THE MIGRATION ATLAS

MOVEMENTS OF THE BIRDS OF BRITAIN AND IRELAND

THE MIGRATION ATLAS

MOVEMENTS OF THE BIRDS OF BRITAIN AND IRELAND

Edited by

**CHRIS WERNHAM, MIKE TOMS,
JOHN MARCHANT, JACQUIE CLARK,
GAVIN SIRIWARDENA & STEPHEN BAILLIE**

T & A D POYSER

LONDON

Published 2002 by T & A D Poyser, an imprint of A & C Black Publishers Ltd.,
37 Soho Square, London W1D 3QZ

ISBN 0–7136–6514–9

A CIP catalogue record for this book is available from the British Library

A & C Black uses paper produced with elemental chlorine-free pulp, harvested from managed sustainable forests.

Typeset by J&L Composition, Filey, Yorkshire.

Printed in Slovenia by Compass Press Limited.

10 9 8 7 6 5 4 3 2 1

Recommended citation:
Wernham, C.V., Toms, M.P., Marchant, J.H., Clark, J.A., Siriwardena, G.M. & Baillie, S.R. (eds). 2002. *The Migration Atlas: movements of the birds of Britain and Ireland.* T. & A.D. Poyser, London.

Dedication

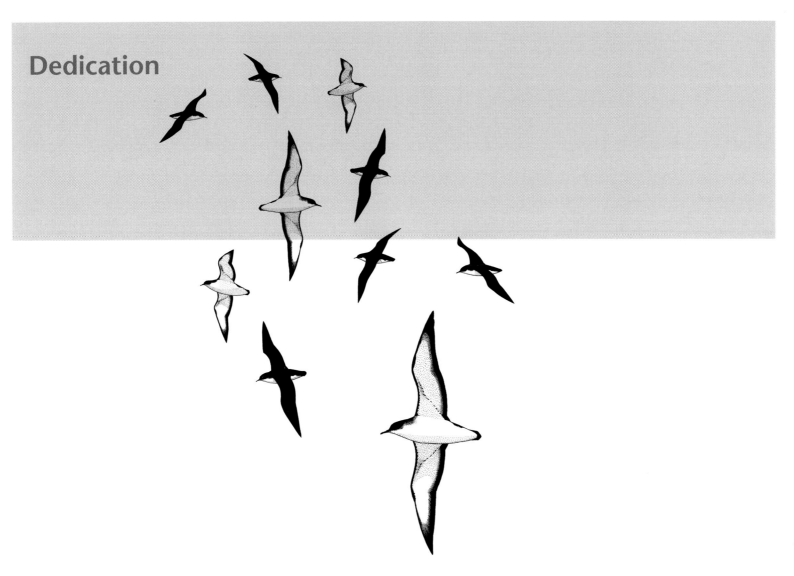

*This book is dedicated to the many thousands of
volunteer bird ringers and bird recorders who have given
their time so freely over many years to gather knowledge
of the movements of British and Irish birds.*

Contents

CONTENTS

CONTENTS

CONTENTS

Foreword

From time immemorial, people have been fascinated by the migrations of birds but it was not until the 19th century that scientific study began in earnest. A major breakthrough came around the turn of the century, with the development of bird rings. The idea was simple: these small, lightweight metal bands, placed loosely around one leg, would carry an address and an individual identification number. Wild birds could be trapped, ringed and released, or they could be ringed in the nest before they could fly. If, at some later date, a ringed bird fell again into human hands, there was a chance that this event would be reported, thus providing information on the movement and longevity of the bird concerned. Even though only a small proportion of ringed birds was later reported, the accumulation of records throughout the 20th century has provided a picture of bird movements previously unimaginable.

For many years, bird ringing in Britain and Ireland has been organised by the British Trust for Ornithology. The many millions of wild birds trapped and ringed here since 1909 have yielded more than 500,000 recoveries, which together provide the vast database on which this book is based. The text and maps bring together information from ringing and other sources on the movement patterns of birds that live in Britain & Ireland year round, and of those that come here from elsewhere to breed or to winter, or that pass through on migration. This is the first time in the history of British and Irish bird ringing that such a synthesis has been attempted. It is hard to thumb through the maps in this book without feeling a sense of wonder. While some bird species make only short movements, remaining throughout their lives in the same small part of the country, others undertake spectacular long-distance journeys to remote parts of the world.

The maps reveal in great detail the network of migration routes that link 'our' birds with other regions. Particularly impressive journeys are undertaken by the Arctic Terns that migrate to winter in the waters around Antarctica, by the Manx Shearwaters that migrate across the Atlantic to winter in the seas off Brazil, and by the Swallows and other small birds that spend their winters in Africa south of the Sahara.

Migration is clearly an important aspect of bird biology, and a significant factor in influencing bird population levels. The three types of question most commonly asked about migratory birds centre on where they go (or come from), how they find their way, and how they manage to fuel such long flights. This book is concerned primarily with the first of these questions: with the breeding areas, wintering areas and migration routes of particular populations. Such knowledge is fascinating in its own right but over the years it has become essential for conservation, as natural habitats are increasingly destroyed by human activity. Clearly, we cannot hope to conserve migrant birds effectively without a firm basis of knowledge, and without a coordinated international effort that provides for the needs of particular populations at different times of year.

The current volume will provide a source of interest for birdwatchers who want to know more about the movements of the birds they see, for conservationists who need to take account of bird movements in the selection of nature reserves, and for students and researchers who wish to address further questions about migration. The book will also form a firm baseline against which future changes in the migration patterns of birds can be measured. That birds can change their migration habits from time to time is now well known. Many species appear to have altered their movement patterns in recent decades as winters have become milder; and, under the influence of global climate change, we can expect many more such changes in the years to come.

The book also highlights gaps in our current knowledge: we still know relatively little about the movements of birds that breed in Ireland and western Scotland where ringers are few, or about the movements of species that breed in Britain & Ireland but winter in those parts of Africa and elsewhere where the chances of a ringed bird being found and reported are extremely low. In time, no doubt, these gaps will be filled, and information will become available from areas so far little known. Migration atlases have already been produced from other parts of Europe and elsewhere, and yet others are in preparation. The British and Irish Ringing Scheme is now integrated with other national European schemes under the auspices of 'EURING' – The European Union for Bird Ringing. So perhaps, in future, we can look forward to the production of atlases that cover even wider geographical scales. In any case, many of the results presented in this book should be seen as a starting point for further migration studies.

Meanwhile, this Atlas represents a significant milestone in the history of bird ringing in Britain and Ireland, and also in the history of the BTO. It forms an important complementary volume to the two breeding bird atlases and the *Winter Atlas*, two of which were produced in fruitful collaboration with the Scottish Ornithologists' Club and BirdWatch Ireland. It is a tribute to the thousands of trained ringers, mostly working in their own time and at their own expense, whose collective efforts over the past century enabled this huge database to be assembled. The book was put together mainly by the team of dedicated BTO staff whose names appear on the front cover, and who extracted and analysed the data, wrote sections of text, and coordinated the whole project. More than 180 other specialists contributed to the 188 detailed species accounts and to the brief accounts for a further 73 regularly occurring but seldom-ringed species. In addition, various corporate bodies and individuals listed later in the book made the whole project possible through their financial support. In every sense, this book is a truly collaborative venture, and a magnificent tribute to all involved.

Ian Newton

Ringing Scheme acknowledgement

The information on the migration and movements of birds contained in this book is derived largely from ring recoveries. The British and Irish Ringing Scheme is operated and part funded by the British Trust for Ornithology.

Part of the Scheme is currently funded by a partnership of the BTO and the Joint Nature Conservation Committee (on behalf of English Nature, Scottish Natural Heritage and the Countryside Council for Wales, and also on behalf of the Environment and Heritage Service in Northern Ireland). The Trust is extremely grateful to the JNCC and its predecessors for their long-term support.

We are also very grateful for long-term support from Dúchas The Heritage Service and its predecessors in the Republic of Ireland.

Dúchas The Heritage Service

We also thank the very many people who have reported ringed birds, and colleagues in other Ringing Schemes and at the EURING data bank with whom ringing and recovery data have been exchanged.

The greatest contribution has been made by the many thousands of dedicated volunteer ringers who have given freely of their time to mark the birds on which this book is based and who have also provided a substantial part of the Scheme's funding.

Acknowledgement to funders

The Migration Atlas project was part funded from British Trust for Ornithology core funds, and through the generous support of its members and ringers. Individual sponsors are acknowledged on the species accounts and other appropriate sections of the book.

**HERITAGE
LOTTERY
FUND**

We are grateful for the support of the Heritage Lottery Fund for the analyses and mapping of the ring-recovery data, which form the basis of this book.

We also thank the Central Science Laboratory for their sponsorship of the Migration Atlas project.

Editors' Preface and Acknowledgements

Chris Wernham, Mike Toms, John Marchant, Jacquie Clark, Gavin Siriwardena & Stephen Baillie

This book represents the first comprehensive summary of the movements of British & Irish birds, placing these movements into a European and global context. At its publication in 2002, bird ringing has been carried out in Britain & Ireland for almost a hundred years, resulting in the marking of more than 25 million birds and generating more than half a million subsequent reports (recoveries) of these individuals. The Ringing Scheme has been an integral part of the BTO since 1937. It is these numerous reports of ringed birds, generated from locations all over the globe, that form the basis of the book, supplemented by information from other sources. Many previous studies have analysed ring-recovery information for individual British & Irish species or groups of species but the results have never previously been collated. Others have reviewed the information on the movements of various species relevant to Britain & Ireland (*eg BWP*) but within a wider remit and, hence, provided less detail specifically for British & Irish populations. This book therefore represents the first comprehensive 'stock-take' of our knowledge of the specific movements of British & Irish bird populations; further, it provides detailed recommendations for future research to improve this knowledge.

The production of a 'Migration Atlas' for British & Irish birds was discussed for many years before funding eventually allowed the initiation of the current project in June 1997. The concept was certainly discussed by Chris Mead and Bob Spencer while they were responsible for running the BTO Ringing Scheme during the 1970s and 1980s, with much encouragement from Trevor Poyser to get such an important book into print following the success of the previous BTO/SOC/IWC atlases of bird distribution. The six of us were therefore greatly honoured to organize and run this milestone project at the BTO. We are extremely grateful to all those (below) who provided the funding and support to allow the project to go ahead.

We hope that readers will find this book a mine of information both on the movements of British & Irish birds and on bird migration in general. Chapter 1 explains the methods by which information on bird movements has been collected and the value of an integrated approach. Chapter 2 describes the development of the thriving British and Irish Ringing Scheme, its contribution to migration studies and also its contributions in other fields of conservation-related research. Bird movement is not only fascinating but also complex, so Chapter 3 draws on the deep knowledge of three invited expert authors to provide a review of the ecology and ecophysiology of migration and how it is influenced by the weather, with an extensive bibliography for further reading. This provides the ecological background for the detailed descriptions of the movement patterns of individual species.

The focal points of the Migration Atlas are the 188 major species accounts and the 73 shorter accounts. There are texts for all the bird species that occur most regularly in Britain & Ireland during the year, whether as breeding species, winter immigrants, passage migrants or in some combination of these categories. For ease of reference, the accounts follow a standard format, as explained in the introductory section of Chapter 6. The main species accounts were written voluntarily by invited experts, each of whom was provided with a standard set of tables of the ring-recovery data, simple analyses and copious maps, as well as guidelines for structuring their text. More than 30,000 maps have been produced over the course of the project, of which more than a thousand are presented within the book. The methods that we used for the standard analyses and mapping are explained in Chapter 4. In addition to the accounts for individual species, we also carried out several sets of cross-species analyses to address specific questions, including the migratory status of individual species in relation to others in the British & Irish bird community, the ecological correlates of the degree of migrancy, differential migration patterns, variation in migration patterns with geographical region of Britain & Ireland and changes in movement patterns through time. Chapter 5 describes the results obtained from these novel cross-species approaches, providing a synthesis of the detailed species-specific migration patterns that are described within the individual species accounts.

We hope that the facts and figures within the Migration Atlas will be of great interest to all students of birds and natural history. The book will also prove to be a valuable tool for conservationists and policy-makers because the need for knowledge of bird movements underpins effective management of their populations through time, at every geographical scale. The accounts and appendices contain the basic facts on each species, as well as a concise explanation of their annual movements. In addition, in Chapter 7, we have provided an appraisal of the level of information that is now available for British & Irish bird communities, a review of the many ways in which such information can contribute to practical conservation, and recommendations for future research to address the existing gaps in our knowledge. We hope that this book will provide a focus for further development of the Ringing Scheme, and for increasing the integrated use of ringing data with other sources of information on bird movements, both from novel high-tech approaches to the monitoring of the movements of individual birds and from broad-scale survey approaches. It will also form a baseline against which future changes in bird movement patterns can be assessed.

This book is the result of truly collaborative efforts by a very large number of people. Over 180 expert authors have given of their time and experience in writing the species accounts in Chapter 6; without their efforts, we could never have hoped to complete such a complex project within the time available. Each account was reviewed by the editors and by an outside expert on the species: we are grateful to all of the following for their assistance with reviewing species accounts or other text: Jake Allsop, Dawn Balmer, Colin Bibby, Richard Bradbury, John Calladine, Nigel Clark, Brian Cresswell, Chris Feare, Tony Fox, Rob Fuller, Bob Furness, Gillian Gilbert, Simon Gillings, Rhys Green, Mike Harris, Baz Hughes, Hugh Insley, Peter Lack, Iain Main, Chris Mead, Carl Mitchell, Andy Musgrove, Ian Newton, David Pearson, Chris Perrins,

Steve Petty, Theunis Piersma, Norman Ratcliffe, Chris Redfern, Jim Reid, Roger Riddington, Peter Robertson, Rob Robinson, Stephen Rumsey, Ken Smith, David Stroud, Ron Summers, Mark Tasker, Moss Taylor, Kate Thompson, Juliet Vickery, Sîan Whitehead, Jerry Wilson and Kevin Woodbridge. We would particularly like to thank Tony Fox and Mike Harris for the huge amounts of time that they both devoted to helping us with the project.

We are grateful to all the following artists that gave so freely of their skills in supplying the fabulous new illustrations that were produced for the book: Ray Bishop, Keith Brockie, Chris Butler, Lawrence Chappell, Mark Cornish, Simon Gillings, Su Gough, Maxine Grover, Brendel Lang, Liz Mackley, Harriet Mead, Dan Powell, Rosemary Powell, John Reaney, Derek Robertson, Rob Robinson, Gerard Russell, Richard Thewlis, Lyn Wells, Andy Wilson and Pete Wilson.

A great many people also helped in various ways with the species accounts in the book, and we thank all of the following for their contributions, on behalf of the authors for the named accounts: Mike Harris (Fulmar); Mike Brooke (Manx Shearwater); Dietrich Ristow & Dean Hashmi (Cory's Shearwater); Jens-Kjeld Jensen (Shag); members of the Swan Study Group (Mute Swan); Richard Hearn & Jens Kristiansen (White-fronted Goose); Carl Mitchell (Greylag Goose); Jon Coleman (Tufted Duck); Mick Marquiss & Malcolm Ogilvie (Goshawk); I. Bainbridge, C. Crooke, A.V. Cross, R.H. Dennis, B. Etheridge, M. McQuaid, D.C. Orr-Ewing, N. Snell & P.J. Stevens (Red Kite); Belgian Ringing Scheme, Hiddensee Bird Ringing Centre, Vogelwarte Radolfzell, Ministerio de Medio Ambiente (Ringing Data Bank), Swedish Bird Ringing Centre, Sempach Ringing Centre, Estonian Bird Ringing Centre, BirdLife Hungary & Latvian Ringing Centre (Hobby); Ævar Petersen (Merlin, Red-necked Phalarope); Richard Bradbury & Jim Reynolds (Golden Plover); Bill Sutherland (Ringed Plover); John Coulson (Herring Gull); Norman Ratcliffe (Black Tern); David Ramsden & the Barn Owl Trust and Colin Shawyer & the Hawk & Owl Trust (Barn Owl); Ian Alexander & Andy Welch (Nightjar); José Pedro Tavares (Tree Pipit); Deryk Shaw (Dunnock); Chris Hindle, Tim Melling, Jan Pritchard, Andy Wilson & Alan Woodcock (Nightingale); David Arthur, Michael Brooke, Tony Cross, Murray Grant, Chris Hewson, Julian Hughes, the late Roy Leverton, Dick Loxton, Chris Rollie, Colin Ryall, Innes Sim & Leo Smith (Ring Ouzel); Ian Lewis (Aquatic Warbler); Bob Edgar (Blackcap); Greg Conway (Yellow-browed Warbler); Andrew Russell (Long-tailed Tit); Paul Bellamy & Bodil Enoksson (Nuthatch); John McMeeking, Margaret Price & their team of workers in Treswell Wood (Treecreeper); Paul Walsh, Alison Taylor & Gavin Fennessy (Carrion Crow); Kjeld Pedersen and the Copenhagen Bird Ringing Centre (Magpie); David Jardine & Robert Rae (crossbills); Dawn Balmer, Derek Robertson & Didier Vangeluwe (Goldfinch); Darren Moorcroft & Richard Bradbury (Linnet); Phil Atkinson, Colin Cross, Keith Duncan, Raymond Duncan, Pete Findley, Joop Jukema, Mike Kimber, Iain Mackay, Mick Marquiss, Nigel Odin, Bob Proctor, Robert Rae, Jim Williams & Eric Wood (Snow Bunting); and Alan Ball (Lapland Bunting).

We would also like to express our own thanks to the following: Stuart Bearhop, the late Peter Evans, Pete Fraser, Stephen Rumsey and David Stroud (who provided material for Chapter 1) and Nicholas Aebischer, Franz Bairlein, Jeff Black, Seb Buckton, Kees Camphuysen, John Coulson, Peter Cranswick, Mark Cubitt, Mary Fox, Tony Fox, Anne Goodall, Andy Gosler, Richard Hearn, Taej Mundkur, Stuart Newson, John O'Halloran, Eileen Rees, Carole Showell, Patrick Smith, Juliet Vickery and Robin Ward (who helped with queries in the reference list).

We are very grateful to the Heritage Lottery Fund for providing half of the funding for the analyses and mapping of the ring-recovery data, providing the essential foundations upon which the Migration Atlas is built. Ringers, BTO members, charitable trusts and commercial organizations supplied the matching funding to make the project possible. Those that supplied the matching funding are mentioned specifically on each species account or other section of the book to which they contributed so generously. In addition, the work on the texts for Arctic and Great Skuas was funded by IFOMA (International Fishmeal & Oil Manufacturers Association). The Central Science Laboratory (CSL) generously became an additional overall sponsor for the project.

We owe our thanks to Rowena Langston and Nigel Clark for undertaking the work to acquire major funding for the project. We also thank Graham Appleton for all his hard work in raising the additional funds required to run the project, and for his careful management of the publicity programme. Jenny Gill kindly assisted Graham with organising the 'Great Bird Auction' to raise funding for the project. We are grateful to Alison McLeod, Sam Rider and Helen Secker for managing the sponsorship database.

Many members of BTO staff assisted with the production of the book. Sophie Foulger performed a thorough in-house copy-editing. Angie Raven acted as general secretary for the project. Angela Rickard and Susan Waghorn helped with the production of the illustrative material. Helen Carrier, Janet Elliott-Simmons and Jane Wells provided additional secretarial assistance. Caroline Dudley and Dawn Balmer assisted with mapping. Andy Musgrove advised on the use of WeBS data. Many other colleagues helped with rearranging work programmes so that the key staff could spend their time on the book; we are particularly grateful to David Noble, Humphrey Crick and the staff of the Ringing Unit for their cooperation in this respect. Members of the BTO's Ringing Committee all offered their support and advice to the project. We are very grateful to Dilys Breese, Andy Elvin, Jeremy Greenwood and Alan Martin for assistance with management of the project.

We are grateful to all the staff at J&L Composition for their advice during typesetting, to Simon Crump and Andy Richford of Academic Press, and to Eveline Taylor for copy-editing. Andy Lawrence and colleagues at Keele University (KUDIS) provided invaluable advice on the electronic maps. In-house proof reading was carried out by the editors. We are extremely grateful to Dawn Balmer, John Calladine, Chris du Feu, Richard du Feu, Sophie Foulger, Verity Hunter, Peter Lack, David Leech, Stuart Newson, Trevor Poyser and Pamela Rhodes for their additional help with proofing, at very short notice.

We would like to express our thanks to the Joint Nature Conservation Committee and Dúchas The Heritage Service in the Republic of Ireland (and their predecessors) for their long-term support for the Ringing Scheme. We also thank colleagues in other ringing schemes and at the EURING data bank, with whom ringing and recovery data have been exchanged. We acknowledge the Wildfowl & Wetlands Trust for their long-term coordination and support for wildfowl ringing in Britain and Ireland.

Our greatest thanks go to all the ringers and ringing groups who have ringed birds in Britain and Ireland since 1909, all those who have reported ringed birds, and the dedicated staff who have processed the reports and entered them into the database. Equally, our thanks go to all those birdwatchers and report editors who have meticulously recorded and published their observations. Without the work of all these people, this project could never have been completed.

Finally, we hope that this book will provide a stimulus for the further bird marking and observational studies that are needed to fill some of the gaps in knowledge that we have identified.

The Nunnery, Thetford, July 2002

1 Learning about bird movements: methods of study

John Marchant

Bird migration is a topic that has intrigued people since at least the early writings of biblical times. The seasonal comings and goings of birds and the unpredictable appearance of unexpected species or numbers have long engaged interest, and are still constant sources of wonder and excitement to anyone who remains in touch with the natural world. Knowledge of the movements of birds finds an application in the case of quarry species, where plans for sustainable harvest must take account of migration patterns and timings. Increasingly, as more bird populations come under threat from direct or indirect human pressures, an understanding of their movements is vital also for effective conservation, enabling remedial actions to be concentrated at the appropriate places and seasons. In addition, birds are more easily monitored than most other animals, and often have a high profile for generating conservation action. Conservation measures designed to help birds may benefit many other organisms, too.

Much of the detailed information about bird migration and movements that now exists has been gathered only during the last 100 years. While incomplete as a review of this large subject, this chapter examines the ways in which patterns of bird movement have been investigated. It also considers what kinds of discoveries might lie in store for the future, as more information is gathered and as new techniques for migration study are developed or become more widely used. It does not attempt to cover methods for investigating migration 'processes', such as physiology, orientation or feeding ecology, because these are not major components of the book as a whole. Some information on migration ecology and ecophysiology, and how these topics are studied, can be found in Chapter 3, however. Neither does this chapter explore the analytical methods that are an integral part of any study of bird movements. There are a number of useful reviews that the interested reader might consult for more information on this topic (see Perdeck 1977, Nichols 1996, Nichols & Kaiser 1999), and the development of such methods is considered further in Chapter 7.

The scope of the *Migration Atlas*

The function of the *Migration Atlas* is to take stock of the information that is available on bird migrations and movements as they involve Britain & Ireland. The data collected since 1909 by the British & Irish Ringing Scheme were the inspiration for this book, and form its core. In each of the main species texts, however, the expert author has combined this bird-ringing information with that from other sources

*This chapter has been sponsored by the
Alan Turner Trust*

discussed in this chapter, as appropriate, to give as far as possible a rounded picture of what is known. We also consider in the book what more we need to discover, and how best to deploy our information to aid the future conservation of birds and their habitats.

The geographical focus of this *Migration Atlas* is Britain & Ireland[1], defined as the United Kingdom and the Republic of Ireland, and their offshore waters, including the Isle of Man but not the Channel Islands (Fig 1.1). As well as forming a biologically meaningful area for discussion, this definition embraces the geographical remit of the British & Irish Bird Ringing Scheme. Although only a tiny part of the earth's surface, Britain & Ireland occupies a very special position on the globe, as far as migrant birds are concerned. It comprises an important part of regular flyways that bring arctic-breeding birds from an area that spans more than 200° of longitude, well over halfway round the world. Our island shores provide a vital refuge or stepping-stone for many populations of birds from further north, from sources as widely separated as the islands of Nunavut in the Canadian Arctic and the Taimyr Peninsula in central Siberia.

There is no universally accepted definition of the term 'migration', even as applied to birds, let alone to other groups of animals. Whereas such spectacular long-distance seasonal movements as those of Brent Geese from the Taimyr Peninsula to southeast Britain, or of Swallows from Britain & Ireland to South Africa, clearly constitute 'migration', we also discuss other kinds of movements that take birds beyond what might be considered their normal home area. Thus, we include regular seasonal shifts of distribution, irregular or nomadic movements, and local dispersals, while attempting to exclude the movements that a typical bird might make during its normal daily activities. Some of the major categories of movement covered in this book are:

'Seasonal' movements
- the seasonal movements of certain populations of particular species along relatively well-defined routes from breeding to non-breeding areas ('true migration');
- the seasonal movements ('dispersal') of individuals away from their breeding areas after the breeding season, and reverse movements in the spring;
- regular or irregular movements within a non-breeding area, during

[1] Throughout the book, we refer to 'Britain & Ireland' when referring to this defined geographical area as a whole, or to 'Britain *and* Ireland' when referring to both Britain and Ireland as separate units.

Fig 1.1 The focal area for the *Migration Atlas*, Britain & Ireland, showing bird observatories, major ringing sites mentioned in the text, and other sites at which regular observations of bird movements are made.

the course of a single autumn/winter/spring period, for example, onward passage movements or movements due to freezing conditions or exhaustion of food supplies;
- movement to a different non-breeding area in one winter from that used in the previous winter.

'Dispersal' movements
- the movements of young birds away from their birthplaces once they have reached independence from their parents ('post-juvenile dispersal');
- the locations of young birds breeding for the first time, in relation to their birthplaces ('natal dispersal');
- the locations of breeding of adults in one year in relation to their breeding places in the previous year ('breeding dispersal').

Even the most sedentary bird species show a degree of natal dispersal (sometimes in only one sex), to avoid the inbreeding that would otherwise occur. Thus, the movements of birds like Tawny Owl and Nuthatch that rarely travel far and generally avoid crossing any stretch of open water are discussed in this book alongside those of the spectacular long-distance migrants, such as Arctic Tern and Swallow.

The various types of movements made by birds, and their place in avian ecology, are discussed in more detail in Chapter 3, and definitions of terms used throughout the book are given in Chapter 4.

Information sources: their value and limitations

The most obvious way to find out about what birds do is to watch them. There is much that can be learnt, at least about the movements of species or populations as a whole, from recording their seasonal changes in distribution and numbers and by observing the timing and direction of their visible movements. Where such observations can be directed into systematic surveys, and nil returns added to the resulting counts to document absences, the information obtained can be treated as properly quantitative. Ringing and other more detailed techniques add further

layers of information, especially as they relate to birds as individuals. Indeed, ringing is essential for a proper understanding of bird migration, because the marking of individual birds from known populations allows their movements to be traced, when individuals from different populations would not otherwise be separable in the field.

The large samples of reports of ringed birds that are now available for many species allow their movements to be interpreted, with caveats that are described more fully in Chapter 4, as representative of those of the populations from which those individuals were drawn. The extensive set of ring-recovery data collected by the BTO's British & Irish Ringing Scheme forms the basis of this book. Most of the contributing authors and members of the editing team are dedicated bird ringers. The story of bird ringing in Britain & Ireland, and the enormous contribution made to conservation science (including migration studies) by the BTO's team of trained volunteer ringers, is summarized in Chapter 2.

There are a few British & Irish species about which we would know almost nothing about their movements, were it not for the efforts of bird ringers. Aquatic Warbler, for example, is a scarce migrant detected most often during mist-netting, and Storm Petrel is a breeding species that is strictly nocturnal above ground at the breeding site, and is difficult to observe at sea, but for which there are many ring-recoveries. Conversely, however, there are several species that breed in Britain & Ireland, including Black-throated Diver, Ptarmigan and Red-necked Phalarope, for which ringing has not yet provided a single recovery involving our area of coverage. A number of regular winter visitors or migrants to Britain & Ireland, such as Red-necked Grebe and Smew, similarly have no ring-recovery data at all for this area. Less obviously, ringing can give only part of the story for some species, because there are groups of birds or subpopulations that, for one reason or another, are inadequately represented in the ring-recovery data. For example, the ringing of seabirds such as Fulmars and Puffins is almost entirely of birds at colonies during the breeding season, leaving open the question of whether birds of very different origins may occur at sea in British & Irish waters at other times of year, especially as there is little or no ringing at many of the potential source colonies for immigrant birds.

Bird ringing is only one of a range of tools at our disposal for studying migration: its results are complemented from a variety of other sources. In meeting the wide scope of this book, therefore, the species texts draw on not just the ring-recovery data, but also on what is known from all kinds of observations and surveys, and from the other sources of information that are available.

Table 1.1 attempts to summarize this web of information gathering, by presenting a classification of the main methods of migration study and the kinds of information obtainable from each.

Observations of changes in seasonal abundance
The pioneer British naturalist Gilbert White, based in Selborne in inland Hampshire, but with correspondents around Britain, seemed uncertain about whether Swallows left the country for the winter or hibernated (White 1789). Early understanding of the regular seasonal movements of birds should not be underestimated, however. People living at many coastal locations must have been familiar with seasonal arrivals and departures, especially of quarry species. Seafarers would have observed that landbirds were occasionally to be encountered far out in the ocean, especially in spring and autumn. The Pink-footed Goose text relates that an Icelandic bishop recorded an accurate summary of these birds' migration between Iceland and Britain & Ireland as early as 1638 (see Chapter 6).

As the pioneers demonstrated, ordinary, unsystematic observations, once assembled and documented, can reveal a great deal about bird movements. Some types of unsystematic observations, and their value for migration studies, are listed in Table 1.2.

The scale of such observation in Britain & Ireland has increased beyond all recognition in recent decades. Today's birders carry powerful optical and photographic equipment and are typically highly skilled in

Table 1.1 An overview of the main kinds of information obtainable from each of the categories of bird migration study discussed in Chapter 1. The number of symbols (maximum four) represents the potential of each method in each area, with respect to movements involving Britain & Ireland, and the number of filled symbols the extent to which that potential has so far been realized.

	Information obtainable on bird movements								
	About the species .... About the individual								
Study method	Seasonal ranges and sites used by populations on passage	True volume of migration/ turnover	Annual variations in volume (*eg* irruptions)	Headings at particular sites and times	Patterns of dispersal	Routes followed by individuals	Variations during lifetime of individuals	Constant surveillance of individuals at study sites	Global surveillance of individuals
Unsystematic observations	●●○[1]	●[2]	●[2]	●					
Systematic surveys	●●○○[1]	●○○○[6]	●○○○[3,6]	●○					
Moon-watching, infra-red and radar		●○[4]	○	●○○[5]					
Orientation testing				●○○○					
Ringing and recapture data from study sites	●○	●○○○[6]	●○○○[6]		●○		○○[7]		
Ring-recoveries away from ringing sites	●○○[8]				●●○○[9]	●●○	●○		
Colour-marking		●○○○[6]	●○○○[6]		●○○[9]	●○○	●○○	●○○	●○
Chemical and biological markers	●○○○								
Data loggers (non-transmitting)				○	○	●○	○		
Transponders (with fixed sensors)		○○	○○				●○	●○○	
Radio-tracking		●○[6]	●○[6]		○○[10]	●○	○○[10,11]	●○○○[12]	
Satellite tracking[13]	????		????	?????[9]	●○○○	○○[14]	●○[15]		●○○○[16]

Notes

1. Speculative, unsystematic observations may yield new faunistic information that is not revealed by systematic surveys of limited scope, which have been designed on the basis of prior knowledge to address specific questions. Systematic surveys with broad coverage (such as atlas-type studies) are required to obtain a reasonably comprehensive picture for many species, however.
2. Unsystematic observations cannot provide measures of the true volume of migration or of annual variations in numbers except in the case of rare species or obvious irruptions. Such aims generally require systematic counts and/or systematic mark–recapture work (see note 6).
3. With the exception of the Wetland Bird Survey (WeBS), systematic surveys of migrant birds have generally been too short term to measure trends.
4. These methods illustrate the volume and direction of bird movements; radar can also measure the speed and altitude of flying birds. They rarely identify birds to species, however, and are restricted in their operation to certain times, sites or weather conditions.
5. Actual observations of headings are influenced by topology and weather and may not be as informative as the results of orientation tests.
6. The true volume of migration and annual variation in numbers will generally require systematic survey and/or systematic mark–recapture work. Measurements of numbers overhead generally require radar and will often be imprecise. Numbers moving through particular sites (turnover measurements) nearly always require both counts and mark–recapture work. The latter can be based on ringing retraps, sightings of colour-marked birds or radio-telemetry (at greater expense but most appropriate for some species that are hard to catch and/or observe).
7. Full computerization of ringing and recapture information from ringers (see Chapter 4) will help with this in future.
8. Results from ring-recoveries will always be somewhat biased by the localized distribution of ringing activities and by variations in the likelihood of ring finding and reporting (see Chapter 4). On broad geographical scales, it may be possible to control quantitatively for some of these biases in future (Chapter 7).
9. Satellite-tracking methods would be the ideal for measuring dispersal if there were records for large numbers of individual birds. Ring-recoveries currently form the most satisfactory method, and are less biased than colour-ring sightings, because search effort for colour-rings is mostly by birdwatchers in likely places for sightings.
10. Assessment of bird movement by ground-based radio-tracking is limited by the size of the area that can be searched. In practice, most radio-tagged birds are lost for good once they leave the study area, unless special effort is made to find them using aircraft.
11. Radio-transmitters currently in use have a lifespan much shorter than the birds that carry them, and a relatively short range.
12. Radio-tracking can be used at night, when other kinds of observation are not possible.
13. The entries for satellite tracking are made on the assumption that costs will not decrease (and hence sample sizes increase) by orders of magnitude in the near future. If they did, the technique would have even greater potential for population-level migration studies (denoted by '????' on table).
14. Satellite-transmitters carried by birds have rarely lasted more than a year when operating continuously but new developments, such as intermittent transmission, are likely to improve their lifespan. Reductions in the size and weight of transmitters should eventually allow their use on small birds.
15. The potential for using satellite technology to monitor individuals at study sites will increase if the accuracy of recording locations improves.
16. Only satellite tracking enables birds to be located wherever they are on the globe.

Table 1.2 The contribution of unsystematic bird recording to migration studies.

Types of unsystematic observations of birds	Value for migration studies
Collecting museum specimens	Establishment of faunistic records (provided that label details are full, correct and credible); generally superseded for this purpose now by photographs, field notes, and biometrics (even DNA samples) of birds trapped for ringing.
Presence/absence notes, or counts, for particular sites and times	Published reports help to establish seasonal ranges of each species, and which sites they use on passage. (Quantification is more useful as part of a systematic survey, see Table 1.3.)
Early and late dates for common migrants, unusual sightings	Published records (*eg* in county bird reports) can support research into phenological trends (*eg* Mason 1995) and, because they are ongoing and open-ended, often provide unexpected information not recorded in systematic surveys.
Observations of visible migration (including sea-watching)	Documentary evidence of direction and strength of movement at particular times and places. (Quantification would be more useful as part of a systematic survey, see Table 1.3.)
Observations of daily foraging and roosting movements	Description of bird movements at a finer temporal scale (within the day) than is possible from conventional ringing.
Finding and reporting rare migrants	Records of rare birds published by the appropriate records committee (usually with supporting details kept on file) may establish new faunistic records at various geographical scales, and help document occurrence patterns and how these change over time.

field identification. More importantly, they network their observations through a range of organizations, reports, journals and web sites, thus allowing world-wide access to the latest news and information. Through mobile telephones, pagers and the Internet, such access can now take just minutes, rather than months or years. Suitable conditions for observing migrants send eager enthusiasts to likely spots to try their luck. The fruit of all this frenzy of observation and communication should be measured not, as some may suggest, as new species for people's lists or by Internet ephemera, but by the volume of published reports and papers that document and synthesize the sightings.

Dates of arrival and departure for regular migrants, and each observation for scarcer species, are documented each year in local and county reports that cover almost the whole of Britain & Ireland. Annual reports and summaries feed into publications that document occurrence patterns over the longer term (*eg Birds in Scotland, Birds in Ireland, Birds in Wales*). Summaries of scarce migrant records throughout Britain, compiled from county bird reports, have been particularly valuable source material for this atlas (*eg* Dymond *et al* 1989, Fraser *et al* 1997, 1999a, b, 2000; Fig 1.2). The recent bibliography of local reports and avifaunas in Britain and the Isle of Man (Ballance 2000), running to more than 500 pages, is an indication of how much British birdwatchers have already achieved in this direction.

Systematic surveys
In Britain & Ireland, and in many other parts of the world, the approach being taken to collect observational data is increasingly directed towards conservation science. If the collection of data becomes systematic, to the extent that absences or low counts are as likely to be recorded as high counts, the conclusions that can be drawn become more rigorous and the value of the information collected much greater. This kind of approach is taken by the BTO and other bodies that organize broad-scale surveys in the UK. By joining organizations such as the BTO, participating in wide-scale surveys and pooling their observations in standardized ways with those of other observers, birdwatchers can make their observations of value not just individually and locally but also collectively and nationally. Various types of systematic bird survey that contribute to migration study are described in Table 1.3.

Aside from bird ringing, discussed more fully in Chapter 2, the national projects most relevant to bird migration have been the breeding atlas surveys (*1968–72 Atlas, 1988–91 Atlas*), and the *Winter Atlas*.

Comparison of the breeding season and midwinter distributions of birds, at the scale of the 10-km squares of the national grid, gives remarkable insights into annual movements, despite the choice of just these two periods to cover the annual cycle. Of species that are present year-round in Britain & Ireland, some may be absent from certain parts of the breeding range during the winter, or appear in new areas at that season. Different combinations of emigration, immigration and partial migration, which mapping alone cannot distinguish, have produced a variety of patterns according to species. The Black-headed Gull, for example, is largely absent from inland southern parts of both Britain and Ireland in the breeding season, and absent from some parts of inland northern Britain in winter (Fig 1.3). Tetrad (2-km square) atlas surveys, undertaken by many county ornithological societies in Britain, give an even greater resolution of bird distribution and allow a closer comparison of changes with topography and habitat (Donald & Fuller 1998).

One problem with breeding and winter atlases in the context of migration study is that the organizers have necessarily had to choose clear boundaries of mapping seasons to suit the majority of the species to be covered, and long enough in duration for observers to achieve good coverage. Some species, however, may undertake major changes of distribution within the periods selected. Oystercatchers, for example, winter almost exclusively on or near the coast but, because they return to inland breeding territories as early as February, they were mapped extensively inland by the *Winter Atlas*; the full non-breeding distribution has therefore never been documented. Another problem, which affects every species, is that not all of the year has been covered; the *Winter Atlas* period was mid-November to the end of February, and that for the *1988–91 Atlas* of breeding distribution was 1 April to 31 July. We do not yet know the detailed distribution of most British & Irish birds during the remaining 4½ months of the year, therefore, although certain inferences can be made from the information that we do have.

Much more can be learnt about seasonal movements by mapping distribution within shorter periods covering more of the annual cycle. The Dutch year-round atlas (SOVON 1987), mapping each species monthly, is able to distinguish the early autumn departure of Wood Warbler, mostly in August, from that of Willow Warbler, mainly in August and September, and Chiffchaff, in September and October. Among winter visitors in the Netherlands, the autumn arrival of Red-breasted Mergansers, beginning in August, is shown to be two months earlier than that of Goosander (Fig 1.4). The whereabouts of Goosanders in Britain in

Fig 1.2 Occurrence of Richard's Pipit in Britain, collated from unsystematic observations of this scarce migrant reported to county bird recorders: (a) weekly totals during 1998; (b) distribution in Britain in 1998, by county. (*Source*: Fraser *et al* 2000, by permission of *British Birds*.)

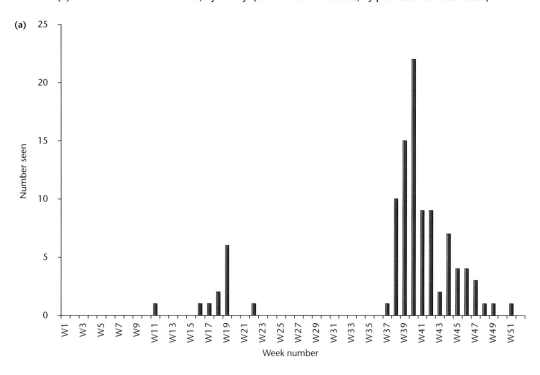

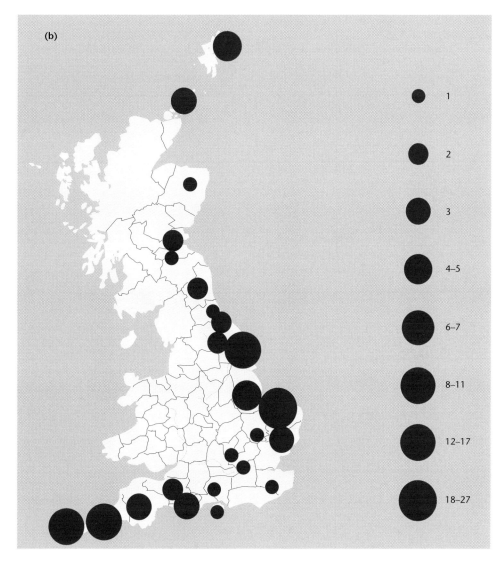

Table 1.3 The contribution of systematic bird surveys to migration studies.

Types of systematic surveys of birds	Value for migration studies, and example references to published work
Systematic short-term collection of presence/absence and count data for particular sites and times	Published reports help to establish seasonal ranges and the sites that are used on passage (*eg* expedition reports).
Regular counts of visible migration and grounded migrants (including bird observatory daily logs and inland watch-points), ideally with daily effort recorded or standardized	Essential background information on the timing and scale of passage; can often be related to weather conditions, which may need to be taken into account during interpretation of the data (*eg* observatory reports; Williamson 1958–62, Sharrock 1973, *R & F*, Dymond 1980, 1991, Riddiford 1991).
Wetland Bird Survey (WeBS, I-WeBS)	WeBS collects monthly counts of all wetland birds at most UK sites and is complemented by I-WeBS in the Republic of Ireland; an increasing number of WeBS sites are counted throughout the year, making it the only UK-wide survey that has covered the spring and autumn migration periods. Monthly totals by site and region show when waterbirds arrive and depart (*eg* Waters *et al* 1998, Cranswick *et al* 1999).
At-sea surveys	Mapping of the abundance of seabirds in British & Irish waters has begun relatively recently and has provided completely new information on seabird distribution and how this changes seasonally (*eg* Blake *et al* 1984, Tasker *et al* 1987, Webb *et al* 1990, Pollock *et al* 2000).
Breeding and winter atlas mapping surveys	Quantitative mapping of seasonal change between summer and winter (*eg* 1968–72 Atlas, Winter Atlas, 1988–91 Atlas).
Year-round mapping surveys	Timing of seasonal movement becomes more apparent than if just two mapping periods are used (*eg* SOVON 1987; Buckland *et al* (1990) plotted seasonal distribution by altitude; Clarke *et al* 1999).

Fig 1.3 The distribution of Black-headed Gulls in Britain & Ireland (a) in the breeding season and (b) in winter. Greater temporal and spatial resolution in future atlas work would help to reveal the timing of the various movements that bring about the change between these two periods of the year. (*Sources: Winter Atlas, 1988–91 Atlas.*)

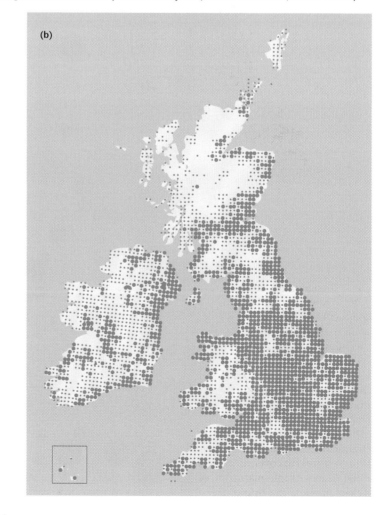

Fig 1.4 Monthly distribution maps of (a) Red-breasted Merganser and (b) Goosander in the Netherlands in autumn. The arrival times of these two species are very different. (*Source*: SOVON 1987.)

(a) Red-breasted Merganser

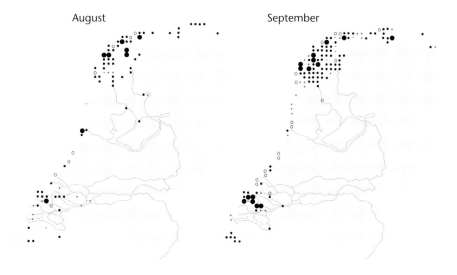

August   September

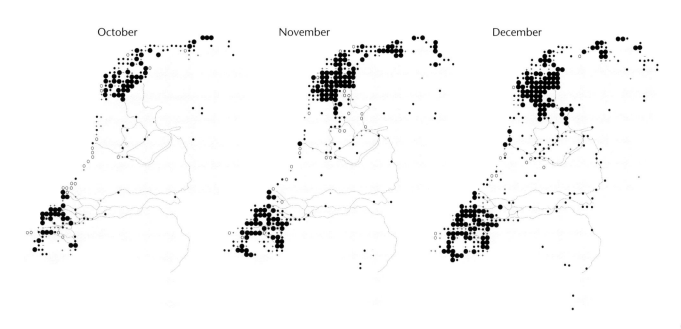

October   November   December

Continued

autumn, though partly covered by WeBS counts, are presently difficult to discover from any published source (see the species account for Goosander in Chapter 6). While the males are generally absent on moult migration (mostly, as ring-recoveries have demonstrated, in Norway), are the females and young still near the breeding waters, or have they too shifted site? This kind of information would potentially emerge for most species from a year-round distribution atlas of birds in Britain & Ireland. Such an ambitious project would be extremely demanding, however, in terms of fieldwork effort and number of volunteers, and is unlikely to be attempted in the near future.

The Australian Bird Count, organized by Birds Australia (the Royal Australasian Ornithologists' Union), sets another fascinating example. Despite vast areas to cover, and relatively few birdwatchers, the survey has resulted in remarkable maps showing seasonal changes in distribution. For some species, the information obtained was completely new and

unexpected (Fig 1.5). If a continuation of this work proves possible, it might refine the information on the seasonal timing of Australian bird migrations, and further discoveries will undoubtedly be made.

Unspecific observations of birds on the move

Close observation of the full moon on a clear night sometimes reveals, to the patient eye, the tiny silhouettes of birds on nocturnal migration. The value of moon-watching for migration study was first documented in the 19th century in the USA (Scott 1881, Chapman 1888, West 1896). In the spring of 1948, coordinated moon-watching at 34 stations between Yucatan and Ontario showed for the first time that small migrant birds returning from Central America cross the Gulf of Mexico on spring migration, and charted their subsequent movements across eastern North America (Lowery 1951). By simple calculations involving the moon's bearing and elevation, counts of birds crossing the moon's

Fig 1.4 *Continued*

(b) Goosander

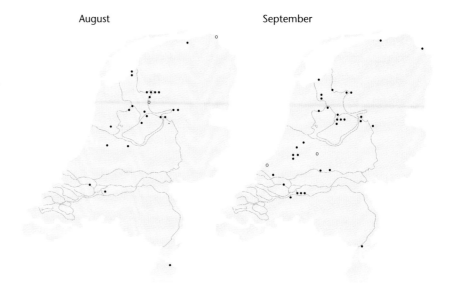

August   September

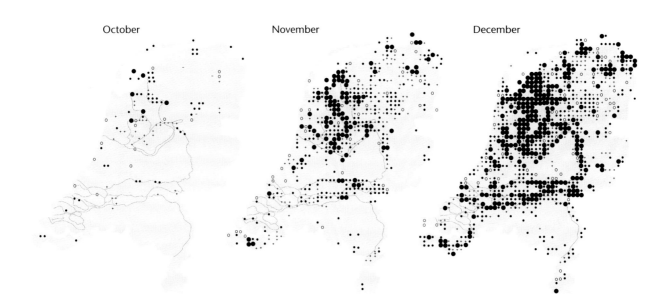

October   November   December

disc can be transformed into estimates of the numbers of birds passing overhead, their direction of movement, and even of their height and speed. It is not possible to identify the birds to species, however, although some can be classified by their shapes and wing action and, since the observers are generally stationed outdoors, they may hear calls that reveal the identity of at least some of the species involved. A severely limiting constraint of moon-watching is that it can only be attempted on a few nights each month, and may even then be spoiled by cloud cover. The numbers of birds passing on cloudy nights or nights without a full moon cannot be estimated by this method.

The popularity of moon-watching was soon overtaken when it was realized that many of the unidentified echoes detected by the new tool of radar, invented for military use during the 1940s, were in fact high-flying birds (*eg* Harper 1959, Lack 1959a). Radar was thus discovered to be another tool that can be used to estimate the volume of migration that occurs at night. As with moon-watching, a major drawback is that it is not possible to know which species are being observed, although modern radar can estimate wingbeat patterns and can allow echoes to be classified

into types. It is not limited by weather or by the phase of the moon, and can equally well detect diurnal migration, some of which may be too high to be observed from the ground. It is generally only available to professional researchers, however, and mostly limited geographically to the locations of suitable fixed radar installations. Powerful and sophisticated radar is needed to estimate the number of individual birds in a flock, which may otherwise appear as just a single echo (Bruderer *et al* 1995a, Buurma 1995). Quantification is not necessarily precise, therefore. Radar of course can estimate the altitude of the birds detected (*eg* Bruderer *et al* 1995b, Bruderer & Liechti 1995). Radar observations are most reliable over the sea or in flat terrain, and work best where observations of migrating birds are unlikely to be swamped by others making short feeding or roosting movements. The first radar studies investigated migration across the North Sea (Lack 1959b, 1960, 1962, 1963). Radar has been used to estimate the volume of migration across desert areas in Africa (*eg* Bairlein 1985b) and Israel (*eg* Bruderer 1994), and even to confirm the absence of bird migration in the region of the North Pole (Gudmundsson & Alerstam 1998a). Most recently, high-precision tracking radar has been

Fig 1.5 Maps showing the (a) autumn, (b) winter, (c) spring and (d) summer distributions of the Grey Fantail in Australia; the colour intensity increases with increasing density of birds per hectare, as detected in a 20-minute survey, while areas for which no data were available are shown in white. Although many areas are occupied all year round, the mapping reveals a strong north–south migration. (*Source*: '*Australian Bird Count: Where do all the bush birds go?*' by Michael F. Clarke, Peter Griffioen & Richard H. Loyn, supplement to *Wingspan* volume 9, number 1 (December 1999), published by Birds Australia.)

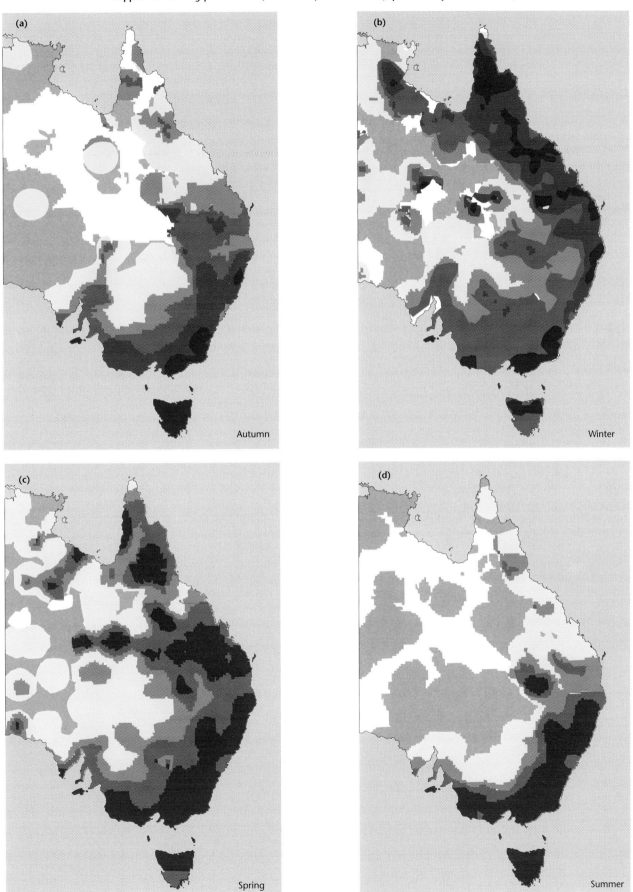

used to study the flight behaviour of migrating birds when crossing the Mediterranean (*eg* Bruderer & Liechti 1998).

Owing to military restrictions, it is most unlikely that there can be coordinated radar studies to track the movements of birds on a broad international scale, although this would undoubtedly be technically possible. There may be more scope for wide-scale surveys using infra-red detection equipment, which, in direct comparison, was more efficient than moon-watching and found as many birds as radar (Liechti *et al* 1995).

Some studies have indicated that the numbers of migrants grounded, for example at a bird observatory, do not correspond very closely to the movements that are known by radar to be occurring overhead (Lack 1962, Lack & Parslow 1962, Parslow 1962, but see also Riddiford 1985). In fine conditions, counts may be low, but turnover high, with many birds overflying watch-points and passing undetected by birdwatchers, whereas, in weather unsuitable for active migration, ground-based counts may be higher than is warranted by the amount of actual bird movement. Ground-based surveys therefore cannot generally be relied upon as a measure of the true volume of migration from day to day. A fuller review and further empirical study of this topic are clearly long overdue. Very recently, the *BirdCast* Project, run by the Audubon Society, Clemson University Radar Ornithology Laboratory, Cornell Laboratory of Ornithology and the US Academy of Natural Sciences, has been using NEXRAD (Next Generation Doppler Radar designed for weather forecasting) to record bird movements on a daily basis during spring and autumn, and asking volunteer birdwatchers to carry out ground-truthing by sending in observations of birds in their gardens and from regular birding sites (see www.birdsource.cornell.edu/BirdCast/home.html).

The major drawback with all of these methods at present is that the specific identity of the birds that are detected is very rarely known for certain. These methods of studying migration have therefore provided little information of relevance to the species-by-species approach adopted by the present book.

Orientation testing

A number of methods have been devised for estimating the migratory drive and the preferred heading of birds held in captivity. These include the Kramer cage and the Emlen funnel, and recent improvements on their basic design (*eg* Berthold 1991, Busse 1995). These methods depend on the assumption that, in the absence of other stimuli, a bird will try to escape from its cage in the direction in which it would be migrating, if free to do so, and with a persistence that indicates its urge to migrate. There is a great deal of evidence that such orientation measurements do show the direction in which unrestrained birds actually migrate.

The main reason that such orientation tests have been made has been to investigate by experiment the mechanisms of orientation and navigation (see Chapter 3). The researcher can discover how the preferred orientation changes in response to induced changes in the environment, for example obscuring or altering the apparent position of the celestial bodies, changing the apparent day-length or the timing of sunrise and sunset, or changing the magnetic field, as experienced inside the cage. This technique has proved to be valuable for investigating many theoretical aspects of migration biology and the heritability of migratory behaviour (*eg* Berthold 1991, 1995, 1996).

A more field-based use of the technique has been to test the orientation of wild-trapped birds, held captive for only a day or so, in particular locations or circumstances (*eg* Rabøl 1973). Rabøl (1985) found that the orientation of continental migrants that had drifted west to the Faeroes in September was generally the same as would be found in the same species in Scandinavia, with only a few birds showing evidence of a change in heading to compensate for their displacement. This result perhaps suggests that many continental migrants appearing on the furthest fringes of western Europe in autumn are likely to perish at sea on their next migratory flight. Recent work of this type has also demonstrated that ring-recoveries may not give a complete picture of

migration routes for populations that pass through large geographical areas where the chances of ringed birds being found and reported are slim (Busse 2000).

Ringing: movements of individuals from A to B

While observations can show how the range of a species may shift seasonally from one area of the globe to another, they cannot show how birds from any particular breeding area are distributed on the wintering grounds. Similarly, for species that occupy the same geographical range all year, observations alone cannot begin to describe the behaviour of individual birds, which may vary from sedentary to dispersive or migratory. The complicated patterns of movement that underlie the seasonal changes in distribution shown by atlas surveys require more-detailed study methods to unravel. This is where ringing and other methods of tracking individual birds become of great importance.

Bird ringing shifts the emphasis of migration studies from the species as a whole to particular individuals that have been marked. The placement of a small, light and unobtrusive metal ring on the bird's leg, inscribed with a unique number and a return address, allows the movements of the individual to be traced if it is caught again or found dead. Ringing provides data that link breeding grounds, migration stopover sites and wintering grounds for individual birds. Ring-recoveries are thus a vital source of information for studying bird movements, and particularly dispersal, for which until very recently they have been the only effective source (Table 1.1).

General details of ringing captures form an extremely valuable survey in themselves: one that is very long-running, wide-scale but unsystematic, and that links species and numbers caught with age and sex, moult status, date, place, habitat, biometrics and other factors. Computerization of historical ringing records is gradually making these data available (see Chapter 2).

Ringing can also valuably take the form of a formal systematic survey. Where ringing effort is standardized, as in the BTO's Constant Effort Sites (CES) scheme during the breeding season (*eg* du Feu & McMeeking 1991, Peach *et al* 1998), and under differing protocols at many bird observatories and other ringing stations, the number of birds captured may indicate the occurrence patterns of birds at the site within and between seasons. Two important large-scale projects, the Mettnau–Reit–Illmitz (MRI) Project (Berthold & Schlenker 1975, Berthold *et al* 1991) and the European Science Foundation (ESF) Network Project (*eg* Bairlein 1997a), have used standardized ringing during migration periods to study the migration timing, habitat use and migration strategies of passerine birds. Ringing and retrapping ('mark–recapture'), ideally combined with count data, allow estimation of the total number of individuals passing through a site during a passage season, the rate of turnover, and stopover duration, given that certain assumptions are met; rigorous analytical methods are now available for obtaining such information from mark–recapture data (*eg* Kaiser 1999, Schaub *et al* 2001).

In situations where birds are difficult to observe, such as in forest and reedbed, or in petrel colonies at night, mist-netting is a valuable tool for discovering the species and numbers of birds that are present. Many rarities have been located during the course of ringing activity, and a number of faunistically important records have become established only after the bird has been caught and examined in the hand (*eg* Cubitt 1995).

Typically, however, returns from ringing provide just two or maybe a handful of known points in a bird's life; at ringing and at finding as a dead bird, or perhaps when retrapped at the ringing site or recaught by another ringer. It cannot be known how far a bird might have travelled between being ringed at point A and being found again at point B, perhaps some years later, but it is almost always a very much longer distance than the straight line by which recoveries are typically summarized on maps. Methods of marking birds so that they are individually recognizable in the field, without capture, or that allow them to be tracked remotely, can increase the number of records per bird and provide information on movements in much more detail.

Colour-marking: following individuals by observation

Conventional ringing with numbered metal rings can often be frustrating for the ringer, because so few of the birds ringed are ever recorded again. Small birds are very seldom found dead; for some species, the rate is less than one bird per thousand ringed — a slender return indeed for the hundreds of hours invested in catching the birds in the first place. Of those small birds that are recorded again, many are retrapped by the ringer at the same site, or by other ringers nearby, and such records give a very limited idea of the movements that may have been undertaken.

Information can be gathered much faster if the birds are marked in such a way that each individual can be recognized at a distance, without the need for recapture (eg Rock 1999). The power of colour-marking, as a supplement to conventional ringing, was first demonstrated for wildfowl (Ogilvie 1972a). Marking may be dye painted on a conspicuous area of the plumage, a combination of coloured plastic rings on the legs, or a numbered plastic leg ring, wing-tag or collar. All marking methods must be approved as safe before they are used. For such schemes to be successful, the ringer must spend time not only in marking birds but also in searching likely sites for resightings. Where the ringer is keen to obtain sightings from other birdwatchers elsewhere, it is imperative that the marks are truly unique, for the species concerned, during the birds' expected lifetime. If this is not known to be the case, any distant resighting might not necessarily be of the individual under study but could be from another colour-marking project altogether. A number of international bodies, such as the Wader Study Group through its Colour-marking Register (see http://www.waderstudygroup.org), try to avoid or minimize overlap between schemes. An overview of colour-marking schemes in Europe, with contact names and addresses, was provided by Flamant (1994) and updated information is now available on the World Wide Web (http://www.cr-birding.be). Further details of colour-marking in Britain & Ireland are provided in Chapter 4. Generally, colour-marked birds are also given a conventional metal ring, to ensure that they are uniquely marked and can be traced through the usual ring-recovery database system.

Colour-marking greatly increases the chances of multiple recordings of the same individual, showing a succession of movements during its lifetime (Fig 1.6). An unforeseen advantage of colour-ringing is that it may also increase the likelihood of a conventional metal ring being reported by the finder of a dead bird, because the colour marks draw attention to the fact that the bird also carries a numbered ring. The addition of single red rings to metal-ringed Grasshopper Warblers has provided at least two important recoveries that apparently would not have been recorded otherwise (S J R Rumsey pers comm).

Information from geese ringed with plastic rings gives opportunities for repeated observations that enable detailed understanding of an individual's movements. At a recent count, the longest duration of observations for a Greenland White-fronted Goose was 17 years and nine months (from July 1979 to March 1997) and the maximum number of resightings was 213 from another individual (D A Stroud pers comm). Multiple resightings like these give information on site-use and social interactions throughout the lifetime of many individual birds. For wildfowl in particular, such as White-fronted Goose, it is remarkable how much of our current knowledge of migration strategies and behavioural interactions now derives from colour-ringing. The importance of information gained from colour-marking is demonstrated in a number of the main species accounts in Chapter 6, including those for Cormorant, Bewick's and Whooper Swans, White-fronted and Greylag Geese, Goosander, Black-tailed Godwit and Puffin. In the future, carefully planned colour-marking studies over wide geographical areas may play a much larger role in investigating the nature of bird dispersal.

Chemical and biological markers

Chemical analysis of the body tissues or body feathers of a migratory bird, or tell-tale signs of other organisms with which it had come into contact, may give clues to locations that it had previously visited or, in the case of DNA, the population to which it belongs. There is scope for major developments in analytical techniques that may make methods such as these of considerable importance for migration studies in the future, alongside more traditional methods.

Genetic markers are already known that can separate individuals reliably at the species level, although for North American waders an initial investigation found that differentiation of populations within a species was most likely to be possible where they were well separated geographically and where philopatry was strongly developed (Haig et al 1997). Future developments of this technique may allow reliable identification of races or subpopulations at any stage of their annual cycle, thus allowing their migrations to be described in detail.

Stable isotopes of several abundant elements, including hydrogen, carbon, nitrogen and oxygen, and also sulphur, strontium and lead, have a distribution that varies spatially in a predictable way, either across broad geographical areas or between bird habitats. The ratio of deuterium (^{2}H) to ordinary hydrogen (^{1}H) in growing-season rainfall, for example, can be represented as a gradient across North America from Florida to the Northwest Territories (Hobson 1999; see Fig 7.1). It is becoming increasingly clear that the relative abundances of these isotopes in the environment are transferred directly to new growth of plant and animal tissue. For animals that have migrated, therefore, isotopic analysis can indicate the geographical locations or habitats in which they previously fed.

A major way in which isotopic analysis has proved its value for ornithology is in allowing distinctions to be quantified between groups of birds, for example North American wood-warblers hatched at different latitudes (Chamberlain et al 1997). Willow Warblers in Sweden show a discontinuity in isotopic profiles around 62°N that corresponds with the distribution of races trochilus and acredula and indicates that these two taxa winter in quite different parts of Africa (Chamberlain et al 2000). In this study, samples were taken from feathers that had been grown during the winter moult. Their chemical analysis does not show the location of the winter quarters but this is indicated by a small number of ring-recoveries in Africa.

The applications of isotopic analysis for studying bird movements are only beginning to be explored. A problem for large-scale studies is the way in which geographical isotopic gradients are overlain by differences in isotope ratios between habitats, such as coastal and freshwater, and between food-plants with differing photosynthetic pathways; these introduce a large degree of uncertainty into the patterns, such that many widely scattered locations might have the same isotopic profile. It is unlikely, therefore, that maps of isotopic distribution, or of genetic markers, will ever be precise enough to identify the origin of a particular individual, in the way that a ring-recovery can. At the population level, however, these methods can suggest broad patterns of movements between breeding and wintering areas, and fill some gaps in what we know from other sources.

At a simpler level, the presence of pollen from spring-flowering plants of the Mediterranean region in the facial feathers of five species of Sylvia warblers caught in Denmark in spring, but not in autumn, has been quoted as evidence that the Mediterranean Basin is an important spring stopover for these birds (Laursen et al 1997).

Remote sensing of individual birds: a new direction for the future

New techniques adopted over the last two decades have enabled a huge leap in our abilities to gather information on bird movements in ways never previously possible (Table 1.1). Remote sensing, by which the presence of an individual in a particular study area, or even its location globally, can be detected automatically at any time of day or night, promises to illuminate many of the mysteries that still remain after a century of recording observations and gathering ring-recoveries.

Various kinds of data loggers or archival tags, reviewed by Calvo & Furness (1992), have been fitted to birds to record their activity or their

Fig 1.6 Map of repeated sightings of an individually colour-ringed Black-tailed Godwit, showing the kind of information obtainable by this method, given effort spent searching for resightings by the ringers and by birdwatchers elsewhere. (*Source*: University of East Anglia/Wash Wader Ringing Group Black-tailed Godwit study.)

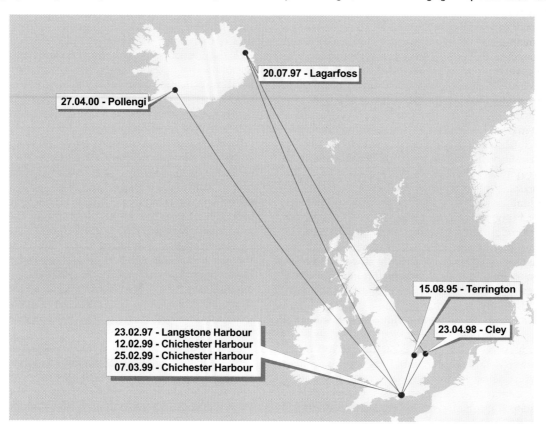

physiology for analysis once the bird has been recaptured and the device removed. Devices that log both time and heading, or those that carry a global positioning sensor, can record the precise path that a bird has followed between captures, for example on a foraging trip away from the nest. If combined with an altimeter or depth-recorder, the journey can even be traced in three dimensions by dead-reckoning calculations (Wilson 2001). Such devices have been used to track a number of Antarctic seabirds. Because of the requirement to retrieve the device by a subsequent recapture, however, the technique has a relatively limited application to studying bird movements.

At Wilhelmshaven in northwest Germany, individual Common Terns at a breeding colony are being studied in extraordinary detail by means of tiny transponders injected under the birds' skin and a large number of sensors, distributed throughout the colony, that cable information about individual birds continually back to a computer (Becker & Wendeln 1997, Becker *et al* 2001). The results give insight into the activity of birds at the colony, throughout the season and at all times of day and night, that would not be obtainable in any other way. Chicks marked in the early years of the study are now returning to breed, some having made brief visits to the site as non-breeders. A large number of individuals can be monitored simultaneously, and over periods that may be as long as the whole lifetime of the birds. The use of such transponders is currently only applicable to situations where the location of birds is predictable to within a few feet, the current maximum range of the sensors. Applications to the study of bird movements are therefore currently limited to recording the presence or absence of individuals at predetermined and very precise locations. If the range of such sensors can be increased, however, the technique could have wider application, for example for measuring turnover at staging sites.

Radio-tracking allows the observer to locate individual birds over a wide area, and sometimes at sites that are difficult to predict (Priede & Swift 1992, Kenward 2001). The birds are equipped with a radio-

transmitter that emits a regular and distinctive signal. Researchers then search likely areas, on foot or by vehicle, using radio receivers and strongly directional aerials that can give a good fix on the bird. Once the bird has been located by its signal, supplementary visual observations of its activity can often be made. This is a well-established technique and many examples of its use are reported in this book. It was first used on larger bird species that were better able to carry the weight of the transmitter but miniaturization now allows its use on much smaller birds, such as tits (Naef-Daenzer 1994) and Robins (*eg* Johnstone 1998, Godfrey & Bryant 2000).

A clear advantage of radio-tracking over any kind of visual observation is that it enables us to discover what individual birds are doing at night. Remarkable successes of the technique have included the discovery of the extent to which Woodcocks (Wilson 1983, Hoodless 1994a) and Nightjars (Alexander & Cresswell 1990, Cresswell & Alexander 1992) use habitats at night that differ from those they occupy during the day. Its value for detecting longer movements of birds is limited, however. Once a signal is lost, the researcher does not generally know whether the bird has moved away or whether the transmitter has stopped working. The range at which a signal can be detected depends greatly on the power of the transmitter, the height above ground of the bird and the receiving system and, to a lesser extent, on the terrain, habitat and the presence of obstacles such as hills or buildings. It is rarely more than a few kilometres, unless the birds are flying at high altitude or being tracked from aircraft, under which conditions signals can often carry an order of magnitude further than at ground level. Widening the search area may sometimes enable a missing tag to be relocated. Searches using light aircraft, taking advantage of the improved range at high altitude and covering very large areas in a short time, were successful in relocating radio-tagged Golden Eagles that had dispersed away from the natal area (Grant & McGrady 1999) and have also been used in a range of other studies. It has even been possible to relocate waders tagged in their wintering areas back in their remote breeding sites, and geese, tagged when breeding, back on their wintering grounds (*eg* Samuel *et al* 1999). For Bitterns, researchers have asked birdwatchers throughout Britain to inform them of individuals that arrive at unexpected sites, so that the birds can be checked for active transmitters; in this way, the search area has been expanded to cover the whole country.

The main drawback of ground-based radio-tracking, in the present context, is that data must be won through intensive effort by observers in the field. Owing to this, and to the technical limitations of transmitters and the methods by which they can safely be attached to birds, few birds have been radio-tracked for as much as a year. There have been few cases where radio-tracking has led to discoveries about migrations of birds, as opposed to more predictable shorter-distance movements and dispersal, because the geographical scale of the observations is usually rather small. For most species that have been studied, the number of individuals radio-tracked has also been small, raising questions about how representative these individuals may have been of the population from which they were drawn.

The most promising recent development in bird migration study has been the combination of satellite technology and radio-tracking. Satellite systems are now operating that can report the location of a ground-based transmitter at daily or hourly intervals, and even in almost real time (*eg* M R Fuller *et al* 1995). Signals that indicate the type of activity that the bird is carrying out can also be relayed (*eg* Ginati *et al* 1995). Solar panels can now supply the power that is required to send such signals, thus increasing the life of transmitters beyond that of the non-rechargeable batteries on which they previously depended.

Some satellite tracks for birds using Britain & Ireland, for example, Cormorants, Whooper Swans, White-fronted Geese and Ospreys, are reproduced in this book. World-wide, satellite telemetry has been used to follow White Storks from Germany to Africa and back (Berthold *et al* 1995, 1997a, b), Lesser Spotted Eagles in Europe and Africa (Meyburg *et al* 1995) and geese in the Arctic (*eg* Gudmundsson *et al* 1995, Clausen & Bustnes 1998). Even the migration of a flightless bird, the Magellanic Penguin, that swims northward from its South American colonies after breeding, has been tracked by satellite (Stokes & Boersma 1998). Tracks are now often reported on the Internet, giving world-wide access to the data as they are received. The following sites were recently active:

African Penguins off South Africa:
(http://www.uct.ac.za/depts/stats/adu/oilspill/sapmap.htm);

White Storks in South Africa:
(http://www.uct.ac.za/depts/stats/adu/wstork00.htm);

Peregrine Falcons in the USA:
(http://www.dom.com/about/environment/falcon/tracking.html);

Ospreys from Britain:
(http://www.ospreys.org.uk/AWOP/Satellite.htm).

The new capability to follow long-distance migratory movements in fine detail is very exciting. Detailed information linking the phenology, location and direction and speed of movements during migration seasons, in relation to weather, will prove extremely valuable in unravelling the choices made by individuals. The results from satellite telemetry provide extremely instructive information on migration routes, albeit for small numbers of individual birds. Regrettably, this technology remains restrictively expensive and outside most volunteer and many professional budgets, but its potential for migration studies is huge.

The need for an integrated approach to migration study

None of the categories of methods described here is a substitute for any other. Rather, they complement each other in the nature of the information provided (Table 1.1). Each has its place in the network of data collection.

Some ornithologists with a particularly rigorous scientific outlook may question the value of documenting sightings in local or county bird reports, or national reports on rare birds, and some do not contribute their own observations. They might say that the fieldwork that produces the information in bird reports is unsystematic and the search effort unmeasurable, and therefore that the data are essentially qualitative, or at best semi-quantitative, and that because the observations reported are highly biased towards particular sites and times of year, they are potentially misleading. But this is to overlook the value of even qualitative observations in providing a broad backcloth to our knowledge of bird migration, to which more rigorous methods of collecting data add detail. With global warming and its associated biological changes well under way, we cannot assume that the information already gathered is adequate. Synthesis of ordinary unsystematic bird records will continue to be needed, therefore.

An integrated approach to migration study is required, in which both non-systematic and systematic bird recording are pursued alongside the latest technological advances. Detailed satellite tracks of a small number of individuals are a wonderful revelation of the movements of these particular birds, but the place in the migration system of the species of a few individuals, perhaps unrepresentative in respect of the time and place of marking, can only be assessed where knowledge from surveys and other observations provides sufficient background.

Ringing provides remarkable insights into the lives of individual birds and will continue to have unique importance in studies of bird migration. Since it often produces only a few records in time and space for each individual, it is likely to be used increasingly in combination with other techniques, such as colour-marking and remote tracking (see Chapter 7). The biases resulting from spatial and temporal variation in the reporting of ringed birds must be considered carefully when interpreting movement patterns derived from ring-recoveries (see Chapter 4). Ringing is generally less reliable than count data for providing the basic information about seasonal occurrence, except in habitats with dense cover, such as rainforest. Observations are constantly necessary, therefore, as a background against which ring-recovery patterns can be interpreted.

While much of this book focuses on information derived from bird ringing, we trust that by integrating ringing and non-ringing information on movements throughout the book, we will show ringers how bird recording is essential for interpreting their data and, equally, show birdwatchers what valuable work ringers have been doing all these years. Contributors of information who are either ringers or birdwatchers, but not both, may not have realized just how closely their activities complement each other, even in a British & Irish context. Cooperation between participants in all areas of bird study will be increasingly important if we are to unravel the remaining mysteries of bird migration. We hope that this book might persuade more people to maximize their contribution to migration study by getting involved in a wider range of relevant, productive and enjoyable methods of study.

2 Ringing in Britain and Ireland

Jacquie Clark & Chris Wernham

The development of bird marking

The earliest recorded examples of marking of birds both involve the use of Swallows as 'homing pigeons' by the ancient Romans, firstly during a siege in the 3rd century BC and, less dramatically, to report the results of races (Mead 1974b). The investigation of bird migration is reported to have begun as early as 750 years ago, when according to a Cistercian prior in Germany, a man attached a small piece of parchment to the leg of a Swallow with a message asking where it went. The bird is supposed to have returned next year with a message from Asia! The annual disappearance of Swallows continued to be of interest and their habit of feeding low over water led to the suggestion that they spent the winter hibernating in ponds. In the 18th century the German ornithologist J L Frisch disproved this theory by marking birds with threads dyed with watercolours: the birds returned the next year with the dyes still visible and he therefore concluded that they had not hibernated under water. Later, more permanent rings were added to falcons by their owners, who sometimes also marked the falcons' quarry and released them. For example, a Grey Heron caught at a heronry in Norfolk in 1844 carried a ring with the inscription 'Colonel Wilson, Didlington, 1829' (Broderick & Salvin in Stevenson 1870). At the end of the 19th century, Lord William Percy started to ring Woodcocks on his estate in Northumberland; 375 birds were ringed between 1891 and 1908 and 58 were later recovered (Rydzewski 1951). However, the rings carried only the letter 'N', for Northumberland, and the year.

The first person to see the possibilities of marking birds with a unique identification number and return address, as on modern rings, was a Danish teacher named Hans Christian Cornelius Mortensen. He first used numbered aluminium rings in 1899, when he placed them on 165 Starlings that he had caught in nestboxes fitted with an automatic closing mechanism (Preuss 2001). Mortensen made his own rings, cutting the aluminium to size, removing sharp edges with sandpaper and stamping the address and number on each. He then put them in a box of sand and asked students to carry the box around in their pockets for days, so that the sand wore the edges absolutely smooth, making the rings safe to fit on birds. Mortensen went on to ring systematically storks, ducks and seabirds. In order to ring ducks, he bought them from the owners of the duck decoy on the Danish island of Fanø. His activities drew the attention of ornithologists in other countries, many of whom then followed his example. Most of Mortensen's research papers were eventually published in English (Jespersen & Tåning 1950).

The development of ringing in Britain & Ireland

Ringing in Britain & Ireland started just 10 years after Mortensen's pioneering work, when two schemes were set up in 1909, one in London founded by Harry Witherby of *British Birds* and one in Aberdeen started by Arthur Landsborough Thomson. The Aberdeen

This chapter has been supported in memory of Adrian and Wendy Cawthorne, who contributed greatly to British & Irish bird ringing

scheme came to an end during the First World War but the Witherby scheme continued, and was handed over to the recently founded BTO in June 1937. Both Landsborough Thomson and Witherby retained strong links with the BTO and the Ringing Scheme through its early development. The rings issued by Witherby were classified just as small, medium, large or extra-large, a far cry from today when there are 20 ring sizes with internal diameters varying from 2 to 26 mm (to ensure a safe fit for birds of all leg shapes and sizes) and a variety of metals are used. Only small numbers of birds were ringed initially but, by the end of 1909, there were already 44 recoveries on file (41 from ringing in Britain & Ireland and three of birds ringed abroad and found here). Interestingly, the earliest recovery recorded in the BTO database involved a Pintail ringed at Fanø by Mortensen himself on 20 October 1908 and found dead on Lough Neagh on 15 April 1909. The first recovery from ringing in Britain & Ireland was of a Meadow Pipit ringed in the nest on 19 June 1909 at Ben Rhydding, Yorkshire, and found dead close by on 9 July 1909 having flown into telegraph wires.

The Witherby Ringing Scheme was run initially from High Holborn, London. Its day-to-day organization was taken over by Miss Elsie Leach during the 1930s, and she moved with the scheme to the BTO. The BTO headquarters were then in Oxford but the Ringing Scheme was housed at the British Museum (Natural History) in London and so was able to adopt the extremely valuable, internationally recognizable address of 'British Museum, London' that is still in use today. Elsie Leach continued to work for the Ringing Scheme until 1963. In 1953, a first contract was issued to the BTO by the Government's nature conservation body, then the Nature Conservancy. This recognition that bird ringing was important for scientific and conservation purposes marked the start of an important association between the Ringing Scheme and the statutory conservation bodies that still continues. It allowed the employment, in 1954, of the first full-time Ringing Officer, Bob Spencer, who started to develop the scientific objectives of the scheme. Bob was also responsible for producing a 16-page booklet summarizing the rules of the scheme and giving advice to ringers, followed by the first *Ringer's Manual*. This has since undergone a number of revisions and has become a comprehensive source of information, rules and guidelines on all aspects of bird ringing (Redfern & Clark 2001). Bob went on to introduce many more innovations to the scheme. For example, he started 'project-ringing' such as the Sand Martin Enquiry (see later); pioneered constant-effort ringing and, in collaboration with Cecil Lambourne, began the development of the full range of rings used today. The Lambourne family continued to supply the BTO with rings until the end of the 20th century.

In 1957, Ken Williamson was appointed as the BTO's Migration Research Officer. Ken, previously a warden at Fair Isle Bird Observatory,

Fig 2.1 The numbers of birds ringed and recovered in Britain & Ireland, by decade. (*Sources*: numbers ringed are taken from the BTO annual ringing reports and numbers recovered from the BTO's ring-recovery database.)

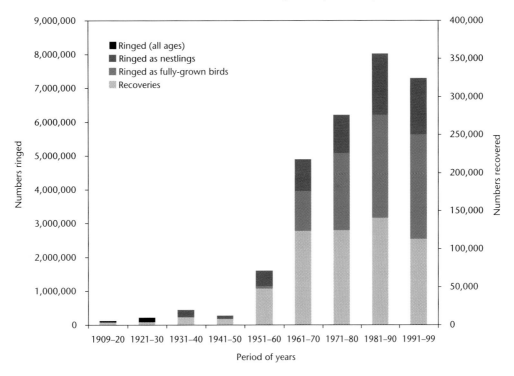

was a pioneer of field taxonomy. Among his many contributions to ringing research, Ken was responsible for writing three ground-breaking guides to the identification of Palearctic warblers (Williamson 1960, 1962a, 1964), developing moult recording and editing the BTO journal *Bird Migration*. He went on to develop the BTO's pioneering scheme for monitoring numbers of breeding birds, the Common Birds Census.

In 1963, the BTO found new premises and united the staff, now including Chris Mead, at Beech Grove in Tring, Hertfordshire. Bob Spencer and Chris Mead saw the Ringing Scheme transformed! There were leaps forward in general administration and computerization. Butted rings made of special alloys were introduced to replace the old-

Fig 2.2 The number of ringers in Britain & Ireland, 1960–99: 'A' permit holders can ring totally independently; 'C' ringers can ring on their own, but are responsible to the holder of an 'A' permit, and 'Trainees' can ring only under direct supervision. (*Source*: BTO annual ringing reports.)

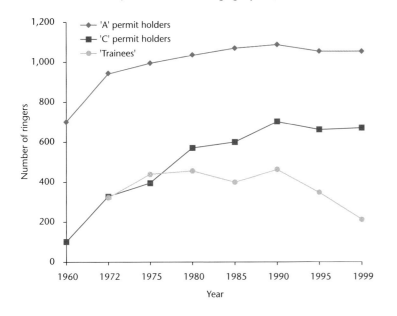

fashioned overlapping ones that had proved subject to excessive abrasion and corrosion. Ringing training courses were introduced and long series at Gibraltar Point and Spurn saw many trainee ringers receive their full permits.

The first meeting of the 'Ringing and Migration Committee' (the forerunner of the current Ringing Committee) was held in March 1964, following 24 previous meetings of the 'Bird Ringing Committee'. Committee members have been involved in decisions on the direction of ringing research and in the initiation of special projects, as well as considering rules and procedures. A permit system for ringers was first introduced in 1956, and official training standards in 1960. The Ringing Scheme began producing a regular newsletter for its ringers, the *Ringers' Bulletin*, in 1957, and its own journal for publishing the scientific results from ringing, *Ringing & Migration*, in 1975. In addition, annual conferences have provided opportunities for ringers to exchange ideas and to hear the results of projects based on their data for over 30 years.

In 1979, the first mainframe computer arrived at Beech Grove, less powerful than a single PC of today but the start of a revolution! Soon recovery records were being typed straight onto the computer, rather than onto carbon-copied forms, and the BTO received a grant from EURING (see later) in the early 1980s, to allow all the back data from BTO-ringed birds to be input. In 1983, a group of dedicated volunteer ringers started work on a suite of computer programs for ringers to use, to input their own ringing data and, later, submit them electronically to the BTO database. The first program (B-RING), and the more recent IPMR (Integrated Population Monitoring Reporter) have gone from strength to strength, allowing ringing and related data to be input, checked, manipulated and submitted to BTO headquarters very efficiently indeed, mainly through the efforts of the ringers themselves (see www.bto.org/ringing/ringsoft/software.htm for further details).

Very little ringing was carried out in Ireland before 1950 (O J Merne pers comm). Systematic ringing began with the establishment of bird observatories in Ireland, starting with Great Saltee in 1950 and continuing with Cape Clear, Tory Island and Malin Head. General ringing in Ireland increased through the 1960s, stimulated by the establishment of a number of ringing groups. In the 1970s in particular,

Fig 2.3 The importance of ringing in the BTO's Integrated Population Monitoring (IPM) Programme. The top of the diagram shows the major BTO schemes that contribute to the programme, the middle shows the types of biological information collected and the bottom shows how and why the information is used: the key places where ringing contributes are shown in red. (*Source*: adapted from Baillie *et al* 1999b.)

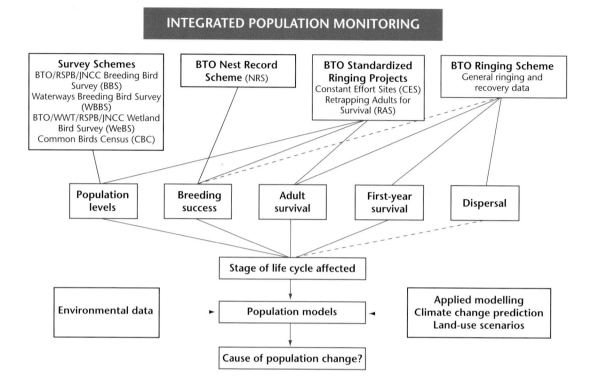

a number of ringing training courses were run in Ireland, involving BTO staff and other experienced British ringers, again greatly encouraging further ringing in Ireland. An Irish Ringing Report has been published in the journal *Irish Birds* since 1975. New wildlife legislation (The Wildlife Act) came into force in the Republic of Ireland in 1976, providing the official licensing for bird ringing. Soon after this, the Irish Government commenced providing annual financial support to the Ringing Scheme and it has remained the British & Irish Ringing Scheme to this day.

Numbers ringed and recovered, the techniques and the ringers

In the early years of the Ringing Scheme, only small numbers of birds were ringed, and therefore recovered (Fig 2.1), with a strong bias towards the ringing of nestlings (see Fig 4.6). Adult birds were caught largely in traps, often the large-scale and permanent Helgoland traps at bird observatories. The first bird observatory in Britain & Ireland was set up in the autumn of 1933 by Ronald Lockley on Skokholm, an island off Pembrokeshire, where Ronald built the first British Helgoland trap. This was rapidly followed by the establishment of the Isle of May Bird Observatory by Midlothian Ornithological Club, following the pioneering work of Miss L J Rintoul and Miss E V Baxter on the island's birds (Spencer 1976). Both observatories were set up with the express purpose of catching and ringing birds on migration. Spencer (1976) details the further establishment of the bird observatory network, including the establishment of the first observatory in Ireland, on Great Saltee, in 1950 (see Fig 1.1 for the current distribution of sites within Britain and Ireland). By 1951, one million birds had been ringed in Britain & Ireland. Rapid changes took place from the late 1950s, with the introduction of new catching techniques. The first mist-net was brought to England in 1956 and demonstrated by Dick Le Sueur and Doug Hook at a meeting of the Bird Observatories Council in Oxford. The use of these nets, imported from Japan, quickly changed the patterns of ringing. Now many more adult birds (particularly passerines) could be caught at a

wider variety of sites (see Fig 4.6). The development of the rocket-net by the Wildfowl Trust in the early 1950s and, in the 1960s, the cannon-net, by Clive Minton of the Wash Wader Ringing Group, led to large increases in the numbers of adult wildfowl and waders (and later also gulls) ringed and recovered. These changes took the number of birds ringed by the scheme to five million by 1966 and, by the end of 1996, over 25 million birds had been ringed, producing over half a million recovery records.

The early increases in the numbers of birds ringed, and therefore in the numbers of recoveries, were initially welcomed, and special projects were initiated to encourage more ringing of particular species. For example, the Sand Martin Enquiry (1959–65), which provided ringers with free rings for Sand Martins after their first hundred birds had been ringed, was particularly successful. Over a quarter of a million Sand Martins were ringed during the project, resulting in more than 11,000 recoveries (C J Mead pers comm). However, the increase in work for the Ringing Scheme staff, not matched by increased funding, later became a problem. Ring prices were increased in 1968 to try to control the numbers of birds ringed. This was not completely successful and, from the beginning of 1970, restrictions on the ringing of a number of species (including Sand Martins at roosting sites) were introduced. Such restrictions must have seemed a good option at the time, but they meant that, for example, very few House Sparrows were ringed for many years. This gap in ringing effort is now making it difficult to understand the causes of the subsequent population decline in this species. More positively, part of the restrictions involved the introduction of special data forms for a limited number of species; some of the data (particularly weights) recorded on these forms have been of great use to researchers in recent years (*eg* Gosler *et al* 1995a). Also, the introduction of free rings for Guillemots, Razorbills and Manx Shearwaters in 1959 in Britain (and 1965 in Ireland) — for the auks, a similar arrangement continuing with support from the JNCC/BTO partnership today — has ensured that sufficient numbers of these species have been ringed each year for monitoring purposes. In the 1980s, it was decided to direct ringing in a positive way, by paying rebates to ringers who had ringed species of conservation interest, as part of the overall scientific development of the scheme (see later). By the end of the 20th century, this approach had been further developed so that ring prices now, where possible, reflect the conservation priority of the species being ringed (Clark *et al* 1998).

The British & Irish Ringing Scheme is now the largest in Europe, with around three-quarters of a million birds ringed each year, generating over 11,000 recoveries (Fig 2.1). Of these recoveries, around 38% are from resident passerines (species where most of the population winters in Europe), 11% from seabirds (excluding gulls), 17% from wildfowl and 10% from migrant passerines (Baillie *et al* 1999b). In 1996, 2,095 ringers were registered with the scheme, of whom 1,073 had 'A' permits (fully independent), 676 had 'C' permits (limited independence) and 346 were 'trainees' (ringing only under direct supervision) (Toms & Clark 1998). Of these, 74% were based in England, 15% in Scotland, 5% in Wales, 4.5% in Ireland and 1.5% outside Britain & Ireland. The numbers of permit holders have shown a gradual increase over time (Fig 2.2) and are now approximately stable, while numbers of trainees were steady for a number of years but have declined somewhat in very recent years. A very high proportion of British & Irish ringers take part in the scheme entirely on a voluntary basis, in their leisure time. The BTO is granted a licence for ringing, to be carried out by its permit-holders, by the UK Government's country agencies (see Boobyer 1999). In the Republic of Ireland, a separate licence, again administered by the BTO through its permit system, is issued by Dúchas The Heritage Service (National Parks and Wildlife). The standards of training for ringers in Britain & Ireland are among the highest in the world. Many ringers from abroad have visited Britain & Ireland to receive training, and BTO ringers have made large contributions by passing on their skills and experience in training programmes abroad.

Development of the Ringing Scheme for science and conservation

Until the end of the 1950s, the work of the BTO focused heavily on migration, with the Ringing Scheme and the Bird Observatories Network at the heart of that work. Although the study of bird movements provided the initial motivation for ringing in Britain & Ireland, ring-recovery data were also being used for pioneering studies of survival, such of those of Lack (1951) and Haldane (1955), even in those early days. Since 1960, the BTO's work has increasingly been directed towards research of high value for applied conservation. The Ringing Scheme has been increasingly important for providing information on migration routes and longevity, as well as for answering more complex ecological questions involving the marking of individual birds.

The close association, continuing since 1953, between the Ringing Scheme and the Nature Conservancy, and its successors, the Nature Conservancy Council and the current Joint Nature Conservation Committee (JNCC), has been extremely important in ensuring that the results from ringing are accessible to conservation policy-makers and practical conservationists. In a review of the contribution of ringing studies to bird conservation (Langslow 1981), Derek Langslow, then the Chief Ornithologist of the Nature Conservancy and also a volunteer ringer, noted how important it was that the Ringing Scheme should continue to evolve. He also highlighted the value of ringing for conservation, notably for seabirds (*eg* to assess the origins of those affected by oiling incidents), top predators (as indicators of the general health of the environment) and a number of small passerines (to gain information on habitat use, site-fidelity, local movements, survival and the effects of habitat change). The scientific objectives of the scheme were reviewed a few years later (O'Connor 1984) and, in 1986, the Ringing Committee decided that a 'Ringing Scheme Objectives Review Group' should be established to lay down the principal scientific aims of the scheme. The Group consulted widely among volunteer ringers and professional ornithologists and there was considerable agreement as to what the major objectives should be (see Baillie *et al* 1999a).

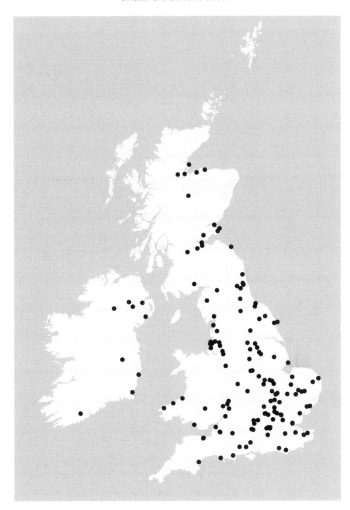

Fig 2.4 Distribution of BTO Constant Effort Sites (CES) operated in Britain & Ireland in 2000.

The British & Irish Ringing Scheme today

In 1995, a joint JNCC/BTO workshop was a major component of the most recent review of the Ringing Scheme (Baillie *et al* 1999b), and the review working group published the current 'Scientific Strategy', containing objectives for the scheme, in 1996 (Baillie *et al* 1999c). The Scientific Strategy will continue to be reviewed at regular intervals, to ensure that the contribution of ringing to conservation science and ornithological research continues to increase. The emphasis in the training given to ringers is now also strongly focused on the gathering, safely, of high-quality data for use in research and conservation. Aspects of data gathering within the Ringing Scheme are considered in Chapter 4 and potential future developments in Chapter 7. This chapter focuses on the conservation-related research work of the Ringing Scheme, which concentrates on two major topics: these are the measurement and understanding of changes in bird populations (population dynamics) and migration and movements.

Measuring and understanding changes in bird populations

Data from the Ringing Scheme are now vitally important in allowing us to measure and understand changes in our bird populations. The BTO has developed a programme of Integrated Population Monitoring (IPM), which brings together information from counts, nest recording and ringing, so that any changes in populations can be identified, the relevant stage of the life cycle can be established and the causes of the observed changes can be investigated (Baillie 1990a, 1991). The Ringing Scheme has a central role in the IPM programme (Wernham *et al* 1998, Baillie *et al* 1999b), contributing in all areas (Fig 2.3).

Fig 2.5 The distribution of active constant-effort ringing programmes in Europe. For each country or scheme, the year that it was initiated and the number of sites operated in 2000 is shown: two separate schemes operate currently in Spain. Most schemes follow the methods developed for the BTO's CES scheme. (*Source*: EURING EURO-CES Project, see Wernham & Balmer 2001.)

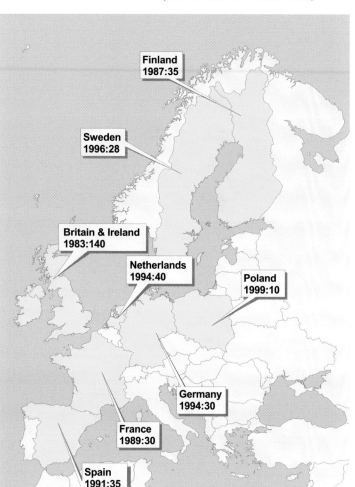

Fig 2.6 The distribution of Retrapping Adults for Survival (RAS) studies of Sand Martins, Swallows and Pied Flycatchers in 2000. This BTO project encourages a geographical spread of studies for each target species, so that regional variations in adult survival rates can be investigated.

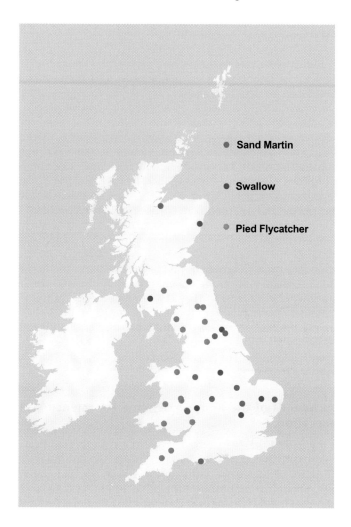

The information from general ringing is enhanced by data from two important special ringing projects. The Constant Effort Sites (CES) scheme involves volunteer ringers in mist-netting in a standard manner between May and August each year at over 140 sites (Fig 2.4), mainly in reedbed and scrub habitats. It has been running since the early 1980s and monitors the breeding numbers, productivity and adult survival rates of around 25 species of common passerine (Peach 1993, Peach *et al* 1990, 1996, 1998). The CES scheme provides the best measure of changes in population size for some species breeding in specialist habitats, such as Reed and Sedge Warblers. It also provides unique information on productivity. This complements information on breeding success from the Nest Record Scheme (Crick & Baillie 1996), because it provides a measure that is integrated across all breeding attempts within each breeding season and includes immediate post-fledging survival, which is difficult to measure by other means. The recaptures between years of individual birds at CES sites provide invaluable information on adult survival rates for species of small birds for which the general rates of recovery from dead birds are very low. Since the development of CES in Britain & Ireland, it has been adopted in a number of other European countries (Fig 2.5) and in North America (*eg* DeSante *et al* 1995, 1999).

The Retrapping Adults for Survival (RAS) project started in 1998, resulting from a recommendation in the Ringing Scheme Scientific Strategy (Baillie *et al* 1999c). The idea is that birds are caught and then retrapped or resighted during the breeding season, in order to measure

adult survival rates. The approach is very similar to that of CES, but uses a single-species approach, with capture techniques, study areas and seasons appropriate to the chosen species. RAS complements the CES scheme and general ringing by targeting species of current conservation concern and those for which survival rates are otherwise poorly monitored (Balmer 2001, Balmer & Wernham 2001). The project aims to increase the number of studies of target species around Britain & Ireland, so that survival rates can be compared between regions. Current target species include Pied Flycatcher, Sand Martin, Swallow and Eider (Fig 2.6).

The measurement of survival rates using data from the British & Irish Ringing Scheme has contributed to our understanding of the causes of the population declines observed for a number of species of conservation concern. For example, a strong relationship has been shown between the survival rates of Sedge Warblers, and their consequent population levels, and rainfall in the Sahel region of West Africa, where British & Irish birds spend the winter (Peach *et al* 1991). For some other Palearctic–African migrants, including Willow Warblers breeding in Britain, research has shown that winter mortality is important in driving changes in population size, although the environmental conditions underlying the relationship need further investigation (Baillie & Peach 1992, Peach *et al* 1995a; Fig 2.7).

Ring-recovery data have also featured prominently in recent research on the causes of widespread declines among farmland birds in Britain & Ireland (Tucker & Heath 1994, Aebischer *et al* 2000). Population

Fig 2.7 (a) Patterns of change (variation in the 95% confidence limits) of indices of abundance of the Willow Warbler breeding populations in northern Britain (blue) and southern Britain (red) in 1984–93, as measured by the BTO Common Birds Census, and (b) the adult survival rates (with 95% confidence limits) of Willow Warblers ringed in southern Britain, calculated using data from the BTO Constant Effort Sites (CES) Scheme. Survival rates in southern Britain fell markedly during the period of rapid population decline in 1990–92, but changed little in northern Britain. Variations in productivity during the same period were not sufficient to explain the population decline. (*Source*: **Peach** *et al* **1995**, by permission of Taylor & Francis Ltd – www.tandf.co.uk/journals.)

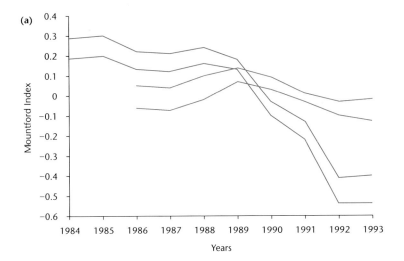

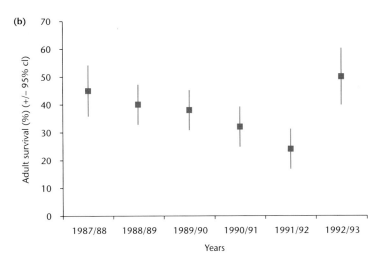

modelling has shown that changes in the first-year survival rates of Song Thrushes (Thomson *et al* 1997), and in the first-year and adult survival rates of Reed Buntings (Peach *et al* 1999), Goldfinches and House Sparrows (Siriwardena *et al* 1999) have been the driving forces behind the changes in their numbers on farmland. Changes in survival rates have in fact contributed to the population changes of at least 13 species of birds on farmland in Britain & Ireland (Siriwardena *et al* 1998b). In contrast, a comparison of survival information from ring-recoveries and information on breeding success has shown that the population decline of Lapwings breeding in Britain has largely been the result of very low productivity rather than reduced survival rates (Peach *et al* 1994).

Ringing data have recently been used to great effect to investigate the reasons behind declines during 1990–98 in the populations of Oystercatchers and Knot wintering on the Wash (Atkinson *et al* 2000). Ring-recoveries were used to measure overwinter survival rates, and recruitment rates were estimated from the juvenile:adult ratios in samples of birds caught during each winter period. The results showed that the decline in Oystercatcher numbers from the winter of 1992/93 onwards was driven by a decline in adult survival rates, coupled with poor recruitment (Fig 2.8a). The overwinter survival of adult Oystercatchers was high, except for three 'kill years' (Fig 2.8b), and was significantly related to measures of Edible Cockle and Edible Mussel abundance in the Wash. Knot showed no trend in overwinter survival; annual recruitment rates explained much of the variation in their winter numbers.

Investigating migration and movements

Most ringing schemes, including the British & Irish one, were originally set up primarily to study bird migration. There has, however, been less emphasis on migration research in Britain & Ireland in recent years, while the population-monitoring value of ringing has been developed. In continental Europe, however, a high level of migration-related work based on ringing data has continued (see Spina 1999). The results from migration research are, of course, vital for conservation, as is demonstrated throughout this book. For example, without information on migration routes and wintering areas (mainly gained by ringing) it would be impossible to identify, and hence conserve, sites that are important for particular populations (*eg* Davidson *et al* 1999, Spina 1999). Information from the British & Irish Ringing Scheme has been used in a number of studies to investigate the movements of waders, particularly in relation to their use of specific estuaries (*eg* Symonds & Langslow 1984, Davidson *et al* 1986a) and in relation to the designation of specific areas as refuges (Rehfisch *et al* 1996). Ring-recovery data play

an essential role in the assessment of cold-weather movements, particularly for waterfowl (Baillie *et al* 1986, Ridgill & Fox 1990, Clark *et al* 1993), allowing measures to be taken to protect populations that have moved in response to cold weather (Stroud 1992).

Information that has been generated by the British & Irish Ringing Scheme on the movements of northern Europe's internationally important populations of seabirds, has been invaluable in recent years because of the ever-present threats from pollution, accidental mortality in fishing nets and depletion of fish-stocks. A number of applied analyses of British and Irish seabird ring-recovery data have been carried out, in relation to observed seabird 'wrecks' and the differential movement patterns of regional subpopulations (*eg* Baillie & Mead 1982, Galbraith *et al* 1986, Heubeck *et al* 1991, Baillie *et al* 1994; see also Harris & Tasker 1999). Such projects allow the seabirds associated with particular mortality events in a given sea area to be traced to a specific breeding colony or group of colonies, thereby identifying more closely the scale and location of the impacts. Potentially important future work on the movements of seabirds in relation to environmental changes is discussed in Chapter 7.

Ring-recoveries of Cormorants and sawbill ducks were used recently to determine the seasonal movements of subpopulations living in different regions and investigate the potential threats to inland fisheries, which are widely perceived to have increased in Britain in the last two or three decades of the 20th century (Rehfisch *et al* 1999). Ring-recoveries were also used to show how the survival rates of British & Irish Cormorants have changed over time and how these changes might influence the population trends and, hence, the potential for future conflicts with the fisheries (Wernham & Peach 1999, Rehfisch *et al* 1999).

Immigration and emigration may be negligible when considering changes in populations that occupy very large areas, such as whole countries or regions of continents, but they may be very important when considering populations living in much smaller areas, such as a particular area of woodland or a specific seabird colony. At this more local scale, immigration and emigration may play an important role in determining population size (or density). Information on immigration to and emigration from breeding populations is therefore essential for conservation purposes, for example for investigating the effects of habitat fragmentation or degradation (both now pandemic) on bird populations. Hence, information on dispersal is of great importance to the BTO's Integrated Population Monitoring programme (Fig 2.3). Ring-recoveries have a key role to play in measuring the distances over which birds disperse (see Table 1.1). Recently, the patterns of natal and breeding dispersal shown by 75 species of birds breeding in terrestrial habitats in

Fig 2.8 The use of ringing data to investigate the decline of wintering Oystercatchers on the Wash, 1990–98: (a) predicted changes in wintering numbers based on survival and recruitment rates (blue) matched the observed numbers closely (red, Underhill Index with final year set to a value of 100) and (b) overwinter (October–March) survival rates of adult Oystercatchers on the Wash, showing the 'kill years' of 1992/93, 1995/96 and 1996/97; red circles show the measured survival rates and blue triangles the rates predicted from the proportion of birds showing suspended moult during December–September each year (with missing data for years when too few birds were caught). (*Source*: Atkinson *et al* 2000.)

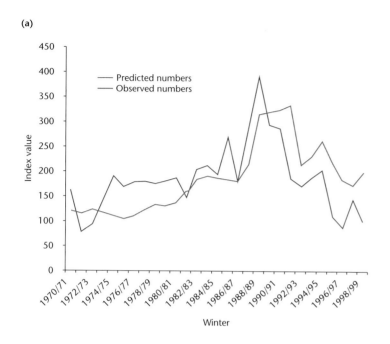

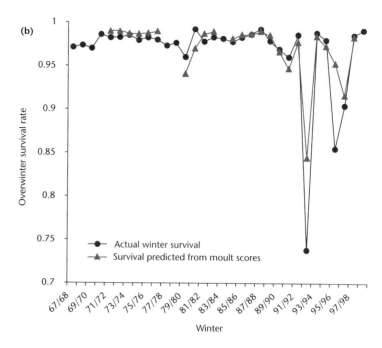

Britain & Ireland have been investigated using ring-recoveries, including the relationships between dispersal distances and a range of morphological, ecological and life-history characteristics (Paradis *et al* 1998). The dispersal patterns from the analyses have since been used in spatial population models for Great Tits living in a hypothetical area with a mixture of farmland and woodland habitats (Baillie *et al* 2000), showing, for example, that for this species population density within an isolated patch of woodland is depressed relative to that in a larger woodland area (Fig 2.9). There is great potential to develop this research, using a combination of new data collection, to look at movements and recruitment between habitats, and further modelling, to provide more information of applied conservation value (see Chapter 7).

The importance of the British & Irish Ringing Scheme for providing key information on bird movements for conservation and scientific purposes was recognized in full when the production of an atlas of bird migration was identified as a priority in both the 1987 and 1996 reviews of the Ringing Scheme. Throughout this book, the conservation importance of the ring-recovery data collected by the scheme since 1909 is highlighted. A synthesis of its current value to conservation is provided in Chapter 7, which also demonstrates that there is still much to learn about movements and that the Ringing Scheme will play a major role in future research on this topic.

Other applied conservation research based on ringing in Britain & Ireland

The information gained from ringing in Britain & Ireland is also put to a number of other applied uses. For example, ring-recovery data from 18 European ringing schemes, including our own, have been used to investigate regional variation across Europe and changes through time in hunting pressures on 20 migratory species; the results suggest that the hunting of some species has decreased (Tucker *et al* 1990, McCulloch *et al* 1992, Fig 2.10; see also Chapter 4). European ring-recoveries of Snipe and Woodcock have also been used to look in greater detail at the patterns of hunting pressure experienced by these species, once again suggesting reduced hunting in more recent years (Henderson *et al* 1993). Potentially important future work on this topic is discussed in Chapter 7.

Information from the British & Irish Ringing Scheme has been used to assess the effectiveness of efforts to rehabilitate injured and oiled birds. Ringing showed that the release of many rehabilitated and captive-bred Barn Owls in the 1970s and 1980s was unsuccessful as a conservation measure, because their survival rates were much lower than those of wild individuals (Percival 1990). It is now recognized that habitat restoration and the provision of nest sites are more effective measures for conserving Barn Owls, and they may be released only as part of carefully planned and licensed projects. Against a background of earlier evidence from ringing that the survival of rehabilitated auks was poor, ring-recoveries of British and Irish Guillemots that had been cleaned and rehabilitated after oiling, have been compared with those of healthy, wild birds. Less than one bird out of every hundred rehabilitated auks survived the following year, and more than 80% died in the first month after release; their survival was less than 1% of the value for healthy, wild Guillemots (Wernham *et al* 1997). These sad results led to a series of recommendations, the principal one being that the effectiveness of different treatment and cleaning regimes should be monitored by following individuals through the rehabilitation process (Wernham & Williams 1999). To this end, many more rehabilitated Guillemots are now being carefully monitored through the cleaning and recuperation period and then ringed with BTO rings, so that their movements and survival can be followed once they are released. The methods of cleaning and treatment of any birds that are known through ringing to have done well after release can then be compared with those of birds that do badly, to assess whether certain treatment regimes work better than others. In time, this could help to refine the rehabilitation process for auks and increase success rates.

Measurements of the body condition of birds may be valuable for predicting their chances of survival, and knowledge of the relationships between condition and survival can be applied directly to conservation. For example, they can be used to predict the effects of severe weather on overwinter survival chances. Many British and Irish ringers routinely collect the kinds of biometrics required to measure body condition, such as scores of fat reserves and muscle size, weights and standard measurements of body size. Research, including that by a 'Biometrics

Fig 2.9 The effects of dispersal on Great Tit population densities, from a model including the observed dispersal distribution derived from ring-recoveries. The graph shows the equilibrium density of birds within a woodland patch (a) of 30 × 30 km and (b) of 10 × 10 km. Densities in the woodland patches were lower than they would be in an area of pure woodland, because emigration from the wood is greater than immigration from the surrounding farmland. Densities within the woodland were even more depressed for a more dispersive migrant species, such as Willow Warbler, and less so for a very sedentary species, such as Dunnock. (*Source*: Baillie *et al* 2000, by permission of *Journal of Applied Ecology*, Blackwell Science Ltd.)

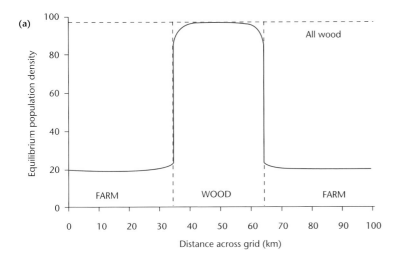
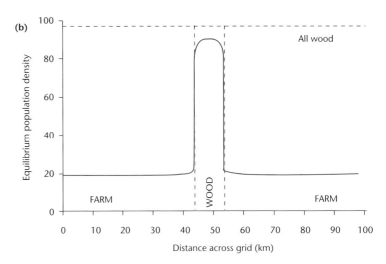

Working Group' of the Ringing Committee, has shown that such measurements can be of great value, especially if they are collected in a standard way as part of a planned trapping study (*eg* Gosler 1991, Gosler *et al* 1995a, b). In the recent study to investigate declines in the 1990s of waders wintering on the Wash (Atkinson *et al* 2000; see earlier), the proportion in catches of adult Oystercatchers that showed an abnormal (slow or suspended) pattern of wing moult was used successfully as a measure of body condition, and shown to be a good predictor of overwinter survival (Fig 2.8b). In that study, the exact mechanism for the relationship between overwinter survival and cockle and mussel stock size was not established but the body condition measurement, based on recording the state of moult of birds caught for ringing, has the potential to be an 'early-warning' indicator for the management of the shellfish stocks. Applied research based on biometrics is likely to become an increasingly important part of the work of the Ringing Scheme (see Chapter 7 for some examples of the part it may play in migration studies).

These and other examples of the great value of data from the British & Irish Ringing Scheme for conservation research are discussed more fully in a number of review articles (Baillie 1995, 2001, Wernham *et al* 1998, Baillie *et al* 1999b). These give the interested reader a little more detail and additional pointers for further study.

The Union of European Ringing Schemes (EURING)

EURING was established in 1963, with the British & Irish Ringing Scheme a founder member and Bob Spencer, the BTO's Ringing Officer, its first General Secretary. Bob said that EURING was 'born out of idealism, and of the practical need for the 30 or more ringing schemes in Europe to be able to speak a common scientific language'. EURING has enabled a high level of cooperation between European Ringing Schemes, of vital importance when studying migrant birds via ringing. Spina (1999) provides further information on EURING, and on some European ringing projects that it has coordinated.

In 1966, EURING produced a first standard coding system for European ring-recovery data, which is now used by all affiliated ringing schemes and allows the efficient exchange of data at the international level. The EURING Data Bank (EDB), based at Heteren in the Netherlands, was set up in 1977 to store European recovery data in a central location, accessible to researchers from all over the world with the agreement of the contributing national schemes (see Baillie 1995). Since 1986, EURING has taken a leading role in promoting analytical techniques and computer

software for research based on ring-recoveries, by encouraging ornithologists and statisticians to participate in EURING Technical Meetings, held every three years since 1986 (see Lebreton & North 1993, Baillie *et al* 1999d).

EURING allows a large pool of enthusiastic European ringers to be mobilized for large-scale projects. For example, the EURING Swallow Project aims to identify the main factors contributing to the decline of European Swallow populations, by studying variations in their dispersal, survival and productivity across Europe and through time, and by investigating their migratory movements, fattening areas and strategies and the wintering grounds of the different populations (Spina 1998a, b; Pilastro & Spina 1999). Since the pilot year in 1997, 25 countries have taken part in the project (Spina 2001). EURING also facilitates collaborative analytical projects based on the European ring-recovery information. In 1997, for example, a joint project between Vogelwarte Radolfzell and EURING was started to research changes in the migratory behaviour of European birds through pan-European ring-recovery analyses, beginning with the White Stork (Fiedler 1998, Sproll & Fiedler 2001). In 2000, the BTO agreed to lead a joint EURING project to develop guidelines for fieldwork and data analysis for constant-effort site ringing at the European scale, in close collaboration with the French Ringing Scheme (CRBPO) and involving a number of other long-running schemes (Wernham & Balmer 2001; see Fig 2.5).

The British & Irish Ringing Scheme. What does the future hold?

The British & Irish Ringing Scheme has a 'Scientific Strategy', which describes a number of fieldwork and analytical projects that are of high priority to develop the research work of the scheme (Baillie *et al* 1999c). Some of the new data collection will place emphasis on structured projects, such as the CES scheme and RAS project (see previously), to enhance the value of the data for conservation and scientific research. For example, pilot projects have already started to investigate the winter movements and overwinter survival of farmland passerines (see Evans *et al* 1999 for a review) and to set up 'Integrated Population Monitoring Sites', where constant-effort ringing, nest recording and census work are carried out in the same study area (Peach *et al* 1997, Wernham *et al* 1999). Many of the research projects described in these sections (such as the work on the survival rates of declining farmland passerines, the projects on Wash waders and the work on the movements and survival

Fig 2.10 (a) Geographical variation across Europe in hunting indices (based on ring-recoveries) for raptors before 1980: the larger the symbol, the higher the hunting pressure; open circles indicate areas with insufficient recoveries for analysis. (b) Changes through time in the hunting index (all countries combined) for Buzzard. The hunting indices for many species, especially raptors, have shown decreases in recent years (due to the introduction of protective legislation). (*Source*: McCulloch *et al* 1992, by permission of *Ibis*.)

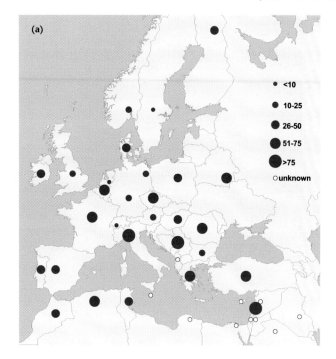

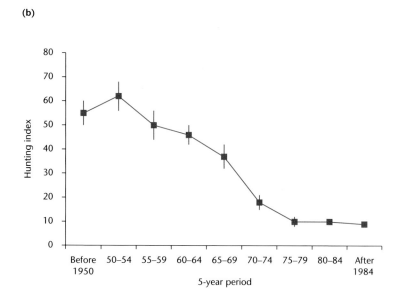

of Cormorants) demonstrate the great value of collecting ring-recovery data over long periods and over large geographical areas. It is important that the Ringing Scheme continues to collect such data for as wide a range of species as possible, because it is impossible to predict which species will become of conservation concern, or conflict with human activities in the future. It will also be important to keep the scheme well publicized, to ensure that recovery rates due to members of the public reporting dead ringed birds remain high enough to produce the valuable records on which the scheme partly depends, as there is some indication that these have started to fall. Ringers will continue to be encouraged to submit all kinds of ringing and recapture data electronically, so that the data are readily available on computer for analyses to be carried out, and analytical work will focus on areas of high conservation priority. Many new ideas for conservation-related

research into the movements of birds will be developed leading on from the publication of this book, and the Ringing Scheme aims to promote some new migration projects based on these ideas in the future (see Chapter 7). Some of these are likely to involve traditional ringing used in conjunction with new technologies, such as remote tracking (see Chapter 1) or tracing techniques (*eg* isotopic or DNA analyses, Chapters 1 and 7), and the Ringing Scheme is likely to broaden the range of types of data that are collected and analysed. Such migration projects will probably involve even closer collaboration with colleagues in the rest of Europe (through EURING) and further afield.

The British & Irish Ringing Scheme, with its more than 2,000 ringers that enthusiastically give of their time and energy, has already contributed a great deal to bird conservation and related research, and exciting times are ahead!

3 Why and how do birds migrate?[1]

Franz Bairlein, Norman Elkins & Peter Evans

Why migrate?

In enabling a bird to travel successfully between two places on the earth's surface, migration involves a complex set of behaviours that must be correctly dovetailed. Some time before the bird sets out, it must prepare for the journey by storing fat as fuel. It must then choose the correct time of year and weather conditions in which to depart. In many instances, it must hold a compass course during flight. On long journeys, it may need to stop to refuel, using a site that (if it is a young bird) it has never visited before and which may hold food resources quite unlike those around its birthplace or departure point. Finally, it must decide when the journey is over. Along the way, a migrant bird may be blown off course by adverse winds or storms, or its navigation system may fail. It may run out of fuel when over the sea or it may find a traditional refuelling site devoid of food. Or it may be attacked by a bird of prey, such as Eleanora's Falcon that makes its living from migrant songbirds.

It is plain, therefore, that migratory behaviour holds many hazards for birds. Why then did it evolve and why is it maintained today? The answers lie in consideration of the various benefits, as well as the costs, of migration. These benefits and costs vary between species and breeding areas, and, as a consequence of differences in age, sex and size, to name but three, between individuals. Natural selection favours individuals that adopt a life style that leads to a higher 'lifetime reproductive success' (LRS) than that of other birds of the same species. LRS is measured by the number of offspring, carrying the genes of a male or female parent, that survive to breed themselves and so contribute to future generations. Any or all of the following can increase LRS: higher year-to-year adult survival (allowing more breeding attempts), more young raised at each attempt, and higher survival rates of young to breeding age. Migration is a behaviour that may assist the maximization of LRS, provided that the mortality risks of the flights are outweighed by the benefits of greater success in rearing more young, for example if migration increases a bird's chances of overwinter survival allowing it extra opportunities to breed.

Seasonal migrations

Most bird food resources vary seasonally, even in the tropics, but probably the most extreme fluctuations affecting breeding success are those that occur at mid- to high latitudes, especially those in insect abundance. Young birds require a diet reasonably high in protein to allow them to grow their muscles and feathers. Meat or insects provide such a diet, whereas not all seeds and very few fruits do. Thus, it is not surprising that in Britain & Ireland many summer migrant species or individuals are insectivorous. These birds take advantage of the longer hours of daylight at higher latitudes in summer, and the surge in insect abundance at a predictable time of year, to raise larger (or more) broods, before they retreat southward towards the tropics in autumn. In their extreme form, such movements can take place between a fixed breeding area and a fixed non-breeding ('wintering') area, but once the restriction imposed by the fixed location of a nest (to which adults have to return to incubate eggs and, often, feed young) is removed, individual birds are free to move if it is advantageous to do so. Movements between nesting attempts also occur in a few species. One of the best known is the Red-billed Quelea, which migrates in relation to the movement of the rainfall front of the Inter-Tropical Convergence Zone in Africa. Closer to home, some Quail are believed to nest in early spring in southern Europe and then to migrate north before laying a second clutch in, for example, southern England. On a more local scale, Bullfinches may move tens of kilometres between individual nesting attempts.

Seasonal migrations also occur in species that feed largely on soil invertebrates, such as earthworms, which bury deeper as continental soils dry out in summer. This explains why Lapwings that breed in continental Europe move west to Britain & Ireland as early as July. Winter cold *per se* is not necessarily the driving force for migration, except in small birds, since body feathers can produce very effective insulation against heat loss, provided that the bird can generate heat fast enough by gaining ready access to food. Many waterfowl leave arctic latitudes and central, continental Europe in autumn because their feeding sites become frozen over, so that they cannot reach the foods locked beneath the ice; for examples, see the maps indicated in the species accounts for Pintail (Fig 4), Pochard and Teal (Fig 5). Individuals of those seed-eating species that rely on seeds of low-growing annual plants usually migrate away from areas where there is a high probability of snow covering the ground, and hence their foods, each winter. For example, Common Redpolls breeding in Finland migrate southeastwards

---

[1] This chapter covers a series of large and complex subject areas. Space enables us to give only a flavour of each topic, and we cannot provide detailed references for every statement. In many specific cases, the relevant species texts in Chapter 6 give further detail. Please refer to the final section on '*Further reading*', and to Table 3.2, to find sources of additional information.

Fig 3.1 Examples of the broad-front migration of songbirds along parallel migration routes within Europe. (a) Movements of Wheatears ringed as nestlings. (*Source*: G Zink, *Der Zug europäischer Singvögel*, Volume 1, © 1987 AULA-Verlag GmbH.) (b) Recoveries of Chaffinches ringed during passage at the Courish Spit in Baltic Russia (closed symbols) and at Col de Bretolet in Switzerland (open symbols). (*Source*: Bairlein 2001, by permission of *Ardea*.)

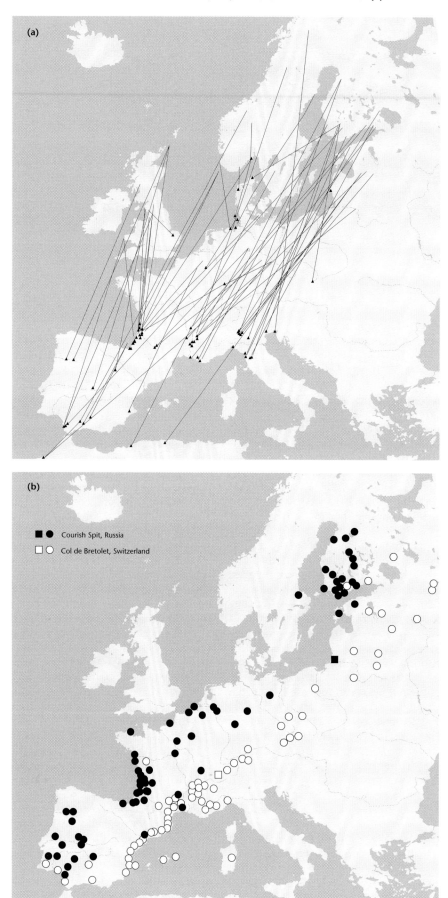

Fig 3.2 Movements of White Storks as shown by ring-recoveries. (a) Recovery locations of White Storks ringed at locations across Europe (updated from Fiedler 1998) and arrows indicating the two main migration routes across Iberia and the Strait of Gibraltar (western route) and along the eastern edge of the Mediterranean (eastern route) (after Nowak & Berthold 1987). (b) Direction of departure since 1970 of more than 4,000 young White Storks during their first autumn migration. Data are pooled in cells of 1 × 1° of latitude and longitude. Birds that moved north, or less than 50 km, are excluded. All cells with at least 10 recoveries are shown. Symbols: red, >75% recoveries in southeastern directions; pink, >50% southeastern; pale blue, >50% southwestern; dark blue, >75% southwestern. More birds from the eastern breeding areas follow the eastern migration route and more from the west the western route but the division is less clear than it had been before 1970. (*Source*: W Fiedler pers comm.)

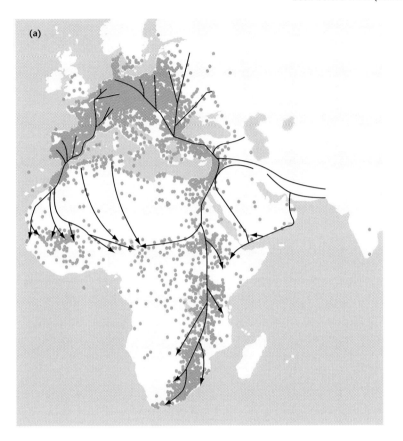

into Russia to wintering areas sufficiently far south that deep snow rarely occurs.

Annual migrations, eruptions and irruptions
The foods of some bird species vary markedly not only with season, but also from year to year. Finches that feed on tree seeds (*eg* Brambling), northern thrushes that take berries (*eg* Fieldfare), and birds of prey (*eg* Short-eared Owl) that feed on small mammals with populations that fluctuate cyclically, like voles and lemmings, all contain some individuals or populations that migrate every year. The proportions and numbers that migrate depend not only on the abundance of food in the breeding areas after the young birds have become independent, but also on the density of the birds themselves; high densities may stimulate emigration. For many species, it is not clear whether these movements away from the breeding areas are true migrations (which would involve preparation for long flights by laying down fat) or whether they are explorations for food that cease as soon as suitable supplies are encountered. Given that parts of the journeys seem to follow similar directions in different years, however, they must involve more than mere nomadic wanderings. Also, Brambling and other species are known to lay down fat for the return journeys to breeding grounds in spring.

If a species' food supply moves around, then its bird predators may also move. Movements of fish to spawning grounds at predictable times of year may have led seabirds to time their movements to harvest these fish. Sometimes this leads to movements in late summer in a direction almost opposite to that in which migration will eventually take them. For example, adult Common Terns from many parts of northern Europe bring their young to the Tees Estuary in northeast England in August, to coincide with movements of young sprats into the shallows. Adults and young terns from the southern North Sea colonies may also join them, however, flying northwards to do so, before all the birds head south in September to spend the winter off the coast of West Africa.

Migration patterns
The migratory routes that birds follow today are the products of natural selection in an ever-changing world. Since the end of the last glaciation some 10,000 years ago, sea-levels have risen and land has disappeared. Regions that were totally covered by ice, and so uninhabitable by birds, are now vegetated and have winter climates that allow survival of all but the smallest species, if appropriate food resources are available.

Although the migrations of most songbirds involve many individuals flying along parallel routes across a broad front (Fig 3.1), those of birds of prey and other soaring birds, such as storks (Fig 3.2a), converge on short sea-crossings, especially at the two ends of the Mediterranean Sea during journeys between Europe and Africa. Soaring birds require help from up-currents of air, from thermal 'bubbles' rising over irregularly heated ground, or from winds being forced up by mountain ridges, and so they avoid flying far over water. Although songbird routes do not concentrate so markedly in this way, recent radar observations suggest that several species do detour around the western end of the Mediterranean in spring, while others pass over Israel. In this way, they may gain some advantage from following winds and so reduce the energy costs of the flight. Indeed, some shorebirds such as Bar-tailed Godwit migrating from northwest Africa towards Siberia require wind assistance if they are to reach their refuelling areas in the Wadden Sea using the fuel load with which they leave Mauritania.

Many songbirds that come to Britain to breed in the summer have been seen by radar to arrive from the south-southeast in spring, and to depart in that direction, on a broad front, in early autumn, even though they then travel through western Iberia (which lies to the south-southwest). Movements from ring-recoveries also suggest this south-southeasterly movement within Britain in autumn and the reverse in spring; for examples, see the maps indicated in the species accounts for Sand Martin (Fig 4), Sedge Warbler (Fig 4a & c) and Willow Warbler (Fig 5b) in Chapter 6. In Iberia, they refuel on their way to tropical Africa, a destination that requires them to change direction again towards the south. Other populations of the same songbird species, having bred in central Europe, also migrate through western Iberia in autumn, travelling at first in a southwesterly direction (Fig 3.1) before turning south. The differences in departure directions of British and continental birds are pre-programmed and inherited, but the accuracy of pre-programming in some individuals (particularly young birds) may not be very high. Straying from the normal path, or 'vagrancy', has often been considered a failure to orient in the 'correct' direction or is attributed to peculiarities of weather (see later). Young, first-time migrants form a high proportion of such vagrants, and their behaviour, if repeatable and heritable, may allow the development of new migratory pathways. For example, although most young German Blackcaps have inherited the tendency to head in south to southwesterly directions to Mediterranean and North African wintering grounds on their first migration, a few inherit the tendency to fly in other directions. When circumstances of climate or food supplies change, some of these 'aberrant' juveniles, which hitherto would have flown to unsuitable wintering areas and died, may reach areas where survival is now possible or even better than in traditional areas. In this way, new migration routes and destinations can evolve. In the case of the Blackcaps in recent years, this has led to wintering in southern Britain and in Ireland. Winter survival in these areas may have increased because winter food resources have improved, while wintering further north and closer to Germany has the possible additional advantage of allowing an earlier return to the breeding grounds. Given that such micro-evolutionary change has occurred rapidly, within a few decades, future climate change could produce many more examples like this.

The possible refuelling areas available on long migrations may cover extensive regions for songbirds that are seeking insects or fruit as food, but they are much more restricted for waterfowl and shorebirds that depend on lakes, saltmarshes or estuaries. Some of the most demanding migrations among birds are undertaken by the Knot, the Siberian breeding population of which flies to northwestern (and some individuals subsequently to southern) Africa by way of a single refuelling site in the Wadden Sea. How often a species needs to refuel depends on its size and shape, and its capacity to carry fat. These considerations have influenced the routes that are used, other factors (such as the favourability of the wind) being equal. To bestow a selective advantage, a route must contain predictably reliable refuelling areas; changing global rainfall patterns may thus lead to changes in migration patterns for these types of species.

Another factor that has shaped migratory routes is the existence of large ecological barriers: the oceans, extensive deserts and mountain ranges for landbirds, and the continents for seabirds. Yet even these may not be absolute barriers. Crossing them may be hazardous, but the alternatives even more so. It has been suggested that many Greenland Wheatears fly direct to northwestern Spain and Africa because a roundabout land-hopping route would add considerably to journey distance and time, and increase the risk of being taken by a predator. Many small songbirds may take a route that avoids crossing the central Sahara but some individuals do so regularly and survive; the relative costs of these two strategies are not known at present.

Other forms of migration
In the same way that many insectivorous birds leave mid- to high latitudes in winter to avoid food shortage and enhance their own survival, some species that breed on hills and mountains (areas which become less hospitable in winter) move in autumn to lower altitudes where food remains accessible. Songbirds such as Twite and waders such as Golden Plover leave the upland moors for nearby coasts and lowland pastures to overwinter. These two-way altitudinal movements closely parallel the movements from north to south seen in many migrants, and from east to west in waterfowl and shorebirds that move from Siberia to Britain & Ireland to obtain the benefits of unfrozen conditions in winter, thanks to the proximity of the Gulf Stream.

Some long-distance migrants do not breed until they are several years old, for example White Storks, seabirds such as terns, and most arctic-nesting shorebirds. The young of these species travel as far as (but not necessarily with) their parents during their first autumn journey and so gain the benefits of higher survival in better 'wintering' areas, often in tropical latitudes. Many of these young do not return in the following spring, or migrate only part way towards their breeding grounds (Fig 3.3), thereby avoiding the full costs of the journey. Interestingly, they do not normally attempt to breed in their wintering areas, though a few White Storks, European Bee-eaters and Booted Eagles have done so in southern Africa. Indeed, they do not normally develop the signs of breeding condition, full adult plumage, territoriality and so on, that indicate physiological readiness to rear young. Those seabirds that travel long distances as juveniles may return progressively nearer to their final destinations as the years pass (eg Fulmars and Gannets), and indeed in later years may visit breeding colonies briefly, after nesting is under way, to prospect for vacant sites (eg Puffins).

Other forms of movement
At the end of the breeding season of each species, the numbers of birds in a nesting area reach their maximum. No longer constrained by attachment to nest sites, birds are able to redistribute themselves and many, particularly juveniles, do so. Individuals of normally resident species tend not to move more than a few kilometres, but in occasional years of very high breeding output, some juveniles may move much further, colonizing habitats where the species does not normally occur and even moving along the coast, as has been recorded at Spurn Point Bird Observatory for Dunnocks and House Sparrows. Whether these individuals were pushed out by active competition from areas close to their birthplace, or chose to search for less crowded feeding areas, is not clear. The young of long-distance migrant species also move around in the weeks after reaching independence from their parents and before departing to their wintering grounds. Such movements, made by both residents and migrants, are often referred to as 'post-juvenile dispersal' but the term is unfortunate as it implies that birds consciously move away *from each other*, rather than making independent decisions as to where to explore. During this period, young birds probably identify possible nesting sites or areas for their first breeding attempts in a subsequent year. Experiments have shown that they have to learn the characteristic reference marks of the area near their birthplace, rather

Fig 3.3 Movements of Sandwich Terns of differing age as shown from ring-recoveries. (a) Locations in May–July of those ringed as nestlings in Britain & Ireland. First-years (red) and most second-years (blue) do not return to breeding colonies for the summer, although most do having reached three years old (grey). (b) Monthly variation in the differences in latitude between ringing and recovery locations of British & Irish Sandwich Terns, by age. Monthly medians (points) and interquartile ranges (bars) are given, showing that most birds do not return to the breeding colonies in summer until their third year of life. Negative values indicate southerly displacement. (*Source*: BTO data.)

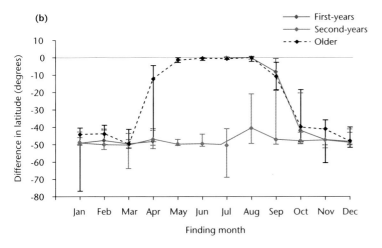

than inheriting that knowledge, and that this occurs during this time of wandering, before migration.

Considerable interest has been shown in the distances that individuals of a species move from their exact birthplaces to their first breeding places, referred to as 'natal dispersal'. The consequences of the movements affect the amount of inbreeding in a population. Individuals may move again between their first and subsequent breeding attempts. This may occur within the same year, as has been shown for Dotterel, or between years, as shown for Pied Flycatchers; this is sometimes found in females but not usually in males (particularly if the males hold territories). In this book, the term 'breeding dispersal' is used to refer to cases where the movement occurs between years. The reasons for such movements are obscure and do not necessarily relate to failure of the first nest. Possibly, in hole-nesting species, individuals late to arrive from migration may fail to find a suitable nest site in years when resident species, such as tits, are abundant, and are thus forced to move elsewhere to nest. For both natal and breeding dispersal, the distances moved tell only the outcome and nothing of the actual route taken or the process by which the individuals changed locations.

Escape movements

The foods of many bird species wintering in Britain & Ireland are not replenished between autumn and spring. As such foods gradually become depleted, the migrants that feed on them (*eg* Redwings on Hawthorn berries) may move slowly to areas that have not been exploited so intensively. But sometimes even undepleted food sources can suddenly be made unavailable: lakes can ice over, pastures and ploughed land freeze hard or be covered with snow. Such rapid changes in weather can stimulate some species to escape by moving promptly, rather than trying to sit it out until conditions improve. Each day of delay in responding to severe weather reduces a bird's fat reserves and hence the distance it can then fly to find accessible food; there is no time to lay down additional fat as happens before true migrations.

Cold-weather movements occur in many wildfowl and many estuarine waders, such as Teal, Oystercatcher and Dunlin, as well as in inland-feeding waders, such as Lapwing and Golden Plover. For example, Oystercatchers are known to have moved from the Netherlands to France, and Dunlin may move from the Wadden Sea to the Wash. Very sensibly under such conditions, birds tend to move with the wind, as this speeds up their escape and reduces the energy costs per kilometre. When cold weather arrives from the north, they may fly southwards to Iberia, when from the east, westwards to Ireland. Return movements follow when wind directions change and bring milder conditions.

Differential migration

In some species or populations in which all individuals leave the breeding areas, the distances travelled and subsequent wintering areas may vary between categories of sex or age (see Chapter 5 for a synthesis of such patterns for British & Irish birds). This is often termed 'differential migration' and, presumably, results from differences in the costs and benefits of moving less far or further from nesting sites. Those birds that winter nearest gain the benefits of shorter return journeys and better chances of acquiring a breeding territory or nest site (such as a natural tree hole), if these are in short supply, because they can respond most quickly to the arrival of spring. They must face a harsher winter climate to do so, however. Since in most groups of birds that do not breed in colonies, it is generally the male (if either of the sexes) that acquires a breeding site, then these would be expected to migrate shorter distances than females; for the latter, ensuring overwinter survival is generally more important than an early return to the breeding area. It is more difficult to predict what effects age should have. If the chances of old and young males acquiring breeding sites are similar, but depend on who arrives first, then there might be no segregation of wintering areas. For a young male that has never bred before, however, it may be more important to survive the winter (in order to have any chance of leaving its genes to posterity) than to ensure early arrival; hence young males may winter further away than adults. Finally, if older males are normally dominant to younger ones in contests over a limited supply of nesting sites, then it will not matter if they winter further away, survive better and return later. In such cases, the young males might be found nearest to the breeding area. Whereas there is good evidence of shortage of nesting sites and competition among males for acquiring these, with some potential first-time breeders failing to do so (as in Pied Flycatchers), there is much less indication that young female songbird migrants may fail to find a breeding site. Yet, if these are in short supply, or if good-quality sites or good-quality males that hold them are scarce, similar arguments should hold about possible differences in distance from the breeding areas at which young and old females spend the winter.

Some of the above outcomes may be affected by body-size differences between old and young males and females. Sexual differences in size normally stem from factors that have nothing to do with migration, such as the need to compete for a partner. In songbirds and wildfowl, males tend if anything to be larger than females, whereas in shorebirds and raptors, males are often smaller. General arguments about the ratio between the area of body surface (which loses heat) and body volume (which generates it) suggest that larger birds should be able to withstand colder climates more easily than smaller birds. Hence the larger males, among many songbird migrants that move within the northern hemisphere, could be expected to winter closer to their breeding areas than the females, even if there is no competition between males for nesting sites. If there is competition, size is a good predictor of the outcome in some species but levels of male sex hormone, testosterone, may also be important and even over-ride size considerations.

In summary, lack of differential migration, and hence a common non-breeding area shared by males and females, old and young alike, would be most likely in migrant species that show no size differences between sex and age classes and are not restricted by shortage of nesting sites on the breeding grounds. Movements over different distances by birds of different sex or age classes result from trade-offs between the costs associated with different wintering areas (related to *predictable* differences in weather-related survival in different areas) and the benefits associated with ease of return to secure a nesting site. Probably there are also different costs associated with different flight distances, if only because these affect the time that must be spent, at risk to predators, acquiring the extra food needed to fuel the flight and, at the mercy of the weather, on the flight itself.

Chapter 5 presents the results of exploratory analyses searching for differential migration patterns among British & Irish birds. It shows that differential migration of the age classes is found widely among seabirds and gulls, and is also shown by some waders (*eg* Lapwing, Oystercatcher and Redshank) and passerines (*eg* Pied Wagtail). In most cases where a difference was apparent, immature birds moved further than adults between breeding and wintering areas. Movements of the two sexes, where this could be tested, showed significant differences for fewer species. Again, the direction of the difference varied; for example, female Pied Wagtails moved further than males but male Hen Harriers moved further than females. Time, within the *Migration Atlas* project, did not allow the testing of any specific hypotheses for explaining differential migration but Chapter 5 presents preliminary results that could later be used for this (also, see Chapter 7 for recommendations for further research on this topic).

Partial migration

In contrast to differential migration, partial migration involves only part of a population leaving its breeding area. The migrating individuals include all age and sex groups, for if only adult males remained resident, for example, this might more correctly be termed an extreme form of differential migration. Partial migration may be 'obligate', when some individuals leave the breeding area every year. Alternatively, 'facultative' partial migration occurs only in some years, when external factors (*eg* poor weather, reduced food resources, or high population density) reduce the 'quality' of the breeding area for wintering. If the reduction is sufficiently great, it may lead to eruption of a large proportion of the population.

In its simplest form, partial migration represents a solution to the problem of year-to-year *variability* in winter weather, and hence in overwinter survival, on the breeding grounds. Those birds that move to more-favourable non-breeding areas avoid the risk of dying in a severe winter near their nest sites. In a normal winter, however, the emigrants face the hazards of a migratory journey and so survive less well than the residents. Two complementary hypotheses have been put forward to explain obligate partial migration. The 'Genetic Hypothesis' suggests that the 'decision' whether to migrate or stay is genetically based and thus depends on the behaviours shown by the parents, as demonstrated by breeding experiments with Blackcaps, Robins and Blackbirds. Some of the offspring of the pairings of males from a migratory race with females from a sedentary population show migratory activity, while others do not. Thus, the proportion of migrants and residents in a partially migrant population could change in response to changes in survival rates in the breeding and non-breeding areas. If there is no particular long-term trend in winter severity, the result would be the maintenance of both behaviours but if the long-term trend is towards better winter survival on the breeding area (*eg* because of global warming), some populations could become chiefly resident. If the opposite occurred because winters became colder (*eg* if Atlantic currents were to reverse, moving the Gulf Stream away from western Britain & Ireland), then populations almost wholly resident at present might become highly migratory. The cross-breeding experiments show that such changes could take place rapidly.

In addition to genetic influences on migratory versus non-migratory behaviour, environmental influences may also be important (the 'Behavioural–Constitutional Hypothesis'). If resources on the breeding areas in autumn are limited in relation to the numbers of potentially resident birds, some individuals may be forced to move away because the only alternative is to stay and die from lack of access to food. In this situation, migratory behaviour may never lead to higher survival than residency, no matter how severe the winter. Robins in Belgium have been shown to behave like this.

Chapter 5 presents the results of exploratory analyses to define the migratory tendencies of British & Irish birds, allowing their degree of migrancy to be scored and compared between species. The chapter also investigates whether the degree of migrancy correlates with a number of factors relating to the biology, ecology and demography of each species and considers further the genetic and environmental control of partial migration.

Leap-frog migration

In some species, not only do all members of certain races or breeding populations migrate while all members of others do not, these phenomena occur in particular spatial sequences, such that resident races breed further south than any migratory races. The latter overfly the residents en route to winter quarters, leaving the residents to winter furthest north (*eg* Redshank, Fig 3.4). Similarly, many Fennoscandian Blackbirds overfly the largely resident population breeding in Britain & Ireland to winter further south. This phenomenon has been termed 'leap-frog' migration.

Several explanations for 'leap-frogging' have been suggested, and there may be no single answer. Mediterranean breeding populations of Yellow Wagtails winter further north in West Africa (Nigeria) than do those that breed in Britain or Scandinavia, and also leave Africa earlier to return to the breeding grounds in the spring. The northernmost wintering birds (the southernmost, Mediterranean breeders) leave Africa before the rains begin, whereas those wintering further south leave for northern Europe some weeks after the rains of the Nigerian wet season have begun. Rainfall cannot be the cue for departure because the pattern is the exact opposite of what would be expected if that were the case. Rather, the timing of departure coincides closely with the differential times at which breeding ranges become suitable during the Palearctic spring. By wintering further south in Nigeria, the northern European wagtails may benefit from the increased insect abundance associated

Fig 3.4 The winter ranges of Redshank from (1) Iceland, (2) Britain & Ireland, (3) Denmark, Germany, the Netherlands and Belgium, (4) Sweden and Norway, and (5) Hungary, showing leap-frog migration of the northern populations of larger birds. (*Source*: Hale 1973, by permission of *Zoological Journal of the Linnean Society*.)

Fig 3.5 Movements (lines) and recovery locations (points) of Canada Geese that have been present in the Beauly Firth, northeast Scotland. Many moulting birds in the Beauly Firth breed in North Yorkshire but birds also come from a variety of other locations. (*Source*: BTO data.)

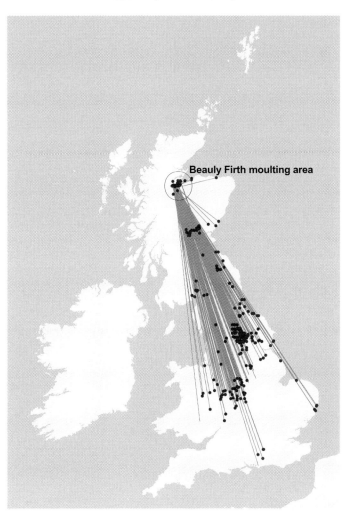

with the start of the rains before departure, and use it to aid fat deposition for the long return journey.

Although the wagtails from different breeding populations do not differ in size, those of several 'leap-frog' species do so, with the resident or short-distance migrant populations that winter furthest north being larger than the migrants in some cases (*eg* Redshank). This suggests that the smaller birds may be forced to move further south in winter to avoid competition with the larger residents. There is evidence that competition among Grey Plovers on a potential wintering site (Teesmouth, northeast England) leads to smaller juveniles moving further, but it is not known whether all these birds were from the same breeding area. Nevertheless, the situation provides a possible model of how some cases of leap-frog migration are maintained, if not how they actually arose. In reality, the ecology underlying the phenomenon of leap-frog migration may be complex, involving variation in competitive ability between individuals (including body-size effects), differential timing of breeding with latitude, the relative quality of different wintering areas, the energetic and predation costs of migration and so on. A large body of literature is accruing on the subject, particularly with reference to waders, and no single or clear explanation is yet apparent.

Moult migrations

Some groups of birds (in Britain & Ireland chiefly wildfowl and seabirds) become flightless while they are replacing their wing feathers (all of which are shed at the same time), in contrast to songbirds (which replace wing feathers sequentially, a few at a time). While they are flightless, ducks and geese could become easy prey to mammals such as the Red Fox. Hence they need a safe moulting site, usually close to, or surrounded by, a large area of water. Feather growth also requires extra energy and nutrients each day, so abundant food allows birds to shorten their flightless period. Not all wildfowl species migrate to moulting areas and, of those that do undertake such movements, not all individuals participate. In particular, some adults may stay with crèches of young ducklings or goslings to defend them against predators.

Among the best-known moult migrations are those in late June and July of Shelduck from throughout Europe to Grosser Knechtsand and other mudflats off the Elbe Estuary in northwest Germany, an area holding very high densities of one of their preferred foods, a small mud-snail *Hydrobia ulvae*. To reach this area, Shelducks from different breeding areas travel in very different directions, those from the Camargue (southern France) flying almost due north and those from Britain east or southeast. Although they complete the moult in only five to six weeks, the British birds do not return directly to their breeding areas but gradually move west and north during the autumn and winter.

In some geese, it is the non-breeding birds (or failed breeders) that migrate before moulting, in the Arctic often travelling north to good feeding areas that are not normally snow-free for long enough for pairs to rear young but are available for the period needed for wing moult. By leaving the breeding areas, these birds incidentally reduce their impact

Fig 3.6 Seasonal movements of (a) Manx and (b) Great Shearwaters. (*Source*: Mead 1983.)

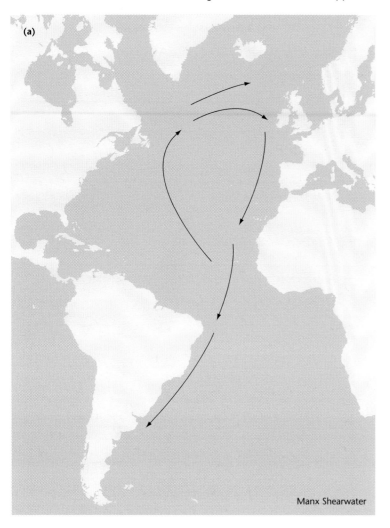

Manx Shearwater

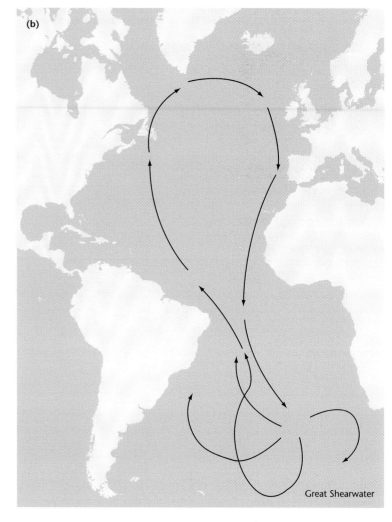

Great Shearwater

on the food supplies there but the 'reason' for leaving must be that their chances of survival are better in the moulting area. Nearer to home, some originally non-migratory Canada Geese, introduced as ornamental waterfowl into North Yorkshire, have established a regular post-breeding migration to moult on the Beauly Firth in Scotland (Fig 3.5).

Not only geese that eat plants and ducks that eat aquatic invertebrates undertake moult migrations. Some fish-eating ducks also do so, for example the Goosanders from upland Britain that travel to Norway. In this species, as in other wildfowl in which the drake has a much more colourful breeding plumage than the duck, moult migration is undertaken chiefly by the drakes, which may desert the incubating ducks before the ducklings hatch.

Among the truly pelagic seabirds, those that come to land only to nest and spend most of the year at sea, some undertake very long migrations, at the end of which they moult, often so completely that their flight capacity is impaired for several weeks. To ensure sufficient food during this period, they converge on areas where fish are particularly abundant. Manx Shearwaters move from Britain & Ireland to the coast of Brazil in autumn, to take advantage of the fish associated with the nutrient-rich Falklands Current (Fig 3.6a). Great Shearwaters, which have bred in the South Atlantic on Tristan da Cunha during the northern winter, move north in April to Newfoundland and then to southwest Greenland (Fig 3.6b), where they moult in July and August while feeding from the rich fishing grounds there.

How do birds migrate? The behavioural physiology of migration and orientation

Soon after fledging and independence from its parents for food, a young migrant bird faces some serious questions. When, for example, should it leave for migration? Which direction should it take? For how long should it travel? What supplies need to be taken? For how long should it stay in the winter quarters? How will it find its way back home for breeding? Could it simply follow its parents? Young of many long-distance migrants have to prepare for migration, and travel, completely alone.

Juvenile development

The first preparation for outbound migration may have already taken place in the nest. Migrants that depart relatively early in the autumn undergo a very rapid juvenile development, beginning even at the embryo stage, in order to prepare for migration in time. Young Garden Warblers hatched in June start juvenile moult at about 20–30 days old and reach the peak much closer to the onset of their migration in August than most Blackcaps, which start at an age of 40–60 days and moult comparatively slowly, before departing in September. Blackcaps hatched in August, however, have an accelerated juvenile development and much reduced juvenile moult, triggered by the decreasing day-length during late summer, so that they too are ready for migration in September. Late-hatched Blackcaps, and fast-developing migrants such as Garden Warblers, also overlap their various developmental processes more than other birds.

Metabolic, nutritional and physiological preparations

After completion of moult, the young bird has to prepare physiologically before embarking on the journey. Long-distance migrants, flying for thousands of kilometres and traversing vast areas that lack opportunities for feeding, such as deserts or oceans, require considerable energy reserves to endure their extraordinary flights. Apart from a few species that are able to feed extensively on the wing (eg terns, hirundines and swifts), many migrants must accumulate large reserves before or between migratory flights. The major store of energy for migration is fat but some species (eg arctic shorebirds) also store considerable amounts of protein, although this can provide only half as much energy per gram as fat. Carbohydrates seem to play no energetic role in migratory flights, but glycogen may serve as the primary fuel for take-off.

The amount of fat that must be stored is related to a bird's overall migratory distance; it also limits the length of a single migratory flight, or the length of the overall migration distance where the flight is interrupted by stopovers without feeding. Some species, such as Turnstone, put on small amounts of fuel at a series of fattening sites spread along the migration routes whereas others, such as Knot and Garden Warbler, store large amounts. Garden Warblers, for example, weigh 16–18 g when breeding, but up to 34 g just before they leave to cross the Sahara Desert. The highest rates of fat deposition, expressed as a percentage of lean body mass, have been found in small passerines,

which may gain 10–13% per day. This percentage rate of mass gain decreases with increasing body mass.

Among the mechanisms suggested for migratory fat deposition, increased food intake ('hyperphagia') is generally regarded as the most important. Increased utilization of ingested food may also play a role, however, and there is increasing evidence for adaptive shifts in diet and nutrient selection. In Garden Warblers, for example, hyperphagia accounts for some two-thirds of the daily increase in reserve accumulation, and an increase in the efficiency of utilization for the rest. Quite a number of species change their diet during pre-migratory fattening. Geese feed selectively on a variety of specific plant species during migration, depending upon particular nutrient requirements, as do several shorebird species; the latter may alter their diet during migratory stopovers and even eat seeds (which can comprise up to 37% of the diet) or berries. Chaffinches change from an insect diet to a seed diet during the period of fuelling and many warblers and other species seek fruit. Migratory fattening in several species (including Garden Warbler) is facilitated by an increased intake of fruits during post-breeding migration and, in some places, just prior to spring migration in Africa. This appears to be a significant adaptation, since fruits are often locally superabundant, thus minimizing the time birds need to spend searching for food. The generally low fibre content of fruits makes them easy to digest, and they seem to be rich enough in nutrients, especially sugars, to meet the specific physiological needs of migrants. Such seasonal frugivory may sometimes simply reflect seasonal changes in the relative availability of insects and fruits but there is now considerable evidence that such shifts are primarily the results of active changes in food preference. Both the degree of frugivory during migration and the species-specific preferences for particular fruits often vary independently of local fruit abundance. In captive birds, there is a significant preference for diets rich in unsaturated fatty acids, and birds fed with a pure saturated fatty acid showed impaired fattening. For species that have to accumulate fats rapidly, the preferential incorporation of unsaturated fatty acids directly from their food may be highly adaptive, reducing the energy costs involved. Recent work in the Mediterranean has also suggested that some warblers may prefer flower nectar over invertebrates when fattening for long-distance flights.

The fat stored by migrants is primarily used to fuel the flight engine, the breast muscle. In some species (eg Bar-tailed Godwit), the flight muscles actually increase in size in preparation for departure. The adaptive role of such 'hypertrophy' is not clear, however. The protein deposition may perhaps provide the extra power needed for migratory flights; equally, it may be necessary to maintain appropriate protein turnover rates, or the breakdown of proteins may facilitate the utilization of fatty acids as fuel. Pre-migratory mass increases of several organs, such as the heart, lungs and intestine, have been reported in some migrant species but the results are sometimes contradictory and their adaptive role, if any, is not yet clear. Similarly, little is known about enzymatic and hormonal changes in relation to migration, although quite a number of hormones may play a role in pre-migratory preparation. Gonadal hormones appear to be involved in the control of fattening and migration in spring, although not in autumn.

Since the migrations of most birds proceed according to rather precise seasonal schedules, the deposition of energy reserves is required at specific times of the year. Numerous studies on a variety of species have indicated that, in temperate-zone migrants, it is the length of the day relative to that of the night ('photoperiod') that is the major environmental factor controlling these processes, as well as many other seasonal phenomena such as breeding and moult. Spring fattening can generally be induced or advanced by experimentally lengthening the photoperiod, whereas autumn migratory disposition in most species appears to develop independently of immediate photoperiodic stimulation although, in field conditions, environmental factors may still act to moderate the pre-programmed schedule.

Initiation of first outbound migration

In several species that migrate rather late in the season, such as Swallows, the first departures often occur as food availability and other environmental conditions begin to deteriorate. For an early migrant, however, such as the Willow Warbler, which leaves when it is still the northern summer, the stimuli for departure are less obvious. In addition, in many species other than those like geese and terns that travel in family groups, the young leave later than their parents and conspecific adults.

The timing of migration is often supposed to be closely associated with the annual change in day-length, which is the most reliable predictor of seasonal change in temperate zones. Changes in day-length cannot account for the timing of northward migration of northern migrants wintering in the tropics, however, where endogenous mechanisms must play an important role in the initiation of migration. Aviculturalists have long known that captive migrants may show increased activity during periods when their wild conspecifics are migrating, and this 'Zugunruhe' (migratory restlessness) has now been systematically recorded in over a hundred species. Migratory restlessness is easily recognizable in those nocturnal migrants that outside the migratory periods are active only by day, although diurnal migrants also show alterations of their activity patterns, flying rather than feeding in the early morning hours. Hand-raised Garden Warblers, for example, kept in captivity in a constant photoperiod, display an annual cycle of nocturnal activity that matches closely that of their free-living conspecifics. Species or populations that migrate long distances exhibit more weeks of more pronounced migratory restlessness than those that travel shorter distances. Taken together, these results indicate that young warblers are equipped with an endogenous programme for timing both the start and the duration of migration. Genetic control of these features has been proved experimentally: the cross-breeding of sedentary Blackcaps from the Cape Verde Islands with migratory ones from central Europe resulted in intermediate patterns of migratory restlessness in their offspring.

When birds are kept under constant conditions for more than a year, the onset of migratory restlessness advances with respect to the calendar year, but the rhythm may run for many years. Circannual rhythms are particularly well developed in long-distance migrants, which have to cope with a tight seasonal schedule and, because of their migrations across many degrees of latitude, experience a variety of photoperiodic patterns. Presumably, the inbuilt rhythms stabilize the annual pattern against the 'noise' that is inherent in the environmental cues; also, they should guarantee an appropriate timing of activities during the times of the year in which birds live in seasonally constant environments or geographical areas with unpredictable weather patterns and resource availability. Under natural conditions, the internal annual cycle is synchronized to environmental cues, primarily to photoperiod. This has been demonstrated most convincingly in experiments in which birds were exposed to seasonal photoperiodic cycles with periods deviating from 12 months (eg six-month cycles); as a rule, the birds' biological rhythms conformed to the altered period of the photoperiodic cycle.

Nocturnal versus diurnal migration

Most migration occurs at night, although most bird species are diurnal during the non-migratory seasons. Nocturnal migration has several considerable advantages. It allows daytime feeding, and hence the accumulation of energy stores. Nocturnal migrants may save energy and time by utilizing atmospheric conditions present at night that facilitate endurance flying, such as cooler or denser air, or reduced headwinds. The avoidance of dehydration may be particularly important, as night-time temperatures are generally lower and relative humidity is higher, reducing evaporative water-loss. Predator avoidance may be a further benefit, and the stars may provide the most suitable compass for orientation.

Nocturnality is not a 'fixed' behaviour, however. Many nocturnal migrants travel both at night and by day, depending on local circumstances. Swallows, for example, are viewed as typical daytime migrants, spending their nights in large roosts during migration. Over the Sahara, however, they appear to switch to travelling by night. Species that rely on thermals for soaring, however, such as pelicans, storks, and several birds of prey, migrate only by day.

The migratory direction

In many and perhaps most migratory species, young birds know instinctively the direction in which they have to depart. Juveniles regularly migrate and reach their species-specific destinations independently of their parents. For example, inexperienced Common Cuckoos migrate to their African wintering quarters irrespective of the migratory behaviour (or lack of it) of their foster parents.

The most convincing evidence that there are innate mechanisms guiding orientation comes from displacement experiments and studies with captive migrants. Starlings breeding in countries of the eastern Baltic migrate across northern Germany and the Netherlands to winter in northern France and southern England. First-year Starlings caught during this autumn flight through the Netherlands and transported southwards by plane to Switzerland continued after release to travel in their original westerly direction, reaching wintering areas in Spain. They followed a given compass direction and did not compensate for their displacement (Fig 3.7).

Even young storks and geese, which normally migrate guided by experienced conspecifics (often their parents), possess a basic innate knowledge of their species- and population-specific directions. Young White Storks hatched near the southern shores of the Baltic (in the former East Prussia) normally migrate southeast across Europe to western Turkey, before heading south to winter in Africa, whereas those from western Germany head southwest through Iberia to Africa. When displaced westwards but released without contact with western storks, the young eastern storks followed their population-specific compass direction and headed southeast. When released with adult western storks, however, the young east-born storks joined the western ones on their southwestward course. Social bonds thus modified their innate compass direction.

The inbuilt nature of migratory directions has also been shown experimentally in the laboratory. Placed in circular orientation cages, inexperienced young birds of several migrant species showed directional preferences that closely match their species- and population-specific migration directions in the wild (see Fig 3.8 for an example of this). Tests carried out in such orientation cages have shown that even changes in migration directions are pre-programmed. Young Garden Warblers held captive in Germany changed their preferred directions during the period corresponding to autumn migration. They tried to head southwest when tested in September or October but in November and December, their preferred direction changed towards the southeast. Birds kept until the following spring and tested again during the period of spring migratory restlessness attempted to head north, like their free-living conspecifics. In Blackcaps, cross-breeding between individuals with southwesterly (from southern Germany) and southeasterly (from eastern Austria)

Fig 3.7 Results of Perdeck's classic Starling displacement experiment: (a) the natural recovery locations of Starlings ringed in the Netherlands and (b) the recovery locations of Starlings that were displaced by plane to Switzerland. Juveniles are plotted as solid symbols and adults as crosses. Displaced juveniles carried on migrating in the same direction as they would have done from the Netherlands, while the adults were able to compensate and return to their usual wintering area. (*Sources*: Perdeck 1958, by permission of *Ardea*, Mead 1983.)

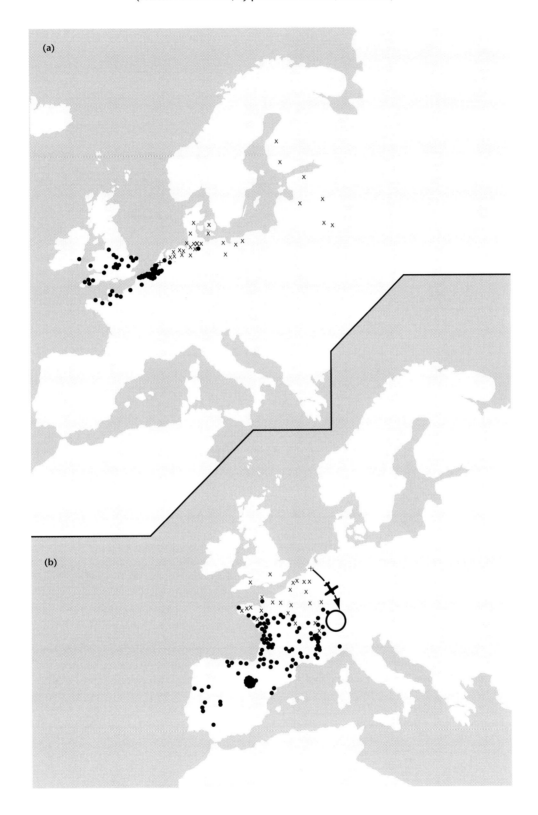

migratory directions resulted in intermediate directional preferences among the offspring, showing that migratory direction, as well as the degree of migratory restlessness (see earlier), is under genetic control in this species.

Orientation on the first outbound migration

Orientation can be achieved in two different ways. Animals may sometimes sense local cues associated with the destination, so that they are guided towards a predetermined goal. Alternatively, as in most cases

Fig 3.8 Seasonal changes in the directional preferences of Garden Warblers (kept in a constant 12-hour photoperiod) during nocturnal migratory restlessness. The circular diagrams summarize the results obtained in the orientation cages during the months shown, with the large arrow showing the mean direction of movement for each test series. The map shows schematically the changes in migratory direction known to occur during the year in the field. (*Source*: Gwinner 1986, *Circannual Rhythms*, by permission of Springer–Verlag.)

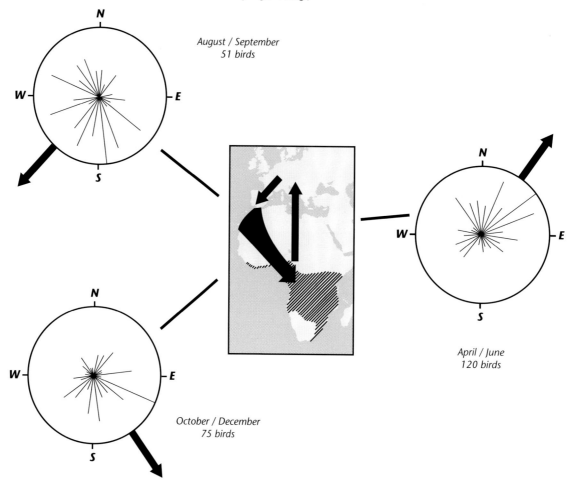

August / September
51 birds

April / June
120 birds

October / December
75 birds

of long-distance migration, such direct cues are not available and orientation must then be established indirectly using an external reference — a compass. Through this, the intended course of migration is converted into an actual direction of movement.

Visual cues

In the simplest case, migrants may use geographical landmarks for orientation. Many seabirds follow coastlines, and rivers may serve as orientational cues for waterfowl. Soaring birds may use mountain ridges. The use of landmarks is probably most important for homing, which, under natural conditions, always follows an active outward movement during which landmarks may be learnt. However, the significance of landmarks in orientation is still unclear.

On current knowledge, the most important visual cues for orientation are the celestial ones: the sun and the stars. Under a sunny sky, Starlings kept in orientation cages during the migration period oriented in the same direction as free-living birds. If the sky became overcast, however, the directional preference disappeared. When their view of the sun's direction was changed using mirrors, the birds oriented at the same angle as the apparent sun. Hence, migrant birds possess a sun compass. This could only give accurate information if regulated by an internal clock, to allow adjustment of direction as the sun moves through the sky. The existence of such a time-compensated sun compass was also first shown in Starlings. Experiments in which Starlings were kept under artificial cycles of day and night, of the same duration as natural time but out of phase, revealed clearly that they use both the

sun's position on the azimuth and the time of the day to orient. The sun can also provide information through the plane of polarization of light. Nocturnal migrants are able to use the characteristic celestial pattern of polarized light at sunset to set their departure direction.

Stars play an important role for nocturnal migrants. On clear nights, caged birds display oriented restlessness, as they do also under an artificial planetarium 'sky'. The selective blocking-out of constellations in the artificial sky has shown that the birds are able to use the natural stellar pattern in directional orientation. The development of a star compass requires learning, however. Birds without early visual experience of stellar information failed to orient but a star pattern need not be the natural one for them to develop this ability. In experiments with several migrant species, even very arbitrary and simple patterns are sufficient if the pattern rotates around a central reference star, which the birds then treat as the northern pole star. In contrast to the sun compass, the birds can use a star compass without knowledge of time.

The use of the earth's magnetic field

As revealed by radar studies, nocturnal migrants can be oriented correctly even under completely overcast conditions, as can caged birds with no perception of the stars. Caged birds lost this ability, however, when isolated from the earth's magnetic field behind metal-reinforced walls. When the magnetic field experienced by captive Robins was rotated using electrical coils so that, for example, magnetic north was shifted to the east while the field's total intensity and inclination as well as other potential directional cues were kept unchanged, the birds altered their orientation accordingly. The magnetic compass used by migrants differs from Man's technical compass, however. Instead of indicating north or south, it distinguishes between pole-ward, where the lines of magnetic force point to the ground, and equator-ward, where they point upwards. Transequatorial migrants face a problem, therefore, because the magnetic field is horizontal, and thus ambiguous with respect to direction, for some distance north and south of the Equator. Laboratory experiments simulating a crossing of the Equator suggest that birds would erroneously continue southward migration in the southern hemisphere under field conditions if they relied solely on the magnetic field. They probably have to use stellar cues to maintain a proper heading while crossing the horizontal magnetic field at the Equator.

Because of its structure and properties, the earth's magnetic field represents a very reliable and omnipresent reference for orientation, both in terms of directional and positional information. Not surprisingly, therefore, the use of a magnetic compass is very widespread among migrating animals, although the mechanism of its sensory perception is still unclear. In birds, there appear to be two distinct magnetoreceptive systems, one sensitive to inclination and another to intensity.

Other possible orientational cues
Several species may have some ability to sense winds aloft as a directional cue. Wind may be used to maintain a compass direction or to select a heading, and there are many reports of upwind or downwind orientation but the pattern is complex and not yet clear. Another possible orientational cue is infrasound emanating from distant mountain ridges, or from waves breaking on the shore. Although the use of infrasound by migrants remains an open question, it is interesting that several migratory species circumvent mountain ridges and change their directional preferences well before they can detect the barrier visually.

Interactions between orientational cues
Many migrants seem able to use multiple cues to maintain appropriate headings under a wide range of weather conditions and at different times and places in their journeys. In nocturnal passerine migrants, there are probably two distinct phases when magnetic and stellar cues interact. During the pre-migratory period, when encoded directional information is being converted into an actual compass course, stellar rotation and magnetic cues interact to produce the migration course but celestial cues dominate. During migration, the star compass, sunset cues and the magnetic compass set the course but the magnetic compass dominates. In cases of disagreement, the other cues are adjusted to fit the ambient magnetic field. On their return to the breeding grounds, birds recalibrate their magnetic compass with reference to the celestial rotation; during migration, they recalibrate celestial cues by the earth's magnetic field. In this way, they avoid conflict between the various cues and always derive the same directional information from whichever cue is available.

Flight performance and migration strategies
Most avian migrants fly, although swimming may contribute significantly among waterbirds such as geese, ducks, divers and auks. Pelicans, storks, birds of prey, albatrosses and petrels cover large distances by soaring. They may either use thermals to gain height and then glide, as do storks and many birds of prey, or glide on wind currents over the waves, as do many ocean wanderers. Most migrating birds, however, use flapping or powered flight. Relatively little is known about the rates of energy expenditure during migratory flights. Metabolism may increase to five to ten times the basal rate, and single flights can last for up to 80–100 hours. The prime fuel is fat; during sustained flights, the oxidative capacities of the flight muscles increase to facilitate rapid metabolism of fatty acids.

After take-off, the migratory bird has to decide on flight altitude and flight speed, as well as when to stop, either for rest or to terminate migration. During flapping flight, birds do not usually fly at their maximum speed, but rather at their most economical. Measured ground speeds are of the order of 30–50 km/h in passerines, and 70–90 km/h in larger birds. As flying consumes energy, migrants have developed adaptations that minimize total flight costs, such as the bounding flight of many small passerines, with alternating flapping and wing-folded phases. Several larger species, such as geese, migrate in V-shaped formation, which saves about 20% of energy compared with non-formation flight.

Migration may take place very close to sea-level in ocean wanderers, or reach altitudes of up to 9,000 m above sea-level in some species, such as when Bar-headed Geese cross the Himalaya. Normally, however, overland migration takes place at much lower altitudes. For example, radar studies have shown that the median height during spring migration over the Swiss lowlands was 400 m by day, but 700 m at night, with 90% of the recordings below 2,000 m. Similar altitudinal distributions were recorded over northern Germany but with autumn migration on average lower than spring migration (430 versus 910 m). Flight altitude also varies in relation to topography and wind conditions. With headwinds, birds fly lower. Lower altitudes are more usual over the land, especially at mountain passes, whereas passerines fly comparatively high during migration over the ocean. In trans-Saharan migrants, flight altitude is related to the energetic and water-balance requirements of the birds.

Migration strategies
A crucial question is how far can a bird fly, given a certain amount of fuel? Aerodynamic theory assumes that there should be a diminishing return from further fattening, because progressively heavier birds will experience increasing flight costs. This function forms the basis for the theory of optimal stopover and departure decisions. The optimal policy for a migrating bird to reach its destination within the appropriate time depends upon the constraints that act on the bird. Time spent, energy costs, and safety from predators are the primary concerns. Natural selection may have favoured individuals that minimize the total energy expenditure for migration, which requires that they always fly with the least power requirements. Such birds should carry only as much fat as is needed to reach the next fuelling site, with a little spare to allow settling in on arrival. Alternatively, birds could be selected to minimize the time spent on migration, either to reach their destination (wintering, breeding or moulting areas) as soon as possible to obtain good territories, or to spend as little time as possible in unknown areas along the migration route. In this case, a high overall speed of migration, including both flight and stopover, would be favoured. Such birds should minimize the time spent on stopover and carry maximum fat loads at departure, to allow long-distance flights without further interruptions for feeding. A third possibility is that predation constitutes such a significant hazard to migrants that they are primarily adapted to minimize the mortality risk associated with migration. In this case, birds should depart with smaller fat reserves than is optimal under time-selected migration, because heavy fat loads may make them more vulnerable to predators.

Considerable recent progress has been made, using dynamic models, in evaluating the adaptive aspects of flight behaviour, fuel deposition, and responses to environmental cues, and in predicting patterns of stopover, fuel load at departure, responses to different fuel-deposition rates, and habitat selection in migrating birds. The strategies used to cover long migratory distances have been shown to differ among species. Some move in many short 'hops', while others negotiate the same distance in one or two very long 'jumps' (for example, the contrasting movements of British & Irish Sedge and Reed Warblers across Iberia). The physiological requirements and ecological and time constraints for 'hoppers' and 'jumpers' are naturally rather different. Moving by a series of short flights requires less on-board fat, and therefore incurs lower carrying costs, but it requires that there are many suitable stopover sites *en route*. Should a site become unsuitable through habitat change, 'hoppers' can generally move easily to the next site. Migration by long-haul flights, in contrast, is expensive, due to the costs of carrying the extra fat in the early stages of the flight, and is risky because the loss of any one stopover site may significantly hamper further migration. Birds may counter these disadvantages by gaining time, since they do not need to search for good feeding grounds at many successive stopover sites, or, since they are familiar with their feeding sites, by being less exposed to predation than are 'hoppers' at their many unknown stopover places.

Staging

Except when crossing major environmental obstacles, such as seas or deserts, many species migrate in short 'hops', with regular stopovers at staging sites, where they replenish their fuel stores for subsequent migratory flights. The choice of appropriate habitat is a prerequisite for optimal migration. Selection of suitable habitat by inexperienced first-time migrants may be relatively easy for waterbirds and waders. They often depend on coastal marshlands or tidal areas, such as the Wash or the Wadden Sea, where young birds may be attracted by staging conspecifics. It may be more problematic for a lone young passerine migrant in a novel environment. Many such migrants may have developed fairly precise habitat preferences as juveniles before departure, through direct experience, but for others the habitats used during staging may be very different from those near their birthplace. There is evidence that some migrants are equipped with distinct instinctive species-specific habitat preferences. The preferences birdwatchers observe during autumn migration at staging sites are astonishingly constant from year to year, despite the fact that most of the resting birds are normally first-time migrants, which select habitat independently from one another. Such precise patterns are unlikely to result from trial and error. In nocturnal migrants, the patterns of habitat choice observed even very early in the morning, when the birds have had little daylight time in which to redistribute themselves, are as distinct as those observed later in the day. Habitat selection is probably guided by fixed principles, perhaps related to the morphological and behavioural characteristics of the species, enabling migrants to settle into novel environments rather quickly and avoid the expenditure of time on roving and exploration. They also separate species and reduce the competition that might otherwise interfere with subsequent feeding and fat deposition.

Appropriate settling at staging sites is particularly important for those migratory species that must cross large ecological barriers like oceans and deserts, such as trans-Saharan passerines, or those that travel in a few long jumps and achieve their most significant fuelling at a few particular staging sites, like several arctic-nesting shorebirds. Knots and Bar-tailed Godwits migrate in one long, non-stop flight from their arctic breeding grounds to the Wadden Sea, where they stay and feed for a couple of weeks until they have accumulated an amount of fat roughly equivalent to their lean body mass. Then they depart for a further non-stop flight to the coast of West Africa. Several trans-Saharan passerines fuel mainly in North Africa during their southward migration. For Garden and Reed Warblers, maximum rates of daily fattening have been observed at staging sites in northern Algeria and northern Morocco; Sedge Warblers on the other hand fatten mainly in France.

Trans-Saharan migration

Some 200 European bird species winter in Africa south of the Sahara. Assuming that the Sahara Desert was a totally inhospitable land for most Palearctic migrants, offering neither food nor shelter, most ornithologists previously believed that migrants wintering in tropical Africa cross it in a single non-stop flight lasting at least 40–60 hours. Support for this assumption came from observations that the fat reserves of many migrants would theoretically enable such long flights. Several recent studies in various parts of the Sahara have revealed, however, that many migrants regularly undertake stopovers in the desert. Nocturnal migrants land at dawn and rest in the shade throughout the day, continuing their migration the following night if they are equipped with sufficient energy reserves to fuel the next flight. Individuals that have low fat reserves stay and replenish them. As the majority of the migrants staging in the desert have sufficient fat, and rest in the shade without feeding, the decision to land seems not to be related to energy demands. But as well as costing energy, flying also produces heat that has to be dissipated if normal body temperature is to be maintained.

At higher ambient temperatures, most heat is lost through the evaporation of body water, but excessive evaporation leads to dehydration. Water generation from the use of fat as fuel during migratory flights can balance evaporative water-loss in part, but a balance can only be achieved at lower ambient temperatures. At moderate and high temperatures, evaporative water-loss exceeds metabolic water production. Thus, over the Sahara, a balance might be achievable only by flying at higher altitudes where the air is cool enough, or by flying at night. When flying high, southbound migrants increasingly face headwinds that increase their energetic demands. If the birds descend, then they face higher ambient temperatures. Non-stop flights across the Sahara Desert are probably only possible, therefore, when tailwinds exist at altitudes with appropriate ambient temperatures. In all other circumstances, birds are forced to make landfall and to rest in the shade, continuing the flight the following night. Thus, there is not a unique optimal trans-Saharan migration strategy, but rather a variety that are used flexibly by migrants so that they can best cope with the prevailing environmental conditions. Whichever strategy is adopted, successful trans-Saharan migration depends on appropriate fuelling before departure.

Termination of outward migration

Soon after leaving the Sahara behind, the first-time migrant has to terminate its migration. Apparently, this is largely internally pre-programmed. In captive migrants, such as Garden Warblers, nocturnal migratory restlessness stops at the time when free-living conspecifics have reached the winter destination.

Termination of the first outbound migration is not, as was once assumed, stimulated by features that are associated with a particular geographical location, such as celestial cues. When captive migrants were displaced to their species-specific wintering grounds early in the migration period, they showed migratory restlessness for as long a period as individuals kept in the breeding area. The Starlings mentioned earlier, displaced to Switzerland during their first outward migration from eastern to western Europe, continued migration to wintering areas at an equivalent distance away in southern Europe. Thus, the timing of termination of migration is pre-programmed. Through this process, migrants normally reach the area where their conspecifics winter. If they have been forced to terminate at unfavourable places, however, the internal 'program' is flexible enough to enable them to move further on. This is also revealed in studies of captive migrants where, if the living conditions are experimentally worsened after termination of programmed migratory activity, the birds react with additional (facultative) migratory activity.

The movements that have been reported for several migrant species within their tropical winter range, particularly in East Africa, may be primarily a reaction to deteriorating environmental conditions, in particular to food depletion. After reaching the northern savanna soon after the rains, they stay for four to six weeks, and may even establish territories. As conditions deteriorate, many of them move on southwards to the southern savannas that received their rains just prior to the arrival of the migrants (Fig 3.9). This type of migration has been best recorded at Ngulia Lodge in Tsavo West National Park in Kenya, where southbound nocturnal migration peaks in November and December. Alternatively, however, these onward movements may also be pre-programmed. Large-scale midwinter movements may be much more common in Africa than has so far been suggested.

Fig 3.9 A schematic representation of the distribution of trans-Saharan migrants in Africa in (a) October, (b) December and (c) February. Darker shading indicates higher numbers of birds, although actual densities depend on habitat. (*Source*: Lack 1990.)

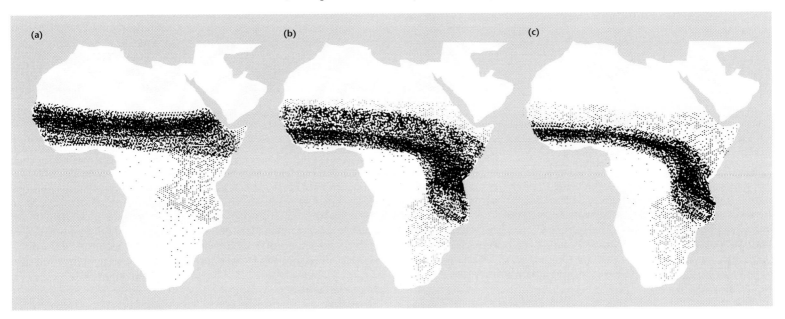

Homeward spring migration

As in first-time outbound migration, first-time homeward migration in spring seems to be initiated by an internal clock. Species wintering at the Equator do not experience the pronounced changes in day-length that, in temperate zones, could stimulate the onset of migration. Nevertheless, they leave the area so precisely that the timing of their arrival on the northern breeding grounds varies little from year to year. The innate nature of the onset of northbound migration is also revealed by captive migrants, which spontaneously resume spring migratory activity after a winter rest in the absence of any change in photoperiod or other seasonal cues. Moreover, Garden Warblers kept in winter in photoperiodic conditions equivalent to a latitude of 20°S initiated migratory activity and testicular growth significantly earlier than conspecifics held under an equatorial photoperiod. This difference may reflect the longer distance to be moved by the individuals wintering further south, and it ensures that both northern and southern winterers arrive at the breeding grounds at the same time.

For many migrant species, the course of the homeward migration is the reverse of the outbound route. These species may therefore use geographical information gathered during southward migration to find their way back home. Small differences between autumn and spring migration routes and overall speeds may be related to an increased urge to return to the breeding grounds in spring, or to differences in environmental conditions such as prevailing winds. For other species, homeward courses differ markedly from outward courses; they undertake 'loop migrations' (for further discussion, see the species accounts for Sand Martin, Whitethroat and, the one of the classic loop-migrants, Red-backed Shrike, in Chapter 6). As shown in the Garden Warbler, the birds may possess an inbuilt knowledge even for their homebound directions. In any case, and in contrast to the first-time outbound migration in autumn, all homing migrants know their final goal, which is generally either their natal area or their previous breeding site. Fidelity to breeding sites, sometimes even to the previous nesting place, is common among many bird species, and even first-time breeders of migratory species often return to the vicinity of their natal sites.

As an alternative to following an inbuilt program, migrants may *navigate* their route, using more than simple compass (directional) orientation. The difference is best illustrated by the displacement experiment described earlier, involving migrating European Starlings (Fig 3.6). Whereas the young birds followed an inbuilt compass direction after displacement, adult birds treated in the same manner were able to compensate, navigating towards their familiar winter quarters in northern France and southern England. True navigation relies on the determination by a migrant of its exact position relative to its goal and the calculation of the direction that leads to the goal, based on a map-and-compass mechanism, followed by orientation in that direction.

The mechanisms of navigation are still poorly known, particularly the cues that are used to establish a map. Quite a number of possible cues have been suggested, ranging from landmarks to olfactory information, but the earth's magnetic field may be the most reliable one, at least for long-distance navigation. Migrants might determine their position relative to a distant goal through magnetic cues that form a gradient map, enabling them to return to the correct vicinity. Then they may use more local cues, associated with the goal, as some kind of topographical map. The map may be acquired both through imprinting or experience at the birthplace and during the first outbound migration, though this cannot help during the first return leg of a loop migration.

Little is known about the control of subsequent migrations. Older migrants have already been through at least one complete migration cycle, gaining experience that may be used during subsequent migrations. Adult British & Irish Gannets and adult German White Storks, for example, winter on average further north than first-time migrants. In other species, winter site-fidelity can be astonishingly high. In a number of tropical locations, colour-ringed trans-Saharan migrants have been shown to return to almost the same bush in the following year. Among Pied Flycatchers, the rate of return to the previous wintering site in West Africa may be as high as breeding site-fidelity.

Weather and bird movements

The role of the atmosphere in influencing the movements of migrants is well known. As discussed earlier in this chapter, astronomical cues from the sun and stars play an important part in the onset of migration and, through orientation cues, in its progress, particularly at mid- and high latitudes. Wind can significantly affect the direction and speed of migration. These elements are as important in determining the movement of scarce and rare migrants into Britain & Ireland as they are to our regular migrants.

During the 1950s and 1960s, much progress was made in relating migration to weather patterns, especially at bird observatories such as Fair Isle. The resulting studies have become 'bread and butter' for migration watchers but radar has shown that movements aloft are rather more complex, since they are affected by atmospheric conditions such as cloud structure, wind direction and wind strength, all of which show considerable variation with altitude. The height at which the birds fly, and the time an individual bird has been on passage since it began its journey, are frequently unknown. The latter is especially relevant to overland migrants, which are able to land at any stage of their journey.

Migration weather

Favourable migration weather in autumn is normally associated with regions of subsiding air associated with anticyclones and polar air masses (Fig 3.10a). In mid- and high latitudes, anticyclones block the normal eastward flow of air round the hemisphere and divert disturbances such

Fig 3.10 Relationships between weather and bird migration in Britain & Ireland, showing standard meteorological maps with temperatures shown in °C. (*Source*: Elkins 1988a.)
  (a) Ideal migration weather over Britain & Ireland and mainland western Europe, with a blocking anticyclone ('H') centred on Scotland (22 September 1977, 1200h).
  (b) A typical situation delaying migration in spring, with a blocking anticyclone ('H') west of Britain and cold northerly winds over Britain and the North Sea (11 April 1973, 0600h). This particular 'block' lasted for two weeks.
  (c) Autumn fall conditions on the east coast of Britain, with arrows showing the subsequent movement of low pressure centres (3 September 1965, 1200h). The area of the English coast that experienced the fall is shown by stippling, the southern limit near Orford Ness in Suffolk being due to onshore wind. On a 4-km walk along the coast at this time, one observer estimated the presence of around 15,000 Redstarts, 8,000 Wheatears, 4,000 Pied Flycatchers, 3,000 Garden Warblers and more than a thousand each of Whinchat, Tree Pipit and Willow Warbler (Davis 1966b).
  (d) Conditions leading to a fall in northern Scotland of migrants bound for Scandinavia (3 May 1969, 1200h). Southerly winds over Iberia and France during the previous two days allowed migrants to move northwards, until they encountered strong easterlies ahead of the front. Fair Isle received one of the largest spring falls on record, including 1,500+ Tree Pipits, 500 Bramblings, 400 Willow Warblers, 300 Ring Ouzels, 45 Wrynecks and 32 Ortolan Buntings.
  (e) Conditions leading to transatlantic landbird vagrancy to Britain & Ireland, with an anticyclone over eastern Canada ('H') giving fine migration weather there, and a rapidly moving front of two small depressions ('O' and 'N') giving a strong westerly airflow in their broad warm sector (4 October 1976, 1200h). Mark 'A' shows the position of low 'O' at 1200h on 3 October, and 'B' the position of low 'N' at 0600h on 5 October. Six Blackpoll Warblers arrived in southwest Britain, 6–9 October.
  (f) Conditions leading to a large (assumed) overland passage of Kittiwakes across central Scotland, due to a large depression ('L') in the North Sea giving strong northwesterly winds, with a ridge of high pressure (and hence lighter winds) off western Scotland (15 November 1973, 1200h). The track of the depression is marked by crosses. Thousand of Kittiwakes were observed moving westwards up the Firth of Forth.

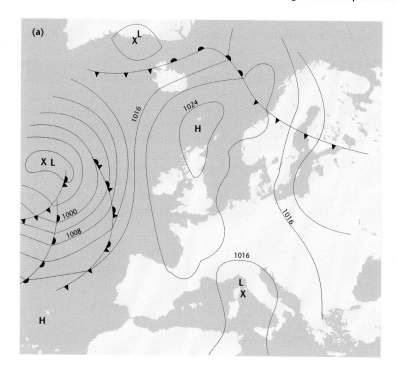

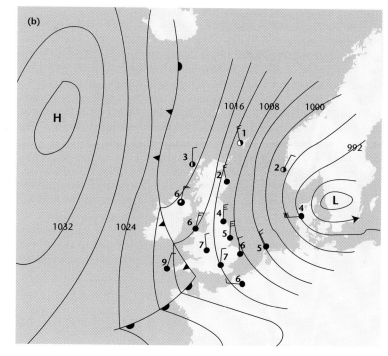

as frontal depressions. Some are persistent and promote suitable conditions over a particular region for several weeks, whereas others are more transient. Ideal autumn migration weather is located within and to the east of an anticyclone or ridge, where there is not only good visibility with significant breaks in cloud-cover (which may aid navigation using the sun and the stars) but also two other factors of importance. The first is a fall in temperature. Clear skies allow nocturnal cooling, and a polar air mass brings cold air from higher latitudes. Among other factors, low temperatures may signal to some migrant species that it is time to leave their breeding grounds. The second factor is wind, which in anticyclonic pressure patterns is generally light and often variable in direction. These conditions enable a migrant to fly with little risk of being drifted from its preferred heading or track. On the arrival of a polar air mass, after the passage of a cold front, winds are frequently very much stronger but are usually favourable in direction, so that migrants can fly downwind at ground speeds greatly exceeding their own still-air capability.

How important favourable weather patterns are for departure depends on the season and the physiological state of the bird. In early autumn, there is little real urgency to migrate, but later, especially if the weather has been adverse for some time, weather patterns assume great importance, and huge waves of birds may leave within a very short period of favourable weather. The longer it has been delayed, the more readily will a bird depart in suboptimal weather. The same applies to the onward passage of grounded migrants. It is not unusual in autumn for fine warm weather to result in migrants moving in the opposite direction to that expected, particularly when assisted by a tailwind. This is known as 'reverse migration' and can often carry migrants into higher latitudes.

In spring, there is a greater urgency to reach the destination, and the worst weather is more likely to be met at the end of the journey than near the beginning. Migrants must ensure that they do not arrive at successive latitudes too early to encounter an adequate food supply. Many species break their migration by using traditional staging posts where they renew fat reserves. The need for a rapid return from the winter quarters to breeding areas often results in movements occurring in weather that is more disturbed than in autumn, and early migrants are particularly at risk. If conditions deteriorate after arrival, some migrants may be required to retreat to avoid starvation. Movements of a

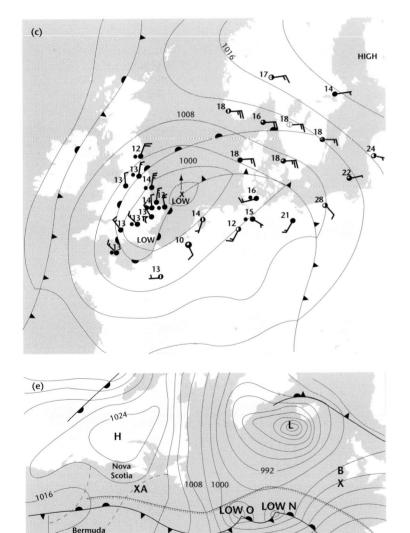

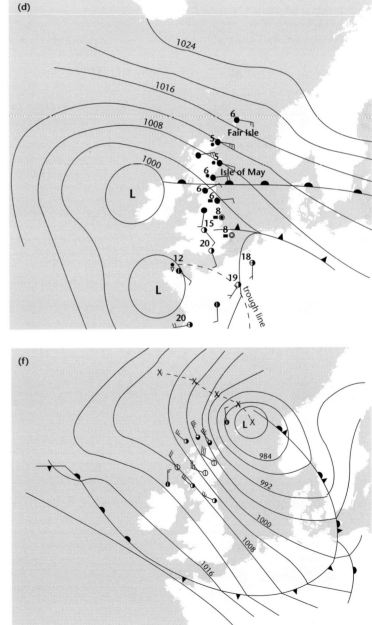

Table 3.1 Rarer species (not included in Chapter 6) that have provided evidence of movement from ring-recoveries involving Britain & Ireland. Short-term ring-recoveries at the ringing location are omitted. Numbers in brackets after the species name are, first, the number ringed in Britain & Ireland 1909–97 and, second, the number of these rings subsequently recovered. For complete listings of species ringed and recovered in Britain & Ireland, see the five-year BTO ringing reports. (*Main sources*: BTO data, Naylor 1996, 1998, Toms & Clark 1998, Toms *et al* 1999, Clark *et al* 2000.)

Species	Summary of ringing and recovery details for birds showing evidence of movement, including birds ringed abroad and recovered in Britain & Ireland
Black-crowned Night Heron *Nycticorax nycticorax* (0, 0)	A 1979 nestling from near Odessa, Ukraine, was seen at Skegness, Lincolnshire, from 30 December onward and found shot dead there on 4 January 1980.
Purple Heron *Ardea purpurea* (0, 0)	A 1967 nestling from Noorden, the Netherlands, was on Fair Isle during 2–31 May 1969 (trapped 16th); and a 1968 nestling from the same place was found dead on Scilly on 30 May 1970.
White Stork *Ciconia ciconia* (0, 0)	Sixteen records (8 originating in Denmark, 4 in Germany and 4 in the Netherlands) of 11 individual birds ringed abroad, some from reintroduction programmes.
American Wigeon *Anas americana* (2, 0)	Two young from New Brunswick, Canada, were shot, both in their first autumns, a female on Shetland on 7 October 1966 and a male in Co Kerry on 12 October 1968; a female ringed on Prince Edward Island, Canada, on 30 August 1977 was shot in Co Galway on 8–9 October the same year; in 1986, a juvenile male ringed in New Brunswick on 13 August was on Fair Isle from 21 September to 3 October (and a first-winter female bearing an American ring was shot in Co Wexford on 30 November).
Blue-winged Teal *Anas discors* (1, 0)	A male ringed in New Brunswick, Canada, in June 1971 was shot in Suffolk on 9 October that year; another, a juvenile ringed in September 1983 in Newfoundland, was shot in Co Offaly the following January.
Red-crested Pochard *Netta rufina* (48, 10)	Nine within-Britain movements (the greatest 214 km between Greater London and Staffordshire); a juvenile ringed in September 1952 in St James's Park, London, was found dead in Hoogeveen, the Netherlands, in January 1953.
Ring-necked Duck *Aythya collaris* (3, 1)	A fully grown bird ringed on 7 September 1967 in New Brunswick, Canada, was shot near Brecon on 26 December 1967; an adult male ringed at Slimbridge, Gloucestershire, on 1 March 1977 was shot at Isertoq, southeast Greenland, in May of the same year.
White-tailed Eagle *Haliaeetus albicilla* (64, 2)	Two within-Scotland movements, of 46 km and 62 km, of birds ringed as nestlings or juveniles and found long dead; a third bird, a 1997 nestling from Wester Ross, was seen alive in Morayshire 8 months later.
Red-footed Falcon *Falco vespertinus* (4, 0)	An adult male ringed in Lot-et-Garonne, southwest France on 25 July 1984 was seen in North Yorkshire on 5 September the same year and then found dead at Thornhill, near Dumfries, about 12 days later.
Kentish Plover *Charadrius alexandrinus* (4, 0)	A first-summer male ringed in Zeeland, the Netherlands, was seen at Dungeness on 10 April 1988.
Ring-billed Gull *Larus delawarensis* (0, 0)	A 1980 chick from New York state, USA, was found dead in Donegal on 28 December 1981.
Caspian Tern *Sterna caspia* (0, 0)	One ringed at Lake Michigan, USA, on 14 July 1927 was found dead at Whitby, North Yorkshire, in August 1939; remains of a 1970 nestling from Finland were found in a fox-earth in Cambridgeshire in July 1972; a 1975 nestling from near Stockholm, Sweden, was found long dead on Yell, Shetland, in August 1976.
Royal Tern *Sterna maxima* (0, 0)	The ring of a first-winter bird at Kenfig, Glamorgan, on 24 November 1979 was only partly read but indicated that the bird had been ringed as a pullus in North Carolina or Virginia, USA (Moon 1983).
Snowy Owl *Nyctea scandiaca* (28, 5)	Three local recoveries of birds ringed as nestlings on Fetlar, Shetland (1973, 1973–74 and 1969–84); another nestling, a female, moved 16 km within Shetland; an adult male ringed on Fair Isle in June 1972 was found long dead in the Outer Hebrides in February 1975. An adult female ringed in southern Norway on 1 April 1992 was found injured on North Uist on 31 May the same year.
Tengmalm's Owl *Aegolius funereus* (1, 0)	The leg and ring of a nestling from Hedmark, Norway, ringed in June 1980, was found in County Durham on 10 January 1981.
Alpine Swift *Apus melba* (1, 0)	One found dead at the St Agnes lighthouse, Scilly, on 24 September 1969 had been ringed as a nestling in Switzerland two months earlier.
Thrush Nightingale *Luscinia luscinia* (84, 0)	A first-year bird ringed in Vestfold, Norway, on 14 August 1984 put on 7.1 g of fat at Beachy Head, Sussex, between 26 August and 1 September the same year (James 1996).

Savi's Warbler *Locustella luscinioides* (59, 2)	One ringed at Brandon Marsh, Warwickshire, in May 1989 was recaught at Tring, Hertfordshire, two months later; also, an adult male ringed at Westbere, Kent, in June 1986 was retrapped there in June 1987 and June 1988.
Paddyfield Warbler *Acrocephalus agricola* (24, 0)	A first-autumn bird ringed on passage in Lithuania on 8 September 1996 was recaught on Fair Isle 11 days later.
Blyth's Reed Warbler *Acrocephalus dumetorum* (24, 2)	Two records of the same individual; ringed on Fair Isle on 22 October 1993, seen next day and later recaught at Sumburgh, Shetland, and finally found dead at the latter site on 31 October; also in 1993, a juvenile ringed at Jönköping, Sweden, on 29 September was recaught at Dungeness on 2 November.
Booted Warbler *Hippolais caligata* (28, 1)	A juvenile ringed at Spurn on 16 September 1993 and still there next day was recaught at Wetteren, Belgium, 19 days later (on 5 October).
Dusky Warbler *Phylloscopus fuscatus* (54, 1)	One ringed on the Calf of Man on 14 May 1970 was found dead near Limerick, Ireland, in early December the same year.
Eurasian Penduline Tit *Remiz pendulinus* (14, 1)	An adult female ringed at Icklesham, Sussex, in October 1988 was recaught in Kvismaren, Sweden, in May 1989; a 1997 nestling from southern Sweden was recaught at Icklesham on 25 October the same year.
Lesser Grey Shrike *Lanius minor* (16, 3)	Two local recoveries of dead birds (at Jarrow, Tyne & Wear, and on Foula, Shetland); also, a male at Seahouses, Northumberland, during 13–28 September 1952 was found dead near Aberdeen, on 15 October the same year.
Woodchat Shrike *Lanius senator* (108, 1)	In 1976, a female trapped on Skokholm on 3 June was recaught at Walberswick, Suffolk, on 20–21 June.
Rustic Bunting *Emberiza rustica* (47, 1)	A female ringed on Fair Isle, present there 12–19 June 1963, was recovered on the Greek island of Chios four months later.
Little Bunting *Emberiza pusilla* (128, 2)	A juvenile ringed on Fair Isle on 27 September 1994 was found dying on Cleeton oil rig in the North Sea, 50 km northeast of Hull, 7 days later; also, an adult ringed at Lewell, Dorset, in November 1993 was retrapped there in February 1994.

similar nature are made in winter ('cold-weather movements') and in summer ('drought displacement') (see the first section of this chapter), during which birds move, normally downwind, into regions where conditions are more benign and food more readily available. In general, warm spring airflows from the south are associated with northward passage, as cold autumn winds are for southward passage. Particularly fine warm weather may induce some spring migrants to overshoot their destination.

Weather conditions that inhibit navigation and continued onward passage are not infrequent (*eg* Fig 3.10b). Their effects may be greater for inexperienced young birds and perhaps for some adults whose navigational skills are poorly developed. Drift by the wind is one of the more serious problems that arise when orientation is hindered. The extent of drift will depend on a particular bird's size, weight, power and speed; strong winds may have least deflecting influence on birds that are fast and heavy. Certain weather conditions result in large coastal falls of migrants, when landbirds are presumed to have drifted off course or become disoriented over the sea (*eg* Fig 3.10c, d). Several studies have indicated that high-flying migrants may not always allow for lateral displacement, so that crosswinds result in extensive drift over land and sea. Low-flying birds are often able to correct for drift by using landmarks, and possibly also features at sea. In overcast weather, migrants may also be able to detect wind direction and actively reorient downwind, although even small cloud breaks allowing a sight of the sun or stars may permit some corrections to orientation, as may the use of the earth's magnetic field (see the previous sections of this chapter on orientation). Radar observations and occasional recoveries of ringed vagrants after return to their normal range (*eg* see the record for Rustic Bunting in Table 3.1) have confirmed that reorientation can occur but the degree to which it can be successful is not yet clear. The effect of

overcast skies and poor visibility at ground level can be difficult to assess. Poor visibility in frontal situations is likely to be associated with precipitation and thick cloud layers aloft but, in subsiding air, fog or low cloud over land and sea is more likely to be topped by clear skies, and migration can continue unimpeded above it.

It must be emphasized that the structure of weather systems with which we are familiar in sea-girt Britain & Ireland can be markedly different to those associated with large continental landmasses because of significant variations in atmospheric temperature and humidity.

The influence of weather on bird movements obviously has great importance in predicting the likely impacts of global climate change, whether due to natural fluctuation or man-induced changes. This issue is discussed in Chapter 7.

Scarce and rare migrants
Alongside the many widespread and common migrant bird species in Britain and Ireland, there are 200 or so that occur either regularly in small numbers or rarely and irregularly. Such birds are of special interest to many birdwatchers. There is no doubt that Britain & Ireland, at the battleground of air masses, are exceptionally well placed to receive unexpected migrants from a wide range of compass directions. In many autumns, a vagrant songbird from North America may be observed alongside one from central Asia.

Scarce and rare migrants in Britain & Ireland are subject to the same atmospheric influences as the more common species. Their occurrence also depends on their population levels, however, as well as on the distance from their normal range and their expected migratory orientation. The route of a migrant on a specific heading will cross certain regions but miss others, whether the species originates from a distant source, such as North America, central Asia or Africa, or from closer at hand within Europe. For rare species, it has been suggested that this may explain why certain rarities show regional variations in occurrence across Britain & Ireland, while other potential visitors are never observed. In all cases, there is a greater likelihood of a vagrant turning up when the population of displaced migrants is high.

Many rarities found here are almost impossible to relate to specific atmospheric conditions. Some of the amazing past occurrences have probably been the outcome of a complex combination of weather influences operating along the bird's route, which can never be resolved without detailed knowledge of its individual history and the actual date of its arrival.

North American species

Autumn arrivals of North American landbirds in Britain & Ireland have been linked to fast-moving weather systems that develop over their normal southward migration routes along the eastern seaboard of North America and through the western Atlantic (eg Fig 3.10e). Two situations give rise to transatlantic movements. Many migrants, such as some Grey-cheeked Thrushes and Blackpoll Warblers, typically fly south over the western Atlantic. Active cold fronts across their route off eastern North America can cause them to become disoriented and then to be displaced rapidly eastward by the fast-moving warm sectors of depressions. Reverse movements in warm southwesterlies over the eastern seaboard may also carry migrants such as Red-eyed Vireos into similar situations. Hurricanes and deep, slow-moving depressions are unlikely to be directly responsible for transatlantic vagrancy since they invariably move too slowly and have too vigorous a circulation for vagrants to survive a crossing. Ships experiencing hurricanes may become inundated with hundreds of migrants, however, that may then be assisted towards Britain or Ireland.

Some shorebirds also follow routes over the western Atlantic in autumn. For these, vagrancy in Britain & Ireland correlates not with Atlantic depressions but with the strength and direction of winds at the altitudes of several thousand metres at which they fly. These winds often blow from different directions to those nearer the earth's surface. More of these vagrants, which include Pectoral, White-rumped and Buff-breasted Sandpipers, appear when transatlantic upper westerly winds are stronger than normal and are displaced into lower latitudes.

Transatlantic vagrancy of one or two species (notably American Robin and Killdeer) may begin with cold-weather movements in the eastern USA, which bring birds into the paths of developing Atlantic depressions.

Asian species

The vagrancy to Britain & Ireland of passerines from northern and central Asia, involving species that normally move south and southeast in autumn, has traditionally been linked to the building winter anticyclone over their source region. However, most depart before this feature has become well established. The increasing numbers of such birds, several species of which reach northern Europe every autumn in varying but often substantial numbers, suggest that other mechanisms are initially involved. It may be that part of the population of several species undertakes exploratory movements on a reverse compass bearing (also sometimes termed 'reverse migration'). Some juveniles of these species may inherit atypical pre-programmed directions for their first migrations and set out westwards towards Britain. Their eventual arrival is then subject to the same European weather patterns that bring Scandinavian migrants to Britain on easterly winds over the North Sea. Into this category come the influxes of Yellow-browed and Pallas's Warblers, as well as those of rarer warblers, pipits and buntings.

Arctic species

Incursions of very cold arctic air in winter from both Nearctic and Palearctic regions are thought to be responsible for the arrival of several northern species. Some are arctic seabirds, such as Ivory and Ross's Gulls. Others, such as Gyr Falcon and Snowy Owl (Table 3.1), are subject to fluctuating populations and periodic shortages of food.

European and African species

The overshooting of birds from southern and eastern Europe and North Africa in spring and early summer is related to prolonged fine anticyclonic conditions over their destination, leading individuals of some species, assisted by suitable winds, to explore beyond the edge of their range. These species include White-winged Black Terns, Lesser Grey Shrikes and Red-rumped Swallows. Several heron species overshoot regularly from the south and this may have led to the recent establishment of a Little Egret breeding population in southern England, which has been allowed to flourish by a run of mild winters. White Storks are dependent upon thermal up-currents for long-distance travel, as also are many large raptors, such as the Black Kite. Sea air does not often provide the sustained thermals that soaring birds need but, if suitable up-currents are embedded in a strong following wind, long sea-crossings are possible.

The autumn occurrence of many scarce species, such as Ortolan Bunting, Red-breasted Flycatcher, Melodious Warbler and Tawny Pipit, has been linked to reverse migration. Such birds reach Britain on warm southerly to easterly winds; some southern individuals (eg Desert Wheatear) have arrived in air masses whose origin has been shown by falls of Saharan dust.

Although food supplies normally control the movements of irruptive species in autumn and winter, some of these (eg Nutcracker) are, again, typically encountered in Britain during spells of winds blowing from continental Europe.

Seabirds

Strong winds blowing onshore or along coasts are often responsible for inshore seabird passage, which may include the rarer shearwaters and petrels that normally remain well offshore, as well as Long-tailed and Pomarine Skuas, Sabine's Gulls and Grey Phalaropes. Severe gales occasionally carry such birds well inland. Concentrations of seabirds also move along with the relatively calm 'eyes' of intense low-pressure systems, such as hurricanes or deep depressions (see the account for Sabine's Gull in Chapter 6). Observations in both North America and Europe indicate that, when these weather systems make landfall on especially dark, moonless nights with dense cloud, some pelagic birds may be unaware of the physical features beneath them and progress well inland. Gale-force conditions at sea may also lead some seabird species to make more local movements to areas where feeding is possible, sometimes leading to overland passage (eg Fig 3.10f).

Vagrancy, or evolution in action?

Many individual unexpected migrants seen on British & Irish coasts may be disoriented, unaware of their location and, given the proximity of the Atlantic Ocean, perhaps unlikely to survive a further flight. It could be argued that such birds, lost and destined to die before passing on their genes, are of no biological significance. Others, however, may be the vanguard of a new subpopulation just beginning to exploit a novel breeding or wintering area, or the remnants of one that is becoming extinct. Species such as Yellow-browed and Pallas's Warblers, that have become much more numerous in western Europe in recent decades, blur the distinction between commonness and rarity. They may indeed be establishing new wintering areas, perhaps alongside other species of similar origins that are currently less frequent in Britain & Ireland. Such observations indicate that 'vagrancy' among birds is indeed a topic worthy of scientific attention.

The movements of a number of scarce or rare species, including Little Egret, Pectoral Sandpiper, Grey Phalarope, Long-tailed Skua, Pomarine Skua, Richard's Pipit, Yellow-browed Warbler and Red-breasted Flycatcher, are discussed in more detail in the short species accounts in Chapter 6. Species that do not warrant a species account, but for which there are interesting ring-recoveries involving Britain & Ireland are

Table 3.2 Suggested references for further reading, by topic.

Topic	Suggested references
Dispersal	Greenwood 1980; Greenwood & Harvey 1982; Paradis *et al* 1998
Differential migration	Ketterson & Nolan 1983; Cristol *et al* 1999; see also Chapter 5
Partial migration	Berthold 1984; Lundberg 1988; see also Chapter 5
Escape movements	Baillie *et al* 1986; Ridgill & Fox 1990; Clark *et al* 1993; Hulscher *et al* 1996; Carey & Dawson 1999
Irruptions/nomadic movements	Newton 1972; Berthold 2001; see also the species accounts for the crossbills, redpolls and Waxwing in Chapter 6
Evolution of migration/migration routes	Baker 1978; Terrill 1991; Berthold 2001 — future changes
Leap-frog migration	Alerstam & Högstedt 1980, 1985; Pienkowski *et al* 1985; Townshend 1985: Grey Plover; Drent & Piersma 1990; Wood 1992: Yellow Wagtail; Meltofte 1996a
Migration physiology	Castro & Myers 1989: flight ranges; Biebach 1992: flight ranges; Gwinner 1990; Berthold 1996; Gwinner 1996: annual cycle
Migration strategies and staging	Bairlein *et al* 1983; Bairlein 1985a, 1988; Wood 1989; Biebach 1990; Berthold 2001
Moult migration	Walker 1970; Little & Furness 1985; Jehl 1990; Alerstam 1990a; see also the Shelduck species account in Chapter 6
Orientation and navigation	Baker 1984; Berthold 1991
Palearctic–African migration systems	Moreau 1972; Curry-Lindahl 1981; Jones 1985; Crick 1992; Lövei 1998
Vagrancy	Nisbet 1959; Dymond *et al* 1989; Williams & Williams 1978; Elkins 1979, 1988b, 1999; Robbins 1980; Baker 1984; Howey & Bell 1985; Alerstam 1990b; Berthold 1991; van Impe & Derasse 1994; Thorup 1998
Weather and bird movements	Elkins 1979, 1988a, 1988b; Richardson 1978: updated in Gwinner 1990; Richardson 1991

listed, with a summary of the available data, in Table 3.1. A handful of these recoveries, notably for Ring-necked Duck, Booted Warbler, Penduline Tit, Rustic Bunting and Little Bunting, suggest return movements of vagrant individuals towards their expected ranges, as do single recoveries for Red-breasted Flycatcher and Common Rosefinch that are referred to in Chapter 6.

Further reading

The ecology, ecophysiology and evolution of bird migration represent large and complex subject areas, of which we have been able to provide only a flavour in this chapter. Due to space limitations, we have included only a few key references within the text. For further general background, we highly recommend *Bird Migration: a general survey* (Berthold 2001) and *Bird Migration* (Alerstam 1990a). These two books are excellent sources of further references on particular subject areas. For those interested in the most up-to-date research on bird migration, two sets of conference proceedings have recently been published: Alerstam & Hedenström (1998) on the subject of '*Optimal Migration*', and the proceedings of the '*Bird Ringing 100 Years*' conference held on Helgoland in 1999, which contains many papers on bird migration (Berthold & Winkel 2000, Jenni & Camphuysen 2001). In addition, we hope that the reference list by topic given in Table 3.2 will help the reader to find more detailed information if required.

4 Analysis and interpretation of the ring-recovery data

Chris Wernham & Gavin Siriwardena

Ring-recovery data form the basis of this book. Their generation involves ringing birds at one point in space and recapturing, resighting or finding some of them dead elsewhere. In drawing conclusions about bird movements from this type of information, there are notable theoretical and practical difficulties that must be overcome. This chapter describes the ring-recovery data used in the book and how they were analysed. It also highlights a number of key issues that must be taken into account when ring-recoveries are used to provide information on patterns of bird distribution and movement.

The analyses for the book were carried out as a two-stage process. First, an initial set of maps, tables and key distance information was produced and supplied to the authors writing the main species accounts for Chapter 6. The authors used this material, together with information on bird movements from sources other than ring-recoveries (see Chapter 1), in compiling their texts. Second, rigorous statistical analyses were undertaken, investigating differences between the movements of groups of birds (age, sex and regional classes), quantifying migratory tendency and analysing how it varies between species. Species-specific results from these analyses have been fed into the main species accounts, and more general patterns across groups of species are discussed in Chapter 5.

In this chapter, we first give a brief overview of the ring-recovery data that are held within the BTO Ringing Scheme database. We then consider some issues that need to be considered carefully when interpreting such data. Finally, we lay out the methods used to analyse the information for this book. We have restricted the technical details to a bare minimum and have kept the more complex explanations of methods separate from the main text. The latter are provided as footnotes for readers with a greater statistical interest!

The BTO ring-recovery database and the data included in the book

In this book, we include information both from birds ringed in Britain & Ireland (and reported anywhere in the world) and from birds reported in Britain & Ireland, but ringed elsewhere. For the purposes of the book, the Isle of Man is included within 'Britain & Ireland' and the Channel Isles are 'abroad'. 'Ireland' includes both Northern Ireland and the Republic.

The term *recovery* is used throughout the book to refer to any report of a ringed bird from the BTO database. For British- and Irish-ringed birds, we have used reports of birds ringed from 1909 (when the Ringing Scheme began) up to the end of 1997 (and reported to the BTO by the end of April 1998). The BTO has been routinely computerizing recovery records of birds ringed in Britain & Ireland since 1968. All earlier recovery records of BTO-ringed birds were also computerized, in the early 1980s, with the aid of a European Union grant via EURING. Baillie *et al* (1999b) give further details of the BTO ring-recovery database.

Until relatively recently, the derivation of qualitative information on where birds went was the primary focus of bird ringing. This is still important today, but the focus has shifted more towards quantitative studies of demography that require fully computerized data (see Chapter 2). The BTO's approaches to data collection and collation reflect this shift in emphasis over time. All records of dead ringed birds are held on computer regardless of the distance moved. Until the late 1990s, recaptures of live ringed birds and resightings of birds with marks that could be read at a distance in the field (such as colour rings or wing tags) were only computerized if they satisfied certain specific criteria[1] or occurred more than a certain distance away from the original ringing

---

[1] 'Reportable retraps' (retrapped within 5 km of the ringing site) were defined as (i) birds having a retrap history that were subsequently recovered dead, (ii) birds ringed as nestlings that survived beyond the calendar year of ringing, (iii) summer migrants retrapped in subsequent summers, (iv) winter immigrants retrapped in subsequent winters, (v) birds ringed on passage and retrapped on a subsequent passage, (vi) records showing 'interesting longevity' (retrapped more than five years after ringing for small birds), (vii) records considered to be of particular interest by the ringer in the light of local conditions and (viii) summer migrants retrapped in winter (December–February) or winter immigrants retrapped in summer (June–July). In addition to the inclusion of the above *controls* (the term used by ringers for records of live birds away from their original ringing site) in the BTO database, a few local *retraps* (birds caught at their original ringing sites) have been computerized each year since 1984 if the time elapsed between ringing and recovery exceeded the period listed as the 'retrap age' in the third edition of *The Ringer's Manual* (Spencer 1984).

[2] For Storm Petrel, all movements of greater than 20 km were processed, and any likely to involve breeding birds (defined as birds retrapped four or more years after being ringed as chicks or juveniles, or three years after being ringed as adults). For Mute Swan and Canada Goose, only recaptures or resightings over 40 km were processed, or those between 5 km and 40 km if thought to be significant by the ringer. For common shore waders (Oystercatcher, Ringed Plover, Grey Plover, Turnstone, Dunlin, Knot, Sanderling, Redshank, Bar-tailed Godwit and Curlew), all recaptures and resightings involving movements over 30 km or movements between estuaries have been processed. For Black-headed, Lesser Black-backed, Herring, Great Black-backed and Common Gulls, the threshold distance for processing live records has been 40 km (it has been 5 km for other gull species). For Sand Martin, the minimum distance for a live record to be processed was 10 km.

site. The reporting distance, introduced in the third edition of *The Ringer's Manual* (Spencer 1984), was 5 km for most species, with a few exceptions[2]. Currently, a high proportion of ringing data is submitted electronically and short-distance movements of live birds will soon all enter the database routinely. For present purposes, however, records of dead birds give the highest-quality information on distances moved by the different species. Records of live ringed birds have generally not been used for analyses of movement distances, because they will tend to overestimate average distances (short-distance movements having been omitted from the database).

Not all records of colour-marked birds are stored in the BTO database. The BTO first requested that all colour-marking schemes should register with the Ringing Scheme in 1966. There are now more than 250 projects active in Britain & Ireland, and the coordination of these programmes for some groups is undertaken by volunteers. Currently, some reports of colour-marked birds come directly to the BTO (approximately 1,000 per year) and the rest are sent to volunteer coordinators for onward transmission to the ringers involved. Those records held only by the volunteer coordinators and individual ringers were not available for use in this book, unless the species-text authors held or had obtained this information themselves. For some species, records of colour-marked birds may give a biased picture of movement patterns because the geographical spread of colour-ringing studies and observers is more clumped than that of general ringing. For this reason, such resightings have generally been omitted from quantitative analyses presented in the book. With the increased data-handling power of computers, the incorporation of colour-mark resighting information into the main BTO database is likely to increase during the next few years.

Reports of foreign-ringed birds recovered in Britain & Ireland have been computerized only since 1979 for some species. For these species, the pre-1979 records were unfortunately not available for analysis or mapping in this book. The numbers of pre-1979 reports of such species are summarized in the '*Ringing and recovery data*' table in each main species account (see Chapter 6) and details are also provided in map legends and within the species accounts, where appropriate.

Some species and races have only been differentiated in the BTO database relatively recently. For example, records of Water Pipits before 1986 were included under Rock Pipit and Scottish Crossbill has only very recently been separated from Common Crossbill. Carrion and Hooded Crows are not differentiated on the database, nor are Feral Pigeon (a form not normally ringed) and Rock Dove. The data do not allow the separation of the redpolls or teal under their new taxonomy (Marchant *et al* 2000). For a few other species, races are differentiated in the database either on plumage characteristics or biometrics (*eg* Dunlin). In all these cases, authors for the main species accounts have interpreted the ring-recovery data in the light of these limitations using their expert knowledge, and have made use of the information available to differentiate races or species whenever possible.

For a number of sensitive species, such as several birds of prey, ringing (nesting) sites are confidential and the exact coordinates are not coded in the ring-recovery database. For such species, records have generally been included if the ringing location was coded to an accuracy of at least half a degree of latitude and longitude (the standard throughout the book, see later). In a few cases, such as Osprey, recoveries have been plotted on maps even if the ringing site was recorded less accurately than this (due to confidentiality), because this did not impair the accuracy of the recovery data.

Until very recently, ringing data were not computerized routinely for birds that were not subsequently recovered. Instead, these were simply checked and filed away on paper forms. The full set of data for all birds ringed has only been computerized for a handful of species, as part of specific research projects. Computerized ringing data on birds that were not recovered were not available, therefore, for the analyses in this book. The total numbers of birds ringed, indicated in the '*Ringing and recovery data*' table in each main species account and used in some analyses here,

were derived from totals lists supplied by ringers at the end of each year and are, no doubt, imprecise. Such totals cannot be segregated by region or into the classes that would be ideal for some analyses. Hence, for the purposes of the book, the degree to which ringed birds were representative of the populations using Britain & Ireland as a whole was assessed solely from the ringing locations of those birds subsequently recovered. This situation is set to improve. Since 1983, ringers have provided annual totals for 22 common passerines ringed between April and September inclusive, split by both age and region. Now that an increasing proportion of the annual ringing data is being submitted to the BTO in computerized form, such information will enter the database routinely, making totals available for analyses in the future. It is unlikely that all the historical ringing data will be computerized in the near future, however.

How representative of wider populations are the birds that have been ringed?

In any scientific research, the results can only be generalized if the sample of individuals studied is representative of the population in question. Hence, if we wish to make statements about the movement patterns of the Meadow Pipits that breed in Britain & Ireland, then we need to ensure that the birds that have been ringed and reported come from a wide enough geographical area and range of habitats (or areas of high and low population density) to be representative of the national populations. Ideally, we would look at the distribution of the ringing locations of all the Meadow Pipits that have ever been ringed and compare these with our knowledge of the distribution of the breeding population (from the *1988–91 Atlas*, for example) to check that all areas are adequately covered by ringing. This was not possible for this book, however, because the full ringing data set has not been computerized for most species. Rather, the ringing locations of only those birds that were recovered subsequently could be used. These are presented in the standard Figure 1 in each main species account (see Chapter 6). For Meadow Pipit, the distribution of ringing locations for birds recovered subsequently (Fig 4.1a) is in marked contrast to the map of abundance from the *1988–91 Atlas* (Fig 4.1b); vast areas of north and west Scotland, where the species is abundant, are not represented in the recovery data, nor are areas of high population density in western Ireland. If we had the full ringing data set, then we would be able to distinguish for certain between two possible interpretations of this difference in distribution: either (i) few birds have been ringed in the north and west of Scotland and in western Ireland, leading to few recoveries or (ii) birds have been ringed there but they have migrated to areas that are different, and have a lower recovery rate, from those visited by birds from further south in Britain. In fact we know from the results for other species that few birds have been ringed in the areas that lack recoveries (see later). The comparison between the map of ringing locations for birds recovered subsequently and the map of breeding abundance is still important, however, as it warns us that the information available on Meadow Pipit movements may not be representative of the movements of birds from the core breeding areas in Britain and Ireland.

The paucity of recovery data for birds ringed in the north and west of Britain, and from Ireland, for Meadow Pipit is reflected in the general situation for all passerines ringed throughout the year and recovered subsequently (Fig 4.2a). The overall pattern for passerines strongly reflects the distribution of areas of dense human population and, hence, of concentrations of ringers. Ringing is biased towards the south and east of Britain, with generally fewer birds recovered that have been ringed further north and west or in Ireland (with the exception of the northeast around Belfast). Exceptions in the north and west, where large numbers have been ringed and recovered, include the 'hot spots' of several bird observatories, such as Fair Isle, North Ronaldsay, the Calf of Man and Bardsey. The bias towards the south and east of Britain is also apparent, to some extent at least, for raptors & owls, waders and wildfowl (Fig

Fig 4.1 (a) Ringing locations in Britain & Ireland during the breeding season of Meadow Pipits later recovered, summarized into blocks of 0.5° latitude and 1° longitude (small circles 1–9 birds ringed, large circles 10–99 birds ringed) and (b) the breeding abundance of Meadow Pipits in Britain & Ireland during 1988–91 (from the *1988–91 Atlas*).

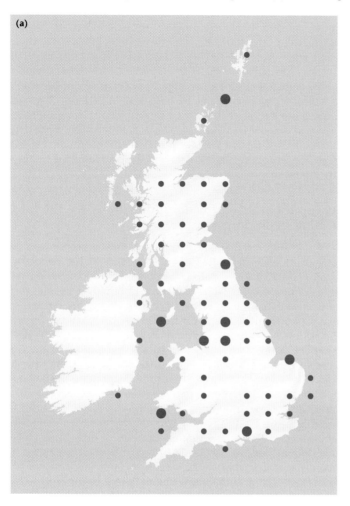

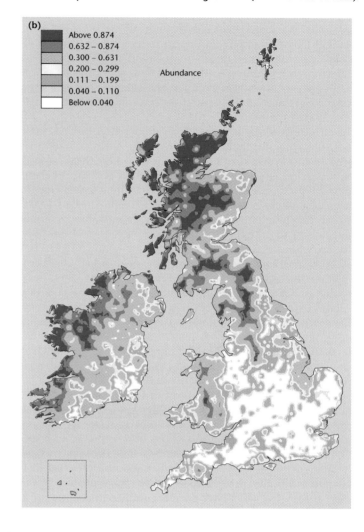

4.2b–d), although the patterns are modified somewhat due to the distribution of the specialist ringers that target these groups. For example, large numbers of waders have been ringed on the Mersey Estuary, and many waterfowl in the Firths of Forth and Tay. For seabirds and gulls, the remoter colonies in northwest Scotland and on the west coast of Ireland have generally been under-ringed, as have those on the Southwest Peninsula (Fig 4.2e). These general biases in the distribution of ringed birds may become either more or less serious for species that have a limited British & Irish distribution. For example, the southeast ringing bias will be less severe for species like Reed Warbler, Lesser Whitethroat and Nightingale that also have breeding distributions concentrated in southern Britain but more severe for species whose distributions are concentrated in the north and west, such as Short-eared Owl, Wheatear, Stonechat, Meadow Pipit and Siskin.

In assessing whether the birds that have been ringed and recovered are representative of the populations under consideration, the seasonal pattern of ringing must also be checked. For many species, such as Dunlin, Black-headed Gull, Blackbird and Blackcap, we know that Britain & Ireland receives passage migrants and wintering birds from continental Europe and northern populations, as well as holding its own breeding populations. The seasonal spread of ringing activity, and, to some extent, the age classes ringed, show the likelihood of the data revealing the movements of such immigrant individuals and those of the British & Irish breeding population. This information is presented in the standard Figure 2 in each main species account. For example, most Wigeon ringed in Britain & Ireland and recovered subsequently have been ringed between September and March (Fig 4.3a). Hence, much is

known about the movements of the populations of immigrant birds that are present in Britain & Ireland on passage and in winter, but almost nothing about the British & Irish breeding population; very few Wigeon have been ringed as ducklings in Britain & Ireland or as breeding adults. Most Blackcaps are ringed in Britain & Ireland during autumn passage between July and October (Fig 4.3b). In common with many other migrant warblers, relatively few are ringed as nestlings to provide information on the dispersal of young of known natal origin. There have also been few ringed in the winter months, to provide information on the precise breeding origins of those that are overwintering in Britain & Ireland in increasing numbers in recent years. In contrast, most Great Black-backed Gulls, in common with many coastal seabird and gull species, have been ringed largely as chicks during the breeding season, with few ringed as fully grown birds during the breeding season, passage periods or in winter (Fig 4.3c). Hence, we know little about breeding dispersal or the breeding origins of passage and wintering populations of some of these species.

Generalizing at the group level (Fig 4.4), many common passerine species are ringed throughout the year in Britain & Ireland, or at least throughout the period when they are present here, so that the recovery data are a qualitatively reasonable representation of populations present throughout the year. The frequency with which the chicks (*ie* birds of definite British & Irish origin) of passerines are ringed varies between species and, in common with other groups, depends on the ease of finding nests and their accessibility for ringing. The chicks of many nestbox species are ringed in good numbers, while those of species with well-hidden nests (*eg* Willow Warbler), nests that are difficult to reach

Fig 4.2 All ringing locations in Britain & Ireland of (a) passerines, (b) raptors and owls, (c) waders, (d) wildfowl and (e) seabirds and gulls, 1909–97, for birds later recovered, summarized into blocks of 0.5° latitude and 1° longitude and with one-fifth of the birds ringed in each symbol size class.

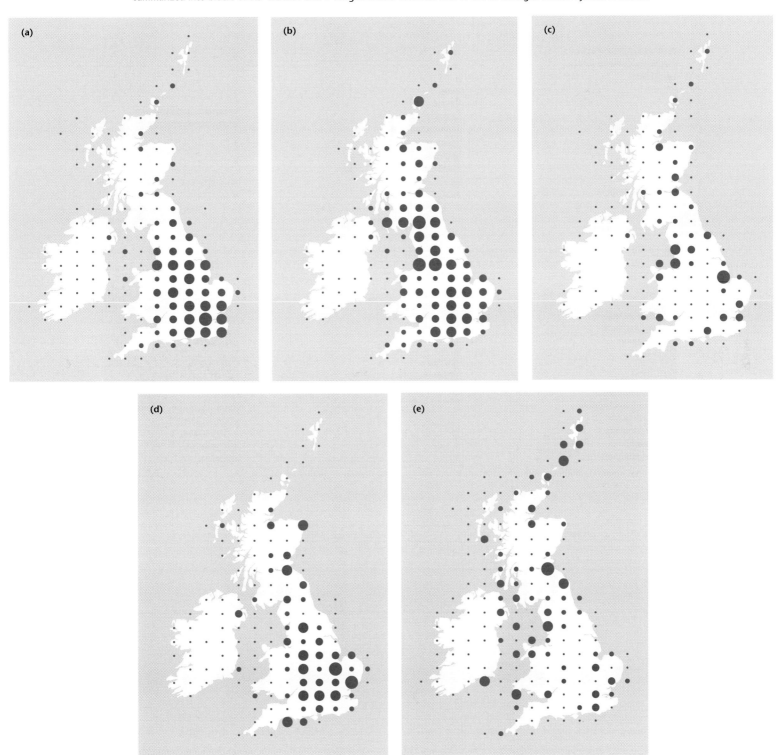

without disturbance (*eg* Reed Warbler) and enclosed nests (*eg* Wren, Long-tailed Tit, Treecreeper) are ringed in much smaller numbers. Most seabirds, raptors and owls are ringed as chicks, because of the practical difficulties in catching adult birds. This means that we know rather little about the composition and breeding origins of populations present in Britain & Ireland outside the breeding season for many species. Exceptions include some of the gulls, which can be caught in relatively large numbers by cannon-netting at waste tips outside the breeding season. In general, the converse is true for waders and wildfowl: fully grown birds present in Britain & Ireland on passage and during the

winter have been caught in large numbers by specialist ringers, such as the Wildfowl & Wetlands Trust (WWT) and the Wash Wader Ringing Group, while fewer are ringed during the breeding season, and very few chicks. This means that we often know more about immigrant populations of these species than those that breed in Britain & Ireland.

For both passerines and raptors & owls, the geographical spread of ringing activity has generally increased over time, particularly with improved coverage in the north and west of Britain (Fig 4.5a, b). Before the arrival of mist-nets in the late 1950s (see Chapter 2), a slightly higher proportion of passerines were ringed as nestlings (around 22% according

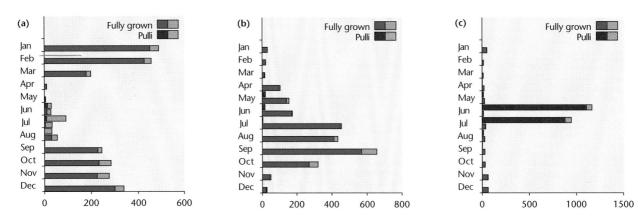

Fig 4.3 Months and age classes of ringing of birds later recovered for (a) Wigeon, (b) Blackcap and (c) Great Black-backed Gull. Dark red and dark blue bars show birds ringed in Britain & Ireland, light red and light blue bars show birds ringed elsewhere and recovered within Britain & Ireland.

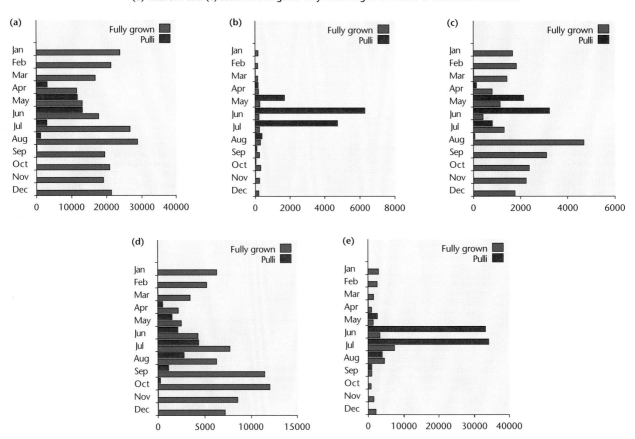

Fig 4.4 Months and age classes of ringing by ecological group for birds later recovered: (a) passerines, (b) raptors and owls, (c) waders, (d) wildfowl and (e) seabirds and gulls. Only birds ringed in Britain & Ireland are included.

to recoveries) than in recent decades (Fig 4.6), and Helgoland traps at bird observatories were of great importance for catching fully grown birds. It is possible that the distribution of habitats in which passerines have been ringed has varied over time (perhaps towards more ringing in gardens) but, without the comprehensive computerization of ringing data and the systematic recording of habitat information at ringing sites (which has been initiated only recently), we are unable to check for such changes. Further analysis of the temporal variation in the geographical distribution of ringing effort would be valuable for the interpretation of observed changes over time in the recovery patterns of some species (such as Blackbirds).

Until the late 1950s, wader ringing showed a northerly bias within Britain (Fig 4.5c), with a high proportion of birds ringed as chicks (Fig 4.6), including particularly large numbers of Lapwing. With the

introduction of rocket-nets in the late 1950s, followed rapidly by that of cannon-nets (see Chapter 2), emphasis switched to the catching of fully grown birds at coastal sites; the proportion of birds ringed as chicks (and subsequently recovered) decreased from 84% in 1909–59 to less than a quarter thereafter (Fig 4.6) and the geographical spread of the ringing activity increased over time (Fig 4.5c).

Similarly, the advent of cannon-netting was of particular importance for the catching of wildfowl, and the distribution of wildfowl ringing activity has increased markedly over time (Fig 4.5d). Before the advent of cannon-nets, ducks were caught in old decoys converted for ringing use during the 1940s and 1950s and in baited traps (eg Wainwright 1957). The numbers and distribution of geese ringed have varied over time due to particular expedition work and targeted studies, many led by WWT (eg see the accounts for Pink-footed Goose and White-fronted Goose

Fig 4.5 Changes in the spatial distribution of ringing activity in Britain & Ireland over time. The maps show all ringing locations in Britain & Ireland in the stated time period for birds later recovered, summarized into blocks of 0.5° latitude and 1° longitude and with one-fifth of the birds ringed in each symbol size class: (a) passerines (1909–59 and 1990–97), (b) raptors and owls (1909–59 and 1990–97), (c) waders (1909–59, 1960–69 and 1990–97), (d) wildfowl (1909–59 and 1990–97) and (e) seabirds and gulls (1909–59 and 1990–97).

(a) Passerines

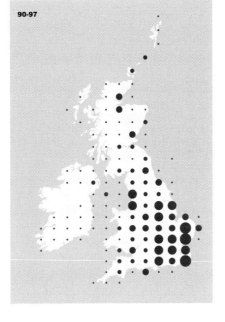

(b) Raptors and owls

Continued

in Chapter 6). The proportion of wildfowl ringed as chicks (and subsequently recovered) increased slightly during the 1970s (to around 20%) but is still at a rather low level (see Chapter 7).

The geographical spread of seabird and gull ringing has also increased somewhat over time (Fig 4.5e). The pattern of change reflects the varying effort put in by specialist ringers and groups through the period, including the increased catching of adult gulls through cannon-netting. In more recent years, proportionally more recoveries have come from birds ringed in the Northern Isles, off the west coast of Scotland (*eg* the Treshnish Isles and Canna), in southeast Ireland (Great Saltee) and from gulls ringed around Bristol, to give some examples. Conversely, proportionally fewer recoveries have come from birds ringed at some other sites (*eg* on the Farne Islands and in Pembrokeshire). The proportion of seabirds that were ringed as chicks (and subsequently recovered) was lower in the 1970s and 1980s (less than 70%) than in the 1990s (95%, Fig 4.6). This probably reflects the initiation of important

long-term monitoring studies that involved the catching and colour-marking of breeding adults in the earlier period and the subsequent demise of a number of these studies in recent years as their funding expired.

Just as the distribution of ringing activity in Britain & Ireland through time is an important consideration when considering how representative are ringed birds of the wider population, so is the distribution of ringing activity abroad for interpreting data for birds recovered within Britain & Ireland. Space does not allow a detailed consideration of changes in ringing activities outside Britain & Ireland but any significant changes that may affect the interpretation of temporal changes in recovery patterns are addressed, whenever possible, in the individual species texts. Fig 4.7 shows the catchment area from which foreign-ringed birds have reached our shores since 1909. This pattern is influenced by both ringing effort in the individual countries and their distance from Britain & Ireland.

Fig 4.5 Continued

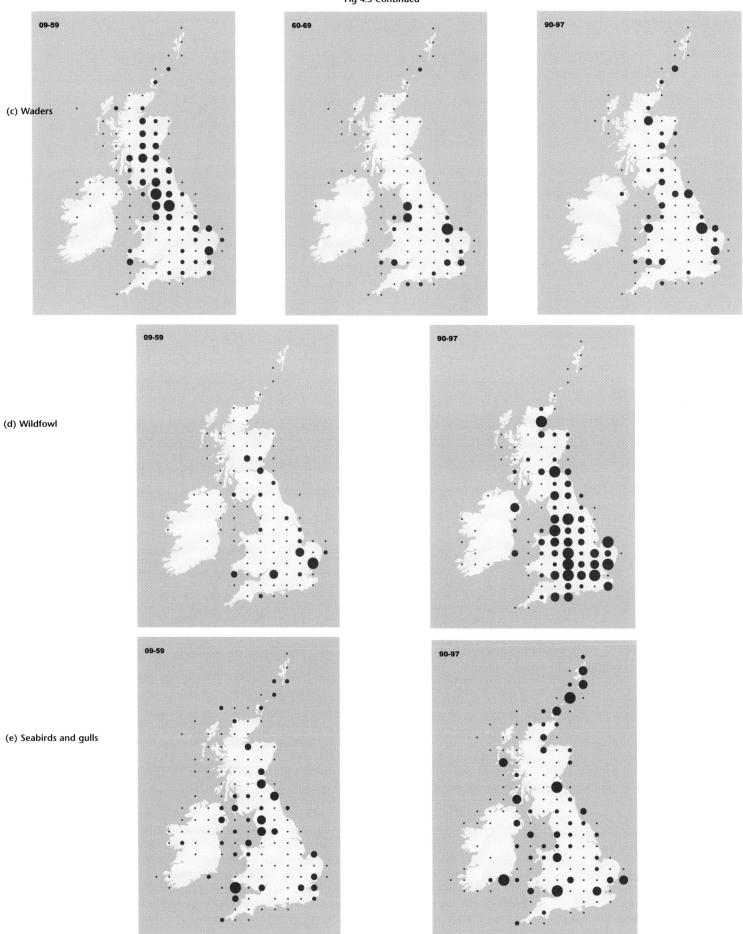

(c) Waders

(d) Wildfowl

(e) Seabirds and gulls

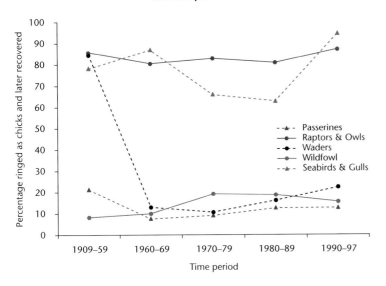

Fig 4.6 Percentages of recovered birds ringed as chicks, by ecological grouping and time period.

allows us to 'correct' the recovery patterns and, hence, to quantify with any certainty the true densities of birds in given geographical areas. By combining and mapping all the recovery locations of dead birds, however, for groups of ecologically similar species, it is possible to produce a broad quantitative indication of spatial variation in recovery chances (Fig 4.8).

For terrestrial species, the chances of recovery are low or nil in many parts of Africa, particularly the sparsely populated desert areas and countries where the first European language spoken is not English; these areas include the Sahara and Kalahari Deserts, much of the remainder of Namibia, Angola and inland parts of much of equatorial West Africa and countries bordering the Gulf of Guinea (*eg* Guinea, Ivory Coast, Cameroon and Gabon, Fig 4.8a). In general, there is better coverage of coastal areas of Africa, with seabird recoveries extending continuously along the west and south coasts, with the exception of large sections of the coast of Namibia (restricted, diamond-mining areas) and part of the coast of Gabon (which is very thickly forested, sparsely populated and French-speaking). The extent to which the limited number of wildfowl recoveries in Africa for some species (*eg* for Garganey and Pintail) is truly reflective of a low number of individuals travelling that far, or is a result of low recovery rates, is still in question.

For all ecological groups, recovery rates are relatively high throughout western Europe (Fig 4.8b), with the exception of sparsely populated areas of northern Fennoscandia and mountainous areas, such as the Alps. Further south and east in Europe, recoveries are sparser. There has been considerable debate as to the extent to which this is a reflection of migratory bird populations in western Europe, using predominantly southwesterly migration routes or of low chances of recovery in these southeastern areas of Europe. For the purposes of this book, which deals predominantly with populations that regularly breed in, or pass through, Britain & Ireland, the interpretation of the low numbers of recoveries in southeast Europe is of greatest importance for the small number of species that are known, from recoveries at other locations, to use a more southeasterly route for migration (*eg* Cuckoo and Lesser Whitethroat). Field orientation experiments, independent of ring-recovery information, suggest that many passerines from populations breeding in eastern Europe migrate in a southeasterly direction, unlike those from western populations. This further shows that ring-recovery rates must be very low in southeast Europe because the migration routes implied by these experiments are not confirmed by recovery patterns (Busse 2000 and references therein). The chances of recovery are also likely to be very low in the extreme northeast of Europe (western Siberia), so that recovery patterns do not adequately represent the true breeding ranges of some populations of wildfowl and waders that winter in Britain & Ireland or move through on passage (*eg* Grey Plover). The recovery patterns of those seabirds that are pelagic outside the breeding season (*eg* most auks, petrels, Kittiwake) suffer from extreme bias due to spatial variation in chances of recovery. Rings can generally only be recovered when birds are washed ashore in areas where there are human populations or are killed due to human activities (see later). Hence, for such species, recovery patterns must be interpreted together with information on distribution and movements from other sources, in this case including at-sea, ship-based surveys (*eg* Tasker *et al* 1984, Stone *et al* 1995), even more so than is necessary for other ecological groups of species.

The spatial biases associated with recaptures by ringers or resightings of colour-marked birds are likely to be even more pronounced than those associated with recoveries of dead birds by members of the public, because of the aggregated nature of the 'observers' in each case. Recaptures will only occur where specialist bird ringers are operating, and resightings where dedicated birdwatchers go out to look for, and report, colour-marked birds. Not surprisingly, most recaptures and resightings for all groups have occurred in densely populated areas of western Europe (Fig 4.9a, b). Recaptures within Britain & Ireland have shown a similar pattern to the ringing locations of recovered birds (Fig

The importance of recovery type

The different types of ring-recovery included in this book can introduce varying biases when interpreting recovery patterns because of the differing spatial distribution of 'observers'. Three types of recovery are defined within the book. Those termed *dead* were found, generally dead, by members of the public; the small number of cases where members of the public (rather than ringers) read the ring numbers of live birds (when they were trapped in a building, for example) were included in this category, because they were likely to be subject to spatial biases similar to those for birds recovered dead (see later). *Recaptures* refer to live ringed birds caught by ringers (mostly by ringers away from the original ringing site, see above) and *resightings* refer to field reports of individually marked birds (such as those with coloured or numbered rings that can be read at a distance in the field).

The numbers of the different recovery types available for each species will influence the ways in which the recovery data need to be interpreted. For example, if most of the records for a species result from recaptures by ringers, then the pattern will necessarily be influenced by the distribution of those ringers. If most of the records come from members of the public, then a further set of considerations relating to this, and to particular finding circumstances (see later) must be addressed. The proportions of the three recovery types available for each species are shown beneath the pie chart (standard Figure 3) in each main species account (see Chapter 6).

The number of recoveries of dead birds from any given geographical location will depend on:

- the number of ringed birds that go there. This is a function of the total number of birds that go to the location and the proportion of that 'population' that are ringed. This is the biological measure that is of interest to us when we are studying movement patterns.
- the number of ringed birds that die there. This depends on spatial variation in the risk of mortality, which may be related to factors such as human hunting pressure (see later).
- the chances that a bird dying there will be found and reported to the BTO. This is likely to depend on habitat and climate (the detectability and resilience of the corpse, the presence of particular scavengers), the density of the human population and the nature of the human population (level of education, knowledge of bird ringing, knowledge of the English language).

When we look at the spatial recovery patterns for a given species all these factors are confounded. We do not have detailed quantitative information on spatial variation in mortality rates or reporting rates that

Fig 4.7 Ringing locations abroad, (a) at the European scale and (b) at the world scale, for birds recovered subsequently in Britain & Ireland and featuring in the book, summarized into blocks of 0.5° latitude and 1° longitude and with one-fifth of the birds ringed in each symbol size class.

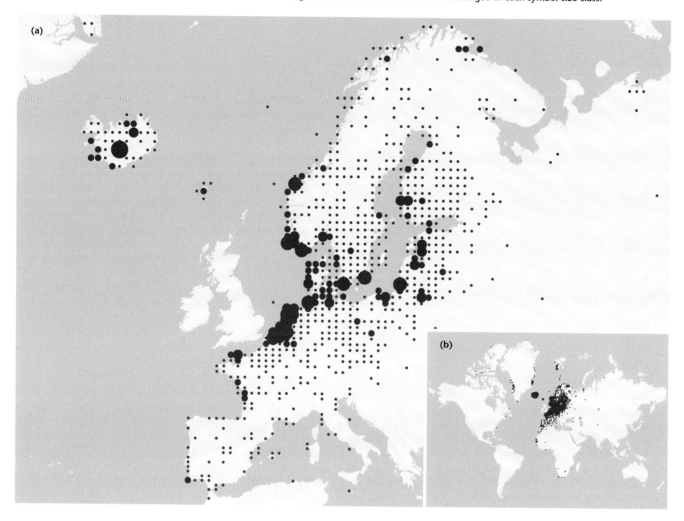

4.2). For passerines, there has been a marked bias towards southeast and central England. 'Hot spots' for passerine recaptures outside Britain & Ireland have occurred in Belgium, where loud tapes of calls were used to attract nocturnally migrating birds, such as finches, for trapping, and at various coastal bird observatories and ringing stations (*eg* Helgoland in Germany, around the coast of Denmark, the south coasts of Norway and Sweden, on Åland off Finland and at Riga in Latvia). 'Hot spots' for wildfowl recaptures have included Iceland, Svalbard, and the Wadden Sea in the Netherlands (mainly geese) and, for waders, Iceland, around Tromsø in northern Norway, Murmansk in Russia, around Turku in southern Finland, Riga in Latvia, the Wadden Sea and Friesian Islands, and southern Portugal. Concentrations of seabird recaptures have occurred off the west coast of Norway around Stavanger, Bergen and on the Lofoten Isles and in the Faeroes (cliff-nesting species), on the Russian Baltic coast around Kaliningrad, on the Baltic coast of Germany, around the Kattegat and off the Netherlands (mainly gulls) and off southern Portugal (particularly Storm Petrels from expedition ringing work). 'Hot spots' for resightings in Europe include central and southern England (particularly studies of Canada Geese, Mute Swans, gulls and Cormorants), Merseyside (gulls), Lambay Island off Dublin and St Margaret's Island in Pembrokeshire (Cormorants), the Forth islands and the Farne Islands (cliff-nesting seabirds and gulls), the Wadden Sea (wildfowl, waders and gulls), the southern Kattegat coast of Denmark and Sweden (gulls), the Gulf of Finland (gulls) and the west coast of Portugal (expedition work to locate Lesser Black-backed Gulls, see species account). Recaptures and resightings in Africa (Fig 4.9c) have been almost exclusively the result of expedition work, with the exception of

the many recaptures in South Africa of Swallows during local ringing projects (*eg* Nuttall 2001). The major concentration on the coast of Senegal (mainly of passerine records but also including a few gulls and waders) resulted from winter expeditions run by British and French ringers to the Parc National du Djoudj in the early 1990s (*eg* Rodwell *et al* 1996, Sauvage *et al* 1998). The other concentrations of records of waders and gulls on the coasts of Morocco and Mauritania have also resulted from expedition work (*eg* Pienkowski 1976, Piersma *et al* 1990).

The importance of finding circumstances

The cause of death of a ringed bird may influence the chances that the bird is found and reported to the BTO (or to another ringing scheme). For example, a bird that is shot by a hunter or brought into a house by a domestic cat must be more likely to be reported than one that dies of natural causes in a wood or on a remote mountaintop. If most recoveries of a species occur through hunting, then their distribution pattern is likely to reflect geographical variation in hunting pressure as well as the true overall distribution of the species. Similar biases could be introduced if pollution incidents (such as oil spills) or capture in fishing nets are major causes of recovery for certain species. If human-related events (such as collisions with buildings or motor vehicles, or capture by cats) cause most recoveries, then the pattern is likely to be heavily biased towards areas of high human population density. This bias towards areas of high human population density is always present in any case, to some extent, because recoveries cannot be gathered in the absence of reporters! The seriousness of this human bias depends on

Fig 4.8 All recoveries from dead birds previously ringed in Britain & Ireland, 1909–97, at the scale of (a) Africa, (b) Europe and (c) Britain & Ireland. Recoveries are summarized into blocks of 0.5° latitude and 1° longitude and with one-fifth of the birds recovered in each symbol size class.

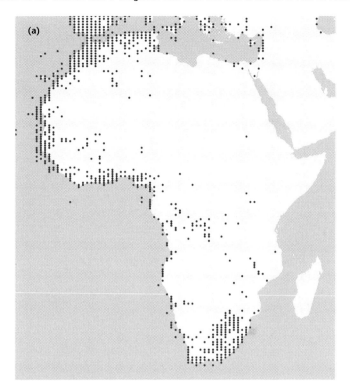

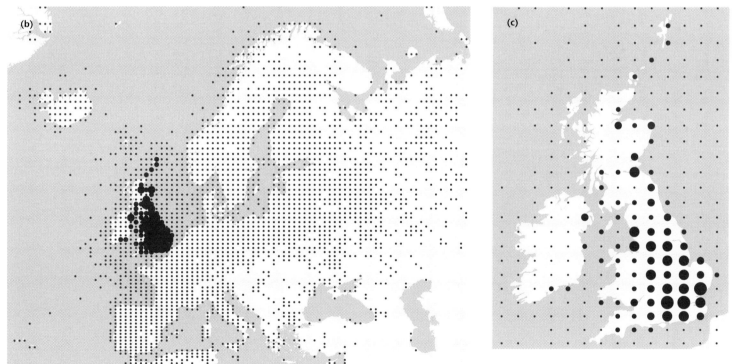

how closely a species is associated with humans; it introduces little bias for House Sparrows, which are generally associated with humans, but more for species that are associated with humans in some areas but are also common in habitats remote from humans (*eg* Blackbirds).

For the purposes of the book, we defined eight major types of finding circumstance: *deliberately taken by Man* (shot, trapped or deliberately poisoned); *human-related* (such as road casualties and birds that hit windows); *accidental capture* (*eg* in fishing nets); *natural (environmental)* (such as due to cold weather); *natural (illness)* (*eg* due to broken bones or disease); *pollution* (such as oiling or electrocution); *domestic predator*;

natural predator; others were lumped under *additional rare classes*. The standard Figure 3 in each main species account shows the proportion of recoveries, for which a cause was reported, that fall into the three largest categories for that species. Each of the eight categories is defined in more detail in Appendix 1. The proportion of the total recoveries of dead birds that had a cause reported is shown in parentheses below the pie chart in each account.

The precise ways in which finding circumstances influence recovery patterns, and to what extent, are complex issues that we have only been able to address in part in this book. To aid interpretation of the

Fig 4.9 All (a) recaptures in Europe, (b) resightings in Europe and (c) recaptures and resightings in Africa, of birds ringed in Britain & Ireland, 1909–97. Records are summarized into blocks of 0.5° latitude and 1° longitude and with one-fifth of the birds recovered in each symbol size class.

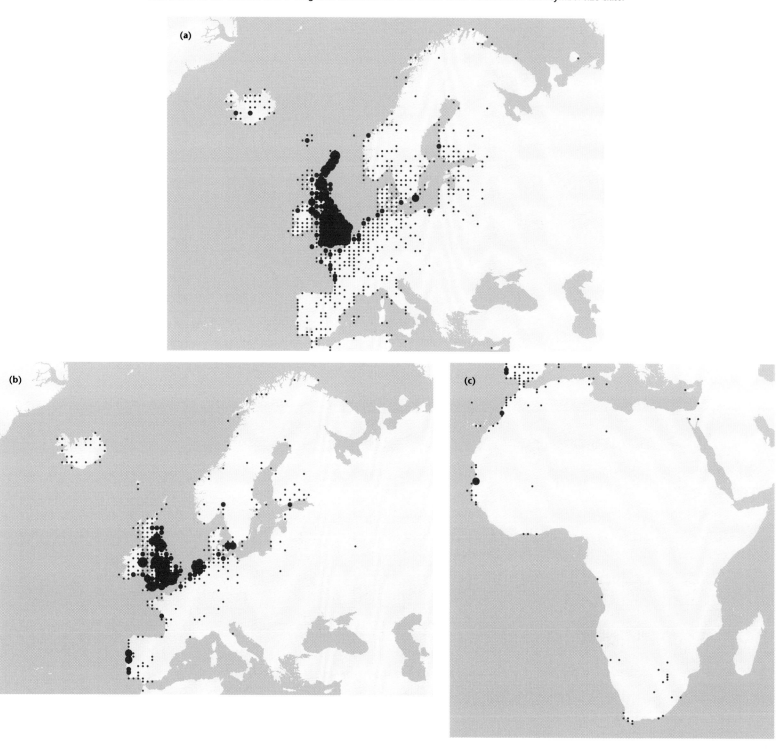

individual species accounts in Chapter 6, the average recovery locations of birds reported due to five different finding circumstances classes thought potentially to cause bias were compared with those for other, more natural causes of recovery for every species with sufficient sample sizes, using the methods described later in the 'Differences in movement patterns within and between species' section of this chapter. The five classes with the potential to cause significant bias were those defined as *deliberately taken by Man, human-related, domestic predator, accidental capture* and *pollution* in Appendix 1a. The average locations of recoveries due to these causes were compared with those due to natural illness,

natural environmental factors and natural predators (as defined in Appendix 1a) combined. Although these latter categories of recovery may also show some spatial bias (*eg* they may be more likely to be reported by professional biologists than the general public), they are probably the nearest we can get to the 'natural' pattern. This analysis was carried out for each species with 10 or more records in each of the two classes in each pairwise comparison. Analyses were carried out both for birds ringed in Britain & Ireland during the breeding season and recovered in winter and for those ringed in Britain & Ireland in winter and recovered during the breeding season. The results for individual

Fig 4.10 Results by ecological grouping of tests for differences in recovery locations between birds recovered in the circumstances indicated and those recovered through natural causes for (a) birds ringed in Britain & Ireland during the breeding season and recovered in winter, and (b) birds ringed in Britain & Ireland during the winter and recovered in the breeding season.

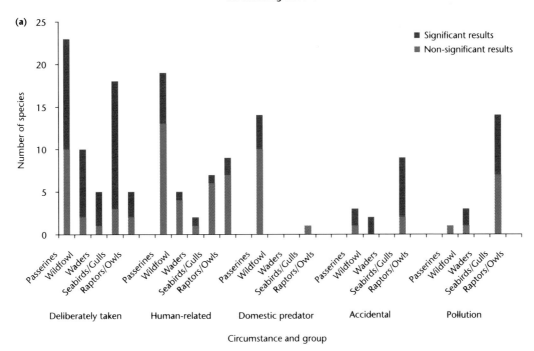

species are flagged in the 'Statistical analyses' table in each main species account (see Chapter 6) and reported in Appendix 1b. For a few species, recovery sample sizes were insufficient to allow direct tests for bias due to finding circumstances but, nonetheless, there was a high proportion of recoveries due to a potentially biasing cause, usually deliberate taking by Man (eg Wigeon and Woodcock, Appendix 1b). For such species, the overall recovery patterns need to be interpreted with caution and with reference to the general biases identified for groups of species discussed later.

Deliberate taking by Man

Deliberate taking by Man, leading to the recovery of rings, represents the most significant cause of bias in recovery patterns, with average locations from this cause differing from those for natural causes for over 50% of the species tested in each of the five ecological groups (Fig 4.10). For some species, the differences in average latitude and/or longitude of recovery between birds deliberately taken and those that died from natural causes were large, sometimes greater than 5° of latitude or longitude (Appendix 1b). Mapping by recovery cause showed that, in general, recoveries of passerines taken deliberately by Man have shown concentrations in Belgium, the southern coast of the Bay of Biscay and the northern Pyrenees, and parts of Iberia, Italy and southeast Europe that are not apparent among birds recovered after dying from natural causes (Fig 4.11a); this is also true, although to a lesser extent, in North and West Africa. These differences, resulting largely from hunting (trapping and shooting), may be responsible for the significant differences in mean recovery location in winter between deliberately taken and 'natural' recoveries observed for some classic partially

Fig 4.11 Comparisons of the distributions of recoveries due to natural causes (all seasons of ringing and recovery) with those due to the other causes indicated for (a) passerines (Deliberately taken by Man), (b) wildfowl (Deliberately taken by Man, Accidentally captured and Pollution), (c) waders (Deliberately taken by Man) and (d) seabirds and gulls (Deliberately taken by Man, Accidentally captured and Pollution). Records are summarized into blocks of 0.5° latitude and 1° longitude and with one-fifth of the birds recovered in each symbol size class.

(a) Passerines

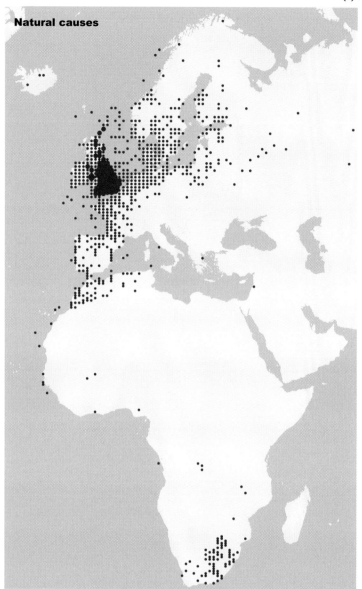

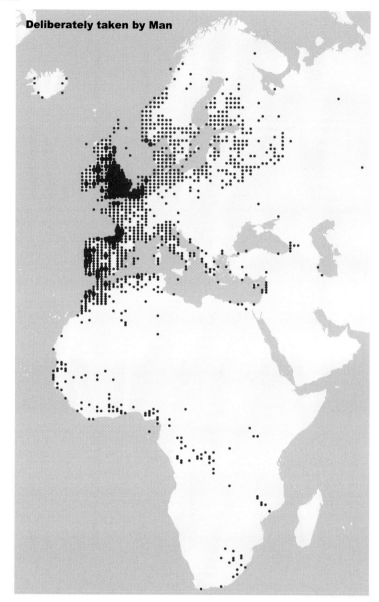

migratory species (Linnet, Meadow Pipit, Goldfinch, Pied Wagtail) and for the thrushes (Blackbird, Song Thrush and Mistle Thrush). The other passerines showing significant differences in winter were some corvids (Raven, Magpie and Jay) and some smaller resident species (Dunnock, House Sparrow and Bullfinch), perhaps as a result of local control measures for at least some of these species. The same may be true for Barn Owl, Kestrel and Sparrowhawk, which also show small but significant differences in the locations of recoveries in winter. For sedentary species in general, the differing average locations of deliberately taken recoveries are not a great cause for concern. The four species of passerine showing significant differences for birds ringed in winter and recovered in the breeding season were all species for which Britain & Ireland is known to have significant wintering populations of continental origin (Fieldfare, Blackbird, Starling and Greenfinch), such that the differences probably result from more 'deliberate taking' on the Continent (of returned immigrants) than in Britain & Ireland (of residents).

For wildfowl, recoveries due to deliberate taking by Man have been the only major source of records in North Africa, Iberia, Italy and much of southeast Europe. They have also been much more extensive in Russia than recoveries due to any other cause (Fig 4.11b). This may explain some but not all of the significant differences between hunted and 'natural' recoveries in mean recovery locations in winter identified for species ringed in Britain & Ireland during the breeding season (apparent for Coot, Moorhen, Canada Goose, Mute Swan, Shelduck, Eider, Tufted Duck and Grey Heron), and for the three species ringed in Britain & Ireland in winter and recovered during the breeding season (Mallard, Teal and Tufted Duck), all of which have large immigrant populations of continental origin. For the more sedentary species, such as Canada Goose, the differences are likely to be the result of local control measures or hunting pressures within Britain & Ireland, and so are of little consequence. For waders, the gross differences in recovery locations between 'deliberately taken' recoveries and those due to natural causes have been similar to those for wildfowl, with concentrations of records

(b) Wildfowl

Natural causes

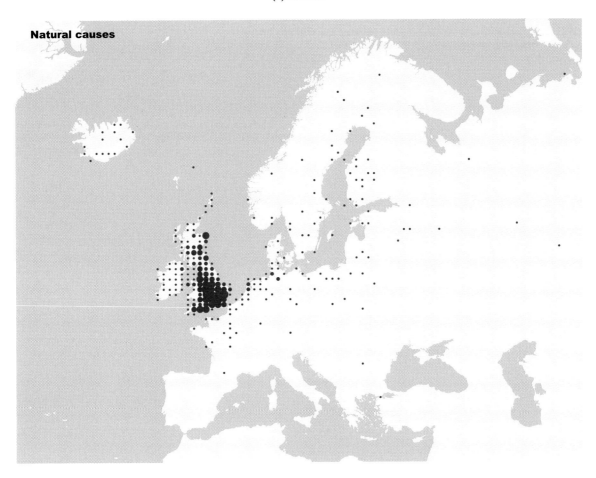

Deliberately taken by Man

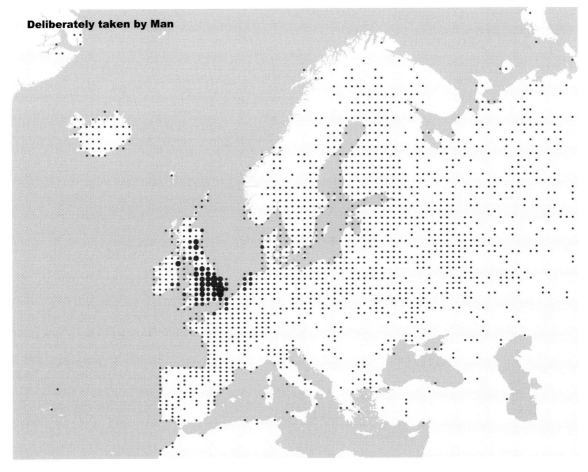

Continued

Fig 4.11 Continued

(b) Wildfowl

Accidentally captured

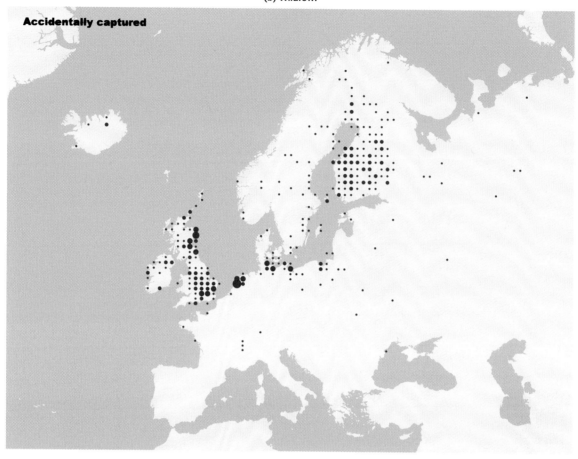

Pollution

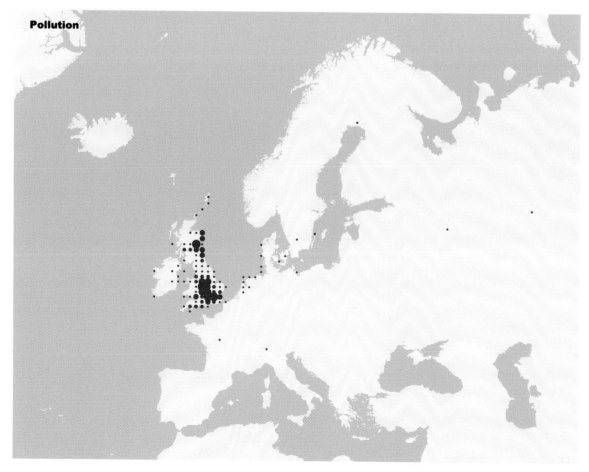

(c) Waders

Natural causes

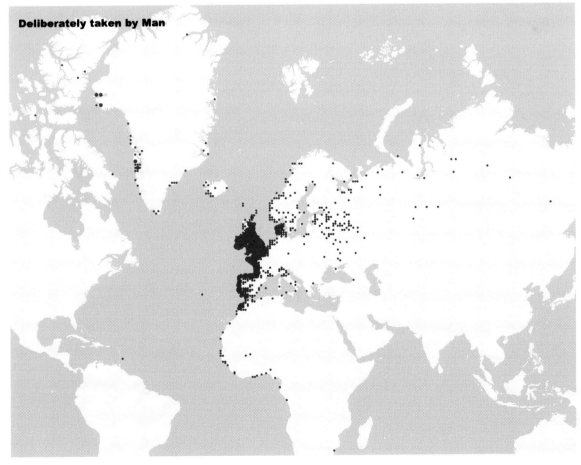

Deliberately taken by Man

Continued

Fig 4.11 Continued

(d) Seabirds and gulls

Natural causes

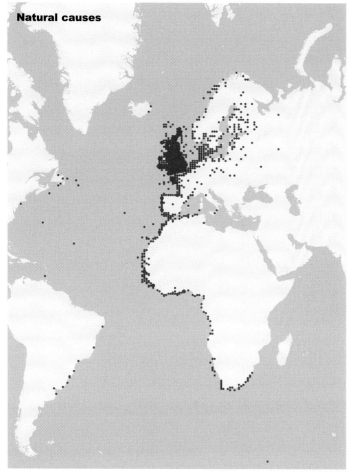

Deliberately taken by Man

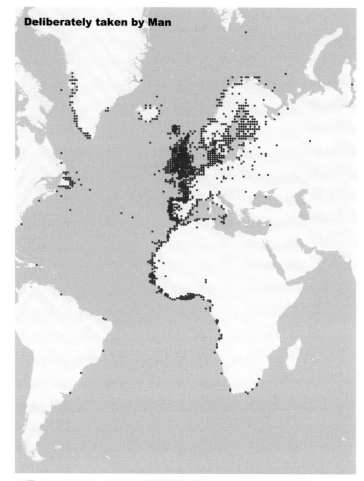

Accidentally captured

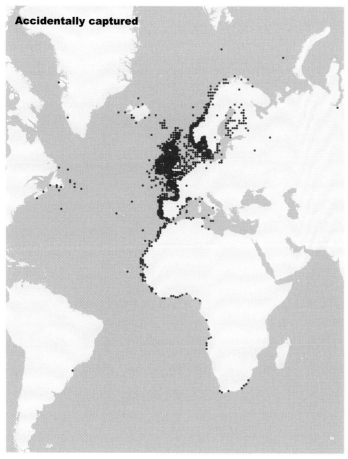

Pollution

of birds deliberately taken on the coasts of France, Iberia and Italy that are not evident through other causes of recovery, and more extensive records across Russia than from other causes, as well as along the coast of West Greenland (Fig 4.11c). These differences probably explain the significant differences in mean recovery locations, between recoveries due to hunting and to natural causes, for Curlew, Lapwing, Oystercatchers and Redshank ringed in Britain & Ireland in winter and recovered during the breeding season.

Birds deliberately taken by Man have been the only source of records of seabirds from West Greenland, and have shown much higher concentrations in Iceland and the Faeroes, and somewhat higher concentrations in the Bay of Biscay and the Iberian coast than recoveries due to natural causes (Fig 4.11d). Significant differences in mean recovery locations in winter for seabirds ringed in Britain & Ireland during the breeding season were apparent for 15 of the 18 species tested (Fig 4.10a), the exceptions being Common Tern, Great Black-backed Gull and Herring Gull. While the differences for these 15 species were mainly due to hunting, those for the two species ringed in winter and recovered during the breeding season (Black-headed Gull and Herring Gull) were probably the result of local control measures (culling at colonies) in Britain & Ireland.

The direct tests for bias in the mean recovery locations of birds deliberately taken by Man carried out for this book only considered recovery locations in winter and during the breeding season, although much hunting activity takes place in the autumn (particularly across southern Europe) and in spring (particularly in North Africa) (Tucker *et al* 1990, McCulloch *et al* 1992). The tests carried out for the book were intended to aid interpretation of other formal statistical testing for migratory tendency and differences between different classes of bird (see later). Much more detailed work at the species level would be required to test for all possible biases in the general recovery patterns (as discussed in the individual species accounts) due to hunting and culling; this would be a useful avenue to explore in future analyses. However, the general ways in which spatial recovery patterns due to deliberate taking differ from those due to natural causes, discussed here, should also be considered when interpreting the patterns of autumn and spring recoveries of species for which a high proportion of recoveries are the result of this cause. Equally, it should be borne in mind for such species that the timing of hunting seasons could affect the interpretation of the timing of migration along flyways.

One of the most detailed appraisals available of the spatial and temporal variation in hunting pressures across Europe was carried out by the BTO in the early 1990s (Tucker *et al* 1990, McCulloch *et al* 1992), using ring-recovery data. That study looked in detail at recoveries of 20 migratory species (five raptors and 15 passerines) from 19 European ringing schemes, using a 'hunting index' that incorporated controls for differences in ringing effort and reporting rates. The work showed that hunting pressure was generally high in western Mediterranean countries (particularly in southern France and northern and southwestern Iberia), in northern Italy and in northwest Africa (Morocco, Algeria and Tunisia) (*eg* Fig 2.10a). Geographical variation in the patterns of hunting pressure affecting individual breeding populations was species-specific, however. In Europe, the majority of migrants were hunted in autumn and winter (August to November), the peak month for hunting becoming later further south. In contrast, in North Africa, almost as many birds were hunted in spring as in autumn, perhaps because those that winter south of the Sahara stop north of the desert to fuel when on spring migration (Moreau 1961). Most species showed a reduction in 'hunting index' values after 1980 (after the protection afforded by the 1979 EC Wild Birds Directive; see Chapter 7) and generally from the 1950s onwards, with the exception of those that remained legitimate quarry species. This reduction was interpreted as at least partly due to a real decline in deliberate taking of birds but could also reflect reduced reporting of hunted species that became protected by law. The reductions were greatest for some raptor species, such as Sparrowhawk, after the

introduction in the mid-1960s to early 1970s of laws to protect such species in many European countries (Bijleveld 1974; see also Fig 2.10b, showing the decline in hunting pressure on Buzzards). The hunting of legitimate quarry species, such as Song Thrush and Skylark, tended to remain stable or even increase in some countries.

Accidental capture
Accidental capture (mainly in fishing nets and fish traps of various types) is a major source of bias in recovery patterns for seabirds and waterfowl. For seabirds, recoveries from this cause have been concentrated around the Bay of Biscay, around Portugal and off the coasts of Norway and southern Sweden (Fig 4.11d). Around Britain & Ireland, such recoveries have been concentrated on the Irish coast and the west coast of Britain. The seabird species for which winter recovery patterns were affected significantly in such ways were Cormorant, Shag, Gannet, Guillemot, Razorbill, Sandwich Tern and Lesser Black-backed Gull, and Black-headed Gull during the breeding season; for Sandwich Tern, however, local factors on the African coast are more likely to have been the cause of the significant result. For wildfowl, recoveries due to accidental capture have shown an important area of concentration in southern Finland (Fig 4.11b), and this pattern is probably responsible for the significant differences for the breeding season recovery patterns of the Mallard, Teal and Tufted Ducks that wintered in Britain & Ireland. The significant differences for Tufted Ducks and Grey Herons ringed during the breeding season and recovered in winter probably have a more local cause, such as the occurrence of a few large fish-farms (protected by nets) near to productive ringing sites. Accidental captures of passerines (largely in crop protection nets) have been concentrated in central and southern England and probably introduce only very local biases into recovery patterns for the species affected (Blackbird, Song Thrush and Blue Tit).

Pollution
Pollution has influenced recovery patterns markedly for seabirds and some wildfowl (Fig 4.11b, d). For both groups, recoveries due to pollution have been more concentrated in Britain & Ireland than recoveries due to natural causes and, for seabirds, concentrations in the English Channel, the North Sea, the Kattegat and the Bay of Biscay have also been apparent. Pollution has resulted in significant differences in the mean locations of winter recovery for seven of the 14 seabird species tested (Cormorant, Shag, Gannet, Guillemot, Razorbill, Kittiwake and Great Black-backed Gull) and two of the three wildfowl tested (Eider and Mute Swan). Only one wader species (Oystercatcher) had a large number of recoveries attributed to pollution and this resulted in significantly differing recovery locations during the breeding season. The recovery patterns due to pollution reflect both localized pollution events, such as oil spills, and chronic pollution 'hot spots', such as the North Sea. For most seabird species, previous BTO analyses have shown that more recoveries of oiled birds occur as a result of chronic pollution than as a result of major oil spills (Baillie 1990b).

Other finding circumstances
In general, human-related causes and capture by domestic predators did not show marked differences in distribution when mapped for the ecological groups of species and compared with recoveries due to natural causes. Significant differences identified at the species level (Fig 4.10) were mainly for passerines and resulted in only local modifications to overall recovery patterns (Appendix 1b). The species affected were Blackbird, Song Thrush, Chaffinch, Dunnock, Greenfinch, Bullfinch, House Sparrow, Starling, Siskin, Robin, Pied Wagtail, Redwing and Jackdaw (*ie* mostly common garden species in Britain & Ireland). These results suggest that, for species where these finding circumstances are the dominant method of recovery, the method of finding is unlikely to bias recovery patterns over and above the general bias associated with the distribution of human populations.

Interpreting temporal changes in recovery patterns

The issues surrounding the effects of different recovery causes on overall recovery patterns become even more complex when investigating whether migration patterns have changed through time. The problem is probably most acute for recoveries due to hunting, as conservation legislation regarding this has changed substantially over the years in a manner far from consistent between individual countries. In most western European countries, shooting seasons have been curtailed to start later and end earlier during the last four or five decades of the 20th century (Tucker *et al* 1990, McCulloch *et al* 1992). For example, the shooting of wildfowl in spring and the early part of the breeding season was banned completely in the USSR (as it then was) in 1976. Such changes may have both reduced the total numbers of recoveries due to hunting from certain areas and led to apparent changes in the timing of migration for some species. Similarly, conservation legislation has changed to restrict the use of some kinds of fishing nets (such as long monofilament gill nets), leading to fewer birds being subject to accidental capture in certain areas.

Within the *Migration Atlas* project, we were able to carry out only exploratory analyses of temporal change in movement patterns (see later). The results from these analyses give an indication of species, or groups of species, for which further detailed investigations, also taking into account temporal changes in recovery circumstances, would potentially be interesting.

Data excluded from the ring-recovery analyses

To ensure that the information derived from the ring-recovery data set was accurate, the data had to be screened to exclude records of lower quality. Sample sizes were maximized for particular analyses but any problematic cases were rejected. Those recoveries for which either the ringing or finding location was uncertain (not known to within half a degree of latitude or longitude) or that had unusual ringing circumstances (making them unrepresentative of the population as a whole) were excluded completely. Unusual circumstances included birds that were held in captivity before release (often being rehabilitated), those in poor condition when ringed, and those that had been used in field experiments or hand-reared. Cases that were reported as 'moved before finding', such as in the front grilles of lorries, were also routinely excluded, except those coded as 'moved by water', which is regular for seabirds and waders found on the shoreline. We know that movement by water can cause considerable bias in recovery patterns for seabirds because generally, only those that reach the shore are found (*eg* Bibby 1981b), but without these records we would have little information on movement patterns for many species. Reports of rings that were found on their own, without any part of the bird, were also excluded because the bird may not have died where the ring was found. Multiple recoveries of the same individual (through sightings of individual marks or recaptures by ringers) were excluded from the main *Migration Atlas* data set, retaining only the first recovery of each individual. While this meant some information was lost, it meant that the statistical analyses were rigorous and were carried out entirely on independent data. In some instances, authors have nevertheless been able to refer in their text to multiple captures, which are often of exceptional value in recording the movements of individual birds; in such cases, the inclusion of such data has been reported explicitly. The standard filtering used for the book excluded approximately 4% of the recoveries of birds ringed in Britain & Ireland and 8% of those ringed abroad and recovered in Britain & Ireland. The recoveries left after the 'filtering' described above are termed *included recoveries* and the total number available is shown for each species in the '*Ringing and recovery data*' table in each species account.

For many of the analyses and maps, recoveries are grouped by month or season. In such cases, recoveries for which the date of ringing or

recovery is inaccurate have either been excluded (statistical analyses) or reported separately (*eg* on some maps). These include reports where the date of ringing or, more usually, the date of recovery was not known to within 15 days, and birds recorded as 'not freshly dead' when found (those corpses thought to be more than about a week old and many known to be much older). Recoveries for which there was no information about the time or method of recovery were also excluded here. Although such reports still give useful information on *where* birds are recovered, they cannot give accurate information on *when* birds are at a given location. For the purposes of this book they are termed *seasonally inaccurate recoveries*, as opposed to *seasonally accurate recoveries*.

Definition of seasons

Where there were a large number of recoveries for a given species, mapping by month (or selected months) has been used to illustrate seasonal movements. However, for many species with smaller sample sizes, pooling into seasonal categories has been necessary for both ease and clarity of mapping. Seasons also had to be defined to allow formal statistical analyses to be carried out. We defined four non-overlapping seasons on a species-specific basis (termed *breeding, autumn, winter* and *spring*), in units of half-months (Appendix 2). For each species, these seasons were based on information from both published and unpublished sources (*BWP*, Campbell & Ferguson-Lees 1972; the distribution of dates on which the nestlings of recovered birds have been ringed; BTO Nest Record Scheme data: Crick & Baillie 1996, H Q P Crick pers comm). Where possible, these definitions followed the rationale of delimiting the main spring and autumn movement periods of populations likely to use Britain & Ireland during the year (if any), so that *breeding* and *winter* remained, nominally, as periods of stability. These two seasons should define periods of the year when migratory movements are at a minimum; for example, the season defined as *breeding* should exclude times when parts of a population may still be on the move. Regardless of the half-month definition of the breeding season, birds ringed as chicks and those ringed or found with coded status 'breeding' have also been included in the breeding season (for ringing or finding) as appropriate. Because the seasons had to be general enough to account for all parts of the ringed populations, they may not be ideal for every population. In a few cases, authors asked us to redefine one or more seasons for the purposes of a specific analysis. The seasons referred to in the individual species accounts, the maps and the statistical analyses are those defined in Appendix 2 unless it is otherwise stated explicitly.

Definition of age classes

For the purposes of this book, birds have been classed as either *chick (pullus), immature* or *adult* at ringing, and *first-year, immature* or *adult* at recovery. When the data for a species include a *chick* class (at ringing) or a *first-year* class (at recovery), the *immature* class excludes the younger birds. When there is no discrete *chick* or *first-year* class, birds of these ages are included with other *immatures*. *Immatures* become *adults* at the start of the breeding season in the year when they attain the defined age of first breeding. The age of first breeding that was adopted (Appendix 2) was taken from published sources (generally *BWP*, or a more recent paper) or was established after consultation with the appropriate expert author. The term *adult* as used here does not therefore imply confirmed breeding. *First-years* become *immatures* or *adults* (depending on the age of first breeding) at the start of the breeding season in the year after they were hatched.

Definition of geographical regions

For a number of analytical and mapping purposes within the book, Britain & Ireland has been subdivided into five geographical regions.

Fig 4.12 Boundaries of the five geographical 'regions' used in the book, defined for the three categories of species: (a) 'terrestrial' (inland species), (b) 'waders' (coastal species) and (c) 'seabirds' (marine species).

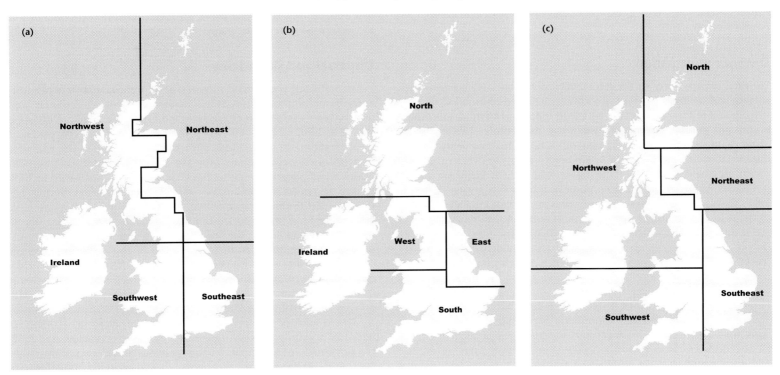

These regions differ between three groups of species — *seabirds, waders* and *terrestrial* — defined so as to reflect the use of habitats within Britain & Ireland by the birds most commonly ringed (Fig 4.12). These regional groups differ from the ecological groups used for analyses in other parts of the book (*eg* Appendix 5). Species for which the *seabird* regional definition was used are truly marine species that are traditionally ringed largely at coastal and offshore seabird colonies (*eg* petrels, cormorants, auks). Those classified as *waders* are those that are ringed largely in coastal habitats (*eg* the typical shore waders, Eider). The *terrestrial* group refers to species that are generally ringed inland, including most passerines and near-passerines, non-coastal waterfowl, some breeding waders and also most of the gulls. The regions were defined so as to be as meaningful biologically as possible, within each group, while maintaining adequate sample sizes in each region for analyses, restricting the regions to a manageable number and allowing a straightforward classification of recoveries using fields already stored within the ring-recovery database. The boundaries for the *terrestrial* class are somewhat complex, largely because of the need to differentiate between drier lowland habitats in the east and south of Britain and wetter upland habitats in the north and west. Although the chosen classes could never be perfect for all species within a group, they divided up the ring-recovery data to allow investigation of broad regional differences, for example in the seasonal movements of regional breeding subpopulations or in the receipt of immigrants from abroad. The group to which each species was allocated for regional division is shown in Appendix 2. In a small number of cases, authors requested that the regional divisions were modified to test specific hypotheses; these are highlighted explicitly in the maps and text when they occur.

Definition of breeding populations

For many migrant or partially migrant species, the birds ringed in Britain & Ireland throughout the year constitute a mixture of individuals from different populations. One of the main aims in the book has been to separate these populations to reveal their differential movements. As a first step in this process, a group of birds was treated as the *British & Irish breeding population*. This included (i) any bird ringed

as a chick in Britain or Ireland, (ii) any bird ringed or found with a coded status of 'breeding' in Britain or Ireland, and (iii) any other bird ringed or recovered in Britain or Ireland during the *breeding* season. For most species, birds ringed as chicks are generally the only ones that can be linked unambiguously to a known breeding population because the coding in the ring-recovery database of ringing status or finding status as 'known breeding' was rare until recently. Thus the definition of the British & Irish breeding population used in this book is not rigorous because the data may include, for example, immature birds from continental breeding populations that have not returned to the breeding area that year (*eg* gulls) or early or late passage migrants still in Britain & Ireland during the season defined as *breeding* (*eg* some duck species). However, the definition acted as a starting point for splitting the data, and has been used throughout this book for mapping and analytical purposes. Where more rigorous definitions have been possible, due to the large quantity of data available, these have been used and explicitly stated in map legends or the text. For example, only individuals ringed as chicks in Britain & Ireland have been categorized as coming from the *British & Irish breeding population* for many seabird species.

The above definition of *British & Irish* birds does not allow rigorous separation of true seasonal movements from dispersal movements (see later) because the data include birds ringed as chicks or juveniles. Hence, for some species with sufficient recoveries, a second data set (termed *British & Irish adults*) was derived including only those individuals ringed as adults during the breeding season in either Britain or Ireland. This more restricted data set was used to look for seasonal movements of the British & Irish breeding population when sample sizes allowed.

Other populations breeding outside Britain & Ireland have been defined on an *ad hoc* basis throughout the book, generally using criteria supplied by the expert authors. In many cases, the breeding origins of birds present in Britain & Ireland outside the breeding season have been shown by plotting 'locations abroad during the breeding season'. Here, the definition of the breeding season is the same as that given in Appendix 2, unless otherwise stated. Many of the maps indicate movements of birds belonging to (i) the *British & Irish breeding population* and (ii) *other or uncertain breeding populations*. In this case, the second group refers to (a) individuals not recorded from Britain & Ireland during the *breeding* season and/or (b) *seasonally inaccurate recoveries* of birds that therefore cannot be confirmed as present in Britain & Ireland during the *breeding* season.

Distance information

For each ring-recovery in the BTO database, the distance between the ringing and recovery locations (in km) is calculated routinely from the ringing and finding coordinates by the Rhumb Line method, following a constant compass bearing between the two points. Two types of distance information have been used in this book. First, we define short-distance movements as those of 20 km or less (as such movements could constitute maximum daily foraging movements, at least for small passerines; Main 1996). The proportion of movements greater than 20 km is often used by species-text authors as an indication of site-fidelity or the sedentary nature of a population. In such cases, all recovery types are included, unless otherwise stated explicitly. The total sample size ('n') is always given as an indication of the confidence that can be placed on the results. For species for which a high proportion of the recoveries are recaptures by ringers other than the original ringer (*controls*), site-fidelity will usually be underestimated because local retraps have not been computerized (see earlier).

Second, absolute distance information is presented throughout the book for various groups of birds and various types of movement. If all the distances in a particular analysis are ranked from lowest to highest, the median is the middle (average) value, $P5$ is the value below which the lowest 5% of the values lie and $P95$ is the value above which the highest 5% of values lie. We have used medians throughout, in preference to means, because the data are unlikely to be normally distributed. Rather than giving complete ranges (and maximum distances moved), we have favoured using the 5th percentile ($P5$) and 95th percentile ($P95$), so as to remove extreme values that are unlikely to be representative (and may be erroneous in some cases). When medians and 5th–95th percentiles are quoted, only recoveries of dead birds are included in the analyses unless stated otherwise. The inclusion of live recaptures in distance analyses would result in distances being overestimated because many short movements are not stored in the database (see earlier). Similarly, resightings have not been included in such analyses because of the potential biases associated with variation in observer effort (which are probably greater than those associated with variation in the reporting rates of dead recoveries). In a few cases, individual authors have compared the longer movements (over 20 km) between classes of bird and, here, recaptures and resightings may have been included because the bias associated with the lack of short-distance recaptures was then assumed to be similar across classes.

Directional information

In the BTO database, the angular direction moved (in degrees and minutes) is also recorded routinely for each ring-recovery; this is calculated assuming a constant bearing throughout the journey. Information on the directions moved by individual birds has not been included routinely in this book, however, for two reasons. First and more important, the position of the islands of Britain and Ireland on the western edge of continental Europe places limits on the directional movements that birds can be recorded as making, particularly to the north and west. Hence, if the dispersal directions of resident passerines were to be compared between different regions of Britain & Ireland, then some complex controls would be required for the areas of land available for dispersal in the various compass directions. This complexity was felt to be beyond the scope of the book. Second, the direction moved between ringing and recovery should not be taken to imply a route followed, because many other locations not on a direct route are likely to have been visited before recovery. Hence we consider the presentation of quantitative directional information to be potentially misleading. Such information has been presented by species-text authors only in a qualitative manner, therefore, with reference to movements shown on the maps.

Dispersal and site-fidelity

When sufficient appropriate ring-recoveries were available, exploratory analyses of post-natal (juvenile), natal and breeding dispersal were undertaken. For *post-natal (juvenile) dispersal*, the median distances moved by birds ringed as chicks in Britain or Ireland and recovered dead in consecutive 30-day periods after ringing (and their 5th and 95th percentiles) were calculated for the first year after ringing. The information presented in this book on *natal dispersal* refers to birds ringed as chicks in Britain or Ireland and recovered during any subsequent breeding season when of breeding age. Information on *breeding dispersal* refers to birds ringed as adults of breeding age in Britain or Ireland during the breeding season and recovered during any subsequent breeding season. Our filtering of the natal and breeding dispersal data sets was not rigorous. For example, birds that were ringed during the breeding season when of breeding age may not necessarily have been breeding (a particular problem for large non-passerines with delayed and variable ages of first breeding).

The results of more rigorous analyses of dispersal patterns of terrestrial species previously undertaken by the BTO (Paradis *et al* 1998) are presented in Appendix 2. This previous work used similar data filtering to that applied for this book, but also excluded birds that were deliberately taken by Man (except shot birds) and implemented additional controls, based on relationships between dispersal distance and direction, to remove birds thought to be ringed or recovered when still on migration.

Analyses of winter movements were undertaken to enable species account authors to comment on winter site-fidelity and the potential importance of severe-weather movements. The winter movements were defined as one of two types: ringed during the winter and recovered in the same winter (*within-winter movements*) and ringed during winter and recovered in any subsequent winter (*between-winter movements*).

Mapping

Because the earth is roughly spherical, any map projected onto a flat surface is inevitably a distortion, in terms of shape, scale, area or direction. A map projection is a systematic representation of part of the surface of the earth; the most commonly applied projections each have different distortions associated with them, either representing a compromise between different types of distortion, or more commonly being faithful to only one spatial or directional characteristic. Bentley (1995) has reviewed the suitability of different projections for mapping the distribution and migration of birds.

The choice of an appropriate projection for use in the *Migration Atlas* was complicated by the fact that readers might wish to interpret individual maps with regard to more than one spatial or directional characteristic, and by the fact that no projection can show scale correctly throughout the whole map. A final and particularly important consideration was the reader's likely perception of how a map of northwest Europe should look, and exactly what shape Britain & Ireland should be. While a number of cylindrical equal-area projections have been suggested as well suited to depicting the relative sizes of bird ranges, because they do not distort area in the way that the familiar Mercator projection does, they give Europe a rather unfamiliar shape.

Because the maps were to be used to illustrate points made in the text, rather than to allow detailed analysis of differences in locations of ring-recoveries and directions of movements, the Mercator projection was selected for virtually all of the maps. This projection introduces massive distortion in areas beyond about 75° north or south of the

Equator but it does produce a familiar-looking map, as well as having the advantage of spacing out the ring-recoveries that fall within most of northwest Europe. However, for a small number of maps involving high-Arctic species, the use of the Mercator projection was clearly inappropriate. In these instances, which are indicated explicitly in the text, the Lambert Equal-Area Azimuthal projection was used instead.

It is important to note that lines linking ringing and recovery locations on the maps do not reflect the routes taken by individual birds. Similarly, distances between the locations of individual recoveries, and between ringing and recovery locations, cannot be compared with one another, and it would be incorrect to state that bird A had moved twice as far as bird B simply because the line on the map is twice as long. Our choice of map projections represents a compromise between a desire to follow the guidelines laid down by Bentley (1995) and by Gudmundsson & Alerstam (1998b) for maps showing ornithological information, and the need to present a suitable 'familiar' image of the world to the reader.

Differences in movement patterns within and between species

The ring-recovery maps shown throughout this book suggest a wide range of movement patterns, some of which appear to differ between age classes, sexes or birds from different areas. Patterns that are apparent visually can be misleading, however, particularly when only small numbers of recoveries are involved. To identify real variation in movement patterns, we need quantitative measures of the confidence that we have in each apparent difference. Such measures are provided by the analytical and statistical techniques that are an integral part of contemporary biology. For the purposes of this book, such techniques have been used both for species-specific tests of movement patterns and for broader cross-species comparisons of important biological phenomena (principally differential and partial migration tendencies and the differing movements of regional subpopulations). The results of the latter analyses are presented and discussed in Chapter 5.

The general analytical approach adopted in the book involves comparisons of groups of ring-recoveries, as represented by their latitudinal and longitudinal coordinates. This is a conceptually simple technique that avoids the potential complications associated with the analysis of movement *directions*. When appropriate, complementary analyses of variation in movement *distance* have also been conducted. The principal approach adopted involves testing for differences in average latitude and longitude separately, a difference in either indicating a difference in location. It is also possible that locations could differ by small amounts in both latitude and longitude, such that the difference would be statistically significant if they were considered in tandem, but not in terms of either latitude or longitude alone. In practice, however, any such differences that may have been overlooked by the standard approach that we adopted are likely to be too small to be of biological importance. Taken together, the estimates of mean latitude and mean longitude and their associated confidence limits (estimates of the reliability of the means, Perdeck 1977) form *centres of gravity* for defined groups of ring-recoveries. This technique has been

useful in this book for summarizing the average locations of ring-recoveries of a particular species in a particular season or month, and for testing for differences in average location between groups of individuals (such as birds of different sex or age). It is highly informative for species with a population of individuals that travel to approximately the same wintering area, for example, but potentially misleading if used for a species comprising subpopulations using discrete migratory routes and wintering or breeding areas. For an extreme case, such as Dunlin, where races wintering in similar areas of Britain & Ireland then migrate to breeding areas as widely spread as Greenland and Siberia, the technique is not appropriate for testing between the movements of groups of birds, unless the races can be considered separately. Such limitations of the technique have been borne in mind when interpreting the results of the various statistical tests carried out for this book.

Data selection and statistical testing

The formal statistical analyses for the book were based on only the BTO data for birds ringed in Britain & Ireland between 1909 and 1997. Birds ringed abroad and recovered in Britain & Ireland were excluded to avoid the potential interpretational difficulties that might be caused by geographical variations in ringing effort abroad. The standard filtering was carried out (as described previously) and only recoveries of dead birds were used. As all the analyses were based on seasonal divisions of the data, only seasonally accurate recoveries were used throughout. All 188 main species covered in the book were considered for testing but some had to be omitted from some or all of the tests because of inadequate sample sizes. Ten recoveries in any group were considered the minimum required for a test between two groups of locations to be conducted because the use of any fewer risked the generation of misleading results. Statistical tests needed to be appropriate to the specific type of data to be analysed[3].

Migratory tendency and seasonal locations

It is well established that many breeding birds, such as Swallow and Swift, migrate south from Britain & Ireland to winter in warmer climates while others, such as many geese, arrive in Britain & Ireland for the winter from their high-Arctic breeding grounds. However, it is only large-scale bird ringing that has allowed us to demonstrate that some species present in Britain & Ireland throughout the year also exhibit migratory behaviour, even if only part of the population is involved or movements are very short. Indeed, we now know that it is rare for bird species not to undergo some form of seasonal movement, even if it is only the adoption of larger home ranges in winter as breeding territories are no longer defended and food becomes harder to find.

For each species, we calculated the average recovery locations in each season (or month if sufficient data were available) for (i) birds ringed in Britain & Ireland during the breeding season and (ii) birds ringed in Britain & Ireland in winter. We tested the differences between (i) the average location of ringing in the breeding season (the British & Irish breeding population) and the average location of recovery in winter (Appendix 3a) and/or (ii) the average location of ringing in the winter (including individuals from breeding populations outside Britain &

---

[3] Latitude and longitude are measured in degrees, which are units on a circular rather than linear scale. Hence, 360° is the same as 0°, and 300° is closer to 0° than to 100°. This means that special statistical methods are required to analyse latitude and longitude data rigorously. A statistical technique known as the Watson–Williams test was used to compare mean latitudes and longitudes. This is equivalent, conceptually, to a *t*-test or an analysis of variance for data on a linear scale (such as wing lengths) (see Zar 1984 or Fowler & Cohen 1995); it is parametric and assumes that each sample comes from a population conforming to the von Mises (or circular normal) distribution. The result of the Watson–Williams test is an '*F* statistic', which is effectively the same as that produced by an analysis of variance and can be looked up to find a significance level in the same tables. Computer programs to conduct these tests were written in SAS software (SAS Institute Inc, North Carolina, USA) following the procedure described by Zar (1984). Confidence intervals (5–95%) for the seasonal mean latitudes and longitudes were calculated using the method suggested by Batschelet (1981). These intervals should be interpreted as indicating that we can be 95% confident that the *true mean latitude and longitude* lie within them; they do not show the range of locations within which 95% of recoveries occurred, which is much larger. Following convention, a probability level of 5% that there is no difference between samples has been used to indicate statistical significance throughout. For some specific analyses, we also tested whether the distances moved by groups of birds between breeding and wintering areas (or *vice versa*) differed. These comparisons were conducted using Wilcoxon tests (SAS Institute 1990, Sokal & Rohlf 1995); these are equivalent to *t*-tests but are non-parametric (based on ranks and making no assumption about the distribution of distances moved) and test differences between medians rather than between means.

Ireland, if present) and the average location of recovery in the breeding season (Appendix 3b), for each of the 188 main species in the book with at least 10 recoveries of dead birds in each appropriate class. The tests show which species are *significantly migrant* and which are genuinely *sedentary*. While the results are essentially trivial in this sense for a species like Swallow, which we know migrates, they are of greater interest for species that have traditionally been thought of as sedentary or partially migratory (often without any widespread formal analysis of their movement patterns).

The results of these analyses were used to assign a *status* to each species (and British & Irish breeding or wintering population), which is the classification presented in the *'Statistical analyses'* table in each main species account. The classification used is explained fully in Chapter 6. Unfortunately, the recovery rates of long-distance migrants can be very low, if they winter in areas with low human population density, and even some common species such as Sedge Warbler and Whitethroat have been recovered dead on their wintering grounds too infrequently to be included in these analyses. For such species, where we know from other sources that they are migrant, with reasonable certainty, this is stated in parentheses in the summary box in each account.

Where natal dispersal and migratory movements are confounded

For many species, a large proportion of the individuals ringed have been ringed as chicks or as young immatures, and the age-structure in the recovery data set therefore shows a similar (although probably slightly different) bias. This could lead to a problem in the interpretation of inter-seasonal movements, particularly for rather resident species, because any difference between the ringing and recovery locations of birds ringed as immatures in the breeding season and recovered in winter will potentially incorporate both movements between breeding and wintering sites and permanent dispersal from natal areas. It is possible, therefore, that some short, apparently migratory movements in fact represent only juvenile dispersal and that the standard tests we have used will overestimate the migratory tendency of some resident species. In an ideal world, this problem would be soluble by the use of recoveries only of birds ringed as adults, but sample sizes do not allow such analyses for many species. Where there were 20 or more recoveries, breeding season to winter, of birds ringed as adults, however, we repeated the comparison of ringing and recovery locations for adults only. The results of these tests are given in Appendix 3, where it is indicated whether or not adult-only comparisons were possible and, if so, whether the results were significant. Where a difference between ringing and recovery locations was no longer significant after immatures were removed from the sample, this may suggest that either (a) the species concerned is not genuinely migratory or (b) only immature birds are migratory. The data do not generally allow these two interpretations to be separated. For species for which no such checking was possible, migration and natal dispersal remain confounded. It should be noted that the same problem affects our analyses of differential migration patterns with respect to age.

Differential migration

Analyses of locations and ringing-to-recovery distances were carried out to investigate the variation in movement patterns with respect to age class and sex for as many species as possible. Only recoveries for which the age class or sex (as appropriate for the specific analysis) was known accurately were included. As before, the recoveries were divided into birds ringed in Britain & Ireland during the breeding season and those ringed in winter. The age-class analyses compared birds recovered as *immatures* and those recovered as *adults* (as defined above). For movements from breeding to winter locations, the tests compared birds ringed as nestlings or immatures, and recovered as immatures, with those ringed and recovered as adults; hence, for immatures, seasonal movements were confounded with dispersal (as described above). The

question asked here was: *'Do adult and immature birds from the British & Irish population have different wintering areas?'*

For movements from winter to breeding locations, the tests considered birds ringed as either immatures or adults and recovered as adults. This minimized the risk of comparing the breeding season locations of breeding adults with those of individuals of pre-breeding age that may not have returned to the breeding grounds (as is common for many non-passerines with delayed first breeding, such as many seabirds, some waders and raptors). In this case, the question asked was: *'Do adult and immature birds that spend the winter in Britain & Ireland come from different breeding areas?'*

For the tests between sexes, the questions asked were: *'Do males and females from the British & Irish population have different wintering areas?'* (for birds ringed in Britain & Ireland in the breeding season); and *'Do male and female birds that spend the winter in Britain & Ireland come from different breeding areas?'* (for birds ringed in Britain & Ireland during the winter).

Differences between the mean latitude and longitude of recovery of immatures and adults, and males and females, were conducted for each of the four seasons using two-sample Watson–Williams tests. Tests of locations in winter (for British & Irish breeders) or in the breeding season (for British & Irish winterers) were the most rigorous for testing for differential migratory tendency. Those comparing locations in spring or autumn could produce significant results if the timing of the seasonal movements or routes taken by the two age classes or sexes differed, and this would not necessarily indicate a final separation on the wintering grounds. However, average locations in spring and autumn were also calculated for comparison with the winter and breeding season results, particularly to assess whether any differential timings or routes of movement were suggested. The distances moved by the two age classes and sexes were compared using Wilcoxon tests for recoveries in the breeding season and in winter (but not in spring or autumn, for the reasons explained above).

The results of these differential migration tests for individual species are given in Appendix 4 and are flagged in the *'Statistical analyses'* table in each main account (see Chapter 6). The more general patterns across species are discussed in Chapter 5.

Biases caused by differences in ringing locations

For tests involving comparison of two groups of recovery locations, such as the tests of the wintering locations of sexes and age classes above, there is a potential problem with interpretation if the average ringing locations of those two groups differ. This could lead to significant differences in recovery locations in the absence of any differential movement. To take account of such potential effects, parallel tests were conducted, using identical statistical methods, comparing the ringing latitudes and longitudes of each pair of recovery samples. The magnitude and direction of any differences found in ringing locations were then compared with the corresponding differences in recovery locations. If the net difference in recovery locations (after subtraction of the difference in ringing locations) was less than 0.2°, then the difference in recovery location was considered to be confounded with the difference in ringing location. The figure of 0.2° was used because it marked, approximately, the smallest significant difference in latitude or longitude identified across the range of Watson–Williams two-sample tests conducted. Where the results of statistical tests were confounded with differences in ringing location, these are highlighted in Appendix 4 and flagged next to the test results in the *'Statistical analyses'* table in each main species account (see Chapter 6). Differing ringing locations will not have influenced the tests of distance because consideration of ringing location was intrinsic to the calculation of the length of each movement.

Biases caused by the confounding of age and sex effects

We considered the effects of age and sex on movement patterns separately, to give the maximum possible sample sizes for each test (because some birds were of unknown sex or age class). This approach meant that the effects of age and sex on movement could be confounded, however, if, for example, the movements of males and females were compared, but more females were immature when ringed than were males (so that any difference detected could actually have been an effect of age and not sex). To check for this possibility, we carried out chi-squared tests on two-by-two contingency tables of frequencies of the different sex (male or female) and age (immature or adult at ringing) classes for all species with sufficient numbers of individuals of both known sex and known age. For a test to be carried out, an expected value of at least five was required in each of the four cells of the table. The results of these tests are given in Appendix 4c. In some cases, the chi-squared test could not be carried out because of insufficient records in one or two cells but it was still possible to state with reasonable certainty that age and sex effects were not confounded. For example, if the tests for differences in movement patterns between the sexes were carried out almost exclusively on adults (less than 10% immatures in the sample), then the effects of age did not influence the result. Such results are coded separately in Appendix 4c. For many sexually monomorphic species, tests of differential migration of the two age classes were possible but the ratios of the sex classes in the two samples could not be tested because most birds were of unknown sex. For such species it is not possible to say for certain that sex differences are not confounded with any observed differences in movement patterns between the age classes. Sexes being similar, however, age differences might be more likely to result in differential movements than sex differences (see Chapters 3 & 5).

Differential movements of regional subpopulations

A number of different hypotheses were tested, based on regional divisions of the recovery data (see Chapter 5). Again, some referred to birds ringed in Britain & Ireland during the breeding season and some to birds ringed in Britain & Ireland in winter. In each case, the hypotheses involved testing differences in mean recovery locations (using Watson–Williams tests, as above), or in distances moved between breeding area and wintering area (using Wilcoxon tests, as above), between birds from between two and five regions. A region was only included in a test if a sample of at least 10 recoveries was available. There was no need to control for differences in ringing location as, by definition, ringing locations differed between regions. For species defined as *sedentary* in the migratory tendency tests (above), this meant that recovery locations were also bound to differ between regions and, therefore, tests of mean location in a given season were inappropriate. For such species, the median distances moved by individuals ringed in the breeding season and recovered in winter were tested. The results of the tests are presented in full in Appendix 5 and are flagged in the 'Statistical analyses' table in each main account (see Chapter 6). Patterns across species are discussed in Chapter 5.

Partial migration: quantifying migratory strategy

We have already described tests designed to reveal whether species are migrant or not; these function by comparing the movement of an average bird between the breeding and winter seasons. These tests have allowed us to assign a level of statistical significance to the movements undertaken by average individuals but, nevertheless, they represent only a very coarse assessment of the migratory strategy of each species. While some birds are genuinely faithful to local areas, and so can justifiably be called sedentary, migrant species exhibit a wide range of strategies. These include obligate long-distance migration, in which whole populations move thousands of kilometres annually, and facultative short-distance migration, in which some birds move in response to local changes in resource availability. Species adopting these extremes and many intermediate alternatives would all be considered 'significant migrants' by the simple tests described above (given adequate sample sizes) but it is clearly of interest to investigate this variation in strategy further.

Between species that do not migrate at all, such as Blue Tit, and species that can be considered to be obligate migrants, such as Swallow, there are a great many 'partial migrants'. A 'partially migrant' species can be defined conservatively as one in which different individuals in a single breeding population have different migratory strategies. Partial migrants might then include species in which almost all individuals migrate long distances, while a minority remain close to their breeding areas, and species in which only a minority leave the breeding grounds (see Chapter 3). Although it has long been recognized that many species undertake such mixed strategies, the classification of migratory behaviour has usually been an *ad hoc* process, making qualitative use of records of greatly reduced winter numbers, of observations in overseas wintering areas and of any ring-recoveries that have occurred. For this book, we have adopted a more objective and quantitative approach to the definition of migratory strategies, allowing species to be classified according to how much of a migrant they are. This classification has been used to score migratory strategies in the 'Statistical analyses' table within each main species account and its derivation is described below. It represents a significant advance on previous general statements.

From the complete sample of recoveries representing breeding season to winter exchanges for each species, the numbers moving different distances provide a picture of the overall migratory strategy of the species concerned. Obligate migrants would be expected always to move large distances, true residents always to move only short distances and partial migrants to be recovered at a range of distances. The exact shape of the frequency distribution of the distances moved provides a means by which migratory strategy can be quantified. For each species, seasonally accurate recoveries of dead birds that were ringed in the breeding season and recovered in winter were extracted from the ring-recovery database. Reasonable recovery sample sizes are required to produce reliable frequency distributions, so analyses were restricted to the 91 species for which 20 or more suitable recoveries were available. A left-skewed frequency distribution, showing a preponderance of short-distance recoveries, would suggest a more resident species (Fig 4.13a) while a right-skewed distribution, showing that long-distance movements dominate, would suggest an obligate migrant (Fig 4.13b). A partial migrant would have an intermediate frequency distribution of numbers of recoveries with distance (Fig 4.13c).

Two different approaches were used to convert the sets of ringing-to-recovery distances into frequency distributions. First, the interval between zero and the maximum distance moved by each species was divided into 20 equal segments, such that recoveries were assigned to categories that varied by species, in terms of absolute values, but were a fixed percentage of the maximum distance (5%) in width. Second, the interval between zero and the approximate maximum distance travelled by a passerine (10,000 km: a Swallow movement) was divided into 100 equal segments, such that recoveries of each species were assigned to quantitatively similar categories. In the latter case, any recovery at a distance of more than 10,000 km was assigned to the maximum distance category. Each of these approaches has its strengths and weaknesses, and each emphasizes a different aspect of a species' migratory behaviour. The first, 'standardized' method allows the distance that constitutes 'a long way' to vary between species. This means that two species that differ in the absolute distances that they move but that have similar proportions of their populations stopping to overwinter, say halfway to their most distant wintering areas, will be regarded as equally partially migrant. This should clearly be a desirable property in an index of migratory behaviour (differences in absolute distances moved are the subject of separate tests as described above). A problem with this first approach is that it relies on the existence of unusually distant recoveries of truly resident species to generate a left-skewed frequency distribution. These are rare, by definition, in resident species and large recovery samples will have to exist before they are found. In their absence, maximum movement distances could be small, indicating no real migration at all but generating a frequency distribution suggesting a partially migrant

Fig 4.13 The process used to produce indices of migratory tendency for this book. The figure shows frequency distributions of numbers of recoveries with distance from ringing locations for (a) a sedentary species (Blue Tit), (b) a migrant (Swallow) and (c) a partial migrant (Goldfinch). These are then converted into standardized cumulative frequency distributions, as shown for (d) Swallow and (e) Goldfinch, and the cumulative distributions for these two species are superimposed: the area between the two lines forms a measure of their dissimilarity (f).

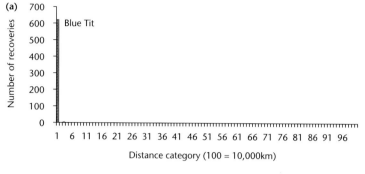

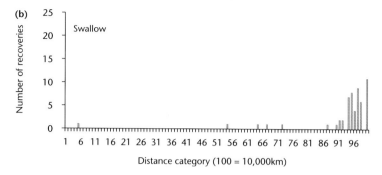

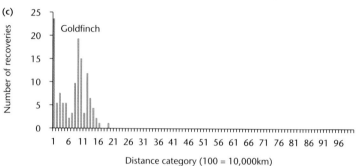

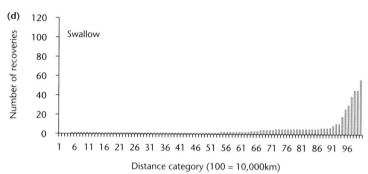

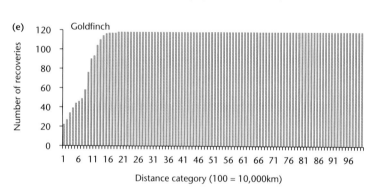

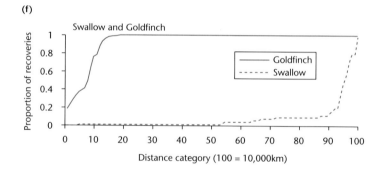

strategy. The second, 'absolute' method aids the detection of truly resident species by allowing them to have extremely left-skewed distributions but could hinder the detection of species with truly partially migrant strategies when the absolute distances moved are small. However, the use of a large number of divisions of the interval between zero and the maximum distance should maximize the sensitivity of any comparison of 'absolute' distributions. Neither the standardized nor the absolute type of frequency distribution provides a clearly superior

measure of migratory behaviour, so the two were used in parallel and the results interpreted in the light of their properties.

Standard statistical procedures were used to allow differences in migratory tendency between species to be expressed in terms of a single index and also to test their significance formally[4]. A procedure called multi-dimensional scaling (MDS) was then used to produce indices of migratory tendency for all species with 20 or more movements between the breeding season and winter[5]. These indices were then used in

---

[4] To quantify the differences between frequency distributions and to convert them into a simple representation of the variation across all species, the distributions were first converted into a cumulative form, standardized into the range of zero to one (ie cumulative proportions of the sample; Fig 4.13d, e) as in the first step in a Kolmogorov–Smirnov test for the homogeneity of two frequency distributions (Sokal & Rohlf 1995). Standardizing the distributions in this way removes any effect of sample size on differences between them. The difference between each pair of species was then quantified by calculating the area between the cumulative frequency curves of the two species (Fig 4.13f). This generated a matrix of *dissimilarity* coefficients that quantified the difference between each species and the others. Such dissimilarities can be thought of as analogous to distances between a set of points in space or on a map (Kruskal & Wish 1978, Manly 1986).

[5] MDS is commonly used to reproduce the spatial locations of sets of points using only the distances between them, in the absence of coordinates (Everitt 1978, Kruskal & Wish 1978, Manly 1986). MDS finds the orientation of a set of points, in a specified number of dimensions, that distorts the original between-point distances as little as possible. The distortion of the original distances in producing a fit with the required dimensionality is measured using a quantity called 'stress': values of around 0.05 or less are generally considered to indicate a good fit of the derived locations to the original distances (Kruskal & Wish 1978). MDS using area dissimilarities has previously been used to quantify and graph the differences between the long-term Common Birds Census trends of 42 species of farmland bird (Siriwardena *et al* 1998a). To produce indices of migratory behaviour from the dissimilarity matrices derived from the standardized and absolute frequency distributions, the matrices were analysed using the MDS procedure of SAS (SAS Institute 1996). Each analysis allowed only a one-dimensional fit (ie the expression of the differences between distributions in terms of values on a single linear scale). The distributions concerned will generally be simple and of a standard shape (sigmoid and asymptotic), so that differences between them can be readily interpreted as differences in the species' tendencies to migrate. The MDS-derived indices of migratory tendency were calculated for each of the standardized and absolute forms of frequency distribution. The 'stress' measures for one-dimensional MDS solutions indicated an acceptable fit for both these approaches to index calculation (0.061 and 0.025, respectively).

comparative, multi-species analyses and the approach was developed further to investigate temporal changes in patterns of migration; the analyses are described in Chapter 5.

In order to classify migratory strategies for the main species accounts, we combined the results of the simple tests of whether species are 'significantly migrant' with the standardized index of migratory tendency described in this section. Species were assigned a score of their migratory tendency of between zero and four. A score of zero was given to any species for which there were significant differences in neither latitude nor longitude between ringing and finding locations for birds ringed in the breeding season and recovered in winter (*ie* species classified as 'sedentary'). All other species were assigned scores between one and four, according to their standardized index of migratory tendency[6]. This process provided an objective, quantitative classification

of migratory strategies that was also easily interpretable. The standardized index values and allocated scores for each species are given in Appendix 3a.

Temporal change in movement patterns

The investigation of temporal changes in movement patterns based on ring-recoveries is complicated by potential concurrent changes in finding circumstances (as discussed previously). The quantitative index of migratory tendency developed for this book (see previous section) can be readily adapted to compare the distribution of winter recoveries for a given species by time periods. This gave a method for carrying out some exploratory analyses of temporal change in movement patterns in this book. The methods specific to these analyses, together with the results and the caveats involved, are discussed in Chapter 5.

---

[6] The 52 species that were found to be 'significant migrants' were ranked in order of their standardized, MDS-derived index. As the distances separating relatively migrant species from one another tended to be larger than those separating relatively sedentary species, the standardized index was log-transformed, using the formula New Index = Log(((Index × −1) − Min(Index)) + 1), and the range in the transformed index between the most and least migrant species was then divided into four equal sections. Species for which index values fell within each section were assigned a score between one (least migrant section) and four (most migrant section).

5 Synthesis of the migration patterns of British & Irish birds

Gavin Siriwardena & Chris Wernham

Birds use a wide range of migratory strategies: some of the possible reasons for the selection of each strategy have been described in Chapter 3, and the strategies used by each of the main species included in this book are highlighted in Chapter 6. Here, we aim to investigate whether any broad patterns in migratory strategy exist across groups of bird species that use Britain & Ireland throughout the year. We cannot hope to cover every possible migratory strategy and group of species in this short synthesis. Rather, we focus on a number of questions, addressing a range of interesting biological phenomena, with particular relevance to bird populations using Britain & Ireland. Where appropriate, we also note the implications of any patterns revealed for the conservation of particular ecological groups of species. Some of the statistical techniques used in our analyses are complex and the details of the methods used are therefore described elsewhere (Chapter 4). We hope that the results will be of general interest.

We first provide a summary of the overall migration patterns of the birds that occur regularly in Britain & Ireland, based on analyses carried out for the *Migration Atlas* project and on information from other sources. We consider briefly how British & Irish populations fit into the wider context of the West Palearctic and contrast our systems with those found elsewhere. Next, we describe a new method of quantifying the degree of migrancy of a population, and therefore a means of comparing migrancy both between and within species, and contrasting the degree of movement between different periods of years. The latter approach may prove particularly useful for future analyses, in the light of the environmental changes that are now thought to be occurring at a global scale. The largest part of the chapter investigates the degree to which differential movements and partial migrations occur within the populations that inhabit Britain & Ireland through the year. We develop further our quantitative assessment of 'degree of migrancy' and use it to consider the physical, social and ecological factors that may determine how much a species migrates and the consequences of migration for other aspects of birds' life histories. Finally, we provide a brief summary of the current state of knowledge concerning the phenomena of differential and partial migration, to put our results into context, and suggest how our approaches might contribute to future research.

Bird migration in Britain & Ireland: an overview

Britain & Ireland occupies an extreme geographical position within western Europe because of its proximity to the North Atlantic Ocean and the influence of the Gulf Stream (Moss 1995). In winter, food generally becomes less available at higher latitudes; for some species, it may become completely inaccessible due to ice or snow-cover, while for others, supplies simply become much reduced. Migration is likely to evolve in any bird population where the net chances of survival can be increased by moving to a new area for the winter compared with staying on the breeding grounds (Lack 1954b).

Across all organisms, there tends to exist a general decrease in species richness with increasing latitude (Fischer 1960, Pianka 1966). In the case of European bird populations, this decrease has been shown to steepen greatly north of 65°N in summer and north of 40°N in winter (Newton & Dale 1996a). A relationship between climate and bird species richness has also been demonstrated within Britain (Turner *et al* 1988). Generally, the numbers of populations that are migrant as opposed to resident are greater at higher latitudes, because seasonal variations in temperature and hence food supplies are larger there than further south (Herrera 1978, Terborgh 1989). Newton & Dale (1996a) provide a revealing summary of climatic variation across the geographical region with which populations present in Britain & Ireland through the year are associated. For example, mean January temperatures exceed 10°C only in southern Spain and North Africa; they are 0–5°C in much of western Europe but below freezing and as low as −15°C in most of Fennoscandia and −20°C in Novaya Zemlya. Minimum winter day-lengths are around 11 h at 35°N, but decrease to zero at the Arctic Circle, which lies only 6° north of Shetland. The season of plant growth lasts six to nine months at 35–50°N but contracts further north to less than three months in Svalbard. In continental western European winters, most still fresh waters north of 55°N freeze but those in Britain & Ireland remain open. Most of the Baltic and Barents Seas are covered in sea-ice during the course of the winter.

Considering Europe as a whole, many species move southward for the winter, while a smaller number of species arrive from further north. North of about 35°N, the emigrants generally exceed the immigrants so that fewer species are present at a given latitude in winter than in summer (Newton & Dale 1996a). Around 23% of west European bird species probably leave Europe completely, many wintering in equatorial areas or further south, while about 3% of wintering species leave Europe in spring to breed elsewhere. The proportion of summer visitors in local avifaunas generally increases with latitude in Europe (Newton & Dale 1996a). A similar relationship with latitude has been demonstrated in eastern North America but, at any given latitude there, 17% more breeding species leave for the winter and 10% more wintering species leave to breed, presumably because temperatures for equivalent latitudes are lower in North America than in Europe (Newton & Dale 1996b). Winter climates increase in severity from the Atlantic coasts of Europe eastwards (Fig 5.1), so that some species that are completely migratory in the east of their European range can be partially migratory or even sedentary as far west as Britain & Ireland. Greenfinch and Chaffinch, for example, are far more migratory where a continental climate of harsher winters and hotter summers prevails. Milder conditions in Britain & Ireland allow some species to be partial migrants that, elsewhere, always migrate away from their breeding grounds (Lundberg 1988).

In summarizing the migratory status of the bird species that breed and winter in Britain & Ireland, we have included all 261 species for which there is either a main or additional species account in this book,

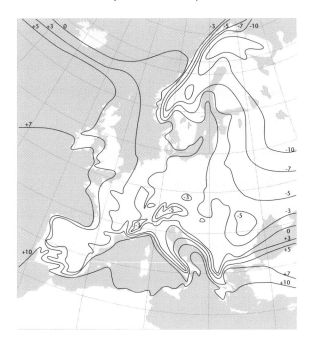

Fig 5.1 Isotherms (lines of equal average temperature in °C) across western Europe in January, showing the general increase in temperature with decreasing latitude, but also the milder conditions on western coasts bordering the North Atlantic Ocean. The severity of winter weather therefore also increases from west to east. (*Source*: Moss 1995.)

and thus all species we define as 'regularly occurring' (see Chapter 6 for the criteria used). Breeding species were divided into three categories: 'long-distance migrants' (of which the average individual winters outside Britain & Ireland), 'short-distance migrants' (migratory but the average individual winters within Britain & Ireland) and 'sedentary'. For those species with adequate ring-recovery data, this process was based on rigorous statistical tests specifically for British & Irish breeding birds (see Chapter 4 and Appendix 3a). For all other species, we drew on information provided in the species accounts. For 11 of the 196 species with British & Irish breeding populations, we found there was too little information to assign a category. The full results are given in Appendix 6a for main species and in Appendix 7 for additional species. In the synthesis that follows, species for which the classifications were based on direct testing of ring-recovery data are differentiated from those where migratory status was assumed. We divided British & Irish wintering species into three categories: 'immigrant only' (no British & Irish breeding population), 'resident only' (no winter immigrants from abroad, and the average British & Irish breeder winters within Britain & Ireland) and 'resident and immigrant' (wintering birds have mixed origins).

Of the 196 species breeding in Britain & Ireland that we could classify, 37% are long-distance migrants (on average wintering outside Britain & Ireland), 22% are short-distance migrants and 41% are sedentary (Fig 5.2a). In their consideration of 418 bird species in Europe as a whole, Newton & Dale (1996a) showed that the proportion of summer visitors in local avifaunas increased with latitude from around 29% of breeding species at 35°N to 83% at 80°N. Our results are in line with their estimate of the proportion of migrants at around 55°N, the approximate middle latitude for Britain & Ireland (Fig 5.3), but demonstrate considerable variation around this average figure, depending on ecological grouping (Figs 5.2b–f). Britain & Ireland supports relatively few breeding waterfowl that are long-distance migrants (14%), reflecting the relatively mild winters that we experience for our latitudinal position, and only around a quarter of our breeding raptor and owl species leave Britain & Ireland for the winter. Around 35% of our breeding passerines and near-passerines are long-distance

migrants but 52% of our seabird/gull species and 67% of waders leave Britain & Ireland for the winter. Unlike terrestrial species, where species diversity decreases with increasing latitude, numbers of breeding marine bird species peak at around 60–70°N, where zooplankton production reaches its maximum in European waters (Newton & Dale 1996a). Many seabird species probably move south for the winter to exploit the large expanses of southern oceans whereas, on a European scale, far fewer marine species move northwards to exploit the northern oceans, which are much less extensive.

The relative proportions of short-distance migrants and sedentary breeding species in Britain & Ireland, shown by our synthesis, may be somewhat biased in that species in the ecological groupings with relatively large numbers of short-distance migrants (seabirds/gulls, waterfowl and waders) tend to have higher recovery rates than the majority of passerines and near-passerines, giving us more power to detect movements. Also, more observational evidence generally exists to support short-distance migration in, for example, waterfowl that are noticeably absent from inland waterbodies in the winter because they have moved to the coast, than for, say, tits that have temporarily deserted their breeding sites in upland woodlands for lowland parks and gardens. Nevertheless, some groups included within our 'passerine and near-passerine' grouping (*eg* the gamebirds) are renowned for their sedentary lifestyles.

Of the 188 species that we considered to winter in Britain & Ireland (Fig 5.4a), information for 32 (17%) was insufficient to determine whether regular immigration occurs. Half of these species are passerines or near-passerines. Of those that we felt able to classify, 33% are resident only, 22% are immigrant only and 44% have both immigrant and resident populations. For Europe as a whole, the proportion of winter visitors decreases with increasing latitude from 36% of wintering species at 35°N to only 8% (mostly seabirds) at 70°N and none at 80°N (Newton & Dale 1996a). The 22% of species that are solely winter immigrants to Britain & Ireland (Figs 5.4b–f) include 13 wildfowl species, nine waders and eight passerines, only four seabirds (three of which are gulls) and one raptor (Rough-legged Buzzard). Britain & Ireland has double the number of species for which resident and immigrant populations mix on the wintering grounds than species that are solely winter visitors, reflecting its attractive winter climate for both foreign-breeding birds and resident populations. Given this great importance of Britain & Ireland for wintering bird populations, our lack of knowledge of the extent of immigration for many species (below and Chapter 7), and even of the existence or otherwise of immigrant populations for 17% of our wintering species, is a major handicap to conservation efforts. Potential ways to rectify this lack of knowledge are addressed in Chapter 7.

Patterns of migration of British & Irish birds

How much of a migrant is each species?
Migratory strategies are frequently described using a classification of species as 'migrants' or 'residents'. With respect to the birds of Britain & Ireland, such a scheme can separate species that clearly always migrate long distances (such as Swallow and Swift) from others that are rarely found to venture more than a few kilometres from their breeding areas (such as Blue Tit and Dunnock). Many strategies are intermediate between these extremes, however, and the variation between species in 'degree of migrancy' is, in reality, a continuum that cannot be described accurately by a simple classification.

Within the research underlying this book, we were keen to explore new, more rigorous and quantitative approaches to the study of bird migration. One such approach was to develop a quantitative method for the definition of migratory tendency — that is, a method by which we could identify where each species lies in the continuum between true residents and true migrants. As well as allowing us to classify strategies objectively, a quantitative system of this kind would allow us to conduct

Fig 5.2 The composition of migrant types within 196 species of bird that breed regularly in Britain & Ireland, for (a) all ecological groupings combined, (b) 102 species of passerine/near-passerine, (c) 19 species of raptor/owl, (d) 25 species of seabird/gull, (e) 15 species of wader and (f) 35 species of wildfowl. Proportions within the migrant types without brackets are derived from species tested directly using ring-recovery data, those in brackets are assumed from other sources of information. 'Long-distance migrants' have average wintering locations outside Britain & Ireland, while 'short-distance migrants' show significant movement between breeding and wintering areas but, on average, still winter within Britain & Ireland (see text for further explanation).

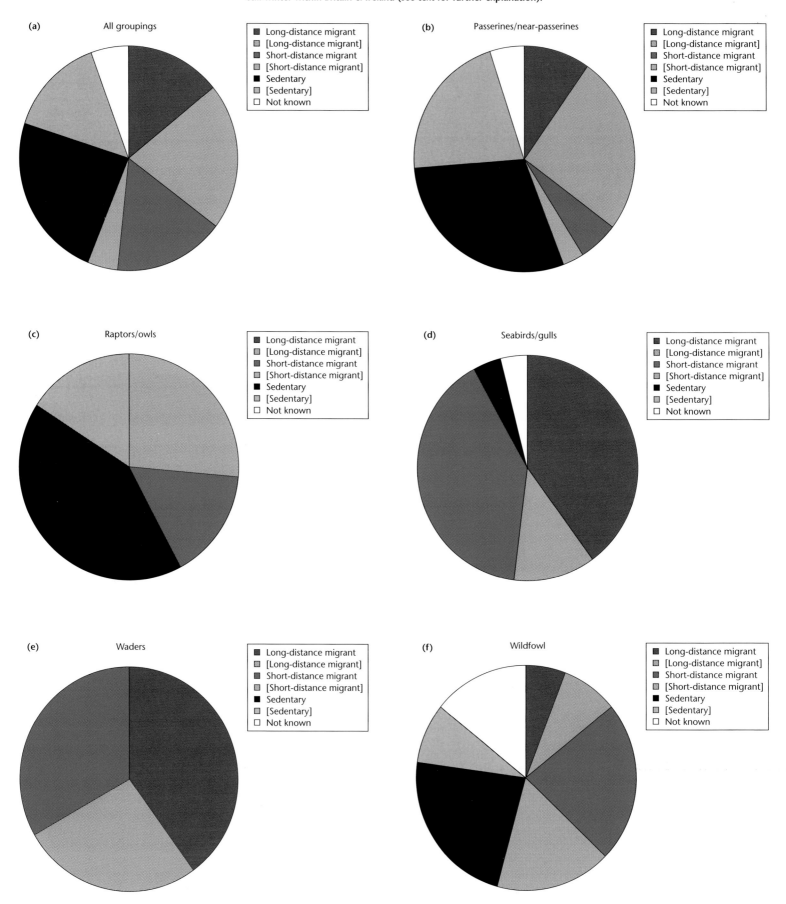

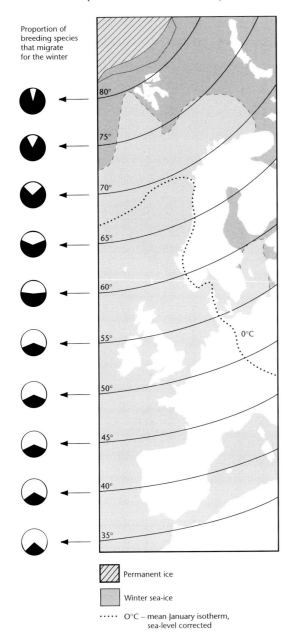

Fig 5.3 Variations with latitude in the proportions (black segments of pie charts) of breeding bird species in western Europe that migrate south for the winter. (*Source*: Newton & Dale 1996a.)

Proportion of breeding species that migrate for the winter

Permanent ice

Winter sea-ice

····· 0°C – mean January isotherm, sea-level corrected

winter of dead birds previously ringed as adults in the breeding season (seasons being as defined in Appendix 2). We constructed movement distance frequency distributions in two ways, differing in the definition of what constitutes a 'long distance'. The *absolute* method considers that a given distance is equally meaningful for each species, so that a species in which the whole population moves 10,000 km is more migratory than one in which all birds move 2,000 km. The *standardized* method defines long distances on a species-specific basis, considering in this case that species where more individuals migrate over distances approaching the maximum that the species moves are more migratory than species where movements approaching the maximum are rare. We have used a standard statistical technique to convert the differences between species in patterns of migration revealed by each type of distribution into two versions of an *index of migratory tendency*. The importance of the distinction between the two methods, and therefore of using both of them, is discussed in Chapter 4 and below. All 91 species with 20 or more relevant recoveries were considered: reliable frequency distributions could not have been produced for species with fewer recoveries.

The basic methods we have used are described in full in Chapter 4 (under *Partial migration: quantifying migratory strategy*). These methods generated the standardized and absolute indices that we have used, first, to characterize the migratory tendency of each species. Subsequently, we have extended the method in several ways to conduct exploratory analyses into the variation within species, looking for differences between breeding and wintering birds and changes over time, and then examining possible evolutionary causes and life-history consequences of migratory behaviour through multi-species comparisons. These analyses, described below, were intended to show some of the uses to which our approach can be put, and the results should not be regarded as definitive. Nevertheless, we have been able to identify interesting patterns that suggest avenues for fruitful further investigation, either using existing ring-recoveries or newly collected information.

Variations in migratory tendency between species
Making comparisons between species in terms of their indices of migratory tendency gives an indication of how much of a migrant each species can be considered to be. The standardized and absolute indices are plotted against each other in Fig 5.5a (see also Appendix 3a): these are raw index values, not the transformed values used to generate the score of migratory tendency for each species account (see Chapter 4). Each index shows a gradient from more migratory (high positive values) to more sedentary (high negative values), so the concentration towards the bottom left of the graph (especially along the 'absolute' axis) shows a large number of species with comparatively sedentary lifestyles. Obligate long-distance migrants, that is species of which all individuals migrate to distant wintering grounds every year, can be seen to form a group discrete from more resident species, especially with respect to the absolute index (more positive index values, towards the top right of Fig 5.5a). Most of the variation in strategy therefore separates the few long-distance migrants with sufficiently large sample sizes for analysis from the majority of relatively non-migratory species. There is also proportionally greater variation among the indices of species with more migratory habits. This pattern suggests that relatively resident strategies or short-distance migrations are the norm and probably the biologically important pattern for many species (*Overview* section, above). The scarcity of ring-recoveries far distant from Britain & Ireland, most notably from Africa, means that long-distance migrants are generally under-represented in all our analyses of movement patterns. Nevertheless, many commonly ringed and recovered species were found to have low migratory tendencies and fell in the concentration near the origin in Fig 5.5a, despite the occurrence of occasional long-distance recoveries. Therefore, although the latter are likely to attract attention, for example in the maps in the species accounts (Chapter 6), they are of little significance in describing the prevalent movement patterns of British & Irish populations. One

statistical tests to explore the ecological and life-history causes and consequences of variations in migratory tendency.

In this section we introduce our new approach to describing a species' migratory behaviour, examine the results of applying the technique to the birds of Britain & Ireland and explore how it might be applied in order to shed light on the evolutionary, ecological and life-history causes and consequences of migration. Our aim here is to provide an overview of the approach and its potential value, describing what it tells us about patterns of migration across species and asking what evidence it can contribute to comparative studies in evolution and ecology. It would be beyond the scope of this book to provide a full investigation of these subjects; comprehensive reviews have been prepared by, for example, Berthold (1996, 1999, 2001). Rather, we wish to show how our approach might complement the results of previous studies.

Our approach uses the differences between the patterns of distances moved by individuals of each species between their breeding and wintering areas to reveal each species' migratory tendency relative to that of each other species. The distances moved refer to recoveries in

Fig 5.4 The composition of migrant types within 188 species of bird that spend the winter regularly in Britain & Ireland, for (a) all ecological groupings combined, (b) 82 species of passerine/near-passerine, (c) 16 species of raptor/owl, (d) 20 species of seabird/gull, (e) 23 species of wader and (f) 47 species of wildfowl. 'Immigrant only' species are those for which there is no regular breeding population within Britain & Ireland, 'resident only' are those species for which there are no regular immigrants from abroad into Britain & Ireland in winter and 'resident & immigrant' species have wintering populations within Britain & Ireland composed of individuals from both local and foreign breeding areas (see text for further explanation).

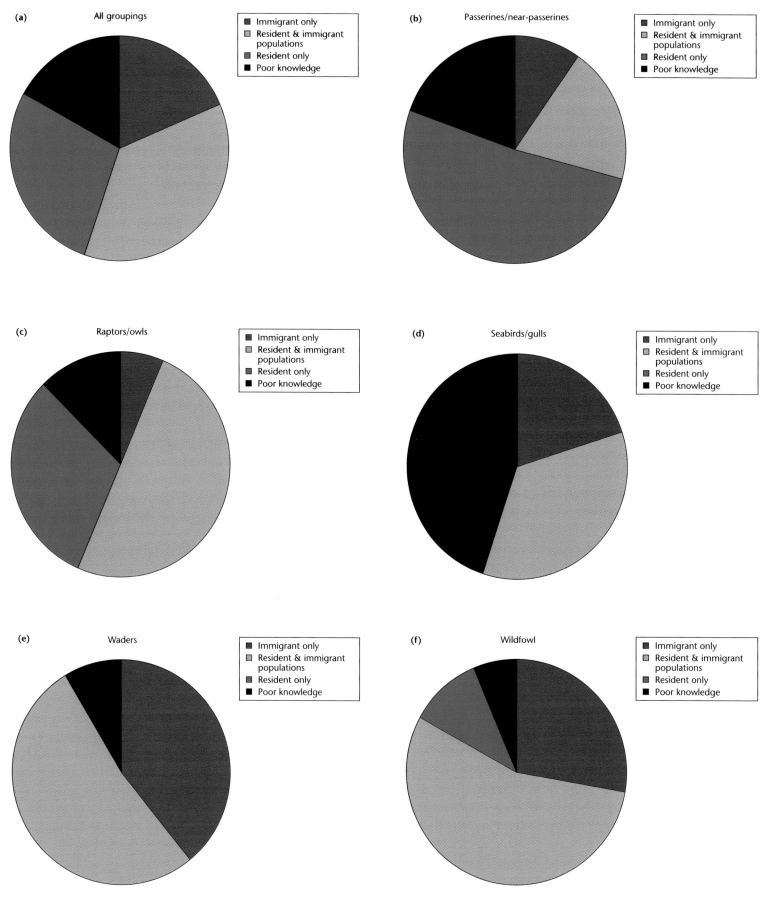

Fig 5.5 Indices of migratory tendency for British & Irish breeding birds: (a) comparisons of the 'absolute' and 'standardized' index values of individual species and (b) comparisons of the ranks of the two index values for individual species (see text for further explanation). The codes used to identify the species are given in Appendix 3a.

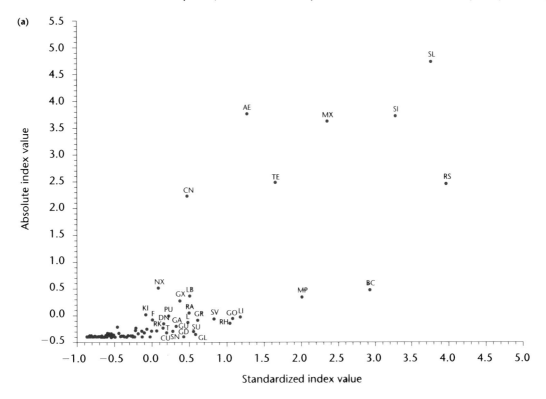

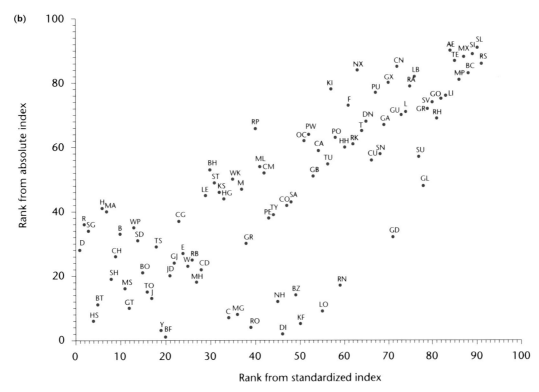

species for which long-distance recoveries could be given an importance out of proportion with their frequency is Blackbird: the recovery sample is one of the largest in the BTO's database and many long-distance and overseas recoveries have occurred. Calculating indices of migratory tendency from the complete recovery-distance distribution for the species suggests that it is largely sedentary (Appendix 3a), however, implying that the long-distance recoveries reflect the large sample size rather than an important strategy undertaken by a significant fraction of

the population. This is supported by our simple tests of whether species are significantly migratory, which showed that British & Irish breeding Blackbirds make, on average, a significant westerly movement between their breeding and wintering grounds, but that this average movement was less than 0.2° of longitude (Appendix 3a). The Blackbird example indicates how, in this context, interesting and unusual recoveries should not be emphasized at the expense of the biologically more important norm for a species that can be revealed by quantitative analyses.

Table 5.1 Differences between the migratory tendencies of populations present in Britain & Ireland in the breeding season and in winter. Species are listed as having more migratory breeding or wintering populations where such a pattern was indicated by the results of comparisons of either or both of the 'absolute' and 'standardized' recovery distributions. Only species with at least 20 suitable recoveries for each of the breeding and wintering populations were included (see text for further explanation).

Differences between populations	Species		
No significant differences	Canada Goose	Sparrowhawk	Moorhen
	Collared Dove	Tawny Owl	Wren
	Dunnock	Robin	Great Tit
	Jay	Magpie	Jackdaw
	House Sparrow	Bullfinch	Yellowhammer
	Reed Bunting		
Breeding population more migratory	Coot	Lesser Black-backed Gull	Pied Wagtail
	Song Thrush	Mistle Thrush	Blue Tit
	Nuthatch	Rook	Greenfinch
	Goldfinch	Linnet	
Wintering population more migratory	Mute Swan	Teal	Mallard
	Pochard	Tufted Duck	Eider
	Oystercatcher	Dunlin	Curlew
	Redshank	Black-headed Gull	Common Gull
	Herring Gull	Great Black-backed Gull	Wood Pigeon
	Barn Owl	Blackbird	Starling
	Tree Sparrow	Chaffinch	

The uneven spread of species (Fig 5.5a) and, in particular, the proximity of genuine partial migrants such as Goldfinch and Linnet to the 'sedentary' cluster, suggested that examining the relative indices for each species as they are presented was unlikely to be very informative. Therefore, we ranked the index values to generate a clearer picture of the relative position of each species (Fig 5.5b). These ranks then formed the basis for the statistical tests examining the causes and consequences of migratory strategies described below. The positions of species in the rank order from most to least migratory tend to be similar between the two indices (Fig 5.5b). The bias in the sample towards relatively sedentary species means that only a small proportion of the variation in strategy is made up of obligate migrant species, so that partial migrants, such as Meadow Pipit, and shorter-distance obligate migrants, such as Blackcap, can be found towards the 'highly migratory' end of the range.

There is a notable group of species off the main diagonal in Fig 5.5b, towards the standardized index axis, that includes Yellowhammer, Buzzard and Little Owl. These are species for which the standardized index suggests a stronger migratory tendency than is indicated by the absolute index. In practice, these species are the ones that demonstrate most clearly why the absolute index is needed in addition to the standardized one: their maximum recovery distances are somewhat short, leading to 'flat', stretched-out standardized recovery distributions that may suggest a partially migratory strategy where none exists.

Probably the most interesting and useful index results involve species in the middle of Fig 5.5b and towards the bottom of Fig 5.5a (but away from the tight cluster at the bottom left). These species lie between genuine residents like House Sparrow and Bullfinch and the long-distance migrants. It is species such as Goldfinch, Linnet, Puffin, Tufted Duck, Oystercatcher and Lesser Black-backed Gull that appear to undertake a range of migratory strategies and could therefore be called partial migrants (but see *Partial migration and the control of migratory tendency*, later). The differences in strategy between individuals may be a result of the effects of genetic diversity, dominance, or factors related to

life histories, such as age- or sex-specific variation. The consensus of researchers to date is that migratory tendency is under strong genetic control (Berthold 1996, 2001) but the detail of how the distances moved by individuals are determined remains unclear. A range of ecological and life-history factors are potentially related to migratory strategy at the species level, and we consider such factors later in this chapter.

Do breeding and wintering populations of the same species differ in migratory tendency?
The principal indices of migratory tendency that are described above (and that were used to inform the classifications used in each species account) were derived only from birds ringed in Britain & Ireland in the breeding season and recovered in winter. One interesting question for species present in Britain & Ireland all year is whether the breeding and wintering populations are equally migratory. In other words, do the birds present in summer and in winter include similar proportions of migratory individuals? If the winter-ringed population is more migratory, this could indicate the presence of winter immigrants from abroad that may not be easily detectable in the field. We were able to examine the recovery-distance frequency distributions for birds ringed in winter in Britain & Ireland and recovered in the breeding season, and compare them with the breeding-to-winter distributions. These analyses complemented those investigating differential migration described later in this chapter.

The two recovery-distance distributions were compared for 47 species[1], all those with at least 20 suitable recoveries from each of the breeding and wintering populations. Both the standardized and the absolute forms of the recovery distributions were compared. The results are summarized in Table 5.1: the breeding and wintering populations differed in migratory tendency for one or both forms of frequency distribution for 31 of the 47 species. Of these 31 differences, 10 were significant only when standardized distributions were used while only one (Mistle Thrush) was significant only when absolute distributions

---

[1] Two-sample Kolmogorov–Smirnov tests (Sokal & Rohlf 1995), which are designed specifically to compare frequency distributions, were used to test for differences between breeding-to-winter and winter-to-breeding recovery-distance distributions.

were used. For 11 species, the breeding population was the more migratory but, for 20 species, it was the wintering one. Non-significant results would be expected if a population were entirely sedentary or if British & Irish birds migrated annually between breeding and wintering grounds within the islands, with no immigration from overseas in either season. Note, however, that all the results refer to the populations of birds sampled by ringing in the breeding season and in winter: this sampling may have been biased with respect to habitat (for example, if proportionally more ringing is conducted in gardens in winter) or geography (for example, if seasonal patterns of ringing activity or recovery reporting vary between regions). Problems with geographical bias could be identified to some extent from comparisons of ringing locations between seasons, but such comparisons would not necessarily reveal bias in habitat coverage because habitat is unlikely to be related simply to geographical location. Time did not permit a full investigation of these issues of bias within the *Migration Atlas* project, so we treat them as caveats to our results while recommending that they should be considered in future developments of these methods.

Nine of the species whose breeding populations were found to be more migratory and only four of those whose wintering populations tended to move further were passerines: this difference is highly significant[2]. This pattern reflects the use of Britain & Ireland as a wintering ground by many non-passerines that also breed in the islands. Passerines are more likely to be partial migrants, the individuals present and ringed in winter being relatively sedentary, but exceptions include Blackbird and Chaffinch, of which large numbers of Fennoscandian breeders are known to winter in Britain & Ireland (see the species accounts in Chapter 6). Most of the differences between wintering and breeding populations listed in Table 5.1 can be explained in this way, but with some exceptions. Influences of dispersal or of geographical or habitat differences between the two samples may underlie the results for some species (*eg* Mute Swan, Coot, Wood Pigeon, Barn Owl, Song Thrush, Mistle Thrush, Blue Tit, Nuthatch, Rook and Tree Sparrow). Habitat bias may be especially likely when the predominant catching methods or types of site for ringing differ markedly between seasons, for example if most summer ringing of a species targets nestlings in nest boxes while most winter ringing is of birds trapped at feeding stations that could have a wide catchment area. Controls for some of these suspected sources of bias could be added to our method in the future so that conclusions can be reached that are more definitive.

Has migratory tendency changed over time?

Changes in migratory tendency over time are of intrinsic interest in biology and can have important implications for conservation (Chapter 7). The case of Blackcaps wintering in Britain & Ireland in increasing numbers, for example (see species account and Chapter 3), raises evolutionary and ecological questions about how and why the species' behaviour has changed, and also has what many would regard as the welcome consequence of increasing winter biodiversity in these islands; experiments suggest that this change has a genetic basis (Berthold & Querner 1995). As components of population change, changes in migratory strategy can have important implications for conservation and management as either causes or consequences of variations in abundance. For example, climate change could cause a decrease in the proportion of a partial migrant's population that migrates, making it less vulnerable to hunting pressure overseas, or migration to distant wintering grounds could be density-dependent such that breeding population increases in Britain have little effect on winter abundance. In general, any improvements to our understanding of past influences

on changes in abundance would aid the development of conservation policies for the future.

The quantitative indices of migratory tendency described above can be readily applied to any set of subdivisions of a population, sample sizes permitting, provided that the ring-recovery data can be reliably separated according to the subdivisions. We applied the method to explorations of variation in migratory strategy over time for each species by dividing the larger of the data sets used in the analyses described above (those with 40 or more recoveries) into two equal parts (around the median recovery year). We then tested the significance of the differences between the *early* and *late* recovery-distance distributions[3]. Although rather coarse, this exploratory temporal analysis had the benefit of maximizing the number of species that could be tested. Ring-recovery sample sizes represent the only constraint on how time periods might be chosen to test more specific or complex temporal hypotheses. The results presented here only provide a guide as to what could be done and indicate where interesting changes might have occurred; they should not, in any way, be taken to form a definitive investigation of historical changes in the migratory strategies of British & Irish birds.

We were able to test for changes in migratory tendency over time for 73 species and for 22 of these found significant or near-significant temporal shifts in recovery-distance distribution by one or both of the standardized and absolute methods of calculating frequency distributions (Table 5.2). Of the 51 species for which there was no significant change with time, 23 had been identified as sedentary by testing the significance of the differences between ringing and recovery locations (Chapter 4). Although these differences were also non-significant for Mute Swan and Buzzard, we found changes in migratory tendency over time for these species, suggesting that the lack of a clear pattern overall may have masked important variation. More generally, for 14 of the species whose migratory tendency changed over time, the difference found was significant by both methods, the other eight cases involving small shifts in distribution or differences in the short-distance movements undertaken by very sedentary species (Appendix 3a). It was more common for species to have shifted towards shorter than towards longer migratory distances (15 and five species, respectively) but there was no clear taxonomic pattern with respect to the direction of change (see Table 5.2). Two other species have undergone more complex changes in distribution (Manx Shearwater and Sandwich Tern), in which the early and late frequency distributions were significantly different, but not in ways that can be interpreted as simple changes in how much the average individual is migratory. These changes might reflect a tendency for some parts of the population to have become more migratory (for example, young birds or birds from one geographical area) while others have become less migratory. They could also equally be artefacts caused by complex temporal changes in finding circumstances (Chapter 4). Such species-specific patterns require further investigation. The year chosen to mark the division of the samples could clearly be critical in determining the temporal changes suggested by an analysis like this and should be considered when the results are interpreted: the years we have used are listed in Appendix 3a.

The common tendency for migratory movements to have become shorter is interesting because it matches the pattern that would be predicted if global warming had increased the climatic suitability of more northerly regions for wintering birds. If so, such changes could occur through a shortening of the distances moved by obligate migrant populations or by the migratory components of partially migrant populations, or by a reduction in the proportion of a population that migrates. Examination of the species involved suggests that an effect of

---

[2] G-test (Sokal & Rohlf 1995): G = 11.50, 1 df, $P < 0.001$.
[3] Data for birds ringed during the breeding season and recovered dead in winter in early (before the median recovery year) and late (after the median recovery year) periods were compared using Kolmogorov–Smirnov tests (Sokal & Rohlf 1995) for each species. 'Standardized' frequency distributions for the periods both before and after the median year were generated using the species-specific maximum distance across the whole data set (early and late combined) (see Chapter 4 for details of the basic method).

Table 5.2 Summary of the results of tests for changes in migratory tendency over time. Species are listed in categories according to whether significant or near-significant ($P<0.1$) changes in migratory tendency were detected when comparing recoveries before and after their median recovery years. Species are listed as having undergone changes if there was a significant change using either or both of the 'absolute' and 'standardized' approaches to creating the index (see text). Species in black text are those found to be sedentary (not significantly migratory) and those in red are significantly migratory (see Chapter 4). Full results and the median year for each species are presented in Appendix 3a.

Summary of changes in migratory tendency	Species			
No significant change	Fulmar	Cormorant	Grey Heron	Greylag Goose
	Canada Goose	Shelduck	Mallard	Pochard
	Hen Harrier	Sparrowhawk	Merlin	Peregrine
	Moorhen	Coot	Ringed Plover	Snipe
	Woodcock	Redshank	Common Gull	Lesser Black-backed Gull
	Herring Gull	Great Black-backed Gull	Kittiwake	Roseate Tern
	Arctic Tern	Stock Dove	Wood Pigeon	Barn Owl
	Tawny Owl	Kingfisher	Swallow	Meadow Pipit
	Wren	Dunnock	Robin	Mistle Thrush
	Blue Tit	Great Tit	Jay	Magpie
	Jackdaw	Rook	Carrion Crow	Raven
	Starling	House Sparrow	Chaffinch	Greenfinch
	Goldfinch	Bullfinch	Reed Bunting	
Movements tend to have become shorter	Gannet	Shag	Eider	Tufted Duck
	Buzzard	Kestrel	Oystercatcher	Curlew
	Great Skua	Black-headed Gull	Common Tern	Puffin
	Pied Wagtail	Song Thrush	Blackbird	
Movements tend to have become longer	Mute Swan	Lapwing	Guillemot	Razorbill
	Linnet			
More complex changes	Manx Shearwater	Sandwich Tern		

global warming is unlikely to be a general explanation, however: they include several seabirds and waders, but not the partially migrant species like Meadow Pipit, Linnet and Goldfinch that might be expected to be affected most (Table 5.2). It is also notable that no temporal change was detectable for 51 of the 73 species tested (only half of which were identified as sedentary in our analyses: Table 5.2), suggesting that large effects of climate change on migratory behaviour were not detected. Adequately controlled tests, focusing on the species and periods most likely to reveal such effects, would be needed to investigate effectively the possible changes to migration patterns due to global climate change. Such research, building on our results above, would make a useful contribution to the current debate on the conservation implications of this topical issue and should be high priority for future work in the field of bird migration.

Comparisons of the directions of the significant temporal changes in recovery distribution with the historical population trends of the species concerned (1988–91 Atlas, Baillie et al 2001) revealed no clear associations of shifts towards shorter or longer migratory distances with particular population-trend directions. It is interesting that a relatively large proportion (9/22) of the species for which significant changes (in various directions) were found were seabirds (Table 5.2, Fig 5.6). Apart from this, and a tendency for passerines to be particularly unlikely to have undergone changes in migratory tendency, there were no clear patterns for particular changes in migratory tendency to be associated with different phylogenetic/ecological groups (Fig 5.6). It is likely, therefore, that the temporal changes in recovery distribution reflect species-specific factors (and perhaps biases such as changes in patterns of ringing and recovery, see Chapter 4 and below) and that these results are best interpreted on a species-by-species basis. Our degree of knowledge of temporal change in the movements of British & Irish birds is examined further in Chapter 7.

Do British & Irish birds show differential migration with respect to age and sex?
The tendency of female Chaffinches to leave Sweden in winter while males tended to remain is probably the most famously documented example of differential migration, and led Linnaeus to name the species *coelebs* ('bachelor'). Differential migration, in the most restrictive use of

Fig 5.6 Summary of the results of analyses to test whether British & Irish breeding bird populations have become more or less migratory through time. The method used compared the frequency distributions of distances moved between breeding and wintering areas for each species before and after the median date of winter recoveries (see text for further explanation).

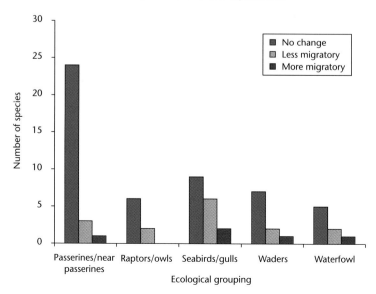

the term, refers to a situation where all individuals within a population migrate, but the distance travelled between breeding and 'wintering' areas varies with age class and/or sex (eg Ketterson & Nolan 1983). Discussion of differential migration covers three sections of this chapter. In this section, we assess whether differential migration is a feature of the lifestyles of the bird species that breed in Britain & Ireland, and those that are present in Britain & Ireland outside the breeding season. We next consider briefly what ring-recoveries can tell us about differences in the timing of migration between sexes and age classes (a further aspect of the phenomenon termed 'differential migration' by Terrill & Able 1988). Finally, we investigate whether the birds that are present in different regions of Britain & Ireland during the year display variations in migratory behaviour.

The question of whether birds of different age and sex differ in their migration patterns is important, both in terms of our understanding of the evolution of migration and for applied conservation. The protection of wintering areas and sites used on passage, as well as breeding areas, is crucial for the conservation of migratory species. A satisfactory network of areas to fulfil this aim effectively can only be established if the movements of all subdivisions of the population are considered. For example, there would be no point in conserving the wintering grounds for the male Ruff that breed in Europe, which are in southern Europe and North Africa, without also conserving those of the majority of females, which are located further south in Africa. Similarly, the protection of sites used for wintering by adult birds is less than effective for their conservation if the sites used by immatures, which will later recruit into the breeding population, are not protected as well. Immatures of a number of species (such as Hen Harrier, Lapwing, Lesser Black-backed Gull and Razorbill) winter further south than adults and may therefore be subjected to different threats on the wintering grounds.

There are a number of suggested reasons why birds of differing age and sex may be segregated on their wintering grounds. Quite often males and females of a given species differ in body size and, often, immature birds are smaller than adults of the same sex. If this is the case, the smaller-bodied sex or age class may seek out a geographical area with a more favourable winter climate (often wintering further south, for those species that breed in northern latitudes). Larger birds can carry more fuel reserves (fat) and endure fasting for longer periods, and so are able to winter further north (Ketterson & Nolan 1976). Gauthreaux (1978, 1982) suggests alternatively that a single force, that of intraspecific social dominance relationships, underlies all forms of segregation on the wintering grounds, ranging from habitat separation of sexes or age classes in sedentary populations to differential migration of ages and sexes, partial migration and intraspecific differences in irruptive behaviour. In the case of differential migration, dominant individuals may migrate only as far as is necessary to reach suitable wintering habitat, while the subordinate sex or age class may either migrate further than the dominant class or occupy lower-quality habitat. Quite often, these two suggested hypotheses are difficult to separate in practice,

because the larger sex or age class is also the dominant one. For example, in some northern species of raptor, such as Sparrowhawk (Belopol'skij 1972, Mead 1973) and Goshawk (Mueller et al 1977), there is a tendency for males to winter further south than females; females are larger than males, and females are also said to be the dominant sex in these species.

The two hypotheses just described both assume that segregation is necessary because of intraspecific competition for resources on the wintering grounds. Differential migration could also result, however, if individuals of one sex or age class experience more intense competition for resources on the breeding grounds, such that it is advantageous for that class to return to the breeding grounds as early as possible (Myers 1981). For example, the sex that establishes territory in the spring would be predicted to return first. Earlier arrival could be achieved by migrating a shorter distance and wintering closer to the breeding area, by earlier departure from the wintering area, or by a combination of these two strategies. Migration is probably both energetically costly and risky for birds. If one sex or age class suffers a higher risk of mortality due to starvation, dehydration or predation during migration, then this may lead them to shorten their migration distance or take a route that lowers the risk (Ketterson & Nolan 1983). In reality, the factors and mechanisms that lead to differential migration are complex and an explanation that involves several factors working together (the 'Multifactoral Hypothesis' of Baker 1978) seems the most likely, the factors and mechanisms probably differing between species.

In the latest comprehensive review of differential migration, Cristol et al (1999) provide detailed tables documenting the species for which differential migration strategies have been proven or refuted and a new modelling approach to show how the factors described above might interact to explain the patterns observed. The authors postulate that some kind of differential migration is usual rather than exceptional because differences in size, social dominance or arrival times on the breeding grounds exist between sexes or age classes for most species. Cristol et al (1999) then reviewed the evidence for the occurrence of differential migration across species and concluded that the phenomenon is much more widespread than has previously been reported. They found only 16 species for which the absence of differential migration had been shown conclusively, as opposed to 146 species for which there was evidence that differential migration could or definitely does occur.

We tested for differences in distance moved and mean recovery locations between males and females, and adults and immatures, for birds ringed in Britain & Ireland during the breeding season and recovered in winter (79 species for age comparisons and 30 for sex comparisons) and for birds ringed in Britain & Ireland during the winter and recovered as adults during the breeding season (46 and 27 species for age and sex respectively). Only recoveries from dead birds were included in the analyses. We did not restrict our analyses of differential movement patterns to species that we had found to be significantly migratory; this was to cover the possibility that migratory tendencies in part of a population, such as one age class, sex or regional subpopulation, had been masked in the larger data set, resulting in the species being classified as a non-migrant. For clarity of interpretation, and to make our results broadly comparable with those from previous studies, we have presented results for 'migrants' and 'non-migrants' (as determined by our rigorous tests, above) separately in the figures. The full results of the analyses are given in Appendix 4 and are summarized by ecological group in Fig 5.7. More detail about the movements of species showing significant differences can be found in their species accounts in Chapter 6.

Passerines and near-passerines
For British & Irish breeding birds (Fig 5.7a), only 10 of the 32 species of passerine or near-passerine that were tested showed differences in distances moved between breeding and wintering areas by the two age classes (Woodpigeon, Pied Wagtail, Song Thrush, Mistle Thrush, Blue

Fig 5.7 Summary of the results of analyses to test for differential migration between (a) immature and adult birds ringed in Britain & Ireland in the breeding season and recovered in winter, (b) male and female birds ringed in Britain & Ireland in the breeding season and recovered in winter, (c) immature and adult birds ringed in Britain & Ireland in winter and recovered as adults in the breeding season, and (d) male and female birds ringed in Britain & Ireland in winter and recovered during the breeding season. In each case, the number of species for which the results of the tests were significant ('SIG', red/pink), non-significant ('NS', blue/pale blue) or non-significant but confounded with differences in ringing locations ('CONF', yellow/pale yellow, see text for further explanation) are shown for each ecological grouping, separately for the distances moved and mean recovery location tests (latitude and longitude). In (a) and (b), bolder shades of colour indicate the results for species that are significantly migrant and pale shades those that are non-migrant. In (c) and (d), bolder shades indicate species with winter immigrant populations into Britain & Ireland and pale shades those for which winter immigration does not occur or is poorly known.

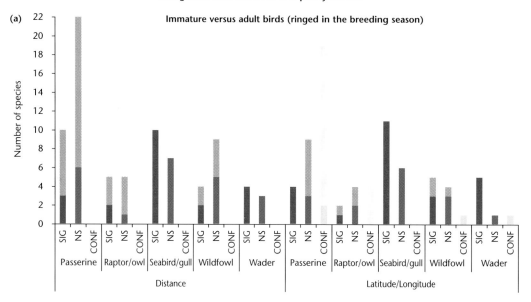

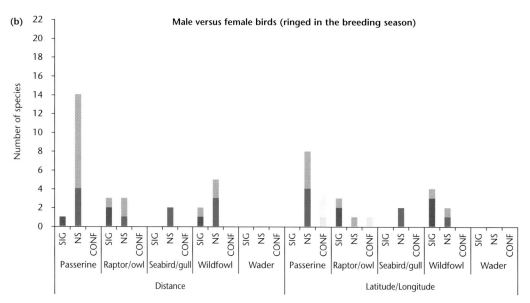

Tit, Jay, Jackdaw, Rook, Starling and Yellowhammer), immatures always moving further than adults. For most of these species, the difference between the two age classes in distance moved was very small (less than 10 km), however, and for only three (Pied Wagtail, Mistle Thrush and Song Thrush) was there a significant difference in the average winter recovery locations of the two age classes. For such comparisons involving terrestrial species where the immature class comprises birds ringed as nestlings, any seasonal movements to wintering areas are confounded with natal dispersal for the immature age class. Comparison of the distances moved by immatures between natal and wintering areas with natal dispersal distances (see Appendix 2) showed that for Blue Tit, Jackdaw, Jay, Rook, Starling and Yellowhammer the distances were similar. For these species, the observed difference between the age classes in distance moved between breeding and wintering areas could be attributed to the process of natal dispersal. For

Mistle Thrush, Song Thrush and Pied Wagtail, immatures were recovered significantly (0.6–1.6° of latitude) further south than adults (and for Pied Wagtail also significantly (1°) further west than adults), suggesting true differential migration of immatures to more favourable winter climates in the south and west. For the two thrushes, the effect is likely to be local (as the median distances moved by immatures were only 9 km and 12 km for Mistle Thrush and Song Thrush respectively) but the average immature Pied Wagtail was recovered 92 km from its natal area in winter. Immature Wood Pigeons moved a median of 28 km (natal dispersal around 10 km, Appendix 2) compared to 6 km for adults, also suggesting a differential movement but not leading to a difference in average wintering area.

Of the 15 species with sufficient sample sizes to test for differences in breeding-to-winter movements for the sexes, only one showed a significant difference (Fig 5.7b). Female Pied Wagtails (median 15.5 km)

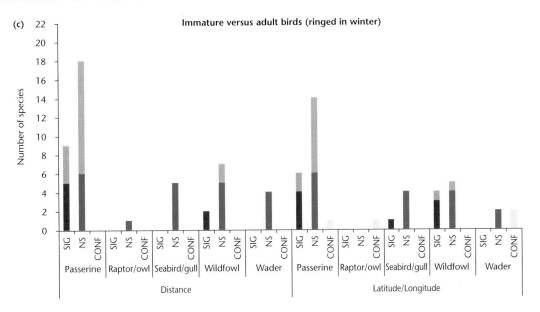

(c) Immature versus adult birds (ringed in winter)

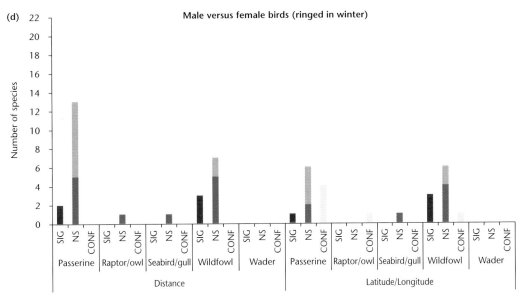

(d) Male versus female birds (ringed in winter)

were recovered in winter significantly further away from breeding areas than males (median 4 km). That the majority of passerines breeding in Britain & Ireland did not show differential migration of the age classes or sexes is not surprising given the suite of species that had sufficient data for testing. The majority of those tested were sedentary species because there were insufficient recoveries from wintering areas to carry out such tests for most medium- and long-distance migrants, or in some cases too few birds of known sex (see the overall winter result column in Appendix 4a). For largely sedentary species, it is possible that segregation of sexes or age classes occurs by habitat in winter, rather than there being differences in the distances moved. Such segregation by habitat is currently poorly known, however. This may be an important area for future study given the possible conservation implications of any differences. For example, if we are to reverse the recent population declines of some farmland passerines in Britain & Ireland (Baillie *et al* 2001), which are thought to be due largely to reduced overwinter survival related to food supply changes (Siriwardena *et al* 1998b), we will need to understand the use of habitats by the different classes within these populations.

There were 27 passerine or near-passerine species for which there were sufficient data to test for age differences in the movement patterns

of birds ringed in Britain & Ireland during the winter and recovered as adults during the breeding season. Significant differences were detected for 11 of these species but they were essentially trivial or, for five species, confounded with differences in ringing locations (Blackbird, Greenfinch, Great Tit, House Sparrow and Rook, see Appendix 4c). For Linnets and Pied Wagtails ringed in Britain & Ireland during the winter, immatures were recovered during the breeding season significantly further from ringing sites than adults but no differences in average breeding locations were apparent. Such a difference could occur if juveniles make exploratory dispersal movements before their first breeding season but a majority still returns to the natal area. Chaffinches ringed in winter as immatures were recovered during the breeding season significantly further north (mean 54.4°N) than those ringed as adults (mean 53.7°N). The average recovery latitudes and longitudes during the breeding season suggested that the majority of ringed birds were from the British & Irish breeding population, hence suggesting, overall, that immatures are more likely than adults to move south in winter. This was not borne out for birds ringed during the breeding season and recovered in winter, however, and the results may be complicated by the presence of a proportion of immigrant birds in the winter-ringed sample (see species account in Chapter 6).

Starlings ringed in winter as immatures were recovered in the breeding season significantly further from the ringing sites (median 11 km) than those ringed as adults (median 6 km). The median distances moved suggested that the majority of birds caught in winter were from the British & Irish breeding population. Birds ringed as immatures were recovered, on average, 0.8° further east (mean 3.5°E) than those ringed as adults (mean 2.7°E), however. That the average recovery locations during the breeding season were east of Britain showed that a proportion of the birds caught in winter were immigrants from continental Europe, and that immatures had come from breeding areas further east than adults (or that more immatures reach Britain & Ireland). The converse was found for Siskins ringed in Britain & Ireland during the winter, with those ringed as adults recovered during the breeding season further from ringing sites (median 498 km) than those ringed as immatures (median 98 km). Their average breeding locations also differed significantly, with those ringed as immatures breeding, on average, 5.5° further west (mean 2.8°W) than those ringed as adults (mean 2.7°E). These results suggest that the majority of immatures ringed in winter are from the British & Irish breeding population, while a higher proportion of adults are immigrant birds. This pattern would result if immatures from the continental European breeding populations winter further south and/or west than the adults (ie further south than Britain & Ireland). Goldfinches ringed as immatures were also recovered in the breeding season significantly further west (mean 2.5°W) than those ringed as adults (mean 1°W) but the mean locations showed that the birds ringed were mainly from the British & Irish breeding population. The result could be due to Britain & Ireland receiving a small proportion of mainly adult immigrants from continental Europe (see the species account in Chapter 6). No age-class differences were detected in the breeding-season recovery locations of birds ringed in winter for some of the classic winter immigrants (such as Fieldfare and Redwing).

Differences in the movement patterns between the sexes for birds ringed in winter and recovered during the breeding season could be tested for 15 species. Differences were found for only two of these species. For Blackbird, a significant but very small difference in movement distances was detected. The movements of immigrants from continental Europe are discussed in detail in the main account for this species (Chapter 6). Female Reed Buntings were recovered in the breeding season significantly further from winter ringing locations (median 29 km) than males (median 2 km), and also further north (mean 54°N) than males (mean 52.6°N). Hence, females may be more likely to move south in winter than males.

Raptors and owls

The immatures of five of the 10 raptor and owl species tested (Hen Harrier, Kestrel, Sparrowhawk, Barn Owl and Little Owl) moved significantly further than adults between the breeding season and winter but for all, with the exception of Hen Harrier, the immature distance may have been heavily influenced by natal dispersal movements. In the case of Kestrel, differences between age classes and sexes were confounded because more immatures than adults were female (see Appendix 4c). It has previously been established that female British Kestrels migrate further than males (Mead 1973, Village 1985a). For Hen Harrier and Long-eared Owl, immatures were recovered significantly further south in winter (by 2.7° and 2° of latitude respectively) than adults. For the small sample available, male Hen Harriers (median 406 km) moved significantly further than females (median only 16 km), so that they were recovered 4.9° further south than the females, as concluded previously by Watson (1977). The female is the larger and the dominant sex in this species. Conversely, in the current analyses, female Sparrowhawks (median 13 km) were recovered in winter slightly but significantly further from the breeding areas than males (median 7 km). Finally, female Peregrines ringed during the breeding season were recovered in winter on average significantly further west (by 0.9°) than males (but not further north), despite their larger size.

Only Sparrowhawk had sufficient recoveries during the breeding season of birds ringed in Britain & Ireland during the winter, and no differences in the movements of the age classes or sexes were detected (sample sizes were small in each comparison).

Seabirds and gulls

For the majority of seabird and gull species, a difference in distance moved or mean winter location (12 species), or both (five species), was detected between immatures and adults ringed during the breeding season (Fig 5.7a). For all 10 species for which a difference in distance moved was detected (Gannet, Cormorant, Shag, Black-headed Gull, Lesser Black-backed Gull, Herring Gull, Great Black-backed Gull, Guillemot, Razorbill and Puffin), immatures moved further than adults. For eight of these species, immatures were recovered significantly further south than adults and for six significantly further west (see Appendix 4a for the full results). Immature Kittiwakes and Sandwich Terns were also recovered significantly further west than adults. Guillemots were exceptional in that immatures were recovered significantly further north and east than adults. The magnitudes of the differences detected between adults and immatures varied. For example, the median distance moved between breeding and wintering areas by immature Black-headed Gulls (141 km) was not especially large compared to that of adults (84 km), resulting in immatures wintering on average only 0.9° further south and 0.5° further west than adults. At the other extreme, the median distances moved by immature and adult Gannets, of 1,380 km and 639 km respectively, resulted in immatures wintering on average 9.4° further south and 2.7° further west than adults. Most adult British & Irish Gannets do not go further south in winter than the Bay of Biscay while first-years winter off West Africa and older immatures show intermediate movement patterns (see species account in Chapter 6).

The majority of seabird species exhibit delayed first breeding, and intraspecific competition during the breeding season is thought to be high. First-year seabirds often remain in the winter quarters for the summer, or in sea areas separate from those used by the breeding adults. As they get older, they generally begin to visit the breeding sites during the summer but they usually arrive later in the spring and depart earlier in autumn than the breeding adults. Our results for seabirds breeding in Britain & Ireland generally confirm broad differences in the migration distances and wintering areas of adults and immatures that were already well established for some species (eg Gannet: Thomson 1974, Nelson 1978; several large gull species: Kilpi & Saurola 1984; the auks: Lloyd 1974; Sandwich Tern: Langham 1971; Kittiwake: Coulson 1966). Of the five species for which we found no differences in the movements of adults and immatures (Common Gull, Common Tern, Fulmar, Great Skua and Roseate Tern), only Roseate Tern showed no suggestion of immatures wintering further south and west than adults. The small sample sizes probably precluded obtaining significant results for the other four species, for some of which previous studies have suggested differences between age classes (eg Fulmar, Macdonald 1977; Great Skua, Furness 1987).

For many of these seabird species, studies of differential migration based on ring-recoveries may be complicated by differences between age classes in their risk of succumbing to certain finding circumstances, which vary geographically. For example, naive immatures may be more susceptible to accidental capture in fishing nets than adults and more such catching may happen further south (eg in the Bay of Biscay and off the African coast) and further west (eg around Newfoundland, see Chapter 4 for more details). We can be reasonably certain that the age classes of seabirds breeding in Britain & Ireland do generally differ in their wintering areas, to some extent, but further detailed quantitative analyses, taking the spatial variation in finding circumstances fully into account, should be carried out if we are to have a clear picture of differences in wintering areas for conservation purposes. For example, this would help us to predict accurately the population effects of a major

winter oil spill in a given sea area, given the age distribution of the seabird species present there.

Although seabirds can often be sexed by a combination of different measurements of body size, most are sexually monomorphic in plumage. For this reason, few birds that are ringed are of known sex, and consequently very little is known about differences between the sexes in movement patterns. In our rigorous analysis of the available ring-recovery data, only two species had more than 10 winter recoveries for birds of each sex and neither had more than 13 recoveries in each group. Although none of the differences was significant, the results suggested that females moved further than males for both Guillemot (male median 777 km, female 953 km) and Shag (male median 43 km, female 95.5 km).

The movements of birds ringed in Britain & Ireland during the winter and recovered as adults during the breeding season were tested for five species of gull (Black-headed, Common, Great Black-backed, Herring and Lesser Black-backed). Only for Herring Gull was a difference detected between the age classes, with birds ringed as adults recovered 2° further north than those ringed as immatures, but no significant difference in the distances moved by the two age classes was apparent. The average latitude and longitude of the recovered birds suggested that most were British & Irish breeders. Since many of the gulls that are ringed in winter have been caught by cannon-netting, often at waste disposal sites, the detected difference may indicate complex interactions between the age classes from different breeding areas caused by social factors operating at such concentrated food sources, or a bias in the composition of cannon-net catches that was not detected by our analytical approach.

Wildfowl
Of the 13 species with sufficient data for testing for differences between age classes, seven showed differences in their movements from breeding to wintering areas. Four of 10 species tested for sexual differences in movement patterns showed significant results. There was no clear pattern across the group. Immature Grey Herons (median 47.5 km) were recovered significantly further from breeding areas than adults (median 22.5 km) but the two age classes did not differ in average wintering locations. For Canada Goose, Eider and Mallard, adults moved significantly further than immatures. For Eider and Mallard, the results were confounded with those for sex, as either more adults than immatures were female (Eider) or more adults than immatures were male (Mallard). For both species, however, males moved significantly further than females between breeding and wintering areas (although the difference was small for Mallard). Differential movements have already been identified for British Eiders; for example, a substantial proportion of adults from the Sands of Forvie move to the Tay and Forth Estuaries for the winter, while most first-year birds do not (see the species account in Chapter 6). The interpretation of small but significant differences in the average wintering locations of the age classes for Mallard and Mute Swan were complicated both by differences in the sex ratios of the two age classes and by significant differences in their average ringing locations. Immature Shelducks and Tufted Ducks were recovered in winter significantly further west than adults (by 4.3° and 1.4° of longitude respectively). For Shelduck, this may be because

immatures undertake the moult migration to the Grosser Knechtsand in Germany earlier than many adults do, while some British adults may remain in Britain through the winter. Female Pochard were recovered in winter significantly further west (by 3.6°) than males, although only a small sample of females was available for analysis. It is well established that the sexes of this species display differential migratory strategies at the European scale (see Carbone & Owen 1995 and the species account in Chapter 6). The small difference in latitude of recovery between the sexes for Tufted Duck was confounded with a difference in ringing locations.

The differential movements of wildfowl ringed in Britain & Ireland during the winter could be tested for 10 species (sex differences) and nine species (age differences). No major differences between the age classes or sexes were found for Eider, Mute Swan, Pink-footed Goose, Pintail or Tufted Duck. Moorhens ringed as immatures in winter moved significantly further to breeding areas (median 6 km) than those ringed as adults (median <1 km) and were also recovered significantly further west within Britain & Ireland (by 1.7°) than adults. Teal ringed when immature were recovered significantly further from winter ringing sites (median 2,123 km) than adults (median 2,022 km) and were recovered 6° further east (mean 33.7°E) than adults (mean 27.7°E). Conversely, adult Wigeon were recovered during the breeding season on average 2.3° further north than immatures, with the mean locations of both age classes falling in northern Russia. In addition, male Wigeon were recovered 10° further east during the breeding season than females and moved on average 800 km further between wintering and breeding locations. Similarly, male Pochard wintering within Britain & Ireland were recovered significantly further east and north than females during the breeding season, reflecting the known differential migration patterns of the species across Europe and that more males than females from overseas remain in Britain & Ireland for the winter (see the species account in Chapter 6). Conversely, female Mallards present in Britain & Ireland during the winter were recovered in the breeding season 4° further east and 1.5° further north than males (with mean latitudes in continental Europe), suggesting that females travel further to reach Britain & Ireland or arrive from continental Europe in greater numbers.

Waders
Sufficient data were available to test the movements of adults and immatures for seven species of wader breeding in Britain & Ireland (Curlew, Lapwing, Oystercatcher, Redshank, Ringed Plover, Snipe and Woodcock), and differences were detected for six species. Immature Lapwings, Oystercatchers and Redshanks were recovered significantly further away from breeding areas than adults, resulting in immatures wintering significantly further south (Lapwing, by 1°) or further west (Oystercatcher, by 1.1°, and Redshank, by 0.9°). Immature Curlews were also recovered significantly further west (by 1.2°) than adults. Two rather counter-intuitive results, adult Snipe moving significantly further than immatures and immature Ringed Plovers being recovered significantly further north (by 4.3°) than adults, may have been artefacts of small sample sizes or 'contamination' of the samples of British & Irish breeders by early or late migrants with varying movement patterns. In a previous analysis demonstrating the leap-frog migration of some European populations of Ringed Plover, however, winter recoveries of British & Irish first-year birds were all within Britain & Ireland, all those abroad being in their second winter or older (Taylor 1980).

None of the wader species breeding in Britain & Ireland, or ringed in Britain & Ireland during the winter and recovered during the breeding season, had enough recoveries of sexed birds to allow comparisons of their movements to or from wintering areas. Although the sex of adults of a number of wader species can be established by a combination of body-size measurements, and some can be distinguished by plumage, most of those ringed during the breeding season will have been ringed as chicks, when they cannot generally be sexed.

The samples of waders ringed in Britain & Ireland in winter and recovered during the breeding season were only sufficient for testing for age differences for four species (Curlew, Dunlin, Oystercatcher and Redshank) and, for all but Dunlin, sample sizes were small in at least one group. Analyses for waders are complicated by the widely separated breeding origins of birds that winter in Britain & Ireland, and the simple statistical tests performed for this book were not suitable to investigate their differential movements. Further information for some species may be found in their accounts in Chapter 6 but the data for several species would doubtless benefit from further, more detailed analyses.

Differential movement patterns of British & Irish birds: Conclusions
How then do our results for British & Irish bird populations compare to those of Cristol *et al* (1999) that suggest that differential migration is the rule rather than the exception? Differential movements by the age classes are certainly the norm for our breeding seabirds (12 of 17 species show them) and our breeding waders (six of seven species), with immatures travelling further than adults and also wintering generally further south or west, where winters are generally milder. There are exceptions, however, like the Ringed Plover, where immatures appear to remain in Britain & Ireland while more adults move further south, perhaps as a result of their dominance on superior wintering areas also occupied by breeding populations from outside Britain & Ireland. The magnitudes of the differences detected also vary greatly between species, with distances moved by the two age classes differing by only a few tens of kilometres in some species (*eg* Black-headed Gull) but by hundreds of kilometres, with a large degree of segregation on the wintering grounds, in others (*eg* Gannet). For seabirds/gulls and waders, we know very little about sex-specific differences in movement patterns and how they may interact with the effects of age, an area that is certainly worthy of further study if suitable sexing techniques can be found (see Chapter 7).

For our breeding raptors/owls, our results suggest that age influences the wintering areas of only two species (Hen Harrier and Long-eared Owl), with immatures wintering further south, but insufficient sample sizes excluded several migrant species from our analyses (*eg* Marsh and Montagu's Harriers, Osprey and Short-eared Owl). Our results suggest that sex differences in movement patterns are widespread among our breeding raptors, detected in four of six species tested, but that the direction of difference varies, influenced at least in part by the sexual dimorphism exhibited by some species (*eg* Hen Harrier). No clear patterns with respect to age or sex emerged for British & Irish breeding waterfowl, although studies that were more intensive have shown that differences do occur for some species, at least within regional subpopulations (*eg* Eider). Our analyses for this grouping were hindered by small sample sizes for several widespread breeding species and by problems of confounded ringing locations for other species with otherwise satisfactory samples of data (*eg* Mallard); the latter group will require more detailed analyses to establish the true patterns of movement with respect to sexes and age classes. For the passerines and

near-passerines, our analyses were biased towards the more sedentary species, which might be less likely to show differential movements of a magnitude that would be detectable using these exploratory analytical methods. Pied Wagtail was one of the few significantly migratory species with sufficient ring-recovery data from the wintering grounds to allow both age and sex differences to be tested, and significant variation with respect to both age and sex was detected. Our knowledge of such movements for most of our other migrant and partial migrant species will only improve if the volume of information collected on their wintering areas can be increased and if better sexing techniques can be developed. Methods for achieving this are suggested in Chapter 7.

For British & Irish wintering populations of passerines, our analyses were once again dominated by resident species for which winter immigrants from abroad are rare. Despite this, the analyses produced some interesting results for the few species for which winter immigration into Britain & Ireland is known to occur. For Chaffinch and Starling, our findings suggest that immature birds come from more distant breeding areas than adults (or that more immigrants were immature than adult), while for Siskin and, to a lesser extent, Goldfinch, our results indicate that any immigrants may be largely adults (perhaps because immatures from continental Europe winter further south than Britain & Ireland). For Blackbird, more immigrants may be female than male (see account in Chapter 6) and for Reed Bunting, our results suggest that British & Irish breeding females may move further from their breeding areas in winter than males. We did not find age or sex differences for the two immigrant thrushes, Redwing and Fieldfare, and had insufficient data to test two other similar species, Waxwing and Brambling. For wintering wildfowl, our results confirm the existence and pattern of differential migration previously identified for some species (*eg* Pochard; Salomonsen 1968, Owen & Dix 1986, Carbone & Owen 1995) and suggest some differential migration between sexes and/or age classes for most duck species for which sample sizes are satisfactory (*eg* Mallard, Teal and Wigeon, but not Tufted Duck). Whether it is males or females, adults or immatures that travel further or winter in Britain & Ireland in differing numbers must be dependent upon the overall wintering distribution of the species (and where Britain & Ireland is placed within this distribution), as well as upon the migration strategies of the species concerned. Our exploratory analyses for Britain & Ireland could be developed further for passerines and ducks by incorporating the data for birds ringed abroad and recovered in Britain & Ireland if appropriate age- and sex-specific data were available for all the countries of origin to allow us to control for spatial variation in numbers ringed. European-scale analyses of the ring-recovery data for these ecological groupings would be particularly useful, however, especially if they also addressed temporal change in such movements and incorporated appropriate controls for spatial and temporal variation in the numbers ringed and for changes in recovery circumstances, and hence recovery rates, over time.

For seabirds/gulls, raptors/owls and waders, we have little knowledge of sex-specific differences in the movements of populations that winter in Britain & Ireland, because so few birds ringed have been of known sex. Differential migration between age classes is well established for many seabird and wader populations, so that the populations present in winter in Britain & Ireland (or its waters) are likely to vary in their age composition. This could also be true for populations of migratory raptors/owls. Because of the complex migration routes of most wintering wader populations, and the difficulties of catching seabirds and raptors/owls outside the breeding season, information on the composition and origins of the populations of species in these groupings that winter in Britain & Ireland will be derived most effectively by analyses carried out at an international scale (see Chapter 7 for examples).

What can ring-recoveries tell us about age- and sex-specific differences in the timing of migration?
If individuals of one sex or age class experience more intense competition for resources on the breeding grounds, such that it is

advantageous for them to return to the breeding grounds as early as possible (Myers 1981), the sex that establishes territory in the spring would be predicted to return first. That sex may achieve earlier arrival, at least in part, by earlier departure from the wintering area. For many species examined previously, males precede females on spring migration, with a few exceptions (see Gauthreaux 1982 for examples). Often studies have shown that older birds migrate before younger birds and, in the extreme case, that younger birds remain on the wintering grounds (*eg* Osprey). The timings across species with respect to age and sex for autumn migration are far more complex (Gauthreaux 1982). For example, the males of several waterfowl species have previously been shown to precede females on migration in autumn but, in several other species, females precede males (*eg* Nilsson 1970), depending on the extent to which the sexes are involved in parental care and on their moulting strategies. Similarly, some studies across a range of bird groups indicate that adults precede juveniles on post-breeding migration, while others show the converse (see Gauthreaux 1982 for further references).

A knowledge of the timing of migrations for different species is critical for their conservation (see Chapter 7), particularly for quarry species, and every effort has been made to provide information on timings for each of the species covered in this book (Chapter 6). Differences in the timings of movements by birds of different sex and age may result in differences in their vulnerability to threats that vary seasonally, such as hunting or accidental capture in fishing nets. In turn, these differences will influence the extent to which losses due to such activities may result in changes to the population trend for each species. We could not carry out a comprehensive analysis of age- and sex-specific differences in the timing of movements for this book. We did carry out some exploratory analyses, however, in an attempt to demonstrate the utility and limitations of ring-recovery data for this purpose, to highlight any broad patterns across groups of species and to suggest species or ecological groupings for which further study might be valuable. The analyses involved testing for differences in mean recovery locations between males and females, and adults and immatures, for birds ringed in Britain & Ireland during the breeding season and recovered in autumn and spring. Only recoveries of dead birds were included in the analyses and both species previously defined as 'migrant' and 'non-migrant' were included (for reasons stated previously). The full results are given in Appendix 4 and are summarized by ecological group in Table 5.3.

British & Irish breeding passerines and near-passerines
Eight species (Swift, Yellow Wagtail, Redstart, Song Thrush, Reed Warbler, Blackcap, Willow Warbler and Pied Flycatcher) showed a difference between adults and immatures in autumn recovery locations (while 12, including migrants like Turtle Dove, Sand Martin, Swallow, Meadow Pipit, Pied Wagtail, Whitethroat, Goldfinch and Linnet, did not). Two (Robin and Swallow) showed a difference in spring (when 14, including migrants like Blackcap and Pied Flycatcher, did not). The results for a large number of species could not be interpreted with certainty in either autumn or spring because differences in ringing and recovery locations were confounded (Table 5.3). For such species, more detailed analyses of the data will be required, taking the variations in ringing location more fully into account. For those species showing significant differences, adults were consistently recovered further south and/or west in autumn, suggesting that they depart the breeding grounds earlier than immatures. In the spring, immature Swallows were recovered on average 5° further south than adults, suggesting that adults return to breeding areas earlier. Data were available for fewer species to test for differences between the sexes and only one difference was found: male Swallows were recovered significantly further west (median 1.9° W) than females (median 0.6° E) in spring.

British & Irish breeding non-passerines
Only one difference was found for raptors and owls: adult Merlins were recovered on average 1.3° further south in autumn, suggesting that they

depart earlier than immatures. Significant differences in autumn recovery locations between immatures and adults were noted for seven of the nine species of waterfowl tested (Table 5.3). For six of these (Eider, Goosander, Mallard, Shelduck, Teal and Tufted Duck), immatures were recovered significantly further south and/or west than adults, the exception being Shoveler (adults significantly further south, based on a small sample of recoveries). For waterfowl species in which part of the population makes moult migrations in autumn (*eg* Goosander and Shelduck), these results could be explained in terms of the earlier departure of adults for the moulting grounds (although the converse seems to be true for Shelduck). Results for the other species require further study, to determine whether they indicate differential timing, dispersal of immatures, or are complicated by 'contamination' of the British & Irish sample with early immigrants. Of six species tested in autumn (Canada Goose, Greylag Goose, Mallard, Pochard, Shelduck and Shoveler), none showed significant differences between the sexes. In spring, females were recovered significantly further west than males (Canada Goose) or significantly further south and west (Mallard). Immature Oystercatchers were recovered significantly further south and west in both autumn and spring than adults, while no differences between the age classes were detected (in autumn) for Lapwing, Redshank, Ringed Plover, Stone-curlew or Woodcock. Differences between the sexes could not be tested for any wader species. For seabirds and gulls, significant differences between the two age classes in recovery locations in spring and autumn were detected in a majority of species with sufficient data for testing, with immatures being found significantly further south and/or west than adults in most cases in both seasons (Table 5.3).

The interpretation of these results is complicated for seabirds/gulls by their delayed maturity (and for other species that do not breed in their first year). Some significant results may reflect true differences in the timings of movements away from colonies but others reflect that immatures, and particularly first-year birds, do not return to colonies and thus are bound to have different recovery locations in 'passage' periods than the adult birds. The issues of differences in reporting circumstances (mentioned above for the analyses of differences in wintering areas) also affect the results. The differences highlighted for seabirds and gulls, and for some other long-lived species with delayed maturity, are addressed more fully in the accounts for each species (Chapter 6) by considering the seasonal recovery patterns in more detail.

Differences in the timing of movements: some conclusions
Our rather crude exploratory analyses of differences in the timing of movements using ring-recoveries were most appropriate for species that breed in the year after hatching (*ie* the majority of passerines, some duck species but rather fewer species from the other ecological groupings). For the migrant passerines, our analyses suggest that adults leave the breeding grounds earlier than juveniles in the autumn but differences between the two age classes were less common in spring (although fewer migrant species had sufficient data for testing in spring). However, the apparent differences in the timing of movements of the two age classes in autumn could be caused by the complications of differences in the number of broods reared. For example, a previous study of Reed Warblers concluded that the overall differences in timing between the two age classes were caused by a spread of hatching dates and not by differences in the speed or timing of movements per se (Insley & Boswell 1978). It should also be noted that adults and juveniles may follow different routes south (see, for example, the species account for Sedge Warbler in Chapter 6), and it could be these that cause the differences in recovery location in autumn rather than large differences in timing. Our rigorous tests of autumn longitudes using only recoveries of dead birds suggested that immatures of a number of species (*eg* Pied Flycatcher, Willow Warbler and Yellow Wagtail) follow routes further east across southern Europe than adults, as suggested for Sedge Warbler (using all recovery types) in Chapter 6.

Table 5.3 Summary of the results of tests using ring-recovery data to investigate age- and sex-specific differences in the timing of autumn and spring migration for birds ringed in Britain & Ireland during the breeding season. For each ecological grouping, season and class of tests, the number of species showing significant test results ('n spp'), the number showing non-significant results ('NS', and in brackets the number of these for which the sample size for at least one class was less than 30 recoveries) and the number of species for which results were confounded with differences in ringing locations ('CF') are shown. For significant results, the direction of the differences detected and number of species showing each specific difference are shown. See text for analytical methods and Appendix 4 for the full results.

		Significant results	NS (small)	CF
	n spp	Direction of differences (and number of species)		
GROUP, SEASON, CLASS				
Passerines				
Autumn (age)	8	Adults further south & west (5); adults further west (3)	12 (5)	19
Spring (age)	2	Immatures further south (1); immatures further west (1)	14 (7)	15
Autumn (sex)	0		6 (0)	6
Spring (sex)	1	Males further west (1)	2 (1)	3
Raptors/Owls				
Autumn (age)	1	Adults further south (1)	1 (0)	5
Spring (age)	0		4 (2)	2
Autumn (sex)	0		3 (0)	0
Spring (sex)	0		2 (2)	0
Seabirds/Gulls				
Autumn (age)	8	Immatures further south & west (3); immatures further south (2); immatures further west (1); adults further west (2)	6 (2)	6
Spring (age)	11	Immatures further south & west (5); immatures further south (3); immatures further west (1); immatures further south & east (1); immatures further east (1)	5 (2)	2
Autumn (sex)	0		1 (0)	0
Spring (sex)	0		0	0
Waterfowl				
Autumn (age)	7	Immatures further south & west (2); immatures further south (1); immatures further west (3); adults further south (1)	2 (1)	5
Spring (age)	1	Immatures further west (1)	0	3
Autumn (sex)	0		6 (0)	0
Spring (sex)	2	Females further south & west (1); females further west (1)	0	0
Waders				
Autumn (age)	1	Immatures further south & west (1)	5 (3)	2
Spring (age)	1	Immatures further south & west (1)	1 (1)	2
Autumn (sex)	0		0	0
Spring (sex)	0		0	0

Because of the low recovery rates from dead passerines, further research on such differential migration movements would be carried out most effectively by ringing through the passage periods at an appropriately distributed network of study sites (where ringing effort is carefully recorded), and would involve international collaboration (*eg* see Spina *et al* 1994 and further discussion in Chapter 7).

Do birds in different regions of Britain & Ireland differ in their movement patterns?

So far in this chapter, we have discussed the results of analyses carried out for the entire populations either breeding or wintering in Britain & Ireland, and considered briefly the implications of general variation in the movements of different age classes and sexes for bird conservation. We now go on to consider whether subpopulations breeding or wintering in different parts of Britain & Ireland have varying movement patterns. The analyses that were carried out, the results and some conservation implications of the findings are presented here separately for a number of ecological groupings of species. Details of the methods

used to define the migratory habit of species and to carry out tests of distances moved and finding locations are given in Chapter 4 and the boundaries for the regional definitions used are shown in Fig 4.12.

Sedentary 'terrestrial' British & Irish breeding populations

For the purposes of this book, we defined species as 'migrant' if the average recovery locations of the entire British- & Irish-ringed population during the winter differed from their average ringing locations during the breeding season. However, more localized movements might still be important for those species defined as 'sedentary' using these methods. For example, some species that are able to utilize upland habitats in the breeding season might have to move to lower ground to find sufficient food or to escape severe weather during the winter months. There is evidence of such altitudinal movements occurring between high mountain areas and lowland areas in continental Europe (*eg* movements of Alpine Choughs, Wallcreepers and Water Pipits in the Alps), where the altitudinal range is large, but such movements are less well known in Britain & Ireland. Although

Fig 5.8 Summary of the results of analyses to test for differences in the distances moved by regional subpopulations within Britain of (a) sedentary terrestrial bird species, (b) migratory terrestrial bird species and (c) seabirds. For all species for which at least two regions differed, regions were ordered by the median distance moved by birds ringed during the breeding season and recovered in winter; the bars for each breeding region indicate the number of species for which birds from the given region showed the longest through to the shortest movements between breeding and wintering areas. When two or more regions had the same median distances, tied scores were allocated. For most species, sample sizes were insufficient to include Ireland in the regional testing (see text for further details). The regional boundaries used are shown in Figure 4.12.

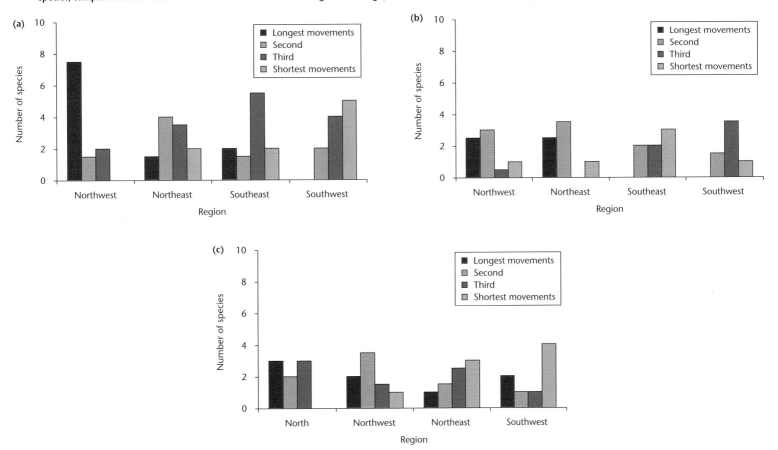

such movements within Britain & Ireland may be smaller-scale than seen on the Continent, a knowledge of seasonal movements made by traditionally 'sedentary' species, even at the local scale, is likely to be important for their conservation, in the same way that a knowledge of the requirements for wintering and passage, as well as for breeding, is essential for the conservation of long-distance migrants. For example, birds that breed around upland farms may move to important wintering areas on lowland pastures or coastal saltmarshes, or some common passerines in upland woods may rely on lowland parks and gardens in winter. Such knowledge is important for our understanding of the dynamics of the populations of such species, of the possible reasons for adverse changes and of the suite of habitats required for their conservation within Britain & Ireland.

We could not test for such movements directly using information from the BTO ring-recovery database because altitudinal information is not currently included. As well as such local altitudinal movements, our analyses of migratory tendency based on all appropriate British & Irish recoveries could have missed important movements occurring at a regional scale, particularly if the sample were dominated by birds (that did not move) from one particular region. The topography and climatic gradients of Britain & Ireland lead us to predict that many terrestrial species might be more likely to undertake movements between the breeding season and winter from the northern regions than from southern ones, both climate and topography playing a part. Similarly, such movements might be more evident from the east than the west, because western areas (and particularly southwestern ones) have milder winters.

We tested for regional differences in the distances moved between breeding and wintering areas by 20 sedentary terrestrial species. There was a general pattern (Fig 5.8a) for the distances moved by breeding birds to decrease from the Northwest (greatest number of species where the longest average movements were from this region), through the Northeast and Southeast, to the Southwest (shortest movements), approximately in the order that might be predicted by comparison of the topography and climate of the four regions. The full results are given in Appendix 5a. Twelve species showed differences in distances moved between at least two of the regions, while eight showed no differences (although sample sizes were small in at least one region for seven of these species). Tests could include Ireland for only four species, for three of which (Grey Heron, Sparrowhawk and Starling) Irish birds moved the shortest or next from shortest distances. Only for Mallard did Irish birds appear to move further than those from most regions of Britain (except the Southeast). The other species showing significant differences between regions of Britain in breeding-to-winter movements were Mute Swan, Greylag Goose, Woodpigeon, Tawny Owl, Robin, Blue Tit, Great Tit and Greenfinch. The results for these species warrant further individual scrutiny, however, particularly to investigate the reasons for deviations from this broad trend. Regional variation in reporting rates, due to differences in human population density, could play a part in the trends, and some species-specific analyses incorporating direct tests of altitudinal movements would make valuable comparisons to our suggested broad pattern. Our exploratory analyses point towards some suitable species with reasonable sample sizes across regions (eg Blue Tit, Great Tit, Robin and Starling).

Migratory 'terrestrial' British & Irish breeding populations

Threats to migratory bird populations can occur on the breeding grounds, on the (geographically distinct) wintering grounds or anywhere along the migration route. If adverse changes in population size or some other demographic parameter are observed, then knowledge of the seasonal pattern of movements may be essential to pinning down the cause and taking remedial, practical conservation action. For example, knowledge that the wintering grounds of British Sedge Warblers were in the Sahel region of West Africa allowed a relationship to be established between Sahelian rainfall and their overwinter survival and, hence, the likely reasons for years of reduced breeding population (Peach *et al* 1991). That link with the wintering area was only established for the British population as a whole. Greater differentiation of the wintering areas within West Africa of regional subpopulations would have the potential to link adverse changes even more closely to environmental causes, however, particularly if some regional subpopulations were declining more than others and were wintering in different areas. There is already limited evidence of segregation of wintering areas for regional subpopulations of at least one British & Irish species of breeding trans-Saharan migrant (see the species account for Sedge Warbler in Chapter 6). Similarly, a detailed knowledge of the high-latitude breeding ranges of some of the wader and wildfowl species that winter in Britain & Ireland would allow adverse changes in specific parts of these remote breeding areas (*eg* as a result of global climate change) to be detected through the monitoring of subpopulations wintering in different parts of Britain & Ireland, if such subpopulations were also known to be segregated on the breeding grounds.

We tested for regional differences in average wintering locations and the distances moved between breeding and wintering areas by 15 migratory terrestrial species. Significant differences between at least two regions in distances moved or average wintering locations were detected for 13 of the 15 species (Canada Goose, Kestrel, Lapwing, Snipe, Woodcock, Curlew, Black-headed Gull, Herring Gull, Lesser Black-backed Gull, Meadow Pipit, Pied Wagtail, Blackbird and Song Thrush). The full results are given in Appendix 5a; the distance results for four regions (excluding Ireland) are summarized in Fig 5.8b and the results from winter recovery locations in Figs 5.9a & b.

In general, migratory birds from the Northwest and Northeast regions were recovered in winter further from their breeding season ringing locations than those from the Southeast and Southwest (Fig 5.8b). The difference was very marked for some species. For example, Pied Wagtails from the Northwest and Northeast moved on average more than 500 km between breeding and wintering areas, whereas those from the Southeast and Southwest moved less than 40 km. Song Thrushes from the Northwest moved on average almost 200 km, whereas those from the other three regions of Britain moved less than 15 km. Despite moving greater distances between breeding and wintering areas, birds from the two northern regions generally still wintered further north than those from the southern regions (Fig 5.9a), rather than making a leap-frog migration. For only two species (Pied Wagtail and Lesser Black-backed Gull) was there any suggestion of birds from more northern regions wintering further south and, for both species, the differences were small (less than 1° of latitude). There was a general tendency for individuals from the west to be recovered further west in winter than those from the two eastern regions (Fig 5.9b). Birds from the Northeast region were the most frequent exception to this rule, being recovered further west than those from one or both western regions in eight species (Kestrel, Lapwing, Woodcock, Curlew, Black-headed Gull, Lesser Black-backed Gull, Meadow Pipit and Song Thrush). With the exception of the Lesser Black-backed Gull and Meadow Pipit, for which average birds from the Northwest were recovered outside Britain & Ireland in winter, the other species all require unfrozen and snow-free ground to find their prey and might therefore benefit most from moving westward (as well as southward) within Britain & Ireland.

Unfortunately, for many long-distance terrestrial migrant species there were too few recoveries of dead birds on the wintering grounds to allow us to include them in the regional analyses described above. We attempted to investigate any regional differences in the movements of such species by carrying out a second set of analyses, in which we divided all overseas autumn or winter recoveries of dead birds previously ringed in the breeding season in Britain & Ireland by their median latitude or longitude of recovery (separate tests for each), such that the autumn or winter recoveries were divided into two groups in each case. We then statistically compared the origins during the breeding season of birds in each pair of groups[4]. These tests were designed to assess, first, whether birds breeding in the west of Britain & Ireland use more westerly migration routes or spend the winter further west than those from eastern breeding areas and, second, whether birds from northern breeding areas winter further north than birds breeding further south, or 'leap-frog' them to more southerly wintering grounds. The full results are given in Appendix 5b. Tests comparing eastern and western recoveries in autumn were carried out for 24 species but significant differences were detected for only four. Birds breeding in eastern areas appeared to follow a more easterly route south for two of these species (Herring Gull and Sedge Warbler) but a more westerly route for the other two (Meadow Pipit and Reed Warbler). The tests based on recoveries on the wintering grounds (possible for 13 species) produced only three significant results (for Black-headed Gull, Herring Gull and Linnet), all indicating that birds breeding in eastern areas also generally wintered further east than those from western breeding areas. The tests comparing birds from northern and southern breeding areas of Britain & Ireland on the wintering grounds abroad were possible for 14 species, of which five showed significant results. Tufted Ducks and Linnets from northern breeding areas generally wintered further north than those from the south, while some 'leap-frogging' was suggested for regional subpopulations of Herring Gull, Pied Wagtail and Swallow (Appendix 5b).

---

[4] For latitude tests, we compared birds ringed in the breeding season north of 54°N with those ringed south of that latitude, and for longitude tests we compared birds ringed in the breeding season in the Northwest and Southwest regions and Ireland ('western' group) with those ringed in the Northeast and Southeast regions ('eastern' group). Regional boundaries are shown in Fig 4.12. By comparing, for example, the proportion of birds in a wintering area east of the median winter recovery longitude from eastern breeding areas with the proportion from eastern breeding areas in the area west of the median longitude of winter recovery, our analyses accounted for potential differences in recovery rates between the two wintering areas and differences in the numbers of recoveries from each of the source breeding areas. Each analysis resulted in a two-by-two contingency table for each species, which we tested with a standard chi-squared procedure. Tests were only carried out for species with expected values of at least 5 in each cell of the table.

Fig 5.9 Summary of the results of analyses to test for differences in average wintering locations between regional subpopulations within Britain & Ireland of (a) migratory terrestrial bird species (latitude tests), (b) migratory terrestrial bird species (longitude tests), (c) seabirds (latitude tests) and (d) seabirds (longitude tests). For all species for which at least two regions differed, regions were ordered in terms of median recovery latitudes (north to south) or longitudes (east to west); the bars for each breeding region indicate the number of species for which any given region fell into one of the four categories from furthest north to south or furthest east to west respectively. Sample sizes were insufficient to include Ireland in the analyses for migratory terrestrial species and to include the Southeast region in the analyses for seabirds (see text for further details and Fig 4.12 for the regional boundaries used).

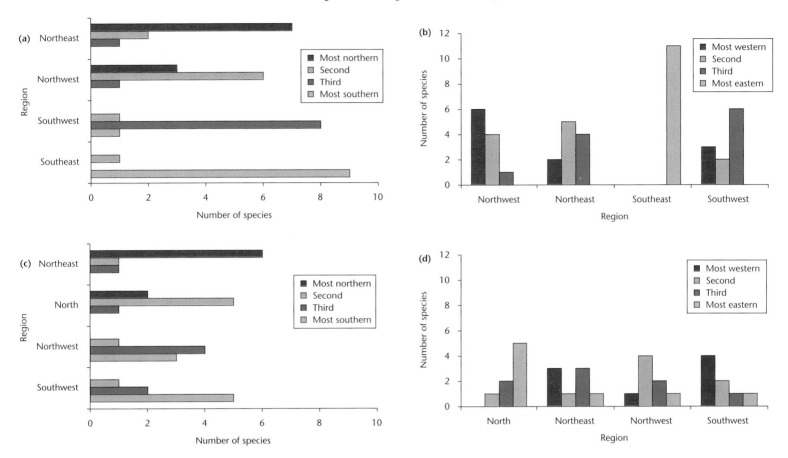

Seabirds from British & Irish breeding populations

Seabirds are perhaps the most difficult group for which to assess differences in wintering areas. Information collected on their distribution at sea (which is often more difficult to collect than for many terrestrial species) cannot differentiate between individuals from different breeding regions, and ring-recovery patterns may be more biased by the localized nature of some of the major causes of recovery (such as accidental capture in fishing nets, and oil spills) than they are for other groups of species (see also Chapter 7). Most recoveries can only be made when birds drift ashore. Despite these problems, and as for other migratory species, effective conservation demands knowledge of wintering as well as breeding areas, and of whether individuals from different breeding colonies are separated spatially outside the breeding season. For example, if there is a major oil spill, or a new large-scale industrial fishery threatens to reduce the prey available for seabirds, then it is important to know the breeding origins of the individuals likely to be affected. This is particularly important for seabirds, since for most species population trends are only detectable with any accuracy when the birds come ashore to breed. Knowledge of the spatial at-sea distribution of individuals from different colonies will also be important in predicting the likely effects of global climate change on seabird populations.

We tested for regional differences in average wintering locations and the distances moved between breeding and wintering areas by 10 seabird species (all of which were short- or long-distance migrants). Sample sizes were insufficient to allow the Southeast region to be included in the summary analyses. Gulls were included in the previous analyses of

'terrestrial' species. Significant differences between at least two regions in distances moved or average wintering locations were detected for nine of the species (Gannet, Cormorant, Shag, Kittiwake, Sandwich Tern, Common Tern, Guillemot, Razorbill and Puffin) but not for Fulmar. The full results are given in Appendix 5a; the distance results for four regions are summarized in Fig 5.8c and the results from winter recovery locations in Figs 5.9c & d.

In general, seabirds from colonies in the North and Northwest regions were recovered further from breeding areas than those from the Northeast and Southwest, although variation between species was considerable (Fig 5.8c). For most species, these varying distances moved resulted in some difference in average wintering locations for birds from the different breeding regions (for all species except Common Tern). There was a general trend for seabirds from the North and Northeast to winter further north than those from the Northwest and, most southerly, the Southwest (Fig 5.9c). Given that, to maintain adequate samples in each group, the Northwest regional boundary extended 2° further south than that for the Northeast region (Fig 4.12), it is perhaps not surprising that some seabirds from the Northwest wintered further south. However, there was some evidence to suggest that individuals from the North 'leap-frog' those from the Northeast to winter further south in some species (*eg* Cormorant, Shag, Kittiwake, Guillemot and Razorbill). Average longitudes of recovery in winter suggested that individuals from colonies in the North remain largely within the North Sea for several species, so that they are the easternmost winterers (*eg* Cormorant, Shag, Razorbill, Puffin; Fig 5.9d). For several species, individuals from the Southwest, perhaps predictably, winter the furthest south and west (Cormorant, Shag,

Guillemot and Razorbill). Because of the biases that might be introduced by the aggregated nature of some of the principal recovery causes for seabirds (Chapter 4), further detailed mapping and analysis would be valuable before rigorous conclusions are drawn. In addition, such assessments should concurrently address variations between the sexes and age classes, which further complicate patterns of regional difference for species with delayed maturity (eg Baillie et al 1994). More detailed information on variations in wintering areas between seabirds from different breeding colonies can be found in many of the species accounts in Chapter 6.

Winter immigrants to Britain & Ireland
Britain & Ireland is well known as an important wintering area for migrant species from further north and east in Europe, particularly for wildfowl and waders but also for some wintering passerines (eg Fieldfare, Redwing and Brambling) and gulls. Results from winter atlas projects (including the national *Winter Atlas*) have given us a basic knowledge of the distribution of such species within Britain & Ireland in winter but cannot indicate the relative distributions of immigrants versus 'residents' for those species for which there are also British & Irish breeding populations. Currently, ringing is the only widely used method of linking immigrant birds with the breeding areas where they originate and, hence, distinguishing their distribution within the wintering grounds from that of 'resident' individuals. Knowledge of the numbers of immigrant individuals into Britain & Ireland outside the breeding season and their distribution is of clear importance for the conservation of such migrant populations, and for Britain & Ireland to fulfil commitments to European Union conservation legislation (see Chapter 7).

Many of the individual species accounts in Chapter 6 detail the breeding origins of the immigrants that enter Britain & Ireland outside the breeding season. We took the consideration one step further by comparing the mean recovery locations abroad during the breeding season of birds ringed in different areas of Britain & Ireland during the winter. We also compared the proportions of birds ringed in Britain & Ireland in winter that were recovered abroad versus within Britain & Ireland during the breeding season, in an attempt to assess whether some regions of Britain & Ireland hold more immigrant individuals in winter than others. One or other of these groups of tests between birds from at least two wintering regions was possible for only 17 species and, among these, sample sizes were often small in one or more regional group. Few data were available for Irish wintering birds. The full results are presented in Appendix 5c.

Differences in average latitude of recovery abroad during the breeding season were detected for seven of the 17 species. For the species for which comparisons between northern and southern regions were possible (Oystercatcher, Black-headed Gull, Common Gull, Herring Gull, Blackbird and Starling), birds ringed in the northern regions of Britain & Ireland in winter were recovered further north during the breeding

season than those ringed further south. For Tufted Duck, birds ringed in winter in the Southwest were recovered almost 3° further north during the breeding season than those from the Southeast. Differences between wintering regions in the mean longitude of recovery abroad during the breeding season were detected for only three species (Black-headed Gull, Oystercatcher and Starling). Black-headed Gulls wintering in the Northwest region were recovered furthest east in continental Europe during the breeding season, and those from the Northeast furthest west, with no suggestion that the regions tested supported different proportions of winter immigrants. Oystercatchers wintering in the East region were on average recovered more than 7° further east in the breeding season than those wintering in other regions of Britain; tests of the proportions recovered abroad (below) also suggested that the East receives more continental immigrants than the other regions (72% of birds ringed in winter in the East were recovered abroad during the breeding season compared to less than 40% from the other regions and only 10% of those from the North). For Starling, birds wintering in the two southern regions of Britain were recovered further east in continental Europe during the breeding season than those from other regions, and once again the tests of proportions recovered abroad suggested the highest proportions of immigrants in the southern regions (and similar proportions in the Northeast, all greater than 25%). The proportions of winter-ringed birds recovered abroad could be tested for nine species only, and significant differences were detected for six of these (Mallard, Oystercatcher, Herring Gull, Blackbird, Starling and Chaffinch). The results suggested that higher proportions of immigrants were found in the Northeast and Ireland (>10%) for Blackbird, in the Southeast for Herring Gull (27%) and Mallard (81%), and in the East for Oystercatcher (72%, above).

As would be expected, given the suite of species for which testing was possible, general patterns in the regional distributions of winter immigrants in Britain & Ireland were not common. There were significant variations in the breeding origins and proportions of winter immigrants between wintering regions but the patterns were generally species-specific. For six species, however, including three gull species, two passerines and Oystercatcher, there was a general suggestion that some segregation of northerly and southerly breeding subpopulations was maintained once birds reach Britain & Ireland. Variation about this pattern must be related to the ways in which these winter immigrants interact with British & Irish breeding populations of each species, and where these native populations spend the winter. The proportions of wintering birds subsequently recovered abroad during the breeding season (Appendix 5c) should not be taken as an indication of the absolute proportions of winter immigrants because of the variations in recovery rates that exist across Europe (see Chapter 4). Generally, breeding-season recovery rates for many species are likely to be higher in Britain & Ireland than across eastern and northern Europe, such that our crude analyses will underestimate the true proportions of immigrants. When the immigrants to the various regions of Britain & Ireland differ in their breeding origins, any spatial variation in recovery rates between the breeding regions will also influence the proportions of immigrant birds that we have estimated. Further understanding of numbers of winter immigrants and their movements and needs within Britain & Ireland is important for the conservation of such migrant species, and potentially also for that of 'resident' species if interaction takes place on the wintering grounds. However, the preliminary analyses undertaken here show how little information is currently available from ring-recoveries to answer such applied questions. This might be remedied in future using a mixture of traditional ringing and novel 'marking' techniques, such as DNA and isotopic signatures (see Chapter 7).

Movements of British & Irish regional subpopulations: some conclusions
Even within the restricted spatial area of Britain & Ireland, our analyses suggested some important geographical variation in bird movement

patterns. More than half of the 20 'sedentary' terrestrial species for which sufficient data were available showed differential movement distances between British & Irish breeding areas and winter recovery locations: in general, individuals from the Northwest of Britain moved the furthest and those from the Southwest the least between breeding and wintering areas, with those from the eastern regions intermediate. Of the four species for which Irish populations could be tested, the Irish birds of three species moved the shortest distances. These results supported the hypothesis that individuals breeding in more northern and eastern areas and areas with a greater extent of upland habitats, that is in areas with less favourable environmental conditions in winter, must move further to find suitable wintering locations than those breeding further south.

Thirteen of 15 migratory terrestrial species exhibited regional differences in the distances moved between the breeding season and winter and/or in average wintering areas. Those breeding in northern Britain generally migrated further than those from the south (and might be expected if they were all moving to a common wintering ground) but the former still generally wintered further north than those from southern populations; there was some suggestion of 'leap-frog migration' for only four species (Herring and Lesser Black-backed Gulls, Pied Wagtail and Swallow). There was also some evidence that the east–west gradation of breeding subpopulations is maintained on the wintering grounds for many species. Species that behaved exceptionally, with subpopulations from the Northeast wintering further west than expected, tended to be those likely to benefit most from unfrozen and snow-free ground in winter, such as Curlew, Lapwing and Woodcock. Nine of 10 species of migratory seabird showed differences between regional breeding subpopulations in their average wintering areas but the patterns were more complex than for terrestrial species: about half the species appeared to preserve some north–south gradation of subpopulations in the wintering areas, while there was some evidence for 'leap-frogging' for the other species. Given the considerable applied importance of understanding how seabird populations mix on the wintering grounds, further analyses of these complex patterns would be valuable, preferably at the international level and using a quantitative approach to differentiate core wintering areas for specific populations and subpopulations (see Chapter 7).

Regional differences in the breeding origins and proportions of winter immigrants into Britain & Ireland were testable for only 17 species, and for 10 of these could be tested between only two of the five regions. Of the seven species for which at least two regions differed in average breeding origins, six (Oystercatcher, three gull species, Blackbird and Starling) demonstrated a general tendency for those in the northern regions of Britain to originate from more northern breeding areas in continental Europe than those wintering further south in Britain. Other significant differences with respect to the longitude of origin and proportions of immigrants tended to be rather species-specific, presumably influenced by the ways in which immigrant populations mix with or replace British & Irish breeding populations once they reach Britain & Ireland. Once again, a greater understanding of such mechanisms is of high applied value for conservation purposes (Chapter 7), in addition to raising interesting ecological and evolutionary questions.

Correlates of migratory tendency

What determines the extent to which a species migrates?

The development of objective and quantitative indices of the migratory tendencies of different species provides an unprecedented opportunity for investigations of the causes and consequences of the range of strategies found. In this section, we describe a range of tests designed to investigate some of the physical, social and ecological factors that might influence the choice of migratory strategy. As with the other analyses in this chapter, the results should be regarded as exploratory: later in the chapter, we explore the caveats associated with our analyses and the future work that would be desirable to make the results more definitive.

Our analyses of the effects of potential influences on migratory tendency involved taking the variation in each of the absolute and standardized indices of migratory tendency between species and testing it against various key variables using statistical tests based on rank values of the indices[5]. We then repeated these tests using only species falling into the passerine and raptor groupings, running a new comparison of recovery-distance distributions and calculating new standardized and absolute indices. Raptors and passerines represent a reasonably homogeneous group of terrestrial species whose migratory strategies may be driven by similar factors. Some relationships might only be detectable using such a set of species. Since it is also likely that the shapes of recovery-distance frequency distributions reflect real populations more closely as sample sizes increase, we conducted further tests restricting the species to those with 50 or more breeding-to-winter movements (considering both all species and raptors and passerines alone). For clarity, we report the results based on 50 or more relevant recoveries for each species only when they were significant and contradicted the more inclusive tests.

The statistical tests described above all implicitly considered the migratory strategy of each species to represent an independent measure of the relationship between the relevant set of characteristics of that species and the index of migratory tendency. However, species in the same genus or family (for example) may share strategies through a single evolutionary 'choice' made by a common ancestor. In this case, the data for each such species can be considered only to represent a repeat measure of a single relationship. We included a specific control for the possible confounding effects of phylogeny in our analyses[6], and we present results both including and excluding this control. The disappearance of a significant difference after the introduction of a control for phylogeny would not necessarily indicate that a difference detected had been false, however: it would merely show that the relationship was confounded with

---

[5] General linear models were fitted, in which the ranks of the species with respect to each index of migratory tendency were either regressed against the ranks with respect to a continuous predictor or compared between the alternative classifications of a categorical predictor. The regression tests were identical computationally to Spearman rank correlations (but were, philosophically, regressions) and the latter comparisons formed Kruskal–Wallis non-parametric analyses of variance (Sokal & Rohlf 1995). The analyses were conducted using the GLM procedure of SAS (SAS Institute 1990). We used non-parametric methods because we did not know how the indices were distributed (ie whether the distribution was normal) and because parametric analyses would emphasize the great variation visible among the more migratory species in Fig 5.5b, and the differences between these species and more sedentary ones, rather than the variation among all 91 species.

[6] Sophisticated statistical techniques that use evolutionary trees to identify independent nodes, either side of which represents an independent observation, are now recommended for rigorous phylogenetic analyses (Harvey & Pagel 1991) but are beyond the scope of the simple overview we present here. Another approach, as used by Dobson (1990), would be to analyse the data simultaneously at different taxonomic levels (ie species, genera and families) and to look for common results across the levels, but three sets of analyses would add complexity to interpretation and probably lead to sample size problems in the family-level analyses. As an alternative, we controlled for interspecific relatedness at (approximately) the superfamily level (Sibley *et al* 1988) by introducing phylogenetic group, a categorical variable, into the general linear models relating the migratory tendency indices (transformed into ranks) to each continuous variable (the latter also being transformed into ranks where appropriate). The groups used are shown in Appendix 3a. The significance of each of the effects was then reassessed with the variation due to phylogeny thus having been removed. These analyses were again conducted using the GLM procedure of SAS (SAS Institute 1990). Phylogenetic controls were not applied to the analyses using categorical variables because many of the categories in each case were entirely confounded with phylogenetic group.

phylogenetic differences. Conversely, any significant effects that are detected only after controlling for phylogeny should not be considered less important biologically than effects that are detectable in the presence of phylogenetic variation. The latter could occur when a relationship with migratory tendency is significant within phylogenetic groups but, when all species are pooled, is obscured by the variation between the groups.

Although we have treated the analyses described in this section as tests of potential *influences on* migratory tendency, it is conceivable that some of the factors are actually *consequences* of migratory behaviour. This also applies (in reverse) to the subsequent section describing tests of the potential influence of migration on life-history variables. As an example of the general problem, we treat body shape as a potential influence on migration, but might it be better viewed as an evolutionary consequence of species-specific migratory strategy, determined by natural selection? Similarly, does diet determine where a species goes, or is diet determined by where the species is forced (by other factors) to feed at different seasons? It is reassuring that these points are basically philosophical: the same or very similar results (depending on whether a control for phylogeny were employed: see below) would be obtained from the tests described if the models were recast conceptually to alter the implied direction of causation. We have left our analyses as describing potential influences on migration (or influences *of* migration in the next section) because we think the directions of causation that we postulate are reasonable, or at least arguably so, and we suggest that concerned readers substitute the more neutral phrase 'relationship between' for 'influence on' or 'influence of'.

How does body size affect migratory tendency?

Larger birds should tend to be less vulnerable to extreme environmental conditions, both thermodynamically and because they can more easily seek out more favourable conditions in local areas, so they may, in general, be less likely to migrate. Size is clearly something that can be measured in many different ways; we have used four continuous variables: body length, wingspan, wing length and weight (all as averages for adult birds, taken from *CBWP*).

There were only three significant results with respect to body size, all indicating that larger species tend to be more migratory (Table 5.4). When the data were restricted to species with 50 or more recoveries, there were no significant results across all the species considered, but significant results were found for all four variables for the raptor and passerine group. However, the results from the standardized and absolute methods conflicted with one another. The results for length, wingspan and weight with respect to the absolute index method support the expectation that larger species would be less migratory. Only one of these results was robust to the control for phylogeny, however, and the results involving the standardized indices that *were* significant after the control was added all indicated the converse pattern, that larger species are *more* migratory. Taken together, these patterns indicate, first, that other factors (*eg* ecological influences) obscure any effect of body size when all species are considered together, even after controlling for phylogeny. Second, larger species among the raptor and passerine groups do tend to be less migratory but this effect relates to the absolute distances that they move, rather than to the proportions of their populations that migrate, and is confounded with phylogeny. This result suggests that body size is related to the dichotomy between migrant and resident strategies as either is adopted at the superfamily level. In contrast, within superfamilies, larger proportions of the populations of larger species tend to migrate. This could indicate that larger species are more likely than their close relatives to move away from their breeding areas, although not necessarily moving very far, perhaps because their size allows them greater mobility.

How does body shape affect migratory tendency?

Body shape (including wing shape) is likely to be closely related to migratory tendency because of the aerodynamic requirements for efficient flight (Norberg 1990). While an efficient body shape might best be viewed as an evolutionary effect rather than a cause of migratory behaviour, there is also likely to be facilitation in the other direction, such that the possibility for the evolution of more extreme migratory behaviour is enhanced among species that already have certain migratory adaptations and habits; this will tend to obscure the distinction between cause and effect. We tested relationships between migratory tendency and body shape through two variables: wing-loading (*ie* weight/wing length) and wing:body ratio (*ie* wingspan/body length), both calculated using figures from *CBWP*. Low wing-loadings and high wing:body ratios would tend to suggest adaptation to promote efficient long-distance flight. Voelker (2001) found that flight morphology among pipits was more strongly related to migratory tendency than to the requirements of display flights, despite the fact that the latter occurred more frequently; it would be interesting to know how general is this over-riding importance of migration in dictating morphology.

The results of our tests indicated that more migratory species tend to have larger wing:body ratios and lower wing-loadings, as would be expected. However, the effect of wing-loading was detectable only when using the absolute index and only for raptors and passerines with 50 or more recoveries, and the effect of wing:body ratio was strong only when all species groupings were included (Table 5.5). The relationships between the absolute index and wing:body ratio were significant both before and after controls for phylogeny had been added (Table 5.5). The effect of wing-loading therefore appears to be related to absolute distances moved rather than to the adoption of a migratory habit. It is either unimportant or, perhaps more probably, obscured by other factors when all species groupings were considered together. The results with respect to wing:body ratio showed that individuals of relatively longer-winged species tend both more often to go further and more often to adopt a migrant strategy, but that only the former pattern was robust to phylogenetic variation. This suggests that morphology is related to the absolute distances moved by individual species, but that it is at a higher taxonomic level that it is related to the selection of a *strategy*.

How does diet influence migratory tendency?

The geographical locations in which birds are able to breed or survive are likely to be determined largely by where suitable food can be found in sufficient quantities. The extent of any seasonal variation in food availability is therefore likely to be a major influence on migratory behaviour. Species more dependent on more seasonally variable foods, such as insects, may be more likely to migrate because they are generally more vulnerable to cold weather than species that take other foods, such as vertebrates or seeds. We looked for differences in migratory tendency among species grouped according to their diets (determined by reference to the broad summaries of year-round adult diet in *CBWP*). These were classified into seven groups: those feeding on fish (*eg* Kingfisher, Common Tern), other vertebrates (*eg* Kestrel), invertebrates (*eg* Swallow), invertebrates with some plant material (*eg* Blackbird), mostly invertebrates but with various other foods too (*eg* Carrion Crow, Black-headed Gull), plant material with some invertebrates (*eg* Chaffinch) and vegetation exclusively (*eg* Canada Goose) (see Appendix 3a). Kingfisher, the single fish-eater in the raptor/passerine grouping, was added to the 'other vertebrate' category when this grouping was analysed alone.

Migratory tendency was strongly related to diet (Table 5.6). Across all species groupings, species with an invertebrate-only or fish diet were the most migratory. For the former (including hirundines and warblers), this reflects the fluctuations in invertebrate abundance through the year while the piscivorous birds are mostly colonial seabirds, which tend at least to disperse away from their breeding areas in winter. The other dietary groups were rather similar to one another in migratory tendency, but were separated more when raptors and passerines were analysed alone, although in different orders in terms of the standardized and absolute indices (Table 5.6). Based on the standardized index, the species

Table 5.4 Relationships between indices of migratory tendency and body size. Results are shown for both the standardized ('Standard') and absolute ('Absolute') methods of calculating the index. For each variable (left-hand column), results are shown both for the basic analyses ('Basic') and those with control for phylogeny ('Phylogenetic'). See the text for details of the analytical methods employed. The direction of the slope of the relationship is shown for all tests significant at the 10% level or below (*eg* 'positive' for length indicates that species with larger body lengths tend to be more migratory). Text colour indicates the significance level: black, significant at the 10% level; pink, significant at the 5% level; and red, significant at the 1% level.

Grouping and analysis method		All species >20 recoveries		Raptors and Passerines >20 recoveries		Raptors and Passerines >50 recoveries	
Number of species		Standard 91	Absolute 91	Standard 46	Absolute 46	Standard 36	Absolute 36
Variable							
Length	Basic						Negative
	Phylogenetic					Positive	
Wingspan	Basic	Positive					Negative
	Phylogenetic			Positive		Positive	
Wing length	Basic						
	Phylogenetic			Positive		Positive	
Weight	Basic						Negative
	Phylogenetic						Negative

Table 5.5 Relationships between indices of migratory tendency and body shape. Text colour indicates the significance level: Black, significant at the 10% level; pink significant at the 5% level and red significant at the 1% level.

Grouping and analysis method		All species >20 recoveries		Raptors and Passerines >20 recoveries		Raptors and Passerines >50 recoveries	
Number of species		Standard 91	Absolute 91	Standard 46	Absolute 46	Standard 36	Absolute 36
Variable							
Wing-loading	Basic						Negative
	Phylogenetic						Negative
Wing:body ratio	Basic	Positive	Positive				
	Phylogenetic		Positive			Positive	

with an 'invertebrate/various' diet (mostly gulls and corvids) were clearly more migratory than the others, so the result probably reflects the movements of the more migratory gulls as well as the winter dispersal of other species away from breeding colonies. Using the absolute index, species with a mixed invertebrate and plant diet were intermediate between invertebrate-eaters and the other groups, showing that some of these species can migrate long distances, presumably to allow them to find sufficient invertebrate food in winter. The general result that species with mixed, vegetation-dominated or terrestrial-vertebrate-dominated diets tend to be less migratory (Table 5.6) probably shows that dietary flexibility and a food supply that varies little seasonally are factors allowing birds to remain near their breeding grounds through the winter.

How does social organization influence migratory strategy?
Social factors could have an important influence on sexual or other variations in migratory strategy among species. For example, birds may benefit in terms of territory acquisition from an early return to their breeding areas, so that the breeding males of many territorial species may tend to travel less far to overwinter. Less territorial species might therefore be expected to have more migratory and more homogeneous strategies. We used a coarse classification of social organization in the

Table 5.6 Tests of the variation in migratory tendency between bird species with different diets. Mean species ranks show the average relative migratory tendency for each group: higher mean ranks indicate a greater migratory tendency. The dietary groups to which individual species were assigned are shown in Appendix 3a. The coding for statistical significance follows that in Table 5.5.

		Mean species ranks	
Diet	Number of species	Standardized index >20 recoveries	Absolute index >20 recoveries
All species			
Invertebrates	17	61.6	58.2
Invertebrates/plant material	16	32.8	41.0
Invertebrates/various	11	40.0	31.9
Seeds/invertebrates	13	29.5	30.0
Vegetation	5	34.4	37.2
Fish	19	65.2	66.6
Other vertebrates	10	34.8	32.1
Passerines and Raptors			
Invertebrates	7	37.6	33.0
Invertebrates/plant material	10	15.3	26.5
Invertebrates/various	6	24.8	12.4
Seeds/invertebrates	12	19.4	21.7
Vertebrates	11	25.7	22.8

breeding season, derived from the descriptions in *CBWP*, to investigate variations in migratory tendency between species: each species was classified as territorial, intermediate (semicolonial or weakly territorial) or colonial (see Appendix 3a).

The extent of territoriality was related highly significantly to migratory tendency, with strongly territorial species tending to be less migratory than colonial and intermediate species (Table 5.7). This pattern was stronger in the analyses using absolute recovery-distance distributions, suggesting that shorter migratory distances, in absolute terms, are particularly associated with strong territoriality. This result supports the hypothesis that residency is promoted by territoriality and the concomitant selection pressure for remaining closer to breeding areas in winter or returning to them earlier in spring. This is a logical corollary of the observation that higher-quality individuals of species that are both territorial and migratory tend to arrive on their breeding grounds earlier (*eg* Francis & Cooke 1986, Møller 1994, Lozano *et al* 1996), which has been shown through the application of game theory to be consistent with a system in which individuals compete for access to high-quality territories via arrival times (Kokko 1999). However, the pattern disappeared when raptors and passerines were considered alone (Table 5.7). In part, this may be due to the domination of the set of species used by the territorial habit, but it probably also reflects the degree to which social organization is confounded with phylogeny.

How does nesting strategy affect migratory strategy?
Whether species build open-cup or hole nests could be an important determinant of migratory behaviour because the number of suitable nest holes may be limiting, potentially providing a selective pressure for residency, shorter migration distances or an early return to the breeding grounds (von Haartman 1968, Alerstam & Högstedt 1981). We made a simple comparison of migratory tendency between species with these two nesting habits (see Appendix 3a for the classification of individual species).

Overall, open-nesting species tended to be significantly more migratory than hole-nesting species by both standardized and absolute approaches, suggesting that the former may indeed be less constrained in annual movements by their breeding strategy (Table 5.8). However,

Table 5.7 Tests of the variation in migratory tendency between bird species with strongly territorial, weakly territorial or semi-colonial ('intermediate') and colonial habits. Mean species ranks show the average relative migratory tendency for each group: higher mean ranks indicate a greater migratory tendency. The groups to which individuals were assigned according to territoriality are shown in Appendix 3a. The coding for statistical significance follows that in Table 5.5.

		Mean species ranks	
Social organization	Number of species	Standardized >20 recoveries	Absolute >20 recoveries
All species			
Colonial	32	52.5	58.0
Intermediate	17	53.0	51.4
Territorial	42	38.6	35.1
Passerines and Raptors (non-significant results for both index types)			
Colonial	7	23.1	21.9
Intermediate	8	27.8	29.9
Territorial	31	22.5	22.2

the pattern was considerably weaker when the species in the raptor and passerine groups were examined alone. The pattern across all groups may therefore partly reflect the more frequent occurrence of hole nesting among species in the raptor and passerine groups, which tend to be relatively sedentary (Fig 5.2), and might actually be caused by other ecological differences. Nevertheless, the prevalence of hole nesting among the passerines and raptors could be a key factor driving their relatively low average migratory tendency. Our exploratory analyses did not allow us to separate the influence of hole nesting from the other differences between the ecological groups.

Table 5.8 Tests of the variation in migratory tendency between bird species with open-nesting and hole-nesting strategies. Mean species ranks show the average relative migratory tendency for each group: higher mean ranks indicate a greater migratory tendency. The groups to which species were assigned are shown in Appendix 3a. The coding for statistical significance follows that in Table 5.5.

Nesting strategy	Number of species	Mean species ranks	
		Standardized index >20 recoveries	Absolute index >20 recoveries
All species			
Open	74	49.0	49.9
Hole	17	33.1	29.1
Passerines and Raptors (standardized results non-significant)			
Open	29	24.3	26.1
Hole	17	22.2	19.0

How does rarity affect migratory tendency?
Population size (rarity) might affect migratory strategy; species with sparser populations will tend to exist at lower densities and therefore potentially experience lower intensities of intraspecific competition, leading to a reduced need to migrate. However, a contrary influence might be that rarer species will often be those for which British & Irish populations are at the edge of the species' ranges, therefore perhaps experiencing less than ideal conditions and being more likely to migrate and to travel further. We tested the influence of rarity on migratory tendency using the estimated UK population size of each species (number of individuals, from Stone *et al* 1997) as a continuous variable.

The indices based on standardized recovery-distance distributions were negatively correlated with population size, both before and after controls for phylogeny were introduced, but there was only one, weakly significant such result using the absolute method (Table 5.9). This suggests that rarer species tend to be more migratory but also that the effect was not related to the actual distances moved and that the relationship is driven by the results for the relatively more sedentary species. The effect of populations at the northern edge of their ranges being more likely to have to move south and west in winter thus appears to be stronger than any effect of intraspecific competition; it is also likely that these species tend to be at lower densities (nationally) than species that could be considered better adapted to habitats in Britain & Ireland year-round. However, this test does not necessarily reflect the true importance of population *density* because populations of individual species will be distributed in varying ways within the landscape according to social organization and variations in habitat.

How does distribution affect migratory tendency?
Species with more restricted distributions (at the scale of Britain & Ireland as a whole) may be those that are nearer the edges of their ranges and therefore those that are less well adapted to utilizing British & Irish habitats year-round. Such species might be more likely to be migratory. We tested the influence of distribution on migratory tendency by using the ubiquity of each species within Britain & Ireland as a continuous variable. Ubiquity was measured as the number of 10-km squares in Britain & Ireland occupied by the species during the period 1988–91, taken from the *1988–91 Atlas*.

Species with restricted distributions tended to be more migratory (Table 5.10), giving strong support to the idea that their populations tend to have to move further to find suitable habitat in winter. There were significant effects on the absolute indices as well as the

standardized ones, particularly when all species groupings were included; this probably reflects the additional influence of species for which distributions are necessarily restricted and which tend to move away from breeding colonies outside the breeding season, such as the colonial seabirds (Figs 5.5a & b).

What are the life-history consequences of migration?
As well as allowing investigations of possible influences on migratory behaviour, our derivation of quantitative indices of migratory tendency makes it possible to perform formal tests of the life-history consequences of differences in migratory strategy. We conducted tests of the relationships between migratory tendency and three important life-history variables: annual survival rate, reproductive effort and the timing of breeding. We once again used analyses based on ranks but, in this case, treated the indices of migratory tendency as predictors of the variation in the life-history factors. As in the previous sections, we also conducted further tests controlling for phylogeny, considered indices derived through both the standardized and absolute approaches, and performed analyses for the 'raptor & passerine' ecological groupings only, as well as for all species combined. Further tests, using only species with 50 or more ring-recoveries suitable for analysis, are only described if they produced different results to those from the more inclusive tests (based on all species with 20 or more appropriate recoveries).

How does migratory strategy affect survival?
Migration may occur, fundamentally, because survival would be low if birds remained in their breeding areas over the winter. Benign conditions in southern wintering grounds might afford higher survival rates to migrants, but migration itself may also be hazardous and lead to high mortality, especially for young birds on their first outward and return journeys (Greenberg 1980, Owen & Black 1989, 1991, Sillett & Holmes 2002). Greenberg (1980) collated survival-rate estimates for a range of Old World and New World passerines and found that migrants (mostly neotropical migrants) tended to have higher survival rates than residents; the pattern he found is confounded with phylogenetic variation, however, his data were variable in quality, and methods of estimation have improved considerably since his study was conducted. We tested the influence of migratory strategy on survival, taking species-specific estimates of average annual adult survival rate from Balmer & Peach (1996) or Siriwardena *et al* (1998b).

When all species were considered together, all the indices of migratory tendency indicated that the more migratory species had higher survival rates (Table 5.11), supporting the idea that more benign wintering conditions might reduce mortality and outweigh any effect of the hazards of migration. This pattern was entirely confounded by phylogeny, however, suggesting that it primarily reflects the higher survival rates of the species making up the seabird and wader groups, which tend to be larger-bodied than the small passerines that dominate the relatively sedentary suite of species. Support for this interpretation was evident in the results for raptors and passerines only: although the tests using species with 20 or more suitable ring-recoveries were non-significant, there was a significant, negative relationship between the absolute index of migratory tendency and the survival of raptor and passerine species for which 50 or more recoveries were available. Hence, the more migratory species tend to have *lower* survival rates; the pattern was significant whether or not a control for phylogeny was applied. Because this result was found only with the absolute index, it can be interpreted as indicating that species that migrate further tend to have lower survival rates. These may reflect mortality during migration, or result from the physiological or energetic pressures involved in preparing for migration or recovering from it.

How does migratory strategy affect reproductive effort?
Current theory predicts that annual reproductive effort should be inversely related to annual survival at the species level, with longer-

Table 5.9 Relationships between indices of migratory tendency and rarity. (See Table 5.5 for a key to abbreviations and coding.)

Grouping and analysis method		All species >20 recoveries		Raptors and Passerines >20 recoveries	
		Standard	Absolute	Standard	Absolute
Number of species		91	91	46	46
Variable					
Population size	Basic	Negative	Negative	Negative	
	Phylogenetic	Negative		Negative	

Table 5.10 Relationships between indices of migratory tendency and distribution (ubiquity). (See Table 5.5 for a key to abbreviations and coding.)

Grouping and analysis method		All species >20 recoveries		Raptors and Passerines >20 recoveries	
		Standard	Absolute	Standard	Absolute
Number of species		91	91	46	46
Variable					
Number of 1988–91 Atlas squares occupied	Basic	Negative	Negative	Negative	Negative
	Phylogenetic	Negative		Negative	

Table 5.11 Relationships between annual survival rates and indices of migratory tendency. (See Table 5.5 for a key to abbreviations and coding.)

Grouping and analysis method		All species				Raptors and Passerines			
		>20 recoveries		>50 recoveries		>20 recoveries		>50 recoveries	
		Standard	Absolute	Standard	Absolute	Standard	Absolute	Standard	Absolute
Number of species		88	88	76	76	40	40	31	31
Variable									
Annual survival rate	Basic	Positive	Positive	Positive	Positive				Negative
	Phylogenetic								Negative

lived species tending to produce fewer young each year. We would expect, therefore, that any relationships between migratory tendency and annual survival would also be reflected in relationships with annual reproductive effort. Greenberg (1980) suggested that migrants are generally less productive than residents, reflecting life-history trade-offs coupled with the higher survival for migrants that he detected (although note the possible problems with that study described above). Additionally, constraints on the length of the breeding season or on the date at which breeding can start (see later) might mean that migrants tend to make fewer breeding attempts, but put more effort into each one. We calculated overall reproductive effort by combining average clutch size, the typical number of broods per year and average egg volume[7] and also investigated these variables independently.

We found a significant negative effect of migratory tendency on reproductive effort but only with the absolute index for raptors and passerines with more than 50 recoveries. Further negative relationships were revealed when controls for phylogeny were added (Table 5.12). This suggests that species that are more migratory tend to invest less in reproduction, contrary to what might be expected given our results for the relationship between survival and migratory tendency for raptors and passerines alone, but in line with the results for all ecological groupings combined (see above). Phylogenetic variation tends to obscure this pattern, however, unlike the situation with respect to survival. Dobson (1990) investigated the relationship between survival and reproductive effort (measured as clutch size and the number of breeding attempts) for British birds and found that the number of broods

[7] Data on these variables were extracted from BWP, CBWP and Crick et al (1994), egg volume being estimated as $(0.67 \times \pi \times (0.5 \times \text{egg width}) \times \text{egg length})$ and overall reproductive effort as (egg volume × clutch size × number of broods).

Table 5.12 Relationships between reproductive effort and indices of migratory tendency. (See Table 5.5 for a key to abbreviations and coding.)

Grouping and analysis method		All species				Raptors and Passerines			
		>20 recoveries		>50 recoveries		>20 recoveries		>50 recoveries	
	Number of species	Standard 91	Absolute 91	Standard 71	Absolute 71	Standard 46	Absolute 46	Standard 36	Absolute 36
Variable									
Clutch size	Basic	Negative	Negative	Negative	Negative				
	Phylogenetic			Negative					
Egg volume	Basic	**Positive**	Positive	Positive	Positive				Negative
	Phylogenetic		Positive		**Positive**				
Number of broods	Basic	Negative	Negative	Negative	**Negative**				Positive
	Phylogenetic	Negative							**Positive**
Reproductive effort	Basic								Negative
	Phylogenetic	Negative	**Negative**	Negative					

was negatively related to survival rate but that there was no clear pattern with respect to clutch size. Interestingly, when we analysed the influence of migratory tendency on the number of broods alone, the results corresponded with those described above for survival (Table 5.11); there were significant negative relationships for the all-inclusive analyses and non-significant ones for the basic raptor and passerine analyses, but a significant positive relationship in the analysis using the absolute index and only raptors and passerines with 50 or more usable recoveries (Table 5.12). When overall reproductive effort was considered, however, this pattern disappeared (Table 5.12), suggesting that Dobson's analysis might have revealed only a part of a bigger picture. The other components of reproductive effort gave rise to more complex patterns, in part reflecting a negative correlation between clutch size and egg volume (Table 5.12).

Overall, our analyses leave the question of the effects of migratory tendency on life-history strategies unclear; further analyses of our index results using more sophisticated phylogenetic controls might permit firmer conclusions to be reached. Perhaps other related variables, such as the energetic demands or growth rates of chicks, or the lengths of their dependency periods, should be added to our measure in some way, to produce a more complete index of reproductive effort (although reliable data on these variables are likely to be hard to find for many species). Research to compare field measurements of demographic rates between comparable migrant and resident birds, at the species or population level, might be a useful alternative analytical approach. There is some evidence for habitat segregation between migrant and resident Blackcaps in Germany, and that productivity is higher in the habitat in which the residents tend to be found (Berthold 1996), but this refers only to a single species in a particular situation and further research is required.

How does migratory strategy affect the timing of breeding?
The adoption of a migratory habit could delay the date on which a species can begin breeding and limit the length of the breeding season. This is because pair formation and territory acquisition can usually occur only after the birds arrive at their breeding grounds and because

they are likely to require a period of recovery before breeding can commence and a period of pre-migratory fattening before their departure in autumn. These requirements could occupy some of the time during which environmental conditions might otherwise allow breeding. Migratory species, which are assumed to be less well adapted to conditions in Britain & Ireland year-round than residents, may also be limited more fundamentally to being able to breed during only short periods of the year. We investigated relationships between migratory tendency and the timing of breeding using two variables: the average laying date and the average length of the breeding season[8].

The results for all species combined clearly showed that the more migratory species tend to begin breeding later but, when raptors and passerines alone were considered, the pattern was significant only in terms of the absolute index (Table 5.13). This suggests, perhaps unsurprisingly, that the pattern is linked more strongly to migratory *distance* than to migratory *behaviour* alone. It is interesting that no corresponding pattern was clearly detectable in the results for the length of the breeding season: we might have expected migrants to have shorter breeding seasons because they seem to start breeding later. Although there was one significant result that suggested such a pattern after a control for phylogeny was employed, the effect was not strong. Many migrants must then, in general, both start and finish breeding somewhat later than more sedentary species. It is interesting that the tendency for more sedentary species to begin laying earlier was not found in the standardized indices for raptors and passerines only, suggesting that later laying is associated more with migratory distance than with the selection of a more migratory strategy, at least among these species. This makes intuitive sense given that travelling time, rather than whether movement tends to occur or not, is likely to be the major constraint on the average date on which breeding starts.

Conclusions about influences on and consequences of migratory tendency
The set of tests of the possible influences on migratory tendency and of its potential life-history consequences, reported above, is not complete: many other possibilities remain to be tested, if suitable data sources for

[8] These data were taken from Campbell & Ferguson-Lees (1972). Laying date was calculated as the day forming the 5th percentile for the distribution of dates observed. The length of the breeding season, in days, was the 95th percentile minus the 5th percentile in the same distribution. Both analyses considered British & Irish breeders only.

Table 5.13 Relationships between the timing of breeding and indices of migratory tendency. (See Table 5.5 for a key to abbreviations and coding.)

Grouping and analysis method		All species >20 recoveries		Raptors and Passerines >20 recoveries	
	Number of species	Standard 88	Absolute 88	Standard 46	Absolute 46
Variable					
First egg date	Basic	Positive	Positive		Positive
	Phylogenetic	Positive	Positive		Positive
Length of breeding season	Basic				
	Phylogenetic	Negative			

the parameters of interest can be found. One potentially important influence on migratory tendency could be population density: species breeding more densely may be more likely to adopt a wider range of migratory habits because their habitat might be unable to support the breeding density year-round. Tests of the importance of density would require species-specific data not only on absolute densities but also on habitat quality, allowing densities to be converted to measures of the degree of saturation of the available habitat. We considered each influence or consequence separately in most cases, to keep presentation and interpretation as clear and straightforward as possible. Clearly, however, potential relationships are rarely likely to be mutually exclusive, and future analyses that thoughtfully combine potential influencing factors would be valuable. It might be valuable to ask, for example, how controlling for the effects of body size on migratory tendency affects relationships with survival (because survival and body size are probably related). The results from our exploratory tests will usefully inform such future work.

We set out only to investigate the potential that our indices of migratory tendency have to contribute to the types of question considered here: we do not claim to have conducted definitive analyses. One important limitation of our work is that the range of migratory behaviours is somewhat biased towards shorter-distance migrants and residents because of the lack of winter recoveries of, for example, many trans-Saharan migrant warblers. Thus, it is possible that different results might be obtained from, say, a test of the influence of migratory tendency on survival if more of the highly migratory species could be included. One way in which this could be done would be to use our indices to define the migratory tendency of intermediate species but to assign migratory tendency values a priori to residents and obligate migrants based on established natural history information on these species. Such a study would not be straightforward because assigning migratory tendencies would have an unavoidable subjective element: the quality of the information being used would have to be assessed with great care so as to avoid perpetuating accepted 'wisdom' that has not been scientifically proven for British & Irish birds.

Notwithstanding these limitations, we have identified several key findings that we highlight for the support that they give to existing hypotheses or for the pointers that they provide towards further valuable research work:

- larger species in the raptor and passerine groups tend to be less migratory but the pattern is more complex and confounded with phylogeny when a wider range of species is considered;
- species with body morphologies better adapted to efficient flight tend to be more migrant, although some of the variation could also be due to other factors that vary with phylogeny;

- the most migratory species tend to be those with invertebrate-only or piscivorous diets (but for differing reasons);
- territorial species tend to be more sedentary than colonial and semicolonial species;
- hole-nesting species tend to be less migratory than open-nesting ones;
- rarer species are more likely to be migratory, but rarity is not related to the absolute distances that species tend to move;
- species with more restricted distributions in Britain & Ireland (ie those at the edges of their ranges) tend to be more migratory;
- across all ecological groupings, the more migratory species have higher annual survival rates but this pattern is confounded with other phylogenetic variation and, among raptors and passerines, the opposite pattern occurs;
- the more migratory species tend to invest less effort in reproduction (egg and clutch production) but the effect is only apparent after controlling for phylogenetic variation; and
- the more migratory species tend to begin breeding later in the year but evidence is only weak that this leads to shorter breeding seasons.

Contexts, caveats and next steps

The analyses described in this chapter represent a quantitative exploration of patterns of migration using the BTO's existing ring-recovery database. Our analyses have not been exhaustive, however, and we can suggest a range of additional tests that could valuably be conducted, with both British & Irish data and those from a larger geographical area. In this section, we explore current knowledge of differential and partial migration, describe certain key caveats to our analyses that should be taken into account in their interpretation, and suggest some avenues for further work that would build on the analyses presented here.

Possible problems with the analyses and potential solutions
In our analyses both of differential migration and of variations in migratory tendency, we tried to make our results as reliable as possible by selecting and classifying recoveries with care, by running appropriate checking analyses and by incorporating controlling methods. We must, nevertheless, note four potential problems with our analyses.

Distribution of ringing effort
First, the caveats about the coverage of Britain & Ireland by ringing over the years described elsewhere (Chapter 4) clearly also apply to the analyses in this chapter: the results will have reflected the migratory habits of birds in areas and periods where ringing effort has been high much better than those of birds from little-sampled subpopulations. For

example, we have very little information on the movements of Irish-breeding terrestrial species or populations of terrestrial species breeding in the far north and west of Britain because of the low ringing effort in these areas. In addition, if a species is distributed through its range or within habitats differentially with respect to sex or age, spatial variation in ringing effort could have introduced biases into our analyses of differential migration. Our knowledge of migration would be advanced both in terms of future studies and retrospectively by further research into the nature and size of potential biases like these in ring-recovery data (see Chapter 7).

Definition of seasons
Second, many of our analyses incorporate seasonality, either in classifying recoveries or in determining whether they should be included or omitted. In all such cases, any birds that have been ringed or recovered at a stage (breeding, passage or wintering) of their individual annual cycle that is different from the stage we have assigned to the date in question for the whole population will introduce 'noise' into the analysis in question. For example, early-departing breeding birds might be ringed or recovered while on passage, but still within the breeding season for the population as a whole (Chapter 4 for further discussion). This issue has particular implications for the analyses of migratory tendency, in which our basic approach assumes that birds ringed in the breeding season are on their breeding grounds and that birds recovered in winter are in a location that can be defined as a 'wintering area'. Violations of the former are merely a methodological problem, curable in principle by using a correct definition (if such a thing exists at the population level) for the breeding season. In winter, however, birds may not have any easily definable destination marking the end of migration. Not only do many species have very large home ranges in winter, making the practical definition of their location difficult, but it is common for large-scale, onward movements to occur within a broad (perhaps continent-wide) wintering area and to form a normal part of annual migratory behaviour (Terrill 1990), perhaps even forming a regular 'loop migration'. Again, such problems will create 'noise' in our allocated index values and thus reduce the power of analyses to detect biologically meaningful patterns; their effects will be greatest where ring-recovery sample sizes are small. Clearly, such movements would also make the derivation of biologically meaningful definitions of passage periods problematic because the spring and autumn migration periods would effectively blend into one another. For this book, we have used species-specific seasonal definitions that represent good compromises for the analyses that we have conducted (see Chapter 4); other specific research might find alternative definitions more appropriate.

Sample-size limitations
The third potential problem with the analyses in this chapter arises from the severe limits placed on some of the analyses that we have been able to conduct by the ring-recovery sample sizes. The implications of small samples for our analyses of migratory tendency are discussed above but there are further general problems for the investigations of differential migration. All standard statistical testing takes account of sample sizes, so we should not have detected many significant differences erroneously (in the absence of bias), but the lack of power to detect differences, and the inability to conduct tests at all, were widespread problems. We used sample size cut-off points of a minimum of 10 ring-recoveries per category to prevent, as far as possible, the false acceptance of results indicating a lack of difference, but the power to detect differences will have been lower for smaller sample sizes. In other words, a true biological difference has to be larger to be detected as statistically significant when recovery sample sizes are smaller. Sample sizes dwindle rapidly as ring-recovery data sets are subdivided to compare the movement patterns of different categories of bird or to investigate finer spatial scales, partly because not all recoveries can be used for all tests (due to a lack of age or sex information or insufficient

seasonal accuracy, for example). This places firm limits on the analyses that can usefully be done with the ring-recovery data set.

Although the data set held by the BTO is probably the largest in the world for a geographical area the size of Britain & Ireland, there is still a great deal of room for improving its volume and coverage (see Chapter 7 for specific recommendations). Measures to improve reporting rates, perhaps through local or national publicity campaigns to increase awareness among the general public, as well as those to increase ringing activity, will make ringing more productive for migration studies. Such changes would be particularly valuable for species and areas where data are currently sparse (*eg* for passerines in Ireland). The quantity of usable data produced by a given number of fitted rings could be increased by some careful targeting of ringing effort towards groups of birds that are more likely to yield useful information. For example, for some groups it might be more useful to ring fully grown birds rather than nestlings, or breeding or wintering birds rather than those on passage. Traditional ringing combined with colour-mark resighting work and the use of capture-mark-recapture trapping also have increasing roles to play. These recommendations are developed in more detail in Chapter 7.

Sample-size limitations were a particular problem for our analyses of differential migration. The small numbers of available ring-recoveries relevant to certain tests mean that many questions of biological interest simply cannot be addressed at a species-specific level. This may mean that future investigations involving fine subdivisions of recovery types might best be done using carefully selected 'model' species, extrapolating the results more generally when appropriate. However, broad multi-species analyses and summaries of the kind we present here are also valuable, since the combination of data from many species can reveal patterns that are common to the species concerned, even if the individual tests are non-significant or have low power. This could be important, particularly with respect to the problem that differences in migratory behaviour between groups of birds of relatively less migratory species are likely to be much more difficult to detect than similar differences within long-distance migrant species, simply because the differences in location or distance concerned are likely to be smaller. The ring-recovery analyses summarized by ecological grouping in this chapter should therefore have been the best possible for detecting broad patterns across large numbers of species. The approach could be extended statistically by using formal 'meta-analysis' techniques or by pooling data for which initial investigations suggest similar systems are in operation. Note, however, that if the true patterns for species within a group are genuinely rather different, any multi-species analysis or summary will not lead to clear overall results and could obscure interesting species-specific information. Broad patterns detected by multi-species analyses nonetheless represent valuable information if they are interpreted with care and they can, in many cases, provide useful guides for future research to be conducted at the species level.

Variations in reporting rate
All analyses of ring-recoveries are potentially complicated by sex-specific, age-specific, spatial and temporal variations in the rate at which dead, ringed birds are recovered and reported (see Chapter 4). With respect to our analyses quantifying migratory tendency, any spatial differences in reporting rate across a species' wintering area would affect the shape of the recovery-distance distribution and any interspecific or temporal variation in this difference would affect the comparisons made here. Any variation in reporting rate with respect to age or sex in the relevant seasons will also have introduced bias into the corresponding analyses of differential migration. Factors such as human population density, hunting pressure (legal and illegal) and the social awareness of and public interest in wildlife in general, and bird ringing in particular, probably all vary spatially and temporally. This will occur increasingly with greater distances in space or time from present-day Britain & Ireland (Chapter 4). Lower reporting rates at greater distances from Britain & Ireland may have led to an underestimation of the migratory tendency of some species, especially for those partial migrants from whose populations at

long-distance migration and fully sedentary behaviour can be viewed as the extremes in a continuum of migratory behaviour, and this philosophy underlies the indexing methods we have used. Lundberg (1988) has drawn an additional, conceptual distinction between partial migration and differential migration, whereby the former describes the existence of two (or more) discrete strategies but the latter involves one strategy expressed to different extents by different sexes or age classes. One classic example of a differential migration is that of a common North American passerine, the Dark-eyed Junco. This species has been studied extensively (*eg* Ketterson & Nolan 1983), and has been used as a model system by many authors (*eg* Dingle 1996, Berthold 1996, 2001); such work provides a context in which we can view the broad patterns found in the differential migration of British & Irish birds. In the Dark-eyed Junco, differential migration occurs with respect to sex and to age, juvenile females tending to move the furthest (Gauthreaux 1982, Ketterson & Nolan 1983). It is clear that, if Junco recoveries were not identified by sex and age, their pattern with respect to distance would suggest a partially migratory strategy. This illustrates how Lundberg's definition can present difficulties in practice, because the determination of sex and age (needed to allow the characterization of a species as a 'true' partial migrant) is often difficult. In addition, and further complicating the picture, Terrill & Able (1988) suggested that 'differential migration' be used as a modifier for other categories of migratory behaviour because age and sex differences can occur within the movements of a partial migrant. We measured migratory tendency using all recoveries, regardless of sex or age, to avoid these problems of definition. This means that partial and differential migration could be confounded, to some extent, in our indices of migratory tendency (although it would be possible, in principle, to exclude differential migrants from analyses identifying partial migrants or to control for age- or sex-specific differences, where they were identifiable, in producing indices of migratory tendency along similar lines, sample sizes permitting).

For the reasons set out above, it may be best to view our indices of migratory tendency as revealing the continuum between a solely resident strategy through a range of *mixed* migratory strategies (including differential migration and true partial migration) to a solely migrant strategy. While studies that define 'partial' and 'differential' migration might suggest that our approach obscures the distinctions between them, we can also argue that the phenomena are sufficiently closely related that separating them is of limited value. In addition, from an applied perspective, such as for conservation purposes, some knowledge of migratory strategy (provided by inclusive analyses that maximize usable data across species) is far better than none at all and can provide an important basis for further targeted research. Both partial and differential migrations involve a mixture of migratory strategies but they differ in the way in which the adoption of a more migratory or a less migratory strategy is controlled.

Most migratory behaviour is under genetic control, as has been shown for passerines by selection experiments and the rearing of chicks in isolation (Berthold 1996, 2001). The rapid establishment of a new wintering habit by central European Blackcaps, which has been shown to have a genetic basis (Berthold *et al* 1992, Helbig *et al* 1994), illustrates the fine level of control and flexibility possible with 'hard-wired' genetics. In passerines, at least, migration is controlled by multiple genetic loci (not single genes; Berthold 1996) and selection experiments suggest that many changes in migratory timing, distance and direction may be micro-evolutionary (Berthold & Querner 1995). This does not mean that changes in behaviour will always be slow, however: for example, a 50% reduction in migratory distance could occur though natural selection in only five years (Berthold & Querner 1995). Nevertheless, some aspects of migration are clearly not controlled entirely by genetic coding. While the fundamentals of winter movements into the tropics and subtropics may be under firm genetic control, it seems likely that the common and widespread onward movements of birds within their wintering areas do at least have something of a facultative, resource-dependent basis (Terrill

least some individuals migrate into Africa (such as Goldfinch), although it should not be assumed that so simple a pattern underlies all the geographical variation in reporting probabilities. Additional biases with respect to age and sex could result from selective hunting (perhaps because more colourful individuals are sought or because one age class or sex frequents areas under high hunting pressure more often) or because corpses differ in conspicuousness, for example if one age class or sex is more likely to be found dead.

It is certain that our investigations of migratory tendency will have been affected by variations in reporting rate and this must therefore provide a caveat to the extent to which they can be regarded as a reliable representation of the migratory patterns of British & Irish birds. However, it may well be that the biases caused by variations in reporting rate are reasonably constant across species (or at least across groups of ecologically similar species) because it is human social factors that are the major influence. Exceptions will clearly occur, such as when certain species are a particularly popular target for hunting, but interspecific comparisons may not generally be seriously affected. Nevertheless, new analyses would need to be conducted to assess whether this is the case and to control properly for the influence of variable reporting rates. Such work would ideally incorporate consideration of the numbers of birds that have been ringed each year and in different areas of Britain & Ireland, data that have not yet been computerized in full for most species (Chapter 4). It would then be possible to produce some estimates of reporting-rate variation, either in zones within and beyond Britain & Ireland or as a function of distance, and to adjust recovery distributions accordingly, before repeating the analyses performed here or employing a more sophisticated analytical approach.

Differential migration, partial migration and the control of migratory strategy

The analyses of differential migration and of variations in migratory strategy described in this chapter are more thorough and more quantitative than any attempted previously, but they are not a complete investigation of the variations in strategy exhibited by British & Irish birds. They were designed, respectively, to identify broad patterns of differential migration across species and to describe temporal and interspecific variations in migratory strategy. Further analyses then showed how the quantitative variation in strategy might be used to study its ecological causes and life-history consequences. We hope that our initial results demonstrate the potential of the approach and will stimulate new thought and research into the ecology and evolutionary biology of migration. To this end, we present in this final section of the chapter a brief summary of current knowledge on differential and partial migration, so that our results may be viewed in context.

By its broadest definition, the phenomenon of partial migration refers to any set of strategies intermediate between all individuals of a species being sedentary and all being migratory, and it is commonly found in many other taxa besides birds (Dingle 1996). In fact, obligate

1990). A simple genetic mechanism would also be unable to account for the irregular irruptive migrations of species like Waxwing (Berthold 1990). In addition, the migrations of geese and cranes are well known to depend on the cultural transmission of routes and timings from parents to offspring (eg Sutherland 1988), although the physiological aspects of migration and behaviours, such as pre-migratory fattening, must presumably have some genetic component.

The refinement of the migrant versus resident dichotomy into a situation of partial migration could, theoretically, also be determined genetically. In such a situation, the costs and benefits of migrancy and residency would probably be frequency-dependent, that is each has an evolutionary advantage when its frequency of occurrence is below a certain level, leading to the establishment of an equilibrium mix of strategies (Swingland 1983). It is also possible that present-day populations are not in equilibrium, with natural selection being in the process of eliminating one strategy or the other (Swingland 1983), but this is unlikely to explain all partial migration, especially for stable populations in stable habitats. Alternatively, there could be a single, conditional strategy in which an individual's behaviour is determined facultatively by physiological or environmental conditions, the bird effectively 'deciding' whether to migrate each year with genetics playing no role in the decision (Swingland 1983). Both of these mechanisms require that the behavioural and physiological processes of migration be encoded genetically. They differ in that the former also requires the 'trigger' for migration to be endogenous and genetically coded, while in the latter case it must be some cue that is related to the availability of resources (Schwabl & Silverin 1990).

Age-related differential migration represents another form of single, conditional strategy, in which the decision on whether (or how far) to migrate is based on age. When migratory behaviour varies with sex, a single strategy could be invoked in a similar way, or the determination of gender itself, which is of course genetic, could be held responsible. Again, the distinction between differential and partial migration is blurred in this case.

If the control of partial migration is genetic, it implies that the differences in strategy are evolutionary adaptations, with equal average pay-offs after equilibrium is reached by frequency-dependent selection. A single conditional strategy, on the other hand, implies that one or other strategy (probably the migrant one) sees the losers of some form of intraspecific competition 'making the best of a bad job' (Dingle 1996). This means that it would be possible, in principle, to test between the two alternatives by comparing the genetic fitness of birds that adopt the two strategies (Lundberg 1988). However, measuring fitness (the production of offspring that enter the breeding population and then breed successfully themselves) is very difficult. As a result, direct comparisons between the genetic and conditional control of partial migration have yet to be conducted, but there is some evidence supporting both possibilities from various species (Lundberg 1988, Sutherland 1988, Berthold 1996).

The strongest evidence for genetic control comes from the selection experiments of Peter Berthold and colleagues, primarily on Blackcaps in Germany (Berthold 1990, 1996, 2001; Berthold & Querner 1995). They found that selection based on the natural variation in migratory activity could produce exclusively migratory or resident behaviour in three to six generations (Berthold 1996). Blackcaps have been recorded as maturing from a migrant to a resident habit (although not the reverse), but even this change can be explained as a genetically coded age-dependent strategy, rather than birds responding to changes in their social status (Berthold 1990, 1996). Consistent evidence for a degree of genetic control has also been found for Great Crested Grebes, Song Sparrows, Blackbirds, Robins and Stonechats, although the existence of a conditional component in the strategy cannot be ruled out (Biebach 1983, Berthold & Querner 1995, Berthold 1996).

Evidence for a contribution of conditional control to partial migration tends to be more circumstantial. Resident Belgian Robins tend to be more socially dominant and migrants may be forced to leave by competition (Adriaensen et al 1990). Higher densities lead to more migratory behaviour in Great Tits (van Balen & Hage 1989) and intraspecific competition seems to force female Pochards to move further (Choudhury & Black 1991). It is possible to formulate genetic hypotheses to explain all of these patterns, as well as others that have been studied but for which the extent of genetic control is unclear, by implicating roles for factors like age-dependence, thus invoking differential rather than partial migration (Berthold 1996). In general, most variation in competitive ability and social dominance will be associated in some way with genetic variation, so that it will always be difficult to separate the two without direct investigations of genetics. In the Dark-eyed Junco, for example, the pattern of differential migration described above features behaviourally subordinate birds being forced to move further by competition, or the birds with the most to gain from an early return to the breeding grounds (which happen to be adult males) choosing to travel less far and trading off winter survival prospects against subsequent breeding success (Ketterson & Nolan 1983). Competition may play no role in the system, however; rather, winter weather may force the smaller, weaker birds to travel further or larger birds may suffer greater mortality during migration, leading them to stop after moving shorter distances (Ketterson & Nolan 1983). All of these possibilities could be viewed as single conditional strategies that are modified by intraspecific competition or environmental influences, but the outcome of each is that a genetically identifiable group, adult males, tends to be less migratory.

Further evidence for the potential importance of conditional strategies comes from work showing that migratory restlessness can be induced experimentally outside the normal times for migration and that food availability can be inversely related to migratory activity (Berthold 1996), suggesting that some migratory behaviour is facultative. Caveats should also be applied to the principal evidence in favour of genetic control, as the work has all relied upon laboratory experiments (Lundberg 1988), wherein birds are clearly not in their natural habitat: natural conditions could conceivably lead to a more frequent induction of conditional strategies. These experiments have also used measurements of *Zugunruhe* (migratory restlessness) in experimental chambers to quantify migratory activity and the distances likely to be moved; this measure must have limited utility in describing migratory behaviour, however.

In practice, differential migration, genetically determined partial migration and facultative partial migration may often prove to be indistinguishable and, in reality, this may only reflect the inter-relatedness of these phenomena. The hypotheses suggested as explanations for differential migration (variations in dominance, body size and benefits arising from earlier arrival; Cristol et al 1999) are exactly the same as those commonly used in explaining partial migration, except that the birds undertaking different strategies are identifiable by age or sex. Distinctions such as Terrill & Able's (1988) suggested division between 'obligate' and 'facultative' partial migrants, the former being regularly migratory species under genetic control, and the latter those that undergo occasional, irregular irruptive movements (such as tits in Fennoscandia; Sandell & Smith 1991) that are at least partly under environmental control, may in practice be only academic. Whatever the details of any mechanism, its results may well match the situation in the Dark-eyed Junco, where birds seem to settle over the winter in locations that optimize the balance between mortality on migration, overwinter survival and subsequent breeding success for the individual (Ketterson & Nolan 1983). The exact mechanism remains uncertain but is certainly very complex in the case of the Junco (Berthold 1996).

The balance of evidence suggests that the adoption of migrant and resident strategies is correlated with genetic variation in partial migrants, but what drives the decisions of individuals in nature with respect to migratory behaviour remains unknown. It might be best to seek a single explanation for all differential and partial migration patterns that is supported by the experimental and field evidence and that does not attempt to divide the continuum of behaviours into discrete sections. One such hypothesis would hold that there are genetically coded thresholds in physiological condition (or some other measure of likely future survival prospects) at which birds will migrate. This might mean that younger birds and females will migrate at higher environmental resource levels (a density-dependent parameter) than older birds and males, for example. Baker (1978) proposed similar thresholds at the species level, rather than the individual level, for 'facultative' migrants. He also proposed environmental migration thresholds for 'obligate' migrants, with the distinction that they would form 'triggers' for a sequence of migratory behaviours rather than direct stimuli, but he acknowledged that there was a grey area between these extremes. Given individual variation in where our proposed thresholds lie, selection experiments could alter their average values and therefore increase or reduce migratory activity at any given resource level; this could also be true for the 'trigger threshold' for Baker's (1978) 'obligate' migrants. However, there could still be rapid facultative responses to changes in environmental conditions, such as short- and long-distance partial migration and irruptions. An interesting corollary of this idea is that no new genetic mutations need be postulated to explain the emergence of novel resident or migrant habits (although the determination of migratory direction is a different matter).

There is clearly still much research to be carried out on the control of migratory strategy and it would be interesting to see the hypothesis that we have outlined above explored further. The types of analyses that we have conducted for this book are unlikely to provide definitive tests of ideas about strategies and mechanisms but comparative work along the same lines could, in particular, provide some correlative, circumstantial evidence. Cristol *et al* (1999) suggested that comparative tests are also the best way forward for research into differential migration. We hope that our indices of migratory tendency and multi-species analyses can contribute in this way, either in their current form or adapted to allow additional comparative studies.

Although some of the issues of definition and mechanisms that we have considered are rather academic and only of interest to biologists, some could also have particular applied importance. In general, knowledge of how migration is controlled could be critical if we are to understand or to predict the effects of environmental change or management on populations of migratory birds. For example, the speed at which a population's migratory habits can respond to changes in environmental conditions could be greatly influenced by the extent to which genetic changes have to occur before there can be changes in behaviour (Sutherland 1988). A number of factors involved in the processes of global climate change may soon provide tests of the adaptability of many bird species. The varying responses of different species to the deterioration of the farmland environment (Siriwardena *et al* 2000) could also reflect variation in adaptability to the changed conditions — migratory flexibility could well be an important factor.

6 Movement patterns of British and Irish birds: main and minor species accounts

John Marchant, Chris Wernham & Mike Toms

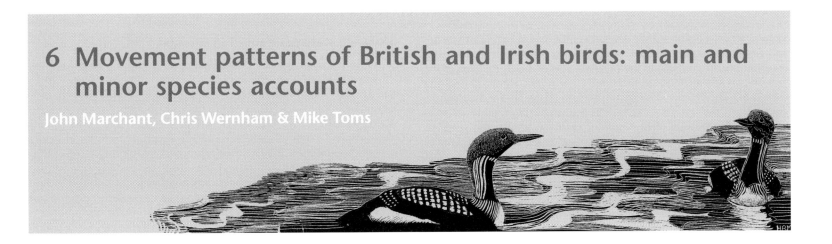

Comprehensive individual accounts follow of the movements of each species, 188 in all, for which there were sufficient ring-recoveries involving Britain & Ireland to use as a baseline for a discussion of their movements (generally 50 recoveries or more). These are followed by shorter accounts for 73 additional species for which there were fewer (or no) ring-recoveries. The additional species selected for inclusion all occur regularly in Britain & Ireland as relatively numerous breeding birds, winterers or passage migrants, according to recent sources (Stone *et al* 1997; Fraser *et al* 1997, 1999a, b; Ogilvie *et al* 1999a, b, 2000). Some in fact are resident species. We did not include national rarities, defined as those species currently listed by the British Birds Rarities Committee, those recently deleted from the list (unless, like Little Egret, they are now regular) and a few species of equivalent status.

With a further four species included within the main species accounts, the main and additional texts cover 265 of the most familiar British & Irish bird species. Purple Heron, White Stork, Red-crested Pochard, Ferruginous Duck, Kentish Plover, Ring-billed Gull, European Bee-eater, Tawny Pipit, Savi's Warbler, Melodious Warbler, Woodchat Shrike, Serin, Ortolan Bunting and Little Bunting are among the most common species that have not been included.

This introduction aims to provide a key, within a few short pages, that will enable the reader to interpret the more complex features of the species accounts. Where appropriate, we direct attention to relevant sections of the detailed methods, in Chapter 4, or to the specialist definitions or results of statistical analyses presented in the *Appendices*.

Structure of the species accounts

The species accounts, whether main or additional, are built around an ordered list of standard topics. The space devoted to each topic, and to the account as a whole, necessarily varies widely between species according to the information that is available and to the aspects of each species' movement biology that are of greatest interest.

Authors have generally begun with a sentence or two that refers to any features of movements that make the species unique or remarkable. World breeding and wintering ranges follow, and an overview of migration routes or flyways globally; in line with our geographical scope, limited reference is made to races that neither occur in Britain & Ireland, nor use flyways relevant to British & Irish populations. There is a brief description of habitats and, especially, of any shifts between habitats that indicate the pattern of movement.

The next section introduces the ring-recovery data, with reference to the standard figures and tables, and comments on the extent to which these data can be taken as representative of the populations using Britain & Ireland through the year. Additional species accounts, which include less information drawn from ring-recoveries, generally omit this section.

Discussion of movement patterns is more-or-less chronological, starting with autumn migration and covering, where relevant, wintering areas and fidelity to wintering sites, onward winter movements, spring migration, post-fledging and natal dispersal, fidelity to breeding sites, irruptions and severe-weather movements. Other interesting aspects of movements are also addressed, including temporal change and any differences between age or sex classes, or between regions. Movements of the British & Irish breeding population of the species, if any, are discussed before those of any foreign-breeding populations that arrive to winter or occur on passage. For foreign breeders, the focus is on their seasonal use of Britain & Ireland rather than the details of their movements as a whole. This section reviews previous ring-recovery analyses for the species and integrates information from other methods of studying migration (see Chapter 1). Results from the formal statistical analyses (see Chapter 4) may be incorporated here.

Accounts conclude with a discussion of any conservation implications of movement patterns, and of the gaps in current knowledge and the further work that is required to fill them, that the author wishes to highlight. Broader syntheses of these topics, for ecological groupings of species, are provided in Chapter 7.

All references cited in the accounts are given in full in the *References* list at the end of the book, with those that have been allocated abbreviated and italicized citations (such as *HBW*) in a separate section. Acknowledgements requested by species account authors for help with their texts can be found in the *Acknowledgements* section at the front of the book.

The first page of each account for the 188 main species has a standard layout for easy reference. In every main account, there is a blue box containing Figures 1–3 that describe the ring-recovery data used in the analyses and a pink box with two tables, describing the amount of ring-recovery data available and the results of various analyses. The form and contents of these standard figures and tables are discussed below.

For each main species, the analysis of the ring-recovery data was funded in part by the Heritage Lottery Fund and in part by a private individual or group sponsor (see *Introduction* and *Acknowledgements* sections at the front of the book). At the top of each main account, we express our thanks to each of these sponsors for their generosity. We are grateful to the Heritage Lottery Fund for the matching funding supplied for every species.

Definitions used in the species accounts

Seasons

For analysis and mapping, four mutually exclusive seasons were defined (to the resolution of half-month periods) for each species (see Chapter 4, p 62). The definitions for the '*breeding*' season and '*winter*' are shown at the top of the 'Statistical analyses' summary table in each main text, while '*autumn*' and '*spring*' are the seasons in-between. For example, if the entries are 'mMay–mAug' under 'breeding' and 'mNov–sMar' under 'winter', then the breeding season is defined as mid-May to mid-August and winter as mid-November to the start of

March. Hence, autumn will be defined as mid-August to mid-November and spring as the start of March to mid-May. References to the 'non-breeding season' or 'outside the breeding season' mean the part of the year that is not defined as 'breeding' (*ie* autumn, winter and spring combined), and is defined for each species in Figure 1b. For the example given above, the non-breeding season will extend from mid-August to mid-May. The seasonal definitions for each species are also listed in Appendix 2. In the few cases where authors requested adjustments to the seasonal definitions for specific analyses, the revised seasonal definitions are stated explicitly in the text or figure legend.

The use of the terms '*seasonally accurate*' and '*seasonally inaccurate*' refers to the accuracy of timing attached to each report of a ringed bird. Those termed '*accurate*' were known to be at the reported location within 15 days (and often within many fewer days) of the date given (see Chapter 4, p 62).

Age classes

Three age classes have been used for age at ringing. A '*pullus*' (or chick) is a bird that has not yet fledged and is still in the nest or nearby. '*Adults*' are birds that have survived until the start of the breeding season in the year when they attain the age of first breeding that has been adopted for these analyses (see Chapter 4, p 62, and Appendix 2). Use of the term 'adult' does not necessarily confirm, therefore, that a bird was indeed breeding. A bird of known age that is neither 'pullus' nor 'adult' is termed '*immature*'.

Three age classes at recovery have been used: '*first-year*', '*immature*' and '*adult*'. If the age of first breeding has been set at 1, a first-year bird becomes an adult at the start of the first breeding season after hatching; otherwise it becomes an immature.

In analyses where there are no separate '*pullus*' or '*first-year*' categories, these younger birds are included with '*immatures*'.

Regions

For some analyses and maps, Britain & Ireland has been divided into five geographical '*regions*', the boundaries of which differ between three groups of species (see Chapter 4, p 62, and Figure 4.12). The group to which each species is allocated is shown in Appendix 2. When maps are shown for regional subpopulations of birds, the regional boundaries are generally indicated on the map (with given regions highlighted by broader boundary lines on the individual maps). In the few cases where the standard regions were modified by authors, to test specific hypotheses, this is highlighted explicitly in the relevant figures or text.

Populations

Generally for the ring-recovery analyses, the term '*British & Irish breeding population*' is defined very broadly, to include any bird ringed or recovered in Britain or Ireland during the 'breeding season', together with any chicks ringed or adult birds coded as of breeding status at other times of year (see Chapter 4, p 63). Where samples of recoveries were large, more rigorous definitions were applied, as explained in map legends and in the text; for many seabird species, for example, only individuals ringed as pulli in Britain & Ireland have been categorized as coming from the British & Irish breeding population.

Many of the maps indicate movements of birds belonging to '*other or uncertain breeding populations*'. These are (i) individuals not recorded from Britain & Ireland during the 'breeding' season and/or (ii) 'seasonally inaccurate recoveries' of birds that, therefore, cannot be confirmed to have been present either in or outside Britain & Ireland during the 'breeding' season.

For most species, birds ringed as chicks are generally the only ones that can be linked unambiguously to a known breeding population. This is because fully grown birds with a ringing or finding status of 'known breeding' have, until relatively recently, rarely been coded as such in the ring-recovery database.

Distance statistics quoted in the text

Distance information may be given in one of two standard ways (see Chapter 4, p 64). First, the *proportion of movements greater than 20 km* (or its converse) is often used to indicate site-fidelity or the sedentary nature of a population. All recovery types are included unless explicitly stated otherwise. The total sample size ('*n*') is given as an indication of the confidence that can be placed on the results. For species for which a high proportion of the recoveries are recaptures by ringers other than the original ringer, use of these data is likely to seriously overestimate distances moved (or underestimate site-fidelity).

Second, absolute distance information can be presented as a median, with the 5th ('*P5*') and 95th ('*P95*') percentiles usually also quoted to give an indication of variability. The median of a set of data is the middle figure when all the values are ranked from lowest to highest and is a good indication of a typical figure; *P5* is the value below which the lowest 5% of the figures lie and *P95* is the value above which the highest 5% lie. Thus '... median 10 km (*P5–95=5–50 km, n=250*)' would indicate that, of 250 recoveries analysed, a typical distance between ringing and recovery locations was 10 km and that 90% of the distances were between 5 and 50 km. These summaries include recoveries of dead birds only, unless otherwise stated.

Standard figures

Figure 1: Ringing locations of birds later recovered

An example is reproduced here as Figure 6.1. The two maps show the distribution of ringing locations *only of birds subsequently recovered*. Each point represents ringing locations summarized to the centre of a block of 0.5° latitude and 1° longitude using size-scaled symbols: small (1–9 birds ringed), medium (10–99 ringed), large (100–999 ringed) and very large (more than 1,000 ringed). Ringing locations can be mapped only for birds that were subsequently recovered because the much larger data set of all birds ringed is only partly computerized. The maps give a general indication of whether the recoveries included in the analysis are representative of populations using Britain & Ireland as a whole, particularly when compared with breeding and wintering distributions of the species in the *1988–91 Atlas* and the *Winter Atlas*. One or other of the maps may be blank if the occurrence or ringing of the species is strongly seasonal.

The periods used to define the two seasons are shown. Just as birds ringed during the breeding season were not necessarily breeding (or on the breeding grounds), those ringed in the non-breeding season were not necessarily confirmed as not breeding. Many of the seabirds ringed in the non-breeding season were early or late birds at the breeding colonies, for example, while many ducks ringed during the breeding season were probably moulting rather than breeding. Figure 1 and Figure 2 (described below) should be used together to build a picture of the classes of bird contributing to the ring-recovery data.

Figure 2: Month of ringing for birds later recovered

This histogram shows the seasonal distribution of ringing dates, split by month of ringing and by age class (Fig 6.2). Once again, only the ringing months and ages of birds that were subsequently recovered can be plotted because the larger data set of all birds ringed is only partially computerized. '*Pulli*' (red bars) are birds ringed as young in the nest (for those that build nests) or that were ringed before they are able to fly (*eg* the young of most waders and wildfowl). The category '*fully grown*' (blue bars) includes all birds ringed after fledging. The darker red and blue parts of the bars refer to birds ringed in Britain & Ireland, and the paler parts to those recovered in Britain & Ireland, having been ringed abroad.

This information helps to indicate how representative are the recoveries included in the analyses of the populations that use Britain & Ireland throughout the year. For example, for a species that is ringed in Britain & Ireland only as chicks in June and July, we may have little or no

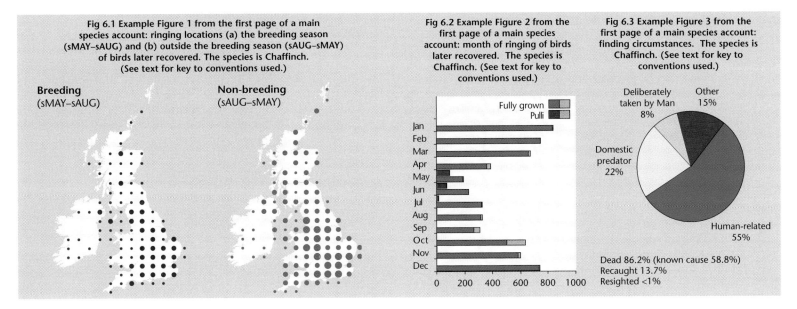

Fig 6.1 Example Figure 1 from the first page of a main species account: ringing locations (a) the breeding season (sMAY–sAUG) and (b) outside the breeding season (sAUG–sMAY) of birds later recovered. The species is Chaffinch. (See text for key to conventions used.)

Breeding (sMAY–sAUG)

Non-breeding (sAUG–sMAY)

Fig 6.2 Example Figure 2 from the first page of a main species account: month of ringing of birds later recovered. The species is Chaffinch. (See text for key to conventions used.)

Fully grown
Pulli

Jan, Feb, Mar, Apr, May, Jun, Jul, Aug, Sep, Oct, Nov, Dec

0 200 400 600 800 1000

Fig 6.3 Example Figure 3 from the first page of a main species account: finding circumstances. The species is Chaffinch. (See text for key to conventions used.)

Deliberately taken by Man 8%
Other 15%
Domestic predator 22%
Human-related 55%

Dead 86.2% (known cause 58.8%)
Recaught 13.7%
Resighted <1%

information on any immigrant populations that may use Britain and Ireland during the winter or passage periods. Conversely, for a wader species ringed only as fully grown birds on estuaries in the spring and autumn, for example, the ring-recovery data will tell us little, if anything, about the movements of any British or Irish breeding birds.

Figure 3: Finding circumstances

The different types of ring-recovery included in this book can introduce varying biases when interpreting recovery patterns because of the differing spatial distribution of 'observers' (see Chapter 4, p 52). The proportions of each type of recovery available for each species are shown beneath the pie chart in **Figure 3** (see example in Fig 6.3). Most birds termed *'dead'* were found dead by members of the public but this category also includes rings read on live birds by members of the public (*eg* when a bird was trapped in a building). These classes were grouped because the recoveries that they produce are subject to similar spatial biases. *'Recaptures'* refer to live birds caught, generally away from the original ringing site, by ringers (termed *'controls'* by ringers) and *'resightings'* refer to reports of live individually marked birds (such as those with coloured or numbered rings that can be read at a distance in the field).

For those recoveries termed 'dead', the proportion that had a *'known cause'* of recovery recorded by the finder is given in parentheses. The cause of recovery may influence the chances that a dead bird will be reported, and recovery causes can therefore influence the geographical spread of recoveries. For birds shot by hunters, for example, the pattern of recoveries might reflect geographical variation in hunting pressure more closely than the true distribution of the species (see Chapter 4,

p 55, for further details). For the purposes of the book, we defined nine major types of finding circumstance: 'Deliberately taken by Man' (shot, trapped or deliberately poisoned), 'Human-related' (such as road casualties and birds that hit windows), 'Accidental capture' (*eg* in fishing nets), 'Natural (environmental)' (such as due to cold weather), 'Natural (illness)' (*eg* due to broken bones or disease), 'Pollution' (such as oiling or electrocution), 'Domestic predator', 'Natural predator' and 'Additional rare classes'. Each of the nine categories is defined in more detail in Appendix 1. The pie chart shows the proportion of recoveries of 'dead' birds with 'known cause' that fall into the three or four largest categories of recovery cause (see example in Fig 6.3).

Ringing and recovery data table

An example of the pink box at the bottom of the first page for each main species is shown here. This box contains both the 'ringing and recovery data' (Table 6.1) and 'statistical analyses' (Table 6.2) tables.

The final column of the top line of the 'ringing and recovery data' table (*eg* Table 6.1) shows the **total** number of birds ringed in Britain & Ireland between 1909 and 1997, based on totals from the BTO Annual Ringing Reports (although some may differ slightly because of late-submitted data and a few errors now corrected). The abbreviation *'BTO-ringed'* means ringed within Britain & Ireland as part of the British and Irish Ringing Scheme. The other figures in the top line of the table are the **percentages** of the total ringed in each of five periods. Although these figures are the best that we have, they should be used as a guide only because totals have been calculated on a relatively *ad hoc* basis until

Table 6.1 Example 'Ringing and recovery data' table from the first page of a main species account. The species is Chaffinch. (See text for key.)

Table 6.2 Example 'Statistical analyses' table from the first page of a main species account. The species is Chaffinch. (See text for key.)

Ringing and recovery data

	<1960	60–69	70–79	80–89	90–97	Total
RINGING						
BTO ringing totals (%)	9	12	18	32	29	844,552
RECOVERIES						
BTO-ringed (%)	14	19	19	28	21	5,900
Foreign-ringed (%)	←	65	→	26	9	779

Statistical analyses

	Breeding population (sMAY–sAUG)	Wintering population (sNOV–mMAR)
Status	SEDENTARY (0)	SHORT-DISTANCE MIGRANT*
Age differences[NS*]	Not significant*	Significant
Sex differences[NS*]	Not significant*	Not significant*
Regional differences	Not significant[4*]	Significant[2]
Finding circumstances	Not significant*	Significant

quite recently (see Chapter 4, p 45). Time constraints prohibited us from seeking similar information on the numbers of birds ringed abroad; in any case, the availability of computerized totals across the other European ringing schemes varies considerably and any interpretation of such totals would thus be problematical without considerable effort to ensure that they were comprehensive.

The lower part of the table shows the total numbers of recoveries of birds ringed in Britain & Ireland from 1909 to 1997, and ringed abroad and recovered in Britain & Ireland (final row), and the **percentages** of those recovered in each of the five periods. Note that the totals will not generally match those previously presented in the BTO Annual Ringing Reports because they refer only to 'included recoveries' (those records remaining after data filtering: see Chapter 4, p 62). For birds ringed abroad and recovered in Britain & Ireland, recoveries before 1979 are not computerized for some species and, therefore, have not been used in the analyses or plotted on maps in the book. For such species, the number of recoveries of foreign-ringed birds in Britain & Ireland up to 1979 is indicated by a single number, with arrows spanning the entire period <1960 to 1979.

For birds ringed in Britain & Ireland, this table gives a general indication of the extent to which the movements discussed in the account are representative of the entire span of years considered. In particular, it gives a qualitative assessment of whether there have been sufficient recoveries in recent years to indicate the current movement patterns of the species. The totals can also be used to calculate approximate recovery rates by time period, although bear in mind the time lag between ringing and recovery for many long-lived species (particularly non-passerines).

Statistical analyses table

This table summarizes the results from formal statistical tests performed on the ring-recovery data for each species (see example in Table 6.2). Separate tests, presented in the first and second columns of the table, were made for birds ringed in Britain & Ireland during the breeding season and recovered in winter ('breeding': essentially the British & Irish breeding population) and for birds ringed in Britain & Ireland during winter and recovered during the breeding season ('winter': winter populations, which are a mixture of resident and immigrant individuals for some species). The seasonal boundaries defined for each category, which differ between species, are given in the column headings.

Statistical methods are described in the *'Differences in movement patterns within and between species'* section of Chapter 4.

Status

This indicates whether the species (and population) is significantly migratory and, for the British & Irish breeding population, the degree to which it is migratory (see Appendix 3 for the full results). The six categories that are used in the table are as follows:

SEDENTARY	Formally tested and no significant difference between ringing and finding locations in the appropriate seasons. [If in square brackets, not formally tested but thought to be sedentary from other information sources.]
SHORT-DISTANCE MIGRANT	Formally tested, significant difference between ringing and finding locations but the average finding location is within Britain & Ireland (50–61°N and 11°W–2°E). [If in square brackets, not formally tested but thought to move only locally within Britain & Ireland from other information sources.]

LONG-DISTANCE MIGRANT	Formally tested, significant difference between ringing and finding locations and the average finding location is outside Britain & Ireland (as defined above). [If in square brackets, not formally tested but it is thought that British & Irish birds winter largely abroad ('Breeding' column) or that Britain & Ireland regularly receives winter immigrants from abroad ('Winter' column) from other information sources.]

For each of the above classes, an asterisk indicates either that a test result was based on fewer than 30 recoveries or that the result was different when only adult birds were tested (see Appendix 3).

The value in parentheses that appears after status classes derived from formal testing in the 'breeding' column is the **migratory score**, with values of 0–4. This indicates the proportion of the British & Irish breeding population that is migratory. Sedentary species have a value of zero. Those that are significantly migrant have values from 1 (largely resident, with a small proportion making migratory movements) through to 4 (largely migratory). The derivation of these scores is explained in full in Chapter 4, p 69.

Passage only	Not formally tested. Britain & Ireland do not hold regular breeding or wintering populations but the species regularly passes through during passage periods (*eg* Curlew Sandpiper).
None	The species is not regularly present in Britain & Ireland during the breeding season (*eg* Whooper Swan) or in winter (*eg* Swallow).
?	Not formally tested, and migratory status cannot be ascertained from current knowledge.

Differences between ages, sexes, regions and finding circumstances
Details of the testing procedures within the 'breeding' and 'winter' categories of the table are summarized below.

Age differences and sex differences
Analyses were carried out to investigate the variation in movement patterns with respect to age class and, separately, sex for as many species as possible. In both cases, a minimum sample of 10 records in each class was required for testing. Analyses for age differences compared immatures and adults (as defined above), and those for sex differences also compared two classes of birds (male and female); recoveries of individuals for which age or sex respectively was uncertain were omitted.

For the 'breeding' category (birds that were ringed in Britain & Ireland during the breeding season), tests for age differences compared the recovery locations in winter, and distances moved, for birds ringed as chicks and immatures and recovered as immatures with those both ringed and recovered as adults. For the 'winter' category, the tests compared the recovery locations during the breeding season, and distances moved, for birds ringed as immatures with those for birds ringed as adults; these birds were all ringed in Britain & Ireland during the winter and recovered as adults in a subsequent breeding season. Tests for sex differences compared the recovery locations and distances moved by males and females, regardless of age class.

For tests such as these that involve a comparison of two groups of recovery locations, there is a potential problem with interpretation if the average ringing locations for those two groups of recoveries differ. To check whether this was the case, parallel tests comparing the ringing latitudes and longitudes of each pair of recovery samples were conducted, using identical statistical methods. Details of the methods are given in the *'Differential migration'* (p 66) and *'Biases caused by differences in ringing locations'* (p 66) sections of Chapter 4 and the full results are provided in Appendices 4a and 4b. Further interpretation of the results across groups of species is provided in Chapter 5.

To check whether the effects of age and sex were confounded within the results (see Chapter 4, p 66), we carried out statistical tests to compare the frequencies of the different sex (male or female) and age (immature or adult at ringing) classes. For a test to be carried out, a minimum of five records for each age-by-sex class was required. The results of these tests are given in abbreviated form after the title 'Age differences' or 'Sex differences' in column one of the table. If a test result is *'significant'*, then the effects of age and sex on movement patterns may be confounded. This means that an apparent effect of age differences on movement patterns may be due, in all or part, to an effect of sex differences, or *vice versa*. The methods are explained in the *'Biases caused by the confounding of age and sex effects'* section (p 66) of Chapter 4 and the full results of the tests are given in Appendix 4c.

Regional differences

For the 'breeding' category, tests were carried out to assess whether movements to wintering areas differed between birds from five British & Irish regions (as defined above). They tested for differences in winter recovery locations (except for sedentary species) and in distances moved (for all species with sufficient data). For the 'winter' category, the recovery locations abroad during the breeding season were compared for birds ringed in different regions of Britain & Ireland in winter. The tests also compared whether the percentage of birds recovered abroad differed between the British & Irish wintering regions. In all cases, a minimum of 10 recoveries was required for any given region to be included in the analyses.

Details of the methods are given in the *'Differential movements of regional subpopulations'* section (p 67) of Chapter 4, and full results are presented in Appendix 5.

Finding circumstances

For each species, the mean latitudes and longitudes of recoveries due to deliberate taking by Man, human-related causes, pollution, accidental capture and domestic predators were each compared in turn to those due to other more natural causes ('other'). A minimum sample of 10 recoveries in each group was required for a test to be carried out and no tests were made where there were fewer than 10 recoveries in the 'other' group. The entries here indicate whether finding circumstances are likely to have introduced significant bias into the recovery patterns presented for the species.

Key to entries in the table

Significant, S $P<0.05$ in at least one test and samples numbering at least 30 recoveries in all classes tested. For 'finding circumstances', more than half of the recoveries of known cause were due to the cause(s) for which the significant result was found.

Significant*, S* $P<0.05$ in at least one test but either at least one sample was smaller than 30 or (for 'age differences' and 'sex differences') differences in ringing and recovery locations were confounded. For 'finding circumstances', more than half of the recoveries of known cause were due to the cause(s) for which the significant result was found but the only significant tests included samples of less than 30 recoveries.

Not significant, NS   No significant results; samples at least 30 in all classes.

Not significant*, NS*   No significant results but either at least one sample was smaller than 30 or (for 'age differences' and 'sex differences') differences in ringing and recovery locations were confounded.

(Not significant), (NS)   For 'finding circumstances', $P<0.05$ in at least one test but fewer than half of the recoveries of known cause were due to the cause for which the significant result was found. For confounding effects of age and sex, differences not tested but unbalanced data make confounding effects unlikely (eg all recoveries in the test for age differences are of birds of one sex).

Not tested (NT)   Insufficient data for testing. For 'age differences' and 'sex differences', fewer than 10 in at least one age or sex class. For confounding effects of sex and age, fewer than five in at least one of the four age/sex categories. For 'regional differences', no two regions had samples of 10 or more. For 'finding circumstances', fewer than 10 in all potential biasing groups.

Not tested*   For 'finding circumstances', fewer than 10 recoveries with finding circumstances categorized as 'other' available but more than 10 recoveries in one of the potentially biasing categories.

Maps of ring-recoveries

The maps are the key to presenting the information on movements for most of the species in the book, and we have attempted to make them clear and unambiguous. Recovery maps have been selected for each species so as best to illustrate the most important aspects of its movements. The number of maps will depend therefore on the complexity of these movements and on the volume and types of ring-recovery data available. Some individual recoveries may appear on more than one map, if a number of different breakdowns of the data are required to illustrate varying movement patterns.

Two map projections have been used. Most maps use the standard Mercator projection, which is suitable for depicting the latitudes encompassing Britain & Ireland and gives these islands a familiar appearance. For maps focusing on the higher latitudes, we have used the Lambert Equal-Area Azimuthal projection (see Chapter 4, p 64, for further details). We have maximized resolution by tailoring map boundaries to the data to be presented but, when maps are intended to be compared directly, their boundaries have been kept identical. In a few cases, obvious outliers in the data, such as a single recovery in North America or Australia, have been removed from maps, and noted instead in the legends, to improve the resolution of the more representative distribution of locations.

Most maps consist of points, showing ringing or recovery locations, or lines, linking ringing and recovery locations, or some combination of the two. When **lines** are used, it is important to realize that these do not imply a route taken, because a bird could have visited many points away from the line between the two locations before being recovered. They also do not necessarily even represent movements made during a single migratory journey (so-called 'direct movements'), unless this is stated explicitly as being the case. In general, we have only used linking lines when it is important to show both the origin and destination of ringed birds. When lines are included with large samples, they are shown in a paler tone than the points, to give an overall impression of movement directions.

On many of the maps, **points** are used to show recovery locations; on others, however, they show the locations in a certain month or season of birds present in Britain & Ireland or abroad in another given month or season. In the latter case, the maps generally show movements in both directions, so that points indicate ringing locations for some individuals and recovery locations for others. For example, a map showing *'the breeding locations of birds present in Britain & Ireland during the winter'* will show the recovery locations, during the breeding season, of birds ringed in Britain or Ireland in the winter and the ringing locations of birds ringed during the breeding season and recovered in Britain or Ireland during the winter. We have not attempted to indicate where more than one recovery occurs at a given location because, often, a large number at a single site reflects a 'hot spot' for recovery (*eg* due to intensive efforts by ringers or high hunting pressure) rather than a concentration of birds (see Chapter 4, p 51). We suggest that greater emphasis should be placed on the overall distribution of the locations on the maps, rather than on the numbers of recoveries at given locations.

We have tried to make the **legends** for each map explicit. All recovery types have been included unless it is stated otherwise. For maps that contain seasonal or monthly divisions of the data (including dispersal movements), any seasonally inaccurate records have been omitted (or are shown with a different colour or symbol to flag up the uncertainty associated with their timing). Recoveries coded as 'confidential' are not included on maps (see Chapter 4, p 45). The number of recoveries presented is stated on most of the maps, particularly when maps forming part of a series are designed to be compared directly. We have generally tried to include all movements, as to leave out those shorter than a certain minimum distance (*eg* 20 km) may give a biased impression of the overall scale of a species' movements. When short movements have been omitted from a map to improve clarity, the sample sizes for both short and long movements have been clearly stated in the map legend. For maps that involve birds ringed abroad and recovered in Britain & Ireland, and where the pre-1979 recoveries have not been computerized, details of the pre-1979 movements relevant to the map have been included in the legend, if they were available.

Other figures and tables

Most other figures and tables have explicit legends and should be understandable without the need to refer to this key. A few commonly used graphs warrant further explanation, however.

For some species, the timing of seasonal movements is illustrated by **graphs of differences between ringing and recovery latitudes and/or longitudes, by month**. These show either the movements of the *'British & Irish breeding population'* (defined earlier), *'British & Irish winterers'* (birds ringed or recovered in Britain & Ireland during the 'winter') or some other defined class. The points shown on these graphs are median differences in latitude or longitude between ringing and recovery locations. For latitude differences, positive values indicate displacement north, and negative values displacement south. For longitude, positive values indicate displacement east and negative values displacement west. Points do not appear for months for which the sample size is less than 10 recoveries for a given class of bird. The bars give the inter-quartile range (25th and 75th percentiles) of the differences as an indication of variability. Months for which this range is wide are likely to be those in which movements are taking place.

In other types of graphs showing median distances moved for various classes of bird and time periods (such as those showing the progress of **post-natal dispersal**), we have included the 25th and 75th percentiles as an indication of variability whenever possible. This may not have been possible where data came from a source other than the BTO database.

When the contents of a figure or table refer to data not held on the BTO database, the source is explicitly mentioned in the legend. Acknowledgements of these contributions can be found in the *Acknowledgements* section of the book.

Red-throated Diver
Gavia stellata

The strange calls of the Red-throated Diver in the breeding season have ensured that this species has a firm place in northern folklore, with its wild cries associated with madness or the moon's cycles; in most languages the name has connections with lunacy (hence the alternative name 'loon'). These calls evoke wild, remote, northern places.

The Red-throated Diver is highly adapted for life on the water, spending most of the year at sea and only coming onto fresh water to breed. The nest site is within a few centimetres of the water's edge, reflecting the difficulty that the species has in moving on land. In Britain, they may nest by the largest lochs, which may hold more than one pair, smaller lochans, or even small pools only a few square metres in area. These lochans and pools are often on open moorland and many sites are on higher ground on ridges or hilltops.

The species is circumpolar in its distribution, with pairs in the high Arctic inhabiting the most northerly points of Greenland, Russia and North America, the bulk of the population nesting north of 60°N (*BWP*). In western Europe, it breeds throughout northern Scandinavia and northern Britain, with a handful of pairs in Ireland. The British & Irish population, one of the most southerly in the world, is largely restricted to the north and west of Scotland, with most confined to Orkney and Shetland, where the population increased notably during the 20th century. The Shetland population was estimated to be about 700 pairs in 1983 (Gomersall *et al* 1984), but had fallen to 430 pairs by 1994 when the total Scottish population was estimated at between 935 and 1,500 breeding pairs (Gibbons *et al* 1997). There had, however, been some expansion of range in mainland Scotland (*1988–91 Atlas*).

The analysis of the data for this species was supported by David Milne QC

In Britain, this species nests only on fresh water and, in most areas, parent birds fly to the sea to catch and bring back individual fish (usually sand-eels) to the young. Most pairs return to their territories in late March and April, the first in the last few days of February in some years, and eggs are laid in late May and early June. The breeding season in Orkney is about a week ahead of that in Shetland (J Williams pers comm). Non-breeding birds, believed to be prospecting immatures, visit suitable larger lochs throughout the season, which can disturb the resident adults. The first chicks fledge late in July, although most fledge during August. The latest fledging date recorded so far in Shetland is 2 October, which was for a chick from a re-laid clutch. The young make their first flight to the sea attended by their parents and then move away from the breeding areas within a few days. The small parties seen migrating south in autumn may well be family groups.

Virtually the entire breeding range is frozen or otherwise inhospitable in winter. Scandinavian birds winter in the southern North Sea and southwards to central France (Eriksson 2000). The British population travels shorter distances to winter than more northerly birds.

Before 1977, only 162 Red-throated Divers had been ringed, but improved methods for catching birds on the smallest of their nesting lochans and better techniques for fitting rings were then developed (Okill 1981). By the end of 1997, 2,664 individuals had been ringed,

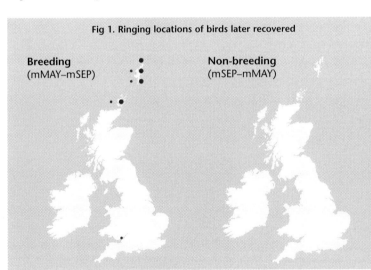

Fig 1. Ringing locations of birds later recovered

Breeding (mMAY–mSEP)   Non-breeding (mSEP–mMAY)

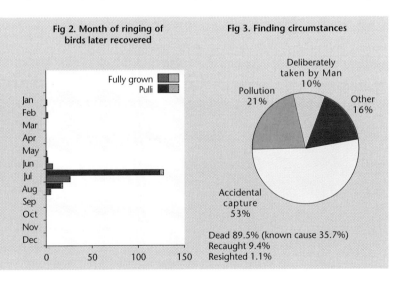

Fig 2. Month of ringing of birds later recovered

Fully grown / Pulli

Fig 3. Finding circumstances

Deliberately taken by Man 10%
Pollution 21%
Other 16%
Accidental capture 53%

Dead 89.5% (known cause 35.7%)
Recaught 9.4%
Resighted 1.1%

Ringing and recovery data

	<1960	60–69	70–79	80–89	90–97	Total
RINGING						
BTO ringing totals (%)	0	2	10	46	41	2,664
RECOVERIES						
BTO-ringed (%)	2	1	6	51	40	181
Foreign-ringed (%)	10	10	20	20	40	10

Statistical analyses

	Breeding population (mMAY–mSEP)	Wintering population (sDEC–sAPR)
Status	SHORT-DISTANCE MIGRANT* (3)	[LONG-DISTANCE MIGRANT]
Age differences[NT]	Not significant*	Not tested
Sex differences	Not tested	Not tested
Regional differences	Not tested	Not tested
Finding circumstances	Not tested	Not tested

Fig 4. Locations outside the breeding season and movements of over 20 km between the breeding and non-breeding season of 46 Red-throated Divers present in Britain & Ireland during the breeding season.

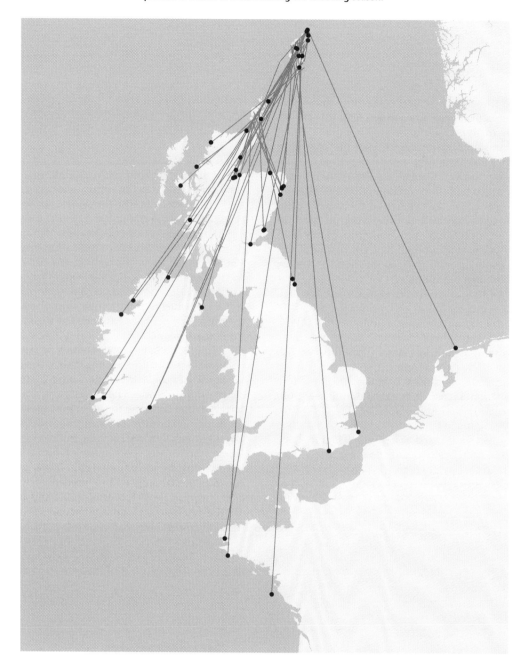

nearly all as part of long-term studies in Orkney and Shetland. This total has generated 194 recoveries, giving a recovery rate of over 7%, which is high for a seabird. Except for a handful of rehabilitated individuals, all recoveries have originated from birds ringed on the Northern Isles (Fig 1) and are of birds ringed during the breeding season as either breeding adults or unfledged chicks (Fig 2). Most adults can be sexed by their measurements, males being larger than females (Okill *et al* 1989).

Of the recoveries with a known cause of death, just over half were birds caught in fishing nets, which reflects the vulnerability of this species to such entanglement (Fig 3). A wide variety of different nets have been responsible, including those used at fish-farms. Birds have been drowned both in discarded netting and in nets set for a variety of fish including Herring, Atlantic Salmon and Skate. A further 21% of recoveries were associated with pollution, mainly from oil. Of those reported as predated, most were during the breeding season when they

become more vulnerable to a variety of mammalian and avian predators.

The recoveries show a generally southerly movement of birds in autumn and winter away from their breeding areas but with a wide distribution around the British & Irish coasts (Fig 4). Sandy coasts are preferred to rocky ones, and wintering habitats are coastal rather than truly maritime. Large numbers of birds overwinter in the wide, shallow, sandy bays and sea-lochs of Ireland and the west coast of Scotland. Immature birds tend to move furthest from their natal areas, some travelling as far south as the coast of central France (Okill 1994); this represents an example of retarded migration.

About a quarter of immatures return to their natal areas in the Northern Isles in the first summer (Okill 1994). The other breeding-season recoveries of first-years have been found along the north coast of Scotland with a scattering through Ireland and with singles in Devon and Norway. Two-thirds of immatures return to their natal areas for

Fig 5. Movements of the 10 foreign-ringed Red-throated Divers recovered in Britain & Ireland.

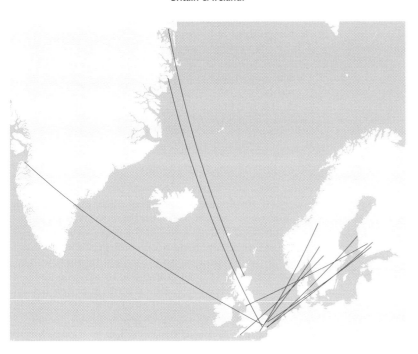

their second summer, with the remainder moving north but spending the summer along the northern Scottish coasts. By their third summer, all birds are returning to their natal areas but the age at which they begin to breed is not fully known. Four birds, all males, have been found breeding in their fourth year, while two females have been found breeding in their sixth.

In Shetland, males returned to breed on average only 2 km from where they fledged; females, however, dispersed more widely and were found nesting on average 38 km from their natal loch (Okill 1992). Since then, a female ringed as a chick in Shetland has been found breeding on Orkney. Once established as breeding birds, most adults return to the same loch in subsequent years; movements to a different breeding loch are always to an adjacent site (Okill 1992).

Recoveries show a peak in May to August and another smaller one in January and February. The summer peak may reflect breeding stress, predation, or the increased probability of finding or reporting individuals as birds move inland to breed. The winter peak may be associated with poor weather conditions making feeding difficult, together with the stresses of moult. Little is known about the moulting period but it is thought that a full moult takes place in early winter or midwinter, when

birds become flightless for some days; during this period, birds would find it difficult to move quickly to sheltered waters or alternative feeding grounds.

Foreign-ringed birds found in Britain, all ringed in the breeding season, have originated from Greenland (both east and west coasts), Finland and Sweden (Fig 5). The majority of these have been in southeast England in winter, perhaps from birds associated with the very important wintering area for Scandinavian divers in the southern North Sea and the Helgoland Bight (Tasker *et al* 1987). The large wintering population in the southern Baltic (Durinck *et al* 1994) is thought to consist of Russian birds as no Scandinavian birds have been recovered in the Baltic in winter (Eriksson 2000). There is some movement out of the Baltic in midwinter, especially during colder weather, but no evidence as yet that Russian birds reach Britain.

Birds arrive on their wintering areas during late September and into October and there is a strong indication that wintering birds are mobile within their wintering areas in response to weather conditions or food supply (*Winter Atlas*). Notably, however, this species is less likely to be found inland than the other British & Irish divers. Large numbers may be recorded from various coasts during winter, for example flocks of hundreds have been seen off the coast of East Anglia from various sites (Taylor *et al* 1999). There is a substantial eastward passage along the south coast of England in April and May, probably involving mainly Scandinavian birds since most British breeders are then already on territory.

The wide distribution of the British population in winter ensures that only small numbers of individuals are at risk from localized pollution events at any one time. However, as nearly all British birds are in inshore waters off northern Scotland during the summer, this means that the population could be highly vulnerable to a major pollution event during these months.

Further investigation is required into the wintering status of divers around all parts of the British & Irish coasts, especially to discover how many birds winter in the southern North Sea and whether their movements are a response to weather, food supplies or other factors. Better understanding is also needed of which migratory routes the different populations follow in spring and autumn.

The use of nets set for fish, sometimes illegally, continues to be a threat to Red-throated Divers in both their summering and wintering areas. The expansion of the marine fish-farming industry throughout much of their breeding range since 1980 has increased the risks of netting casualties and disturbance. On the breeding grounds, human access and consequent disturbance can cause breeding failure and continues to be an issue, especially on larger lochs that are used for recreation.

Dave Okill

Little Grebe

Tachybaptus ruficollis

The Little Grebe is a common British & Irish bird that is rarely observed in flight and probably migrates nocturnally. The nominate race breeds throughout temperate Europe (north to almost 60°N in the west), northwest Africa, Turkey and Israel; two other races occur in the West Palearctic (in the Caucasus and Iraq) and six more elsewhere in the Old World (*BWP*). None of the races other than *ruficollis* is likely to reach Britain & Ireland.

Little Grebes breed on fresh waters that are mainly shallow and often small; some open water must be available, and preferred habitat includes muddy bottoms often with submerged aquatic vegetation (*BWP*). Oligotrophic waters are avoided. British & Irish nest-site preference is for reedbeds, or dense formations of other water-fringing plants, on a wide range of water types: rivers and streams, lakes and ponds, and artificial waters, such as canals, dykes and reservoirs (Moss & Moss 1993). Outside the breeding season, many breeding sites become inhospitable, and the species occurs on more open waters and on sheltered coasts and estuaries.

The nominate race winters throughout the west of its breeding range but leaves Scandinavia and central and eastern Europe in the winter, when it occurs along Atlantic and Mediterranean coasts. Differences between breeding and wintering ranges suggest a major east–west component to movement in the autumn. Ring-recoveries generally throw little light on flyways: breeders from northwest Europe move south to southwest, those from central and west-central Europe move west-northwest to southwest, and those from east-central and southeast Europe move west to south (*BWP*).

The analysis of the data for this species was supported by Moss Taylor

Regular observations suggest that most British Little Grebes disperse from their breeding areas and winter elsewhere, often on the coast (Vinicombe 1982), where small flocks are observed. WeBS counts show that maximum numbers are counted in September and October, and that by January over one-third of birds have left the larger waters where counts tend to be most frequently made (Cranswick *et al* 1999). The *Winter Atlas* shows that the species remains distributed throughout its inland breeding areas during the midwinter months, although in much smaller numbers. Some early-returning breeding birds may well have been included in the *Winter Atlas*.

Little Grebes are very difficult to trap and appear largely to have been ringed by a small number of specialists at very few locations. Only 1,259 Little Grebes had been ringed in Britain or Ireland by the end of 1997, and just 42 of these had been recovered (Figs 1 & 2). Maps of ringing locations within both the breeding season and the non-breeding season for birds subsequently recovered (Fig 1) show great biases when compared with the *1968–72* and *1988–91 Atlases* and the *Winter Atlas*. Most ring-recoveries are of birds ringed at Abberton Reservoir, Essex. A scattering of birds have been ringed in the non-breeding season elsewhere in eastern England south of the Humber, but hardly any birds ringed at any season outside this part of the species' range have been recovered. Two foreign-ringed birds have been recovered in Britain.

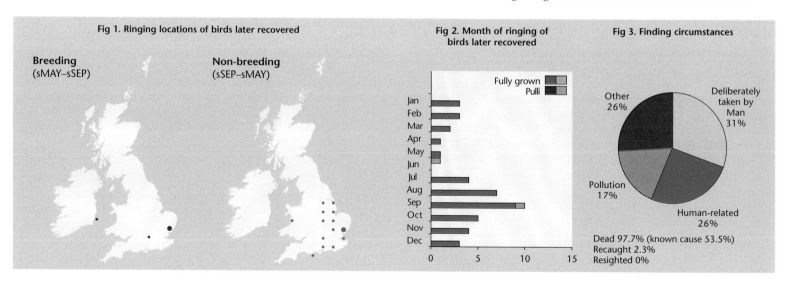

Fig 1. Ringing locations of birds later recovered

Breeding (sMAY–sSEP)

Non-breeding (sSEP–sMAY)

Fig 2. Month of ringing of birds later recovered

Fully grown
Pulli

Fig 3. Finding circumstances

Other 26%
Deliberately taken by Man 31%
Pollution 17%
Human-related 26%

Dead 97.7% (known cause 53.5%)
Recaught 2.3%
Resighted 0%

Ringing and recovery data

	<1960	60–69	70–79	80–89	90–97	Total
RINGING						
BTO ringing totals (%)	13	20	26	22	19	1,259
RECOVERIES						
BTO-ringed (%)	26	17	28	21	7	42
Foreign-ringed (%)	0	50	0	50	0	2

Statistical analyses

	Breeding population (sMAY–sSEP)	Wintering population (sNOV–sMAR)
Status	[SHORT-DISTANCE MIGRANT]	[LONG-DISTANCE MIGRANT]
Age differences	Not tested	Not tested
Sex differences	Not tested	Not tested
Regional differences	Not tested	Not tested
Finding circumstances	Not tested	Not tested

Fig 4. Recovery locations and movements of over 20 km for the 55 included recoveries of Little Grebes ringed or recovered in Britain & Ireland, with those present in Britain & Ireland during the breeding season (red) differentiated from those from other or uncertain breeding populations (grey).

Of the 44 usable recoveries, 43 were of birds found dead, and for 23 of these birds, the cause was known. The most commonly attributed causes of death were deliberate taking by Man (31%), human-related (26%), and pollution (17%). These causes of death are more likely than natural deaths to have resulted in the bird's corpse being found. Seasonal differences in mortality rates are suggested by the fact that 17 of the 32 seasonally accurate recoveries (53%) were in the four midwinter months. This supports the finding, based on nest record cards (Moss & Moss 1993), that the species is susceptible to severe winter weather.

In total, 43 birds recovered dead had moved a known distance, with a median of 21 km (P5–95=0–1,653 km). Only 11 recoveries can be attributed to British & Irish breeders: the median distance moved for these birds was 14 km (P5–95=0–215 km). Owing to the severe bias in ringing locations and very small samples, no conclusions can be drawn about differential locations for birds ringed and recovered in different seasons.

The movements involving birds ringed or recovered abroad show that Little Grebes generally follow east–west routes, apart from those making short journeys across the English Channel, which moved between southeast and southwest (Fig 4). Three such birds were ringed between September and November and recovered between eight days and four months later, and were probably ringed when they had already left their breeding area, which may have been on the Continent. Birds breeding at inland sites are thought to disperse to nearby coasts (Vinicombe 1982) but there is little evidence of this from the recoveries of birds ringed in the breeding season: three out of 10 of these birds moved more than 20 km (Fig 4). Three were ringed at the same site in Essex; they were recovered in the London area, Oxfordshire and Humberside, the latter being the only south–north movement recorded between summer and winter. The Oxfordshire and Humberside birds were both ringed as breeding adults. Seven other birds ringed at Abberton between late July and early October were recovered 8–23 km away in the same autumn or winter. There is no information on juvenile dispersal. There has been only one movement within a winter (6 km) and three between winters (one over 20 km, within Essex). There is no other information showing movements of birds ringed outside the breeding season.

The two foreign ring-recoveries are both particularly interesting. One bird was ringed in Denmark in September of its first year and recovered in Hertfordshire the following January, having moved 918 km west. The other bird was ringed close to the northern limit of the breeding range in Latvia, as a juvenile, and recovered in Lancashire in its second winter, 1,653 km west. This confirmed the supposition that birds breeding in northern parts of their range in the Baltic region would need to move west in the winter to avoid frozen conditions.

Despite the extensive count data, there are still many unknowns about Little Grebe migration. The maximum total counts recorded by WeBS account for only about a quarter of the supposed British & Irish breeding population, although the two long-distance ring-recoveries prove that Britain & Ireland receive migrants from northern Europe. Many wintering birds must be on small waters and rivers which are not covered by WeBS, and we do not know why so many birds leave the counted sites during the early winter, well before the approach of the breeding season. Ringing has not been able to complete the picture but, since the Little Grebe is not a species of conservation concern, it is unlikely that there will be priority to increase ringing effort and spread our knowledge beyond the centre of activity in Essex. Perhaps only a radio-tracking survey using satellites would reveal much about the movements of this secretive species.

Dorian Moss

Great Crested Grebe
Podiceps cristatus

Though not adept at take-off, the Great Crested Grebe is a competent flyer and capable of substantial migrations. Its breeding range is determined by the availability of large, shallow, eutrophic lakes and is expanding in many areas following the creation of new eutrophic waters such as reservoirs and gravel-pits. It can also be found at atypical linear locations such as canals, moats and broad slow-flowing rivers. Most populations contain substantial migratory, dispersive and non-migratory elements (*European Atlas*). The nominate race *cristatus* has a wide distribution in the West Palearctic, from Fennoscandia southwards to fragmented populations along the Mediterranean coastal fringe of North Africa, and eastwards to Korea and the Sea of Japan. Two further subspecies are recognized; these are *infuscatus* which breeds in isolated pockets in eastern and southern Africa, and *australis* of eastern Australia and parts of New Zealand (*BWP*).

Great Crested Grebes are now abundant in Europe and breeding in 32 countries. In just a few locations, the breeding population exceeds 2,000 adult birds: the IJsselmeer in the Netherlands (3,000), Lake Vesijärvi in southern Finland (2,200–3,200) and Lake Neuchâtel (4,600) in western Switzerland (*European Atlas*). Recent research at the Northern Irish stronghold at Lough Neagh and its smaller satellite lakes (Lough Beg, Portmore Lough and Lough Gullion) has investigated the breeding population of almost 4,100 adult grebes; this is by far the most important breeding site in Britain & Ireland and one of the foremost sites in the West Palearctic (Perry 2000).

In Britain & Ireland, Great Crested Grebes are found on large lowland lakes, reservoirs, meres and gravel-pits with riparian fringe vegetation,

The analysis of the data for this species was supported by Ken Perry

reeds being the preferred breeding habitat. They are less widespread in western and northern England, and largely absent from the oligotrophic lochs of northern Scotland (*CBWP*). Ideally, breeding pairs prefer areas of open water to facilitate a long take-off run for flight, and the paucity of larger lakes, especially in southern Ireland, limits population densities (*Birds in Ireland*).

Outside the breeding season, Great Crested Grebes are often solitary, especially when feeding, though occasionally they form congregations of a hundred or more. Whereas most are non-territorial in winter, some individuals defend small temporary foraging territories in coastal areas, and others are sedentary and remain all year on freshwater territories if weather conditions permit. The majority of wintering grebes in Britain return to their breeding areas from mid-February onwards (*BWP*). In Ireland, some Lough Neagh migrants remain on the coast until April, and upon return to their breeding grounds find that the resident birds have commenced breeding in the best nesting areas, pushing the late arrivals into lower-quality nesting habitat (Perry 2000). In the Netherlands, colour-ringed territorial males were found to return to their breeding areas usually in January, followed about 50 days later by females (van der Poel 1985). Late-breeding adults with a brood can be recorded in December and in mild winters nesting may begin as early as January (A M van der Poel pers comm). Similarly, nesting birds have

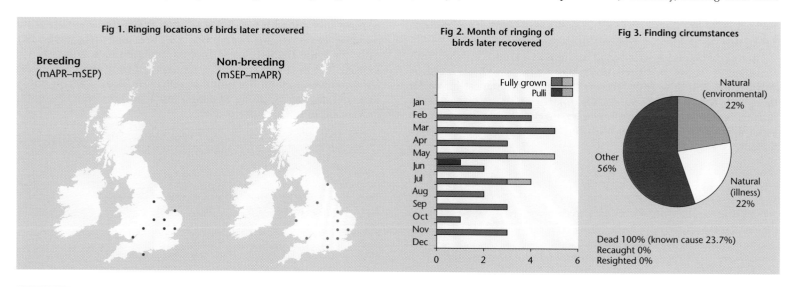

Fig 1. Ringing locations of birds later recovered

Breeding (mAPR–mSEP)

Non-breeding (mSEP–mAPR)

Fig 2. Month of ringing of birds later recovered

Fully grown
Pulli

Fig 3. Finding circumstances

Natural (environmental) 22%

Other 56%

Natural (illness) 22%

Dead 100% (known cause 23.7%)
Recaught 0%
Resighted 0%

Ringing and recovery data

	<1960	60–69	70–79	80–89	90–97	Total
RINGING						
BTO ringing totals (%)	7	20	25	30	18	350
RECOVERIES						
BTO-ringed (%)	0	17	29	43	11	35
Foreign-ringed (%)	0	33	33	33	0	3

Statistical analyses

	Breeding population (mAPR–mSEP)	Wintering population (mNOV–mFEB)
Status	[SHORT-DISTANCE MIGRANT]	?
Age differences	Not tested	—
Sex differences	Not tested	—
Regional differences	Not tested	—
Finding circumstances	Not tested	—

Fig 4. Locations and movements of over 20 km of Great Crested Grebes. Recovery locations and movements of British & Irish breeders between breeding seasons (red, 7) are differentiated from locations outside the breeding season and movements between the breeding and non-breeding season for birds present in Britain & Ireland during the breeding season (blue, 13), and all other movements and recovery locations (grey, 19).

been recorded in January in Britain, and young in February (Griggs 1998).

Marked shifts are shown in British & Irish populations with, at times, large numbers of Great Crested Grebes overwintering on inland waters or moving from smaller lakes to gather on the larger English lakes and reservoirs, such as Rutland Water, Chew Valley Lake and Grafham Water. Great variations in numbers have been noted between years, with winter peaks halving or doubling during the 1990s at seven of the 10 principal sites. Of the wintering sites monitored annually by WeBS in Britain that carry at least fifty birds, inland waters carried a mean of 52% of grebes with 48% recorded at the coast. In Northern Ireland, similar proportions are found, with 48% of wintering grebes at two large inland sites and the remainder on the sea-loughs of the north and east coast (Waters et al 1998).

Movements away from the nesting areas in Britain can begin in late July and August and moult takes place on the wintering grounds between August and October. In Ireland, non-breeding adults and unsuccessful breeders at Lough Neagh leave many of the larger colonies early and pre-migratory dispersal movements from the lake occur as early as June. From the first week of July, increasing numbers move to their traditional marine wintering site at Belfast Lough to reach a peak of more than 2,000 birds by September. This movement, which takes place before the annual moult, involves a minimum flight distance to the coast of 23 km (Perry 2000). Great Crested Grebes renew their flight feathers in a simultaneous wing moult, mainly between August and October, resulting in an extended period of impaired flight capability. At a few locations affording safety from predators and where sufficient food resources are available, such as the IJsselmeer, assemblages of 10,000–40,000 may gather (Piersma 1988b). In other parts of western Europe, full or partial moult can take place on the breeding grounds and gradual dispersal to the coast can continue as late as November (CBWP).

Historic difficulties in trapping strategies and methodology have resulted in low numbers of adults being caught and ringed in Britain & Ireland, and the tarsi of many well-developed but still dependent juveniles when caught are frequently found to be too small to carry a ring. Adults have been found to enter fixed or floating cage traps baited with dead fish only rarely and, while popular and successful in the USA

(Lindmeier & Jessen 1961, Snow et al 1989, King et al 1994), nocturnal attempts to dazzle-trap roosting adults from boats, using hand-nets, have had similarly poor results, although limited successes were experienced at Chew Valley Lake (Hughes et al 1990). Recent experimental trapping at Lough Neagh over a 10-day period, and using large-mesh two-shelf mist-nets placed in shallow, sheltered inlets at the end of the breeding season, have resulted in the capture of 16 adult grebes. In contrast, studies in continental Europe and particularly in the Netherlands record much higher trapping success, including catches of incubating territorial adults on urban canals and moats from a boat, using a long-handled catching net (A M van der Poel pers comm).

Great Crested Grebes have been ringed in Britain & Ireland almost exclusively as adults and although only 350 were ringed in total during 1909–97, 11% of these birds were recovered. Analysis of recoveries to date broadly reflects the breeding distribution in southern England but shows an absence of recoveries from other parts of Britain & Ireland (Figs 1 & 2). Almost a quarter of all recoveries can be attributed to a known cause of death (Fig 3). Anecdotal evidence from discussions with commercial fishermen points to higher levels of human-related mortality due to the accidental capture of many grebes in fishing nets on some of the larger lakes.

The migration routes of Great Crested Grebes within Britain & Ireland are poorly known; the small number of recoveries show predictable seasonal movements between inland breeding sites and the coast, but in a confused pattern of directions (Fig 4). In Ireland in 1998, four unrelated adults radio-tagged in August were tracked from their breeding sites at Lough Neagh, and by October all were relocated at Belfast Lough. These movements are indicative of the proportion of adult birds, together with some young, that leave their breeding grounds to winter on the coast. Some birds, especially late breeding pairs with their young, remain all winter on the breeding grounds (Perry 2000).

Little is known of the preferred timing of the return migration. Migrating grebes are occasionally noted diurnally but there is evidence that most passage may be nocturnal. One adult found at dawn in late March 1998 near high-tension cables on the outskirts of Belfast suggests a return migration flight-line from Belfast Lough direct to Lough Neagh over an illuminated route (Perry 2000).

There seems to be little consistency from year to year in the direction and extent of population movements from inland waters to the coast across the continental range of Great Crested Grebes (van der Poel 1984, Adriaensen et al 1993, Meltofte 1996b); the strength and direction of such movements may be driven largely by climatic variations. Some of the largest autumn and winter concentrations are found on the IJsselmeer in the Netherlands, with peaks of c 40,000 (Vlug 1976, Piersma et al 1986), and on the eutrophic lakes of western Switzerland (BWP), with at times c 22,000; at Lake Neuchâtel numbers fluctuate from less than the total summering population in severe winters to much higher numbers in milder winters (Antoniazza 1998, Perry et al 1999). The patterns of migration in Europe and the relative importance of different wintering areas have changed greatly since the 1970s, with many population increases found in the south Baltic (Adriaensen et al 1993). In particular, the winter total of 15,000 or so grebes in Denmark shows the conservation importance of the region as a wintering site for its own breeding population and for immigrants (Meltofte 1996b). Although some Fennoscandian birds may stay on the breeding grounds in mild winters, or winter on the Baltic or Wadden Seas, most move southeast to winter mainly in southeastern Europe, especially around the Black Sea (Adriaensen et al 1993). Studies in Denmark have shown that at least 43% of the total inland freshwater population moves to coastal sites in winter (Meltofte 1996b).

Analysis of Dutch ring-recovery data shows that of nine grebes ringed as juveniles, two moved southwest into northern France, while adults (n=24) wintered locally (42%), or when their feeding areas froze moved southwest (21%) or eastwards (37%) (van der Poel 1984). It is suggested by Adriaensen et al (1993) that southeasterly movements, particularly from Finland and Sweden during October–November, show a real migration route. Exceptional movements have included a Dutch-ringed grebe recovered near the Caspian Sea (van der Poel 1984) and two grebes ringed in Sweden and Finland and recovered in Turkey (Adriaensen *et al* 1993).

There were five movements of Great Crested Grebes to or from continental Europe during 1909–97 (Fig 4) but, with a national total of only 38 recoveries, it is difficult to quantify the degree of exchange between Britain & Ireland and the Continent. The collection of further data is needed.

Many British & Irish Great Crested Grebes depend on a small number of traditional coastal environments that are also used by commercial freight and oil tankers. Foraging and roosting sites are frequently located close to shipping lanes, with the risk of environmental contamination from accidental oil spillage. Legislation protects many estuaries, but in some cases the deeper waters are not effectively protected; at Belfast Lough, for example, further consultation is under way to extend the protected area to include all areas used by the wintering population of *c* 2,100 grebes, thus reducing the threat to this high proportion of the Northern Irish Great Crested Grebe population.

In the future, it would be extremely useful to monitor dispersal, population shifts and habitat use through increased ringing effort and the use of radio-tagging. This would promote a greater understanding of the complex seasonal movements of Great Crested Grebes and their dependence on certain wintering areas and breeding sites. The extent of interchange between Britain and continental Europe is still unknown.

Ken Perry

Northern Fulmar (Fulmar)

Fulmarus glacialis

Fulmars are pelagic birds that live in the colder and macroplankton-rich parts of the North Atlantic and North Pacific Oceans (Furness & Todd 1984). The species' range and numbers in the Atlantic have increased dramatically during the last couple of centuries. For example, the Fulmar colonized Newfoundland and Labrador during the 1970s (Nettleship & Lock 1973), and numbers in Britain & Ireland almost doubled between 1969–70 and 1985–87 (Lloyd *et al* 1991). The reason for these changes is unclear, although an increase in food availability following Man's vastly increased whaling and then fishing activities must have played a part (Fisher 1952). Or some sudden genetic change may have allowed the species to colonize new areas (Wynne-Edwards 1962).

The nominate race *glacialis* breeds in Svalbard, the Barents Sea, Jan Mayen, Iceland, the Faeroes, Britain, Ireland, Norway, Helgoland, Normandy and Brittany (*BWP*). In the western Atlantic, it breeds mainly in West Greenland and the islands of the eastern Canadian Arctic, south as far as Newfoundland. Fulmars of the high Arctic have smaller bills and lower weights, and the populations have a higher proportion of dark morphs ('Blue Fulmars') than do those in lower latitudes. The Pacific subspecies *rodgersii* breeds from Alaska to the Kuril Islands; its measurements most closely match those of the Antarctic Fulmar *F. glacialoides*, which is generally regarded as the ancestral form (Wynne-Edwards 1952). In the western Palearctic, Fulmars occur year-round across the entire marine sector south from the polar pack-ice to about 50°N, with a slight shift south in the winter out of the most northerly seas into less cold waters, some reaching 40°N. The Fulmar's range,

The analysis of the data for this species was supported by David Milne QC

therefore, encompasses vast tracts of ocean where there is little chance of a ringed bird being reported.

Following its range expansion, the Fulmar breeds in most coastal counties of Britain and Ireland, and numbers continue to increase. The species is most abundant in northern Scotland, where it breeds on virtually all coasts that have cliffs or steep coastal banks. In recent years, there has been a spread inland to quarries and cliffs and, in some areas, sand-dunes and man-made structures have been colonized (Anderson 1982).

The ringing locations of birds later recovered agree broadly with the breeding distribution but numbers are heavily biased towards colonies in the far north, notably Orkney and Shetland: that is, colonies where birds have more-or-less direct access to the North Sea (Fig 1). Fulmars on St Kilda have a different diet and make much longer foraging trips than those on Shetland (Furness & Todd 1984), for example, so a difference in the patterns of recoveries from birds at northern and western colonies is to be anticipated but, as yet, there are too few recoveries from birds ringed in the west to look for such differences.

The bulk of recoveries (more than 70%) come from birds ringed as chicks (Fig 2). As fully grown birds rarely alight on land, other than at actual or prospective breeding sites (*CBWP*), relatively few are ever ringed. The recoveries are even more biased towards younger birds since

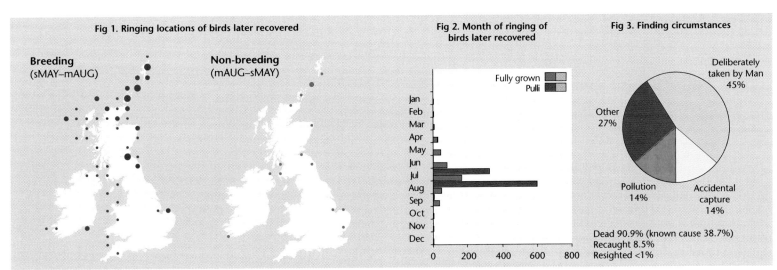

Fig 1. Ringing locations of birds later recovered

Breeding (sMAY–mAUG)   Non-breeding (mAUG–sMAY)

Fig 2. Month of ringing of birds later recovered

Fully grown / Pulli

Fig 3. Finding circumstances

Deliberately taken by Man 45%
Other 27%
Pollution 14%
Accidental capture 14%

Dead 90.9% (known cause 38.7%)
Recaught 8.5%
Resighted <1%

Ringing and recovery data

	<1960	60–69	70–79	80–89	90–97	Total
RINGING						
BTO ringing totals (%)	5	13	21	39	22	98,975
RECOVERIES						
BTO-ringed (%)	5	9	21	37	28	1,334
Foreign-ringed (%)	←	43	→	48	9	23

Statistical analyses

	Breeding population (sMAY–mAUG)	Wintering population (mNOV–sMAR)
Status	SHORT-DISTANCE MIGRANT (2)	?
Age differences[NT]	Not significant*	—
Sex differences	Not tested	—
Regional differences	Significant[3]*	—
Finding circumstances	(Not significant)	—

Fig 4. Locations in the breeding season of (a) 151 immature and (b) 112 adult Fulmars ringed as pulli in Britain & Ireland.

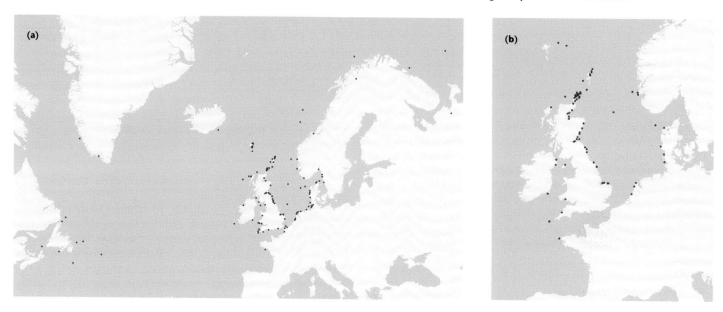

Fig 5. Locations outside the breeding season of (a) 385 immature and (b) 44 adult Fulmars ringed as pulli in Britain & Ireland.

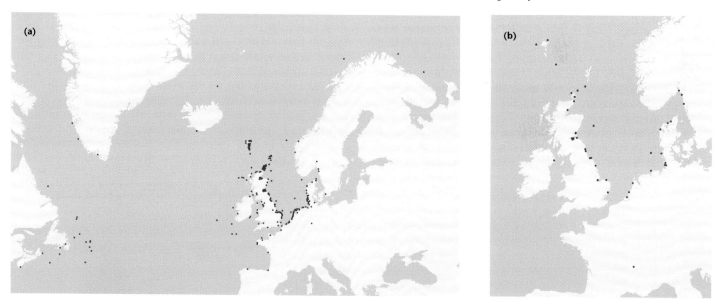

Fulmars do not reach sexual maturity until they are nine years old (Dunnet *et al* 1979), by which time many of the aluminium rings used up to the 1960s will have fallen off. Where recovery circumstances were known (for 39% of birds recovered dead), about half were birds deliberately taken by Man (Fig 3). More than half of these 'hunted' recoveries came from the Faeroes, with the proportional contribution to the overall total varying considerably: 12% of all recoveries during the 1950s, 3% in the 1960s and rising to 15% during the 1990s. Pollution and accidental capture each contributed 14% to recovery causes. These potential biases should be borne in mind when interpreting the recovery patterns, particularly if considering temporal changes.

After fledging, young Fulmars spend perhaps four years at sea, during which time they disperse widely and probably never visit land. They then spend a further five summers visiting potential nesting areas. During this period of immaturity, the longest of any British bird, recoveries are dispersed widely throughout the eastern and western Atlantic, Norwegian and Barent Seas, and the Arctic (Macdonald 1977), with rather little difference in the distribution of recoveries coming from within and outside the breeding season (Figs 4a & 5a). The majority of

the distant records occur within the first four years of life (Macdonald 1977). There are recoveries in the western Atlantic in all months except February, so perhaps some young individuals remain there for one or more years. The absence of recoveries in the central Atlantic, where direct observations show Fulmars to be present, presumably reflects the very low chance of obtaining a recovery in areas where there is no fishing activity. The contrasting concentration of recoveries in the North Sea, especially in winter, may be due to a high chance of a dead bird being found and reported. There is a suggestion that a higher proportion of birds from western colonies cross the Atlantic (Fig 6), but this could be an artefact due to there being fewer recoveries than expected from west Scotland and Ireland. The geographic spread of recoveries once birds are adult is greatly reduced (Figs 4b & 5b) but still there is little difference in recovery distribution in and outside the breeding season. There is one quite exceptional inland recovery in France. There are too few recoveries of birds of known sex to look for differences in movement patterns between the sexes, but a long-term study on Orkney showed that males spend longer than females at nest sites during the winter (pers obs), suggesting that females could range further when not breeding.

Fig 6. All included exchanges of Fulmars between (a) the north (433) and (b) the northwest (58) of Britain & Ireland and abroad.

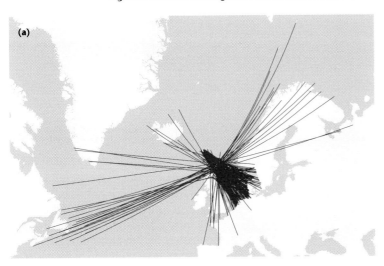

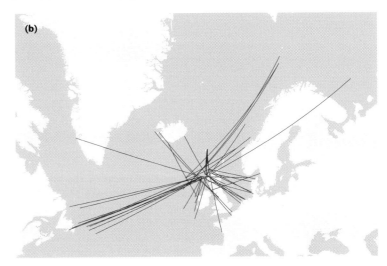

Fig 7. Movements of over 20 km and recovery locations of Fulmars ringed as pulli in Britain & Ireland and recovered in a subsequent breeding season when of breeding age. There were 36:82 movements under:over 20 km but only those over 20 km are plotted.

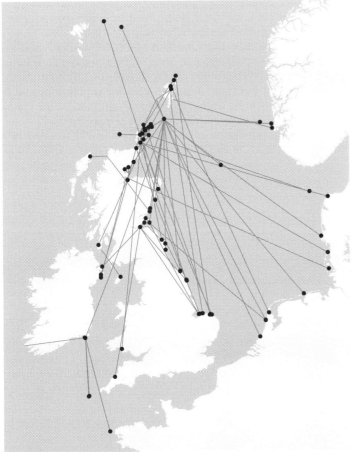

Fulmars attend colonies for most of the year, though numbers are noticeably depressed in midwinter, and in May, when many breeders are absent for a few weeks prior to egg-laying (Dunnet *et al* 1963). These observations are supported by at-sea surveys, which have shown low densities in most areas around Britain & Ireland between December and February, with densities increasing during March and April and high from May to July, both around the colonies and in feeding areas, such as at the shelf edge to the north and west of Scotland and on the Dogger and Rockall Banks (Stone *et al* 1995). From August to November, densities increase in the North Sea south of the Firth of Forth (where they are generally lower during the main part of the breeding season), as far as 53°N. Densities in the English Channel, the Southwest Approaches and the extreme southern part of the North Sea remain low all year round. During the late spring, recoveries point to an increase in the numbers of Fulmars in the North Sea, particularly off Denmark and the Low Countries, perhaps linked to high salinity, good water clarity and stratification giving concentrations of zooplankton and small fish in the vicinity of the German Bight (Garthe 1997). From May onwards, the density of Fulmars in the southern and eastern North Sea increases, probably as non-breeding birds move into the area to moult (Lloyd *et al* 1991).

Fig 7 includes the recovery locations of birds that were present (although not necessarily breeding) at colonies away from where they were ringed as chicks but, since incubation stints can be as long as 11 days, which allows birds to travel hundreds of miles (Macdonald 1977, Hamer *et al* 1997), many of the summer recoveries of birds of breeding age are well within the normal foraging range of birds either breeding or visiting colonies. Once a pair of birds has bred, they generally remain together for several successive breeding seasons and changes of nesting site are rare, except in cases of nesting failure (Dunnet *et al* 1963). Most Fulmars nest on sheer cliffs or isolated stacks where breeding birds are difficult to catch. This explains the paucity of wider-scale data on the colony fidelity of both chicks and adults.

Twenty-two foreign-ringed Fulmars have been found in Britain & Ireland. Seven of these were ringed at sea, and one of these (ringed off Labrador in July) was later found breeding on Great Saltee. The others came from Iceland, the Faeroes, Denmark, Norway and Svalbard. It remains unclear what proportion of the Fulmars seen off the shores of Britain & Ireland are of foreign origin.

Fulmars spend most of their life at sea, where data collection is expensive and fraught with logistical difficulties. Although plenty of information on the activities of British & Irish Fulmars at the breeding colonies now exists, much remains unknown. Many of the unanswered questions relate to their sea-based life. For example, there is little known about where breeding birds go when they forage at sea, the factors that determine the accessibility and distribution of food, or where birds are in general when at sea outside the breeding season. It is unlikely that ringing alone can answer these questions, and remote tracking may have much to offer (Falk & Moller 1995). The breeding success of the older breeders, some aged 30 or more, has not been compared with that of younger adults. The issues surrounding the exchange of birds between colonies in Britain & Ireland and those elsewhere are also largely unexplored.

Alexander Anderson & Peter Cosgrove

Manx Shearwater
Puffinus puffinus

Manx Shearwaters are transequatorial migrants, nesting in burrows and active on the surface of their island colonies only at night. British & Irish birdwatchers are familiar with their passage movements off west-coast headlands.

In the eastern Atlantic, Manx Shearwaters breed in the Westman Islands off Iceland, the Faeroes, Britain, Ireland, Brittany, Madeira, the Canary Islands and the Azores (Brooke 1990, Monteiro *et al* 1999). Within the past 50 years, this species has also become more common as a breeding species in the western Atlantic, with an established colony in Newfoundland and sporadic records from other locations in New England and Canada. However, the Bermuda population is now apparently extinct (Brooke 1990). The temperate populations are long-distance migrants, with the majority of British & Irish birds wintering in the western South Atlantic, most commonly off the coast of Brazil. The movements of the subtropical North Atlantic populations are unknown (*BWP*). A sibling species, Mediterranean Shearwater *P. yelkouan* has recently been separated (Bourne *et al* 1988, BOU 1991). Five additional closely related taxa are recognized in the Pacific.

There are three main centres of population in Britain & Ireland (Lloyd *et al* 1991, *1988–91 Atlas*): the small isles off western Scotland, principally Rum (Wormell 1976); Skomer, Skokholm and Middleholm off southwest Wales (Smith *et al* 2001); and various islands off Kerry. Much smaller numbers are present at some 30 other locations (Lloyd *et al* 1991). Ideally, Manx Shearwaters require breeding sites free of mammalian predators including rats (Brooke 1990). They are typically pelagic birds of the continental shelf, avoiding inshore waters outside the breeding

The analysis of the data for this species was supported by the Copeland Bird Observatory

season (*BWP*), and feed within a few metres of the water surface by surface or plunge diving (Brooke 1990). During the breeding season, they are associated with seasonal fronts, most notably the Irish Sea Front, where prey may be concentrated near the surface (Stone *et al* 1994, Begg & Reid 1997). There is no detailed information on the distribution of pelagic seabird species in their main wintering grounds off southern Brazil (Neves & Olmos 1998). However, the River Plate Estuary, at the southern boundary of this area, has high primary productivity in the austral summer (J L Orgeira pers comm) associated with mixing of subantarctic and subtropical water masses, and is noted for its seabird concentrations, including Manx Shearwaters (Cooke & Mills 1972).

The greatest ringing effort, generating recoveries for both adults and birds ringed as pulli, has been at the Pembrokeshire colonies (Fig 1). Substantial ringing effort has also occurred at the relatively small colonies adjacent to the Bardsey and Copeland bird observatories, with many fewer being ringed at the major colonies on Rum and the Kerry islands. Fully grown birds can be caught on the surface at night from March to September (Fig 2), especially during moonless nights in June and July (Brooke 1990). Chicks are easily caught when 'exercising' at their burrow entrances prior to fledging, from mid-August to early October.

A major ringing programme was initiated on Skokholm in the 1930s, with over 15,300 birds, mainly fully grown, ringed between 1936 and 1939

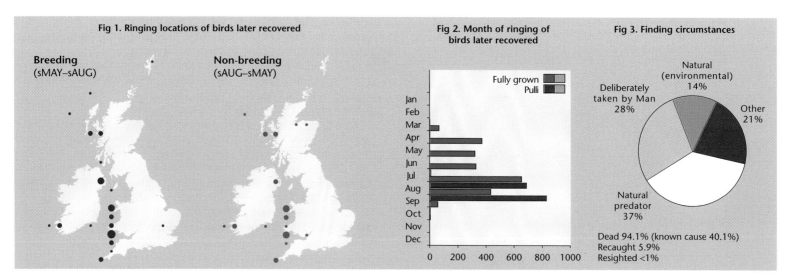

Fig 1. Ringing locations of birds later recovered

Breeding (sMAY–sAUG)

Non-breeding (sAUG–sMAY)

Fig 2. Month of ringing of birds later recovered

Fig 3. Finding circumstances

Natural (environmental) 14%
Deliberately taken by Man 28%
Other 21%
Natural predator 37%

Dead 94.1% (known cause 40.1%)
Recaught 5.9%
Resighted <1%

Ringing and recovery data

	<1960	60–69	70–79	80–89	90–97	Total
RINGING						
BTO ringing totals (%)	31	32	16	13	8	283,170
RECOVERIES						
BTO-ringed (%)	26	31	17	18	7	3,768
Foreign-ringed (%)	←	88	→	13	0	8

Statistical analyses

	Breeding population (sMAY–sAUG)	Wintering population (sNOV–mJAN)
Status	LONG-DISTANCE MIGRANT (4)	NONE
Age differences	Not tested	—
Sex differences	Not tested	—
Regional differences	Not tested	—
Finding circumstances	Not tested	—

(Lockley 1942, 1953). Prior to this, it was known that Manx Shearwaters occurred off Brazil in the northern winter, but their provenance was unknown. Unfortunately, the short life of the aluminium rings used prior to the introduction of harder metal (Monel) rings in 1958 severely limited the potential information return from this early effort (Harris 1964a), and it was not until October 1952 that the first British-ringed Manx Shearwater was recovered in South America (Brooke 1990). In the 40 years since Monel rings were introduced, many shearwaters, mainly pulli, have been ringed at the Pembrokeshire colonies, the majority up to 1976, when ringing ceased on Skokholm (Brooke 1990).

Manx Shearwaters exhibit a high degree of philopatry (Brooke 1990); few are recaptured alive away from their ringing site and the vast majority of recoveries are of dead birds. Hence, despite their long lifespan, which can extend to over 50 years (BTO data), there are few recaptures of individuals away from the breeding colonies, and this limits the conclusions that may be drawn from the data. The cause of death has been reported in 40% of cases (Fig 3). Nearly a third of these are birds deliberately (28%) or accidentally (3%) captured by Man. These recoveries introduce geographical bias into the data set as the great majority are from the Bay of Biscay where fishermen captured substantial numbers of Manx Shearwaters for food, bait and recreation up to at least the 1970s (Brooke 1990). A further 8% of reported causes of death are human-related and this may also add bias to the data as such birds are more likely to be discovered than those dying in more remote locations (including at sea). Conversely, the pelagic habits of Manx Shearwaters outside the breeding season considerably reduce the chances of ringed birds being discovered in their wintering grounds or on passage.

Brooke (1990) undertook a detailed analysis of BTO ring-recoveries of Manx Shearwaters to 1987. This text builds upon his interpretation of movement patterns, which he gained from a detailed examination of the movements of various year classes and of some key individual birds.

At the Pembrokeshire colonies, the first fledglings depart in mid-August, with numbers peaking in early to mid-September and a few stragglers remaining until early October (Brooke 1990). The timing of breeding is sometimes slightly later on Rum (Thompson 1987). Parents desert the chicks for variable periods prior to fledging; hence adults on average depart the breeding colonies before the young of the year. By the end of October, the species is all but absent from European waters (Stone et al 1994). In late August, large numbers of Manx Shearwaters move south along the Atlantic coast of the Outer Hebrides (Burton & Burton 1963) and major southward autumn-passage movements have also been observed from Erris Head in western Ireland (Phillips & Lee 1966). Early autumn concentrations of Manx Shearwaters, presumably feeding up in preparation for migration, have been recorded in association with the Irish Sea Front (Stone et al 1994).

During August to October, the majority of recoveries of Manx Shearwaters ringed in Britain & Ireland are of dead birds found in Britain or France (Fig 4a). In the early migration period, fledglings in particular may be blown inland by autumnal gales (Brooke 1990). However, from September there is a rapid build-up of recoveries along the east coast of South America, and the majority of recoveries between November and mid-January are from this area, principally north from the River Plate at Montevideo, latitude 35°S, to Rio de Janeiro, latitude 23°S (Fig 4b). The median distance travelled between ringing and recovery for Manx Shearwaters ringed in the breeding season and recovered in winter is 9,328 km ($P5$–95=26–$11,261$ km, n=61) and this large distance can be covered remarkably quickly. Brooke (1990) cited an example of a fledgling recovered dead on the coast of Brazil just 16 days after being ringed on Skokholm. The bird was estimated to have been dead for at least three days when recovered, giving a minimum average speed of 740 km per day.

The occurrence of mass movements of Manx Shearwaters along the west coast of Ireland in autumn suggests that birds from the Hebridean colonies initially head south via this route, rather than by entering the Irish Sea (Phillips & Lee 1966). The route taken once birds leave French

and Spanish waters cannot be determined with any certainty as there are few records from mid-ocean. However, recoveries from the Canary Islands and adjacent African coast in September, one from Ghana in October (Fig 4a), and another of uncertain date from Angola, suggest that at least some birds follow eastern Atlantic coasts a considerable distance south before heading across the Atlantic towards southern Brazil and Uruguay. Such a route would take advantage of the northeast trade winds (Brooke 1990). Brooke (1990) cited an absence of autumn recoveries of fledglings from northern Brazil as possible further evidence in favour of this route. However, there have been a few September recoveries from this northern part of Brazil (Fig 4a) and the question of the southward migration route remains to be resolved.

During the spring (mid-January to end April), there is a major decline in recoveries from South America, coinciding with a rapid increase in recoveries from Spain, France, Britain and Ireland (Fig 4c) as Manx Shearwaters migrate back to their breeding grounds. By the height of the breeding season (May to July), the great majority of recoveries are from Britain & Ireland, with the median distance travelled from point of ringing being less than 1 km (Fig 4d). Prior to the 1980s, sardine fishermen in the Bay of Biscay also captured substantial numbers of ringed birds in the late spring and during the breeding season. These were thought by Lockley (1942, 1953) to be breeding birds from the Pembrokeshire colonies, but Brooke (1990) concluded that, with the exception of breeding females during their pre-laying exodus (Harris 1966, Perrins & Brooke 1976), the majority were in fact probably non-breeders. In addition, observations at sea in the 1980s provided no evidence of birds commuting from Pembrokeshire to the Bay of Biscay (Stone et al 1994).

Even less is known about the spring migration route than the autumn journey. A few adult birds have been recovered south of the River Plate in late winter and early spring, the most southerly being from the vicinity of Puerto Madryn, latitude 42°46'S, in January. A January cruise by Cooke & Mills (1972) found Manx Shearwaters as far south as 49° and there have also been winter and spring sightings at c 51°S in the Falkland Islands (Woods 1988, White et al 1999). There has also been a recovery near Cape Town, but in unknown circumstances, of an adult from Copeland. Although the origin of such birds is unknown, these records would be consistent with an anticlockwise loop migration in the South Atlantic, as suggested by Thomson (1965). However, the absence of known winter or spring recoveries along the west coast of southern Africa (Figs 4b & c) together with the general paucity of sightings in this area and their concentration in the winter months (Sinclair & Rose 1982), do not support this hypothesis.

There is evidence to suggest that, once in the North Atlantic, Manx Shearwaters follow a more westerly migration route in spring than in the autumn (Thomson 1965, Brooke 1990). There have been spring recoveries of adults (here defined as birds at least five years old) in North Carolina, the Azores and mid-Atlantic (Fig 4c) and, in contrast with the autumn (Fig 4a), a complete absence of recoveries in the vicinity of West Africa. In addition, systematic sea-borne surveys off the coast of North Carolina have recorded peak numbers of Manx Shearwaters in February and March (Lee 1995).

As previously stated by Brooke (1990), there is no evidence to suggest any difference in migratory movements between Manx Shearwaters ringed at the Pembrokeshire colonies and the smaller numbers ringed elsewhere in Britain & Ireland.

While the general picture that emerges from ring-recoveries is of British & Irish Manx Shearwaters of all ages wintering in the western South Atlantic and returning to their breeding colonies in the summer, there are some noteworthy exceptions to this pattern. There are some winter recoveries from France and Iberia (Fig 4b), which, together with sightings in the southern Bay of Biscay in the same months (Lockley 1953), suggest that not all British & Irish birds undertake a transequatorial migration. In addition, there are some breeding season recoveries, predominantly of immature birds (defined here as less than

Fig 4. Locations in (a) autumn (461:82:188), (b) winter (36:14:10), (c) spring (15:46:254) and (d) the breeding season (20:159:718) of Manx Shearwaters ringed in Britain & Ireland. Those recovered as adults (blue) and first-years (grey) are differentiated from immatures (red). Sample sizes of the classes (first-year: immature: adult) are shown.

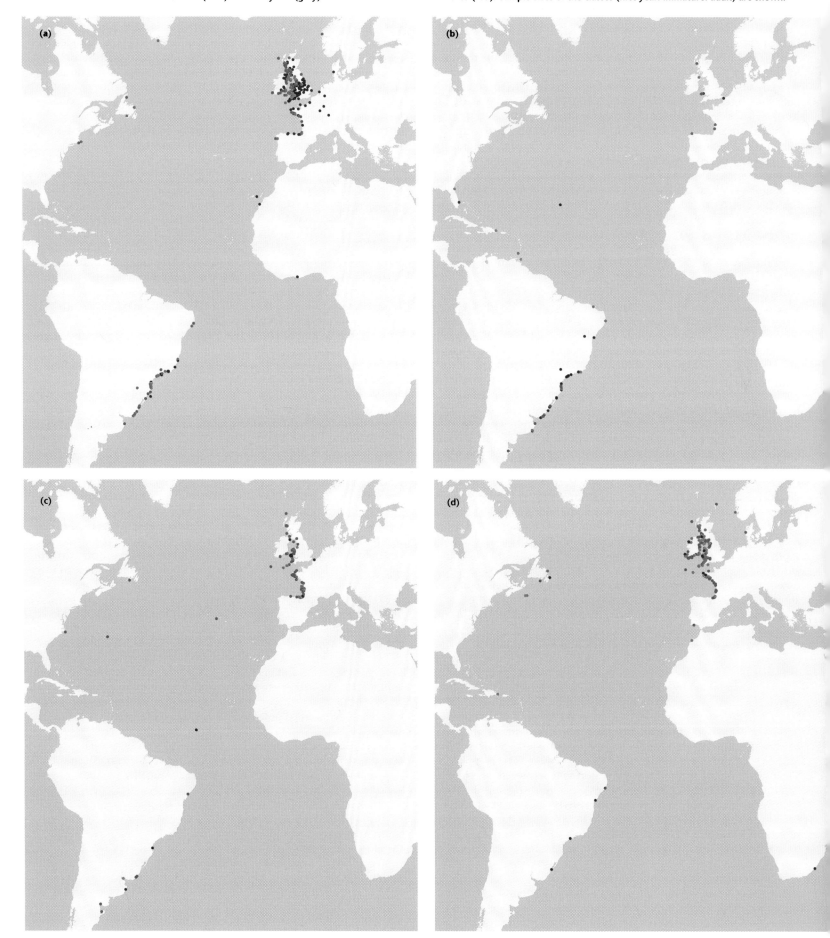

Fig 5. Movements of over 20 km and recovery locations of Manx Shearwaters ringed as pulli in Britain & Ireland and recovered in a subsequent breeding season when of breeding age. There were 146:92 movements under:over 20 km but only those over 20 km are plotted.

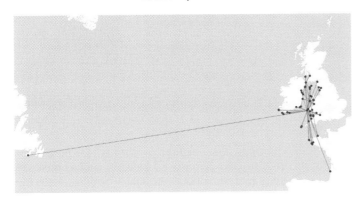

five years old), from both the southwest and northwest Atlantic (Fig 4d). Brooke (1990) noted that the majority of such recoveries are of one-year-old birds and that the western North Atlantic now appears to be an important summering area for these young birds. Post (1967) described a marked increase in summer sightings off the northeastern United States and Canada from the 1950s, followed since the mid-1970s by a similar increase off the southeastern States (Lee 1995). This penetration into the western North Atlantic by Manx Shearwaters coincided with the formation of the first North American colony, at Middle Lawn Island, Newfoundland, in the 1970s. Recoveries at or near this colony strongly indicate that some of the colonists originated from the Pembrokeshire colonies (Storey & Lien 1985) (Fig 5). There have also been a number of winter recoveries of immature birds in the Caribbean (Fig 4b) and Manx Shearwaters have been sighted off the southeastern United States in all months of the year (Lee 1995). It seems possible that some of those birds that spend their first summer off North America may subsequently winter in the greater Caribbean area (Brooke 1990).

An analysis of ring-recoveries on Skomer and Skokholm concluded that, while male Shearwaters apparently normally return to their natal colony to breed, around half of females may emigrate, if only to immediately adjacent colonies within the same island group (Brooke 1978). In addition, the possibility of birds visiting several colonies when immature (Harris 1972) means that caution must be exercised before concluding that a bird has definitely moved between colonies (Brooke 1990). However, there have to date been 92 records of birds ringed as fledglings at Irish Sea colonies being recaptured as adults at locations 20 km or more distant (Fig 5), constituting 40% of all recorded natal dispersal movements. The majority are of birds from Skokholm or Skomer

recaptured on Bardsey or Copeland, the nearest colonies regularly worked by ringers, and a number of these birds have been recaptured at the same colony in two or more years (Brooke 1990). Once Manx Shearwaters begin to breed, they are highly faithful to their colonies and there have been only five records of birds ringed when of breeding age during the breeding season being recaptured over 20 km distant in a subsequent breeding season (from a total of 11 such breeding dispersal movements). There have been no confirmed records of either natal or breeding dispersal between the Irish Sea and Hebridean colonies.

There is no evidence from ringing or other sources of through passage in British & Irish waters of Manx Shearwaters from breeding populations abroad. The eight foreign-ringed birds that have been recovered in Britain & Ireland have all involved exchanges with French colonies.

In the Bay of Biscay, large numbers of shearwaters used to be taken by fishermen for food or sport (Lockley 1953, Brooke 1990), but numbers of Manx Shearwaters recovered in this region have declined markedly over the past 20 years, from 265 in 1960–79 to just six in 1980–97. Several factors may have contributed to this, including a significant reduction in ringing effort at the Pembrokeshire colonies, legal protection in France since 1975 (Bernard Cadiou pers comm) and a possible decline in the birds' use of the southern part of the Bay of Biscay (Brooke 1990, Stone et al 1994). However, while mortality of Manx Shearwaters in fisheries has apparently declined in the Bay of Biscay, the potential for such impacts in the wintering grounds has yet to be assessed. Four Manx Shearwaters recovered dead off South America were either deliberately or accidentally taken by Man and long-line fisheries over the Patagonian Shelf south of Puerto Madryn, latitude 42°30'S, and off the River Plate at 35–37°S, take significant bycatches of Procellariiformes, particularly Black-browed Albatrosses (eg Schiavini et al 1998). Shearwaters have not been recorded as a bycatch in these fisheries, but Great Shearwaters have been caught by demersal long-liners off southern Brazil in the austral winter (Neves & Olmos 1998). These Brazilian fisheries are expanding (Neves & Olmos 1998) and, although the large baits used in some sectors of the industry may effectively exclude smaller Procellariiformes, such as the Manx Shearwater, from capture (Júnior 1991), the possible implications for Manx Shearwaters wintering in these waters are unknown.

Large-scale ringing of Manx Shearwaters in Britain & Ireland has taught us much about their seasonal migration and post-natal movements. However, more remains to be discovered, particularly with respect to migration routes, fidelity to wintering sites and movements of first-year and second-year birds. In future, satellite-tracking of individual birds may help to resolve these tantalizing questions about the long-distance journeys of this extraordinary bird.

K R Thompson

European Storm-petrel (Storm Petrel)

Hydrobates pelagicus

The Storm Petrel is Britain's smallest seabird and is truly pelagic, only coming ashore under the cover of darkness to breed (or to prospect for breeding sites) among scree slopes, boulder beaches, cracks in peat banks, dry stone walls, and collapsed buildings of all kinds (with a particular fondness in the Northern Isles for Pictish brochs). In Britain and Ireland, breeding colonies are more or less restricted to remote islands and skerries on the west coast, from the Isles of Scilly to Shetland, with the largest colonies (more than 10,000 pairs) found in the west of Ireland (Lloyd *et al* 1991). Elsewhere, Storm Petrels breed in Norway, the Faeroes, possibly Iceland, and there is a subpopulation in the Mediterranean that appears to be largely resident (Hashmi & Fliege 1994). North Atlantic birds disperse southwards in the autumn to the seas off western and southern Africa, and into the Indian Ocean.

Up to the mid-1970s, Storm Petrels were captured mainly by interception by mist-nets as they visited colonies. Since then, the high responsiveness of birds to tape-recordings of the 'purr' call on coastal sites far away from colonies has resulted in ringers catching birds in many locations, where there is little likelihood of nesting, around Britain, including the east coast (Milton 1996), in Portugal, and in Norway, the Faeroes, Ireland and Iceland (Figs 1 & 4). Some 100,000 birds have been ringed in this way in Shetland alone. This technique selects for the population class known as 'wanderers' or 'wandering pre-breeders', however (Mainwood 1976). The differences between the 'wanderer' and 'breeder' classes include arrival dates, recapture rates, ectoparasite burden, presence of a brood patch, biometrics and behavioural features (Furness & Baillie 1981, Fowler *et al* 1984, 1986).

The analysis of the data for this species was supported by Dave Okill & Jim Fowler

'Wanderers' probably come inshore to prospect for potential nest sites, and also to visit colonies. The presence of such individuals in samples of birds caught at colonies generates heterogeneity in the sample, thus greatly inflating mark–recapture estimates of the size of a colony (Love 1978). However, samples of birds tape-lured away from colonies are considered to represent a homogeneous population class, are equal in sex ratio (Fowler *et al* 1986) and have been shown to disperse randomly without significant bias towards recapture location, so that they are ideal subjects for mark–recapture studies (Fowler 1985); older birds, which are rarely attracted, are probably failed breeders. For example, there are consistent estimates of about 60,000 birds available for capture in this way in any year in Shetland waters (Fowler & Hounsome 1998).

Most birds recovered have been ringed in July and August (Fig 2). The vast majority of recoveries are also breeding-season recaptures of 'wanderers' at tape-lures (Fig 4a), or recaptures in colonies, where a 20-year-old retrap is not unusual (indeed, the retrapping of a colony-ringed bird in the same colony more than 4 years after ringing provides strong evidence of a breeding bird). Less than 5% of the recoveries refer to dead birds and a cause of recovery has been attributed to over half of these (Fig 3); around half have been taken by a natural predator, a further 24% accruing from the activities of humans. Winter recoveries are mainly

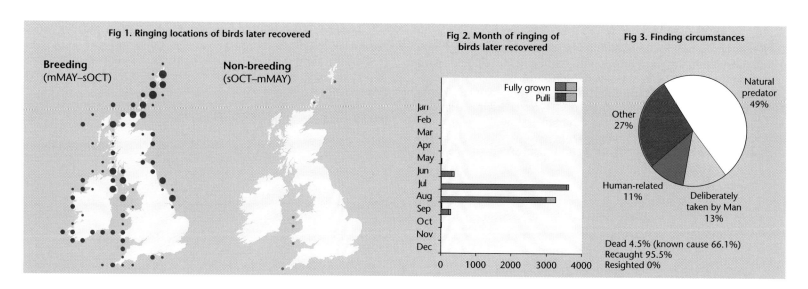

Ringing and recovery data

	<1960	60–69	70–79	80–89	90–97	Total
RINGING						
BTO ringing totals (%)	2	12	25	33	29	340,725
RECOVERIES						
BTO-ringed (%)	0	2	12	34	52	7,167
Foreign-ringed (%)	0	2	1	5	91	437

Statistical analyses

	Breeding population (mMAY–sOCT)	Wintering population (sDEC–sMAR)
Status	LONG-DISTANCE MIGRANT*	NONE
Age differences	Not tested	—
Sex differences	Not tested	—
Regional differences	Not tested	—
Finding circumstances	Not tested	—

Fig 4. All included exchanges between Britain & Ireland and abroad, and recovery locations of Storm Petrels recovered during (a) the breeding season (29:839), (b) autumn (16:2), (c) winter (28:1) and (d) spring (16:0). Dead recoveries (red) are differentiated from live recaptures (blue). The large number of live recaptures during the breeding season is mainly due to the tape-luring of wandering immatures. Sample sizes of the recovery types (dead recoveries:live recaptures) are shown.

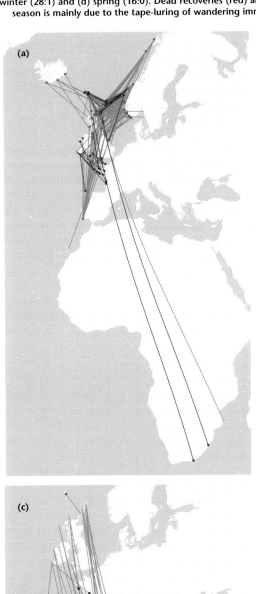

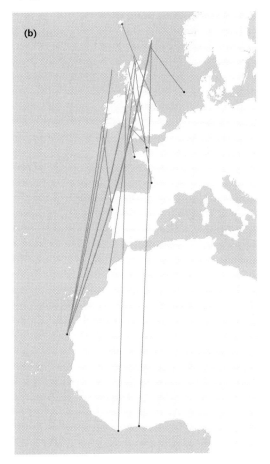

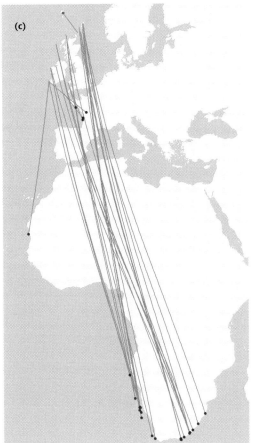

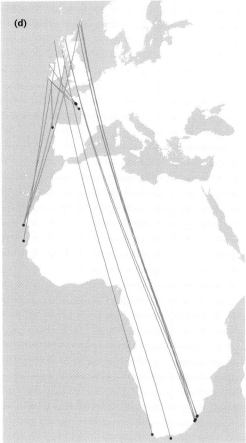

Fig 5. Movements of over 200 km made by 51 Storm Petrels within three days of being captured. Most of these movements were made during July and August, although a small number took place in June and September.

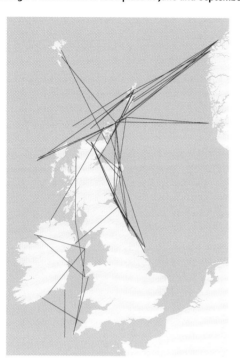

storm-wrecked birds on African beaches or captures aboard fishing vessels (Fig 4).

Breeding birds arrive at colonies from the end of April and, when not in burrows, are presumed to disperse into the North Atlantic or North Sea to feed (Scott 1970). Because recoveries of known breeding birds are so scarce, little is understood about their movements. Chicks fledge during September and October and migrate to waters around the coast of southern Africa (Fig 4). Numbers of birds captured at tape-lures peter out during September but it is probable that departure for winter quarters takes place over a protracted period. At this time, many birds enter the Mediterranean Sea (Hashmi & Fliege 1994) but, in the absence of ring-recoveries to link these to an alternative population, there is no assurance that these are not Mediterranean breeders. Storm Petrels appear off West Africa from the middle of November. Although some may winter further north off Mauritania (*BWP*), most birds probably spend the period from December to April off southwest and South Africa (Fig 4). Northward movements offshore occur in West Africa in March and April, while records further south later in the spring are probably of birds of pre-breeding age (*BWP*). Surveys at sea around Britain and Ireland have recorded the highest densities between June and August, with far lower densities from September onwards, perhaps as a result of the departure of the non-breeding part of the population (Stone *et al* 1995, Pollock *et al* 2000). Densities decline further through October and November and very few have been recorded between December and April.

It is believed that British & Irish birds do not return northwards in their first year but do so two or three years later, when they form the 'wanderer' class. Thus, of 517 chicks ringed on Mousa (Shetland) since 1990, 18 have been recaptured subsequently in Shetland at a tape-lure, 14 two years later and 4 three years later (J D Okill & M Bolton pers

Fig 6. Locations outside the breeding season, and movements between the breeding and non-breeding season, of Storm Petrels present in the breeding season in (a) Scotland (46) and (b) Ireland, Wales, the Isle of Man and the Isles of Scilly (23).

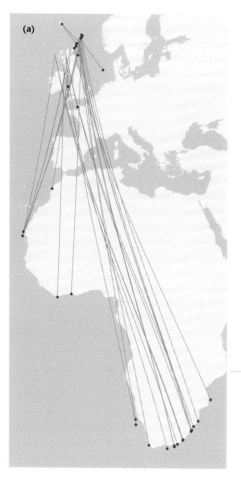

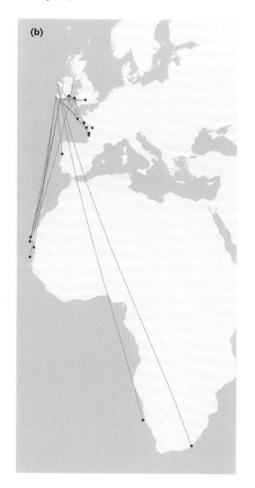

comm). Recaptures of tape-lured birds decline logarithmically in subsequent years (far more rapidly than can be explained by mortality alone); as the birds mature into breeders, they probably become faithful to a colony and cease to be vulnerable to attraction to tape-lures.

Storm Petrels are rarely seen from land and are difficult to observe from ships, so direct observations tell us little about their migrations or seasonal abundance. However, tape-luring Storm Petrels in Portugal throughout the summer has shown that most birds were attracted and captured within a short period of about three weeks in June (Harris *et al* 1993), although there was also evidence of a small early peak in May. Some individuals from these samples were recaptured in Shetland as few as 25 days after ringing, suggesting a minimum northward migration rate of about 116 km per day (assuming the shortest route across the Bay of Biscay). There is also strong evidence of a second large influx of birds into Shetland waters towards the end of July. There appears to be no corresponding second passage past Portugal that might account for the later influx, and its origin is currently unknown (Fowler & Hounsome 1998). Attempts to attract birds to tape-lures in Portugal in autumn have proved fruitless, suggesting that the southward passage takes place further out to sea.

Once in northern waters, immature birds are vulnerable to attraction to tape-lures, and movements between ringing sites all over the eastern North Atlantic, from the Western Isles of Scotland to the Lofoten Isles of Norway and sites in the Faeroes and Iceland, can be extremely rapid (Fig 5). From Shetland, overnight movements to Orkney, or two- or three-day movements to Norway, are not unusual (Fowler & Swinfen 1984, Fowler *et al* 1996). The birds breeding in Irish Sea and western Irish colonies may represent a separate subpopulation (Furness & Baillie 1981b) and interchanges between the 'northern' ringing sites and sites at the Calf of Man, Copeland and in Eire are uncommon. Moreover, there are pronounced differences between the patterns of recoveries shown by birds from these populations, with a greater tendency for the Irish Sea birds to be recovered in the Bay of Biscay (Fig 6).

The main gap in our knowledge of Storm Petrels relates to age-specific migration patterns, especially those of adult breeding birds. Whilst birds tape-lured away from colonies can safely be considered as belonging to the 'wanderer' class, birds caught in colonies (even without the use of tape-lures) may be either breeders or immatures, which therefore cannot be linked to a known breeding location with any certainty. It is admittedly difficult to ring large numbers of Storm Petrel chicks but persistence with this (as is currently being undertaken on Mousa, Shetland, for example) would help to plug the gaps. Some tape-luring in the Cape Verdes or the Canary Islands during spring might help to track the northerly migration, while summer expeditions to southern Greenland, and even eastern North America, might help to reveal the full extent of the wandering propensity of this species.

Jim Fowler

Leach's Storm-petrel (Leach's Petrel)

Oceanodroma leucorhoa

Leach's Petrels are the most oceanic of birds breeding in Britain & Ireland. The nesting colonies are on the most remote oceanic islands (Lloyd *et al* 1991) and their main European feeding areas in the deep Atlantic are over and beyond the edge of the continental shelf (Stone *et al* 1995). These two facts, coupled with the species' habit of being found above ground at the colonies only by night, makes this species one of the least known of those breeding in Britain & Ireland.

Leach's Petrels breed in large numbers on both sides of both the North Atlantic and North Pacific Oceans. Breeding has recently been proved off South Africa (Whittington *et al* 1999) and has long been suspected off New Zealand. The taxonomy of the species is controversial. Nominate *leucorhoa* breeds in the North Atlantic and the North Pacific from Alaska west to Hokkaido, while a small number of subspecies breed south of the range of the nominate form (*BWP*); in the eastern Pacific three distinct populations breed at different times on Guadalupe Island (Power & Ainley 1986). All populations use the higher latitudes for breeding and migrate towards and beyond the Equator outside the breeding season (*BWP*).

In Britain & Ireland, the species breeds only on remote islands, free of mammalian predators, off northern Scotland and on the Stags of Broadhaven in County Mayo, although other sites in Ireland were probably used for breeding in the 1800s (*1988–91 Atlas*). The largest colonies are on St Kilda (Tasker *et al* 1988) and many of the small overall number of recoveries relate to birds ringed there (Fig 1). Most ringing has occurred at colonies; some has been carried out at tape-luring sites on other coasts but has not generated any recoveries to date (Fig 1).

The analysis of the data for this species was supported by David Milne QC

Most recoveries have come from birds ringed in July (Fig 2). Over 90% of the recoveries have been recaptures by ringers, also mostly in July; the wandering of non-breeders between colonies causes this peak (Wilbur 1969). Natural predators were responsible for the two recoveries of dead birds for which a cause of death was given (Fig 3). Birds dying at sea are unlikely to be found owing to the relatively small size and fragility of the species, and there are few ring-recoveries that shed light on the migration of this species. Nearly all records are of recaptures between known breeding sites, with the exceptions being between known breeding sites and other islands in Orkney, Shetland and Norway (Fig 4). Given the difficulty of locating small colonies of this species, it might even be possible that these latter islands are, or were, breeding sites also.

More is known of the migration of this species from observations from land and at sea of birds of unknown breeding origin. Relatively large numbers of Leach's Petrels are sometimes seen inshore along the west European Atlantic seaboard following autumnal and winter storms. For example, strong passages occur regularly off the Wirral. In a remarkable day on 17 September 1978, 663 passed close inshore at Hilbre Island (Craggs 1982). The numbers involved in these influxes are sufficiently large that birds from the western Atlantic must be involved (Boyd 1954, Hémery & Jouanin 1988). This is reinforced by the recovery of a nestling ringed in Newfoundland and found dead in Spain (*BWP*),

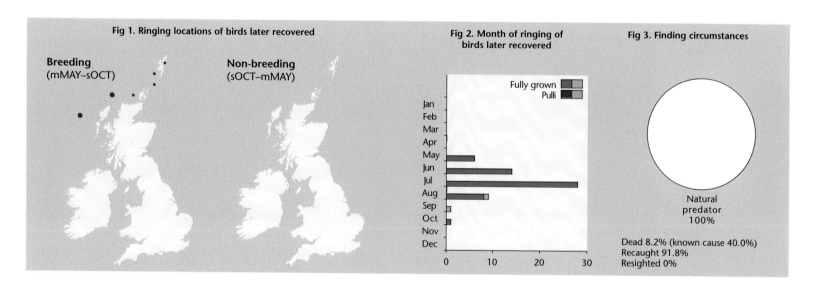

Ringing and recovery data

	<1960	60–69	70–79	80–89	90–97	Total
RINGING						
BTO ringing totals (%)	8	6	30	45	11	11,009
RECOVERIES						
BTO-ringed (%)	3	20	34	24	19	59
Foreign-ringed (%)	←	0	→	0	100	2

Statistical analyses

	Breeding population (mMAY–sOCT)	Wintering population (sDEC–sMAR)
Status	[LONG-DISTANCE MIGRANT]	NONE
Age differences	Not tested	—
Sex differences	Not tested	—
Regional differences	Not tested	—
Finding circumstances	Not tested	—

Fig 4. Recovery locations and movements of over 20 km for the 61 included recoveries of Leach's Petrels ringed or recovered in Britain & Ireland.

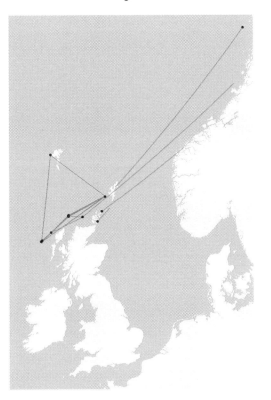

and of a breeding bird ringed in New Brunswick, found in France in January (Hémery & Jouanin 1988). Records at sea indicate that there are many Leach's Petrels in the tropics north of the Equator in the eastern Atlantic between October and January (Bourne 1992), with some moving to the South Atlantic. Hémery & Jouanin (1988) estimated that there are between 300,000 and two million birds in the Bay of Biscay during this same period. Wrecks of Leach's Petrels in Britain & Ireland tend to occur earlier in the autumn than the peaks in occurrence further south (pers obs). At-sea surveys around Britain & Ireland have produced dispersed records of Leach's Petrel during September to November, and very few records from December to April; during May to August the birds are concentrated over the edge of the continental shelf and in the deeper waters off northwest Scotland (Stone *et al* 1995, Pollock *et al* 2000).

Leach's Petrels, like other tubenoses, have a relatively long period of immaturity, perhaps around five years according to studies in the western Atlantic (*BWP*). There is currently no information, from ringing or other sources, on whether these pre-breeding birds behave any differently from the rest of the population; it is likely that, as with Storm Petrel, they wander between breeding sites during the breeding season.

There are no obvious threats to these birds at sea but introduced mammalian predators, particularly rats and cats, are a serious menace at breeding colonies. The small number of long-distance movements between potential breeding areas, demonstrated by the ring-recoveries, suggests that suitable islands that are restored to a predator-free condition are likely to be recolonized by Leach's Petrels. Where such restoration has been carried out off North America, tape-lures have been used to attract birds back to the islands. Much further knowledge of the movements of British & Irish birds outside the breeding season is required, some of which could be gained through targeted ringing despite the very low recovery rates for this species.

Mark L Tasker

Northern Gannet (Gannet)

Morus bassanus

The Northern Gannet, with its dazzling white plumage, black wingtips and 2 m wing span, is perhaps the most impressive of all Britain's seabirds and has long attracted the attention of ornithologists and bird-ringers. It is endemic to the North Atlantic with two largely discrete but morphologically similar populations, in Canada and in Europe. About 60% of the east Atlantic population nests in Britain & Ireland (Murray & Wanless 1997). The remaining colonies are located in France, the Channel Islands, Helgoland, the Faeroes, Iceland, Norway and (a recent colonization) Russia. The Gannet is a bird of the open sea although skeins of birds returning to colonies or migrating can be seen from many British and Irish headlands. Most feeding takes place over the continental shelf well away from land, with concentrations in areas of high marine productivity. Although birds cross Scotland using the Forth–Clyde corridor, the species is normally seen inland only when storm-driven. Typically, birds from European colonies migrate southwards at the end of the breeding season (Thomson 1974, Nelson 1978, Barrett 1988, Veron 1988). The migration is especially strong among first-years, with many birds from the east Atlantic reaching Senegal and some crossing the Equator in the Gulf of Guinea. Some birds enter the Mediterranean but as yet no Icelandic-ringed Gannet has been recovered there. A single Icelandic-ringed bird has been reported from northwest Greenland (Petersen 1998). Canadian Gannets migrate as far south as Florida and some enter the Gulf of Mexico (Nelson 1978); a few cross into the east Atlantic (Walker 1996).

Typically, gannetries are situated on remote islands, which are often difficult to land a boat on. However, once ashore it is often possible to

The analysis of the data for this species was supported by Ron and Jean Shanks

ring large numbers of chicks. Very few adult Gannets are ringed and most recoveries come from chicks ringed on the Bass Rock, Hermaness, Ailsa Craig and Scar Rocks in Scotland, Grassholm in Wales and Great Saltee in Ireland (Figs 1 & 2).

Almost half of the recoveries indicate a cause of death (Fig 3). The most common was accidental capture on baited fishing lines or drowning in nets often well offshore (34%), a further 24% were deliberately killed for food, either by shooting or caught on baited lines, and 22% were due to pollution. The importance of these causes varied geographically, with oiling being highest on North Sea coasts (72%), whereas direct human predation and entanglement in fishing gear, combined because it is often difficult to separate deliberate from accidental capture, was the most common cause in the open sea (69%). Deliberate killing appears to have been most frequent in the Mediterranean, Africa, the Faeroes and Norway. The incidence, or perhaps only the reporting, of deliberate killing appears to have declined over the last 50 years. It is noteworthy that the pelagic recoveries appear to give a somewhat better indication of the at-sea range than is the case for most other seabirds (Fig 4), though the species' use of seas to the west and especially the northwest of Britain & Ireland is still underestimated (Stone *et al* 1995).

Several factors make the interpretation of the numerous recovery data difficult. In addition to the biases mentioned above, the Gannet has a

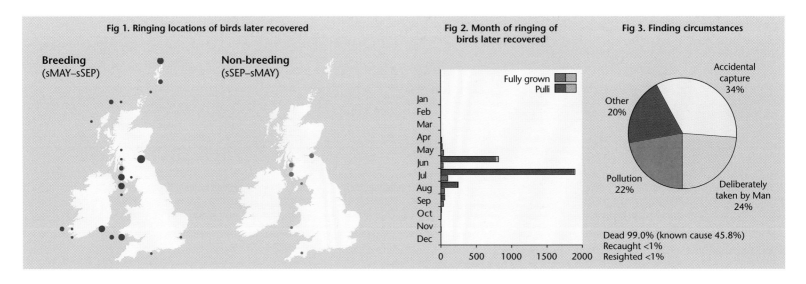

Fig 1. Ringing locations of birds later recovered

Breeding (sMAY–sSEP)

Non-breeding (sSEP–sMAY)

Fig 2. Month of ringing of birds later recovered

Fully grown / Pulli

Fig 3. Finding circumstances

Accidental capture 34%
Other 20%
Pollution 22%
Deliberately taken by Man 24%

Dead 99.0% (known cause 45.8%)
Recaught <1%
Resighted <1%

Ringing and recovery data

	<1960	60–69	70–79	80–89	90–97	Total
RINGING						
BTO ringing totals (%)	33	21	11	19	16	62,328
RECOVERIES						
BTO-ringed (%)	24	27	19	14	17	3,218
Foreign-ringed (%)	←	24	→	40	36	111

Statistical analyses

	Breeding population (sMAY–sSEP)	Wintering population (sDEC–sMAR)
Status	LONG-DISTANCE MIGRANT (2)?	
Age differences[NT]	Significant	—
Sex differences	Not tested	—
Regional differences	Significant[4*]	—
Finding circumstances	Significant	—

Fig 4. Recovery locations of (a) first-year (908), (b) second- to fourth-year (820) and (c) fifth-year and older (639) Gannets ringed or recovered in Britain & Ireland.

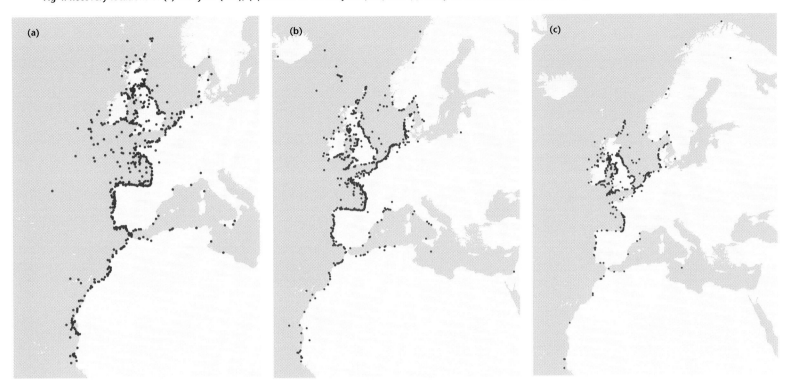

prolonged breeding season and adults attend colonies from January (occasionally even December) to November, with chicks fledging from August to October. Immatures (*ie* up to and including the fourth year) attend colonies for several seasons prior to breeding and there is a variable age of first breeding. There is clearly considerable variation in migratory patterns since birds in all stages of plumage development can be seen in all parts of the range throughout the year. Despite these problems, the general pattern of migration is well documented by both direct observations of migrating birds and the results of ringing (see Thomson 1974, Nelson 1978, 1997).

Juveniles are independent of their parents at fledging. Typically they make a short flight down from the breeding ledges and land on the sea within a few kilometres of the colony. Most are too heavy to take off again and consequently begin their migration by swimming. Once light enough to take off they generally move south immediately, although a few

juveniles from the Bass Rock apparently go north and west around northern Scotland before setting off southwards to wintering grounds south of the Bay of Biscay. Most young travel further south to Morocco, some get as far as Senegal and a few reach the coast of Guinea-Bissau (12°N) (Fig 4). Birds from west-coast British and Irish colonies and those from the Channel Islands (Veron 1988) arrive in the Bay of Biscay, and presumably their wintering grounds, well before those from the Bass Rock.

Migration, particularly of young birds, can be rapid. For example, a juvenile from Ailsa Craig, whose precise fledging date was known, was recovered exhausted in Morocco within 14 days. Six juveniles caught on the water below the colony on Noss, Shetland, and recovered 10–16 days later had moved, on average, 60 km per day (maximum 155 km per day) (Wanless & Okill 1994). From August onwards immatures and some adults enter the Mediterranean, and although numbers of recoveries and sightings decrease to the east of Italy, a few reach Israel. The greatest

Fig 5. Variation in the distances moved by juvenile Gannets with time after ringing as pulli. Medians for 30-day periods (points) and interquartile ranges (bars) are shown.

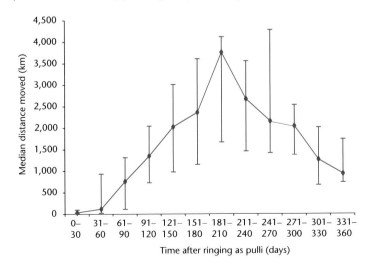

Fig 6. Monthly variation in the differences in latitude between ringing and recovery locations of Gannets present in Britain & Ireland during the breeding season. Monthly medians (points) and interquartile ranges (bars) are shown.

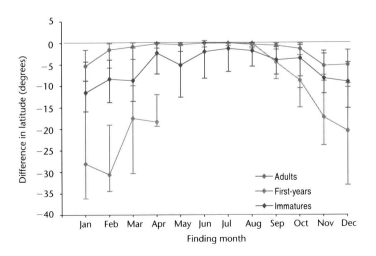

Fig 7. Locations during winter of Gannets that were present in the north (18, red squares), northeast (208, grey circles), northwest (73, blue circles) and southwest (89, blue squares) of Britain & Ireland during the breeding season.

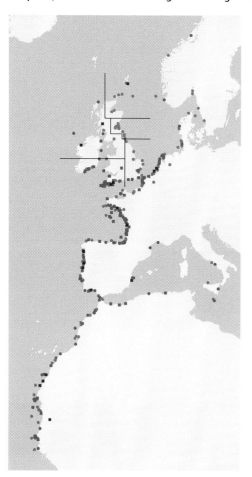

Fig 8. Movements of 85 Gannets ringed abroad and recovered in Britain & Ireland. The 27 pre-1979 foreign-ringed Gannets (France & the Channel Isles 24, Iceland one, Norway one and Germany one) are not shown.

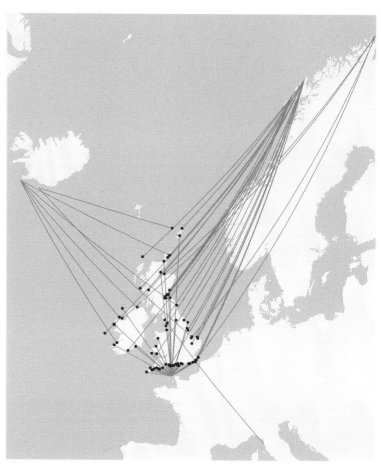

distances reached by first-year birds are achieved about 200 days after ringing and birds then start to return north (Fig 5). Information on the return movement is difficult to interpret but it appears that most individuals come at least part-way back to the colonies in the first year of life. Some, however, appear to spend a year or two south of the Bay of Biscay. Recoveries of immatures tend to be further south than those of adults (Fig 6). A few individuals visit breeding colonies during their first summer but most delay this for a year or two. As they get older, birds generally winter further north (Fig 4) but, even so, some experienced adults still get as far south as Senegal (Nelson 1978). A few birds spend the summer in the Mediterranean and there is a bizarre record of a pair nesting on a small boat anchored near Marseille in 1993 (Fernandez & Bayle 1994).

The distributions of Gannet recoveries from different areas of Britain & Ireland (Fig 7), and recoveries from other European ringing schemes show that birds from all east Atlantic colonies intermingle in the winter (Barrett 1988, Veron 1988, Petersen 1998, unpublished data from the Norwegian Ringing Scheme).

Gannets ringed in the Channel Islands and France (73 birds), Norway (29), Iceland (seven), Italy (one) and Germany (one) were recovered in Britain & Ireland up to the end of 1997 (Fig 8). Norwegian birds migrate mainly via the North Sea, though there was one summer recovery in the Irish Sea. Birds from the Channel Islands occur in the waters all around Britain & Ireland. A total of five Gannets ringed at the Canadian colonies of Funk and Bonaventure Islands has been reported from the east

Atlantic south of 60°N (Harris & Wanless 1999). Three were in their first winter and two were in the fourth year of life. One of the latter was found oiled in western Ireland in March, when most Gannets of this age would be expected to be prospecting for nest sites and moving shorter distances than immatures. Possibly this bird had moved across the Atlantic in its first year and then remained in the east until it was ready to nest.

Most Gannets probably return to their natal colony to breed. However, there are a few records that indicate emigration, including several British birds recruiting into newly formed colonies in Norway. Gannets may also move between long-established colonies, as shown by a chick from Eldey (the largest Icelandic colony) that was subsequently found breeding on the Bass Rock (the second-largest colony in Britain & Ireland).

The migration patterns and wintering areas of the Gannet are now well documented. These data will form a valuable baseline against which to assess whether changes in the marine environment, predicted to occur as a result of global warming, have any impact on Gannet distribution. In addition, analyses in progress suggest that the recovery data can be used to estimate the survival rates of adult and immature Gannets. A formal analysis of temporal and spatial variation in the recovery rates would be well worth undertaking.

Sarah Wanless

Great Cormorant (Cormorant)

Phalacrocorax carbo

Cormorants are large fish-eating birds that have become much more common inland over the past 30 or so years, both outside the breeding season and, following the establishment of new colonies of tree-nesting birds in the early 1980s, also in the breeding season (Kirby & Sellers 1997). Coastal colonies almost exclusively comprise birds of the nominate race, but the new inland colonies also contain birds of the continental race, which have somewhat distinct movement patterns outside the breeding season (Hughes *et al* 2000).

The nominate race *carbo* breeds along the coasts of the North Atlantic, between easternmost Canada and the Norwegian coast in the north and northwest France in the south, and is only partially migratory or dispersive. The continental race *sinensis* inhabits central and southern Europe (Sweden and the area south and east of the Baltic) and much of Asia, and is migratory throughout most of its range (Hughes *et al* 2000). Some *sinensis* may overwinter near the breeding areas, however, the proportion to some extent dependent on the severity of winter weather (*BWP*). *Sinensis* breeding in western Europe migrate south-southwest and those of eastern Europe south-southeast, with much longitudinal scatter; many move as far south as the Mediterranean Basin (*BWP*, Reymond & Zuchuat 1995). Those breeding in the Balkans, by the Black Sea and in Turkey may be merely dispersive in winter, but some may winter in the eastern Mediterranean (*BWP*). The two other Western Palearctic races, *maroccanus* (coasts of northwest Africa) and *lucidus* (West and southern Africa and inland East Africa), are believed to be only locally dispersive (*BWP*). A further race, *novaehollandiae*, inhabits Oceania.

The analysis of the data for this species was supported by Joy and Ian Castle

Most British & Irish Cormorants are of the nominate race, which breeds largely on rocky cliffs and offshore islands, with the exception of a few long-standing colonies associated with inland freshwaters in Scotland, Wales and Ireland. Cormorants of the continental race *sinensis*, the populations of which increased rapidly in mainland Europe in the latter part of the 20th century (van Eerden & Gregersen 1995, Baccetti & Cherubini 1997), are now known to constitute part of the subpopulation that has been breeding on inland fresh waters in southeast England and the Midlands since the early 1980s (Sellers *et al* 1997, Goostrey *et al* 1998). Most British & Irish breeders and their young winter in coastal areas but an increasing proportion has been using inland freshwater habitats in winter in recent years (Rehfisch *et al* 1999).

Cormorants have been ringed almost exclusively as nestlings at breeding colonies (Figs 1 & 2). The distribution of coastal ringing effort broadly reflects the distribution and size of breeding colonies shown in the *1988–91 Atlas*, except for under-representing colonies on the northwest and southwest coasts of Ireland, the south coast of England and the Southwest Peninsula. As yet, there have been relatively few recoveries (dead) of Cormorants metal-ringed at the relatively new inland breeding colonies in England, which only became established in the early 1980s. However, information on the movements of this

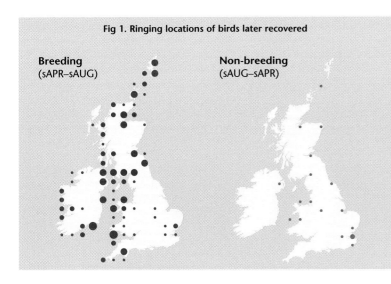

Fig 1. Ringing locations of birds later recovered

Breeding (sAPR–sAUG)

Non-breeding (sAUG–sAPR)

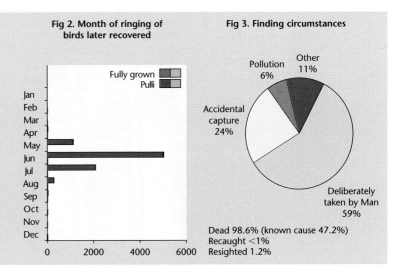

Fig 2. Month of ringing of birds later recovered

Fully grown
Pulli

Jan Feb Mar Apr May Jun Jul Aug Sep Oct Nov Dec

0   2000   4000   6000

Fig 3. Finding circumstances

Pollution 6%
Other 11%
Accidental capture 24%
Deliberately taken by Man 59%

Dead 98.6% (known cause 47.2%)
Recaught <1%
Resighted 1.2%

Ringing and recovery data

	<1960	60–69	70–79	80–89	90–97	Total
RINGING						
BTO ringing totals (%)	7	16	18	33	26	63,627
RECOVERIES						
BTO-ringed (%)	13	20	24	25	18	8,569
Foreign-ringed (%)	←	22	→	34	45	74

Statistical analyses

	Breeding population (sAPR–sAUG)	Wintering population (sNOV–sFEB)
Status	SHORT-DISTANCE MIGRANT (2)	[SHORT-DISTANCE MIGRANT]
Age differences[NS*]	Significant	Not tested
Sex differences	Not tested	Not tested
Regional differences	Significant[S*]	Not tested
Finding circumstances	Significant	Not tested

Fig 4. Locations outside the breeding season, and movements of over 20 km between the breeding and non-breeding season, of coastal Cormorants present in the (a) northeast (678), (b) northwest (2,022), (c) north (611) and (d) southwest (1,746) of Britain & Ireland during the breeding season.

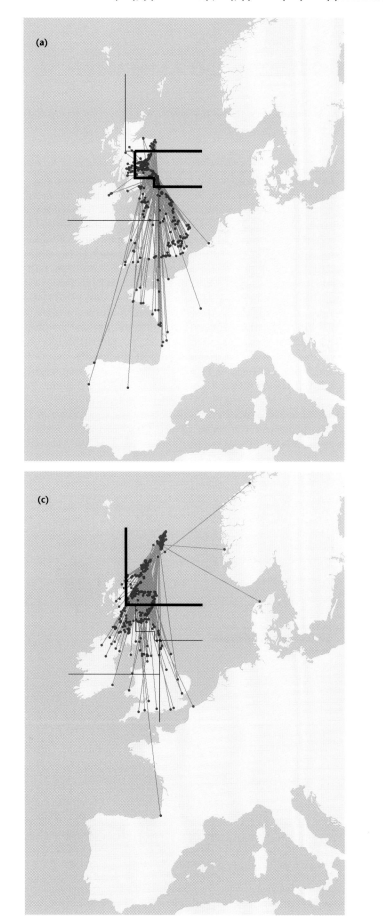
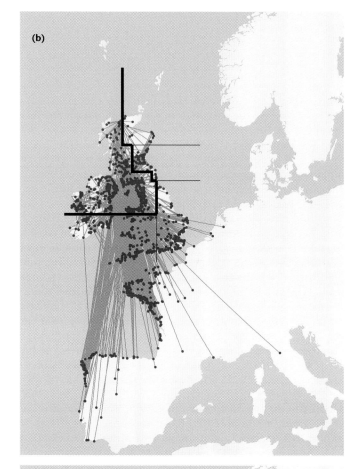
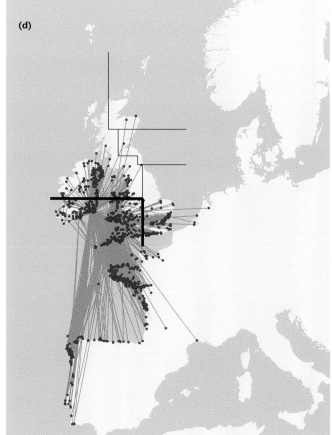

Fig 5. Locations outside the breeding season of (a) 990 adult and (b) 5,601 immature coastal Cormorants that were present in Britain & Ireland during the breeding season.

Fig 6. Monthly variation in the differences in (a) latitude and (b) longitude between ringing and recovery locations of coastal Cormorants present in Britain & Ireland during the breeding season. Monthly medians (points) and interquartile ranges (bars) are shown.

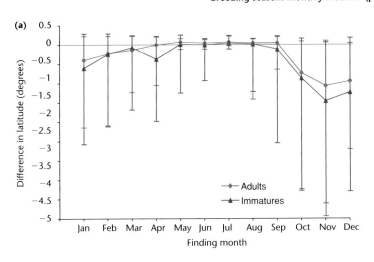

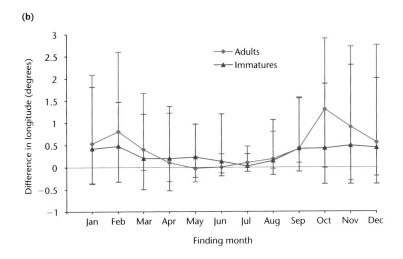

subpopulation is rapidly increasing through the colour-ringing of nestlings at most of these sites.

Almost half of all Cormorant recoveries are attributed to a known cause of death. The majority of these have been deliberately taken by Man or accidentally captured in fishing nets (Fig 3). These causes of mortality are likely to have varied both spatially and temporally across Europe since ringing began, and the legal status of Cormorants has also varied, potentially influencing whether ringed birds that were shot have been reported. Any such changes must be considered when interpreting the recovery patterns.

Many Cormorants breeding at coastal colonies in Britain & Ireland remain close to their breeding areas outside the breeding season, while others move further south to winter, and are recovered between northern France and the south coast of Portugal (Fig 4). A small number have been recovered east of Britain, during both the breeding and non-breeding seasons, from the west coast of Norway south to northern Italy;

these have been mostly immatures (Fig 5). The autumn movements of coastal breeders take place from July onwards, with return movements from November to May (Fig 6). Some juveniles move away from their natal colony within a couple of weeks of fledging (R M Sellers pers obs). Immature British & Irish Cormorants from coastal colonies have not shown any gross differences from those of breeding age in the pattern or timing of movements, although immatures have been slightly more likely to winter inland in Britain than adults (Rehfisch *et al* 1999; Fig 5). The median distance moved by immature birds between the natal colony and wintering areas was 222 km ($P5-95=25-1,069$ km, $n=1,695$), significantly further than that of adults (median=179 km, $P5-95=13-1,060$ km, $n=310$). There are too few birds of known sex to look for differences in movement patterns between the sexes. Surveys of Cormorant winter roosts (mainly of *sinensis*) across western Europe and as far south as Tunisia suggested that females and juvenile birds moved further south away from the breeding areas than adult males and showed

Fig 7. Movements of foreign-ringed Cormorants into Britain & Ireland. Those recovered in Britain & Ireland during the breeding season (13, red) are differentiated from those recovered outside the breeding season (33, blue) and from those of unknown seasonality (12, grey). The 16 pre-1979 foreign-ringed Cormorants (France 7, Denmark 2, Germany 2, Belgium 2, the Netherlands 2 and Norway 1) are not shown.

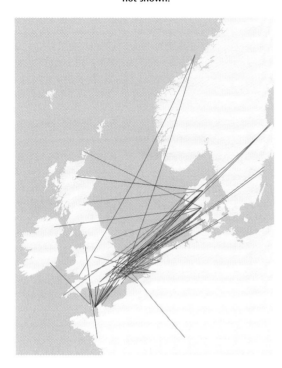

Fig 8. Temporal change in the percentage of Cormorant recoveries outside the breeding season that have occurred inland in Britain. Points show the percentages recovered inland (with 95% confidence limits – bars) and the line shows the significant trend (*Source*: Rehfisch *et al* 1999, © Crown copyright. Crown copyright material is reproduced with the permission of the Controller of HMSO and the Queen's Printer for Scotland.)

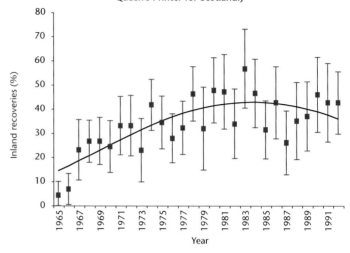

a preference for milder climates. There may also be variation in the timing of movements between the different sex and age groups, and in the length of time that they stay in their winter quarters, which may complicate the interpretation of the apparent differences in the locations of their wintering areas. The proportions of the sex and age classes in roosts across Europe may also vary according to the severity of the winter weather (van Eerden & Munsterman 1995).

British & Irish Cormorants from different breeding areas differ in the average direction and distance of movements during the non-breeding season, and in the extent to which seas and land-masses are crossed (Stuart 1948, Coulson 1961, Balfour *et al* 1967, Coulson & Brazendale 1968, Summers & Laing 1990, Rehfisch *et al* 1999). The degree to which British & Irish Cormorants have penetrated south into France and (mostly) northern Spain outside the breeding season appears to depend on the relative proximity of these wintering areas to their breeding area (Fig 4). Most of the birds reaching Iberia have been from breeding colonies in Ireland or a region comprising southwest England and southern Wales. Many of those reaching France have been from the latter region but have been joined there by birds from northwest England and northern Wales, and smaller numbers from the Farne Islands. Most Cormorants from Scotland and Northumberland remain in Britain outside the breeding season but some exchange occurs between the east and west coasts. Similarly, movements between areas bordering the Irish Sea occur outside the breeding season. Cormorants from the Northern Isles and the north of Scotland rarely move further south than northern England. Movements across the North Sea have been very rare (Fig 4). The more easterly average longitude of recoveries outside compared with within the breeding season (Fig 6) reflects movements of Cormorants away from their breeding strongholds in the west of Britain (particularly Wales), and in Ireland (Rehfisch *et al* 1999), to utilize winter resources in southern England, where, historically, few Cormorants have bred.

Cormorants are thought to be relatively faithful to wintering sites. Colour-ringed birds from the colonies at St Margaret's Island in Pembrokeshire and at Grune Point on the Solway Firth have been observed at the same sites both within and between winters (R M Sellers pers obs, M Carrier pers comm, Rehfisch *et al* 1999). A more rigorous analysis of sightings of British & Irish colour-marked Cormorants is needed to estimate the true rates of fidelity to wintering sites, however. A study of individually recognizable Cormorants using winter roosts in western France (Yésou 1995) showed that, while many individuals passed rapidly through roosts (probably on passage to other wintering areas), long-stayers were markedly faithful to the same roost in subsequent winters; many of these long-stayers were birds from St Margaret's Island in Wales.

Between years, British & Irish Cormorants do not appear to show the large variation in degree of movement exhibited by the closely related Shag (Coulson & Brazendale 1968), although a detailed analysis has yet to be undertaken. Short-term movements away from the coast to inland sites may occur, however, as a result of unfavourable weather conditions, such as gale-force winds (Rehfisch *et al* 1999). Birds wintering inland probably also move to rivers and coasts in freezing conditions (B Hughes pers comm).

Recoveries of Cormorants ringed as nestlings at coastal colonies, and recovered when of breeding age during the breeding season, show that more than 60% returned to breed at or near their natal colony, while only 20% were recovered more than 100 km distant (Rehfisch *et al* 1999). The median natal dispersal distance of 33 km shown by recoveries of dead Cormorants (P5–95=0–428 km, n=379) may be too high, however, because up to 10% of Cormorants of breeding age may abstain from breeding in any given year (Lloyd *et al* 1991) and may remain distant from their breeding colonies. Observations of colour-ringed Cormorants suggest that probably less than 5% breed at colonies other than the natal colony (Lloyd *et al* 1991), so that fidelity to the breeding colony is thought to be high. Most immature British & Irish Cormorants appear to spend the breeding season close to existing breeding colonies, although some have been recovered in northwest France and some as far south as northern Spain.

Most Cormorants that have been ringed in continental Europe and subsequently recovered in Britain & Ireland have been ringed during the breeding season, mainly as nestlings (97%), and have been recovered as immatures in southeast England outside the breeding season (Fig 7). Those few foreign-ringed Cormorants recovered in England during the

Fig 9. Locations outside the breeding season of (a) 408 first-year and (b) 338 older Cormorants ringed as pulli at the four inland colonies shown. Local sightings from Abberton, Hanningfield Reservoir, Colman's, Alton Water and Loompit Lake have been excluded. (*Source*: G R Ekins personal data.)

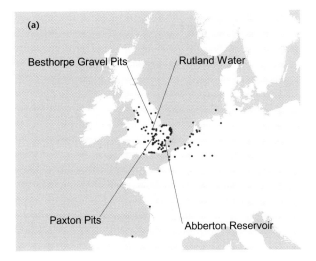

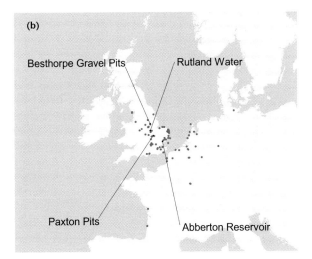

Fig 10. Seasonal changes in distance from the natal colony of Cormorants ringed as pulli at Abberton Reservoir, Essex. Means (points) and 95% confidence limits (bars) are shown for each of three age classes. (*Source*: Hughes *et al* 2000.)

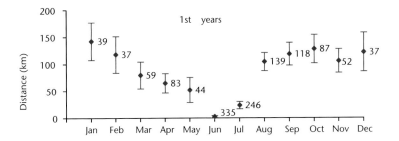

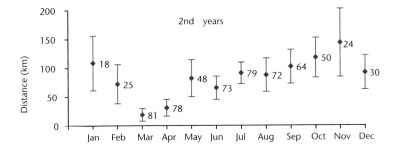

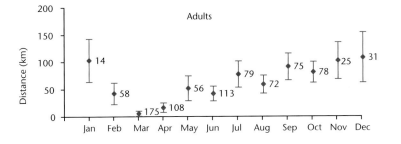

breeding season have mostly been associated with the relatively newly formed inland breeding colonies (below). The ring-recovery data show that the proportion of coastal-breeding British & Irish Cormorants wintering inland in Britain increased between the mid-1960s and the mid-1980s, and then stabilized or decreased slightly (Rehfisch *et al* 1999) (Fig 8). Most of this increase occurred prior to the period of rapid increase in continental populations of *sinensis*. Since 1980, immigrants from continental Europe have comprised about 2.5% of the British wintering population (excluding those from the inland colonies in England). Taking into account the numbers ringed in each country of origin, numbers entering Britain in winter from the Netherlands and Denmark have increased since 1980 (Rehfisch *et al* 1999).

The extent to which immigrants from continental Europe have contributed to the establishment of the inland breeding colonies in southeast England is still a subject of debate, but genetic analyses have confirmed that the birds breeding at these colonies are a mixture of *carbo* and *sinensis*, and have suggested that the two races are probably hybridizing within them (Goostrey *et al* 1998). Recent research suggests that the gular pouch alone can be used to correctly assign around 80% of individual Cormorants to either *carbo* or *sinensis* (Newson 2000). Results using this technique have confirmed those from DNA studies suggesting that most birds breeding inland in Britain are *sinensis* but that the proportion of *carbo* is higher at Abberton than at the other inland colonies. The same work suggests that around 20% of Cormorants wintering inland in England are *sinensis*. Colour- and metal-ringing have proved that inland breeders originate from both coastal British & Irish *carbo* and continental *sinensis* colonies. Seventy-one marked *sinensis* individuals from six European countries were sighted in Britain & Ireland between 1985 and 1995 (Sellers *et al* 1997), 18 of these during the brood-rearing period for inland breeders (April–July). Six such birds have attempted to breed at inland colonies in England, three successfully. Coastally bred *carbo* ringed in Wales (two) and Cumbria (two) have also been recorded at inland colonies.

Cormorants ringed as nestlings at the inland breeding colonies show movement patterns more like *sinensis*, which migrate further from the colonies in winter (Bregnballe *et al* 1997), than those of nominate *carbo* (Ekins 1996, Hughes *et al* 2000, Fig 9). Although around three-quarters of these inland breeders winter within Britain (Hughes *et al* 2000), there have been many resightings and recoveries of dead birds in mainland Europe, mainly in the Netherlands and France; 90% of these overseas movements have involved birds aged three years or younger (Hughes *et*

Fig 11. Locations of adult satellite-tagged Cormorants (a) 27,486 and (b) 27,487 from Grafham Water tracked from June to August 1996. Transmissions accurate to less than 10 km (red) are differentiated from those for which the accuracy was poorer than 10 km (grey). (*Source*: Hughes *et al* 1999, © Crown copyright. Crown copyright material is reproduced with the permission of the Controller of HMSO and the Queen's Printer for Scotland.)

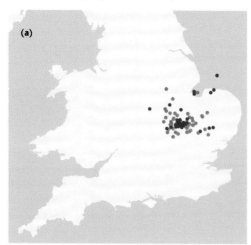

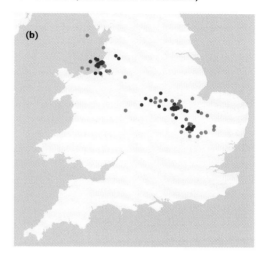

al 2000). Of birds from the largest inland colony, at Abberton, 9% of resightings but 26% of recoveries of dead birds have occurred abroad; the latter may represent the most accurate estimate of the proportion wintering abroad, because resighting effort is probably much lower in mainland Europe than in Britain. Juveniles disperse very rapidly from Abberton within two months of fledging, which occurs mostly in June. By August, they are on average over 100 km from the colony (Fig 10); few remain at the colony by September (Ekins 1996). The mean recovery distance remains at 100–150 km until February, when first-year birds move closer to the natal colony, but many do not return completely (the mean recovery distance is still over 50 km in May). The recovery distances of second-year and adult birds gradually increase between late summer and early winter; they do not disperse as far as first-years, and they return to colonies earlier (between January and March, Fig 10). At Abberton, there is some evidence that Cormorants begin breeding when two years old, and some may attempt to breed in their first year (G R Ekins pers obs). For 45 birds ringed as nestlings at Abberton and resighted during the breeding season when at least three years old, the mean natal dispersal distance was 101 km (range 12–255 km, Newson 2000).

A small sample of four adult Cormorants fitted with satellite-transmitters at Grafham Water in late summer, and assumed to be breeding birds from the inland tree-nesting colony at Paxton Pits Nature Reserve, provided interesting information on their post-breeding movements (Hughes *et al* 1999, Fig 11). In 1996, one bird remained within a 15 km radius of Grafham Water for six weeks and left for the north coast of Norfolk in early August, taking three days to make the journey. The second bird remained at Grafham Water for only 12 days, moved to Rutland Water for a further six days, flew 80 km to Staffordshire for a day and then flew a further 125 km northwest (in less than 6 hours) to reach the Irish Sea coast at Seaforth, Liverpool Bay (Fig 11). Two birds marked in July 1997 remained at inland sites in central England for the duration of transmitter function (12 days and 62 days respectively). A further two adult birds fitted with satellite-tags in January 1997 stayed within 40 km of their inland tagging sites in central England during the midwinter period (duration of transmitter function 25 and 47 days).

The large numbers of Cormorants wintering inland in Britain & Ireland in the last 30 years have increased the perception held by anglers and fisheries managers that Cormorants affect their fish stocks, particularly inland in southern England. Although recoveries have shown that the inland wintering population comprises Cormorants from a mixture of breeding areas within Britain & Ireland, those from some areas (*eg* Wales) have shown a greater tendency to winter inland than others (*eg* those from the Northern Isles), perhaps because of differences in their established routes to wintering areas (Rehfisch *et al* 1999); for example, Cormorants from the Welsh colonies have been shown to cross southern England to winter along the east coast ever since ringing began (Coulson & Brazendale 1968) and since 1965 it is the Welsh Cormorants that have shown the greatest tendency amongst coastal breeders to winter inland in Britain (Rehfisch *et al* 1999). Birds from the newly established inland colonies have also contributed to the enlarged winter population, as around three-quarters of them remain in Britain for the winter (Hughes *et al* 2000).

Given that widespread ringing has already allowed the detection of substantial changes in the wintering behaviour of British & Irish Cormorants, it is important that sufficient numbers continue to be marked annually to monitor any future changes. Colour-ringing has an important role to play in establishing the origins of birds breeding at inland colonies in England and the seasonal movements of individuals bred at those colonies. Any further expansion of inland breeding will only be fully understood, and any changes in the movement patterns of this somewhat distinct group of birds identified, if annual colour-ringing continues at the established colonies. Further systematic colour-ringing and resighting of Cormorants at a wide geographical spread of coastal colonies could provide important additional information on natal and breeding dispersal, age of first breeding and the prevalence of breeding abstinence, which is essential for accurate modelling of regional population changes. It would also increase knowledge of winter site-fidelity, which is essential for addressing conflicts between the birds and inland fisheries.

Chris Wernham, Graham Ekins & Robin M Sellers

European Shag (Shag)

Phalacrocorax aristotelis

The Shag is a medium-sized colonially breeding seabird endemic to the rocky coasts and islands of the northeast Atlantic and Mediterranean. The total population is currently put at 85,000 pairs, of which over half nest in Britain & Ireland (Wanless & Harris 1997). We have, therefore, a special responsibility to monitor the movements and survival of this species. The breeding range of the nominate race *aristotelis* extends from Russia south to the Atlantic coast of Iberia. In most areas juveniles, immatures, and many adults disperse from the colonies after breeding. Although dispersal has a generally southward bias, only populations in the far north of Norway and Russia are truly migratory. Only 10% of recoveries of birds ringed north of 62°N have been reported on coasts of southwest Norway and none have crossed to Britain (Galbraith *et al* 1986, Norwegian Ringing Scheme unpublished data). Some populations have fairly consistent year-to-year dispersal whereas in others there are marked annual differences in the extent of movements. Despite extensive ringing, not a single Icelandic bird has been recovered outside Icelandic waters (Petersen 1998). Individuals of the Mediterranean race *desmarestii* are sedentary but nothing is known of the movements of *riggenbachi*, which nests in very small numbers along the Atlantic coast of Morocco.

Shags are ideal subjects for ringing studies. They nest in large accessible colonies, adults as well as chicks can be ringed in numbers and, unlike most seabirds, adults are easily sexed by size and voice. The ringing and recovery totals are the highest of any British & Irish seabird except the Herring Gull. Recoveries come from colonies from the extreme northern tip of Britain (Hermaness at 61°N) to the Isles of Scilly

The analysis of the data for this species was supported by David Milne QC

(50°N) (Fig 1). The Shag has by far the longest breeding season of any British seabird and recoveries come from chicks ringed between late April and October (Fig 2). Three colonies, at the Isle of May, Farne Islands and Great Saltee, have each provided more than a thousand recoveries. Detailed analyses have been published on the movements of birds ringed on the Farne Islands (Potts 1969), Isle of May (Galbraith *et al* 1981), Puffin Island, Anglesey (Moss 1992), and in northwest Scotland (Swann & Ramsay 1979).

Only a quarter of the recoveries give details of the cause of death (Fig 3). Accidental capture (mainly in fishing nets and lobster creels, though Shags get caught in an amazing array of objects) accounts for 36% of these, 22% were shot and 18% of reports mention oil or other pollutants. Methods of recovery vary with the location and time; for instance 40% of recoveries of birds ringed in the Western Isles up to 1950 were shot compared with 3% from southeast Scotland in the 1970s (Swann & Ramsay 1979, Galbraith *et al* 1981). The proportions shot and caught in nets are both now substantially lower than they were 30–40 years ago whereas the proportion reported as being oiled has increased. Shags have undoubtedly benefited from the removal of bounties offered for Cormorant beaks by fishery boards since the introduction of the Wildlife and Countryside Act in 1981. Currently there is rather limited interest in eating the species whereas prior to 1981, when it became

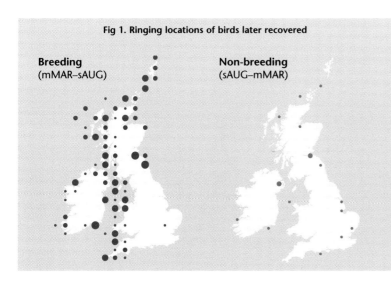

Fig 1. Ringing locations of birds later recovered

Breeding (mMAR–sAUG)

Non-breeding (sAUG–mMAR)

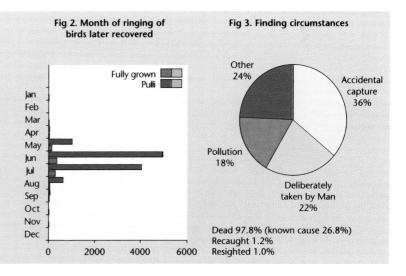

Fig 2. Month of ringing of birds later recovered

Fully grown / Pulli

Fig 3. Finding circumstances

Other 24%
Accidental capture 36%
Pollution 18%
Deliberately taken by Man 22%

Dead 97.8% (known cause 26.8%)
Recaught 1.2%
Resighted 1.0%

Ringing and recovery data

	<1960	60–69	70–79	80–89	90–97	Total
RINGING						
BTO ringing totals (%)	5	17	19	41	19	177,093
RECOVERIES						
BTO-ringed (%)	7	18	23	31	22	11,576
Foreign-ringed (%)	←	21	→	40	38	42

Statistical analyses

	Breeding population (mMAR–sAUG)	Wintering population (sNOV–sFEB)
Status	SHORT-DISTANCE MIGRANT (2)	[SHORT-DISTANCE MIGRANT]
Age differences[NS*]	Significant*	Not tested
Sex differences[NS*]	Not significant*	Not tested
Regional differences	Significant[4]	Not tested
Finding circumstances	(Not significant)	Not tested

139

Fig 4. Recovery locations of Shags ringed in Britain & Ireland for those (a) recovered as immatures during the breeding season (2,106), (b) recovered as adults during the breeding season (1,156), (c) recovered as immatures outside the breeding season (4,068) and (d) recovered as adults outside the breeding season (598).

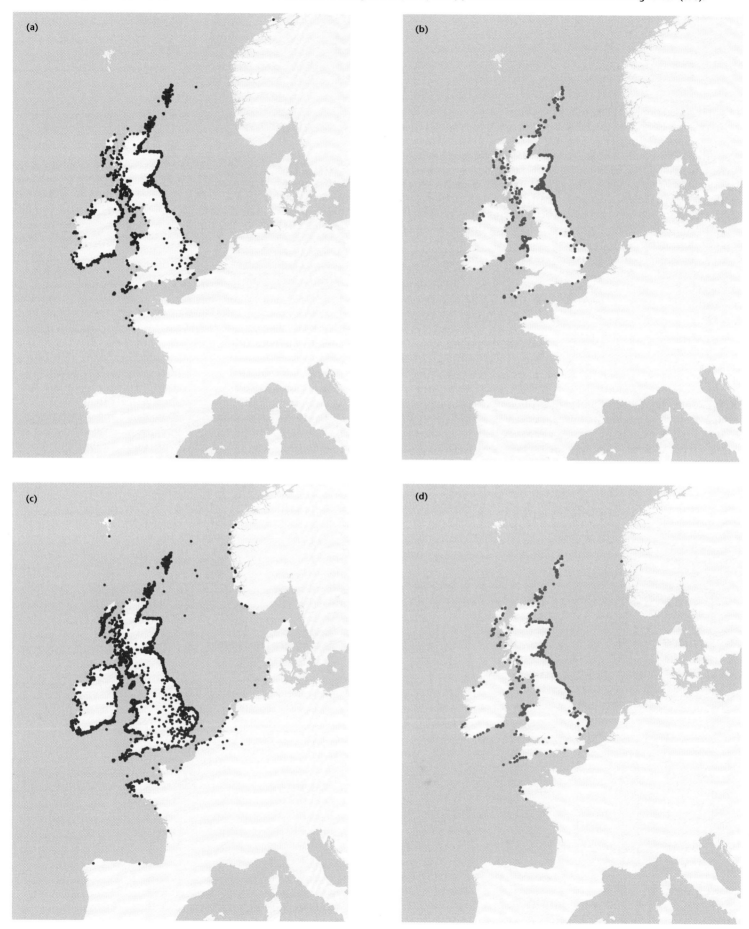

Fig 5. Recovery locations of Shags that were ringed in the (a) north (294:1,405), (b) northeast (1,327:3,683), (c) northwest (564:2,160) and (d) southwest (458:1,678) of Britain & Ireland. Sample sizes of movements under:over 20 km are given but only those over 20 km are plotted.

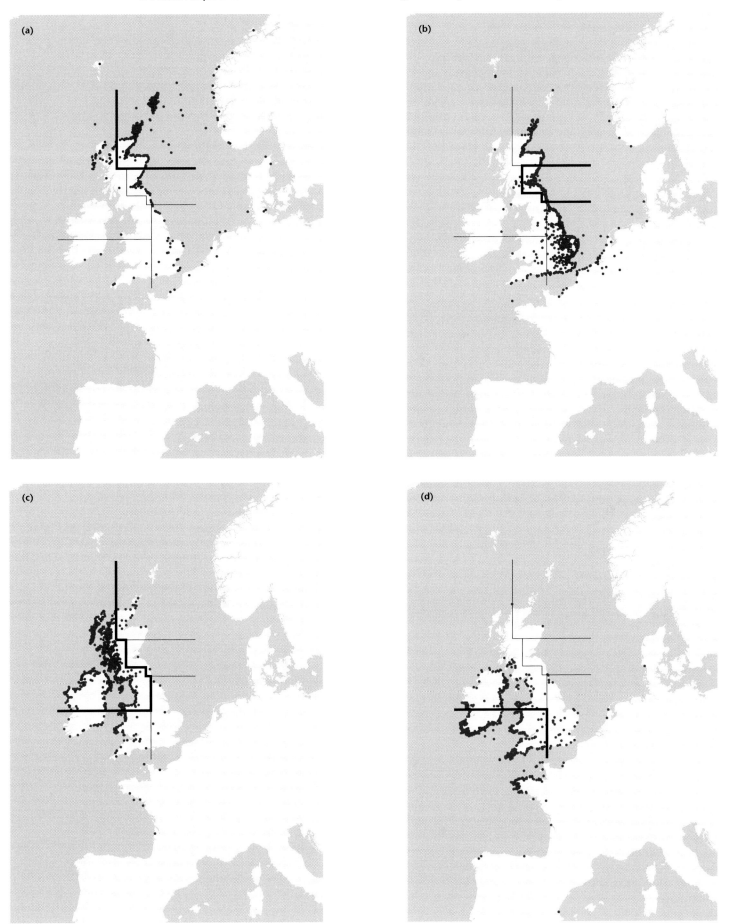

illegal, large numbers were killed in parts of the Western Isles for human consumption (Swann *et al* 1994). Capture in nets is particularly common in Ireland (69% of recoveries) and France (45%). These factors must be borne in mind when interpreting recoveries but the general patterns of movements are clear. The large numbers reported as 'found dead on beach' indicate the effect severe weather can have on this species.

British & Irish Shags disperse widely (Fig 4) but many older birds remain throughout the year within 50–100 km of even the most northerly colonies, and are displaced only by extreme weather or food shortage. The Shag is an inshore feeding species and is virtually never seen out of sight of land. It rarely spends long resting on the sea, except when diving, probably because, like some other cormorants, its plumage is not completely waterproof (Wanless & Harris 1992, Johnsgard 1993). Wide stretches of water apparently impose a severe constraint on movements. A few northern birds are recovered in Norway but many of the offshore recoveries of Shags in the central North Sea are on boats or oil rigs, which raises the possibility that some at least of birds reported from Scandinavia could have had a 'ship-assisted' crossing.

After they have fledged, young are fed for several weeks and then move slowly away from the colony; the monthly median recovery distance reaches its maximum (114 km, *n*=308) 4–5 months after ringing. The actual date is meaningless since birds fledge any time between June and October. Immatures, especially those in their first and second winters, disperse much further than do adults and have a much greater tendency to occur inland (Fig 4). These inland recoveries are clumped and most occur in well-documented wrecks (Potts 1969). In Britain, wrecks are an east-coast phenomenon and follow long periods of generally onshore (easterly) winds. Birds appear to have difficulty foraging, and often are forced far south to where there are limited safe roosting places and either die on the coast or fly inland, where they usually suffer a similar fate, albeit after weeks or even months (Potts 1969). However, even very large wrecks, such as one in the Moray Firth in February 1994 during which 331 ringed Shags (mainly from colonies to the south) were reported, can occur without more than the odd bird being reported inland (Harris & Wanless 1996). Wrecks are far less a feature of Shag biology in west Britain (Swann & Ramsay 1979), and there are few inland recoveries from Ireland and Wales (Fig 5). During the spring and early summer birds of all ages return to near the colonies, which results in a contraction of the recovery area.

There are no obvious differences between the sexes in either the pattern of recoveries or the median distances moved by birds recovered dead (female 56 km, *n*=186; male 63 km, *n*=200), but birds have a longer average recovery distance when they are immature (here taken as the first three years of life; 77 km, *n*=6,095) than they do when older

(44 km, *n*=1,261). This difference between age classes was shown to be statistically significant in the formal analysis.

Shags from different regions have quite different patterns of recovery (Fig 5). Birds from the northeast disperse along the east coast of England and Scotland both south and north (though with only one recovery in Shetland) with some 'overshooting' into mainland western Europe. Individuals from the north move less, though with an inevitable southerly bias. Most of the recoveries from Scandinavia are of Shags ringed in Shetland. Shags from the northwest are generally less migratory with most recoveries occurring within the region and showing no obvious bias in the direction of dispersal. In the southwest, birds from Great Saltee are recovered within Ireland with many movements being to the west and north; this contrasts markedly with the south and east movements of birds from Wales and southwest England. Fig 5 perhaps indicates the barrier that the open sea poses to Shag movements. The only population where individuals appear to routinely overfly the sea is that on the Isles of Scilly since numbers are reported in France, a distance of at least 200 km. There is a single recovery of a Welsh bird in the western Mediterranean (Fig 5) within the range of *desmarestii*.

The few foreign-ringed Shags recovered in Britain & Ireland have all come from the Channel Islands or northwest France. It is possible that Shags from the population of around 2,000 pairs breeding on the Faeroes (*European Atlas*) move south to the coasts of Scotland in winter but with only around 50 ringed there since 1923 (Jens-Kjeld Jensen pers comm), the chances of a recovery to confirm this are slim.

The retrapping of birds at colonies indicates that 92–95% of young Shags that survive recruit as breeders within 12 km of the natal colony (Aebischer 1995a). Most interchanges involve movements of less than 100 km, mainly between colonies in the Firth of Forth and the Farne Islands but long-distance movements have included chicks from Foula (Shetland) found breeding on Great Saltee (934 km) and the Farne Islands (505 km). Breeding adults show high colony fidelity with less than 1% changing; the few movements that do occur often follow heavy mortality caused by algal blooms (red-tides) or unusually severe wrecks (Coulson *et al* 1968, Aebischer 1995a, Wanless & Harris 1997).

The BTO database of Shag recoveries is a valuable resource. It has been used to great effect in the study of Shag migration (references above) and, in conjunction with retrapping at colonies, survival (Harris *et al* 1994, Catchpole *et al* 1998). Despite the undoubted biases associated with temporal and spatial changes in recovery circumstances, this species has great potential as a monitor of environmental conditions over a wide area of Britain & Ireland if ringing continues at its present level.

Mike P Harris & Bob Swann

Grey Heron
Ardea cinerea

The Grey Heron feeds mainly on fish caught in shallow water. It is the largest heron species in Europe and has the most northerly geographical range. Like many Palearctic freshwater fish-eating birds, northern populations are migratory, moving south and west for the winter, but the warming influence of the Gulf Stream enables Grey Herons breeding in Britain & Ireland to remain year-round.

The main factors that influence the availability of fish for herons and egrets are the size and productivity of wetlands, water levels and temperature. The birds have their easiest fishing when water margins recede and concentrate fish into shallow pools. At the other extreme, high water levels or low temperatures reduce fish availability. Fish activity is markedly reduced as temperatures fall and, for herons, the most difficult conditions of all prevail when slow-moving waters are iced over. The seasonal movements of Grey Herons are thus mostly influenced by rainfall patterns in the southern part of their range, and by temperature in the north. Where seasonal fishing conditions are annually predictable, Grey Herons make regular migratory movements but, in addition, they sometimes make less predictable movements associated with drought or freezing cold.

The nominate *cinerea* extends across the whole of the Palearctic eastwards to Sakhalin Island, and northwards in the west to include Fennoscandia, but not Iceland. Southwards it includes much of Africa and India (Hancock & Kushlan 1984). The subspecies *jouyi* inhabits the Far East, *firasa* is found in Madagascar and *monicae* only in the Banc d'Arguin, Mauritania. Populations of *cinerea* from the northern Palearctic move west and south to winter in western and southern

The analysis of the data for this species was supported by G H Green & R M Bishop

Europe, trans-Saharan Africa and southern Asia. Migrating herons use flapping flight; they do not need to soar on thermals so they can migrate at night and on a broad front.

In Britain & Ireland, Grey Herons use a variety of freshwater wetlands, brackish estuaries and marine shallow rocky shores (Marquiss 1993). Some habitats are used only at specific seasons, *eg* peat bogs and some freshwater marshes are mainly used in early spring when frogs are available. Standing fresh waters are heavily used in summer and autumn as water levels fall and prey become concentrated in shallow water. These same fresh waters become unavailable in winter when glazed in cold periods, while other habitats can sustain herons year-round. For example, lowland streams and river margins rarely freeze in British or Irish winters. The most predictable year-round fishing for herons is on estuaries and rocky marine shores. These habitats almost never freeze but daylight and tide can restrict the amount of fish that can be caught (Richner 1986). In general, there is an exodus from the uplands in winter and more birds are then found in lowland habitats and on the coast (*Winter Atlas*).

Most Grey Herons are ringed as nestlings (Figs 1 & 2) and about 11% are recovered. There is potential bias in that fewer are ringed in northwest Britain and in Ireland (Fig 1), and many of those recovered are deliberately killed by Man (32% of those with known cause of death, Fig

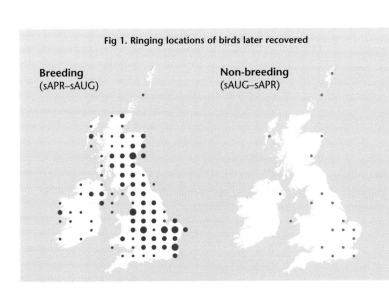

Fig 1. Ringing locations of birds later recovered

Breeding (sAPR–sAUG)

Non-breeding (sAUG–sAPR)

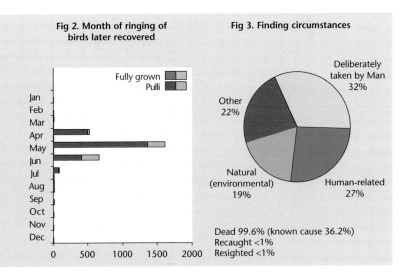

Fig 2. Month of ringing of birds later recovered

Fig 3. Finding circumstances

Deliberately taken by Man 32%

Other 22%

Natural (environmental) 19%

Human-related 27%

Dead 99.6% (known cause 36.2%)
Recaught <1%
Resighted <1%

Ringing and recovery data

	<1960	60–69	70–79	80–89	90–97	Total
RINGING						
BTO ringing totals (%)	19	9	17	33	21	22,752
RECOVERIES						
BTO-ringed (%)	26	12	24	25	13	2,425
Foreign-ringed (%)	35	14	24	18	9	534

Statistical analyses

	Breeding population (sAPR–sAUG)	Wintering population (mNOV–sFEB)
Status	SEDENTARY (0)	[LONG-DISTANCE MIGRANT]
Age differences[NT]	Significant*	Not tested
Sex differences	Not tested	Not tested
Regional differences	Significant[5]*	Not tested
Finding circumstances	(Not significant)	Not tested

Fig 4. Variation in the distances moved by juvenile Grey Herons with time after ringing as pulli. Medians for 30-day periods (points) and interquartile ranges (bars) are shown.

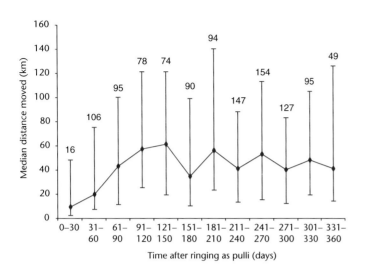

3) or at least have had a human-related accident or death (27%). Nevertheless, the map of the ringing locations for birds later recovered very much reflects the pattern of Grey Heron abundance (*1988–91 Atlas*), so the broad patterns of movements might well reflect the movements of the population at large.

Grey Herons breed early (*BWP*) and most ringed nestlings will have fledged in June. The progressive increase in median recovery distances

with time (Fig 4), suggests that general dispersal movements occur over the first five months. Thereafter, median recovery distances are less, but still exceed the 28-km median natal dispersal distance (of birds ringed as pulli and recovered in a subsequent breeding season when of breeding age). These recovery distances may be representative of the live population, in which case birds disperse for up to five months after fledging, later returning towards the natal site to breed. An alternative explanation is that birds that survive to breeding age are those that have dispersed less far. There are only a handful of sequential locations for live birds, and too few recoveries of birds ringed when fully grown, to explore these alternative explanations. The one 'breeding dispersal' movement on record (a bird both ringed and recovered as an adult) moved 6 km between breeding seasons, well within the recorded daily movements of radio-tagged Grey Herons during the breeding season (van Vessem & Draulans 1987, Marion 1989).

Ringed nestlings have been recovered in all months of the year but more frequently in two periods. Recoveries peak first in May and June, soon after fledging. Many of these could be birds that die through inexperience rather than by chance, as young herons are less competent than adults at fishing (Draulans & van Vessem 1985). The second peak in recoveries is in the three coldest months of the year, December to February. With the onset of cold weather, many fishing sites become untenable and, as adult Grey Herons defend good sites (Richner 1986), young birds must move or perish. In prolonged severe cold, many young Grey Herons die (North 1979) and recovery distances tend to be greater (Marquiss *et al* 1983), suggesting they can wander far before perishing.

The dispersal of juveniles is in all directions, but with much longer distances to the south (Fig 5a) in stark contrast to the relatively short natal dispersal distances (Fig 5b). However, because more first-year birds

Fig 5. Movements of over 20 km and recovery locations of Grey Herons ringed as pulli in Britain & Ireland and recovered (a) outside the breeding season (379:806) and (b) in a subsequent breeding season (109:170). Sample sizes of movements under:over 20 km are given but only those over 20 km are plotted.

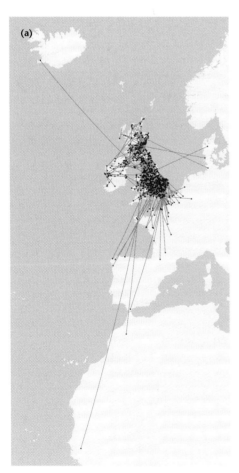

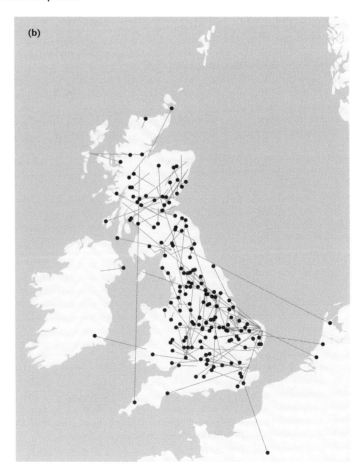

Fig 6. Movements of 347 foreign-ringed Grey Herons recovered in Britain & Ireland during the winter (September–March).

progressively from 12% prior to 1940 to 2% in the 1990s but the reasons are unclear. Many of these recoveries are of shot birds so the trend might reflect the progressively greater protection afforded to Grey Herons in continental Europe over this time. Another explanation might be that the British & Irish population has had a small migratory component that has declined with the amelioration of winters here.

The pattern for foreign-ringed Grey Herons recovered in Britain & Ireland (Fig 6) is completely different to that of home-bred birds. Most foreign-ringed birds originate from the north and east. Just over half of these recoveries (53%) involved birds from Norway, with good numbers also from Denmark (14%), the Netherlands (13%) and Sweden (11%). Most were ringed as nestlings, and these movements reflect the well-documented annual migrations of northern populations (Rydzewski 1956, Hancock & Kushlan 1984, *BWP*). Most birds from the Netherlands were recovered in the south of Britain, whereas those from Norway were predominantly found in the north, particularly Scotland and Ireland. In general, Norwegian birds that winter in Britain arrive in September to October and return to their breeding colonies by March (Roalkvam 1994).

The Grey Heron population in Britain has steadily increased for almost 40 years since the very low number in 1964 (Marquiss 1989, Crick *et al* 1998). In the 1960s, the population was heavily affected by persistent pollution of fresh waters with organochlorines and was recovering from a particularly severe winter. Since then pollution has apparently been less of a problem, severe weather is less frequent and fish are probably more prolific than formerly with the artificial stocking of many waters. In the 1980s, there was some persecution of Grey Herons associated with their depredations at fish-farms (Carss 1994) but this is apparently no longer the case, as farmers can take non-lethal measures to protect their stock. There are probably more Grey Herons in Europe now than there have been for a century.

Despite the species' current ubiquity, there are some fundamental gaps in our knowledge of Grey Heron movements. As outlined above, we have little information on the annual patterns of movement of adult birds. The population shift towards the coast in winter is implied from counts – what is required are documented movements of birds between breeding and wintering sites. Those that breed inland, particularly in the uplands, probably winter on the coast where they must then compete for foraging sites with local residents and also winter immigrants from abroad.

move further and die in harsh winters, cold-weather movements are likely to be over-represented on Fig 5a, perhaps obscuring the pattern for most winters. There are movements in both directions across the Irish Sea. Foreign recoveries of British & Irish nestlings are only 3.3% of the total; most are in France, with fewer in Belgium, Spain and the Netherlands. Occasional recoveries have been from Iceland, Norway, Denmark (two), Germany (two), Portugal, Morocco and the Gambia. The proportion of dead recoveries in foreign countries has declined

Mick Marquiss

Mute Swan
Cygnus olor

The Mute Swan is the largest species of bird regularly found breeding in Britain & Ireland, and one of the best known and most easily recognized of wildfowl, even by non-birdwatchers. Often considered as sedentary, its movements and migrations, in Britain & Ireland at least, have been largely overlooked. While overseas recoveries are rare, it is one of the few species that undergo a distinct moult migration within Britain. On the Continent, however, many populations are partially or wholly migratory (*BWP*).

The natural range extends across Eurasia from Ireland to Manchuria but is highly discontinuous. The species has been introduced into North America, Japan, South Africa, Australia and New Zealand, as well as to parts of Britain & Ireland, the Faeroes and elsewhere in Europe (*BWP*). While central European and Scandinavian populations are wild and avoid proximity to Man, in Britain and certain other western European countries, Mute Swans have had a long history of domestication and use for food (Ticehurst 1957), though wild populations probably bred historically (Birkhead & Perrins 1986).

In addition to annual movements associated with moult migration, northern and eastern populations show regular winter movements south and west in search of ice-free conditions (Wieloch 1991). This pattern may be changing, as there is evidence of recent shorter-distance movements, and many moult sites have also changed (*European Atlas*). Particularly cold weather in late winter may cause Estonian and Latvian breeding populations to move west in large numbers to Denmark (Kuresoo 1991), while in southeast Europe birds move south to the Caspian and Black Sea coasts (*BWP*, Serebryakov *et al* 1991).

The analysis of the data for this species was supported by Joe & Ann Hardman

The British population of some 26,000 birds (Delany *et al* 1992) is found on a wide range of lowland aquatic habitats, from municipal park lakes to coastal inlets and marshes, and often in close proximity to Man (Kirby *et al* 1994). A further 7,000 or so birds are found in Ireland (Rüger *et al* 1986). Their breeding distribution (*1988–91 Atlas*) shows that the only area avoided by nesting swans is land over 300 m above sea-level. The highest breeding densities occur in lowland river basins and in isolated Scottish areas in the Orkneys and Outer Hebrides (Spray 1992, Delany *et al* 1992). The winter distribution is largely similar (*Winter Atlas*), except for localized movements to coastal waters, particularly in cold weather, and onto freshwater marshes and agricultural fields (*eg* Kirby *et al* 1994, Chisholm & Spray 2002).

Most ringing of Mute Swans in Britain & Ireland has been undertaken by a relatively small number of ringers, members of the Swan Study Group, working on detailed regional studies. Fortunately, these studies have covered a variety of habitats and regions, from the wild birds in the Outer Hebrides and Ireland to those living in close proximity to Man in the English Midlands and south; the recoveries therefore represent the overall population relatively well (Fig 1). Many of these studies are long-term and involve the use of large, individually marked colour-rings (Ogilvie 1972a). In addition, the Mute Swan was the first British breeding species to have been studied using

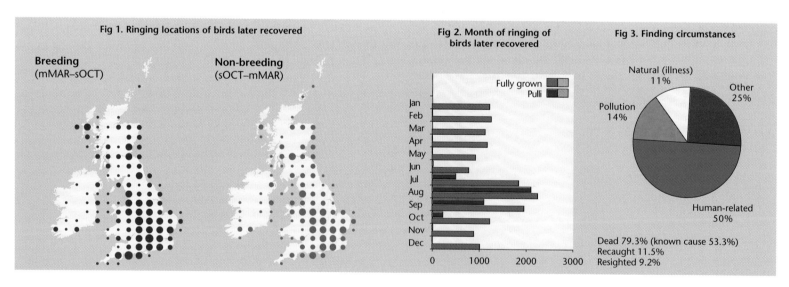

Fig 1. Ringing locations of birds later recovered

Breeding (mMAR–sOCT)

Non-breeding (sOCT–mMAR)

Fig 2. Month of ringing of birds later recovered

Fully grown
Pulli

Fig 3. Finding circumstances

Natural (illness) 11%
Other 25%
Pollution 14%
Human-related 50%

Dead 79.3% (known cause 53.3%)
Recaught 11.5%
Resighted 9.2%

Ringing and recovery data

	<1960	60–69	70–79	80–89	90–97	Total
RINGING						
BTO ringing totals (%)	1	24	14	25	37	82,000
RECOVERIES						
BTO-ringed (%)	1	27	20	27	25	19,704
Foreign-ringed (%)	8	23	23	38	8	13

Statistical analyses

	Breeding population (mMAR–sOCT)	Wintering population (mDEC–mFEB)
Status	SEDENTARY (0)	SEDENTARY
Age differences[NS]	Significant*	Significant*
Sex differences[NS]	Not significant	Not significant
Regional differences	Significant[S]*	Not tested
Finding circumstances	(Not significant)	Not significant

Fig 4. Variation in the distances moved by juvenile Mute Swans with time after ringing as pulli. Medians for 30-day periods (points) and interquartile ranges (bars) and sample sizes are shown.

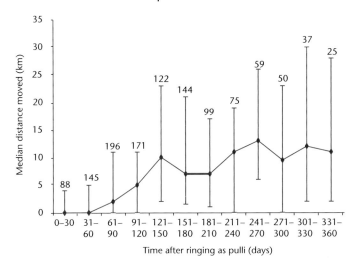

Fig 5. Movements of over 20 km of 631 Mute Swans ringed in Britain & Ireland in June–September and recovered during winter (October to mid-February), with known first-year birds excluded. Some major moulting sites are also indicated.

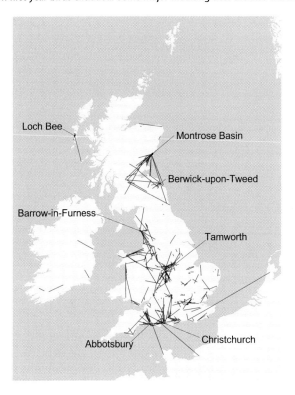

individually identifiable neck-collars in the Outer Hebrides (Spray & Bayes 1992).

The ringing of Mute Swans is very seasonal (Fig 2), with an emphasis on catching broods as complete units, before they fledge in autumn and disperse from their natal territory. For fully grown birds, the annual period of flightlessness during wing moult provides an opportunity to catch large numbers at traditional moult sites in July and August. Individual catches of over 500 swans have been achieved in this manner at Abbotsbury in Dorset and at Berwick-upon-Tweed in Northumberland, with other large catches at the Loch of Strathbeg and at Montrose Basin (northeast Scotland), Loch Bee (Outer Hebrides) and at several sites in the English Midlands.

Dead swans are obvious and this fact, combined with the detailed nature of regionally focused studies and the birds' close relationship to Man, means that the recovery rate of 24% is among the highest for any species in Britain & Ireland. It should be noted that sightings and retraps under 40 km have not been routinely included in the database, unless considered particularly significant.

Just over half of all Mute Swan ring-recoveries are attributed to a known cause of death (53%) and exactly half of these are the result of human-related circumstances, to which must be added a further 14% resulting from pollution and 8% from birds deliberately taken by Man (Fig 3). The incidences of collision with overhead wires and of lead poisoning are particularly high. In a study using British & Irish ring-recoveries to examine Mute Swan mortality resulting from collisions with overhead wires, Perrins & Sears (1991) recorded that 22% of reported deaths (which are themselves non-random) involved birds that had flown into wires, though in some areas this figure can be much higher (Coleman et al 1991, Spray 1991). The overall picture reflects seasonal changes in flying activity, with very few deaths in the summer moult period, and with deaths due to wires decreasing with age.

A number of studies have investigated lead poisoning, which can result when swans looking for grit ingest anglers' lead weights or lead gunshot (Sears 1988, Spray & Milne 1988, O'Halloran et al 1991, Sears & Hunt 1991). Not only do overall mortality rates vary geographically and across years (angling lead was banned in 1987 in England and Wales) but also seasonally and with the source of lead (gunshot or anglers' weights).

A major problem in analysing movements of Mute Swans in recent years has been the growth and activity of Swan Rescue Centres. In the course of their rescue and rehabilitation, some birds have been released at different locations from where they were caught, with large numbers released at certain favoured sites, and rings have sometimes been removed. It is difficult to know exactly how many swans are involved, and many are handled more than once, but with individual centres reporting over 400 swans handled in one year, the figure must run into thousands. The figures presented in Perrins & Martin (1999) could suggest a figure of 5,500 birds passing through Swan Rescue Centres in England and Wales each year (C Perrins pers comm). Not only will this artificially increase survival rates, it is becoming impossible to be certain whether reported movements were natural or assisted. For instance, two ringed birds from East Lothian were rediscovered in Harrogate, Yorkshire, while another from Berwick-upon-Tweed was found dead in Somerset. In each case, it is now known they were transported south 'for treatment' and then escaped or were released hundreds of miles from their original point of capture (C Spray pers obs).

Young Mute Swans ringed in Britain & Ireland disperse from their natal sites either with their parents, as lone individuals, or as brood units but their survival and the distance travelled do not appear to differ between these cases (J Coleman pers obs). Fig 4 shows clearly how the first movements do not generally occur until early winter and the median monthly distance travelled in their first year does not exceed 13 km. These first dispersal movements are usually into the nearest flock and of 132 first-year birds recovered dead in a Midlands study area only 6% were more than 32 km from their natal site (Minton 1971, Coleman & Minton 1979). In Ireland, Collins & Whelan (1993, 1994) have shown that the average distances of first movement of cygnets to six different flocks were 6, 7, 10, 11, 19 and 42 km, with no individual movement over 90 km.

Perrins (1991) has examined the survival rates of young Mute Swans in Britain and has shown that the pattern of mortality seems to be largely similar across the country. Once the cygnets start to leave their natal area in October, monthly death rates rise sharply and remain high until April, at which time the birds settle down to spend the summer, and eventually moult, in one location. Coleman et al (2001) have shown that of 1,647 swans for which their exact age was known at time of death, 75% died in their first two years, so this period of life is

Fig 6. All included exchanges of Mute Swans between Britain & Ireland and abroad, with those ringed in Britain & Ireland (45, red) differentiated from those ringed abroad (13, black).

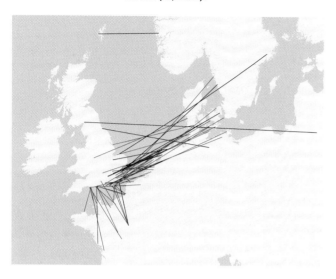

particularly important within the context of the analysis of overall movement patterns.

Once Mute Swan juveniles have dispersed and settled into a non-breeding flock, it becomes more difficult to ascertain the pattern of movements from aggregated national data. Detailed studies of flocks in Ireland by Collins & Whelan (1994) and in the English Midlands by Minton (1971) have clearly shown the nature and extent of interchange between flocks in these pre-breeding years. One particular feature from the Midlands study is the avoidance of movements over high ground, with the vast majority of flights using valleys and low-lying areas. This situation is repeated in northeast Scotland and northeast England (C Spray & J Coleman pers obs) where movements concentrate along the coastal plain and major valleys, with no records from the Pennines or Grampian uplands. Even in low-lying areas such as the Thames, the birds keep closely to the river systems and only infrequently fly across the higher ground (C Perrins pers comm).

Collins & Whelan (1994) showed that Irish swans move more than their English Midland counterparts, and suggest that the distance between flocks, which is larger in Ireland, is the key factor. Minton (1971) reported significant movements between flocks less than 25 km apart but this rapidly falls off as flock separation increases. Only 3% of all recorded movements were over 48 km (5% if incomers to the study area are included) and only 1–2% moved over 80 km. In Ireland, Collins & Whelan (1994) observed 55% of swans in two or more flocks, of which 20% were seen in three and 2% in four different flocks. Both studies reported that movements between flocks become less frequent with age. Of 50 birds moving over 48 km between flocks, and where the exact year of movement was recorded, 23 moved in their first year, 21 in their second and only four and two in the third and fourth years respectively (Minton 1971).

The median natal dispersal distance derived from 307 British & Irish recoveries is 14 km. Detailed studies have shown that birds move much further away from their natal site during the early adult years but return to pair and nest closer to it (Coleman & Minton 1979). Three times as many females as males nested within 1.6 km of their natal site, while conversely twice as many males as females nested over 8 km away. In total, some 51% of birds made their first breeding attempt within 8 km of their natal site and 93% within 24 km (Coleman & Minton 1979). More recent data from the same study area (Coleman et al 2001) have shown that significantly more females (50%) took up territories within 5 km of their birthplace than males (33%). Once Mute Swans have become established as breeders, their movements tend to be even more

restricted, and the median distance for breeding dispersal derived from 182 recoveries is only 2 km. Scott (1984) has shown that for many pairs it is important to stay on a breeding territory over winter to ensure no other pair can take over an apparently empty territory. She showed that winter temperature and available food supply were the critical factors that could cause territorial pairs to abandon a site.

Overlain on the patterns of juvenile, natal and breeding dispersal is the pattern of movement associated with the Mute Swan's annual moult migration. Like other waterfowl, Mute Swans drop all their flight feathers at once, a strategy that necessitates the location of a safe site with abundant food. While breeding adults with young moult on territory, failed breeders join non-breeding adults and juveniles at traditional moulting sites. Minton (1971) reports the moult movement as starting in mid-May and ending in mid-June, with the return largely in September. Counts of the moulting flock at Berwick show a slightly later movement into the flock with departure in September (Spray et al 1996) but that individual swans may be in wing moult from May to the end of October (pers obs).

Since in moult catches a large number of swans are ringed at a restricted number of sites, the catchments of the key study sites can be identified (Fig 5). The resultant pattern also clearly shows the avoidance of movements over high ground, the Berwick and Montrose birds moving either along the coastal plain or via the Tweed and Forth Valleys, rather than inland over the hills. Aerial surveys and ringing at Montrose have shown that an influx of nearly 200 swans occurs at the time of the moult, rather than just a local redistribution (Spray & Atkinson 1991). They subsequently disperse to the south and southwest. At Berwick, a similar pattern occurs with birds from the Tweed Valley and the Northumbrian coastal plain arriving to moult. They then disperse inland up the Tweed or south as far as Tees-side (pers obs).

For 143 birds moulting at Montrose, their choice of moult location has been identified in subsequent years. Males showed greater fidelity to moult sites than females and adults greater fidelity than first-years, with 38% of first-year females being reported moulting in a different flock in a subsequent year (Spray & Atkinson 1991). In 19 of the 22 instances where birds moved to an alternative site, it was to Berwick, 100 km south.

For established breeders and other Mute Swans severe winter weather can cause a major disruption to more usual movement patterns and can also induce severe mortality (Boyd & Ogilvie 1964, Harrison & Ogilvie 1967, Spray 1981, Perrins 1991). The last extensive period of cold weather in Britain, the 1962/63 winter, produced a very high number of swan recoveries, both of British-ringed birds abroad and foreign swans found in Britain. Together with other records, they show a distinct pattern of movement centred on the southeast with birds from the Netherlands and Denmark, as well as movements to and from France and the English south coast (Fig 6). This cold-weather movement may be equivalent to that recorded further east in Europe on a more routine basis, and may be just the western end of such winter migrations (Kuresoo 1991, Wieloch 1991). The range of dates of the recoveries and the disproportionate number ringed in Britain and recovered abroad (rather than vice versa) may just be a reflection of timing and relative ringing intensity – the implication being many were 'foreign' swans over here, returning to the Continent.

The British population of Mute Swans continues to increase (Kirby et al 1994) and a new national survey is due to be undertaken in 2001. Paradoxically this increase may become a conservation issue as the species comes into greater conflict with Man over damage either to fisheries (Trump et al 1994) or to agricultural crops (Chisholm & Spray 2002). At the same time, there are indications that lead poisoning has not disappeared totally and there are always threats to large flightless aggregations of moulting birds from oil or other pollutants. The nature and extent of the operation of Swan Rescue Centres needs to be more fully understood before further detailed analyses of population dynamics and movements can be undertaken.

Chris Spray, Bert Coleman & Jon Coleman

Tundra Swan (Bewick's Swan)

Cygnus columbianus

The Bewick's Swan in Eurasia, race *bewickii*, is a high Arctic breeder that nests on Russian tundras from the Kanin Peninsula across to the Chukchi Sea. A pair in Lithuania in the summers of 1997 and 1998 (S Svazas pers comm) was nesting well to the south of the normal breeding range. The western population, most recently estimated at 29,000 birds (Beekman 1997), migrates to winter mainly in the Netherlands and Britain, with less than 10% (1,000–2,000 birds) reaching Ireland (Delany *et al* 1999). A regular wintering flock of up to 135 birds has become established on the Camargue, to the south of the main wintering range, since the mid-1960s (Monval & Pirot 1989). Large concentrations (up to 50% of the population) are found at key staging sites in Estonia, the Gulf of Finland and the White Sea region in spring and autumn (Luigujoe *et al* 1996, Rees *et al* 1997a, Nolet *et al* 2001). Birds in the eastern part of the range follow a separate flyway to winter in Japan, China and Korea. There is thought to be a third population, of *c* 500 birds, which winters in the south Caspian region, most notably in northern Iran, but the breeding distribution and current status of these birds remain uncertain. Reports of birds seen in the Ukraine, Greece and Turkey may also be from this group (Rees *et al* 1997a, Delany *et al* 1999). The nominate race *columbianus* is native to North America, although there is evidence of occasional breeding in far eastern Siberia where it may interbreed with *bewickii*. It also occurs as a vagrant in Western Europe (Evans & Sladen 1980, Rees *et al* 1997a).

Upon arrival in Britain & Ireland, the swans show few major shifts in distribution during the winter months, other than local changes of feeding site. Cold-weather movements from mainland Europe are

The analysis of the data for this species was supported by Lailan and Robin Young

mainly to established sites. Previously, Bewick's Swans fed primarily on aquatic and marshland plants and on flooded pasture, but they have used arable land increasingly since the early 1970s (Rees *et al* 1997a & c). Similar patterns have been noted in the Netherlands, where the birds still select pondweeds upon arrival in autumn but, having depleted these, switch to arable land and grassland later in the season (Dirksen *et al* 1991). Large flocks occur in different parts of Britain & Ireland, with internationally important numbers recorded at sites in southeast, southwest and northwest England and in southeast Ireland (Rees *et al* 1997c, Colhoun 1998, Cranswick *et al* 1999). This apparent tendency to target particular sites, compared with the Whooper Swan's southwesterly shift in distribution as winter progresses, has been attributed to Britain & Ireland being at the outermost reaches of the Bewick's Swan's migratory range (Rees *et al* 1997c).

For many years Bewick's Swans were ringed only at Slimbridge, Gloucestershire, where birds have been marked with metal rings since 1961 and with additional colour-rings since 1967. The building of swan-pipes at Caerlaverock, Dumfries, and at Welney, Norfolk, in 1980 extended the ringing programme to other parts of Britain, with a fourth pipe at Martin Mere, Lancashire, being brought into use in 1990 (Fig 1). Opportunistic catches elsewhere (at Pensthorpe, Norfolk, and Little Downham, Cambridgeshire) have added to the numbers ringed in

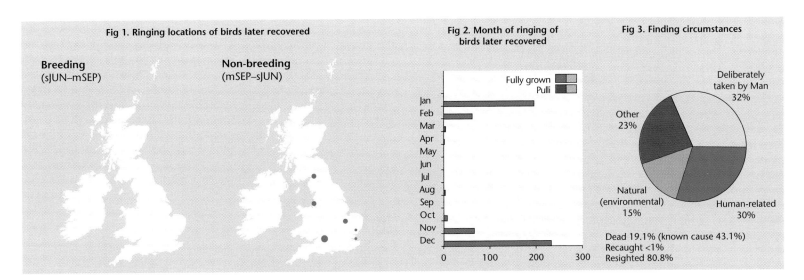

Fig 1. Ringing locations of birds later recovered

Breeding (sJUN–mSEP)   **Non-breeding** (mSEP–sJUN)

Fig 2. Month of ringing of birds later recovered

Fully grown / Pulli

Fig 3. Finding circumstances

Deliberately taken by Man 32%
Other 23%
Natural (environmental) 15%
Human-related 30%

Dead 19.1% (known cause 43.1%)
Recaught <1%
Resighted 80.8%

Ringing and recovery data

	<1960	60–69	70–79	80–89	90–97	Total
RINGING						
BTO ringing totals (%)	0	10	33	28	30	2,035
RECOVERIES						
BTO-ringed (%)	0	1	14	69	16	569
Foreign-ringed (%)	33	0	0	0	67	3

Statistical analyses

	Breeding population (sJUN–mSEP)	Wintering population (sDEC–mMAR)
Status	NONE	[LONG-DISTANCE MIGRANT]
Age differences	—	Not tested
Sex differences	—	Not tested
Regional differences	—	Not tested
Finding circumstances	—	Not tested

Fig 4. Recovery locations for all included recoveries of Bewick's Swans ringed or recovered in Britain & Ireland, with dead recoveries (109, red) differentiated from resightings (462, blue) and recaptures (1, black).

southeast England. Dutch ringers started a regular marking programme for Bewick's Swans wintering in the Netherlands in 1985; more recently, birds have also been caught at migratory sites in Germany, Denmark and Estonia, and on the breeding grounds in the Russian Arctic. Most swan catches in Britain are made in midwinter (Fig 2). The small number of rings recovered from birds marked in August emanate from collaborative studies by Russian, British, Dutch and Danish scientists in the Nenetskiy District of northern Russia, begun in 1991. Although 491 Bewick's Swans have been marked in the Netherlands since the mid-1980s (T Haitjema pers comm), few have been recovered in Britain, and none in Ireland, reflecting the high level of winter site-fidelity in this species (Evans 1979a, Rees 1988).

Of 47 swans found dead for which the finding circumstances were reported to the BTO, 30% had collided with man-made structures, mainly power lines, and 32% had been deliberately taken by Man, despite national legislation banning the hunting of Bewick's Swans throughout its migratory range (Fig 3). Some 32% of live adult swans X-rayed in Britain between 1990 and 1996 were found to be carrying gunshot in their body tissues (Rees et al 1997a) again indicating the importance of illegal hunting as a cause of mortality, but there may still be biases attributable to regional variation in reporting rates, and to difficulties in diagnosing less obvious (including natural) causes of death. The cause of death reported for 18 birds recovered in Britain & Ireland indicated that two (11%) were shot and eight collided with man-made structures, whereas nine (69%) of 13 recoveries from Russia were ascribed to hunting. Death from natural causes predominated in seven reports from the Netherlands. In all areas, however, the sample sizes are low. A separate study based on post-mortem examination of 150 Bewick's Swans recovered in Britain reinforces the view that flying accidents, diagnosed for 27% of adults and 34% of juveniles, are the main reported cause of death in Britain; lead poisoning was recorded for 16% of adults, and 7% of adults had been shot dead (Brown et al 1992). Recoveries from the different age categories do not indicate age differences in recovery rates (Fig 2), since 57% of all birds ringed to 1997 were adults, 16% were yearlings and 27% were juveniles (WWT unpublished data). More detailed assessment of annual survival rates, however, indicates that mortality is higher between the first and second winters than in subsequent years (Scott 1988). The same study found no significant difference in survival between the sexes.

Bewick's Swans migrate from their breeding grounds along the arctic coast of Russia to the White Sea, then head southwest across Karelia to

the Gulf of Finland and the Baltic coast, following both northern and southern shores of the Baltic to wintering grounds in northwest Europe (Rees et al 1997a). Resightings and recoveries of colour-ringed birds (Evans 1982, Rees 1991), and more recently a satellite-tracking programme (Beekman et al 1996), have confirmed the migratory route, with only three recoveries occurring well outside this range (Fig 4). Two of the out-of-range recoveries were from Astrakhan and the third from Perm, on the western side of the Ural Mountains, indicating that these birds had changed flyways and joined the small group wintering in the south Caspian region (Rees 1991, Rees et al 1997a). The resighting of a British-ringed Bewick's Swan in Iceland also was exceptional, since only one or two individuals of the species are seen in Iceland each summer. The bird was marked at Welney, a winter destination for many Icelandic Whooper Swans since the early 1980s (Rees & Bowler 1997), so presumably it joined the Whoopers on migration in spring.

The monthly distribution of recoveries reflects the timing of the Bewick's Swan's migration (Figs 5a & b). The birds begin to leave the breeding grounds in early September, although most families remain until later in the month (Mineyev 1991). Passage through the Baltic is usually in October but continues into November in mild autumns (Luigujoe et al 1996, Rees et al 1997a). The first birds arrive on the wintering grounds in mid- or late October, with numbers reported in the Netherlands, Britain and Ireland increasing in November and during midwinter (Fig 5a). Return migration from Britain & Ireland begins in February, with major movements to staging sites in Germany in March, along the Baltic in April and northwards to the breeding grounds in May (Fig 5b). All healthy Bewick's Swans return to the breeding grounds in spring, with migration occurring both at night and in the day (Rees & Bowler 1991, Beekman & Laubek 1997). The onset of migration is regulated by day length, indicating the broad migratory season, and also by other environmental factors, notably wind direction, which determine the departure date. Thus, once photoperiod has indicated the onset of the migratory season, final departure is influenced by wind direction, with the swans preferring to migrate on northeasterly tail winds in autumn and southwesterly tail winds in spring (Evans 1979b, Rees 1982). The recovery locations suggest that the birds use a number of staging areas but, since several were shot, recovery locations may not reflect the most important sites. Satellite-tracking indicates that the swans use just two or three stopover sites during the journey of 3,000–3,500 km between the breeding and wintering ranges, which fits with energetics studies that estimate a potential flight range of 1,450 km before the need to feed and replenish reserves (Beekman et al 1996). Counts and ring resightings confirm, however, that the clusters of recoveries in Estonia, the White Sea region and the Pechora Delta (Fig 4) do indeed represent vital staging and breeding areas for swan species (Rees et al 1997a, Nolet et al 2001). Flight speed varies with wind speed and direction, and also with the birds' fat-loading (Pennycuick et al 1996), but the birds should complete a 1,450 km flight in 24 hours at an average speed of 60 km/h, which seems appropriate for the species (based on Pennycuick et al 1996, Ogilvie 1972b). Nevertheless, spring migration takes several weeks, since trans-continental migrants use staging areas, not only in order to rest and accumulate body reserves (Drent et al 1981), but also to wait for conditions to improve during the journey north (Rees & Bowler 1991). Autumn migration may be more rapid and direct, since the birds are less likely to encounter adverse weather during their journey south. Certainly, Bewick's Swans are more likely to be reported at migratory sites in spring than in autumn (Evans 1982), and the numbers staging in Estonia are usually higher in spring (Luigujoe et al 1996).

Long-term studies of Bewick's Swans in Britain have shown a high level of winter site-fidelity in this species; some 40–50% of adults and yearlings recorded at Slimbridge each winter have been identified at the site in previous years (Rees 1988). There is also some evidence for fidelity to particular stopover sites, although further analyses are needed to confirm this point (Rees & Bacon 1996). The swans are generally

Fig 5. Locations of Bewick's Swans in (a) October (28), (b) November (115), (c) December (145), (d) January (63), (e) February (69), (f) March (89), (g) April (15) and (h) May (6).

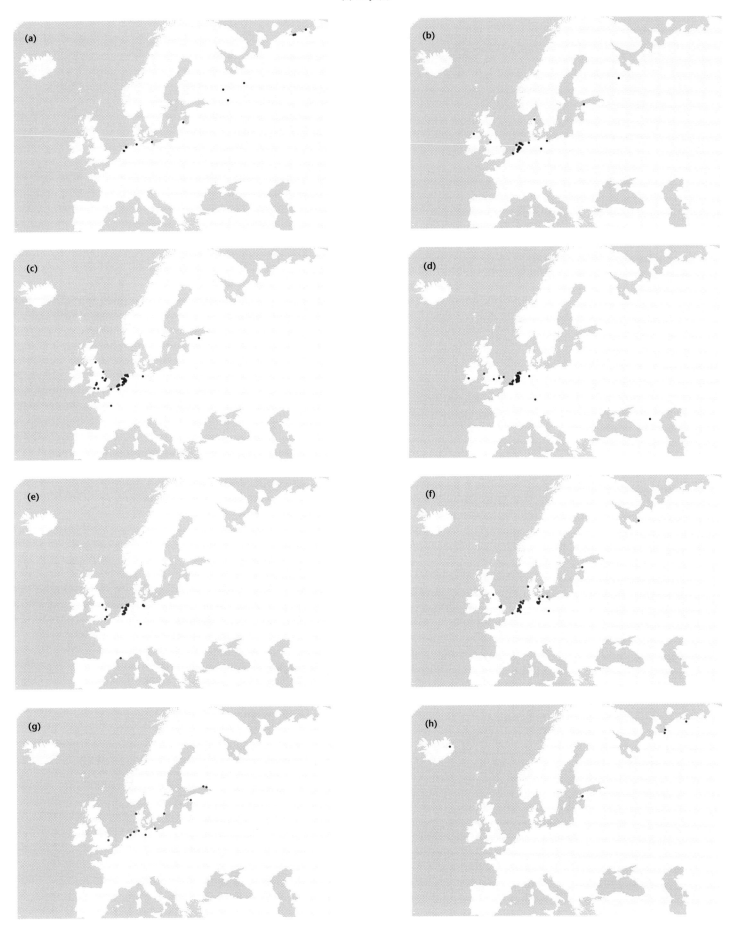

Fig 6. Locations outside the breeding season of (a) 263 female and (b) 260 male Bewick's Swans ringed outside the breeding season in Britain & Ireland.

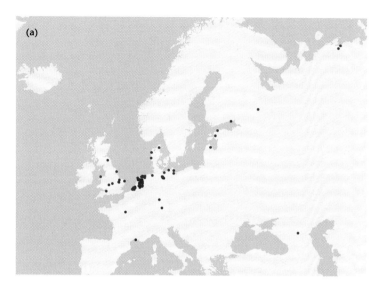

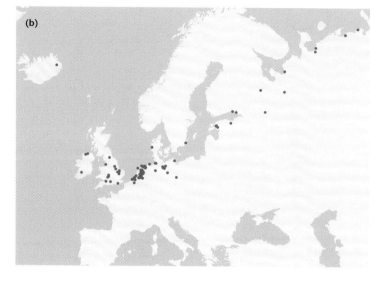

monogamous, with paired birds remaining together throughout the year and offspring associating with their parents throughout the first winter. Thus there is little difference in recovery distribution recorded for males and females, although females occasionally are recovered south of the main wintering grounds in the Netherlands, Britain and Ireland (Figs 6a & b). These birds may have changed wintering site or, in the case of one individual, to a different flyway, following a change of mate. A study of the dispersal of ringed birds in the wintering range has confirmed that males show a higher level of winter site-fidelity, and that they tend to

determine the wintering site for a new pair (Rees 1987). Thus, although a change of wintering site would in most cases be to other parts of the main wintering areas, both northerly and southerly movements away from the ringing site may be more evident in females. It is also possible that, if the birds were unpaired, the recoveries may reflect sex differences in dispersal reported for duck species, with females having a more southerly distribution (Choudhury & Black 1991, Carbone & Owen 1995). This cannot be substantiated, however, without information on the sex ratios of unpaired birds at different latitudes.

Fig 7. All included exchanges of Bewick's Swans between the (a) northwest (16), (b) southwest (458) and (c) southeast (48) of Britain, and abroad.

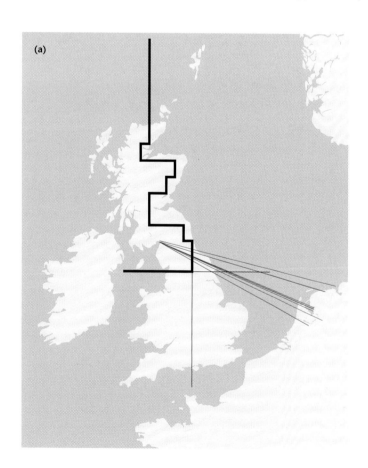

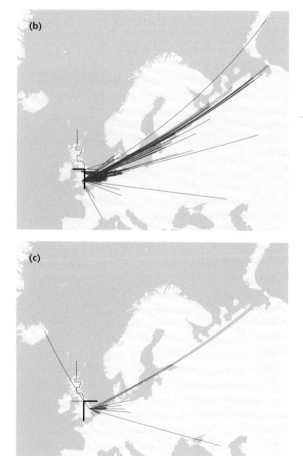

Although subadult birds generally are more likely to disperse than adults, the recovery distribution for immature Bewick's Swans is broadly similar to that of the adult birds, confirming earlier studies which showed that birds marked as first-winters are likely to return to the same wintering site in their second winter, where they frequently associate again with their parents (Evans 1979c). There is evidence that pairing and breeding status does affect a swan's dispersal patterns, however; analysis of resightings showed that single swans are seen at more sites within a winter season than paired birds, which in turn are seen at more sites than family parties (Rees & Bacon 1996).

Bewick's Swans follow a relatively narrow migration route to the breeding grounds, but there is some evidence that birds wintering in different parts of Britain may have different migratory patterns, with those ringed in northwest England (at Martin Mere) and southwest Scotland (at Caerlaverock) having a more northerly distribution than those marked in southern Britain when reported or recovered in the Netherlands or Germany (Figs 7a, b & c). More extensive analyses of 21,915 sightings of colour-ringed Bewick's Swan reported between 1966 and 1994 gave similar results (Rees & Bacon 1996). These showed that swans marked in northwest England were significantly more likely to be reported in Denmark, Germany and Northern Ireland than those marked in the southwest, which were seen more frequently in the Netherlands and other parts of Britain. A similar pattern was noted for swans ringed in southwest Scotland except that a high proportion (44%) of reports were from other British wintering sites. Within-season analyses are needed to determine if these are attributable to individuals staging on the Ouse Washes and in northern England en route to Caerlaverock but, since most Bewick's Swans in Britain winter on the Ouse Washes, it is likely that most birds both enter and leave Britain via East Anglia, with an unknown proportion of swans from more northerly sites in Britain & Ireland flying directly to the continental mainland. Birds ringed in the southeast had a more southerly and easterly distribution, being resighted mainly in the Netherlands and Germany; none were reported from Ireland.

Bewick's Swans tend to congregate at comparatively few sites outside the breeding range; up to 90% of the population may occur on 10 or fewer sites, making them susceptible to changing conditions in these areas (Beekman et al 1994). Population size has increased substantially since the 1960s but regional trends vary; most growth from the mid-1980s to the mid-1990s has been accommodated by wintering sites in the Netherlands (Koffijberg et al 1997, Delany et al 1999), whereas numbers have fluctuated in Britain and declined in Northern Ireland in recent years (Cranswick et al 1999). The loss of aquatic vegetation, the swans' traditional diet, due to eutrophication and drainage at migratory and wintering sites, has encouraged the birds to feed on arable land and pasture where they come into conflict with farmers. Water quality remains a concern at the swans' wetland habitats, but management programmes for restoring aquatic ecosystems are currently under way in the Netherlands, where the swans are increasingly using restored sites and colonizing new areas (Beekman et al 1994, Koffijberg et al 1997, Dirksen et al 1998). Further analysis of within-winter movements recorded for marked birds would help to describe the network of sites and habitats used by the swans in winter, and any variation there has been in site selection over the years that may be attributable to environmental factors, including habitat restoration and weather conditions. Comparatively little is known about dispersal patterns in the breeding range, although variation in breeding density in the European Arctic is well established (Mineyev 1991), and site-fidelity is evident for territorial and breeding pairs (Shchadilov et al 1998). Habitat loss due to oil and gas exploration, and increased disturbance at nest sites due to the associated human activity, remain a major threat to the species (Beekman et al 1994, Rees et al 1997a). The level of illegal hunting, which appears to occur throughout the range, remains a concern and its effect on population parameters should be monitored closely.

Eileen Rees & John Bowler

Whooper Swan
Cygnus cygnus

Whooper Swans are amongst the heaviest of migratory birds; adult males caught in Britain weigh on average 10.2 kg, and one bird in Denmark was recorded at 15.5 kg (Rees *et al* 1997b). They breed in a broad band of subarctic and taiga habitats across northern Eurasia, from Iceland and northern Scandinavia in the west to Mongolia, northern China and the Russian Far East. The Icelandic breeding population migrates mainly to Britain & Ireland (Garðarsson 1991), with some 500–1,300 birds remaining in Iceland through the winter (Garðarsson & Skarphéðinsson 1985, Cranswick *et al* 1996). Co-ordinated midwinter censuses in Britain, Ireland and Iceland indicate that, following an apparent increase in numbers during the late 1980s, the Icelandic population has stabilized at around 16,000 birds, or even begun to decline (Cranswick *et al* 1996, Delany *et al* 1999). A further 59,000 birds from the Fennoscandian and northwest Russian breeding population winter in continental Europe (Laubek *et al* 1999). The level of movement between the two populations, and the extent to which this varies between years, is still not known but estimates are of at least 200 Finnish breeding birds visiting Britain (Laubek *et al* 1998) and of up to 600 Icelandic birds wintering in Europe (Garðarsson 1991).

Nesting habitat in Iceland varies from low-lying marshes amid agricultural fields to upland pools, bogs and lakes set in glacial moraine at altitudes of up to 700 m (Garðarsson & Skarphéðinsson 1984, Einarsson 1996, Rees *et al* 1997b). Historically, the swans wintered on freshwater lakes and marshes, brackish lagoons and coastal bays across northern Britain & Ireland (Owen *et al* 1986), but agricultural fields were used occasionally in the 1940s and more regularly since the 1960s (Kear 1963, Sheppard 1982). Surveys of swans wintering in Britain & Ireland

The analysis of the data for this species was supported by Robert, Audrey & Niall Lightfoot

in the 1990s found less than 15% of the Whooper Swans on arable land, although flock sizes were larger at these sites than elsewhere (Cranswick *et al* 1996, Rees *et al* 1997c). Feeding-site selection appears to differ in continental Europe, where some 75% of Whooper Swans wintering in Denmark feed on farmland, mainly on winter cereals and oilseed rape (Laubek 1995). Areas of open water remain important to provide secure roosts throughout the wintering range.

Regular colour-ringing of Whooper Swans in Britain commenced during the 1979/80 winter, following the building of swan-pipes for catching birds wintering at Caerlaverock, Dumfriesshire, and at Welney, Norfolk (Fig 1). Fewer than 50 have been caught at Welney because numbers wintering on the Ouse Washes were relatively low (100–300 birds) during the early 1980s. By the 1994/95 winter, when over a thousand birds were first recorded at the site (Rees & Bowler 1997), the swan-pipe had fallen into disrepair. A high proportion of the birds wintering at Caerlaverock are caught each winter, however, and several hundreds have been marked at Martin Mere, Lancashire, following the construction of a new swan-pipe there in 1990. Small numbers have been colour-ringed elsewhere, including South Uist in the late 1980s, northeast England throughout the 1990s, southwest Wales in March 1991 and in Northern Ireland, particularly at Castle Espie, since the 1992/93 winter. Birds caught on Fair Isle were marked with metal rings only, and four of the 12 recovered were from a single family. A few

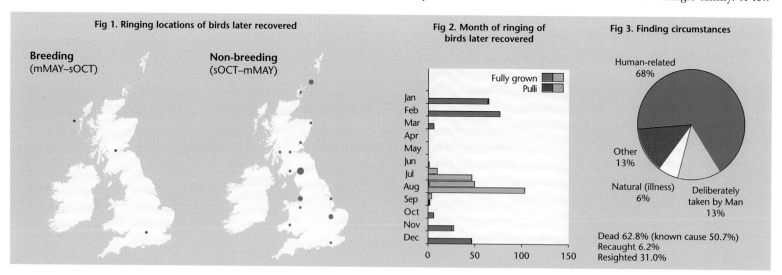

Fig 1. Ringing locations of birds later recovered

Breeding (mMAY–sOCT)

Non-breeding (sOCT–mMAY)

Fig 2. Month of ringing of birds later recovered

Fully grown
Pulli

Fig 3. Finding circumstances

Human-related 68%

Other 13%

Natural (illness) 6%

Deliberately taken by Man 13%

Dead 62.8% (known cause 50.7%)
Recaught 6.2%
Resighted 31.0%

Ringing and recovery data

	<1960	60–69	70–79	80–89	90–97	Total
RINGING						
BTO ringing totals (%)	0	4	1	43	52	1,206
RECOVERIES						
BTO-ringed (%)	0	3	2	34	60	229
Foreign-ringed (%)	0	10	5	34	51	220

Statistical analyses

	Breeding population (mMAY–sOCT)	Wintering population (sDEC–mMAR)
Status	NONE	LONG-DISTANCE MIGRANT*
Age differences	—	Not tested
Sex differences	—	Not significant*
Regional differences	—	Not tested
Finding circumstances	—	Not tested

Fig 4. Within-winter movements of Whooper Swans (a) from Britain to Ireland (188) and (b) from Ireland to Britain (140), for the winters 1979/80 to 1998/99 inclusive. This figure is based on both recoveries and resightings of colour-marked birds. (*Sources*: WWT and Irish Whooper Swan Study Group data.)

(a)

(b)

oversummering or feral Whooper Swans have been caught and marked during their late-summer moult. An individual ringed in Sussex in February 1963 was with a group of Mute Swans, so may also have been a feral bird.

The first of the Icelandic Whooper Swan ringing programmes was initiated in the 1960s, when 400–500 birds were marked with metal rings. A few hundred birds from moulting flocks at Mývatn, Snæfellsnes, Vopnafjörður and Alftafjörður were marked with neck-collars in the early to mid-1980s (Brazil 1983, Garðarsson 1991). Annual colour-ringing of breeding and non-breeding birds at three sites in northern Iceland (Skagafjörður, Mývatnsheiði and Jökulðalsheiði) since 1988 has developed into a detailed long-term study of the population. Ringing has been less intensive in southern Iceland but birds overwintering on Tjörnin in central Reykjavík have been caught and ringed opportunistically since 1990. Individuals from the Fennoscandian and northwest Russian population have been marked with neck-collars in Sweden since 1977 (Mathiasson 1991), in Denmark since 1979 (Preuss 1981) and in Finland since the 1980s (Laubek *et al* 1998), but only seven ring-recoveries reported to the BTO, four from Finland and three from Denmark, were from continental ringing sites, compared with 213 from Iceland. The wide distribution of ringing sites in Iceland has helped to ensure that birds' movements can be monitored in most parts of the wintering range. This has been particularly important in Ireland, where few birds have been caught and where relatively few British-ringed Whooper Swans are observed, despite a programme of intensive ring-reading since the early 1990s. A high proportion of recoveries are from birds of known age, having been marked as pulli or juveniles (38% of 229 recoveries from British-ringed birds and 36% of 213 recoveries of Icelandic-ringed birds; Fig 2).

Of 282 ringed birds whose death was reported, the cause of death was known for 143. Of these, 68% died in human-related circumstances (including colliding with man-made structures), a further 13% were

illegally shot or deliberately taken by Man and 6% died of natural illness; seven birds were taken by natural predators and five died through pollution (Fig 3). Earlier studies found that the main cause of death in Britain, Ireland and Iceland is flying accidents, mostly collisions with overhead wires (Brown *et al* 1992, Einarsson 1996). X-rays taken of birds caught in Scotland also showed that, despite protection from hunting throughout the range, some 10% of birds had lead shot in their body tissues (Rees *et al* 1990). This level is lower than that reported for Bewick's Swans (see Bewick's Swan account), which have a longer migration and cross more international boundaries, but serves to emphasize that illegal hunting of swans also occurs in Britain, Ireland or Iceland, and probably in all of these countries.

Although the distribution and number of recovery sites does not emphasize the main wintering areas for the birds, it does broadly reflect the known distribution, with the swans having a predominantly northerly distribution in Britain but being widespread in Ireland (Cranswick *et al* 1996). Over 1,000 Whooper Swans wintering on the Ouse Washes, southeast England, the most important site for the species in Britain (Rees & Bowler 1997), are at the southernmost edge of the range. Recoveries from the breeding range show that the swans are also widespread in Iceland, except for the central glacial regions. There is a similar proportion of the two sexes in the population (47% males in a sample of over 4,000 caught in Britain and Iceland by December 1997), and members of a pair remain together over many years (Rees *et al* 1996).

Earlier studies have shown a high level of site-fidelity in this species. For instance, some 78% of swans marked in southwest Scotland during the early 1980s returned to the same site for at least one further winter (Black & Rees 1984) and 57% of nest sites were occupied by a pair where both members of the pair had nested on the same territory the previous year (Einarsson 1996). Nevertheless, individuals move readily between Britain and Ireland within a winter season (Fig 4), with northern areas of

Fig 5. Satellite tracks for Whooper Swans on (a) autumn migration: swans JSC (red), CPA (blue) and CIA (black), and (b) spring migration: swans AJU (red) and JAP (blue). (*Sources:* Pennycuick *et al* 1996, 1999, by permission of *Ibis* and *Journal of Avian Biology*.)

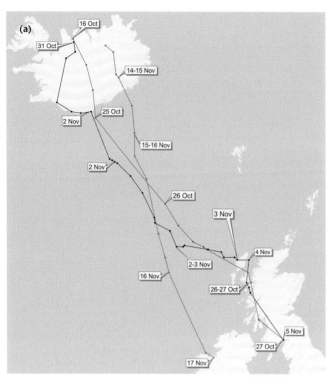

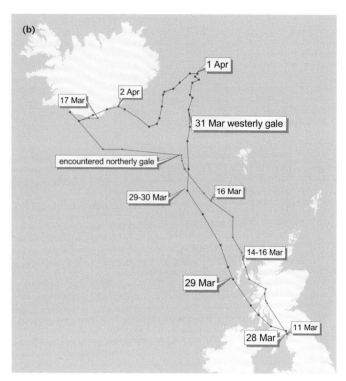

Ireland, in particular, being used as staging sites by swans wintering in Britain, as well as by those wintering elsewhere in Ireland (McElwaine *et al* 1995). Movement was marginally more frequent from Britain to Ireland (55% of 411 within-winter movements between Britain and Ireland reported to WWT by 1998) than in the other direction, perhaps reflecting a gradual southward shift in distribution as the winter progresses, and a more direct flight to the breeding range (Rees *et al* 1997c).

Cygnets migrate with their parents in autumn and remain with them during the first winter but may return to Iceland independently in the spring. Although they are less likely than Bewick's Swans to associate with their parents thereafter, 79% of birds ringed at Caerlaverock during their first winter returned to the same site in subsequent years (Black & Rees 1984).

Autumn migration commences in late September or October, with departure for the breeding grounds occurring mainly in March and April (Rees *et al* 1997b). The 800 km minimum flight between Britain & Ireland and Iceland is probably the longest sea-crossing undertaken by any swan species, taking between 12.7 and 42.4 hours for six satellite tracks of Whooper Swans on autumn migration, and 32 to 101 hours for four swans followed in spring (Pennycuick *et al* 1996, 1999; Fig 5). At least two of the swans tracked during spring migration encountered strong headwinds or sidewinds when halfway to Iceland, including a bird that spent four days at sea (Pennycuick *et al* 1996). A third individual took 36 hours to fly a straight track from southeast Iceland to Donegal Bay (Pennycuick *et al* 1999; Fig 5), confirming that some swans fly directly from Iceland to Ireland. All three birds survived but it seems that persistent adverse weather during migration could have a major effect on survival rates. The predominantly overseas journey between Britain & Ireland and Iceland means that there are no migratory sites separate from the breeding or wintering areas; none of the satellite-tracked swans used the Faeroes. Wintering sites in northern Britain and Ireland, such as Loughs Foyle and Swilly in Ireland (McElwaine *et al* 1995), are important as landfall or departure areas, with key staging sites in south and southeast Iceland, notably Lónfjörður (up to 7,000–8,000 birds; Einarsson 2000) and Þykkvibaer (over 1,000 birds; Ó Einarsson pers comm), similarly being used in autumn and spring.

Although the first birds to reach Britain & Ireland in autumn may arrive at sites throughout the range, including the Ouse Washes, there is a shift in the distribution of the population as a whole during the winter, from the northern regions of Scotland in October and November to sites in England and southern Scotland in midwinter (Rees *et al* 1997c). This could be due to swans wintering in the southern part of the range generally migrating later than the rest of the population or, more likely, that many birds use regions closer to their Icelandic breeding grounds on arrival in Britain & Ireland, then disperse southwards as the winter progresses. Movements of individuals within Ireland support the latter view, with birds first seen at Loughs Foyle and Swilly subsequently identified at Loughs Neagh and Beg, and in counties further south (McElwaine *et al* 1995).

Birds from eastern Britain appeared more likely to be recovered in eastern or central Iceland, and vice versa, but birds moved between western Britain and all parts of the breeding range (Fig 6). There were relatively few recoveries from southern Iceland probably because ringing, and thus recaptures, were mainly at study sites in the northern part of the country. Most movements between Britain and continental Europe were to or from eastern Britain, although two birds ringed in southwest Scotland were recovered in Norway and the Netherlands respectively. As for western Britain, movements of birds between Ireland and Iceland also were wide-ranging. Thus, despite the movement between eastern Britain and eastern Iceland, the pattern differs from results of earlier analyses which found that swans seen in Ireland were significantly more likely to come from Skagafjörður (northwest Iceland) than from two ringing sites further east (McElwaine *et al* 1995), and that Whooper Swans migrate from Iceland on a broad front (Garðarsson 1991). This may be due to all recoveries submitted to the BTO being presented here, rather than focusing on autumn distribution patterns in Britain & Ireland, thus not controlling for redistribution during the winter. Further analyses, using all resightings, are planned to clarify movements between the breeding and wintering sites. Even when all sightings are considered, however, only 51 (1%) of over 4,700 swans colour-ringed in Britain and Iceland have been reported in continental Europe, 38 in Denmark, seven in the Netherlands, two in Norway, and one bird in each of Finland, Germany, France and Spain.

Fig 6. All included exchanges of Whooper Swans between Britain & Ireland and other parts of Europe, with those involving Iceland (360, red) differentiated from those involving Norway, Denmark, Sweden and Finland (10, blue).

Ringing of Whooper Swans in continental Europe confirmed that movement to Britain & Ireland of swans from the Fennoscandian and northwest Russian population also occurs in winter. Several families from 447 Whooper Swans marked with neck-collars in Finland in the mid-1990s have been sighted in Britain, mainly in southeast England (Laubek *et al* 1998), and the first marked bird from this population was identified in Ireland, at Lough Neagh, in February 1999. Since neck-collared birds were seen in southeast England in both the 1995/96 and 1996/97 winters, migration from the Continent may be a regular pattern, although the extent to which this is influenced by weather conditions remains uncertain (Rees *et al* 1997b, Laubek *et al* 1998). Ringing of Whooper Swans in different parts of Finland indicates that distribution in winter is related to breeding locality, with birds from southern Finland being more likely to visit Britain than those ringed further north. The latter are more likely to winter in Denmark (Laubek *et al* 1998). Denmark, Germany and southern Sweden remain the main wintering areas for the Fennoscandian and northwest Russian population, with cold weather increasing movement to the Netherlands and Germany in some years (Delany *et al* 1999, Laubek *et al* 1999).

The Whooper Swan's scattered distribution, and the tendency to feed on temporary wetlands or non-wetland habitats in the day (Rees *et al* 1997b), means that the monthly wildfowl counts may miss a substantial proportion of the population (Owen *et al* 1986), making it difficult to evaluate population trends prior to the introduction of coordinated international censuses in 1986. The British population was put at not more than 4,000 birds in the early 1960s (Boyd & Eltringham 1962) compared with counts of 4,980 to 5,200 in Great Britain since the mid-1980s (Salmon & Black 1986, Kirby *et al* 1992, Cranswick *et al* 1996). Total population size was estimated at around 4,000 in 1984 and 1985

(Garðarsson & Skarphéðinsson 1984, Garðarsson 1991), rising to 16,700 during the first international census in January 1986 (Salmon & Black 1986) and just over 18,000 in January 1991 (Kirby *et al* 1992), indicating real population growth over this period. Population trends in the mid-1990s, and a count of 15,800 in the January 1995 census, indicate that numbers may now have stabilized or begun to decline (Cranswick *et al* 1996). There were no major changes in Whooper Swan distribution recorded in the 1991 and 1995 censuses, although birds in England were more concentrated in 1995, with counts of 250 in Lancashire and 500 in Norfolk/Cambridgeshire, perhaps due to the presence of a safe roost in an area of intensive agriculture (Cranswick *et al* 1996, Rees & Bowler 1997).

Further analysis of counts made during the international censuses, held at five-yearly intervals, should indicate whether the distribution in Britain & Ireland is becoming more clumped, and analysis of ring-resightings will assess the level of movement between sites. The marked increase in the Fennoscandian and northwest Russian population over the last decade (Delany *et al* 1999, Laubek *et al* 1999) may result in more substantial movements of Whooper Swans from the Continent to Britain & Ireland in future years, particularly if there is cold weather elsewhere in Europe, which should be evident through sightings of birds ringed in Finland or Denmark. Spring or autumn censuses in Iceland should be undertaken in conjunction with the midwinter international censuses, to determine whether immigration from the Continent is having a significant effect on population estimates for the Icelandic breeding population, and to describe any variation in the movement of continental birds to Britain & Ireland.

Eileen Rees, Kendrew Colhoun, Ólafur Einarsson, Graham McElwaine, Ævar Petersen & Sverrir Thorstensen

Pink-footed Goose
Anser brachyrhynchus

High skeins of Pink-footed Geese moving across British skies are the very essence of visible migration. Whilst the status of Pinkfeet in Britain & Ireland up to the late 19th century was virtually unknown, and their absence during April to September a complete mystery, farmers in Iceland had known of the existence of the 'mountain goose' for many centuries. In 1638, Gísli Oddsson, the Bishop of Skálholt in southern Iceland, wrote: 'I speak of fowl which come from abroad; throughout the winter they do not dwell among us and are not even observed . . . every year in autumn they make for the neighbouring countries of England, Ireland and Scotland . . .' (quoted by Scott & Fisher 1953). These are remarkable statements when we consider the ideas then prevalent about bird migration.

Today, although the Pink-footed Goose is a familiar bird in Britain it has a very limited world distribution and numbers no more than 260,000 individuals. Through extensive ringing we now know that there are two wholly migratory populations of Pink-footed Geese. One breeds in Svalbard, migrates through Norway and Denmark to winter in the Netherlands and Belgium, and numbers some 35,000 birds (Madsen *et al* 1999). The other breeds in central Iceland and east Greenland and winters almost exclusively in Scotland and England (Fig 6). This population has increased in number from *c* 30,000 in the 1950s to *c* 225,000 in 1999 (Mitchell *et al* 1999). Very few Pinkfeet winter in Ireland, the maximum count during winter 1997/98 being 27 birds at Lough Swilly (Colhoun 2000).

Knowledge of the movements, phenology and winter distribution of the Iceland/Greenland population is underpinned by the extensive ringing effort of the Wildfowl Trust in the 1950s (Boyd & Scott 1955,

The analysis of the data for this species was supported by the friends and families of Jenny Gill & Graham Appleton

Scott *et al* 1955). Peter Scott, Hugh Boyd and their colleagues and volunteers caught 13,561 Pinkfeet using rocket-nets during the 1950s (Scott 1953). During the decade, catches were invariably in the autumn, and the distribution of the ringing sites of recovered birds broadly reflected the distribution of Pinkfeet in Scotland and England (Fig 1), except northeast Scotland, which is under-represented. In addition to those caught in Britain, a further 14,000 were captured on the breeding and moulting grounds in central Iceland (Scott & Fisher 1953, Scott *et al* 1955). Knowledge of the movements (Boyd 1955, Fox *et al* 1994a), and population dynamics (Boyd & Scott 1955, Boyd 1956) of the species was greatly advanced.

After 1961, virtually no Pink-footed Geese were caught in Britain or Iceland. The Wildfowl Trust (now WWT) began a new investigation into their winter ecology in 1986. The principal catching sites were Martin Mere (Lancashire), Loch Leven (Kinross), and sites close to the Ythan Estuary (Aberdeenshire), and, as in the 1950s, the majority of birds were caught in October to February (Fig 2). In addition to the standard metal ring, these birds were fitted with plastic leg rings, allowing multiple sightings of the same individual. Latterly some birds were fitted with plastic neck-collars.

In 1987, 77 Pinkfeet were caught in Greenland and, in 1988, 27 in Iceland. From 1996, however, WWT, in association with the Icelandic Institute of Natural History, began a new effort to catch moulting birds

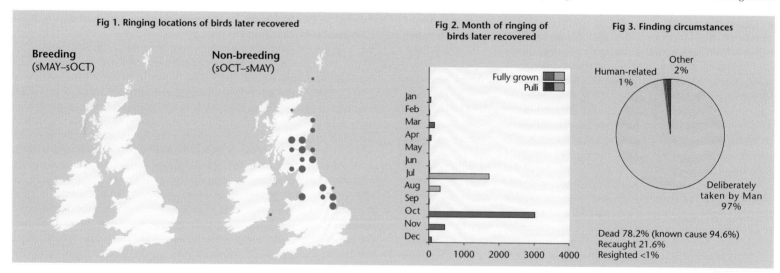

Fig 1. Ringing locations of birds later recovered

Breeding (sMAY–sOCT)

Non-breeding (sOCT–sMAY)

Fig 2. Month of ringing of birds later recovered

Fully grown
Pulli

Jan / Feb / Mar / Apr / May / Jun / Jul / Aug / Sep / Oct / Nov / Dec

0 1000 2000 3000 4000

Fig 3. Finding circumstances

Other 2%
Human-related 1%
Deliberately taken by Man 97%

Dead 78.2% (known cause 94.6%)
Recaught 21.6%
Resighted <1%

Ringing and recovery data

	<1960	60–69	70–79	80–89	90–97	Total
RINGING						
BTO ringing totals (%)	83	0	0	5	12	14,219
RECOVERIES						
BTO-ringed (%)	60	26	3	1	9	3,801
Foreign-ringed (%)	90	8	0	0	1	2,062

Statistical analyses

	Breeding population (sMAY–sOCT)	Wintering population (sNOV–sAPR)
Status	NONE	LONG-DISTANCE MIGRANT*
Age differences	—	Not tested
Sex differences	—	Not significant*
Regional differences	—	Not significant[2]*
Finding circumstances	—	Not tested*

Fig 4. Temporal and spatial distribution of sightings of colour-marked Pink-footed Geese in different parts of Britain. (*Source*: WWT data.)

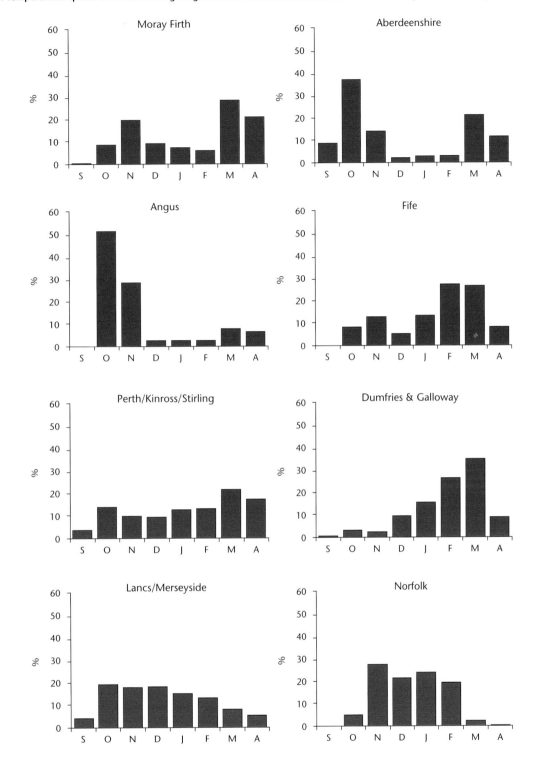

in central Iceland and, up to 1999, over 2,000 birds had been newly ringed.

The Pink-footed Goose is a popular quarry species and it is not surprising that 97% of all known causes of death are from shooting (Fig 3). While the distribution of recoveries undoubtedly reflects hunting activity, this may not be as big a problem as, for example, for common duck species, since goose hunters actively seek out Pinkfeet in many of their traditional haunts.

Analysis of recovery and resighting data, particularly involving individually marked birds, has revealed the extent of movements within the winter in Britain, and confirmed the timing of passage through

Scotland and Iceland (Fox *et al* 1994a). The main departure from the east Greenland breeding/moulting areas commences in late August towards Iceland to join the breeding/moulting stock there. Pink-footed Geese generally start to arrive in Britain from their breeding grounds in early or mid-September, with numbers then increasing up to mid-October (Fig 4). The arrival is pronounced at well-defined staging areas, especially in northeast Scotland (Loch of Strathbeg), eastern Scotland (*eg* Dupplin Lochs, near Perth) and the Lothians and Borders areas (*eg* West Water Reservoir), where lesser numbers remain to winter. Peak numbers occur at major sites generally in the middle of October with over 95% of the whole population counted on as few as 30 sites (Mitchell *et al* 1999).

Fig 5. Recovery locations and movements of over 20 km of Pink-footed Geese ringed during October and November in Perth & Kinross (244, red) and Lancashire (54, blue), and recovered before the end of the following January.

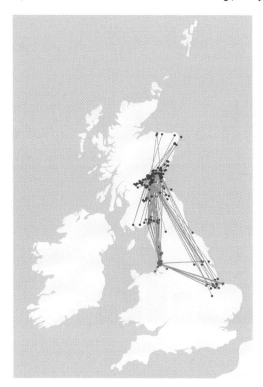

Fig 6. Recovery locations and all included exchanges of Pink-footed Geese between Britain & Ireland and abroad. Those exchanges involving Iceland or Greenland (2,324, red) are differentiated from all others (14, grey).

There is considerable redistribution in late autumn and early winter especially to sites further south, particularly to Lancashire and Norfolk, with peak numbers occurring in Norfolk through January (Fig 4). Pink-footed Geese start to move north again as early as February when numbers peak on the Fylde and in the Solway Firth. Pre-migratory peaks in numbers on the Ythan Estuary, Loch of Strathbeg and on the Moray Firth are recorded in late March (Fig 4). The return passage to Iceland starts in mid-April, with visible migration occurring through the Western Isles. This appears to differ little from patterns observed early in the 20th century (Berry 1939). The first arrivals in Iceland have been recorded from *c* 18–24 April, with the majority arriving in late April and early May (Fox *et al* 1992).

Despite an eightfold increase in numbers, the winter distribution has remained essentially the same as in earlier years. Recent intensive studies of feeding distribution around Loch Leven showed a similar feeding distribution to patterns observed during 1968–70 (Newton & Campbell 1973, Hearn & Mitchell 1995). The main winter habitat is thought to have been saltmarsh (Owen 1976), but from the late 19th century, the species has moved inland to feed on farmland, taking advantage of reservoirs, other freshwater bodies and estuaries for roosting (Owen *et al* 1986). Generally, Pink-footed Geese use stubble fields in autumn, gleaning the spilt grain, then moving to root crops (if available in midwinters, but with grassland predominating after autumn in most studies of habitat use (*eg* Newton & Campbell 1973, Forshaw 1983, Bell 1988)). Radio-tracking in northeast Scotland has confirmed this within-winter mobility for individual Pink-footed Geese. Tagged birds had large feeding ranges (21–69 km^2), although they appeared to have core areas of activity (Giroux & Patterson 1995); they also showed similar shifts in roosting sites, changing sites approximately every 10 nights between December and April, sometimes as a result of human disturbance or harsh weather (Giroux 1991).

Direct recoveries of birds reported dead within the winter of their capture provide further information on the movements of individuals. Birds caught in southeast, east-central and northeast Scotland dispersed throughout the wintering grounds, particularly demonstrating the importance of sites in southeast Scotland as an autumn staging area (Fig 5). Lancashire-caught birds dispersed to eastern England and to southwest Scotland in midwinter (Fig 5).

Resightings in subsequent years showed a 75% return rate to Lancashire of birds individually marked there (Fox *et al* 1994a). Sightings in staging areas also show a high degree of site-fidelity, sometimes to individual fields (pers obs). However, 43% of all geese seen in successive winters were reported from a different site. Most of these movements corresponded with the general within-winter pattern described above and so do not indicate a lack of wintering site-fidelity in individual birds. Until larger numbers of individual case histories are available, it will not be easy to determine whether different wintering groups have different migratory patterns, or whether individuals differ in their winter movements according to the conditions prevailing in particular seasons. This level of site-fidelity fits within a flexible wintering strategy that takes wintering birds through a series of different localities in response to local food availability and occasionally disturbance. This dispersal strategy underpins the ecological success of the Pinkfoot in adapting to changes in the availability of food brought about by major changes in British agriculture in recent decades. The population seems adept at exploiting a patchy but rich food supply subject to sudden extensive changes in distribution and abundance.

There have only been a handful of recoveries involving movements of Pinkfeet between the Iceland/Greenland and the Svalbard populations (Fig 6). However, Ebbinge *et al* (1984) suggested that this modest interchange might be sufficient to promote gene-flow between the two populations.

There is a need to understand the population processes underlying the increase in numbers that has occurred in the last 40 years. Continued monitoring of movements and mortality patterns through individual marking are basic requirements for the immediate future. There is equally an urgent need in Britain to quantify the distribution and scale of alleged agricultural damage.

Carl Mitchell

White-fronted Goose

Anser albifrons

Britain & Ireland holds a unique position for this circumpolar goose, lying at the end of two flyways. The Greenland White-fronted Goose *flavirostris* is the most morphologically distinct of the species' five races. Its single population nests solely in west Greenland (occurring mainly in low arctic tundra at 66–73°N), and is unusual among arctic-breeding geese in undertaking two separate long-distance migratory flights, each of over 1,000 km, between its wintering and breeding areas.

Russian Whitefronts, of the nominate race *albifrons*, breed at low densities across a 4,500-km range, from the Kanin Peninsula (44°E) east to the Kolyma River (155°E). Traditionally, they have been split into two population groupings. Those breeding west of the Chatanga River on the Taimyr Peninsula belong to a West Palearctic group that migrates west and southwest to winter in Europe and southwest Asia. To the east, an East Palearctic group migrates southeast to winter in southeast and east Asia (Rogacheva 1992, Mooij *et al* 1999). Scott & Rose (1996) considered there to be four sub-groups within the West Palearctic: in western and central Siberia (wintering in northeast and northwest Europe), in western and central Siberia (wintering in central Europe), in northern Siberia (wintering around the Black Sea and in Turkey), and in northern Siberia (wintering around the Caspian Sea and in Iraq).

There is no overlap of range or migration routes between *flavirostris* and *albifrons*, and these are treated largely separately in the following account. Two further races, *frontalis*, which breeds from the Kolyma River to Queen Maud Gulf in Canada, and *gambelli*, winter in North America, with Russian populations of *frontalis* also wintering in east Asia (*BWP*).

The analysis of the data for this species was supported by Eve Tigwell Consultancy

In Britain & Ireland, *flavirostris* has always been restricted to northern and western areas — Wales, northwest England (deserted since the 1950s as a regular wintering area; Ruttledge & Ogilvie 1979), west and northern Scotland, and Ireland. In contrast, *albifrons* occurs in relatively small numbers at a few traditional sites in southern England, and formerly Wales. Numbers occurring in England have declined during the last 50 years, a trend attributed to progressive 'short-stopping'; birds are apparently wintering further east in continental Europe in response to the milder winters of recent years. Numbers in Britain peak during severe winters in continental Europe.

The extent of the historic British & Irish wintering areas of *flavirostris* was originally determined by the distribution of western lowland, peatland areas, which did not regularly freeze in winter and where geese could feed on the underground parts of bog plants. Through the 20th century, low-intensity farmland within the traditional range has come to be used, while most flocks retain some use of peatlands as roost sites (Ruttledge & Ogilvie 1979, Fox *et al* 1994b, 1998, 1999b). On some wintering areas, however, Greenland Whitefronts now feed on intensive grasslands (Mayes 1991). In Iceland, spring and autumn staging occurs on lowland farmland in the south and west; here, the birds use intensive farmland, as well as more natural wetlands including lakes, marshes, peatlands and saltmarshes (Francis & Fox 1987, Fox *et al* 1999a, b). In

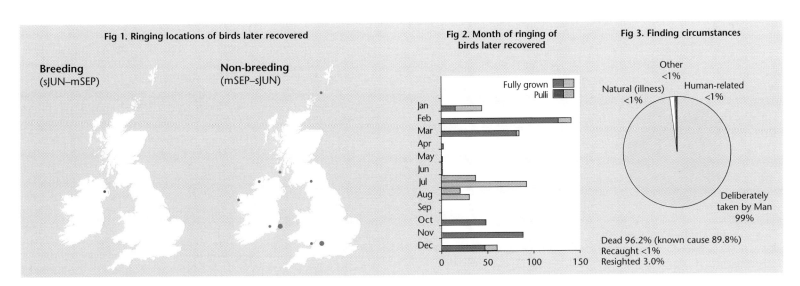

Fig 1. Ringing locations of birds later recovered

Breeding (sJUN–mSEP)

Non-breeding (mSEP–sJUN)

Fig 2. Month of ringing of birds later recovered

Fully grown
Pulli

Fig 3. Finding circumstances

Other <1%
Natural (illness) <1%
Human-related <1%
Deliberately taken by Man 99%

Dead 96.2% (known cause 89.8%)
Recaught <1%
Resighted 3.0%

Ringing and recovery data

	<1960	60–69	70–79	80–89	90–97	Total
RINGING						
BTO ringing totals (%)	24	4	1	35	36	2,148
RECOVERIES						
BTO-ringed (%)	27	21	1	25	27	410
Foreign-ringed (%)	53	32	8	6	1	293

Statistical analyses

	Breeding population (sJUN–mSEP)	Wintering population (mDEC–mMAR)
Status	NONE	[LONG-DISTANCE MIGRANT]
Age differences	—	Not tested
Sex differences	—	Not tested
Regional differences	—	Not tested
Finding circumstances	—	Not tested

Fig 4. Recovery locations and all 391 included exchanges of Greenland White-fronted Geese between Britain & Ireland and abroad.

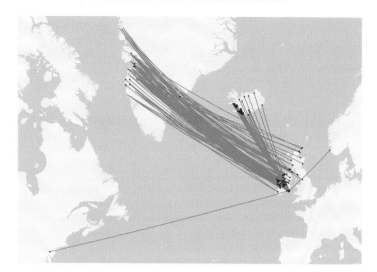

Fig 5. Locations of sightings (197, red), and recoveries of dead birds (8, black), of 66 Greenland White-fronted Geese ringed in Isungua, Greenland (circled).

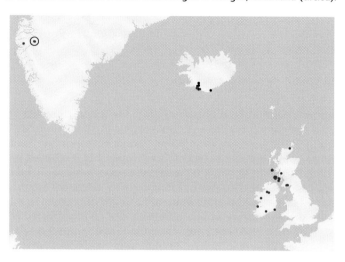

Greenland, a range of low-arctic wetland types are used for staging, nesting, brood-rearing and moult (Fox *et al* 1983, Fox & Stroud 1988, Glahder 1999a).

On the wintering grounds, European Whitefronts, in contrast, use various forms of coastal, estuarine and seminatural grassland. Throughout most of its range, however, recent decades have seen increasing numbers wintering on intensively managed rotational grassland (Mooij *et al* 1999). Whitefronts generally feed within 10 km of secure winter roost sites (Mooij 1993). During spring migration, habitat selection progressively changes from a selection of managed agricultural habitats to natural wetlands as birds approach the breeding areas; typically a range of low-arctic wet moss–sedge tundra types (Rogacheva 1992).

Knowledge of the migration of *flavirostris* has benefited from three distinct phases of ringing activity using progressively more sophisticated techniques. The Greenland Bird Ringing Scheme, operated from Copenhagen's Zoological Museum, encouraged the capture and ringing of geese with conventional metal leg rings by hunters and others (Salomonsen 1956). This resulted in the ringing of 1,319 geese during 1946–74 from substantially the whole of the breeding range. To the mid-1980s, these gave 362 recoveries including 168 from Britain & Ireland and three unexpected recoveries from Canada and one from Norway (although the presence of a regular wintering flock in southwest Norway has recently been suggested; Fox & Francis 2002). These recoveries demonstrated significant leap-frog migration, with a tendency for birds nesting in more northerly areas of western Greenland to winter in southern Ireland, and for birds from further south in Greenland to winter in the west and north of Scotland (Salomonsen 1950, Kampp *et al* 1988).

A second phase of ringing activity, using individually coded plastic marks in addition to metal rings, began in 1979. Initially, just plastic leg rings were used, with 96 birds marked in Greenland in 1979 (Belman 1981) and a further 89 there in 1984. Marking with neck-collars (in addition to leg bands) commenced at Wexford Slobs in Ireland in 1983. In a continuing annual programme operated by the Irish National Parks and Wildlife Service, a total of 1,452 birds have been ringed in Ireland (1,381 at Wexford, but also 57 at Sheskinmore, County Donegal and 14 at Lough Owel, County Westmeath). A total of 37 birds have also been marked on Islay in Scotland, one bird in Lancashire, and 72 in west Iceland. Neck-collars have also been used in Greenland in 1989, 1992 and 1997. Over 47,000 resightings or recaptures of 1,982 individually marked geese, mainly on the wintering grounds but also on Icelandic staging areas and a few also in Greenland, had been made by over 200

observers by May 1999; these have given many detailed insights into the movements and behavioural ecology of this population (Belman 1981, Kampp *et al* 1988, Warren 1990, Wilson *et al* 1991, Warren *et al* 1992a, b, 1993, Bell *et al* 1993, Fox *et al* 1999a).

A third phase of migration research, a programme of satellite telemetry to study spring migration, began in 1996 (Glahder *et al* 1996, 1997, Fox *et al* 1999a, Glahder 1999a). Transmitters placed on six geese in spring 1998, and eight in 1999, have yielded very detailed data on spring and summer movements, currently being analysed (Glahder *et al* pers comm). This programme will yield unique insights into the day-by-day decisions made by individuals during migration, of essential importance to understanding the range of migration strategies adopted and their implications.

For nominate *albifrons*, most data derive from conventional ringing undertaken especially in the Netherlands where over 20,000 have been ringed since the 1950s (Doude van Troostwijk 1974, Ebbinge 1991, Mooij *et al* 1996). In Britain, 612 were ringed to the end of 1981 (Owen *et al* 1986), mostly between 1948 and the 1960s by WWT, at or near Slimbridge (Mitchell & Ogilvie 1996). Small numbers were colour-ringed at Slimbridge in the late 1990s (34 in February 1997 and 19 in February 1998). On the Russian breeding grounds, conventional ringing of moulting birds has been undertaken since the 1960s (Borzhonov 1975, Rogacheva 1992). Since 1989, 848 geese have been individually marked with coloured leg rings or neck-collars.

The recovery data held by BTO, summarized in Figs 1 & 2, are a small subset of the ringing data available for each population. Most knowledge of movements now derives from individually marked birds, data on which are curated independently. Of *albifrons* ringed abroad, only those conventionally ringed in the Netherlands are represented in the British & Irish recoveries held by BTO, although a colour-ringed Whitefront marked on the Taimyr Peninsula in summer 1991 was seen at Slimbridge the following winter (Mooij 1993), and a German neck-collared bird was seen at Slimbridge for several winters in the mid-1990s (R Hearn pers comm). All recoveries of the race *albifrons* from ringing in Britain have been from the Severn Estuary (Fig 1).

The vast majority (98%) of Whitefront recoveries are of birds shot (Fig 3). For *flavirostris*, this reflects also the findings of the complete holdings of the Greenland Ringing Scheme up to the late 1980s (Kampp *et al* 1988), in which 89% of 352 birds where recovery circumstances were known had been shot. The annual number of marked birds recovered from Iceland, as a proportion of those known to be alive, has shown a significant decline since 1980, reflecting a decline either in

Fig 6. Recovery locations during (a) September–November (33) and (b) March–May (43) of nominate *albifrons* White-fronted Geese ringed in England.

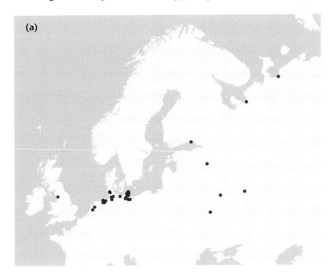

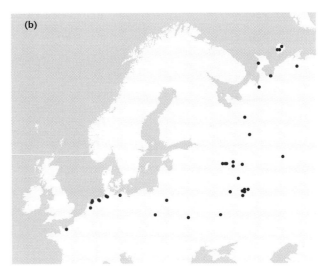

reporting rate or in hunting impact; the adult annual survival rate has shown no significant trend since 1984 but has likely been higher during the latter period than when the population was subject to hunting on the wintering grounds (Fox *et al* 1998).

Broadly, *flavirostris* displays a leap-frog pattern (Salomonsen 1950, Kampp *et al* 1988) but with wide dispersal of birds ringed in any one breeding area of Greenland to many wintering sites (Belman 1981, Wilson *et al* 1991; Figs 4 & 5). An extreme example was of a small flock of 11 moulting non-breeders captured in 1979. By 1987/88, seven had been seen or recovered from nine widely spread sites throughout Scotland and Ireland.

The timing of autumn departure from Greenland to Iceland, and the route used, are not precisely known. Salomonsen (1950) indicated that birds progressively gathered in large, post-breeding flocks close to the ice-cap prior to departure, with some non-breeders moving slowly southwards beginning in late July and August, but that the autumn migration had never been witnessed and was possibly nocturnal. In Iceland in autumn, recoveries have been reported from 30 August to 31 October, although most come from the period 23 September to 15 October along with most sightings of marked birds (Fox *et al* 1999a). The duration of autumn staging for any individual is probably about a month. The first *flavirostris* arrive on their British & Irish wintering areas typically in late September or early October, although the main arrival on Islay and in Wexford may not occur until the third week of October. In some years, counts and resightings indicate some later arrivals at Wexford into November. Birds that winter at Wexford have not infrequently been first observed on Islay, Kintyre or other Scottish sites, staying for some days (Warren *et al* 1992a).

Resightings of individually marked birds have demonstrated extreme site-fidelity within and between winters (Wilson *et al* 1991, Warren *et al* 1992a). In an analysis of movements of wintering geese at Wexford, Warren *et al* (1992a) showed that, on average, only 2.8% moved sites within winters, mainly to or from Scotland before or after the Wexford midwinter peak. Within-winter movements were made by all age and sex classes. The same analysis showed that, on average, 14.3% of Wexford-ringed geese that were seen in two consecutive winters (1,026 resightings) changed site, most moves being away from Wexford. Overall this equated to an annual average net emigration rate of 9.2%. Between-winter movements were made by all age classes, although significantly more made them in their second and third winters (*ie* aged 1–3 years old), probably linked to pair formation at this time.

Greenland Whitefronts leave their wintering areas in the second or third week of April and fly to Iceland. There have been some sightings of

marked birds wintering at Wexford staging briefly on Islay or in the Outer Hebrides. One bird marked with a satellite transmitter in 1997 stayed for 10 days in Northern Ireland before onward migration to Iceland on 16 April.

The birds stage in Iceland for up to a month in two main areas, the southern and western lowlands (Fox *et al* 1999a). Spring migration phenology appears to differ between these, with earlier arrivals in the southern lowlands with peak numbers on 24–26 April in 1990–92, compared with a more rapid build-up to peak numbers in western staging areas, on 18–22 April in 1997–99, where substantial numbers remain into May each year. Although these differences could relate to differences in migration period in the years concerned, they may also relate to different migration strategies of birds using the two areas (Fox *et al* 1999a). The limited evidence suggests that few birds use both staging areas in the same season.

Most Whitefronts have departed from Iceland around 6 May with few birds present in the western lowlands after 10 May. All evidence indicates that geese fly direct from Iceland to east Greenland, crossing the coast in the Angmassalik area (Salomonsen 1979, Stroud & Fox 1981, Alerstam *et al* 1986, Glahder *et al* 1999). The route from the east to west coast at this point crosses the Greenland ice-cap at its lowest point (2,400 m asl), and is a 1,300–1,900-km direct flight from Iceland to the breeding areas. Passage takes place in flocks of up to 15 birds (Alerstam *et al* 1986). First sightings in the central part of the breeding range occurred during 2–7 May in the years 1979–96 (Fox & Stroud 1988, Glahder 1999b).

Early thawing lowland areas are used on arrival for feeding, a few such areas having a crucial role in breeding energetics (Fox & Ridgill 1985, Glahder 1999a, b). There is evidence from marked birds that northerly breeding birds (Irish winterers) stage within Greenland (Fox & Ridgill 1985, Glahder *et al* 1999) moving north between lowland areas presumably in response to local patterns of thaw. Data from resightings (GWGS unpublished data) suggest that individuals use the same breeding areas in different years, although observations are limited.

The annual post-breeding moult takes place locally within the breeding range. In the central part of the breeding range, there is a local movement to higher-altitude lakes to moult. Salomonsen (1967a) suggested that birds moulting in the north of the range were supplemented by geese moving up from the south; there is one recent resighting to support this suggestion, and aerial surveys have located significant moulting flocks in areas that are unlikely to be favourable breeding habitat.

The movements of *albifrons* are known in rather less detail. European Whitefronts leave their arctic breeding areas in September and early October, and movement to the wintering grounds is progressive over the

Fig 7. Recovery locations and all included exchanges between (a) southeast England (21, blue) & (b) southwest England (197, red) and abroad of nominate *albifrons* White-fronted Geese.

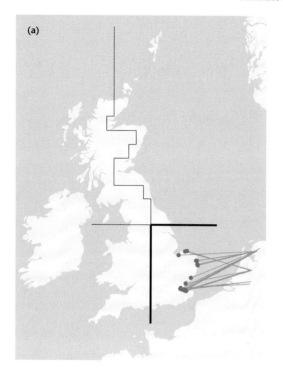

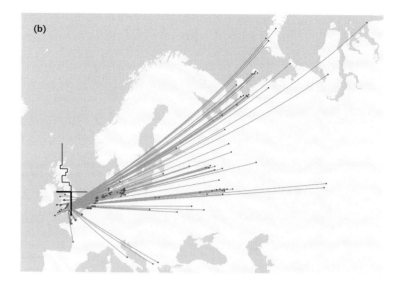

next two months. On the basis of recoveries, geese ringed in England appear to arrive via central Russia and central Europe rather than following a more northerly route along the Baltic coast (Fig 6a). The locations of many recoveries closely match known traditional staging areas identified by Mooij *et al* (1999). Thus geese appear to move along the coast of the Kara Sea, past Kanin to the south coast of the White Sea before heading due south. There are October recoveries from the Volga and Kama Basins as well as from the Oka River Basin (Fig 6a). By November, geese appear on the German coast of the Baltic as well as in the Netherlands and Belgium. Earliest arrivals in England are in November, although peak numbers do not usually occur until late January or early February (Owen *et al* 1986).

There are only two recoveries within the same winter, both birds ringed at Slimbridge and recovered subsequently from the Dutch Delta area and the Lower Rhine area of northern Germany. These movements probably reflect birds returning towards breeding areas in late winter. Most interchange between different wintering areas has been of birds ringed at Slimbridge being recovered in later years in France, Belgium, the Netherlands and northern Germany. There have been a few recoveries that indicate significantly changed wintering areas between years, with single February recoveries of English-ringed geese from Italy, Greece and Macedonia (Fig 7b).

Return migration from England begins in early March and most geese have left Britain by the second half of the month (Owen *et al* 1986). Many English-ringed birds remain during March in the Netherlands, although with numbers in the Lower Rhine area and as far as the staging areas of Pripyat River Basin and the Biebrza Basin in Poland (Fig 6b). By April, most recoveries are between Belarus and central Russia, with the Volga and Kama Basins, and the Oka River Basin again used for staging. In May, birds move northwards, with recoveries in the Novgorod area, although by the end of the month many have reached the most westerly arctic breeding areas located on the Kanin Peninsula and Kolguyev Island (45–50°E). One mid-May recovery from the Omsk region, east of the Urals (69°E), may suggest a flightline to more easterly arctic breeding areas. By June, all geese are on nesting grounds, even in areas further east. Early Russian literature suggests that

the use of specific staging areas is variable between years and that migration routes may show periodic shifts (see Mooij *et al* 1999).

There are very few recoveries from the breeding grounds from ringing in England (Fig 7). Syroechkovskiy *et al* (1992) plotted all recoveries between 15 May and 31 August in northern Russia of 16,671 Whitefronts ringed in the Netherlands between 1953 and 1987. This showed major concentrations of recoveries around the Kanin Peninsula, Kolguyev Island and the Pechora Peninsula and Delta, with other significant concentrations of recoveries further east on Vaygach Island, and the coast of the east Kara Sea, and to the north along the Nenets coast from Kanin to *c* 55°E. Given the close relationship between English and Dutch wintering geese (Fig 7), it might be supposed that these westerly breeding areas of Dutch birds are also those used by English wintering birds. Indeed, Boyd (1966) showed a strong relationship between the annual productivity of Whitefronts wintering at Slimbridge with July weather conditions on Novaya Zemlya. The observation at Slimbridge, however, of a colour-ringed Whitefront from the Taimyr much further east than these areas, as well as a bird ringed at Slimbridge and recovered on Dickson Island in eastern Taimyr (80°E; Fig 7b), indicate that a proportion of birds may come from much further east.

Patterns of moult migration of Russian birds are poorly known. Rogacheva (1992) indicated that birds move to remoter, less disturbed waterbodies to moult. Very large concentrations are found in some regions suggesting significant influxes from surrounding breeding areas.

As with *flavirostris*, recent colour-ringing has shown European Whitefronts to have a dispersal pattern such that birds from one Russian breeding area disperse widely to many wintering areas (Mooij & Kostin 1997). Mooij (1993) summarized recoveries and sightings of individually colour-ringed geese captured on the Taimyr Peninsula since 1989. Of 523 geese marked, 53 were resighted in various localities from southwest England to Kazakhstan. Mooij (1993) discussed the possible genetic implications of such dispersal which, given pairing in winter (as suggested by van Impe 1978), would encourage gene-flow between otherwise widely separated breeding areas.

The considerable site-fidelity of *flavirostris* throughout the annual cycle that has been demonstrated by individual marking has highlighted

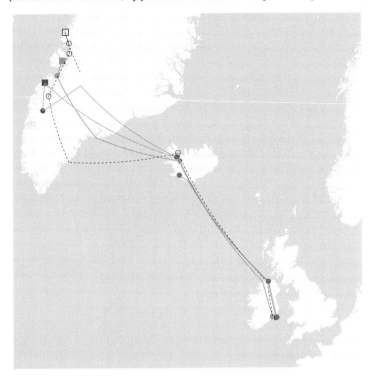

Fig 8. Summering locations (squares), staging areas (circles) and migration routes as revealed by satellite tracking for four Greenland White-fronted Geese in 1997 and 1998, after initial capture on their wintering grounds in Wexford, Ireland. K3F (grey) and K3A (red) are distinguished from H3Z (blue) and K2A (broken black line). (*Source*: Glahder *et al* 1999, by permission of *Dansk Ornitologisk Forenings Tidsskrift*.)

While maintaining existing ringing programmes at major sites, for the purposes of long-term comparisons, ringing elsewhere should be a priority. Similarly, catching has occurred at just two central, inland parts of the breeding range in recent decades and catches from elsewhere in Greenland would yield considerable information.

The period following breeding until the return to wintering areas is the most poorly known in the annual cycle of *flavirostris*. Late-summer local movements in Greenland, the timing of departure and route taken from Greenland to Iceland, and local movements in Iceland in the autumn are all unknown. Satellite telemetry gives opportunities for such studies.

To date, the ringing of European Whitefronts has occurred at just a few locations in a small number of northwest European countries, principally in the Netherlands, England and Germany. The degree to which currently defined biogeographical populations are discrete is far from understood but this issue will only be resolved with a new programme of coordinated marking in south and east Europe, which would have great potential. Further catching and colour-marking on the Russian breeding areas would also assist in delimiting the complex population structure of the species.

The eco-physiological significance of staging in spring and autumn is unknown either at the population or individual level. Unlike the Greenland race, which undertakes long migration over oceans or ice-caps with limited staging possibilities, the European race migrates entirely over the continental land-mass. There are numerous possible, and several known, staging areas (Mooij *et al* 1999), but it is not known how many are used in a single migration season, what is the duration of stopover for individual geese, nor whether the same areas are used by individuals in different seasons or years.

Results from individual marking, and more recently from satellite telemetry (Fig 8), have highlighted significant differences in movements between individuals. Understanding the detailed choices made by individuals both in winter and during migration will be essential to elucidate the different migration strategies adopted and their eco-physiological implications (Fox *et al* 1999a, Glahder 1999a).

The varied consequences of climate change throughout the Whitefront's range are likely to be the most severe long-term threats to all its populations. Recent modelling has predicted significant losses of tundra in a number of areas where European Whitefronts currently breed at high densities (Zöckler & Lysenko 2000). Modelling the consequences of circumpolar habitat loss, these authors estimate a halving of the species' global population size by 2077–99. These projections take no account of possible negative consequences for the population of the effects of a changed climate on habitats used at other times of the year.

the particular importance of site-based protection for this population. Consequently, a major part of population conservation relies on the identification and wise use of national and international networks of important sites (D A Stroud 1992, Fox *et al* 1998, 1999b). Given the occurrence in Britain & Ireland during winter of the entirety of this subspecies, the governments of UK and Ireland have particular international responsibility for its conservation. Although the range of European Whitefronts is very large, highly traditional sites are also used throughout the year. High proportions of particular flyway populations use some of these sites, and a number of Russian staging areas, not all formally protected, are of great significance.

Despite the major advances in understanding in recent years, there remain many gaps and uncertainties in our knowledge of Greenland White-fronted Goose movements. Ringing activity to date has been concentrated at a few major locations. It is not known whether the behaviour of birds using these areas is typical of others at smaller wintering sites, where population trends are different (Fox *et al* 1998).

David Stroud, Tony Fox & Alyn Walsh

Greylag Goose
Anser anser

With their loud honking contact calls and their V-shaped skeins, Greylag Geese must be one of the most visible of all migrating birds.

The Greylag Goose is the typical goose of temperate and boreal wetlands (*BWP*). The nominate race *anser* breeds in Iceland, Scandinavia and around the Baltic, with a remnant population in northwest Scotland. The eastern race *rubrirostris* breeds across the former USSR, east of the Black Sea. In central and eastern Europe, intermediates occur, part of a cline of variation between the two races. Although birds from some breeding populations winter within the breeding range, the majority of birds are migratory. Birds from the eastern race move south to winter from Turkey through Iraq and Iran into Pakistan and India. Eastern European birds winter mainly around the eastern Mediterranean, chiefly in North Africa. Birds from central Europe and Scandinavia winter in the Netherlands and Spain, whilst Icelandic birds winter mostly in Scotland (Madsen *et al* 1999).

The native population of Scottish Greylags has recently increased in north and west Scotland and has spread to the Inner Hebrides (*1988–91 Atlas*). Birds breed on islets or around the shores of lochs, amongst peat bogs or along riversides usually adjacent to areas of permanent pasture. Progeny from this population have been used to reintroduce the species to much of lowland Scotland and England (Owen & Salmon 1988). These reintroduced populations are associated particularly with lochs, reservoirs and gravel-pits surrounded by parkland or agricultural land, which provide ideal year-round feeding opportunities. Wintering birds from Iceland are associated with agricultural areas in low-lying parts of the country, mostly in eastern Scotland.

The analysis of the data for this species was supported by the Central Science Laboratory

Ringing of Greylag Geese has not been uniform in either time or place, mainly due to the difficulty in catching the birds. Ringing studies have been conducted in the range of the native birds on the Uists, Coll and Tiree, and at Loch Loyal in Sutherland, whilst studies of reintroduced birds have been undertaken in central and southwest Scotland and southern England, particularly by the Sevenoaks Ringing Group in Kent (Fig 1). All these studies (except those in central and southwest Scotland) have involved the use of plastic leg rings and, since 1994 in Scotland, plastic neck-collars, in order to increase resighting rates. Catches of birds during the breeding season take place mainly during June and July when broods or flightless moulting adults can be rounded up (Fig 2). Winter catches of Icelandic birds in Scotland have been made mostly in October and November, at a few sites by rocket nets during 1950–66 by the Wildfowl Trust, and more recently by cannon-nets in the 1990s at Loch Eye in Easter Ross by the Highland Ringing Group (HRG) in association with WWT. Since 1996, there has been a joint WWT/Icelandic Institute of Natural History ringing project in Iceland, marking both goslings and flightless adults (Mitchell & Sigfusson 1999). The few winter catches of reintroduced birds have been mainly made in southern England.

Most Greylag Goose recoveries (85%) have a known cause of death and, not surprisingly, for a quarry species, in 96% of cases they have

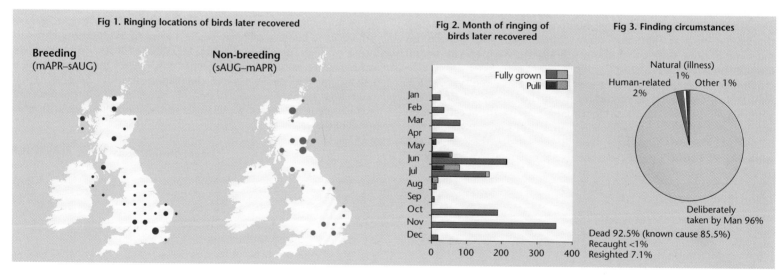

Fig 1. Ringing locations of birds later recovered

Breeding (mAPR–sAUG) **Non-breeding** (sAUG–mAPR)

Fig 2. Month of ringing of birds later recovered

Fully grown
Pulli

Jan, Feb, Mar, Apr, May, Jun, Jul, Aug, Sep, Oct, Nov, Dec

0   100   200   300   400

Fig 3. Finding circumstances

Natural (illness) 1%
Human-related 2%   Other 1%

Deliberately taken by Man 96%

Dead 92.5% (known cause 85.5%)
Recaught <1%
Resighted 7.1%

Ringing and recovery data

	<1960	60–69	70–79	80–89	90–97	Total
RINGING						
BTO ringing totals (%)	8	17	5	22	48	7,097
RECOVERIES						
BTO-ringed (%)	15	21	4	23	37	1,244
Foreign-ringed (%)	18	15	4	40	22	89

Statistical analyses

	Breeding population (mAPR–sAUG)	Wintering population (sDEC–mFEB)
Status	SEDENTARY (0)	[LONG-DISTANCE MIGRANT]
Age differences[NS]*	Not significant*	Not tested
Sex differences[NS]*	Not significant*	Not tested
Regional differences	Significant[2]*	Not tested
Finding circumstances	Not tested*	Not tested

Fig 4. Locations outside the breeding season and movements of over 20 km between the breeding and non-breeding season of 374 Greylag Geese present in Britain & Ireland during the breeding season. All exchanges involving Iceland during April have been excluded, because some Icelandic breeders are still present in Scotland during this month.

Fig 5. All 325 included exchanges of Greylag Geese between Britain & Ireland and abroad.

been deliberately taken, mainly shot, by Man (Fig 3). This means that there is a seasonal bias to recoveries, with most occurring during the shooting seasons in Britain & Ireland (September to February) and Iceland (August to November).

Greylag Geese breeding in Britain are largely sedentary (Fig 4). According to BTO data, the median distance moved by goslings in their first year of life was only 10 km ($P5–95=0–35$ km, $n=28$). Birds individually marked in late summer in the Uists dispersed up to 30 km within the islands between their breeding and wintering areas (Mitchell 1999). Only five of over 500 marked were recovered away from the islands. One moved north to Lewis and four were observed in the Inner Hebrides (Mitchell 1999), one of which (a colour-ringed individual) was suspected of breeding on Tiree (A Leitch pers comm). One recovered in Iceland in a subsequent season was presumed to be an Icelandic bird that had summered on the islands (Mitchell 1999). This is also likely to apply to a bird ringed as an adult in Tayside in July and recovered in Iceland (Fig 4). Birds marked on Tiree in summer 1998 remained on the island, moving only short distances throughout the winter (mean 3.6 km, $n=85$), whereas 74% of birds individually marked on Coll moved to Tiree for the winter, giving a mean dispersal distance of 24 km ($n=40$, A Leitch pers comm). Birds from the native breeding population in Sutherland move up to 50 km towards the coastal plains of north and southeast Sutherland and low-lying parts of central Caithness during the non-breeding season, returning to the inland straths from mid-February (F L Symonds pers comm). During the autumn, some of these birds mix with visitors from the Icelandic breeding population and this results in temporary movements of a few native birds into south and east Scotland. More exceptional were two birds ringed at Loch Loyal in summer and recovered together in winter in the Netherlands.

The reintroduced populations also appear very sedentary (Fig 4). Young (1972) quoted an average recovery distance of 20 km ($n=31$)

from the population in southwest Scotland, whilst BTO data suggest a median dispersal distance of only 11 km ($n=130$) for birds breeding in southeast Britain, and 7 km ($n=31$) for birds breeding in the southwest. These low median distances hide the fact that odd individuals make longer movements, such as from southwest Scotland to Lincolnshire, and Kent to the Netherlands. One Irish bird crossed the North Channel to Galloway.

Most of the migratory birds wintering in Britain & Ireland are from the Icelandic breeding population (Fig 5). They arrive in Scotland between late September and early November (*Birds in Scotland*) and winter in Orkney and Caithness, around the Moray Firth, in Aberdeenshire and in east-central Scotland, with smaller numbers in southwest and southeast Scotland, Northumberland, Cumbria and Ireland (Mitchell & Sigfusson 1999). Much of the analysis that follows involves data from recent HRG/WWT studies using sightings of birds marked with plastic collars and leg rings. This shows that on arrival in Easter Ross many birds move swiftly into eastern and Central Scotland, whilst others move north into Caithness and Orkney, then as the winter progresses there is a gradual movement south (Swann 1998). Further movements can be initiated by spells of snowy weather, but many Greylags can remain through quite severe blizzards, grubbing their way through the snow to find food. Although some birds are faithful to a site all winter, this is not the general rule. There appears to be considerable within-winter movement of Icelandic birds throughout the entire range.

Although most movements are southerly (Fig 6a), other birds move north, particularly from Grampian into the Moray Firth area and from the Moray Firth to Orkney and Caithness (Fig 6b). This is possibly due to birds responding to changes in food supplies and different levels of disturbance in different parts of Scotland. Partly as a result of these movements, Greylags are not necessarily faithful from one winter to the next to a particular area. Of 120 collared birds seen in one

Fig 6. (a) Southerly (68) and (b) northerly (54) within-winter (December–February) movements of Greylag Geese in Britain & Ireland, from sightings of colour-marked birds. (*Source*: Highland RG/WWT data.)

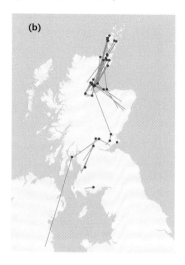

Fig 8. (a) Southerly (7) and (b) northerly (29) same-spring (March–April) movements of Greylag Geese in Britain & Ireland, from sightings of colour-marked birds. (*Source*: Highland RG/WWT data.)

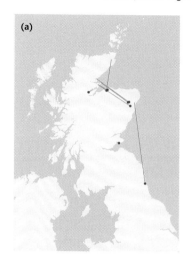

midwinter period (December–February), 41% had relocated to an entirely different part of the country the following midwinter. From mid-March through to late April, birds depart for their breeding grounds in low-lying parts of Iceland (Fig 7). This again is a very visible migration, as skeins of geese can be observed flying north through the Scottish glens and over the Hebrides. During this time some birds are still quite mobile and a percentage move back to northern Scotland each year prior to their final departure (Fig 8). Observations of marked birds show, however, that the majority remain at their final wintering site, from where they return directly to Iceland. Not surprisingly, as birds tend to keep together in family parties, no significant differences were detected in the distances moved between the sexes or between adults and immatures.

Fig 7. Locations in Iceland of Greylag Geese ringed in Britain and recovered in Iceland (226, red points), ringed in Iceland and recovered in Britain (72, red squares) and ringed in Iceland and recovered in Ireland (8, blue points). There were no birds ringed in Ireland and recovered in Iceland. Only recoveries of dead birds, and those which were present in Britain & Ireland outside the breeding season, are included.

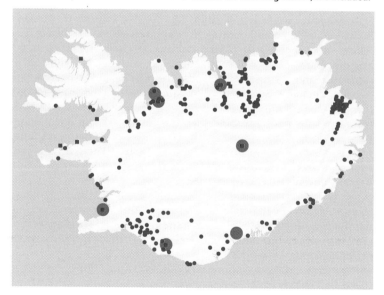

The few recoveries of Icelandic Greylags wintering in Ireland appear to show a westerly distribution, with no recoveries linking Ireland and the eastern third of Iceland (Fig 7). There have been changes in the recovery locations of Greylags recovered in Britain through time, with there being far fewer recoveries latterly of birds in Ireland and northern England (Boyd 1959a). This is partly related to a northward shift in the wintering areas of the Icelandic population (Mitchell & Sigfusson 1999).

Ringed birds from other breeding populations have been reported occasionally in Britain (Fig 5). These include two birds ringed in the Netherlands and one from Belgium. An adult from the population breeding in Poland, ringed there in June, was found in Devon the following November. Ringing in Scotland in the 1950s resulted in three recoveries in southern Norway and one in Denmark. Two birds ringed in northern Norway have been recovered in Britain in subsequent winters, and there have been seven records of neck-collared birds from recent studies in Norway and southern Sweden in southeast England (L Nilsson pers comm). Another Swedish bird appears to have relocated to Britain; it now winters in northeast England and moves north to summer in Central Scotland (Insley 1997).

The ringing of Greylag Geese is important for a number of conservation reasons. The birds are considered by some to be a pest on agricultural land in Scotland (Patterson *et al* 1989) and farmers can apply to SNH for licences to shoot Greylags out of season. A knowledge of the movements of the birds will help ascertain where conflicts are most likely to occur. In the far north, it is important to know whether birds from the native breeding populations are involved, as they are covered by Schedule 1 protection under the 1981 Wildlife and Countryside Act, whereas Icelandic birds are not. The ringing of Greylag Geese is very project-based and usually organized by particular ringing groups, backed by WWT. It is this ringing that currently underpins our basic understanding of Greylag Goose populations in Britain. A continuation of this ringing programme will be necessary if we are to monitor reasons for changes in populations and how these may influence movements. This is particularly relevant at the moment when, as native and reintroduced populations continue to increase, the Icelandic population is now starting to decline (Waters *et al* 1998).

Bob Swann & Ivan Brockway

Canada Goose
Branta canadensis

The Canada Goose is the most numerous goose in the world. In their native North America most races are highly migratory. Up to 12 races are recognized, birds tending to be darker in colour towards the west and smaller towards the north of their breeding range, which covers nearly all of Canada, Alaska and northern USA (Delacour 1959, Palmer 1976a, Madge & Burn 1988). Larger races tend to be more sedentary than the smaller races, the latter wintering further to the south.

Canada Geese were introduced into Europe and Australasia, the first arriving in Britain during 1665 into St James's Park, London, followed by additions to collections in London, Norfolk, Yorkshire and Nottinghamshire (Lever 1977, Owen 1983, Madsen *et al* 1999). Large feral populations of Canada Geese also exist in Norway (*c* 2,000 breeding pairs), Sweden (*c* 5,000 breeding pairs) and Finland (*c* 3,500 breeding pairs) from where they migrate south to winter in France (several hundreds), the Netherlands (*c* 2,000) and Germany (up to 30,000). There are small resident populations elsewhere in Europe including Ireland (*c* 1,000), France, Germany, the Netherlands, Italy, Switzerland and the Ukraine. There is also a feral population of more than 40,000 in New Zealand (Blair *et al* 2000).

The large size and coloration of birds in the British & Irish feral population suggest they are derived mainly from the nominate race *canadensis*, with possibly some contribution from the Giant Canada Goose *maxima*. In North America, most Canada Geese are highly migratory, with the larger races undertaking pronounced moult

The analysis of the data for this species was supported by the Central Science Laboratory

migrations (Sterling & Dzubin 1967, Wege 1980, Zicus 1981, Davis *et al* 1985). Feral populations in Fennoscandia show distinct migratory patterns, while those in Britain & Ireland are regarded as being largely sedentary, although there is a pronounced moult migration.

Although widespread by 1900, the British population remained below 4,000 birds until the 1950s (Blurton-Jones 1956). At this time, discrete subpopulations were evident and there was apparently little or no natural interchange between them. Since then, numbers have undergone an accelerating rate of increase and in 1991 were estimated to be 61,000 (Delany 1993). This increase may partly be due to natural colonization of newly created habitats, such as reservoirs and gravel-pits, but was probably greatly facilitated by translocations of geese by the then Wildfowlers' Association of Great Britain and Ireland and by the Wildfowl Trust (Kirby *et al* 1999). The motivation for the former organization was to provide new shooting opportunities (Bedingfield 1961, Ruxton 1962), and for the latter organization to alleviate local agricultural conflicts (Ogilvie 1969). As recently as 1980–83, White-Robinson (1984) was able to confirm the existence of largely discrete subpopulations in a colour-ringed population in Nottinghamshire. However, most of the recent population increase has been absorbed within the already established range of the species by a process of

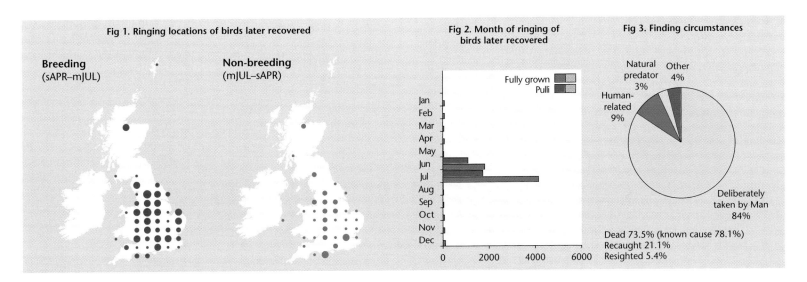

Fig 1. Ringing locations of birds later recovered

Breeding (sAPR–mJUL)

Non-breeding (mJUL–sAPR)

Fig 2. Month of ringing of birds later recovered

Fully grown
Pulli

Fig 3. Finding circumstances

Natural predator 3%
Other 4%
Human-related 9%
Deliberately taken by Man 84%

Dead 73.5% (known cause 78.1%)
Recaught 21.1%
Resighted 5.4%

Ringing and recovery data

	<1960	60–69	70–79	80–89	90–97	Total
RINGING						
BTO ringing totals (%)	2	8	31	30	29	56,925
RECOVERIES						
BTO-ringed (%)	0	6	39	32	22	9,307
Foreign-ringed (%)	0	0	17	0	83	6

Statistical analyses

	Breeding population (sAPR–mJUL)	Wintering population (sNOV–mFEB)
Status	SHORT-DISTANCE MIGRANT (1)	SEDENTARY*
Age differences[NS]	Not significant	Not tested
Sex differences[NS]	Not significant	Not tested
Regional differences	Significant[4]	Not tested
Finding circumstances	Significant	Not tested

Fig 4. Movements of over 20 km and recovery locations of 1,731 Canada Geese using the Beauly Firth area (marked with a black circle). Only movements within Britain & Ireland are plotted: a single movement to central Russia is not shown.

Fig 5. Movements of over 20 km and recovery locations of Canada Geese in Britain & Ireland (7,565) excluding those using the Beauly Firth area (see Fig 4). Only movements within Britain & Ireland are plotted: movements to France (7), the Faeroes (2) and the USA (1), and from Norway (4), Sweden (1) and the USA (1) are not shown.

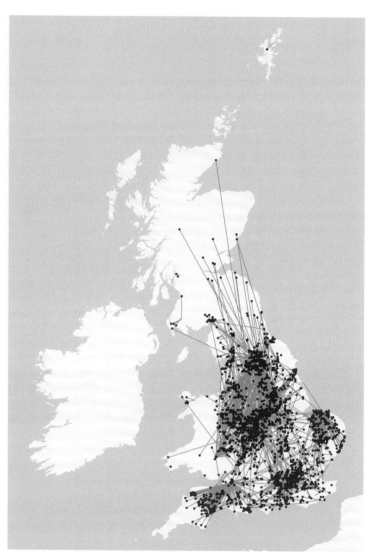

infilling and local increase, rather than a marked extension of range. Hence, distinct subpopulations may no longer be apparent, although the species is still relatively localized in Scotland, west Wales and Ireland (Delany 1993).

Canada Geese have been ringed at a wide spread of sites in Britain but Irish birds have yet to be marked to any degree (Fig 1). Most Canada Geese (95%), whether adult or pullus, have been ringed during the June and July moult period when family groups may join non-breeders and failed breeders to form large flocks (Fig 2). These flightless geese congregate at suitable safe sites such as flooded gravel-pits, lakes and reservoirs. The majority (60%) of these birds have been adults. Canada Geese have often attracted the interests of local ringing groups, especially following establishment of new moult sites, although concentrated sustained ringing effort over long periods has been confined to a few sites. This source of bias must be borne in mind when analysing movements, especially when considering changes through time. Breeding birds may moult in smaller family groups (Lessells 1985), while others may move considerable distances to join aggregations of non-breeders. In some areas, therefore, adults ringed and recovered will be biased towards birds of pre-breeding age and failed breeders, because they are over-represented in the larger moulting flocks. The minimum reportable distance set by the

British & Irish Bird Ringing Scheme for sightings or live captures of Canada Geese is 40 km which is greater than the median distance between ringing and recovery sites of birds found dead (11 km, $P5-95=0-399$, $n=6,839$) and so these will also be biased towards longer movements. Local studies (eg in Nottinghamshire) show that there are great numbers of movements of between 10 km and 40 km (between feeding, roosting and breeding sites) but these were not available for the current analyses.

Over 56,000 Canada Geese have been ringed in Britain and these have resulted in over 9,000 usable ring-recoveries. Most recoveries (74%) are of dead birds and a cause of death can be attributed to 78% of these (Fig 3). A large proportion (84%) are deliberately taken by Man and a further 9% die of human-related causes. Of those deliberately taken, 93% were reported as shot, presumably for sport, the remainder being culled (Austin et al 1996). Given that the open season extends from September to January (and to February on the coast) it follows that most recoveries of Canada Geese occur in autumn and winter.

Fledged young Canada Geese usually remain in loose family groups. Later in the autumn the family parties break up, and juveniles may wander more widely (BWP). In general, females wander less than males (Lessells 1985). At this time some Canada Goose populations shift from their upland breeding areas to lowland areas (Garnett 1980). By the onset of winter, most lowland nesting Canada Geese are thought to have returned to the vicinity of their breeding areas, probably ranging over distances of only a few kilometres (Owen *et al* 1986). They may form large winter concentrations on waters that carry only small breeding populations, however (White-Robinson 1984).

The sedentary nature of the Canada Goose population in Britain is clear from the pattern of ring-recoveries. Since the earliest recoveries of Canada Geese in 1951, the median recovery distance for dead birds has ranged between 4 and 29 km (median=11 km) between years. The only exception was when the median distance rose to 432 km due to four recoveries in France, out of seven recorded that year, during the severe winter weather in Britain of January and February 1963. Subsequent severe winters have not resulted in similar responses (Austin *et al* 1996).

The typical distances observed between ringing and recovery probably fall well within the daily patterns of movement of Canada Geese, especially in autumn following the break-up of moulting flocks. Canada Geese frequently move several kilometres between feeding areas and safe roost sites, especially in autumn (Garnett 1980, Baker 1985, Parkin & McMeeking 1985, Owen *et al* 1986), which has allowed them rapidly to colonize new breeding and feeding sites within their existing range (Delany 1993). Small numbers of Canada Geese regularly move over greater distances (Lessells 1985). When these birds do establish new populations, these increase extremely rapidly (Owen *et al* 1994).

The most spectacular movement undertaken by Canada Geese within Britain involves movements of birds from England north to the Beauly Firth where several hundreds congregate into a moulting flock (Walker 1970). This mirrors the northward moult migrations in North America. Those moult migrations allow non-breeding birds or failed breeders to take advantage of rich food supplies that lie beyond the normal breeding range during an energetically expensive period of the annual cycle. The British long-distance moult migration involves only a small proportion of the population; the majority of these birds originate from Yorkshire and the West Midlands of England (Fig 4).

Excluding the Beauly Firth moult migration, ring-recoveries show no marked directional trends other than those explained by the physical barriers of the coastline and large expanses of upland (Fig 5). Canada Geese ringed in North Norfolk, and at Chew Valley Lake in Avon, show a southward bias in their movements, those from the English–Welsh border tend to move northeast, and birds from London tend to move southwest. Those ringed in the English Midlands and Yorkshire display no marked directional bias. All these movements occur over relatively short distances, however, and some of these apparent directional trends may be partly explained by the distribution of habitats in which birds are more likely to be shot (and so recovered) relative to the ringing sites, rather than directional trends in the movements of the birds themselves. There have also been two recoveries of English-bred birds in the Faeroes, where Canada Geese now breed, the recovery dates suggesting moult migration (Mead & Clark 1987).

There have been six foreign-ringed Canada Geese recovered in Britain & Ireland and 12 foreign recoveries of birds ringed in Britain. Four birds ringed in Norway and one in Sweden have been recovered in Britain although one of the Norwegian birds was captive-bred. These recoveries could involve birds participating in the regular migration of these populations that had taken a more westerly course than normal. The three wild Norwegian Geese were all wintering in northeast Scotland when shot (Clark *et al* 1996). The Swedish bird, ringed as a pullus, was seen in southeast England during its second winter, subsequently returning to Sweden where it was shot in its 13th winter (Mead *et al* 1993).

A small number of recoveries involved very long distances. These include one recovery from the River Ob in west Siberia and two movements between Britain and the USA (one in each direction). The first might have involved a bird from the Fennoscandian population that reached Britain and then overshot the return journey. One possible explanation for the transatlantic movements is that they involve Canada Geese from the East Atlantic breeding populations of North America that have attached to and migrated with flocks of Greenland White-fronted Geese. Both cases involved between-winter movements (Appleton *et al* 1997). There are currently at least 2,500 pairs of Canada Geese breeding in west Greenland, with numbers having increased dramatically since the late 1980s, and it seems likely that more transatlantic recoveries will be reported in the future (Fox *et al* 1996, Malecki *et al* 2000).

The growth of the Canada Goose population has been accompanied by increased pressure for measures to control them. To ensure well-informed political decision-making, and that any measures taken will be effective, it is essential to understand Canada Geese movements within their home ranges and the potential for new birds to replace any that are culled. It is the analysis of data obtained from sustained ringing of Canada Geese that will provide the necessary information. The most informative data come from field observations of colour-ringed individuals. This technique has enabled movement patterns for local populations to be followed throughout the year and avoids the problems associated with seasonal biases in ring-recoveries. It is clear that the patterns of local movement vary between different parts of the country and are probably driven by differences in the character of the local habitat (Austin *et al* 1996). It is therefore important to base any initiatives to manage Canada Geese on detailed analysis of movements of the target population. For many areas, these data already exist. The ability of Canada Geese to find and colonize newly created habitats suggests that removal of birds is unlikely to be effective, as they would quickly be replaced. Past experience has shown that the translocation of birds should always be resisted.

Love them or hate them, we must live with Canada Geese. Although, when they occur in large numbers, they may constitute a nuisance to some, they do provide wildlife interest for many people in otherwise impoverished habitats.

Graham E Austin, Phil J Belman & John McMeeking

Barnacle Goose
Branta leucopsis

An attractive small goose, the Barnacle is traditionally a maritime species, breeding in the high Arctic and wintering along the coasts of Britain & Ireland and the mainland of continental Europe. Three separate natural populations of Barnacle Geese occur in the Western Palearctic and these were shown by early ringing to have separate migration routes and breeding grounds (Boyd 1961). The western group, which breeds in east Greenland, and the central population, from Svalbard, both winter exclusively in Britain & Ireland. The third group, which winters in the Low Countries and Germany, includes breeders from high-arctic Russia and latterly from various temperate islands of the Baltic. The Baltic population became established only in the early 1970s (Forslund & Larsson 1991); the birds merge with the quarter million or so arctic breeders that winter mostly in the Netherlands (Ganter *et al* 1999).

A new population became established in Iceland in the 1990s; there were 66 individuals there in 1999 and 52 of these were caught, giving rise to resightings on Islay and Tiree (R Hearn pers comm). Another, introduced group consists of almost a thousand birds that are resident in Britain but this is not thought to constitute a self-sustaining population (Delany 1993, Vinicombe *et al* 1993).

No subspecies are separated; examinations of measurements from the three natural populations indicate similar size and conformation, and no plumage differentiation has been described (Owen 1980).

The Barnacle Goose is primarily a grazer, feeding on tundra in summer and lowland grasslands and saltmarshes on migration and in winter. Traditionally the species grazed short saltmarsh swards on the

The analysis of the data for this species was supported by Brian Payne

mainland or on islands washed by salt spray. As pastures have been improved at its traditional haunts the species has increasingly moved onto these, consequently moving further inland, both in winter (Owen *et al* 1987, Percival 1993) and on migration (Black *et al* 1991, Percival & Percival 1997).

Very large numbers of individuals in each population have been marked, many thousands with easily readable engraved plastic rings, and this has confirmed that interchange between the populations is extremely limited, despite the proximity of their winter ranges (Ebbinge *et al* 1991, Owen & Black 1991, WWT unpublished data). All populations are currently protected over large parts of their range so the recent ring-recovery rates tend to be low, but information on the migration routes, the timing of movements and other aspects come also from studies using marks readable in the field and from other observations. Ring-recoveries reported to the BTO (Figs 1–4) represent a tiny fraction of the hundreds of thousands of resightings that have been made on the breeding, staging and wintering areas.

Barnacle Geese are occasionally seen in southeast England in winter, and ring-recoveries confirm that some of these are stragglers from the Russian or Baltic populations. However, many sightings could be of feral birds that have escaped from wildfowl collections, where many have been kept full-winged. In 1990, there were about a thousand feral birds

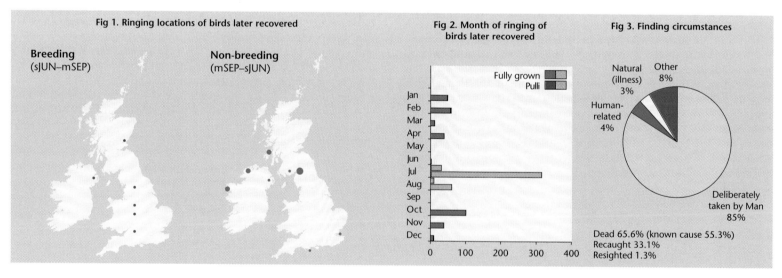

Fig 1. Ringing locations of birds later recovered

Breeding (sJUN–mSEP)

Non-breeding (mSEP–sJUN)

Fig 2. Month of ringing of birds later recovered

Fully grown / Pulli

Fig 3. Finding circumstances

Natural (illness) 3%
Other 8%
Human-related 4%
Deliberately taken by Man 85%

Dead 65.6% (known cause 55.3%)
Recaught 33.1%
Resighted 1.3%

Ringing and recovery data

	<1960	60–69	70–79	80–89	90–97	Total
RINGING						
BTO ringing totals (%)	0	11	30	20	39	4,065
RECOVERIES						
BTO-ringed (%)	1	13	31	29	26	313
Foreign-ringed (%)	6	54	19	12	9	434

Statistical analyses

	Breeding population (sJUN–mSEP)	Wintering population (sDEC–mAPR)
Status	NONE	LONG-DISTANCE MIGRANT*
Age differences	—	Not tested
Sex differences	—	Not tested
Regional differences	—	Not tested
Finding circumstances	—	Not tested

in Britain (Delany 1993) but none would have been ringed with BTO rings and so they are not represented in the recovery maps. There is a single bird appearing on the recovery maps that originated from a free-flying flock kept by the Swedish Sportsman's Association (Fig 4). The two wild populations, breeding in Greenland and on Svalbard, are discrete and are treated separately in the following account.

The first sizeable catch of the Svalbard population was 685 birds in Hornsund, Svalbard, in 1962. This was followed by catches on the Solway in 1963, when 316 were caught including 94 of the Svalbard-ringed geese, and further catches in Svalbard and the Solway. The colour-marking programme started in 1973 and more than 7,000 birds have been marked with individually coded rings (Ogilvie & Owen 1984, WWT unpublished data).

In autumn, the geese leave the breeding grounds around the end of August, moving first to staging areas on Svalbard close to the rearing areas as soon as the young are able to fly (Prop et al 1984). Then a proportion of the population, probably the majority, at least in some seasons, move to Bear Island, by far the southernmost island in the Svalbard group, before flying to Britain. Birds arrive in Britain on a broad front, from the Northern Isles to Yorkshire. Most arrive in the Solway between 20 September and 10 October, though in some seasons stragglers remain further north and west (Owen & Gullestad 1984). Satellite-tracking studies have shown that birds may stop several times for short periods on islands along the Norwegian coast or even on the sea, though not for long enough to feed and replenish their body reserves (Butler & Woakes 1998).

All the birds stay in the Caerlaverock area for some time. As numbers in the population have increased, however, dispersal now occurs early in the winter to other parts of the Solway, particularly around Southerness

to the west and Rockcliffe Marsh to the east. There are very few records of birds moving out of the Solway in winter and then only in small numbers, even in severe weather. In April and early May, the birds are largely found at Rockcliffe Marsh from where they depart between mid-April and mid-May (Owen et al 1987).

They fly to a staging area just south of the Arctic Circle in Helgeland in western Norway and stay there for two or three weeks before moving to Svalbard in the second half of May. The birds return to the same small islands or even parts of islands in the staging area year after year (Gullestad et al 1984). New haunts have become occupied as the population has increased in size and on larger islands some birds have become used to foraging on agricultural pastures further inland (Black et al 1991). Some geese stop on Bear Island on the way to the nesting sites and they may visit snow-free areas on the main island of Svalbard before nesting (Mehlum 1998). As is the rule for geese, individuals are extremely loyal to their breeding areas, returning to the same sites year after year. No moult migration has been recorded; the distribution of mature non-breeders and of immature geese during the summer is consistent with the suggestion that the birds moult close to their nesting sites and that immatures return to their natal area to moult (Owen et al 1988).

Ringing of geese from the Greenland population started in 1961 when 609 rings were fitted in Greenland. Recoveries from these and from the very large numbers of birds subsequently ringed in Britain, Ireland and Greenland have confirmed that, with the exception of a few stragglers, all the Greenland birds winter in Britain & Ireland, as had been predicted by Boyd (1961). During the 1980s and 1990s, 2,584 birds were marked with individually coded plastic rings in Scotland, mainly on Islay, with 39 in Sutherland (Percival 1991, S M Percival pers comm), and resightings of these have been made at most stages of the life cycle.

In Ireland, a long-term study on the west coast involved the ringing of 816 Barnacle Geese on the Inishkea Islands, County Mayo (giving rise to 18,000 sightings), and 176 at Sheshkinmore, County Donegal (Cabot & West 1983, Ogilvie et al 1999c). Four expeditions to Greenland in the 1980s also contributed 939 individually marked birds (Cabot et al 1984, S M Percival pers comm).

The birds leave the breeding grounds in late August and September, heading for staging grounds in southeast Iceland. Some birds stay in the uplands of Iceland (above 200 m) if these remain snow-free, but most occupy marshes and agricultural pastures in the lowlands (Ogilvie et al 1999c). They move to Britain & Ireland progressively through the autumn; recoveries show that birds are at both staging and wintering areas in September and October but are absent from Iceland from November to mid-April. The species is legal quarry in autumn in Iceland and around 2,000 are shot each year (Icelandic Wildlife Management Institute data).

There are indications that some birds may stop in Scotland on the way to Irish wintering grounds but numbers on Islay, where the majority of the work in Scotland has been done, are relatively stable after the migratory period (WeBS data). Individual geese are loyal to their wintering sites, both within and between winters, and there is a link between winter distribution and ringing location in summer in that birds are recorded together at both sites more frequently than expected (Percival 1991).

Geese leave the wintering grounds in mid-April and arrive in the lowlands of northwest Iceland, where they stay for three or four weeks, feeding on improved grasslands (Percival & Percival 1997). Apart from the introduced birds in Britain, only occasional (probably injured) birds of either population summer here. The Greenland breeders move to their nesting areas in late May. There is evidence of a moult migration of part of the population to a site in Jameson Land, east Greenland, but the distances travelled to this site are unknown (Ogilvie et al 1999c).

The map of ring-recoveries (Fig 4) shows these movements in outline, although there are few recoveries from the Svalbard population on migration in Norway, and none from Bear Island. It appears that birds from Russia or the Baltic may occur at times on the Solway, as well as in East Anglia. Barnacle Goose is only an accidental species in Spain, so the recovery there was exceptional.

The Greenland population has been the source of much conflict between farmers and conservation agencies, especially on the island of Islay in the Inner Hebrides, where numbers have increased considerably in recent decades. At the same time, numbers have been static or have declined in the traditional haunts on Hebridean islands and in Ireland. Problems also arise in Iceland, especially in spring.

Studies of the movements of flocks and individual birds in the Svalbard population have contributed enormously to its conservation at all stages of its life cycle. Observations of marked individuals have enabled the identification of all the important sites used throughout the life cycle, and steps have been taken in Britain and Norway to safeguard breeding, moulting, staging and wintering areas. The information has been brought together into a Flyway Management Plan that will result in co-ordinated monitoring, research and conservation throughout the birds' range (Black, 1998). The Greenland population, though more numerous than the Svalbard stock, is, however, still small and relatively vulnerable. There is a need for co-ordinated action within a Flyway Management Plan on the conservation of the population and its integration with the modern agricultural landscape.

Myrfyn Owen

Brent Goose

Branta bernicla

Brent Geese are long-distance migrants nesting in the high Arctic, with arguably one of the most energetically costly migrations of any waterfowl species. With a circumpolar breeding distribution at latitudes largely beyond 70°N, and in some places north of 80°N, breeding and wintering grounds are separated by up to 8,000 km, and migration may involve non-stop flights of over 3,000 km.

Globally there are three named subspecies of Brent Goose, divided between seven distinct populations or flyways. The Dark-bellied Brent Goose, nominate *bernicla*, forms the largest population, breeding predominantly on the Taimyr Peninsula in the central Russian Arctic, and wintering in northwest Europe, from the Atlantic coast of France to the Danish Wadden Sea. Populations of Light-bellied Brent Geese, *hrota*, are divided into four main flyways, one breeding largely in the Svalbard archipelago (but also in northeast Greenland and Franz Josef Land) and wintering around the North Sea, a second breeding in the eastern Canadian high Arctic and wintering almost exclusively in Ireland, and a third (known as Atlantic Brant) breeding in the southeastern Canadian Arctic and wintering on the Atlantic coast of the USA. The fourth *hrota* population (known as Grey-bellied Brant) is genetically and geographically quite distinct (Shields 1990), breeding in the western Canadian high Arctic, and wintering on the Pacific coast of the USA. Finally, the Pacific or Black Brant, *nigricans*, has two main populations. One of these breeds in the Russian Arctic, east of the Taimyr Peninsula, and winters on the coasts of China, Japan and Korea. The other, more numerous, breeds in Alaska and the southwestern Canadian Arctic, and winters on the Pacific coasts of Mexico and the USA, mixing to some extent with Grey-bellied Brant.

The analysis of the data for this species was supported by North Down Ringing Group

Brent Geese nest on open tundra, usually in coastal areas, in large river deltas, or on offshore islands, and often in association with gull colonies or raptors, a strategy that affords some protection from ground predators. Brood-rearing frequently takes place on areas of richer vegetation associated with fresh water. On wintering and staging areas, Brent Geese are exclusively coastal, preferring mudflats where they feed on eel-grass and green algae, and, in some areas, saltmarsh where they feed on a wide variety of plants. In several parts of the wintering range, particularly that of the nominate race, coastal pasture and arable crops have increasingly been used to supplement intertidal resources as the sizes of populations have grown (Vickery *et al* 1995, Andrews *et al* 1996).

The British & Irish ringing data for Brent Geese (Figs 1–3) are relatively sparse when compared with many other species but there are a number of other sources of information that, combined with general ringing, provide good information on migratory patterns. These include several intensive colour-marking schemes: in southeast England (St Joseph 1979), and arctic Canada (Maltby-Prevett *et al* 1975) in the 1970s, in the Netherlands and Germany in the 1980s (Ebbinge & St Joseph 1992), and in Northumberland and Denmark (Clausen & Percival 1992) and arctic Russia (Ebbinge *et al* 1999) in the 1990s. In addition, there have been two studies using satellite-telemetry to track Light-bellied Brent Geese migrating to Canada (Gudmundsson *et al* 1995) and to Svalbard and

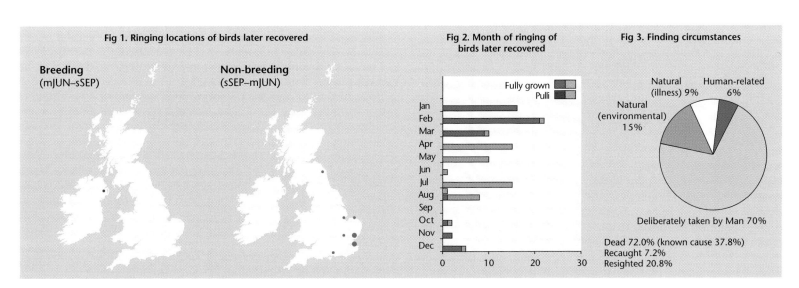

Fig 1. Ringing locations of birds later recovered

Breeding (mJUN–sSEP)

Non-breeding (sSEP–mJUN)

Fig 2. Month of ringing of birds later recovered

Fully grown / Pulli

Jan, Feb, Mar, Apr, May, Jun, Jul, Aug, Sep, Oct, Nov, Dec

0 10 20 30

Fig 3. Finding circumstances

Natural (illness) 9%
Human-related 6%
Natural (environmental) 15%
Deliberately taken by Man 70%

Dead 72.0% (known cause 37.8%)
Recaught 7.2%
Resighted 20.8%

Ringing and recovery data

	<1960	60–69	70–79	80–89	90–97	Total
RINGING						
BTO ringing totals (%)	1	1	23	10	65	916
RECOVERIES						
BTO-ringed (%)	2	6	70	7	15	54
Foreign-ringed (%)	6	10	42	27	15	71

Statistical analyses

	Breeding population (mJUN–sSEP)	Wintering population (sDEC–mMAR)
Status	NONE	[LONG-DISTANCE MIGRANT]
Age differences	—	Not tested
Sex differences	—	Not tested
Regional differences	—	Not tested
Finding circumstances	—	Not tested

Fig 4. All 110 included exchanges of Brent Geese between Britain & Ireland and abroad.

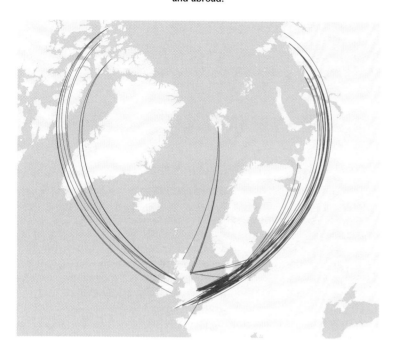

Greenland (Clausen & Bustnes 1998). Because it is relatively easy to achieve near-complete counts of Brent Geese on the wintering areas, information on population-level movements can also be assessed from monthly count data (*eg* Cranswick *et al* 1997).

The broad migration routes followed by British & Irish Brent Geese can be illustrated by the pattern of recoveries abroad (Fig 4). The separation of the three populations' flyways is clearly demonstrated, as are the links between the main wintering and breeding grounds. However, the number of connections largely represents the intensity of ringing effort and likelihood of recovery rather than the number of birds actually making the movements shown.

The connections between southern and southeastern Britain and arctic Russia represent the Dark-bellied Brent Goose population. The most northeasterly of the points shown are on the Taimyr Peninsula, representing the core of the breeding range, although some breeding also occurs as far west as the Kanin Peninsula (Filchager & Leonovich 1992, *European Atlas*). The White Sea, although represented by only four exchanges with Britain (Fig 4), is a critically important staging area for this population, since it is likely that the majority of birds and perhaps the entire population, stops here to feed during both the autumn (September) and spring (June) migrations (Bianki 1979, Clausen 1997). In the winter range, there is a shift in the population from northeast to southwest and back again over the course of the winter (Ebbinge *et al* 1999). In late September and October, large concentrations occur in the Wadden Sea of Denmark, Germany and the Netherlands. By November, the population is concentrated in Britain and France, and in January and February these two countries frequently hold virtually the entire population, divided roughly equally between them. The return migration begins in late February, and by May the majority of the population is again concentrated in the Wadden Sea. Migration may be either nocturnal or diurnal, and takes place almost exclusively over sea along coasts, although overland movements are occasionally recorded (Harrison 1979).

Within Britain, numbers of Dark-bellied Brent Geese build up from late September to a maximum in January, with most birds leaving for staging areas in the Wadden Sea in March. However, there is some regional variation in this pattern (Fig 5). Numbers build up earliest on the outer Thames Estuary, particularly on extensive eel-grass beds at

Foulness and Leigh-on-Sea (St Joseph 1979), and a large proportion of the wintering population passes through this area in October and November. The smaller populations in Dorset and south Devon also peak relatively early, with an early December maximum and onward movement to other sites as intertidal food resources in these areas are depleted. Most other regions broadly follow the national pattern, with peak numbers in the midwinter period from December to February, although significant numbers remain on the Wash and in north Kent into May. Although virtually the entire population leaves Britain in the spring, a few tens of birds commonly linger in parts of southeast Britain into the summer months. These patterns have changed over the years in response to a growing population. Whereas, around 1950, Britain hosted a substantial proportion of the Dark-bellied Brent Goose population only in the southeast and in midwinter, estuaries are now occupied well into autumn and spring at locations as far west as South Wales and as far north as the Humber (Summers *et al* 1996).

Colour-ring resightings indicate that site-fidelity is generally high in winter. Most marked geese were rarely or never seen away from preferred sites but others were highly mobile, apparently tracking the availability of eel-grass across the winter range (St Joseph 1979, Ebbinge & St Joseph 1992). The connection between Britain and France in Fig 4 perhaps represents this more mobile portion of the population. It is not known whether certain classes of bird are more likely to be site-faithful in winter, although there are some clear class differences in the timings of arrival and departure. Families with young tend to arrive later in the autumn but move further south and west in midwinter (Lambeck 1990), while young, non-breeding birds tend to migrate later in the spring (Summers *et al* 1996). Families stay together over the winter, breaking up only as the spring migration approaches (Reed 1993).

The connections between northeast Britain, northern Denmark, and Svalbard (Fig 4) illustrate the main breeding and wintering sites used by the Svalbard Light-bellied Brent Goose population. The majority of the population breeds in the Tusenøyane island group in the south of Svalbard. Historically, the first migratory destination in the autumn was Denmark, from where a substantial proportion moved on to Lindisfarne in northeast England; a large proportion of the population, however, now migrates directly to Lindisfarne (Clausen *et al* 1998). In the spring, the population concentrates in Denmark before migrating north. Although it is thought that there may be some staging on the Norwegian coast or on Byørnøya (Bear Island), between Norway and Svalbard, no major staging concentrations have yet been recorded (Clausen *et al* 1999). Two other important breeding areas, one in Franz Josef Land to the northeast of Svalbard, and another, recently confirmed, at the northeastern tip of Greenland (Clausen & Bustnes 1998), are not represented in the ring-recovery data.

Within Britain, Svalbard Light-bellied Brent Geese historically wintered widely along the east coast, from the Moray Firth to North Norfolk. However, although small numbers are still periodically recorded across this range, the population now winters almost exclusively at Lindisfarne. Geese arrive there from the beginning of September, peak between October and December, and move to Denmark by early March (Clausen *et al* 1998).

The breeding range of the Canadian Light-bellied Brent Goose population is still incompletely documented, although connections to Canada (Fig 4) give a rough indication of the likely geographical range covered by this population in summer. The recoveries fail to illustrate the crucial staging area on the west coast of Iceland, where it is likely that the entire population rests for two to three weeks during both autumn (September) and spring (May) migrations (Gardarsson & Gudmundsson 1996). This area is of particular importance because it provides the main feeding opportunity to fuel before and after the arduous crossing of the Greenland Sea and ice-cap (Gudmundsson *et al* 1995).

Small numbers of Canadian Light-bellied Brent Geese winter regularly on the Channel Islands and in Brittany, and there are sporadic

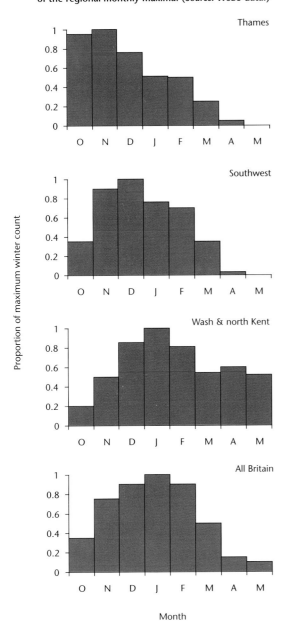

Fig 5. The winter phenology of Dark-bellied Brent Goose numbers in different parts of Britain for the period 1989–93, expressed as proportions of the regional monthly maxima. (*Source*: WeBS data.)

records from the Hebrides, parts of which were used more regularly by this population in the early 20th century (Merne *et al* 1999). However, the vast majority of the population winters on the coast of Ireland. The most important single site is Strangford Lough, which is used by over 75% of the population between late September and November (Ó Brian *et al* 1986). Following autumn staging in the north of Ireland, the population disperses to estuaries distributed around most of the Irish coast, concentrated in the southeast but largely absent from the far southwest (Ó Briain & Healy 1991).

There is no evidence of weather-related movement in Canadian Light-bellied Brent Geese (Ó Briain & Healy 1991) but extreme cold weather causing estuaries to freeze can cause southward and westward movements of Svalbard Light-bellied and Dark-bellied Brent Geese. For the Svalbard population, cold-weather movements may result in increased numbers at Lindisfarne, unusual records elsewhere in Britain, and some build-up in the Netherlands (Clausen *et al* 1999), although more recently Lindisfarne has consistently held almost the entire population in midwinter, regardless of the weather (Clausen *et al* 1998). Cold-weather movements of Dark-bellied Brent Geese into Britain and France also occur but there is no published information on the extent of such movements. Since a relatively small proportion of this population now spends the midwinter period in the part of its range most prone to freezing conditions, it may be that cold-weather influxes of Dark-bellied Brent Geese into Britain are now less evident than in the past. Cold weather in spring may also delay the growth of crucial food resources on saltmarshes in the Wadden Sea staging areas and this can lead to delay or even some reverse in the spring migration of Dark-bellied Brent Geese (Ebbinge & St Joseph 1992).

During migration, Brent Geese of all populations tend to congregate at key staging sites. This heavy reliance on a small number of sites at critical points in the annual cycle makes them particularly vulnerable to habitat loss or degradation at these sites and is the main source of conservation concern for these populations. Within Britain & Ireland, the related questions of intertidal habitat availability, agricultural conflict and disturbance also have conservation implications. Since the early 1970s for Dark-bellied Brent Geese, and now increasingly for the other populations, foraging on agricultural land in preference to the traditional intertidal habitats has led to crop damage and hence to conflict with farmers (Vickery *et al* 1995, Andrews *et al* 1996). Meeting the resulting demands for pest management without compromising the conservation of the geese represents a substantial problem for which there are many suggested approaches (*eg* Vickery & Gill 1999) but, as yet, no generally accepted solutions.

Although our knowledge of the migratory pathways used by Brent Geese wintering in Britain & Ireland is good, some significant gaps remain in our understanding of detailed patterns. In particular, a full quantitative analysis of colour-ring resighting data is needed to clarify the effects of age, sex and reproductive status on differences in migratory strategy, particularly for the Light-bellied populations.

J Marcus Rowcliffe & Juliet A Vickery

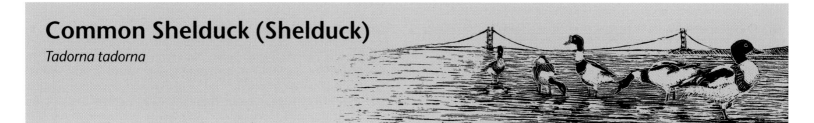

Common Shelduck (Shelduck)
Tadorna tadorna

The large, brightly coloured Shelduck is a familiar bird of estuaries and muddy shores, throughout Britain and Ireland, where it feeds on small invertebrates sieved from the surface layers of the mud. The species has a wide distribution in the Palearctic, from the west of Ireland to western China, divided into five geographic populations, three in western Eurasia (Scott & Rose 1996, Rose & Scott 1997) and two in eastern Eurasia (Miyabayashi & Mundkur 1999). Although these populations do not differ significantly in measurements or in plumage (Patterson 1982), they occupy very different habitats; most of the western birds occupy shallow muddy shores and estuaries, with a small proportion breeding on inland fresh waters, while the eastern birds live mainly on saline inland waters in semi-arid areas (*BWP*). The seasonal pattern of movement also differs between the two populations, with the eastern birds moulting in their breeding areas and then migrating south to wintering grounds in south and southeast Asia whereas most western Shelducks have a well-defined moult migration to the Helgoland Bight in northwest Germany followed by a gradual return to the breeding areas. A small minority of British & Irish Shelducks, however, moult locally.

The ringing of Shelducks has been distributed generally throughout the species' British & Irish range, especially in the breeding season (Fig 1), although few birds have been ringed in Ireland. In the non-breeding season, there has been over-representation of northeast Scotland, where a long-term study was based on ringed birds on the Ythan Estuary (Patterson 1982).

Ringing in Britain & Ireland has been almost equally divided between ducklings or juveniles in July-August and older birds caught

The analysis of the data for this species was supported by the Rye Bay Ringing Group and the Wetland Trust

mainly in early spring, with a peak in March (Fig 2). Foreign-ringed birds have been caught mainly while flightless on the moulting grounds, in August.

A quarter of ring-recoveries involving birds found dead indicated a cause of death but, of this minority, 53% were taken deliberately by Man (Fig 3), while in a further 17% death was attributed to a human-related cause, including pollution and accidental capture. Ring-recoveries are therefore likely to be biased towards sites and seasons where hunting pressure is high and to places where pollution incidents have occurred.

The Shelducks breeding in Britain & Ireland do not migrate to a wintering area but have a well-defined moult migration, involving most fully grown birds in the population. First-summer immatures and second-summer pre-breeders begin their departure from breeding areas as early as mid-June (Lind 1957). They are followed by adults that have failed in breeding, leading to a peak of passage in the first half of July. Some successful adults caring for ducklings stay behind and moult later. All of a large number of departures seen in northwest England occurred around sunset, normally in clear weather and with a following wind (Coombes 1949, 1950, Allen & Rutter 1956, 1957, 1958, Morley 1966). The birds from most areas appear to fly directly to the main moulting area in the Helgoland Bight of the Wadden Sea (Fig 4), presumably in a single overnight flight, where they join birds from Scandinavia and the

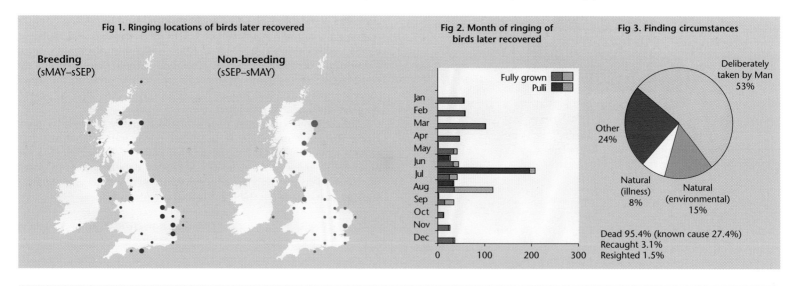

Fig 1. Ringing locations of birds later recovered

Breeding (sMAY–sSEP)

Non-breeding (sSEP–sMAY)

Fig 2. Month of ringing of birds later recovered

Fully grown
Pulli

Fig 3. Finding circumstances

Deliberately taken by Man 53%

Other 24%

Natural (illness) 8%

Natural (environmental) 15%

Dead 95.4% (known cause 27.4%)
Recaught 3.1%
Resighted 1.5%

Ringing and recovery data

	<1960	60–69	70–79	80–89	90–97	Total
RINGING						
BTO ringing totals (%)	11	24	25	18	22	8,092
RECOVERIES						
BTO-ringed (%)	6	19	34	23	18	723
Foreign-ringed (%)	21	35	29	11	5	168

Statistical analyses

	Breeding population (sMAY–sSEP)	Wintering population (sDEC–sMAR)
Status	SHORT-DISTANCE MIGRANT (3)	SHORT-DISTANCE MIGRANT*
Age differences[S]*	Significant*	Not tested
Sex differences	Not tested	Not tested
Regional differences	Not tested	Not tested
Finding circumstances	(Not significant)	Not tested

Fig 4. Locations during July, August and September, and movements of over 20 km between the presumed breeding and moulting areas, of 31 Shelduck of at least one year of age that were present in Britain & Ireland during March–June.

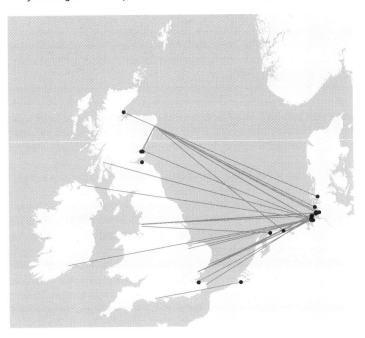

Fig 5. Locations in winter (October–February) of 46 Shelduck of at least one year of age that were present in Britain & Ireland during March–June.

Fig 6. Locations in their first year of life of 103 Shelduck ringed in Britain & Ireland as pulli or as juveniles during March–June.

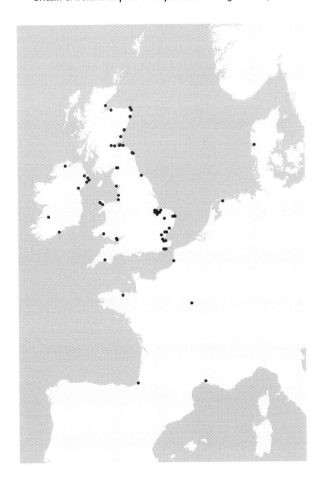

Fig 7. Movements of 18 Shelduck present in Britain & Ireland during the winter (October–February) and abroad during March–June.

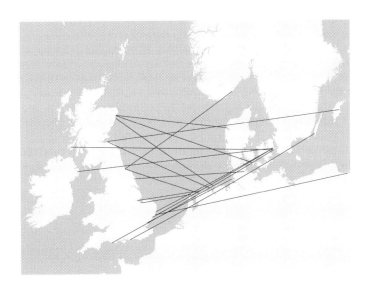

Baltic (Meltofte *et al* 1994). Shelduck numbers in the central moulting ground, the vast mudflats of the Grosser Knechtsand (Goethe 1961), remain high from about mid-July to the end of August (Oelke 1969), with few remaining after mid-September. The pattern of recoveries of ringed birds from the different parts of Britain & Ireland shows that most of the population goes to the same area for moulting (Fig 4).

The return leg of the moult migration appears to be gradual and less direct, with recoveries of British & Irish Shelducks on the European mainland coast concentrated near the moulting grounds until December, and an increased proportion in southeast England in January. In a sample of 74 Shelducks ringed while moulting on the Grosser Knechtsand and recovered in Britain & Ireland between October and March (up to 1980), 46% were found between the Wash and Kent, whereas only 32% of those recovered in the breeding season were found there (Patterson 1982), suggesting a winter concentration in the southeast (Fig 5). From here, the returning birds appear to move from one major estuary to another (Pienkowski & Evans 1979), since most have wintering concentrations much larger than the local breeding population (Hori 1969, Tubbs 1977), with peak numbers occurring progressively later at more northerly sites (Young 1964). However, it is possible that Shelducks from the far north of Britain may bypass the south of England by a more direct return, since most winter and early spring recoveries of birds ringed on the Ythan Estuary in Aberdeenshire were from northeast England and east Scotland, with very few south of the Humber (Patterson 1982).

Instead of taking part in the moult migration to the Helgoland Bight, a small proportion of British & Irish Shelducks moult locally in large estuaries including Bridgwater Bay on the Severn (Perrett 1951, Eltringham & Boyd 1960, 1963, Eltringham 1961), the Forth (Bryant & Waugh 1976, Pienkowski & Evans 1978, 1979, Bryant 1978, 1981), the Humber (Tasker 1982) and the Wash (Bryant 1981). The origin of these birds is difficult to determine. Ring-recoveries of moulting birds are not usually distinguishable from those of the local breeding or wintering population and coloured rings can rarely be seen, since moulting birds stay on the water or on remote mudflats. There has been speculation that the Shelducks moulting in Bridgwater Bay originate in Ireland but there have been no recoveries of Irish birds there, in contrast to the numbers in the Helgoland Bight (Fig 4). Pienkowski & Evans (1979) were able to identify colour-ringed birds in the Forth immediately before and after the moult period and found that most were one-year-old and two-year-old birds from local populations. The other British moulting areas may also be occupied by birds of local origin, so that only short-distance movements will be made by the minority (under 10%) of British & Irish Shelducks that moult there.

From mid-April to mid-June, most adult Shelducks are sedentary in their breeding areas, with very small distances between ringing and recovery sites. Breeding adults show a high level of site-fidelity; in the Ythan population in 1970–78, 85–93% of colour-ringed breeders returned each year. None was found in searches of other estuaries up to 200 km away and it is likely that most of the missing birds had died. There was no difference in site-fidelity or in movement patterns between the sexes (Patterson 1982).

Juvenile Shelducks do not take part in the moult migration; they stay behind in the breeding area after the adults have left and later disperse during the autumn. They first move in all directions but later tend to travel southwards (Patterson 1982), most within Britain & Ireland but some as far as the south of France (Fig 6). The long-distance dispersers return to Britain & Ireland by March, after which time all of the recoveries are within the breeding distribution. The percentage of colour-ringed juveniles that returned to the Ythan in 1969–77 (usually in May, at the end of their first year) varied from 8% to 32% with a mean of 18.7% (Patterson 1982). It is not known how many of the remainder had settled in other populations; although none was seen living elsewhere, a few rings were recovered in other areas in later years.

Some Shelducks from continental Europe migrate to Britain & Ireland, mainly the south, for the winter; this is shown by breeding-season recoveries in Scandinavia and around the Baltic of birds ringed in Britain & Ireland in winter and recoveries in Britain & Ireland during winter of birds ringed in these countries in the breeding season (Fig 7). Shelducks may also migrate to Britain & Ireland from northwest Germany, the Netherlands, Belgium and northern France but such possible movements are difficult to distinguish from the moult migration without more detailed analysis.

It is clear that the main movement of the British & Irish Shelduck population, the moult migration, is dependent on the well-being of the mudflats in the Helgoland Bight. These could be threatened by pollution of the Rivers Elbe and Weser or by developments at their mouths, which could influence water flow and silt deposition. However the status of this area as a Ramsar site, with the political recognition of the international Wadden Sea, and the commitment of the governments of Germany, Denmark and the Netherlands to its 'wise-use' gives a measure of optimism that future conservation threats to this key area will be averted. The return movement depends on a chain of major estuaries within Britain & Ireland, so it is vital that these are protected if the species is to continue to thrive.

Ian J Patterson

Mandarin Duck
Aix galericulata

The breeding plumage of the Mandarin drake is the most spectacular of any bird on the British List. Although first introduced to England from its home in the Far East before 1745, the species' naturalized population in England (principally in east Berkshire, Surrey and southern Buckinghamshire), Scotland and Wales is descended from accidental escapes and deliberate releases from avicultural collections since the 1930s. Mandarins occur in Ireland only as vagrants, presumably from England (*Birds in Ireland*). The British population, which numbers at least 3,500 breeding pairs (Davies & Baggott 1989), is of conservation significance, since it is an important component of the total world population of 25,180 pairs. In Japan, where there are an estimated 13,340 pairs, recent figures suggest that the species has staged a recovery and trends revealed from midwinter censuses indicate a stable population (Brazil 1991, Callaghan & Green 1993). In common with the only other member of the genus, the Wood Duck of North America, the Mandarin is monotypic.

Mandarins are natives of the eastern Palearctic, where they occur mainly in the Russian Federation, China, Korea and Japan. Here, the Mandarin formerly bred from around 40°N on the Chinese mainland, principally in the Tung Ling (Eastern Tombs) Forest, north of Beijing, to around 51°N on Sakhalin and the Kuril Islands in Russia and to about 55°N on the main Uda River in the Russian Far East. Between these extremes, Mandarin once nested in North Korea; in the Kirin Forest in Manchuria; throughout the catchments of the Amur and Ussuri Rivers; and on the Japanese islands of Kyushu (mainly at Isahaya east of Nagasaki), Honshu (principally on Lake Ashi near Tokyo at about 36°N

The analysis of the data for this species was supported by Peter Stevens

and around Mount Fuji) and Hokkaido. Today, the Mandarin's much reduced breeding range comprises eastern Siberia, centred on the valleys of the Amur and Ussuri Rivers; China, where the species breeds locally in the northeast in Heilungkiang and eastern Kurin, and perhaps still in Hopei (Savage 1952, *BWP*, Shurtleff & Savage 1996, Miyabayashi & Mundkur 1999); and Japan, mainly on Hokkaido.

The principal reason for the decline of the Mandarin in its native range during the past hundred years has been loss of habitat due to widespread deforestation, especially in the birds' two main breeding grounds, the Tung Ling and Kirin Forests, as a result of human settlement after the Manchu emperors were deposed in 1911 (Savage 1952).

In their native range, Mandarin are both migratory and dispersive. Between late August and early November, breeders in the Russian Maritime Territories, Manchuria and Hopei migrate south, some via Korea, to winter quarters in southeastern China, mainly south of the Yangtze River, from around 23°N in Kwangtung Province to approximately 27–29°N in Kiangsi and Chekiang Provinces; at least some Mandarin breeders migrate south from the Primorskiy Kray Territory to winter in Japan (Ostapenko 1997); they return north, already paired, between late March and early May (Savage 1952, *BWP*, Shurtleff & Savage 1996). On the main Japanese islands, there is a tendency towards some

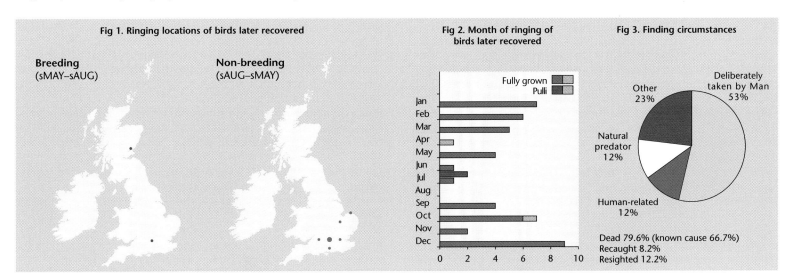

Fig 1. Ringing locations of birds later recovered

Breeding (sMAY–sAUG)

Non-breeding (sAUG–sMAY)

Fig 2. Month of ringing of birds later recovered

Fully grown
Pulli

Fig 3. Finding circumstances

Deliberately taken by Man 53%
Other 23%
Natural predator 12%
Human-related 12%

Dead 79.6% (known cause 66.7%)
Recaught 8.2%
Resighted 12.2%

Ringing and recovery data

	<1960	60–69	70–79	80–89	90–97	Total
RINGING						
BTO ringing totals (%)	0	0	2	43	54	1,316
RECOVERIES						
BTO-ringed (%)	0	0	4	40	55	47
Foreign-ringed (%)	0	0	0	0	100	2

Statistical analyses

	Breeding population (sMAY–sAUG)	Wintering population (sNOV–sFEB)
Status	[SHORT-DISTANCE MIGRANT]	[SHORT-DISTANCE MIGRANT]
Age differences	Not tested	Not tested
Sex differences	Not tested	Not tested
Regional differences	Not tested	Not tested
Finding circumstances	Not tested	Not tested

Fig 4. Recovery locations and movements of over 20 km for the 47 included recoveries of Mandarin ringed or recovered in Britain & Ireland. A bird ringed in Berkshire and recovered in Russia, together with a bird ringed and recovered locally in Tayside, are not shown.

similarly lost the migratory instinct (Shurtleff & Savage 1996), as apparently have others established, or formerly established, in Austria, Belgium, Germany and the Netherlands (Baillie & Groombridge 1996). Elsewhere in Europe, *BWP* records Mandarin as accidental visitors to Finland, the former Czechoslovakia, the former Yugoslavia, Italy and Spain, and also to the Faeroes.

The loss of the instinct to migrate, which has contributed towards the Mandarin's naturalization in Britain and elsewhere, has, however, been a factor inhibiting the species' extension of range, though in Britain and probably other countries there is a tendency to some seasonal dispersal. In late September, after the end of the breeding season and the emergence of the drakes from eclipse plumage, Mandarin, especially in southeastern England, gather on the larger lakes to form extensive autumnal flocks. Normally they do not return to their breeding localities until the following spring, although in a mild winter they may sometimes do so by early February or even late January (pers obs).

Ring-recoveries of Mandarin have originated from several parts of the species' British range but most have arisen from ringing in the Surrey stronghold between September and March (Figs 1 & 2). There are few recoveries of known cause, most of which have been from birds taken deliberately or which were otherwise human-related (Fig 3).

In Europe, Mandarin movements tend to be longitudinal, rather than latitudinal as in the Far East (Ostapenko 1997). Although in Britain the Mandarin is non-migratory, ring-recoveries have revealed some remarkable and swift long-distance flights to and from the near Continent, and even one to European Russia (Fig 4). Apart from the foreign recoveries included in the maps and tables, a bird from St James's Park in London was subsequently reported in Hungary in 1931; two birds from Norway were shot together in Northumberland in 1962; of two captive birds ringed in the Channel Islands in July 1980, one was recovered in Avon and the other in Devon in the following December; and a drake ringed in Berkshire was later recorded in St Petersburg in Russia (Bowey 1992). This last individual may perhaps have been caught up with other migrating ducks. We do not know whether the movements from the Netherlands to Surrey and from Surrey to France indicate attempts to escape from severe winter weather, nor whether the ringing of Mandarin may be biased towards semicaptive individuals and others with a reduced fear of Man. Clearly there is much still to be learnt about the foreign dispersal of Britain's naturalized Mandarin population.

Away from breeding areas in Britain, there are sometimes noticeable seasonal peaks in occurrence that indicate when birds are on the move. In Yorkshire, Northumberland and County Durham, for example, the peak period for occurrence (nearly all drakes) is between late March and early May (Bowey 1992, Wilson & Slack 1996); this phenomenon has been tentatively ascribed to young males seeking new territories (Bowey 1992). A smaller autumnal peak occurs in late October and November, raising the possibility that these birds may be imitating the movements of their Asian counterparts (Wilson & Slack 1996).

Clearly, the conservation of a non-migratory population is easier to achieve than is that of one that does migrate. Although the Mandarin is officially classified in its native range only as of 'least concern' (BirdLife International 2000), all necessary steps still need to be taken for the species' conservation in both Britain and the Far East.

The reason for the abandonment of the seasonal migration of Mandarin (and indeed of other aliens such as the Canada Goose) is unknown; an obvious possible explanation is that in the more temperate climate of their adopted homeland the need for migration no longer exists; this may well be true but is so far unproven. Further research should eventually shed light on the many unknown factors relating to the nature of the Mandarin's local movements and dispersal both inside and outside Britain.

Christopher Lever

southward dispersal in autumn. Elsewhere in the Far East, Mandarin have been recorded as far west as Mongolia, Upper Assam and Manipur in eastern India, and eastward to the Ryukyu Islands, Hong Kong and Taiwan (*BWP*). In recent years, Mandarin have been sighted in Vietnam, northern Thailand and Nepal (Shurtleff & Savage 1996), suggesting the possibility of some future extension of range.

In contrast to most other Palearctic wildfowl, Mandarin are birds of the mid-latitude temperate deciduous broad-leaved forest zone, where they frequent slow-flowing or standing fresh waters bordered by a dense growth of marginal trees and shrubs, especially where they overhang the water's edge to provide good cover, and where there is an abundance of reeds, sedges and other emergent vegetation. They require plenty of arboreal and scrub cover for concealment, and if alarmed take readily to the air, being, like Teal, capable of rising steeply and fast from confined spaces and dense cover. Mandarin nest in holes in mature trees up to 15 m or more from the ground, in hollow tree stumps, in fallen logs and even occasionally among roots at or near ground level (Lever 1987, 1990). They readily accept artificial nestboxes even where natural holes occur (Davies & Baggott 1989). In Britain, Mandarin compete for nesting sites with such hole-nesting birds as Jackdaws and even with introduced Grey Squirrels.

The success of the Mandarin in becoming so well established in the wild in southeastern England, and to a lesser extent elsewhere in Britain, can be attributed to a number of factors. First, the species fills a vacant ecological niche for a hole-nesting perching duck; second, the founder stock was composed of individuals chosen from the survivors of a shipment in 1928 from Hong Kong to Paris, which were themselves the survivors of a much larger number originally captured in their winter quarters in southern China, and were thus inherently the strongest individuals and, coming originally from northern China and the Russian Maritime Territories, were derived from a wide genetic base (Lever 1990); and third, Mandarin in Britain, like the also-introduced Canada Goose, have lost the instinct to migrate, and are thus able to become established in the wild without the distraction of the need for migration (*European Atlas*). An introduced population of Mandarin in California, USA, has

Eurasian Wigeon (Wigeon)

Anas penelope

The Wigeon is one of the best-known ducks in northwest Europe. The characteristic, far-carrying whistle of the male is a familiar sound to the birdwatcher and large winter flocks are a common sight on British & Irish estuaries and inland waters.

Wigeon breed between *c* 50°N and *c* 70°N across northern Europe and Asia, from Iceland and northern Britain across Scandinavia and northern Russia to the Bering Sea coast (Rogacheva 1992, *BWP*). The species is highly migratory, leaving the breeding grounds in late summer to winter across almost the whole of the temperate zone of Europe and Asia, with concentrations in coastal areas of western Europe, the Mediterranean and Black Sea regions, Caspian Sea lowlands, Iraq and Iran east to southern and eastern China and Japan. Wigeon also winter along the Nile Valley as far south as Sudan and Ethiopia (Scott & Rose 1996). Males moult their flight feathers between late May and July, and the females between late June and early September. Males congregate at important moult gatherings, recorded at many localities in Russia, including the Volga Delta, lakes in the Urals and the upper Pechora, and in Estonia, southern Sweden, Denmark and Iceland. The main departure from the breeding or moulting grounds takes place in September and the main arrival on the winter quarters is in October and November. Wigeon leave their winter quarters in northwest Europe and the Black Sea region in the second half of March and early April but do not arrive on their breeding grounds in northern Russia before the second half of May (Owen & Mitchell 1988).

No discrete populations are identifiable but five main wintering groups can be separated. Winter estimates suggest 1,250,000 in northwest

The analysis of the data for this species was supported by David Musson

Europe, 560,000 in the Black Sea and Mediterranean Basin, 250,000 between southwest Asia and northeast Africa, another 250,000 in south Asia, and 100,000–1,000,000 in eastern Asia (Rose & Scott 1997). Birds from these groups may well mix on the breeding grounds and at major moulting areas, although the different population trends might suggest that northwest European birds are separate from the Black Sea and Mediterranean groups (Delany *et al* 1999).

Wigeon breed on shallow freshwater marshes, lakes and lagoons, often surrounded by scattered trees or open forest. They winter in coastal marshes, freshwater and brackish lagoons, estuaries, bays and other sheltered marine habitats. Wigeon consume an almost entirely vegetable diet throughout the year. Food is obtained either on land by grazing while walking, on water from the surface or, less often, under water by immersing their head and neck. Wigeon are highly gregarious outside the breeding season, tending to form close aggregations, often of enormous numbers, on the wintering grounds. Britain & Ireland holds a number of internationally important sites for wintering Wigeon, notably the Ribble Estuary, the Ouse Washes, the Swale Estuary and the Somerset Levels (Pollitt *et al* 2000).

Wigeon catching in Britain & Ireland has been almost restricted to the winter months, with 86% of the ring-recovery sample having been caught between September and February (Figs 1 & 2). Despite their abundance,

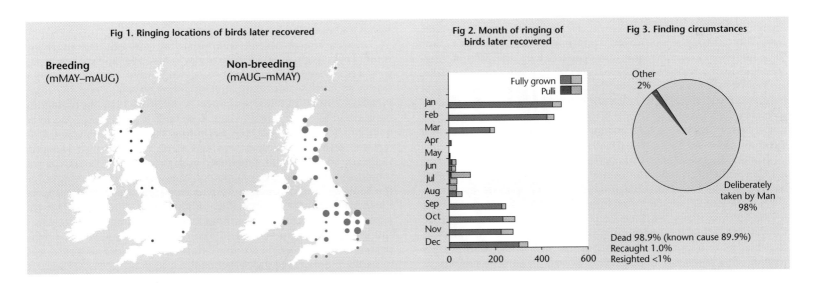

Fig 1. Ringing locations of birds later recovered

Breeding (mMAY–mAUG)

Non-breeding (mAUG–mMAY)

Fig 2. Month of ringing of birds later recovered

Fully grown
Pulli

Fig 3. Finding circumstances

Other 2%

Deliberately taken by Man 98%

Dead 98.9% (known cause 89.9%)
Recaught 1.0%
Resighted <1%

Ringing and recovery data

	<1960	60–69	70–79	80–89	90–97	Total
RINGING						
BTO ringing totals (%)	11	9	19	24	37	18,144
RECOVERIES						
BTO-ringed (%)	18	12	28	20	22	2,115
Foreign-ringed (%)	28	25	22	17	7	453

Statistical analyses

	Breeding population (mMAY–mAUG)	Wintering population (sDEC–mMAR)
Status	SEDENTARY*	LONG-DISTANCE MIGRANT*
Age differences[NT]	Not tested	Significant
Sex differences[NT]	Not tested	Significant*
Regional differences	Not tested	Not significant[3]*
Finding circumstances	Not tested*	Not tested*

Fig 4. Recovery locations, and movements of over 20 km, of Wigeon ringed as pulli or first-years during May–August, and recovered before the end of January in the following year (24, red) or subsequent to that (15, blue).

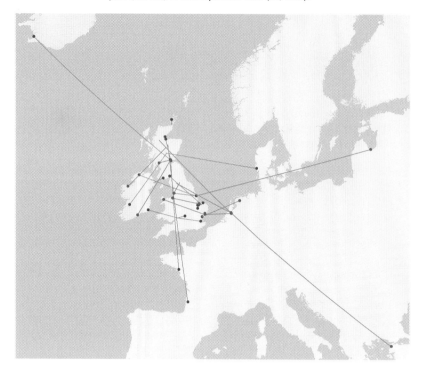

rather few birds have ever been ringed. Up to 1986, 9,500 birds had been caught, mainly in decoys and large cage traps operated by the WWT in the southeast of England, especially Essex, Suffolk and Norfolk. However, in the following seven years, the WWT encouraged local cannon-netting groups to focus more attention on the species as part of a project investigating within-winter movements. This resulted in a further 4,500 birds being caught, with large samples being trapped in areas away from the southeast of England, particularly in Scotland (Mitchell *et al* 1995). Approximately 50% of the ring-recovery sample were ringed as first-winter birds. Very few Wigeon were ringed as pulli in Britain & Ireland (just 1% of the ring-recovery sample) and this contrasts with the 30% of ring-recoveries for foreign-ringed Wigeon that come from birds ringed as pulli.

The Wigeon is a quarry species throughout its range, and substantial numbers are taken annually. In the UK, it is the third most-taken quarry species, with an annual bag of *c* 60,000 (Harradine 1985). Almost all ring-recoveries for which the finding circumstances are known are a direct result of birds being shot (Fig 3).

Just under a half (47%) of all ring-recoveries were from within Britain & Ireland. These include within-winter movements, and birds returning to winter quarters after breeding. A substantial number of ring-recoveries (16% of the sample) were reported from European Russia, reflecting both hunting pressure there and the importance of the area for breeding birds. Conversely, 44% of the Wigeon ringed abroad and recovered in Britain & Ireland were trapped in the Netherlands, with a further 28% from Iceland. This highlights ringing effort as well as hunting pressure as obvious sources of bias in interpreting the ring-recovery data.

Britain supports a small breeding population, most recently estimated at some 300–500 pairs (*1988–91 Atlas*). The main breeding areas are in the Pennines, the uplands of east and central Scotland and in the far north. Nesting attempts are rare in Ireland (*Birds in Ireland*) although the species may be breeding there unnoticed in some years (*1988–91 Atlas*). Although the number of Wigeon breeding in Britain & Ireland has increased during the last century they continue to make a negligible contribution to the wintering stock. Most birds ringed as pulli or juveniles in Britain dispersed within Britain & Ireland during the first winter (Fig 4). Recoveries in subsequent seasons included singles in

Latvia and Turkey. However, Duncan (1992a) noted the high degree of natal philopatry shown by females and ducklings at a breeding colony in Upper Deeside, Scotland.

The first birds returning from breeding grounds in continental Europe can arrive back in Britain & Ireland as early as August, with a steady increase in numbers through the autumn months. The maximum numbers of Wigeon are counted in Britain & Ireland almost invariably in January (Cranswick *et al* 1999). Departure is most pronounced in late March and April and is well synchronized.

The recoveries of Wigeon demonstrate the large area from which our winter flocks originate (Fig 5). Recoveries in May and June are principally from Fennoscandia to European Russia with many recoveries coming from east of 40°E, including striking concentrations along the rivers Pechora, Yenisei and Ob, seemingly a result of high local hunting pressure. In July and August when some birds would be expected to be moulting (and some possibly beginning migration) recoveries were reported from the breeding area and along the Baltic Sea and near Denmark. Recoveries in September and October were found in the breeding area and along the migratory route along the coastal regions of the Baltic Sea and onwards to western Europe. In March and April, the number of recoveries was smaller, although it is noteworthy that the majority were along inland countries south of the Baltic Sea, suggesting a spring migration more southerly than that of the autumn. A similar phenomenon has been observed in European White-fronted Geese ringed in southern Britain and the Netherlands.

Winter recoveries of Wigeon ringed on the breeding grounds in Iceland were predominantly from northwest Europe with the majority from Scotland and Ireland (Owen & Mitchell 1988). Some have been found in Russia and elsewhere in continental Europe in later years, probably as a result of abmigration. Icelandic Wigeon are joined here, and outnumbered, by those breeding in Fennoscandia and especially Russia. There is redistribution within Britain & Ireland during the winter, presumably of Icelandic birds moving south and of continental ones moving west (Mitchell *et al* 1995). There is substantial turnover of Wigeon in Britain during the winter, as early arrivals are shot or pass through to Ireland, France and Iberia. The number of Wigeon using Britain &

Fig 5. Locations during (a) May–June (263), (b) July–August (266), (c) September–October (585) and (d) March–April (76) of Wigeon present in Britain & Ireland during part of the year.

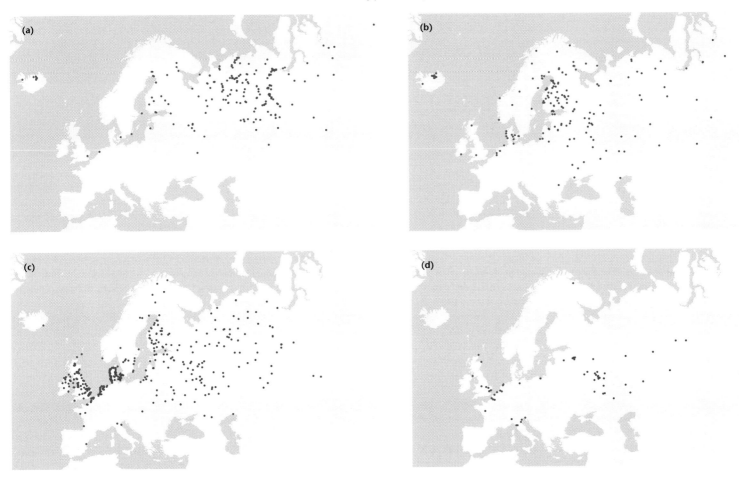

Ireland during the winter is probably half as much again as are present at the January peak, although this remains supposition.

Wigeon undertake significant cold-weather movements of varying magnitude depending on the severity of the winter. Increases occur in east and west Britain, Ireland and north and west France in severe winters, and dramatic increases occur in Iberia in very severe winters (Ridgill & Fox 1990).

Based on 37 recoveries of Wigeon that had been ringed in the Netherlands and recovered in subsequent winters at the same locality, Donker (1959) suggested that Wigeon would, at times, visit the same place in several consecutive years either as a migrant or as a winter visitor. This was also confirmed by Mitchell *et al* (1995), who showed that of 753 Wigeon recovered wintering back in Britain & Ireland after at least one migration to the breeding grounds, 22% were recovered within 25 km of the original ringing site. At Caerlaverock, Dumfries, where individually marked Wigeon were intensively studied over three winters, 61% of birds were seen in a subsequent winter. With a relatively low survival rate, this suggested that virtually all the birds assumed to be alive returned to the site at least once during the winter after ringing. Mitchell *et al* (1995) also suggested that Wigeon passing through Britain, especially during the autumn months, to wintering sites further west and south may be using the same staging sites in consecutive winters. Use of wintering sites can change relatively quickly in response to external influences: the negative impacts on wintering sites at Lindisfarne and Strangford Lough have led to rapid declines, whilst the creation of hunting-free refuges in Denmark has resulted in huge increases in the numbers staging at such sites (Madsen 1998).

The estimated adult survival rate is *c* 64% (Bell & Mitchell 1996) while that for juveniles is lower (Boyd 1962). An even sex ratio of first-winter birds in winter flocks, compared with an adult ratio of 1.23 males per female (pers obs), suggests that the adult female survival is lower than that of adult males. The median time between ringing and recovery was 771 days for males and 567 days for females, also suggesting higher survival rates for males (Owen & Mitchell 1988). The proportion of young in winter flocks fluctuated annually between 21% and 46% during 1989–96 (pers obs), and this is reflected in the proportion of young in bag samples and the ring-recovery sample (Mitchell 1997).

The population wintering in northwest Europe showed an apparent rate of increase of 7.5% per annum during 1975–94 (Rose 1995), but there are signs that part of the Russian breeding population declined at the same time, reflected in the decline seen in the Black Sea and Mediterranean population. The number of birds wintering in the west Mediterranean probably decreased by 45% in the same 20 years, while the number wintering in the Black Sea or east Mediterranean may now be less than half the number present in 1982 (Rose 1995).

The autumn and spring passage sites in the Baltic, Belarus and Russia suggest that other important passage sites must exist in other areas right across Europe en route between the breeding and wintering grounds. Most of the wintering sites in northwest Europe and the Mediterranean region are protected, as are the known key passage sites. In contrast, the two most important sites in the Caspian Basin, but very few of the remaining 38, are fully protected (Scott & Rose 1996). Implementation of conservation measures at these known, but unprotected sites is clearly an immediate priority. Further ringing and ideally satellite-tracking would help to identify further sites at which conservation measures are high priority.

Carl Mitchell

Gadwall
Anas strepera

The Gadwall appears to be something of an opportunistic duck species. Its herbivorous, surface-feeding nature would normally confine the species to the shallower parts of the most productive of wetland systems. However, its kleptoparasitism of coot species in the Old World (Amat & Soriguer 1984) and the New World (LeSchack & Hepp 1995), and of other species of herbivorous waterfowl, enable this dabbling duck to exploit food resources in deeper water far beyond its normal reach. Its favoured breeding habitats in continental Europe, and prairie wetlands, semipermanent ponds and lakes in grassland in continental North America, freeze in winter so, inevitably, the Gadwall is a winter migrant.

The recent expansion in breeding (5% per annum) and wintering numbers (15% per annum) in Britain has also been associated with the increase in nutrient-rich artificial wetland habitats there (Fox 1988, Fox & Salmon 1989) as elsewhere in Europe. This initial colonization of Britain & Ireland is considered to have been aided by introductions of the species starting in the middle of the 19th century, but the very recent increase in breeding and wintering numbers in northwest Europe appears not to be linked to any such process. In the western Palearctic, largest numbers occur in the Black Sea/Mediterranean Basin, south of the distribution of many dabbling ducks. On the basis of limited ring-recovery data, it remains difficult to identify precise biogeographical populations of the Gadwall (Scott & Rose 1996). However, it does appear that the modest northwest European wintering population (originating from Fennoscandia, western Russia and central Europe) may be largely discrete from the larger numbers breeding in a zone from south-central

The analysis of the data for this species was supported by the Rye Bay Ringing Group and the Wetland Trust

areas of the former USSR to Siberia, which winter around the Black and Caspian Seas. In North America, its breeding range was traditionally centred in the west, with strongholds in the prairie pothole region. However, in the second half of this century it has spread eastwards, where it is conspicuously associated with wildlife refuges, reservoirs, sewage treatment works and other artificial or modified habitats (Henny & Holgersen 1974, LeSchack *et al* 1997). The winter range extends from southern Alaska east to southern Ontario and south to Mexico, but with greatest concentrations along coasts, especially in Louisiana and adjacent Gulf coasts (Bellrose 1980).

A modest but increasing breeding population of about 800 pairs occurs in Britain & Ireland, concentrated in the British south and east in association with the most productive wetlands (*1988–91 Atlas*). In winter 1997/98, some 13,000 Gadwall were counted in Britain & Ireland, approximately 7% of the western Palearctic population, but over 40% of the estimated numbers in northwest Europe (Cranswick *et al* 1999, Rose & Scott 1997). Peak counts used to occur in Britain in autumn. Increasingly, however, numbers reach a maximum in midwinter, when the dispersing native populations are supplemented by birds originating in the east and northeast (Fox & Salmon 1989). It is generally considered that the faster rate of increase in numbers counted in midwinter (compared with autumn) suggests a more rapid expansion among this element of the

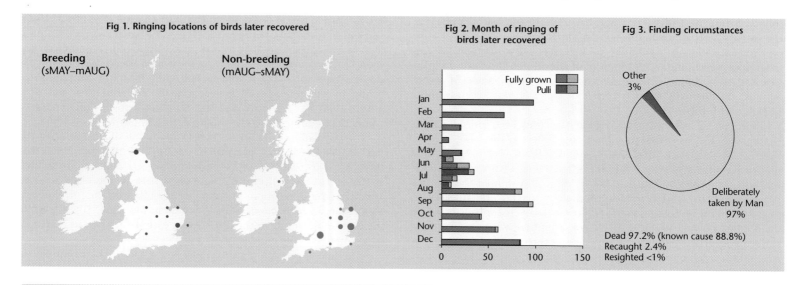

Fig 1. Ringing locations of birds later recovered

Breeding (sMAY–mAUG)

Non-breeding (mAUG–sMAY)

Fig 2. Month of ringing of birds later recovered

Fully grown
Pulli

Fig 3. Finding circumstances

Other 3%

Deliberately taken by Man 97%

Dead 97.2% (known cause 88.8%)
Recaught 2.4%
Resighted <1%

Ringing and recovery data

	<1960	60–69	70–79	80–89	90–97	Total
RINGING						
BTO ringing totals (%)	2	5	21	40	32	5,488
RECOVERIES						
BTO-ringed (%)	5	5	20	49	21	626
Foreign-ringed (%)	31	4	22	25	18	55

Statistical analyses

	Breeding population (sMAY–mAUG)	Wintering population (sDEC–sMAR)
Status	LONG-DISTANCE MIGRANT* (2)	LONG-DISTANCE MIGRANT*
Age differences	Not tested	Not tested
Sex differences	Not tested	Not tested
Regional differences	Not tested	Not tested
Finding circumstances	Not tested*	Not tested

Fig 4. Recovery locations for all included recoveries of Gadwall ringed or recovered in Britain & Ireland, with dead recoveries (662, red) differentiated from resightings (3, black) and recaptures (16, blue).

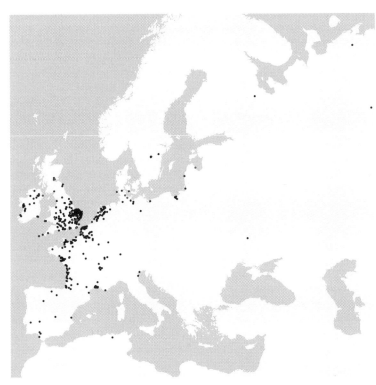

population than for the native British & Irish one. Subsequently, birds move to France, Spain and the Mediterranean for the winter (Fox & Mitchell 1988). Gadwall nesting in southeastern Europe are considered to winter in the Mediterranean alongside birds breeding very much further east in Russia (*BWP*).

Because the Gadwall was relatively scarce in Britain & Ireland until about 1970, relatively few had been ringed there. Most individuals were caught in autumn and winter at the WWT ringing stations at Abberton

Reservoir in Essex, Nacton Decoy in Suffolk, and Borough Fen Decoy near Peterborough (Fig 1). In more recent times, the establishment of feral populations associated with the wildfowl collections at Slimbridge (Gloucestershire) and Castle Espie (County Down) have led to extensive marking of these and decoyed wild birds at these sites (Fig 1). The seasonality of capture reflects abundance, with greatest numbers generally in the winter months, but with large numbers of juveniles caught in August and September (Fig 2). Hunting was the source of the vast majority of Gadwall whose rings were recovered (Fig 3). The distribution of all 626 usable recoveries of Gadwall ringed in Britain & Ireland is shown in Fig 4, together with 55 recoveries of foreign-ringed Gadwall captured in Britain & Ireland.

Most ring-recoveries from British & Irish pulli have been from France, the Netherlands, Spain, Italy or Denmark in the autumn or winter after ringing (Fox & Mitchell 1988), with recoveries in subsequent seasons from France, the Netherlands and Ireland (Fig 5a). Post-breeding recoveries of Gadwall in the Netherlands during autumn confirm the status of the IJsselmeer as an important moulting area for adults and staging area for immatures of this species (Salomonsen 1968). In addition, there are records of birds marked in November in Britain moving to the same area after as little as 17 days (Fox & Mitchell 1988). Hence the northern part of the Netherlands is undoubtedly of some importance in autumn for this population, both as a moult site and prior to winter dispersal (SOVON 1987). Ring-recoveries indicate that only some 13% of British- & Irish-ringed Gadwall caught during the summer remained in Britain & Ireland until late February; on this basis, there seems little justification for regarding the Gadwall population as sedentary, as might be expected if the population was derived solely from introduced stock. British & Irish summer-ringed Gadwall show little dispersal outside their general range (Fig 5b).

Based on birds ringed abroad, between a half and a third of the Gadwall wintering in Britain & Ireland originate in eastern Europe (including the Czech Republic and the Baltic States). Recoveries of BTO- and foreign-ringed birds also show that Icelandic and Scottish breeders tend to winter in Ireland (Fox & Mitchell 1988). Hence it would seem that the wintering stock comprises immigrants from the north and east that supplement the resident element of the local breeding population (Fig 6).

Fig 5. Recovery locations of Gadwall ringed in the breeding season in Britain or Ireland as adult (red) or as pullus or immature (blue) and recovered (a) before the start of the following breeding season (17:36) or (b) after the start of the following breeding season (21:18). Sample sizes of the age classes (adult:pullus or immature) are given.

(a)

(b)

Fig 6. Locations in the breeding season of 50 Gadwall present in Britain & Ireland outside the breeding season.

More than two-thirds of all Gadwall ringed in Britain & Ireland (either in their first winter or as adults) and recovered in the same year in autumn or winter had made only local movements, suggesting a relatively resident winter population. Nevertheless, between the analyses of Owen *et al* (1986, based on data up to 1982) and Fox & Mitchell (1988, using data gathered up to January 1988), the proportion of Gadwall ringed at the major stations of Abberton and Slimbridge that were recovered overseas had almost doubled. This suggests birds were increasingly likely to move to continental Europe, perhaps as a result of severe cold spells in the winters of 1983/84, 1984/85, 1985/86 and 1986/87. Spring and summer recoveries in Denmark, Germany, Poland and Russia all suggest the same common breeding origin of these birds. Male Gadwall were more likely to disperse overseas than females, and adults were less likely to be recovered in Ireland or Britain than juveniles of either sex, although the differences did not attain statistical significance (Fox & Mitchell 1988).

Although there are a few recoveries of British- & Irish-ringed Gadwall, marked in any season, from the French Mediterranean coasts, there are no recoveries from the Black Sea and eastern Mediterranean areas where this species is so abundant; this suggests that these populations may largely be discrete.

Gadwall are amongst the earliest of dabbling ducks to pair in autumn or early winter, since paired individuals are behaviourally dominant over unmated individuals and gain access to food resources (Paulus 1983). Intriguingly, Gadwall is one of the few dabbling duck species where sequential monogamy is strongly suspected; pair-bonds are only briefly interrupted for the duration of the male moult migration (Fedynich & Godfrey 1989, Köhler *et al* 1995).

As for many other species of dabbling duck, Britain & Ireland sits at a crossroads for migrating Gadwall, accepting breeding birds from Iceland, the Netherlands, Denmark, northern Germany, Poland, the Baltic States and northwest Russia, some of which continue into France, Spain and North Africa, as well as contributing modest numbers from the resident breeding population which are either sedentary or go south for the winter. Small sample sizes preclude more detailed analyses of the existing ringing database. As a species showing a conspicuous increase in numbers in the last 30 years, however, continued ringing effort to monitor changes in Gadwall migratory behaviour, survival and dispersal would seem an important research priority for the immediate future.

A D (Tony) Fox

Eurasian Teal (Teal)
Anas crecca
Green-winged Teal
Anas carolinensis

The Teal (now treated as two species) is one of the smallest dabbling ducks and has a holarctic range, breeding throughout the temperate zone and extending into the sub-Arctic. Teal winter mainly to the south of their breeding range and are highly responsive to cold spells, which cause rapid and extensive onward movement.

The British breeding population is estimated at 1,500–2,600 pairs, and there are a further 400–675 pairs in Ireland (*1988–91 Atlas*). These birds appear to be mainly resident, although some may move south into France and Iberia in severe weather. At least 200,000 individuals winter in Britain & Ireland, arriving from breeding grounds that extend from Iceland through Scandinavia to northwest Siberia (Cranswick *et al* 1999). This represents around half the northwest European winter population of *c* 400,000 birds (Rose & Scott 1997), the remainder, in normal winters, being distributed mainly in Denmark, the Netherlands and northern France. Up to three million Teal breed in Siberia and winter in the eastern Mediterranean, the Black Sea, East Africa, the Indian subcontinent and in east and southeast Asia (Shevareva 1970). Separate forms occur in the Aleutian Islands (*nimia*; less than 10,000 birds) and throughout North America (*carolinensis*; in excess of two million birds) (Rose & Scott 1997). The latter is now treated as a separate monotypic species (BOU 2001).

Teal breed in a variety of freshwater habitats, from large lakes to tiny pools, and at altitudes of up to 2,000 m. They will occupy similar wetlands in winter but occur in largest numbers on large, sheltered estuaries, extensive inland floods and large reservoirs with areas of mud and shallows. Teal are dependent for feeding on shallows and wet mud

The analysis of the data for these species was supported by the Mahee Island Ringing Station

and, as these are the first parts of a wetland to freeze in cold spells, have developed a strategy of migrating as soon as this occurs (Ogilvie 1983).

More Teal have been ringed in Britain & Ireland than any other species of wildfowl except Mallard. Relatively few recoveries have been obtained of Teal ringed during the breeding season, and few of the ringing locations (Fig 1) are in northern or western Scotland where the breeding population is most concentrated (*1988–91 Atlas*). Outside the breeding season, the ringing locations are more representative of the winter distribution in the southern half of Britain, though less so in the northern half and in Ireland (*Winter Atlas*). The various duck decoys operated by WWT in the last 50 years all caught this species, and cage traps at Abberton Reservoir were particularly successful. Of over 55,000 Teal ringed in the period 1949–77, more than 37,000 were caught at Abberton and 9,000 at Borough Fen Decoy, Northamptonshire (Ogilvie 1983). Teal trapped or mist-netted at a wide variety of other sites have also provided recoveries.

Of 13,949 recoveries from dead birds, 60% were of birds sexed at ringing as males, 34% were of females and 6% of the birds were of unknown sex. This reflects the bias in sex ratio in numbers ringed, since males arrive some weeks ahead of the females, and the largest catches were consistently made during October–November (Fig 2).

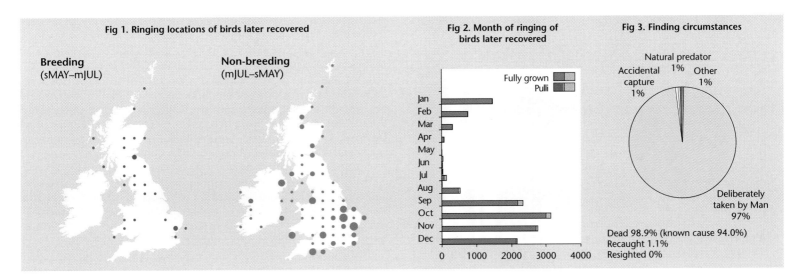

Fig 1. Ringing locations of birds later recovered

Breeding (sMAY–mJUL)   Non-breeding (mJUL–sMAY)

Fig 2. Month of ringing of birds later recovered

Fully grown / Pulli

Fig 3. Finding circumstances

Natural predator 1%
Accidental capture 1%   Other 1%
Deliberately taken by Man 97%

Dead 98.9% (known cause 94.0%)
Recaught 1.1%
Resighted 0%

Ringing and recovery data

	<1960	60–69	70–79	80–89	90–97	Total
RINGING						
BTO ringing totals (%)	34	25	15	12	15	85,654
RECOVERIES						
BTO-ringed (%)	34	32	18	9	7	13,505
Foreign-ringed (%)	←	82	→	15	3	3,045

Statistical analyses

	Breeding population (sMAY–mJUL)	Wintering population (mNOV–sMAR)
Status	SHORT-DISTANCE MIGRANT (2)	LONG-DISTANCE MIGRANT*
Age differences[NT]	Not significant*	Significant
Sex differences[NT]	Not tested	Not significant
Regional differences	Not tested	Not significant[2]
Finding circumstances	Not tested*	Significant

Fig 4. Locations outside the breeding season and movements of over 20 km between the breeding and non-breeding season of 96 Teal ringed as pulli, or as juveniles (before mid-July), or recorded as breeding in Britain & Ireland.

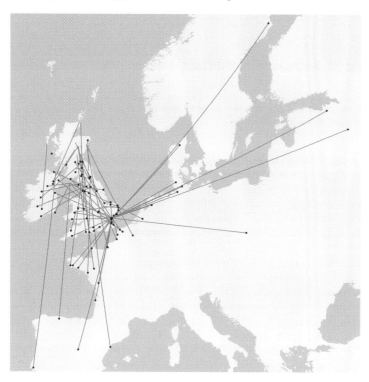

Fig 6. Recovery locations and all 22 included exchanges of Teal between Britain & Ireland and Iceland.

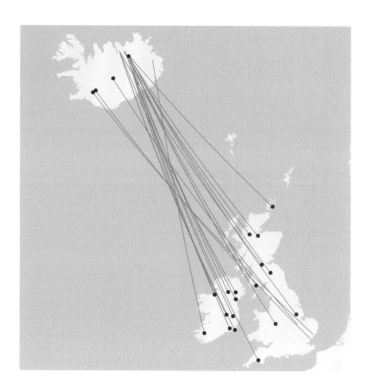

Fig 5. Seasonally accurate locations during May–June of 378 Teal using Britain & Ireland during the year.

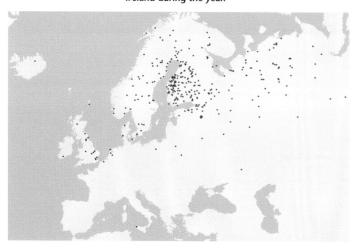

The Teal is a quarry species throughout its range, which is reflected in the 97% of recoveries deliberately taken by Man (Fig 3); nearly all of these birds will have been shot. As with all quarry species, the pattern of recoveries in space and time is influenced very heavily by hunting pressure, which itself varies geographically and has changed seasonally and across years as hunting regulations have altered.

The small amount of ringing of Teal bred, or thought from the date of ringing to have been bred, in Britain & Ireland has produced a few useful recoveries. Our local breeding stock remains mainly within Britain & Ireland, with southward movement in the winter (Duncan 1992b). Under the influence of severe weather, they may move further south or west, taking some into Iberia (Fig 4). It is possible that some of the birds trapped in early July could have been early immigrants, and this may explain some of the eastward movements between Abberton and abroad.

Teal wintering in Britain & Ireland, as well as those passing through to areas further south, come from breeding grounds in Iceland, northern Europe, the Baltic States and a large area of the Russian Federation north of about 55°N and extending eastwards to about 60°E, with rather few from further east (Fig 5). Examination of Teal ring-recoveries for birds known to be from foreign breeding populations (*ie* those with confirmed breeding status), and present in Britain & Ireland during part of the year, shows a similar breeding range but with a much reduced sample size (*n*=26) compared to that shown in Fig 5. This reinforces the importance of Britain & Ireland for birds from across a wide breeding range. It is believed that most of the Icelandic population, which amounts to some hundreds of pairs, winters within Britain & Ireland (*BWP*), with a slight bias towards Ireland and the northern half of Britain (Fig 6). Icelandic-ringed Teal have also been recovered in continental Europe from Denmark south to Portugal, with scattered records from Scandinavia, Greenland and the Azores (A Petersen pers comm).

Small but increasing numbers of *carolinensis* have been recorded annually in Britain & Ireland, with up to 30 new individuals recorded annually in recent years in addition to regular returnees (Fraser *et al* 1999b). Since only the males can be identified successfully in the field, the true number of *carolinensis* wintering in Britain & Ireland may be somewhat higher than published figures suggest.

Males desert incubating females to undertake a moult migration, forming large concentrations on the Russian breeding grounds, with small groups elsewhere (Salomonsen 1968). Some birds move long distances, *eg* from Karelia and the Ob catchment south to the Volga Delta (*BWP*). Moulting birds in the Netherlands may include northwest European breeders as well as some from further afield, including Poland (*BWP*).

Ogilvie (1983) found evidence of the effect of weather conditions on breeding Teal in northern Europe from a very detailed analysis of ring-recoveries. In drought years, poor breeding led to early movement away from the breeding areas, sometimes to the north or east, perhaps of birds still seeking suitable nesting conditions. Continued drought seemed to advance autumn migration, whatever the local effects on breeding

Fig 7. Seasonally accurate locations during (a) July (148), (b) September (1,646) and (c) November (1,449) of Teal using Britain & Ireland during the year.

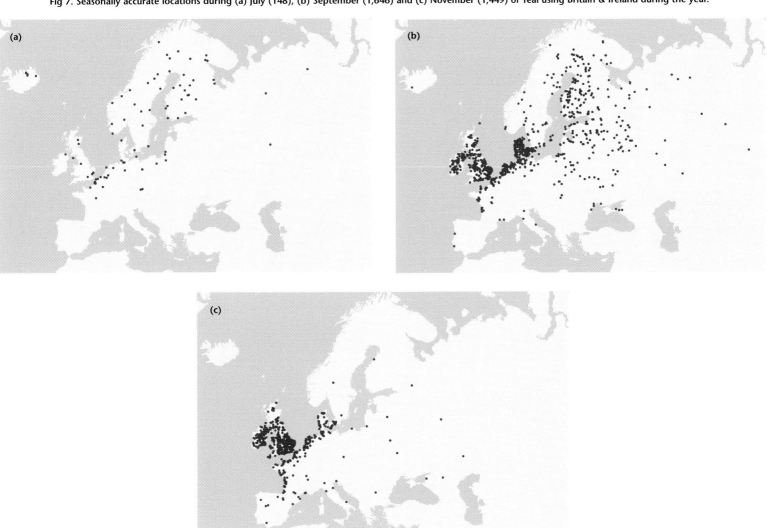

performance. Studies of breeding ducks in North America, of a kind not carried out in Europe, have shown a clear correlation between temperature and precipitation and the onset of nesting (*eg* Sowls 1955, Mendall 1958, Keith 1961).

The autumn migration of Teal is very prolonged, with birds, mainly males, already leaving the breeding grounds from late June, but some are still moving towards the wintering grounds in November (Fig 7). Ogilvie (1983) was able to correlate autumn dispersal with timing of arrival on the breeding grounds and with autumn weather. In general, cold summers led to an early departure from the breeding grounds, with birds heading southwest, even when conditions were wet. In fine summers, which in the majority of cases followed fine springs and an early arrival, there would be a later than average departure. In other words, an early start does not seem to be a reason for an early departure. Indeed the opposite seems to be true, with the birds remaining to exploit the still suitable conditions.

Once on the wintering grounds, Teal will remain unless freezing weather conditions affect their shallow water habitat. The most common cold-winter movement of wintering Teal from Britain & Ireland is south or southwest into France and, especially in the coldest spells, Iberia (Fig 8). Some sites in Spain and France are only important during hard weather (Ridgill & Fox 1990). Ogilvie (1983) found that in some years females clearly moved earlier than males but, if the cold continued, the males caught up. In other years, however, the males seemed to move as

soon as the females, and occasionally before. While the movements into Iberia correlated well with the coldest and most prolonged spells, the relative movement of the sexes did not. Although the main movement of British-ringed Teal in cold weather is south into continental Europe, as it is for Teal ringed in Denmark and the Netherlands, there are also displacements of particularly Dutch-ringed Teal westwards into Britain & Ireland. It seems that there are certain circumstances that send them west rather than south, though sometimes both happen. Similar movements, especially of males, appear to take place in prolonged dry spells (Ogilvie 1983). When the cold-weather movement took place in December or January, there was ample evidence from the recoveries of a quite rapid return to the normal wintering area. In the three most severe winters when February was especially cold (1954, 1956 and 1963), few if any birds returned north to Britain & Ireland and presumably set off from their cold-weather refuge direct to their breeding grounds (Ogilvie 1983).

There are insufficient recoveries of birds ringed in the breeding season and recovered in a subsequent breeding season from which to establish the pattern of abmigration. However, the between-winter movements (Fig 8b) suggest that a degree of abmigration does occur, with some individuals ringed in Britain & Ireland recovered in subsequent winters around the Black Sea and eastern Mediterranean. This change in wintering location strongly suggests a switch between breeding populations and is indicative of abmigration.

Fig 8. Movements of over 20 km and recovery locations of Teal ringed in winter and recovered in (a) the same winter (441:961, red) or (b) a subsequent winter (356:1,339, blue). Sample sizes of movements under:over 20 km are given but only those over 20 km are plotted.

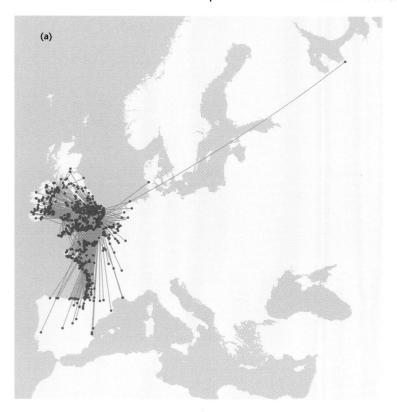

The spring return of Teal from Britain and Ireland to their northern European breeding grounds begins in late February and continues well into May. Ogilvie's (1983) analysis showed that the distribution of recoveries on the breeding grounds varied from year to year, the birds not always returning to the same areas each summer. The apparent cause of this variation was the weather conditions on the breeding grounds when the birds arrived. In some years, there were spring and summer recoveries from much further to the north and east in Scandinavia and Russia than normal. This could be correlated with spring weather in northern Europe that was drier and warmer than average. Conversely, in other years, when the weather was wetter and cooler, the main area of recoveries was concentrated further to the west and south.

Ogilvie (1983) concluded that the Teal shows a remarkable capacity for responding to local conditions, whether of drought, excessive rainfall or freezing, which involves them at times either in almost continual movement or, alternatively, the cessation of movement for months at a time, all carried out on a continental scale. The fluidity that this implies has considerable conservation implications. A wetland in Spain, for example, that might be used less than once a decade as a cold-weather refuge, has as great an importance to the population as one at which the birds winter in all other years (Ridgill & Fox 1990).

Little is known about the breeding and natal dispersal of Teal from the British and Irish breeding populations. Such information is only likely to come from targeted ringing of breeding birds but, as for other wildfowl species, this would be a difficult undertaking. Continued ringing of a more general nature, particularly of birds using Britain & Ireland during the winter, is important if the use of cold-weather refuges is to be monitored successfully.

Malcolm Ogilvie

Mallard
Anas platyrhynchos

Adaptability to a wide range of wetland habitats is a feature of this, one of the world's most common dabbling ducks. Mallard are encountered throughout the middle latitudes of northern Eurasia and North America from the Arctic tundra to the subtropical zone, on or by standing or flowing fresh water, brackish estuaries and lagoons or coasts where the saline water is shallow, fairly sheltered and within sight of land. Essentially the Mallard is a still- and shallow-water bird, usually limited to water depths of less than a metre for foraging.

With six million individuals in North America and 12 million in the Palearctic, this is the most abundant and widespread of northern hemisphere dabbling ducks (Delany *et al* 1999). Most northern breeding populations are migratory, and extensive ringing has demonstrated various flyways with overlapping wintering areas (Shevareva 1970, Scott & Rose 1996).

In north, east and central Europe, most Mallard migrate south and west for the winter. However, in temperate northwest Europe, including Britain & Ireland, Mallard are largely sedentary or dispersive. Here, the Mallard does not move long distances during cold weather, usually shifting to the nearest open water, especially at the coast, in severe winters (Ridgill & Fox 1990). The winter population in northwest Europe also contains immigrants drawn from a wider area. Most Icelandic breeders winter in Iceland, the remainder in Britain & Ireland. Those from northwest Russia, Fennoscandia, the Baltic States, northern Poland and Germany winter from Denmark to northern France, including Britain & Ireland (Scott & Rose 1996).

The Mallard was the principal catch of duck decoys for many centuries. Most of the 200 or more decoys built in Britain went out of use

The analysis of the data for this species was supported by David Harper

before 1900 but some were converted for ringing during the 1940s and 1950s and the last commercial decoy, at Nacton, Suffolk, became a ringing station in 1967. Mallard have also been caught in baited traps, mainly based on the design developed at Abberton Reservoir, Essex (Wainwright 1957). As with many wildfowl species, large-scale capture of Mallard in Britain & Ireland has largely been confined to professional ringing stations (Fig 1).

Most British & Irish duck ringing has been concentrated at a very few sites, mostly in southern England, introducing bias if the behaviour of southern English birds were different from those further north. When examining quantitative problems such as the proportion of immigrants in the winter stock, such problems are difficult to overcome. For instance, a higher proportion of birds ringed at Abberton were migrants than those marked at Borough Fen Decoy, Cambridgeshire, and Slimbridge, Gloucestershire (Boyd & Ogilvie 1961).

Most Mallard ringing within Britain & Ireland has been concentrated in the early autumn with 26% of birds later recovered being caught in September (Fig 2). Of these, 70% were juveniles and 29% were adults. However, over all months, 47% were ringed as juveniles and 48% as adults, the remainder being ringed as pulli. At Borough Fen Decoy between 1957 and 1967, 49% of the catch of over 17,000 Mallard was male (Ogilvie & Cook 1971), although the ring-recoveries show a slight bias towards males, which account for 60% of birds of known sex.

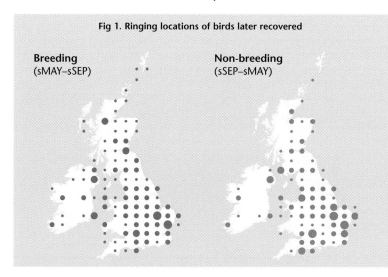

Fig 1. Ringing locations of birds later recovered

Breeding (sMAY–sSEP)   **Non-breeding** (sSEP–sMAY)

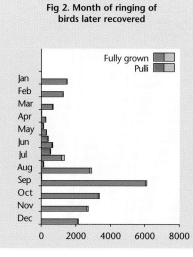

Fig 2. Month of ringing of birds later recovered

Fully grown / Pulli

Jan, Feb, Mar, Apr, May, Jun, Jul, Aug, Sep, Oct, Nov, Dec

0 2000 4000 6000 8000

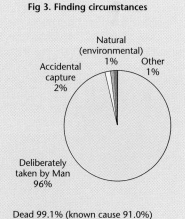

Fig 3. Finding circumstances

Natural (environmental) 1%   Other 1%
Accidental capture 2%
Deliberately taken by Man 96%

Dead 99.1% (known cause 91.0%)
Recaught <1%
Resighted <1%

Ringing and recovery data

	<1960	60–69	70–79	80–89	90–97	Total
RINGING						
BTO ringing totals (%)	18	30	23	19	9	158,583
RECOVERIES						
BTO-ringed (%)	17	34	29	15	6	23,951
Foreign-ringed (%)	26	29	36	7	2	743

Statistical analyses

	Breeding population (sMAY–sSEP)	Wintering population (sNOV–sMAR)
Status	SEDENTARY (0)	LONG-DISTANCE MIGRANT*
Age differences[S]	Significant*	Not significant
Sex differences[S]	Significant*	Significant
Regional differences	Significant[S]	Significant[4]*
Finding circumstances	Not significant	Significant

Fig 4. Recovery locations of 1,729 Mallard ringed during the breeding season in Britain & Ireland as pulli or juveniles and recovered before the end of January in the following year.

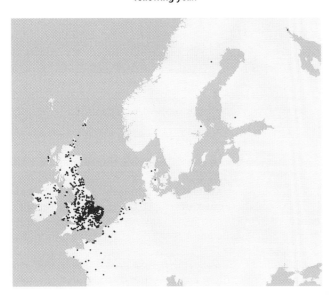

The majority (96%) of Mallard recoveries for which the finding circumstances were known had been shot (Fig 3); there is a high probability that such recoveries are reported. Shooting seasons vary from country to country and this largely determines the probability of recovery. On the other hand, Mallard dying from other causes are more likely to be reported from the well-populated areas of western Europe than the vast wildernesses of Scandinavia and Russia (Owen *et al* 1986). Annual survival rates for Mallard are low, with estimates of around 58% for adults and 32% for juveniles (Boyd 1962). Mortality rates are so high that after only a few years the great majority of the recoveries have been notified. Thus, 88% were notified within 4–5 years (Ogilvie & Cook 1971, 1972).

Of over 24,051 included ring-recoveries of Mallard ringed in Britain & Ireland, 82% were recovered within the two islands, 4% in the Netherlands and 3% in Denmark. Conversely, of 743 included ring-recoveries for Mallard ringed abroad and recovered in Britain or Ireland, 31% were ringed in Denmark, 18% in Belgium, 16% in the Netherlands and 13% in Sweden. These proportions are doubtless influenced strongly by ringing effort.

Britain supports an estimated 100–130,000 breeding pairs (Stone *et al* 1997) with an estimated further 23,000 pairs in Ireland (*1988–91 Atlas*). Recoveries of juveniles and adults caught in the breeding season, May–August, show little emigration after breeding. The median direct recovery distances, for birds presumed to have been ringed close to their hatching areas and recovered before February of the following year, of juvenile male and female Mallard were 13 km (P5–95=0–252 km, n=495) and 17 km (P5–95=0–200 km, n=727) respectively (Fig 4). Many of these young birds were somewhat sedentary: 56% of males and 63% of females were recovered less than 20 km from where they were ringed, about the maximum range of daily movements between roost sites and feeding areas (Bossenmaier & Marshall 1958). Some ventured further, with 29 being recovered in northern France (1.7% of direct recoveries) and 10 in the Netherlands (0.6%).

Adults ringed during the breeding season similarly showed little post-breeding dispersal. The median direct recovery distances of adult male and female Mallard which were presumed to have been ringed close to their breeding areas were 22 km (P5–95=0–430 km, n=465) and 12 km (P5–95=0–198 km, n=259) respectively (Fig 5). Some 47% of males and 67% of females were recovered less than 20 km from the ringing site. Slightly more adults than juveniles ventured further south during the autumn and winter months, with 1.7% (13) being recovered in northern France and 1.7% in the Netherlands. Local dispersal of breeding birds and ducklings appears to follow topographical features favourable to Mallard (Ogilvie & Cook 1972).

Considerable ringing has taken place in the autumn (September–November) at Abberton Reservoir. Within-winter movements longer than 20 km (before February) show dispersal to other areas in southern England and occasionally on to southern Ireland and a few to northern France (Fig 6). This sample includes many birds presumably of continental origin passing through Abberton to ultimate wintering destinations further south and west. The same pattern of turnover presumably occurs at other staging sites in southern and eastern Britain.

Abmigration, measured as the proportion of birds ringed during the breeding season in Britain & Ireland and recovered during a subsequent breeding season in continental Europe (Fig 7), was greater for males (n=87) than for females (n=57), 51% compared with 28% respectively, confirming the findings of Ogilvie & Cook (1971). In their study, the proportion of all males recovered in Denmark, Poland and Germany (75%) was significantly higher than for other areas (Ogilvie & Cook 1971).

The winter pattern of monthly WeBS counts indicates a gradual increase in numbers through the autumn, and this is confirmed by ring-

Fig 5. Recovery locations of (a) 465 male and (b) 259 female Mallard ringed in the breeding season in Britain & Ireland as adults and recovered before the end of January in the following year.

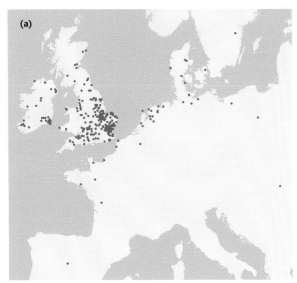

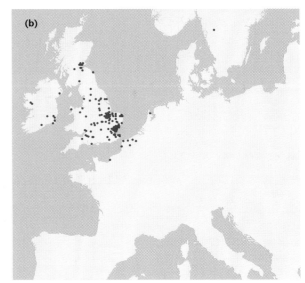

Fig 6. Recovery locations and movements of over 20 km of 183 Mallard ringed at Abberton Reservoir during September–November as adults and recovered before the end of January in the following year.

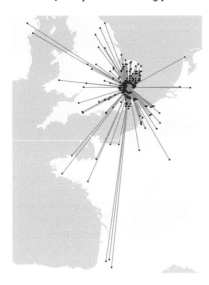

Fig 7. Locations abroad of 44 male and 16 female Mallard ringed during the breeding season in Britain & Ireland as adults and recovered abroad in a subsequent breeding season.

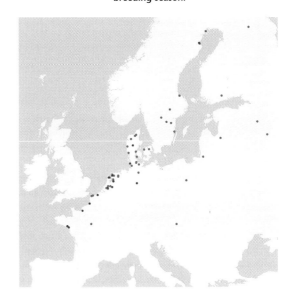

Fig 8. Locations abroad in the breeding season of 638 Mallard ringed in Britain & Ireland during winter.

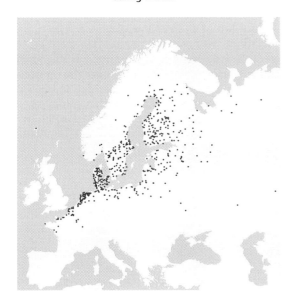

Fig 9. Pattern of temporal change in the percentage of Mallard ringed during winter in Britain & Ireland and recovered abroad during the breeding season, with the exclusion of those deliberately taken by Man.

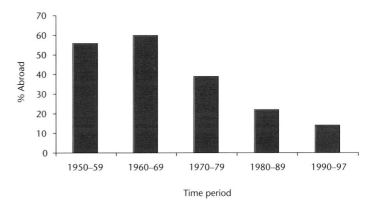

recoveries (Matthews 1963, Ogilvie & Cook 1971). Shooting takes a considerable toll of Mallard in autumn but this is thought to be more than compensated for by winter immigrants. Ring-recoveries suggest that up to three-quarters of winter birds in Britain & Ireland are immigrants, with 638 of the 863 birds ringed in Britain & Ireland in winter being recovered abroad during the breeding season. These birds come from a very wide area (Fig 8) including Fennoscandia, Russia, Poland, Denmark, Germany, the Netherlands, Belgium and France (Boyd & Ogilvie 1961, Ogilvie & Cook 1971, Mitchell *et al* 1990).

The northwest European population has been stable over the past 20 years (Rose 1995) and numbers wintering in the Mediterranean Basin appear to have doubled in the same period. Conversely, winter numbers in east-central Europe have fallen by 60% since the mid-1970s, and numbers in the Black Sea and east Mediterranean region have fallen by 75% since 1986 (Rose 1995). Very recently, Cranswick *et al* (1999) reported a 40% decline in the British wintering stock in the 10 years up to 1998. This decline in midwinter numbers may be partly due to a reduction in the contribution of non-native stock. For example, of Mallard ringed

during November to February, at a time when the winter stock consists of a mixture of local birds and continental immigrants, and recovered during the breeding season, the proportion recovered in continental Europe was above 50% in the 1950s and 1960s, whereas in the 1980s this had decreased to below 25% (Fig 9).

Any analysis of patterns of winter numbers and recovery patterns is complicated by the deliberate release of hand-reared birds, many of which are not marked. Boyd & Harrison (1962) showed that hand-reared birds are rather more sedentary than genuine wild birds and that releases result in bigger stock in the immediate vicinity. For quarry species such as Mallard, birds that are shot early in the season are, in effect, replaced by continental immigrants later in the winter. The overall numbers of Mallard change little through the winter season (WeBS data). The count data suggest a population of around half a million post-breeding birds in September and only a few more at peak in January. The 600,000 or so Mallard reported to be shot annually (Harradine 1985) is thus equivalent to the estimated peak population. However, an estimated 400,000 Mallard are said to be released by shooters annually (Harradine 1985), although many of these would be shot in early September, or stay on small release ponds where they would not be included in the WeBS data. It is, however, unsatisfactory that for such an important species as the Mallard, more accurate estimates of population size, turnover and the impact of shooting are not available.

Carl Mitchell, Roy King & Tony Cook

Northern Pintail (Pintail)

Anas acuta

The Pintail is an elegant dabbling duck with a holarctic distribution, breeding widely over northern temperate and arctic zones, extending further north than any other dabbling duck, and wintering south through the temperate zone to the tropics, almost reaching the Equator in Africa. There are no identifiable races.

Britain has a very small breeding population (a minimum of 11–51 pairs, Ogilvie *et al* 2000), and there is a handful of breeding records from Ireland (*1988–91 Atlas*). These birds are thought to be mainly sedentary, remaining within Britain & Ireland. Britain & Ireland is the winter quarters for birds from breeding areas further north and northwest, as well as lying on the western edge of a major flyway from northwest Siberia to subtropical West Africa involving a population of perhaps 1.25 million birds (Rose & Scott 1997). Around 28,000 birds winter in Britain (Kirby 1995), and a further 1–3,000 in Ireland (*Birds in Ireland*), out of a northwest European total of *c* 60,000 in midwinter. The breeding range continues eastwards through northern Russia and there are ill-defined boundaries of the European flyways with others. Populations totalling at least a further million birds take Pintail to wintering areas in East Africa, the Middle East, the Indian subcontinent, and in China and Japan. The North American population of at least two million birds probably winters exclusively within southern North America and Central America.

Pintail breed mainly on eutrophic lowland wetlands, which may be on coastlines, sheltered among forests and scrub or exposed on the open tundra. Larger open waters, both fresh and salt, are used for the summer moult. Wintering in Britain & Ireland principally takes place on sheltered estuaries, but the birds may also use nearby fresh waters, including floods,

The analysis of the data for this species was supported by Chris & Mike Evans

as well as feeding on farmland, *eg* corn stubbles. Elsewhere, wintering areas include extensive fresh waters, as in West Africa. Pintail show a clumped distribution in winter within northwest Europe, with large concentrations at a small number of sites and few elsewhere, a pattern not seen in North American or east Asian populations.

Pintail have been ringed in smaller numbers in Britain & Ireland than most other dabbling ducks, which more readily frequent the principal duck-trapping stations, nearly all of which are on freshwater wetlands. Very few Pintail have been ringed during the breeding season. Ringing carried out during the non-breeding season has been concentrated at just five localities in southern and southeastern England, one in northwest England and one each in northern and southeast Ireland (Figs 1 & 2), although this does reflect to a reasonable degree the winter distribution of the species (*Winter Atlas*).

Nearly two-thirds of all Pintail ringing took place during 1967–81, when the Wildfowl Trust operated Nacton Decoy on the Suffolk coast, which was consistently far more successful at catching Pintail than any other ringing station. The few good years since 1981 (just five years out of 16 exceeded ringing totals of 100) were due to one-off catches in swan traps at Slimbridge and at Martin Mere. However, even in the best period, the numbers being ringed can hardly be considered representative of the total wintering population. The ringing has been

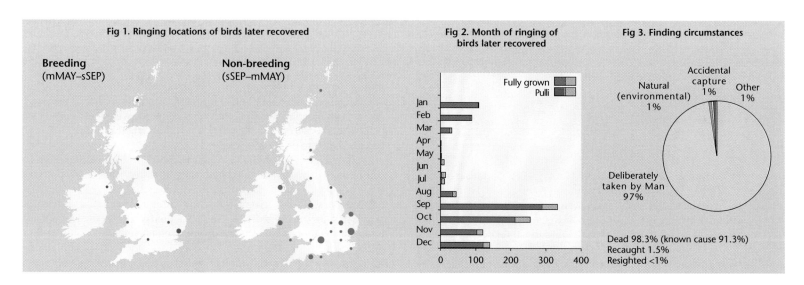

Fig 1. Ringing locations of birds later recovered

Breeding (mMAY–sSEP)

Non-breeding (sSEP–mMAY)

Fig 2. Month of ringing of birds later recovered

Fully grown
Pulli

Jan, Feb, Mar, Apr, May, Jun, Jul, Aug, Sep, Oct, Nov, Dec

0 100 200 300 400

Fig 3. Finding circumstances

Natural (environmental) 1%
Accidental capture 1%
Other 1%
Deliberately taken by Man 97%

Dead 98.3% (known cause 91.3%)
Recaught 1.5%
Resighted <1%

Ringing and recovery data

	<1960	60–69	70–79	80–89	90–97	Total
RINGING						
BTO ringing totals (%)	8	23	41	16	13	6,659
RECOVERIES						
BTO-ringed (%)	10	18	45	20	7	995
Foreign-ringed (%)	13	31	35	18	2	181

Statistical analyses

	Breeding population (mMAY–sSEP)	Wintering population (sDEC–mMAR)
Status	SEDENTARY*	LONG-DISTANCE MIGRANT
Age differences[NS]*	Not tested	Not significant*
Sex differences[NS]*	Not tested	Not significant*
Regional differences	Not tested	Not tested
Finding circumstances	Not tested*	Not tested*

Fig 4. Locations in the breeding season of 68 Pintail present in Britain & Ireland
during the winter. A recovery in North America is not shown

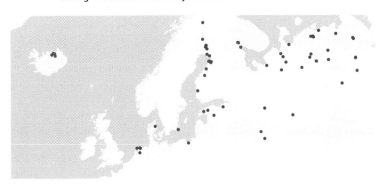

concentrated in the autumn and winter periods (Fig 2), which will have
sampled both the birds remaining to winter in Britain & Ireland and
those passing through on autumn migration. Very few birds on spring
passage will have been caught.

The Pintail is a quarry species throughout its range, which is reflected
not just in the overwhelming proportion of ring-recoveries deliberately
taken by Man (97% of those of known cause), virtually all of which will
have been shot, but also in the massive 91% of all ring-recoveries that
have a known cause (Fig 3). As with other quarry species, the distribution
of recoveries geographically, through the seasons, and between years,
will be greatly influenced by hunting pressure; caution must therefore be
exercised in interpreting recovery patterns.

There has been almost no ringing of Pintail of unarguably British or
Irish origin, and just eight pulli and juveniles ringed in June and July
have provided recoveries. Six of these were recovered within Britain &
Ireland and the remaining two overseas. With such a small sample it is
impossible to comment on whether Pintail breeding in Britain & Ireland
are sedentary or not.

The Pintail that winter in Britain & Ireland, or pass through on
migration, come from widely dispersed breeding grounds stretching
from Iceland eastwards through Fennoscandia and the Baltic States, with
the bulk of the recoveries from the Russian Federation north of 60°N and
east to about 80°E (Fig 4). Three individuals from the North American
breeding population have been recovered in Britain & Ireland — two
recovered in September and the other in January — indicating no more
than occasional transatlantic vagrancy and similar to the other North
American wildfowl.

Males leave the breeding grounds from late May onwards, once
the females have begun incubation, and many undertake extensive

movements to moulting sites where they may gather in large numbers.
Some of the known locations where moulting birds congregate include
the lower Ob River Basin and adjacent Yamal Peninsula in western
Siberia, Lakes Tengiz and Kurgaldzhino in Kazakhstan and the delta of
the Volga in Russia, much further south (BWP). Flocks of moulting males
on the IJsselmeer, the Netherlands, are also likely to have originated
from the Russian breeding grounds. Some males from breeding
populations in Scandinavia and Denmark typically undergo moult
within the breeding range, either in small parties or alone (Salomonsen
1968). The recoveries of birds in July and August on the Black and
Caspian Seas, as well as in the Netherlands as early as July, may indicate
moult migration (Fig 5a). There are also recoveries well to the south of
the breeding range in September (Fig 5b). With the completion of wing
moult, the males continue towards their wintering grounds; males pass
through Denmark from the end of August to the middle of September,
while the adult females and juveniles follow on somewhat later
(Salomonsen 1968). It is not known whether any males remain on the
breeding grounds with the females, nor is it known where the Icelandic
breeders moult and when they arrive in Britain & Ireland. Two Icelandic-
ringed Pintails have been recovered in Britain & Ireland during October,
both during the year in which they were ringed: one was an adult male,
the other an unsexed individual ringed as a pullus.

WeBS data show a double peak in the monthly indices (October and
December), which only occurs in some years, notably the late 1980s
and early 1990s. Cranswick et al (1999) suggest that this results from
differences in the timing of movements of different subpopulations and
their relative occurrence in Britain & Ireland, with the possibility that
Icelandic birds may arrive early in winter and disperse, to be followed by
the arrival of continental birds pushed further west by suitable weather
conditions. By September–October only stragglers are left far to the east,
while the bulk of the population has arrived in northwest Europe with
small numbers moving on south to the Mediterranean, though some of
these may have flown there directly from their moulting area (Fig 5b). It
can be assumed that the males arrive ahead of the females, as is common
for many species of ducks (Salomonsen 1968), but there are insufficient
recoveries for the sort of detailed breakdown that might confirm this.
Those Pintail passing through Britain & Ireland appear to move to
wintering areas around the Mediterranean and into West Africa (Fig 6).
It is interesting that the pattern of winter recoveries does not follow the
south-southwest pattern of most other dabbling duck species dispersing
from Britain & Ireland. However, there are insufficient ring-recoveries
with which to examine this in more detail.

The majority of winter recoveries occur within Britain & Ireland,
with just small numbers further south. Some of these reach beyond the

Fig 5. Locations of Pintail in (a) July & August (94) and (b) September & October (340). Two individuals in North America are not shown.

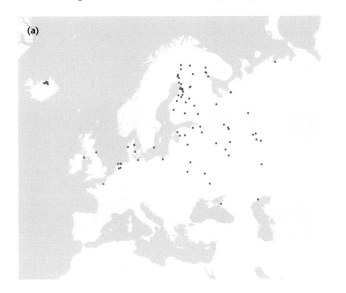
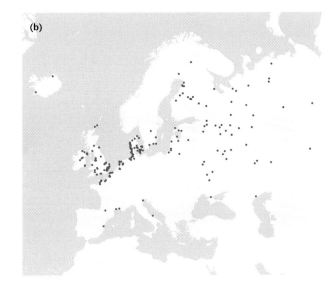

been documented, with movements from Danish, German and Dutch coasts, seemingly to Britain & Ireland, northern France and Iberia (*BWP*, Ridgill & Fox 1990), although there is an apparent reluctance to move further south across the Sahara to the main West African wintering grounds (Scott & Rose 1996). The ring-recovery data, for birds found dead only, support a degree of within-winter movement, with a median of 42 km (P5–95=0–626 km, *n*=42). As would be expected, this is considerably less than the value for between-winter movements of 304 km (P5–95=0–877 km, *n*=94).

The spring return takes place early in the year with birds departing from North and West Africa during February and March. WeBS data suggest that departures of winter birds and spring passage through Britain & Ireland are completed by April and by this time the first recoveries appear in Russia. The picture is biased, however, by the ending of all shooting seasons in western Europe during February and March. Spring passage may involve some degree of overland movement, as revealed by inland recoveries during spring and an absence during autumn, and this may lend support to the suggested loop migration (*BWP*). However, only a small number of recoveries are involved and the pattern of shooting effort may have an influence.

The Pintail has an 'unfavourable conservation status' in Europe, reflecting declines on many of the breeding and wintering grounds. These declines prompted a reduction in the 1% threshold for international importance within northwest Europe during the last review (Rose & Scott 1997), together with a review of population trends within Britain (Kershaw 1998). The declines are thought to be a result of the loss of suitable wetland habitat across the breeding and wintering range, particularly evident in the Mediterranean region. Locally, the over-exploitation of hunted stocks may also be a significant threat (Tucker & Heath 1994). In addition to the conservation management of breeding areas, the maintenance of key sites for wintering populations has been highlighted as being essential for the successful conservation of this species. Ring-recovery data could provide an important tool by which Pintail populations and their extensive movements could be followed. This still requires further developments to address some of the unknowns, however, such as refining the routes of flyways and establishing the degree of interchange between populations, as well as controlling for the effects of recovery biases associated with the spatial and temporal patterns in hunting pressure. Additional ring-recovery data are needed to examine the pattern of winter movements of Pintail using Britain & Ireland earlier in the year, particularly in comparison with other dabbling duck species.

Malcolm Ogilvie

Mediterranean towards the major wintering area in West Africa, especially Senegal and east through Nigeria as far as Chad. Not surprisingly, the handful of recoveries from this region does not reflect the size of the wintering population there, which numbers hundreds of thousands (Brown *et al* 1982). There are no apparent differences in winter recovery patterns related to either age or sex of the birds but sample sizes are small. Marked fluctuations in the numbers of birds occurring in the main wintering areas suggest a degree of interchange between the sites (Scott & Rose 1996). Cold-weather movements have

Garganey
Anas querquedula

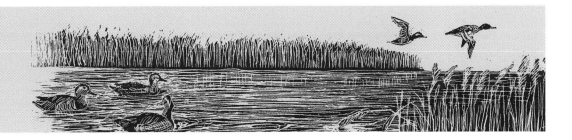

The Garganey has the distinction of being the only wildfowl species that is a summer visitor to Britain & Ireland. The breeding range spans the Palearctic from Britain and France eastward to Sakhalin Island and Kamchatka (*BWP*). The vast majority of West Palearctic breeders winter in the northern tropics just to the south of the Sahara, with only small numbers in the Mediterranean Basin (*BWP*). In Senegal and the Gambia, the Garganey is by far the most common Palearctic duck in winter, with up to 93,000 birds recorded in some years (*BWP*). There are two main migratory routes followed by European breeding populations in autumn. British breeders, along with those in the Netherlands, France and western Germany, tend to follow a southerly route across the Mediterranean to Morocco and Algeria, or southeast to Italy and the Balkans, then probably direct across the Sahara (*BWP*). Populations breeding further east in Europe, and some from northern Russia east of the Urals, tend to migrate southwest to southern France and Italy, on their way to Africa. Other Asian birds winter in West or East Africa, or in southern Asia from eastern Iran, to Sri Lanka, Thailand and Hong Kong (*BWP*).

In Britain & Ireland, Garganey are found breeding mainly in central and southeastern England, notably in East Anglia, Lincolnshire and Essex. The current breeding population is estimated at between 15 and 125 pairs (Stone *et al* 1997). Larger numbers occur in some years, when birds can be found as far north as Scotland and Yorkshire and west into Wales and Ireland, where breeding attempts are less than annual (*Birds in Ireland*). The Garganey is rarely found in estuarine

The analysis of the data for this species was supported by Moss Taylor

habitats, preferring narrow or fragmented and sheltered areas of fresh water with plenty of edge vegetation. In its winter quarters it can be found in river floodplains and other shallow, lowland waters, including coastal lagoons.

The distribution of the ringing sites of birds that have been recovered does not adequately reflect the localized and scattered breeding distribution in Britain; in particular the main breeding stronghold, the Ouse Washes, is not represented (Fig 1). Up to 1997, 475 birds had been ringed, and 16% subsequently recovered. The majority of birds ringed in Britain & Ireland and subsequently recovered were ringed as juveniles (39%) and adults (18%) between July and September (Fig 2). Only 8% have been ringed as pulli. The majority of recoveries for this species were made during the period 1950–79, with very few birds recovered subsequently. This may be a reflection of hunting pressure but is also linked with the numbers of birds ringed during this period. There has been a major decline in the numbers of Garganey ringed in Britain since the 1970s: a total of 334 birds ringed by 1970 represents 70% of the grand total up to 1997. Most of the ringing has taken place at Slimbridge, Gloucestershire, Abberton Reservoir, Essex, Borough Fen Decoy, Cambridgeshire, and Deeping Lake, Lincolnshire. There have been 14 recoveries of foreign-ringed Garganey to date, 10 of these from

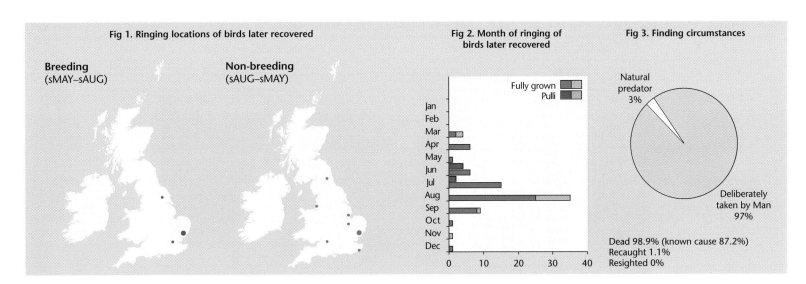

Fig 1. Ringing locations of birds later recovered

Breeding (sMAY–sAUG)   **Non-breeding** (sAUG–sMAY)

Fig 2. Month of ringing of birds later recovered

Fully grown / Pulli

Fig 3. Finding circumstances

Natural predator 3%
Deliberately taken by Man 97%

Dead 98.9% (known cause 87.2%)
Recaught 1.1%
Resighted 0%

Ringing and recovery data

	<1960	60–69	70–79	80–89	90–97	Total
RINGING						
BTO ringing totals (%)	28	41	19	7	6	475
RECOVERIES						
BTO-ringed (%)	22	45	22	4	7	73
Foreign-ringed (%)	79	21	0	0	0	14

Statistical analyses

	Breeding population (sMAY–sAUG)	Wintering population (sNOV–sMAR)
Status	[LONG-DISTANCE MIGRANT]	[LONG-DISTANCE MIGRANT]
Age differences	Not tested	Not tested
Sex differences	Not tested	Not tested
Regional differences	Not tested	Not tested
Finding circumstances	Not tested	Not tested

Fig 4. Recovery locations and movements of over 20 km of Garganey present in Britain & Ireland during (a) autumn (32), (b) winter (8) and (c) spring (10).

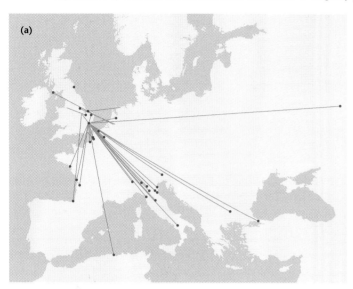

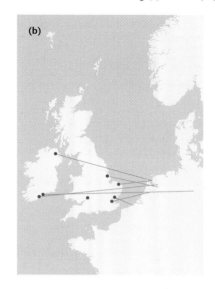

the Netherlands, and all during the period 1930–69. The finding circumstances are known for 87% of the ring-recoveries, and 97% of these were of the category 'deliberately taken by Man' (Fig 3). There are biases in the ring-recovery data due to spatial variation in hunting pressure, with southern European countries, notably France (29%) and Italy (29%) accounting for the majority of ring-recoveries reported as being deliberately taken. There are a small number of ring-recoveries from elsewhere, including two each in Russia and Algeria and singles in Kazakhstan and Mali; these are also attributed to Man.

Most recoveries of birds were made during the spring and autumn migrations. Autumn migration begins in July, with a large peak in observations in August, and stragglers extend the passage into November

(Owen *et al* 1986). Occasional birds winter in Britain; there were winter records at 10 sites in 1997/98, a mild winter (Cranswick *et al* 1999). There is evidence of immigration of Garganey during autumn and winter into Britain & Ireland. Of the 14 recoveries of foreign-ringed birds, 10 were recovered in winter in Britain & Ireland (Fig 4). In Britain & Ireland most adult Garganey are ringed in July and August; whether these birds constitute successful breeders within the country or passage migrants from the Continent is uncertain. Of the few known adults ringed during the breeding season, only one has been recovered in the same county during the same season and year.

Adult and immature birds ringed outside the breeding season show similar movements within the same season, generally moving

Fig 5. Recovery locations and movements of over 20 km of Garganey ringed in the breeding season in Britain or Ireland as adult (red, 6:5) or as pullus or immature (blue, 5:8). Those recovered before the start of the following breeding season (circles) are differentiated from those recovered after the start of the following breeding season (squares). Sample sizes of the classes (before:after the start of the following breeding season) are shown.

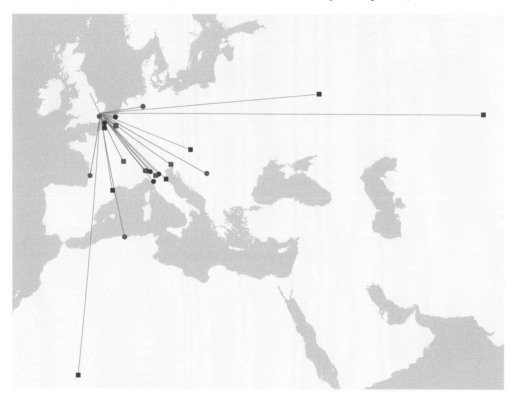

south-east across Europe. There is also no major difference in movements between the sexes, although there is evidence of moult gatherings of males from late May onwards, when the birds are flightless for several weeks; the Volga Delta in the north Caspian is the main known staging area (*BWP*). Onward migration of these birds to the winter quarters takes place from late July through to October.

Spring migration begins in February, peaking in March, and most adults return to their breeding grounds during April. Recoveries peak in March in France and Italy, highlighting the passage through the western Mediterranean. There is some evidence of loop migration taking place with return flights from West and East Africa tending to be via Italy and the Balkans.

There are insufficient ring-recovery data with which to fully investigate breeding site-fidelity and the degree of abmigration. However, two adults ringed in southeast Britain in the breeding season have been recovered in a subsequent breeding season in France, and birds ringed as pulli or juveniles in Britain have been recovered in subsequent breeding seasons in Italy and as far east as Russia (Fig 5). Birds ringed in Britain & Ireland in the breeding season have been recovered as far east as the Russian Federation or south to Morocco in autumn, and further east to Kazakhstan in spring. There is therefore evidence of an intermixing of passage and wintering populations of Garganey across Europe.

Although not globally threatened, Garganey have shown evidence of a decrease not only in Britain but also within central Russia between 1972 and 1989 (Scott & Rose 1996). The recovery circumstances highlight the pressure from spring and autumn hunting across the Mediterranean, although the overall effect of this hunting pressure on the population in western Europe is unclear. There is an ongoing threat of land drainage in the northern tropics, where large-scale irrigation and river diversion projects could lead to a loss of wintering habitat (Scott & Rose 1996). In contrast, most remaining Garganey breeding sites in Britain are on nature reserves, where drainage poses less of a threat. There is also the threat of drought in the winter quarters and general climatic changes, which may have an effect on the numbers of birds surviving to breed the following summer.

There is obviously a need to increase the ringing of this species in the form of long-term ringing and recapture studies at the main breeding sites in Europe. There are very few retrap data and the actual numbers of birds ringed in Britain & Ireland have decreased markedly in the last 20 years, with no new birds ringed in 1995 and only five in 1997 (Appleton *et al* 1997, Toms *et al* 1999). This is most likely a result of the decline in large-scale duck ringing operations but may also reflect a general decline in numbers visiting Britain & Ireland during the summer months. Being such an elusive species, the location and confirmation of breeding is often difficult. These facts alone make the practicalities of increasing ringing effort for Garganey, compared with other species, difficult.

During late summer and autumn there tends to be a general influx of Garganey into areas of Britain & Ireland where breeding is unlikely to have occurred (J H Marchant pers comm). Targeting ringing in these areas may assist in identifying the origin of such birds. However, in practice, the value of such ringing is limited due to the overall mobility of the species and the evidence of abmigration, which would lessen the chances of obtaining retrap data. It would also depend to a certain extent on the level of ringing of this species in other European countries. Increasing ringing effort in the known breeding strongholds, such as the Ouse Washes, may assist in assessing the productivity of Britain as a breeding area for this species. There is also a need for more expedition ringing within the key wintering quarters in parts of Africa and also southwest Asia, where no ringing studies have yet been undertaken (Scott & Rose 1996).

Bridget Griffin

Northern Shoveler
(Shoveler)
Anas clypeata

The analysis of the data for this species was supported by the Rye Bay Ringing Group and the Wetland Trust

The specialized bill and feeding ecology of the Shoveler means that it favours wetlands with abundant zooplankton; such habitats tend to be ephemeral, where other plankton-feeders, such as fish, cannot survive year-round. Shoveler tend to be most abundant, therefore, in highly productive waters that dry out in summer. Perhaps as a consequence, throughout its distribution in the northern hemisphere, the species has a more southerly distribution than most other dabbling duck species (*BWP*). The Shoveler can have a dramatic impact upon the Cladoceran and Ostracod prey it exploits in late summer and autumn respectively, removing significant portions of these populations (Pirot & Pont 1987), such that regular onward movement to more distant wintering areas is inevitable. At the same time, the Shoveler can consume up to 10% of its body weight per day, despite the small size of its prey, enabling the establishment of extensive fat reserves (Pirot & Pont 1987). Hence, it is not surprising that the species tends to be highly migratory throughout its range. In the Western Palearctic, the largest numbers winter in the Black Sea, Mediterranean Basin and Sahelian Africa, with comparatively few in northwest Europe (Scott & Rose 1996). In North America, it is most common as a breeding bird in the mixed prairie lands of Canada and the Dakotas, wintering from California southwards into Mexico, Central America and the West Indies (Bellrose 1980).

Britain supports over a thousand breeding pairs, concentrated in the south and east, and there are about a hundred pairs in Ireland (*1988–91 Atlas*). In autumn and winter, some 10,000 Shoveler occur in Britain, 2% of the estimated population in the Western Palearctic. Peak counts occur in Britain in October, when birds from northwest continental Europe, eastern Fennoscandia, the Baltic States and western Russia supplement local breeders; subsequently, both local breeders and immigrants move on into France, Spain and the Mediterranean for the winter (Kirby & Mitchell 1993). Breeding birds from central and southeastern Europe are considered to winter in the Mediterranean Basin where they mix with birds from further east in Russia (Dement'ev & Gladkov 1967, *BWP*).

As with most wildfowl species, large-scale capture of Shoveler has largely been confined to sites with professional ringing operations. The ringing effort during the breeding season has been very much concentrated at Abberton Reservoir, Essex, where a WWT ringing station was operative for many years (Fig 1). Outside the breeding season, ring-recoveries originate mostly from birds caught at the WWT centre at Slimbridge, although the Trust's ringing stations at Abberton Reservoir and Borough Fen Decoy near Peterborough also contributed significant numbers to the totals. Greatest numbers of Shoveler were captured in July–September, with smaller numbers spread evenly throughout the rest of the year (Fig 2). The vast majority of Shoveler recoveries were from birds killed by hunters (Fig 3) and care must be taken, therefore, in interpreting the patterns of recoveries, since these are biased by patterns of hunting activity.

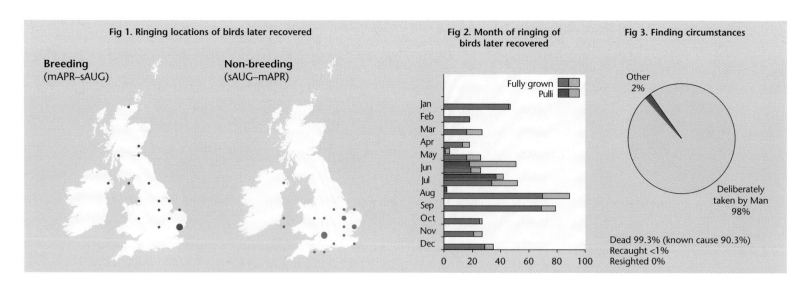

Fig 1. Ringing locations of birds later recovered

Breeding (mAPR–sAUG)

Non-breeding (sAUG–mAPR)

Fig 2. Month of ringing of birds later recovered

Fully grown
Pulli

Fig 3. Finding circumstances

Other 2%

Deliberately taken by Man 98%

Dead 99.3% (known cause 90.3%)
Recaught <1%
Resighted 0%

Ringing and recovery data

	<1960	60–69	70–79	80–89	90–97	Total
RINGING						
BTO ringing totals (%)	17	22	29	21	11	2,784
RECOVERIES						
BTO-ringed (%)	22	30	22	20	6	451
Foreign-ringed (%)	17	43	25	7	8	138

Statistical analyses

	Breeding population (mAPR–sAUG)	Wintering population (sDEC–sMAR)
Status	LONG-DISTANCE MIGRANT* (3)	LONG-DISTANCE MIGRANT*
Age differences[NS]*	Not significant*	Not tested
Sex differences	Not tested	Not tested
Regional differences	Not tested	Not tested
Finding circumstances	Not tested*	Not tested*

Fig 4. Recovery locations of Shoveler ringed in the breeding season in Britain or Ireland as adult (red) or as pullus or immature (blue) and recovered (a) before the start of the following breeding season (18:47) or (b) after the start of the following breeding season (19:23). Sample sizes of the age classes (adult:pullus or immature) are given.

Fig 5. Locations in the breeding season of 101 Shoveler present in Britain & Ireland outside the breeding season.

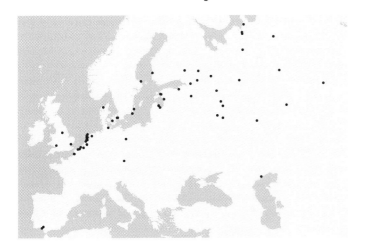

On limited evidence, British & Irish Shoveler generally do not disperse away from natal sites immediately after fledging. The median dispersal distance for birds ringed as pulli was 56 km ($P5$–95=0–874, n=11) in the third month after ringing. This pattern supports the idea that the peak counts in autumn comprise locally bred birds supplemented by migrants from the Continent. Birds ringed as pulli or immature birds in Britain & Ireland (n=47), or as adults during the breeding season (n=18) and recovered before the subsequent breeding season, show wide dispersion (Fig 4a). Most were recovered along the North Sea coast (Denmark, Germany, the Netherlands and France) with smaller numbers from the Mediterranean and North Africa. Generally, however, British-ringed Shoveler captured from mid-April to late July predominantly move to north and west France, the Iberian Peninsula and North Africa, due south of their natal or breeding area, which is presumably the main wintering region for this stock. Two birds caught in the breeding season in eastern Britain were recovered in Ireland in subsequent winters, however, and Kirby & Mitchell (1993) also suggested that small numbers of winter recoveries in Britain & Ireland hint at some birds being resident. What is clearer is that some British summer-ringed Shoveler do not return to Britain to breed (Fig 4b). There were five indirect recoveries from Russia, two males, a female and two unsexed birds; of these two were shot in April, the other three during the breeding season.

The winter locations of Shoveler using Britain & Ireland during autumn confirm Britain, Ireland, France, the Iberian Peninsula and North Africa as the winter quarters of these ducks, although there are also two records in Italy. Spring recoveries of Shoveler using Britain & Ireland throughout the year suggest that birds return through northwestern France on their pre-nuptial migration.

Ring-recoveries show that Shoveler using Britain outside the breeding season originate from breeding populations scattered across northern Europe from France through the Baltic to Russia (Fig 5). Immigrants to Ireland have a similar origin and, in addition, a single recovery links Ireland to Iceland where there is a very small breeding population. Shovelers ringed elsewhere in May and June and recovered in Britain & Ireland (n=48) and those ringed in autumn or winter and recovered during the breeding season overseas (n=12) mostly come from a narrow latitudinal band between 50°N and 65°N, stretching across Europe and central Asia to about 60°E. Exactly half of the 24 Shoveler caught in winter in Britain & Ireland and recovered in subsequent winters come from the same countries, with the rest from western continental coasts, suggesting relatively high winter fidelity to these islands. Only two birds have been recovered from the Mediterranean Basin, where so many Shoveler ringed in Britain & Ireland in other seasons have been recovered.

During periods of severe weather, the shallow waters, which are the typical habitat of Shoveler, are amongst the first to freeze. Hence, the species often shows large-scale movements out of Britain (and other North Sea coasts) with the onset of sub-zero temperatures as in early 1987 (Salmon 1987). There is good evidence from the International Waterbird Census that movements of Shoveler out of Britain, the Netherlands and north and west France in severe weather correlate with increases in Spain and Portugal (Ridgill & Fox 1990). However, for Shoveler ringed throughout northern Europe, the same authors could find no significant differences between recovery distances for birds recovered during cold weather periods compared to those recovered in mild periods in adjacent years, nor any overall significant increases in numbers of recoveries for this species. Hence it may well be that the Shoveler, despite its preference for shallow water habitats, has evolved a migration strategy that in most winters ensures it is rarely present in those wetlands subject to severe weather at critical times of the winter cycle.

A D (Tony) Fox

Common Pochard (Pochard)
Aythya ferina

The Pochard became established as a breeding species in Britain & Ireland during the early 19th century, although it has expanded slowly and the estimated breeding population is only 400 pairs, restricted mainly to the east of England and eastern Scotland (*1988–91 Atlas*). There is, however, an estimated wintering population of 83,700 birds, representing 24% of the northwest European population, and occurring in 47% of 10-km squares in Britain & Ireland (*Winter Atlas*, Kirby 1995, Cranswick *et al* 1999). Numbers of Pochard wintering in Britain doubled between 1948/51 and 1960/62 and continued to increase into the early 1970s in line with numbers in northwest Europe (Fox & Salmon 1988). Numbers declined slightly in the late 1970s but have stabilized since then (Kershaw *et al* 1998). Much of the increase in wintering numbers has been attributed to the creation of man-made habitats such as gravel-pits and reservoirs as well as sympathetic management of floodlands (Fox & Salmon 1988).

The breeding range is wide, spanning temperate latitudes across Eurasia to southeastern Russia and northeastern China, mainly between 45°N and 60°N (Scott & Rose 1996). The species formerly bred in North Africa, and is an irregular breeding bird in Iceland. Although the Pochard is monotypic, three subpopulations have been recognized based on their wintering areas in northwest Europe, Black Sea/ Mediterranean and southwest Asia (Monval & Pirot 1989, Scott & Rose 1996).

Pochard are predominantly migratory. Northern and eastern populations are highly so, wintering as far south as West Africa, the

The analysis of the data for this species was supported by Cicely and John Port

Arabian Peninsula and occasionally the Equator in East Africa (Scott & Rose 1996). In contrast, they are present throughout the year on breeding areas in temperate regions of western and southern Europe. The breeding populations of Denmark, Fennoscandia, north Germany, Poland, the Baltic States and northwest Russia, north of about 50°N and east to about 76°E, migrate west and south to winter in western Germany, Switzerland, the Netherlands, Britain, Ireland, France, Iberia, and northwest Africa (Boyd 1959b, *BWP*, Fox & Salmon 1988). Birds wintering in the Black Sea/Mediterranean region come from southern and central Europe, southern Russia, and Kazakhstan and other central Asian republics (*BWP*, Monval & Pirot 1989, Scott & Rose 1996). Birds wintering in southwest Asia probably originate mainly from the central Asian republics and western and central Siberia. Not all individuals follow the expected pattern, however, and there is some exchange of birds between the different groups (*BWP*).

Moult migration has been observed in some populations of Pochard (Salomonsen 1968). Moult gatherings of males are frequent in western Europe, sometimes involving considerable numbers. For example, up to 20,000 have been recorded at Ismaninger Reservoir, Bavaria, and up to 50,000 at the IJsselmeer in the Netherlands (Salomonsen 1968, *BWP*). Further east, many sites carry relatively small numbers of moulting

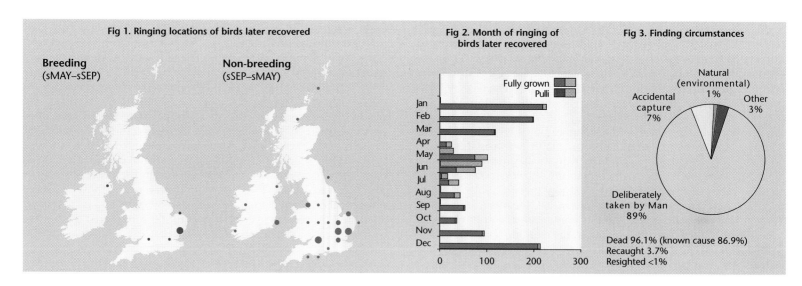

Ringing and recovery data

	<1960	60–69	70–79	80–89	90–97	Total
RINGING						
BTO ringing totals (%)	1	2	14	43	39	14,066
RECOVERIES						
BTO-ringed (%)	3	5	14	54	24	1,093
Foreign-ringed (%)	3	15	31	34	17	271

Statistical analyses

	Breeding population (sMAY–sSEP)	Wintering population (sDEC–sMAR)
Status	SHORT-DISTANCE MIGRANT* (2)	LONG-DISTANCE MIGRANT*
Age differences[NT]	Not tested	Not significant*
Sex differences[NS]	Significant*	Significant
Regional differences	Not tested	Not significant[2]
Finding circumstances	Not tested*	Not tested*

Fig 4. Locations in winter and movements of over 20 km between the breeding season and winter of 63 adult Pochard present in Britain & Ireland during the breeding season.

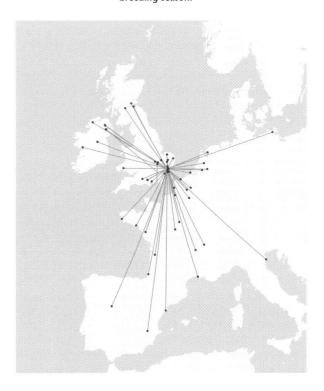

Fig 5. Locations in the breeding season of 232 adult Pochard present in Britain & Ireland outside the breeding season.

males and birds may moult on or close to their breeding grounds (*BWP, European Atlas*).

The Pochard is basically a steppe-dweller, stopping short of tundra and inhabiting taiga and boreal forest zones only thinly (Fox & Salmon 1988, *CBWP*). It favours nutrient-rich waters less than 6 m deep, including well-vegetated marshes, swamps, lakes and slow-flowing rivers with areas of open water. In winter, the species occurs mostly on larger lakes and reservoirs. Fresh water is preferred at all seasons, although birds will move to coastal and inshore maritime habitats, for example in cold weather, and will even breed in sheltered marine bays (Olney 1968, *BWP*, Phillips 1991, Scott & Rose 1996, *CBWP*).

Recoveries from ringing in the breeding season in Britain & Ireland have come from birds caught in Northern Ireland, North Norfolk, the London area and Gloucestershire (Fig 1). This is a poor reflection of the breeding distribution of Pochard in Britain & Ireland, and indeed many birds may have been moult-migrants rather than part of the local breeding population. The distribution of non-breeding season ringing in Britain & Ireland is slightly more extensive, although concentrated in the southeast of England at Abberton Reservoir, Essex, Blunham, Bedfordshire, and at Slimbridge, Gloucestershire (Fig 1).

Most Pochard (76%) ringed in Britain & Ireland have been ringed between November and March (Fig 2). Only 15% of birds have been ringed during the breeding season (May–August) and hardly any birds have been ringed as pulli. Of birds ringed abroad and recovered in Britain & Ireland, the majority have been ringed during the breeding season (86%), with 49% ringed as pulli (Fig 2).

The vast majority of Pochard recoveries (96%) are of dead birds. Of the 87% of recoveries where the cause of death is known, 89% have been deliberately taken by Man, almost all shot by hunters (Fig 3). The geographical pattern of recoveries will therefore depend to a large extent on the distribution of hunting pressure and reporting rates. More than half of the recoveries of Pochard ringed in Britain & Ireland have come from overseas, mainly France (13%), the Russian Federation (13%; 8% in Europe and 5% in Asia), Poland, the Netherlands, Germany and the Ukraine.

Of birds ringed abroad and recovered in Britain & Ireland, almost two-thirds (62%) had been ringed in Latvia. The percentage of British & Irish recoveries of Latvian-ringed birds increased from 19% in the 1960s to 81% in the 1990s while that of Danish-ringed birds decreased from 29% to 6% over the same period. While it is not possible to control for the effect of temporal variation in ringing and recovery patterns, there is evidence for an increase in Pochard numbers in Latvia due to protection (*BWP*). Smaller numbers had been ringed in the Czech Republic, Switzerland, Germany, the Netherlands, Lithuania, the Russian Federation, Poland, Finland, France, Estonia and Spain.

There is very little information on the movements of British & Irish breeding Pochard as few known breeders or young have been ringed. Pochard may undertake a moult migration to Britain & Ireland during June and July (Salomonsen 1968). Generally, therefore, it is not known whether fully grown birds caught in late summer are local breeders or continental immigrants. Many British breeders appear to remain within Britain & Ireland during the winter, although few are resident on the breeding waters (*BWP*, Fox & Salmon 1988). There is also evidence that some birds move further south and west to winter in France and Spain (*BWP*, Fox & Salmon 1988). Ringing data suggest that Pochard present in Britain & Ireland during the breeding season winter predominantly in Britain, Ireland, France and the Netherlands with a few travelling as far as Spain (Fig 4). In autumn, there is some movement of birds from southeast England to sites in south and southwest England, Ireland and southeast Scotland, as well as to northeast France and the Netherlands, with a few birds moving to western France, Spain, Germany and Denmark. The median recovery distance for all movements of birds using Britain & Ireland during the breeding season was slightly higher for females (350 km) than for males (297 km) and females were recovered significantly further west than males during the winter.

As very few pulli are ringed in Britain & Ireland, there is little information on post-fledging and natal dispersal. Of six birds ringed as pulli or immatures in Britain & Ireland during the breeding season and recovered before the following breeding season, two were recovered in Ireland, one in northeast France, one in southeast France, one in Morocco and one in the Ukraine.

Although sample sizes are small, adult birds ringed in Britain & Ireland during the breeding season have been recovered in subsequent breeding seasons as far as 65°E in the Russian Federation as well as in Finland, Estonia, the Netherlands, Poland, Belarus and Britain. Whether this indicates an exchange of birds between different breeding areas is not clear, and more ringing data for known British & Irish breeders are required.

Fig 6. Movements of over 20 km and recovery locations of Pochard ringed in winter and recovered in a subsequent winter. There were 29:128 movements under:over 20 km but only those over 20 km are plotted.

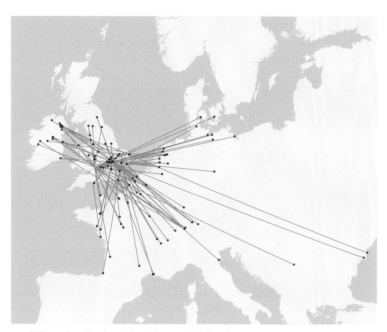

Fig 6. Movements of over 20 km and recovery locations of Pochard ringed in winter and recovered in a subsequent winter. There were 29:128 movements under:over 20 km but only those over 20 km are plotted.

Wintering Pochard in Britain & Ireland come mainly from the Baltic countries and the former USSR east to at least 61°E, although there have been recoveries of British-ringed birds from beyond 76°E (Boyd 1959b, Fox & Salmon 1988) (Fig 5). Generally males begin to arrive on moulting sites in early June, numbers peak in mid-July and birds disperse in late August and September (*BWP*). In 1966, 1,500 birds arrived at Loch Leven in late July, whereas in other years the summer influx has not exceeded 200 birds (*Birds in Scotland*). Summer influxes of 2–3,000 birds also occur at Abberton in July and August, although again numbers can be irregular (Salmon 1981). Moulting birds ringed at Abberton have been recovered during the breeding season in the former USSR (especially Latvia), Germany, Denmark, Poland and the Netherlands and Belgium, and in the winter season in Britain, Ireland, France and Spain (Fox & Salmon 1988). There has been a general decline in the use of southeast England by moulting birds in September since the mid-1970s and an increase in the southwest, especially at Cotswold Water Park (Owen *et al* 1986, Fox & Salmon 1988). Moulting flocks have also been recorded in Orkney (Fox & Salmon 1988). In Ireland, flocks of several thousand mainly male Pochard on Loughs Corrib, Cullin and Derravaragh in late summer have been assumed to be moulting birds (*Birds in Ireland*). Some females may also join the moulting males, particularly during August (Salomonsen 1968).

Most birds move westwards from the breeding areas from September. The median difference in longitude between ringing and recovery locations of Pochard ringed in Britain & Ireland in winter was 26°E in August compared to 17°E in September, 11°E in October and 1°E in November, indicating a gradual westward movement across continental Europe during autumn. Ring-recoveries appear most widely dispersed in September. By November, most of the wintering birds have reached Britain & Ireland, the Netherlands or France. The peak autumn migration in western maritime countries is generally October to November, with males moving about two weeks earlier than females (*BWP*). There is considerable regional variation in the timing of the winter peak in Britain & Ireland. Numbers in northeast Scotland peak in October, and those in the Northern Isles in November, and then fall sharply, suggesting a passage of birds through these areas in early winter (Kershaw *et al* 1998). In the Outer Hebrides and the Borders, numbers also peak in autumn and relatively few stay to winter (*Birds in Scotland*). Numbers in the south and west of Britain peak in January while in east, northeast and central England numbers are greatest in February (Kershaw *et al* 1998).

While winter ringing and recovery patterns indicate that many Pochard winter regularly in Britain & Ireland, a substantial number of birds have been recorded in Britain & Ireland one winter and on the Continent in another, with some as far away as Italy, the former Yugoslavia and the Ukraine, suggesting that a proportion of birds may wander widely over the wintering range (Fig 6) (*BWP, European Atlas*). The median distance of between-winter movements was 330 km, suggesting that there is low fidelity to wintering sites. Recoveries reveal movements between Britain & Ireland and France (especially the north and east), the Netherlands and Denmark, in particular. There is considerable movement within Britain & Ireland between winters including movements between southern England and Ireland, and between southern and northern England.

Spring passage may begin in February in mild winters but most birds leave the wintering areas in March and early April (*BWP*). Numbers are lower in February in all regions of Britain except east-central England and northeast England, which might indicate that birds in the south and west of Britain are starting to move eastwards (Kershaw *et al* 1998). Numbers fall sharply in March in most regions as birds depart mainly eastwards to the Continent. British & Irish wintering birds have been recovered as far east as Belarus and the Ukraine in March, even though the median difference in longitude between ringing and recovery locations is only 1°E. By April, the majority of wintering birds have moved east, with birds present on breeding areas in Poland and the Russian Federation, some birds being recovered from beyond 60°E. The return movement is rapid, with males preceding females, and breeding waters are occupied from early March in temperate regions and from early May in Siberia (*BWP*).

Shallow eutrophic waters favoured by Pochard are susceptible to freezing and this tends to concentrate birds on ice-free waters during cold weather (Fox & Salmon 1988). Such cold-weather movements within Britain & Ireland are common, and birds may move to coastal maritime habitats in hard weather (Fox & Salmon 1988, *Birds in Wales*). During the severe weather of January 1979, 5,800 Pochard appeared on the Inner Thames estuary, presumably in response to freezing of inland waters (Fox & Salmon 1988). In the severe winter of 1981/82, when many estuaries were frozen, there were concentrations of Pochard at Poole Harbour, Severn Estuary, Hamford Water, Teesmouth and on the Firth of Forth during the cold spell (Fox & Salmon 1988). Some winter visitors move out of Britain to northern and western France during cold weather, as for example in 1978/79 and 1981/82 (Salmon 1982, Baillie 1984, Baillie *et al* 1986, Ridgill & Fox 1990). Recovery data also suggest that some British-wintering birds move south to France during cold weather but more recoveries are needed to confirm this (Baillie *et al* 1986). From the 57 within-winter recoveries, seven birds ringed in Britain during the winter have been recovered the same winter in northern France.

The species also shows large-scale cold-weather movements south and west from the Baltic and Wadden Sea regions (Scott & Rose 1996). Some Dutch-wintering birds probably move to Britain in hard weather, although the effect might be masked by British birds moving to France and Spain (*BWP*, Fox & Salmon 1988). In the cold weather of January 1979, Pochard numbers in the Netherlands fell by about 50,000 compared with the previous year's count, with parallel increases in Britain and north and west France (Ridgill & Fox 1990); three within-winter recoveries of birds ringed in the Netherlands were from southeast England.

In Europe, Pochard undergo differential migration of the sexes with females settling further south on the wintering grounds after the autumn migration (Salomonsen 1968, Choudhury & Black 1991, Carbone & Owen 1995). This is probably due to intersexual aggression forcing females to migrate further south (Choudhury & Black 1991, Carbone & Owen 1995) although, at a site level, Marsden & Sullivan (2000) found that, despite behavioural dominance by males, females did not occupy areas of lower invertebrate density or suffer reduced feeding rates compared to males. Salomonsen (1968) suggests that the segregation of males and females on the wintering areas may be the

Fig 7. Locations overseas and all included exchanges of Pochard between (a) southeast Britain, (b) southwest Britain, and (c) Ireland, and abroad.

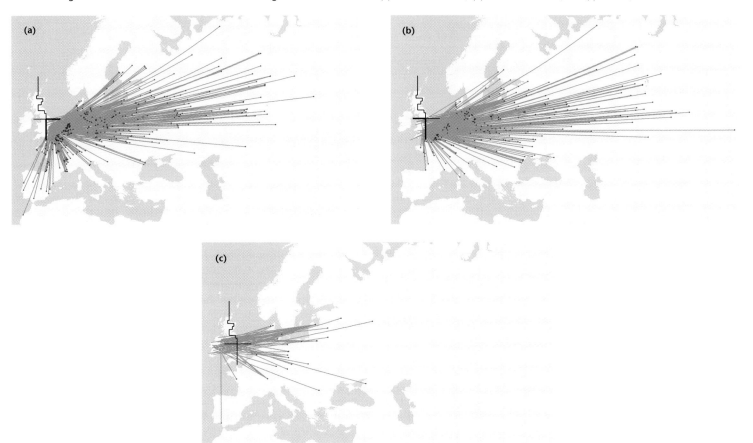

result of the different moult migrations, since males arrive earlier in the winter quarters and so force some females to continue their migration to areas beyond those occupied by the males. At a European scale, Carbone & Owen (1995) found that the male:female ratio was strongly correlated with latitude, with approximately 3:1 at 57°N and 3:4 at 37°N. Pochard wintering in Britain show amongst the highest male:female ratio (7:3) of any British duck (Owen & Dix 1986). Within Britain & Ireland, males predominate in the north, with a ratio of over 8:1 at 59°N but only 3:2 at 50°N (Owen & Dix 1986).

Since the majority of recovery data relate to southern England, it is difficult to determine if there are any differences in movement patterns for different regions in Britain & Ireland (Fig 7). Few Irish birds have been recovered further east than about 25°E with most birds originating from Latvia. In contrast, recoveries of birds from southeast and southwest England extend across the Russian Federation to 60°E and beyond.

Overall, Pochard ringed as adults move shorter distances than birds ringed as immatures. The median distance moved by adults was 701 km between ringing and recovery, compared with 1,115 km for immature birds recovered as adults, and 1,538 km for immatures recovered as immatures.

The differential migration patterns shown by male and female Pochard have conservation implications for the species. Females may suffer higher winter mortality due to the longer migration distances and by having to winter on habitats of poorer quality (Owen & Dix 1986, Carbone & Owen 1995). Additionally, Pochard survival rates in southern Europe may be lower as a result of higher hunting pressure (Owen & Dix 1986, Carbone & Owen 1995). If female mortality rates are higher, this could contribute to the uneven sex ratio and affect productivity (Carbone & Owen 1995).

The causes of the increase in numbers of wintering Pochard in Britain & Ireland and in northwest Europe in the 1960s and 1970s, and the slight decline in numbers in the 1980s are not fully understood (Fox & Salmon 1988). In particular, there are major gaps in our knowledge of cold-weather movements and of interchange between the different population groups. The different wintering populations exhibit different long-term trends in population size, yet some interchange between these populations clearly does occur (Rüger *et al* 1986, Fox & Salmon 1988). Further research into the precise origins of the Pochard wintering in Britain & Ireland and data on the mortality and productivity of the species are needed to understand their population dynamics in western Europe (Fox & Salmon 1988).

Melanie Kershaw

Tufted Duck
Aythya fuligula

The Tufted Duck is a familiar sight to birdwatchers in Britain & Ireland, being the most numerous and widespread diving duck, during both the breeding season and the winter months. This monotypic species breeds in a band that extends from approximately 45°N to 70°N (Scott & Rose 1996) and stretches across the Palearctic from Iceland to Kamchatka (*BWP*). It is largely migratory, with smaller, more sedentary populations in the temperate areas of western Europe. Birds from the eastern half of this breeding range winter in a band stretching eastwards from Pakistan across northern India and southeast China to Japan (*BWP*). Those breeding in the centre of the range, from around 70°E to 110°E, move south and west to winter predominantly along the Caspian coast of Iran. In western regions, two further subpopulations are distinct in winter (Scott & Rose 1996), although there is overlap with the Caspian population and their delineation on the breeding grounds is unclear. Those breeding in Fennoscandia and the Russian Federation east to around 65°E move south and west to winter in countries bordering the Baltic, North Sea and Atlantic. Birds breeding further east move into central Europe, the eastern Mediterranean and Black Sea regions, with important concentrations on the high-altitude lakes of Switzerland and western Austria (Monval & Pirot 1989, Scott & Rose 1996). The Icelandic population moves southeast, predominantly into Ireland.

In western Europe, a marked range expansion and population increase occurred in the late 19th and early 20th centuries (*BWP*). Two factors are thought to be primarily responsible for this expansion. The rapid creation of artificial inland waters, such as gravel-pits and reservoirs, has provided a new and extensive habitat, which the Tufted

The analysis of the data for this species was supported by the Rye Bay Ringing Group and the Wetland Trust

Duck has exploited successfully. In addition, these slow-moving waterbodies have also provided suitable habitat for the spread of the introduced Zebra Mussel and, where it occurs, this mollusc has become the staple food item of the Tufted Duck (Olney 1963).

In Britain, the Tufted Duck was first recorded breeding in 1849 (*1988–91 Atlas*). Colonization of Ireland followed in 1877 (*Birds in Ireland*) and now some 7,000–8,000 pairs breed in Britain (Owen *et al* 1986), with a further 1,750–2,000 pairs in Ireland (*1988–91 Atlas*). Between the *1968–72 Atlas* and the *1988–91 Atlas* the breeding population in Britain increased by 15% and spread to new areas in southwest England. In Ireland, however, the breeding population declined by 24%, most notably at Lough Neagh, where numbers fell from 1,000 pairs in the 1960s to 300 in 1987 (*1988–91 Atlas*). In contrast, wintering numbers have been among the most stable of all wildfowl species for the past 25 years (Waters *et al* 1998), with an estimated population of 90,600–100,600 in Britain & Ireland (Kirby 1995, Colhoun 1998, Waters *et al* 1998), representing approximately 13% of the northwest European population (Kirby 1995). Lough Neagh is the only site supporting internationally important wintering numbers of Tufted Duck in Britain & Ireland.

When breeding, Tufted Ducks show a strong preference for lowland areas, largely avoiding more northerly tundra zones and southerly steppe-desert zones (*BWP*). In recent decades, they have increased in

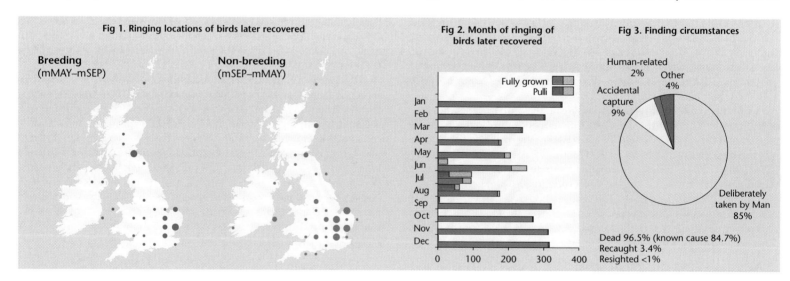

Fig 1. Ringing locations of birds later recovered

Breeding (mMAY–mSEP)

Non-breeding (mSEP–mMAY)

Fig 2. Month of ringing of birds later recovered

Fully grown
Pulli

Fig 3. Finding circumstances

Human-related 2%
Other 4%
Accidental capture 9%
Deliberately taken by Man 85%

Dead 96.5% (known cause 84.7%)
Recaught 3.4%
Resighted <1%

Ringing and recovery data

	<1960	60–69	70–79	80–89	90–97	Total
RINGING						
BTO ringing totals (%)	3	7	23	44	23	31,189
RECOVERIES						
BTO-ringed (%)	5	10	26	41	17	2,984
Foreign-ringed (%)	27	22	29	17	5	221

Statistical analyses

	Breeding population (mMAY–mSEP)	Wintering population (sDEC–mMAR)
Status	SHORT-DISTANCE MIGRANT* (2)	LONG-DISTANCE MIGRANT*
Age differences[NS]	Significant*	Not significant
Sex differences[NS]	Significant*	Not significant
Regional differences	Not tested	Significant[2]
Finding circumstances	Significant	Significant

Fig 4. Locations in (a) autumn (39), (b) winter (44) and (c) spring (4), and movements of over 20 km between the breeding and non-breeding season, of Tufted Ducks from the British & Irish breeding population (ringed as ducklings or as adults with confirmed breeding status).

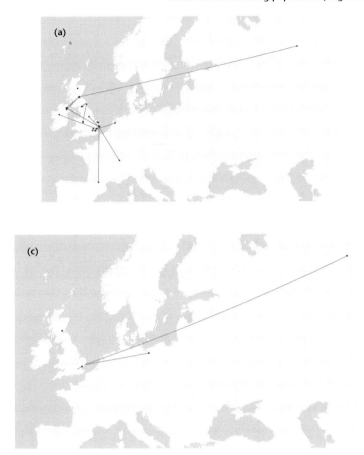

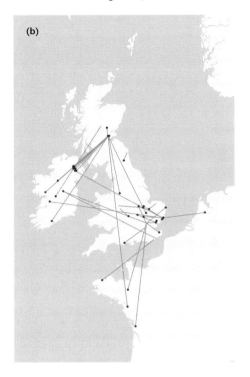

oceanic regions in the west of the range and are no longer predominantly continental in distribution (*CBWP*). During the winter, they can be found across a broad range of wetland habitats, and have adapted well to those new environments provided by Man, preferring those sheltered from strong wave action (*CBWP*).

The distribution of ringing locations for Tufted Duck ring-recoveries (Fig 1) is largely concentrated in the southeast of England, both during the breeding season and winter months. Almost no Tufted Ducks have been ringed in Ireland. Ringing has occurred more evenly through the year than for most other ducks (Fig 2) and this is largely due to a period of concentrated summer ringing at Loch Leven in the late 1960s and early 1970s (Ogilvie 1987). However, of 2,984 recoveries, over 70% were ringed between September and March. Overall, just over half were ringed as juveniles, and only 3% as pulli (Fig 2). In contrast, 221 foreign-ringed birds that have been recovered in Britain & Ireland were ringed mostly in June or July (72%, Fig 2). Most were ringed as pulli (47%) or as unaged fully grown individuals (42%).

The cause of death is known for 85% of the recoveries and the majority of these were deliberately killed (Fig 3). The distribution of recoveries is therefore strongly influenced by the distribution of hunting pressure. Over 90% of recoveries in Britain, Denmark, France, Ireland and the Russian Federation were from birds killed deliberately. In Germany and the Netherlands, however, more than half were from birds captured accidentally, usually in traps set for other species.

The majority of breeding Tufted Ducks remain within Britain & Ireland for most of the year (Ogilvie 1987) and only short movements are made from breeding to wintering areas. Recoveries of Tufted Ducks ringed during the breeding season and recovered during winter are clearly concentrated in Britain & Ireland, many close to where they were ringed (Fig 4). However, there are regional differences, particularly in the

direction of movement. Examination of autumn and winter movements of birds from the five main regions of Britain & Ireland shows a strong contrast between birds breeding in southeast Scotland and southeast England (Fig 4). Recoveries from other regions are not numerous enough to reveal any patterns of movement. Tufted Ducks from southeast England move to three main areas during the winter. The majority stay within England, moving to East Anglia, the Midlands and the southwest. The two other key wintering areas for these birds are the IJsselmeer (SOVON 1987) and Ireland. It is likely that at least some of the movements to Ireland are prompted by cold weather (Ridgill & Fox 1990). However, count data from the Netherlands indicate that numbers there seem to decrease by 30–40% during cold winters (Ridgill & Fox 1990). Movements to the Netherlands may therefore indicate short-distance winter migration, although whether these movements are short-term or for much of the winter cannot be determined from available data. A smaller number of recoveries, primarily in France and Iberia, also seem to indicate cold-weather movements of English-breeding Tufted Ducks.

In contrast, breeding Tufted Ducks from Scotland show a strong propensity to move southwest into Ireland for the winter (Fig 4). In this sense, their autumn migration is analogous to other northern populations that migrate southwest to winter in northwest Europe. Ogilvie (1987) showed that recoveries of females and immatures ringed at Loch Leven are four times as likely to move into Ireland than south into England. Southerly movement into England and France is most likely as a result of cold weather and movements to the IJsselmeer and Iberia are atypical for Scottish Tufted Ducks.

Both within-winter and between-winter site-fidelity for the British & Irish breeding population cannot be clearly determined as recoveries of winter-ringed birds do not allow us to determine which breeding

Fig 5. Movements of over 20 km and recovery locations of Tufted Ducks ringed as pulli in Britain & Ireland and recovered in a subsequent breeding season when of breeding age. There were 1:10 movements under:over 20 km but only those over 20 km are plotted.

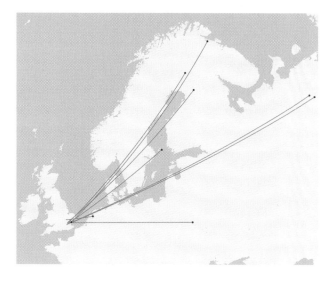

Fig 6. Locations in the breeding season, and all movements, of 289 Tufted Ducks present in Britain & Ireland during winter.

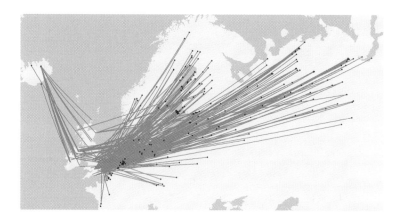

population the birds were from. Inferences can be drawn from looking at recoveries for all wintering Tufted Ducks, and this aspect is discussed later.

During the summer, in addition to the breeding population, Britain, and to a lesser extent Ireland, also supports an unknown proportion of adults from other breeding areas that have undertaken a moult migration (Salomonsen 1968). These birds start to arrive before the end of the breeding season here and, therefore, assessing the dispersal of genuine breeding birds becomes difficult. However, detailed studies elsewhere in Europe have shown that philopatry, in females at least, is extremely high, with nearly all surviving birds returning to breeding sites used previously (Blums et al 1996). The ring-recoveries show a predominantly northeasterly movement from southeast England to areas where most of the British & Irish wintering population originates, mainly Finland and northwest Russia. However, it is likely that these are the return movements of moult migrants rather than British breeding birds dispersing to new areas to breed. Some breeding dispersal also occurs to parts of Britain & Ireland and France, although the number of recoveries is small and suggests that most breeding dispersal occurs at a local scale.

Recoveries of pulli in subsequent breeding seasons indicate that there is some degree of natal dispersal to Finland, northwest Russia and, to a lesser extent, more southerly latitudes of eastern Europe (Fig 5). This recovery pattern is likely to be strongly influenced by the distribution of hunting effort during the summer months, however. All recoveries showing such natal dispersal originated from southeast England. However, there are too few recoveries in subsequent breeding seasons (n=9 found dead) of birds ringed as pulli from which any inference can be drawn about the extent of natal dispersal. Studies in Latvia have suggested that the degree of long-distance natal dispersal of Tufted Ducks seems to be higher than for Pochard (Blums et al 1989). The timing of natal dispersal can be judged from 43 recoveries of pulli made during the first 12 months after ringing. Between the third and fourth months after ringing as a pullus, the median distance dispersed increases from less than 100 km to 240 km, although some movements greater than 200 km are made as early as the second month.

A small number of immature birds have been recovered in Iceland during subsequent breeding seasons, but the majority of recoveries of immatures are within Britain & Ireland, concentrated around ringing centres in southeast England and at Loch Leven, with some additional recoveries from Northern Ireland. Ogilvie (1987) found that there was a

marked movement of Loch Leven birds to Ireland, all but one of which (n=87) were females or juvenile males, but did not mention the seasonality of these recoveries.

The majority of foreign birds arriving to moult are male, with less than 10% of females undertaking a moult migration (Salomonsen 1968). Some males begin leaving the breeding grounds in June, with moult migration reaching its peak in late July (BWP). Females migrate later than males, arriving at moulting sites in August (Salomonsen 1968). Ogilvie (1987) highlighted 60 recoveries of male Tufted Ducks ringed at Abberton Reservoir, Essex, in June. Although just 15 of these were recovered during May–August, four of these were in Russia and a further three were found there at an unspecified time of year. The remaining summer recoveries were all from Britain, with one exception in eastern Germany, suggesting that the birds undertaking a moult migration to Britain are principally from easternmost parts of the European range. Autumn recoveries in eastern Europe of summer-ringed birds suggest that individuals may not return each year to Britain to moult, preferring to moult closer to their breeding areas in some years.

Ring-recovery data from Britain & Ireland are inconclusive about whether there are spatial differences in wintering areas between male and female Tufted Ducks from Britain & Ireland. Male Tufted Ducks ringed during the breeding season move further (median distance of 249 km) than females (median=58 km). However, this summer-ringed sample is likely to contain a bias of male moult-migrants. Females from these more distant breeding grounds arrive later than many males and are therefore unlikely to be ringed in Britain & Ireland during the breeding season.

Most Tufted Ducks seen in Britain & Ireland are winter visitors from more northerly latitudes in European Russia, Fennoscandia and Iceland. Eastern birds winter primarily in Britain and the Icelandic population is concentrated in Ireland (Fig 6).

The distribution of ringing locations for foreign-ringed Tufted Ducks recovered in Britain & Ireland are clearly concentrated around the Baltic region. Most birds were ringed in Finland (10%, primarily near Helsinki), Estonia (6%), Latvia (13%, primarily in the Gulf of Riga), Sweden (5%) and Denmark (14%). A further 15% of recoveries are from birds ringed in the Netherlands, primarily the IJsselmeer. The largest proportion of foreign recoveries, however, (27%, n=60) comes from Iceland, primarily Lake Mývatn.

Autumn migration for the majority of the population begins in September and birds start to arrive on the wintering grounds during early October (BWP). In Britain & Ireland, peak numbers typically occur in December or January, possibly as a result of cold-weather movements (BWP), although Ridgill & Fox (1990) found that Britain & Ireland did not receive any major influx of Tufted Duck during cold weather.

Fig 7. Movements of over 20 km and recovery locations of Tufted Ducks ringed in winter and recovered in (a) the same winter (65:34, red) or (b) a subsequent winter (89:175, blue). Sample sizes of movements under:over 20 km are given but only those over 20 km are plotted.

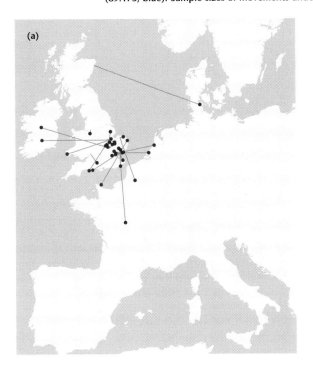

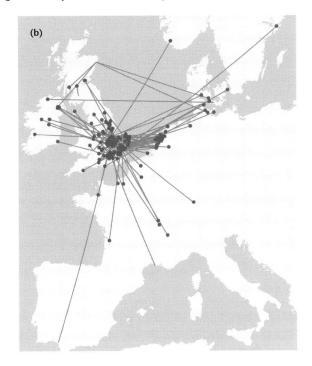

Within-winter recoveries of Tufted Ducks suggest that movements are localized (median=14 km, P5–95=0–347 km, n=98). Colour-marking studies in northeast England appear to confirm this and have suggested that while Tufted Ducks are very mobile during the winter, with a minimum of 40% utilizing more than one site during the course of a winter, they remain faithful to northeast England as a whole (J Coleman pers comm). Between-winter movements indicate that a proportion of Tufted Ducks may move to other areas in subsequent winters (median=56 km, P5–95=0–766 km, n=252). These movements closely resemble those made by British & Irish breeding Tufted Ducks during the autumn and winter, with the majority confined to southeast England and the IJsselmeer (Fig 7). Additional small numbers of birds move to cold-weather refuges such as France and Ireland. Those moving east to Denmark probably indicate the direction of early spring migration. Colour-marking in northeast England, however, has shown that at least 50% of Tufted Ducks return to the same sites in subsequent winters (J Coleman pers comm).

Changes in the distribution of ring-recoveries during cold weather show that the majority of these movements are from Scotland, eastern England and western Britain to southern England and Europe south of the Wadden Sea, primarily France and Spain (Baillie et al 1986), although Ridgill & Fox (1990) found significant increases in cold-weather recoveries in north, east and west Britain, and Ireland, as well as France and Iberia. Some birds undoubtedly move south and west into Ireland, although the incompleteness of the count data does not allow verification of this (Ridgill & Fox 1990).

Cold weather may also affect Tufted Duck survival. Ridgill & Fox (1990) found that recovery rates increased significantly during cold weather. In southern Sweden, following an especially cold winter, Tufted Duck numbers decreased markedly in subsequent winters when compared to other diving ducks in the same region, such as Goldeneye and Long-tailed Duck (Nilsson 1984a). It was suggested that, as the least efficient diver of these three species, Tufted Ducks become stressed in less severe conditions than other species. After the hard winter of 1970, emaciated Tufted Ducks were found commonly along the coasts of southern Sweden.

Spring migration may begin as early as late February in mild years, with males preceding females, and arriving at breeding areas as early as

late March in Fennoscandia and mid-May in the Russian Federation (BWP). Departure from Britain & Ireland peaks in April and May and in west and central Europe spring migration is largely complete by mid-April (CBWP).

Tufted Ducks wintering in northwest Europe are typical of many other ducks in exhibiting allohiemy of the sexes, with females migrating later and further than males to winter at more southerly latitudes (eg Salomonsen 1968, Perdeck & Clason 1983). The ratio of male:female Tufted Duck wintering in Britain was found to be 1.4:1 and has been estimated at 1.3:1 using data from the rest of the European wintering range (Owen & Dix 1986). Nilsson (1970) found that the sex ratio of Tufted Ducks changed with flock size. Males predominated in areas with large numbers, whereas females predominated in areas with low numbers and smaller flocks.

Ringing has allowed ornithologists to identify key breeding areas and delineate the flyways for western subpopulations of Tufted Duck. This information has been of great benefit to conservationists in designating key areas used by Tufted Ducks during their breeding, wintering and migration cycles. However, there is still much to be learned. The African–Eurasian Migratory Waterbird Agreement (AEWA) specifically identifies ringing as one of the actions required to conserve migratory waterbirds. Most duck ringing in Britain & Ireland is concentrated into a few key areas and in many cases does not provide a representative sample of ringed birds. Ringing away from these areas, especially in the case of the widely dispersed Tufted Duck, should be encouraged.

Greater levels of ringing, especially of breeding birds and pulli, would facilitate a better understanding of Tufted Duck populations. Particular aspects that need closer attention include turnover rates, the use by individuals of composite sites and the degree of overlap between birds wintering in northwest Europe and those in central Europe and the Caspian region. These have important implications for facets of conservation such as population estimates and site designations. In addition, more studies using colour-marking and radio-transmitters should be encouraged. Finally, less biased techniques for measuring productivity need to be developed.

Richard Hearn

Greater Scaup
(Scaup)
Aythya marila

The analysis of the data for this species was supported by E Bartlett

Although breeding only sporadically (most recently in Northern Ireland in 1997), Scaup occur in Britain & Ireland mainly during the winter. In the 1960s and 1970s, the peak midwinter population numbered tens of thousands but in the next two decades 5–10,000 was more usual (Kirby *et al* 1993). The breeding distribution of Scaup is circumpolar with the nominate race *marila* occurring eastwards from Iceland through northern Fennoscandia to western Siberia and *mariloides* extending from eastern Siberia to northern America. While those breeding in southern Scandinavia may move only short distances to winter on nearby coasts, the westernmost European breeding populations are believed to winter mainly in the North and Baltic Seas, and it is presumed that those wintering on the Black and Caspian Seas are likely to be from the Siberian breeding population.

There is a small moulting flock in the IJsselmeer but the majority of Scaup appear to moult on or closer to their breeding grounds. While some birds may arrive at wintering sites as early as September, the main passage into and through the Baltic is not until October, with the main arrivals in Britain and Ireland starting late in the month. The exact timing of passage is perhaps determined by weather conditions further east and north. The spring return starts to get under way in late February with the main passage through the Baltic occurring in April (*BWP*).

Around the Baltic and North Sea, most Scaup winter in marine coastal waters where they typically feed on molluscs such as mussels. Lagoons and coastal lakes may also be used but normally only small numbers occur further inland on freshwater lakes and reservoirs. Scaup tend to congregate in large flocks and it has been estimated that 90% of the wintering population in northwest Europe is concentrated at fewer than 10 major sites (Tucker & Heath 1994).

The majority of Scaup in Britain & Ireland are at sites where it is impossible to catch them, so the majority ringed have been caught while wintering at sites where specialist trapping operations for diving ducks have been undertaken, such as the Ythan Estuary, Aberdeenshire, and Abberton Reservoir, Essex (Figs 1 & 2). Thus ringed birds may have been unrepresentative to the extent that they were using habitats not favoured by the bulk of the wintering population. Similarly, although no detailed assessment has been carried out of ringing effort on wintering and breeding grounds abroad, the data on recoveries ringed abroad are dominated by the intensive ringing work carried out in Iceland. Finally, there are also some temporal anomalies. The majority (80%) of recoveries of Scaup ringed in Britain & Ireland occurred between 1950 and 1979. This covered the period when peak wintering numbers in Britain were markedly higher than before or since (Kirby *et al* 1993) and when greatest numbers were actually being ringed. Recoveries of foreign-ringed birds, mainly those ringed in the breeding season in Iceland, show an even earlier peak with 75% having been made before 1960 and reflecting a period of intense ringing activity at that time.

With so few recoveries of Scaup ringed in Britain & Ireland, a better picture of migration patterns can be obtained by considering these

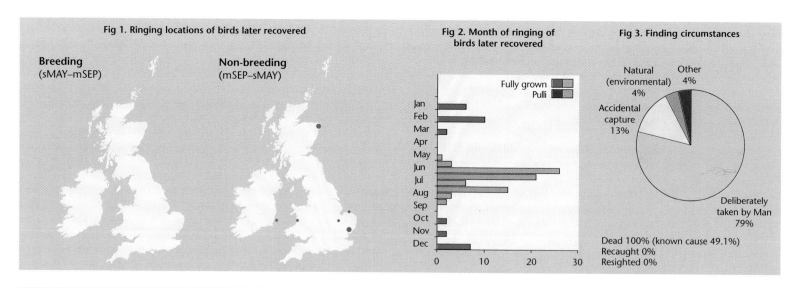

Fig 1. Ringing locations of birds later recovered

Breeding (sMAY–mSEP)

Non-breeding (mSEP–sMAY)

Fig 2. Month of ringing of birds later recovered

Fully grown
Pulli

Fig 3. Finding circumstances

Natural (environmental) 4%
Other 4%
Accidental capture 13%
Deliberately taken by Man 79%

Dead 100% (known cause 49.1%)
Recaught 0%
Resighted 0%

Ringing and recovery data

	<1960	60–69	70–79	80–89	90–97	Total
RINGING						
BTO ringing totals (%)	12	40	17	17	14	205
RECOVERIES						
BTO-ringed (%)	21	41	17	7	14	29
Foreign-ringed (%)	75	8	6	9	1	77

Statistical analyses

	Breeding population (sMAY–mSEP)	Wintering population (mNOV–mMAR)
Status	NONE	[LONG-DISTANCE MIGRANT]
Age differences	—	Not tested
Sex differences	—	Not tested
Regional differences	—	Not tested
Finding circumstances	—	Not tested

Fig 4. All 92 included exchanges of Scaup between Britain & Ireland and abroad.

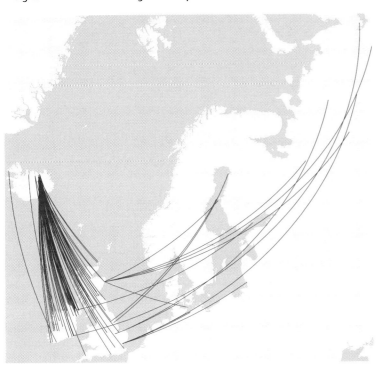

together with the slightly greater number of recoveries here of foreign-ringed birds. These 106 recoveries consist of a mix of adults and juveniles ringed in the winter in Britain & Ireland and adults and pulli ringed in the breeding season in Iceland and Finland. All recoveries were recorded as dead, almost half of which are attributed to a known cause (Fig 3). Of these, over three-quarters were deliberately taken, wildfowlers in Britain & Ireland alone accounting for 65%, and a further 14% taken accidentally.

Considering the data as a whole, and despite the relatively small sample of recoveries, it is clear that Scaup wintering within Britain & Ireland are drawn from populations breeding across almost the whole range of the nominate race (Fig 4). Individuals ringed in Britain & Ireland have been recovered in Iceland, four countries abutting the North Sea and the Baltic, and from various locations in Russia eastwards to beyond the Urals at 70°E. The bulk (96%) of the foreign-ringed birds were from Iceland, the remainder being from Finland. Although birds breeding in Iceland appear to be particularly well represented in Ireland, it is notable that one of the two most easterly recoveries beyond the Urals was from a bird ringed in Ireland (Fig 4). Thus, while Icelandic breeders may make up the greater proportion of the total population present, particularly in the north and west, wintering flocks anywhere within Britain & Ireland are also likely to include birds that breed in Fennoscandia and further east into western Siberia.

Four Scaup ringed in winter in Britain or Ireland were recovered in a subsequent winter, two within 20 km of where they were ringed. The other two, ringed in Aberdeenshire and in Essex, were found respectively off the Danish and German coasts of the Baltic.

Unfortunately, since 1980, there has only been one recovery abroad (in Russia) of a Scaup ringed in Britain & Ireland and only eight recoveries (seven from Iceland) of foreign-ringed Scaup. Although these still indicate that the wintering population is made up of Scaup from all parts of the breeding range, there is strong circumstantial evidence to suggest that the wintering population in Britain & Ireland is now largely Icelandic in origin (Scott & Rose 1996).

During the 1960s and 1970s (the period when most recoveries of Scaup occurred), the main site for Scaup was the Firth of Forth, which at times held more than 30,000 and where they fed in sewage-polluted waters off Edinburgh. Numbers at this site always peaked markedly in late December and early January and high counts were usually sustained for only a few weeks. Many of the Scaup that visited the Forth therefore spent most of the winter period outside Britain & Ireland. This was also the time when numbers breeding in Iceland are believed to have declined substantially (Salmon 1988). It thus seems highly probable, and consistent with the recovery data, that a substantial proportion of the Scaup then occurring in eastern Britain, and perhaps further west, were from the Scandinavian and Russian breeding populations, with these birds spending much of the winter further east in the IJsselmeer, the Wadden Sea or the western Baltic. The decline in wintering numbers in the mid-1970s, attributed at least in part to improved treatment of Edinburgh sewage (Campbell 1984), may simply be because, with reduced feeding opportunities, eastern Scotland no longer attracted or retained birds spending most of the winter further east.

In more recent years, and following an apparent recovery in the Icelandic breeding population, the principal wintering sites in Britain & Ireland have been in more western areas, notably Lough Neagh (atypically a freshwater site), the Solway and Loch Indaal on Islay. In contrast to the Forth in the 1960s and 1970s, and Salmon's (1988) suggestion of a November peak in western populations, numbers in Northern Ireland (principally Lough Neagh) now tend to build up steadily throughout the winter, sometimes peaking as late as March (Cranswick et al 1999). A similar pattern has been described for the Solway (Quinn et al 1997). Autumn peaks at some sites and sustained or peak numbers throughout February and March would be consistent with flocks arriving from and waiting to depart to Iceland.

In common with other ducks wintering in flocks in coastal areas, Scaup are vulnerable to the immediate effects of pollution, notably oil. Loss of preferred feeding areas is likely to cause flocks to move elsewhere, although the disappearance of the large flocks in the Forth might suggest that such movements would be to areas other than in Britain & Ireland. Because Scaup are normally nocturnal feeders, disturbance, in particular by wildfowlers, is unlikely to be a problem. On Lough Neagh, Scaup largely feed on midge larvae, which are present in huge numbers. Although there is regular and widespread wildfowling on the Lough, there appear to be ample areas for them to roost and feed without undue disturbance. Accidental drowning in nets set for fish poses a threat to flocks in some locations. Although the total numbers of Scaup wintering in British & Irish waters represent only a small proportion of the total European wintering population of over 300,000 (Laursen et al 1992), Britain & Ireland may hold a substantial proportion of the Icelandic breeding population. The fate of the Icelandic population, and therefore the wintering population in Britain & Ireland, may depend heavily on how changes at key sites are managed by these countries.

Although it has been possible to use the limited data that are available to identify the broad areas from which Scaup wintering within Britain & Ireland are drawn, much of the detail remains obscure. While strong links have been established between the Icelandic breeding populations and wintering sites within Britain & Ireland, it is not clear to what extent other breeding populations, particularly in the western parts of the Fennoscandian range, may also focus here. Further information on site-fidelity would be useful to establish the extent to which breeding subpopulations may be dependent on single sites or groups of sites. Obtaining such information would require a major increase in ringing activity within the main breeding areas.

Lennox Campbell

Common Eider (Eider)
Somateria mollissima

Eiders have a northerly breeding distribution and some populations migrate over a thousand kilometres south for the winter. However, other populations of this hardy seaduck are remarkably sedentary and remain in, or close to arctic waters throughout the year. Britain and Ireland both lie at the south of the species' range and our breeding populations undertake relatively short seasonal movements or are sedentary. Some continental birds visit the east coast of Britain in winter and Eiders from the British population sometimes pair with them and recruit to continental populations.

The circumpolar breeding distribution extends to about 80°N and shows only a slight southward shift in winter (*BWP*). Movements generally follow coastlines but land-crossings are sometimes used to shorten the migration routes (Alerstam *et al* 1974, Gauthier *et al* 1976). The nominate race breeds mainly in Britain, Ireland, the Netherlands, Fennoscandia, Estonia, and northwest Russia including Novaya Zemlya. A few birds occur well outside this range, including a small, mainly wintering population in Switzerland and a small wintering population in the Mediterranean, with regular numbers around the mouth of the Rhône in southern France and the Gulf of Venice in the northern Adriatic (A Fox pers comm). Additionally, there is a small breeding population in the Ukrainian Black Sea (*European Atlas*). Many of the Eiders from the Baltic, particularly adult males and immatures, undertake spectacular moult migrations to southwest Jutland, the German Wadden Sea and the Danish side of the Kattegat in June and July (Salomonsen 1968, Schmidt 1983). Birds from these moulting concentrations disperse to the Danish islands, the southwest Baltic off

The analysis of the data for this species was supported by Mark Penty

Germany and the Wadden Sea to winter and are joined in these areas by the remaining Eiders from the Baltic. Much of the inner Baltic freezes in winter rendering it unsuitable for seaducks. The breeding population of Eiders in the Dutch Wadden Sea is essentially resident. First-year birds disperse in a predominantly southwesterly direction and a few reach Britain (Swennen 1990). Birds from the arctic coasts of Russia and Norway exhibit a variable degree of westerly movement in winter, probably linked to temperatures. Birds from the west coast of Norway are thought to be fairly sedentary but some from south Norway join western Swedish birds to winter in Danish waters (*BWP*, Noer 1991).

The Faeroes has its own resident endemic race, *faeroeensis*. The race *borealis* occupies the arctic North Atlantic extending from Franz Josef Land west through Svalbard, Iceland, Greenland and as far as the Baffin Island region of Canada (*BWP*). Many birds from Svalbard move south to winter in the Norwegian Sea but others remain off Svalbard during the winter where there are breaks in the sea-ice. The Icelandic population is resident apart from some southerly winter movement within the country. Eiders of the race *borealis* breeding in Greenland and Canada show moderate southerly movements within those areas.

There are three other races: *dresseri* occupies the Atlantic coast of North America from Maine to Labrador, *sedentaria* is restricted to Hudson Bay and *v-nigrum* occurs in northwest North America and along

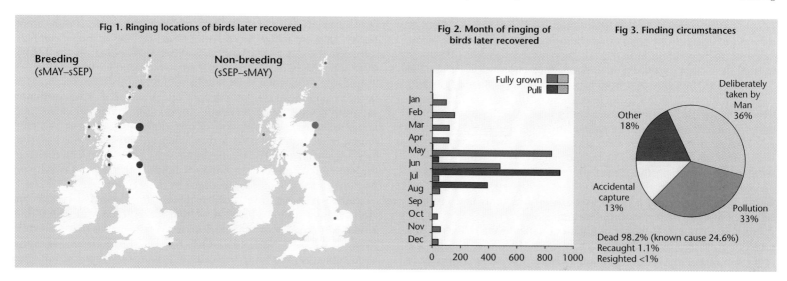

Fig 1. Ringing locations of birds later recovered

Breeding (sMAY–sSEP)

Non-breeding (sSEP–sMAY)

Fig 2. Month of ringing of birds later recovered

Fully grown
Pulli

Fig 3. Finding circumstances

Deliberately taken by Man 36%

Other 18%

Accidental capture 13%

Pollution 33%

Dead 98.2% (known cause 24.6%)
Recaught 1.1%
Resighted <1%

Ringing and recovery data

	<1960	60–69	70–79	80–89	90–97	Total
RINGING						
BTO ringing totals (%)	7	35	29	26	3	18,667
RECOVERIES						
BTO-ringed (%)	2	25	32	31	10	3,389
Foreign-ringed (%)	←	38	→	38	23	13

Statistical analyses

	Breeding population (sMAY–sSEP)	Wintering population (mNOV–mMAR)
Status	SHORT-DISTANCE MIGRANT* (1)	SEDENTARY
Age differences[S]	Significant*	Not significant
Sex differences[S]	Significant*	Not significant
Regional differences	Not tested	Not tested
Finding circumstances	(Not significant)	Not significant*

Fig 4. Recovery locations in November–February of (a) 129 first-year and (b) 123 older Eiders ringed as ducklings at the Sands of Forvie, northeast Scotland.

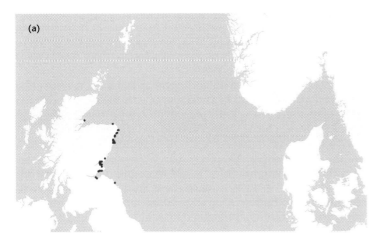

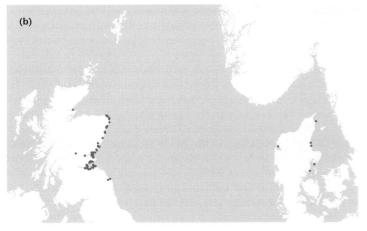

Fig 5. Locations abroad in April–June (11, red), July–October (21, blue) and November–March (6, grey) of Eiders ringed in Britain & Ireland during the breeding season.

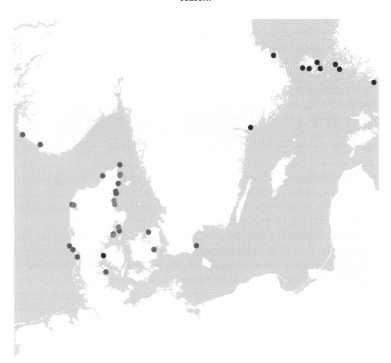

the coasts of east Siberia. The range of movement patterns shown by these populations is similar to that of the European races described above (Reed 1975, Palmer 1976b, Reed & Erskine 1986).

Eiders are almost entirely restricted to coastal and marine habitats where they feed mainly on Blue Mussels but also on other molluscs, crustaceans and echinoderms. Prey is obtained principally by diving but birds may also feed by head-dipping or up-ending in shallow areas. Thus Eiders require prey concentrations at depths that are suitable for diving (usually up to 3 m; *BWP*) and avoid coasts with excessive exposure to rain or strong winds. In Britain & Ireland, most large concentrations occur on estuaries. Nesting takes place on islands or at other coastal

Table 1. Summary of distances moved between ringing and recovery for Eiders ringed in the defined breeding areas and recovered dead throughout the year (all age classes combined).

Area of ringing in the breeding season	Number of recoveries	0–10 km %	11–50 km %	>50 km %
Sands of Forvie	2,277	52	21	27
Farnes & Coquet	955	67	26	6
Firths of Forth and Tay	69	49	46	5
Orkney & Shetland	31	90	7	3
Strathclyde	21	57	38	5
Eastern Scotland north of Grampian	16	75	6	19
Northwest Scotland	15	67	27	6

locations where mammalian predators are scarce or absent and where there is both access from the sea and nesting cover. Females will take their ducklings to foraging sites up to 20 km from the nesting areas (Bustnes & Erikstad 1993).

Eiders breed around the coasts of Scotland and northern England, their range extending south to Coquet Island in the east and Walney Island in the west. Breeding birds also occur along the north coast of Ireland. Most of the Eider ringing carried out in Britain & Ireland has taken place on the British northeast coast, mainly at the Ythan Estuary and Sands of Forvie, Grampian (Baillie & Milne 1997), Coquet Island, Northumberland (Coulson 1984), and the Farne Islands (Fig 1). Thus 97% of recoveries are of birds ringed in this area compared with the 47% of British & Irish Eiders that are found there (*Winter Atlas*).

Female Eiders are easily caught while incubating, either by hand or with a landing net, and they quickly return to their nests on release. It is also relatively easy to round up large ducklings. Thus 43% of recoveries are of birds ringed as females during the breeding season and 32% are of birds ringed as ducklings (Fig 2). The recovery sample includes relatively few records of birds ringed between September and April. Trapping of all age and sex classes throughout the year can be achieved using grain-baited funnel traps, by dazzling or by cannon-netting at high-tide roosts. Such efforts have been restricted mainly to the Forvie study, however. These techniques are most suitable for relatively sheltered situations where Eiders are reliably present, and birds from offshore flocks are almost never trapped.

Eiders dying close inshore in eastern Britain have a good chance of being washed up on beaches and found by members of the public. Thus 17% of Eiders ringed in Britain & Ireland have been recovered, and three-quarters of these are simply reported as found dead. Shooting, oil pollution and accidental captures in fishing nets are the main identifiable causes of death for recovered birds (Fig 3). Recovery rates are likely to be reasonably uniform within major regions of Britain & Ireland but will differ between them. Unmeasured differences in recovery rates between eastern Britain and the Continent make it impossible to estimate the exact proportion of birds that emigrate to the Baltic (below).

The movements of Eiders ringed on the east coast of Britain have been analysed in detail (Baillie & Milne 1989). Over three-quarters of the

Eiders breeding at the Sands of Forvie spend the winter on the Tay and Forth Estuaries (Fig 4). Adults move a short distance south of Forvie, but within Grampian, in July and August to moult off Murcar (Campbell & Milne 1983). Many birds then move back to Forvie in September prior to the main southward migration later that month. Numbers at Forvie decline progressively from October to March as further birds disperse southward, some eventually reaching the main wintering grounds of the migratory segment of the population. The majority of winter-ringed adults remain at Forvie throughout the year but there are a considerable number of recoveries away from Forvie during the summer, indicating that some of the Forvie wintering population breeds elsewhere. For instance, one female Eider ringed at Forvie in February was recorded breeding on the Isle of May in three subsequent summers. Pioneering analyses of egg albumen proteins in the 1960s indicated that there were genetic differences between migratory and sedentary components of the Forvie population (Milne & Robertson 1965). However, more recent work indicates that any such differences are unlikely to remain stable due to the effects of dispersal.

Many first-year birds from Forvie remain there throughout the winter, but others disperse up and down the coast, a few eventually reaching the adult wintering grounds (Fig 4; Baillie & Milne 1989). First-year birds that move away from Forvie do not return there during their first summer. Birds begin following the adult migration pattern during their second year, which corresponds to the earliest age at which females start to breed (Baillie & Milne 1982). It should be noted that an age of first breeding of three was used for the analyses of ring-recovery data presented in this volume, because most female Eiders start to breed when they are three or four years old (Baillie & Milne 1982).

Nearly all Eider ringing on the Farnes and Coquet Island has been of adult females caught on nests. Many of these birds move north to winter on the Tay and Forth Estuaries (Baillie & Milne 1989) where they overlap with wintering birds from Forvie. Despite this overlap of wintering ranges, only a few Forvie-ringed females have been recovered breeding in Northumberland. The small number of recoveries of birds ringed on the Tay and Forth Estuaries as ducklings or breeding females suggest that the breeding population of this area is mainly sedentary, as might be expected in an area that is able to support greatly increased numbers in winter.

The limited data on Eiders ringed along the coast of Scotland from just north of Grampian round to Strathclyde suggest that movements of these populations are quite limited (Table 1). Apart from the east coast from Grampian to Northumberland, only two records involve movements of over 100 km, one from the east of Highland Region to Grampian and one within northwest Scotland. A single movement of 40 km from the west of Highland Region to Strathclyde is the only other record of a bird moving between regions, outside Grampian to Northumberland. Movements of the breeding population in the north of Ireland have not yet been studied.

Eiders, like many waterfowl, pair during the winter and females are generally philopatric. Thus, if a male pairs with a female from a different breeding area, he will usually follow his mate back to her natal area, a process known as abmigration. Most females reared at Forvie returned there to breed, but over half of the males emigrated to other breeding populations (Baillie & Milne 1989).

Forty-three Eiders ringed as ducklings or breeding adults at Forvie have been recovered abroad (Fig 5). These movements appear to result mainly from abmigration into the Baltic population, with 27 out of 28 records for birds of known sex being males. Autumn and winter records are mainly from Danish waters, while virtually all breeding-season recoveries are from the central Baltic. This nicely reflects the seasonal movements of Baltic Eider populations. Thus, Eiders wintering off the east coast of Britain are likely to include immigrants from continental breeding populations. Eight foreign recoveries of winter-ringed birds from Forvie support this, the recoveries coming from similar areas of the Baltic to the recoveries in Fig 5. The five males in this sample may have been British birds that joined the continental population by abmigration but the three females are likely to have been wintering birds from continental Europe. Similarly, many of the male Eiders reared in the Dutch Wadden Sea pair with overwintering females from the Baltic and thus recruit into the Baltic breeding population (Swennen 1990).

The small number of records of foreign-ringed Eiders recovered in Britain & Ireland all fit with the general dispersal patterns of Eiders from nearby continental populations (Swennen 1990). There are eight records of birds ringed as ducklings in the Netherlands and recovered on the east coast of Britain from Fife to Kent, all but one record being in winter. The record of a duckling ringed in the Netherlands and recovered in Cork in its first December of life is exceptional. A single bird from the German Friesian Islands and three birds from Denmark were recovered on the east coast between Lothian and Northumberland, a slightly more northerly distribution than that of the Dutch birds.

Eider populations expanded considerably during the 20th century, but their populations remain sensitive to predation at breeding colonies, to mortality from oiling and other marine pollution and to the loss of feeding grounds. Concentrations, in particular at moulting and wintering areas, increase this vulnerability. The species is long-lived and has a low reproductive rate, so recovery from any major losses would be slow (Coulson 1984, Baillie & Milne 1997). Much better data on movements from populations throughout Britain & Ireland are needed to assess which breeding populations are at risk from mortality in particular areas.

Stephen R Baillie

Common Goldeneye (Goldeneye)
Bucephala clangula

Although established as a regular Scottish breeding species since 1970 (now numbering c 100 pairs; Stone *et al* 1997), Goldeneye are much more abundant and widespread in Britain & Ireland during the winter, when small numbers occur all around the coasts and estuaries, and on lochs, lakes, reservoirs and rivers. Up to a dozen sites in the United Kingdom regularly hold flocks of 400 or more, and peak wintering numbers during the 1990s have been around 32,000 (Stone *et al* 1997). Breeding Goldeneye require mature forest and water, and their circumpolar breeding distribution roughly coincides with that of the boreal forest zone. The nominate race *clangula* extends eastwards from Scotland, through Fennoscandia and northern Russia into eastern Siberia, while *americana* is found from southern Alaska east to Newfoundland. The Scottish population, which has thrived because of a scheme to place nestboxes at suitable woodland sites close to water, is centred on the Spey Valley, but is now spreading more widely.

Although some may make only local movements from their breeding grounds to winter in nearby coastal waters, for example those in southern Sweden, the majority of birds breeding in Fennoscandia and western Russia are believed to migrate southwards or westwards to the Baltic and North Seas; some, however, winter as far south as the Mediterranean coast of France and eastward to the Black Sea. Birds ringed in Finland have been recovered from as far west as France and eastwards to the Black Sea, and one from the Kola Peninsula in western Russia was recovered in Switzerland. The large flocks that have been recorded in the Caspian Sea are thought to be drawn from more easterly breeding populations.

The analysis of the data for this species was supported by Peter Wilson

Some 300,000 Goldeneye are estimated to winter in western Europe (Scott & Rose 1996). Large flocks, probably consisting of non-breeding birds and moulting birds from the Swedish and Finnish populations, arrive at Limfjorden in Denmark and other sites in the Baltic from June onwards. Birds start to return to their wintering grounds from late August onwards, although the main movement does not take place until November. Most Fennoscandian birds are believed to pass through the Baltic, but those from northern Sweden and Norway may fly direct to sites around the North Sea. Birds start to move north and east from February onwards, although the main passage from more northerly wintering sites, such as eastern Scotland and southern Sweden, is not until March (Nilsson 1969, *BWP*).

In most of western Europe, the majority of wintering Goldeneye and the major concentrations occur on coastal waters and in estuaries. In the 1960s and 1970s, large flocks were found at coastal sewage outfalls, particularly in eastern Scotland (Pounder 1976), but as a result of various improvement schemes most of these birds have now gone (Campbell 1984). The main wintering site in Britain & Ireland is now the freshwater Lough Neagh, in Northern Ireland, which together with nearby Lough Beg regularly holds a peak of more than 5,000 birds. Small groups may occur on all sorts of freshwater locations and the *Winter Atlas* showed that Goldeneye were the fourth most widespread duck, after Mallard, Teal and

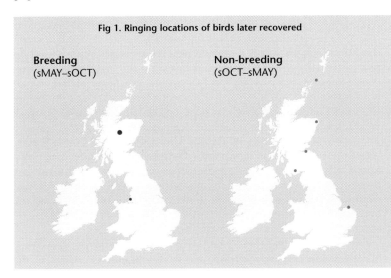

Fig 1. Ringing locations of birds later recovered

Breeding (sMAY–sOCT)

Non-breeding (sOCT–sMAY)

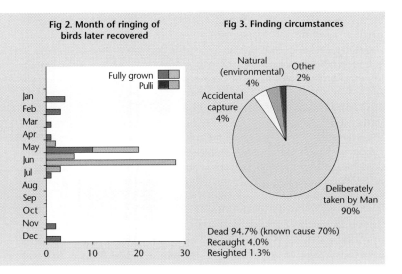

Fig 2. Month of ringing of birds later recovered

Fully grown
Pulli

Jan, Feb, Mar, Apr, May, Jun, Jul, Aug, Sep, Oct, Nov, Dec

0   10   20   30

Fig 3. Finding circumstances

Natural (environmental) 4%
Other 2%
Accidental capture 4%
Deliberately taken by Man 90%

Dead 94.7% (known cause 70%)
Recaught 4.0%
Resighted 1.3%

Ringing and recovery data

	<1960	60–69	70–79	80–89	90–97	Total
RINGING						
BTO ringing totals (%)	2	13	10	27	48	276
RECOVERIES						
BTO-ringed (%)	0	24	8	24	44	25
Foreign-ringed (%)	12	30	30	14	14	50

Statistical analyses

	Breeding population (sMAY–sOCT)	Wintering population (mDEC–sMAR)
Status	[SHORT-DISTANCE MIGRANT]	[LONG-DISTANCE MIGRANT]
Age differences	Not tested	Not tested
Sex differences	Not tested	Not tested
Regional differences	Not tested	Not tested
Finding circumstances	Not tested	Not tested

Fig 4. All included exchanges of Goldeneye between Britain (36, red) & Ireland (23, blue) and abroad.

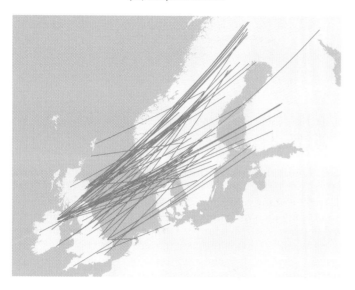

Tufted Duck, being recorded in half the 10-km squares in Britain & Ireland. As in Sweden (Nilsson 1969), numbers inland tend to decrease as winter progresses, perhaps in response to weather, but other factors, such as food depletion, may be involved (Duncan & Marquiss 1993).

The majority of Goldeneye ringed during the breeding season in Britain & Ireland are on Speyside (Fig 1), where they are caught as part of the nestbox scheme. Outside the breeding season, Goldeneye are usually found in situations where they are difficult to catch, and those that are caught and ringed are usually the by-product of other catching operations rather than the specific target. The ringing locations of birds ringed in the non-breeding season and later recovered, although small in number, are widely spaced and include coastal, estuarine and inland sites (Fig 1). Although there are none from the main wintering site at Lough Neagh, there is no reason to suggest that the recoveries are particularly biased regionally or in terms of habitat. Similarly the distribution of ringing locations of foreign-ringed recoveries in Britain & Ireland shows a reasonably wide spread across the core of the breeding range in Fennoscandia.

With only 25 recoveries of Goldeneye ringed in Britain, and none in Ireland, a more reliable picture of overall migration patterns can be obtained by combining these with the 50 recoveries that are available of birds ringed abroad. The latter consisted entirely of birds ringed during the breeding season in May, June and July, only 25% of which were young hatched that year (Fig 2). Nearly all of the recoveries were from dead birds and a cause of death was given for 70%. Deliberate taking in Britain or Ireland, presumably mainly by wildfowlers, accounted for 82% of these (Fig 3).

Nine birds ringed in the breeding season in Scotland have been recovered, one in Northern Ireland, and the rest, only two of which were in winter, either relatively close to the breeding area or in other parts of Scotland or northern England. These limited data suggest that the Scottish breeding population undertakes only a relatively short migration and winters within Britain & Ireland.

The ringing or recovery locations abroad of 50 Goldeneye recovered or ringed in Britain & Ireland are clearly demonstrated in Fig 4. Forty-three were in Sweden, nine in Finland, four in Norway and one each in the Netherlands, Germany and Russia. Although the majority of records for Scotland appear to involve Goldeneye from Norway and northern

Sweden, and those for eastern and southern England a greater proportion from southern Sweden and Finland, the very wide mix recorded in Ireland, including the most easterly from Russia, suggests that the wintering population in Britain & Ireland as a whole is drawn from the whole Fennoscandian breeding population. This concurs with the results of a review of all recoveries available up to August 1967 of Goldeneye ringed in Sweden and Finland (Nilsson 1969). Of the total of 202 recoveries, 87 (43%), mainly in Sweden, were of Goldeneye moving to and from their breeding grounds, in September and October or between March and May. More than half the 115 winter recoveries were from Danish (52) and north German (11) coastal regions but with a further third from Sweden (11), Norway (10) and Britain & Ireland (18). A scattering of recoveries of Finnish-ringed Goldeneye from the Mediterranean, the Black Sea and inland central Europe suggests that the Finnish breeding population may tend to migrate further south than those from other Fennoscandian countries.

Although numbers at many sites in Britain & Ireland peak in midwinter, numbers tend to be sustained at relatively high levels for the rest of the winter, often with a second peak in March (Cranswick *et al* 1999). In the 1960s and 1970s in the Firth of Forth, when several thousand Goldeneye joined the large flocks of Scaup at sewage outfalls off Edinburgh, numbers tended to show a marked midwinter peak (Campbell 1978), suggesting that, like Scaup, they were being attracted for a short time by the rich feeding conditions around sewage outfalls, before moving on to spend the rest of the winter elsewhere. Increasing numbers at various sites in late winter suggest some form of pre-migratory gathering. With the main breeding areas all lying well to the east in Fennoscandia, it is improbable that birds would move westwards at this time from their main wintering areas further east and, as has been suggested for northeast Scotland (Duncan & Marquiss 1993), it is likely that these influxes are made up of birds that wintered, possibly inland and dispersed in smaller numbers, elsewhere in Britain & Ireland.

Like other waterfowl wintering in flocks in coastal areas, Goldeneye are vulnerable to the immediate effects of pollution, notably oil. Although some flocks continue to gather at sewage outfalls and may thus, like those at Edinburgh in the 1970s, be affected by improved sewage treatment, the widespread distribution of Goldeneye suggests that there is no shortage of suitable wintering sites and that, where concentrations occur, it is simply because the birds are taking advantage of a particularly rich food source. Even within the main wintering site, Lough Neagh, Goldeneye are widely dispersed and its overall importance is mostly due to its large size and rich aquatic invertebrate fauna. Because Goldeneye normally feed by day, they may be vulnerable to disturbance by wildfowlers, although there is no evidence to suggest that this is a significant problem, even on heavily shot sites such as Lough Neagh, where there appear to be ample areas for them to roost and feed without undue disturbance. Accidental drowning in nets set for fish poses a threat to flocks in some locations and although, along with losses from wildfowling or oil pollution, it is unlikely at current levels to have any impact of the Fennoscandian populations, it could have a disproportionate effect on the still-small Scottish breeding population.

Although the available ringing data do establish the broad patterns of movements between breeding and wintering grounds, much of the finer detail is missing. For example, it is not known to what extent birds are faithful to particular breeding or wintering sites. A marked increase in ringing activity, particularly in Fennoscandia and Russia, would be needed to provide this additional information. The origins of the birds that started the breeding population in Scotland remain obscure.

Lennox Campbell

Goosander

Mergus merganser

The Goosander's remarkable and recently discovered moult migration, performed mostly by drakes, makes its movement patterns unique among British & Irish birds. This, the largest of the fish-eating sawbill ducks, has colonized Britain & Ireland relatively recently and continues to expand its range and population size.

Goosanders are found in temperate and boreal zones almost throughout the Holarctic. The nominate race *merganser* breeds across northern Eurasia from Iceland and Britain to the Bering Sea, with an outpost of around a thousand pairs in the Alps and a few breeders elsewhere in southern Europe (Scott & Rose 1996, *European Atlas*). The race *orientalis* breeds in the mountains of southern Asia between Afghanistan and western China, and *americanus* from California and Alaska east to New England and Newfoundland (*HBW*). Many southerly parts of the breeding range are occupied all year. Icelandic birds are resident but other northerly breeders migrate to milder climates for the winter, in Europe reaching Britain, France, the former Yugoslavia, Greece, and the Black and Caspian Seas.

The winter range covers almost all of Britain but single birds or small groups penetrate only occasionally into Ireland (*Winter Atlas, Birds in Ireland*). Most wintering birds are found inland on lakes, gravel-pits and broad rivers, with many in lowland areas such as the Fens and the Thames Valley, but some occur on sheltered estuaries and bays, especially in eastern Scotland (*eg* Aspinall & Dennis 1988). In the vicinity of the breeding areas, birds may be seen all year; elsewhere, most arrive between November and January, much later than other wintering ducks (see Fig 1.4 in Chapter 1), and depart during March.

The analysis of the data for this species was supported by the Northumbria Ringing Group

The winter population suggested from WeBS counts is about 8,900 birds, approximately 6% of the 150,000 estimated to winter in northwest Europe as a whole (Rose & Scott 1994).

Breeding in Britain was first proved in 1871, in Perthshire. The range has spread subsequently to include much of mainland Scotland, northern England south to Yorkshire and Lancashire and along the Pennines to Derbyshire, Wales, and parts of Cornwall and Devon (Meek & Little 1977a, *1988–91 Atlas*). One pair was proved nesting in County Donegal between 1969 and 1978 (*Birds in Ireland*), and another in the *1988–91 Atlas* period, but establishment in Ireland is still awaited. The British breeding population had reached about 2,600 pairs by the time of the *1988–91 Atlas*, and has continued to expand both in range and density since that time (Rehfisch *et al* 1999). Females nest in holes, often in trees, rabbit burrows or holes in crags and occasionally in banks covered in thick heather; they will also use nesting boxes. Most nests are close to fast-flowing rivers in upland areas.

The ringing of Goosanders in Britain has fallen into two categories, separated by season and largely by locality (Figs 1 & 2). Most birds subsequently recovered were trapped on the breeding rivers between May and August, as unfledged ducklings or attendant females (*eg* Meek & Little 1977b). Also, some breeding females have been ringed at the nest, in nesting boxes or in natural sites, late in incubation. Some birds

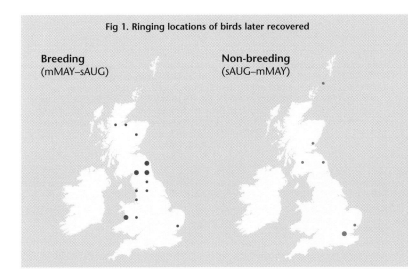

Fig 1. Ringing locations of birds later recovered

Breeding (mMAY–sAUG)

Non-breeding (sAUG–mMAY)

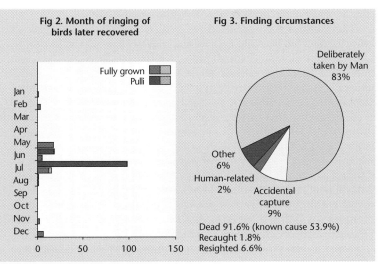

Fig 2. Month of ringing of birds later recovered

Fully grown / Pulli

Fig 3. Finding circumstances

Deliberately taken by Man 83%

Other 6%

Human-related 2%

Accidental capture 9%

Dead 91.6% (known cause 53.9%)
Recaught 1.8%
Resighted 6.6%

Ringing and recovery data

	<1960	60–69	70–79	80–89	90–97	Total
RINGING						
BTO ringing totals (%)	4	3	37	31	24	1,292
RECOVERIES						
BTO-ringed (%)	4	4	43	33	16	160
Foreign-ringed (%)	50	17	0	17	17	6

Statistical analyses

	Breeding population (mMAY–sAUG)	Wintering population (mDEC–mMAR)
Status	SHORT-DISTANCE MIGRANT* (2)	[LONG-DISTANCE MIGRANT]
Age differences	Not tested	Not tested
Sex differences	Not tested	Not tested
Regional differences	Not tested	Not tested
Finding circumstances	Not significant*	Not tested

Fig 4. Locations in autumn, and movements of over 20 km between the breeding season and autumn, of Goosanders present in Britain & Ireland during the breeding season. Males (2, blue) and females (9, red) are differentiated from those of unknown sex (35, grey). Resightings are not shown.

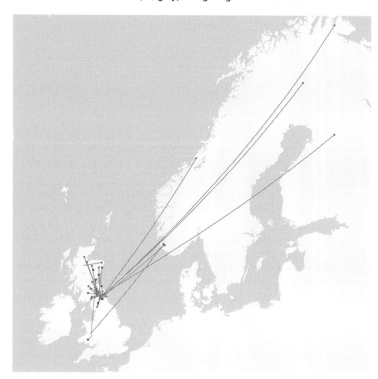

Fig 5. Locations in winter, and movements of over 20 km between the breeding season and winter, of Goosanders present in Britain & Ireland during the breeding season. Males (7, blue) and females (4, red) are differentiated from those of unknown sex (15, grey). Resightings are not shown.

have been fitted with numbered, coloured wing-tags that enable them to be recognized individually in the field. Most trapping in the breeding season has been carried out at sites in Northumberland and at Hoselaw Loch, Borders. The distribution of ringing in winter is quite different, with most recoveries stemming from birds caught in large duck-traps at sites in or near London between November and February.

The increase and spread of Goosanders during the 20th century brought them into conflict with fishing interests at a number of sites (eg Carter & Evans 1988). The legal protection that is afforded to them (but only since 1981 in Scotland) allows for the species to be 'controlled' under licence, so that many birds have been shot on the breeding rivers. Deliberate killing by Man is therefore by far the most widely reported cause of death (Fig 3). A further 9% have been accidentally captured in fishing nets and a further 2% are also human-related. Over the last 40 years the legal status of the species has varied, potentially influencing whether or not ringed birds that have been shot have been reported. Changes in the law, and in the behaviour of hunters as well as ringers, have undoubtedly influenced the recovery information. Since hunting pressure within Britain is concentrated at certain breeding rivers, where the species is viewed as an economically important pest, it is likely that birds elsewhere are greatly under-represented in the ring-recoveries.

Goosanders on the breeding grounds show a distinct annual cycle of occurrence (Marquiss & Duncan 1994a). Along the Scottish River Dee, weekly counts showed that Goosanders were most abundant along the upper river in spring and summer, on the lower river in late summer, autumn and winter, and on lochs in late winter and spring. Once the females have completed their clutches and are incubating, the breeding males gather on inland waters where they are joined by one-year-old males during late May. Remarkably, fully grown males are almost totally absent from the breeding grounds during June to October, although a few hundred have been recorded as moulting in the Beauly Firth and Longman Bay in the Highlands. The complete disappearance of the majority, long a mystery, is now known to be due to a moult migration to the area of the four large fjords around the North Cape in northernmost Norway

Fig 6. Wing-tag sightings of Goosanders marked (a) as pulli in Northumberland since 1976 (19,31) and (b) as fully grown birds at Hoselaw Loch, Borders, in May 1982 and 1984 (5,9). Those relocated during March–August (red) are differentiated from those relocated during September–February (blue). Hoselaw Loch is denoted by a black square. Two individuals ringed at the Loch and seen in Tana Fjord, Norway, in September are not shown. Individuals may appear more than once. Sample sizes for the classes (March–August, September–February) are shown. (Source: Northumbria Ringing Group data.)

(a)

(b)

Fig 7. Recovery locations and overseas movements of Goosanders present in Britain & Ireland during winter. Those known to be from a foreign breeding population (2, red) are differentiated from all others (16, grey).

(Little & Furness 1985). The majority of western European drakes, estimated to be about 35,000 birds, eventually gather in the Tana Fjord during September, having completed their annual moult. The females moult within Britain after raising their broods to fledging (Fig 4).

On hatching, Goosander chicks are led to the river, where broods may cover long distances downstream prior to fledging. In autumn, some adults and young birds remain on the breeding rivers, while others move to estuaries or sheltered coasts (Aspinall & Dennis 1988). The pattern of autumn and winter movements appears to be complex (Figs 4 & 5). Migrant males do not begin to return from Norway until November; between then and January, they rejoin the females and first-winter males on waters close to the breeding areas. Except during June–August, birds often roost communally at night on secluded lakes and reservoirs, arriving mostly in the hour before sunset and departing before sunrise, and spreading out onto surrounding waters to feed by day (Smaldon 1993, Marquiss & Duncan 1994b).

Birds wing-tagged as ducklings in Northumberland, and those tagged as fully grown adults in the Borders, show considerable spread into southern Scotland and south to the English Midlands during the winter (Fig 6a). There is some evidence that birds ringed as pulli in Northumberland penetrated further south into England & Wales after 1976 than previously, in accordance with the expansion of the breeding range (Rehfisch *et al* 1999). Most birds winter within 150 km of their natal or breeding sites. Multiple tag-sightings indicate that some British breeding adults are faithful to particular wintering sites. One bird, for which co-ordinates for mapping were not available, was ringed as a pullus in Northumberland and shot near Laval in Brittany in mid-March four years later.

Most birds return to their nesting areas by late March. Ring-recoveries and sightings suggest a wide range of natal dispersal distances (Rehfisch *et al* 1999). Six of 25 pulli recovered in the breeding season were found within 20 km of the ringing site. By contrast, another bird ringed as a pullus was recovered in northwest Russia in May three years later, possibly an abmigrant. The limited evidence suggests that female breeding site-fidelity is high. One female was found nesting in the same tree in two years. Another two birds ringed as breeding adults were recovered within 12 km in a subsequent breeding season.

Only one ring-recovery, in Essex, has shown a British-bred bird penetrating far into the areas of Britain where the Goosander is purely a non-breeding visitor, and furthermore, despite these areas being well-watched, there have been no sightings there of tagged British-bred birds (Figs 4–6). Exchanges of ringed birds with abroad appear to support the contention that the large majority of Goosanders of both sexes seen in lowland England are winter visitors from the Continent (Fig 7). Arrivals originate mainly in northern Fennoscandia and western Russia, birds from southern Scandinavia and from south of the Baltic being largely resident close to their breeding sites (*BWP*). The possibility remains, however, that some birds in southern Britain in winter may be British in origin, perhaps investigating potential new breeding areas as part of continued range expansion. Foreign-ringed birds have been reported from widely scattered areas of eastern Britain but most have been found in lowland England. The single recovery in Lancashire in December of a bird ringed as a pullus in Norway in the same year (Fig 7) suggests that there is at least a small degree of mixing of continental and British birds in winter. A recovery of a Goosander ringed in Surrey in winter and recovered in the Netherlands three winters later (Fig 7) indicates that individual continental birds may not visit Britain every winter. This accords with the observation that influxes may occur into Britain during severe weather in western Europe, as in 1979 (Chandler 1981).

The widespread perception of Goosander as a pest species is likely to continue to threaten its presently favourable conservation status. The gaps in our knowledge of the diurnal and seasonal movements of individual birds, and of the patterns of dispersal, hamper the argument over the kinds of measures, if any, that should be taken to control the increase and spread of the breeding population. Further marking studies are therefore highly desirable, both to clarify the seasonal movements of birds breeding in different regions of Britain and their degree of overlap with the wintering ranges of immigrants from the Continent.

Brian Little & John H Marchant

Red Kite
Milvus milvus

The Red Kite, known for its forked tail and scavenging habits, is now increasing in Britain. As a result there is a greater chance of seeing this rare but charismatic raptor even in those regions where it has yet to recolonize, since young birds disperse widely in their pre-breeding years. The nominate race *milvus* has an essentially European range covering mainly France, Germany, Poland, Spain, Sweden and Switzerland but with smaller populations in adjacent countries, including Britain (*European Atlas*). In Ireland, it is recorded only as a vagrant (*Birds in Ireland*). Small isolated populations also occur in eastern and southern Europe and possibly North Africa (Evans & Pienkowski 1991, *European Atlas*) but are fragmented and declining, while Red Kites seen in the Middle East are now likely to be only wandering birds (Evans & Pienkowski 1991). Those populations breeding in northern and central Europe are partially migratory but since the late 1950s overwintering has developed, although this only involves a small proportion of the total central European population (*BWP*, *European Atlas*). The small populations in Corsica (Patrimonio 1990), Italy (Cortone *et al* 1994) and Wales (Davis *et al* 2001) are largely sedentary while in Iberia the resident breeding population is joined in winter by large numbers of migrants from northern and central Europe (Heredia *et al* 1991, Viñuela 1997). Small numbers also winter in North Africa (Urcun & Bried 1998a) and stragglers have been recorded as far east as India (Prakash 1989) and Bangladesh (Sarker & Sarker 1985). The only other race *fasciicauda* is restricted to the Cape Verde Islands (*BWP*), where it has interbred with Black Kites and is now endangered, possibly extinct (Hazevoet 1995).

The analysis of the data for this species was supported by Ursula Bowen

Within Britain, conservation action has expanded the breeding range of the Red Kite by re-establishing populations in England and Scotland through the translocation and release of birds mainly of continental origin (Evans *et al* 1997), and by encouraging recovery of the native population in Wales (Davis 1993, Cross & Davis 1998). In addition, a breeding pair of Red Kites, possibly natural immigrants from the Continent, has been discovered recently in Suffolk (Carter 1998). The basic landscapes favoured by Red Kites are those which offer extensive open areas for foraging but which also contain a patchwork of woodland for nesting and roosting. Prior to 1989, these requirements were associated with the relict oakwoods, sheep-grazed rough grassland, meadows and moorland of central Wales (Walters-Davies & Davis 1973). Today, however, Red Kites are also recolonizing wooded lowland mixed-farmland landscapes, similar to those used by Red Kites in northern and central Europe.

The distribution and amount of ringing (Fig 1) broadly reflects the distribution and size of the breeding populations in Britain, although pairs in the re-established populations produce more young per breeding attempt than those within Wales (I M Evans *et al* 1999). Red Kites are ringed almost exclusively as nestlings in June and July (Fig 2). Since 1968, a high proportion of the annual production of young has

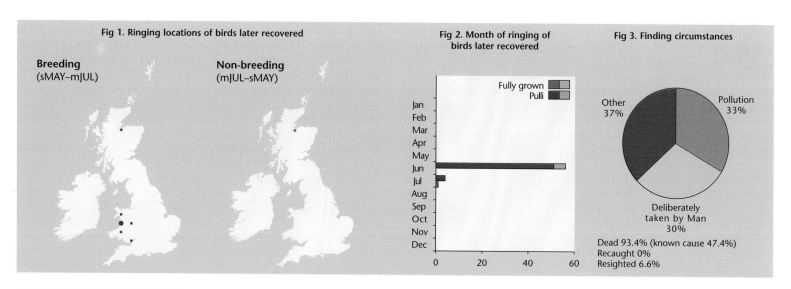

Fig 1. Ringing locations of birds later recovered

Breeding (sMAY–mJUL)

Non-breeding (mJUL–sMAY)

Fig 2. Month of ringing of birds later recovered

Fully grown
Pulli

Fig 3. Finding circumstances

Other 37%
Pollution 33%
Deliberately taken by Man 30%

Dead 93.4% (known cause 47.4%)
Recaught 0%
Resighted 6.6%

Ringing and recovery data

	<1960	60–69	70–79	80–89	90–97	Total
RINGING						
BTO ringing totals (%)	0	2	10	19	70	1,220
RECOVERIES						
BTO-ringed (%)	0	0	9	43	48	56
Foreign-ringed (%)	0	0	60	40	0	5

Statistical analyses

	Breeding population (sMAY–mJUL)	Wintering population (sNOV–mFEB)
Status	[SEDENTARY]	[LONG-DISTANCE MIGRANT]
Age differences	Not tested	Not tested
Sex differences	Not tested	Not tested
Regional differences	Not tested	Not tested
Finding circumstances	Not tested	Not tested

Fig 4. Dispersal of Red Kites ringed as nestlings in the Welsh breeding area (large filled circle) and recovered more than 50 km from their natal areas during the period 1968–97. (*Source*: P E Davis & A V Cross.)

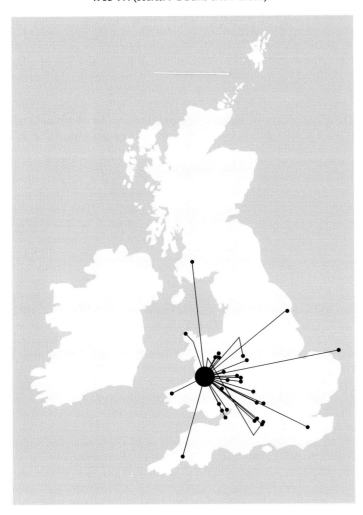

Fig 5. Furthest locations of Red Kites ringed as nestlings in aviaries or at nest sites within their respective release areas in England and Scotland. (*Source*: I M Evans *et al* 1999, by permission of *Bird Study.*)

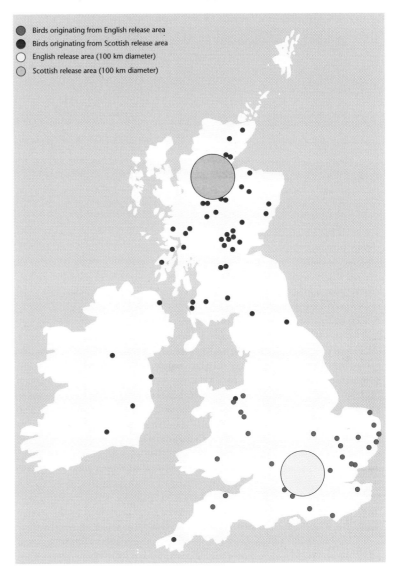

been ringed annually in Wales, as part of the efforts to monitor and conserve the population (Davis *et al* 2001). In addition, all Red Kites that were translocated to and released in Britain and a high proportion of their young have also been ringed, although only information from naturally fledged birds has been included in the analyses below. Recently, the efficiency of gathering information on movements by Red Kites in Britain has been greatly assisted by fitting wing-tags, colour-rings and radio-transmitters to some of the ringed birds (Newton *et al* 1989, Evans *et al* 1997, Davis *et al* 2001).

Just under half of all the ring-recovery data record a known cause of death (Fig 3), of which 63% involved birds poisoned or deliberately taken by Man and 37% involved trauma or other natural causes. Similar percentages for these categories of mortality were reported from the Welsh population (which included ringed and unringed individuals) by Davis *et al* (2001), in which the cause of death was recorded for 64% of recoveries. In comparison, studies on ringed, radio-tagged and wing-tagged Red Kites in England and Scotland (I M Evans *et al* 1999), attributed the highest proportion of recoveries (71%) with a known cause of death. The majority of these died through the abuse, misuse and approved use of pesticides and this is clearly a major nature conservation issue for this species in Britain.

In Wales, most first-year Red Kites remain within 40 km of their natal areas (Davis *et al* 2001). However, Red Kites have been found up to 390 km from their natal areas in Wales during their first year (Davis *et al* 2001). The majority of these movements were in an easterly direction (Fig 4), although dispersal within Wales was markedly orientated southwestwards (Davis *et al* 2001). Three birds that were seen at more

than 100 km from their natal areas returned subsequently to Wales and at least one has bred. These recoveries suggest that in Wales only a small proportion of juvenile Red Kites disperse far from their natal areas in their first autumn or winter and that in some birds this movement occurs very soon after fledging (Walters-Davies & Davis 1973, Davis *et al* 2001).

In the recently naturalized populations in southern England and northern Scotland, the pattern of juvenile dispersal differs along with the provenance of the breeding stock and the latitude of the breeding locations. This has been shown by I M Evans *et al* (1999) where first-year birds of Swedish origin released in northern Scotland showed a greater tendency to disperse and to travel greater distances (up to 830 km) than those of mainly Spanish origin released in southern England (which dispersed up to 272 km). Birds released in northern Scotland also dispersed predominantly in a southerly or southwesterly direction prior to their first winter and returned the following spring. Recent sightings of naturally fledged birds dispersing from northern Scotland generally accord with this pattern (Etheridge *et al* 1998, 1999); the sighting of a first-year Red Kite 1,017 km away in Iceland, however, shows that there can be exceptions. Dispersing first-year Red Kites from the more sedentary population in southern England show no directional preference (Fig 5) and may disperse in late summer/autumn or in the following spring after wintering in their natal area. Females were more

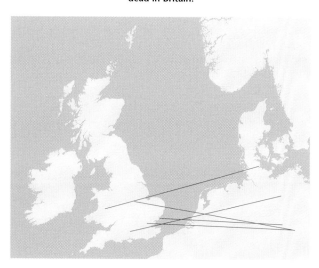

likely than males to disperse and tended to disperse further overall than males (I M Evans *et al* 1999).

Information on the movements of native Red Kites of breeding age indicates that these birds are largely sedentary once they have established a breeding territory, although there may be some movement following nest failure and during winter when individuals form communal roosts (Davis *et al* 2001). Newton *et al* (1989) first showed that birds were highly philopatric, while Davis *et al* (2001) report average natal dispersal distances to first breeding site of 11.7 km for male and 13.7 km for female Red Kites; the furthest distances recorded were 58 km for males and 53 km for females. In addition, some young birds occupied non-breeding territories prior to breeding in another, up to 30.5 km away (Newton *et al* 1989). Translocated birds (I M Evans *et al* 1999) also showed a high degree of philopatry with median distances of up to 9.4 km but Scottish birds dispersed further. Generally, once translocated birds had started breeding, they exhibited a similar pattern to the native population in Wales. However, translocated birds released in one locality have bred in other release areas more than 100 km away (Etheridge *et al* 1999, M McQuaid pers comm) and around 50 km from their release sites (I M Evans *et al* 1999). In southern England, a pair has bred around 50 km from the release area but in an area where others have attempted to breed and where Red Kites from the Chilterns regularly occur.

Recoveries of Red Kite pulli ringed in Sweden confirm that they migrate predominantly southwest to the main wintering areas in Spain, central and southwest France. Some also move south and winter in Italy and possibly southeast Europe. There may also be some abmigration as some ringed birds were recovered in neighbouring breeding populations (Poland and Germany) during spring and summer (Kjellén 1994). The rapid increase of the Swedish population since the early 1970s has been associated with more and more birds overwintering in Sweden. However, the number of mainly juvenile Red Kites leaving Sweden each autumn is also increasing along with population size (Kjellén 1996). A similar

pattern of behaviour has been reported for Red Kites in Switzerland (Müller 1997), Germany (Ortlieb 1982, George 1997) and eastern France (Urcun & Bried 1998a). Consequently, large numbers of Red Kites (mainly juveniles) from northern and central Europe still winter within Spain, with the greatest concentration on the northern plateau of Castilla y León (Viñuela 1996). Smaller numbers winter in Portugal (Abreu 1989), while up to 1,500 winter on the northern slopes of the western Pyrenees (Sagot 1991). Counts of migrating raptors indicate that the western Pyrenees is the major flyway into Spain for Red Kites, with peak passage during October (Urcun & Bried 1998a). Prior to 1989, annual bird reports for the eastern and southern counties of England also report peak numbers of vagrant Red Kites during spring and autumn, thought to comprise drifted migrants travelling between their wintering areas in southern Europe and breeding areas in central and northern Europe (I Carter pers comm).

The first overseas recovery of a Welsh Red Kite was reported in December 1999. This bird was in its fifth year and was found dead in County Wexford, Ireland (A V Cross pers comm), finally corroborating previous suggestions that vagrant Welsh birds occur in Ireland (*Birds in Ireland*). However, prior to this date, one Welsh bird was seen perched on a gas rig off the Norfolk coast, 390 km from its nest (Davis *et al* 2001) and a ringed offspring of a Welsh bird released in southern England was reported dead in its fourth year near Brussels, Belgium, in December 1997 (D A Stroud pers comm). Only one other Red Kite from southern England has been recovered dead abroad. This was a first-year bird (of Spanish origin) found 272 km away in northern France. Only the more migratory naturalized populations in Scotland tend to be seen or found dead abroad, with most overseas recoveries in Ireland. However, the recovery of a dead first-year bird in northeast Spain in May 1999, 1,598 km from its natal site in northern Scotland (B Etheridge pers comm), raises the possibility that some individuals may also winter in the same areas as Red Kites from northern and central Europe. Indeed, the recovery of a Scottish Red Kite, which had been seen previously in southern Ireland, dead in southwest England (McGrady *et al* 1994), and the Icelandic recovery, suggests that sea-crossings may not be a significant barrier to dispersal. This is also supported by the fact that not all Red Kites seen in Britain are from the native and naturalized populations, since passage and overwintering by continental Red Kites has also been confirmed by ringing (Fig 6). Some of these movements by continental birds may also represent natural colonization, since recent genetic evidence indicates that immigrant Red Kites have joined the breeding populations in Wales (May *et al* 1993) and England (I M Evans *et al* 1999).

No doubt the intensive efforts to ring Red Kites in Britain will continue into the future as this species remains of high conservation concern. Consequently, our knowledge of the movements of Red Kites is likely to improve further, particularly as other marking methods, in combination with ringing, are being used extensively. Effort needs to be directed particularly towards quantifying the true impact of persecution on both dispersing and sedentary individuals. In addition, a comprehensive analysis of the movements of colour-marked and radio-tagged Red Kites is needed to improve our knowledge of dispersal behaviour in the different populations of Red Kites now breeding in Britain and the extent to which this influences range expansion (Lensink 1997).

Ian M Evans, Peter E Davis & Lorcan O'Toole

Eurasian Marsh Harrier (Marsh Harrier)

Circus aeruginosus

The Marsh Harrier, the largest of the British species of harrier, is a partial migrant, with some individuals overwintering in Britain, and others moving to southern Europe and northwest Africa or south of the Sahara. With such a wide wintering range, it is perhaps not surprising that this adaptable and opportunistic species has increased in numbers both in Britain and abroad, following earlier declines due largely to persecution and the effects of organochlorine pesticides (Underhill-Day 1984, 1998). In Ireland, the species has become more common on passage during recent years but there has been no evidence of breeding (Milne & O'Sullivan 1997). The nominate race occupies suitable lowland habitat throughout Europe, extending north to about 63°N and south and east to Turkey, Iran and central Asia. In winter, birds from northern and northwest Europe move south, most either stopping in the Mediterranean Basin or crossing the Sahara to winter in central and southern Africa as far south as the Transvaal (*BWP*). In southern Spain and northwest Africa, the breeding race is *harterti* and is believed to be resident (*BWP*). The eastern race *spilonotus* breeds in eastern Asia and winters in India and the Far East. To the south, on Madagascar and Réunion, there are two further races, *macrosceles* and *maillardi*, while *spilothorax* occurs in New Guinea, *approximans* on the central Pacific islands, and *gouldi* in Australasia. Of these, only southern populations of *gouldi* seem to be migratory (Brown & Amadon 1989).

In Britain, Marsh Harriers nest within extensive reedbeds and areas of arable cultivation. In farmland, they nest in smaller reed stands or rough grass in creeks or ditches, or in the crops themselves, mostly

The analysis of the data for this species was supported by Wicken Fen Group

winter cereals, oilseed rape or, latterly, linseed (Image 1987, Underhill-Day 1990). Elsewhere in Europe, they are found in similar habitat, as well as in sedge, rush and reedmace beds, on saltmarshes and in stands of tall herbaceous vegetation (*eg* Schipper 1978, Buczek & Keller 1994). In winter, Marsh Harriers are found in a range of wetland habitats, including reedswamps, flooded grasslands, saltmarshes and ricefields, but some hunting takes place over dry habitats, including crops and semi-desert (Thiollay 1989, Arroyo *et al* 1995).

Apart from two birds ringed as juveniles, all Marsh Harriers ringed and recovered were ringed as pulli. With few exceptions, ringing took place in the main breeding areas within East Anglia (Fig 1), and only one bird was ringed outside the breeding season, in September (Fig 2). All pulli were ringed during June or July and the sex of most was not known. During the period 1920–97, an estimated 3,817 young birds fledged (Underhill-Day 1984, 1998). Of 1,283 birds ringed, only 50 (3.9%) have been recovered, with nearly half of all recoveries during 1990–97. Where the cause of death was known (Fig 3), 85% of deaths were directly linked to human activity.

Most recoveries of British-ringed birds have been within Britain, with 60% of all recoveries during the period June–August. The median distances travelled before recovery may be biased towards British

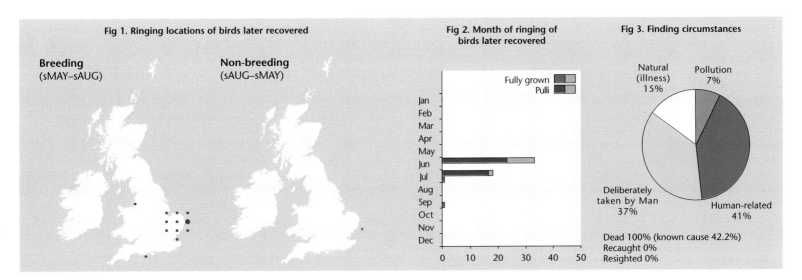

Fig 1. Ringing locations of birds later recovered

Breeding (sMAY–sAUG) Non-breeding (sAUG–sMAY)

Fig 2. Month of ringing of birds later recovered

Fully grown
Pulli

Fig 3. Finding circumstances

Natural (illness) 15%
Pollution 7%
Deliberately taken by Man 37%
Human-related 41%

Dead 100% (known cause 42.2%)
Recaught 0%
Resighted 0%

Ringing and recovery data

	<1960	60–69	70–79	80–89	90–97	Total
RINGING						
BTO ringing totals (%)	9	1	4	21	65	1,283
RECOVERIES						
BTO-ringed (%)	26	4	8	18	44	50
Foreign-ringed (%)	7	7	21	50	14	14

Statistical analyses

	Breeding population (sMAY–sAUG)	Wintering population (mNOV–sMAR)
Status	[LONG-DISTANCE MIGRANT]	?
Age differences	Not tested	—
Sex differences	Not tested	—
Regional differences	Not tested	—
Finding circumstances	Not tested	—

Fig 4. Movements of over 20 km and recovery locations in (a) July, August and September (17:9) and (b) October–February (9:2, points) and April (2:2, triangles) of Marsh Harriers ringed as pulli in Britain & Ireland. First-year birds (red) are differentiated from older birds (blue), with seasonally inaccurate recoveries shown with open points and broken lines colour coded by age. Sample sizes of the classes (first-year birds:older birds) are shown.

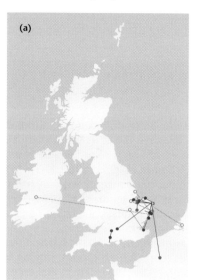

recoveries because the chance of a ring being found and reported may be higher in Britain than in less densely populated areas abroad. For all birds, the median distance travelled before recovery was 172 km.

There is limited evidence to suggest that some birds may disperse before migration, as there is little difference in the median distances moved between 31–60 days (75 km), and 61–90 days (89 km) after ringing. Moreover, recoveries of juveniles during July, August and September in the year in which they were ringed as pulli are from all quadrants of the compass, but half are between north and west. Of the recoveries in October, the majority are between south and southwest (Fig 4a & b). A Danish-ringed nestling has also been found in East Anglia in September. During 1986–92 at the Falsterbo Peninsula in Sweden, Kjellén (1993) found that median autumn dates for migrating juveniles (which were not sexed by observers) and adult females were similar, with adult males passing through generally a week or two later. Finlayson (1992) recorded no difference in timing between the sexes on autumn migration over the Strait of Gibraltar.

Most recent sightings of adult birds wintering in Britain have been of females (*Winter Atlas*). In the Netherlands, Zijlstra (1987) recorded more adult females than males overwintering. Further south in Charente-Maritime in western central France, 79% of marked adults were found during winter within 25 km of their first known nesting site, and 63% of juveniles also overwintered within 10 km of where they were fledged. There was no significant difference between the proportions of each sex that stayed (Bavoux et al 1992, 1994).

There are no reliable dates for departure from Britain, although most birds probably leave during September–October, and recovery patterns suggest that they move south through France and Iberia, either wintering in northwest Africa or moving south down the African coast (Fig 4b). The movement of foreign-ringed birds from north and northwest Europe shows a similar pattern, with recoveries from north and northwest Africa south as far as the Equator. In Senegal, Arroyo et al (1995) found that only 15% of wintering Marsh Harriers were adult

males. In partial migrants, where the larger, more powerful sex is likely to compete more successfully for food during the winter, one usually expects the larger birds to stay and the smaller sex to move away. Marsh Harriers show pronounced sexual dimorphism, with females larger than males, and it seems that the males are less likely to overwinter in those breeding areas, including Britain, where most of the population is migratory. Whether males move further or faster on migration than females is unclear.

Although no foreign-ringed individuals have been found breeding in Britain, an adult bird ringed in the Netherlands was recovered in a breeding area in May, and given the history and population fluctuations of this species, it seems probable that there is some recruitment into our breeding population from abroad. Several foreign-ringed juveniles have also been recovered in Britain during May and June. No British-ringed birds have been recovered abroad as adults during the breeding season.

The few spring recoveries in Portugal and northern France suggest that birds return along similar routes to those taken in autumn (Fig 4b). Arroyo et al (1995) reported that Marsh Harriers had almost disappeared from their wintering areas in Senegal by March. The peak spring-passage time for males over the Strait of Gibraltar is from mid-February to late April, with most females passing over from late April to mid-May (Finlayson 1992). Spring passage by males in Italy was mostly in March (36%) and April (62%), significantly earlier than females, most of which passed through in April and May. First-summer birds were later still, with most seen in May (Gustin & Pizzari 1998). Median arrival dates at breeding locations in Britain did not differ significantly between males (4 April) and females (1 April), although female arrivals were spread over a longer period (Underhill-Day 1990).

Colour ringing of pulli was undertaken during 1983–86 and, in subsequent years, birds of both sexes were recorded breeding near their natal area. A female was also found breeding some 180 km from where she was fledged. In Charente-Maritime, Bavoux et al (1998) found that birds frequently nested not far from their natal site. The colour-ringing project also confirmed that British Marsh Harriers of both sexes can breed in their second year, and that some juveniles return to Britain in the summer of their first year (pers obs).

There is evidence that first-year and adult Marsh Harriers wintering in Charente-Maritime, France, were at risk from lead poisoning through ingestion of lead shot carried by their prey. Birds with blood lead concentrations greater than 150 µg/dl may have a lower annual survival probability than birds with lower lead levels in their blood (Pain et al 1997 & pers comm). British birds also overwinter in areas where lead shot is used, which may put them at similar risk, although the recent banning of lead shot for shooting over wetlands in Britain may reduce this.

With a high proportion of birds ringed as pulli and a limited number of recoveries, we have little information on the movements of Marsh Harriers, including any differences in timing, routes and wintering destinations between the sexes and age groups. Further ring-recoveries should also provide more information on pre-migratory dispersal by juveniles, and on natal and breeding dispersal. There is only limited information on the population dynamics of Marsh Harriers and additional data would improve our understanding of such matters as lifetime productivity, age of first breeding, life expectancy and mortality. In view of the recent tendency towards nesting in crops, further information on philopatry and consistency in choice of nesting habitat would also help us to assess the future conservation needs of this species.

John Underhill-Day

Hen Harrier

Circus cyaneus

The Hen Harrier is the most widespread and familiar of the three species of Palearctic harrier that breed regularly in Britain & Ireland. It is also the least migratory, with many individuals present throughout the year in their Scottish stronghold, thus making them the most northerly wintering harriers in the world (Watson 1977). However, because in their first autumn some Scottish- and Welsh-born birds undertake long movements into southwest Europe, the Hen Harrier in Britain & Ireland is best described as a partial migrant. In contrast, northern European populations withdraw completely from their nesting grounds, to winter as far south as the Mediterranean shores of North Africa (*BWP*). Hen Harriers have a wide global distribution, with the nominate *cyaneus* extending east through Europe on a broad belt across central Asia to Kamchatka. In winter, these eastern populations migrate as far south as Iran, northern India, Myanmar and Vietnam (Watson 1977). The Nearctic race *hudsonius,* the 'Northern Harrier', breeds in Canada and the prairie states of USA and winters in the southern states and into Central America.

Hen Harriers are capable of high soaring and flapping flight, and are not confined to narrow migration corridors, and thus occur in relatively small numbers at raptor migration watch-points (*BWP*). At Falsterbo, Sweden, passage commences in mid-August but most birds fly through in the period mid-September to late October with no obvious peaks, adults preceding juveniles (Kjellén 1992). Many harriers from these Fennoscandian populations are bound for wintering grounds in the southwest, particularly in France, Iberia and the Low Countries (*BWP*). Autumn migration through the Pyrenees shows a similar broad peak

The analysis of the data for this species was supported by Brian Etheridge

extending into early November (Urcun & Bried 1998b). In the breeding season, the species is typically associated with heather moorland and newly afforested uplands throughout Scotland, Ireland and Wales, with a tiny population on the grousemoors of northern England (*1988–91 Atlas*). In autumn and winter, Hen Harriers can be seen in open country throughout both Britain and Ireland, but low-lying coastal areas in south and east England and southwest Scotland are particularly favoured (*Winter Atlas*).

Watson (1977) analysed the 143 ring-recoveries of Hen Harriers available to the end of 1973. Since then, intense interest in the species has led to a large increase in the number of young ringed, so that the number of ring-recoveries has more than doubled. Most of the ringing has been carried out in Scotland (Fig 1), and is a reflection of the wide distribution and abundance of Hen Harriers in that country (*1988–91 Atlas*). In addition, a recent RSPB study carried out in Scotland and Wales involved the fitting of uniquely marked wing-tags to 1,600 nestling Hen Harriers of known sex (Etheridge *et al* 1997) and resulted in almost 900 sightings outside the breeding season.

Around 95% of the ring-recoveries of British & Irish Hen Harriers were from birds marked as nestlings (Fig 2). The fully grown birds that were marked were mostly breeding adults or fledged juveniles. The cause of ring-recovery was recorded in only 38% of the returns and, of these,

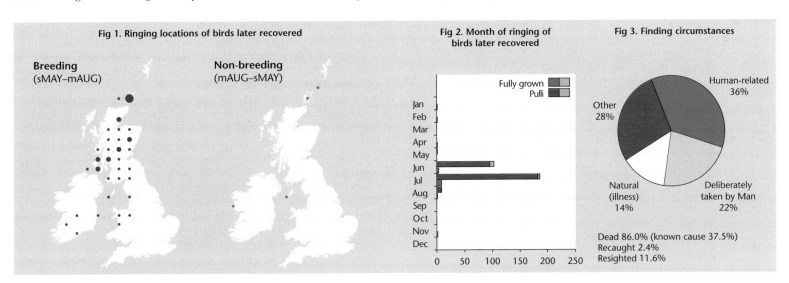

Fig 1. Ringing locations of birds later recovered

Breeding (sMAY–mAUG) Non-breeding (mAUG–sMAY)

Fig 2. Month of ringing of birds later recovered

Fully grown / Pulli

Fig 3. Finding circumstances

Human-related 36%
Other 28%
Natural (illness) 14%
Deliberately taken by Man 22%

Dead 86.0% (known cause 37.5%)
Recaught 2.4%
Resighted 11.6%

Ringing and recovery data

	<1960	60–69	70–79	80–89	90–97	Total
RINGING						
BTO ringing totals (%)	6	10	16	26	42	7,069
RECOVERIES						
BTO-ringed (%)	13	16	19	19	33	363
Foreign-ringed (%)	0	13	47	40	0	15

Statistical analyses

	Breeding population (sMAY–mAUG)	Wintering population (mNOV–sMAR)
Status	SHORT-DISTANCE MIGRANT (2)	[LONG-DISTANCE MIGRANT]
Age differences[NS*]	Significant*	Not tested
Sex differences[NS*]	Significant*	Not tested
Regional differences	Not tested	Not tested
Finding circumstances	Not significant*	Not tested

Fig 4. Locations in autumn (red) and winter (blue) and movements of over 20 km between the breeding season and autumn or winter of (a) male (25:27) and (b) female (21:19) Hen Harriers present in Britain & Ireland during the breeding season. Sample sizes of the classes (autumn:winter) are shown. Wing-tag sightings are not included.

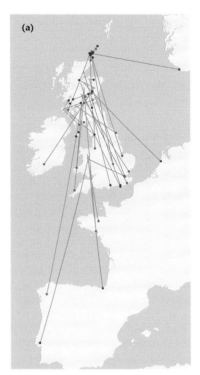

killed by Man and that few, if any, are reported by the person responsible for the killing, even under alternative recovery categories (Newton 1979).

Hen Harriers breeding in Orkney have been the subject of intensive ringing studies for over 50 years (eg Balfour & Cadbury 1979, Picozzi 1984) and have produced the largest number of recoveries, the majority occurring before the species underwent its recent major decline there (Meek et al 1998b). Some Orkney birds, particularly young of the year, move south in autumn into eastern and central Scotland, and a few have reached Ireland and England as far south as the Wash and East Anglia in winter (Fig 4). There are also 10 recoveries showing movements across the North Sea into coastal areas of Norway, Denmark, northern Germany and the Netherlands (most of which are omitted from Fig 4 because they were made by birds of unknown sex); such movements from Britain & Ireland are almost exclusively from Orkney. Despite the large numbers ringed, no Orkney-ringed bird has been recovered in extreme southern England, France or Iberia. Moreover, there are many recoveries within Orkney outside the breeding season, confirming that some birds are resident there (Fig 4). In mainland Scotland, the majority of ring-recoveries and sightings of wing-tagged Hen Harriers come from young in their first autumn and winter. Post-fledging sightings of tagged birds up to mid-September suggest most young are still in inland habitats, though many have moved from moorland onto agricultural land. These dispersal movements, the majority under 100 km, have no marked directional preference. A number of individuals, particularly females, have travelled well to the north and east of the natal moors. Many young Scottish-born Hen Harriers overwinter; 53% of sightings of tagged males and 65% of sightings of tagged females were reported in Scotland during their first winter (November–February). In older birds these percentages increase to 70% for males and 75% for females. The median distance moved by those remaining is 65 km for males and 27 km for females. Over 55% of tagged males that wintered in Scotland were seen on agricultural ground less than 100 m above sea-level, whereas only 38% of tagged females were found wintering at this altitude and most (53%) were above 200 m on heather moorland. Marquiss (1980) provided evidence to show that in Scotland many more female Hen Harriers winter on high ground because they can better exploit the larger prey items there, while the smaller males move to coastal farmland where smaller prey are available.

Most of the juvenile males that depart south from Scotland in autumn originate in the Highlands. Wing-tag sightings of these birds in late September and during October indicate a migration route through the Southern Uplands and into England by following the Pennine Hills or the Irish Sea coast. The east coast between Lothian and Yorkshire is largely avoided. Some birds continue down to southwest England and there is a cluster of sightings of tagged juvenile males between Dorset and the Scilly Isles in late October and November. Many are seen at coastal headlands, suggesting imminent departure across the English Channel. Moreover, the occurrence of sightings and ring-recoveries in Brittany indicates that southwest England is the main departure point for juvenile male harriers heading south onto the Continent. The 160-km crossing of the English Channel between Devon and the Brittany coast is evidently no barrier and is the most direct route to wintering areas in southwest France and northwest Iberia. Further evidence of the importance of this migration route comes from the lack of a concentration of sightings at the short sea-crossing in southeast England and the absence of both tag-sightings and ring-recoveries of Scottish birds in northern France between Cherbourg and Calais. Small numbers of first-year male Hen Harriers (5% of sightings outside Scotland), mainly wing-tagged as chicks in the west and north Highlands, have been reported in winter from Ireland. These movements to Ireland are supported by several ring-recoveries. The percentage of the Scottish population actually wintering in Ireland is probably very much higher than 5%, but is under-recorded due to the scarcity of observers and the consequential low reporting rates of marked birds. A few young males, ringed or tagged in Scotland, have been recorded wintering in

over half (58%) were attributed to Man's activities, including 22% shot, poisoned or trapped (Fig 3). In their study of Hen Harrier persecution on Scottish grousemoors, Etheridge et al (1997) were able to demonstrate that 11–15% of the total population of breeding females in Scotland, except those in Orkney, were killed by gamekeepers each year, amounting to 55–74 females. Furthermore, many of the adults and some of the broods destroyed had been previously ringed and wing-tagged but none were subsequently reported. This was not unexpected given the legal protection now afforded to all birds of prey. However, it corroborates the idea that ring-recoveries currently under-record the number of raptors

HEN HARRIER

Fig 5. Movements of the 15 foreign-ringed Hen Harriers recovered in Britain & Ireland.

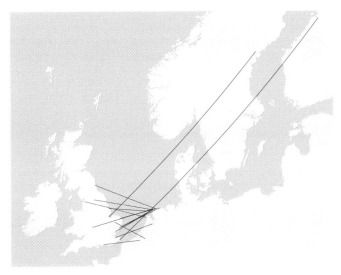

coastal areas of southwest Wales, in southwest England or in low-lying areas of south and east England.

Only 35% of winter sightings of tagged juvenile female Hen Harriers were reported outside Scotland. A fifth of this total, all birds tagged in the west Highlands in Argyll or on Islay, were reported from Ireland. The remaining 28% of records came from the moors of northern England and from coastal areas of eastern England between the Humber and East Anglia. Sightings of wing-tagged females along the south coast of England in autumn and winter were scarce, and the only indication that female Hen Harriers cross to the Continent is a single sighting of a Scottish-tagged chick on passage through Jersey in late October. This difference in autumn movement between the sexes is well demonstrated by comparing the ring-recovery maps for male and female Hen Harriers ringed in Britain & Ireland (Figs 4a & b). Males are much smaller than females and the tendency for the sexes to utilize different wintering areas (supported by the statistical analysis of the ring-recovery data, with males recovered significantly further south in winter) and habitats outside the breeding season may prevent competition between them and is linked to differences in the size and availability of their preferred prey (Newton 1979).

Young Hen Harriers of both sexes hatched in southwest Scotland are much more sedentary outside the breeding season than young from populations further north or in Wales. The majority of ring-recoveries and tag-sightings have occurred within 100 km of the natal moors and there are only occasional sightings, mainly of males, on the Isle of Man or in the south of England. There are no continental recoveries or sightings, and the main wintering area for the few that leave Scotland lies along the east coast between the Thames and Humber Estuaries. A higher proportion of resident birds in southwest Scotland could be linked to relatively mild winters and to the greater availability of prey species for both sexes.

The small population of Hen Harriers breeding in Wales has provided several interesting autumn and winter recoveries and sightings. There are no recoveries or sightings of first-winter males within Wales. Reports indicate that the main wintering areas are in east and southern England and along the Biscay coast of France, with an exceptional bird reaching Portugal (Fig 4). Welsh-born female Hen Harriers reveal a concentration of winter recoveries and sightings on the Wash and in East Anglia (Fig 4), with only a few remaining in Wales or occurring on the downs of southern England. There are no records of Welsh Hen Harriers either from Ireland or from Scotland (Fig 4). Nor are there any records of Irish-born Hen Harriers outside Ireland and the data, although limited, suggest that locally bred birds are largely resident, the population augmented in winter by a small number of first-year birds from north and west Scotland. Older birds from Scottish and Welsh populations in

subsequent winters were less likely to be found at long distances from the breeding moors, although a few individuals of both sexes were resighted in favoured winter haunts in eastern and southern England.

Most females start breeding at one year old and males at two (Etheridge et al 1997). It can therefore be assumed that most female and probably many male Hen Harriers ringed as pulli and recovered dead in a subsequent breeding season were at or close to their nesting site. The median distance between natal site and assumed breeding site for 22 birds recovered dead, of both sexes, was 21 km. Etheridge et al (1997) gave details of natal dispersal from a much larger sample of individually wing-tagged birds in relation to land use. Males moved further than females in all land-use categories: median distances for those hatched on grousemoors were 38 km (females 10.5 km), on other moorland 14 km (9.5 km) and in conifer forests 150 km (51 km). Wing-tagged male and female Hen Harriers usually nested in the same area in successive years, the median distance moved between nest sites being only 0.7 km.

The main wintering areas in Britain for Hen Harriers are southwest Scotland and southern and eastern England (Winter Atlas, Clarke & Watson 1990), where communal roosts are regularly counted. Grey-plumaged males (second-winter and older) make up on average 34% of the birds recorded at these roosts (Clarke & Watson 1997). In southern and southwestern England, the proportion of grey-plumaged males can reach 41–46% (Howells 1986, Castle & Clarke 1995). The ring-recovery and wing-tag data suggest very few British-breeding adult males occur in southern and southwestern England in winter. The origin of the majority of grey males must therefore lie on the Continent. The same is probably true for females, too, as only a small proportion of the brown birds attending communal roosts in eastern and southern England are found to be wing-tagged, despite the large numbers marked in Scotland and Wales. The inference is that the bulk of the winter population in southern and eastern England must consist of foreign birds (Clarke & Watson 1997). Supporting evidence comes from 11 recoveries in England outside the breeding season of nestlings and adults ringed in the Netherlands, where the population consists of 130–150 pairs (Bijlsma 1993). The presence of north European birds is indicated by a Finnish-ringed bird in Kent and a bird from northern Sweden on the Wash (Fig 5). The lack of further recoveries of Fennoscandian birds may be due to the low numbers of Hen Harriers ringed in these breeding areas (Clarke & Watson 1990). Furthermore, England may be visited in numbers only when severe weather displaces birds wintering on the Continent. Such conditions occurred in the midwinter influx of 1978/79 when over 750 Hen Harriers were counted along the east and south coasts of England (Davenport 1982).

Hen Harriers in Britain & Ireland have specific habitat requirements. The retention of inland bogs, rank grasslands and coastal grazing marshes in the main wintering areas in Ireland, southwest Scotland and southern and eastern England would benefit the species. However, the greatest contribution to the conservation of Hen Harriers in all seasons would be the adoption of a more tolerant attitude by landowners, hunters and gamekeepers (Etheridge et al 1997, Stott 1998). A wing-tagging study at the English Hen Harrier stronghold in the Forest of Bowland, Lancashire, is now under way and producing valuable results (D Sowter pers comm). Greater ringing effort directed towards this species is required both in Ireland and on the Isle of Man to increase the limited knowledge of the movements of these two populations. The deployment of a lightweight satellite-transmitter suitable for use on Hen Harriers would greatly benefit further research into their seasonal movements, and allow the origins of the wintering population in southern and eastern England to be identified. This information is urgently required because the numbers found wintering in Britain have been in steady decline for the last 10 years, and the reduction may be a reflection of what is happening on the breeding grounds (Clarke & Watson 1997).

Brian Etheridge

Montagu's Harrier
Circus pygargus

The Montagu's Harrier is the smallest and rarest of the three species of harrier breeding in Britain & Ireland, and the only one which is wholly migratory. The breeding distribution is confined to northwest Africa and Europe south of latitude 60°N and eastwards to central Siberia, with scattered populations in Turkey and northern Iran (*BWP*).

Populations from northwest Europe winter south of the Sahara but remain in the northern tropics, while birds from eastern Europe and central Asia winter in eastern Africa from the Sudan as far south as South Africa; birds from Siberia and northern China move to India and southeast Asia during the winter months (*BWP, European Atlas*). Across much of the European range of Montagu's Harrier, breeding populations declined from the 1960s onwards until some stabilization and recovery began during the 1980s. The declines were particularly severe in northwest Europe and Iberia, with numbers stable or increasing in Fennoscandia and the former Soviet states (Galushin 1994). Currently three-quarters of the European population is believed to nest in Russia with a further 15% in southern France and Spain (*European Atlas*).

In Britain, the numbers fell from a post-1945 peak of 30 nests in 1953 to just one by 1975. Subsequently there has been a slight increase with up to 12 nests reported annually during the 1990s (Underhill-Day 1990, RSPB pers comm). Recoveries of ringed birds have followed a similar pattern, with 81% of all recoveries occurring before 1970. The Montagu's Harrier was formerly a widespread if very local breeding bird in Britain with, at various periods of the 20th century, populations in the East Anglian fens and Breckland heaths, the rough grasslands,

The analysis of the data for this species was supported by Slapton Bird Observatory of Devon Birdwatching & Preservation Society

heaths and young conifer plantations of south and southwest England and south Wales, plantations and dunes on Anglesey and moorlands in northern England and Scotland (Underhill-Day 1990). In Ireland, Montagu's Harriers have been very rare breeding birds during the 20th century (*Birds in Ireland*). The distribution of ringing sites reflects this historical distribution (Fig 1), although in recent years most breeding attempts have been recorded from arable areas in East Anglia, mostly in winter cereals or oilseed rape, with sporadic breeding attempts in crops and on heathland elsewhere.

The low wing-loading and long primaries of Montagu's Harriers compared with other harriers (Nieboer 1973) may be an adaptation to longer migratory journeys (Clarke 1996). Montagu's Harriers winter south of the Sahara in the semi-desert and savanna grasslands of West and central Africa, and in East Africa through a range of similar vegetation zones. Hunting takes place over open habitats including burnt, dry and inundation grasslands, wetlands, ricefields and other cultivated areas, and scrublands.

All Montagu's Harrier ring-recoveries were of birds ringed as pulli between June and August (Fig 2), and 90% of those recovered had been found dead before reaching the presumed breeding age at the beginning of their third year. Human activity was implicated in about 83% of recoveries for which there was a suggested cause of death (Fig 3). Others

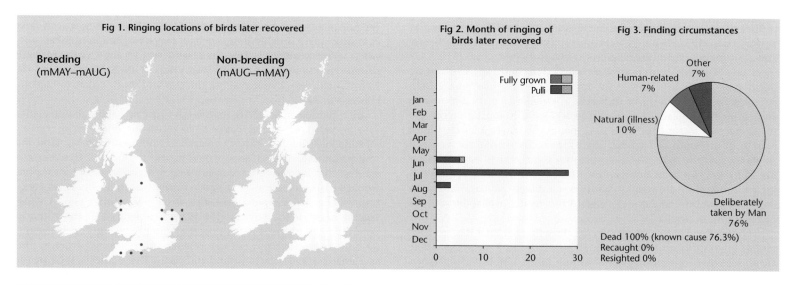

Fig 1. Ringing locations of birds later recovered

Breeding (mMAY–mAUG)

Non-breeding (mAUG–mMAY)

Fig 2. Month of ringing of birds later recovered

Fully grown / Pulli

Fig 3. Finding circumstances

Other 7%
Human-related 7%
Natural (illness) 10%
Deliberately taken by Man 76%

Dead 100% (known cause 76.3%)
Recaught 0%
Resighted 0%

Ringing and recovery data

	<1960	60–69	70–79	80–89	90–97	Total
RINGING						
BTO ringing totals (%)	48	13	1	19	20	461
RECOVERIES						
BTO-ringed (%)	76	5	0	11	8	37
Foreign-ringed (%)	100	0	0	0	0	1

Statistical analyses

	Breeding population (mMAY–mAUG)	Wintering population (mOCT–mMAR)
Status	[LONG-DISTANCE MIGRANT]	NONE
Age differences	Not tested	—
Sex differences	Not tested	—
Regional differences	Not tested	—
Finding circumstances	Not tested	—

Fig 4. Locations in autumn (18, red) and winter (1, blue), and movements of over 20 km between the breeding and non-breeding season, of Montagu's Harriers present in Britain & Ireland during the breeding season.

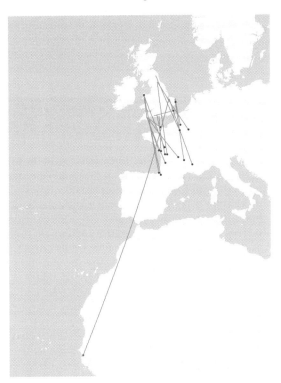

died from natural causes, including one bird whose remains were found in an Eagle Owl's nest.

All ring-recoveries before mid-August were in Britain or northern France but from mid-August birds were recovered elsewhere in France, with most recoveries in September and a few in October. At the Strait of Gibraltar, birds (presumably failed or non-breeders) are noted passing south as early as July, with the last during October (Finlayson 1992). Within 30 days of ringing, juveniles had travelled a median distance of 237 km, within 31–60 days 380 km and within 61–90 days 737 km. In one case, a juvenile had moved 672 km in no more than nine days (Image 1992). Most birds moved in a generally southerly direction (Fig 4), so that juveniles ringed in East Anglia and northwest England were recovered in northeast and southeast France, whilst birds from Wales and south and southwest England were recovered in southwest France, several close to the coast, as far south as the Spanish border. Recoveries of foreign-ringed birds suggest that most northwest and central European birds move south, crossing the Mediterranean from Iberia or the South of France. A few birds travel via Malta or the Italian Peninsula to Cap Bon in Tunisia, with a small number moving further east. Birds returning in the spring seem to follow similar routes (Finlayson 1992, Garcia & Arroyo 1998). There has been only a single recovery of a foreign-ringed bird, from the Netherlands, a first-year bird found in East Anglia in June 1929.

Only one British-ringed bird has been recovered in Africa, in Senegal in February, but other northwest European birds have been recovered from northwest Africa, Benin, Sudan, Chad, Nigeria and Senegal (BWP, Nikolaus 1987, Arroyo et al 1995, Garcia & Arroyo 1998).

During 1926–84, the mean arrival date at the breeding grounds for male Montagu's Harriers in Britain was 7 May and for females 6 May,

although during the last 50 years there has been a trend for birds to be seen earlier (Underhill-Day 1990). Montagu's Harriers pass over the Strait of Gibraltar in greatest numbers during the first third of April, a little earlier than through Italy where the median date for adults of both sexes was April 12, with first-year birds passing through about a month later (Finlayson 1992, Gustin & Pizzari 1998).

Of seven birds ringed as nestlings and recovered as adults in June or July, three were found less than 20 km from the natal area and four elsewhere. Of the latter, the most distant was a bird ringed in Devon and found dead in Finistere, France (236 km), and a female ringed as a nestling on Anglesey and found dead near its nest in Dumfries (219 km). The others, both ringed in Norfolk, had travelled about 75 km. Colour-ringing programmes in Britain have shown that some males and females return to breed in their natal area, although two females breeding in East Anglia had been colour-ringed in France and in Scotland respectively. At a time when practically all known young reared in Britain had been colour-ringed for the previous 10 years, there were still a number of unringed, presumably foreign-bred birds in the breeding population. These results all suggest considerable variation in behaviour.

Montagu's Harriers arrive later in spring than Marsh Harriers but leave during the same period after breeding (BWP). This may reflect the fact that some Marsh Harriers winter close to their breeding areas, whereas the Montagu's Harrier remains a long-distance migrant. There are a few winter records of Montagu's Harriers in Britain & Ireland, mostly adult females (Clarke 1996).

Despite decreases in persecution in parts of their range, it seems probable that Montagu's Harriers are still at risk from hunters, particularly in autumn during their passage through southern Europe. With numbers so low in much of northwest Europe, such persecution could have a significant effect on populations. Following the withdrawal of organochlorine pesticides in northwest Europe, Montagu's Harrier numbers in Britain initially increased but less so than for a number of other trans-Saharan migrant raptors. It has been suggested that this is connected with the onset of drought in the wintering areas in the Sahel (Underhill-Day 1990). Montagu's Harrier eggs analysed during the early 1980s in Italy and Britain showed low levels of organochlorine contamination (Arca & Mason 1985, Underhill-Day 1990). Following the end of the Sahel drought with heavy rains in 1987, locust populations increased and during 1986–90 some 14 million hectares in northern Africa were treated with insecticides, mainly fenitrothion (Keith & Bruggers 1998). Grasshoppers have been found to be predominant in the diet of wintering Montagu's Harriers (Thiollay 1985b, Cormier & Baillon 1991, Arroyo et al 1995), and although no direct evidence of pesticide-related mortality has been found in the African wintering areas, it is possible that the use of fenitrothion, which can kill birds even at low concentrations (Steedman 1988, Keith & Bruggers 1998), has exerted further downward pressure on harrier numbers. Montagu's Harrier numbers in Fennoscandia and the former Soviet Union have remained stable or increased during the last 20 years (Forsman 1993, Galushin 1994, Rodebrand 1996), and this may reflect better survival rates in those birds wintering in areas further south and east than those from northwest Europe wintering in west and central Africa south of the Sahara.

Considerable efforts have been made in a number of European countries, including Britain, to protect Montagu's Harriers during the breeding season, and continued ringing should be a high priority as we need to know more about migration routes, causes of mortality and the extent of the African wintering areas.

John Underhill-Day

Northern Goshawk (Goshawk)

Accipiter gentilis

Goshawks had ceased to breed regularly in Britain by the 1880s. Their demise was largely the result of massive deforestation since the Middle Ages but latterly due to persecution (Marquiss & Newton 1982b, Petty 1996a). Then followed a period with only sporadic breeding attempts until the 1950s. Falconers started to import Goshawks from Europe from around this time. Some of these birds escaped while others were deliberately released, resulting in a number of small, isolated breeding populations becoming established (Kenward *et al* 1981). Numbers increased only slowly at first, but since the late 1980s some populations have increased rapidly. The success of these re-established populations was due to a reversal of two factors that had caused the initial decline. First, extensive conifer forests planted since the 1920s were now old enough to provide secluded areas for breeding. Second, the density of gamekeepers had declined greatly since the demise of Goshawks in the 19th century (Tapper 1992) and most of the new forests were free of such persecution. Today this spectacular, if secretive raptor can be seen in many parts of Britain. Goshawks are not known to have bred in Ireland, although records have increased since 1965 (*Birds in Ireland*). Most of these were in southern Ireland during September–November and January–March, and are probably linked to the increasing British population, although the American race (*atricapillus*) has been recorded in Ireland.

Goshawks are widely distributed in the Holarctic, where at least nine races have been described (Howard & Moore 1998). Our present population originates mainly from birds imported from Fennoscandia, although some of the earliest imports also came from central Europe

The analysis of the data for this species was supported by Tony and Trisha Irwin

(Marquiss 1981). Thus, the founder birds were probably all nominate *gentilis*, which occupies Europe apart from northern Fennoscandia (race *buteoides*) and Corsica and Sardinia (race *arrigonii*).

In Britain, Goshawks prefer large forests during the breeding season and often build their nests in conifers (Petty 1996b). However, they occasionally breed in small broad-leaved woods where nothing else is available, but they are then more susceptible to disturbance. Goshawks are often considered to be woodland raptors, but they will hunt extensively over open habitats when prey is abundant. Outside the breeding season, they visit estuaries to hunt wildfowl and waders, and lowland farms with plentiful supplies of pigeons, corvids and winter thrushes.

The ringing locations of birds later recovered (Fig 1) broadly reflect their breeding range in Britain (*1988–91 Atlas*), although few recoveries have been reported from the small populations in southeastern England and North Yorkshire. Most recoveries come from the main population clusters in Britain, which are in Wales and the Forest of Dean, the southern Pennines, the English/Scottish Borders and northeast Scotland. Almost all recoveries are of birds that were ringed as nestlings (Fig 2). Most broods are ringed in June, with a few early and late broods being ringed in May and July respectively. The number of nestlings ringed annually has increased substantially (Fig 4). This mirrors the

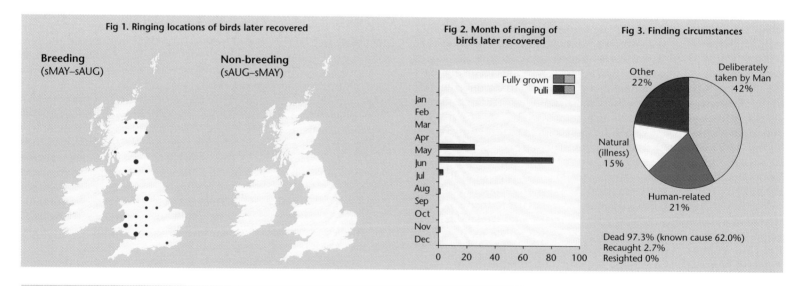

Fig 1. Ringing locations of birds later recovered

Breeding (sMAY–sAUG)

Non-breeding (sAUG–sMAY)

Fig 2. Month of ringing of birds later recovered

Fully grown
Pulli

Fig 3. Finding circumstances

Other 22%
Deliberately taken by Man 42%
Natural (illness) 15%
Human-related 21%

Dead 97.3% (known cause 62.0%)
Recaught 2.7%
Resighted 0%

Ringing and recovery data

	<1960	60–69	70–79	80–89	90–97	Total
RINGING						
BTO ringing totals (%)	0	0	2	23	75	3,251
RECOVERIES						
BTO-ringed (%)	0	0	9	37	54	110
Foreign-ringed (%)	←	0	→	0	100	1

Statistical analyses

	Breeding population (sMAY–sAUG)	Wintering population (mNOV–sMAR)
Status	[SEDENTARY]	[SEDENTARY]
Age differences	Not tested	Not tested
Sex differences	Not tested	Not tested
Regional differences	Not tested	Not tested
Finding circumstances	Not tested	Not tested

Fig 4. The number of nestling Goshawks ringed annually 1976–97.

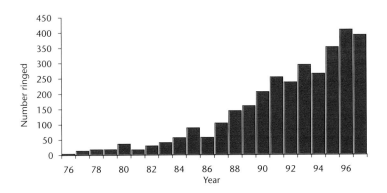

Fig 5. Recovery locations and movements of over 20 km for the 111 included recoveries of Goshawks ringed or recovered in Britain & Ireland.

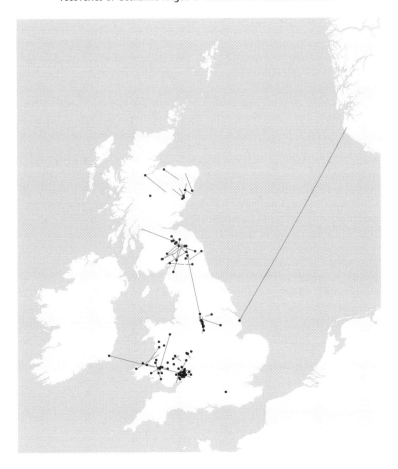

population size of Goshawks in Britain, with small numbers in the 1970s, a slow increase to the mid-1980s, followed by a sharp rise, which culminated in around 400 nestlings per annum being ringed by 1997. The estimated size of the breeding population in 1994–95 was 400 pairs (Petty 1996a). With over 50% of the recoveries coming in the period 1990–97, and over 90% since 1980, the pattern of recoveries over time reflects the increased ringing effort and interest in this species, as well as its increase in numbers.

The nominate race is largely sedentary, although some populations in northern Fennoscandia and eastern Europe may be partially migratory (*BWP*). Data on migrating raptors from Falsterbo, southern Sweden, show that Goshawks are one of the least recorded species (Kjellén 1998). However, counts showed more annual variation than any other raptor species. This appears to reflect annual fluctuations in productivity, as most were of juveniles, which may be linked to cyclic changes in the abundance of grouse, one of the main prey groups in Fennoscandia (Sulkava *et al* 1994). Adults, all males, comprised only 4% of birds recorded at Falsterbo. Around 70% of the juveniles were also males, indicating that females are either sedentary during the winter or have a more northerly distribution. In northern USA and Canada, Goshawks (race *atricapillus*) exhibit more pronounced movement patterns linked to the abundance of Snowshoe Hare, one of their main prey species, whose numbers fluctuate in approximately 10-year cycles. During the increase and peak phases of the cycle, breeding success is high, with birds staying in their breeding areas year-round (Doyle & Smith 1994). When hare numbers crash, Goshawks become more nomadic and large-scale movements to the south sometimes occur (Mueller *et al* 1977). Compared to Goshawks that inhabit the boreal forest, those in temperate and Mediterranean zones have food supplies that are more varied and collectively less prone to large annual fluctuations. This results in little annual variation in breeding performance and many individuals, particularly adult males, stay near to their territories all year. Thus, throughout the Holarctic, it appears that movement patterns of Goshawks are closely linked to fluctuations in food availability.

The cause of death was known for 62% of ring-recoveries involving birds found dead (Fig 3). Of these, 42% were deliberately taken by Man, in spite of Goshawks having full legal protection. Dispersing juveniles are attracted to Pheasant release-pens, and this is presumably where most are killed. The scale of illegal killing is likely to be under-represented by these data, as many ringed birds that are killed are not reported. This appears to be reflected in the low recovery rate of ringed Goshawks (3.4%) compared to other raptors of a similar size (8.2% for Peregrine and 6.2% for Buzzard). The next most important category is other human-related deaths (21%). Most recoveries are reported during June–October, with a peak in August. This appears to reflect a high natural mortality in newly independent birds. A smaller peak in recoveries occurs in April, at a time when incubation has started but when prey numbers are still generally low. Peaks in mortality occur at similar times of the year in Sparrowhawks (Newton 1986).

The movement of juveniles away from nesting areas takes place once their flight feathers are fully grown (Kenward *et al* 1993), from late July to late August. Median dispersal distances of British juveniles in 30-day periods after ringing showed no clear pattern over the first six months, ranging between 9 km and 31 km. There is evidence from other studies that juvenile males disperse further than juvenile females, prior to settling to breed. In migration counts in the USA and Sweden, juvenile males outnumbered juvenile females (Mueller *et al* 1977, Kjellén 1998), and juvenile males moved further than juvenile females in the Netherlands and Sweden (Marcström & Kenward 1981, Bijlsma 1993). Marcström & Kenward (1981) considered that juvenile males were inherently more liable to move than juvenile females.

Combining all British data, the median distance moved between ringing and recovery locations for dead birds was 21 km, with an indication that movement distances were shorter in Wales and the Forest of Dean than further north. The median distance moved between ringing and recovery for Goshawks ringed as pulli and subsequently found dead was 47 km (P5–95=12–94 km, *n*=27) for birds from the northeast and northwest. Statistically, this was significantly greater than the median distance of 18 km (P5–95=0–114 km, *n*=79) moved by birds from the southeast and southwest. Similar patterns have been recorded elsewhere. Juveniles reared in northern Sweden moved further than those reared in southern Sweden (Höglund 1964), while immatures from mid-Norway moved three times further than those from southern Norway (Halley 1996).

The national ringing data provide little information on natal dispersal. In the English/Scottish Border population, median natal dispersal distances were significantly greater for females (32 km) than males (15 km) (Petty & Anderson 1996). Similar results were obtained in the Netherlands (Bijlsma 1993). Thus it appears that, while juvenile males initially disperse further than juvenile females, they return closer than females to their natal area to breed. The national ringing data also provide little information about post-breeding dispersal patterns of adults. Observations suggest that most males stay near to their territory during the winter, but females appear to be more mobile and may have separate wintering ranges (Squires & Ruggiero 1995); neither aspect has been quantified, however.

The recovery data suggest that the main population clusters (Wales and the Forest of Dean, southern Pennines, English/Scottish Borders and northeast Scotland) are isolated from one another, as there has been only a single movement between clusters (Fig 5). It may be a few years yet, therefore, before the various populations are close enough to allow interbreeding.

Pairs can be found in breeding areas from as early as February and sometimes throughout the year in rich lowland areas (Toyne 1995). Goshawks are frequently seen displaying in late winter or early spring in areas with no history of breeding, and many of these observations could be of wintering birds. In lowland areas where food is plentiful, females may spend most of the year within the home range where breeding occurs. However, in many upland forests, adult females and yearlings are rarely seen during September–February. Similarly in Scandinavia, juveniles leave the forests to winter in agricultural areas (Widén 1985).

There has been one recovery of a foreign-ringed Goshawk in Britain (Fig 5). This was ringed as a nestling in southwestern Norway in June 1994 and was trapped and released alive at Theddlethorpe Dunes in Lincolnshire on 17 October the same year. Many birds are ringed annually in the Netherlands (Bijlsma 1993) but none have been reported from Britain. This suggests that sporadic records of Goshawks along the east coast prior to their re-establishment in Britain were likely to have originated from Norway rather than from continental populations nearer to the UK. There has been one recovery only of a British-ringed Goshawk outside Britain. This was a male bird, ringed as a pullus in Dyfed during June 1995 and recovered in Wexford some three months later.

The main threat to Goshawks occurs just after the breeding season, when dispersing juveniles are attracted to Pheasant release-pens and many are illegally killed. Research is needed into the design of release-pens and the use of deterrents and other management techniques to reduce Goshawk predation. Breeding success of most populations in Britain is similar to that of Goshawks in continental Europe but in a few areas the theft of eggs and chicks can greatly reduce the production of young. Potential conflicts between breeding Goshawks and timber-harvesting operations have been largely overcome (Petty 1996b).

Steve J Petty

Eurasian Sparrowhawk (Sparrowhawk)

Accipiter nisus

As a major predator of small birds in Britain and Ireland, the Sparrowhawk is one of our most common and widespread birds of prey. It has an extensive breeding range, in forest and woodland throughout the Palearctic from Ireland across Eurasia to Japan. From south to north within this range, populations become increasingly migratory and north European birds winter southwards to the Mediterranean region. The Sparrowhawks that breed in Britain & Ireland are non-migratory and relatively sedentary. After a period of post-fledging dispersal in August and September, which can occur in any direction, most juveniles settle and remain in the same general area throughout their lives. Their numbers are augmented in winter, however, by migrants mainly from northern Europe. These birds arrive mainly in September and October; some remain throughout the winter, while others pass on to wintering areas in the Low Countries and France. The return passage occurs mainly in April.

Sparrowhawks nest in fairly thick woodland, either broad-leaved or coniferous. In Britain, they are especially fond of conifer plantations 20–40 years old trees, which offer ideal structural conditions. Younger plantations, before they have been thinned, tend to be too thick for them, while older plantations tend to be too open. Within suitable woodland, Sparrowhawks often breed in the same restricted localities year after year; they build a new nest each year, near old ones, so that their regular nesting places can be recognized by groups of nests of varying ages. The birds are much less restricted in their foraging areas, and hunt in a wide range of habitats from dense forest, through farmland, to open moorland and sea-coast, wherever suitable small-bird prey species occur.

The analysis of the data for this species was supported by the Rye Bay Ringing Group and the Wetland Trust

In recent decades, Sparrowhawks have become frequent in urban areas, attracted by the small birds at garden feeders.

Sparrowhawk recoveries have come from birds ringed in most parts of the British & Irish breeding range but are by no means evenly spread. Concentrations of recoveries occur around localities where particular ringers or ringing groups have concentrated on Sparrowhawks, and obvious deficiencies in ringing have occurred in parts of western Scotland and west-central Ireland (Fig 1). Many have been ringed as nestlings, while throughout the year others have been trapped and ringed as fully grown individuals (Fig 2). Many continental migrants have been trapped at bird observatories and other ringing sites in the east of Britain.

About two-thirds of recoveries were attributed to a known cause of death and most of these were human-related, referring to birds that were shot or that died from collisions with wires, windows and other obstacles (Fig 3; see also Newton *et al* 1999). The impetuous hunting behaviour of Sparrowhawks may predispose them to this type of accident. The main causes of recovery have changed greatly over the years, however, with shot birds predominating in the early decades of the 20th century and accident victims in the later ones (Newton 1986, Newton *et al* 1999). The cause of death leading to most recoveries in the last 20 years has been collisions with windows.

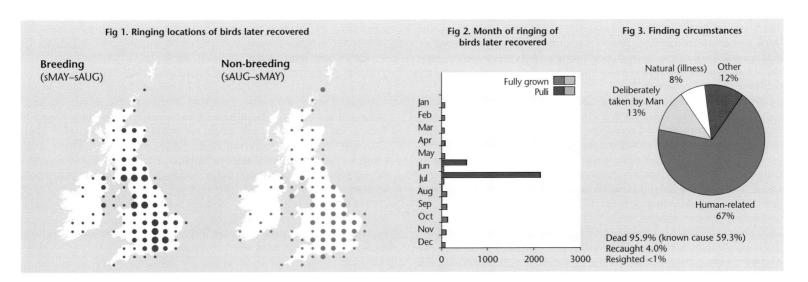

Fig 1. Ringing locations of birds later recovered

Breeding (sMAY–sAUG)

Non-breeding (sAUG–sMAY)

Fig 2. Month of ringing of birds later recovered

Fully grown / Pulli

Jan, Feb, Mar, Apr, May, Jun, Jul, Aug, Sep, Oct, Nov, Dec

0   1000   2000   3000

Fig 3. Finding circumstances

Natural (illness) 8%
Other 12%
Deliberately taken by Man 13%
Human-related 67%

Dead 95.9% (known cause 59.3%)
Recaught 4.0%
Resighted <1%

Ringing and recovery data

	<1960	60–69	70–79	80–89	90–97	Total
RINGING						
BTO ringing totals (%)	4	2	20	38	37	36,587
RECOVERIES						
BTO-ringed (%)	5	1	18	40	35	3,583
Foreign-ringed (%)	22	9	16	22	31	55

Statistical analyses

	Breeding population (sMAY–sAUG)	Wintering population (mNOV–sMAR)
Status	SEDENTARY (0)	SEDENTARY
Age differences[NS]	Significant	Not significant*
Sex differences[NS]	Significant	Not significant*
Regional differences	Significant[S*]	Not tested
Finding circumstances	(Not significant)	Not significant*

Fig 4. Distribution of distances moved by male and female Sparrowhawks ringed as pulli in Britain & Ireland and recovered in a subsequent breeding season when of breeding age.

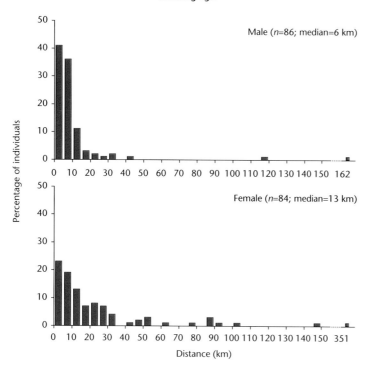

Fig 5. Movements of over 20 km and recovery locations of Sparrowhawks ringed as pulli in Britain & Ireland and recovered in a subsequent breeding season when of breeding age. There were 186:53 movements under:over 20 km but only those over 20 km are plotted.

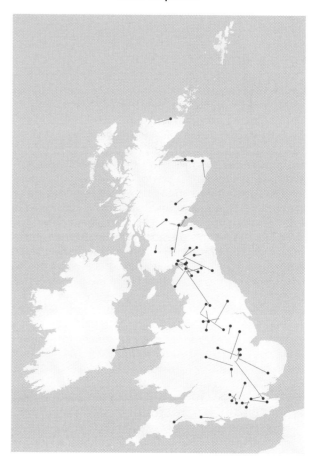

After leaving the nest, at about four weeks of age, the young stay in the immediate vicinity for about another four weeks, still fed by their parents. At the end of this period, at about eight weeks old, they become independent of parental care, and disperse away from the nest area. As shown by ring-recoveries (Newton 1986), as well as by radio-tracking (Wyllie 1985, Frumkin 1994), siblings move independently of one another, and in any direction. They remain on the move for a relatively short period, however, no more than two to four weeks, before settling. Thereafter, as ringing reveals, the majority of individuals remain in the same area for the rest of their lives. Thus, during August and September, ring-recoveries of juveniles tend to get progressively more distant from the natal territory but from October onwards the recoveries reveal no further outward movement.

Of 239 birds ringed as nestlings and recovered in a later breeding season (taken as May–July), 78% had moved less than 20 km between natal site and presumed breeding site, and only a small minority had moved beyond 100 km, with a median distance of 8 km (Figs 4 & 5). Among the 170 birds that were sexed, males moved generally shorter distances than females (median distances 6 km and 13 km respectively). Of 14 Sparrowhawks ringed as adults in the breeding season and found dead in a later breeding season, 12 had moved less than 20 km (median=2.5 km). Likewise, of 32 Sparrowhawks ringed in one winter and recovered the next, 29 had moved less than 20 km (median=4 km). These movements are more meaningful when viewed in relation to the normal foraging ranges of the birds. In south Scotland, radio-marked Sparrowhawks frequently hunted within 1–2 km of their nesting or regular roosting sites, and occasionally up to 5 km or more (Marquiss & Newton 1982a, Newton 1986). Hence, many of the birds that had moved no more than a few kilometres between ringing and recovery sites may have been within the same home range.

In general, therefore, compared with some other birds of prey that breed in Britain, Sparrowhawks appear remarkably sedentary, especially after the initial post-fledging dispersal. On the records available, however, dispersal distances were significantly longer in the northwest than in other parts of the country. Combining the records for all times of year, some 55% of individuals ringed in northwest Britain had moved

more than 20 km from the ringing site, compared with 28%, 23% and 23% in the northeast, southwest and southeast, and 24% in Ireland.

Given the usual natal dispersal distances of Sparrowhawks, one would expect some cross-Channel interchange, with birds raised on one side breeding on the other. So far, the only hint that this might occur is a single recovery of a female ringed as a pullus in the Netherlands and recovered on 29 May the next year in Suffolk. No nestling ringed in Britain or Ireland has yet been recovered in continental Europe, although several have moved from Britain to Ireland. There is no evidence for any directional preference among the movements of British-bred birds, or for any other seasonal displacements that would indicate regular migration.

Fidelity of adults to their nesting territories was studied in south Scotland by live-trapping adults at their nests in successive years (Newton 1986, Newton & Wyllie 1992). Of birds that were caught in more than one year, 68% of 50 males and 69% of 399 females were on the same territory in both years, the remainder having moved to different territories. Comparing age groups, the frequency of territory changes was greatest between the first and second years of life, and became progressively less between the second and third years, and between the third and fourth years. The figures for the three age groups were 53%, 29% and 24% in females, and 43%, 36% and 28% in males. Within each age group, birds were more likely to change territory after a nest failure than after a success. A change of territory was usually associated with a change of mate, and followed by an improvement in nest success.

Territories seemed to vary in quality, as measured by their frequency of occupancy and breeding success (Newton 1991). Territory quality

Fig 6. Recovery locations and all included exchanges of Sparrowhawks present in Britain & Ireland outside the breeding season and abroad (a) during the breeding season (26) and (b) outside the breeding season (51).

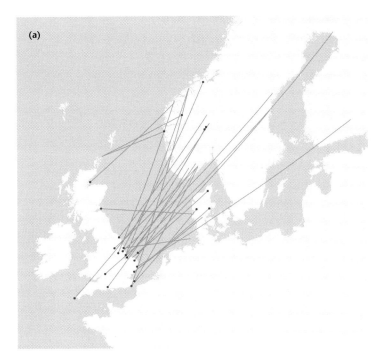

(a)

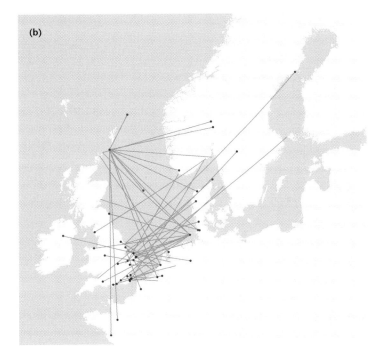

(b)

emerged as another factor that influenced the movements of breeders, in that birds tended to stay on high-grade territories after successful breeding but to move away from low-grade territories, whether successful or not the previous year. Thus site-fidelity among breeding Sparrowhawks was related to the age, sex and previous nesting success of the bird, and to the quality of the territories themselves.

Many birds which changed territories from one year to the next moved only to an adjacent territory but others moved greater distances, females further than males. The median distance moved by males between breeding sites of successive years was 0.8 km and the maximum was 19 km, while the equivalent figures for females were 1.5 km and 27 km. Although recorded distances may have been constrained by the size of the study area, they should have been comparable between the sexes, and the longest distance recorded for females was similar to the longest distances for breeding dispersal recorded in the national ring-recoveries. Moreover, comparable data obtained for a different area in east-central England gave roughly similar results, in terms of factors affecting territory changes and distances moved (Newton & Wyllie 1992), as did the small number of appropriate ring-recoveries of dead birds (median=2.5 km, n=14).

Unlike the Sparrowhawks that are resident year-round in Britain, those in northern Europe are migratory or partly migratory, moving generally southwest in autumn to winter at lower latitudes. To judge from ring-recoveries, most of the continental Sparrowhawks that winter in Britain come from Norway and Denmark, with fewer from Sweden and fewer still from Finland (Fig 6). This would be expected because, like many other birds, Sparrowhawks tend to maintain the same west–east distribution in their wintering areas as in their breeding areas, with Norwegian birds decreasing in proportion from west to east through the west European wintering range, and Finnish birds increasing. Many other Sparrowhawks found in Britain outside the breeding season were ringed across the Channel in the Low Countries (Fig 6). These birds could have originated from either the northern or middle latitudes of Europe but as most of these birds were ringed in August–November, or in April, they almost certainly included some north European birds on

passage to and from Britain. Nonetheless, recoveries also suggest that some Dutch birds winter in Britain, with movements recorded in both directions. While most recoveries of continental birds were from eastern parts of Britain, others were from western parts, with one in Ireland.

Many recoveries of birds ringed at migration time on Fair Isle and on the east coast of England, at Spurn Point (Yorkshire) and Gibraltar Point (Lincolnshire), imply an autumn passage of Sparrowhawks from northern Europe, through eastern Britain, to wintering grounds in the Netherlands, Belgium and France, and back again in spring. Finally, some recoveries revealing movements between Britain and the Continent were likely to involve birds caught at different points on the migration route in different years. Some birds were ringed in their first autumn or winter in Britain and recovered in northern Europe in a later winter, indicating that some individuals migrated in their first year but not later.

These various recoveries fit well with observations of Sparrowhawk movements around Britain, and with the records of bird observatories. A small passage is seen regularly on Fair Isle and Shetland, while a stronger passage is known on the east coast, mainly from early September to mid-November, and a less marked return mainly in April (Newton 1986). Ring-recoveries imply that some north European birds do not leave Britain until mid-May, when local birds are on eggs.

Because British Sparrowhawks are resident here year-round, any changes in their status must be due unequivocally to events in Britain. But such events could also affect the populations of northern Europe. In particular, the use in Britain of organochlorine pesticides from the late 1940s to the mid-1980s is likely to have affected not only British birds but also north European ones. The recovery of Sparrowhawk numbers apparent in winter sightings during the 1980s and early 1990s would thus have involved continental as well as British birds. The main gaps in our knowledge centre on western Ireland, where few Sparrowhawks have been recovered, but it would be surprising if birds in this region behaved differently from those in the rest of Britain & Ireland.

Ian Newton

Common Buzzard (Buzzard)

Buteo buteo

Buzzards are essentially sedentary in Britain & Ireland. Nevertheless, their movements show a number of interesting features that may be linked to migratory habits in other parts of their range. Buzzard movements also reflect the current recolonization of eastern Britain. Extensive radio-tagging of Buzzards in southern England has complemented ringing to reveal the complexity of these movements.

The Buzzard in Britain & Ireland belongs to the nominate race *buteo*. The species' winter food in many areas is dominated by invertebrates, primarily earthworms, and the digestive system is better adapted than in other raptors for a poor diet (Barton & Houston 1993). However, the species also takes vertebrate prey, which are important for breeding (Tubbs 1974, Graham *et al* 1995, Swann & Etheridge 1995) and some Buzzards may also feed mainly on small mammals in winter. Feeding on worms in winter makes Buzzards vulnerable to frosts, and snow-cover makes even small rodents hard to hunt.

As a result of its winter diet, the Buzzard becomes migratory in areas with prolonged snow-cover in winter. The sedentary nature in Britain & Ireland is possible in an oceanic climate but affects a tiny fraction of individuals of a species that occurs across Siberia to approximately 96°E, and thus has the largest global distribution of any *Buteo* (BWP). Buzzards in Fennoscandia mostly migrate in winter, with a passage of around 20,000 annually over Falsterbo (Kjellén 1992, 1998). East of Fennoscandia, the race *vulpinus* (Steppe Buzzard) is a transequatorial migrant, with hundreds of thousands passing annually over well-known Middle Eastern watch-points such as Eilat (Yosef 1995b, Leshem & Yom-Tov 1996).

The analysis of the data for this species was supported anonymously

The ringing locations during the breeding season (Fig 1) represent where Buzzards are most abundant in Britain (*1988–91 Atlas*), only missing a small scattering of breeders throughout the southeast. In Ireland, however, there has been a substantial increase in population size in the north since the 1968–72 survey (*1988–91 Atlas*) and this is not represented in the ringing locations of recovered birds. The majority (95%) of Buzzards were ringed as pulli, 85% in June (Fig 2). Almost all recoveries represented deaths (98%). Of the 49% where causes of death were attributed, 49% were caused by human-related accidents and 21% deliberately by humans (Fig 3). Overall, 82% of the recorded deaths were caused by human activities, including pollution and accidental capture. However, the ringing data stem in part from a time when Buzzards were unprotected, and persecution may still be widespread in the north (Elliott & Avery 1991). An analysis of 160 recoveries since 1970 in southern Britain gave 67% human-related deaths and a further 17% killed deliberately. This compared with 34% human-related accidents, plus 26% killed, among 50 deaths of Buzzards radio-tagged in southern Britain. Even though human-related deaths are overestimated in ring-recoveries, a majority of Buzzard deaths are nevertheless caused by human activities.

With the Steppe Buzzard clearly adapted for migration in its morphology and behaviour (Spaar 1995, Spaar & Bruderer 1997), and

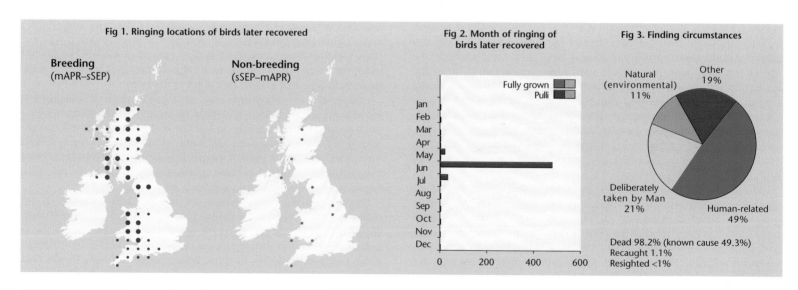

Fig 1. Ringing locations of birds later recovered

Breeding (mAPR–sSEP)

Non-breeding (sSEP–mAPR)

Fig 2. Month of ringing of birds later recovered

Fully grown
Pulli

Fig 3. Finding circumstances

Natural (environmental) 11%
Other 19%
Deliberately taken by Man 21%
Human-related 49%

Dead 98.2% (known cause 49.3%)
Recaught 1.1%
Resighted <1%

Ringing and recovery data

	<1960	60–69	70–79	80–89	90–97	Total
RINGING						
BTO ringing totals (%)	11	6	20	28	35	8,967
RECOVERIES						
BTO-ringed (%)	8	6	30	29	28	559
Foreign-ringed (%)	←	0	→	0	100	1

Statistical analyses

	Breeding population (mAPR–sSEP)	Wintering population (sNOV–sMAR)
Status	SEDENTARY (0)	?
Age differences[NT]	Not significant*	—
Sex differences	Not tested	—
Regional differences	Not tested	—
Finding circumstances	(Not significant)	—

Fig 4. Movements of over 20 km between the breeding and non-breeding season and locations outside the breeding season of Buzzards present in northern (blue) and southern (red) Britain & Ireland during the breeding season (132:122). Sample sizes of movements under:over 20 km are given but only those over 20 km are plotted.

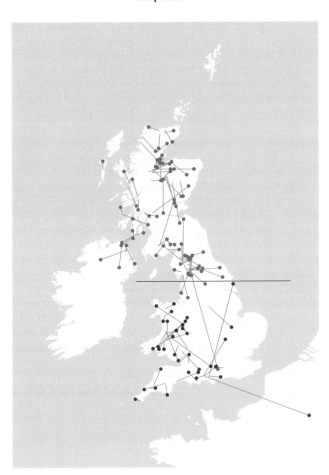

Fig 5. Dispersal distances of radio-tagged juvenile Buzzards in Dorset. Medians for seasons (points), 95% confidence limits (bars) and sample sizes are shown. (*Source:* authors' own data.)

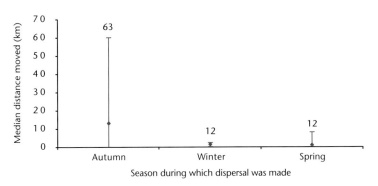

mean that Buzzards tend to move back towards their natal areas after initial dispersal but the issue is not that simple. Radio-tracking showed that young Buzzards start making long excursive flights when they are about 70 days old, when their feathers have hardened (Tyack *et al* 1998), and may then explore up to 25 km from their nests without dispersing (Nore *et al* 1992, Walls & Kenward 1995). However, about half of the young also dispersed from natal areas by their first October. The birds leaving in their first autumn moved longer distances than those leaving later in winter and the following spring, when another third of the young Buzzards dispersed (Fig 5). After leaving the natal area, birds often changed home range more than once before settling but none moved after their third summer. In the spring, they made philopatric visits back to their natal areas, earlier each spring until they bred either there or, more frequently, where they had settled (Walls & Kenward 1998).

The pattern of recovery distances revealed by ringing (Table 1) is understandable if one remembers that the recoveries are of dead birds. The radio-tracking results suggest that first-year recoveries represent early failures. The ones that leave early, and travel long distances, are the first birds to leave large broods, and also tend to settle in inferior habitats that contain much arable land (Walls *et al* 1999, Kenward *et al* 2001). They may be at a competitive disadvantage and more likely to die young than those that remain behind and in circumstances that make them more likely to be recovered. Later, some of the recoveries for other long-distance dispersers may move closer to home as a result of philopatric movements. The pattern of shorter dispersal distances through the first year and observed in the ringing data may therefore partly reflect philopatry but probably also a recovery bias with long-distance dispersers being more likely to die and be recovered than short-distance ones. Philopatry could be an advantage for a bird that has moved to a wintering area away from its breeding site because its natal area is certainly suitable for breeding even if the wintering area is not.

There would be no bias in recovery distances for birds counted only after they had survived for several years. When movements were only recorded as distances from natal nests to first breeding, then the median movement of 17 ringed Buzzards was only 5 km, and 95% were within 30 km. The equivalent distances for 21 radio-tracked Buzzards were very similar (median 4 km and 85% within 30 km).

large migrations recorded even for nominate *buteo* in parts of its range (*BWP*, Urcun & Bried 1998b), the median figure of 15 km moved by British & Irish birds looks rather small scale. There have been only three recorded movements to and from the European mainland in more than 500 ring-recoveries. One from the New Forest was killed in its first autumn in northeast France, one ringed near Inverness was recovered near the German border with Belgium, and a bird ringed in Belgium in winter was later recorded near Dundee. None of the continental records were more than 300 km from the Pas de Calais. With only one recovery from mainland Europe, it is difficult to assess the origins of the regular winter influxes of Buzzards on the east coast of Britain. There is no evidence from any source that Buzzards are more migratory in northern Britain. The two long movements recorded in the north, against one in the south, reflect the ringing of around twice as many birds in the north (Fig 1).

When movement distances recorded by ringing and radio-tagging in southern Britain were compared, there were no significant differences (Walls & Kenward 1995, 1998). Ring-recovery distances were also very similar in northern and southern Britain (Fig 4). However, there was a strong seasonal trend in the ring-recovery data, similar to that found on the Continent. In Germany, the Netherlands, Belgium and France, 75% of juvenile recoveries were southwest (*BWP*), consistent with the majority of birds moving southwest in winter but older birds being back in their breeding areas. A similar situation was recorded for German Buzzards, where summer recoveries were within 50 km of natal sites for only 37% of birds in their second summer but for 57% in their third and 84% in their fourth (Mebs 1964). This trend might be interpreted to

Table 1. Recovery distances in their first year (km) of Buzzards marked as pulli or newly fledged juveniles (before the end of August).

Season	Median	5%	95%	n
Autumn (Sep–Oct)	21	0	161	73
Winter (Nov–Feb)	18	0	106	104
Spring (Mar)	19	0	125	33
Summer (Apr–Aug)	13	0	91	77

Fig 6. Monthly variation in the differences in longitude between ringing and recovery locations of immature Buzzards that were present in Britain & Ireland during the breeding season. Monthly medians (points) and interquartile ranges (bars) are shown.

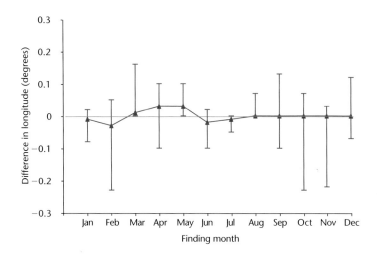

The radio-tracking of 114 young Buzzards confirmed ringing observations that migration is rare for British birds. Only one bird made regular movements between a summer and a winter area, 8 km apart. Two others were each recorded twice returning for spring visits to a Dorset study area from the east, after being untraceable from searches of southern Britain from the air in winter. They may therefore have crossed the English Channel. A 'winter-sensitive' species is likely to contain a small proportion of individuals with a genetic tendency to migrate because their genes will provide a great advantage if there is a run of severe winters.

The ring-recovery data suggest a tendency for immature Buzzards to move east from their ringing sites, especially in the autumn just after leaving the nest (Fig 6). Since the recoveries date back to a time when Buzzards were restricted to the west (Tubbs 1974), there may have been a historical bias in the direction the birds could disperse. However, this tendency also became significant by the second calendar year for radio-tracked Buzzards that originated from Dorset, which has no westerly restriction. It resulted from a tendency of dispersers to settle in newly colonized areas to the east, where density was presumably low (Walls & Kenward 1998). In Ireland, some of the few recoveries over 20 km tend to be biased south and west into uncolonized areas rather than across to Britain (Fig 4).

We may conclude that ring-recovery data can usefully be complemented by radio-tracking to provide a detailed description of movements. Using information from other sources, the data can be analysed to understand how the movements and survival of individuals relate to habitats and the density of conspecifics (Kenward et al 2001). Such analyses, together with experimental releases, are helping to unravel the complex interplay of movements and demography that leads to recolonization. An understanding of recolonization processes is urgently needed for large raptors, in order to understand when conservation goals may best be met by reintroductions, as for White-tailed Eagles and Red Kites, and when it may be more effective to let natural processes unfold. Population modelling shows that the relatively small proportion of Buzzards deliberately killed by Man in southern Britain is well below a level that might hinder population expansion. The increasing extent of arable land may prove to be a problem for Buzzards in the long term, but for the time being the rapid completion of recolonization is to be expected.

Robert Kenward & Sean Walls

Golden Eagle
Aquila chrysaetos

Golden Eagles in Britain & Ireland are largely sedentary and adults that have acquired breeding territories are unlikely to move more than a few kilometres for the remainder of their lives. Non-breeding juvenile and immature eagles, by contrast, disperse over distances up to 150 km from their natal area (Watson 1997). No Golden Eagles ringed in Britain have been recovered abroad, nor have any birds ringed outside Britain been recovered within Britain & Ireland.

This pattern of very restricted movements is typical throughout much of the bird's holarctic range. However, in the more northerly populations of continental Eurasia and North America many young Golden Eagles do migrate southwards over several thousand kilometres each winter (Fremming 1980, Millsap & Vana 1984, Sherrington 1993). Further north still, in the subarctic populations of northern Russia, Alaska and Canada, virtually all Golden Eagles, including territorial adults, are long-range migrants. Long-range migration probably occurs over a relatively broad front in continental Eurasia (*BWP*). In western North America, there is a relatively concentrated Golden Eagle flyway along the Rocky Mountains where, in the Mount Lorette area of Alberta, over 450 Golden Eagles in a day have been seen passing south in early October, and more than 800 birds per day heading north in the same locality in late March (Sherrington 1993).

The breeding range of Golden Eagles in Britain & Ireland is nowadays restricted to the comparatively remote, mountainous areas of northwest Britain (*1988–91 Atlas*). Outside Scotland, nesting occurred in several areas of northern England until the late 18th century, in the mountains of Snowdonia in Wales up to the middle of the 18th century,

The analysis of the data for this species was supported by the Scottish Ornithologists' Club

and quite widely in western Ireland until the late 19th century (Holloway 1996). Today, all but one or two of the 420 or so breeding pairs are confined to Scotland, mainly in the Highlands and on the islands off the west coast (Dennis *et al* 1984, Green 1996a). The mild, oceanic climate of northern and western Scotland, where typically there is abundant winter food in the form of deer and sheep carrion (Watson *et al* 1992), ensures that territorial adult eagles have no need to migrate.

Ringing data offer only the scantiest of insights to the movements of Golden Eagles in Britain. There have been less than 40 recoveries since numbers of eagle nestlings began to be ringed some 40–50 years ago. Of these, only around 20 contain relatively complete information – a tiny sample that must be treated with great caution. In addition to ring-recoveries, some data are now available on natal dispersal from a small number of Golden Eagles that have been radio-tagged and tracked over several months (Grant & McGrady 1999).

All Golden Eagle ring-recoveries are from birds ringed as nestlings at breeding sites (Figs 1 & 2). The distribution of ringing locations broadly reflects the species' breeding range (*1988–91 Atlas*), although ringing effort has been relatively low in the far north of the range (Fig 1). Cause of death was reported for just 16 of the ring-recoveries and, of these, over 80% were either directly caused by Man or were in some way human-related (Fig 3). This high incidence of human-related mortality

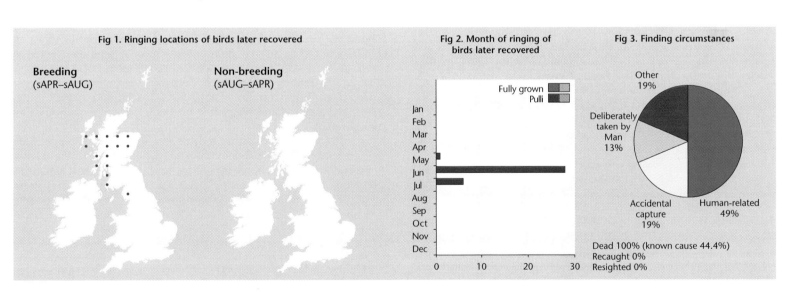

Fig 1. Ringing locations of birds later recovered

Breeding (sAPR–sAUG)

Non-breeding (sAUG–sAPR)

Fig 2. Month of ringing of birds later recovered

Fully grown
Pulli

Fig 3. Finding circumstances

Other 19%
Deliberately taken by Man 13%
Accidental capture 19%
Human-related 49%

Dead 100% (known cause 44.4%)
Recaught 0%
Resighted 0%

Ringing and recovery data

	<1960	60–69	70–79	80–89	90–97	Total
RINGING						
BTO ringing totals (%)	4	5	18	45	29	957
RECOVERIES						
BTO-ringed (%)	0	6	38	28	28	36
Foreign-ringed (%)	0	0	0	0	0	0

Statistical analyses

	Breeding population (sAPR–sAUG)	Wintering population (sDEC–sMAR)
Status	[SEDENTARY]	[SEDENTARY]
Age differences	Not tested	Not tested
Sex differences	Not tested	Not tested
Regional differences	Not tested	Not tested
Finding circumstances	Not tested	Not tested

Fig 4. Recovery locations and movements of over 20 km for the 36 included recoveries of Golden Eagles ringed or recovered in Britain & Ireland.

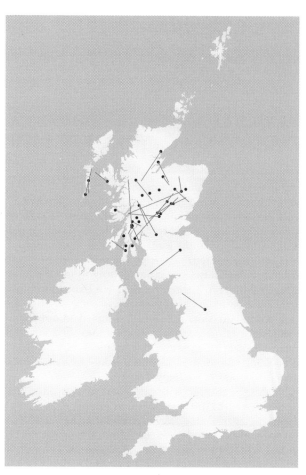

is broadly comparable with that found in other samples of dead eagles in Britain. For example, in some 100 Golden Eagle autopsies, by the Scottish Agricultural Science Agency and ITE, at least 50% of deaths were attributable directly or indirectly to humans (Watson 1997). In these studies, the most common forms of death were poisoning and shooting or trapping, with smaller numbers killed by collisions with wires or by electrocution. These figures probably under-record the frequency of illegal killing, since corpses found by the people who are responsible for the deliberate poisoning or shooting of eagles would tend not to be reported.

As would be expected for a relatively long-lived bird, Golden Eagles do not normally enter the breeding population until they are three or more years old. Our knowledge of the behaviour of juvenile and immature Golden Eagles is very patchy when compared with the quite detailed information available on breeding adults. The small sample of ring-recoveries gives only a tantalizing glimpse into the dispersal behaviour of these non-breeding birds (Fig 4). For all 36 usable ring-recoveries, the median distance between ringing location and recovery is 44 km ($P5$–95 = 0–136 km).

Earlier analyses (Watson 1997, Grant & McGrady 1999) have reported some evidence that Golden Eagles in their first year or two of life tend

to disperse greater distances (mean 67 km, range 11–161 km, $n=22$) than birds three or four years old (mean 33 km, range 7–47 km, $n=8$). This apparent tendency for birds to return closer to their natal area as they approach breeding age has also been reported for Golden Eagles in Switzerland, based on information from ring-recoveries (Haller 1982).

Work by Grant & McGrady (1999) with radio-tagged birds in Argyll has thrown some light on the immediate post-fledging behaviour of Golden Eagles. Two nestlings from different nests, one male and one female, were fitted with radio-transmitters and followed for 15 months and 10 months respectively. The male bird remained within the home range of his parents for approximately 185 days post-fledging, and thereafter was reported at varying distances up to 75 km from the natal territory during the next nine months. The female bird began to make excursions from the parental home range as early as 70 days after fledging, thereafter spending time both outside and inside the parental home range until some 95 days after fledging. She was then reported at distances up to 35 km from the parental range before the last contact was made some 10 months after fledging.

Grant & McGrady (1999) observed that the areas where their independent juveniles were located were most frequently either areas unoccupied by territorial adults, or on the peripheries of other home ranges. For long periods during their study, the radio-tagged young eagles were impossible to locate, despite wide-ranging searches. The authors concluded that once the young eagles began to leave the parental territory, they wandered widely, returning only occasionally and for relatively brief periods, to the vicinity of the parental territory.

One further source of information on dispersal behaviour comes from recent records of Golden Eagles in Ireland. For more than 20 years, there have been no breeding records from Ireland, but since around 1970 at least 26 individual Golden Eagles have been recorded there (D Scott & L O'Toole pers comm). Presumably these birds all originated in Scotland, the majority crossing to Ireland from the Mull of Kintyre. The great majority of these sightings were of birds in County Antrim, although occasional birds have turned up in Donegal. Most records (20) were first sighted in the six-month period from February to July, with just six records between August and January. This timing may reflect a period of more active 'dispersal' by non-breeders (most birds were immatures or sub-adults) during a period when territorial birds in Scotland would be actively involved in territorial behaviour linked to nesting. With such a small number of records from Ireland in recent years, it is unlikely that Golden Eagles will recolonize naturally. If Golden Eagles are to become re-established in Ireland, and possibly further south into England and Wales, it will require a planned reintroduction programme.

Clearly much more work is needed if we are to understand more fully the movements of juvenile and immature Golden Eagles. The evidence from the Argyll telemetry study is that much can be learnt using this technique, and certainly it has provided as many insights into the pattern of dispersal behaviour as have 50 years of casual ringing. The continuing pressures on Golden Eagles from illegal killing, and the particular pressures on wandering young eagles from human persecution, further argue for more studies of post-fledging dispersal using radio-tracking.

Jeff Watson

Osprey
Pandion haliaetus

The Osprey is one of Britain's best-known birds. Its large size, distinctive plumage and spectacular fishing behaviour have been written about since the time of Shakespeare. The demise and extinction of the Osprey from Britain & Ireland has been extensively chronicled (Waterston 1966), and the successful recolonization of Scotland since the early 1950s is even better known (Dennis 1983). Each spring their return is eagerly reported by the media and the RSPB's Osprey observation hide at Loch Garten, set up in 1959, has become world-famous.

This is one of the most cosmopolitan and adaptable raptors in the world. There are five distinctive subspecies, with the nominate *haliaetus* breeding throughout the Palearctic range. Populations breeding in the northern latitudes of Europe, Asia and North America are highly migratory while those in tropical and subtropical regions are resident or move relatively short distances (Poole 1989). Ospreys breeding in northwest Europe migrate in a generally south or southwest direction to winter in West Africa. Those breeding further east in Finland and Russia tend to migrate southwards to winter in central and East Africa, although some birds from the Finnish population winter in West Africa (Österlöf 1977).

In the early years of recolonization, Ospreys nested in Strathspey, Inverness-shire, where the habitat of freshwater lochs, rivers and native Scots Pine forests was similar to the nesting habitat of the species in Scandinavia. Since then, the range has extended into wooded farmland and coastal plains from Caithness to southern Scotland, but most nests are located from east Sutherland to Perthshire and Argyll. Over 90% of present-day eyries are in the eastern half of Scotland, whereas over 90%

The analysis of the data for this species was supported by Roy Dennis

of known historical eyries were in the western half (Dennis 1995a). Scottish Ospreys nowadays fish in estuaries and the open sea as well as freshwater sites, including trout ponds. The known population rose to 26 pairs by 1980, 52 pairs by 1987, 94 pairs by 1994 and to 136 known pairs in 1999. The rate of range expansion has been slow, at an average of 3.4 km per annum over 40 years (Dennis 1995b).

Since 1967, young Ospreys have been ringed in their eyries in Scotland with BTO rings and Darvic colour rings, usually individually identifiable (Figs 1 & 2). In 1982, and since 1995, small numbers of adults have been caught for ringing. Tail-mounted transmitters have been fitted for special studies and more recently satellite-transmitters have also been used.

Recoveries southward from Scotland have come from England (23), Wales, Ireland (three), the Netherlands, Belgium (two), France (11), Poland, Croatia, Spain (six), Portugal (four), Morocco (two), Algeria, Mauritania (two), Senegal (four), the Gambia (five), Guinea (two), Guinea-Bissau and Benin. Summer recoveries have been in Norway, Sweden, the Faeroes and Iceland.

Almost 60% of all recoveries for Ospreys found dead can be attributed to a known cause, with equal numbers (23%) of birds reported as being deliberately taken by Man, accidentally captured or dying as a result of natural circumstances (Fig 3). A further 20% were human-related or the

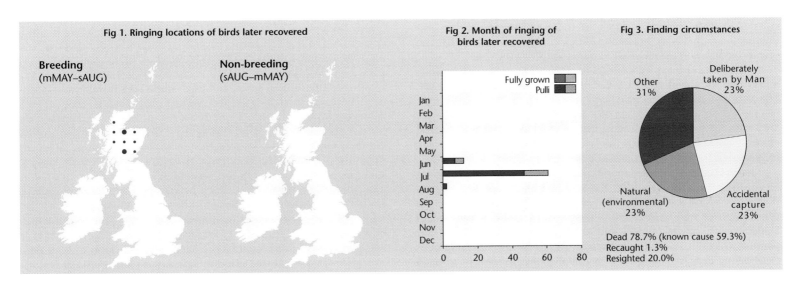

Fig 1. Ringing locations of birds later recovered

Breeding (mMAY–sAUG) **Non-breeding** (sAUG–mMAY)

Fig 2. Month of ringing of birds later recovered

Fig 3. Finding circumstances

Dead 78.7% (known cause 59.3%)
Recaught 1.3%
Resighted 20.0%

Ringing and recovery data

	<1960	60–69	70–79	80–89	90–97	Total
RINGING						
BTO ringing totals (%)	0	1	11	32	56	1,247
RECOVERIES						
BTO-ringed (%)	0	0	9	20	71	56
Foreign-ringed (%)	42	11	16	21	11	19

Statistical analyses

	Breeding population (mMAY–sAUG)	Wintering population (sNOV–mMAR)
Status	[LONG-DISTANCE MIGRANT]	NONE
Age differences	Not tested	—
Sex differences	Not tested	—
Regional differences	Not tested	—
Finding circumstances	Not tested	—

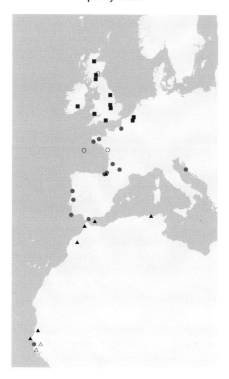

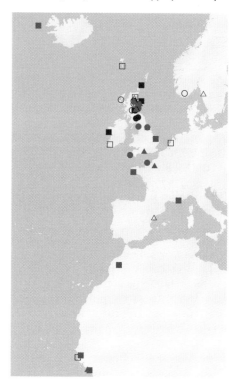

result of pollution. Since 1975, there has been a decrease in the number of birds in Europe reported as shot (pers obs). Ospreys regularly visit fish-farms and while some individuals get caught and die in the anti-predator nets used at such sites, others are released alive, including some fitted with either BTO or Darvic rings (pers obs). Some of the recoveries attributed to pollution refer to birds becoming entangled in fishing line. The problem stems from their catching fish that are trailing hooks and broken line. Fishing debris, including hooks and bubble-floats, is found in eyries and on rare occasions in the mouths of youngsters at ringing time.

Most young Ospreys in Scotland fly for the first time in the second half of July and spend about a month post-fledging around the nest site. The flying young are provided with freshly caught fish by the male parent. The family disperses in the second half of August and early September, with the female leaving first and followed next by the oldest chick. The male remains until the last of the brood is ready to depart. Ospreys migrate individually and not as family groups.

The recoveries of young Ospreys ringed in Scotland are shown in Fig 4. The earliest date away from the breeding area was 14 August in Hampshire (pers obs). All but two of the ring-recoveries during the dispersal period were to the south of the ringing site. Only seven birds of 1,204 Swedish ring-recoveries were reported making similar northerly journeys (Österlöf 1977). The pattern of ring-recoveries for young birds undertaking their first southward migration shows movement through northwestern France, into Spain and Portugal and on to Morocco, before they reach West Africa. There are two exceptions: one in Croatia on 20 October and one in late August in Poland, the latter not appearing on Fig 4 because it was not recovered until 1998 (beyond the end of the Atlas period). Interesting records are from Algeria on 1 December, showing that some juveniles are still in North Africa in early winter, and a Moroccan recovery in late February, which also suggests northerly wintering. Most juveniles are believed to spend their first summer in Africa south of the Sahara (Österlöf 1977, Saurola 1994). A recovery in Guinea in early August supports this view but another in Spain in September shows that some move north to Europe.

The migration routes of older birds (Fig 5) follow a similar pattern to and from West Africa. Autumn movements can be quite rapid as revealed through the use of satellite-transmitters. Scottish adults usually start to reappear on their breeding territories in late March and most return in the first half of April. Sightings and recoveries in Ireland and southwest England suggest they make a long sea-crossing to and from France or Spain. Ospreys are known as strong-flying broad-front migrants which do not need to rely on hot-air thermals or narrow sea-crossings, such as occur at Falsterbo and Gibraltar (Kjellén et al 1997). A three-year-old male seen in Cornwall on 19 April had probably just made the long sea-crossing from northern Spain, and three weeks later it was found freshly dead near its natal area in the Scottish Highlands. There are two recoveries from fishing boats, one 200 km southwest of Brittany and the other on the Great Sole Bank, 230 km west of the Isles of Scilly. Scottish Ospreys, nesting at the western extremity of the European range, are more likely to undertake long sea-crossings and in so doing are likely to suffer increased mortality in bad weather. It is also possible for them to miss Scotland on the return journey, as suggested by a two-year-old that landed on a fishing boat northwest of Iceland on 25 April 1978.

There are insufficient ring-recoveries to look at either natal or breeding dispersal. However, colour-ring sightings at breeding sites in Scotland show that males are more likely to breed closer to their natal sites than females, as was found in Scandinavia and in North America (Österlöf 1977, Poole 1989). Of 26 males, eight such sightings were within 10 km of their natal site, while only two of 28 females were within 10 km. Breeding adults as old as 22 years have been identified and there are two recoveries at 16 years of age.

As well as being faithful to their nest sites as adults, Ospreys are believed to prefer to winter in the same areas in successive winters. Six of nine Ospreys marked at the mouth of the Sénégal River returned to the same place the following winter (Prevost 1982). A colour-ringed Scottish juvenile seen in the Gambia in its first winter was identified at the same place in the following two winters (pers obs). Migrating birds probably also use favoured sites in successive years; for example a

Fig 6. Migration tracks of a juvenile female Osprey released at Rutland Water (red) and an adult female Osprey caught near Nairn, Scottish Highlands (blue), derived from satellite tracking. (*Source*: Anglian Water Osprey project.)

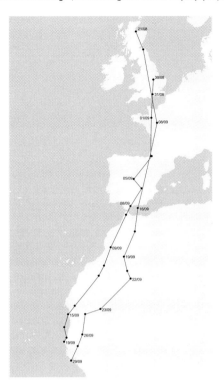

Fig 7. Movements of 19 Ospreys ringed abroad as pulli and recovered in Britain & Ireland.

colour-ringed juvenile seen in southern Spain from 29 September to 2 October 1991 was seen at the same place by the same observer during 5–10 April 1993 (pers obs).

A small number of Ospreys have been fitted with satellite-transmitters as part of the Anglian Water Osprey Project to translocate young Ospreys from Scotland to Rutland Water Nature Reserve to help restore a breeding population in England (Dennis & Dixon 1999). Transmitters were fitted to five birds in England and six in Scotland; migration tracks for two of the birds are shown in Fig 6. Similar studies have been carried out in Sweden, Germany and North America (Kjellén *et al* 1997). These results not only confirm the known pattern of migration to West Africa but have added much detail. Of the five Rutland Water juveniles, three made the journey to Africa, one was killed against a high-voltage power line and one only reached Dover before its signals were lost. A female departed on 31 August and reached southern Senegal on 19 September, having flown 4,878 km in 20 days. She then moved 230 km back north to a wintering site. The other two birds made extended journeys after visiting west Cornwall. One spent three weeks in Brittany before moving on to winter in Mali, while the other stopped off in eastern France before migrating to reach Senegal by 9 October. The Scottish juvenile migrated southwestwards through Ireland and then to Portugal, before its signal was lost.

Three breeding females in northern Scotland were also tracked. One was still in Strathspey on 26 August and reached its wintering site in Senegal on 27 September, after spending 15 days in Spain. Another from Strathspey flew to Extremadura in Spain in late August and wintered there on two large reservoirs. The third left on 2 September and stopped over in France or Spain before starting a 13-day journey from southern Spain to reach Guinea-Bissau on 29 September. An 11-year-old breeding male that was satellite-tagged was still feeding young in Strathspey until 13 September. It moved slowly south through Britain to cross the English Channel on 26 September and, after a six-day stopover in southwest Spain, it headed out to sea from Portugal for a nocturnal crossing to Morocco. It then wintered in Mauritania. Finally, a two-year-old male, ringed as a chick in Norway and later tagged in Strathspey, spent most of September in northwest England. It left northern France on 29 September and reached Guinea-Bissau on 17 October.

In addition to the native population, Ospreys from Fennoscandia also occur in both Britain and Ireland. It is not believed that Ospreys regularly migrate through Britain & Ireland, except perhaps through the extreme south and east of England. Most exchanges with Fennoscandia probably involve birds that have been drifted across the North Sea by bad weather. Recoveries of foreign-ringed birds have come from Sweden (15), Finland (three) and Norway (one) (Fig 7). Both male and female Ospreys from Sweden and Norway have been found breeding in Scotland and were, and still are, instrumental in the recovery of the species in Britain. The male of the second pair in Strathspey in 1963 had been ringed as a chick near Stockholm in 1960.

The information from the satellite-transmitters has already given us new information on routes, speeds and stopover points during autumn migration. It has shown sea-crossings and changes in direction en route as well as proving that migration can be nocturnal in this species. There is much more to learn on wintering strategies, spring migration and the behaviour of juveniles in their first summer. We need to know more about the importance and conservation status of individual stopover sites, the extent and frequency of sea-crossings, the effects of man-made hazards, especially overhead power lines on estuaries and fresh waters, and the location and conservation status of the most important wintering sites in Africa.

Roy Dennis

Common Kestrel (Kestrel)

Falco tinnunculus

Kestrels are small falcons, common throughout Britain & Ireland, and with a widespread distribution across Europe, Asia and Africa. They hunt from perches or in hovering flight and feed on a variety of prey such as small rodents, lizards, birds and invertebrates. This variety of diet enables them to occupy most open habitats including moorland, farmland and even city centres. Kestrels do not build their own nests but rely on finding nesting sites on rock ledges, in tree holes or in the disused stick nests of other birds. This limits their breeding distribution to places where there are suitable sites. They take readily to nestboxes, however, and nestbox schemes in various parts of Europe have provided a considerable amount of ringing data in recent years.

Within Britain & Ireland, Kestrels are most abundant in areas of rough grassland or farmland that support high populations of voles. Breeding populations are highest in south Scotland, north and southeast England, and lowest in northwest Scotland and parts of southwest England and Wales (*1988–91 Atlas*). They are also low in Ireland, where Short-tailed Voles are absent and where they must rely mainly on Woodmice and small birds. Kestrels cannot catch prey under thick snow and they are not very adept at catching small birds, so their winter distribution and migratory habits are largely related to the incidence of snow-cover. The breeding populations of much of northeast Europe are totally migratory, the northern limit of the winter distribution roughly following the line of permanent snow-cover. Immediately south of this line breeding populations are partially migratory, while those in southern areas are largely sedentary.

The analysis of the data for this species was supported by Kestrel Productions Ltd

Kestrels from the migratory populations winter in lowland Europe and some travel as far as Africa. There is evidence of leap-frog migration among Scandinavian birds, with those breeding in northern Sweden wintering further south than those from the south (Wallin *et al* 1987). Movement in continental Europe is mainly southwest in autumn, and most long-distance migrants probably winter in West Africa as far south as Nigeria and Ghana (Mead 1973, Brown *et al* 1982). Unlike broad-winged raptors, Kestrels can migrate long distances over water, and they regularly cross the North Sea. Nonetheless, there is some concentration of migrating Kestrels at each end of the Mediterranean and at Cap Bon, Tunisia. Northern European birds are funnelled through the Iberian Peninsula, and Spanish recoveries of foreign-ringed Kestrels include individuals from Britain, Belgium, the Netherlands, Germany and Sweden (Mead 1973). Kestrels migrating across the centre of the Mediterranean and ringed at Cap Bon have been recovered mainly in central Europe, Russia and as far east as Kazakhstan (Dejonghe 1989). The origin of birds using the east end of the Mediterranean is less certain but it is likely that most breed north and east of the Black and Caspian Seas and winter in East Africa.

The distribution of ringing sites within Britain & Ireland, for Kestrels that have been subsequently recovered, reflects the abundance of

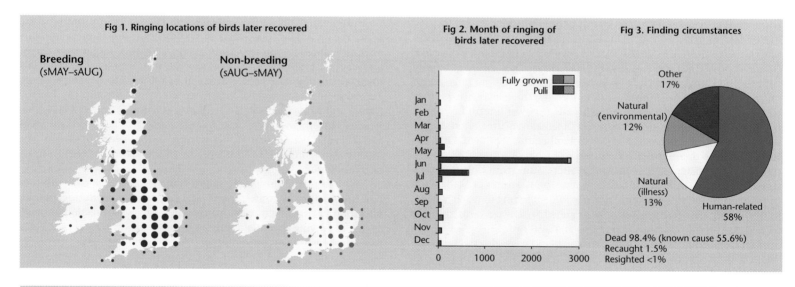

Fig 1. Ringing locations of birds later recovered

Breeding (sMAY–sAUG)

Non-breeding (sAUG–sMAY)

Fig 2. Month of ringing of birds later recovered

Fully grown
Pulli

Fig 3. Finding circumstances

Other 17%

Natural (environmental) 12%

Natural (illness) 13%

Human-related 58%

Dead 98.4% (known cause 55.6%)
Recaught 1.5%
Resighted <1%

Ringing and recovery data

	<1960	60–69	70–79	80–89	90–97	Total
RINGING						
BTO ringing totals (%)	5	8	21	31	34	46,788
RECOVERIES						
BTO-ringed (%)	8	12	26	33	20	4,116
Foreign-ringed (%)	9	6	21	30	33	127

Statistical analyses

	Breeding population (sMAY–sAUG)	Wintering population (mNOV–sMAR)
Status	SHORT-DISTANCE MIGRANT (1)	SEDENTARY*
Age differences[s]	Significant	Not tested
Sex differences[s]	Significant*	Not tested
Regional differences	Significant[s]*	Not tested
Finding circumstances	(Not significant)	Not tested

246

Fig 4. Distances between ringing and recovery locations of Kestrels ringed as pulli early (before 23 June) or late (after 23 June) in the breeding season. Medians for months (points) and interquartile ranges (bars) are shown.

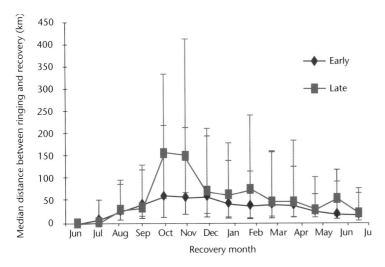

Fig 5. Locations outside the breeding season of (a) female (202) and (b) male (193) Kestrels that were present in Britain & Ireland during the breeding season.

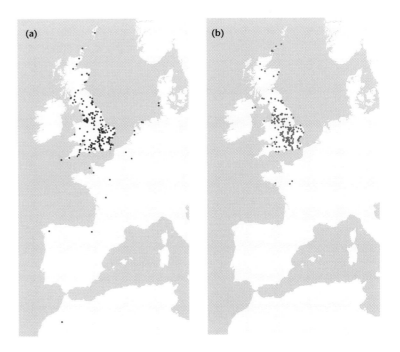

breeding pairs, though Ireland is under-represented (Fig 1). Kestrels raise a single brood each year and most nestlings are ringed between late May and mid-July (Fig 2). A few studies in areas as far apart as south Scotland and southeast England have also ringed fully grown birds (caught at the nest or with decoy traps in winter). In continental Europe, there have been long-term studies of Kestrels in Fennoscandia (notably Finland) and the Netherlands, making these countries the main sources of foreign-ringed recoveries in Britain & Ireland.

Ring-recoveries have mainly been made in the most populated areas of Britain. The cause of death was recorded in just over half of the recoveries where birds were found dead, and 58% of these were human-related (Fig 3). The Kestrel's familiar habit of hovering near road verges may make it vulnerable to collisions with motor vehicles, and this reported cause of death rose substantially between the 1950s and 1980s (Village 1990). This may further bias the recovery locations to areas of high human population density, such as southeast and central England. However, recovery locations are likely to be a reasonable guide to movements in Britain & Ireland.

Young Kestrels disperse from the nest from July onwards. Although most recoveries at this stage are within a few tens of kilometres of the birthplace (70% within 75 km), some are from much further afield (Village 1990). This movement away from the nest seems to be in random directions and some birds move very quickly. One nestling ringed on 17 June in Dumfriesshire was recovered 24 days later in Aberdeen, 300 km away (Village 1990). Such long-distance dispersal is rare but may explain the occasional recovery of British-ringed nestlings in places such as Norway. This pattern of a random post-fledging dispersal seems to happen elsewhere in Europe (eg Belgium; Adriaensen et al 1997, 1998), and a number of first-winter Kestrels find their way to southeast England from France, Belgium and the Netherlands. Siblings sometimes end up some distance from the nest on adjacent wintering territories, suggesting they may have moved together (Village 1990).

Long-distance, migratory movements become apparent in recoveries from September onwards. The concentration of recoveries in southeast England is more than could be accounted for by its high human populations. It seems likely that some birds from south Scotland and upland areas of north England move into central and southeast England. Juveniles ringed as nestlings from northern areas move further to their wintering recovery locations (median=135 km, n=206) than those from southern Britain (median= 40 km, n=362) and, apart from those reared in counties bordering the English Channel, are more likely to be recovered on the Continent (Snow 1968).

Despite these longer migrations of some birds from the north, the bulk of juveniles ringed in the north are also recovered there, suggesting

that most do little more than disperse from their natal areas to the first available winter territory. This idea is supported by the longer distances moved by late-fledged young compared with those fledged early in the season, a difference that is maintained to some extent in the first summer (Fig 4), and may be related to the fact that early-fledged birds are more likely to breed near their natal site in their first year than those fledged from late broods, both in Britain (Village 1990) and in the Netherlands (Dijkstra et al 1990). Work based on ring-recovery data from Kestrels ringed as nestlings in Belgium has also shown that dispersal rates and distances vary markedly between cohorts hatched in different years, and that both are negatively correlated with annual food availability (dispersal activity being lower in good years, Adriaensen et al 1998).

The migrating juveniles are joined by adults, especially from upland areas of northern Britain, where the bulk of the breeding population moves away in winter (Village 1990). In a partially migratory population in south Scotland, pairs split in autumn and territories were occupied by individuals. Breeders that remained behind were joined by dispersing juveniles that set up territories in vacant areas. Where one member of a pair remained behind it was invariably the male, and the proportion of males in the population was highest during a winter with low vole numbers (Village 1990). A similar finding is reported from Austria (Gamauf 1987). Some separation of sexes among the wintering population of Kestrels in Europe, with females apparently travelling further south, on average, than males (Fig 5) is suggested but not supported by statistical analysis. In farmland areas of eastern England, where pairs remained together in winter, females formed a higher proportion of the wintering population than in south Scotland; the overall sex ratio, however, was still slightly biased towards males (Village 1990). Further work is needed to see if females predominate on wintering grounds in southern Europe or Africa.

Individuals may return to the same wintering territories from year to year. In farmland areas in eastern England, three wing-tagged Kestrels were seen on winter territories in successive years but not in the intervening summer. One of these was a female seen for three successive winters on the Cambridgeshire fens (Village 1990).

Fig 6. Movements of Kestrels ringed abroad during the breeding season as pulli (65, red) or adults (3, black) and recovered in Britain & Ireland during autumn or winter.

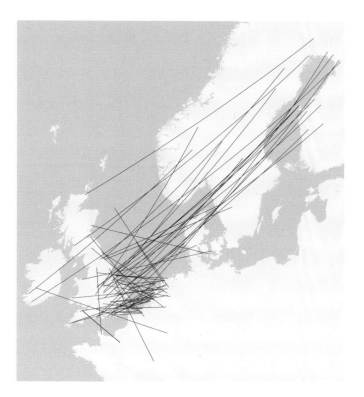

Fig 7. Movements of over 20 km and recovery locations of Kestrels ringed as pulli in Britain & Ireland and recovered in a subsequent breeding season when of breeding age. There were 146:140 movements under:over 20 km but only those over 20 km are plotted.

Observations on autumn migration routes such as Falsterbo in Sweden (Kjellén 1992) and in the Schwabian Alps (Gatter 1972) found that 'brown' birds (juveniles or adult females) migrated before adult males. At any location, juveniles generally migrate further than adults. Overall, winter recoveries are further from the birthplace for birds recovered in their first winter (median=47.5 km, P5–95=0–643 km, n=832) than subsequent ones (median=3 km, P5–95=0–398, n=30). This may not reflect what birds actually do, because it is not possible to separate truly migrant birds from sedentary ones. If immatures that settle permanently near their birthplace are more likely to survive than those that disperse, then adult recoveries could include a higher proportion of sedentary birds as an artefact.

Ring-recoveries of known breeding birds outside the breeding season are comparatively rare in the data set but the longest movements are all from birds in northern England or Scotland. Several of these are from a detailed study in south Scotland, which showed that some breeding adults travelled into northern and central England and even as far as western France in one instance. Wing-tagged breeders from this same study were seen in nearby low ground in successive winters and bred in the upland study area in the intervening summers (Village 1990). These birds were among the first to return to the breeding grounds in spring, and may have moved to lower ground when snow covered their breeding territories. In contrast, ringed adults from a comparable study in eastern England were mostly recovered close to their breeding territories (Village 1990). Even in cold weather, the English adult birds seemed able to survive by catching small birds, which were more numerous than in the Scottish Southern Uplands in winter. Juveniles in the English study were less able to cope with harsh weather, and 70–80% of wing-tagged individuals disappeared (probably dying rather than moving) during cold winters, compared with only 30–55% during mild ones.

The period of autumn migration is usually over by November. Behavioural studies have shown a decline in territorial fighting after October, as territory boundaries are established. Experimental removal of

territory holders has shown that lost birds are not replaced in winter, and there seems to be little midwinter movement (Village 1990).

The wintering population in Britain & Ireland also contains some birds from countries bordering the North and Baltic Seas (Fig 6). Most of the ring-recoveries are of immature birds ringed abroad in the nest and recovered in Britain or Ireland the following autumn or winter. These birds may arrive for differing reasons: some seem to be dispersing westwards or northwards from countries such as France, Belgium and the Netherlands. The distances involved are within those expected for dispersing juveniles, and if this movement is random dispersal rather than directed migration, it is likely that the southeast of Britain will receive a number of birds in their first winter from abroad. One of these immature birds was recovered in the west of Ireland, suggesting that some may continue moving until they reach the seaboard. A similar pattern holds for juveniles from Fennoscandia, and there are a number of recoveries of birds ringed in the nest in Sweden or Finland. The majority of these were recovered in southeast or southwest England but, again, a couple were found on the west coast of Ireland. These dispersing juveniles may remain in Britain & Ireland to breed but some definitely return. A few of the winter recoveries in lowland England were adults that had probably nested the previous summer, and this area may be a significant wintering ground for some of the Fennoscandian breeding population. Sightings of Kestrels from North Sea oil platforms peak in autumn and spring (Riddle 1986), suggesting that Kestrels which cross the North Sea include true migrants as well as dispersing juveniles.

Spring migration of European Kestrels lasts from February to May, with a peak in March and April. Long-distance migrants leave Africa from early March onwards and most have gone by April (Brown et al 1982). In south Scotland, the first migrants joined the winter residents in late February and the last arrived in early May (Village 1985b). Kestrels wintering near to the breeding grounds may return as soon as conditions permit and return was earlier following a mild winter than after harsher ones. Detailed studies at breeding grounds in northern Europe suggest that adults arrive before juveniles and males slightly before females

(Village 1985b, Palokangas *et al* 1992), the reverse of the situation in autumn. This agrees with trapping data from Cap Bon (Dejonghe 1989): first-year birds made up 38% of all captures in March (*n*=509) but 78% of captures in May (*n*=1,234); while among adults, males made up 69% of captures in March (*n*=367) but only 38% in May (*n*=269).

The return migration includes first-year birds as well as adults and, in Britain, recovery distances from birthplace decrease for both northern- and southern-reared Kestrels as they approach their first summer (Village 1990). The ringing data are difficult to interpret in terms of natal or breeding dispersal. There seems to be some return of juveniles to their natal areas but this may be biased if, as seems likely, juveniles settling near their natal sites are more likely to survive their first winter than are those that move further afield. The pattern of natal dispersal, with a median distance of 21 km (*P*5–95=0–254 km, *n*=265), is consistent with the idea that at least some Kestrels that settle following their post-fledging dispersal may remain on those territories and breed (Fig 7). There is little information from ring-recoveries on how far Kestrels move between breeding attempts. Movements between sites in particular study areas suggest most individuals rarely move more than 3 km, though longer movements would be difficult to record in such local studies (Village 1990). Comparisons between the sexes suggest that females are slightly more likely to change sites between breeding attempts than are males, and those females that change move slightly further than do males.

The greater frequency of migration in northern Kestrels is associated with a slightly higher turnover at nesting territories than in more sedentary populations in eastern England; though, even in these latter areas, there is a 60–70% chance of a change of individuals between successive breeding attempts at the same nesting site (Village 1990). Within the south Scotland study area, males that left the area in winter and then returned were less likely to pair with the same partner (22% of 28 cases) than males that remained in the area over winter (53% of 26 cases) but there was no such difference in females. Overall, mate-fidelity was similar to that in more sedentary populations, so migration did not seem to have as much effect on population turnover as might have been expected (Village 1990). The main factors influencing fidelity to nest or mate seemed to be breeding success (more chance of change after breeding failure) and age (less change in site or mate in older birds).

The influence of food supply on movements by Kestrels is difficult to measure directly. In broad terms, the seasonal migration is due to Kestrels moving away from parts of northern Europe where prolonged snow-cover makes small mammals unavailable to birds that hunt by sight. In years of very high vole abundance, however, a few individuals remain even in northern Fennoscandia (Korpimäki 1994). In these northern parts of their range, Kestrels settle in spring according to the local vole abundance, so numbers rapidly track the year-to-year fluctuations in prey abundance (Korpimäki 1994). Return rates of ringed breeding Kestrels in this study area were low, suggesting individuals may move considerable distances between breeding attempts in search of areas where voles are abundant. There is some evidence that Kestrels may be able to locate such areas because they can detect high concentrations of vole urine, visible in ultraviolet light (Viitala *et al* 1995). In areas where winters are less severe, Kestrels are more sedentary and individuals are likely to remain on their breeding areas in winter. These populations are also less prone to dramatic changes in vole abundance, so remaining in one place may offer the best chance of successful breeding.

Ring-recoveries have given a reasonably full picture of the movements of Kestrels in Europe, though more information is needed on differential migration of ages and sexes. In areas where part of the breeding population migrates, it would be interesting to know whether particular individuals migrate in some years but not in others, what makes an individual become a migrant rather than a winter resident, and more about the costs and benefits of migration versus winter residency on the breeding grounds.

Andrew Village

Merlin
Falco columbarius

The Merlin is the smallest breeding raptor in Britain & Ireland. It is essentially an open-country falcon particularly associated in these islands with nesting on upland moorland. Birds from this region tend to winter at lower altitudes, within 100 km of their natal area, but a few move much further south and into continental Europe (Mead 1973, Heavisides 1987). Additionally the region is an important wintering destination for the Icelandic race *subaesalon*.

The Merlin has an extensive northern holarctic range; there are nine subspecies breeding in northern Europe, northern and central Asia and North America. It is mostly migratory throughout its range although some populations are sedentary, particularly in the extreme west. The nominate race, breeding in North America, is the only one to include birds which move south of the Equator (*BWP*). The subspecies *subaesalon* breeds in Iceland and winters mainly in Britain & Ireland, with some remaining in Iceland and others reaching continental Europe. The range of the race *aesalon* extends from Ireland to northwest Siberia.

In common with the other falcons, Merlins do not build a nest, but utilize the old stick nests of other species, particularly corvids, or lay their eggs in a scrape on the ground. In general, Merlins avoid dense forest and bare or very steep areas. Nests in trees are usually in sparse shelter belts or isolated trees. In recent decades, however, Merlins in Britain have moved into edge sites in conifer plantations usually bordering onto suitable open hunting country (Newton *et al* 1986, Parr 1991, Little & Davison 1992, Orchel 1992).

The majority of birds in this region do, however, nest on the ground (Bibby & Nattrass 1986). Moorland managed for Red Grouse is

The analysis of the data for this species was supported by Grampian & Tayside Merlin Study Group

particularly attractive to the species. It is fortunate that a number of long-term breeding studies involving ringing have been carried out throughout Britain, including most of the main breeding areas (Fig 1a). Numbers of birds ringed in Ireland and subsequently recovered are comparatively small. Most of the birds recovered have been ringed as nestlings.

Some have been ringed as breeding adults and a small number of birds have been ringed or controlled during migration, particularly on Fair Isle, or in wintering areas (Figs 1 & 2). Two-thirds of all recoveries were reported with a known cause of death (Fig 3). Of these, the majority (59%) were recorded as human-related, which includes a range of accidental death circumstances that result in the corpse being likely to be found. An earlier analysis of finding circumstances showed that the proportion reported as killed by Man, in Britain & Ireland, steadily decreased from around 70% in the 1920s to about 4% in the 1980s (Heavisides 1987).

Most young Merlins in Britain & Ireland have fledged by late July and have become independent within about 10 days (pers obs) or 2–3 weeks (Newton *et al* 1978). Movements away from the breeding areas are then usual. Although some birds linger in suitable areas throughout the winter, provided that suitable prey remain available, there is a general movement to lower elevations (*BWP*). Although perhaps more often

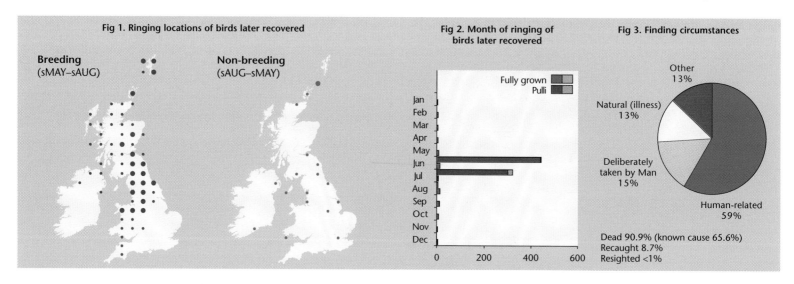

Fig 1. Ringing locations of birds later recovered

Breeding (sMAY–sAUG)   Non-breeding (sAUG–sMAY)

Fig 2. Month of ringing of birds later recovered

Fig 3. Finding circumstances

Other 13%
Natural (illness) 13%
Deliberately taken by Man 15%
Human-related 59%

Dead 90.9% (known cause 65.6%)
Recaught 8.7%
Resighted <1%

Ringing and recovery data

	<1960	60–69	70–79	80–89	90–97	Total
RINGING						
BTO ringing totals (%)	5	3	11	33	48	13,197
RECOVERIES						
BTO-ringed (%)	11	5	14	35	34	797
Foreign-ringed (%)	11	11	14	50	14	28

Statistical analyses

	Breeding population (sMAY–sAUG)	Wintering population (sNOV–sMAR)
Status	SHORT-DISTANCE MIGRANT (1)	[LONG-DISTANCE MIGRANT]
Age differences[NS]	Not significant	Not tested
Sex differences[NS]	Not significant*	Not tested
Regional differences	Not tested	Not tested
Finding circumstances	(Not significant)	Not tested

Fig 4. Movements of over 20 km between the breeding season and (a) autumn (55:235), (b) winter (15:109) and (c) spring (16:51) and locations outside the breeding season of Merlins present in Britain & Ireland during the breeding season. Sample sizes of movements under:over 20 km are given, but only those over 20 km are plotted.

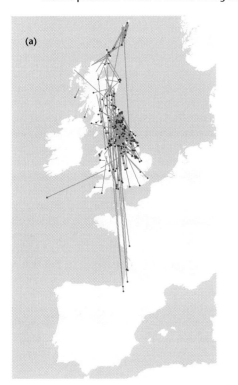
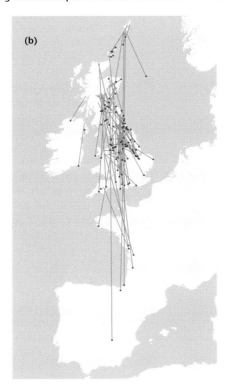
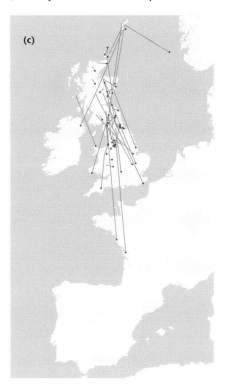

noted in coastal areas outside the breeding season, the recovery data show that birds disperse to both coastal and lowland inland areas throughout Britain & Ireland. Small numbers of birds appear to cross to continental Europe and a few migrants have been recovered on ships or oil platforms in the North Sea and the Atlantic Ocean (Fig 4).

The majority of British & Irish Merlins clearly remain within Britain & Ireland throughout the year (Fig 4). The median recovery distance of all recoveries found dead is calculated as 68 km. Using only birds of known sex, the median recovery distance is 86 km for females ($n=203$) and 83 km for males ($n=128$). Based on the ring-recoveries, there appears to be no significant difference between the sexes in distance of movements away from breeding areas or in average wintering areas. However, a study in Northumberland (Kerr 1989) based on wintering birds identified in the field as either adult males or females/immatures, suggested that adult males are less likely to move away from inland breeding sites than other birds. On Shetland, however, where some of the breeding birds overwinter, very few adult males are recorded during the winter period (Ellis & Okill 1990).

Movements between the breeding season and autumn, winter and spring respectively from Britain & Ireland (Fig 4) illustrate that most movements are south from the breeding areas and that some birds from most parts of the British breeding range have reached continental Europe. Median recovery distances are greatest between the breeding season and winter (99 km) and least between breeding seasons (33 km). Intermediate median distances between breeding season and spring (60 km) and autumn (67 km) reflect movements to and from natal and breeding areas. The ring-recovery data suggest some degree of natal dispersal (median=41 km, $n=55$), although there are too few birds of known sex recovered to allow examination of potential sex-related differences.

There is little evidence of much movement of birds between Britain and Ireland. Only two Merlins ringed in Britain during the breeding season were later recovered in Ireland; both were from Scotland. No

Merlin ringed in Ireland; during the breeding season has yet been recovered outside Ireland.

All overseas recoveries from Britain & Ireland are shown in Fig 5. In an earlier analysis, approximately half of Merlins recovered abroad were in their first year and older birds, up to eight years old, were recovered abroad (Heavisides 1987). The majority of foreign recoveries have been in France (20) with four in Spain, two each in Belgium and Germany, and one in the Netherlands. Five birds have been recovered at sea. Two of these were Shetland birds, one of which was found aboard a ship off Norway and the other on a gas platform in the Forties oilfield. A Merlin ringed as a nestling in Tayside was found the following April well north of its natal area on a ship off the Faeroes. A bird ringed in Wales was found on a ship in the Atlantic south of Ireland. The fifth bird, ringed in March of its first winter in southeast Ireland, was found dead in June, two years later, aboard a ship off Iceland. This would appear to be the only known record of an Icelandic bird, ringed while wintering in Britain & Ireland, and subsequently recovered as it approached its intended breeding area in Iceland.

The Icelandic race *subaesalon* was earlier thought to be separable primarily on longer wing measurements for both sexes. This led to the belief that the majority of Merlins trapped on Fair Isle during passage were of this race (Williamson 1954b, *BWP*). Subsequent measurement of birds in Shetland, Orkney and in northern mainland Scotland showed that northern British Merlins were mainly within the Icelandic size range (Robertson 1982, Picozzi 1983, Rebecca 1987). The ringing of 188 Merlin nestlings in Shetland during 1976–80 resulted in 13 controls on Fair Isle (Okill *et al* 1980). A single Orkney-ringed bird was also controlled there in 1980. No Icelandic- or Scandinavian-ringed birds have been controlled on Fair Isle. The cumulative evidence now strongly supports the view that the origin of these passage birds caught on Fair Isle is mainly Shetland.

During the period 1909–97, 28 Icelandic-ringed Merlins were recovered in Britain & Ireland (Fig 5). These recoveries were concentrated in Ireland and the west of Britain, and all were recorded outside the

Fig 5. Movements of British- & Irish-ringed Merlins recovered abroad (34, red) and of Icelandic-ringed Merlins recovered in Britain & Ireland (27, blue). Points show recovery locations.

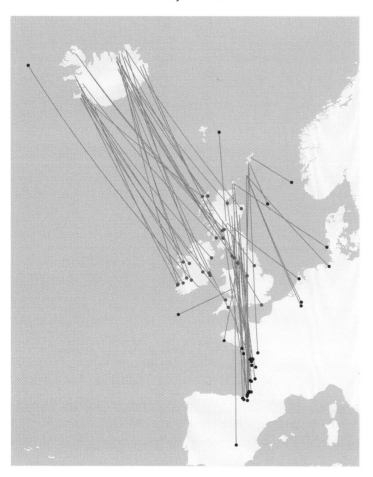

recoveries of Icelandic-ringed Merlins, with over 70% reported in Britain & Ireland and just a single individual reported in Fennoscandia. The remaining recoveries come from the Faeroes, France, Spain, Greenland and the Azores (A Petersen pers comm).

Merlins are frequently recorded on North Sea oil or gas platforms during migration, especially in autumn (Butler 1982). Between 1979 and 1987, 81 individuals were recorded, the majority from the Central and North sectors, 44 and 24 respectively, with only a few in the East and South, seven and six respectively (Rebecca 1989). The only known ring-recovery on a platform was of a nestling ringed in Shetland during June and recovered in November of the same year in the Forties oilfield. Ring-recoveries of birds ringed in Norway (Haftorn 1971) and Sweden (Olson 1980) include significant numbers in near continental Europe including Germany, Belgium, France, the Netherlands, Spain and Italy but only two in Britain and none in Ireland.

The two British recoveries of Merlins ringed in Scandinavia are coincidentally both from County Durham: a nestling ringed in Swedish Lapland during July 1976 was recovered on 10 October of the same year, and a juvenile trapped near the southern tip of Norway on 17 September 1992 was recovered around a month later. The natal area of the latter is unknown and it might have been a Shetland bird that then reoriented towards a more usual British wintering destination. The distribution of *subaesalon* across Ireland and western Britain, together with the recovery of a Shetland-ringed bird on a gas platform and the paucity of recoveries of Scandinavian birds of this species in Britain & Ireland, all support Rebecca's (1989) assertion that the majority of birds recorded from the North Sea are probably of British origin.

After earlier concerns about possible declines in Merlin populations, a survey in 1993–94 (Rebecca & Bainbridge 1998) suggested that the British population size was about 1,300 pairs and, in most areas, numbers had increased or had remained stable since an earlier survey in 1983–84 (Bibby & Nattrass 1986). Ringing studies and recoveries confirm the importance of large areas of open country at high elevations for breeding, and at lower elevations for passage and wintering.

Further studies, including more trapping of breeding adults, colour-marking and radio-tagging, would increase our knowledge of natal and breeding dispersal, the sizes of hunting ranges and the degree of exchange between breeding areas. Continued long-term monitoring of the impacts of land-use changes in the uplands on breeding populations of Merlins is a clear conservation need.

Alan Heavisides

breeding season. Specimens identified as *subaesalon* have been collected in southwest Norway, the Netherlands, Belgium and France (*BWP*). In view of the established size overlap (above), the possibility should now be considered that at least some of these birds might have been from northern Britain. This is supported by the pattern of the 38 overseas

Eurasian Hobby (Hobby)

Falco subbuteo

The Hobby is the only British falcon whose entire population migrates to tropical Africa in winter, joining three other species from Europe, Lesser Kestrel *Falco naumanni*, Red-footed Falcon *F. vespertinus* and Eleonora's Falcon *F. eleonorae*, in exploiting the abundant insect food of the wetlands and savannas. The Eurasian Hobby breeds throughout the Palearctic between Britain and Japan, inhabiting generally open terrain but also broken forest within the temperate, continental and sub-boreal climatic zones encompassed by the July isotherms of 15°C and 32°C and at altitudes ranging from sea-level to over 2,000 m above sea-level in continental regions. Its range in western Europe lies between the Mediterranean and the Arctic Circle in Sweden, Finland and Russia.

All of the western Palearctic Hobby populations migrate to Africa, while most of the east Asian population probably winters in the Indian subcontinent and in parts of southeast Asia. It is not known where the 'migratory divide' occurs (*BWP*). Furthermore, the precise wintering destinations of each of the regional Hobby populations remain uncertain due to a lack of ring-recoveries from the tropics.

Possessing swift, agile flight and acute vision, the Hobby is able to chase and capture aerial prey including a large variety of both bird and insect species between the sizes of Starling and ants. The fact that insects provide a large part of its diet both constrains its choice of breeding areas to those of relatively warm summers with comparatively low rainfall, and rewards its long-distance autumn migration with an immense abundance of food, notably flying termites, in subtropical regions. The Hobby also depends for breeding on the availability of

The analysis of the data for this species was supported by the Arden Ringing Group

disused stick nests of various species, principally Carrion Crow, that are located where the nesting bird is afforded open access and a wide outlook. A shortage of such nests may limit the species' breeding density in some areas (Chapman 1999).

The Hobby's current breeding range within Britain lies south of a line between the Humber and Mersey and extends into the Welsh Marches, with isolated records to the north and west (*1988–91 Atlas*). Very few Hobbies have been recorded in Ireland and no breeding has been reported from there (*Birds in Ireland*). Nesting in the lowland habitats of heathland, forestry and mixed farmland at densities ranging between one and five pairs per 100 sq km, its current population of an estimated 1,350 pairs (Chapman 1999) has probably resulted from a pronounced increase in recent years, albeit to former levels in parts of its range. Hobbies generally return to their breeding sites from late April to mid-May, then undergo courtship and nest selection before laying in mid-June. Young birds fledge around mid-August and both they and the adults migrate south during September, with the latest birds being recorded up to mid-October.

Ringing of Hobbies has generally been of pulli, adults mainly being trapped accidentally in mist-nests. Ninety-five percent of the 1,179 Hobbies ringed in Britain between 1909 and 1997 were pulli. Fig 1 shows the general location of ringing sites. The 37 recoveries from

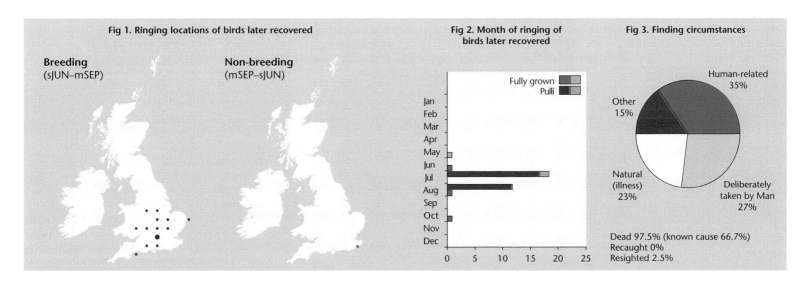

Fig 1. Ringing locations of birds later recovered

Breeding (sJUN–mSEP)

Non-breeding (mSEP–sJUN)

Fig 2. Month of ringing of birds later recovered

Fully grown / Pulli

Fig 3. Finding circumstances

Human-related 35%
Other 15%
Natural (illness) 23%
Deliberately taken by Man 27%

Dead 97.5% (known cause 66.7%)
Recaught 0%
Resighted 2.5%

Ringing and recovery data

	<1960	60–69	70–79	80–89	90–97	Total
RINGING						
BTO ringing totals (%)	4	4	18	31	42	1,179
RECOVERIES						
BTO-ringed (%)	8	8	8	41	35	37
Foreign-ringed (%)	33	0	0	33	33	3

Statistical analyses

	Breeding population (sJUN–mSEP)	Wintering population (mNOV–sAPR)
Status	[LONG-DISTANCE MIGRANT]	NONE
Age differences	Not tested	—
Sex differences	Not tested	—
Regional differences	Not tested	—
Finding circumstances	Not tested	—

253

Fig 4. Recovery locations and movements of over 20 km for the included recoveries of Hobbies ringed (37, red) or recovered (3, blue) in Britain & Ireland.

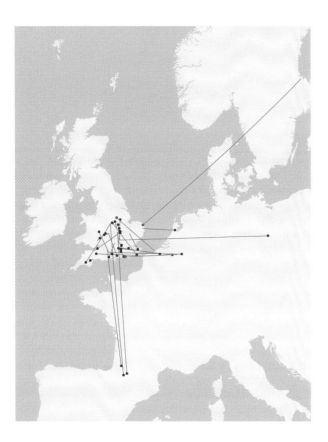

Fig 5. Movements of over 500 km made by Hobbies ringed by other European ringing schemes. (Data provided by the Belgian Ringing Scheme, Dutch Ringing Centre, Hiddensee Bird Ringing Centre, Vogelwarte Radolfzell, Ministerio de Medio Ambiente (Ringing Data Bank), Swedish Bird Ringing Centre and Sempach Ringing Centre.)

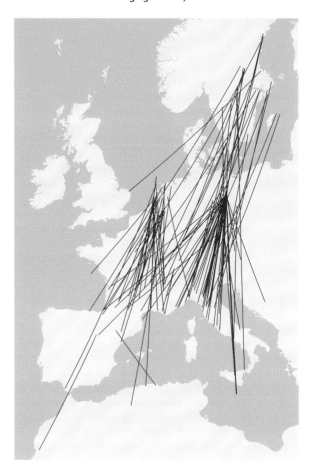

British ringing demonstrate a relatively low recovery rate (3.2%) and include only eight abroad: three in Belgium, two in France, one each in Germany and the Netherlands, and one on board a ship some 1,000 km west of Portugal (Fig 4). A British-ringed Hobby recovered in Portugal has been excluded from the current analysis because of uncertainties over its ringing location.

Birds ringed as pulli accounted for 34 (92%) of the recoveries (Fig 2) and all but one were of birds found dead. Fig 3 collates the various finding circumstances for the two-thirds of birds for which the cause of death was known, and shows that 62% of these were deliberately taken by Man or died through other human-related causes. Ten birds were recovered as juveniles, 14 as second-year birds and 13 as older birds, including one aged 12 years. In addition, single birds from Sweden, Belgium and the Netherlands have been found in Britain (Fig 4). Notably, one record is of an adult Hobby that flew 345 km from Belgium to Nottinghamshire in only two days during early May.

As little inference about migration can be drawn from these few recoveries of British birds, it was more profitable to set them within the context of ring-recoveries from continental Europe. As there has not been a single recovery of a ringed Hobby south of the Sahara, it is possible only to make suppositions about the destination of migrating birds in autumn from ring-recoveries in countries bordering the Mediterranean, the relative numbers of Hobbies counted at migration watch-points and documented information about the species in tropical Africa.

Typically for a falcon, and with its low wing-loading, the Hobby is capable of sustained flight over long distances. The fact that a tiny fraction of its European population (excluding Russia) of 20–27,000 breeding pairs (Chapman 1999) is seen at migration bottlenecks – only

Cap Bon in Tunisia and Malta recording more than 250 birds during a migratory season – demonstrates that birds must migrate on a broad front. There is also evidence for their flying at considerable height: for instance, an African observer estimated that Hobbies rose to 600 m or more within a thundercloud (Brown 1976), while hunting birds ascended over a mountain pass to 1,000–2,000 m above ground (Pfander 1992). Only adverse weather conditions seem to force Hobbies and other raptors down within visible range over Malta; high pressure conditions including low wind strength probably favour their crossing the Mediterranean at great height (Beaman & Galea 1974).

The largest reported passage of Hobbies in Africa was from Kenya where 'flocks of hundreds together may pass in a long stream, each bird well separated from its neighbour, at a height of several hundred feet above the ground' (Brown 1976). Over 100 juveniles hunting dragonflies on the Croatian coast in October was probably an exceptional concentration of migrants (Natorp 1951). Otherwise in Europe, migrating Hobbies are observed singly or in groups of two to five birds during passage.

To provide a more meaningful body of data, nine other European ringing schemes were consulted. Together with Britain, a total of 5,720 Hobbies were ringed during 1909–98, of which 203 (3.5%) were subsequently recovered. In order to ascertain any distinct migratory directions, an arbitrary distance of at least 500 km was chosen and all such recoveries plotted on a map (Fig 5). Of the 107 qualifying records, all the birds were ringed as pulli apart from four. Ninety-three of the recoveries were of Hobbies on autumn migration, usually their first; the remainder were either on spring migration or were recovered as corpses over the winter, except for a bird recovered during February in Algeria where it could possibly have wintered. From these few recoveries there is no great variation among individuals in the general direction taken during migration.

The map shows overall a south to southwesterly movement in autumn, which, if projected, would suggest that Hobbies are heading for West Africa. However, we cannot rule out a possible bias in favour of birds dying (usually shot) and being reported in France, Italy, Spain and the Barbary coast of North Africa, where hunting pressure is high. Hobbies may migrate southwest in western Europe before altering course in Africa to the southeast. The species' main wintering area is believed to be the Zambezi Basin between 10° and 20°S (Chapman 1999).

Hobbies have been recorded on autumn passage in the Guinea savannas of West Africa between Senegal and Cameroon, and wintering in the Ivory Coast (Thiollay 1985a), although such records are few. The cessation of rains in late October triggers an abundance of locusts, grasshoppers and other potential insect prey. Hobbies may well migrate eastwards from this region as do, for example, Swifts. They are quite capable of crossing the equatorial rainforest in order to reach the savannas of Zimbabwe, Zambia, Malawi, Botswana and Mozambique, where many more birds are seen during November–March (even allowing for observer bias in a region where there are more birdwatchers). Hobbies from eastern Europe probably migrate to this region, because the few ring-recoveries of birds ringed in Finland and Latvia, including one recovery from Egypt, suggest a south-southeasterly migration route. They are possibly joined by birds that breed in Russia east of the Urals and in the central Asian states (Chapman 1999).

The recoveries in subsequent breeding seasons of seven (mature) British Hobbies ringed as pulli indicate a median natal dispersal distance of 25 km. This figure is similar to that obtained from an analysis of Russian ring-recoveries, which gave a mean dispersal distance of 39 km from their natal sites (Galushin 1974). A German colour-ringing study established that 87% of male Hobbies, but only 11% of females, had returned to their natal area (Fiuczynski 1978).

Considering the high proportion of recoveries of Hobbies that had been shot on migration through southern Europe, it is one of several vulnerable species that highlight the continuing need for better law enforcement in those countries. However, the number of birds involved is unlikely to have an impact on the Hobby's European breeding populations. The question of how the species is faring in its wintering quarters and on migration through Africa is hard to answer due to the lack of ring-recoveries there.

Anthony Chapman

Peregrine Falcon

Falco peregrinus

The ancient name Peregrine is supposedly derived from the medieval observation that the bird was a wanderer, though this may have been an impression based mainly on knowledge in non-breeding areas. Modern understanding is that this almost cosmopolitan species group migrates to a degree determined largely by the movements of its prey populations, though the young tend in general to disperse from their natal area in seeking a place of their own. Hickey & Anderson (1969) summarized the migratory tendencies of the 19 subspecies of Peregrines as restricted to the five northern races. Within at least four of these subspecies, they suggested that there exists a continuum of behaviour, individuals in the more southerly latitudes being non-migratory, those in the north moving considerable distances, these latitudinal gradients in turn strongly modified by the climatic amelioration produced by the influence of oceans. Hence, the migratory behaviour of Peregrines also tends to increase eastwards across Eurasia and North America.

Only the nominate race of the Peregrine inhabits Britain & Ireland, since the occasional birds from Scandinavia are also of this subspecies, and claimed sight records of North American *anatum* are of doubtful validity. The breeding habitat is mainly in areas where cliffs provide nesting sites, notably on rocky coasts and rugged uplands but as the species has adapted widely to nesting in quarries and on man-made structures, it has come increasingly to include developed and even urban lowlands. Many established breeders are virtually sedentary in their nesting haunts throughout the year (*cf* Mearns 1982) but juveniles and non-breeding adults may turn up almost anywhere, and the *Winter Atlas* shows appreciably more occurrences in eastern and lowland areas

The analysis of the data for this species was supported by Jim Wells

than in spring and summer. Some Scottish Highland Peregrines breeding at high altitudes may leave their nesting grounds for lower levels during winter (D N Weir pers comm), and at least some birds in the barren northwest and the Western and Northern Isles appear to move out to unknown areas (Ratcliffe 1993). Prolonged frost and snow-cover can also cause a temporary desertion of upland haunts in general, as birds seek less severe conditions on lower ground.

After a collapse in population from 1956 to 1963, to about 40% of pre-World War II numbers, attributed to the persistent organochlorine insecticides of agriculture, the Peregrine in Britain & Ireland has recovered to unprecedented high breeding levels after these chemicals were banned. In 1991, a UK-wide survey gave an estimated breeding population of 1,265 pairs, representing an increase of 145% on the 1930–39 level (Crick & Ratcliffe 1995). A parallel survey in the Republic of Ireland that year gave a total of 350–355 occupied territories, 140% above the pre-1950 estimate (Norriss 1995). This remarkable increase in numbers may be attributed to four main factors: the phasing-out of persistent organochlorine insecticides, and the decline of their residues in the Peregrine's food chain; increased protection effort for Peregrines, with an educational-publicity programme on birds of prey; the high numbers of domestic pigeons providing a prolific food supply in many districts; and the species' resilience in adapting to new nesting habitats,

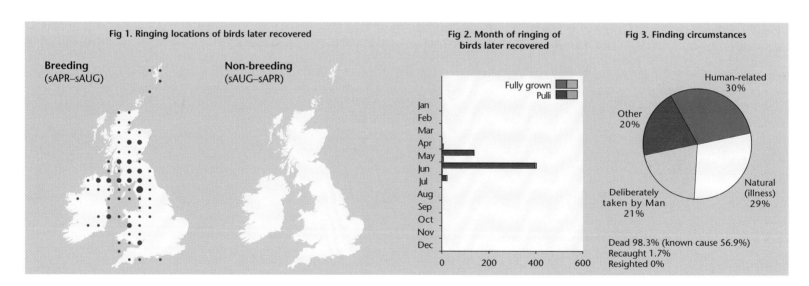

Fig 1. Ringing locations of birds later recovered

Breeding (sAPR–sAUG)

Non-breeding (sAUG–sAPR)

Fig 2. Month of ringing of birds later recovered

Fully grown
Pulli

Fig 3. Finding circumstances

Human-related 30%

Other 20%

Deliberately taken by Man 21%

Natural (illness) 29%

Dead 98.3% (known cause 56.9%)
Recaught 1.7%
Resighted 0%

Ringing and recovery data

	<1960	60–69	70–79	80–89	90–97	Total
RINGING						
BTO ringing totals (%)	2	1	15	44	38	6,845
RECOVERIES						
BTO-ringed (%)	3	0	12	46	39	564
Foreign-ringed (%)	57	0	0	14	29	14

Statistical analyses

	Breeding population (sAPR–sAUG)	Wintering population (mNOV–sMAR)
Status	SEDENTARY (0)	[LONG-DISTANCE MIGRANT]
Age differences[NS]	Not significant*	Not tested
Sex differences[NS]	Significant*	Not tested
Regional differences	Not tested	Not tested
Finding circumstances	Not significant*	Not tested

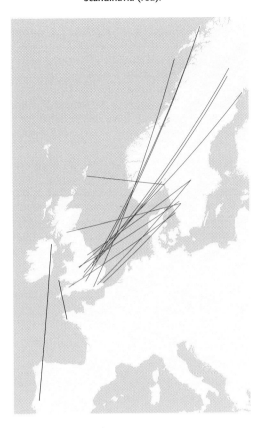

Fig 4. All 16 included exchanges of Peregrines between Britain & Ireland and abroad. Those ringed in Britain & Ireland (black) are differentiated from those ringed in Scandinavia (red).

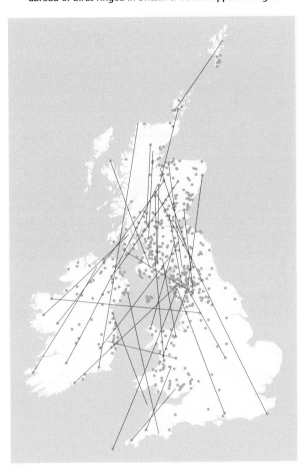

Fig 5. Recovery locations and movements of over 200 km for the 562 included recoveries of Peregrines ringed or recovered in Britain & Ireland. The two recoveries abroad of birds ringed in Britain & Ireland appear in Fig 4.

in quarries (both old and active), man-made structures, and easily accessible nest sites in small rocks, steep banks or even on the ground. Sample surveys of selected areas since 1991 show that a slow increase in the breeding population has continued in general, extending now to southeast England, but not the far north of Scotland, where marine pollutants are suspected to be a residual problem. Completely new nesting territories are reported every year from many areas, and numbers in many districts are not yet at saturation, though in a few areas pairs have dropped out again and reduced the high densities.

Ringing effort is somewhat biased geographically (Fig 1), having depended on the dedication of a small number of enthusiasts. Cumbria in the northwest has been a special focus of attention, and this has been led by G Horne with the astonishing personal total of 1,042 birds ringed and 106 recovered. Relatively neglected regions, with considerable numbers of breeding Peregrines, are southwest England, South and North Wales (coastal and inland), the Isle of Man, the western and northern Highlands (coastal and inland), the Scottish islands, and southern and western Ireland (coastal and inland). The ring-recovery data may thus not reflect the true picture of movements for all these regions, especially in the Highlands and Islands, where migratory tendencies may well be greatest.

Nearly all the Peregrines recovered in Britain & Ireland were ringed as nestlings at around three or four weeks old, in May and June (Fig 2). Cause of death was established for 57% of the 568 birds recovered dead. Of this sample, 51% involved human agency, with 29% through illness and 12% resulting from natural (environmental) causes (Fig 3). Surprisingly, 3.4% of the sample died from natural predation. It can be assumed that many birds for which cause of death was unknown were deliberately and illegally destroyed, as these are the ones for which the true cause would be most likely to be concealed.

Only 14 foreign-ringed Peregrines have been recovered in Britain, all from Scandinavia (Fig 4), confirming the tendency of this northerly European population to migrate southwest or south-southwest. The small numbers of records reflect both low ringing effort and the heavily depleted state of the Fennoscandian Peregrine population following severe decline through persistent pesticide effects. This population 'crash' was itself attributed to the migratory tendencies of these northern birds, which became greatly exposed to pesticidal contamination in their wintering haunts on the farmlands of Europe south of the Baltic and across the North Sea. Most of the foreign-ringed recoveries here were in the southern and mainly lowland half of Britain (Fig 4) but they do not show what proportion of birds currently wintering in these districts is from overseas. There have been no recoveries of Peregrines in a reverse direction, and the only two British- or Irish-ringed birds found outside these two countries had travelled south, to France and Portugal (Fig 4).

While some Peregrines can breed at one year old, the majority do not do so until aged two years or more. In the meantime, they join a non-breeding population whose numbers, distribution and movements are little known. These non-breeders replenish gaps caused by mortality in the breeding population, and many probably live in the same areas.

For 554 birds ringed in Britain & Ireland and later found dead, the median distance travelled was 45 km, with little difference between regions; 55% had moved less than 50 km, 78% less than 100 km, and only 6.7% 200 km or more. Comparison of Fig 5 with Fig 1 suggests that the geographical pattern of recovery is not very different from that of ringing. For birds of known sex, 157 females moved somewhat farther (median 49 km) than 150 males (median 34 km) but the sexes did not differ in their average wintering locations. In an earlier analysis of data up to 1990 (358 recoveries), Mead (1993) found that first-year birds tended to travel shorter distances from birthplace than older birds; the present study, however, shows little difference in median distance between birds recovered while still immature and those which survived into adulthood. While there is no appreciable difference in median distance of movement according to season of recovery, in the Northwest (the only region with significant samples), the proportion of birds recovered more than 20 km from their ringing site was 65% in spring, 83% in autumn and 90% in winter. Movements shown by British & Irish ring-recoveries have no discernible pattern of orientation, and appear to be almost random in direction. For seasonally accurate recoveries, there appear to be no marked differences in geographical pattern of recovery according to month throughout the year.

Virtually the only information on Peregrine movements as adults comes from the study by Mearns & Newton (1984) involving the capture and recapture of breeding birds at the nest in southern Scotland. Of 68 females handled in a subsequent year, 61 had stayed on the same territory while seven moved to a different one, while all of six males were on the same territory. Thirty-nine of these birds had been ringed previously as nestlings, and 24 males had dispersed a median distance of 20 km, while 15 females had travelled a median of 68 km. The authors concluded that Peregrines in southern Scotland made their longest movements during their first year of life, and that, once established as breeders, they mostly remained faithful to their breeding territories. Since, in most cases, breeders cannot be separated from non-breeders amongst adults found dead, it would need a much more concentrated ringing effort on both classes to find out whether breeders in any region tend to be the more sedentary of the two throughout the year.

While the data are largely of birds ringed as nestlings, and give evidence of their dispersal, they would also point to any true migration that might occur as, indeed, the Scandinavian records show. They confirm there is scant evidence that the Peregrine in Britain & Ireland is a migrant, in the sense of regularly travelling after the breeding season to distant winter quarters and reversing the journeys by the following spring. It is possible that some birds in the far north of Scotland are local migrants, but until more ringing data are available for the region this must remain conjecture.

While most British & Irish Peregrines do not move far from their natal areas in their normal dispersal, there are a sufficient number of records of birds travelling over 200 km to suggest a capacity for fairly rapid spread from one breeding district to colonize or repopulate others at some distance (Fig 5). These long-distance movements include eight from Britain to Ireland, and one in the reverse direction. The data do not, however, imply that our Peregrines have made any measurable contribution to recent recovery of the continental European population, especially in Fennoscandia.

Derek A Ratcliffe

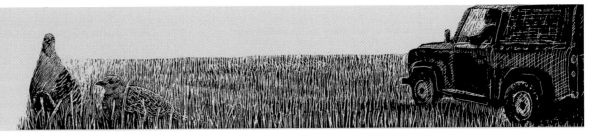

Grey Partridge
Perdix perdix

The Grey Partridge was once the most numerous gamebird in Britain & Ireland. Indeed, in many areas it was the most abundant bird on farmland. In the 20th century, however, annual stocks of the bird fell by around 5½ million birds, or 95%.

Although some populations in the east of the range are migratory, the Grey Partridge must normally be one of the most sedentary of birds. It prefers to walk rather than fly, and usually moves no further than is necessary to feed or roost. One pair, watched continuously for 15 hours 5 minutes, walked 1,200 m, but flew only four times covering a total of 180 m (Blank 1980). Only in avoiding deep snow, which the species has to do since it feeds entirely on the ground, and in finding a mate, is there a need to stray from its sedentary mode.

The range of the Grey Partridge centres on latitude 49°N and extends in Eurasia from Ireland to Mongolia and in North America, where it has been introduced as a gamebird, from coast to coast, with a little less than 2% of the world population found in Britain & Ireland (Potts 1986). Nominate *perdix* breeds in a band from Ireland, Britain and Sweden to Greece and Bulgaria. A further four west European races occupy northern Spain, France, Italy, and an area of the Dutch/German border (*BWP*). To the east of nominate *perdix*, three races are found in eastern Europe or to the east of the Urals. Birds imported for restocking in Britain & Ireland have come mainly from Hungary, prior to 1914, and from Denmark in the early 1960s, and have involved the nominate subspecies. It is also this race that has been introduced to North America.

The Grey Partridge is historically a bird of the relatively treeless grasslands that are now largely given over to the production of cereals. Its

The analysis of the data for this species was supported by Peter G Phillips

presence in Britain is not, however, due to the presence of arable farming, as has sometimes been claimed. Judging from widespread and numerous subfossil deposits, it has been present in Britain & Ireland, whenever the climate permitted, for arguably 475,000 years (Pitts & Roberts 1998).

The most preferred nest sites are the dry grassy banks that today pass for steppe remnants, for example those along hedgerows. As soon as the chicks 'dry off', the broods are taken into cover, ideally cereal crops or tall relatively sparse grasses, where they can wander freely looking for insect food out of sight of aerial predators. Once the cereal harvest is over, the coveys glean the stubbles or graze subsequent crops, dispersing very little, although flying at dusk to open, preferably ploughed fields for roosting. Pair formation takes place in February whereupon the birds search for suitable nest sites. Where all the essential kinds of habitat are close together, as they were on traditional ley farms, and still are today in a few cases, the Grey Partridge can afford to be sedentary.

Grey Partridges have been ringed in private schemes back to at least 1667, but few modern analyses have been completed, nor would many be viable given that, in sharp contrast to the national Ringing Scheme, the data were not stored systematically. Also, unlike the present sample, many of these ringed birds were hand-reared rather than wild-caught.

The locations of ringing (Fig 1) show the expected higher frequency towards the south and east. The distribution of dates of ringing of the

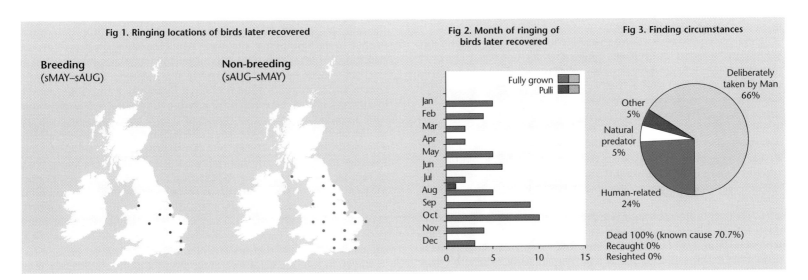

Fig 1. Ringing locations of birds later recovered

Breeding (sMAY–sAUG) Non-breeding (sAUG–sMAY)

Fig 2. Month of ringing of birds later recovered

Fully grown / Pulli

Fig 3. Finding circumstances

Deliberately taken by Man 66%
Other 5%
Natural predator 5%
Human-related 24%

Dead 100% (known cause 70.7%)
Recaught 0%
Resighted 0%

Ringing and recovery data

	<1960	60–69	70–79	80–89	90–97	Total
RINGING						
BTO ringing totals (%)	9	24	26	25	15	1,129
RECOVERIES						
BTO-ringed (%)	7	40	21	26	7	58
Foreign-ringed (%)	0	0	0	0	0	0

Statistical analyses

	Breeding population (sMAY–sAUG)	Wintering population (sNOV–mFEB)
Status	[SEDENTARY]	[SEDENTARY]
Age differences	Not tested	Not tested
Sex differences	Not tested	Not tested
Regional differences	Not tested	Not tested
Finding circumstances	Not tested	Not tested

Fig 4. Recovery locations and movements of over 20 km for the 58 included recoveries of Grey Partridges ringed or recovered in Britain & Ireland.

recoveries through the seasons is much as one would expect, though with a surprising secondary peak in May and June (Fig 2). The circumstances of recovery confirm what we would expect from a gamebird, namely the predominance of hunting (Fig 3). However, most recoveries had been ringed in the period 1960–78 during which shooting accounted for less than 17% of all deaths, not 66% as the ringing data imply; contrary to the impression given by the recoveries, predation is by far the more important cause of death (Potts 1986).

The basic patterns of Grey Partridge seasonal movements have been defined using radio-telemetry and by observing individually marked birds. The methods used have varied greatly but a clear picture emerges. From the first nesting scrape to hatching, the home range is about 2–3 ha (Döring & Helfrich 1986, Birkan & Angibault 1990), suggesting the birds move little more than 150 m from the nest, rising to 2–11 ha in North Dakota (Carroll *et al* 1995).

Once the chicks are hatched, their parents move them according to the supply of insect food. Home range sizes for unfledged chicks in cereals averaged 0.8 ha where pesticides were not used but rose to 2.2 ha where they were used (Rands 1986). Where habitats are complex, the home ranges of fledged broods are 3–6 ha (Döring & Helfrich 1986) but, where field size is greater, the ranges increase to 10 ha or more (Birkan *et al* 1992, Carroll *et al* 1995). From the cereal harvest onwards, home ranges increase still further in size and extend in Hampshire to around 80 ha, overlapping as they do so (Blank & Ash 1956), or to around 100 ha or more in North Dakota (Carroll *et al* 1995). As in summer, the extent of movement depends to a large extent on the supply of food and cover.

In contrast to the west European populations, the race *robusta* east of the Urals is migratory. Working at sites between Lake Baikal and Mongolia, Litun (1982) established that there are regular movements of up to 470 km, with surviving birds returning in spring. Where the snow normally lies for five months or more, or is greater than 50 cm for one month, such movements appear to be annual.

Controversy has surrounded the migratory behaviour of the race *lucida* which occurs in eastern Europe, westward to a line roughly from the mid-Baltic to the Black Sea. It is clear from the older literature, such as that of Naumann (1833), that extensive wandering packs were typical, in numbers up to 500, sometimes in response to snowfalls or sudden thaws. Often appearing from the east, they were compared with the eruptive Pallas's Sandgrouse. In severe winters, large numbers migrated south along the Volga, with some flocks reaching as far west as Odessa (Formozov 1946). The only modern study is that of Nikiforov (1992)

who followed 106 coveys in Belarus. Eight of the coveys were found to be migratory, with no fixed abode. Just as reported by earlier writers, these migratory birds were often in large coveys or packs, their average size being 26. In contrast, the sedentary coveys occupied normal home ranges of 30–150 ha and averaged 10 birds per covey. Whatever made the few coveys so nomadic is not known, but Nikiforov thought it was the result of coveys joining and producing a sort of 'migratory state' rather in the manner of Red Grouse that form restless packs in response to severe weather.

Elsewhere in the range of the nominate race, wandering birds, known in Germany as '*Zughühner*' (wandering partridges) and in France as 'roquettes' (rockets) are less frequent. Buffon (1781) supposed there was a wandering race of smaller birds with brown breasts, yellow legs and a longer bill. Flocks were seen as far west as Normandy and their journeys were described as 'not halting'. They did respond to calls of local birds, however, thus revealing their affinity. In fact, a separate name was not justified, partly because many of the characters were those of younger birds (Temminck 1820).

Wherever they are, all Grey Partridges emerging from winter in coveys undergo two distinct movements, firstly to seek mates and secondly to explore, with the mate, a suitable nest site. The females pair within their winter range while, unusually among birds and in distinct contrast to the Red-legged Partridge, the young males disperse (Blank & Ash 1956, Jenkins 1961). Straight-line distances travelled during the exploration phase averaged 2.2 km in Wisconsin, where nesting habitat was scarce (Church *et al* 1980), but much less than this at Damerham, Hampshire, where potential nest sites were abundant. On this study area, over a thousand wild Grey Partridges were caught, ringed and released from 1950 to 1956 inclusive. Distances moved by those individually marked (with back tabs) from September to the territory where the pair nested were: adult males 265±87 m; adult females 186±22 m; first spring males 525±101 m and first spring females 428±76 m (Game Conservancy Trust unpublished). Males generally were in surplus as is normal in Grey Partridges and, as many young males were never able to find mates, they moved the furthest. Nevertheless, of a total of 172 first-spring males that survived to April only two moved more than 3 km, with the furthest reaching 8.3 km. None of the thousand birds individually marked at Damerham were known to travel further. In the light of this, that two (3%) of the 58 British ring-recoveries had travelled more than 20 km is surprising (Fig 4), especially when at least one was a female in its first spring. It is, however, more in line with studies in Sussex and overseas of Grey Partridges reared and released; excluding birds shot in their first autumn, an average 2% of recoveries were beyond 20 km in five studies (Paludan 1963, pers obs). In the studies on the Sussex Downs, the extreme limit of dispersal was 40 km, reached by two birds (0.4%), but the record goes to an Italian Grey Partridge of Danish origin that reached 139 km. Why these Marco Polos of the Grey Partridge world should travel so far is a mystery. It does suggest, however, that some of the birds lost, assumed dead, during intensive studies of individually marked birds may in fact have moved beyond the limit of detection. The problem is greatest with small areas. Thus 10% of Grey Partridges left an area of 2.6 km² (Jenkins 1961) compared to only 2% that left one of 12.5 km² (pers obs).

Given its role as a barometer of biodiversity in the countryside, most current interest centres on the implementation of the UK Biodiversity Action Plan for the Grey Partridge. The potential for restoration of numbers is shown by more than 80 schemes on private estates. A combination of less-intensive cereal-growing, proper management of set-aside and systematic control of nest predators is effective, but uptake is thwarted by severe economic factors. The situation in Ireland may be too late even for drastic and urgent action. Only 6–8 pairs remain in the whole country (B Kavanagh pers comm), whereas densities were at one time frequently over 2 pairs per km² (eg Seigne 1930).

G R Potts

Water Rail
Rallus aquaticus

Although the Water Rail is widespread in Britain & Ireland throughout the year, many aspects of its ecology remain poorly understood. Despite the appearance of a weak and ungainly flight over short distances, Water Rails are capable of long-distance movements and birds from eastern Europe have been recovered in Britain during the winter.

There are four subspecies of Water Rail; the nominate race *aquaticus* occurs from Britain & Ireland north to southern Fennoscandia and south to North Africa, extending across central Europe east as far as Omsk and northern Kazakhstan. It is mainly resident in the North Sea countries, southwest Europe and the Mediterranean Basin but migratory or partially migratory elsewhere. The populations in the south and west are mainly resident whilst those of the north and northeast are predominantly migratory, wintering in North Africa, Arabia and eastern Pakistan (*BWP*). Water Rails from north and central Europe generally move south and southwest and spend the winter mainly in Britain and France (Flegg & Glue 1973, de Kroon 1980). Individuals of the race *hibernans*, which breeds in southern Iceland, have been reported to occur on Scottish islands during passage (*Birds in Scotland*) and in Ireland during winter (*Birds in Ireland*), although most of the Icelandic population probably migrates to the Faeroes in winter. Of the two remaining races, *korejewi* (of southwest and central Asia) is a partial migrant, while *indicus* (of eastern Asia) is thought to be largely migratory (Taylor & van Perlo 1998).

Water Rails breed over much of Britain & Ireland, with particular strongholds in Ireland and East Anglia (*1988–91 Atlas*). Breeding territories usually include still or slow-flowing water with tall, dense vegetation, typically sedge, Common Reed or bulrush. Such habitats exist on the

The analysis of the data for this species was supported by RailTrack

RAILTRACK

vegetated margins of wetlands and areas with a patchy mosaic of waterlogged vegetation (*European Atlas*). The winter population in Britain & Ireland has a similar distribution to the breeding season, but with a trend for more coastal records in the west (*Winter Atlas*). Habitat occupancy during the winter is broadly similar to that in the breeding season, but harsh weather can result in the use of a wider range of habitat types. Water Rails grounded during migration will use the nearest available cover and have been observed in scrubby grasslands and bracken patches.

Although the distribution of ringing-site locations during the breeding and non-breeding seasons reflects the wide distribution of Water Rails, it is noticeable that the high breeding numbers in Ireland are under-represented (Fig 1) and that a few ringing groups or observatories contribute disproportionately. As Water Rails neither fly at a convenient height for capture in mist-nets, aggregate in open habitats nor build conspicuous nests, they are difficult to catch and ring in large numbers. Although some studies have demonstrated how walk-in traps can yield large catches of birds (de Kroon 1979) and produce information on local movements (Jenkins *et al* 1995), low annual ringing totals are the norm in Britain & Ireland; not only are fully grown birds rarely trapped by ringers but chicks are hardly ever ringed (Fig 2). Furthermore, very few fully grown birds are ringed during May–August. As a result, the sample sizes for particular seasons, regions, sexes and life-stages are often too small to provide anything more than a hint of the true patterns.

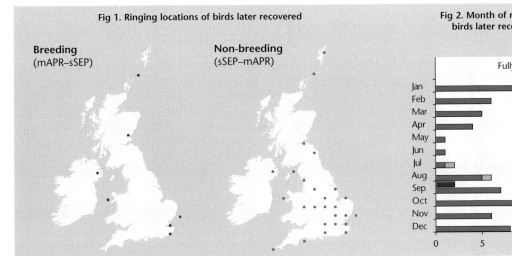

Fig 1. Ringing locations of birds later recovered

Breeding
(mAPR–sSEP)

Non-breeding
(sSEP–mAPR)

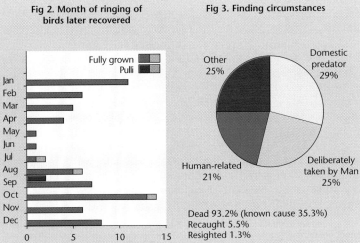

Fig 2. Month of ringing of birds later recovered

Fully grown
Pulli

Fig 3. Finding circumstances

Other 25%
Domestic predator 29%
Deliberately taken by Man 25%
Human-related 21%

Dead 93.2% (known cause 35.3%)
Recaught 5.5%
Resighted 1.3%

Ringing and recovery data

	<1960	60–69	70–79	80–89	90–97	Total
RINGING						
BTO ringing totals (%)	10	23	20	20	26	3,968
RECOVERIES						
BTO-ringed (%)	17	33	19	19	13	70
Foreign-ringed (%)	←	90	→	3	6	31

Statistical analyses

	Breeding population (mAPR–sSEP)	Wintering population (mNOV–sMAR)
Status	[SEDENTARY]	[LONG-DISTANCE MIGRANT]
Age differences	Not tested	Not tested
Sex differences	Not tested	Not tested
Regional differences	Not tested	Not tested
Finding circumstances	Not tested	Not tested

Fig 4. Recovery locations and movements of over 20 km for the 73 included recoveries of Water Rails ringed or recovered in Britain & Ireland.

Of the 73 usable Water Rail ring-recoveries, only five were resighted or recaptured alive. The remaining 68 ring-recoveries were of birds found dead and for 24 of these the finding circumstances were reported. Human activity, either directly (hunting) or indirectly, accounted for 75% of these recoveries (Fig 3) and patterns of ring-recoveries will therefore be influenced by the distribution of human activity.

Young Water Rails begin their dispersal in July (*BWP*) but, as only five ringed juveniles and no chicks have been recovered between July and August, the ringing data cannot confirm this. Recoveries of birds ringed in Britain & Ireland between the months of April and August have generally been within 20 km of the ringing site, but one instance of a bird subsequently recovered in Germany suggests that not all our breeders are resident. There were two long-distance movements within Britain, the longest involving a bird that moved from Tayside to Gwynedd (417 km).

The British & Irish Water Rail population is augmented in the winter by continental birds (*Winter Atlas*) and, to a lesser extent, by birds from Iceland (Taylor & van Perlo 1998). Given that breeding Water Rails in Britain & Ireland are residents (*BWP*), and assuming natal dispersal occurs only over short distances, all recoveries of birds on the Continent probably represent migrants that wintered in Britain, with the majority coming from Germany (Fig 4). Britain & Ireland receive an unknown proportion of the breeding populations of central Europe, with the remainder wintering mainly in France (de Kroon 1980).

Land drainage and reclamation of marshes have had detrimental effects on Water Rail populations in recent years. Breeding surveys in Germany (*European Atlas*) and winter trapping in Mid Wales (Jenkins *et al* 1995) have found Water Rails capable of maintaining very high population densities. Large wetlands in Britain & Ireland, especially coastal sites, may be essential for the conservation of migrants from the Continent and from higher-altitude sites within Britain & Ireland, although the relative importance of wetlands in Britain & Ireland in the winter to migrants from elsewhere has not been quantified.

There are many important aspects of Water Rail movement and migration patterns that remain poorly documented. Small-scale movements, either in response to environmental change (*eg* freezing) or as natal dispersal (in particular), require more data. However, the extreme difficulty in catching Water Rail chicks effectively prohibits the future acquisition of extensive information on the dispersal from breeding sites. Other gaps in our knowledge, such as whether the winter migrants that return to central Europe do so on a loop migration as suggested by Flegg & Glue (1973), simply require the annual ringing totals to increase significantly to provide additional recoveries. Such an increase in ringing should also lead to a higher proportion of ringed birds caught and released.

Richard K B Jenkins

Common Moorhen (Moorhen)

Gallinula chloropus

In its breeding habits the Moorhen is a fascinating species, being both a co-operative breeder (Gibbons 1987, Leonard *et al* 1989) and an intraspecific brood parasite (Gibbons 1986, McRae 1997). However, in its movements it is unexceptional, with British & Irish breeding birds being highly sedentary (*BWP, Winter Atlas, 1988–91 Atlas*). There is some migratorial interest, however, in that resident Moorhens are joined by immigrants from parts of northwest Europe in autumn and winter. With this one exception, there is little to enthuse the student of bird migration and as a consequence the movements of British & Irish birds have been little studied.

The Moorhen occurs in all of the world's major zoogeographical regions except Australasia. All Palearctic birds belong to the nominate race. During the breeding season, it is a bird of wetlands and is found anywhere there is sufficient eutrophic fresh water and emergent vegetation necessary for feeding and nesting. Its winter habitats are similar, when it may form small flocks. In extreme winter weather, its preference for inland fresh waters can lead to seasonal displacement as waterbodies freeze. Probably because of this, it is absent from northernmost Europe, including Iceland, and is a summer migrant to much of eastern Europe, from Finland, the Czech Republic and Romania eastward (*BWP*). Further west in continental Europe, the species becomes a partial migrant, with some birds resident all year. In Belgium, for example, about 40% of the breeding population emigrate in the winter, mainly southwest to northern France, while immigrants arrive from countries to the northeast, principally the Netherlands, northern Germany, Denmark and southern Sweden (del Marmol 1994). The winter range of emigrant Fennoscandian birds and

The analysis of the data for this species was supported by the Rye Bay Ringing Group and the Wetland Trust

others from northern Europe extends south to Iberia, Italy and even North Africa (*BWP*, Engler 2000). Some European and North African birds winter south of the Sahara (*BWP*).

The Moorhen's breeding and wintering distributions in Britain & Ireland are very similar (*Winter Atlas, 1988–91 Atlas*). The distribution of ringing locations in Britain from the breeding and non-breeding seasons are similar to one another and to its breeding and wintering distributions (Fig 1). The distribution of Irish Moorhens is, however, markedly under-represented by ringing locations. Ringing dates for recoveries are weighted towards autumn and early winter (Fig 2), when the proportion of juveniles caught increases.

Virtually all recoveries of ringed Moorhens are of dead birds; less than 1% were recaught away from the ringing location. The cause of death is known for slightly fewer than half of these dead recoveries (Fig 3). Although there are many biases in these data, the proportion deliberately taken by Man (probably mostly shot) is surprising even though the Moorhen is a legal quarry species in Britain and elsewhere. A comparison of those countries for which the cause of death was known for more than a handful of recoveries suggests that legal quarry status influences the proportion of recoveries deliberately taken by Man. The species is legal quarry in Britain where a quarter (127/494) and in France where most (7/9) were deliberately taken. In Ireland and the

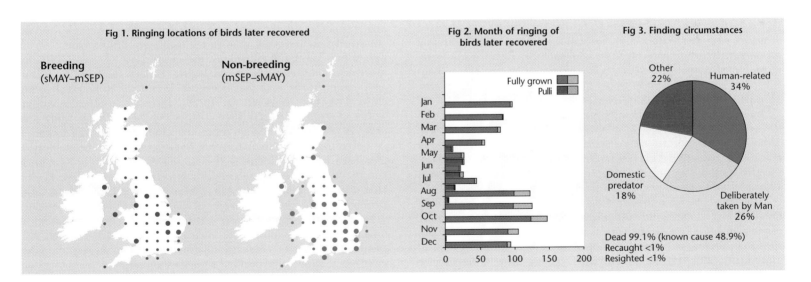

Fig 1. Ringing locations of birds later recovered

Breeding (sMAY–mSEP)

Non-breeding (mSEP–sMAY)

Fig 2. Month of ringing of birds later recovered

Fully grown
Pulli

Fig 3. Finding circumstances

Other 22%
Human-related 34%
Domestic predator 18%
Deliberately taken by Man 26%

Dead 99.1% (known cause 48.9%)
Recaught <1%
Resighted <1%

Ringing and recovery data

	<1960	60–69	70–79	80–89	90–97	Total
RINGING						
BTO ringing totals (%)	18	23	21	21	17	27,586
RECOVERIES						
BTO-ringed (%)	17	35	23	19	6	963
Foreign-ringed (%)	9	39	37	9	6	127

Statistical analyses

	Breeding population (sMAY–mSEP)	Wintering population (mNOV–sMAR)
Status	SEDENTARY (0)	SHORT-DISTANCE MIGRANT
Age differences[NT]	Not significant*	Significant*
Sex differences	Not tested	Not tested
Regional differences	Not tested	Not tested
Finding circumstances	(Not significant)	(Not significant)

Fig 4. Locations in winter, and movements of over 20 km between the breeding and non-breeding season, of 139 Moorhens present in Britain & Ireland during the breeding season.

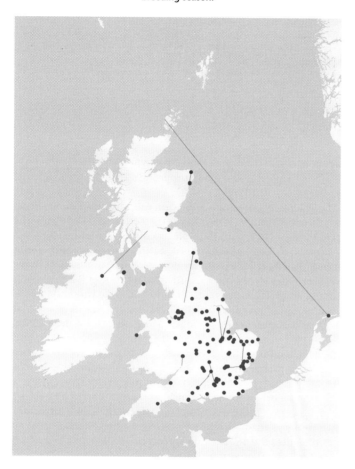

Fig 5. Locations abroad in the breeding season of 54 Moorhens present in Britain & Ireland outside the breeding season.

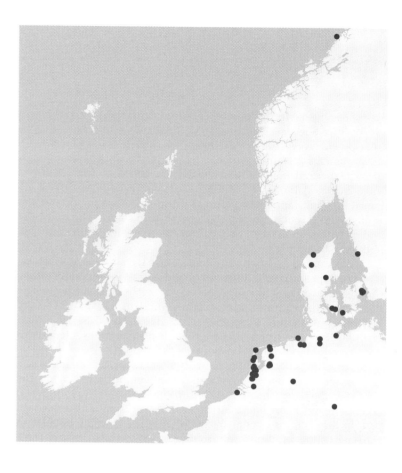

Netherlands, where it is not legal quarry, the cause of death was known for seven recoveries in each, and only a single bird was deliberately taken (in the Netherlands). Nearly 80% of birds ringed in Belgium and recovered in France were deliberately taken by Man (del Marmol 1994). Hunting pressure in France thus seems to be comparatively high. Nearly three-quarters of all human-related causes are collisions with cars, as Moorhens will often attempt to scuttle across minor roads near their territories, rather than flying, thus making them prone to traffic accidents.

A detailed study of Moorhen biology has shown that juveniles begin to leave their natal territories at about 60–100 days of age (Gibbons 1987). Although sparse, the recovery data support this as median recovery distances of birds ringed as chicks were less than a kilometre until about the fifth month after ringing, when three birds had all moved between 13 and 18 km.

Movements between the breeding season and winter of birds using Britain & Ireland during the breeding season show the sedentary nature of the population (Fig 4). Movements between the breeding season and spring or autumn, although not shown, are similar. Ninety percent of movements (287/319) are of less than 20 km. Three long-distance movements, one from Orkney to the Netherlands and two from Fair Isle to Denmark (not shown), were probably of migrating birds ringed during the breeding season. There are insufficient recoveries to allow an examination of either breeding or natal dispersal.

Despite the extreme sedentary nature illustrated by the ring-recovery data, some limited movements do occur between the breeding and non-breeding seasons. Ten percent moved more than 20 km, with little difference between northern Britain (16%, 6/38 in northeast and northwest Britain combined) and southern Britain (11%, 26/248 in southeast and southwest combined). More revealingly, perhaps, 14% (22/161) of birds in southeast Britain moved more than 20 km, while less

than 5% (4/87) of southwest-breeding birds did. Although the precise reason for this is unclear, it is tempting to suggest that this is because of milder conditions in the southwest, which mean that fewer cold-weather movements are necessary than in the southeast. Unfortunately, this is not borne out by the data as the proportion of longer-distance movements in the southeast was higher between the breeding season and autumn (21%, 7/33 movements of more than 20 km) and spring (18%, 5/28) than winter (13%, 10/78). There are insufficient within-winter movements to take these analyses further, although only four (12%) of the 33 within-winter movements were of more than 20 km.

Given their sedentary nature, it is not surprising that the majority of Moorhens ringed in Britain & Ireland and whose recovery location is known (963 in total) were recovered in Britain (87%) and Ireland (8.6%). Most of the rest were recovered in nearby continental Europe, especially Denmark (1.3%), the Netherlands (1.1%), France (0.9%) and Germany (0.7%). Similarly, among nearly 130 foreign-ringed birds recovered in Britain & Ireland, most were ringed in the Netherlands (66.1%), Denmark (17.3%) or Germany (9.4%). These data suggest a limited interchange with neighbouring European countries.

A proportion of the birds that spend the non-breeding season in Britain breed on the nearby Continent, with the Netherlands and Denmark acting as important sources of winter immigrants to Britain & Ireland (Fig 5). Although there are records from farther afield, for example a bird ringed in spring on Fair Isle was recovered during the breeding season in northern Norway, such records are rare. There are no particularly marked differences between juveniles and adults nor males and females in these movement patterns, although numbers of known-sex recoveries are very small.

Two-thirds of all movements between Britain & Ireland and continental Europe (115/172) are to and from southeast Britain.

Although this may be partly because higher numbers of Moorhens and ringers are found in this area, it may also be because of the shorter flight distances that these reluctant flyers would need to make over the sea.

The timing of movements from Britain to the Continent can be determined from an examination of the latitudinal and longitudinal shifts made between ringing and recovery of birds that winter in Britain & Ireland. In April, these birds move north and east, most likely reflecting the movements of winter immigrants back to their continental breeding grounds. Both the latitudinal and longitudinal shifts are relatively small, however, most likely a consequence of the large number of British and Irish residents present within this data set. The median latitudinal and longitudinal shifts of British & Irish breeders were zero in every month of the year, and those shifts that were made were substantially less than those of wintering birds.

Nearly three-quarters of the foreign-ringed birds recovered in Britain & Ireland were ringed during August–November. Although it might be expected that more birds are caught at this time of year, simply because the population is swelled by juveniles, this proportion was substantially less for birds ringed in Britain & Ireland (44%). This difference is probably due to an enthusiasm for trapping continental breeding birds moving southwest towards Britain during autumn passage and it is likely that immigrants move into Britain at this time.

There are many gaps in our knowledge of the movements of British- & Irish-breeding Moorhens. Although a number of studies have been undertaken, none have examined natal and breeding site-fidelity or juvenile dispersal in any detail. In addition, our knowledge of the breeding locations of winter immigrants is likely to be unrepresentative. Although existing data suggest most interchange is with nearby continental countries, it is possible that they come from a wider geographical area in which little ringing is undertaken.

David Gibbons

Common Coot (Coot)

Fulica atra

Despite the Coot's status as a common resident and winter visitor on freshwater lakes and reservoirs in Britain & Ireland, much remains to be learnt about its movements. Coot are common breeding birds of the lowlands throughout Britain & Ireland, with an estimated population of 54,600 birds (*1988–91 Atlas*), yet there are few reports of visible migration of birds, despite the clear increase in numbers during the winter (*Winter Atlas*, Taylor *et al* 1999).

The nominate race, *atra*, breeds throughout the Palearctic in western Europe and North Africa as far east as Japan, south to Sri Lanka, and north to 65°N in Fennoscandia and Siberia. Throughout this range, Coot typically inhabit large, still or slow-moving waterbodies, including lakes, ponds, gravel-pits, rivers, open marshes and saltpans, preferring fairly shallow waters, with areas of open, deeper water (Taylor & van Perlo 1998).

The majority of Coot breeding in eastern Europe and the western region of the former USSR move south and west through the Baltic States into central Europe to winter (*BWP*). Others move along the Baltic coast to countries along the North Sea, the Atlantic coast of France and Iberia, with some reaching northwest Africa. Coot wintering in the Balkans, Italy and Tunisia may originate from central Europe (*BWP*, Monval & Pirot 1989). The winter distribution in Britain & Ireland is broadly similar to that in summer, with the exception that the resident breeding population is supplemented by birds from northwest Europe (*BWP*), taking the wintering population to over 200,000 birds (*Winter Atlas*). Moult migrations, as seen in geese and swans, are also known to take place. Very large moulting flocks have been reported on the

The analysis of the data for this species was supported by the Rye Bay Ringing Group and the Wetland Trust

Ukrainian coast and Baltic Sea during June–August, although little is known about the origin or movements of these birds (*BWP*).

Like many waterfowl, Coot are difficult to catch and are ringed mostly by specialists. The distribution of ringing sites of birds later recovered (Fig 1) clearly reflects the ringing effort rather than the species' distribution within Britain & Ireland. Nonetheless, British & Irish ringing during 1909–97 generated 1,011 usable recoveries, and there were 41 from birds ringed abroad. Recovered birds were mostly ringed outside the breeding season, between August and March (Fig 2). Almost 57% of birds recovered were fully grown when ringed, and a further 39% were juveniles or in their second year. The cause of death is known for more than half of the recoveries (Fig 3). Of these, 61% were deliberately taken by Man, presumably by shooting. Because many Coot recoveries were generated from hunting, there will clearly be a bias in their timing, toward the hunting season, and also in their location, in that hunting is restricted to certain regions, areas within those regions, and habitats.

The Coot in Britain & Ireland are presumed to be mostly sedentary during the breeding season and observations suggest that some individuals are on the same waters all year (*BWP*). Adults are flightless for a time during wing moult in June–September and, although little studied, moult migrations are known to occur. Regular concentrations

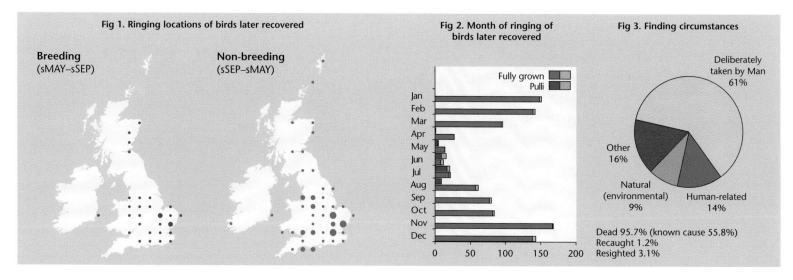

Fig 1. Ringing locations of birds later recovered

Breeding (sMAY–sSEP)

Non-breeding (sSEP–sMAY)

Fig 2. Month of ringing of birds later recovered

Fully grown
Pulli

Fig 3. Finding circumstances

Deliberately taken by Man 61%

Other 16%

Natural (environmental) 9%

Human-related 14%

Dead 95.7% (known cause 55.8%)
Recaught 1.2%
Resighted 3.1%

Ringing and recovery data

	<1960	60–69	70–79	80–89	90–97	Total
RINGING						
BTO ringing totals (%)	11	14	25	27	22	14,817
RECOVERIES						
BTO-ringed (%)	16	18	23	24	19	1,011
Foreign-ringed (%)	15	27	34	15	10	41

Statistical analyses

	Breeding population (sMAY–sSEP)	Wintering population (mNOV–sMAR)
Status	SEDENTARY (0)	LONG-DISTANCE MIGRANT
Age differences[NT]	Not significant*	Not tested
Sex differences	Not tested	Not tested
Regional differences	Not tested	Not tested
Finding circumstances	Significant	Not tested

Fig 4. Locations in autumn, and movements of over 20 km between the breeding season and autumn, of 38 Coot present in Britain & Ireland during the breeding season.

Fig 5. Movements of 23 Coot abroad during the breeding season and present in Britain & Ireland during winter.

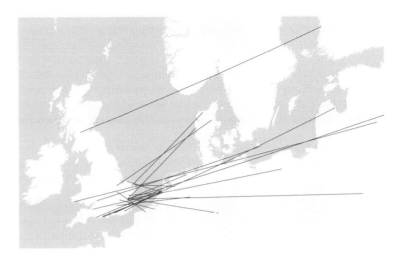

Fig 6. Movements of over 20 km and recovery locations of Coot ringed in winter and recovered in a subsequent winter. There were 60:86 movements under:over 20 km but only those over 20 km are plotted.

of moulting birds have been recorded along the Black Sea coast of the Ukraine, on the Bodensee (German/Swiss border) and in northern Denmark (Taylor & van Perlo 1998). Such concentrations are probably more widespread; late-summer concentrations on Abberton (4,000 birds) and Hanningfield (3,000 birds) Reservoirs are thought to involve moulting birds (Cox 1984). Large concentrations of Coot have previously occurred on other waterbodies within Britain (eg the Broads, Taylor et al 1999), but have since declined, most probably because of declining water quality. Numbers counted for WeBS begin to increase in July, reach a fairly steady level between September and December, and decrease again evenly during January–April (Cranswick et al 1999). Although the changes in numbers suggest that migration is happening on a large scale, it is almost never observed; even short movements between waters must therefore take place entirely at night. Thus there is very little evidence from sources other than ringing with which to unravel movement patterns.

The median distance moved by birds using Britain & Ireland during the breeding season and found dead was 16 km (P5–95=0–447 km, n=158), although, with the breeding season defined as being from May to the end of August for the current analysis, this may include some birds from outside Britain & Ireland that undertook a moult migration to sites in southeast England. Autumn movements of Coot using Britain & Ireland during the breeding season (median=108.5 km, P5–95=0–1,141 km, n=20) include a number of long-distance movements from southeast England to southwest France and Spain (Fig 4), with at least three-quarters of these involving young birds ringed between mid-July and the end of August and recovered the same year. The available sample sizes are too small to allow an examination of differences in movements between regions within Britain & Ireland.

Brown (1955) in his analysis of Coot migration in Britain examined 58 recoveries and reported a general trend of movement, on a broad front, in a northeast/southwest direction. He also suggested that there was a narrow movement along the south Baltic, North Sea and north French coasts and concluded that Coot moved into Britain to winter and also probably occurred on passage (Brown 1955). Although the seasonal sample sizes are small, there is some suggestion from the ring-recovery data for birds ringed as adults in Britain & Ireland that median distances moved between the breeding season and autumn, and between the breeding season and winter, are longer than between other seasons. This may indicate that some Coot breeding in Britain & Ireland do undertake regular movements from breeding sites to wintering grounds some distance away. However, the influences of moult migration and of hard-weather movements are likely to confound this pattern of movement further.

Cold-weather movements may bring Coot from continental breeding populations into Britain, particularly to the southeast (Fig 5). Sheppard (1993) reported that cold-weather movements also bring Coot into Ireland, and this is supported by the presence of large concentrations of Coot at Lough Corrib and at Loughs Neagh and Beg during winter (*Birds in Ireland*, Colhoun 1998). However, Irwin & O'Halloran (1997) reported no change in the numbers (through emigration or immigration) of a wintering Coot flock at Cork Lough during 1995/96. The ring-recovery data contain 74 within-winter movements with a median distance moved of 1 km ($P5-95=0-425$ km) and 140 between-winter movements with a median distance moved of 50 km ($P5-95=0-818$ km). While these data show that Coot using Britain & Ireland in winter may change wintering areas between years (Fig 6), there is little long-distance

movement within a winter. Small-scale movements have been reported in Britain as birds move from small ponds, subject to freezing, to the ice-free reservoirs and lakes. A colour-ringing study by J A Horsfall suggested that Coot make frequent small-scale movements throughout the winter (*Winter Atlas*).

With only 4% of British & Irish breeding Coot recoveries coming from birds ringed as pulli, there is no information available on natal dispersal. Similarly, the ring-recovery data provide no information on breeding dispersal. The colour-ringing of Coot as part of intensive local studies may be the only way in which information on natal and breeding dispersal can be gathered, since few pulli or breeding adults are ringed during more general ringing.

A more detailed understanding of Coot movements is required if we are to plan effective conservation strategies for this species. The Coot has been overlooked and it would certainly benefit from the kind of detailed study afforded to many duck species, especially since there are similarities in their movement patterns and in the threats to their conservation. Despite their widespread distribution and the familiarity of the species to most people, we still have very little detailed knowledge on the movements of this common bird. Perhaps their nocturnal migration pattern will require elucidation through new technologies such as satellite- and radio-tracking.

John O'Halloran

Eurasian Oystercatcher (Oystercatcher)

Haematopus ostralegus

With their striking pied plumage and shrill calls, Oystercatchers are a familiar sight on the coasts and estuaries of northwest Europe. They breed widely on the coasts of Britain & Ireland and also inland, especially in northern Britain. In Aberdeen, they even nest on rooftops. Outside the breeding season they occur mainly on the coast, with large concentrations on estuaries.

The Oystercatchers that occur in Britain & Ireland belong to the nominate race, *ostralegus*, which breeds in Iceland, on the coasts of Europe and east to the Pechora River in Russia. Northern populations show a stronger tendency to migrate than those from further south. The main wintering areas, characterized by mean temperatures above 0°C, are around the coasts of the North and Irish Seas. Smaller numbers occur north to southwest Iceland and southwest Norway as well as on the shores of the western Mediterranean and along the Atlantic coasts of France, Spain and West Africa south to Guinea-Bissau. There are two other races: *longipes* breeds inland from Ukraine to west Siberia and migrates to distinct wintering areas on the coast from northeast Africa to northeast India; and *osculans* breeds along the coast from the Yellow Sea to Kamchatka and winters mainly in southern China. In addition, the South Island Pied Oystercatcher *finschi* of New Zealand is sometimes considered to belong to this species (*HBW*). The Palearctic races are the most migratory of the world's oystercatchers.

The nominate race, *ostralegus*, numbers about 875,000 individuals in winter and is divided into two subpopulations by the North Sea. The 'Atlantic' population, of about 200,000, breeds in Iceland, the Faeroes, Britain and Ireland and winters in Britain and Ireland. The 'continental'

The analysis of the data for this species was supported by the Lancaster and District Birdwatching Society

population is found mainly in the Low Countries and Scandinavia and has major concentrations in the Wadden Sea (500,000) and the Delta area of the southwest Netherlands (100,000). The Atlantic and continental populations are regarded as distinct because the interchange between them is very limited (Hulscher *et al* 1996).

On the coasts of Britain & Ireland, Oystercatchers nest on rocky shores, shingle beaches, saltmarshes, clifftops and among sand-dunes. The first inland breeding probably occurred in Grampian in the 1840s (Holloway 1996). The habit then spread throughout Scotland and, in the 1940s, into northern England. Nowadays, inland breeding, typically on shingle beaches or islands in gravel-pits or by rivers, is common as far south as Mid Wales and Suffolk (*1988–91 Atlas*). After nesting, inland breeders move quickly to the coast. Between August and February, practically all Oystercatchers occupy coastal habitats, especially estuaries where their main food resources are the larger invertebrates, particularly Edible Mussels and Edible Cockles.

Although the Oystercatchers that have been recovered have been ringed during the breeding season throughout their range in Britain & Ireland, the largest numbers have been caught on estuaries at other times of the year, mainly using cannon-nets (Figs 1 & 2). This effort has been stimulated partly by migration studies and partly by investigations concerned with the impact of Oystercatchers on shellfish stocks. Many

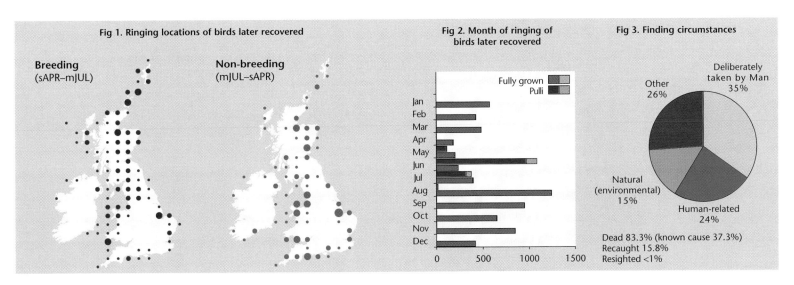

Fig 1. Ringing locations of birds later recovered

Breeding (sAPR–mJUL)　　Non-breeding (mJUL–sAPR)

Fig 2. Month of ringing of birds later recovered

Fully grown / Pulli

Jan Feb Mar Apr May Jun Jul Aug Sep Oct Nov Dec

0　500　1000　1500

Fig 3. Finding circumstances

Other 26%
Deliberately taken by Man 35%
Natural (environmental) 15%
Human-related 24%

Dead 83.3% (known cause 37.3%)
Recaught 15.8%
Resighted <1%

Ringing and recovery data

	<1960	60–69	70–79	80–89	90–97	Total
RINGING						
BTO ringing totals (%)	5	18	26	30	21	130,856
RECOVERIES						
BTO-ringed (%)	3	15	28	31	24	7,996
Foreign-ringed (%)	12	15	23	27	22	242

Statistical analyses

	Breeding population (sAPR–mJUL)	Wintering population (sOCT–sMAR)
Status	SHORT-DISTANCE MIGRANT (2)	SHORT-DISTANCE MIGRANT
Age differences[NT]	Significant	Not significant
Sex differences	Not tested	Not tested
Regional differences	Not tested	Significant[5]
Finding circumstances	(Not significant)	(Not significant)

Table 1. Summary of distances moved between ringing and recovery for all recoveries of dead Oystercatchers present in Britain & Ireland during the breeding season.

Region	Median (km)	P5 (km)	P95 (km)	n
North	213.5	0	982	1,072
West	35.5	0	915	328
East	27	0	1,628	258
Ireland	13.5	0	857	22
South	6	0	1,100	246

In Britain & Ireland, breeding Oystercatchers are partial migrants; some stay close to the nesting areas but the majority move south. Inland breeders, however, all move at least as far as the nearest coast soon after the chicks have fledged. The tendency to migrate and the distance moved, for all recoveries reported from dead birds, is greater in the breeding population of northern Britain than further south (Table 1). In part, however, this arises because inland breeders, most of which are in northern Britain, make an additional journey to the coast.

Juveniles stay close to their natal area for the first six to eight weeks after fledging (median=0, P5–95=0–25 km, n=189). Most then migrate, further on average than adults and also with juveniles from northern Britain moving further than those from Ireland and the south (Fig 5). Some return movements are evident from about the February of the first winter with median distances between ringing as pulli and recovery falling from 463 km (P5–95=0–1,558 km, n=167) at 61–210 days (approximately September–January) after ringing to 161 km (P5–95=0–890 km, n=93) at 211–360 days (approximately February–June) after ringing. Most immatures winter at about the same distance from their natal area in their first as in subsequent winters (Figs 4 & 5).

Oystercatchers do not reach sexual maturity until they are three years old and most do not breed until much later. Age of first breeding is mainly three to six years for females and five to eight years for males (Ens et al 1996). Many immatures spend their second and third summers far from their natal areas, often in the same place that they have spent the winter (Goss-Custard et al 1982; Fig 5). They return to their breeding grounds from their fourth summer onwards. They also show a strong tendency to breed close to where they themselves were reared: 71% of 121 recoveries of birds ringed as chicks and recovered in the breeding season when of breeding age were within 20 km.

birds have also been colour-ringed, particularly since 1976 in connection with studies by CEH based on the Exe Estuary. In comparison, relatively few Oystercatchers have been ringed as breeding adults. However, with over a thousand recoveries from birds ringed as chicks, the movements of Oystercatchers from the British & Irish breeding population are fairly well known (Fig 2).

Only 37% of Oystercatcher recoveries are attributed to a known cause of death. Of these, 59% arose from the activities of Man (Fig 3). Many were birds hunted in France (where it is still legal) or culled to protect British Edible Cockle fisheries. This was done in Morecambe Bay and the Burry Inlet where, together, 27,000 Oystercatchers were shot during 1956–74. Culling failed to stop the decline in cockles and has not been tried since (Prater 1981).

Fig 4. Locations in their (a) first winter (164) and (b) second, third and fourth winters (122), and movements of over 20 km, of Oystercatchers ringed as pulli in Britain & Ireland.

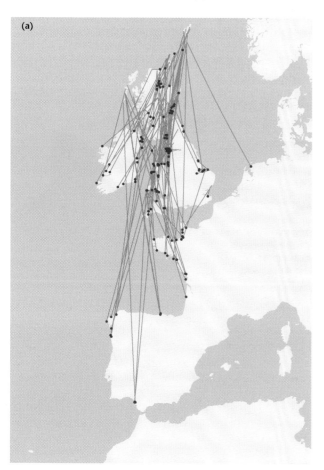

(a)

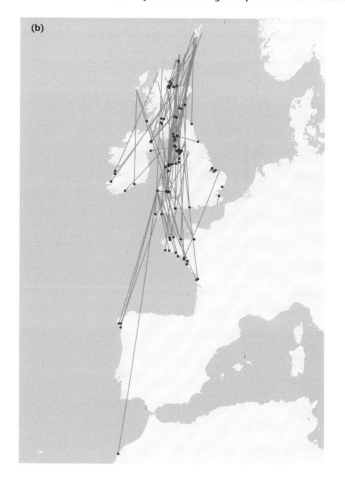

(b)

Fig 5. Summary of distances moved between ringing and recovery of Oystercatchers ringed as pulli in Britain & Ireland and recovered dead during the winter (October–February) or the breeding season (April–mid-July). Note that 'first breeding season' refers to the year of hatching. Monthly medians (points) and interquartile ranges (bars) are shown.

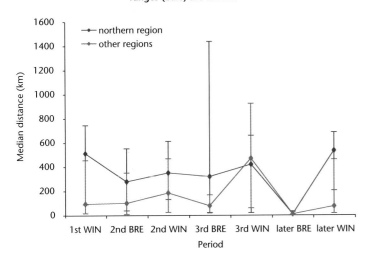

Fig 6. Locations in autumn (12, red), winter (37, blue) and spring (4, grey), and movements of over 20 km between the breeding and non-breeding season, of adult Oystercatchers present in Britain & Ireland during the breeding season.

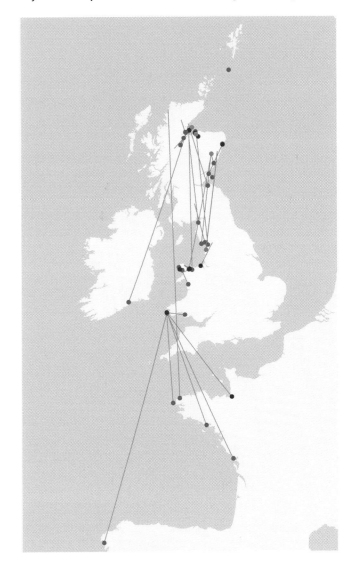

Recoveries of breeding adults suggest that the majority (89%, *n*=53) remain within Britain & Ireland and that passage is mainly down the west coast. Only a few cross the English Channel to winter on the coasts of France or Spain (Fig 6). Breeding birds are extremely site-faithful to their nesting areas with 89% (25/28) of recoveries in subsequent breeding seasons within 20 km of the original ringing site. Similarly, Oystercatchers show high site-fidelity to wintering sites, with 60% of 672 between-winter recoveries being within 20 km of the ringing site.

Outside the breeding season, both Britain and Ireland are visited by large numbers of Oystercatchers that breed abroad (Fig 7). In Ireland, most immigrants are from Iceland and the Faeroes, and there is little evidence of any onward movement to France or Iberia. In north and west Britain, they are from Iceland, the Faeroes and Norway. In east Britain, they are mostly from Norway and the Low Countries. Strikingly, all links with Finland and Russia so far have been with the Wash. In south Britain, breeding areas from Iceland east to Estonia are represented. There are also exceptional recoveries linking Britain with Greenland (one bird shot in April 1979 was ringed at Poole Harbour, Dorset, in January 1975, and a second, also shot, was reported in 1991 having been ringed on the Wash in March 1982) and Bear Island (found long dead in June 1977 having been ringed at Walney Island, Cumbria, in January 1969) where Oystercatchers are rare visitors. Most of these immigrants arrive in August and September and begin their primary moult almost immediately. The moult takes about 100 days (Dare & Mercer 1974) after which some birds move to wintering grounds further south and west although the majority remain through the winter. A few birds cross to the Wadden Sea or the French coast, but the importance of France is likely to be exaggerated as 97% of the Oystercatchers recovered there have been shot. In spring, adults return to the breeding grounds leaving the immatures to remain on the wintering site throughout the summer (Anderson & Minton 1978, Hulscher *et al* 1996).

Generally, Oystercatchers benefit from abundant food supplies and suffer low rates of predation. Individuals may reach a considerable age. Indeed, the oldest ringed Oystercatcher recorded in Britain & Ireland was over 31 years old. Winter mortality in southwest England averages only 5.2% in juveniles and 1.4% in adults (Durell *et al* 2001). Low temperatures affect the ability of Oystercatchers to fulfil their food requirements, especially if the mudflats freeze or they become covered with ice-floes (Goss-Custard *et al* 1996). In Britain & Ireland, such conditions occasionally lead to increased mortality and local movements of birds to milder regions. In contrast, severe weather leading to mass mortality and large-scale movements occurs in the Wadden Sea at least once every nine years (Hulscher *et al* 1996).

Oystercatchers may also suffer food shortages leading to mortality and emigration if invertebrates fail to reproduce, as on the Wash during the winter of 1992/93 (Atkinson *et al* 2000). Similar events have followed over-exploitation of shellfish and land reclamation, especially in the Netherlands (Lambeck *et al* 1996). The health of Oystercatcher populations acts as a barometer of the health of shellfish populations. Continual monitoring of Oystercatchers will be important for the conservation of Oystercatchers and the estuarine environments on which they depend in the non-breeding season.

Humphrey Sitters

Fig 7. Locations abroad during the breeding season of Oystercatchers that were present in the (a) north (50), (b) east (472), (c) south (100) and (d) west (197) of Britain and in (e) Ireland (29) outside the breeding season.

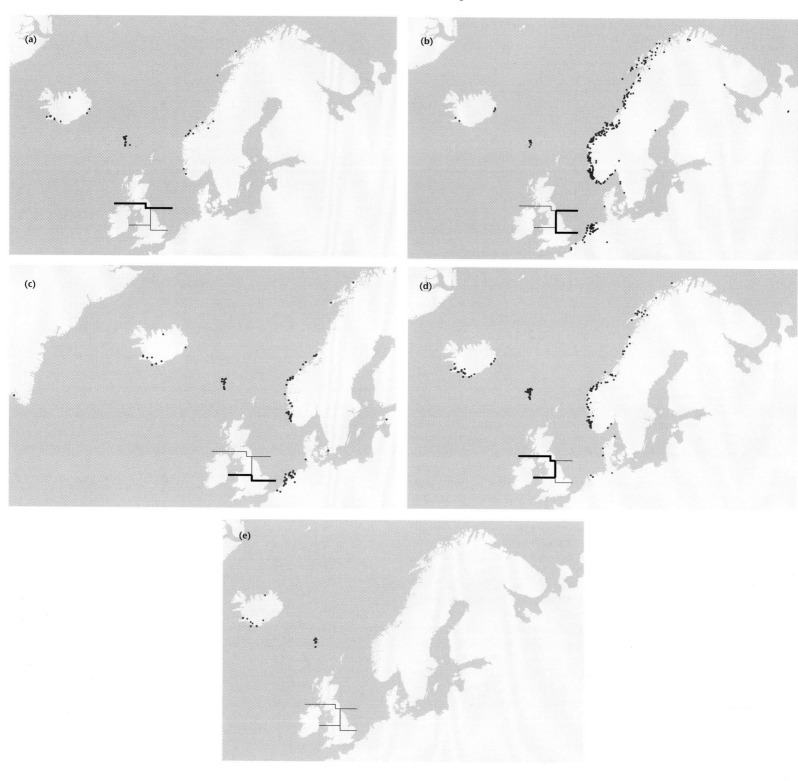

Stone-curlew
Burhinus oedicnemus

The Stone-curlew is the only European representative of the thick-knees, a small family of nine species of largely nocturnal plover-like birds, all of which frequent sparsely vegetated, open habitats in arid zones, beaches, dunes and river sandbanks. There they stalk large surface-active invertebrates, and sometimes small mammals, birds and reptiles, by night, using their huge, downward-pointing, owl-like eyes to detect prey in dim light (Martin & Katzir 1994, Green *et al* 2000). Stone-curlews and other thick-knees probably rely upon nights that are long and warm enough for successful foraging on their invertebrate prey. They therefore occur mainly in the tropics and subtropics. Northern populations of the Stone-curlew, the only species whose breeding range extends outside the subtropics, undertake long-distance migrations to avoid winter cold. Birds from breeding populations in northern and central Europe move south to the Mediterranean region and West Africa in winter, whilst those from central Asia migrate to the Middle East and East Africa (*BWP, HBW*).

Six subspecies are recognized of which two are confined to the Canary Islands. The nominate race, which is the only one known to occur in Britain & Ireland, breeds in England, France, Iberia and eastwards to the northern Balkans, Ukraine and the Caucasus. Other races breed from North Africa eastwards through Greece, Turkey, south-central Asia, and the Indian subcontinent to Indo-China (*HBW*).

In Britain, Stone-curlews are at the northernmost edge of their world range and are confined as breeding birds to southeastern England. The species is a rare vagrant to Scotland, Wales and Ireland (*Birds in Scotland, Birds in Ireland, Birds in Wales*). They have declined markedly in numbers and distribution across much of Europe during the 20th century (Tucker

The analysis of the data for this species was supported by British Sugar plc.

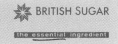
BRITISH SUGAR
the essential ingredient

& Heath 1994) but have recently been increasing in England after a huge decline since the 1930s. Stone-curlews return to England in March to breed on seminatural chalk grassland and heaths where vegetation remains short and sparse because of the free-draining soil, low nutrient levels and grazing pressure from livestock and especially rabbits. In areas with suitable soils, pairs also nest among those spring-sown arable crops that are established latest in the spring (Green *et al* 2000). From July until departure in October or November, independent juveniles and moulting adults gather to loaf on traditional roosting grounds by day and disperse to feed at night.

The distribution of ringing is representative of the numbers of pairs in each of the two main breeding areas, the Breckland region of East Anglia and Salisbury Plain (Fig 1). Stone-curlews have been ringed only as chicks, except for about 50 adults trapped as part of a special study in the 1980s (Fig 2). About half of the recoveries are from overseas, mostly in the non-breeding season. Most recoveries in Britain occur in March to September (Green *et al* 1997). A high proportion of recoveries occur in uncertain circumstances (Fig 3) but deliberate killing, mostly by shooting, or capture is the most frequently identifiable cause of death and occurs in France, Iberia and North Africa in spite of statutory protection in most countries. Collisions with overhead utility lines and fences are a frequent cause of death in Britain and presumably occur when birds are flying to foraging areas at night.

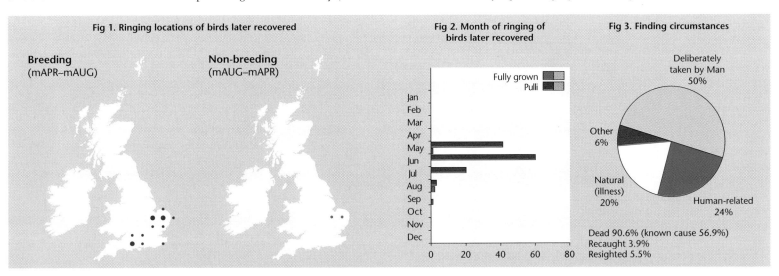

Fig 1. Ringing locations of birds later recovered

Breeding (mAPR–mAUG) Non-breeding (mAUG–mAPR)

Fig 2. Month of ringing of birds later recovered

Fully grown
Pulli

Fig 3. Finding circumstances

Deliberately taken by Man 50%
Other 6%
Natural (illness) 20%
Human-related 24%

Dead 90.6% (known cause 56.9%)
Recaught 3.9%
Resighted 5.5%

Ringing and recovery data

	<1960	60–69	70–79	80–89	90–97	Total
RINGING						
BTO ringing totals (%)	13	1	5	26	54	2,673
RECOVERIES						
BTO-ringed (%)	11	2	7	40	40	128
Foreign-ringed (%)	0	0	0	0	0	0

Statistical analyses

	Breeding population (mAPR–mAUG)	Wintering population (mNOV–sMAR)
Status	LONG-DISTANCE MIGRANT*	NONE
Age differences	Not tested	—
Sex differences	Not tested	—
Regional differences	Not tested	—
Finding circumstances	Not tested	—

Fig 4. Latitude of recoveries starting in July of the year of hatching, of Stone-curlews ringed as pulli in Britain & Ireland and recovered (a) up to the end of June in their first year and (b) subsequently.

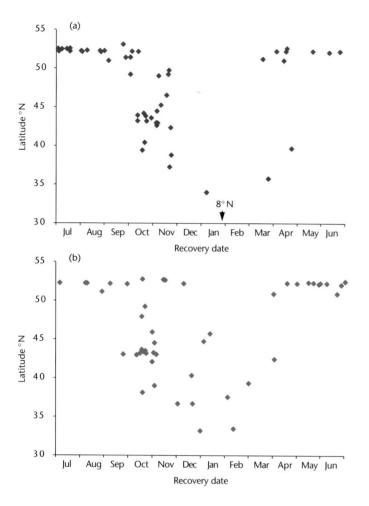

Fig 5. Locations in (a) autumn (43:6) and (b) winter (13:3), and movements of over 20 km between the breeding and non-breeding season, of Stone-curlews present in Britain & Ireland during the breeding season. Birds present in southeast Britain (red) are differentiated from those present in southwest Britain (blue). Sample sizes of the regions (southeast:southwest) are given.

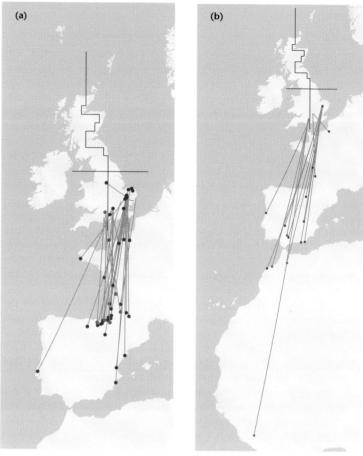

The mean latitude of recovery shifts rapidly to the south in October though occasional adults remain on the post-breeding gathering grounds until November or December (Fig 4). Recoveries of British Stone-curlews during the autumn migration are mainly in western France and northeastern Spain (Fig 5a), but birds can reach southern Spain and North Africa by November. There is no indication that birds from the two main subpopulations in England (Breckland and Salisbury Plain) use different migration routes or wintering areas (Fig 5; Green *et al* 1997). There is one recovery of a first-winter bird in midwinter, well to the south of the poorly known wintering range in West Africa (Sierra Leone; Fig 5b). The dearth of other recoveries of young birds during the middle of their first winter (Green *et al* 1997) suggests that a high proportion may migrate to arid, sparsely populated parts of North and West Africa, where the chance of reported recoveries is low. Most adults winter further north in France or Spain (Fig 4). Most Stone-curlews breed for the first time when two years old (Green & Griffiths 1994), but breeding-season recoveries of both immatures and adults are mainly on the breeding grounds (Fig 4).

Ring-recoveries in Mallorca and the Netherlands (Fig 6) suggest that birds returning to the breeding grounds in England in spring may follow a more easterly route than that used in autumn. This is supported by observations in spring of colour-ringed birds in the Netherlands and Belgium, some of which have later been found breeding in Breckland. There are no recoveries in Britain of Stone-curlews ringed overseas and no indications from counts or observatory records of significant passage of birds from other breeding populations through Britain.

Fig 6. Recovery locations in April–June of Stone-curlews ringed in Britain & Ireland.

Although Stone-curlews of breeding age have been recovered in the Netherlands during the breeding season, they were not in known breeding areas. Hence, there are no clear examples of natal dispersal of a British-bred bird to an overseas breeding population. However, such movements and reciprocal natal dispersal of Stone-curlews hatched on the European mainland into England seem quite probable, though difficult to detect (Green *et al* 1997). Colour-ringing has shown that a small proportion of Stone-curlews hatched in Breckland disperse to breed on Salisbury Plain and vice versa. These movements mainly involve young females. Colour-ringing has also shown that small isolated breeding areas (*1988–91 Atlas*) often receive exchange breeding birds with the main subpopulations. These movements are probably important for the future maintenance of the fragmented range of the species in England.

Continued accumulation of ring-recoveries will improve knowledge of migration routes and wintering areas, but the most important questions that remain about Stone-curlew movements concern natal dispersal and the exchange of birds with the European continent. These questions are unlikely to be answered by metal ringing alone. The best prospect is a coordinated international programme of colour-ringing of chicks and searching breeding populations for ringed birds. In the longer term, as technology develops, satellite telemetry could provide useful information.

Rhys E Green

Little Plover
(Little Ringed Plover)
Charadrius dubius

Although the piping calls of Little Ringed Plovers now grace many wetland sites in Britain, it remains a scarce breeding bird and, in Ireland, colonization has not yet begun (Parrinder & Parrinder 1975, Parrinder 1989, *1988–91 Atlas*). Unlike Ringed Plover, it is completely absent in the winter months. The Palearctic race *curonicus* has a very wide breeding distribution extending from the Canaries, Britain and the Gulf of Bothnia to mid-China and Japan; its main wintering grounds lie between the Tropic of Cancer and the Equator. Resident races occur in India and in southeast Asia. In Europe, *curonicus* is absent only from northern Scotland, Ireland, Iceland, western Scandinavia and the northern tundra (*European Atlas*). Almost all birds from the West Palearctic winter south of the Sahara in a broad band from Senegal to Kenya, with a few in North African wetlands and the Mediterranean Basin (*BWP*).

Little Ringed Plovers began to spread in northwest Europe in the 1930s (*HVM*) and the first British breeding pair was located in Hertfordshire in 1938 (Ledlie & Pedlar 1938). Prior to this expansion, it was typically a bird of lowland rivers with extensive shingle bars, and of sandy or gravelly lakeshores with very little vegetation. Gravel extraction and the construction of new reservoirs created similar conditions in many new areas north and west of its original distribution. Now, over much of northwest Europe, only a small percentage of birds are found on the natural river systems. In Britain, the rivers of much of the south and east do not have suitable gravel banks, but by 1991 there were at least 60 pairs in Wales, of which 50 were on riverine shingle (*1988–91 Atlas*). The British breeding population has been estimated most recently at 825–1,070 pairs (*1988–91 Atlas*). Future colonization of Ireland is likely

The analysis of the data for this species was supported by British Sugar plc

(*Birds in Ireland, 1988–91 Atlas*). On the wintering grounds, south of the Sahara, Little Ringed Plovers are found scattered in small numbers in many types of wetland where marginal vegetation is limited, including small, temporary rainwater pools.

Owing to its scarcity and recent arrival in many areas, relatively few Little Ringed Plovers have been ringed in Britain & Ireland. Since colonization began in the southeast, most recoveries have been of birds ringed in this area (Fig 1). The majority were of birds ringed as pulli (72%) (Fig 2). There are few ring-recoveries, the majority of which (58%) were either retrapped or resighted. Of the 18 birds with a known cause of recovery, 12 were deliberately taken by Man (nine of these in France) (Fig 3). Although this indicates that Little Ringed Plovers are under some pressure while migrating through Europe, most of the birds killed by hunters were taken before 1980; this may indicate that hunting pressure is easing or that the reporting rate from hunters has fallen.

Juveniles from first broods remain on their natal sites for a few weeks but, if the adults lay a second clutch, the young may disperse as early as late June. Five recoveries of pulli in the second month after ringing show a median distance of 100 km, but all these birds remained within south and central Britain. Exploration at this season may be a key factor in the ability of Little Ringed Plovers to locate and colonize newly available breeding habitat. From July to early September, juveniles occur widely on wetlands

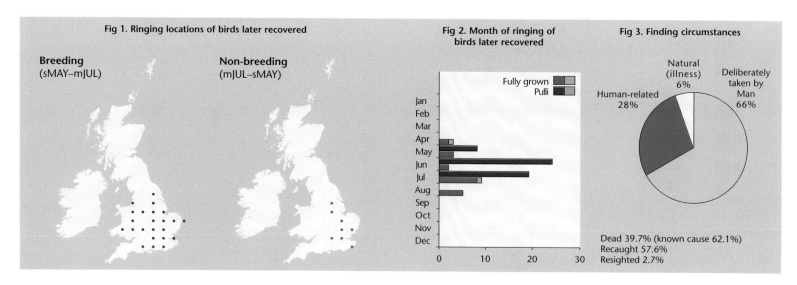

Fig 1. Ringing locations of birds later recovered

Breeding
(sMAY–mJUL)

Non-breeding
(mJUL–sMAY)

Fig 2. Month of ringing of birds later recovered

Fully grown
Pulli

Fig 3. Finding circumstances

Natural (illness) 6%
Deliberately taken by Man 66%
Human-related 28%

Dead 39.7% (known cause 62.1%)
Recaught 57.6%
Resighted 2.7%

Ringing and recovery data

	<1960	60–69	70–79	80–89	90–97	Total
RINGING						
BTO ringing totals (%)	5	13	25	28	29	4,810
RECOVERIES						
BTO-ringed (%)	7	14	34	20	25	71
Foreign-ringed (%)	0	0	100	0	0	2

Statistical analyses

	Breeding population (sMAY–mJUL)	Wintering population (sNOV–sMAR)
Status	[LONG-DISTANCE MIGRANT]	NONE
Age differences	Not tested	—
Sex differences	Not tested	—
Regional differences	Not tested	—
Finding circumstances	Not tested	—

Fig 4. Locations in (a) autumn (34, red) and (b) winter (1, blue) and spring (8, grey), and movements of over 20 km between the breeding and non-breeding season, of Little Ringed Plovers present in Britain & Ireland during the breeding season.

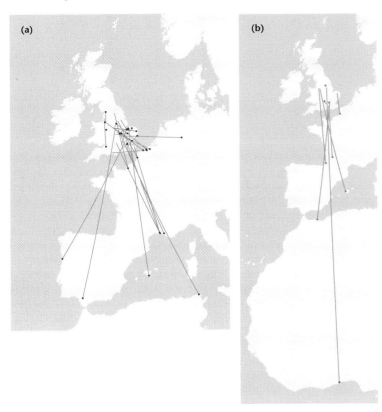

(a)

(b)

where there is no suitable breeding habitat, such as reservoirs and sewage-farms where dropping water levels expose substantial areas of mud.

Autumn departure starts in late July and by the end of that month a number of birds have already crossed the Channel, as shown by four July recoveries in France and one in Germany. By late August, quite a number of birds have already reached the Mediterranean coasts. They appear to move southward on a broad front, although there is a concentration of recoveries in the Camargue, which may be an important staging post for the species (Fig 4a). Some birds have already reached Senegal by August (Olsson 1975, *BWP*). By mid-September few Little Ringed Plovers remain in Britain, and only rarely are stragglers seen in October.

Thereafter little is known about the range of birds that breed in Britain except for a single recovery in southern Togo in January (Fig 4b). This is within the known winter range of the species and, judging by the spread of autumn and spring recoveries, all of which are to the west of 10°E, most British breeders are likely to winter in the western Sahel region (Fig 4).

Northward migration of Little Ringed Plovers from Africa to Europe is thought to be on a broad front, but birds returning in spring may take a more easterly route than in autumn (*BWP*). Little Ringed Plovers start to arrive back in Britain as early as the second week of March, and by late March many are already back on suitable breeding areas (*BWP*). However, birds continue to return through April. All three recoveries in March have been in France, implying a rather rapid and direct return north (Fig 4b).

Few natal or breeding dispersal movements have been recorded from ringing in Britain & Ireland. Results from a German study show that, on average, first-time breeders were found 33.2 km from their natal area; the furthest distance moved was 250 km but 50% of birds were within 10 km of their natal area. Breeding fidelity was higher, with the mean distance moved being just 5.5 km (maximum 102 km: *HVM*). It is not surprising that some birds disperse relatively widely, as most Little Ringed Plovers breed in essentially transient habitats that may exist for only a few years before restoration, vegetation growth or leisure developments intervene, and potential breeding sites may be widely scattered.

Little Ringed Plovers breeding in western Europe migrate on headings between south-southwest and south-southeast in autumn; there is a strong tendency for birds from Sweden and Finland, however, to move south or southeast and these birds may winter on the Persian Gulf or in East Africa (Olsson 1975, *BWP*). Despite these overall headings, some of the many Little Ringed Plovers in southeast England in July and August may be expected to be birds that originate in continental Europe, but there is no evidence as yet that this is the case. A total of eight off-course migrants recorded in Shetland up to 1996, and between May and September (Osborn *et al* 1999), may have been either British or continental in origin. Two birds ringed abroad and recovered in Britain, from Spain in April and France in July, were ringed during passage periods and the latter, ringed as a juvenile, was found breeding in Britain the following year.

The current status of the Little Ringed Plover in Britain is largely dependent on continuing sand and gravel extraction to produce a constant supply of new sites, to replace those lost over the years as they are worked out and restored or otherwise developed. There is now substantial pressure to reduce our dependence on land-based sands and gravels, however, and to exploit the larger marine resources. The populations of Little Ringed Plovers nesting on riverine shingle face other pressures. Regulated flows along rivers lead to more vegetation growth on shingle banks, which can make them unsuitable, while periodic releases of water from upland reservoirs can flood out nests. The latter are likely to increase if global warming increases storminess.

As yet, relatively little is known about the migrations of this species. Certainly it would be difficult for ringing to add much to our understanding, given the apparently wide scatter of routes taken by British birds, but improved techniques such as colour-marking may eventually help. Detailed studies looking at the use of sites, dispersal and productivity would undoubtedly help the efficiency of conservation management at breeding sites.

Tony Prater

Ringed Plover
Charadrius hiaticula

Ringed Plovers are found breeding on almost all of Britain & Ireland's coastlines and their shrill alarm calls and elaborate predator-distraction displays are a feature of almost any suitable beach in the breeding season. Britain & Ireland supports around 10,000 breeding pairs (*1988–91 Atlas*) and also provides wintering or stopover sites for a significant proportion of the East Atlantic Flyway populations. It is in this context that Ringed Plovers are amber-listed as a Bird of Conservation Concern in the UK (Gibbons *et al* 1996a).

The species is widely distributed through arctic, subarctic and temperate areas but is replaced by a sibling species, Semipalmated Plover *Charadrius semipalmatus*, over much of the Nearctic. The nominate race, *hiaticula*, occurs from Svalbard and southern Fennoscandia south to Brittany and west to Iceland, Greenland, and the eastern coasts of Ellesmere and Baffin Islands, Canada. A second race, *tundrae*, breeds along the coast and tundra of northern Fennoscandia and Russia and winters in eastern and southern Africa (*BWP*).

During the breeding season the species is numerous on wide sand or shingle tidal beaches with suitable nesting places above the high-water mark. Most Ringed Plover breeding in England are found on such beaches on the east coast. A high proportion (40%) of the British and Northern Irish population is found on the Outer Hebrides, Orkney and Shetland (Prater 1989); Hebridean machair alone holds around one-fifth of the British population (*1988–91 Atlas*). The lack of suitable substrate for nest sites may account for their scarcity along southwest coasts (Pienkowski 1984). There is some evidence for a decline in the coastal breeding population, and human disturbance has been implicated as

The analysis of the data for this species was supported by the Sandwich Bay Bird Observatory Trust

the cause (Briggs 1983, Pienkowski 1984, Liley 1999). Breeding also occurs in a variety of inland habitats, including gravel-pits, riverine shingle and even car parks! Since the 1970s, there has been a significant shift inland and during the *1988–91 Atlas* 17% of the population in England bred at inland sites. Wintering sites are coastal although narrow exposed shores, largely in northwest Scotland and southwest Britain are avoided (*Winter Atlas*).

The ringing locations for ring-recoveries are a reasonable reflection of the breeding distribution of Ringed Plovers in Britain, although the high populations in northwest Scotland and, particularly, Ireland are under-represented (Fig 1). Ringed Plover are present all round the coastline of Britain & Ireland in the non-breeding season (*Winter Atlas*). This is not reflected in Fig 1; the ringing locations of birds later recovered are biased towards areas of dense human population and the activities of specialist ringing groups and ringers. Fully grown birds are ringed all year, but particularly on passage in May, August and September, and many pulli during May–August (Fig 2). Just over half of the recoveries of dead birds with a known cause were 'deliberately taken' (Fig 3), and this may introduce bias into the distribution of recoveries.

Patterns of movement of British & Irish breeders away from the breeding sites are still poorly understood. There are some general trends, with southern and eastern populations tending to move southwest to

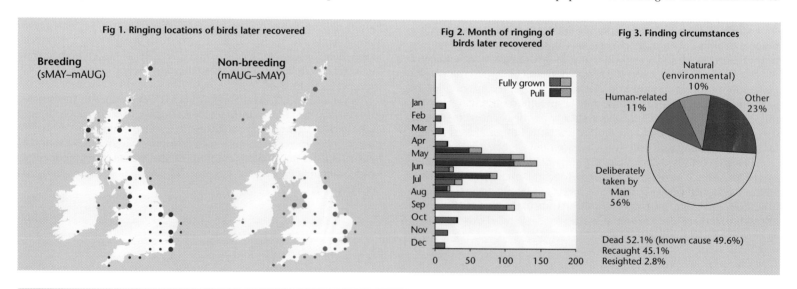

Fig 1. Ringing locations of birds later recovered

Breeding (sMAY–mAUG)

Non-breeding (mAUG–sMAY)

Fig 2. Month of ringing of birds later recovered

Fully grown
Pulli

Fig 3. Finding circumstances

Natural (environmental) 10%
Human-related 11%
Other 23%
Deliberately taken by Man 56%

Dead 52.1% (known cause 49.6%)
Recaught 45.1%
Resighted 2.8%

Ringing and recovery data

	<1960	60–69	70–79	80–89	90–97	Total
RINGING						
BTO ringing totals (%)	9	10	27	34	21	47,272
RECOVERIES						
BTO-ringed (%)	8	10	29	35	18	764
Foreign-ringed (%)	4	14	32	34	16	134

Statistical analyses

	Breeding population (sMAY–mAUG)	Wintering population (sNOV–sMAR)
Status	LONG-DISTANCE MIGRANT* (1)	[LONG-DISTANCE MIGRANT]
Age differences[NT]	Significant*	Not tested
Sex differences	Not tested	Not tested
Regional differences	Not tested	Not tested
Finding circumstances	Not significant*	Not tested

Fig 4. Locations outside the breeding season (June–July) and movements of over 20 km between the breeding and non-breeding season of 255 Ringed Plovers present in Britain & Ireland during the breeding season.

Fig 5. Recovery locations and all 71 included exchanges between Britain & Ireland and abroad of Ringed Plovers present in Britain & Ireland during spring (April–May).

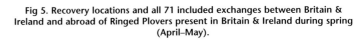

Fig 6. Recovery locations and all 37 included exchanges between Britain & Ireland and abroad of Ringed Plovers present in Britain & Ireland during winter.

Brittany, Ireland and the West Country, and the western and northern populations tending to move south (Fig 4). However, colour-ringing studies have demonstrated that individuals from one breeding location may winter at widely separated sites. For example, birds ringed at a breeding site in northwest Norfolk and recovered outside the breeding season show that, while some adults remain on the breeding grounds, others travel as far north as Lothian, as far south as Brittany, and as far west as Ireland. Others, mostly immatures, remained on the east coast and moved north (Liley 1999). Multiple sightings of colour-ringed individuals from the British breeding population over a single non-breeding period have shown that passage birds travel overland to their wintering locations, stopping at gravel-pits and estuaries *en route* rather than following coastlines.

Although individuals breeding in Britain & Ireland show only slight latitudinal shifts between wintering and breeding sites, populations from northern breeding locations winter far to the south: a 'leap-frog' migration. As Fig 5 highlights, passage migrants from breeding populations in Canada, Greenland, Iceland and Fennoscandia pass through Britain and Ireland, mainly along the coasts around the Irish Sea, on their way to wintering destinations in Spain and West Africa. These birds winter as far south as Benin and Ghana and start moving north in April, only reaching breeding grounds in Fennoscandia and Iceland in May. While British & Irish breeders are defending breeding territories in February (Pienkowski 1984), there are no recoveries in Greenland until June, after the annual snowmelt on the breeding grounds has occurred (Pienkowski 1984). Thus stopover sites are used by a progression of passage migrants, heading to sites increasingly further north, from February through to May. Return passage occurs in August on both the east and the west coasts of Britain, with birds being recovered from southern Spain at this time, and by September it would appear that all have left their northern breeding grounds.

Recoveries from Fennoscandia during the breeding season have been largely of birds ringed on the east coast of Britain in spring, while most recoveries of birds ringed on the west coast (mainly in the Irish Sea) have been recovered breeding in Iceland or Greenland. There is a suggestion of loop migration as there are a number of exchanges of Ringed Plovers between the Irish Sea area in spring and the east coast on return passage in autumn.

Male and female Ringed Plovers both return to their breeding grounds in February (*BWP*, Pienkowski 1984). They are highly faithful to their breeding site (Jackson 1994) and colour-ringing studies in Northumberland (Pienkowski 1984) and Norfolk (Liley 1999) have found that over 80% of adults present in a given year return in the next.

Britain & Ireland is extremely important both for breeding Ringed Plovers (about 80% of the nominate race breed here; Prater 1989) and as a passage and wintering area, as individuals from breeding populations all around the North Sea, from Fennoscandia, Iceland and Greenland utilize the coastline at different times of the year (Figs 5 & 6). Any loss of estuarine habitat will reduce the availability of stopover sites for long-distance migrants as well as wintering birds and local breeders.

The wide variety of wintering locations and the apparently complex patterns of dispersal during the non-breeding season are, as yet, poorly understood. The mixing of individuals from differing populations has been shown in other members of the genus (Haig 1987), but the scatter in wintering locations used by British-breeding Ringed Plovers would seem unusual. Long-term colour-ringing studies may well shed light on differences in survival and breeding success for individuals wintering at different sites; this aspect of the species' life history is certainly worth further investigation.

D Liley, J Barlow & J Middleton

Eurasian Dotterel (Dotterel)

Charadrius morinellus

With its sex role reversal in the breeding season, confiding behaviour and remote and magnificent nesting habitat, the Dotterel is one of the most unusual species in the British breeding avifauna. Curiously, the Dotterel does not breed in Iceland, despite the presence of apparently suitable habitat, nor in Ireland where montane vegetation may be too lush, and so Britain represents the most westerly breeding location in a range that extends across most of the Palearctic and even, sporadically, into Alaska. While vast, the breeding range is disjunct and often centred around mountain ranges, reflecting the Dotterel's preference for alpine habitat. Even in the Arctic, Dotterels appear to be most common at higher elevations. Although Dotterels breed across to northeastern Siberia in the east, the Taimyr Peninsula in the north and the Altai Mountains of Mongolia and Italian Apennines in the south, no races are recognized (*BWP*). Wintering grounds are also disjunct and extend from Morocco in the west across semi-arid parts of North Africa to Iraq in the east. Ring-recoveries of European birds indicate that those originating from westerly breeding areas winter more in the western part of the winter range, and that birds from further east have a more easterly distribution (*BWP*, Nankinov 1996, Whitfield *et al* 1996). There is probably considerable mixing of birds with different origins, although most of the birds wintering in northeastern Africa and the Middle East probably originate from Siberia.

The Dotterel is one of only a handful of British breeding species that are montane specialists, and its preference for montane (low alpine) dwarf shrub, moss and lichen heaths means that the vast majority breed in the Highlands of Scotland (Galbraith *et al* 1993a, b, Whitfield 2002). Densities and breeding numbers are highest in the more extensive and

The analysis of the data for this species was supported by Murphy's Wildlife Holidays

continental plateaux of the eastern and central Scottish Highlands. Numbers nesting in England and the Southern Uplands of Scotland have always appeared to be much smaller than in the Highlands (Galbraith *et al* 1993a, Strowger 1998) but the most recent estimate is of only two breeding attempts (Whitfield 2002). Wintering habitat is less well known, although semi-desert, low-intensity agriculture and steppe-like habitats are all used (Smith 1965, *BWP*, Duncan *et al* 1993).

Locations in Britain of birds ringed during the breeding season and later recovered largely mirror the breeding distribution; very few recoveries exist of birds ringed at other seasons (Fig 1). Most recoveries are from birds ringed as pulli (Fig 2). The vast majority of breeding birds that are ringed are males, as most are caught on the nest or with young chicks and in this species the male alone cares for most nests and all broods of chicks.

A high proportion of recoveries, principally in winter, are associated with humans, with the majority having been deliberately taken by Man (Fig 3). While the circumstances of recovery are notoriously biased towards causes associated with people, Hable (1980) has expressed concern about the possible influence on Dotterel populations of hunting on the wintering grounds. Limited observations in Morocco found little evidence of Dotterel being a quarry species (Duncan *et al* 1993) but this issue is worthy of further investigation.

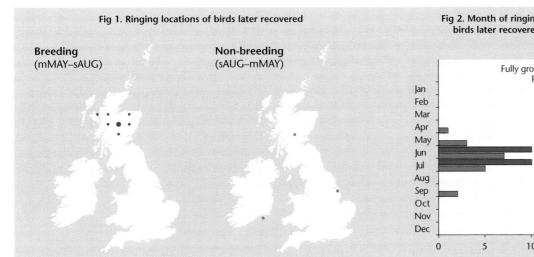

Fig 1. Ringing locations of birds later recovered

Breeding (mMAY–sAUG)

Non-breeding (sAUG–mMAY)

Fig 2. Month of ringing of birds later recovered

Fully grown / Pulli

Fig 3. Finding circumstances

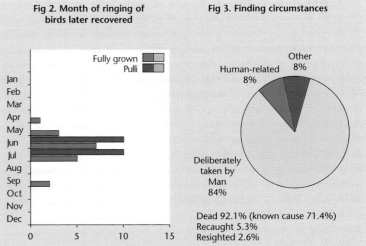

Other 8%

Human-related 8%

Deliberately taken by Man 84%

Dead 92.1% (known cause 71.4%)
Recaught 5.3%
Resighted 2.6%

Ringing and recovery data

	<1960	60–69	70–79	80–89	90–97	Total
RINGING						
BTO ringing totals (%)	1	2	7	45	45	2,168
RECOVERIES						
BTO-ringed (%)	0	3	11	39	47	38
Foreign-ringed (%)	0	0	0	0	0	0

Statistical analyses

	Breeding population (mMAY–sAUG)	Wintering population (mOCT–mAPR)
Status	LONG-DISTANCE MIGRANT*	NONE
Age differences	Not tested	—
Sex differences	Not tested	—
Regional differences	Not tested	—
Finding circumstances	Not tested*	—

Fig 4. Locations in (a) winter (13:2) and (b) autumn (3:5), and movements of over 20 km between the breeding and non-breeding season, of Dotterel present in Britain & Ireland during the breeding season. Those known to be first-years (red) are differentiated from older birds (blue). Sample sizes for the classes (first-years:older) are shown.

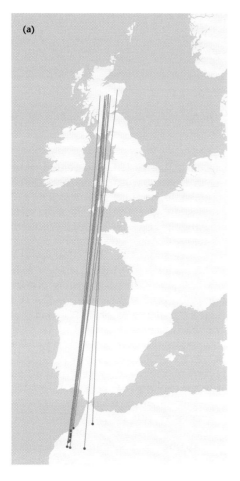

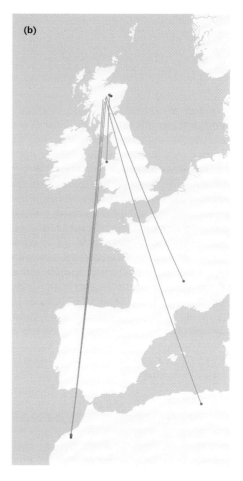

Pre-migratory dispersal of post-breeding adults and juveniles begins in late July in the Scottish Highlands and continues through August. Sightings of colour-ringed birds show that flocks tend to congregate on higher plateaux and summits and can consist of birds from numerous breeding sites. Birds also move between different post-breeding gatherings, but there are no obvious directional patterns in dispersal. Adults, predominantly males at this season, are in body moult and beginning to moult flight feathers (pers obs).

Moult in European birds is presumably suspended during autumn migration and completed on the wintering grounds, which for Scottish-ringed birds are in Morocco (Fig 4a). Two recoveries in late autumn, one in Algeria (Fig 4b) and one in Spain (Whitfield *et al* 1996), may represent wintering destinations or birds still to reach their wintering area. Autumn recoveries are on a broad front between the Scottish breeding grounds and the Moroccan wintering area, and involve mainly juveniles (Whitfield *et al* 1996, Fig 4b). Autumn sightings in Britain & Ireland away from the breeding areas are few and mostly concern juveniles seen singly or in pairs at coastal sites in September or October, most frequently in the south and west. Most Scottish birds probably migrate to the wintering grounds in a single flight (Whitfield *et al* 1996). Birds from more easterly breeding areas probably utilize migratory staging areas, judging by the distances to wintering grounds and observations of flocks in intermediate latitudes (Nethersole-Thompson 1973, *BWP*). A relationship between recovery date and latitude in Morocco suggests that Dotterel are itinerant during the winter and move progressively south, possibly tracking changes in food availability (Whitfield *et al* 1996).

The return to breeding areas apparently begins in late February and March (*BWP*), although the first birds do not usually appear in temperate

western Europe until mid-April and spring passage can continue through to late May (D P Whitfield *et al* pers obs). Spring passage occurs on a broad overland front (Whitfield *et al* 1996) and spring migratory stopovers can be traditional at either upland or lowland sites but seldom involve very large numbers of birds (*BWP*). Parties of up to 20 are annual for a few days each spring on flat or rolling arable fields in the Cambridge area (Bircham 1989). Sightings of colour-ringed birds (Whitfield *et al* 1996), and a greater number of observations away from breeding areas in spring, suggest that more birds stop off on spring migration than in autumn, but the small numbers seen in spring compared to breeding numbers further north indicate that a high proportion of western European Dotterel must reach the breeding grounds without stopping (*BWP*, Whitfield *et al* 1996).

Arrival of birds on the Scottish breeding grounds begins in late April but most arrive in early May. Flocks or 'trips' of birds in spring on Scottish breeding sites can involve paired and unpaired birds, and include birds that will breed on the site or on other Scottish sites and birds bound for more northerly breeding areas (D P Whitfield *et al* pers obs). Such gatherings have been described as 'mating arenas' (Owens *et al* 1994) but a large body of evidence suggests that this interpretation is flawed (D P Whitfield *et al* pers obs). While courtship display and pairing activity do occur in flocks, most activity involves feeding. The presence of flocks is strongly related to the availability of larvae of the Mountain Cranefly, which has a two-year life cycle, and so congregations in spring often show a strongly biennial occurrence. 'Trips' are highly mobile and dynamic in composition and later in May can include breeding birds.

A long-term colour-ringing programme in the Scottish Highlands has shown that Dotterel can move between different breeding sites in May. There is no obvious geographical pattern to these pre-breeding movements in spring. Site-fidelity of breeding males is highly variable between sites and years, but around a third of males return to the same site to breed in the following year. A male that breeds successfully is more likely to return to the same site to breed the following year than a male that fails, and return rates of males that lose their eggs to a predator are lower than for other causes of failure. If a male does not return to the same site his other breeding site can be up to several hundred kilometres distant. Similarly, if a male fails and then initiates a replacement breeding attempt within the same year, about a third stay on the same site but the remainder move to a different site. One male nested on the Hardangervidda in southern Norway in one year and in eastern Scotland in a subsequent year (S Rae pers comm); another failed in northern Scotland and initiated a replacement clutch in Norway in the same year. Given the vastness of the Norwegian breeding grounds and the scarcity of observers there, it seems likely that such movements are routine (D P Whitfield *et al* pers obs).

Very few females have been ringed as breeding birds, and the sample ringed is biased towards those that have helped to incubate a late clutch. Site-fidelity of this sample is not significantly different to males, but this is probably because such females represent a group of birds that stay in Scotland through much of the breeding season, attempting to pair with males that lose their eggs (D P Whitfield *et al* pers obs). One female ringed on a site in the central Highlands was seen the next year in Orkney, immediately following a period of easterly winds, and so may have been in Fennoscandia or further east in the initial part of the breeding season. She returned to the ringing site in the central Highlands a few days after the Orkney sighting (R Smith pers comm). The sex ratio is equal during the initial phase of clutch completion. It then appears that the majority of females leave Scotland after abandoning a first mate and their clutch; in the remaining population there is only about one female to every 10 males (D P Whitfield *et al* pers obs). These females do not appear to head south, as there are no observations of passage birds in summer (*BWP*). Rather it is likely that they head for later breeding areas further north in the search for additional mates, judging by sex ratios at later breeding sites in Norway (Kålås & Byrkjedal 1984). Such movements, both within and between breeding seasons, are a powerful factor inhibiting geographical variation in this species.

Natal philopatry is strongly sexually biased: very few females return to their natal site. Patterns of male natal philopatry are very similar to adult male site-fidelity (D P Whitfield *et al* pers obs). Ring-recoveries and sightings of birds ringed as chicks confirm a breeding link with countries to the northeast of Scotland. A chick ringed in Scotland was reported from Denmark in a subsequent autumn (*BWP*) and another Scottish chick was seen as an adult in southern Norway during spring (pers obs).

In light of the increasing evidence for a high degree of breeding dispersal, it seems likely that the description of certain long-distance recoveries as aberrant (*BWP*) may have been inappropriate. A September migrant ringed in Ireland was found the following June at Krasnoyarsk in Siberia (86°E) and a Scottish bird has been seen in August in Svalbard (pers obs).

While the itineracy of the Dotterel, both on the breeding grounds and on the wintering grounds, is fascinating, it also presents unusual conservation problems. Relatively little is known about Dotterel on their wintering grounds and they may be vulnerable to modern changes in agriculture (*European Atlas*). Their apparent mobility in winter will make it more difficult to establish the impacts of any detrimental human activities (Whitfield *et al* 1996). A recent national survey in Britain has identified a significant reduction in breeding numbers since the late 1980s (Whitfield 2002). Although the pattern of change does not suggest a climatic influence on the breeding grounds, the Dotterel's mountain habitats are particularly vulnerable to climate change. Monitoring breeding populations and identifying causes of fluctuations in numbers within national boundaries is difficult without reference to other countries; a national decline might reflect overall numbers or a shift to another country. It is important that researchers identify an appropriate scale at which to monitor Dotterel populations. While continued ringing effort will help in this regard (particularly with females), other techniques such as genetic sampling and, once feasible, satellite tracking are probably needed. Collaboration and co-ordination are required internationally. Although the challenges for the future are high, it will surely be worth meeting them: this is a remarkable bird.

D Philip Whitfield

European Golden Plover (Golden Plover)
Pluvialis apricaria

The haunting piping calls of breeding Golden Plovers are a characteristic summer sound of many areas of upland moorland in the north and west of Britain and Ireland. Approximately 23,000 pairs (1–2% of the world population) of Golden Plovers breed in Britain & Ireland (*1988–91 Atlas*, Byrkjedal & Thompson 1998) but only about 400 of those are in Ireland. This contrasts with up to 650,000 birds that winter here, mostly in Ireland (Kirby & Lack 1993).

The breeding range extends from Ireland and Iceland in the west, across the tundra to central Siberia in the east (*BWP*). In general, populations move south in a broad band during the autumn to their wintering grounds, which stretch from Britain & Ireland and the southern North Sea countries south through Iberia to northernmost Africa and east to the eastern Mediterranean Sea, the Middle East and the Caspian Sea. The details of movements of populations from different regions are complex. In Britain & Ireland, the species is a partial migrant (*BWP*), those remaining for the winter mixing with birds from the north. Northern birds, mainly of the form 'altifrons', in the westernmost populations tend to leap-frog over British & Irish breeders (Pienkowski *et al* 1985). Peaks in the migration of adults are several weeks ahead of those of juveniles (*BWP, HVM*). Spring migration begins for the southernmost wintering populations in mid-February and follows two broad routes. One runs from northwest Africa and Iberia up through the Low Countries and Britain & Ireland, where numbers peak in April and May, and on to breeding grounds in Iceland, Fennoscandia and sometimes Siberia. The other route tracks across the Mediterranean and eastern Europe before crossing to Siberia (Byrkjedal & Thompson 1998).

The analysis of the data for this species was supported by Andrew Forbes

Golden Plovers breed mainly on unenclosed upland moorlands within Britain & Ireland (*1988–91 Atlas*). Highest densities occur on blanket mires (such as those dominated by Hare's-tail Cottongrass), wet heaths and rough grassland. The highest densities in England have been recorded on calcareous grassland (Ratcliffe 1976). During migration and winter this species is found predominantly on grassland and cultivated land in the lowlands (Barnard & Thompson 1985), with only 10–15% of the population occurring on coastal mudflats (Byrkjedal & Thompson 1998).

The ring-recoveries involving Britain & Ireland provide only limited information. The distribution of ringing sites from which recoveries originated (Fig 1) is a poor match to both breeding and wintering distribution (*1988–91 Atlas*, Kirby & Lack 1993). About half the recoveries were from birds ringed as adults, many of which were ringed during migration periods (Fig 2).

Hunting is the main cause of death reported for ring-recoveries (Fig 3). In Britain 62%, and in Ireland 96%, of recoveries with a known cause of death were taken deliberately by Man. Golden Plovers are still legal quarry in many European countries, including the UK, Ireland, France, Portugal, Denmark and Norway. The numbers killed in these countries may be large. Given that up to 100,000 birds are taken annually in France (Byrkjedal & Thompson 1998), it is perhaps revealing that so few British or Irish rings have been recovered there.

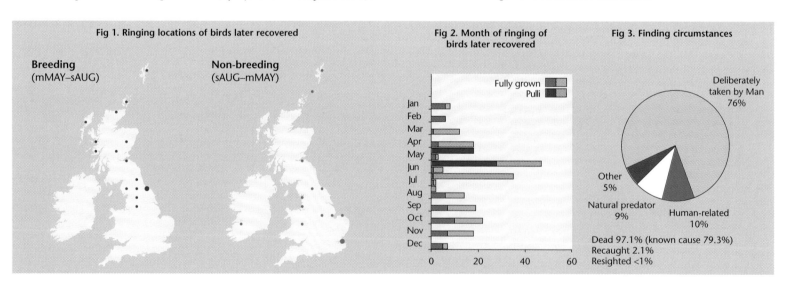

Fig 1. Ringing locations of birds later recovered

Breeding (mMAY–sAUG)

Non-breeding (sAUG–mMAY)

Fig 2. Month of ringing of birds later recovered

Fully grown
Pulli

Jan, Feb, Mar, Apr, May, Jun, Jul, Aug, Sep, Oct, Nov, Dec

0 20 40 60

Fig 3. Finding circumstances

Deliberately taken by Man 76%

Other 5%

Natural predator 9%

Human-related 10%

Dead 97.1% (known cause 79.3%)
Recaught 2.1%
Resighted <1%

Ringing and recovery data

	<1960	60–69	70–79	80–89	90–97	Total
RINGING						
BTO ringing totals (%)	9	10	27	31	23	5,543
RECOVERIES						
BTO-ringed (%)	14	21	20	27	17	104
Foreign-ringed (%)	49	25	8	9	9	135

Statistical analyses

	Breeding population (mMAY–sAUG)	Wintering population (sDEC–mMAR)
Status	LONG-DISTANCE MIGRANT* (3)	[LONG-DISTANCE MIGRANT]
Age differences	Not tested	Not tested
Sex differences	Not tested	Not tested
Regional differences	Not tested	Not tested
Finding circumstances	Not tested*	Not tested

Fig 4. Locations in autumn (10, red), winter (23, blue) and spring (3, grey) of Golden Plovers present in Britain & Ireland during the breeding season.

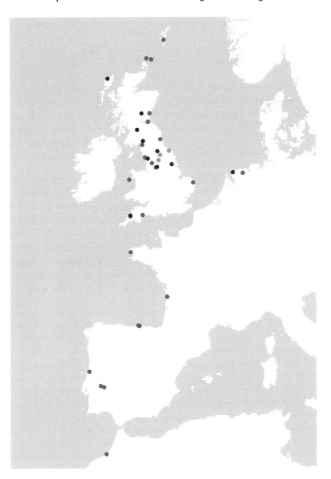

Fig 5. All included exchanges of Golden Plovers between Britain & Ireland and abroad. Those abroad during the breeding season (50, red) and passage periods (66, grey) are differentiated from those abroad during winter (29, blue). The 21 seasonally inaccurate exchanges are not shown.

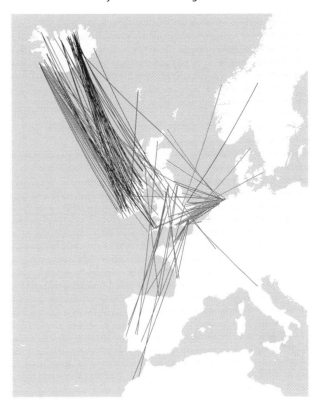

Adult and young Golden Plovers probably leave their British moorland breeding grounds and surrounding fields within a few weeks, or even days, of the young reaching independence (Parr 1980, Whittingham *et al* 1999). During August and September, flocks often build up on coastal sites, though peak counts for these sites and those used for roosting inland, such as gravel-pits, are often in midwinter (Cranswick *et al* 1995). A small number of autumn recoveries of Golden Plover breeding in Britain suggest that they may remain within Britain (median=39 km, P5–95=13–544 km, *n*=9) (Fig 4). There is one record from the Netherlands, and a female with chicks in Upper Teesdale on 23 June was resighted three weeks later on the Humber Estuary, over 200 km away (pers obs). Nine birds (five adults, four pulli) ringed on the breeding grounds in the north Pennines, County Durham, between 1992 and 1996 were all resighted in subsequent autumns in British coastal areas (pers obs).

Some British breeders remain in Britain in the winter, but others migrate long distances (Fig 4). It is notable that there were no recoveries of British breeders wintering in Ireland. Although populations may winter less than 100 km from their breeding grounds (Bannerman 1961, Parr 1992), wide-scale departures with the onset of severe winter cold have been noted in Britain & Ireland (Kirby & Lack 1993) and in other European countries (*HVM*, Yeatman *et al* 1991). These movements are presumably a response to cold weather preventing birds from feeding on frozen ground; birds return soon after a thaw (Fuller & Youngman 1979). Such movements could result in increased overwinter mortality; mean winter soil temperature and total winter rainfall explained 69% of the variation in adult survival rates of Lapwing, which undertakes similar cold-weather movements (Peach *et al* 1994). Flocks of wintering Golden Plovers have been reported using traditional areas each year (Fuller & Youngman 1979). However, use of individual sites within the range of

traditional areas, for roosting and foraging, may show wide fluctuations within and between years (Kirby & Lack 1993, Cranswick *et al* 1995, Byrkjedal & Thompson 1998).

Most British breeders are back on their breeding grounds by late February (Fig 4), though some birds wintering nearby may visit them throughout the winter (Ratcliffe 1976, Byrkjedal & Thompson 1998). During periods of good weather during the winter, birds will visit the breeding grounds and often stand around in pairs dispersed over the moor before returning to pasture fields when harsh weather returns (Ratcliffe 1976, pers obs). Egg-laying does not commence until April or May in most parts of Britain (Ratcliffe 1976, Byrkjedal & Thompson 1998).

The evidence from ring-recoveries indicates that winter immigrants and passage migrants in Ireland differ in origin from those in Britain. Golden Plover wintering in Ireland are predominantly Icelandic breeders, all but two overseas ring-recoveries involving Ireland being to or from Iceland (Fig 5); there is little evidence of British or Scandinavian breeding Golden Plover wintering in Ireland. In Britain, however, there appears to be a mixture of British, Scandinavian and Icelandic breeders, with the Icelandic breeders predominantly found in the west (Fig 5). Britain & Ireland (particularly Ireland) is clearly an important wintering area for Icelandic breeding Golden Plovers. Of 157 exchanges between Iceland and abroad, 87 (55%) were within Britain & Ireland and 61 of these (39%) involved Ireland (Gudmundsson 1997).

There is only one recovery in Britain & Ireland of a Golden Plover present in Scandinavia (Norway) in the breeding season, but many birds present on passage in the Netherlands have been recorded in Britain, mainly in the southeast (Fig 5). Other birds present on passage in the Netherlands have been recorded breeding in Russia, Finland and Scandinavia (*BWP*). Some of these Golden Plover will remain in Britain in winter; others use France, Iberia or Morocco (*BWP*), where birds caught on passage in southeast Britain and breeding birds from northern England are both found in winter.

Although concentrated in Europe, the Golden Plover does not appear to be threatened (Tucker & Heath 1994), because its core populations in Iceland and Norway are stable in numbers. In Britain & Ireland, declines have been documented between the *1968–72* and *1988–91 Atlases*, most noticeably in the Borders, in the central area and Highlands of Scotland, in Wales and in parts of Ireland. Changes in quality of breeding habitats have been suggested as the cause of some of these changes (*1988–91 Atlas*, Byrkjedal & Thompson 1998). As some British breeders make use of wintering grounds outside Britain & Ireland, these areas may be of considerable importance for conservation, in conjunction with suitable year-round habitats in Britain. Ireland, in particular, appears to be of considerable importance to the Icelandic breeding population.

Two intensive studies in Britain have suggested that overwinter survival is important in regulating breeding populations (Parr 1992, Yalden & Pearce-Higgins 1997). The availability of suitable winter habitat may therefore be important for the conservation of Golden Plover. Such conservation measures may be necessary both in Britain and abroad. In Britain, older fields that support greater earthworm densities (Barnard & Thompson 1985) are particularly favoured within regularly used wintering ranges. Land management schemes that encourage the retention of older pastures on lowland farmland should benefit wintering Golden Plovers. Much pasture land has been converted to arable, not only in Britain (Fuller & Lloyd 1981, Byrkjedal & Thompson 1998) but also in the rest of Europe (Tucker & Heath 1994). Further research is required to discover whether this change has affected the numbers or distribution of Golden Plovers.

Ring-recoveries have shown that some British breeders move abroad, and wide-scale movements occur in response to periods of cold weather. However, little is known about the extent and frequency of these movements. We do not yet know how long they remain in these dispersed wintering grounds or to what extent such movements influence site-fidelity of individual birds in the wintering or breeding grounds. A study using colour-ringed birds which are either radio-tracked, or preferably satellite-tagged, should provide valuable insights into Golden Plover movements.

Mark Jonathan Whittingham

Grey Plover
Pluvialis squatarola

Grey Plovers breed in the high arctic regions of Russia and North America, mainly along the belt of lowland tundra between the tree limit and the coast. From these areas birds migrate to wintering areas throughout much of the world, making the Grey Plover one of the most globally widespread of all species of wader; the wintering range extends to the coastlines of Africa, south and east Asia, Australasia and South America (*BWP*). The coasts of Britain, Ireland and the nearby Continent provide the most northerly wintering areas in the world for the species.

No subspecies are described but there is slight geographical variation, with size increasing from Atlantic to Pacific coasts across both continents (*BWP*). Birds caught at coastal sites in autumn and spring have been found with levels of pre-migratory fat sufficient to allow non-stop overland flights of several thousand kilometres between staging posts (Branson & Minton 1976). The global migration routes between breeding and wintering areas probably follow the principal flyways of other arctic-breeding wader species; the details of many of these routes, however, are not well understood.

In Britain & Ireland, Grey Plovers occur both as passage migrants and as winter visitors; there is also a small summering population of non-breeding immature birds. All these birds come from the Russian-breeding populations (Branson & Minton 1976). Passage migrants through Britain & Ireland winter on the coasts of southwest Europe and Africa as far south as the Gulf of Guinea. Birds wintering in South Africa are thought to follow more eastern migration routes. Birds wintering in Asia, Australasia and America come from the populations breeding in eastern Siberia and in arctic North America.

The analysis of the data for this species was supported by the Wash Wader Ringing Group

Away from the breeding areas Grey Plovers are almost entirely confined to the coasts, particularly those with extensive mudflats. Studies of the feeding behaviour of Grey Plovers on their wintering areas have shown that individuals use the same feeding areas from tide to tide, and from year to year (Dugan 1982, Townshend 1985). There is competition for feeding sites, and this may have a bearing on migration (Townshend 1985, Turpie 1995).

Numbers of wintering birds in Britain have increased significantly in recent years, rising from under 10,000 in 1970 to over 43,000 around 1990, with these increases being mirrored by similar increases in other areas of continental Europe, in particular the Wadden Sea and the Dutch deltas (Moser 1988, Cayford & Waters 1996), and in Africa (Smit & Piersma 1989).

The distribution of Grey Plovers in Britain & Ireland is largely southeastern at all seasons, with most birds present in the area from the Wash to the Solent (Pollitt *et al* 2000). Grey Plovers are relatively scarce in Scotland and Ireland. The Wash is the most important estuary in Britain for Grey Plovers in terms of numbers, with a mean peak count of 10,478 (94/95–98/99) and a highest winter peak count of 17,404 in 1994/95 (Pollitt *et al* 2000). The ringing locations in Britain & Ireland for ringed birds recovered (Fig 1) largely match the distribution of wintering birds (*Winter Atlas*), although some sites in the west are not represented

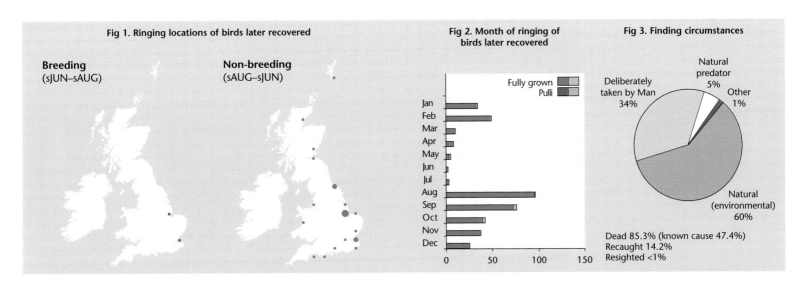

Fig 1. Ringing locations of birds later recovered

Breeding (sJUN–sAUG)

Non-breeding (sAUG–sJUN)

Fig 2. Month of ringing of birds later recovered

Fully grown / Pulli

Fig 3. Finding circumstances

Natural predator 5%
Deliberately taken by Man 34%
Other 1%
Natural (environmental) 60%

Dead 85.3% (known cause 47.4%)
Recaught 14.2%
Resighted <1%

Ringing and recovery data

	<1960	60–69	70–79	80–89	90–97	Total
RINGING						
BTO ringing totals (%)	0	12	21	40	27	9,236
RECOVERIES						
BTO-ringed (%)	1	7	18	36	39	378
Foreign-ringed (%)	0	10	20	50	20	10

Statistical analyses

	Breeding population (sJUN–sAUG)	Wintering population (mNOV–mMAR)
Status	NONE	[LONG-DISTANCE MIGRANT]
Age differences	—	Not tested
Sex differences	—	Not tested
Regional differences	—	Not tested
Finding circumstances	—	Not tested

Fig 4. Locations during (a) April–July (27:19), (b) August–October (65:12) and (c) November–March (220:45) of Grey Plovers using Britain & Ireland. Seasonally accurate recoveries (red) are differentiated from those not seasonally accurate (grey). A further recovery in Ghana is not shown because it was transported within Britain before release. Sample sizes of the classes (seasonally accurate:seasonally inaccurate) are shown.

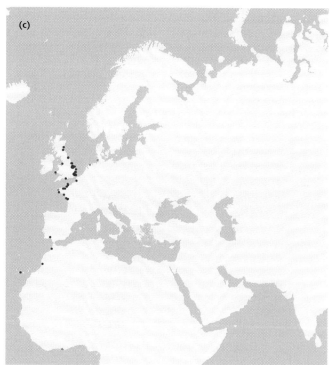

despite holding internationally important numbers of Grey Plover. Most birds were ringed between August and February (Fig 2). The patterns of ringing and recovery are probably broadly representative of the species as it occurs in Britain & Ireland.

Most recoveries (85%) relate to dead birds; where the cause of death is known, the majority (60%) relate to natural environmental factors, including birds found dead on the tideline in cold weather (Fig 3). In addition 34% of known causes of death are of birds killed by hunters

(mainly by shooting); all of the birds recovered overseas with a known cause of death were taken by hunters, and this may bias the recovery pattern.

Movements of Grey Plovers based on ring-recoveries are shown in Fig 4. Three recoveries in the breeding season (June–July) were from the western end of the breeding range in northern Russia. The two remaining recoveries in Russia were both in August, one within the breeding range, and the other on the White Sea coast where the bird was presumably

Fig 5. Movements of over 20 km and recovery locations of Grey Plovers ringed in winter and recovered in the same winter (17:2, red) or a subsequent winter (41:7, blue). Sample sizes of movements under:over 20 km are given but only those over 20 km are plotted.

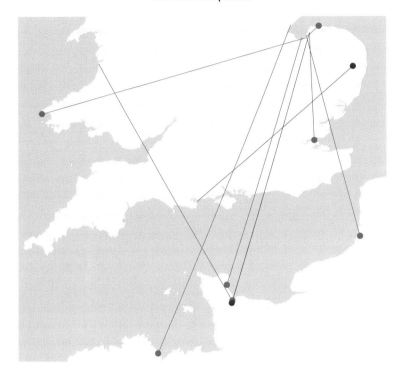

Fig 5. Movements of over 20 km and recovery locations of Grey Plovers ringed in winter and recovered in the same winter (17:2, red) or a subsequent winter (41:7, blue). Sample sizes of movements under:over 20 km are given but only those over 20 km are plotted.

on passage. The recoveries in Denmark, mainly in autumn, suggest that the coast of Denmark provides an important staging post for passage migrants.

In Poland, passage of Grey Plovers begins in early July with adult females, followed by adult males and then juveniles (Krupa 1997). The first adult Grey Plovers arrive in Britain & Ireland towards the end of July, and the first juveniles in early September. Peak autumn numbers occur in September (WeBS count data). Adults can readily be separated into two broad groups: those that are not in active wing moult and remain for a relatively short period while putting on weight prior to departure for wintering areas further south; and those that commence (or recommence) wing moult and remain at least until the moult is completed (Branson & Minton 1976). Numbers fall in October and November as the passage populations move to wintering areas further south and west. Ring-recoveries add considerably to our understanding of the behaviour of these populations (Fig 4). Two recoveries in Ghana indicate the southernmost limit, so far established, of the wintering areas of the passage populations: one of these birds was recovered as early as 21 September, indicating the rapidity with which some birds reach wintering areas in Africa. The remaining overseas recoveries in winter have so far been confined to France, Spain, and Morocco (Fig 4c).

Movements of birds ringed in winter and recovered in the same or subsequent winters are shown in Fig 5. In total, 48 between-winter and 19 within-winter movements of Grey Plovers have been reported. Of these, only nine (seven between winters and two within) had moved over 20 km. For recoveries of dead birds, the median movement between winters was 4 km (P5–95=0–406 km) and within winters was only 2.5 km (P5–95=0–417 km). This indicates the strong site-fidelity of the species to its wintering areas, both within a season and from year to year, a pattern which has been well established through studies of the feeding behaviour of individuals (eg Townshend 1985). Some Grey Plovers do

move in response to cold weather; seven of a group of birds colour-marked on the Tees in a cold spell in January and February 1979 were, despite regular searches, not seen again until a further period of severe weather in January 1982 (Townshend 1982). It also appears that a small proportion of birds that carry out their autumn primary wing moult in Britain & Ireland move to other sites for the remainder of the winter, and count data suggest that some birds that have spent the earlier part of the winter in the Netherlands later move to the east coast of Britain. On the Tees, up to 50 adult Grey Plovers that had already moulted appeared in November and early December. Returning adult Grey Plovers displaced some juveniles that had already taken up territory, whilst other juveniles abandoned territories at this time; of 46 colour-marked juveniles present on the estuary in October, 29 had left by December (Townshend 1985).

Competition for winter feeding sites may have a bearing on the behaviour of certain birds, in particular juveniles, which may be forced to move to wintering areas further south. Two displaced juveniles were recovered, in the same autumn, up to 900 km to the south (Townshend 1985). There is evidence from the proportion of first-year birds in ringing catches at the Wash (pers obs) that numbers of juveniles increase in Britain towards the end of the winter; this may indicate the return of birds that have spent the earlier part of the winter further south, but could equally be onward movement of juveniles from the Wadden Sea or a movement from open coasts.

Return spring passage in Britain & Ireland becomes evident in March when numbers rise rapidly from midwinter levels (WeBS count data). Numbers remain high well into May when many adults are observed in full summer plumage. By June, almost all Grey Plovers remaining in Britain & Ireland are first-summer birds. There is no evidence from ring-recoveries that any first-year birds return to the breeding areas in their first summer.

There are a number of indications that Grey Plovers are under pressure on their British wintering areas. Studies of feeding point to the pressures on individuals to protect their own feeding patch (Townshend et al 1984). About one-third of adults arriving in Britain in autumn have already moulted typically two or three primaries, presumably because it is beneficial for those birds to begin moult as early as possible to reduce demands later in the winter. About 40% of adults are unable to complete their wing moult in autumn, and arrest their moult with typically three primaries unmoulted; these birds resume their moult in the following spring (Branson & Minton 1976). A study of the weights of waders at the Wash has shown that Grey Plovers appear to be particularly sensitive to severe weather conditions (Johnson 1985). The number of recoveries of dead birds along high-tide lines in cold weather indicates that, after Redshank, the Grey Plover is the next most vulnerable species in severe winter weather (Clark et al 1993).

Much remains to be discovered about the migrations of the various populations of Grey Plover. Relatively little is known about the breeding areas and it is unknown whether there is a geographical separation between the breeding areas of the passage and wintering populations that occur in Britain & Ireland. There is potentially much to be learnt by comparing the annual life cycles of those populations which make the relatively short journey to wintering areas in the North Sea but have to endure relatively hard winters, and those which make much longer journeys to wintering areas south of the Equator but have less arduous conditions in their wintering areas. The species remains potentially one of the most rewarding of the waders for further study.

Nicholas Branson

Northern Lapwing (Lapwing)

Vanellus vanellus

The Lapwing in Britain & Ireland is a well-known breeding, passage migrant and wintering species found in a wide range of open habitats. The familiar tumbling display flight and '*pee-wit*' call are signs of spring in upland areas, while migrating flocks mark the onset of cold weather, as they move south and west in search of unfrozen ground.

The Lapwing is the most widely distributed and migratory member of the *Vanellinae*, breeding across the whole of Eurasia (Hayman *et al* 1986). Birds from the western part of the Continent migrate westwards and southwest in winter, to areas with a mild, maritime climate. Of birds breeding in central Europe, some move west or northwest, reaching the Low Countries, Britain and Ireland, whilst others go southwest into Italy and southern France (Imboden 1974). Wintering Lapwings east of Turkey are found between 20°N and 40°N (*BWP*). Occasional vagrants cross the Atlantic, particularly after severe weather, and cause great excitement; these included one English-ringed chick in 1927.

Breeding Lapwings in Britain & Ireland are birds of open farmland and moorland, nesting from sea-level up to altitudes of 500 m in England (*BWP*) but up to 800 or 1,000 m in Scotland (Baxter & Rintoul 1953). There are concentrations of breeding Lapwings in the north of England, the Scottish Borders, the Outer Hebrides and eastern Scotland but very few breed in western Scotland, Wales, the southwest of England and southern and western Ireland (*1988–91 Atlas*). There has been a large decline in the number of Lapwings since the *1988–91 Atlas*. A 1998 survey recorded a 49% decline in England and Wales to a population of 62,923 breeding pairs (95% confidence intervals 55,268 to 74,499) (Wilson *et al* 2001). The largest declines

The analysis of the data for this species was supported by the Rye Bay Ringing Group and the Wetland Trust

were recorded in southwest England and Wales and have led to a range contraction.

After breeding, birds gather in small flocks typically of up to 500 birds (*eg* Cook 1992, Gladwin & Sage 1996). These summer flocks, which may form as early as late May or June, are often associated with gravel-pits or other waterbodies.

The distribution of ringing sites, for birds later recovered, is broadly representative of the British distribution of the species in the breeding season and in winter but Ireland, where relatively few Lapwing are ringed, is greatly under-represented in both seasons (Fig 1). The great majority of recoveries are from birds ringed as pulli, adults being difficult to trap (Fig 2). Just over half of the recoveries of dead birds are categorized as having been deliberately taken by Man (Fig 3); hunting accounted for more than 85% of all recoveries in France, Ireland, Portugal and Spain but only 17% in Britain & Ireland. Hunters in southern Europe may kill many birds displaced from Britain after the onset of cold weather but a detailed analysis of recoveries from the period 1960–89 showed a decline in the proportion of ring-recoveries attributable to hunting (Peach *et al* 1994); there has also been an overall decrease in reporting rates (Catchpole *et al* 1999). In 1960–69, 41% of first-year and 51% of adult recoveries could be attributed to hunting, compared to 14% and 21% in 1970–79 and 10% and 22% in 1980–89.

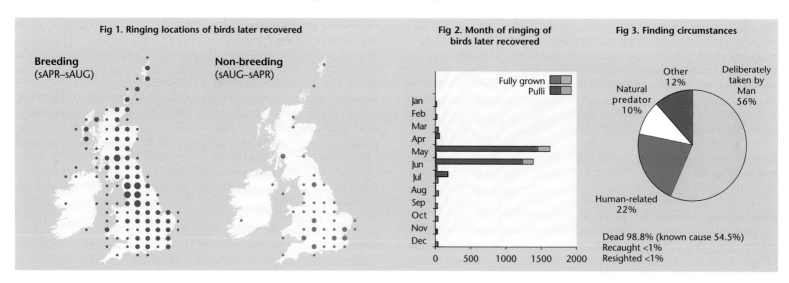

Fig 1. Ringing locations of birds later recovered

Breeding (sAPR–sAUG)

Non-breeding (sAUG–sAPR)

Fig 2. Month of ringing of birds later recovered

Fully grown
Pulli

Fig 3. Finding circumstances

Other 12%
Deliberately taken by Man 56%
Natural predator 10%
Human-related 22%

Dead 98.8% (known cause 54.5%)
Recaught <1%
Resighted <1%

Ringing and recovery data

	<1960	60–69	70–79	80–89	90–97	Total
RINGING						
BTO ringing totals (%)	35	10	17	22	17	201,983
RECOVERIES						
BTO-ringed (%)	45	17	13	16	9	3,209
Foreign-ringed (%)	60	16	12	10	2	387

Statistical analyses

	Breeding population (sAPR–sAUG)	Wintering population (mNOV–sFEB)
Status	LONG-DISTANCE MIGRANT (2)	LONG-DISTANCE MIGRANT*
Age differences[NT]	Significant	Not tested
Sex differences	Not tested	Not tested
Regional differences	Significant[4]	Not tested
Finding circumstances	Significant	Not tested

Fig 4. Locations in winter of Lapwings present in the (a) northeast (81), (b) northwest (351), (c) southeast (112) and (d) southwest (164) of Britain during the breeding season. The two winter recoveries of Lapwings present in Ireland during the breeding season are not shown.

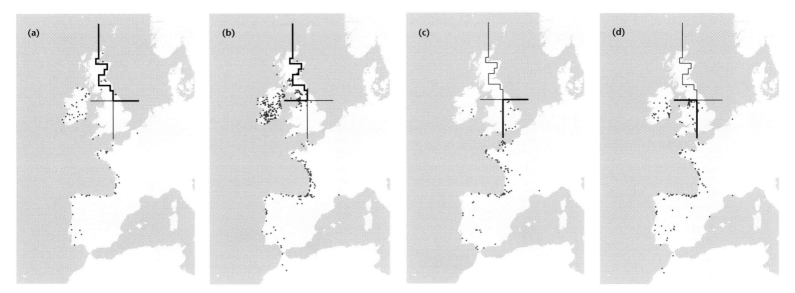

These results may show the influence of the two cold winters during the 1960s, when many British-ringed Lapwings moved to, and were shot in, France and Iberia, rather than any decrease in hunting pressure.

Lapwings breeding in Britain are only partially migratory. Some Lapwings winter close to their breeding areas (*BWP*) whilst others may move substantial distances (Fig 4). Birds from the southeast of Britain predominantly move south in winter, those from the northwest move mainly southwest, with a more mixed pattern for the other two regions. The formal statistical analysis confirmed that more birds from the northern regions tend to move west into Ireland rather than south onto the Continent, whilst the opposite is true for birds from the south. A previous analysis (Spencer 1957) showed that all winter ring-recoveries of Lapwings ringed south and east of the Humber–Severn line within England were in France and Iberia. Birds ringed in northern and western Britain were recovered mainly in Ireland, with a few in the far south of France and Portugal. Lapwings start to arrive in Iberia in October but the highest numbers are recorded in January, as winter conditions limit food availability (Asensio 1992). Lapwings on the Continent in winter tend to be found around the coast where it is easier to feed (Asensio 1992); this is reflected in the distribution of winter locations of birds that are in Britain & Ireland in the breeding season (Fig 4).

Lapwings from continental Europe start to arrive in Britain as early as late May, with the majority of birds arriving between late September and early November (Gillings 1999). Early continental birds moult in Britain, others complete the North Sea crossing while in moult (Appleton & Minton 1978), but most moult in continental Europe (*BWP*). Birds leave the breeding grounds promptly at the end of the breeding season, so after July there are no recoveries from Russia of birds ringed in Britain & Ireland in winter, and in September foreign recoveries are all along the North Sea coast. Flocks in Britain in late summer contain birds of both British and continental origin.

The numbers of Lapwings in Britain & Ireland increase during the autumn, with further arrivals as frosts occur in Europe bringing the British winter population to over one million (*Winter Atlas*). Wintering birds are found in flocks of up to several thousand birds on arable and pastoral farmland and on coasts, often centred upon traditional sites. In Buckinghamshire, for instance, the Vale of Aylesbury probably holds some 20,000 birds in midwinter (Lack & Ferguson 1993).

In cold weather, when fields are frozen, wintering Lapwings move west and south and appear more in estuarine habitats. Sometimes movements may be local and birds will return after a few weeks, but cold-weather movements can be dramatic. Examples include 4,500 passing southwest over Tring, Hertfordshire, in 50 minutes on 9 December 1967

(Gladwin & Sage 1996), 8,900 flying west over Kenfig Dunes, Glamorgan, in three hours on 27 December 1965 (Hurford & Lansdown 1995) and 10,200 in 2.5 hours over Portsmouth, Hampshire, on 30 January 1972 (Clark & Eyre 1993).

Annual adult survival rates of Lapwings are significantly correlated with winter air temperatures (Peach *et al* 1994). In the particularly cold winters of 1961/62 and 1962/63, there were 23 and 56 (respectively) recoveries in the Iberian Peninsula, compared to an average of 5.6 per year for the other 38 winters between 1958 and 1997. A detailed analysis of the results from the *Winter Atlas* (Kirby & Lack 1993) showed the response of Lapwings to changing weather conditions in the winter time. In 1981/82, most birds left the British mainland during a period of cold weather which lasted from the second week of December to mid-January, with numbers building up again in eastern England in February. In the two mild winters of 1982/83 and 1983/84, the distribution of Lapwings remained relatively constant throughout the months of November to January. There are no recoveries linking Ireland with Iberia or elsewhere in southern Europe. This could suggest a lack of onward movement from Ireland to Iberia, even in hard winters, but may simply reflect the small numbers of Lapwings ringed in Ireland.

With the arrival of spring, birds of continental origin return to their breeding areas (Fig 5). March recoveries include birds wintering in southwest Europe, and others moving into Denmark and southern Norway to breed. By April, there are records in the rest of Fennoscandia, and as far east as Moscow, with recoveries further east in May. By the time that these eastern individuals have reached their breeding grounds, the first birds can be seen returning to Britain from the Continent; presumably these are failed breeders.

In Britain, Lapwings may be back on territory in February (Galbraith 1989). A study in northern England has shown breeding Lapwing to be highly site-faithful, almost always nesting in the same or adjacent fields (Thompson *et al* 1994). However, Lapwings in arable farmland will have to respond to changing cropping patterns from year to year. In this case, it is suspected that birds will be faithful to a restricted natal region but there are no data to confirm this. Analysis has shown that 61% of recoveries of pulli in subsequent summers are within 10 km of the natal site, and only 11% are more than 100 km distant (Thompson *et al* 1994). Similar figures for natal philopatry have been found in other studies. For example, in Denmark 54% of pulli were less than 10 km from the ringing site (62% within 20 km; Bak & Ettrup 1982), and Imboden (1974) found that, across Europe, 70% of Lapwings returned to within 20 km of their natal site. Of birds returning to their natal area in northern England, 67% bred in their first summer, with 27% arriving back in the second

Fig 5. Seasonally accurate locations during (a) March (36), (b) April (34) and (c) May (123) of Lapwings present in Britain & Ireland during part of the year. Those ringed as pulli in Britain & Ireland, and therefore of definite breeding origin, are not shown.

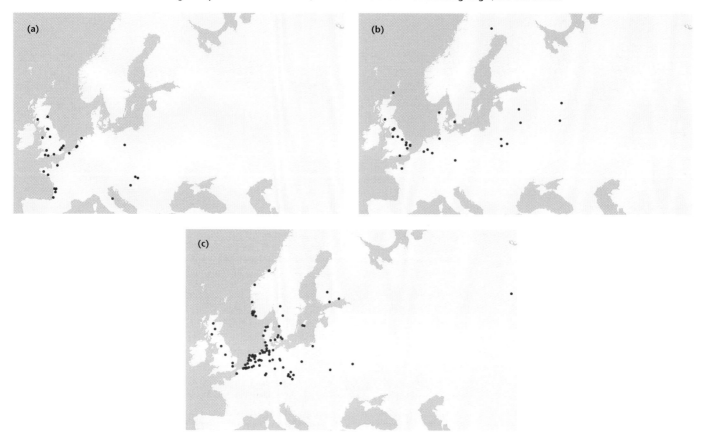

year and 6% in the third (Thompson *et al* 1994). The national data show that large numbers of fledged pulli return to their natal areas from their second summer onwards, but a few birds from all regions move to completely different breeding areas (Fig 6). There are insufficient data to suggest where pre-breeding birds spend their first summer. There is no apparent difference between the migration pattern for the two sexes, although the earliest arrivals in breeding areas are often males.

One of the most unusual aspects of Lapwing migration is that, although most British-bred Lapwings return to their natal areas to breed, a number of birds undertake abmigration (Mead *et al* 1968). There are several instances of pulli from Britain being found breeding in Russia and other countries, the furthest east being 68°E in Russia (Fig 6). The

Fig 6. Movements of over 20 km and recovery locations of Lapwings ringed as pulli in Britain & Ireland and recovered in a subsequent breeding season when of breeding age. There were 259:66 movements under:over 20 km but only those over 20 km are plotted.

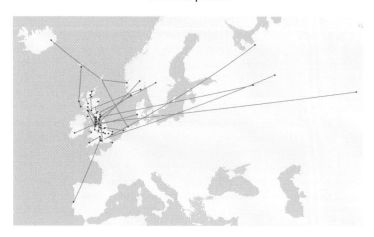

continental recoveries are assumed to be of birds which have undertaken spring migration with birds of eastern origin, either from wintering areas within Britain or from further south. Most of these birds are three or more years old when recovered, with one 12-year-old bird, suggesting that these individuals have been breeding at these sites for several years. Some species of migratory wildfowl undertake abmigration, having formed pair bonds on the wintering grounds. This is unlikely to be the mechanism for abmigration in Lapwing, which may be simply a result of migrating with the 'wrong' flock. Such abmigration increases gene-flow between populations and may explain the absence of subspecies of Lapwing (Mead *et al* 1968).

Lapwing populations are decreasing throughout western Europe (*European Atlas*), with declines being attributed to a reduction in the amount of available breeding habitat (Galbraith 1988, Wilson *et al* 2001) and to poorer breeding performance (Peach *et al* 1994). Wilson *et al* (2001) found that both arable and pastoral farmland is important for Lapwings. They suggest that recent changes in land management are likely to have reduced the amount of suitable habitat for Lapwings and resulted in breeding populations being concentrated on nature reserves. Sensitive management both of reserves and of the wider countryside will be important for the future of this species. Britain and Ireland are critically important wintering areas for birds from large areas of Europe. Little is known about changes that may be taking place in the winter, which may also affect mortality and hence population levels.

Insufficient adult Lapwings are caught. Even in the 1970s and 1980s when there was increased use of cannon-nets, the average annual catch was only 325 adults per year, compared to 3,600 pulli. Catches of wintering birds would provide important conservation information for the species. It has been shown that some birds are site-faithful between winters, so it should be possible to learn more about annual survival rates and also about the migratory responses of birds to cold weather.

Graham Appleton

Red Knot (Knot)
Calidris canutus

Knots are exclusively high Arctic breeders and make some of the longest non-stop migrations of any wader. Outside their breeding season Knots are wholly coastal, mollusc-feeding specialists (Piersma *et al* 1998), depending almost entirely on extensive mud and sandflats in large estuaries and embayments where they occur in dense flocks of many thousands of birds. They reach these by making flights of up to 5,000 km between very few staging areas. Analyses of ringing and recovery information, combined with international collaboration on catching, marking and counting, has played a major role in developing the present detailed understanding of the annual migrations of Knots occurring in western Europe, and elsewhere (Piersma & Davidson 1992, Davidson & Piersma pers obs).

Almost all Knots occurring in Britain & Ireland are of the race *islandica*. Large British estuaries are of major importance in winter, as autumn moulting sites, and as early spring staging areas where Knots rapidly accumulate large stores of fat and protein before flying to stage in western Iceland or in northern Norway (Piersma & Davidson 1992, Boyd & Piersma 2001b). The *islandica* population (450,000 birds) is now relatively stable after a period of steady increase during the 1980s, which represented a partial population recovery after disastrous breeding seasons in the mid-1970s (Piersma & Davidson 1992, Davidson & Piersma pers obs). Some first-year Knots of the nominate *canutus* are known to have occurred in some autumns on estuaries of the east coast of England before migrating on to West African wintering grounds, but this population stages in autumn and spring almost exclusively in the Wadden Sea (Boyd & Piersma 2001a).

The analysis of the data for this species was supported by Ray & Sally Hallam

Knots of the race *islandica* breed in northern Greenland and the Queen Elizabeth Islands of high Arctic Canada, west to Prince Patrick Island, chiefly north of 75°N (Piersma & Davidson 1992). Those in Greenland breed on the east coast north from 70°N and on the west coast north from about 75°N (Meltofte 1985). The racial affinity of the very small Svalbard breeding population is uncertain but is probably *islandica*. Those from Canada and Greenland migrate through west Iceland to overwinter in western Europe as far south as western France, with small numbers reaching Spain and Portugal and perhaps northern Morocco. The core wintering grounds are the large estuaries of the southern North Sea and western Britain, with around 70% of all *islandica* present in midwinter in Britain & Ireland (Davidson & Piersma pers obs). These Knots return to the Arctic in April and May via northern Norway or Iceland (Piersma & Davidson 1992). The nominate subspecies *canutus* breeds largely on coastal tundras of the Taimyr Peninsula, and perhaps the Yakutsk region of Siberia (Tomkovich & Soloviev 1996). During northward and southward migration, it stages in the Wadden Sea *en route* to the wintering areas along the Atlantic coast of Africa from Mauritania to South Africa, with over 75% on the Banc d'Arguin in Mauritania (Dick *et al* 1987, Piersma & Davidson 1992). There may also be a very small discrete wintering population in the eastern Mediterranean and Arabian Gulf, probably either *islandica* or

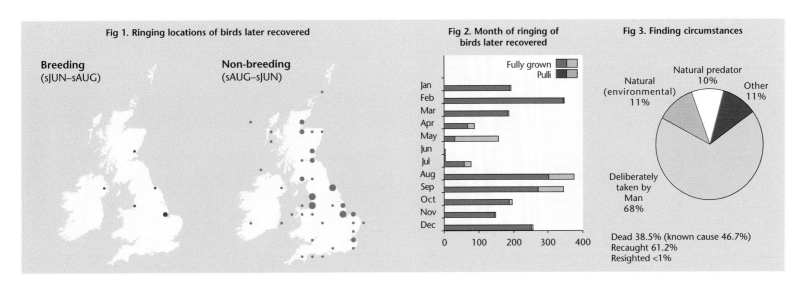

Fig 1. Ringing locations of birds later recovered

Breeding (sJUN–sAUG)

Non-breeding (sAUG–sJUN)

Fig 2. Month of ringing of birds later recovered

Fully grown
Pulli

Fig 3. Finding circumstances

Natural (environmental) 11%

Natural predator 10%

Other 11%

Deliberately taken by Man 68%

Dead 38.5% (known cause 46.7%)
Recaught 61.2%
Resighted <1%

Ringing and recovery data

	<1960	60–69	70–79	80–89	90–97	Total
RINGING						
BTO ringing totals (%)	0	21	41	24	14	90,683
RECOVERIES						
BTO-ringed (%)	0	10	52	26	12	2,028
Foreign-ringed (%)	12	9	39	25	15	345

Statistical analyses

	Breeding population (sJUN–sAUG)	Wintering population (sDEC–sAPR)
Status	NONE	LONG-DISTANCE MIGRANT*
Age differences	—	Not tested
Sex differences	—	Not tested
Regional differences	—	Not significant[2]*
Finding circumstances	—	Not significant*

Fig 4. Locations in (a) July–September (607), (b) October–March (1,013), (c) April–May (464) and (d) June (81) of Knot using Britain & Ireland.

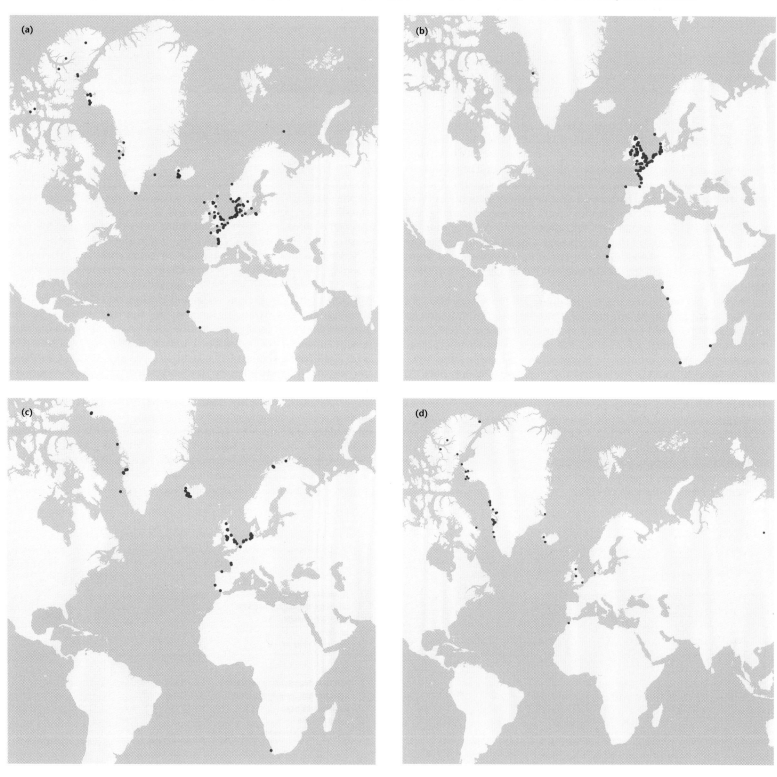

canutus, but whose origins and migration routes are unknown (Davidson & Piersma pers obs).

Other subspecies breed discontinuously in the high Arctic, north from about 60°N (Piersma *et al* 1996). The rare *rogersi* breeds in far eastern Siberia, probably mostly on the Chukotskiy Peninsula, and spends the non-breeding season in southeast Australia and New Zealand. Knots breeding on the New Siberian Islands, formerly considered *canutus,* are now considered a separate population, probably all wintering in northwest Australia (Piersma & Baker 2000). The subspecies *roselaari* is the

least known. On morphometric evidence, it breeds on Wrangel Island and northern Alaska but its non-breeding distribution and migration routes are unclear. It probably overwinters in Florida and Texas and possibly the north coast of South America (Piersma & Davidson 1992). *Rufa* breeds in the central Canadian Arctic and migrates south through James Bay and the Atlantic coast of the Americas to overwinter on the Atlantic coast of southern Argentina (Piersma & Davidson 1992).

Knots breed only at low density, on dry tundras, often close to the coast (*BWP*). Nests are extremely well concealed on sparsely vegetated

Fig 5. Movements of over 20 km and recovery locations of Knot ringed in winter and recovered in the same winter (45:37, red) or a subsequent winter (169:92, blue). Sample sizes of movements under:over 20 km are given but only those over 20 km are plotted.

The seasonality of ringing of Knots in Britain & Ireland matches well their known pattern of occurrence. Most Knots later recovered had been ringed in the period August to March (Fig 2). A larger proportion in autumn and spring were foreign-ringed, at times when many Knots are on migration staging areas. The remoteness of their Arctic breeding grounds means that few Knots have been ringed there, either as chicks or adults, and there are only three recoveries of Knots ringed as pulli.

Of almost 2,400 Knot recoveries involving Britain & Ireland, 61% have been recaptured by ringers. The distribution of these recoveries will be affected by the distribution of ringing activity. Of the 38% of recoveries found dead, 47% had a cause of death attributed (Fig 3). Of these, over two-thirds were deliberately taken by Man. Knots were formerly hunted over much of their wintering range, and remain a quarry species in France, from where 22% of these recoveries originate. Over one-third (34%) of recoveries recorded as deliberately taken by Man come from Greenland: in years of severe spring weather, Knots gather around human settlements where they have been taken by indigenous peoples (Alerstam et al 1986).

Almost all the recoveries of Knot involving Britain & Ireland are attributable to the islandica race, and their distribution illustrates well the range of this race, with the exception of the paucity of records from Greenland and Canadian breeding areas (Fig 4).

Only 14 recoveries (0.6%) are from western or southern Africa, in the wintering range of nominate canutus (Fig 4). These were all (except one bird ringed in southeast Ireland) ringed in eastern and southern England in August and September, between 1963 and 1984, all but two being ringed as juveniles. Almost half were ringed on the Wash in early September 1963. Large numbers of juvenile Knots were present at this time, along with unusually large numbers of Curlew Sandpipers and Little Stints, attributed by Dick et al (1987) to persistent northeasterly winds pushing birds further west than usual as they returned from the Siberian breeding grounds. The occurrence of canutus Knots in Britain & Ireland is believed to be exceptional, involves mostly juveniles (which generally disperse more widely than adults in autumn), and has not been definitely recorded since 1984 (Boyd & Piersma 2001a). This is remarkable since almost the whole population stages in autumn in the Wadden Sea, barely 250 km to the east of eastern England, before flying probably non-stop to their major wintering grounds on the coasts of Mauritania and Guinea-Bissau. Even more exceptional is the single record of an adult also ringed in eastern England in autumn and recovered in the Lesser Antilles, on the wrong side of the Atlantic for either of the Knot populations occurring in Britain & Ireland.

The sexes share incubation duties but most females leave soon after hatching and chicks are mostly guarded to fledging by males only (BWP). Adults, initially failed breeders and females after eggs hatch, leave the breeding grounds from early July, with most departures between mid-July and early August. Recent evidence indicates that birds leave after storing sufficient fat for a non-stop flight across Greenland to western Iceland (R I G Morrison pers comm). Almost all birds stage in western Iceland for an average of two to three weeks to refuel between mid-July and mid-August, with the main passage of adults occurring in late July and early August (Piersma & Davidson 1992). Juveniles leave the breeding grounds later than adults, arriving in Iceland from mid-August and with most birds leaving by early September.

From Iceland islandica Knots make a non-stop flight to moulting areas in Britain and the Wadden Sea. First arrivals can be as early as mid-July, but most adults arrive in August and juveniles in September. Adults then undergo a full moult of flight and body feathers. Some islandica Knots (more juveniles than adults) pause in southwest Norway and Denmark, and the south Baltic coast of Germany and Poland where they mix with canutus Knots (Piersma & Davidson 1992). In some years, some birds briefly use emergency staging areas in northern parts of Britain (pers obs) or Ireland. During moult, birds concentrate in the Wadden Sea and a few large estuaries in Britain, notably the Wash, the Dee and Ribble Estuaries, and Morecambe Bay. Birds are distributed throughout the

rocky slopes. Outside the breeding season, Knots are wholly coastal, staging and wintering on large embayments and estuaries where they feed in large, dense flocks on extensive areas of firm sandy mud, and to a lesser extent on weed-covered rocky shores and outcrops, notably when staging in Iceland and Norway (BWP, Alerstam et al 1992). Knots sometimes fly many kilometres from feeding to roosting sites, which are usually undisturbed shorelines and high sand-spits, and sometimes adjacent fields and lagoons, where they gather in flocks of often many thousands (BWP, van Gils & Piersma 1999).

The great majority of Knots ringed or recovered in Britain & Ireland have been caught, chiefly with cannon-nets, at roosts on large estuaries, especially the Wash and, earlier, in Morecambe Bay and the Ribble Estuary. Ringing locations of birds ringed during the non-breeding season reflect this (Fig 1) and broadly reflect the non-breeding distribution of the birds. Relative to wintering numbers, the Tees Estuary, where there has been an intensive long-term ringing programme, is over-represented in the recoveries, and the Greater Thames Estuary, Humber Estuary, Solway Firth and especially Ireland are under-represented. The few birds ringed in Britain & Ireland during the 'breeding season' are some from the small first-year oversummering population and some of the earliest returning adults (chiefly failed breeders). Outside Britain & Ireland, substantial numbers of islandica have been ringed during autumn moult and early spring in the Wadden Sea, in Iceland in the 1970s during autumn and late spring, and in northern Norway in late spring in the mid-1980s (Piersma & Davidson 1992). Catching and ringing in northern Norway revealed for the first time that Knots staging there in May are of the race islandica, rather than canutus as had previously been thought (BWP, Davidson et al 1986b).

Wadden Sea in autumn, where they occur simultaneously with many *canutus* Knots (Nebel *et al* 2000), but there is evidence of geographical segregation of the populations within the Wadden Sea (Meltofte *et al* 1994).

From October to December birds disperse to wintering grounds, many moving west from the Wadden Sea to Britain, and northwards and westwards in Britain & Ireland from estuaries such as the Wash (Fig 5). There is also considerable movement during winter between British estuaries, which at least includes birds moving northwards up the east coast of England and Scotland and across Britain from east to west coasts (Dugan 1981). Movements between estuaries are considered to be a response to annual variations between and within estuaries in the availability of their mollusc food supply (*eg* Piersma *et al* 1993). From December to March, Knots are generally less mobile between estuaries than at other times of year, and recaptures of ringed birds indicate that many occur on the same estuaries in successive years. There is no ringing evidence to suggest that Knots make major movements in direct response to severe winter weather, as do some other wader species. Numbers counted in the Wadden Sea during icy winters are lower than in mild winters. This may suggest some cold weather response (Meltofte *et al* 1994) but could be a result of the difficulties of making a complete count of birds when the Wadden Sea is iced over.

In the second half of March, many *islandica* Knots return eastwards to the Wadden Sea, particularly to Schleswig-Holstein, where 60–75% of the population begins a body moult into breeding plumage and accumulates nutrient stores (Prokosch 1988). The other 25–40% remain mostly on British estuaries, congregating, as in autumn, on the larger sites such as the Wash and Morecambe Bay. In the first two weeks of May (Fig 4c), birds leave early-spring sites (in the Wadden Sea mostly before the arrival of *canutus* from West Africa), and fly direct to late-spring staging areas in Iceland (chiefly the west coast) and northern Norway. Birds from many wintering sites mix on early-spring staging areas, and birds staging in early spring in both the Wadden Sea and Britain mix on late-spring sites (Davidson *et al* 1986b, Piersma & Davidson 1992). Knots from all regions of Britain occur in both Iceland and in northern Norway but it is unclear, owing to the small number of birds ringed there, whether Knots wintering in Ireland reach northern Norway as well as Iceland in spring. Arrival in Iceland and northern Norway is from late April, with most birds arriving in the first and second weeks of May (Piersma & Davidson 1992). Birds stage in these areas, completing body moult and rapidly regaining nutrient stores, for only about two weeks (Norway) to three weeks (Iceland). There is then a highly synchronous departure on a largely non-stop flight to Arctic breeding grounds in the last week of May (Piersma & Davidson 1992). Two fjords (Balsfjord and Porsangerfjord) are used in Norway, with 60–80,000 birds (*c* 20% of the population) occurring there. There is considerable annual variation in distribution between the two fjords, with movements of colour-ringed birds between them in different years: Knots possibly use the more southerly Balsfjord more in years of heavy ice-cover in Porsangerfjord (Piersma & Davidson 1992). First breeding-ground arrivals are in the last days of May, with most in early June (Meltofte 1985, Morrison & Davidson 1990).

Almost all *islandica* Knots are believed to return to their breeding grounds after their first winter. Only a few thousand remain on British & Irish estuaries (Prater 1981) and a similar number in the Wadden Sea (Meltofte *et al* 1994), totalling less than 3% of the population. These are almost all first-years, probably those that have been unable to store sufficient nutrient reserves to undertake the long flight to Iceland or Norway.

Knots, more than many other waders, are particularly vulnerable to climate change and other habitat impacts. This is a result of their specialist habits of high Arctic breeding, mollusc-feeding, long-distance migratory flights which require considerable, rapid accumulation of nutrient and fuel stores, and dependence on a few major staging and wintering sites (Piersma & Davidson 1992, Piersma & Baker 2000). Pivotal to *islandica* survival is the Wadden Sea which supports about 75% of staging birds. Other critically important locations are the Wash, Ribble and Greater Thames Estuaries (together supporting 45% of wintering birds), western Iceland (*c* 80% of staging birds) and Balsfjord and Porsangerfjord in northern Norway (*c* 20% of staging birds in spring). Overall 24 of the 36 sites of international importance for *islandica* Knots are British or Irish estuaries (Davidson & Piersma pers obs); these form a vital part of the wintering network as well as some being important also as moulting and spring staging sites. Most key European sites are protected by national and international legislation but major parts of the network in northern staging areas remain unprotected, and the efficacy of the protected areas in safeguarding Knots is unclear (Fox *et al* pers comm).

Deducing the overall migration system requires a flyway-scale analysis of Knot ring-recoveries. International co-operation to improve accessibility of the flyway-scale ringing data for Knots is an urgent prerequisite. Such analysis should ideally take into account the bias from the distribution of ringing effort, through better accessibility to data on the numbers of birds ringed at different places and times (Davidson *et al* 1999). This information is needed also for more detailed analysis of the movements within and between winters, and site-fidelity on British & Irish estuaries. Time-series analysis of the effects of population changes on the migration phenology of *islandica* Knots is needed, but is constrained by the lack of recent ringing in Ireland and spring ringing in northwest England (where numbers have declined). More ringing in these regions is a priority and would throw further light on the spring movements of Knots from Britain & Ireland through Iceland and northern Norway. To amplify this, and to discover if other changes in phenology have occurred since the 1970s, also needs further ringing in Iceland in both spring and autumn, since almost all the ringing of Knots there took place in the early 1970s when the population was in rapid decline. There is evidence of local population declines in areas with intensive mechanical shell-dredging (especially for Cockles), an increasingly widespread activity that requires monitoring (Piersma & Koolhaas 1997).

Knots may be a key indicator species for early warning of the impacts of climate change on migratory Arctic birds. Predicted changes in weather patterns, and increased storminess, will increase the need for emergency stopover sites if adverse headwinds increase in frequency, since otherwise Knots could be prevented from reaching the Arctic in sufficiently good condition to breed successfully (Lindström & Agrell 1999). Continued catching, ringing and analyses of these data to monitor their migration behaviour will become increasingly important.

Nick Davidson

Sanderling
Calidris alba

Sanderlings are long-distance migrants, breeding on the high-arctic tundra. In winter, they are characteristic of oceanic sandy beaches, where they scurry along the tide edge, probing the wet sand to feed on marine invertebrates. Their non-breeding distribution is world-wide in this habitat, particularly in temperate and tropical zones. They have a discontinuous holarctic breeding distribution, occurring on the northernmost coasts and islands where the breeding season is very short and unpredictable, and in some years too short to enable successful breeding (*BWP*).

The main breeding areas are in Canada, from Prince Patrick Island east and south to Ellesmere, north Baffin and Southampton Islands, in northeast and northwest Greenland, in Siberia, from the Yenisei to the Lena Deltas, on Severnaya Zemlya and the Novosibirskie Islands and in Svalbard (*CBWP*). Sanderlings from the Canadian Arctic migrate as far south as Tierra del Fuego; the southward journey is mainly along the Atlantic coast (Myers *et al* 1984, 1990). Northward migration is principally through the interior, via the Gulf of Texas, and along the Pacific coast. Sanderlings from northeast Greenland migrate through northwest Europe as far south as West Africa and possibly South Africa (Summers *et al* 1987, Wymenga *et al* 1990, Gudmundsson & Lindström 1992). Siberian breeders migrate along several flyways to widespread non-breeding destinations. Some cross Asia to the coasts of the Indian Ocean and southwest Pacific, as far as Tasmania and New Zealand (Watkins 1993, Higgins & Davies 1996). Others migrate west and south, through the North, Caspian and Black Seas to European and African wintering grounds, as far as South Africa (Summers *et al* 1987).

The analysis of the data for this species was supported by the North Solway Ringing Group

Birds wintering in Africa migrate northwards on a broad front along the West African coast or overland, across the Sahara to the Mediterranean (Summers & Waltner 1978). Then they continue via the Caspian Sea to Siberia, or along the east Atlantic coast, to northwest Europe, en route to Siberia or possibly Greenland. It is thought that the northward migration to Siberia entails three long flights with two refuelling stops. This assumes a flight range of 5,000 km, a departure weight of *c* 95 g and a total journey time of approximately seven weeks, which is supported by ring-recoveries (Summers *et al* 1987).

Sanderlings breed on arctic tundra, preferring small patches of vegetation (T Piersma pers comm). Outside the breeding season, they frequent mainly oceanic sandy beaches exposed to wave-wash or the sandier, outer parts of estuaries (Prater & Davies 1978, Summers *et al* 1987, Higgins & Davies 1996). They are attracted to heaps of kelp washed ashore, as these provide an important source of food when insect larvae hatch from the decomposing seaweed. Sanderlings also occur on shingle or rocky shores, and mudflats, but to a lesser extent. Only rarely do they use habitats such as saltpans or lagoons, or inland freshwater sites.

Over much of the wintering range, Sanderlings are widely dispersed in small numbers. Relatively few sites on each flyway are of major importance in winter. The northern limit to the European wintering grounds is Denmark, although a few remain in the Baltic in mild winters

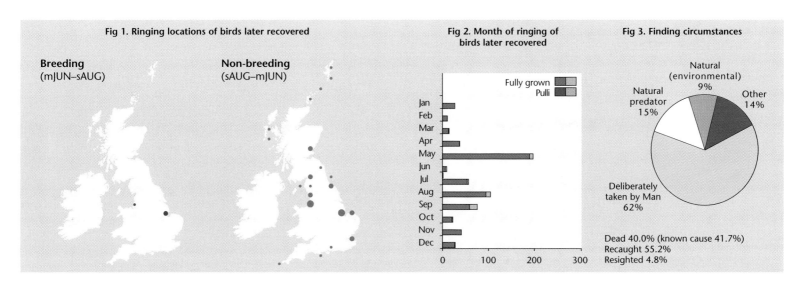

Fig 1. Ringing locations of birds later recovered

Breeding (mJUN–sAUG)

Non-breeding (sAUG–mJUN)

Fig 2. Month of ringing of birds later recovered

Fully grown
Pulli

Fig 3. Finding circumstances

Natural (environmental) 9%
Natural predator 15%
Other 14%
Deliberately taken by Man 62%

Dead 40.0% (known cause 41.7%)
Recaught 55.2%
Resighted 4.8%

Ringing and recovery data

	<1960	60–69	70–79	80–89	90–97	Total
RINGING						
BTO ringing totals (%)	0	16	39	30	15	25,674
RECOVERIES						
BTO-ringed (%)	1	4	35	42	17	572
Foreign-ringed (%)	15	9	30	15	30	46

Statistical analyses

	Breeding population (mJUN–sAUG)	Wintering population (sDEC–sMAY)
Status	NONE	[LONG-DISTANCE MIGRANT]
Age differences	—	Not tested
Sex differences	—	Not tested
Regional differences	—	Not tested
Finding circumstances	—	Not tested

Fig 4. Locations during (a) mid-July to end November (187), (b) December to mid-March (115) and (c) mid-March to mid-July (248) of Sanderlings using Britain & Ireland throughout the year.

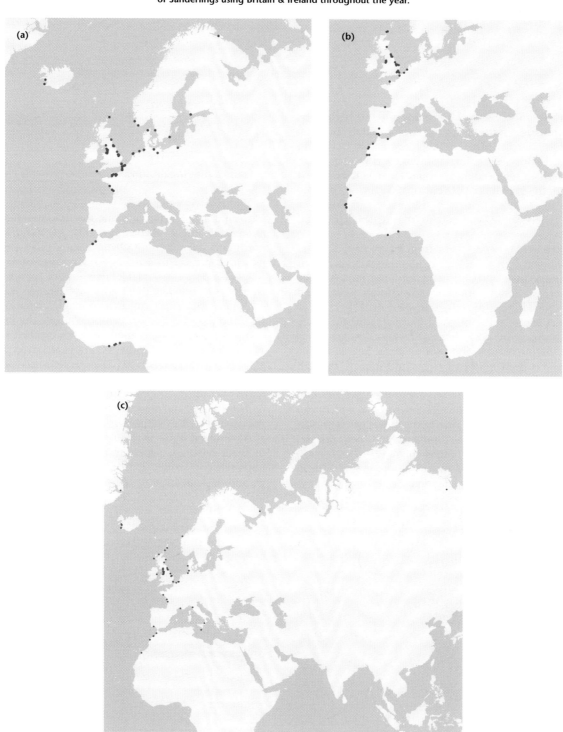

(CBWP). In Britain & Ireland, the Ribble complex is of international importance in winter and during spring and autumn passage (Cranswick *et al* 1999). There are several sites which qualify as nationally important in winter. Just a few sites account for the majority of birds ringed in Britain & Ireland (Fig 1). In particular, the Wash, Tees, Ribble, Morecambe Bay and Solway Firth contribute most to the results from ringing. Consequently, recoveries may over-emphasize movements to and from these sites. Most Sanderling recoveries are of adults that have been ringed during spring or autumn passage (Fig 2).

Most recoveries of birds ringed in Britain & Ireland are in Britain (70%), Iceland (7%), France (7%) and Morocco (5%). This largely reflects

ringing and observation effort in the case of the first two and hunting in the case of the last two, and a high probability of reporting. Similarly, recoveries in Britain & Ireland of foreign-ringed birds are mostly from Iceland and Norway where there has been considerable research and ringing effort. Of over 600 recoveries, 55% have been recaptured by ringers, mostly in Britain, which will influence the distribution of these recoveries. Finding circumstances are known for only 42% of dead recoveries and of these, 62% were deliberately shot or trapped (Fig 3), which may bias their distribution.

Britain & Ireland is an important migration staging and moulting destination, and wintering area for Sanderlings. In autumn, the southward migration from arctic breeding grounds is through Iceland, the Baltic and North Sea countries to Britain, starting in July (Fig 4a). In winter, Sanderlings are distributed along the Atlantic coast from Britain southward through continental Europe and the West African coast to its southern tip (Fig 4b).

Intensive colour-ringing studies have been pursued on the Tees Estuary in northern England since the mid-1970s and augment the ring-recoveries (Evans *et al* 1980). Adults return to the Tees from the second half of July onwards and peak in numbers in late August or early September, while juveniles begin to arrive in late August, peaking in late September or early October. Several strategies are apparent: some birds stop briefly before moving on, others moult and refuel before onward migration, some moult and remain on the Tees, and another group moults elsewhere before arriving at the Tees (Cooper 1987). October and November are the months of post-moult movement. Influxes to the Tees from the Wash have been identified at this time from ring-recoveries and from resightings of colour-ringed birds, as well as onward movement from the Tees by birds that have moulted there, for example northwards along the Northumberland coast. Autumn migration along the east coast of Britain is much more marked than in spring, with the Wash being an important stopover site, increasingly so since 1990 (Fisher 1998, Taylor *et al* 1999). While some birds moult and refuel prior to onward migration, others remain at the Wash through the winter (Branson 1985).

Sanderlings from both Greenland and Siberia occur in Britain during autumn migration; those arriving from Greenland may include some birds from breeding grounds in Canada. Several autumn sightings in Britain of birds colour-ringed in northeast Greenland confirm the presence of birds from this breeding area (*BWP*). It has been suggested that birds of Siberian origin moult and overwinter in Britain & Ireland (Cooper 1987, Branson 1993, Taylor *et al* 1999), while nearctic birds stop over before continuing along the East Atlantic Flyway to wintering destinations further south, as far as South Africa (*BWP*). However, the separation may not be this clear-cut. There is evidence that birds of Siberian origin migrate to South Africa after moulting in northwest Europe (Summers *et al* 1987, Wymenga *et al* 1990). The passage of birds through the Baltic in autumn, on their way to wintering grounds on the northeast coast of England, might suggest Siberian breeding origin, although it does not preclude the possibility of birds coming from northeast Greenland or Svalbard (Gudmundsson & Lindström 1992). It is difficult to distinguish Sanderlings of different breeding origin, as there is little geographical variation. The paucity of recoveries from known breeding grounds also prevents clarification at present.

In Britain, spring migration begins as early as the second half of March on the east coast but is more pronounced along the west coast (Ferns 1980, Goodall 1984). Spring counts peak on the Tees in late April or early May and on the Wash in early or mid-May with the arrival of northbound migrants that use the Wash as a migration stopover (Ferns 1980, Cooper 1987, Taylor *et al* 1999). Sightings at the Wash in late March and early April indicate that some Tees winterers also use the Wash in spring, so there is not a straightforward progression northwards through Britain. On the Solway, numbers peak in the second half of May (Clark *et al* 1982), with influxes known to occur from the Wash. First-year birds are later to depart.

Sanderlings that migrate through Britain & Ireland in spring include birds that have spent the winter in Britain, or in countries further south, and are destined for breeding grounds in Siberia and Greenland (Prater & Davies 1978, Gudmundsson & Lindström 1992, Wilson 1997). One adult Sanderling, ringed at Heacham on the Wash in spring, was found dead in late June, a few years later, on the River Lena in the Siberian Arctic, having been killed by a raptor. Northward migration is on a broad front along the east Atlantic coast and through the Mediterranean, northwest Europe, and the Baltic (Fig 4c). Onward migration through Iceland and Scandinavia may represent separation of Greenland and Siberian birds although, as found for Knots (Davidson *et al* 1986b), waders may migrate to Greenland via Norway. Colour-ringed

Sanderlings from the Tees wintering population have been seen regularly in Iceland during spring migration. Birds staging in Iceland are thought mostly to breed in northeast Greenland, although many may overfly Iceland and head for the Canadian Arctic (Wilson 1981, Gudmundsson & Lindström 1992, Wilson 1997).

Many Sanderlings apparently undertake a northward migration, at least part of the way to breeding grounds, in their first year (*BWP*). Small numbers of summering adults and first-year birds are present in various locations along the flyway, including Britain & Ireland. Consequently, there is no difference in age-related migration routes, just in the extent of movement by individuals. Sample sizes are too small to investigate sex-related differences in movement patterns.

Ring-recoveries show that Sanderlings are very site-faithful, returning to the same spring and autumn staging and wintering sites year after year. They are also long-lived, the current record being over 17 years. One individual, ringed at the Wash, was recaptured 13 times in the course of 12 years. Individuals show a marked consistency in their use of sites in different winters (Evans *et al* 1980, Cooper 1987, Myers *et al* 1988, Roberts 1991); however some individuals regularly move over larger areas than others, being more likely to move in response to the availability of temporarily abundant food sources. The few between-winter movements recorded may indicate change in wintering location, although some may represent progression along the flyway in late autumn or early spring. Birds tend to be more mobile in their first year than subsequently, for example at least some juveniles ringed at the Wash in their first winter subsequently overwintered on the Tees after autumn passage via the Wash (Cooper 1987). Five within-winter movements all relate to exchanges between the Wash and the Tees. Colour-ringing studies on the Tees indicate that Sanderlings may undertake cold-weather movements in periods of severe winter weather or leave earlier than usual in those cold winters (Cooper 1987). Several resightings away from the Tees confirmed that these birds had moved away, for example one individual was seen at Filey in North Yorkshire in January 1982 and another was seen near Dundee in February 1982. The lower overwinter survival in these cold winters indicates that the birds were adversely affected and may have moved in search of more favourable conditions.

In marked contrast to the high degree of site-faithfulness in winter and during migration, limited results from the breeding grounds on the Taimyr indicate low site-fidelity, particularly by female Sanderlings (Tomkovich & Soloviev 1994), although Parmelee (1970) found instances of adult males returning to nest close to their previous nesting location in the Canadian Arctic. It is thought that natal philopatry is low due to the unpredictable nature of the habitat and conditions (Tomkovich & Soloviev 1994).

The highly variable breeding success, owing to the vagaries of the arctic breeding season, combined with pronounced site-faithfulness to a small number of non-breeding sites of significance, leaves the Sanderling vulnerable to potentially large-scale change on any key site. International cooperation is essential for effective conservation of this long-distance migrant. The Agreement on the Conservation of African–Eurasian Migratory Waterbirds of the 'Bonn Convention', which came into force in 1999, requires nations to take coordinated measures to conserve migratory waterbirds. Hopefully, its implementation will benefit Sanderlings.

Further ringing and colour-marking, especially on the breeding grounds, would help to consolidate links between breeding and wintering areas and to confirm the relative importance of Britain & Ireland to Sanderlings of different breeding origins. This would require an intensive and well-coordinated study to generate sufficient observations throughout the network of countries along migration routes. Specific issues that could be addressed include confirming the breeding origins of Sanderlings that overwinter in Britain & Ireland and determining whether or not any Canadian birds join the East Atlantic Flyway.

Rowena Langston

Curlew Sandpiper
Calidris ferruginea

Curlew Sandpipers are passage migrants in Britain & Ireland between distant parts of the high Arctic and wintering grounds mainly in Africa. Passage is annual in autumn and in smaller numbers in spring, but large influxes occur in some autumns. These influxes have been related to population peaks and weather conditions encountered on migration.

The relatively restricted breeding range of Curlew Sandpipers extends from the northern Yamal Peninsula (*c* 70°E) to the Lena Delta (*c* 128°E), centring on the Taimyr Peninsula, but a few extralimital breeding attempts have been recorded east to Alaska and west to Vaygach Island (Underhill 1995, *CBWP*). In contrast, the widespread wintering grounds range from the Canary Islands, through Africa and Indian Ocean coasts, to Australia and New Zealand. The northernmost regular wintering areas are in northwest Africa, Israel and Iraq, although a few individuals occur further north (*BWP*, Shubin 1998). In Britain, only exceptional records of single birds lie outside the period April to November.

The breeding habitat is high-Arctic shrubless tundra. The margins of boggy depressions and pools are favoured for nesting, and riverbanks and coast are used once the young can fly. Sandy tidal beaches, estuaries, inland lagoons and other shallow waters are used on passage. In winter, Curlew Sandpipers use a wide range of coastal and inland wetland habitats including tidal mudflats, sand-spits, estuaries, brackish lagoons, saltpans, paddyfields, marshes, lakes and rivers (*BWP*).

More than 2,000 Curlew Sandpipers have been ringed in Britain & Ireland, resulting in fewer than 40 recoveries. Very few birds have been ringed on spring passage, none of which has been recovered. The

The analysis of the data for this species was supported by Chris Smith

numbers ringed and distribution of ringing in autumn broadly reflect the patterns of occurrence (Figs 1 & 2). Most birds were ringed in years of large influxes, usually in the east and south of Britain. The majority of Curlew Sandpipers migrating through Britain in the autumn are juveniles, and these comprised 80% of those ringed on the Wash (Adams 1995). Curlew Sandpipers are scarcer in Ireland; even single birds are very rare in spring, although treble-figure flocks have occurred in autumn (*Birds in Ireland*). The sample with known recovery circumstances is tiny (Fig 3).

The pattern of recoveries depends heavily on ringing effort, as ringers catch 70% of Curlew Sandpipers recovered (Fig 4). The birds recovered near the Black Sea, all killed in autumn, contrast markedly with the distribution of ringing recaptures. These recoveries probably under-represent the numbers of birds using the northern and western Black Sea on migration. Estimates of numbers at the Sivash Gulf, Ukraine, suggest 50,000–60,000 Curlew Sandpipers pass through in spring and 80,000–140,000 in autumn, although high turnover may mean that these numbers are underestimates (Chernichko *et al* 1991).

Adult male Curlew Sandpipers leave the breeding grounds immediately after mating, most having commenced migration by mid-July (Underhill *et al* 1993). Adult females raise the young alone and leave the breeding grounds when either nesting fails, or the young are

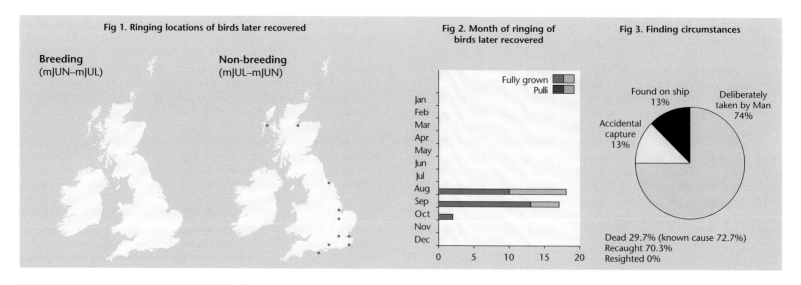

Fig 1. Ringing locations of birds later recovered

Breeding (mJUN–mJUL)

Non-breeding (mJUL–mJUN)

Fig 2. Month of ringing of birds later recovered

Fully grown
Pulli

Fig 3. Finding circumstances

Found on ship 13%
Deliberately taken by Man 74%
Accidental capture 13%

Dead 29.7% (known cause 72.7%)
Recaught 70.3%
Resighted 0%

Ringing and recovery data

	<1960	60–69	70–79	80–89	90–97	Total
RINGING						
BTO ringing totals (%)	5	29	27	25	13	2,126
RECOVERIES						
BTO-ringed (%)	0	12	40	20	28	25
Foreign-ringed (%)	8	8	8	50	25	12

Statistical analyses

	Breeding population (mJUN–mJUL)	Wintering population (sOCT–sMAY)
Status	PASSAGE ONLY	PASSAGE ONLY
Age differences	—	—
Sex differences	—	—
Regional differences	—	—
Finding circumstances	—	—

Fig 4. Recovery locations and movements of over 20 km of Curlew Sandpipers present in Britain & Ireland during the autumn. Birds found dead (8, red) are differentiated from those recaptured (24, blue).

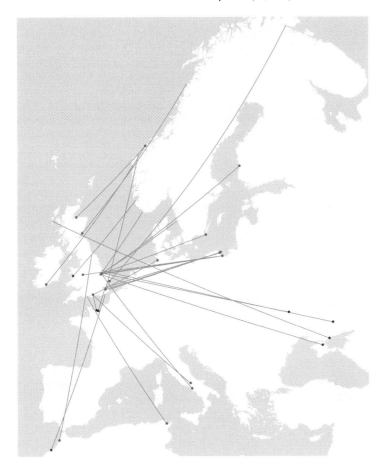

Fig 5. Annual abundance of Curlew Sandpipers in Norfolk on autumn migration. (*Source*: Norfolk Bird & Mammal Reports.)

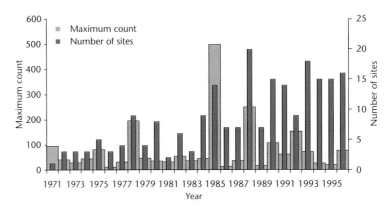

independent. The juveniles are the last to commence migration, from early August, with the last leaving the tundra in early September (Syroechkovski & Lappo 1994). Adult males precede females in the Baltic (Wilson *et al* 1980) and in Italy (Baccetti *et al* 1991), and arrive in Morocco from late July, two to three weeks before females (Pienkowski 1976). Autumn passage through Britain & Ireland normally commences with the arrival of adults in late July and early August, and passage of adults peaks in early August. In contrast to the pattern elsewhere, there is no difference in the timing of adult male and female passage on the Wash, and males outnumber females by two to one (Adams 1995).

The earliest juvenile passage has been recorded from mid-July, but the main passage begins in late August. Juvenile passage peaks in early September and stragglers are found through October and into November. The size of the autumn influx, particularly of juveniles, can vary greatly from year to year. Curlew Sandpipers are usually recorded as single birds, or in small flocks, with parties of more than 40 being exceptional (Taylor *et al* 1999). However, in years of large influxes, flocks of up to 500 birds have been recorded in Britain (Moser 1985) and over 200 in Ireland (*Birds in Ireland*).

Meltofte *et al* (1994) estimated that 5–10% of the adult east Atlantic flyway population stage in the Wadden Sea, making it the nearest regular significant staging area to Britain. It is not surprising, therefore, that most large influxes have occurred in autumn in the east and south of Britain (*eg* Stanley & Minton 1972, Moser 1985). Autumn 1988, when the largest influx was in the north and west, was an exception to this pattern. Kirby *et al* (1989) suggested that Curlew Sandpipers were diverted further west and north than normal, migrating down the Norwegian coast and arriving first in the Northern Isles. Several Curlew Sandpipers ringed in Norway that autumn were recovered in Scotland or Ireland in the same autumn (Fig 4). During the autumn of 1969, a bird

ringed in Belgium was recovered 16 days later in Barbados, West Indies (Kuyken & Burggraeve 1971).

The weather conditions over Scandinavia and the Baltic at the time of migration are a major factor controlling the size of an autumn influx into Britain. The effect is most marked when unstable cyclonic conditions with easterly winds persist throughout the time of the birds' migration. However, breeding success and breeding numbers are probably also important factors as they determine the number of juveniles on their first migration, and therefore influence the potential size of any influx. Breeding success is influenced by unpredictable Arctic weather conditions and the lemming cycle; predators such as Arctic Foxes switch between lemmings and waders depending on which is more abundant. The interaction between these factors resulted in exceptional numbers of Curlew Sandpipers passing through Britain & Ireland in 1969, 1985 and 1988 (Kirby *et al* 1989). Counts from Norfolk illustrate the changing numbers of Curlew Sandpipers reaching Britain each year (Fig 5).

In winter, Curlew Sandpipers are found in southern and western Africa and southwest Europe. Important wintering areas in West Africa include Guinea-Bissau (D A Stroud pers comm), the Banc d'Arguin, coastal Mauritania and Keta and Songor Lagoons in Ghana (Piersma & Ntiamoa-Baidu 1995). The status of the species between Nigeria and Namibia is only vaguely known.

Because of differences in the timing and rate of adult moult of Curlew Sandpipers in South Africa and Mauritania, it has been suggested that the wintering populations of west and southern Africa are separate (Pienkowski *et al* 1976). Recent work has suggested that Curlew Sandpipers have a loop migration. Those passing through the Sivash Gulf, Ukraine, in the autumn appear to winter in central, south and eastern Africa. Curlew Sandpipers staging in the Sivash Gulf in spring, however, use the East Atlantic Flyway in the autumn (with some reaching Britain) and winter in West Africa (Nikolaus & Chernichko 1995).

Underhill (1995) suggested, however, that Curlew Sandpipers exhibit an 'all-to-all' migration strategy in which there are no specific links between particular localities. The distribution of recoveries, spanning a large proportion of the breeding areas from each wintering area, the negligible breeding site-fidelity (in contrast to Dunlin; Tomkovich & Soloviev 1994), and lack of subspecific differences, provide evidence in support of this migration strategy for Curlew Sandpiper. Further evidence is provided by the four Curlew Sandpipers ringed on the Wash in autumn and killed on the eastern migration route in a subsequent autumn (Fig 4), although it should be noted that three of these birds were ringed in autumn 1969, during an exceptional influx to Britain & Ireland. Site-fidelity has, however, been demonstrated on staging areas in Morocco and the South African wintering grounds (Elliott *et al* 1976, Pienkowski 1976). Zeiske (1995) showed adult male Curlew Sandpipers to be more site-faithful than females on stopover sites on the Elbe

Estuary, German Bight. He suggested that males may use a more traditional migration strategy, with long-distance flights, due to their more predictable timing of autumn departure. In contrast, the females cannot predict the timing of their migration, because it depends upon the outcome of their nesting attempt, and may adopt a more flexible approach, making shorter flights and selecting the best of known staging sites.

Little is known about movements within the winter. Departure from temporary wetlands in Senegal has been recorded in late January, but varies from year to year depending on when the wetlands dry out; birds departed in the direction of the Atlantic coast (Hötker *et al* 1990).

Sightings of Curlew Sandpipers in northwestern Europe are scarce in spring compared with autumn, but birds are commoner in spring in Algeria, Tunisia, Libya and Malta. The Banc d'Arguin, the Moroccan coast and also, to a variable extent, the Ebro Delta in northeast Spain are important moulting areas (Figuerola & Bertolero 1995) as is the Sivash Gulf (Nikolaus & Chernichko 1995).

Britain & Ireland are of only marginal importance for Curlew Sandpiper conservation. Kirby *et al* (1989) noted that the most regularly occupied estuaries do not necessarily hold the largest numbers of Curlew Sandpipers. This may be because regular migrants and influxes of juveniles on autumn passage occupy different sites. It is possible that the population consequences of staging-site destruction for these two groups of birds may differ, although birds that previously used Wisbech Sewage Farm, on the western border of Norfolk, appear to have spread to more sites when it closed in 1986 (Fig 5).

The pattern of migration of Curlew Sandpipers through Britain & Ireland, and elsewhere, remains unclear. Ringing more birds on spring passage, and adults in autumn, would provide more information about spring passage and regular autumn migrants through Britain & Ireland. Information on the wintering grounds is incomplete and expeditions to West Africa would provide more information.

Sue Adams

Purple Sandpiper
Calidris maritima

Although the breeding range and habits of the Purple Sandpiper are unremarkable for an Arctic wader, there are two features of its wintering ecology that distinguish it from other sandpipers: it lives primarily on exposed rocky shores and occurs further north than any other sandpiper, even extending into the cold and darkness beyond the Arctic Circle. Winter birds in north Norway have developed a bigger digestive system than those wintering further south, allowing them to process more food and therefore generate sufficient heat to survive the winter (Summers *et al* 1998).

The Purple Sandpiper breeds over a large part of the Arctic, from eastern Canada to the Taimyr Peninsula in Russia. Between these limits there are populations in Greenland, Iceland, Svalbard, Norway, Sweden, and a tiny population in Scotland. All populations winter along North Atlantic shores, in the USA (south to Maryland), Canada, southwest Greenland, Iceland, and down the western European coasts from the Kola Peninsula to northern Spain (*BWP*). None occur in the Pacific, where a close relative, the Rock Sandpiper, adopts a similar role.

Most of the breeding populations of Purple Sandpiper migrate relatively short distances compared with other sandpipers, though the species still exhibits the full range of migration strategies: two populations (Iceland and west Greenland) are resident; two (south Canada and Russia) move to the nearest ice-free coast; and two (Svalbard and Norway) move south of the nearest coast, which is occupied by larger birds from another population (a chain migration). Only the north Canadian population is believed to migrate a long distance, leap-frogging the resident populations in Greenland and Iceland (Summers 1994).

The analysis of the data for this species was supported by Andy Mitchell & Lyn Wells

The nesting habitat of Purple Sandpipers is tundra, though this varies in character depending on location. In Franz Josef Land (82°N), the tundra zone is classed as polar desert, composed mainly of mosses, lichens and frost-lifted stones on bare ground. In the southern part of the range, they nest in the Arctic-alpine zone of the mountains of Norway, on ridges with Crowberry, *Vaccinium* species and Dwarf Willows. On the coast of Iceland, some nest relatively densely among the stones, moss, lichens and Crowberry in Arctic Tern colonies. Those Purple Sandpipers nesting close to the coast make use of beaches, where they feed on shrimps and springtails (Leinaas & Ambrose 1992).

The Purple Sandpiper is primarily a winter visitor to Britain & Ireland, and is found on all coasts where there is suitable habitat. During migration and whilst wintering, the main habitat is wide and exposed rocky shores, where they feed on winkles, Blue Mussels and shrimps. Where rotting seaweed piles up on the high-water mark, Purple Sandpipers feed on the larvae, pupae and adults of kelp flies at high tide (Summers *et al* 1990).

The distribution of ringing sites of Purple Sandpipers later recovered largely reflects their distribution in Britain but also shows that many data have been generated by ringing groups in eastern Scotland (Fig 1). The Purple Sandpipers wintering in Ireland are not represented in the recoveries. As with most Arctic waders, Purple Sandpipers tend to be

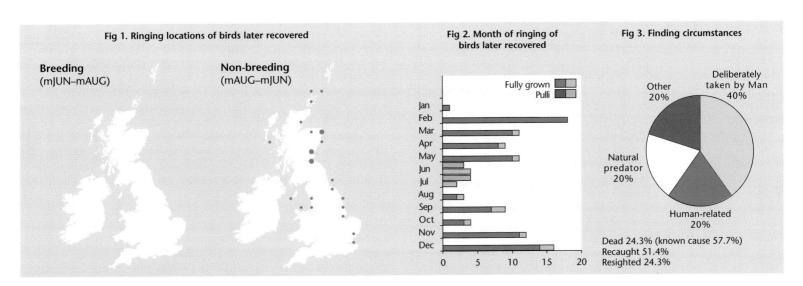

Fig 1. Ringing locations of birds later recovered

Breeding (mJUN–mAUG) Non-breeding (mAUG–mJUN)

Fig 2. Month of ringing of birds later recovered

Fully grown / Pulli

Fig 3. Finding circumstances

Deliberately taken by Man 40%
Other 20%
Natural predator 20%
Human-related 20%

Dead 24.3% (known cause 57.7%)
Recaught 51.4%
Resighted 24.3%

Ringing and recovery data

	<1960	60–69	70–79	80–89	90–97	Total
RINGING						
BTO ringing totals (%)	1	4	17	57	21	6,401
RECOVERIES						
BTO-ringed (%)	0	2	24	51	23	84
Foreign-ringed (%)	4	0	17	57	22	23

Statistical analyses

	Breeding population (mJUN–mAUG)	Wintering population (sDEC–mAPR)
Status	NONE	[LONG-DISTANCE MIGRANT]
Age differences	—	Not tested
Sex differences	—	Not tested
Regional differences	—	Not tested
Finding circumstances	—	Not tested

Fig 4. All 61 included movements of over 20 km and recovery locations of Purple Sandpipers ringed or recovered in Britain & Ireland.

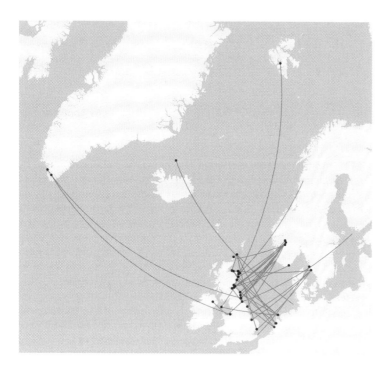

Fig 5. The distribution of short-billed and long-billed Purple Sandpipers wintering in Britain. The area of each circle is proportional to the number of birds. (*Source*: Nicoll *et al* 1988, reproduced by permission of *Ibis*.)

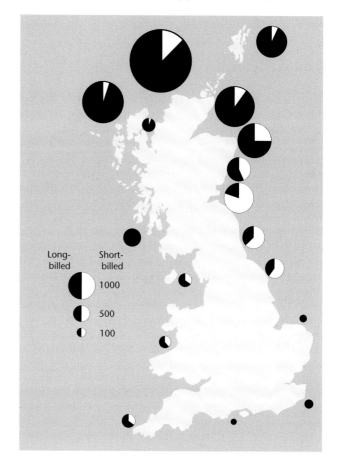

ringed during migration or while wintering (Figs 1 & 2). Dazzle-netting and cannon-netting have been the main techniques for capture. The majority (76%) of recoveries of Purple Sandpiper involving Britain & Ireland have been recaptured or resighted. Just over half of the small number of recoveries of birds found dead have a known cause and, of these, 40% were deliberately taken by Man (Fig 3); this may affect the distribution of recoveries. In addition, there is little chance of obtaining recoveries on the northern breeding grounds, where the birds occur at a low density and there are few people to report rings. To try to overcome this problem, British ringers have caught and colour-ringed Purple Sandpipers on the breeding grounds in Norway (Rae *et al* 1986) and Iceland (Summers *et al* 1988a) in order to generate sightings on the wintering grounds. Colour-ringing schemes have also been carried out in England, Scotland, Germany, the Netherlands, Sweden and Svalbard and have provided much of our knowledge about the migrations of Purple Sandpipers.

Biometrics have also helped in determining the migration patterns. Some breeding populations differ sufficiently in their average wing and bill lengths to make it possible to match measurements taken from breeding birds with samples of birds caught in winter. They also exhibit greater sexual size dimorphism than any other calidrid sandpiper (Summers *et al* 1990). Thus, measurements of bill length can be used to determine racial origin and sex ratio. However, where different breeding populations winter together, as in Britain, interpretation of bill-length distributions is not straightforward (Nicoll *et al* 1988). Nothing is known about the migrations of the tiny British breeding population, which probably originated from the Norwegian breeding population.

Of all the populations, the migration of the birds which breed in Norway and winter on the coasts of eastern Britain is the best known. There have been three ring-recoveries on the Hardangervidda (a mountain plateau in southern Norway), and 16 sightings on the British coast of birds colour-ringed there (Rae *et al* 1986) (Fig 4). These birds start arriving in eastern Britain in the first half of July and immediately start moult. Many remain throughout the winter and depart for Norway in April or May (Atkinson *et al* 1981).

Purple Sandpipers that breed in Norway have smaller bills and wings than the other populations, and comprise about a quarter of the British

wintering population. The majority occur on the east coast between Aberdeenshire and Yorkshire (Nicoll *et al* 1988) (Fig 5). Most of the Purple Sandpipers wintering in the rest of Britain are long-billed, and these long-billed birds comprise about three-quarters of the British wintering population (Nicoll *et al* 1988). Although the winter populations that occur on North American shores originate from Canada, there are several strands of evidence which suggest that the majority of the British & Irish winter population also originates from Canada. There are several ring-recoveries showing that Purple Sandpipers wintering in the southern North Sea and eastern Scotland pass through Orkney in spring (Corse & Summers 1999). Although they could still potentially be heading northeast, northwest is more likely. Further, there have been six movements of Purple Sandpipers in Iceland in spring linked with wintering sites in the Netherlands (three), Spain (one) and Scotland (two) (Hjálmarsson 1982, Boere *et al* 1984, Corse & Summers 1999). However, because the Icelandic breeding population is apparently entirely resident (Summers *et al* 1988a), these recoveries cannot refer to the Icelandic birds. Rather, Iceland appears to be used as a refuelling site for onward migration (Wilson 1981). There are also ring-recoveries linking England with southern Greenland (Fig 4). Again, this was probably not their final destination, because Purple Sandpipers breeding on the south and west coasts of Greenland also seem to be resident (Salomonsen 1967a). Finally, there is one recovery that bridges the last section of the presumed migration route; a bird ringed in Iceland in late May was recovered on Baffin Island, Canada (Morrison 1984).

Biometric evidence supports the idea that a proportion of Canadian Purple Sandpipers migrates to northwest Europe. The bill and wing lengths of Purple Sandpipers wintering in north and west Britain are longer than those of the Norwegian Purple Sandpipers, and match with museum specimens of birds from Baffin Island but not with birds from

Fig 6. Mean bill lengths (vertical lines) ± 1 s.d. (black bars) for male (smaller values) and female (larger values) Purple Sandpipers from different breeding populations. Also shown are the three means ± s.d.s for wintering birds in Britain, where the frequency distribution for bill lengths is trimodal (from Nicoll *et al* 1988). The males and females from Norway match with the shortest and middle modes of the British wintering birds. Although the Icelandic breeders match with the middle and large modes of the British birds, their wing lengths do not (Summers *et al* 1988a). Therefore Canadian birds are suspected to comprise the long-billed birds wintering in Britain. (*Source*: published data, by permission of *Ibis* and *Ringing & Migration*.)

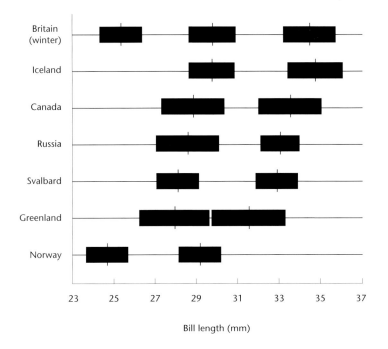

Bill length (mm)

Iceland (which has the largest Purple Sandpipers) or Greenland (Summers *et al* 1988a, Summers 1994) (Fig 6). The long-billed birds also complete their migration later than Norwegian Purple Sandpipers, arriving in Britain in October having moulted elsewhere.

There have been several recoveries of colour-ringed Purple Sandpipers in southern England, where the winter population is very small. These were ringed in western Sweden in May, on northward migration. Measurements made in southeast England indicate that they are long-billed birds, and therefore not from the Norwegian population. Also, their route suggests they are not part of the Canadian population. Hake *et al* (1997) linked these birds to the migration through the Baltic to north Russia.

Recently, there has been a ring-recovery in Svalbard of a bird ringed on the Aberdeenshire coast in November (Fig 4). This suggests that there

may be a fourth population of Purple Sandpipers wintering in Britain. The bill measurements of Svalbard Purple Sandpipers are intermediate between those of the Norwegian and Canadian birds (Nicoll *et al* 1991), but do not form a peak in the bill-length distribution of Purple Sandpipers caught in Britain (Nicoll *et al* 1988). Therefore, it is assumed that they do not form a major part of the British wintering population. Furthermore, colour-ringing in Svalbard and western Sweden has shown that this population mainly migrates down the coast of Norway and that many winter in western Sweden (Hake *et al* 1997).

Several colour-ringing studies have reported strong site-fidelity by Purple Sandpipers, both within a winter and between winters (*eg* Burton & Evans 1997, Dierschke 1998). However, changes in winter quarters do occur, and a fuller picture emerges when searches are widened. Purple Sandpipers ringed on the Isle of May ranged along the mainland shores of Fife and East Lothian (Atkinson *et al* 1981). A radio-tracking study showed that some movements between the island and mainland (8 km) were roost flights to the island at night, whilst other movements were irregular (Summers 1995).

The Purple Sandpiper is not well represented in the WeBS counts and there is little information on trends in numbers. The 1984/85 Winter Shorebird Count gave an estimate of 16,000 for Britain and Northern Ireland (Moser & Summers 1987), a value that was slightly modified by Nicoll *et al* (1988) to 19,000. In 1998/99, a second national survey was carried out and has shown a 20% decline in Purple Sandpiper numbers (Browne *et al* 1996, M M Rehfisch pers comm). This result was supported by counts in East Lothian where there was an 88% decline between the 1970s/80s and 1990s (Dott 1997). At present, the cause of these changes is not known. Not all populations have shown recent declines. Counts on the island of Sanday, Orkney, showed no decline between winters 1982/83 and 1991/92 (Corse & Summers 1999).

Rocky shores are not threatened by reclamation, as other wader habitats are, but are affected by sewage outfalls, which may enhance invertebrate populations. Cleaner sewage systems may therefore be making the shores less attractive to Purple Sandpipers. Purple Sandpipers sometimes become contaminated by oil pollution but birds that have been lightly oiled appear to survive (Dierschke 1994b).

There are still some basic gaps in our knowledge of the migrations of Purple Sandpipers. For example, there is no direct evidence that the long-billed birds that comprise the bulk of the British wintering population come from Canada. Also, we need to confirm that the Purple Sandpipers that occur in southeast England originate in Russia. Colour-ringing on the breeding grounds is the approach most likely to confirm these migration routes.

Ron Summers

Dunlin
Calidris alpina

Dunlin has a circumpolar breeding distribution at low Arctic and boreal latitudes which comprises a complex array of subpopulations each with its own wintering range and migration route. All populations winter at temperate and tropical latitudes, almost exclusively coastally and north of the Equator.

As many as 11 races have been recognized (Greenwood 1986, Wenink *et al* 1996), of which only three occur in Britain & Ireland (Hardy & Minton 1980). The *arctica* race, with a population of only some 15,000 individuals, breeds in northeast Greenland and occurs only briefly on passage in spring and autumn to and from its winter quarters in West Africa. The *schinzii* race, which has a total population of about 800,000 individuals, breeds mainly in Iceland and southeast Greenland, with smaller populations in Britain & Ireland and southern Norway, and winters mainly in West Africa. There is also a small and diminishing population breeding in the coastal marshes around the Baltic, and these may winter on the Atlantic coast of Europe (Smit & Piersma 1989). The third race, nominate *alpina*, breeds in northern Fennoscandia and across western Siberia. Birds from at least as far east as the White Sea come to western Europe to moult and winter (*BWP*) and there is now evidence from ring-recoveries that birds from at least as far east as the Yamal Peninsula winter in Britain & Ireland. More easterly breeding *alpina* winter in the Mediterranean Basin and as far east as western India. Pacific and American races winter mainly in southern China and on both coasts of the USA.

It has been suggested that two other races occur in Britain. The first is *sakhalina* from breeding areas in eastern Siberia, tentatively identified

The analysis of the data for this species was supported by Nigel & Jacquie Clark

from the measurements of a few large individuals (Harrison & Harrison 1971, 1972); these, however, fall within the upper part of the ranges for *alpina* and so cannot be separated from them on the basis of measurements alone. The second is *centralis* from central Siberia, which many authors no longer distinguish from *alpina*.

Nesting habitat is mainly wet tussock and mire, normally at low densities. Within Britain & Ireland, fewer than 10,000 pairs of Dunlin breed on moorland in the north and the west of both islands; densities are high on the machair in the Western Isles and on the unafforested flow country in northern Scotland (*1988–91 Atlas*). Outside the breeding season over half a million Dunlin occur on the coast (Pollitt *et al* 2000), especially in large muddy estuaries. Small numbers may occur on any inland wetland, most frequently as juveniles on autumn passage.

The preference for Dunlin to breed at low density means that very few birds have been ringed on the breeding grounds. This gives considerable problems in interpreting the migration patterns of this species since it is not usually possible to be certain of the breeding population to which any individual belongs. Ring-recoveries are nevertheless of prime importance in unravelling the patterns. Very few Dunlin had been ringed in Britain & Ireland before the early 1960s, when rocket-nets and then cannon-nets were used to catch waders on the Wash. Since the development of cannon-nets, large numbers of

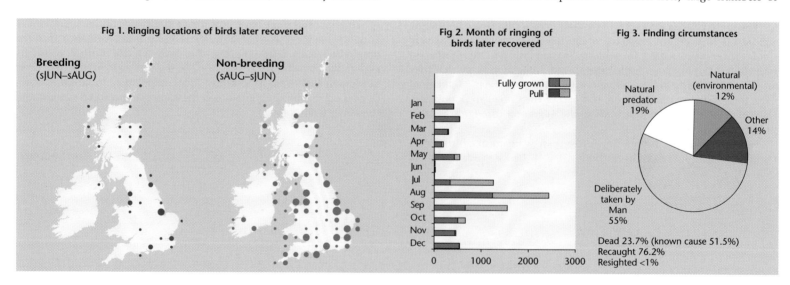

Fig 1. Ringing locations of birds later recovered

Breeding (sJUN–sAUG) Non-breeding (sAUG–sJUN)

Fig 2. Month of ringing of birds later recovered

Fully grown / Pulli

Fig 3. Finding circumstances

Natural predator 19%
Natural (environmental) 12%
Other 14%
Deliberately taken by Man 55%

Dead 23.7% (known cause 51.5%)
Recaught 76.2%
Resighted <1%

Ringing and recovery data

	<1960	60–69	70–79	80–89	90–97	Total
RINGING						
BTO ringing totals (%)	1	17	38	27	17	386,189
RECOVERIES						
BTO-ringed (%)	1	13	41	31	14	5,518
Foreign-ringed (%)	4	15	35	28	17	3,403

Statistical analyses

	Breeding population (sJUN–sAUG)	Wintering population (mOCT–sAPR)
Status	LONG-DISTANCE MIGRANT* (2)	LONG-DISTANCE MIGRANT*
Age differences[NT]	Not tested	Not significant*
Sex differences	Not tested	Not tested
Regional differences	Not tested	Not significant[2]*
Finding circumstances	Not tested	Not tested

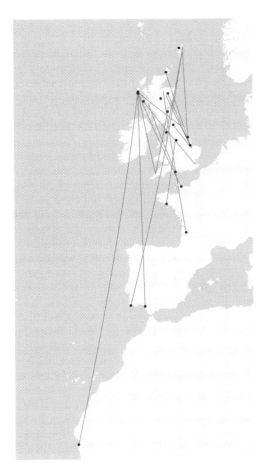

Fig 4. Recovery locations and movements of over 20 km of 24 Dunlin ringed as pulli in Britain & Ireland or recorded as breeding when present in Britain & Ireland.

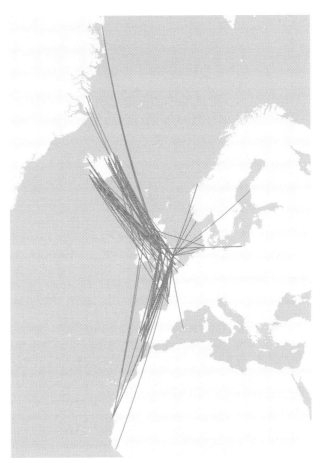

Fig 5. Overseas movements (involving Britain & Ireland) of Dunlin known to be *arctica* or *schinzii* but excluding *schinzii* known to be part of the British & Irish breeding population (shown in Fig 4). Movements involving birds abroad during June–July (36, red) and September–March (13, blue) are differentiated from those abroad at other times or seasonally inaccurate (63, grey).

Dunlin have been caught each year by a few specialist wader groups. Smaller numbers have been caught using wader mist-nets. Large numbers of Dunlin are also ringed around the Baltic, where the low tidal range allows the use of walk-in traps. As a result, the distribution of ringing sites for recoveries relates more closely to the distribution of wader ringing groups than to that of Dunlin (Fig 1).

Most recoveries are of birds ringed at passage times and when many birds are moulting (Fig 2). Over three-quarters of the recoveries of Dunlin involving Britain & Ireland have been recaptures by ringers. This also gives a bias towards the sites and times where and when ringers are active. Half of the 2,000 birds found dead have no known cause of recovery, while half of the remainder were deliberately taken by Man mainly in the 1960s in France, Britain or Iberia (Fig 3).

As Dunlin breed at a wide range of latitudes, the first birds may arrive on their British & Irish breeding grounds in April, while high-Arctic breeders may not arrive on the breeding grounds until 10 June. Female Dunlin leave the breeding grounds a few days after the young have hatched. Sometimes British & Irish *schinzii* may leave as early as mid-June, leaving the male to care for the chicks until they become independent at two to three weeks old. Once the males depart, the juveniles congregate in small groups before starting southward migration in late July. Thus there is no time during the breeding season when only local breeding birds are present in Britain & Ireland, making it impossible to define a clear start or end to the breeding period.

Ring-recoveries known to refer to the native population are very few but suggest that, while most visit West Africa, a few winter more locally (Fig 4). There are only four movements of British breeding adults recorded on autumn passage sites; all of these bred in northern England or Scotland and passed through the Wash between 13 July and 2 August. Remarkably,

two were caught in the same catch of 500 Dunlin on 31 July 1988. Given that the large number of Dunlin caught during August–October in Britain has resulted in only one recovery of a British breeding bird, it is likely that most adult British breeding Dunlin have left the country by the middle of August. There was one winter recovery, however, that suggests that a few individuals breeding in Britain & Ireland spend the winter in northwest Europe: this bird was ringed on 24 December in Kent and subsequently resighted with chicks on the Isle of Coll.

There were five autumn recoveries of juveniles from the British *schinzii* population; one in the Gironde on 26 July, two in Cornwall in August, one in Yorkshire in early September and one was found long dead in the Gironde, France, in October, which may have died much earlier in the autumn. So far, there have been only two recoveries of British breeding birds from the main wintering grounds of *schinzii* Dunlin in Mauritania — an adult in November and a first-winter bird in early April.

Given that the substantial amount of ringing of Dunlin in western Europe in winter has resulted in only one recovery on the British breeding grounds, it is most likely that recoveries in spring will be of passage birds that have wintered in Africa. These birds leave Africa on northward migration between the end of March and mid-May (Piersma *et al* 1990). The earliest spring passage recovery of a British breeding bird is from Poole Harbour on 5 April, with three recoveries occurring in May — one in Portugal on 8 May and singles on 23 May in Lancashire and at Teesmouth. Very few *schinzii* migrate back to the breeding grounds in their first summer. A few do move north, as is shown by the recovery of a Dunlin that was ringed as a pullus in the Pennines in 1913 and shot in France on 10 May the following year.

The *schinzii* race also breeds in southern Norway and the five recoveries of definite breeding birds from this area indicate that they

Table 1. The occurrence of Dunlin from Iceland and Greenland in different regions of Britain & Ireland in spring and autumn.

Months in Britain & Ireland	Ireland %	North %	South %	West %	East %	Total (n)
April/May	0	5	10	85	0	20
July/Aug/Sept	9	6	18	40	27	33

Table 2. The occurrence of Dunlin from Mauritania in different regions of Britain & Ireland in spring and autumn.

Months in Britain & Ireland	Ireland %	North %	South %	West %	East %	Total (n)
April/May	11	0	33	56	0	9
July/Aug/Sept	4	8	4	20	64	25

occur in spring and autumn in Britain & Ireland (Fig 5). A detailed analysis of all recoveries relating to the Baltic population, however, suggested that they wintered in western Europe between Britain & Ireland and Iberia (Jönsson 1986). It is likely that some do winter in Britain & Ireland, as measurements suggest that a few Dunlin wintering on the Severn Estuary are of the *schinzii* race (Clark 1983).

It is very difficult to separate ring-recoveries for the two races breeding in Iceland and Greenland. There are only four exchanges between Britain & Ireland and Greenland that can definitely be attributed to *arctica*. Nine definite Icelandic breeders have been recorded in Britain, five on spring passage and four in the autumn. There are considerably more recoveries that refer to birds with a connection to Iceland or Greenland, but which cannot be split between the races (Fig 5). Table 1 summarizes the recoveries of these birds in spring and autumn in Britain & Ireland. These data show that during spring passage most Dunlin (85%) destined for Iceland or Greenland stage on the west coast of Britain, where they are mainly found on Morecambe Bay, the Dee Estuary and the Solway Firth. In autumn, birds are much more dispersed with many occurring on the British east and south coasts, as well as in the west. After leaving Britain & Ireland in autumn, *schinzii* Dunlin winter mainly in Mauritania, with smaller numbers from Senegal north to Morocco (*BWP*). A summary of movements between Britain &

Ireland and Mauritania is given in Table 2. As expected, it shows that Mauritanian wintering birds are concentrated on the west and south coasts in spring, but in autumn there are three times as many movements involving the east coast as the west, in contrast to the movements to and from Greenland and Iceland. This strongly suggests that some of the birds wintering in Mauritania do not pass through Britain & Ireland in spring.

Nominate-race Dunlin from northern Fennoscandia and European Russia are the most abundant population in Britain & Ireland outside the breeding season, and form the vast flocks on our winter estuaries. Their distribution and timing of movements, in relation to the annual moult, differ substantially from those of the two races already discussed.

Most of the recoveries relating to Dunlin come from the *alpina* race; there are, however, only four recoveries of *alpina* that are definitely from pulli or known breeders. All four came from the extreme west of the *alpina* range in northern Norway, although this may reflect bias in ringing effort. One was ringed as a chick on 25 June and controlled 40 days later in Kent. A second bird ringed as a chick was controlled in its first winter in Dyfed, while two adults caught on the Wash in autumn were controlled while breeding in Norway. Fig 6 shows all seasonally accurate recoveries that involve Dunlin from within the breeding range of *alpina*. It is likely that some of these will have been caught while still on passage to or from their exact breeding locations, especially those on the coast, thereby giving a westerly bias to the distribution (Leslie & Lessells 1978).

After breeding, there is a relatively prolonged movement to the wintering grounds that spans the period of the main annual moult. In July and August, many adult Dunlin migrate through the Baltic and arrive on the Wadden Sea and the Wash to moult (Fig 7a). For *alpina* from the western part of the breeding range and wintering in Britain & Ireland, the main moulting location is the Wadden Sea, although substantial numbers also moult at the Wash and a few other British estuaries (Boere 1976). Some birds, especially those breeding in the east of the range, undergo at least part of their annual moult while on passage through the Baltic or on their breeding grounds. There is a second wave of movement across western Europe and into Britain & Ireland in October–November, as birds that have moulted on the Wadden Sea or on the Wash move on to more westerly wintering sites.

Table 3 investigates the timing of occurrence in Britain & Ireland of *alpina* Dunlin from north of the Arctic Circle. This shows that only 13% (three) of the Dunlin from east of 35°E were found in Britain & Ireland during autumn, when they would be expected to be undergoing their

Fig 6. Seasonally accurate movements and locations outside Britain & Ireland of all Dunlin from east of 10°E and north of 65°N. Those present in Britain & Ireland during July–September (95, red) are differentiated from those present during the rest of the year (143, blue).

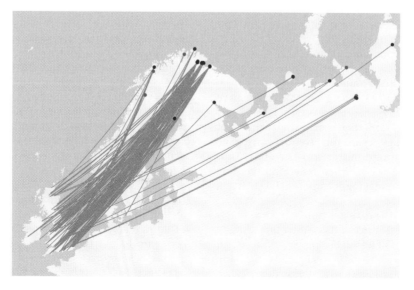

Fig 7. Seasonally accurate locations in (a) July–August (1,644), (b) September–October (577) and (c) April–May (166) of Dunlin present in Britain & Ireland in midwinter (December to February inclusive).

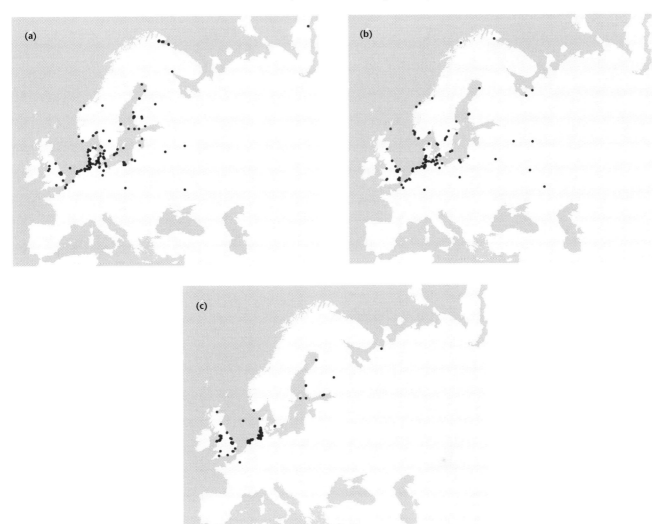

annual moult, whereas about 40% of the other two groups were caught at this time. This fits with evidence that Dunlin from the east of the *alpina* range tend to start moult while still on the breeding grounds (Greenwood 1983, Gromadska 1989). Many of those from the west arrive on the moulting grounds before starting to moult; there they start replacement of four or five of the inner primaries simultaneously (Holmgren *et al* 1993).

The Wash and, to a lesser extent, the Thames and Morecambe Bay are extremely important for moulting populations of *alpina* Dunlin. Fig 7b gives the locations in late autumn (September–October) of Dunlin that were present in winter in Britain & Ireland. By this time, most of the

schinzii migrants will have passed through but it is not possible to know for sure whether the birds mapped were definitely moulting. This clearly shows that Dunlin that have moulted on the Wadden Sea move westward to Britain after their moult is completed.

Juvenile *alpina* Dunlin migrate on a much broader front than adults, with many occurring at inland sites in Europe and on the west coast of Norway (Fig 8). They leave the breeding grounds later than adults and arrive in Britain & Ireland mainly in September and October (Clark 1983).

As Dunlin that winter in Britain & Ireland are most likely to be *alpina*, the movements of this population can also be ascertained by looking at the movements of birds from definite wintering grounds. Dunlin are highly site-faithful to their winter roost sites, both within and between years. On the Wash, 92% of recaptures were within the same section of the estuary (Rehfisch *et al* 1996) and a similar situation was found on the Moray Firth (Rehfisch *et al* pers comm). Fig 9a shows the 47 within-winter, and Fig 9b the 206 between-winter movements of Dunlin. There is remarkably little movement of Dunlin within a midwinter period, but more birds (although still a small proportion) move wintering sites between winters. Between-winter movements are predominantly east–west and may be related to Dunlin and other waders moving further west in colder winters (G E Austin pers comm). Once first-winter birds have chosen their wintering site they are as site-faithful in future years as adults, with a median movement of 14 km

Table 3. The timing of occurrence in Britain & Ireland of Dunlin from different parts of the *alpina* breeding range north of the Arctic Circle.

Occurrence in Britain & Ireland	Norway/Finland	Murmansk coast and Kola Peninsula	White Sea to Yamal Peninsula
July–Sept %	37	44	13
Oct–June %	63	56	87
Total (*n*)	154	80	23

Fig 8. Ringing locations abroad of 460 Dunlin that
were ringed as juveniles and were recovered
in Britain during midwinter
(December to February inclusive).

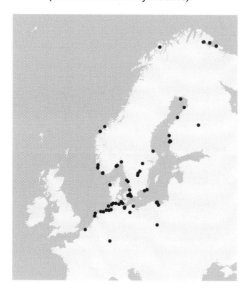

Fig 9. Recovery locations of Dunlin (a) within the same winter (15:32) and (b) in
subsequent winters (55:151) and movements within midwinter periods (December to
February inclusive). Birds ringed in their first winter (red) are differentiated from those
ringed as adults (blue). Sample sizes of the age classes (first-winter:adult) are given.

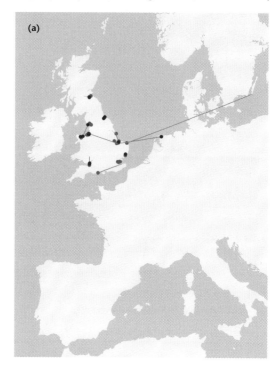

(P5–95=0–488 km, *n*=70) compared with 13 km (P5–95=0–461 km, *n*=156) for adults. This median movement is well within the distance travelled daily by Dunlin within large estuaries.

In spring, most adult *alpina* Dunlin congregate on the Wadden Sea prior to departure to the breeding grounds, although the Wash is also important (Fig 7c). On the northernmost breeding grounds, some birds may still be arriving as late as 10 June. In their first summer many *alpina* do not return to the breeding grounds but tend to move part-way back, only to return early to their moulting grounds. There are few data for second-summer birds but it appears from the breeding-season recoveries that most, if not all, return to the breeding grounds.

There have been two previous detailed analyses of the movements of Dunlin wintering in Britain & Ireland (Clark 1983, 1989). These both show that there were statistically significant differences in the patterns of recoveries for birds using different parts of the same estuary. Whether these differences were the result of birds of different body-size or sex selecting different areas on passage and in winter, or whether they were the result of there being different migration routes for different populations, is unclear. Recent work on the genetics of Dunlin populations (*eg* Wenink *et al* 1996) does not detect variation in Dunlin populations at a fine-enough scale to answer this question at present.

Aside from its own breeding population, Britain & Ireland probably hosts most Icelandic and Greenland Dunlin on passage, and is a winter destination or refuge for a large proportion of the *alpina* Dunlin that breed from Fennoscandia to the Yamal Peninsula. Britain & Ireland, therefore, has a very special responsibility for Dunlin conservation. We still know little about the importance of British & Irish estuaries for British breeding Dunlin, and remarkably little about the breeding area of British & Irish wintering Dunlin. How important are east-coast estuaries for Icelandic Dunlin and *arctica* in autumn? A detailed analysis of the existing recoveries, together with all the biometrics that have been collected, is long overdue but is a daunting task. The value of this approach has been apparent for a long time and much progress has been made (*eg* Pienkowski & Pienkowski 1983). With advances in computer technology, and the greatly increased availability of computers to volunteers, it may now be possible to bring together the biometrics that have been collected. A substantial programme of ringing on a number of sites on the *alpina* breeding grounds, possibly using colour marks, could increase our understanding of whether particular sections of the *alpina* population are concentrated on certain estuaries or types of habitat in winter.

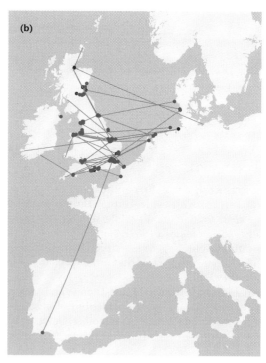

Even in the last 40 years there has been considerable variation in the distribution of wintering Dunlin as the size of the British & Irish wintering population has changed (Pollitt *et al* 2000). Regular monitoring will assess any further changes in the movement patterns, and enable conservation decisions to be undertaken in the light of these changes. This is likely to become increasingly important if intertidal areas are affected by sea-level rise and Dunlin breeding areas move north, and wintering areas east, as a result of global warming.

Nigel Clark

Ruff
Philomachus pugnax

The spectacular breeding plumage and courtship behaviour of Ruff make them unique among British & Irish waders. They are strikingly sexually dimorphic, with males being significantly larger than females and developing the colourful breeding plumage from which the name arises. Within Britain & Ireland there are small breeding and wintering populations but much larger numbers occur on passage.

Ruff breed from Scandinavia to the Bering Strait, and also at more southerly latitudes in the West Palearctic, from southern England and France east to Kazakhstan (*BWP, European Atlas*). They are a common breeding bird in Fennoscandia and Russia but breed in much smaller numbers elsewhere in Europe (*European Atlas*). Within Britain, Ruff were virtually extinct as a breeding species by the end of the 19th century and none bred between 1922 and 1963 (*BWP*). There are now small numbers present in eastern and northeastern Britain; the Ouse Washes, Cambridgeshire, was the first reported breeding site and now seems to be the most regular. Leks have been reported from 5–21 sites in the last decade but breeding is extremely difficult to prove. It is suspected that females may join leks on passage but then subsequently breed further north (van Rhijn 1991). Breeding in Ireland has never been suspected (*1988–91 Atlas*).

By contrast, Ruff have only been recorded wintering in Britain & Ireland since 1934, after which their numbers increased rapidly to over 1,000 in the 1970s, and then declined to a winter population of only a few hundred (Prater 1981). In 1998/99, around 400 birds were recorded by WeBS counts in midwinter (November–January), although many more were recorded on passage, with a peak count of around 1,300 in

The analysis of the data for this species was supported by the Royles family

September (Pollitt *et al* 2000). The majority of Ruff winter in Africa south of the Sahara, with a much smaller number wintering in Europe, North Africa, the Middle East and India (*BWP*). Even birds from the northeast of the Siberian range are present in Africa in winter (*BWP*). During the breeding season, Ruff inhabit lowland wet grassland and marshes. Outside the breeding season they use a variety of wetland habitats including pasture, ricefields, gravel-pits, sewage-works but occasionally intertidal areas (*BWP*).

Around 20 Ruff are ringed annually in Britain & Ireland, mostly during passage periods at sites such as gravel-pits, sugar beet factories, estuaries and sewage-farms (Figs 1 & 2). Little is therefore known about the movements of the British breeding and British & Irish wintering populations. The majority (74%) of Ruff recoveries from dead birds can be attributed to a known cause, 84% of these being taken by Man (Fig 3); these comprised 12 each from France and Italy and five each from Mali and Spain. The timing and distribution of Ruff recoveries is therefore likely to be affected by temporal and spatial variations in hunting pressure.

The first autumn arrivals of adult Ruff occur in Britain in July. At sites around the Wash at least, most of these birds are males (Gill *et al* 1995); this early return is probably the result of males playing no part in parental care (van Rhijn 1991). The first juvenile birds occur slightly

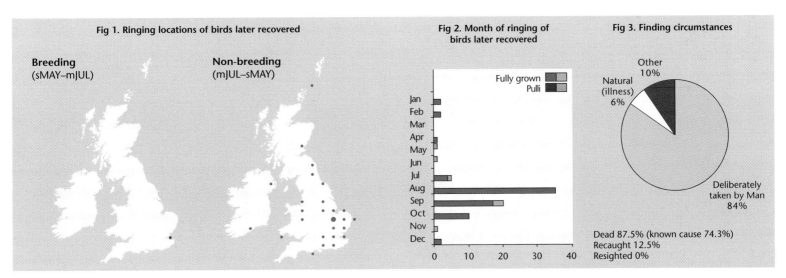

Fig 1. Ringing locations of birds later recovered

Breeding (sMAY–mJUL)

Non-breeding (mJUL–sMAY)

Fig 2. Month of ringing of birds later recovered

Fully grown / Pulli

Fig 3. Finding circumstances

Other 10%
Natural (illness) 6%
Deliberately taken by Man 84%

Dead 87.5% (known cause 74.3%)
Recaught 12.5%
Resighted 0%

Ringing and recovery data

	<1960	60–69	70–79	80–89	90–97	Total
RINGING						
BTO ringing totals (%)	6	41	23	21	9	2,403
RECOVERIES						
BTO-ringed (%)	5	45	25	25	0	73
Foreign-ringed (%)	14	43	29	14	0	7

Statistical analyses

	Breeding population (sMAY–mJUL)	Wintering population (mOCT–sMAR)
Status	[LONG-DISTANCE MIGRANT]	[LONG-DISTANCE MIGRANT]
Age differences	Not tested	Not tested
Sex differences	Not tested	Not tested
Regional differences	Not tested	Not tested
Finding circumstances	Not tested	Not tested

Fig 4. Seasonally accurate locations of Ruff in (a) July–September (20), (b) October–February (21), (c) March–April (15) and (d) May–June (8). A single recovery in the far east of Russia during May–June is not shown.

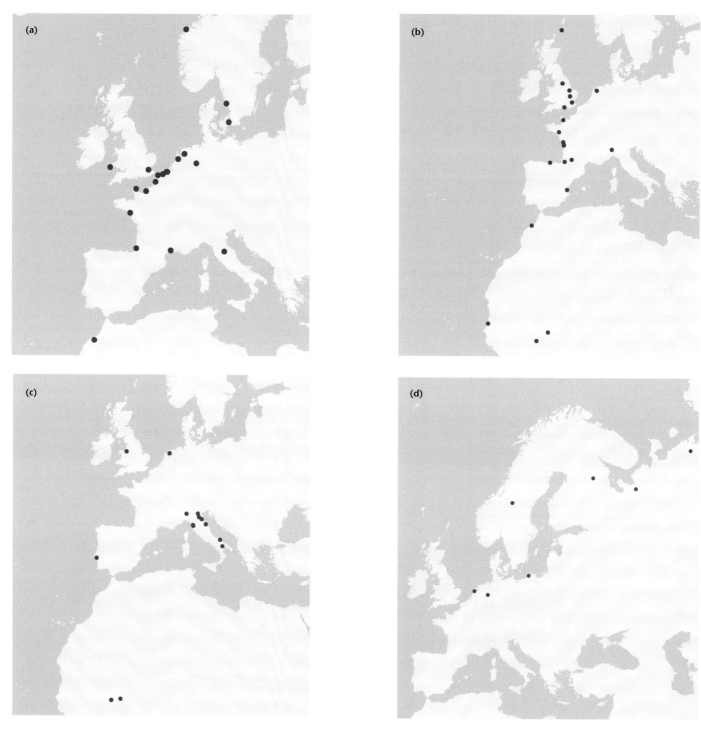

later in August. Passage in Norfolk peaks in August to October with counts of up to 150 individuals (Taylor *et al* 1999).

During autumn passage there is a general south-southwesterly migration through Europe but on the return spring passage there is an easterly shift in distribution (*BWP*, Koopman 1986). Recovery data from Ruff ringed in Britain & Ireland reflect this seasonal pattern of movement. In the main autumn passage months of July to September, most recoveries are concentrated around the coastline of western Europe, from the Netherlands to France and North Africa (Fig 4a). From October to February, recoveries are more widespread, extending from Shetland through western Europe to the wintering grounds of Senegal and Mali (Fig 4b). Prater (1973) noted that midwinter arrivals of Ruff in Britain & Ireland were likely to be of birds wintering in continental

Europe until the onset of hard weather. The pattern of return migration in spring differs from the autumn migration in that the March recoveries are centred around Italy (Fig 4c) where there are large concentrations of Ruff on spring passage (OAG Münster 1989, Serra *et al* 1990, Baccetti *et al* 1998). Recoveries of Ruff ringed in Sweden also show a more easterly spring than autumn migration route (*BWP*). This pattern is unlikely to reflect hunting pressure in Italy as most hunting of migratory species in Europe occurs on autumn passage (Tucker *et al* 1990, Henderson *et al* 1993). There are a small number of recoveries of birds during May and June in northern Europe and Russia, including one bird recovered in the Russian Far East (Fig 4d).

There is a strong male-bias in the sex ratio of Ruff caught in Britain & Ireland, particularly during the winter months (Prater 1973, 1981). By

Fig 5. Sex ratios of Ruff in different wintering areas, based on ringing studies. Numbers indicate sample sizes. (*Source*: OAG Münster 1996, by permission of *Journal für Ornithologie*.)

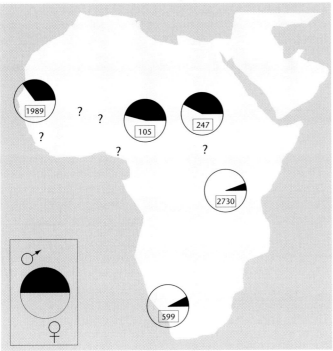

Fig 6. Locations in November–March of Ruff present in Britain & Ireland during passage. Males (18, blue) are differentiated from females (7, red) and from those of unknown seasonality (6, grey, all male).

contrast, the sex ratio in the African wintering grounds ranges from 65% female in Senegal to 90% in Kenya (Pearson 1981) and South Africa (Münster 1996; Fig 5). Among birds present in Britain & Ireland during spring and autumn passage, males in winter were mostly in Europe and North Africa and females were in West Africa, where one bird has been reported from Senegal and four from Mali (two from each of two sites) (Fig 6).

A study of the moult strategies of male and female Ruff in Britain suggests that they may be related to the different migration patterns of the sexes (Gill *et al* 1995). Male Ruff caught in the autumn around the Wash had between four and six primary feathers in the early stages of active moult. By contrast, females caught at the same time either had not started moult or had a maximum of three growing primaries. Female Ruff found in Britain on autumn passage therefore appear to be either passing through without moulting or moulting while migrating. By moulting only a small number of feathers at a time, females may be minimizing the area of missing feathers in their wings, and therefore the reduction in flight efficiency (Gill *et al* 1995). In the Netherlands, Koopman (1986) also found that in autumn a higher proportion of male Ruff were in active moult compared to females, which were either not moulting or had replaced only a small number of feathers.

Ringing has so far provided little information on either the origins or subsequent movements of juveniles on autumn passage in Britain & Ireland. Such information is difficult to gather in a species which is caught in such small numbers but is an important component of any international conservation efforts.

The turnover of individuals as birds move on from Britain & Ireland to wintering grounds further south means that many more Ruff may occur on autumn passage than count data suggest. Studies using colour-marking of birds caught on passage would provide a greater understanding of the total number of Ruff occurring in Britain & Ireland and of the sites of greatest importance during passage periods. The reasons for the apparent loop migration require further investigation as does the importance and conservation status of the inland wetland sites used. Ruff are known to occur consistently on a small number of widely distributed wintering sites within Britain & Ireland, suggesting a high degree of winter site-fidelity, although this has not been quantified. Colour-ringing studies may also be the best way to advance our knowledge of winter site-fidelity.

Jennifer Smart, Jennifer Gill, Jacquie Clark & Nigel Clark

Jack Snipe
Lymnocryptes minimus

Despite its apparently weak flight, the Jack Snipe is a powerful migrant, with some populations commuting from Siberia to trans-Saharan Africa. It is a winter visitor and passage migrant to Britain & Ireland and is widely distributed, although nowhere common. Across much of England the species is only reported from a small number of widely separated traditional sites (each holding typically just a handful of birds) usually in open wetland habitats where feeding conditions are suitable all winter. Chance encounters with Jack Snipe are very unusual, as individuals are only seen when flushed by someone walking very close to them; they are therefore undoubtedly also overlooked during wildfowl and wader counts. Jack Snipe are probably absent from moorland and mountainous districts. There are as yet no reliable data on the size of the winter population. It has been suggested that, based on a comparison of one Jack Snipe for every eight Common Snipe in shooting bags, 100,000 birds may occur in Britain & Ireland (*Winter Atlas*) with 20–30,000 of them in Ireland (*Birds in Ireland*). These figures may be as much as an order of magnitude too high (Stone *et al* 1997) as Jack Snipe, once flushed, are easier to shoot than Common Snipe.

The breeding range lies between 55°N and 70°N and extends from northern Fennoscandia across Siberia to 160°E (*BWP*). Although poorly studied, the European Russian breeding population may be about 100,000 pairs, and there are believed to be about 25,000 pairs in Scandinavia, mainly in northern Finland and northern Sweden (*European Atlas*). Annual fluctuations may take place, apparently in response to severe weather and cyclic predator abundance (*European Atlas*). The winter range includes the western maritime countries of

The analysis of the data for this species was supported by Martin & Kath George

Europe and North Africa and extends patchily across southern Europe as well as in a broad band across Africa, mainly north and just south of the Sahara Desert, and in Asia Minor. Jack Snipe breed mainly in mild low-lying regions, largely inland. Nest sites are often on *Sphagnum*-covered peat mounds in open but well-vegetated tracts of soft bog (*BWP*). In the winter quarters, they may be found in many types of wet habitats including bog, fen, marsh, saltmarsh and flooded arable land (*BWP*). In Denmark, Jack Snipe move to streams when other wetland habitats freeze over (Pedersen 1989).

There is a southwesterly movement on a broad front across Europe in autumn, beginning in August and lasting to November. Migrant birds reach the northern and eastern coasts of Britain in mid-September (*Winter Atlas*), while in Ireland most birds arrive in October and November (*Birds in Ireland*). Return passage occurs mainly in April (*Winter Atlas*).

The distribution of the ringing sites of ringed birds recovered (Fig 1) largely reflects the distribution of Jack Snipe in Britain but the total lack of recoveries of birds ringed in Ireland is striking. Although the Jack Snipe is not rare in Britain & Ireland, its small and apparently thinly spread population and secretive habits ensure that few are ringed. Indeed, only 15 were ringed in Ireland between 1975 and 1997 (Forsyth 1998 and previous reports). Recoveries of Jack Snipe are all of birds ringed when fully grown in the non-breeding season. There is a peak in October, when

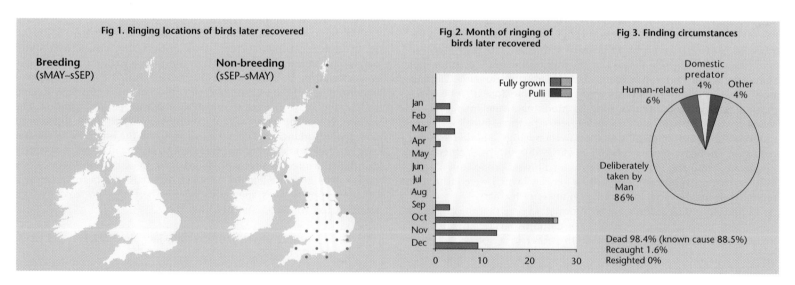

Ringing and recovery data

	<1960	60–69	70–79	80–89	90–97	Total
RINGING						
BTO ringing totals (%)	7	20	35	21	16	3,315
RECOVERIES						
BTO-ringed (%)	13	43	28	10	7	61
Foreign-ringed (%)	←	94	→	0	6	16

Statistical analyses

	Breeding population (sMAY–sSEP)	Wintering population (mNOV–sMAR)
Status	NONE	[LONG-DISTANCE MIGRANT]
Age differences	—	Not tested
Sex differences	—	Not tested
Regional differences	—	Not tested
Finding circumstances	—	Not tested

Fig 4. Recovery locations and movements of over 20 km for the 62 included recoveries of Jack Snipe ringed or recovered in Britain & Ireland.

both winter immigrants and passage migrants arrive (Fig 2). Most recoveries (86%) are of birds deliberately taken by Man, presumably mainly shot, reflecting the snipes' status as legal quarry (Fig 3).

Sixteen foreign-ringed birds have been recovered in Britain & Ireland, mostly prior to 1979. These came from Norway (one), Sweden (three), Finland (one), Germany (three), Denmark (three), Belgium (four) and the Netherlands (one). Birds ringed in Britain & Ireland have been recovered mainly in southern England or Ireland, with France providing the most foreign recoveries (Fig 4). Well over half of all recovery dates (59%) have been in December or January. The ring-recoveries show that there is an autumn passage movement through Britain with eight birds ringed in autumn subsequently recovered in autumn and winter in France, Iberia and Tunisia (Fig 4). There is no evidence of any onward movement from Ireland.

The median distance moved by the 61 Jack Snipe ringed in Britain & Ireland and subsequently found dead was just 6 km ($P5$–95= 0–$1,242$ km), probably reflecting the species' relatively sedentary behaviour in the winter months. The data suggest that at least some individuals show winter site-fidelity. No within-winter movements have been recorded but, of 14 birds ringed in winter and recovered in a subsequent winter, the median distance moved was 4 km ($P5$–95= 0–932 km). There is a suggestion from the recoveries that Jack Snipe ringed in the north of Britain move further than those ringed in the south (north: median=160 km, $P5$–95=0–$1,796$ km, n=12; south: median=4 km, $P5$–95=0–932 km, n=48).

Other European ringing data add to our knowledge of the species' movements (BWP). Single Norwegian birds have been found in winter in France, Spain and Portugal, and one ringed in Denmark in September was found in Finland. In Russia, a Czechoslovakian bird was found at 40°E in September and a German bird at 44°E in August. There are no recoveries in trans-Saharan Africa, but five birds have been found in Morocco (from Germany, Netherlands and Belgium), and one in Algeria (from Germany), all in winter. Danish, German, Dutch and Swiss birds ringed in autumn and winter have been found in Italy, France and the Iberian Peninsula, and a German bird has been found in Greece in December. There are no ring-recoveries for birds wintering in Asia Minor. This population, together with that wintering in East Africa, is presumed to originate in Siberia (BWP).

Reasonably accurate estimates are available for the wintering and breeding populations of most wading bird species in Europe and elsewhere. However, this is not so for the Jack Snipe. Because of its unobtrusive nature, it is very difficult to census and its true status remains in doubt. No population trend for either wintering or breeding birds is available, and the possibility of unrecorded declines is a serious conservation concern. This is of particular concern for a quarry species as, at present, it is impossible to judge if the level of hunting is sustainable. The loss of wetland habitat, both on the edges of the breeding range and on its wintering grounds, has probably diminished its numbers (Pedersen 1994, *European Atlas*). Research is needed to establish monitoring methods and also to gather more evidence of links between specific parts of the breeding and wintering ranges.

Patrick Smiddy

Common Snipe (Snipe)
Gallinago gallinago

The Snipe is a cryptic wader of bogs, fens and wet meadows, which feeds by probing for invertebrates in damp or waterlogged ground. Frozen winter conditions and baked summer substrates are avoided, forcing Snipe in northern Eurasia to undertake extensive seasonal movements across the Continent, many to Africa or the Oriental region.

The nominate race *gallinago* breeds widely from Ireland and northern Spain to eastern Siberia, and *faeroeensis* in the Faeroes, Iceland, Orkney and Shetland. Closely related species or subspecies occur across Africa as well as North and South America. Within Europe, breeding Snipe are especially abundant in Fennoscandia but become progressively scarcer and more scattered further south (*European Atlas*). Subarctic and boreal populations, from Iceland to Russia, are highly migratory, moving to southern and western European countries, such as the Low Countries, France, Iberia, Britain and Ireland, with the approach of harsh winter weather; many individuals travel further, to beyond the Sahara.

Although Snipe breed throughout Britain & Ireland, extensive drainage and general damage to wetland habitats, particularly in the lowlands of England, Wales and Ireland, has increasingly restricted and localized the distribution (*1988–91 Atlas*). The highest breeding densities and most continuous distribution occur across the wetter northern and western regions of Britain & Ireland, where blanket bogs and rough, wet grasslands still persist. Snipe are less localized in winter, foraging widely across scattered wetland or damp habitats, where even the smallest of boggy patches in field hollows or ditches can be utilized. Highest concentrations tend to occur around the fringes of lowland lakes and ponds and at times on flooded grasslands.

The analysis of the data for this species was supported by the Rye Bay Ringing Group and the Wetland Trust

Compared with the breeding distribution, Snipe ringed during the breeding season exhibit a more southerly bias with relatively few birds having been ringed in remote areas of Scotland and most of Ireland (Fig 1). Nesting Snipe are ringed in an unusually long breeding season but over 60% of all ringed birds that are later recovered were ringed outside the breeding season (Fig 2). At this season, the bulk of the population shifts into lowland wetlands in the south and west of Britain, as well as Ireland, but Ireland is grossly under-represented as a ringing location of birds that have been recovered (Fig 1). Owing to its status as a legal quarry species, over 90% of ring-recoveries are from birds deliberately taken by Man and so the recoveries are influenced most strongly by the distribution of hunting (Fig 3).

The median distance moved by Snipe between the breeding season and winter is 272 km (P5–95=0–817 km, n=65, dead recoveries only). Autumn movements begin in August and continue throughout September and October, returning during late March and April to reach their breeding grounds in May (*BWP*). Ring-recoveries show that Snipe breeding in northern Britain may move to Ireland for the winter, whereas those breeding in southern Britain are more likely to be found on the Continent, with one bird reaching North Africa (Fig 4). Indeed, Snipe breeding in southern Britain move further on average than those breeding in northern Britain (Table 1).

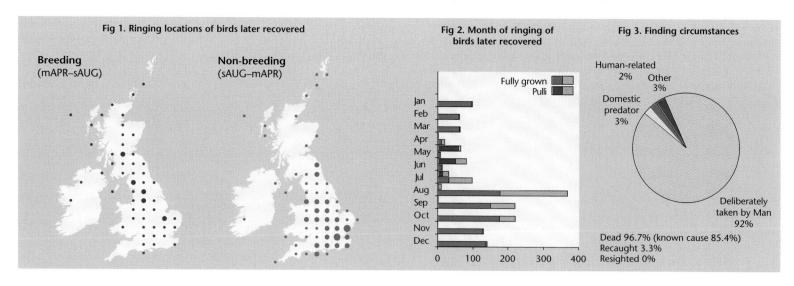

Fig 1. Ringing locations of birds later recovered

Breeding (mAPR–sAUG)

Non-breeding (sAUG–mAPR)

Fig 2. Month of ringing of birds later recovered

Fully grown
Pulli

Fig 3. Finding circumstances

Human-related 2%
Other 3%
Domestic predator 3%
Deliberately taken by Man 92%

Dead 96.7% (known cause 85.4%)
Recaught 3.3%
Resighted 0%

Ringing and recovery data

	<1960	60–69	70–79	80–89	90–97	Total
RINGING						
BTO ringing totals (%)	14	23	32	23	10	32,299
RECOVERIES						
BTO-ringed (%)	17	36	27	15	5	1,171
Foreign-ringed (%)	13	23	37	18	10	460

Statistical analyses

	Breeding population (mAPR–sAUG)	Wintering population (mNOV–sMAR)
Status	SHORT-DISTANCE MIGRANT (2)	LONG-DISTANCE MIGRANT*
Age differences[NT]	Significant*	Not tested
Sex differences	Not tested	Not tested
Regional differences	Significant[3]*	Not tested
Finding circumstances	Not tested*	Not tested

Table 1. Summary of the distances moved between ringing and recovery for Snipe present in Britain during the breeding season. Only dead recoveries are included.

Region	n	Median (km)	P5 (km)	P95 (km)
Northeast	17	11	0	536
Northwest	59	6	0	817
Southeast	42	72.5	0	1,769
Southwest	49	106	0	581

Most recoveries abroad of Snipe ringed in Britain & Ireland have been killed by hunters along the Atlantic coasts of France and Iberia. These recoveries suggest a pattern of movement that sees birds arriving in Britain & Ireland from northern and eastern continental Europe, only to continue their journey south with the progress of winter. The majority (93%) of 'hunted' individuals from the British & Irish breeding population, however, are shot on home territory (92% of all recoveries are 'hunted'; Henderson *et al* 1993), lending weight to the idea that this population is more sedentary than those in central Europe, where 20% of Snipe are 'hunted' on home territory (98% of all recoveries are 'hunted'), or Fennoscandia where 7.3% of Snipe are 'hunted' on home territory (although hunting pressure is lower here accounting for only 78% of all recoveries).

The British & Irish ring-recoveries for Snipe populations abroad suggest that in some years, up to a million birds could arrive in Britain & Ireland, to dwarf the local winter population of at least 70,000 individuals (Stone *et al* 1997). The recovery rate in Britain & Ireland for Snipe pulli (birds from known populations) is around 5% for Fennoscandia and Germany, but represents 13% of all recoveries of Fennoscandian-ringed pulli and 23%

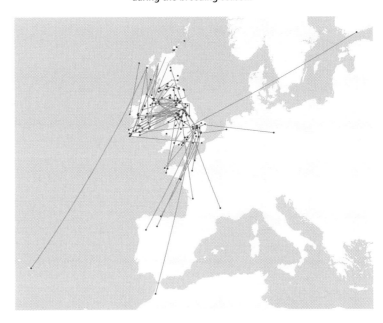

Fig 4. Locations outside the breeding season and movements of over 20 km between the breeding and non-breeding season of 166 Snipe present in Britain & Ireland during the breeding season.

of all recoveries of German-ringed pulli (Henderson *et al* 1993). Estimates of over 300,000 breeding pairs for Fennoscandia and 10,000 breeding pairs for Germany (*European Atlas*) and two fledged offspring per nest (*BWP*) imply that around 165,000 individuals may arrive in Britain & Ireland if recovery rates of pulli are representative of all unringed birds. More importantly, 94% (36/39) of all Icelandic-ringed recoveries were found in Britain & Ireland (two in France, one in Portugal). Icelandic recoveries may

Fig 5. All included exchanges of Snipe between (a) northern Britain (16), (b) southern Britain (56), and (c) Ireland (51), and abroad.

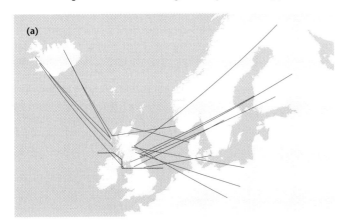

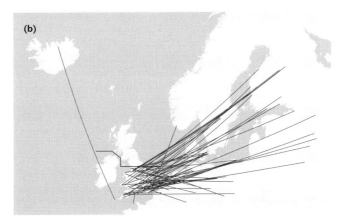

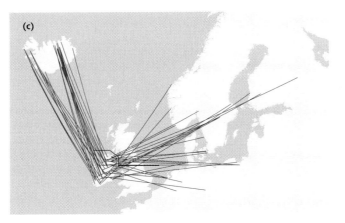

Fig 6. Movements of over 20 km and recovery locations of Snipe ringed in winter and recovered in (a) the same winter (42:30) or (b) a subsequent winter (82:64). Sample sizes of movements under:over 20 km are given but only those over 20 km are plotted.

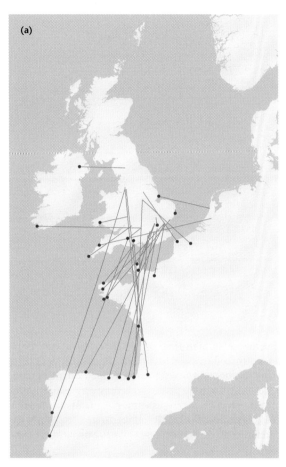

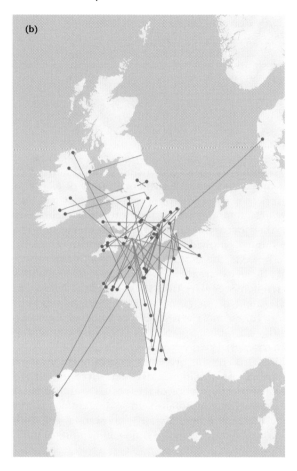

be under-reported elsewhere in Europe but hunting pressure in Britain & Ireland is, if anything, lower than in France and Iberia (Henderson *et al* 1993) where many Fennoscandian-ringed birds are reported but few Icelandic-ringed birds are found. Overall, between 200,000 and 300,000 pairs of Snipe breed in Iceland (*European Atlas*, Petersen 1998) so, with juveniles, up to a million birds may leave Iceland in winter (Petersen pers comm). Most fly to Ireland and probably northwest Britain (Fig 5). Even assuming an unknown level of early-autumn mortality, certainly three-quarters of a million to a million adults and juveniles must visit Britain & Ireland in winter from Iceland, northern and central Europe. Ireland, and possibly northwest Scotland, are clearly vital regions for *faeroeensis* in winter. Elsewhere, Norwegian-ringed birds form only 6% of all foreign-ringed recoveries in Britain & Ireland but this represents 44% of all Norwegian- ringed Snipe that have been recovered (*BWP*), indicating that Britain & Ireland may also be an important destination for birds travelling through Norway.

Some Snipe originate from as far afield as the Baltic States, Russia and the Czech Republic (Fig 5). Apart from Iceland, Snipe present in Ireland outside the breeding season originate from Fennoscandia and northern Europe as far east as Poland (Fig 5a). Snipe that are in southern Britain outside the breeding season are from Fennoscandia and northern Europe as far east as western Russia (Fig 5b). Snipe present in northern Britain outside the breeding season are found breeding over a similar range, although the furthest east that recoveries have been reported from is Finland, and no exchanges between northern Britain and the Russian breeding population have been recorded (Fig 5c).

Although numerically fewer German-ringed birds have been recovered in Britain & Ireland than Fennoscandian-ringed birds, a higher percentage of recoveries of German-ringed (23%) than Fennoscandian-ringed pulli or juveniles (13%) have been from Britain & Ireland (Henderson *et al* 1993), indicating the relative importance of Britain &

Ireland for birds of German, and possibly central European origin. In addition, while recoveries of birds ringed in eastern Europe are rare (reflecting the relatively low level of ringing effort), 50 British- & Irish-ringed Snipe have been recovered from Russia (38), the Baltic States, Ukraine and Belarus, representing almost 25% of recoveries found beyond Britain & Ireland and France. Once again this underlines Britain & Ireland's position as an important wintering or stopover destination for Snipe breeding or travelling, not only through northern Europe, but also through the central and eastern European region (Fig 5).

A few individuals of the North American race *delicata* have been reported in Ireland and western Britain (BOU 1999) but most records are poorly substantiated.

There is evidence of movements in response to cold weather with 30 movements over 20 km within the same winter (Fig 6a) and 64 between winters (Fig 6b), although some of these may be onward movement.

Population trends for breeding Snipe in Britain & Ireland in the last 25 years indicate a serious widespread decline, by as much as 90% in lowland areas of England (O'Brien & Smith 1992, Crick *et al* 1998). Although Snipe are widely hunted in Britain, Ireland and abroad, it is almost certainly not hunting pressure that has caused the decline in the breeding population in Britain & Ireland in the last 20 years, since hunting pressure on Snipe has, if anything, been in decline in Europe since the 1950s (Aebischer *et al* 1999). Instead, the loss of wetland habitats, following extensive programmes of land improvement and drainage in parts of Ireland (Henderson *et al* 2000) as well as southern Britain (*1988–91 Atlas*), has been the most potent threat to this species' breeding status in Britain & Ireland. Ireland and Britain have special responsibilities for *faeroeensis*, yet no monitoring is in place and the movements of British-breeding *faeroeensis* are unknown.

Ian Henderson

Eurasian Woodcock (Woodcock)

Scolopax rusticola

The Woodcock is an elusive, cryptic wader frequenting woodland. It has a widespread breeding distribution within Britain & Ireland but breeding densities tend to be low and it is generally only the peculiar roding displays of the males that betray the birds' presence. It is perhaps in autumn, when our resident birds are supplemented by a large influx of migrants from continental Europe, that most Woodcock are encountered. Even then, one is seldom treated to more than a fleeting glimpse of the bird as it jinks away through the trees.

The Woodcock's main breeding areas are Russia and Fennoscandia, with over 90% of the European population occurring in these regions (*European Atlas*). Much smaller numbers breed in Denmark, Germany, the Netherlands, Belgium and France, as well as in Britain & Ireland. The populations of Russia and Fennoscandia are migratory, wintering throughout western and southern Europe, but particularly in France, Spain, Britain, Ireland and Italy, while those of northwestern Europe are largely sedentary.

During the breeding season, Woodcock favour primarily deciduous and mixed woods with a good understorey of shrubs and dense ground cover for nest concealment, although conifer plantations are used up to the thicket stage. However, outside the breeding season they tend to use woodland only for resting during the day and feed largely by night on rough and improved pastures. During the peak autumn migration, many are found on coastal dunes in eastern Britain and in favoured wintering areas, such as Cornwall, gorse scrub and rhododendron thickets afford sufficient diurnal shelter.

The analysis of the data for this species was supported by Peter Wilson

The Woodcock has long been prized as an elusive and challenging quarry species throughout Europe. Owing to this sporting interest, several estates throughout northern England and Ireland were banding birds before the formal British & Irish Ringing Scheme was introduced in 1909. For instance, at the instigation of the Duke of Northumberland, Lord William Percy, the gamekeepers on the Alnwick estates ringed some 600 Woodcock chicks between 1891 and 1921. The recoveries from these birds provided the first information that most British Woodcock are sedentary.

The distribution of ringing locations in the breeding season of birds later recovered broadly matches the breeding range given in the *1988–91 Atlas*, reflecting the northern strongholds of the species (Fig 1). Some parts of the wintering range, particularly in Scotland and Ireland are under-represented although the ringing locations during autumn and winter highlight a more southerly concentration of wintering Woodcock. The majority of Woodcock have been ringed as chicks during a prolonged breeding season (April–August) but reasonable numbers have also been ringed during autumn migration (Fig 2).

The Woodcock remains an important quarry species and therefore has a ring-recovery rate that is relatively high compared to that of most other waders. Of all recoveries of dead birds with a known cause, 94%

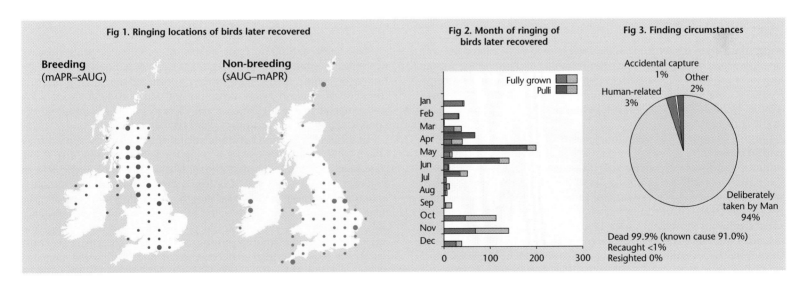

Fig 1. Ringing locations of birds later recovered

Breeding (mAPR–sAUG)

Non-breeding (sAUG–mAPR)

Fig 2. Month of ringing of birds later recovered

Fully grown / Pulli

Jan, Feb, Mar, Apr, May, Jun, Jul, Aug, Sep, Oct, Nov, Dec
0 100 200 300

Fig 3. Finding circumstances

Accidental capture 1%
Human-related 3%
Other 2%
Deliberately taken by Man 94%

Dead 99.9% (known cause 91.0%)
Recaught <1%
Resighted 0%

Ringing and recovery data

	<1960	60–69	70–79	80–89	90–97	Total
RINGING						
BTO ringing totals (%)	60	3	12	15	10	9,404
RECOVERIES						
BTO-ringed (%)	60	5	11	14	10	730
Foreign-ringed (%)	15	17	25	23	20	287

Statistical analyses

	Breeding population (mAPR–sAUG)	Wintering population (mNOV–sMAR)
Status	SHORT-DISTANCE MIGRANT (1)	LONG-DISTANCE MIGRANT*
Age differences[NT]	Not significant*	Not tested
Sex differences	Not tested	Not tested
Regional differences	Significant[5]*	Not tested
Finding circumstances	Not tested*	Not tested*

Fig 4. Locations in autumn & winter and movements of over 20 km between the breeding season and autumn & winter of Woodcock present in (a) northern Britain (315) and (b) southern Britain & Ireland (90) during the breeding season.

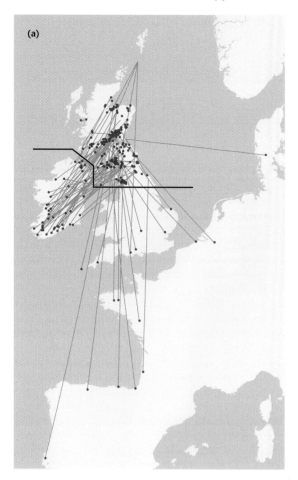

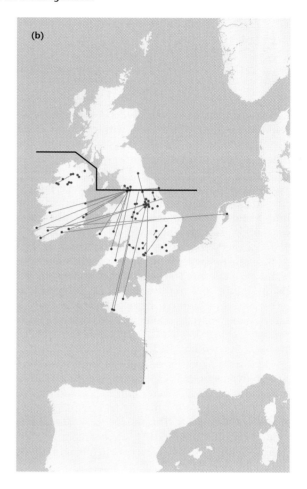

are attributable to hunting (Fig 3). Recoveries need to be interpreted with care, therefore, because there have been changes in the shooting seasons and some countries (Russia, Belarus, Estonia, Latvia, Lithuania, Romania, Hungary, Poland, the former Czechoslovakia, the former Yugoslavia, Austria, Denmark and Sweden) still permit the shooting of roding birds in the spring.

British & Irish Woodcock are typically sedentary throughout the year. Whereas most species of wader leave their breeding grounds in late summer, the majority of British & Irish Woodcock remain faithful to their natal or breeding sites during the winter, with 51% being recovered within 10 km of the place of ringing and 68% within 30 km (Hoodless & Coulson 1994). However, a proportion of the population clearly does make significant movements, with 13% of the winter recoveries made at distances of more than 500 km. Nevertheless, there is no evidence that these were hard-weather movements, as British & Irish Woodcock move no further from their natal or breeding sites in cold winters (mean air temperature in central England below 3°C) or during cold spells within winters (Hoodless & Coulson 1994).

Birds originating in Scotland or northern England seem to be more likely to make a long-distance movement. The longest-distance recoveries were mainly of birds from northern Britain, which tended to move south or southwest to Ireland, France, Spain, Belgium, Portugal or Denmark (Fig 4). The fact that the majority of these recoveries were made before 1 January is again indicative that the movements were not made in response to inclement weather. This suggests that a small proportion of British & Irish breeders are truly migratory, leaving northern Britain as birds from Fennoscandia and Russia are arriving.

Woodcock exhibit a high degree of philopatry, with 76% of recoveries in subsequent breeding seasons of birds ringed as chicks in Britain & Ireland being made within 10 km of the ringing location (Hoodless & Coulson 1994). Recaptures of ringed birds in an intensive study suggest that a high proportion of breeding adults return to the same breeding site in subsequent years (Hoodless 1994a).

Of 45 chicks ringed in Britain & Ireland which were recovered during March to September in years following the year of ringing, five (11%) were found abroad, in Sweden (three), Norway and Russia, all between 1932 and 1948 (Hoodless & Coulson 1994). While this proportion is undoubtedly exaggerated by the shooting of roding birds abroad, and hence gives a misleading impression of the true extent of long-distance dispersal by young birds, this genetic exchange is interesting and important. Such abmigration in other species is often explained by the pairing of British & Irish and continental birds before the migrants depart in spring. This explanation seems unlikely in the Woodcock since there is no evidence of pair formation prior to migration and long-term pairing is very unlikely in this polygynous species.

Records from bird observatories suggest that the first of the migrant Woodcock usually arrive in Scotland during the second week of October, with the first birds reaching southern England and Ireland about 10 days later (Williamson 1958–62, Hoodless & Coulson 1994). This is supported by the increase in numbers ringed (from recoveries) in October and November (Fig 2). The earliest recovery of a foreign Woodcock was on 12 October. It is widely believed that falls of Woodcock usually occur first on the east coast each autumn and certainly some of the largest numbers shot in a day in England have been on Pheasant shoots in the eastern

Fig 5. Recovery locations and movements overseas of Woodcock either ringed abroad and recovered in Britain & Ireland or ringed in Britain & Ireland during winter (October–February) and recovered abroad. Woodcock present in (a) northern Britain (55) are shown separately from those present in (b) southern Britain (176) and (c) Ireland (80).

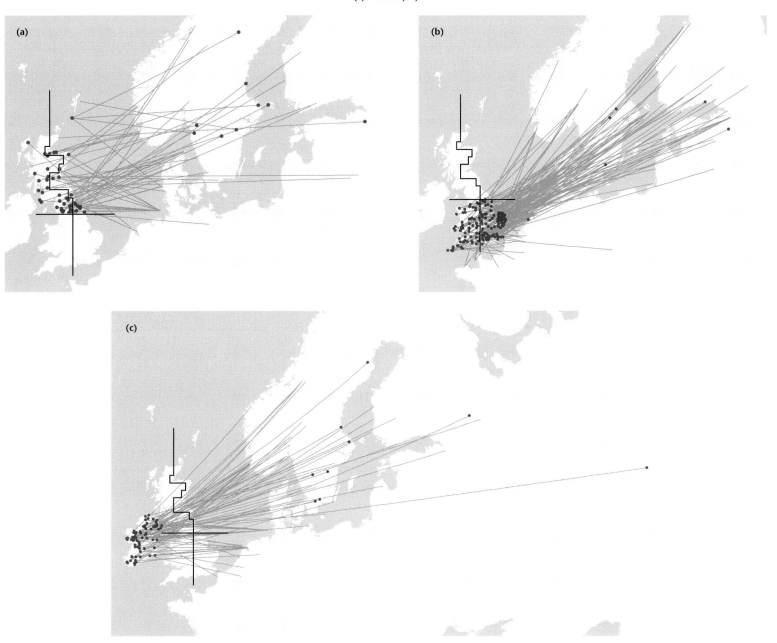

counties of Norfolk, Lincolnshire and Northumberland, where Woodcock constituted only incidental quarry. Shooting literature suggests that large falls often occur around the time of the full moon in late October and particularly in November, the latter being regarded as 'the Woodcock moon'.

The largest number of Woodcock recorded at any of the observatories tends to be at Fair Isle, where about 50 per day are seen during peak passage in average years, although more than a thousand were recorded on 27–28 October 1976 (*Birds in Scotland*). The influx of overwintering migrants continues until late December and is such that the British wintering population may number 800,000 individuals (Hirons & Linsley 1989), meaning that migrant Woodcock outnumber residents by about 13:1 in midwinter. The North Sea crossing can undoubtedly be treacherous on occasion and there are scattered reports of Woodcock 'wrecks' during adverse weather, particularly westerly gales, at the time of the autumn migration. A severe storm in the autumn of 1928 is said to have resulted in thousands of Woodcock drowning off the Lowestoft–

Yarmouth area, with one fishing boat picking up 470 (Seigne 1930, cited by McKelvie 1990).

Using information on the size of breeding Woodcock populations on the Continent, the numbers ringed, and the proportion of ringed individuals recovered in Britain & Ireland, it is possible to estimate the approximate proportions of the British & Irish winter population originating in various countries as 37% from Russia & Latvia, 25% from Finland, 14% from Britain, 12% from Sweden and 10% from Norway (Hoodless & Coulson 1994). Examination of the origin of foreign birds according to the region of recovery suggests that there is a tendency for Woodcock from different continental breeding grounds to winter in different parts of Britain & Ireland (Fig 5). Birds wintering in Scotland and northern England appear to originate largely from Norway, Sweden and Denmark, with a relatively small proportion breeding further east. In contrast, the majority of Woodcock wintering in southern England and Wales seem to originate from Finland, Russia and Latvia. Ireland receives birds from throughout the northern European breeding range.

Comparison of the mean recovery latitudes of foreign-ringed and British- & Irish-ringed Woodcock during November to January suggests that the majority of foreign birds are to be found further south in Britain & Ireland than British & Irish birds during this period. The highest densities of wintering Woodcock are found in southwest England and Wales and consequently these regions are where the largest numbers are shot. Information from ring-recoveries has revealed that a high proportion of the Woodcock in these areas are foreign migrants (Hoodless & Coulson 1994) and hence a large proportion of all Woodcock killed in Britain each winter are undoubtedly of continental origin. Conversely, the relatively small numbers of Woodcock shot in northern England and Scotland before mid-October will belong to local breeding populations. The impact of hunting on the Woodcock is very difficult to assess but recent evidence suggests that there has been a decline in hunting pressure on this species in Britain and in Ireland since the 1960s (Henderson et al 1993).

While the proportions of ringed Woodcock recaptured in intensive studies in Ireland and Cornwall were relatively low (13% and 18.5% respectively; Wilson 1983, Hoodless 1994b), comparison of an annual adult survival rate calculated from the Cornish data with the adult survival rate from all British & Irish ring-recoveries suggests that wintering site-fidelity may be as high as 80% (Hoodless 1994b).

On the basis of the mean Woodcock hunting bags per county during a mild winter (1979/80) and a cold winter (1980/81), Tapper & Hirons (1983) have suggested that there is a redistribution of Woodcock within Britain during cold winters. Certainly during the severe winter of 1962/63, unusually large numbers of Woodcock were concentrated in the southern and western counties of England and Wales and significant numbers were among the many dead birds reported (Ash 1964, Dobinson & Richards 1964). However, Woodcock can generally withstand four or five days of freezing conditions and given that there is no evidence from ring-recoveries that British & Irish Woodcock move farther from their natal or breeding sites in cold winters, it is probable that, in most cases, such movements only involve continental migrants. It seems plausible that the resident and migrant birds might follow different strategies, since the residents will probably benefit from remaining in the same place owing to familiarity with the site, whereas the migrant Woodcock may increase their chance of finding an unfrozen feeding area by moving elsewhere. There is no direct evidence that more Woodcock move to Britain from the Continent in cold winters, but there is a suggestion of this from increased numbers of sightings of Woodcock on the coast (Dobinson & Richards 1964, Marchant 1982, BWP).

The majority of continental migrants depart during late February and early March, but it is interesting to note that some foreign-ringed birds (4% of all foreign recoveries) remained in Britain throughout March and into April (up to 15 April), by which time most resident females would have mated and laid eggs (Hoodless & Coulson 1998). There are no records of any remaining in Britain or Ireland to breed.

There is speculation, as yet unsupported by sufficient data, that continental Woodcock may exhibit differential migrations according to age and sex, as do some migratory ducks. Age ratios among wings supplied by hunters in the early 1980s showed a consistently high proportion of young birds in Cornwall (Harradine 1988) and a female-biased sex ratio has been recorded on one large sporting estate there (Hoodless 1994b). However, the hunting pressure on Woodcock in Cornwall tends to be higher than in most of the rest of Britain and this shooting mortality may maintain the high young:old ratio (Hirons 1988). To discover whether there is indeed any differential migration, large samples of birds shot at different latitudes will have to be examined. Sadly, too few Woodcock are caught by ringers to help answer this question and, in any case, only a small proportion of birds can be sexed with confidence from external measurements.

Andrew Hoodless

Black-tailed Godwit
Limosa limosa

Black-tailed Godwits are elegant wading birds that are common within Britain & Ireland in the non-breeding season but have only a very small breeding population. Of the three subspecies, the nominate *limosa* breeds across western Eurasia, principally in the Netherlands, Denmark, Germany and the former USSR, with small numbers in Britain. It winters largely in Africa, south of the Sahara but also in the Iberian Peninsula. By contrast, *islandica*, which breeds principally in Iceland but with a few pairs in northern Scotland and northwest Norway, winters largely in Britain, Ireland and western France, with smaller numbers in Spain and Portugal. The third subspecies, *melanuroides*, breeds in eastern Siberia and winters from the Bay of Bengal to Taiwan and the Philippines, and south to Australia (*BWP*). The nominate *limosa* is presently undergoing significant declines in numbers across the range, which are believed to be linked to intensification of farming practices (Busche 1994). The Icelandic subspecies, however, is currently increasing in number (Prater 1975, 1981, Cranswick *et al* 1999).

During the breeding season, Black-tailed Godwits inhabit lowland wet grassland and marshes. Outside the breeding season they use a variety of habitats; *islandica* use principally estuarine mudflats but also grassland and coastal lagoons; *limosa* occur largely inland in the Sahel, Rift Valley and Lake Victoria areas. In Britain & Ireland, the winter habitat is mainly estuarine mudflats although wet grasslands, coastal lagoons and reservoirs are also frequented.

The breeding population in Britain & Ireland (*limosa*) is only approximately 60 pairs (*1988–91 Atlas*). Consequently very few breeding Black-tailed Godwits have been ringed in Britain & Ireland, although in

The analysis of the data for this species was supported by Les Hatton, Peter Potts & Jenny Gill

recent years chicks hatched at the two main breeding sites in eastern England have been colour-ringed in order to assess the extent of movement of birds between the British and continental breeding sites. The vast majority of Black-tailed Godwits have been ringed in the non-breeding season (Figs 1 & 2) and are consequently of the Icelandic subspecies. Ringing of these birds has tended to take place on coastal passage sites such as the Wash and Eden Estuaries and on wintering sites such as the Solent harbours. Very little ringing of Black-tailed Godwits has taken place in Ireland.

Black-tailed Godwit ringing data are somewhat unusual in that recent colour-ringing studies of this species in Britain have resulted in over half of all recoveries being observations of individually colour-marked birds. The distribution of these colour-ring sightings is therefore influenced by the location of these studies in the east and south of England and east Scotland. Of the small number of ringed birds that died from a known cause, approximately one-third were deliberately taken by Man and another third resulted from human-related causes; this may have influenced the pattern shown by recoveries of dead birds (Fig 3).

The British breeding population arrives back from the end of March onwards and has left for the wintering grounds by the end of July. Although very few breeding Black-tailed Godwits have been ringed in Britain & Ireland, the single recovery of a British breeding adult to date,

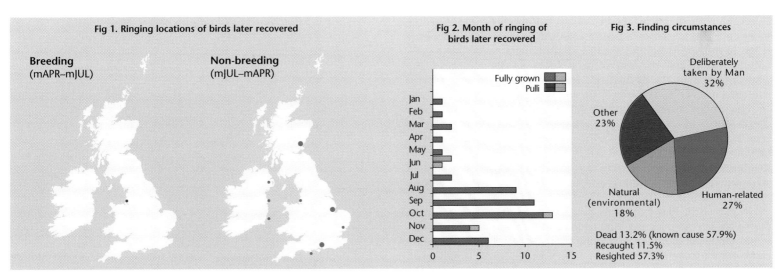

Fig 1. Ringing locations of birds later recovered

Breeding (mAPR–mJUL)   Non-breeding (mJUL–mAPR)

Fig 2. Month of ringing of birds later recovered

Fully grown
Pulli

Fig 3. Finding circumstances

Deliberately taken by Man 32%
Other 23%
Human-related 27%
Natural (environmental) 18%

Dead 13.2% (known cause 57.9%)
Recaught 11.5%
Resighted 57.3%

Ringing and recovery data

	<1960	60–69	70–79	80–89	90–97	Total
RINGING						
BTO ringing totals (%)	0	5	14	28	52	1,767
RECOVERIES						
BTO-ringed (%)	0	2	6	9	83	116
Foreign-ringed (%)	0	0	33	33	33	6

Statistical analyses

	Breeding population (mAPR–mJUL)	Wintering population (mOCT–mFEB)
Status	[LONG-DISTANCE MIGRANT]	[LONG-DISTANCE MIGRANT]
Age differences	Not tested	Not tested
Sex differences	Not tested	Not tested
Regional differences	Not tested	Not tested
Finding circumstances	Not tested	Not tested

Fig 4. Recovery locations in (a) autumn (42), (b) winter (38), (c) spring (16) and (d) the breeding season (20), and movements of over 20 km, of Black-tailed Godwits present in Britain & Ireland during part of the year.

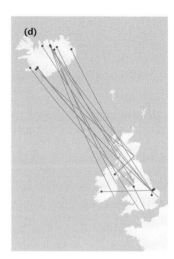

from an unknown location in Guinea-Bissau in November 1990, suggests that they winter south of the Sahara. Of the Black-tailed Godwits hatched in Britain that have been colour-ringed, none have been observed in late autumn or winter, suggesting that these birds do not remain in northern Europe. In addition, these birds appear to have a high degree of natal philopatry, with none having been recorded breeding elsewhere in Europe to date (N Ratcliffe pers comm), and there is no evidence of *limosa* from continental breeding populations occurring in Britain & Ireland on passage.

Confirmation that the Black-tailed Godwits that winter in Britain & Ireland are of the *islandica* race is provided by the large number of recoveries and sightings of British-ringed birds in Iceland and the four godwits ringed in Iceland that have subsequently been recovered in Britain (Fig 4; Fig 1.6 in Chapter 1). Black-tailed Godwits ringed in Britain & Ireland in the non-breeding season have only been recorded breeding in Iceland. Multiple observations of colour-ringed birds throughout the range have shown that Black-tailed Godwits tend to be highly site-faithful within and between winters. The Icelandic subspecies also winters in France, the Netherlands and Denmark, and alongside the wintering *limosa* population in Spain and Portugal.

The seasonal maps of sightings and recoveries show the pattern of distribution of Icelandic breeding Black-tailed Godwits (Fig 4). On arrival from Iceland in July and August the godwits frequently congregate in large moulting flocks on coastal sites. Colour-ring sightings have shown that Black-tailed Godwits arriving on the north and east coast in autumn show different patterns, timings and movements from those arriving on the south coast.

In the north and east, Black-tailed Godwits are generally ringed during the late summer moulting period and then tend to move further south during autumn (Fig 4a). During winter, many are to be found on east-coast estuaries, with smaller numbers moving to the south coast, Ireland and the Netherlands (Figs 4b & 5). On spring passage, many move from the east coast to inland sites in East Anglia, Lancashire and Ireland before returning to Iceland during April and May (Figs 4c & d). Although there is little ringing information from Ireland, count data also show these birds to move to inland sites in spring prior to migration (*Birds in Ireland*).

Colour-ringing of Black-tailed Godwits on the south coast has shown these birds to be much more sedentary: autumn recoveries are largely local movements or occasionally movements to France and there are few winter movements (pers obs). These birds also use inland sites in late winter and spring (pers obs). Fig 4d shows the movement back to Iceland during the breeding season.

The breeding population of *limosa* in Britain is very small and restricted in range. This subspecies is declining across its breeding range and ringing data are extremely important in demonstrating the extent to which birds hatched at the British sites return to their natal breeding grounds, and hence the potential for habitat management to increase local population size.

Fig 5. Locations in winter, and movements between autumn and winter, of colour-marked Black-tailed Godwits. Winter locations for those birds that did not move (blue) are differentiated from those that did move (red). Lines may represent more than one movement between two sites, since there are 95 movements in total. (*Source*: J A Gill.)

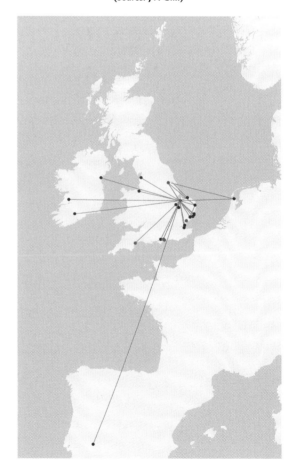

Ringing data have also demonstrated the relatively restricted distribution of the Icelandic-breeding subspecies. In particular, during autumn and spring passage the birds are dependent upon a small number of sites that are often interlinked. Protection of these sites is therefore an important component of maintaining the favourable conservation status of these birds; ringing plays a key role in identifying these sites and quantifying population turnover within sites. Observations of colour-ringed birds have proven particularly effective in estimating turnover and hence allowing calculations of local population sizes. Multiple observations of colour-ringed birds have also provided uniquely valuable information on the links between passage, wintering and breeding sites.

The major gaps in our knowledge of wintering Black-tailed Godwits concern the habitat selection, movements and survival of first-year birds and the large numbers of godwits that winter in Ireland. Over half of the Icelandic subspecies may winter in Ireland but as yet there is very little information on the distribution and movements of this section of the population. Similarly, the proportion of *islandica* that winter further south than Britain & Ireland is currently unclear, as *islandica* and *limosa* mix in some areas. Ringing and observations of colour-ringed birds will allow the currently declining *limosa* and increasing *islandica* populations in these areas to be distinguished.

Jennifer Gill, Les Hatton & Peter Potts

Bar-tailed Godwit
Limosa lapponica

The sight of massive towering flocks of Bar-tailed Godwit shimmering in the weak winter sunlight is a feature of several of the larger estuaries in Britain & Ireland. Bar-tailed Godwits are passage migrants and winter visitors to the British and Irish coasts and perform a remarkably synchronized long-distance migration that extends far into the southern hemisphere.

The breeding distribution of Bar-tailed Godwits is characterized by a number of discrete breeding areas in the Arctic tundra. The nominate race *lapponica* breeds from northern Fennoscandia and the Kola Peninsula across western Siberia to the Taimyr Peninsula. Further east there is a zone in which differentiation from the eastern race *baueri*, which occurs from western Siberia to western Alaska, is apparently incomplete. In winter, *lapponica* is found on the estuaries of northwestern Europe, the West African coast and sparingly further south in Africa and on the western shores of the Indian Ocean, and *baueri* on the shores of western India and from southern China and Sumatra to western Polynesia, Australia and New Zealand. The wintering population of about 125,000 birds in western Europe is concentrated around the North Sea and is likely to originate from the European and west Siberian breeding populations. In West Africa, the majority of wintering birds (600,000–700,000 birds) are likely to come from breeding populations in the Siberian Taimyr and Yamal Peninsulas (Drent & Piersma 1990); these birds migrate through western Europe.

In Britain & Ireland, Bar-tailed Godwits are confined to estuaries and large numbers tend to occur only on relatively few large, sandy estuaries. Important sites include the Wash, Thames Estuary, Dundalk Bay, other

The analysis of the data for this species was supported by Graham Appleton

estuaries in the Irish Sea and Lindisfarne (Cranswick *et al* 1999). Smaller numbers are found on most other British & Irish estuaries.

As with most wader species in Britain & Ireland, ringing effort has been concentrated on relatively few estuaries (Fig 1). The Wash stands out as having the most recoveries compared with other British & Irish estuaries. The ringing dates of birds later recovered show that Bar-tailed Godwits are ringed throughout the year but with most ringing being undertaken in the autumn, particularly August (Fig 2). Over 40% of recoveries of dead birds have a known cause, with the majority of these (70%) having been taken by Man (Fig 3). The distribution of recoveries of dead birds is therefore likely to have been influenced by the distribution of hunters.

Bar-tailed Godwits do not breed in Britain & Ireland. Ring-recoveries from known breeding areas are sparse but indicate that birds from two populations pass through Britain & Ireland (Fig 4). These populations are birds that breed in northern Fennoscandia and western Russia, and those breeding further east to central Siberia. In the breeding season, only small numbers of immature and non-breeding adult birds occur in Britain & Ireland. In winter, again there are two areas where ringed birds have been found (Fig 4). The first is around the North Sea and English Channel coasts, and the second along the coast of West Africa, especially the Banc d'Arguin in Mauritania and in Guinea-Bissau.

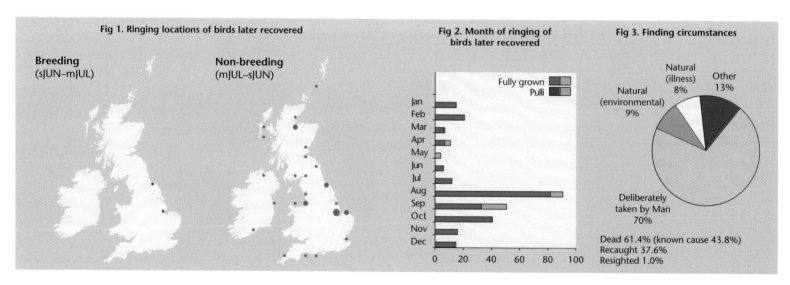

Fig 1. Ringing locations of birds later recovered

Breeding (sJUN–mJUL)

Non-breeding (mJUL–sJUN)

Fig 2. Month of ringing of birds later recovered

Fully grown
Pulli

Fig 3. Finding circumstances

Natural (illness) 8%
Other 13%
Natural (environmental) 9%
Deliberately taken by Man 70%

Dead 61.4% (known cause 43.8%)
Recaught 37.6%
Resighted 1.0%

Ringing and recovery data

	<1960	60–69	70–79	80–89	90–97	Total
RINGING						
BTO ringing totals (%)	0	6	24	52	18	10,500
RECOVERIES						
BTO-ringed (%)	0	5	23	49	24	251
Foreign-ringed (%)	26	13	26	23	13	39

Statistical analyses

	Breeding population (sJUN–mJUL)	Wintering population (sNOV–sAPR)
Status	NONE	[LONG-DISTANCE MIGRANT]
Age differences	—	Not tested
Sex differences	—	Not tested
Regional differences	—	Not tested
Finding circumstances	—	Not tested

Fig 4. Recovery locations and all included exchanges of Bar-tailed Godwits between Britain & Ireland and abroad. Those abroad in the breeding season (5, red) and winter (34, blue) are differentiated from those abroad during other, or unknown, periods (100, grey).

Fig 5. Locations in winter, and movements of over 20 km between autumn and winter, of 50 Bar-tailed Godwits present in Britain & Ireland during autumn.

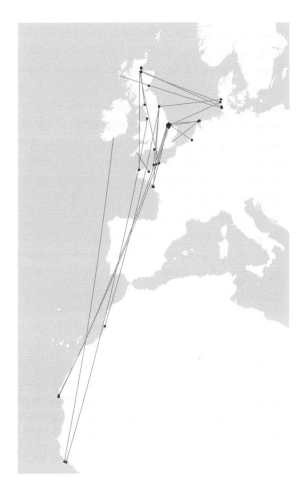

After breeding, adult birds arrive back on British estuaries from the end of July. Large numbers are seen flying past Ottenby in Sweden and some of these birds stop off to moult on the shores of the Wadden Sea or on English or Scottish estuaries (Prater 1981, *Birds in Scotland*). Large moulting flocks occur in particular on the Wash and the Ribble Estuary (Prater 1981). Arrival dates of August in Ireland (*Birds in Ireland*) suggest that small numbers moult there as well. Ring-recoveries show that after being caught on east-coast estuaries, some birds move south and west to winter in Normandy, Brittany and the Channel Islands as well as to wintering areas in West Africa (Fig 5). Prater (1981) also remarks that some birds, after moulting in the Wadden Sea, move into Britain in winter and this has been shown to be the case for some birds trapped on the Wash (Atkinson 1996).

Within Britain & Ireland, the migration and movements of Bar-tailed Godwits are best-known for birds using the Wash (Atkinson 1996). Bar-tailed Godwits arrive back on the Wash in August to moult and then the majority of the population stay on the Wash during winter (Atkinson 1996; Fig 5). A similar pattern is likely for the other main wintering sites. A small but, at present, unknown proportion move and have been found subsequently on other British and continental European estuaries in winter.

On the Wash, catches after 10 August — when most birds have started moult — contain a number of non-moulting birds with smaller-than-average wings and bills. Bar-tailed Godwits vary in size across their breeding range and these smaller birds may be from populations breeding further east, probably in western Siberia or on the western end of the Taimyr Peninsula (Atkinson 1996). These birds, which make up 10–15% of the total birds caught on the Wash in mid- to late August, are presumably on their way to wintering grounds in West Africa, where they moult.

Juvenile birds start to arrive on their wintering grounds later than adults. On the Wash, as elsewhere in England, juveniles arrive *en masse* in September. There have been several same-year recoveries on the Wash of birds ringed as juveniles in Norway, and also juveniles ringed elsewhere and found on the Wash in subsequent years, showing that juveniles may sample estuaries before choosing an estuary to winter on (Atkinson 1996). Bar-tailed Godwits do not breed in their first year. An unknown proportion spend their second summer in the wintering

grounds where they start moult in June, approximately six weeks before adult birds.

Adult birds ringed on the Wash are largely site-faithful during subsequent moulting and winter periods. However, small numbers have been recovered in the Dutch and German Wadden Sea during following years (Atkinson *et al* 1996).

At the end of the winter, the birds wintering around British & Irish coasts move to the Wadden Sea to undergo pre-migratory fattening before returning to the breeding grounds. The major movement from the Wash and other main wintering sites starts in February and continues through March (Fig 6). These birds fatten in the Wadden Sea before departing to Scandinavia and northern Europe (Prater 1981, Prokosch 1988, Atkinson 1996). These birds have left the Wadden Sea by the time those that wintered in West Africa return to fatten for the journey to their Siberian breeding areas. The average departure date from the Banc d'Arguin in Mauritania was 25 April and these birds fly non-stop to the Wadden Sea, arriving several days later (Piersma *et al* 1990). There are no recoveries of birds in intervening areas in North Africa or Spain, Portugal or France, and other research shows that spring migration from the Banc d'Arguin is extremely quick and generally non-stop.

During this period, there is another peak in the number of Bar-tailed Godwits in southeastern Britain, a month after the main exodus of wintering birds. An offshore easterly passage involving thousands of birds is noted annually off Sussex and south Kent, peaking in the last week of April or early May. Peak daily totals have included 4,009 off Worthing on 24 April 1984 (James 1996) and in 1973 over 8,000 were recorded at Dungeness, including 4,188 on 26 April. At Breydon Water in Norfolk, numbers peak so regularly in spring that 12 May has been

Fig 6. Locations in (a) March–April (35) and (b) May (28) of Bar-tailed Godwits present in Britain & Ireland during part of the year. A single recovery in Africa in March is not shown.

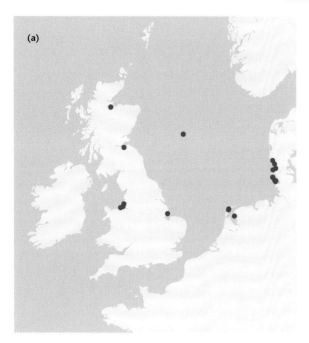

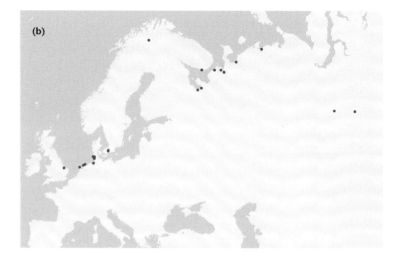

known as 'Godwit Day' (Taylor *et al* 1999). These records undoubtedly refer to the migration of the birds that wintered in West Africa.

Ring-recoveries indicate that, after leaving the Wadden Sea in spring, most birds overfly the Baltic and make a first stop in coastal areas around the Kola Peninsula and the White Sea, where a number of ringed birds have been shot and subsequently reported. These are probably birds staging before moving to breeding areas, although some birds do breed in this area. Whether these birds are from the Fennoscandian or Siberian breeding populations is unknown.

On the breeding grounds, the number of recoveries is low due to the low density of breeding birds and the remote, often inaccessible, nature of their nesting sites (Fig 4). There is one inland record of a bird recovered in May in northern Scandinavia that was probably on its breeding ground, and one inland on the Kola Peninsula in July. The west Siberian breeding birds are represented by two birds recovered in May and July on the West Siberian Plain between the Ob and Yenisei rivers. The most easterly recovery of a bird during the breeding season is one recovered just to the east of the River Yenisei at the extreme western end of the Taimyr Peninsula. This bird was ringed on the Wash in August 1985 and recovered at Lake Essey (68°N 102°E) in Krasnoyarsk region in Russia in April 1994. It had just started to moult when it was caught on the Wash on 20 August, which suggested that it belonged to the European wintering population. Bill and wing lengths also supported this as they were in the extreme upper range for Siberian-breeding birds. This doubt, coupled with the fact that the hunter who shot this bird reported it as a female Ruff, means that this record should be treated as doubtful.

The evidence for differential migration between the sexes is intriguing. In the population that winters around the North Sea and Atlantic coast of Britain, there is a consistently higher proportion of males in catches. These biases are so consistent between catches either by mist-netting or cannon-netting that catching bias towards a particular sex is unlikely. Approximately 70% of the birds caught in the Moray Firth and between 57% and 75% of birds caught in the Wash are males (Swann 1981, Atkinson 1996). On the Wash, where catches have been made throughout the calendar year, the proportion of males in the catches increases from July to December, stays approximately constant until June and then drops again in July (Atkinson 1996). It may be that more females winter elsewhere, either in a geographically different region or separated by habitat, or that there is an unequal sex ratio due to differential survival or other factors. In the West African wintering population, there is evidence that females winter further south than males as the proportion of males is lower in Guinea-Bissau (52%) than the more northerly Mauritania (69%) (Piersma *et al* 1990).

The Bar-tailed Godwit, along with several other species of wader, is reliant on a very small number of sites and is therefore vulnerable to habitat change. The key site in Europe is the Wadden Sea, which, at different times of year, hosts both populations of Bar-tailed Godwit. In Britain & Ireland, the northwest European wintering population is increasing for unknown reasons but reduced hunting pressure in the wintering areas may be a factor. Much has been learnt both in Africa and Europe about the wintering ecology and migration strategy of this species. However, in Britain & Ireland the largest question concerns what happens to wintering birds in late winter and spring. The numbers of birds caught in Britain & Ireland from December to May is extremely small and very little is known about the wintering or spring migration strategies during this time.

Phil Atkinson

Whimbrel
Numenius phaeopus

The bubbling call of migrating Whimbrel, familiar along our western coasts in early May, is an evocative reminder of the spectacular wader assemblages which gather to breed during the short summers in the far north. Whimbrel are long-distance migrants, breeding in the boreal, subarctic and low arctic zones of Eurasia and America and wintering in the southern hemisphere or in the tropics of the northern hemisphere, mainly along coasts (*BWP*). In Britain, they are close to the southern limits of their breeding range and, although the small British population has increased recently, they remain a far northern speciality with 95% of the 413–471 breeding pairs being found in Shetland (Richardson 1990). None nest south of the Grampians or in Ireland. Whimbrel are also familiar along all coasts of Britain & Ireland as passage migrants in spring and autumn, and occasional singletons spend the winter in the south and southwest (*Winter Atlas*).

The nominate race *phaeopus* occurs in Britain & Ireland, having a breeding range extending from northeast Greenland east to central Siberia and wintering mainly along the western and southern coasts of Africa and on the islands and coasts of the western Indian Ocean (*BWP, European Atlas*). Birds from this race migrate across Africa and Europe, both along coastal routes and overland, with migrants occurring regularly in the African Sahel and Sahara. The large numbers migrating to and from east and southeast Africa via the Middle East are thought to be of Siberian origin (*BWP*). Of the three other races distinguished, *variegatus* breeds in eastern Siberia and winters from the Bay of Bengal to Melanesia, Micronesia and Australasia while *hudsonicus* occurs in the Americas (*BWP*). The race *alboaxillaris* is believed to breed in the

The analysis of the data for this species was supported by John McMeeking

steppes of the lower Volga southeast of the Urals and to winter along the western Indian Ocean, within the wintering range of *phaeopus*, but the validity of the race is dubious (Scott 1999).

Moorlands and heathlands characterized by short hummocky vegetation are the favoured breeding habitats of Whimbrel in Britain, with highest breeding densities on the serpentine heaths of Shetland (Grant 1991). Breeding areas tend to be at low to moderate altitudes throughout the range (*BWP*). Wintering birds generally occupy coastal habitats, such as intertidal mudflats, creeks, saltmarshes and open sea beaches, while on migration both coastal and inland habitats, such as wetlands and meadows, are used as staging sites (Beretzk *et al* 1959, Ferns *et al* 1979, *BWP*).

The ring-recovery data for Whimbrel are sparse. As expected, breeding-season ringing locations of birds later recovered are concentrated in Shetland (Fig 1) with the small number of southern locations arising from birds on passage between mid-May and the start of August. Only 13 recoveries are of birds ringed as pulli (Fig 2). Ringing locations outside the breeding season (Fig 1) are concentrated in the south and reflect the distribution of many of the main staging sites along the coast of Britain, but show few of those in Ireland (*Birds in Ireland*). The majority (89%) of the recoveries are of dead birds, with over 60% of these being birds deliberately taken by Man (Fig 3). Thus, the

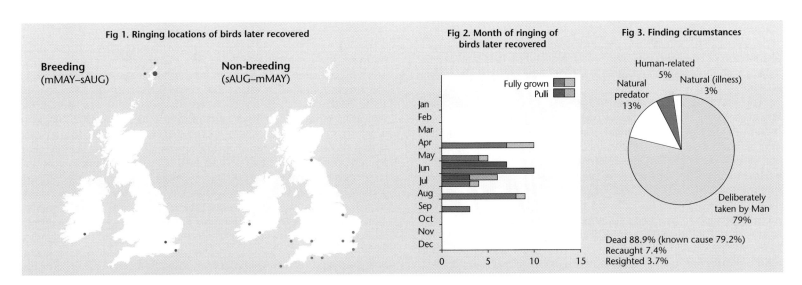

Fig 1. Ringing locations of birds later recovered

Breeding (mMAY–sAUG)   **Non-breeding** (sAUG–mMAY)

Fig 2. Month of ringing of birds later recovered

Fully grown / Pulli

Fig 3. Finding circumstances

Human-related 5%
Natural predator 13%
Natural (illness) 3%
Deliberately taken by Man 79%

Dead 88.9% (known cause 79.2%)
Recaught 7.4%
Resighted 3.7%

Ringing and recovery data

	<1960	60–69	70–79	80–89	90–97	Total
RINGING						
BTO ringing totals (%)	2	11	19	45	23	2,112
RECOVERIES						
BTO-ringed (%)	2	11	20	38	29	45
Foreign-ringed (%)	33	11	22	33	0	9

Statistical analyses

	Breeding population (mMAY–sAUG)	Wintering population (mNOV–mMAR)
Status	[LONG-DISTANCE MIGRANT]	NONE
Age differences	Not tested	—
Sex differences	Not tested	—
Regional differences	Not tested	—
Finding circumstances	Not tested	—

Fig 4. Locations in autumn (7, red), winter (3, blue) and spring (3, grey), and movements of over 20 km between the breeding and non-breeding season, of Whimbrel present in Shetland during the breeding season.

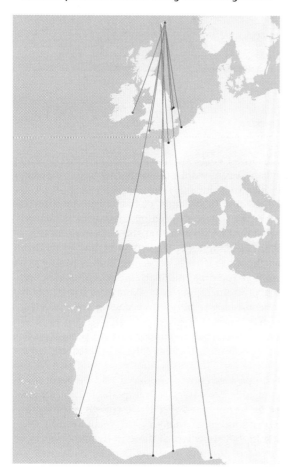

Fig 5. Exchanges between Britain & Ireland and abroad of Whimbrel present in Britain & Ireland during autumn (10, blue), spring (12, black) and the breeding season (3, red), and those of uncertain seasonality (5, grey), excluding those present in Shetland during the breeding season.

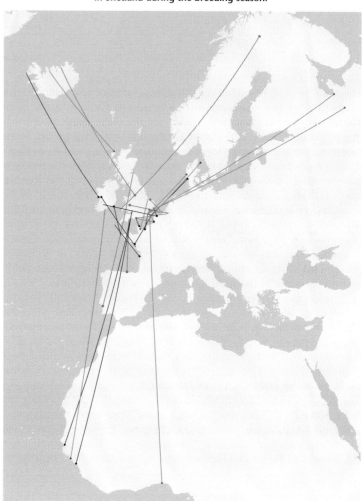

distribution of recoveries from birds ringed in Britain & Ireland may be biased according to the occurrence of hunting, as well as ringing activities.

The southward migration of Whimbrel from Shetland and other British breeding localities begins in mid-July, with failed breeders presumably first to depart. Females sometimes desert their brood a few days before fledging (Grant 1989), and such females may also be among the earlier migrants. Broods in Shetland begin to move off their heathland breeding territories in late July, when most chicks have reached the fledging stage, and small, loose flocks comprising both recent fledglings and adults occur on the islands through late July and August (pers obs). The small number of autumn recoveries of birds ringed on British breeding grounds (Fig 4) suggests that they may tend to use staging sites on the southeast coast of England and on the north coast of France during their southward migration. British breeding birds appear to winter mainly in West Africa (Fig 4). There have been two recoveries of birds on spring passage in the southwest of Britain & Ireland (Fig 4). During spring migration, little time may be spent travelling from staging sites in the southwest of Britain & Ireland to their northern breeding territories. Thus, one colour-ringed bird sighted at Dawlish Warren in Devon in early May was recorded on its breeding territory on Fetlar, Shetland, four days later (John Nicholls pers comm).

Arrival on the breeding grounds in Shetland begins in late April, with most breeding birds having returned by mid-May. The average arrival dates for males are two to three days earlier than for females and fidelity to breeding territories in Shetland is higher for males than females. Thus,

during a three-year study, 87% of males and 68% of females returned to breed on the same study site as in the previous year — a difference that was not attributable to differential survival between the sexes (Grant 1989, 1991). Such high levels of breeding site-fidelity are likely to be typical of Whimbrel in other parts of their range (eg Skeel 1983), as is usual in monogamous wader species which exhibit biparental care (Oring & Lank 1984). Birds do not appear to return to the breeding grounds until at least their second or third years, as indicated by the large numbers which spend the northern summer in the African wintering areas (BWP). Certainly, chicks in Shetland which were colour-ringed in 1987 and 1988 to denote their hatching year were not sighted during intensive searches of the study areas in 1988 and 1989. Sightings of these birds in subsequent years have come mainly from the island of Fetlar, on or close to the main ringing sites, with a record from Shetland Mainland (approximately 38 km from the closest ringing site) being the furthest known movement (pers obs). Thus, at least a proportion of the Shetland-reared chicks return to breed near their natal sites.

The vast majority of Whimbrel that occur on passage in Britain & Ireland will be from the large breeding populations in Iceland, the Faeroes, Fennoscandia and northwest Russia (BWP). Birds ringed on passage in Britain & Ireland have been recovered in Finland (one) and northwest Russia (two), while three recoveries in Britain & Ireland have come from birds ringed on the Icelandic breeding grounds (Fig 5). Birds from these populations also winter in West Africa, many presumably in the same areas as British breeders (BWP). Wing lengths of birds caught on passage in Britain suggest that long-winged birds (typical of Icelandic,

British and, presumably, Faeroese breeders; Salomonsen 1947, Grant 1989) are more prevalent on passage in western Britain (particularly in spring), while shorter-winged birds (typical of continental breeders; Salomonsen 1947) are prevalent in southeast Britain (Ferns *et al* 1979). However, there is clearly overlap of migration routes since the single Finnish recovery was ringed in western Britain.

The main autumn passage in Britain & Ireland is from July to September and peaks in August, when the total WeBS counts for Britain and Northern Ireland have ranged from 602 to 1,155 in recent years (Waters *et al* 1998, Cranswick *et al* 1999, Pollitt *et al* 2000).

During autumn passage, the majority of birds occur along the North Sea coast and in southern England (Prater 1981). Recoveries are too few to indicate the routes taken from passage sites in Britain & Ireland to the African wintering areas, but the occurrence of passage birds suggests a rapid movement of birds through western Europe to Iberia and then down the Moroccan coast to Mauritania. Weight gains of birds on the Wash in autumn suggest that they have sufficient reserves for direct flights to Mauritania (*BWP*).

Northward migration from the African wintering grounds begins in March, with the spring passage in Britain & Ireland beginning in earnest in April and peaking in early May. Spring passage in Britain & Ireland has a more westerly distribution than the autumn passage and between 1972 and 1975 74% of passage Whimbrel counted in Britain in May occurred at sites around the Severn Estuary, compared to 8% during autumn passage (Ferns *et al* 1979). The peak annual spring passage count of *c* 2,500 in Britain & Ireland for 1969–75 was due largely to these concentrations around the Severn Estuary, particularly on the Somerset Levels (Prater 1981). Since then, there has been a substantial decline in numbers using the Somerset Levels (Green & Robins 1993), though large spring concentrations are now known to occur elsewhere in the west of Britain & Ireland (*eg Birds in Ireland*). Recent WeBS total counts for Britain and Northern Ireland in May range from 697 to 2,066 (Cranswick *et al* 1997, 1999, Waters *et al* 1998). Weight gains of birds on the Severn Estuary in spring suggest that they have sufficient reserves for direct flights to Iceland (*BWP*).

During both spring and autumn passage, numbers of birds are greater in continental Europe than in Britain & Ireland (*BWP*), though it is clear from the ring-recovery data that birds using staging sites in northwest Europe may also stage in Britain & Ireland. There are no recoveries linking passage birds in Britain & Ireland with the large spring passage through parts of central Europe.

Throughout Europe the spring passage of Whimbrel is characterized by the large concentrations that occur at a small number of known major staging sites, where Whimbrel presumably find safe roosting sites close to rich feeding areas (*eg* Beretzk *et al* 1959, Ferns *et al* 1979, Zwarts 1990). The substantial decline in the use of the Somerset Levels by spring passage Whimbrel is associated with a long-term lowering of the water table which is likely to have reduced the extent of damp rough grazings, previously the main foraging habitat of Whimbrel at this site (Ferns *et al* 1979, Green & Robins 1993). Thus, major spring passage staging sites may be vulnerable to land-use or management changes that affect foraging habitats. The effects of such declines in the 'quality' of major staging sites will depend upon the availability of alternative sites and how quickly Whimbrel need to build up sufficient reserves in order to arrive onto the breeding grounds in time to breed successfully. Zwarts (1990) suggests that Whimbrel do need to gain weight rapidly in limited time at European staging sites.

Given the paucity of ring-recovery data for Whimbrel, there are clearly many gaps in our knowledge of the precise migration routes and the full extent of the wintering areas both for the British breeding population and the populations which occur on passage in Britain & Ireland. The extent to which birds are dependent upon a network of staging sites is largely unknown, as is the degree to which they may be limited by the occurrence of suitable staging sites. Little information is available on the extent to which birds from different breeding areas overlap in their migration routes, their use of particular staging sites and in their wintering ranges. Differences between the sexes and between adult and immature birds in these respects are also unknown.

Murray Grant

Eurasian Curlew (Curlew)

Numenius arquata

The haunting call of the Curlew must be one of the most familiar sounds of the countryside of Britain & Ireland. It is heard from breeding birds on the moorland edge, or wet pastures, and from Fennoscandian or Russian migrants in winter.

Curlews breed across a wide band of northern Eurasia from Ireland, France and Norway east to central Siberia. They are absent from the Far East, the Americas, Iceland and the Faeroes. The nominate race *arquata* breeds across Europe and intergrades with the eastern race *orientalis* around the Urals (*BWP*). The distribution of the race *orientalis* extends almost to 130°E across Siberia. Most birds from west of the Urals undertake a southerly or southwesterly autumn migration to Atlantic or Mediterranean coasts or coastal fringes (*BWP*). Some western *orientalis* winter in the eastern Mediterranean (*BWP*), but this race migrates further than the nominate race, wintering around the coasts of Africa, the Arabian Peninsula, India and eastwards throughout southern Asia as far as Japan (*BWP*).

Breeding Curlews are still widespread across Britain & Ireland, despite recent declines, particularly in the lowlands, where they are now thinly and patchily distributed (O'Brien & Smith 1992, *1988–91 Atlas*, O'Brien 1996). They nest on heather moorland, for example on Orkney where the highest British & Irish nesting densities are recorded (*1988–91 Atlas*), and on moorland edge pastures and in-bye farmland across northern Britain. Latest estimates suggest there are far greater numbers than previously thought; perhaps as many as 89,000 pairs, though they may well be in decline (O'Brien 1996, O'Brien & Murray 1998).

The analysis of the data for this species was supported by the Headquarters, Army Training Estate (North East)

Southeast of a line from the Humber to the Severn their distribution is limited to unimproved areas of wet pasture and lowland heath.

In winter, Curlews in Britain have a largely coastal distribution, with concentrations on large estuaries like the Wash, Morecambe Bay and the Solway, where they feed on intertidal invertebrates on the mudflats (*Winter Atlas*). However, they are also widely found on rocky coasts (Moser & Summers 1987), and many birds, especially males, commute inland onto grass fields, seeking earthworms (Townshend 1981). In a few areas of Britain, there are flocks wintering entirely inland (*eg* Elphick 1979). In Ireland, inland wintering is common throughout the western half of the country, with particular concentrations in the Shannon Valley. Birds here feed mostly in grass fields, taking advantage of the lack of frozen ground this far west (*Winter Atlas*).

The distribution of breeding-season ringing sites in Britain of birds subsequently recovered broadly reflects the distribution of breeding Curlews today; Ireland, however, is under-represented (*1988–91 Atlas*; Fig 1). For the first fifty years of the Ringing Scheme, very few fully grown Curlews were ringed in Britain but, since the 1960s, with the development of cannon-netting, there has been much ringing of fully grown Curlews around both the British and Irish coasts (Fig 1), throughout the year (Fig 2). The winter distribution probably reflects

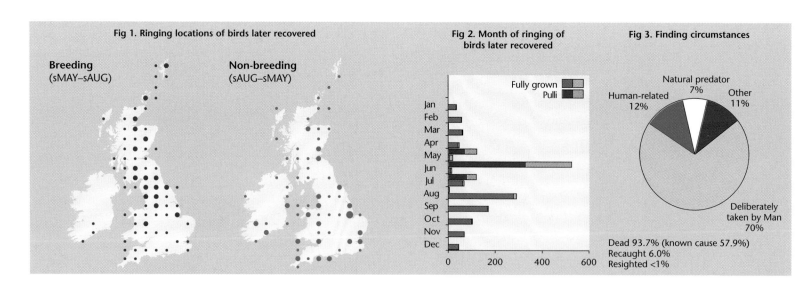

Fig 1. Ringing locations of birds later recovered

Breeding (sMAY–sAUG) Non-breeding (sAUG–sMAY)

Fig 2. Month of ringing of birds later recovered

Fully grown
Pulli

Fig 3. Finding circumstances

Natural predator 7%
Human-related 12%
Other 11%
Deliberately taken by Man 70%

Dead 93.7% (known cause 57.9%)
Recaught 6.0%
Resighted <1%

Ringing and recovery data

	<1960	60–69	70–79	80–89	90–97	Total
RINGING						
BTO ringing totals (%)	17	14	23	26	21	38,851
RECOVERIES						
BTO-ringed (%)	17	18	25	26	14	1,418
Foreign-ringed (%)	31	27	21	11	10	348

Statistical analyses

	Breeding population (sMAY–sAUG)	Wintering population (mOCT–mMAR)
Status	SHORT-DISTANCE MIGRANT (2)	LONG-DISTANCE MIGRANT
Age differences[NT]	Significant	Not significant*
Sex differences	Not tested	Not tested
Regional differences	Significant[4]*	Not tested
Finding circumstances	Significant	Not tested

Fig 4. Locations outside the breeding season, and movements of over 20 km between the breeding and non-breeding season, of Curlews that were ringed in the (a) northeast (33:52), (b) northwest (101:105) and (c) southeast & southwest (25:52) of Britain. Winter recoveries (red) are differentiated from autumn, spring and seasonally inaccurate recoveries (grey). Sample sizes of the classes (winter recoveries:other recoveries) are shown.

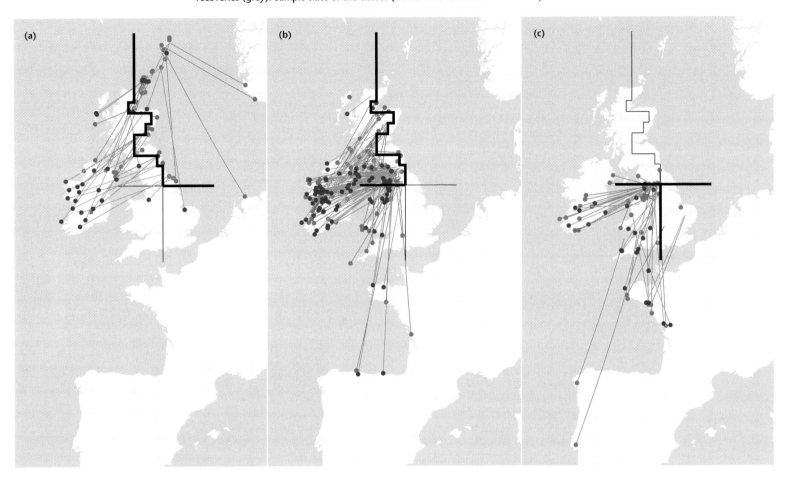

Fig 5. Locations during the breeding season of 338 Curlews present in Britain & Ireland during the non-breeding season.

more the effort of specialist wader ringers, especially at the Wash, where ringing between 1959 and 1998 has generated 305 recoveries (Kew *et al* 1999), than the distribution of Curlews.

Over half (58%) of ring-recoveries of dead Curlews have a known cause. Of these, 70% were deliberately taken by Man (Fig 3). Higher figures, 90% in Ireland, 94% in Denmark and 100% in France and Iberia, reflect the continuing quarry status of the species across much of Europe in winter. The legal protection afforded to Curlews in Britain in 1981 will undoubtedly have reduced recovery rates and influenced recovery statistics.

Most autumn movements of British & Irish breeding Curlews begin in August, though early movement of failed breeders and females (which often leave the males to tend the chicks) occurs in July. Long-distance movements of juveniles also begin in August, and over winter only about a quarter are still within 100 km of their natal site (Bainbridge & Minton 1978). Inland passage is rarely observed after August, and by the end of September, most adult birds are also probably on their wintering areas.

The majority of British-breeding Curlews undertake a southwesterly autumn migration to the British west coasts or into Ireland, where they spend the winter. The majority of birds from north of Morecambe Bay move into Ireland or onto the British northwest coast, though a few birds from northwest England migrate to south Wales and the Atlantic coasts of France and Spain (Fig 4a & b). Birds breeding in southern Britain also move southwest, into southern Ireland, south Wales, southwest England and onto the French coast and south to Portugal (Fig 4c). Although substantial numbers of Curlews winter on the coasts

Fig 6. All included exchanges of Curlews ringed abroad as pulli and recovered in the (a) northwest (38), (b) northeast (29), (c) southwest (60) and (d) southeast (118) of Britain and in (e) Ireland (48).

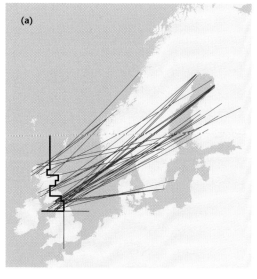
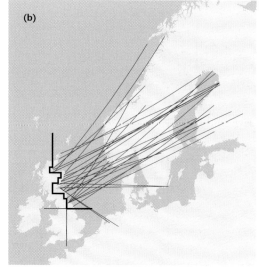
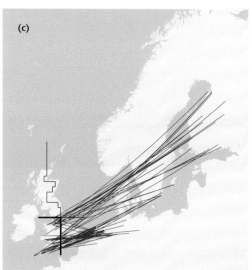
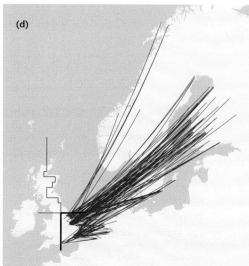
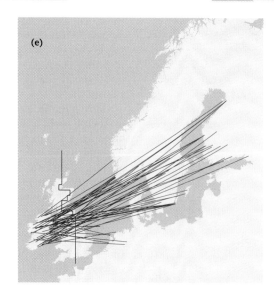

of Morocco and the Mediterranean (*BWP*), no British- & Irish-ringed bird has been found south of Portugal. Few British-breeding Curlews are found on the east coast of Britain in winter; the vast majority of birds found there are winter visitors from further north and east (Bainbridge & Minton 1978). There is very little evidence of birds crossing the North Sea eastwards. There have been two recoveries in Norway of birds ringed as pulli on Shetland (Fig 4a), and two birds each in Denmark, Germany and the Netherlands; although these were caught in Britain in the breeding season, only one was ringed as a pullus (Fig 4a) and the others may well have originated on the Continent. There are too few data from Ireland to determine the wintering locations of birds breeding there but it is presumed that most stay within Ireland for the winter.

There is little evidence of onward movement through the winter, or of shifts between winters. The median distance between ringing and recovery for birds both ringed and found dead in winter, including birds of continental origin, is only 5 km (P5–95=0–382 km, *n*=110), and 81% of such recoveries before 1976 were within 30 km of their ringing site (Bainbridge & Minton 1978). Both British and continental birds are thought to spend winter on the sites where they had moulted during the autumn (Boere 1976, Bainbridge & Minton 1978). There is some evidence of onward movement of Curlews in severe winter weather; in 1962 there was a cold-weather movement into France and Iberia from southwest England (Bainbridge & Minton 1978).

Returning migrants may reappear inland as early as late January, and many southern breeding sites are reoccupied during February; most March recoveries of British adult breeding birds are close to their natal areas (Fig 5, Bainbridge & Minton 1978). The data suggest that, on average, first-year birds winter further south and west than adult birds. The centre of gravity of recovery locations of birds found dead is over a degree further west for birds recovered as immatures when compared to adults. Curlews do not breed in their first summer, and Bainbridge & Minton (1978) showed that 55% of one-year-old birds recovered between March and August were over 100 km from their natal site, many staying in their winter areas for their first summer. Older, breeding birds display strong fidelity to their natal and breeding areas. Bainbridge & Minton (1978) found that 94% of birds at least two years old that were recovered between April and June were found within 100 km of their natal areas. Including the more recent data, the median recovery distance of all birds ringed and found dead in the breeding season was only 3.5 km (P5–95=0–1,238 km, *n*=102), although the median distance for natal dispersal was 20 km (P5–95=5–384 km, *n*=22).

Britain & Ireland receive many Curlews from continental Europe in the autumn. Radar studies have shown an early immigration of Curlews into East Anglia in late June and early July (Lack 1962); these are presumably failed breeders and early-departing females from continental breeding areas. In July, counts on the Wash can exceed 4,000 birds, all adults. Foreign juvenile birds begin to arrive at the Wash in September (Bainbridge & Minton 1978). Most of these birds originate from western Norway as far north as the Lofoten Islands, the southern half of Sweden and its Baltic coast, or Finland. A few recoveries show some birds coming from as far east as the Urals in Russia, though until 1954 only 45 Curlews had been ringed in the former USSR, so the data may under-represent the proportion of birds from Russia that winter here (Bainbridge & Minton 1978). Some birds also arrive from Germany, Denmark, the Netherlands and Belgium (Fig 5). Northern Britain receives Curlews ringed as pulli in Fennoscandia but almost none from mainland Europe (Fig 6a & b). Southern Britain appears to receive most of its birds from Finland, Sweden, Germany and the Low Countries (Fig 6c & d). A few Norwegian birds have been found in the southeast but none in the southwest. Ireland appears to receive birds from all parts of northern Europe, except the coastal north of Norway (Fig 6e).

The spring departure of foreign Curlews appears to be later than the spring movement of British breeding birds. Whilst the latest British birds are on their breeding grounds by April, many Curlews are still present on estuaries until May. In northeast England, two passages, one in March and one in May have been described by Brady (1949) and Evans (1966a), who suggested that birds remaining on the coast in April are of Scandinavian origin. There are no data to allow the timing of departure of birds breeding in Germany and the Low Countries to be determined. The birds that remain on estuaries throughout the summer are likely to be one-year-old birds that have stayed on their wintering grounds for their first summer.

Curlews are site-faithful both to their breeding grounds and in winter; this has implications for their conservation, as birds seldom move between estuaries. Losses of intertidal area on individual estuaries may therefore have serious implications for the Curlews that winter there.

There are two areas warranting further investigation to understand the migration of Curlews in Britain & Ireland. Little is known of the wintering grounds of Irish breeding birds; we presume they winter mainly in Ireland but there are no data to confirm this. Only the further ringing of Curlew chicks or breeding adults in Ireland will resolve this matter. Second, the pattern of recovery information may well have changed in Britain since the 1981 Wildlife & Countryside Act, when Curlews were removed from the list of quarry species. It has been suggested that many birds moved a few kilometres inland to feed when the shooting season started (Bainbridge & Minton 1978), and perhaps habits will have changed since then, as well as patterns of mortality. Davidson (1998) suggested there had been a 22% increase in the numbers of Curlews wintering in Europe between the late 1980s and 1990s; perhaps the change in shooting laws has helped the species to increase.

Ian Bainbridge

Common Redshank (Redshank)

Tringa totanus

The analysis of the data for this species was supported by the Mahee Island Ringing Station

The Redshank is a familiar sight to birdwatchers in Britain & Ireland throughout the year. Many of the British & Irish breeding population of Redshank remain in the country during winter, when they are joined by large numbers of Icelandic breeders and a few birds from the Continent. More continental breeders are present in Britain & Ireland on passage.

There is considerable variation in size between birds from different parts of the breeding range. The largest, Icelandic breeders (*robusta*), winter furthest north, from southern Iceland to around the North Sea. A small number winter as far south as the Vendée in France (Fournier & Spitz 1969), with stragglers possibly reaching Morocco (*BWP*).

The Redshank that breed between Ireland and the Urals are generally considered to belong to the nominate race (*BWP*). The smallest *totanus*, from northern Fennoscandia, appear to winter furthest south, with many reaching West Africa. Intermediate birds from west-central Europe winter between the English Channel and Senegal, with a concentration in the Bay of Biscay, Iberia and the western Mediterranean. The largest, from Britain, Ireland and the eastern North Sea, winter on the Atlantic coasts of Europe (Hale 1973, *BWP*). Both morphometrics and ring-recoveries have shown that Redshank in Morocco, with few exceptions, are from the breeding populations of the Baltic area and the eastern North Sea coast (Pienkowski 1975). Further south in Mauritania, most of the wintering Redshank appear to be from the breeding populations in northern Scandinavia and the North Sea (Dick 1975, Wymenga *et al* 1990). In Guinea-Bissau, the majority of Redshank are short-winged

and, usually, short-billed, suggesting that they originate largely from the northern Scandinavian population (Wymenga *et al* 1990). Most *totanus* from further east in Europe winter in the Mediterranean Basin (*BWP*).

Redshank breeding in central Asia, from the Urals to the Amur Basin and south to northern India, and wintering from the eastern Mediterranean eastward to China and Indonesia, are of four further races (*BWP*).

In Britain & Ireland, breeding Redshank are found on inland wet grassland and on coastal marshes; they are concentrated on lower ground in the northern half of Britain, with some additional local concentrations in Ireland and on coastal saltmarsh in southeast England (*1988–91 Atlas*). The population in the early to mid-1980s was estimated to be 33,000–36,000 pairs (Reed 1985) but, since then, numbers of breeding Redshank have declined on inland wet grassland sites, possibly due to agricultural change (*1988–91 Atlas*). Declines had not been detected on saltmarshes by 1985 (Cadbury *et al* 1987) but a further survey in 1996 showed a decline of about 23% since 1985 which was probably explained by an increase in grazing density (Brindley *et al* 1998, Norris *et al* 1998). The distribution of Redshank in winter is mainly coastal, with up to 100,000 birds (both *totanus* and *robusta*) present (Pollitt *et al* 2000). Some birds winter inland in southern Britain

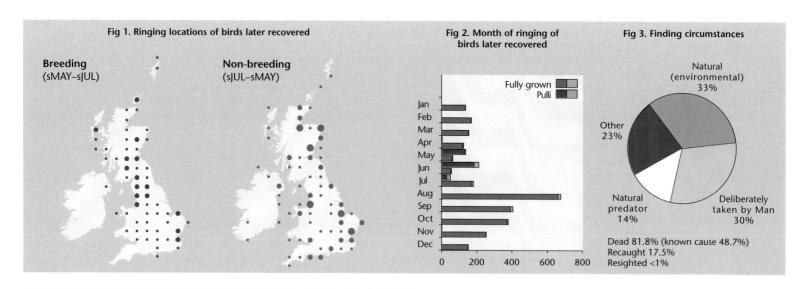

Fig 1. Ringing locations of birds later recovered

Breeding (sMAY–sJUL)

Non-breeding (sJUL–sMAY)

Fig 2. Month of ringing of birds later recovered

Fig 3. Finding circumstances

Natural (environmental) 33%

Other 23%

Natural predator 14%

Deliberately taken by Man 30%

Dead 81.8% (known cause 48.7%)
Recaught 17.5%
Resighted <1%

Ringing and recovery data

	<1960	60–69	70–79	80–89	90–97	Total
RINGING						
BTO ringing totals (%)	6	10	29	38	18	97,969
RECOVERIES						
BTO-ringed (%)	5	11	25	36	23	3,038
Foreign-ringed (%)	15	15	30	26	15	110

Statistical analyses

	Breeding population (sMAY–sJUL)	Wintering population (mOCT–sMAR)
Status	SHORT-DISTANCE MIGRANT* (2)	LONG-DISTANCE MIGRANT*
Age differences[NT]	Significant	Not significant*
Sex differences	Not tested	Not tested
Regional differences	Not tested	Not tested
Finding circumstances	(Not significant)	Not significant*

336

Fig 4. Movements of over 20 km between the breeding and non-breeding season (autumn and winter only) and locations outside the breeding season of Redshank present in the (a) north of Britain (146), (b) west of Britain (174), (c) east & south of Britain and in Ireland (81) during the breeding season.

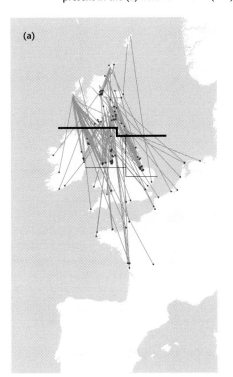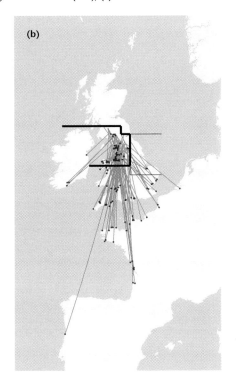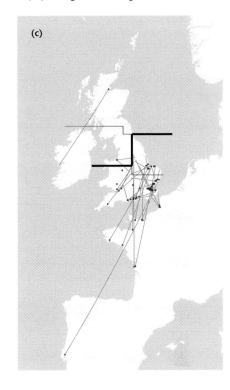

Table 1. Distances moved by Redshank ringed in Britain as pulli or as adults in the breeding season and recovered dead in winter.

Region of ringing	Ringed as adults				Ringed as pulli			
	Median distance (km)	P5 (km)	P95 (km)	n	Median distance (km)	P5 (km)	P95 (km)	n
North	526	333	825	9	465	0	1,368	35
East	—	—	—	—	457	0	793	6
West	88	0	845	37	297.5	0	900	28
South	12	4	321	10	45.5	0	930.5	20

NB: there was only one adult from the East and none from Ireland.

and in Ireland, moving to the coast if there is a series of prolonged frosts (*Winter Atlas*). There are also substantial numbers of Redshank in Britain and Ireland during the passage periods, with 28 sites in the UK having peak counts of more than 1,200 birds (Pollitt *et al* 2000).

Only 14% of recoveries are of Redshank ringed in the breeding season. The ringing locations of these birds broadly mirror the distribution of the breeding population (*1988–91 Atlas*) but there are notable gaps in Ireland and parts of northern and western Scotland (Fig 1). Similar gaps are apparent when comparing the distribution of ringing locations outside the breeding season with the pattern shown in the *Winter Atlas*. Nearly half the recoveries of Redshank ringed in Britain & Ireland were of birds ringed between July and October (Fig 2) that may have been on passage. As the race of Redshank can only be ascertained by calculations using a combination of measurements (Summers *et al* 1988b), the breeding origin of these birds is not clear. Only 12% of recoveries are of birds ringed as nestlings (Fig 2), reflecting the relatively small numbers of pulli that are ringed.

Almost half of all Redshank recoveries have a known cause of death (Fig 3). Of these, a third (421) were due to environmental factors, largely cold weather (393). Redshank are particularly susceptible to the effects of

cold weather (Davidson & Evans 1982, Clark *et al* 1993, Insley *et al* 1997). For example, over 1,500 dead birds were collected on the Wash in February 1991, while many further corpses were no doubt washed out to sea (Clark *et al* 1993). Such events will bias the distribution of recoveries through time, and may also change the geographical pattern of recoveries if birds have moved from their normal wintering areas in response to the cold weather before dying. There is little evidence, however, for large-scale movements of Redshank in response to cold weather. A further 30% of recoveries with known cause were deliberately taken by Man. Such recoveries vary both spatially and temporally with hunting laws and their observance. Notably, of the 119 recoveries with known cause in France of Redshank ringed in Britain & Ireland, 118 were killed by hunters.

The Redshank that breed in Britain & Ireland begin to leave their breeding grounds in June. Resightings of colour-ringed Redshank from South Uist showed that some have already left the breeding grounds by mid-June, with the bulk of the resightings being away from the breeding area by the end of July (Jackson 1999). Wintering Redshank start to return to the Lavan Sands (North Wales) in early July (Moss 1990). Many British & Irish birds remain in Britain & Ireland for the winter (Fig 4). Inland breeders move to the coast but coastal breeders in the south may stay

Fig 5. All included exchanges of Redshank between Iceland and (a) the north of Britain (103), (b) Ireland and the west of Britain (42) and (c) the south and east of Britain (60).

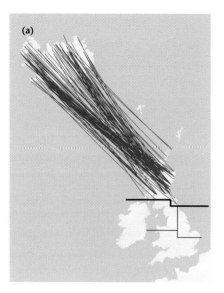
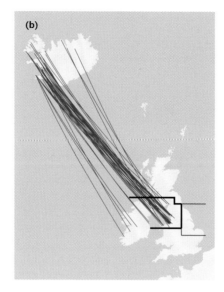
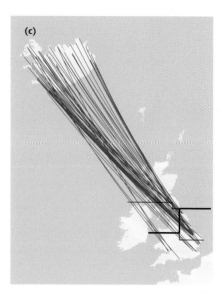

Fig 6. All included exchanges between Britain & Ireland and abroad (excluding exchanges with Iceland) of Redshank present in Britain & Ireland during (a) autumn (106), (b) winter (40) and (c) spring (16).

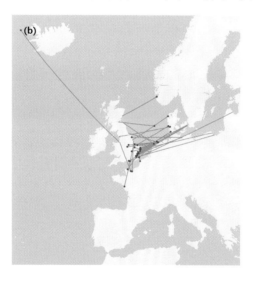
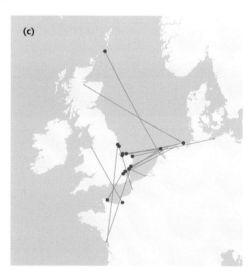

within 10 km of their natal area (*BWP*). The median distance moved between the breeding season and winter by all Redshank ringed in Britain & Ireland in the breeding season and later found dead is only 229 km (P5–95=0–973 km, *n*=125). Many move further south, however, with some birds reaching the Low Countries, France and Iberia (Fig 4). Hale (1980) suggested that Redshank migrate further away from their breeding grounds in their first winter than later in life, when there may be a selective advantage in remaining closer to the breeding grounds. The recoveries support this: the median distance moved by Redshank ringed as pulli and recovered in their first winter was 289 km (P5–95= 12–1,368 km, *n*=51), in later winters it was 105 km (P5–95=0–993 km, *n*=38) and for all adults ringed in the breeding season when of breeding age and recovered in winter it was 45.5 km (P5–95=0–845 km, *n*=34).

Most *totanus* probably leave the north of Britain for the winter. Using morphometrics, it has been estimated that about half of the Redshank in eastern Scotland in September are *totanus* (the rest being Icelandic breeders) but that the proportion of *totanus* had dropped to 10% during December–March (Summers *et al* 1988b). None of the birds colour-marked on South Uist in the breeding season has been resighted there in

winter. Reports outside the breeding season were spread from the Clyde Estuary, southwest Scotland, to Charente-Maritime in southern France, with a concentration around the southern part of the Irish Sea and the south coast of Ireland (Jackson 1999; Fig 4). Recovery distances indicate that British-breeding Redshank from the north of the country migrate further than their southern counterparts (Table 1).

There are very few recoveries from which to assess breeding and natal dispersal. However, eight of nine movements of breeding birds between breeding seasons were of less than 20 km, and six of these birds were back on the same breeding grounds. The one movement of greater than 20 km involved a bird from Lancashire that was recaptured in Jersey on 30 June and would have already been on passage. There is some evidence of natal dispersal in that eight of 18 recoveries of pulli Redshank found in a subsequent breeding season had moved more than 20 km. Intensive breeding studies on the Ribble Marshes, Lancashire, have shown a high degree of both natal and breeding philopatry (Thompson *et al* 1988, Thompson & Hale 1989). Breeding site-fidelity was found to increase with age but was lower in birds that had not bred successfully in the preceding year. In addition, up to a third of chicks seen alive near

Table 2. Seasonality of exchanges of Redshank between Britain & Ireland and France (including the Channel Islands).

Season in Britain & Ireland	Season in France				
	Autumn	Winter	Spring	Breeding	Total
Autumn	32	26	6	2	66
Winter	3	2	0	0	5
Spring	2	3	0	0	5
Breeding	31	22	4	1	58
Total	68	53	10	3	134

fledging returned to breed at their natal site. The mean natal dispersal distance of birds breeding in their first three years was just 615 m, although birds moving further were less likely to be detected (Thompson & Hale 1989).

There is a population of 50,000–100,000 breeding pairs of *robusta* in Iceland but only 500–1,000 birds remain there in winter (Petersen 1998). Birds are present on the Icelandic breeding grounds until August, although some adults reach Britain & Ireland in late June (*BWP*). Icelandic Redshank are found throughout Britain & Ireland in winter (Fig 5); wintering Redshank in northern Scotland appear to be almost exclusively from Iceland, with the proportion of *robusta* decreasing towards the English south coast. There is a suggestion that the Redshank that winter in the west of Britain and in Ireland come from the more westerly parts of the breeding area in Iceland, whereas *robusta* in the rest of Britain & Ireland come from breeding areas spread throughout Iceland (Fig 5).

In winter, Redshank in Britain & Ireland (a mixture of British & Irish and Icelandic breeders) are very site-faithful. For 333 Redshank found dead, both ringed and recovered in winter, the median movement was just 2 km (*P5–95*=0–150 km), although there have been a few long-distance movements between winters, probably in response to cold weather. A study of colour-marked birds on the Firth of Forth, and studies using recaptures on the Wash and the Moray Basin, also found a high level of site-fidelity in winter (Symonds *et al* 1984, Rehfisch *et al* 1996, Rehfisch, Insley & Swann pers comm). The Redshank that nest in Britain & Ireland return to their breeding grounds in March and April. Icelandic Redshank leave Britain & Ireland in the same period to return to their breeding grounds (*BWP*).

It is difficult to be clear about the individual origins and destinations of the 223 seasonally accurate recoveries of Redshank moving between Britain & Ireland and countries other than Iceland (Fig 6). Some are no doubt either Icelandic or British & Irish breeders, ringed on passage and wintering on the near Continent or in the Bay of Biscay. Continental-breeding birds are known to both winter in southeast England and pass through en route to and from more southerly wintering grounds. There have been six recoveries in Africa (four from Morocco and singles from Nigeria and Senegal), all from birds ringed on the east coast of Britain in autumn; four were in Africa in the winter and the remaining two were in Morocco on passage and would also have wintered in Africa. These

birds are likely to have been from the northern European and Baltic breeding populations. Redshank exchanges between Britain & Ireland and Iberia have involved a mixture of birds that have been either wintering in Iberia or on passage to Africa, and include three winter recoveries from autumn ringing in southeast England. There have been 134 exchanges between Britain & Ireland and France, including the Channel Islands, almost half of which involved birds that were in Britain & Ireland in the breeding season (Table 2). The majority were in France in autumn and may either have been on their wintering grounds or en route to wintering grounds further south. A further 39% were in France in winter. There have been two within-winter movements involving France (one in November and one in January). It is possible that the November recovery was of a bird that had not yet settled for the winter but the January movement, along with some other winter recoveries in France, may have occurred due to cold winter weather. There have also been four exchanges between Britain & Ireland and Belgium, 43 with the Netherlands, eight with Germany and 11 with Denmark; again a number of these movements probably involved a change of wintering site as a result of cold weather. The nine birds located north or east of Denmark (four in Norway, two in Poland and singles in Finland, Sweden and Latvia) included birds wintering in Britain & Ireland as well as passage birds that probably wintered further south.

Hence Britain & Ireland is an important area for breeding, wintering and passage Redshank from a number of populations. Numbers wintering in Britain & Ireland are relatively stable, although a provisional international estimate suggests an increase since the 1980s of 34% in the number of *robusta*. This may be balanced, however, by an apparent decrease of 55% in the number of wintering *totanus* (Davidson 1998). It is possible, therefore, that the composition of the wintering population of Redshank is changing, although this is not apparent from counts and it is not clear how many *totanus* that breed to the north and west of Britain & Ireland winter here. Further information on the balance of the races present could be gained from catching and measuring more Redshank. However it would be difficult to assess any change in the proportions of the two races present as measurements of 'tarsus and toe', a relatively new measurement, are required to determine the proportion of *robusta*. Further information on the proportion of the Icelandic breeding population present in winter would also help to assess the importance of Britain & Ireland as a major wintering area for *robusta*. The apparent tendency for *robusta* breeding in the west of Iceland to winter in the west of Britain & Ireland, and of those breeding in the east to winter in the east, also merits further investigation. If such a geographical split of the population exists this may have important conservation implications.

There is a need to investigate the decline in numbers of breeding Redshank in Britain & Ireland. Numbers have fallen on both agricultural land and saltmarsh; it seems likely that this is an effect of reduction in the amount and quality of breeding habitat. Indeed, a study of the overwinter survival of Redshank found little year-to-year variation amongst adults (Insley *et al* 1997). There needs to be further research both to establish the cause of the decline and the time of year when adverse changes are occurring, and to investigate methods for reversing the fall in numbers through habitat creation and management.

Jacquie Clark

Common Greenshank (Greenshank)

Tringa nebularia

The Greenshank is a familiar migrant in Britain & Ireland, occurring widely at both coastal and inland waters in spring and autumn. Breeding Greenshank are found almost exclusively in the uplands of north and west Scotland and the species is wholly absent as a breeding bird from England, Wales and Ireland (*1988–91 Atlas*). Despite this restricted breeding distribution, Greenshank are a familiar sight to most birdwatchers, with regular passage movements occurring throughout Britain & Ireland during the autumn and spring. Several hundred Greenshank overwinter in Britain & Ireland, mainly in the west and in Ireland, which may hold three-quarters of this wintering population (Nethersole-Thompson & Nethersole-Thompson 1979, *Winter Atlas*, Pollitt *et al* 2000).

Greenshank breed throughout northern Fennoscandia and eastward across the former Soviet Union to Kamchatka (*BWP*). The Scottish population of the Greenshank is on the western edge of the world breeding range of the species. Greenshank are migratory throughout their world range with birds generally wintering far to the south of their breeding range. While a small proportion of the Western Palearctic breeders winter coastally in western Europe, the majority are trans-Saharan migrants wintering south of 20°N (*BWP*). Russian birds are thought to winter in central, eastern and southern Africa and also through southern Asia and Australasia (*BWP*).

Greenshank breed commonly throughout the taiga and forest zones of the Palearctic (*BWP*), where they inhabit forest marshes, forest clearings and areas of scrub punctuated with lakes and bogs. By contrast, breeding Greenshank in Scotland are now mainly confined to the

The analysis of the data for this species was supported by members of the Farlington Ringing Group

poorly drained, boulder-strewn peat soils of the northern and western Highlands where the landscape is more open. A wide variety of feeding habitats is used by Greenshank on passage and in the winter quarters. Favoured inland habitats include lakes, reservoirs and sewage-farms, while on the coast Greenshank may be found on estuaries, saltmarsh, lagoons, mangrove swamps and muddy shores.

There have been few ring-recoveries of Greenshank to or from Britain & Ireland, and the distribution of ringing sites of birds later recovered does not reflect the distribution of Greenshank in either the breeding or non-breeding season (Fig 1). The majority (73%) of recoveries are of birds ringed in August and September whilst on autumn migration (Fig 2). Most of these birds were caught on the south coast of England, so the ring-recovery data are biased towards this area (Fig 1). There are very few recoveries of Greenshank that were ringed in winter or on the breeding grounds (Fig 2). Of Greenshank recovered dead, the cause of death was known for 33 birds, almost all of which (91%) had been deliberately taken by Man (Fig 3). Of these, 67% were taken in France, 13% in Britain & Ireland, and the remainder in Denmark, southern Europe or Africa.

Greenshank return to their Scottish breeding grounds in late March and depart from mid-June through until August. Typically, the female

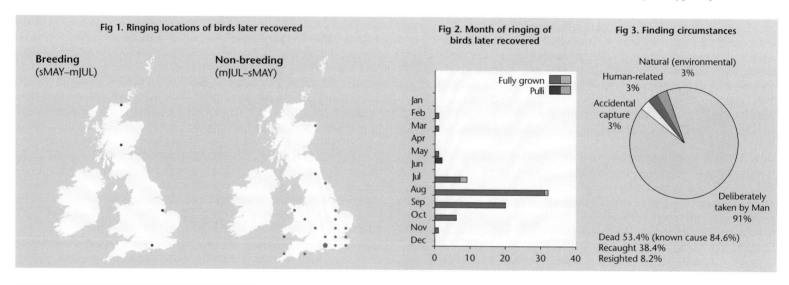

Fig 1. Ringing locations of birds later recovered

Breeding (sMAY–mJUL)   Non-breeding (mJUL–sMAY)

Fig 2. Month of ringing of birds later recovered

Fully grown / Pulli

Fig 3. Finding circumstances

Natural (environmental) 3%
Human-related 3%
Accidental capture 3%
Deliberately taken by Man 91%

Dead 53.4% (known cause 84.6%)
Recaught 38.4%
Resighted 8.2%

Ringing and recovery data

	<1960	60–69	70–79	80–89	90–97	Total
RINGING						
BTO ringing totals (%)	3	18	28	32	19	2,035
RECOVERIES						
BTO-ringed (%)	4	13	17	33	33	70
Foreign-ringed (%)	0	0	0	100	0	3

Statistical analyses

	Breeding population (sMAY–mJUL)	Wintering population (sOCT–sAPR)
Status	[LONG-DISTANCE MIGRANT]	[LONG-DISTANCE MIGRANT]
Age differences	Not tested	Not tested
Sex differences	Not tested	Not tested
Regional differences	Not tested	Not tested
Finding circumstances	Not tested	Not tested

Fig 4. Recovery locations and movements of over 20 km for the 73 included recoveries of Greenshanks ringed or recovered in Britain & Ireland.

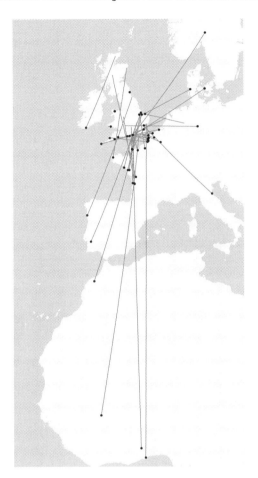

departs in late June or early July, often before the young have fledged. Care of the young is then left to the male who remains with the brood through July. The juvenile birds generally depart for the wintering grounds last. Only three Greenshank ringed on the breeding grounds have subsequently been recovered, and all were shot: one in southern Ireland (Cork) and the other two in southwest France. Clearly, the lack of ring-recoveries for the Scottish breeding population makes an accurate assessment of its movements almost impossible. However, data on the timing of movements suggest that the Scottish breeding population may winter in Ireland and western Britain as well as southwest Europe and northwest Africa (Nethersole-Thompson & Nethersole-Thompson 1979). In Ireland and western Britain, numbers of Greenshank remain high throughout the winter. Return passage from this area usually takes place in March and is almost complete by late April (Nethersole-Thompson & Nethersole-Thompson 1979); this coincides with the late March arrival of Greenshank on the breeding grounds in Scotland. Although this suggests that many Scottish breeding birds winter in Ireland and western Britain, it is not clear when Greenshank from other wintering areas would reach the Scottish breeding grounds.

Breeding Greenshank are highly site-faithful. In one study in northwest Scotland, breeding adults were found to return to the same area to breed in consecutive years. On a number of occasions, Greenshank even used the same nest scrape in consecutive years (Nethersole-Thompson & Nethersole-Thompson 1986, Thompson et al 1988). While there is some evidence to suggest that young birds may return to breed in the general area of hatching, a number of young birds undoubtedly

disperse to other areas to breed. As with Redshank, natal dispersal distances may be longer for females (Thompson et al 1988).

Immature Greenshank may make longer journeys to their wintering grounds than adult Greenshank. From a sample of 26 birds of known age at ringing, 19 adults moved a median distance of 407 km and seven immature birds moved a median distance of 813 km. Alternatively, immature Greenshank may spend more time in the wintering areas than adults. Non-breeding Greenshank have been recorded summering on the wintering grounds in southern Europe and north Africa (BWP).

There is a passage of Greenshank through southern Britain in autumn (Fig 4). It would appear that Greenshank breeding in northeast Europe leave the breeding grounds from July through to September and slowly make their way south and west to winter in southwestern Europe and North Africa (BWP). Many of these birds pass through Britain and probably Ireland in the autumn. Greenshank occur in the Solent largely in the autumn, although there is a small wintering population, and over 150 have been colour-ringed at Farlington Marsh (P M Potts & D A Bell pers comm). Colour-ringing has shown that, during autumn, Greenshank are highly site-faithful both within and between years. Recoveries suggest that these birds may be part of the Scandinavian breeding population (Fig 4). There is also some evidence to suggest that these birds may stop off elsewhere around the North Sea before arriving in the Solent. On arrival in the Solent, some birds start to moult, increase weight slowly and may remain for over three months, whilst others put on weight rapidly and do not moult (P M Potts & D A Bell pers comm). It is likely that these two groups of birds have different wintering destinations and they may also be from different breeding populations. On leaving the Solent, some birds move to southwest Britain (P M Potts & D A Bell pers comm), while most migrate to West Africa (Fig 4). Colour-ring sightings in April and May from continental Europe and eastern England suggest that the return migration of Solent birds follows a more easterly route.

A survey of breeding Greenshank in the UK in 1995 (Hancock et al 1997) found evidence of a range contraction in the previous 25 years. There were also some large regional population changes. A long-term study of a population of Greenshank breeding in northwest Scotland recorded a decline in numbers in the 1980s, probably as a result of habitat change (deterioration of pool complexes due to use of all-terrain vehicles; Thompson & Thompson 1991). It is hoped that the habitat will recover but the population may not be able to respond. Habitat loss, especially as a result of afforestation, may be having an adverse effect on other populations. It will be important to repeat the 1995 survey to estimate the population trend and establish whether the range, and possibly numbers, of breeding Greenshank are continuing to decline.

Global warming and consequent changes in climate and sea-level are likely to have a major impact on the availability of coastal feeding sites for Greenshank. While a slight increase in winter temperatures might benefit Greenshank wintering in Britain & Ireland and extend their wintering range to the east, a rise in sea-level may result in the loss of some important coastal feeding sites. The loss of existing feeding habitat would have an impact on both wintering and passage birds.

Our understanding of the general pattern of movement is undoubtedly hampered by the lack of recoveries of known breeding birds and birds ringed as pulli. While Greenshank have been known to breed at one year of age (Nethersole-Thompson & Nethersole-Thompson 1986), it is clear that some birds delay breeding until their second or later years (BWP). While some first-year birds may be present on the breeding grounds, others may remain on the wintering grounds throughout the breeding season (BWP). The Greenshank is afforded special protection under the Wildlife & Countryside Act (1981) and the EC Birds Directive. While large tracts of known breeding habitat are also protected, it is of major concern that we know so little about where Scottish birds go once they leave the breeding grounds.

Patrick S Thompson

Green Sandpiper
Tringa ochropus

The distinctive calls and eye-catching white rumps of Green Sandpipers make the birds obvious when flushed, although they can be very cryptic when feeding or resting undisturbed. They are predominantly passage birds in Britain & Ireland with a few staying throughout the winter. Breeding has been proved, however, in Cumbria in 1917 and Inverness in 1959 (BOU 1971).

Green Sandpipers breed in the boreal forest zone from Norway and Germany to the Sea of Okhotsk, typically in wet forest and wooded river valleys, laying their eggs in old songbird nests and squirrel dreys (*BWP*). Birds from the Western Palearctic spend the winter in northwest Europe, around the Mediterranean, and in Africa both north and south of the Sahara Desert.

Green Sandpipers in Britain & Ireland occur predominantly in central and southern England and in Wales, with a few in northern England, Scotland and Ireland. There is very little evidence to suggest any major differences in the distributions of birds on passage compared with those that stay through the winter (*Winter Atlas*). There are, however, big shifts in the habitats used in the two periods, with gravel-pits and freshwater lagoons of all types used during passage, and sites with flowing fresh water, such as streams and watercress beds, used in winter (Smith *et al* 1992a). Very few birds are found on coastal saltwater sites at any season, with estuary counts throughout Britain & Ireland rarely reaching three figures.

There have been only 40 recoveries of Green Sandpipers involving Britain & Ireland, of which seven were from birds recaught by other ringers. The distribution of ringing sites of birds later recovered is very

The analysis of the data for this species was supported by Ken Smith & Barry Trevis

similar to that in the *Winter Atlas*, with most birds in the southeast and Midlands of England and just a few in the north (Fig 1). The distribution of recoveries by month of ringing (Fig 2) shows that most were from birds ringed on autumn passage during July to September, with rather few ringed in winter. Although the autumn is when most birds are present in Britain & Ireland, they are probably also more likely to be caught by ringers then. In autumn small groups of birds are a more attractive proposition to ringers than winter singletons; the adult birds are in full wing moult (Kittle 1975), making them relatively easy to trap, and the juvenile birds are likely to be relatively naive at this season.

Of the recoveries for which the circumstances of death were reported, 79% (19) were deliberately taken by Man (Fig 3). This is at first surprising given the protected status of the species, but 27 of the 33 dead recoveries were from before 1980, when hunting pressures may have been higher. In common with many other species (*eg* Catchpole *et al* 1999, Wernham & Peach 1999), the recovery rate has fallen in recent decades. Amongst birds ringed before 1980, 2.7% were recovered by the general public compared with only 1.1% for birds ringed between 1980 and 1995.

Green Sandpipers are one of the earliest migrant waders to return from the breeding grounds in autumn, with the first birds appearing in Britain & Ireland in mid-June. Peak numbers do not occur until July and continue through to September or early October. The first birds to arrive

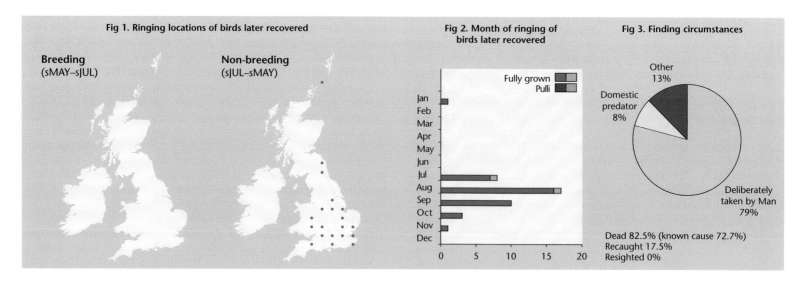

Fig 1. Ringing locations of birds later recovered

Breeding (sMAY–sJUL) **Non-breeding** (sJUL–sMAY)

Fig 2. Month of ringing of birds later recovered

Fully grown / Pulli

Fig 3. Finding circumstances

Other 13%
Domestic predator 8%
Deliberately taken by Man 79%

Dead 82.5% (known cause 72.7%)
Recaught 17.5%
Resighted 0%

Ringing and recovery data

	<1960	60–69	70–79	80–89	90–97	Total
RINGING						
BTO ringing totals (%)	7	24	30	24	15	1,559
RECOVERIES						
BTO-ringed (%)	11	29	34	18	8	38
Foreign-ringed (%)	0	0	50	50	0	2

Statistical analyses

	Breeding population (sMAY–sJUL)	Wintering population (sOCT–mMAR)
Status	NONE	[LONG-DISTANCE MIGRANT]
Age differences	—	Not tested
Sex differences	—	Not tested
Regional differences	—	Not tested
Finding circumstances	—	Not tested

Fig 4. Recovery locations and movements of over 20 km for the 40 included recoveries of Green Sandpipers ringed or recovered in Britain & Ireland.

In late autumn, those birds that remain for the winter tend to move to feeding sites with flowing water and become more solitary in their habits and may even become territorial (Smith *et al* 1992a). Birds are highly faithful to both their passage and wintering sites with colour-ringing studies showing return rates of over 80% from one year to the next (Smith *et al* 1992a). Birds often return to precisely the same piece of riverbank, although they are quite capable of shifting site if their favoured area becomes unsuitable for any reason. Radio-tracking has shown that, even in winter, birds continue to use gravel-pits and lagoons as overnight roost sites, whilst spending the day feeding at watercress beds and beside streams (Smith *et al* 1999).

Count data in Britain & Ireland give little indication of any return northward passage in spring (*Birds in Scotland, Birds in Ireland, Birds in Wales*). The peak departure time of wintering colour-ringed birds from Hertfordshire was mid-April with the last bird seen on 3 May (Smith *et al* 1992a).

The distribution of recoveries is consistent with a south-southwest departure from Britain after arrival from the Baltic area (Fig 4). There are no ring-recoveries as yet involving Ireland. Although nationally there are rather few recoveries of birds ringed in the winter period, there is some evidence that they are less likely to move from their ringing site than birds trapped in autumn. Three Green Sandpipers ringed in Britain in winter have been recovered dead in a subsequent winter (there are no within-winter movements). One bird was back on the same site and another had moved just 8 km, but one, ringed in mid-October, was recovered 475 km away in France and was presumably a late migrant. On the other hand only 13 of 28 recoveries of autumn-ringed birds remained within Britain & Ireland.

One of the remaining mysteries is the breeding area of the birds that occur in Britain & Ireland. There have been no recoveries here of birds ringed as pulli on their breeding grounds. The only published study of recoveries of pulli was of birds ringed in Finland up to 1978 (Saurola 1979), which were recovered in the Netherlands, France and Switzerland. In addition, recoveries of pulli from Norway to Spain, and from Sweden to Denmark, Spain and France, are reported in *BWP*. The only British recovery that gives any clue is an August-ringed juvenile subsequently found in northern Sweden in mid-June, which suggests northern Scandinavia as a likely breeding area.

There is some circumstantial evidence to support a northerly origin for the birds wintering in Britain & Ireland. The median departure date in spring of wintering birds in Hertfordshire was 7 April, with many staying until the end of the month (Smith *et al* 1992a). By early April most birds in the southern part of the Green Sandpiper's breeding range are already on territory (*BWP*), so at least some of our wintering birds are likely to be northerly breeders.

Ken W Smith

are adults and are likely to be females as these often leave the breeding areas early, leaving the unfledged young in the care of the males (*BWP*). The first young birds are recorded in late July or early August in Britain & Ireland. During autumn, birds often form small groups at gravel-pits and freshwater lagoons with unvegetated muddy fringes.

During July and August, the adults moult their body and flight feathers whilst the juveniles replace their body feathers only. Some adults suspend their primary moult and continue their passage with the outermost primaries unmoulted (Kittle 1975) whilst the others complete their moult in Britain & Ireland.

Common Sandpiper
Actitis hypoleucos

The Common Sandpiper is a characteristic breeding bird of stony upland rivers and reservoirs for its short summer breeding season, but is more widespread during its migrations south in the summer and autumn. The breeding population of Britain & Ireland is believed to migrate to West Africa, south of the Sahara. A few birds winter further north, in Europe (including southern Britain and around the Mediterranean) but their provenance is unknown. The species has a wide Palearctic distribution, from Ireland across to Siberia and from about 40°N to 70°N. Birds from the west of the range migrate to Africa, where the species occurs throughout the southern half of the continent in the boreal winter; birds breeding in Siberia winter in India and throughout southeastern Asia, Melanesia and Australia, but the line of division, if it exists, between these two breeding populations is not certain. Migration seems to occur on a wide front across the whole of the range; unlike the coastal waders they do not seem to use flyways.

The European population is believed to number around 882,000 pairs, most of these breeding in Fennoscandia (Piersma 1986). They migrate in a south-southwesterly direction in autumn, which brings some of them through southeast England. The population of Britain & Ireland is estimated to be 18,300 pairs (*1988–91 Atlas*), and these migrate more directly southwards. The breeding sites are upland rivers characterized by stony, shingle beaches and margins that provide both good feeding sites and good cover for the young chicks; territories are typically about 200 m long. Deeper 'black' water and boulders are less suitable, providing instead habitat for Dippers and Grey Wagtails. Upland reservoirs and lakes that have stony shorelines swept bare by

The analysis of the data for this species was supported by T W Dougall, P K Holland & D W Yalden

storms in winter and exposed by draw-down in summer are also suitable breeding habitat. On migration they visit a much wider range of shorelines, muddy and sandy as well as stony, but they appear to prefer fresh water throughout their range, and are scarcer in maritime habitats. In Africa, they do not gather in large flocks, like other wintering waders, but seem to take up territories, of a similar length to their breeding territories, along rivers and lake shores.

The distribution of ringing sites of Common Sandpipers later recovered reflects the distribution of the species in the breeding season although two study areas, the Peak District and the Southern Uplands, stand out (Fig 1). Outside the breeding season ringing localities are concentrated in southeast England with two sites, Abberton Reservoir, Essex, and Wisbech Sewerage Farm, Cambridgeshire, the major contributors (Fig 1). Common Sandpipers in Ireland are under-represented in the recovery data. Recoveries show that the majority of Common Sandpipers are ringed during the breeding season and in autumn. Nearly all pulli later recovered were ringed in June (Fig 2). Over half of all recoveries of birds where the cause of recovery was known were deliberately killed (Fig 3), and this limits the knowledge of both migration and survival patterns. Stiefel *et al* (1985) reported that 49% of recoveries in their study were of birds that had been shot and only 22% had been recaptured. Meissner (1997) remarks, however, that this

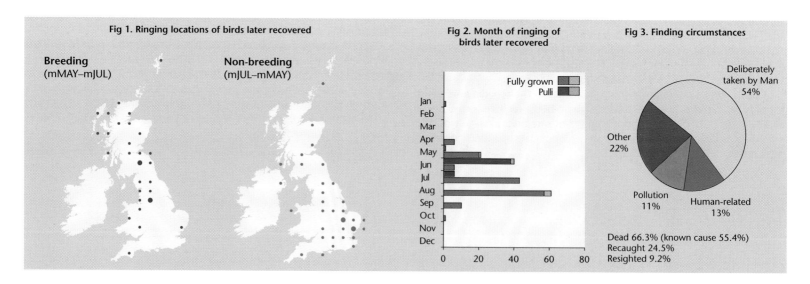

Fig 1. Ringing locations of birds later recovered

Breeding (mMAY–mJUL) Non-breeding (mJUL–mMAY)

Fig 2. Month of ringing of birds later recovered

Fully grown / Pulli

Fig 3. Finding circumstances

Deliberately taken by Man 54%
Other 22%
Pollution 11%
Human-related 13%

Dead 66.3% (known cause 55.4%)
Recaught 24.5%
Resighted 9.2%

Ringing and recovery data

	<1960	60–69	70–79	80–89	90–97	Total
RINGING						
BTO ringing totals (%)	20	22	22	22	13	18,232
RECOVERIES						
BTO-ringed (%)	13	25	26	19	16	189
Foreign-ringed (%)	0	29	29	43	0	7

Statistical analyses

	Breeding population (mMAY–mJUL)	Wintering population (sOCT–mMAR)
Status	[LONG-DISTANCE MIGRANT]	?
Age differences	Not tested	—
Sex differences	Not tested	—
Regional differences	Not tested	—
Finding circumstances	Not tested	—

Fig 4. Locations outside the breeding season and movements of over 20 km between the breeding and non-breeding season of 44 Common Sandpipers present in Britain & Ireland during the breeding season.

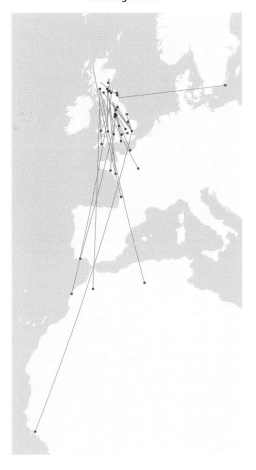

Fig 5. Recovery locations for all 71 included exchanges of Common Sandpipers between Britain & Ireland and abroad. Note that movements of birds definitely present in Britain & Ireland during the breeding season are excluded from this figure.

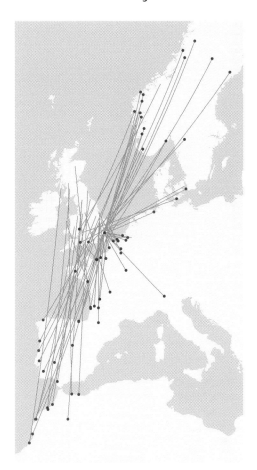

pattern has changed within the last 15 years; 43% of his recoveries were recaptures, and only 23% had been shot.

The very short breeding season of this species is one of its fundamental characteristics. The breeding season in Britain begins with establishment of territories in the last week of April. Earliest clutches are laid in early May, so the first chicks hatch in the last week of May and result in fledglings in mid-June. Adults that fail, and some females whose chicks have reached about 14 days old, may leave the breeding grounds by mid-June, and head south very quickly. By mid-July, when most young have reached independence, the breeding grounds are deserted. Juveniles seem to migrate more slowly than the adults (Brown 1974) but Peak District juveniles have been recovered in southern England within 10 days of fledging. Recoveries in France, Spain and Morocco as early as June, but more generally in July, August and September, indicate the general path and tempo of the southward movement. However, the pattern is confused by overlap with the Scandinavian birds, which breed from late May through June and July, and are still moving northwards through southeastern England when British birds are well into their breeding cycle. The most remarkable feature revealed by the ring-recoveries is the geographical separation of these two populations, so far as overseas recoveries are concerned. Birds present in Britain in the breeding season migrate southwards (Fig 4). Birds ringed in southeast Britain appear to be largely from Scandinavia, recovered there in subsequent breeding seasons or to the southwest on migration (Fig 5). A few Scandinavian birds occur in southwest and northeast Britain but most recoveries there are from the British breeding population.

Exchanges of Common Sandpipers between Africa and European breeding or passage areas suggest that birds breeding in Russia winter in East Africa, whilst those breeding further west also winter further west

(Fig 6). Although there have been no recoveries of British breeding birds in Africa between October and March, if they migrate parallel to birds from Scandinavia and Russia they should winter in the southwestern extremity of West Africa. There is only one recovery of a bird ringed in Britain & Ireland and found south of the Sahara. This bird, one of the presumed Scandinavian migrants, was recovered in Guinea-Bissau in September. There has been one other report of a British-ringed Common Sandpiper that may have been wintering south of the Sahara. This bird, ringed as a pullus in Yorkshire, was found in November in the radiator of an aircraft at Moscow that had come from Accra via Conakry, Bamako and Belgrade.

There is some evidence to suggest that Common Sandpipers wintering in Africa may be site-faithful. Of 65 birds ringed between 1984 and 1993 in Senegal, where they were probably overwintering, nine (14%) were recaptured in later winters, a higher recapture rate than for any of the other waders there (Sauvage et al 1998). There is only one comparable recovery in Britain & Ireland to support winter site-fidelity: a bird ringed in Hampshire in January 1974 was found dead at the same site in March 1975.

One recovery in March and seven in April from Morocco, Portugal, Spain and France, of birds ringed in Britain whilst adults, indicate that the northward return is faster than the autumn migration. Established breeders return quickly to their previous territories, and sometimes suffer severe mortality when unseasonal late snow covers their breeding grounds (Holland & Yalden 1991). Early return may ensure re-acquisition of their territory, or may allow renesting if the first attempt fails. Territory holders are very site-faithful, not just to the general area, but to their specific territory. Of 306 returns to the Peak District study area in subsequent years, 257 (84%) were to the same, or a neighbouring territory.

Fig 6. Recovery locations and movements of Common Sandpipers ringed (a) on passage in eastern Europe (Germany, Poland and the former Czechoslovakia, red), (b) in Russia during the breeding season (blue) and (c) in Africa and recovered back in the breeding areas (grey). (*Sources*: Stiefel *et al* 1985 and Meissner 1997, by permission of *Ornis Fennica*.)

From sightings of colour-ringed birds, adult survivorship in the Peak District is generally around 75% per annum, but drops to 50% or less in years with cold late April weather, such as 1981 and 1989; averaged over 12 years, the figure is 61%. Ringed chicks have about a 40% chance of surviving to fledging (Holland & Yalden 1991, 1994). They appear not to return routinely to their natal territories, and the few ring-recoveries suggest that they may disperse up to 200 km. Of 457 chicks and 102 fledglings ringed in the Peak District over 21 years, only 15 returned to their natal area (Holland & Yalden 1994).

Southbound Scandinavian migrants pass through the Gulf of Gdańsk from mid-July to September, matching their movements through southeast England at this time; passage of adults is earlier than that of juveniles, mostly in late July, and numbers reach a peak in the first half of August, as juveniles move through (Meissner 1996). Records of peak migration across western Europe, which must be this peak of juvenile movement, were collated by OAG Münster (1984). For southern Scotland and northern England, the peak was 26 July, but in southern England, the Netherlands and Hungary it was 14 August. The peak of migration passed through southern Germany around 18 August and southern France on 23 August. This rather slow average rate of progress, contrasting with some recoveries of adults already back in North Africa by July, highlights the flexible migration strategy of the species. Some birds accumulate up to 30 g of fat in or near their breeding grounds in late July, within 10 days of the end of the breeding season (Holland *et al* 1982). They should be able to fly at least 2,500 km non-stop with these reserves, sufficient to reach North Africa. Perhaps they fatten up again there, and make a similar long hop to West Africa. Moreau (1967) reports this species as a regular migrant visitor to oases in the Sahara, suggesting that it is a regular cross-Saharan migrant, and also implying that it uses a long-hop migration pattern. However, other observers report birds migrating with low weights, small fat reserves and short stopover periods, consistent with a short-hop migration strategy (Baccetti *et al* 1992, Meissner 1997). It is uncertain whether these two patterns represent a difference between populations, a difference between adults and juveniles, or a difference between years and feeding opportunities in different sites.

Two major uncertainties are revealed by this analysis. Although it seems likely that Common Sandpipers breeding in Britain & Ireland winter in West Africa (Fig 6), the absence of any midwinter recoveries of British or Irish breeding birds means that this cannot be confirmed. We are therefore unable to evaluate the possible effects on the breeding population of habitat loss or climatic changes on the wintering grounds. It is usually assumed that the retreat in range documented by the *1988–91 Atlas* is a consequence of poorer conditions on the breeding grounds. However, it is evident that poor recruitment following catastrophic declines is the major problem. This could be a consequence of habitat loss in the wintering areas. A comparison of population trends amongst birds breeding in Britain & Ireland and those breeding in Scandinavia may help to explain this. As the wintering grounds of these birds probably overlap, any difference in population trend would imply that the problem is on the breeding grounds. The second uncertainty also concerns population changes. Since wide dispersal from natal sites to adult breeding territories seems usual (as reflected in the poor return rates of chicks), better information on first-year survival and recruitment is needed to understand population dynamics properly. Filling both these gaps will need more ringing effort, and some luck with recoveries from Africa.

P K Holland & D W Yalden

Ruddy Turnstone (Turnstone)

Arenaria interpres

With their striking tortoiseshell breeding plumage and almost world-wide wintering distribution, Turnstones are one of our most familiar waders. Five populations have been recognized, four involving the nominate race *interpres*. Three of these populations (all *interpres*) occur in Britain & Ireland. The Canada/Greenland population breeds on Axel Heiberg and Ellesmere Islands in northeast Canada and in northern Greenland, and winters on the eastern Atlantic seaboard, mainly from the North and Irish Seas to Iberia, with smaller numbers in Iceland, southwest Norway and northwest Africa. The Fennoscandian population breeds on or near much of the Norwegian and northern Baltic coastlines, and in Estonia and Murmansk. Most birds winter in northwest and West Africa, with others on North Sea and western Mediterranean coasts. The Central Siberian population breeds on arctic tundra from the White Sea to central Siberia and winters in southern Africa, the Middle East, and the shores of the eastern Mediterranean and Indian Ocean. Elsewhere, an East Siberian/West Alaskan population winters in Southeast Asia, and Australasia, and on West Pacific islands and the northeast Pacific coast. An East Alaskan/Canadian population, race *morinella*, which breeds further south than the Canada/Greenland population, winters from the southeast USA and Mexico south to central Chile and Argentina (Branson *et al* 1978, Clapham 1979, *BWP*, Summers *et al* 1989).

Isolated pairs may breed in north Scotland on very rare occasions but otherwise only non-breeding birds use Britain & Ireland, with a preference for open coastline, especially rocky shores. The vast bulk of wintering birds are from the Canada/Greenland population, many using Iceland as a migratory stopover, with a small minority of Fennoscandian

The analysis of the data for this species was supported by Ted Ponting

breeders. Some Fennoscandian birds use Britain & Ireland on autumn passage, although most use continental European coasts, and Central Siberian birds can occur as autumn vagrants (*BWP*).

Most Turnstone recoveries involving Britain & Ireland stem from birds ringed in Britain on passage or in winter, mainly between August and May (Figs 1 & 2). Relatively few birds have been ringed on the remote tundra breeding grounds, and foreign-ringed recoveries are mostly restricted to the main periods of migration. Ringing effort within Britain & Ireland is slightly biased towards larger estuaries such as the Wash, the Ribble and Morecambe Bay whereas Turnstones are most abundant on non-estuarine open coasts (*Winter Atlas*, Cayford & Waters 1996). Only 40% of recoveries of dead birds included a report on the finding circumstances (Fig 3) but over a third of these were deliberately taken by Man. This may have an effect on the distribution of recoveries.

On average, departure from the breeding grounds and autumn arrival at the wintering grounds begins with failed breeding birds of both sexes, followed by successful adults, females first, and finally juveniles (Whitfield 1985, D P Whitfield & L Partridge pers obs). The first adults return in late July but the main influx is in early August and is usually complete by the end of August. The first juveniles appear on the wintering grounds in early August and continue to arrive well into September. The return of adults is characterized by raised levels of

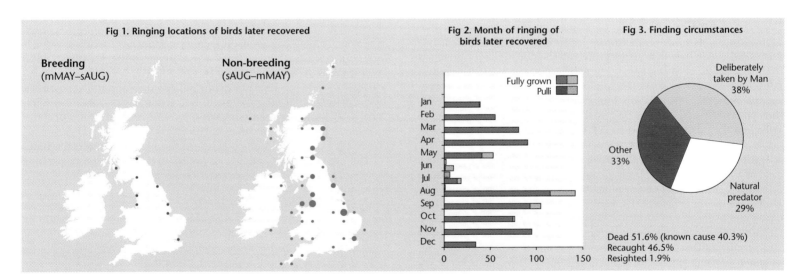

Fig 1. Ringing locations of birds later recovered

Breeding (mMAY–sAUG)   **Non-breeding** (sAUG–mMAY)

Fig 2. Month of ringing of birds later recovered

Fully grown / Pulli

Fig 3. Finding circumstances

Deliberately taken by Man 38%

Other 33%

Natural predator 29%

Dead 51.6% (known cause 40.3%)
Recaught 46.5%
Resighted 1.9%

Ringing and recovery data

	<1960	60–69	70–79	80–89	90–97	Total
RINGING						
BTO ringing totals (%)	2	10	33	40	16	28,723
RECOVERIES						
BTO-ringed (%)	1	5	38	39	17	732
Foreign-ringed (%)	18	13	29	25	14	76

Statistical analyses

	Breeding population (mMAY–sAUG)	Wintering population (mOCT–sAPR)
Status	NONE	LONG-DISTANCE MIGRANT*
Age differences	—	Not tested
Sex differences	—	Not tested
Regional differences	—	Not tested
Finding circumstances	—	Not tested

Fig 4. Locations during the breeding season (41, red) and winter (108, blue), and movements of over 20 km, of Turnstones present in Britain & Ireland during autumn.

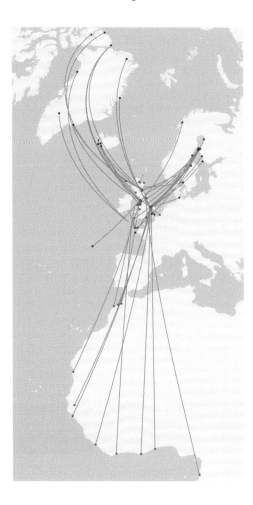

Fig 5. Movements of over 20 km and recovery locations of Turnstones ringed in winter and recovered in the same winter (23:3, red) or a subsequent winter (89:46, blue). Sample sizes of movements under:over 20 km are given but only those over 20 km are plotted. One movement from Scotland to the USA is not shown.

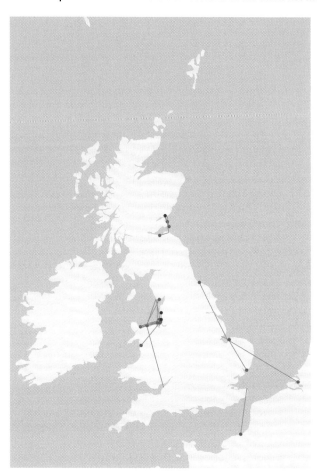

aggression as dominant–subordinate relationships are re-established (Whitfield 1985). The first arriving juveniles appear to adopt preferred feeding techniques in the best feeding areas and enjoy higher survival rates; later arriving birds use less preferred techniques and have poorer survival. This suggests that it is important for breeding adults to fledge their young as early as possible to give their young a better chance of early arrival on the wintering grounds (D P Whitfield & L Partridge pers obs). Adults may start body moult on the breeding grounds but the main moult of flight feathers occurs after arrival on the wintering grounds. Iceland is used by Canada/Greenland birds on autumn migration but many British & Irish wintering birds probably return by a direct flight from the breeding grounds or nearby (Wilson 1981, Whitfield & Magnusson 1987). Canada/ Greenland migrants wintering in Britain & Ireland use southwest Norway far more in autumn than during spring. Many Canada/Greenland birds and Fennoscandian birds that arrive in Britain & Ireland on autumn migration do not remain for the winter (Fig 4). These birds lay down reserves before flying to wintering grounds further south in France, Iberia or Africa. The coastline of continental Europe is used more by migrating Fennoscandian Turnstones than Britain & Ireland (Branson *et al* 1978).

Wintering Turnstones are typically highly site-faithful, both within and between winters (Metcalfe & Furness 1985, Whitfield 1985, Metcalfe 1986, Summers *et al* 1989, Burton & Evans 1997). Individuals tend to occupy the same patch of shoreline in flocks of stable membership usually in every winter for their whole life (D P Whitfield & L Partridge pers obs). Any movements tend to be within 20 km and, in the short term, related to tidal changes in food availability (Whitfield 1985, Metcalfe 1986). Over the course of a winter, the home range appears to vary in size

in relation to the seasonal stability of food supplies in areas occupied in early winter. Smaller home range size is related to greater seasonal stability of food supplies (Whitfield 1985, D P Whitfield & L Partridge pers obs), and local movements tend to increase in late winter and spring (Whitfield 1985, Metcalfe 1986, D P Whitfield & L Partridge pers obs). Wintering Turnstones form dominant–subordinate social relationships with other individuals but dominance does not affect the size of winter home range (Whitfield 1985, D P Whitfield & L Partridge pers obs, *cf* Metcalfe 1986).

The high winter site-fidelity shown by studies of colour-ringed birds is confirmed by the ring-recoveries. Of 26 within-winter recoveries of birds found dead, there are only three records of movements over 20 km, although between winters 34% of 135 recoveries were over 20 km from the site of ringing (Fig 5). A single transatlantic movement must be regarded as highly aberrant. This involved a bird ringed as a juvenile in Lothian, Scotland, in November 1986 that was recovered in December 1989 at Beaufort, North Carolina.

Once movements associated with settlement during the autumn migration period are over, juveniles and first-winter birds appear to be as sedentary as older birds (Metcalfe & Furness 1985, Whitfield 1985). Some very old birds (*ie* at least 10 years old) change their pattern of local movements (D P Whitfield & L Partridge pers obs). There appear to be no sexual differences in winter movements even though females are subordinate to males and can adopt different feeding specializations (Whitfield 1985, 1990).

Turnstones wintering in Britain & Ireland start to leave their wintering grounds as early as late February but the main exodus is in April and May (Branson *et al* 1978, Metcalfe & Furness 1985, Whitfield 1985). Recoveries

Fig 6. Locations during the breeding season (21, red), winter (49, blue) and autumn (30, grey), and movements of over 20 km, of Turnstones present in Britain & Ireland during spring.

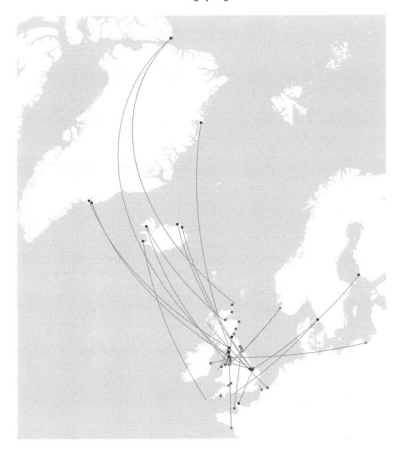

Fig 7. Locations during the breeding season (36, red) and spring (50, grey), and movements of over 20 km, of Turnstones present in Britain & Ireland during winter.

data reveal no geographic trend in pre-migratory movements within Britain & Ireland and indicate that such movements are neither common nor involve long distances. Spring movements through Britain appear to be complex. Some birds leaving wintering areas in late April and early May have gained sufficient fuel stores to reach Iceland (Branson *et al* 1979, Clapham 1979, Ferns 1981). Others may fatten at intermediate sites, such as the Solway Firth (Moser & Carrier 1983) and move northwards in a series of steps (Ferns 1981). Some birds leaving in late May lay down much greater stores and are thought to bypass Iceland, flying direct to breeding grounds in northeast Greenland (Clapham 1979, Wilson 1981). At least some foreign-wintering Turnstones use Britain & Ireland on spring migration. Most of these birds are of the Canada/Greenland population, although a few appear to be Fennoscandian birds breeding in the Baltic (Fig 6). Body moult into breeding plumage may be largely completed at wintering or passage sites.

Gudmundsson & Gardarsson (1993) estimate that around half of the West Palearctic wintering population of Turnstones use Iceland as a spring staging post. Most occur at intertidal areas in west Iceland (see also Wilson 1986). The vast majority of birds that gather there appear to breed in northwest Greenland and northeast Canada, reached by a crossing of the south Greenland ice-cap (Gudmundsson 1993). This route is confirmed by recoveries of British & Irish wintering birds (Fig 7). At a passage site in northeast Iceland, relatively more birds appear to migrate to northeast Greenland (Whitfield & Magnusson 1987). Individuals appear to be faithful to spring migratory tactics (Metcalfe & Furness 1984, pers obs). Males leave spring staging posts and arrive on the breeding grounds a few days before females (Whitfield & Magnusson 1987, pers obs).

Turnstones have high return rates to breeding territories (Bergman 1946, T Partanen & O Hildén pers comm, pers obs). Despite high site-fidelity at all stages of the annual cycle, individuals that winter together do not usually breed at the same site. The wintering grounds of Turnstones breeding at a site on Ellesmere Island included the Netherlands, northern France, North Wales and southern Portugal (pers obs).

Immature Turnstones may either stay in Britain & Ireland (not necessarily at their wintering site), spend the summer in Iceland or migrate to the breeding grounds (*BWP*). Immatures begin their main annual moult before the return of adults from the north.

There is a suggestion that there are differences in the origins of Turnstones using the different regions of Britain & Ireland (Fig 8). Turnstones using western regions appear more likely to migrate to more westerly parts of the Canada/Greenland breeding range (northwest Greenland and northeast Canada) (at least some using west Iceland as a stopover) than birds using eastern regions. Turnstones from eastern Britain appear more likely to breed in northeast Greenland and to use east Iceland as a stopover, if a stopover is used. This pattern may be explained if there is no difference in the breeding areas of Turnstones wintering in different parts of Britain & Ireland but birds that winter in France or further south are more likely to originate from the more distant western part of the breeding range and tend to use western Britain & Ireland as a stopover (Clapham 1979, Ferns 1981). A second possibility is that the breeding areas of Turnstones wintering in eastern Britain tend to be different to the breeding area of birds wintering in western Britain & Ireland, with birds wintering in eastern Britain more likely to breed in the eastern part of the breeding range. While these two explanations are not mutually exclusive, some support for the latter is provided by two colour-ringing studies of wintering Turnstones, one in southwest Scotland, the other in southeast Scotland. Turnstones from the southwest site left much earlier in spring than birds from the southeast site; southwest birds departed as early as February whereas almost half of the southeast birds did not leave until the last two weeks of May (Metcalfe & Furness 1985, Whitfield 1985). This implies that

Fig 8. Exchanges between (a) eastern (31) and (b) western (44) Britain & Ireland and abroad. Only movements to the northwest of Britain & Ireland are shown.

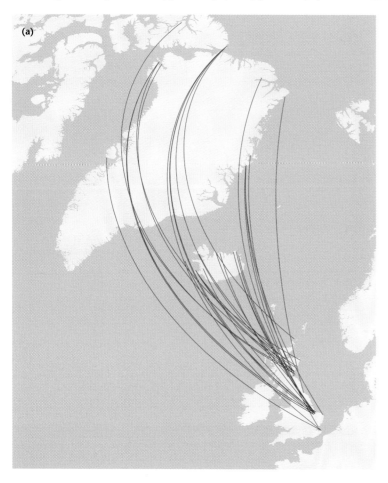

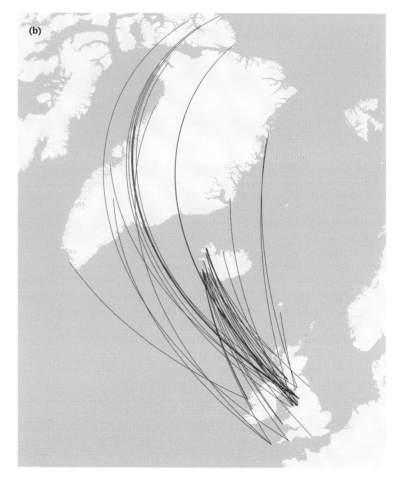

southwest birds were more likely to stage in Iceland (and so further implying they were more likely bound for northwest Greenland or northeast Canada) and that southeast birds were more likely to fly direct to northeast Greenland. Several southwest birds have been seen on spring passage in west Iceland (N B Metcalfe pers comm), whereas no southeast birds have been reported from Iceland even though more southeast birds have been colour-ringed (pers obs).

The possible tendency for an east–west split in the breeding origins of non-breeding Turnstones using Britain & Ireland is worth further

analysis, as it could have implications for any regional differences in the marked recent declines that have been reported in British & Irish wintering Turnstone populations (Browne *et al* 1996, Dott 1997). The cause of these declines (and declines in other non-estuarine wintering waders) should be investigated as a matter of considerable urgency. The role of Britain & Ireland in the movements of the Fennoscandian population is also worthy of further attention.

D Philip Whitfield

Arctic Skua
Stercorarius parasiticus

The Arctic Skua is a piratical seabird that breeds in small numbers in northern Scotland and widely around the Arctic and sub-Arctic. It is a transequatorial migrant that is closely associated during migrations and in winter with flocks of terns and small gulls from which it can steal food (Kapanen 1977, Paterson 1986, K A Wood 1989, Wuorinen 1992, Yosef 1995a), though it can also prey on small birds (Belisle & Giroux 1995).

The breeding range is almost continuous in the Arctic, extending coastally southward to Scotland, Sweden, Kamchatka, the Aleutians, and the southern shore of Hudson Bay. Major wintering areas include Australia, South Africa and southern South America (Furness 1987). Birds from some of the Arctic populations will migrate overland, for example across North America or from Siberia to the Indian Ocean. The birds that migrate along the coasts of Britain and Ireland include the small numbers that breed in Scotland but also birds from the large populations in the north of Europe (Furness 1987).

There is a regular easterly spring passage offshore from Sussex, from early April to early June, peaking in early May (James 1996), while others pass western Ireland and the Western Isles of Scotland. Most birds move singly or in small groups, at speeds estimated at 37–50 km/hour (Newnham 1984). Arctic Skuas occur in two plumage phases, distinguished by the colour of their underparts. In Scotland, dark birds predominate, and in southern Scandinavia up to 95% of birds may be dark-phase, but at high latitudes virtually all birds are light-phase. The migrations of these birds differ in timing and so the proportions of light and dark birds on coasts change through the migration seasons (Arcos 1997). In Sussex it has been observed that the proportion of light-phase

The analysis of the data for this species was supported by the Fair Isle Bird Observatory Trust

FAIR ISLE LODGE AND BIRD OBSERVATORY

birds increases during the spring, as later-migrating birds head for progressively more northerly breeding grounds (Newnham 1984).

Arctic Skuas tend to migrate and winter along coasts, often lingering for some time where there are aggregations of terns and small gulls such as in estuaries (Taylor 1979). They will settle to rest on the shore or on water. Their breeding sites are on the arctic tundra or on moorland and rough grassland close to seabird colonies, especially where there are large numbers of breeding terns, Kittiwakes or Puffins.

Most Arctic Skuas have been ringed as chicks at colonies in Shetland and Orkney (Fig 1), but some have been trapped as adults, on their nests or while defending chicks (Fig 2). Of the known finding circumstances (Fig 3), nearly one-third were of birds deliberately taken by humans, some shot as vermin or for food. Nearly one-quarter were killed by predators. In Orkney and Shetland, the predators are often Great Skuas, which can kill Arctic Skua adults when fighting for territories and kill fledglings and chicks for food. The data on recoveries of ringed adults tend, as a result, to reflect where studies of breeding Arctic Skuas are carried out, and so present a biased picture. Trapping adults on the nest has been concentrated on Foula and Fair Isle, both in Shetland, where long-term studies have been carried out. However, ringing of chicks has been widespread in Shetland and Orkney so that there are many records of intercolony movements and of site-fidelity.

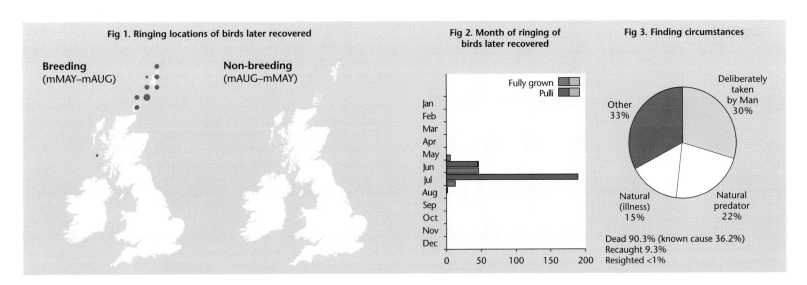

Fig 1. Ringing locations of birds later recovered

Breeding (mMAY–mAUG)

Non-breeding (mAUG–mMAY)

Fig 2. Month of ringing of birds later recovered

Fully grown
Pulli

Jan, Feb, Mar, Apr, May, Jun, Jul, Aug, Sep, Oct, Nov, Dec

0 50 100 150 200

Fig 3. Finding circumstances

Deliberately taken by Man 30%

Other 33%

Natural (illness) 15%

Natural predator 22%

Dead 90.3% (known cause 36.2%)
Recaught 9.3%
Resighted <1%

Ringing and recovery data

	<1960	60–69	70–79	80–89	90–97	Total
RINGING						
BTO ringing totals (%)	7	8	30	26	29	12,449
RECOVERIES						
BTO-ringed (%)	5	9	25	38	23	299
Foreign-ringed (%)	0	0	0	0	100	1

Statistical analyses

	Breeding population (mMAY–mAUG)	Wintering population (mNOV–sAPR)
Status	[LONG-DISTANCE MIGRANT]	NONE
Age differences	Not tested	—
Sex differences	Not tested	—
Regional differences	Not tested	—
Finding circumstances	Not tested	—

Fig 4. Recovery locations during the breeding season of (a) 106 adult and (b) 40 immature Arctic Skuas ringed in Britain & Ireland during the breeding season.

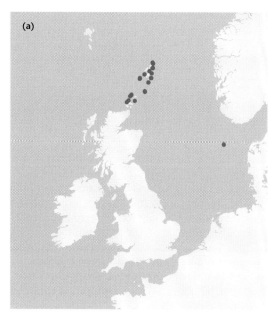

Fig 5. Seasonally accurate locations outside the breeding season of Arctic Skuas ringed during the breeding season. Those recovered as adults (20, blue) are differentiated from those recovered as immatures (47, red).

Recoveries at colonies of adults that had been ringed as chicks show considerable numbers of movements between Shetland colonies but the majority of ringed adults had been hatched at the colony in which they recruited. There are no records of adults moving to breed at another colony once they have established a territory, though some birds take a year off from breeding if feeding conditions are poor (Catry *et al* 1998a) and may then remain at sea through most or all of the summer.

Scottish adult Arctic Skuas return to colonies during late April, but birds breeding in the Arctic may not occupy breeding grounds until June, and some of these may occur along both British and Irish coasts in May. This is the month when the percentage of dark-phase birds is lowest in the North Sea (Tasker *et al* 1987). In autumn, Arctic Skua numbers in the North Sea and west of Britain & Ireland are highest in August and September (Tasker *et al* 1987, Webb *et al* 1990). Fledglings and adults from Scottish colonies tend to begin their southward autumn migration during August. Most birds seen at sea in the North Sea in autumn were classified as dark-phase (Tasker *et al* 1987), suggesting that few Arctic breeders pass through the North Sea in autumn. Only one foreign-ringed Arctic Skua has been recovered in Britain or Ireland: this was ringed in Finland and found in North Norfolk.

Migration routes taken by Scottish Arctic Skuas cannot be identified from the few recoveries away from Scotland. Indeed, recoveries in Syria and the Congo Basin may indicate where Arctic Skuas should not go rather than where they normally occur! Given the small size of the population and the relatively high proportion of chicks that are ringed it is unlikely that further ringing effort will identify details of migration routes or population-specific wintering areas.

A more important conservation-related issue may be the extent to which our breeding population is self-sustaining. The Arctic Skua is one of our least numerous and most geographically restricted breeding seabirds. There is a need to determine whether colonies in different areas of Scotland are supported by immigration of birds from other areas of Scotland, and whether there is any recruitment from colonies overseas. This might best be achieved by a combination of trapping adults ringed as chicks and undertaking molecular studies of genetic differences between populations.

Ringing of Scottish Arctic Skuas shows that almost all recoveries during the breeding season of birds of breeding age (assumed in this analysis to be four years and older) occur at colonies (Fig 4a). This is also true for most recoveries of immature birds during the breeding season, though some young immature birds remain in wintering quarters through the summer or move to high latitudes such as Greenland (Fig 4b). Autumn and winter recoveries (Fig 5) show the movement of birds from colonies in the Northern Isles through the North Sea, then down the coasts of Europe and Africa. These probably winter predominantly off southern Africa, though two winter recoveries of immature birds from South America suggest that some Scottish Arctic Skuas cross to the western South Atlantic. Two recoveries from the eastern Mediterranean (Syria and the Lebanon, both of uncertain seasonality) and two from far inland in Africa (a January recovery in Sudan and one of uncertain seasonality in the Congo Basin) suggest that some Scottish Arctic Skuas may migrate overland, perhaps to the Indian Ocean. A very few Arctic Skuas winter as far north as the Mediterranean (Arcos 1997), and there are occasional winter sightings in British waters.

Bob Furness

Great Skua
Catharacta skua

A large predatory seabird that avoids land except to breed on a few remote islands and coasts, the Great Skua is the only member of the genus *Catharacta* that breeds in the northern hemisphere. Its three close relatives in the Antarctic and sub-Antarctic exemplify an extreme range of migration patterns (Furness 1987). Brown Skuas of the Chatham Islands are resident at the islands throughout the year, while birds from many other Brown Skua colonies, and the Chilean Skua, show limited dispersal or short-distance migrations. The South Polar Skua is a transequatorial migrant, famed for the longest displacement ever recorded by a ringed bird, from the Antarctic continent to Greenland. The Great Skua is a modest migrant by comparison with the South Polar Skua, very rarely reaching as far south as the Equator, and rarely moving far east or west of the Greenwich meridian (Thomson 1966, Furness 1978).

After only short migrations to winter off the coasts of southern Europe, adult Great Skuas at Scottish colonies return to the same breeding territory each year, and their offspring mostly try to establish a territory within a few hundred metres of their birthplace (Klomp & Furness 1992a). However, juveniles may be forced inland by unfavourable conditions in autumn and become lost over the continent of Europe. Ringed juveniles have been found on the central reservation of an autobahn in southern Germany, in a town in Switzerland, and attacking the residents of a duck-pond in Poland. Immature birds often wander south, west and north of the range occupied by older birds, producing recoveries in South America, USA, Greenland, Svalbard and northern Russia. While about half of the entire world population of the

The analysis of the data for this species was supported by Steve & Verity Hunter

Great Skua breeds in northern Scotland, there are large colonies in Iceland and small ones in the Faeroes. In recent years, the species has colonized Norway, Svalbard, Bear Island and northern Russia. All of these new colonies include birds originally ringed at colonies in Scotland, so that the few birds that do not recruit to breed where they were hatched can move considerable distances to found new colonies or join small growing populations.

In Iceland, most Great Skua colonies are on glacial gravel plains of the south coast. In Scotland, Great Skuas breed on moorland or rough grassland on remoter islands in Orkney and Shetland. Very few breed on mainland Scotland or on islands with large human populations or with predominantly agricultural habitats. The other North Atlantic breeding areas are similar in habitat to the preferred remote islands of Orkney and Shetland. Great Skuas migrate between these breeding habitats and their wintering areas in shallow seas off southern Europe with minimal contact with land. On migration, Great Skuas tend to remain at least 2–5 km from coasts, and so the numbers that can be counted from coastal observatories or sea-watching points tend to be far less than can be seen from a boat a few kilometres offshore. Great Skuas are seen in large numbers on passage, from shore, only when weather conditions drive them onto coasts (when there are strong onshore winds or when the visibility is greatly reduced by fog). Only incapacitated or sick birds

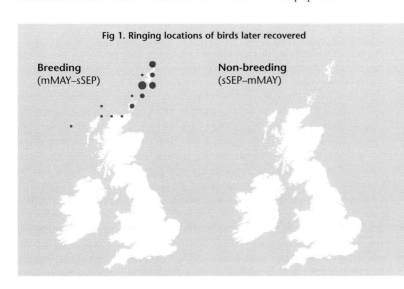

Fig 1. Ringing locations of birds later recovered

Breeding (mMAY–sSEP)

Non-breeding (sSEP–mMAY)

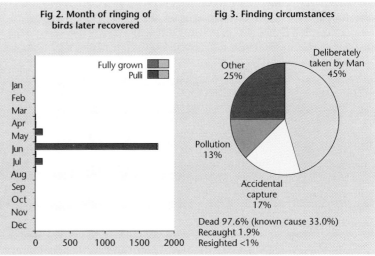

Fig 2. Month of ringing of birds later recovered

Fully grown / Pulli

Fig 3. Finding circumstances

Deliberately taken by Man 45%

Other 25%

Pollution 13%

Accidental capture 17%

Dead 97.6% (known cause 33.0%)
Recaught 1.9%
Resighted <1%

Ringing and recovery data

	<1960	60–69	70–79	80–89	90–97	Total
RINGING						
BTO ringing totals (%)	3	16	37	23	21	65,633
RECOVERIES						
BTO-ringed (%)	2	27	44	20	7	1,956
Foreign-ringed (%)	—	77	—	20	3	35

Statistical analyses

	Breeding population (mMAY–sSEP)	Wintering population (mNOV–mMAR)
Status	LONG-DISTANCE MIGRANT (2)	?
Age differences[NT]	Not significant	—
Sex differences	Not tested	—
Regional differences	Not tested	—
Finding circumstances	(Not significant)	—

Fig 4. Recovery locations outside the breeding season of (a) immature (658, red) and (b) adult (111, blue) Great Skuas ringed in Britain & Ireland during the breeding season.

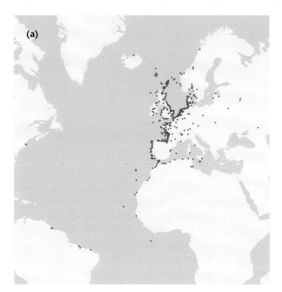

occur on land during migration or winter. Equally, Great Skuas travel only rarely into pelagic waters, but tend to remain over the shallow seas of the continental shelf. Some long ocean crossings must be undertaken, however, to produce ring-recoveries of Scottish birds from South America and Greenland, and for Icelandic Great Skuas to reach either North America or mainland Europe.

Most ringing of Great Skuas has been undertaken at Foula, west Shetland (Fig 1), and almost all ringing has been of chicks (Fig 2). The numbers of Great Skuas in Scotland have increased from a tiny population at only two breeding sites in Shetland at the end of the 19th century. Shetland-ringed Great Skuas now breed at virtually all Scottish colonies, so there is unlikely to be any genetic difference in migration behaviour between birds from different parts of Scotland. Great Skuas from west-coast colonies may migrate south directly down the Atlantic coast of Europe, however, whereas many from the Northern Isles migrate into the North Sea before moving from there into the Atlantic. This funnelling of Orkney and Shetland birds into the North Sea could perhaps generate differences in migration timing or wintering area.

Monel rings on Great Skuas show virtually no wear, so recoveries of older birds are not biased by loss of rings or illegible inscriptions (Furness 1978). The majority of recoveries of known cause are from birds deliberately or accidentally taken by humans, however, many having been shot or drowned by fishing nets or baited lines (Fig 3). These recoveries are frequent in some countries and rare, or rarely reported, in others, so that a biased picture of Great Skua distribution may be created. Indeed, it can be argued that the majority of recoveries of Great Skuas indicate where birds should not have been. This is certainly true of those recovered on land in Europe as a result of storms. The majority of Great Skuas that avoid such hazards are likely to die at sea and their migrations are extremely unlikely to be reported.

Autumn migration starts with the immature birds that have visited colonies. These immature birds (mostly three to eight years old but some even older) tend to migrate away from the colony from late June, with most immatures having left the colonies by late July (Klomp & Furness 1990, 1992b). Most juvenile Great Skuas disperse from colonies during August, though a few may linger around the colony until October. Adults tend to remain defending their territory until at least late July even if they lose their eggs, since early departure can lead to the territory being taken over by another bird, though a few do take years off from breeding (Catry et al 1998a). Most adults move south during late August but a few may stay at the colony into October and occasionally even later. Peak numbers are seen on autumn migration in September in the North Sea (Tasker et al 1987) but in October to the west of Britain &

Ireland (Webb et al 1990). Avoidance of coasts leads Great Skuas to occur only in the outermost parts of estuaries during migration, and to migrate out of the North Sea mostly via the north coast of Scotland in autumn rather than through the southern North Sea and English Channel. Thus the predominant migration of Great Skuas off the east coast of England and Scotland in autumn is northwards, then south, down the west coast. Autumn migration of Great Skuas tends to be leisurely, the birds often staying for some time in areas where feeding conditions are good. Aggregations of fishing boats often provide an attraction for Great Skuas, especially during spring and late summer (Tasker et al 1985), but migration tends to be as individuals or small groups. There is no evidence of Great Skuas remaining in family groups or stable aggregations through the autumn migration. Autumn recoveries of adult Great Skuas typically occur close to colonies or in the southern North Sea. Juveniles show a wider distribution with recoveries inland as well as along the European coasts.

During winter, adult Great Skuas are recovered mostly in the Bay of Biscay, on the Iberian coast and in the western Mediterranean. In all of these areas, Great Skuas often associate with fishing fleets scavenging discarded fish. Immatures are recovered in the same wintering area but also further to the south off the coast of West Africa where there are no recoveries of adults (Figs 4a & b). A few recoveries of Great Skuas have been reported from South America and the USA, and these tend to be immature birds during the winter. Spring migration occurs during March and April, with established breeders arriving at colonies from late March. Newly recruiting birds arrive later, and immatures last of all. The youngest immatures to visit colonies are three years old and they return mostly during June (Klomp & Furness 1992a). Some birds that are two or three years old remain in the southernmost 'wintering' areas during the summer while others, as well as older immatures, migrate far north, reaching Canada, Greenland, the Arctic Ocean and penetrating east to Russia (Fig 5a). Adults (defined in this analysis as birds seven years old and older) migrate back to their breeding colonies for the summer, with only a few recovered during summer in their wintering area or at high latitudes; indeed, there are few breeding-season recoveries of adults away from the main colonies of Orkney and Shetland (Fig 5b). Since the age of first breeding of Great Skuas varies from four to over 10 years old, the few recoveries away from colonies in summer are likely to be of relatively old immature birds or of adults unfit to return to breed.

The analysis of the latitudes of recoveries in different months (Fig 6) shows the tendency for Great Skua autumn migration to be slow and ill-defined, the median movement south from colonies being only a few degrees latitude per month from August to December. In contrast, the

Fig 5. Recovery locations during the breeding season of (a) immature (380, red) and (b) adult (264, blue) ringed in Britain & Ireland during the breeding season. The ringing locations of two birds ringed abroad and recovered in Britain & Ireland during the breeding season as immatures are shown as grey squares.

Fig 6. Monthly variation in the differences in latitude between ringing and recovery locations of Great Skuas present in Britain & Ireland during the breeding season. Monthly medians (points) and interquartile ranges (bars) are shown.

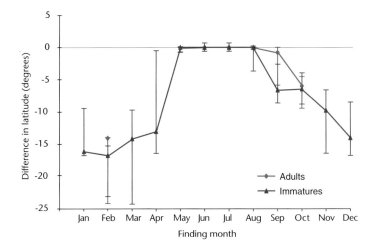

spring migration is more clearly defined, with recoveries remaining around 15 degrees south of colonies until April, then occurring at colonies in May. Rapid spring migration is to be expected as, the earlier in May that birds lay, the higher their breeding productivity (Catry *et al* 1998b).

Icelandic and Faeroese Great Skuas have mostly been ringed with soft metal rings rather than with steel or monel rings, so that few have been recovered at breeding age. The limited evidence suggests that there is very little movement of birds between the Scottish, Faeroese and Icelandic breeding populations. Some Icelandic and Faeroese birds pass the coasts of Britain and Ireland in spring and autumn, however, and between 1979 and 1997, rings from one Faeroese and 17 Icelandic Great Skuas were recovered in Britain & Ireland, most during autumn migration. The Scottish and Icelandic populations apparently differ in their migration routes. The Icelandic ringing data suggest that some of their birds migrate to the Grand Banks, off Newfoundland, whereas very few Scottish Great Skuas have been recovered in the northwest Atlantic.

The different movement patterns and timings of the migrations of different age classes imply that hazards to which Great Skuas are exposed may often affect particular segments of the population. Several of the youngest immature classes in particular tend to be very widely dispersed from South America to the high Arctic, and would be unaffected by catastrophic mortality at a breeding area. High hunting pressure or likelihood of entrapment in fishing gear may be met, especially in certain regions (for example virtually all recoveries from Greenland are from shooting), but the dispersal of birds will tend to reduce local impacts on the population as a whole.

Probably the greatest uncertainty regarding Great Skua migrations is the extent to which patterns are determined by the distribution and behaviour of commercial fisheries. Studies of Great Skuas at sea in wintering areas and on migration suggest that they associate strongly with fishing fleets to feed on discards (Furness 1987, Tasker *et al* 1987). It would probably be necessary to equip birds with data loggers or satellite-transmitters to determine the extent to which their winter range and movements are affected by commercial fishing.

Bob Furness

Black-headed Gull

Larus ridibundus

The delicate Black-headed Gull is well known all year round to many people, whether they live inland or by the sea. Black-headed Gulls often associate with Man, as they find their food from cultivated land, sports fields, rubbish-tips and sewage-works, and even take food from human hands offering morsels in the centres of cities and towns.

Black-headed Gull populations are migratory, partially migratory or dispersive (*BWP*). They are spread throughout most of Europe, central Asia, the extreme southeast of Russia, northeast China and northeast North America and are found wintering as far south as West and East Africa, India, Malaysia, and the Philippines, and in America as far south as Mexico and the Lesser Antilles. In the last half-century they have been found breeding for the first time in southern Europe (Spain, Italy and Sardinia). Those breeding in Fennoscandia and Baltic countries migrate to the western European seaboard or to the Mediterranean. Typically, Russian breeding birds migrate southwestwards in autumn, towards the eastern Mediterranean, Black Sea and Transcaucasia, possibly reaching the Middle East and East Africa. Those from the Netherlands and Belgium winter on the west coasts of Europe, with some reaching northwest Africa, and those from Germany and Switzerland migrate partially south and southwest, using the major rivers, such as the Rhône, as their route. French birds also use rivers such as the Loire to move to the Atlantic for the winter, and move down the Rhône Valley to Mediterranean coasts. Some birds from Switzerland and eastern France cross north Italy using the Po Valley to winter in the Adriatic. Most eastern European birds move to the Mediterranean with some moving northwest along the Rivers Elbe and Rhine to reach the

The analysis of the data for this species was supported by the Mid-Kent Ringing Group

western seaboard (*BWP*). Many British & Irish breeders winter within Britain & Ireland but a small proportion move further south to winter in France and Iberia.

In Britain & Ireland, the Black-headed Gull is widespread during the breeding season, nesting colonially on coastal saltmarshes and sand-dunes, inland freshwater lakes, marshes, gravel-pits and upland tarns (*1988–91 Atlas*; Fig 1.3a in Chapter 1). It is estimated that the population in the breeding season is 147,400 pairs in Britain and 53,800 pairs in Ireland (*1988–91 Atlas*). During the winter months, the Black-headed Gull is the most numerous gull in England and Wales and numbers in Britain are estimated at 1.9 million (Stone *et al* 1997), representing quite a high proportion of the 2.5 million pairs thought to breed in Europe and Russia (*European Atlas*). At this time, Black-headed Gulls are found throughout Britain & Ireland, both inland and at the coasts, with the exception of the uplands of northern England, central Wales and the Scottish Highlands (*Winter Atlas*; Fig 1.3b). The gulls feed on the coasts, at rubbish-tips and on farmland, especially at times of field cultivation when invertebrates are brought to the surface. Pastures and recreational fields are extensively used when there has been heavy rainfall and the birds can easily flush out worms to the surface by puddling. Large winter roosts form on sheltered coasts and estuaries and on large inland waterbodies, reservoirs in particular (Bowes *et al* 1984).

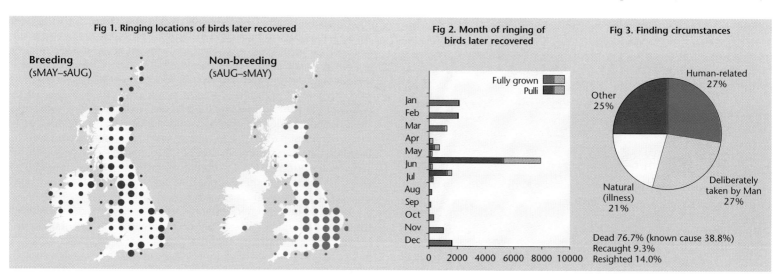

Fig 1. Ringing locations of birds later recovered

Breeding (sMAY–sAUG)

Non-breeding (sAUG–sMAY)

Fig 2. Month of ringing of birds later recovered

Fully grown
Pulli

Fig 3. Finding circumstances

Human-related 27%
Other 25%
Natural (illness) 21%
Deliberately taken by Man 27%

Dead 76.7% (known cause 38.8%)
Recaught 9.3%
Resighted 14.0%

Ringing and recovery data

	<1960	60–69	70–79	80–89	90–97	Total
RINGING						
BTO ringing totals (%)	15	20	14	33	17	326,492
RECOVERIES						
BTO-ringed (%)	13	15	15	34	23	15,832
Foreign-ringed (%)	←	50	→	33	17	8,412

Statistical analyses

	Breeding population (sMAY–sAUG)	Wintering population (sNOV–sMAR)
Status	SHORT-DISTANCE MIGRANT (1)	LONG-DISTANCE MIGRANT*
Age differences[NT]	Significant	Not significant
Sex differences[(NS)*]	Not tested	Not significant*
Regional differences	Significant[5]	Significant[4]
Finding circumstances	(Not significant)	Significant

Fig 4. Locations outside the breeding season of (a) 2,162 immature and (b) 2,275 adult Black-headed Gulls that were ringed as pulli in Britain & Ireland. An immature bird recovered in the Azores is not shown.

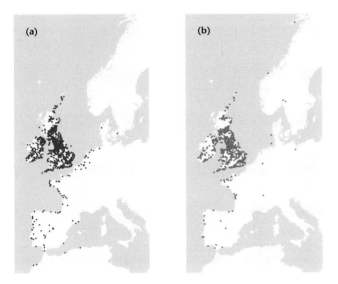

Fig 5. Variation in the distances moved by juvenile Black-headed Gulls with time after ringing as pulli. Medians for 30-day periods (points) and interquartile ranges (bars) are shown.

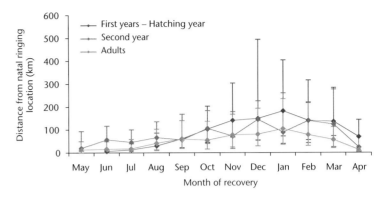

Many Black-headed Gull recoveries result from birds ringed as young at colonies throughout Britain & Ireland (Figs 1 & 2) and in Europe, generally reflecting the overall distribution of breeding colonies (*1988–91 Atlas, European Atlas*). In the mid-1970s, large-scale cannon-netting of gulls started at rubbish-tips, and to a lesser extent on beaches, outside the breeding season, resulting in a large increase in the numbers of both juvenile and adult birds caught, especially in southeast England and East Anglia (Figs 1 & 2). Also as a consequence of this catching, a greater number of foreign-ringed birds have been recorded in Britain, and a larger number of recoveries have come from abroad since that time.

The cause of death is known in 39% of recoveries reported dead (Fig 3). In over 50% of these cases, death resulted from human-related activities, including hunting. Many recoveries result from culls at breeding sites, or from birds being hit on the road or by aircraft or flying into wires (Grant 1974, Flegg & Cox 1975, Flegg & Morgan 1976). Gulls are hunted in various parts of Europe and this has been the main cause of recovery in several countries, particularly in Fennoscandia and Iberia. Disease has accounted for 21% of recoveries of known cause and, in particular, the use of refuse-tips by gulls (Horton *et al* 1983) may have played a part in the prevalence of botulism, which has killed off large numbers of gulls (Ortiz & Smith 1994). Spatial and temporal variations in such causes of recovery must be borne in mind when interpreting recovery patterns for the species.

Most British & Irish Black-headed Gulls remain in Britain & Ireland throughout the year but a small proportion (mainly immature birds) move south to France and Iberia, and even North Africa (Radford 1962, Flegg & Cox 1976; Fig 4). After fledging (on average around mid-June; *BWP*), young generally remain within 50 km of their natal site for two months, after which a gradual movement further away from the colonies takes place (Fig 5). The maximum monthly median distance from the colony reached by first-year birds is 184 km in January. After this time, first-year birds appear to move back towards the natal area but only by May do first-year birds on average come within 50 km of the natal colony (Fig 5). The recoveries from April to August suggest that Black-headed Gulls remain, on average, further from their natal colonies during the breeding season in the year following hatching than in subsequent years. Probably fewer than half of the one-year-olds that arrive back at colonies actually breed, most Black-headed Gulls starting to breed when two years of age (Patterson 1965), though some not until three (*BWP*). Recoveries suggest that the dispersal of adults of breeding age away from the colonies takes place from August onwards; adults are most distant from their colonies (a median of 105 km) in January and

return movements take place thereafter, with birds reaching the breeding colonies again by April (Fig 5).

As suggested in Fig 5, immature Black-headed Gulls travel significantly further between the colonies and wintering locations (median 141 km, P5–95=12–1,391 km, n=587) than adults (median 84 km, P5–95=7–583 km, n=547). Immatures also winter significantly further west (by 0.6° longitude) and further south (by 0.9° latitude) than adults.

Black-headed Gulls from different areas of Britain & Ireland show some variation in their patterns of movement outside the breeding season (Fig 6). Although all those from Britain winter predominantly in Britain, those from the northwest and southwest appear to have the highest degree of westerly movement into Ireland and those from the southeast, and to a lesser extent the southwest and northwest, a strong component of southerly movements into France and Iberia. Many Irish birds appear to winter within Ireland or on adjacent Irish Sea coasts, with few recoveries to the south on the Continent (Fig 6). While some of this variation might be accounted for by differences in the numbers of birds ringed in each region (and hence the likelihood of more distant recoveries), the formal statistical analyses showed significant differences in average wintering areas and in distances moved by birds from the regional subpopulations. Black-headed Gulls from the northeast moved furthest between breeding and wintering locations (median 163 km, P5–95=11–1,404 km, n=112) and also wintered the furthest west of the four groups of British birds, supporting the strong westerly component to their movements into Ireland. Those from the northwest (median 105 km, P5–95=11–534 km, n=373), southwest (median 108 km, P5–95=11–1,263 km, n=217) and southeast (median 113 km, P5–95=6–1,323 km, n=359) moved similar distances between breeding and wintering areas. Birds from the southeast remained further east (by 2° longitude) in winter than those from the two western regions. Black-headed Gulls from Ireland moved the shortest distance for the winter, a median of only 82 km (P5–95=5–1,404 km, n=73).

The natal dispersal of Black-headed Gulls is, on the whole, fairly local and mostly restricted to movements within Britain & Ireland (Radford 1962, Flegg & Cox 1976; Fig 7). The ring-recoveries indicate a median natal dispersal distance of 15 km (P5–95=0–231 km, n=915). Only a handful of birds originally ringed as pulli appear to have dispersed to the Continent to breed, although two birds were found in Fennoscandia in these circumstances. As the age of first breeding was here assumed to be two years, when most Black-headed Gulls begin breeding, but up to one-third may not breed until their third year, some of the movements shown in Fig 7 may have been made by pre-breeding birds. The ring-recoveries also suggest that breeding dispersal occurs mostly over short distances, with a median of 29 km (P5–95=0–1,877 km, n=78). Once again, some of the longer movements may relate to birds ringed or recovered when not actually breeding but the medians for natal and breeding dispersal change little if an age of first breeding of three rather than two years is assumed.

Fig 6. Movements of over 20 km between the breeding and non-breeding season and locations outside the breeding season of Black-headed Gulls ringed as pulli in the (a) northeast (447), (b) northwest (1,075), (c) southeast (976) and (d) southwest (590) of Britain and in (e) Ireland (216). A bird ringed in the northeast region and recovered in the Azores is not shown.

(a) 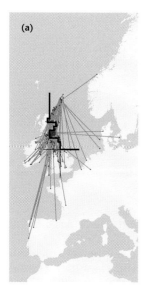 (b)  (c)  (d) 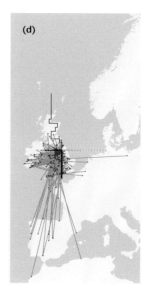 (e)

The numbers of Black-headed Gulls increase greatly in the winter months, with many birds moving from northern and eastern Europe into Britain & Ireland, particularly into the east and southeast of England (Horton *et al* 1984). MacKinnon & Coulson (1987) estimated that 71% of Black-headed Gulls wintering in England and Wales were of continental origin. These birds exploit the warmer weather, safe roosting sites and the readily available food, mostly provided by Man. Birds arrive from all over northern Europe, particularly the Netherlands, Denmark, Fennoscandia and the Baltic States (Fig 8). The gulls also come from as far east as Russia and inland in Germany, Poland, Belarus and the Czech Republic. There is some evidence to suggest that gulls from Iceland also move to our shores for the winter, probably mostly into Ireland and Scotland (*BWP*; Fig 8).

Fig 7. Movements of over 20 km and recovery locations of Black-headed Gulls ringed as pulli in Britain & Ireland and recovered in a subsequent breeding season when of breeding age. There were 540:422 movements under:over 20 km but only those over 20 km are plotted.

The arrival of Black-headed Gulls into Britain & Ireland from elsewhere in Europe takes several months, with birds starting to arrive in July (Fig 9). The birds that arrive in Britain & Ireland at this time include those newly fledged, especially from the Low Countries, which hold the nearest overseas colonies. Arrival can occur in any month from July onwards, with increasing numbers of birds present from mid-September to late October and peak numbers of ringed birds of continental origin recorded in Britain & Ireland in January and February (*BWP*; Fig 9). Observations of Black-headed Gulls from oil platforms in the North Sea confirm the timing of autumn movements (Tasker *et al* 1986). Birds breeding furthest east in continental Europe may arrive slightly earlier and leave slightly earlier than those from further west (Fig 9), probably reflecting the length of journey to be made. The later peak (in February) in Britain & Ireland for birds exchanging with the Netherlands may indicate that some Dutch birds only reach our shores in severe winter weather conditions. Fig 9 also presumably reflects the months of unfavourable weather when mortality may be high. MacKinnon & Coulson (1987) found that the arrival dates in Britain & Ireland of adults showed no relationship to the distance from their natal colonies. However, among birds from the colonies furthest away from Britain & Ireland, immatures were shown to arrive later than adults.

Although Black-headed Gulls from abroad may be found throughout Britain & Ireland in winter, they tend to settle in particular areas of the country (Horton *et al* 1984, MacKinnon & Coulson 1987). Many are recovered in southeast England. Generally, gulls from Fennoscandia and the Baltic States have a more northerly distribution in Britain than those from the Low Countries, Germany and the Czech Republic (Fig 8). On average, those birds wintering in the northwest and northeast regions of Britain that were subsequently recovered abroad during the breeding season were found significantly (2° latitude) further north than those wintering in the southwest and southeast.

Local movements of Black-headed Gulls within Britain & Ireland occur in both winter and the breeding season. In summer, there are local movements between the colonies and the feeding sites, which are usually at nearby rubbish-tips, sewage-works, rivers or on sea-coasts. In winter, the movements between roosts and feeding sites, especially rubbish-tips, can be up to about 50 km (Horton *et al* 1983). These local movements may vary depending on weather conditions and, for coastal birds, the tidal cycle (Grant 1974).

Wintering Black-headed Gulls appear to be very site-faithful. Studies in London (Widgery 1970, Christmas *et al* 1986, Gosling 1986)

Fig 8. Locations during the breeding season and associated movements of Black-headed Gulls that were present in the (a) northeast (185), (b) northwest (119), (c) southeast (2,375) and (d) southwest (959) of Britain and in (e) Ireland (30) during the winter.

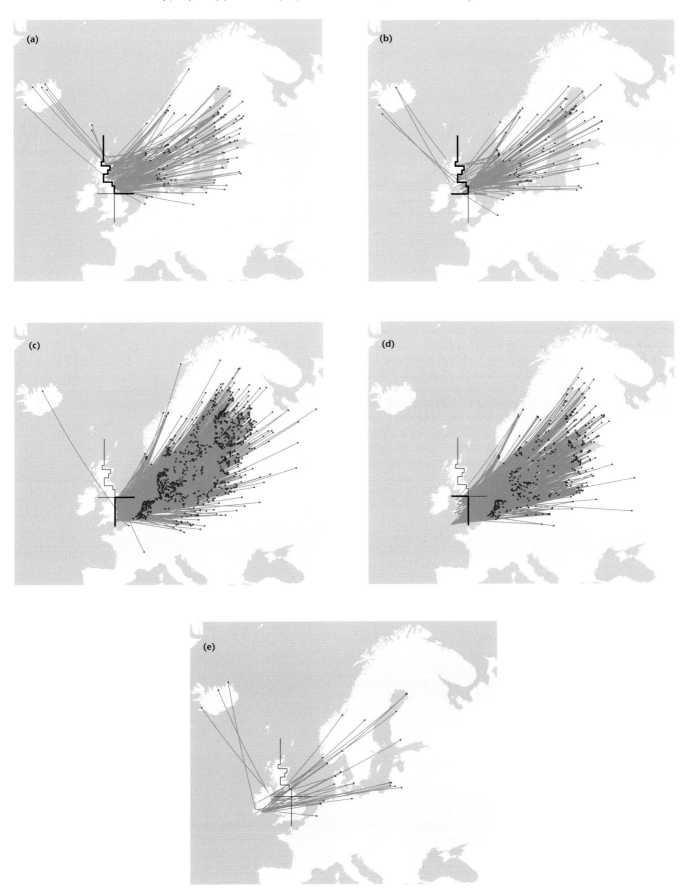

Fig 9. Seasonality in Britain & Ireland of Black-headed Gulls exchanging with the areas abroad indicated. Birds ringed as pulli in Britain & Ireland have been excluded.

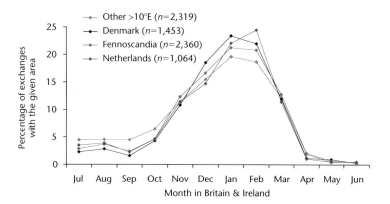

Fig 10. Movements of over 20 km and recovery locations of Black-headed Gulls ringed in winter and recovered in (a) the same winter (175:152, red) or (b) a subsequent winter (401:936, blue). Sample sizes of movements under:over 20 km are given but only those over 20 km are plotted.

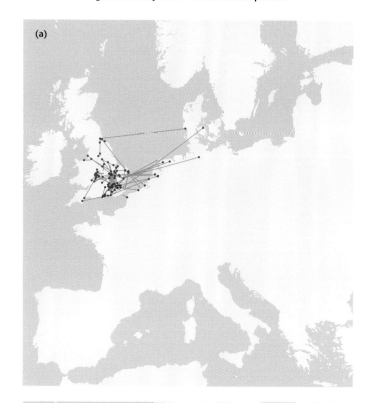

have shown that birds used the same feeding and resting sites over several years, irrespective of the age of the bird or the countries from which they originated. Some seem to be site-faithful for part of the winter and then move to another area, to which they are then equally faithful. Catches at rubbish-tips have shown that many birds return year after year to the same sites, or nearby if a tip has closed down (pers obs). The national ring-recoveries confirm a relatively high level of winter site-fidelity; within a winter, the median distance moved is only 10 km ($P5$–95=0–141 km, n=216) and this increases to 49 km ($P5$–95=0–847 km, n=737) for birds ringed in winter and recovered in a subsequent one. Some of the longer movements within and between winters (Fig 10) may relate to birds moving into Britain & Ireland later in the winter period (for example, from the Low Countries), while others may be movements due to poor winter weather conditions in some years.

Movements back to breeding areas abroad start in February and peak in March. By April, migration back to the breeding sites is largely complete (Fig 5). Tasker *et al* (1986) observed a peak in counts made from oil platforms in the North Sea during these months. MacKinnon & Coulson (1987) suggested that German and Danish birds leave earlier than those breeding in the Low Countries and the eastern Baltic. A small proportion of continental Black-headed Gulls remain in Britain & Ireland throughout the breeding season (Fig 5), with a slightly larger number of immatures than adults (MacKinnon & Coulson 1987); these birds were not predominantly from any particular area of Europe.

Although there have been many studies of Black-headed Gull migration, there are still some unknowns. For example, it is not known whether birds from the same natal colonies migrate together or feed together at the same sites during the winter months. Further, more-detailed analyses of the large quantity of existing ring-recovery data could help to answer these and other questions. There is also much scope for more intensive studies using colour-ringing to follow individual birds from natal and breeding to wintering areas and to study the exchange of breeding birds between colonies.

Mark Fletcher

Mew Gull (Common Gull)

Larus canus

Common Gulls are far less common in Britain & Ireland than their name suggests and, in many places, are highly seasonal in their occurrence. The British & Irish breeding distribution is largely restricted to Scotland, particularly north of the Central Belt, and northwest Ireland (Lloyd *et al* 1991). Only outside the breeding season, when large numbers of continental individuals occur, are Common Gulls seen widely throughout Britain & Ireland.

The nominate subspecies *canus* breeds in Iceland, the Faeroes and southward into France, Belgium, the Netherlands, Germany and Poland, with the bulk of the population nesting in Fennoscandia, Britain & Ireland and the Baltic States (*European Atlas*). East of the White Sea, *canus* grades into *heinei,* which extends eastwards to the Lena River and is replaced by *kamtschatschensis* in eastern Siberia. The race *brachyrhynchus* breeds in northwest North America (*BWP*). Common Gulls are migrants or partial migrants. In winter, the species ranges southward to the Bay of Biscay on the Atlantic seaboard but further, to around 20°N, on Pacific coasts.

In Britain & Ireland, nesting colonies occur both inland, often near fresh water, and along the coast, and are generally small, though exceptionally large aggregations occur, such as the Mortlach Hills in northeast Scotland (Lloyd *et al* 1991). Inland breeding colonies are very susceptible to ground predators and some of the previously large inland colonies in Scotland, such as that in the Coreen Hills, have declined substantially, at least partly due to this cause. From late July to April, Common Gulls are a familiar sight along the coast, inland on agricultural land (Vernon 1972) and in more urban environments. In

The analysis of the data for this species was supported by Mrs Emily Helen M Chapman in memory of her late husband Edward Ascough Chapman 1908–95

Scotland, most birds present in the non-breeding season winter on farmland (Douse 1981), with other birds feeding along the coast (where large night-time roosts form) and in urban habitats such as parks and playing fields. Some birds may also feed on rubbish-dumps. Inland, and especially in the English Midlands and southeast, large night-time roosts gather on the larger lakes and reservoirs (Bowes *et al* 1984).

The distribution of Common Gulls ringed in Britain & Ireland during the breeding season and subsequently recovered reflects very well the breeding distribution (Fig 1). There has been, however, a strong bias in ringing outside the breeding season towards southeast England (Fig 1), when compared with the wintering distribution of Common Gulls (*Winter Atlas*). Most recoveries from British & Irish ringing were from birds ringed as pulli (63%), as were 77% of the foreign-ringed recoveries in Britain & Ireland (Fig 2). The ringing of pulli abroad is probably patchily distributed across the likely source area for migrants into Britain & Ireland, and not all areas will be represented (*European Atlas*). Of birds ringed when fully grown and subsequently recovered, many were cannon-netted in January and February.

Most recoveries are from dead birds (89%) with fewer birds recaught or resighted. The majority (58%) of Common Gull recoveries have some anthropogenic cause (either human-related or deliberately taken by

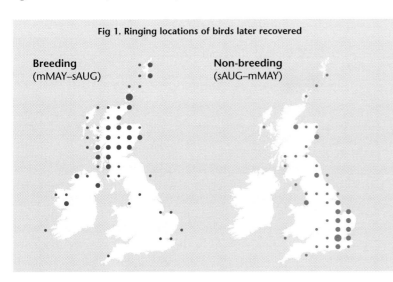

Fig 1. Ringing locations of birds later recovered

Breeding (mMAY–sAUG)

Non-breeding (sAUG–mMAY)

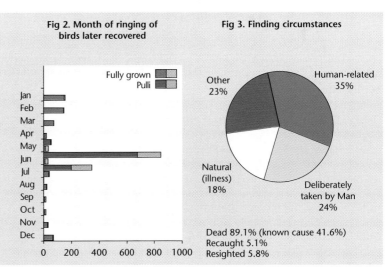

Fig 2. Month of ringing of birds later recovered

Fully grown
Pulli

Jan, Feb, Mar, Apr, May, Jun, Jul, Aug, Sep, Oct, Nov, Dec

0   200   400   600   800   1000

Fig 3. Finding circumstances

Other 23%
Human-related 35%
Natural (illness) 18%
Deliberately taken by Man 24%

Dead 89.1% (known cause 41.6%)
Recaught 5.1%
Resighted 5.8%

Ringing and recovery data

	<1960	60–69	70–79	80–89	90–97	Total
RINGING						
BTO ringing totals (%)	7	5	17	42	29	65,362
RECOVERIES						
BTO-ringed (%)	12	8	19	40	21	1,485
Foreign-ringed (%)	←	73	→	17	10	1,572

Statistical analyses

	Breeding population (mMAY–sAUG)	Wintering population (mNOV–sMAR)
Status	SHORT-DISTANCE MIGRANT (1)	LONG-DISTANCE MIGRANT
Age differences[NT]	Not significant*	Not significant*
Sex differences	Not tested	Not tested
Regional differences	Not tested	Significant[2]*
Finding circumstances	(Not significant)	Not tested

361

Fig 4. Recovery locations of Common Gulls ringed as pulli in Britain & Ireland and recovered as (a) immatures outside the breeding season (349), (b) adults outside the breeding season (102), (c) immatures during the breeding season (46) and (d) adults during the breeding season (85).

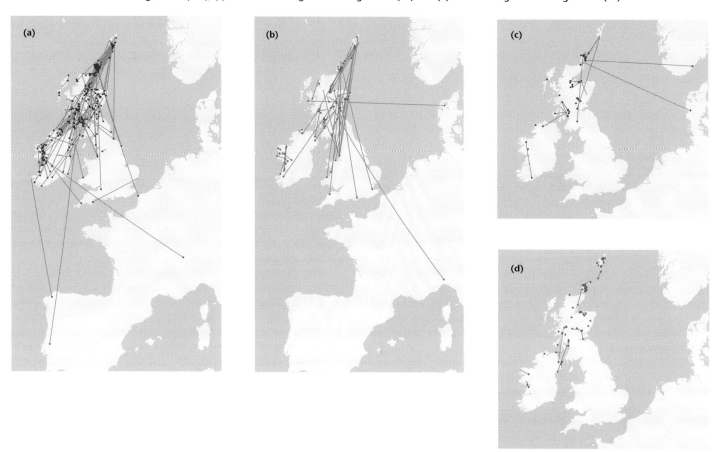

Man, Fig 3). Of the Common Gulls recovered abroad, some 57% were taken deliberately, probably mostly by shooting; the comparable figure for birds recovered in this way in Britain & Ireland was only 14.5%. Given the prevalence of shooting as a recorded cause of death, the pattern of recoveries is certain to be biased somewhat by the distribution of this activity. Since many parts of the breeding range of Common Gulls are sparsely populated, and hunting and shooting are more prevalent in coastal areas in many countries, then a bias towards coastal recoveries might be anticipated (except perhaps in Britain & Ireland).

It has long been known that British & Irish Common Gulls are partial migrants (Radford 1960). Birds ringed as pulli move in a generally southerly or south-southwesterly direction (Fig 4) throughout autumn, reaching their furthest median distance of 168 km from the point of ringing some 121–150 days after ringing (around November; n=19). The data for birds ringed as pulli also suggest that some juvenile Common Gulls are sedentary, while others may move considerable distances, as the 5% limit was 0 km and the 95% limit was 1,851 km for the period 121–150 days after ringing. The formal statistical analyses did not demonstrate any differences in the distances moved, or the average wintering areas, of immatures compared with adult birds. Despite the range of distances moved by the two age classes, most recoveries occur within Britain & Ireland (Fig 4). A small number of British & Irish Common Gulls, all immature birds, have been recovered in Spain and France in winter, which fits the general trend of movement in a south-southwesterly direction.

Common Gulls ringed in the northeast (median=126 km, n=38) moved a similar distance to those from the northwest (median=108 km, n=45) between the breeding season and winter. Some birds from breeding areas in Scotland crossed to Ireland for the winter (Fig 4). The

small sample of 14 Irish-ringed birds moved a median of only 54.5 km between the breeding season and winter. Colour-ringing of birds in western Ireland showed that some birds move east, occasionally into western Britain and as far east as the Netherlands, while others move south to the Irish coasts and, infrequently, to France and Spain (European Atlas).

The limited information available from ring-recoveries suggests that some first-year birds spend the summer close to their natal areas, while others remain some distance away, including single birds in Norway and Denmark (Fig 4). Immature Common Gulls are generally absent from the inland part of their English wintering range during the breeding season (eg Trodd & Kramer 1991), perhaps indicating that they withdraw somewhat towards breeding areas; those that remain further south in the breeding season tend to be coastal. In Estonia, small flocks of one- and two-year-olds visit colonies early in the breeding season (BWP). Recoveries of dead Common Gulls ringed as pulli indicate that natal dispersal is restricted, with a median distance of only 7 km (P5–95=0–57 km, n=82). There are no equivalent data for breeding dispersal but, as for other gull species, fidelity to breeding sites is thought to be high (Onno 1965).

Continental Common Gulls generally move in a westerly direction, onto the northwestern seaboard of the North Sea from Denmark south towards Brittany for the winter (BWP). Norwegian breeders migrate in a southwesterly direction, crossing the North Sea in large numbers, and joining the resident breeding birds in Scotland during the non-breeding season. Ring-recoveries show that Common Gulls wintering in Britain & Ireland originate particularly from Norway, Sweden, Finland, Denmark, the Baltic States and western Russia (Fig 5). If a European population estimate of 524,000 breeding pairs is accepted (European Atlas), then the

Fig 5. Recovery locations and movements of Common Gulls (a) ringed abroad as pulli and recovered in Britain & Ireland (325) or (b) ringed outside the breeding season in Britain & Ireland as fully grown birds and recovered abroad (257).

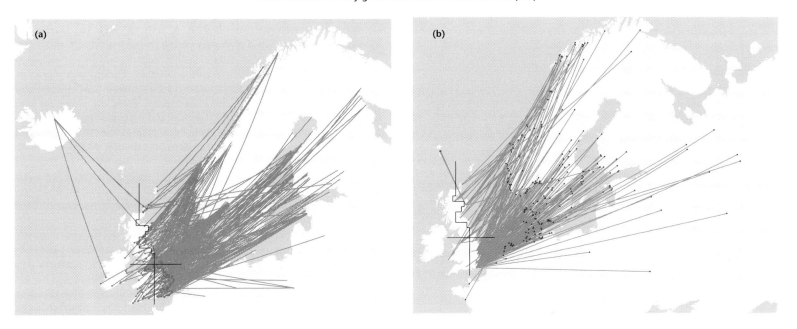

Fig 6. Movements of over 20 km and recovery locations of Common Gulls ringed in winter and recovered in (a) the same winter (15:18) or (b) a subsequent winter (19:37). Sample sizes of movements under:over 20 km are given but only those over 20 km are plotted.

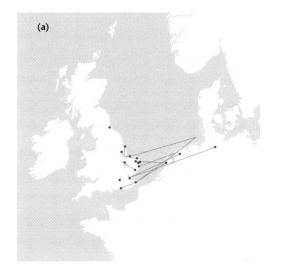

estimate of the wintering population of some 702,000 birds (*Winter Atlas*) suggests that Britain & Ireland is probably the most important wintering area for European breeders.

Migration into Britain starts in August or September, as shown by arrivals of Common Gulls into Shetland (Berry & Johnston 1980) and all along the British east coast, and continues into midwinter. Counts of Common Gulls within the River Ythan catchment peaked in October and November in the years 1978–80, thereafter declining until the return passage in spring (Douse 1981). There may be two routes into Britain: across the North Sea into eastern Scotland and northeast England; and across the Channel and southern North Sea, for birds moving westwards along the coastline of the northwest European countries. There is some tendency for birds from northern Norway to winter further north and birds from Denmark and the Baltic States further south (Fig 5). This trend is by no means distinct, however, and it is likely that many birds migrating into Britain across the northern North Sea then move further south during the winter.

Adult birds leave the Finnish breeding grounds shortly after the juveniles have fledged, and move westwards into Denmark, the Netherlands and Belgium, with the earliest recoveries in Britain occurring in December; the juveniles leave later (Kilpi & Saurola 1985). Birds from the northern part of Finland may move into Sweden and then into Denmark. There is clear evidence in these Finnish populations of birds from northern colonies wintering further north on average, a pattern consistent with the distribution of British recoveries. Danish Common Gulls also move westwards, with some moving into Britain & Ireland, giving a peak in recoveries in January and suggesting a gradual shift westwards as winter progresses, before birds start to return (Munk 1951, Sorenson 1977). These studies also showed that Common Gulls originating in Denmark wintered as far south as the Garonne Estuary in France and even northern Spain. The majority of recoveries of Norwegian Common Gulls in Scotland occur in the period August to November (Haftorn 1971). A small number of birds also reach Scotland from Iceland and the Faeroes (Fig 5), though as the

Fig 7. Locations abroad during the breeding season of Common Gulls ringed as fully grown birds outside the breeding season. Birds recovered as immatures (3, red) are differentiated from those recovered as adults (127, blue).

populations of Common Gulls in these two locations are small (*European Atlas*), the numbers involved are likely to represent a very small component of the total numbers wintering in Britain & Ireland. Once Common Gulls reach their wintering areas they may remain there throughout the midwinter period; ring-recoveries showed that the median distance moved within a winter was only 8 km (*P*5–95=0–499 km, *n*=27), although a few birds moved considerably further, for example between southern England and Denmark (Fig 6). Birds located in different winters had moved a median of 63 km (*P*5–95=1–778 km, *n*=40). While some of these winter movements (Fig 6) could result from onward passage within the midwinter period, they may also support the suggestion that some birds from countries on the near Continent, such as the Netherlands, may migrate to Britain & Ireland only in very cold winters (*BWP*).

In northeast Scotland, the proportion of immatures feeding on agricultural land increases during the winter (Douse 1981), perhaps due to differential movements of adults and juveniles or differences in habitat selection. However, there is little evidence that there is any wider-scale age-related segregation in wintering areas.

The return passage from Britain & Ireland back to continental breeding areas occurs over a shorter period, mostly in March and April. In England, a strong northeasterly visible migration is noted inland at this season (*eg* Vernon 1969, Trodd & Kramer 1991). Large flocks of Common Gulls have been recorded leaving northeast Scotland in April (Bourne & Patterson 1962), and observations from oil platforms also suggest a narrow period within which the return migration occurs (Tasker *et al* 1986). Interestingly, recoveries of immature Common Gulls ringed outside the breeding season in Britain & Ireland and recovered on the Continent in the breeding season are few compared to those of adults birds (Fig 7); the overall recovery pattern poorly reflects the known breeding distribution (*European Atlas*). It is known that few Common Gulls return to breeding areas in Finland at the end of their first year (Kilpi & Saurola 1985).

Some recoveries of Common Gulls in Britain & Ireland originate from the putative zone of intergradation of the nominate race with *heinei*, and occasional individuals showing characters of this latter race have been observed or trapped (Osborn 1985, BOU 1994).

Large declines in the numbers of Common Gulls in the big breeding populations of Norway, Denmark and Estonia have been reported (Tucker & Heath 1994). Although the reasons for these reported declines are uncertain, human disturbance and ground predators, such as introduced Mink may be partly responsible (*European Atlas*). The main areas of conservation concern most likely relate to the breeding grounds rather than to conditions on the passage and wintering grounds for these populations.

Little is known so far of the phenomenon of partial migration among British & Irish breeding Common Gulls, and particularly of the movements of the birds once they reach adulthood. Colour-ringing schemes, producing multiple sightings of individual birds might help to fill some of the missing details. Current understanding of winter immigration into Britain & Ireland is limited by the distribution of pulli ringing on the Continent. New studies in Russia would help to improve our knowledge and perhaps establish how many *heinei* winter within western Europe. Some further work on the taxonomic status of wintering Common Gulls in Britain would be worthwhile, and further examination of biometric data from wintering birds would go some way to achieving this.

Andrew Douse

Lesser Black-backed Gull
Larus fuscus

The Lesser Black-backed Gull breeds in colonies along the coasts and at some inland sites in Britain & Ireland. During the last 50 years, however, some radical changes in breeding numbers, breeding locations and migratory behaviour have taken place, bringing into sharp focus the gaps in our knowledge of the movements of this species.

Britain & Ireland is the stronghold of the race *graellsii*, with over 88,000 breeding pairs (Lloyd *et al* 1991). This race also breeds in western Europe as far south as central Portugal, in Iceland, the Faeroes (*European Atlas*) and also Greenland. The race *intermedius*, which breeds in Denmark, southern Norway and southern Sweden, occurs in Britain & Ireland in small numbers at all times of the year, though particularly in autumn and spring (*BWP*). Lesser Black-backed Gulls breeding in the Netherlands and Germany, which are possibly intergrades between *graellsii* and *intermedius* (Post & Lewis 1995), occur in Britain in larger numbers, especially in autumn and winter. The nominate race, a declining breeder in Finland, northern Norway and northern and eastern Sweden, migrates south-eastwards to winter in East and central Africa; one Finnish-ringed nestling has been recovered in Britain and there have been relatively few claimed sightings.

Lesser Black-backed Gulls traditionally nest on level or undulating ground, including dunes, small islands and moorland, rather than on rocky cliffs, and are less restricted to coastal regions than the other large gulls (*BWP*). They forage in a range of environments, including at sea by fishing and piracy, on agricultural land, where they take soil invertebrates, and at rubbish-tips. Their particular skill in scavenging may have enabled the race *graellsii* to become very successful throughout its range (Spaans

The analysis of the data for this species was supported by Peter Rock & Ian M Spence

et al 1994). Lesser Black-backed Gulls in Britain were quick to take advantage of the proliferation of landfill sites since 1950 for feeding, and breeding numbers increased fifteenfold and more, between the mid-1950s and the mid-1970s (Lloyd *et al* 1991). As a result, new nesting areas were used and increasing numbers started to use urban rooftops, often at some considerable distance inland (Monaghan & Coulson 1977, Raven & Coulson 1997).

Approximately 5,000 Lesser Black-backed Gulls have been ringed annually in Britain & Ireland in recent years. The majority are ringed as nestlings between June and August and the ringing locations broadly reflect the species' northerly and westerly breeding distribution as shown in the *1988–91 Atlas* (Figs 1 & 2). In winter, however, the distribution of the Lesser Black-backed Gull shifts southwards and eastwards (*Winter Atlas*), and fully grown birds have been ringed at rubbish-tips in central and southern England, producing many recoveries (Figs 1 & 2).

The Lesser Black-backed Gull is sometimes viewed as a pest. As a consequence, many of the ring-recoveries are of birds shot or otherwise deliberately killed, both in Britain & Ireland and abroad (Fig 3), with implications for interpretation of the recovery patterns. Since 1960, a near doubling of the recovery rate has been largely due to colour-ringing; recovery rates in excess of 54% are achievable, with multiple returns from individual birds becoming commonplace (Rock 1999).

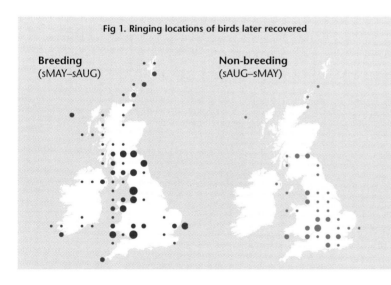

Fig 1. Ringing locations of birds later recovered

Breeding (sMAY–sAUG) Non-breeding (sAUG–sMAY)

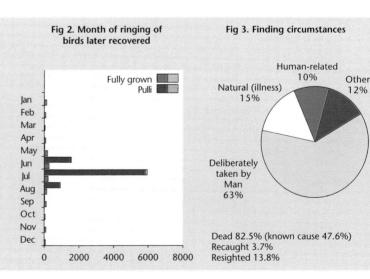

Fig 2. Month of ringing of birds later recovered

Fully grown
Pulli

Jan, Feb, Mar, Apr, May, Jun, Jul, Aug, Sep, Oct, Nov, Dec

0 2000 4000 6000 8000

Fig 3. Finding circumstances

Human-related 10%
Other 12%
Natural (illness) 15%
Deliberately taken by Man 63%

Dead 82.5% (known cause 47.6%)
Recaught 3.7%
Resighted 13.8%

Ringing and recovery data

	<1960	60–69	70–79	80–89	90–97	Total
RINGING						
BTO ringing totals (%)	15	25	9	26	25	152,532
RECOVERIES						
BTO-ringed (%)	9	16	19	27	29	9,617
Foreign-ringed (%)	←	28	→	43	28	243

Statistical analyses

	Breeding population (sMAY–sAUG)	Wintering population (mNOV–sMAR)
Status	LONG-DISTANCE MIGRANT (2)	SHORT-DISTANCE MIGRANT*
Age differences[NT]	Significant	Not significant*
Sex differences	Not tested	Not tested
Regional differences	Significant[4]*	Not tested
Finding circumstances	(Not significant)	Not significant

365

Fig 4. Locations of Lesser Black-backed Gulls ringed as pulli in Britain & Ireland and recovered (a) as immatures in winter (648), (b) as adults in winter (243), (c) as immatures during the breeding season (630) and (d) as adults during the breeding season (1,780). For the winter period the immatures include first-years, while for the breeding season the immatures do not include those birds recovered during the year of their birth.

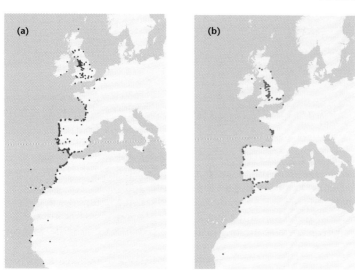

Expedition work has also been carried out to find colour-ringed birds abroad (Rock 1993, 1994, Askins *et al* 1996).

British & Irish Lesser Black-backed Gulls, along with other European *graellsii* and *intermedius*, generally migrate southwards along the western seaboard of continental Europe, most wintering in Iberia, with lower numbers in western North Africa and a few moving as far south as the Gulf of Guinea (Fig 4). Most recoveries have been coastal but there are inland recoveries, of all ages, in Iberia and West Africa. Many immatures

Fig 5. Winter recovery locations and movements of over 20 km of Lesser Black-backed Gulls ringed as pulli in Britain & Ireland and recovered in (a) 1909–69 (327) and (b) 1970–97 (577).

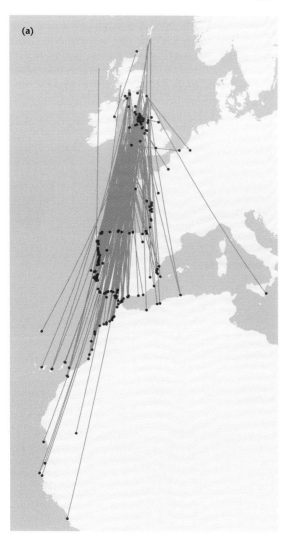
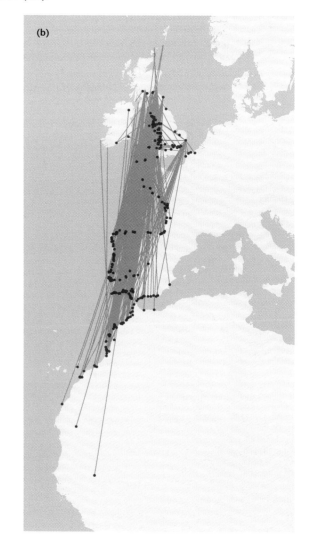

Fig 6. Recovery locations and all included exchanges with abroad of Lesser Black-backed Gulls that were present in the (a) northwest (28), (b) northeast (29), (c) southeast (110) and (d) southwest (177) of Britain and in (e) Ireland (11). Only those birds not known to be part of the British & Irish breeding population are shown.

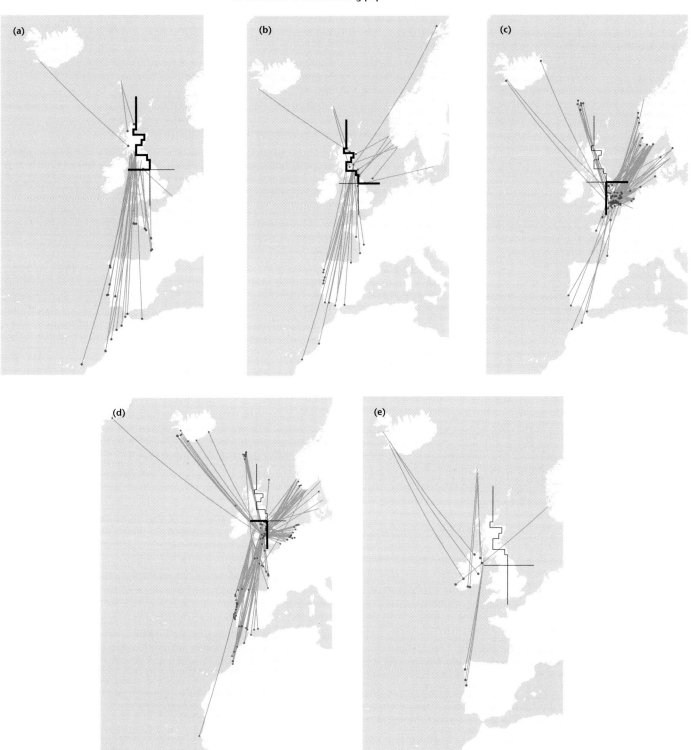

remain in southern latitudes until they are ready to breed (Fig 4) at four years or more (*BWP*). At least between 1965 and 1975, many birds migrated less far and for shorter periods, to the point where the status of the species as a true or typical migrant became less clear (Baker 1980). Now, British & Irish Lesser Black-backed Gulls of all ages are to be found in all parts of their range at all times of the year.

The onset of the autumn movements by Lesser Black-backed Gulls is a protracted affair. It starts in the second half of July but some birds that will later migrate are still near colonies at the beginning of October (pers obs). After fledging, juvenile birds, often accompanied by their parents, make short flights away from the breeding colony, returning in the evenings to roost at the nest site. The young birds appear subsequently to make longer, exploratory flights, sometimes to other breeding colonies (pers obs); the median recovery distance for days 31–60 after ringing is 29 km ($n=410$). Many, however, probably start their migrations by the end of August, and, by the end of October, the majority will have left Britain & Ireland, since the median recovery distance is 1,261 km ($n=175$).

Lesser Black-backed Gulls often fly distances of 100 km or more daily in search of food (pers obs) and should be easily capable of similar flights when migrating. One adult moved 600 km in four days from Worcestershire to Vendée, France (pers obs). When reaching a good feeding area, a bird sometimes stays for up to four weeks before moving on (pers obs). The largest numbers of migrating birds seen in Portugal and Morocco pass by in clear weather with light following winds (Rock 1994). During periods of bad weather, large numbers of migrating or wintering Lesser Black-backed Gulls move considerable distances from the coast into more sheltered estuaries, rivers and reservoirs (R Rufino pers comm). Good feeding opportunities inland will also attract large numbers of birds.

First-year and immature birds tend to wander further than adults (Baker 1980, *European Atlas*; Fig 4). Formal statistical analyses show that the median distance between breeding areas and recovery locations was 1,201 km (P5–95$=$25–2,567 km, $n=153$) for adults and significantly greater at 1,701 km (P5–95$=$38–2,892 km, $n=495$) for immatures. Immatures recovered in winter were, on average, 3° further south and 1.5° further west than adults. However, flocks in southernmost Morocco and western Sahara in winter appear to be composed mostly of adults (up to 90%; Rock 1994, M Marsh pers comm), and further investigation will be necessary to understand the origins of these birds. There is evidence from colour-ringing that some adults are faithful to wintering areas from one year to the next but also that some adults may be found at sites several hundreds of kilometres apart in different winters (pers obs). Whether adults actually change their wintering areas, or whether they are more generally mobile during the winter months deserves further study.

Lesser Black-backed Gulls return to the colonies between mid-February and April (*BWP*). Some birds, however, can be seen in colonies in January, especially on fine days (pers obs). It is possible that these early birds have overwintered nearby or have returned early by shortening the time spent on migration.

Old accounts stress that the Lesser Black-backed Gull was migratory, leaving Britain & Ireland in winter and, even in 1950, only a few hundred were recorded in northwest England and North Wales in December and January (Barnes 1952). Winter numbers in Britain & Ireland rose steadily to an estimated 70,000 birds by 1985 (*Winter Atlas*), with similar numbers recorded in 1993 (Waters 1994). The new landfill sites in Britain after 1950 offered ample food for many Lesser Black-backed Gulls in winter. Autumn migration patterns have also changed since the 1970s–1980s; it is nowadays not just a coastal migrant in continental Europe but many thousands are to be seen inland, especially in Spain and Portugal (Garcia & Guzman 1990, Cantos 1993). Although there have been notable changes in the occurrence of Lesser Black-backed Gulls in winter, particularly increased numbers in southern Britain (Baker 1980), there has not been a large change in the proportion of British- & Irish-ringed birds recovered dead in Britain & Ireland compared to abroad in winter (15% before and 22% after 1970, of a total of around 300 winter recoveries in

each period); nor has there been any major change in the overseas distribution of British & Irish breeding birds during winter (Fig 5).

Many Lesser Black-backed Gulls return to their natal colony to breed; the median natal dispersal distance from recoveries of dead birds is 5 km (P5–95$=$0–167 km, $n=1,677$). However, the proportion that returns appears to be lower than in the Herring Gull (Wanless *et al* 1996). The limited data, mainly from colour-ring sightings, suggest that philopatry is much higher among males than females (pers obs). Recoveries of dead, ringed birds, for which the sex is known, support this difference: the median natal dispersal distance was less than 1 km ($n=23$) for males but 21 km ($n=7$) for females. Intriguingly, a small proportion (less than 2%) of Lesser Black-backed Gulls from urban sites in Bristol recruited into more traditional, rural colonies to breed (pers obs). Lesser Black-backed Gulls of both sexes show a high degree of fidelity to breeding sites once they have become established and will often return to the same mate and to exactly the same territory and the same nest used in previous years (*BWP*, pers obs).

The autumn and winter population of British & Irish Lesser Black-backed Gulls is swollen by influxes of Icelandic, Faeroese and continental *intermedius* and *graellsii* (Fig 6), the timing of which apparently depends upon weather conditions on the Continent (N van Swelm pers comm). Foreign-ringed birds recovered in Britain & Ireland have come from Norway, the Netherlands, the Faeroes, Iceland, Belgium, Denmark, Sweden, Spain, the Channel Islands and Finland. Almost 60% of these are likely to be *intermedius*, from Norway, Sweden and probably from Denmark too. This is in stark contrast to the single recovery of a Finnish-ringed *fuscus* in Suffolk in 1961. Given the marked decrease in the population size of *fuscus* (Strann & Vader 1992), it is uncertain whether this race still occurs in Britain & Ireland. The majority of foreign-ringed Lesser Black-backed Gulls have been found in the south of Britain, and in particular in the southwest, but not in Ireland (Fig 6). Most large, inland flocks have dispersed by mid-April, presumably as native and foreign breeders return to their colonies.

The increase in Lesser Black-backed Gull numbers since the mid-1950s has continued in the urban environment (Raven & Coulson 1997), whereas some but not all coastal populations have subsequently declined (Loxton & Hope Jones 1994). The overall trend has resulted in the Lesser Black-backed Gull being listed as of moderate conservation concern in the UK. Despite this, some populations continue to be perceived as a problem and culling continues in some areas. Continual monitoring is a requirement that follows from the legal status of the species in Britain. Ringing has an important role to play, particularly in determining the origins of our increasing wintering population, the population dynamics of the species, changes in migratory behaviour and the need, if any, for regional variations in management strategies for the species. Very recently, the first three Lesser Black-backed Gulls (one *intermedius* and two *fuscus*, all adults) fitted with satellite-transmitters have been successfully tracked to their winter quarters (J Kube pers comm). The results will surely prove fascinating and should help in the planning of future studies that could shed more light on the migratory behaviour of this and other large gull species.

Peter Rock

Herring Gull
Larus argentatus

An opportunist with an ability to exploit a range of feeding and nesting areas, the Herring Gull is the most abundant and familiar of the large gulls breeding in Britain & Ireland, and often associates with human activities and artefacts. The species is frequently perceived as a pest and general nuisance and has been subject to intensive measures to control local populations (*eg* Thomas 1972, Coulson 1991). These perceptions and also the relative ease of marking and observing large numbers of birds have contributed to the unusually great scientific attention paid to the species.

The Herring Gull has a holarctic distribution, nesting at middle and boreal latitudes but, except in Siberia, not in the high Arctic. Most coastal breeding areas can be occupied throughout the year. When not breeding, the range extends further south and even to the northern tropics. The species belongs to a group of complex taxonomy on which there are many and varying opinions. Of the '*argentatus* group', which breeds in northwest Europe, northerly populations are the most migratory; birds from the White Sea move overland to winter in the Baltic and those from the Murmansk coast follow the coast of Norway to winter around the southern North Sea (*BWP*). More-southerly populations are thought to be generally dispersive, with many birds remaining in the same region through the year and relatively few birds moving between the Baltic and North Seas (*BWP*). The race *argenteus* breeds in Britain & Ireland where it can be found throughout the year. In winter, many nominate *argentatus* (identified by their larger size and their wingtip patterns) occur in eastern Britain (Stanley *et al* 1981, Coulson *et al* 1984b).

The analysis of the data for this species was supported by Dick Loxton

Birds of the '*cachinnans* group', which breed from western France southwards and around the Mediterranean, and at somewhat higher latitudes across central Asia, are also thought to be dispersive, with some western birds reaching Senegal and even the Gulf of Guinea (*BWP*). Yellow-legged birds of the *cachinnans* group (for which there is now a growing consensus for specific status) are occurring in Britain & Ireland with increased frequency, mostly in late summer and especially in the southeast of Britain (*eg* Baker 1998); most have been attributed to the western race *michahellis*, but some *cachinnans* from the Caspian Sea region may also occur (Anon 2000). There have also been isolated records of the nearctic *smithsonianus* in Ireland and western Britain.

In Britain & Ireland, the majority of Herring Gulls breed at or close to the coast, with few stretches unoccupied, the most extensive unoccupied areas being in the east of England (*1988–91 Atlas*). The range of breeding habitats includes cliffs, beaches, moorland and urban rooftops. Some offshore islands have thousands of pairs, and many colonies are shared with Lesser Black-backed Gulls (Lloyd *et al* 1991). In such mixed colonies, there is a chance of misidentification of chicks, and some long-distance recoveries of Herring Gulls probably refer to migratory Lesser Black-backed Gulls. When not breeding, Herring Gulls can be found everywhere around and off the coasts of Britain & Ireland and widely inland (*Winter Atlas*). While the Herring Gull has catholic tastes

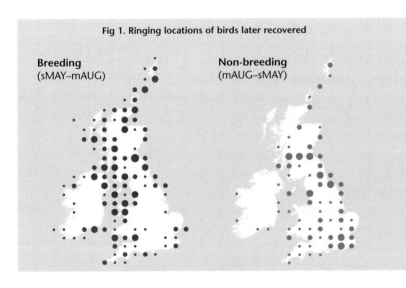

Fig 1. Ringing locations of birds later recovered

Breeding (sMAY–mAUG)

Non-breeding (mAUG–sMAY)

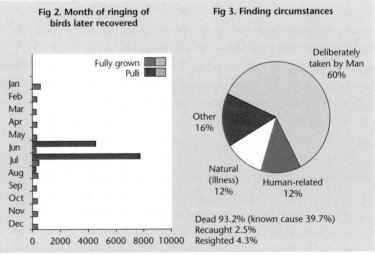

Fig 2. Month of ringing of birds later recovered

Fig 3. Finding circumstances

Deliberately taken by Man 60%

Other 16%

Natural (illness) 12%

Human-related 12%

Dead 93.2% (known cause 39.7%)
Recaught 2.5%
Resighted 4.3%

Ringing and recovery data

	<1960	60–69	70–79	80–89	90–97	Total
RINGING						
BTO ringing totals (%)	10	26	18	29	17	278,276
RECOVERIES						
BTO-ringed (%)	5	16	33	34	13	16,599
Foreign-ringed (%)	←	54	→	38	8	286

Statistical analyses

	Breeding population (sMAY–mAUG)	Wintering population (mNOV–sMAR)
Status	SHORT-DISTANCE MIGRANT (1)	SHORT-DISTANCE MIGRANT*
Age differences[NS*]	Significant	Significant
Sex differences	Not tested	Not tested
Regional differences	Significant[5*]	Significant[4*]
Finding circumstances	Not significant	(Not significant)

Fig 4. Movements of over 20 km and recovery locations of Herring Gulls ringed as pulli in Britain & Ireland and recovered in a subsequent breeding season when of breeding age. There were 3,285:766 movements under:over 20 km but only those over 20 km are plotted.

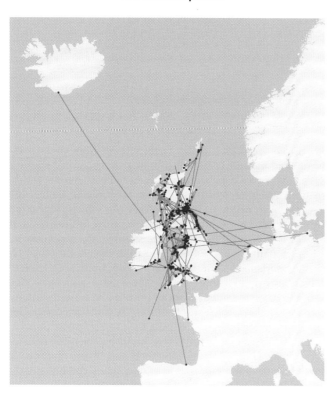

Fig 6. Movements of over 20 km and recovery locations of Herring Gulls ringed in winter and recovered in a subsequent winter. There were 33:128 movements under:over 20 km but only those over 20 km are plotted.

Fig 5. Movements of over 20 km and recovery locations of Herring Gulls ringed during the breeding season in Britain & Ireland as adults and recovered in a subsequent breeding season. There were 30:19 movements under:over 20 km but only those over 20 km are plotted.

Fig 7. Monthly variation in the differences in latitude between ringing and recovery locations of Herring Gulls ringed in Britain & Ireland as pulli. Monthly medians (points) and interquartile ranges (bars) are shown.

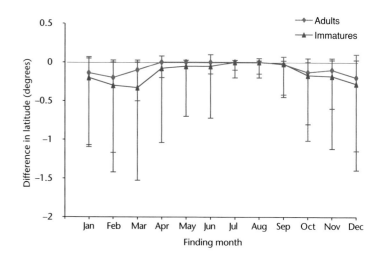

in food (including rubbish, fishing-vessel discards, soil invertebrates, eggs, chicks and carrion), its speciality, if any, is for feeding in the intertidal zone (Mudge & Ferns 1982, Noordhuis & Spaans 1992).

Within Britain, ringing effort at breeding colonies has covered most of the range, but much of Ireland remains under-represented (Fig 1). The majority of the recoveries come from birds ringed as pulli (Fig 2), but large numbers of fully grown birds have also been ringed, notably in

central Scotland, northeast and southeast England, where specific studies have been undertaken and cannon-netting groups have been active. Over 70% of ring-recoveries from dead birds, where the cause of death is known, were deliberately taken by Man or had other human-related causes (Fig 3). This no doubt reflects the large numbers culled and also the effort made to search the resulting corpses for rings. Over 4% of all recoveries were of resightings, showing the effectiveness of marking large

Fig 8. Movements of over 20 km between the breeding and non-breeding season and locations outside the breeding season of Herring Gulls ringed as pulli in the (a) northwest (253:832), (b) northeast (359:1,092), (c) southeast (10:41) and (d) southwest (359:883) of Britain and in (e) Ireland (103:202). Sample sizes of movements under:over 20 km are given but only those over 20 km are plotted.

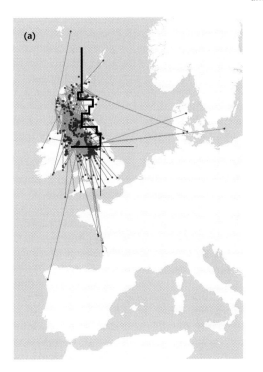
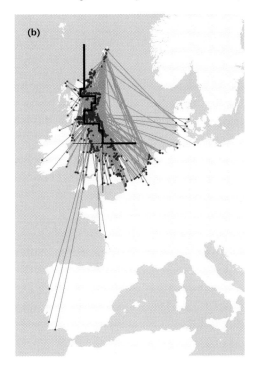
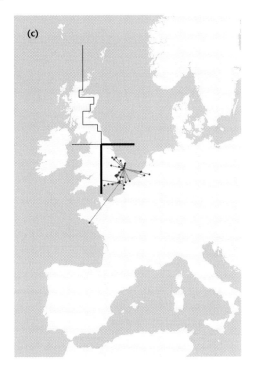
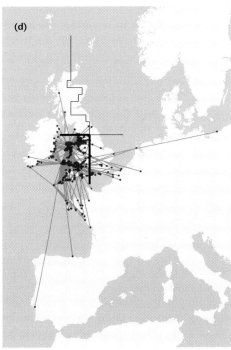
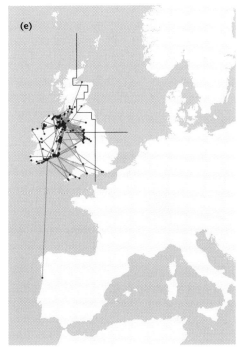

gulls with rings to be read in the field, such as individual combinations of colour-rings.

Most ring-recoveries of dead British & Irish Herring Gulls at all seasons, and for all ages and both sexes, were within a few tens of kilometres from their sites of ringing (median=15 km, $P5–95=0–284$ km, n=10,567). As the data are dominated by birds ringed at breeding sites, most recoveries occur close to those colonies. Numbers are therefore swollen by the many recoveries from birds culled at the breeding colony, but the natural mortality of Herring Gulls also peaks during the breeding season (Chabrzyk & Coulson 1976).

The median distance between sites of ringing Herring Gull pulli and where they were recovered when of breeding age in the breeding season is

less than a kilometre, which suggests high philopatry. However, the proportion of surviving individuals which do return to the natal colony doubtlessly varies and is sometimes as low as 30% (Coulson 1991, Wanless et al 1996). Some few individuals do move considerable distances (Fig 4).

Once a breeding site is established, tenacity to it can be remarkably high, even with high levels of disturbance such as culling or natural predation (Coulson et al 1982a, Southern et al 1985). At an undisturbed site, less than 10% of breeding individuals moved their nest sites more than 30 m within a colony between years and there was no evidence of movements to neighbouring colonies (pers obs). Even so, some recoveries of adults during the breeding period are distant from the breeding colony (Fig 5). These will include birds probably four or five

Fig 9. All 398 included exchanges of Herring Gulls between Britain & Ireland and abroad, excluding those ringed in Britain & Ireland as pulli. Points show recovery locations.

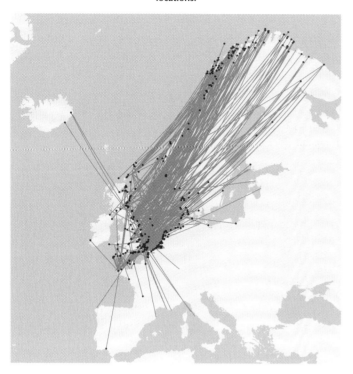

The formal statistical analysis detected some slight regional variation in the distances moved between breeding and wintering areas, with birds from Ireland appearing more sedentary (median 34 km) than birds from the northwest, northeast or southwest of Britain (medians 75–85 km). More local variations (Fig 8) are probably a result of regional geography and the availability of resources, such as fishing discards from fish quays, and suitable intertidal areas for more natural foraging (Harris 1964b, Coulson & Butterfield 1985); birds from the east of Ireland appear to disperse further than might be expected from the latitudinal trend, and those from North Wales not as far. Studies of colour-ringed birds moving into northeast England show that these birds originate from the whole east coast of Scotland, including Orkney and Shetland (J Coulson pers comm). The first adults arrive in late July, the latest not until December, with a peak in September and October. Most pass through, presumably to southern England. Adult male Herring Gulls tend to arrive and depart earlier than females, and some males have returned to Scotland by December, at a time when some females from the same area are still moving south. Many of the Scottish birds stay only a few weeks in northeast England but are seen there again in following years, usually in the same month, suggesting that some individuals execute the same movement pattern each year (J Coulson pers comm).

Movements along coasts and across water appear more frequent than overland movements. There are numerous recoveries of east-coast British birds on both sides of the North Sea. Similarly, Herring Gulls appear to cross the Irish and Celtic Seas readily. Despite the many inland recoveries, and indeed the large number of Herring Gulls that use inland reservoirs and refuse-tips, cross-country ring-recoveries between western and eastern coasts of Britain are surprisingly few. Even at sea most Herring Gulls remain within 25 km of breeding colonies or otherwise close to the coast, with most of those further out following ships at sea (Tasker et al 1987, Garthe 1997). Exchange between Herring Gulls breeding on the east and west sides of Britain may be less than 4% per generation (Coulson & Butterfield 1985). This restricted gene-flow within Britain has been suggested as a causal mechanism for slight plumage variations between regions (Coulson et al 1982b). This is somewhat counter to expectations for a species with a low degree of natal philopatry. Even though the Herring Gull is relatively well studied, there is still a need to investigate the interactions between colonies and the recruitment mechanisms.

The nominate race argentatus, which breeds in northern Europe, occurs in Britain in greatest numbers from September to February (Coulson et al 1984b). There are many recoveries of argentatus from northern Scandinavia and the Kola Peninsula wintering in Britain & Ireland, mostly on the British east coast or in adjacent inland counties (Fig 9). Recoveries involving inland areas of England include a high proportion of these northern birds. In addition to the foreign exchanges with northern Europe and nearby continental coasts, there are a few recoveries involving the Mediterranean, southern Iberia and Morocco. Six pulli ringed in the Mediterranean region and recovered in southeast England (one from Spain, two from Italy and three from France) are likely to have been michahellis. Unfortunately, the difficulties of identifying chicks at mixed colonies raises the possibility that some recoveries of British & Irish Herring Gulls from Iberia and Morocco may in fact have been Lesser Black-backed Gulls. One Spanish recovery was of a bird ringed in Shetland as an adult, however, and unlikely to have been misidentified.

Herring Gulls have long been perceived as requiring management, for the conservation of other species or for reasons of public health, but their own conservation needs and intrinsic interest should also be recognized. Britain & Ireland has about half the population of breeding argenteus (Lloyd et al 1991), and eastern Britain appears to be seasonally important to argentatus. While continued monitoring and further large-scale ringing are needed, the data already accumulated deserve further analysis, for example to determine whether the observed declines are linked to regional changes in survival rates.

years old that have not yet begun to breed, and also adults abstaining from breeding; up to 40% of Herring Gulls with breeding experience have been found not to breed in any one season (Calladine & Harris 1997). Relatively low levels of natal site-fidelity, but a high tenacity to the breeding area once established, has also been shown by smithsonianus in the Great Lakes region of North America (Gabrey 1996).

Post-fledging movements by Herring Gulls in Britain & Ireland are most marked from August onwards, some two to three months after hatching. Although many Herring Gulls, of all ages, spend some time close to their colonies after fledging, there is a general dispersal that leads to fewer birds being recorded at progressively greater distances from their origin, rather than a shift to a specific wintering zone (Parsons & Duncan 1978). Supporting this are numerous recoveries of birds ringed in winter and found elsewhere in subsequent winters (Fig 6).

Herring Gull dispersal is in all directions but there is a marked tendency for southward autumn movements from the colony. Recoveries of immatures are scattered more widely than adults during the period April to June, reflecting their lesser ties to a breeding colony (Fig 7). Of recoveries of Herring Gulls ringed in Britain & Ireland, the most distant from their breeding or natal areas, and also those inland, are dominated by immature birds; a trend also found for Herring Gulls specifically from the Isle of May (Parsons & Duncan 1978). The formal analysis revealed a significant difference in distances moved between breeding and wintering areas between adults (median=45.5 km, P5–95=2–504 km, n=268) and immatures (median=88 km, P5–95=5–533 km, n=695). Immatures were also recovered significantly further south (by 0.5°) than adults during the winter. This alone need not reflect a real tendency for longer movements among younger birds, because adults spend less time (and therefore have less chance of being recovered) away from their breeding areas than immatures do, even outside the breeding season; older immatures spend progressively longer at or close to their natal or future breeding areas (Coulson & Butterfield 1985). Indeed, studies of colour-ringed adults show that they can be present at their breeding colonies all year, except for just a few weeks through the winter; females tend to be away for longer, and periods of absence are not synchronized through a colony (Coulson & Butterfield 1986).

John Calladine

Great Black-backed Gull

Larus marinus

The appearance in winter of Great Black-backed Gulls on eastern coasts, inland areas and other localities where they do not breed indicates that this species is at least partially migratory. A monotypic species, the Great Black-backed Gull breeds widely on North Atlantic and some Arctic coasts. In North America most breeding occurs between 40° and 60°N, whereas in Greenland breeding extends well north of the Arctic Circle on both the east and west coasts. In the northeast Atlantic, the breeding range reaches as far north as 79°N (in Svalbard) but most occur south of 70°N. With the exception of northeast Scotland and Norway, the species is largely absent as a breeder on North Sea coasts. A few birds breed on northern coasts of the Bay of Biscay.

Migration strategies are varied. Limited post-breeding dispersal takes place in North American breeding populations, mainly south along the coast, with some movement west to inland sites (Sauer *et al* 1997). Breeding populations in Greenland and Iceland are sedentary or only partly migratory. In contrast, Fennoscandian populations undertake a definite post-breeding migration; Arctic Ocean nesters migrate southward, probably passing the North Cape first, rather than flying overland; and birds from breeding colonies around the Baltic winter in the western Baltic and Kattegat (Durinck *et al* 1994).

The Great Black-backed Gull is associated with coastal habitats throughout the year. In the breeding season, rocky coastlines with grassy areas for nesting support the greatest numbers of birds; exposed headlands and stacks that allow easy access to the sea are favoured. At least half of the British & Irish population breeds on temperate Atlantic islands, where colonies, numbering many hundreds of pairs in a few

The analysis of the data for this species was supported by Russell McAndrew

places, are shared with other seabirds, some of which are preyed upon or parasitized for food. In the winter, the bird is found in a wide range of coastal types. Those on sandy or muddy shores exploit coastal food supplies, such as shellfish and other littoral organisms, and may also make local movements to inland refuse-tips. During midwinter, many thousands of Great Black-backs in Britain, along with Scandinavian Herring Gulls, commute relatively short distances between feeding areas on refuse-tips and roosts on large inland reservoirs.

Most (84%) of the Great Black-backed Gulls subsequently recovered were ringed as chicks, mainly in June and July. The ringing locations of these broadly reflect the breeding distribution of the species in Britain & Ireland (Figs 1 & 2) and there would appear to be little bias in the pattern of recoveries with respect to breeding location. However, outside the breeding season, ringing localities have an eastern bias, which reflects ringing effort rather than distribution (Fig 1). Of foreign-ringed birds recovered in Britain & Ireland since 1979, 90% were ringed as pulli (Fig 2), mainly in Norway.

The causes of death of ringed Great Black-backed Gulls are known for just over a quarter of recoveries; over half of these were human-related, mostly involving deliberate persecution (Fig 3). Most recoveries of known cause are made in Britain, Ireland or Norway, and are unlikely to bias interpretations of migratory movements. Other causes of death,

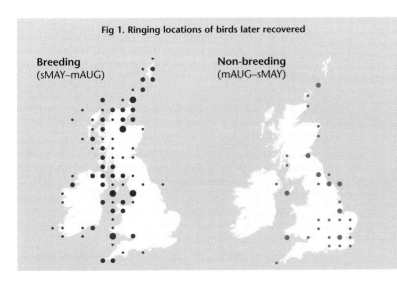

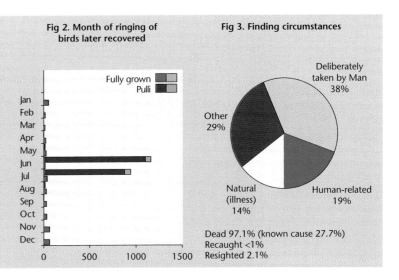

Fig 1. Ringing locations of birds later recovered

Breeding (sMAY–mAUG) Non-breeding (mAUG–sMAY)

Fig 2. Month of ringing of birds later recovered

Fully grown
Pulli

Fig 3. Finding circumstances

Deliberately taken by Man 38%

Other 29%

Natural (illness) 14%

Human-related 19%

Dead 97.1% (known cause 27.7%)
Recaught <1%
Resighted 2.1%

Ringing and recovery data

	<1960	60–69	70–79	80–89	90–97	Total
RINGING						
BTO ringing totals (%)	5	10	24	33	28	56,950
RECOVERIES						
BTO-ringed (%)	6	16	24	29	24	2,378
Foreign-ringed (%)	←	59	→	27	14	339

Statistical analyses

	Breeding population (sMAY–mAUG)	Wintering population (mNOV–sMAR)
Status	SHORT-DISTANCE MIGRANT (2)	LONG-DISTANCE MIGRANT
Age differences[NT]	Significant*	Not significant*
Sex differences	Not tested	Not tested
Regional differences	Not tested	Not tested
Finding circumstances	(Not significant)	Not tested

Fig 4. Monthly variation in the differences in (a) latitude and (b) longitude between ringing and recovery locations of Great Black-backed Gulls present in Britain & Ireland during the breeding season. Monthly medians (points) and interquartile ranges (bars) are shown.

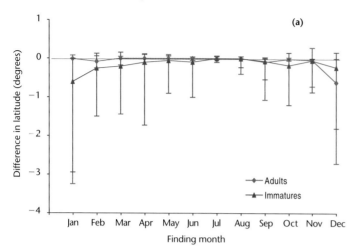

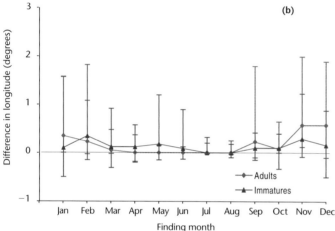

such as pollution, are not likely to exhibit any clear geographical or seasonal pattern, and recoveries of birds that have died from illness (14% of known deaths) show no geographical bias, despite localized reports of deaths attributed to botulism (Sutcliffe 1986).

Breeding Great Black-backed Gulls in Britain & Ireland are mainly sedentary, and are rarely found far from their breeding locations (Harris 1962, *Birds in Ireland*). Although there is no evidence of large-scale post-breeding migration by adults, some do disperse short distances, mainly eastwards. This movement persists until midwinter when there is further southward movement, again over relatively short distances (up to around 60 km) (Fig 4). These movements contribute to the rather ubiquitous winter distribution and occur in response to feeding opportunities, especially at urban refuse-tips, notably in northern and central England. Such movements are less common in Ireland and northern Scotland. There is a gradual return to the coastal breeding sites in late winter and spring, this being completed several weeks before breeding begins again in May (Fig 4). Notwithstanding these local movements, winter site-fidelity is very high (Coulson *et al* 1984a).

The movements of Great Black-backed Gulls ringed as pulli tend to be over similar distances to those attained by Herring Gulls. First-year and immature Great Black-backed Gulls range further than adults; the median distance moved between breeding and wintering locations was 54.5 km ($P5$–95=0–930 km, $n=54$) for adult birds but significantly greater at 115 km ($P5$–95=13–720 km, $n=165$) for immatures. Immatures

also winter, on average, 1.4° significantly further west than adults. Post-fledging movements by British & Irish birds follow a similar temporal pattern to those of adults after the breeding season (Fig 4). Most movements would appear to be inland or, for western populations on islands, to the mainland (*ie* in easterly and southerly directions). Most of the movements are less than 100 km but there are some exceptions, particularly relating to immature birds (Fig 5). For example, 18 birds ringed in the breeding season in northern Britain were recovered in the non-breeding season in Denmark and the Low Countries; three from the northwest were recovered in the Netherlands and northern France; and 13 from the southwest reached the Atlantic coasts of France and Iberia. An additional bird from the southwest region was located in Norway outside the breeding season. All but three of these recoveries have been in autumn or winter.

During their first months of life, Great Black-backed Gulls are recovered at increasingly greater distances from their natal sites, from a median distance of 13 km shortly after fledging ($n=138$) to 256 km in December ($n=38$); by May they are recovered closer to their natal areas once more (median=98 km, $n=20$). As breeding birds show high breeding site-fidelity (Cramp *et al* 1974), there appears then to be an increasing tendency to return to the natal areas during the first three years of life before breeding, culminating in the largely sedentary strategy of the breeding adult. This pattern is confirmed by the data for all birds recovered dead. Limited natal dispersal results in birds settling to breed near their natal sites (at a median distance of 13 km for birds recovered dead, $P5$–95=0–158 km, $n=233$). This latter result should be treated with caution, however, as 72% of the 79 relevant recoveries that had a cause attributed were deliberately taken by humans.

Harris (1962) cautiously suggested that birds from more northerly breeding locations move further than the more southerly populations, and this is borne out by the present data. The median recovery distance for birds present in northern Britain during the breeding season and later recovered dead was 39 km ($n=514$), and for birds ringed in the northwest and southwest 33 km ($n=546$) and 23 km ($n=339$) respectively. Similarly, of those birds present in northern Britain in the breeding season and located in the non-breeding season, 76% had moved more than 20 km; the respective values for the northwest and southwest regions are 69% and 67%. Given these small differences, however, Harris' (1962) caveat remains valid: birds from remote northerly locations may be less likely to be recovered close to the ringing site than birds from southern areas, where the human population is higher.

While movements of British & Irish breeders account for much of the widespread distribution of the Great Black-backed Gull in Britain & Ireland in winter, they alone cannot explain its east-coast component or the large numbers in the North Sea. Ringing on the east coast of England in winter has shown that many of these wintering birds are Norwegian migrants (Coulson *et al* 1984a; Fig 6). Birds from arctic Norway and the Murmansk region migrate in July westwards and southwards to Britain. This large-scale movement occurs along the northern coasts of Norway and Russia and follows the Norwegian coast south, where these birds are joined in crossing the North Sea by successively more southerly Norwegian breeders. They begin arriving on the east coast of Britain, especially the southeast region, again in July. Numbers peak in September, from which time high numbers are maintained throughout the winter. Only occasionally do Norwegian birds reach western Britain and few have been detected in Ireland. In contrast, a few birds from the partly migratory Icelandic and Faeroese breeding populations visit northwestern Britain & Ireland but only rarely reach the east coast.

Although there is some movement into and out of wintering areas, fidelity to these, inland and coastal, is generally high in adults, both within and between winters, although immatures wander more widely (Coulson *et al* 1984a).

Gull numbers remain high until February when they begin the return migration to their breeding areas; there is a suggestion that males

Fig 5. Locations outside the breeding season and movements of over 20 km between the breeding and non-breeding season of Great Black-backed Gulls present in the (a) north (344), (b) northwest (356), (c) northeast and southeast (13) and (d) southwest (174) of Britain & Ireland during the breeding season.

(a)

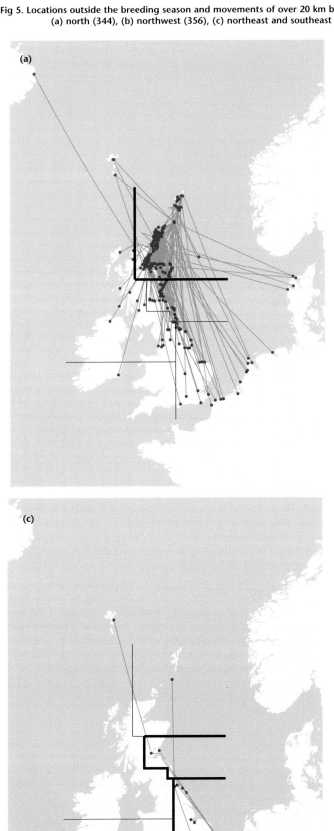

(b)

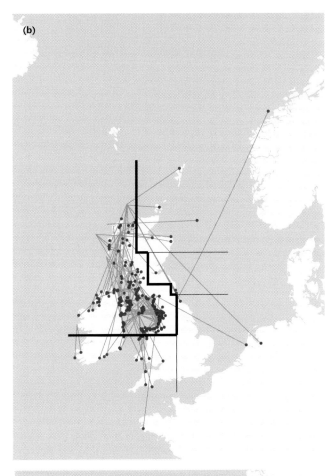

(c)

(d)

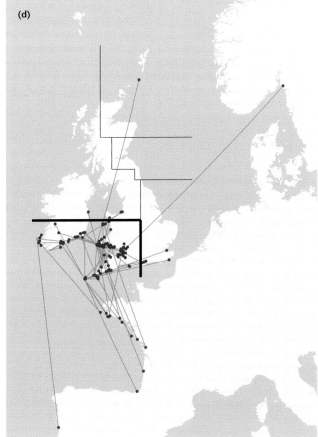

Fig 6. Locations abroad during the breeding season and associated movements between the breeding and non-breeding season of the 129 Great Black-backed Gulls that were present in Britain & Ireland outside the breeding season.

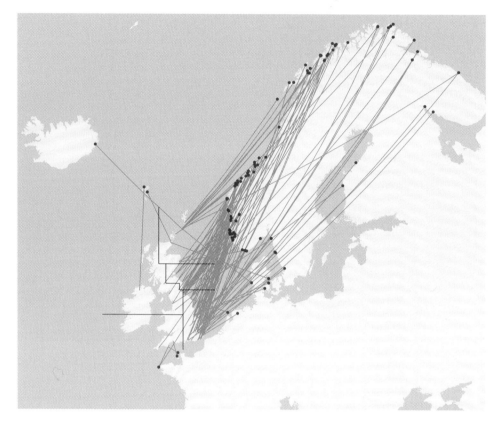

leave slightly earlier than females (Coulson *et al* 1984a). By March, very few are seen inland or in eastern areas. Many adults are recorded from oil rigs during spring migration, whereas immatures predominate between April and August (Blake *et al* 1984, Tasker *et al* 1986).

Most Great Black-backed Gulls recorded from northern North Sea oil rigs are seen during autumn and spring (Tasker *et al* 1986). During autumn migration the number of birds in the northern and central North Sea is very high, perhaps more than 150,000, and the whole North Sea region may support over 300,000 birds (more than 45% of the world population) in winter (Skov *et al* 1995). Surveys at sea indicate that birds range most widely and in greatest numbers between November and February (Stone *et al* 1995). Daily fluctuation in numbers in coastal parts of eastern England in winter may be governed by feeding conditions at sea (*Winter Atlas*). Outside the breeding season, especially in autumn and winter, most Great Black-backed Gulls feed on fisheries discards and more are recorded at trawlers that are fishing than when no trawlers are present (Tasker *et al* 1987, Furness *et al* 1992).

Although a very high proportion of the world population of Great Black-backed Gulls winters in the North Sea region, there is little widespread threat to the species at this time. They are widely dispersed and as one of the more aerial species of gulls they are at little risk from oil pollution.

Several questions remain about Great Black-backed Gull movements, however, that may be addressed through the establishment of colour-marking schemes. The provenance of Great Black-backed Gulls wintering in western areas of Britain & Ireland is poorly known. While most of these may turn out to be relatively local breeders, a proportion may originate from the Faeroes and perhaps Iceland. Colour-marking schemes in the Faeroes and Iceland would highlight the scale of immigration from these areas, as well as shedding light on movements between the two island groups. Similarly, a ringing programme in northern Norway and Murmansk might determine whether birds from these populations also winter in the Baltic, in addition to supplementing our knowledge of their use of wintering areas in Britain. Daily movements of wintering birds in Britain & Ireland also deserve further study in order to assess the relative use of refuse-tips and at-sea sources of feeding. The extent to which these depend on weather might again best be studied with a colour-marking scheme.

Jim Reid

Black-legged Kittiwake (Kittiwake)

Rissa tridactyla

The Black-legged Kittiwake is an arctic species, breeding in areas of the North Atlantic and North Pacific Oceans where typically the sea temperatures never exceed 10°C. The exceptions are those breeding in warmer waters in western Europe (southern Norway, Helgoland, Denmark, Britain, Ireland, France and Spain). Breeding colonies exist along the arctic coast of Russia and extend into the North Pacific and to Alaska (*BWP*). There are two subspecies: *tridactyla* breeding and wintering in the Atlantic Ocean and *pollicaris* in the Pacific. It is not clear where the transition between the two subspecies occurs along the arctic northern coast of Asia or whether there is a total separation in their distribution. Nevertheless, some birds breeding in the Arctic Ocean have long flights to the wintering areas in the Pacific and Atlantic Oceans. Some *tridactyla* may winter in the Pacific, since there is one recovery of a chick ringed in the Barents Sea and later found on the Kamchatka coast of the Bering Sea (Bianki & Gerasimova 1960).

The Kittiwake is the most numerous breeding gull in Britain & Ireland, nesting mainly on precipitous seacliffs and, in a few places, on ledges of buildings. It has even nested on flat ground among terns. Its numbers increased throughout the 20th century and many new colonies now exist, while most of the old colonies have increased dramatically in size (Coulson 1963, 1983, Lloyd *et al* 1991). Throughout its range, adults are present at the breeding colonies for only about half of the year. Outside the breeding season, the Kittiwake is the most oceanic of the gulls and it is distributed across the North Atlantic Ocean. During that time, only small numbers are seen along the coastlines of Britain and Ireland, except for occasional large, inshore movements

The analysis of the data for this species was supported by the late Keith Huxley

associated with atmospheric depressions and strong onshore winds. Many of the birds involved in these movements are probably not of British or Irish origin, since by this time Kittiwakes from many breeding areas have mixed in the Atlantic and North Sea.

Some accounts of the Kittiwake state that it is 'not truly migratory' or that individuals simply disperse (*eg BWP*). However, Kittiwakes breeding along the western section of the Arctic Ocean totally vacate the breeding area, and the birds all move in a similar direction into the Atlantic. This would be considered a migration under most definitions. Once in the Atlantic, individual Kittiwakes from the whole breeding range are probably nomadic, as their distribution and movements are undoubtedly influenced by weather conditions as well as the distribution of their (mainly unknown) food supplies. Nevertheless, while there is considerable mixing in winter, birds from more northern breeding areas tend to remain to the north of those from the southern end of the breeding range (Coulson 1966), although it is not clear how this distribution is achieved.

Most ringing of Kittiwakes has been carried out in northeast England and southeast Scotland, mainly on the Farne Islands, the Isle of May and at colonies on Tyneside. However, as numbers have increased, new colonies have become established on more accessible sites, and now the ringing that has generated recoveries is taking place at more sites

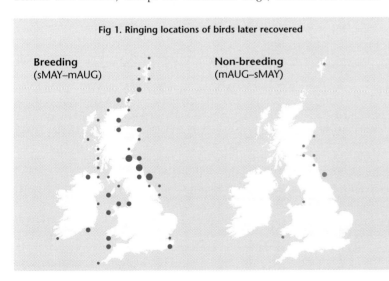

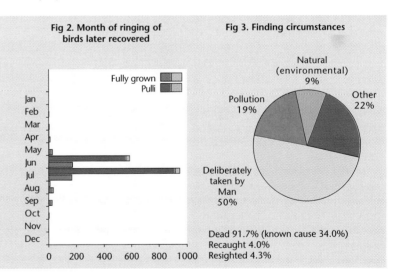

Fig 1. Ringing locations of birds later recovered

Breeding (sMAY–mAUG)

Non-breeding (mAUG–sMAY)

Fig 2. Month of ringing of birds later recovered

Fully grown
Pulli

Fig 3. Finding circumstances

Natural (environmental) 9%

Pollution 19%

Other 22%

Deliberately taken by Man 50%

Dead 91.7% (known cause 34.0%)
Recaught 4.0%
Resighted 4.3%

Ringing and recovery data

	<1960	60–69	70–79	80–89	90–97	Total
RINGING						
BTO ringing totals (%)	12	16	20	36	16	112,065
RECOVERIES						
BTO-ringed (%)	12	24	22	25	17	1,908
Foreign-ringed (%)	←	46	→	48	6	124

Statistical analyses

	Breeding population (sMAY–mAUG)	Wintering population (mNOV–sMAR)
Status	SHORT-DISTANCE MIGRANT (2)	?
Age differences[NT]	Significant	—
Sex differences	Not tested	—
Regional differences	Significant[5]*	—
Finding circumstances	(Not significant)	—

Fig 4. Recovery locations and movements of over 20 km of Kittiwakes (a) recovered in autumn as immatures (202), (b) recovered in autumn as adults (45), (c) recovered in winter as immatures (114) and (d) recovered in winter as adults (84).

throughout Britain and Ireland (Fig 1). There are, as yet, too few recoveries from birds ringed in the west to allow satisfactory comparison to be made between those breeding on the North Sea and Atlantic coasts. More than three-quarters of the recoveries refer to birds ringed as nestlings (Fig 2).

Most Kittiwakes have been recovered in the breeding season and early autumn. They are unlikely to be recovered in winter, because they are oceanic, although most of the mortality appears to occur at this time (pers obs). The causes and locations of Kittiwake recoveries have been also influenced by the activity of hunters, or by fishermen shooting Kittiwakes for bait (Fig 3). Such activities have been extensive in Greenland, off Newfoundland (Montevecchi & Tuck 1987) and, to a lesser extent, in the Bay of Biscay, and these areas tend to produce disproportionately larger numbers of recoveries than, for example, Labrador or the coast of northern Europe. The proportion of recoveries attributed to shooting has decreased in the last 40 years or so, as a result of the decline in the use of this species for food and fishing bait. As a result, a distinctly lower proportion of recoveries are now reported from Greenland, Newfoundland and the Bay of Biscay, although the distribution of Kittiwakes in the Atlantic has probably not changed. Despite the oceanic nature of the species for much of the year, over 95% of Kittiwake recoveries are on the coast, or within 10 km of the shore. A few of the remainder are well inland, mainly in Europe, and even fewer occur in offshore waters.

A clearer insight into the movements of Kittiwakes can only be obtained by combining recoveries with direct observations of their distribution at sea (eg Wynne-Edwards 1935, Rankin & Duffey 1948, Stone et al 1995). Such surveys show that, in the winter half of the year, Kittiwakes are spread across the whole of the North Atlantic, south to about 30–35°N. In late spring, Kittiwakes of all ages vacate the deep oceanic areas and concentrate near the European, Greenland and North American coasts.

Ring-recoveries from Britain & Ireland have a strong westerly component, and young birds reared in Britain have reached Greenland within six weeks of fledging (Fig 4a). Since young Kittiwakes are not fed by their parents after they leave the nest sites, successful (and rapid) dispersal to reach good feeding sites is probably critical for the survival of the juvenile birds. Occasionally there are reports of mass mortalities of recently fledged Kittiwakes. In the late summer and early autumn, the dispersed young Kittiwakes move south, producing winter recoveries around Newfoundland and the Grand Banks (Fig 4c). This pattern is repeated in two-year-old birds and, on average, these birds are then even further away from their natal area than in their first year of life (Coulson 1966). Some young Kittiwakes probably remain on the other side of the Atlantic, off Newfoundland and Greenland, for two years or more, since the contraction of their range each spring and summer into coastal waters produces a discontinuous distribution in the Atlantic, with a large, isolating gap in mid-ocean (Rankin & Duffey 1948). It appears that birds

Table 1. The distribution of recoveries of immature Kittiwakes by month in North America and Greenland, and in latitudinal zones in European waters. Note the tendency for the place of recovery of immature birds to move south during October and November and to return north in the spring. Because there were few recoveries from February to May on the west of the Atlantic and in March and April in European waters, the proportions have been pooled for these months. Note also the lower percentage of birds recovered in the North Sea and in Britain & Ireland between November and February inclusive.

	Aug	Sep	Oct	Nov	Dec	Jan	Feb	Mar	Apr	May	Jun	Jul	Total
West Atlantic													
Greenland	35	20	11	1	0	0	2	1	0	1	7	11	89
Canada/USA	2	5	11	5	4	3	1	0	0	4	1	3	39
Greenland (%)	95	80	50	17	0	0	←	45	→		88	79	—
East Atlantic													
North	3	2	1	2	1	1	2	1	0	1	1	2	17
B&I/North Sea	141	35	15	16	14	26	19	18	37	25	52	108	506
Biscay	1	0	2	9	6	6	6	0	1	3	0	1	35
South	1	0	3	6	3	5	6	1	0	0	0	0	25
B&I/North Sea (%)	97	95	71	48	58	68	58	90	97	86	98	97	—
North* (%)	60	100	17	12	10	8	14	←	33	→	25	100	67	—

Area definitions: North (north of 60°N), Britain & Ireland and North Sea (48°N–60°N), Biscay (43.5°N–48°N) and South (south of 43.5°N)
*The birds from European waters that were north of 60°N are shown as a percentage of the recoveries, excluding those in the Britain & Ireland and North Sea region (which dominate throughout).

which cross the Atlantic move north towards Greenland in summer and south again towards Newfoundland waters in winter, or that additional birds make the transatlantic crossing (Table 1). Birds in their third year are, on average, distinctly closer to their natal areas than a year previously and many (but not all) are clearly and actively returning 'home'.

Some young Kittiwakes start visiting colonies when two years old, usually between late May and July when breeding is well advanced (Coulson 1959). Breeding first occurs when at least three years old, and some individuals do not breed until six years old (Wooller & Coulson 1977, Porter & Coulson 1987).

Recoveries on the European side of the Atlantic show evidence of the same seasonal north–south change of distribution (Table 1). In autumn, young of the year are recovered mainly within the North Sea or off the coast of northern Europe. By late autumn and winter, recoveries tend to be further south, extending into the Bay of Biscay and along the west coast of Iberia, with a single recovery off the North African coast and a few recoveries which show that some British birds penetrate into the western Mediterranean (Fig 4b & d). Presumably these winter recoveries represent the edge of the broad band of Kittiwakes wintering across the whole of the Atlantic to Newfoundland, Nova Scotia and the northeast states of the USA. However recoveries of Kittiwakes from Britain & Ireland are all north of 40°N on the coast of North America, whereas they reach 30°N on the coast of northwest Africa.

Outside the breeding season, Kittiwakes make extensive movements to avoid atmospheric depressions and being forced onto continental coasts (or even inland) by strong, onshore winds. These responses result in spectacular movements, for example, when a depression moves into the southern part of the North Sea. Under such conditions, huge numbers move north along the east coast of Britain (eg Elkins & Williams 1969, Henderson 1974, Mather 1986, Taylor et al 1999), presumably eventually spreading into the Atlantic.

Ringed Kittiwakes have been reported inland in several European countries, mainly in the late autumn and winter, and most frequently in western France, inland from the Bay of Biscay. Other records come from the Czech Republic and Germany, and the most distant of all was found in the Ukraine (BWP). Many of these birds were probably ill and were unable to resist displacement caused, for example, by persistent strong onshore winds. Most Kittiwakes seen inland probably die within a few days.

The aluminium rings used on Kittiwakes until 1960 had a short life of less than four years before they became illegible or fell off (Coulson & White 1955). Since most Kittiwakes were ringed as chicks, little information accumulated about the movements of adults until more durable rings were introduced. This produced the mistaken idea that only young Kittiwakes made transatlantic flights. In recent years, birds of breeding age have been reported from Greenland and Newfoundland, mainly in the winter. It is now clear that transatlantic flights are made by all age classes and that these are probably just the extremes of the much larger winter numbers that occur in mid-Atlantic. Older Kittiwakes leave their colonies late and return early (Coulson & White 1960). As a result, the chances of old birds making transatlantic flights are probably reduced. On the other hand, Kittiwakes in adult plumage are regularly seen in winter in mid-Atlantic and some may make transatlantic flights. Relatively few adult Kittiwakes have been ringed and there is only one record of a known breeding adult making a transatlantic flight. It was ringed, when nesting for the first time, at North Shields on Tyneside and then reported dead in Nova Scotia during the following winter.

Most Kittiwakes ringed and recovered have been marked in northeast England and sparse recoveries of birds from other regions allow only the most general of comparisons. To date, the impression is of little difference in the movements of Kittiwakes from individual colonies or areas within Britain & Ireland.

On a larger scale, analyses of recoveries of Kittiwakes ringed in the Murmansk region of Russia show that these birds tend to winter further north in the Atlantic than British & Irish birds (Dementiev 1956, Coulson 1966). They do not penetrate further south than 45°N on the European side of the Atlantic and are also relatively less frequent in Canada. Thus the winter distribution of Kittiwakes from different breeding areas does not involve a complete mixing of birds from all areas. Over 100 foreign-ringed Kittiwakes have been recovered in Britain & Ireland, most originating from Norway, Russia, France or the Channel Isles, with smaller numbers from Denmark, Iceland, the Faeroes and Sweden, and singles from Germany and Greenland.

Most surviving male Kittiwakes return to their natal colony to breed but only a small minority of females do so, although most nest in colonies within a few kilometres of their birthplace (Coulson & Nève de Mévergnies 1992). Virtually none nest between 50 and 500 km from their natal colony but about 15% of young Kittiwakes disperse

Fig 5. Movements of over 20 km and recovery locations of Kittiwakes ringed as pulli in Britain & Ireland and recovered in a subsequent breeding season when at least three years old. There were 112:165 movements under:over 20 km but only those over 20 km are plotted.

considerable distances (over 500 km), sometimes involving movements across the North Sea (Coulson & Nève de Mévergnies 1992) (Fig 5). However, there is no firm evidence of Kittiwakes ringed as chicks in Europe remaining and breeding in colonies in Greenland or Canada. Confirmed cases of emigration and breeding have been reported, with birds moving from Norway to England and from England to France, Sweden and Helgoland. Despite some colour-marking of Kittiwake chicks, so far none are known to have visited their natal colony before moving elsewhere (pers obs).

Provided that breeding is successful in the colony, adult Kittiwakes return to the same colony year after year (Aebischer & Coulson 1990). In situations where the breeding success in the colony is low, for example through predation, disturbance or ectoparasites, many adults may move to breed in neighbouring colonies (Danchin & Monnat 1992).

Much of what remains to be discovered about the movements of Kittiwakes relates to their life at sea outside the breeding season. Nothing is known of winter movements in the same and in successive years by the same individual, but this is only likely to be established when satellite telemetry can be used to follow individuals, since ringing will not produce these data for the Kittiwake. In Britain, the annual mortality rate of adult Kittiwakes averages about 20% in males and about 17% in females (Aebischer & Coulson 1990) and most mortality occurs outside of the breeding season, when the birds are oceanic. The annual mortality rate for British birds is in marked contrast to the 7% found for both sexes in the Pacific (Hatch et al 1993). This interesting difference deserves further study.

J C Coulson

Sandwich Tern
Sterna sandvicensis

Sandwich Terns are common in coastal waters of Britain & Ireland in summer, attracting attention by their loud calls and vigorous plunge-diving for fish. In Europe, the nominate race *sandvicensis* nests in almost all coastal countries, with 45,000–50,000 pairs breeding on Atlantic and North Sea coasts, and smaller numbers by the Black Sea, the Sea of Azov, the northwest Mediterranean and the Baltic (*European Atlas*). Further east, the Caspian holds 40,000 pairs representing 50% of the Sandwich Tern population in the former USSR (*HBW*). Colonies in the Netherlands currently hold 10,000–12,500 pairs. Although there were up to 40,000 pairs in the 1940s, the Dutch population decreased to 650 in 1965 as a result of pesticide use (*European Atlas*); the subsequent increase in numbers has been paralleled by a similar increase in Britain & Ireland from 6,000 pairs in 1962 to 18,400 in 1985–87 (Lloyd *et al* 1991). The race *acuflavida* breeds on the eastern seaboard of North America extending to the southern Caribbean, and winters south to Peru and Uruguay. A yellow-billed race, *eurygnatha*, is a local breeder from Venezuela south to Patagonia along the eastern coast of South America (*HBW*).

In Britain & Ireland, Sandwich Terns breed in dense colonies at scattered locations on more exposed ocean coasts and inshore islands, and locally on inland lakes in Ireland. These colonies account for up to 10% of the total world population. Over 60% of British & Irish Sandwich Terns are concentrated in a few colonies in three main areas along the east coast of Britain: northeast Scotland, Northumberland and Norfolk (Lloyd *et al* 1991). The Northumberland colonies of Coquet Island and the Farne Islands are particularly important and together hold 4,000–5,000 pairs.

The analysis of the data for this species was supported by Colin Raymond

The breeding population of Ireland was 4,400 pairs in 1985–87 (Lloyd *et al* 1991) with the largest numbers at Strangford Lough.

The Sandwich Tern is migratory throughout the West Palearctic; birds from Britain & Ireland, the Netherlands, Denmark and Germany have common wintering quarters in West Africa (Møller 1981a), while those breeding in the Black Sea area winter in the eastern Black Sea and through the Mediterranean west to Spain, Portugal, Morocco and occasionally further south (*BWP*). Birds from the land-locked Caspian population winter mainly in the Persian Gulf and Arabian Sea, some reaching India and Sri Lanka (*BWP*).

Up to the end of 1997, over 151,000 Sandwich Terns had been ringed in Britain & Ireland, 97% of those later recovered being ringed as nestlings in June and July (Figs 1 & 2). A few fully grown birds have been ringed at breeding colonies, and during August and September on migration. Of the total included recoveries, 85% were reports of dead birds, and the remainder were recaptures (11%) and resightings (4%) of birds around the coasts of Britain & Ireland, the Netherlands, Denmark and Sweden. Recoveries of known cause represent 58% of the total recoveries of dead birds, and three-quarters of these were killed deliberately by humans (Fig 3). Most recoveries due to hunting come from wintering quarters in West Africa, with Ghana and Senegal

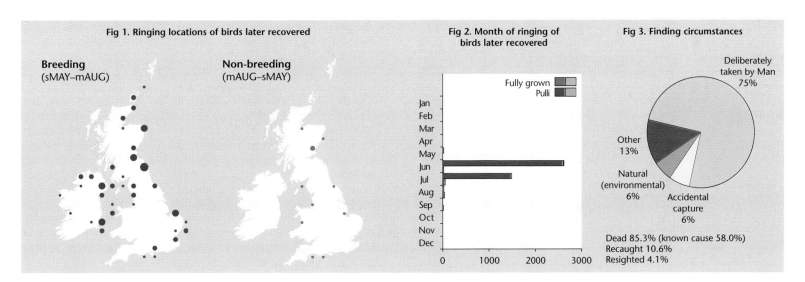

Fig 1. Ringing locations of birds later recovered

Breeding (sMAY–mAUG) Non-breeding (mAUG–sMAY)

Fig 2. Month of ringing of birds later recovered

Fully grown / Pulli

Fig 3. Finding circumstances

Deliberately taken by Man 75%
Other 13%
Natural (environmental) 6%
Accidental capture 6%

Dead 85.3% (known cause 58.0%)
Recaught 10.6%
Resighted 4.1%

Ringing and recovery data

	<1960	60–69	70–79	80–89	90–97	Total
RINGING						
BTO ringing totals (%)	23	24	22	22	10	151,985
RECOVERIES						
BTO-ringed (%)	10	22	29	24	15	4,230
Foreign-ringed (%)	←	67	→	9	24	46

Statistical analyses

	Breeding population (sMAY–mAUG)	Wintering population (mOCT–mMAR)
Status	LONG-DISTANCE MIGRANT (3)	NONE
Age differences[NT]	Significant	—
Sex differences	Not tested	—
Regional differences	Significant[S]	—
Finding circumstances	Significant	—

Fig 4. Locations in (a) August (197:12:255), (b) September (121:15:105) and (c) October (163:18:58) of Sandwich Terns ringed as pulli in Britain & Ireland. Those recovered as juveniles (red) and one-year-olds (blue) are differentiated from those recovered as older birds (grey). Sample sizes of the age classes at recovery (juveniles:one-year-olds:older birds) are shown.

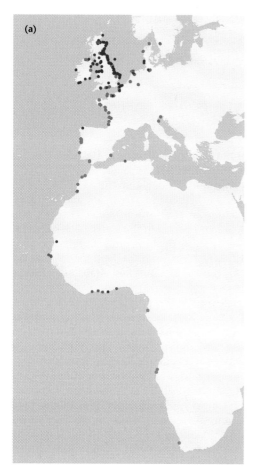
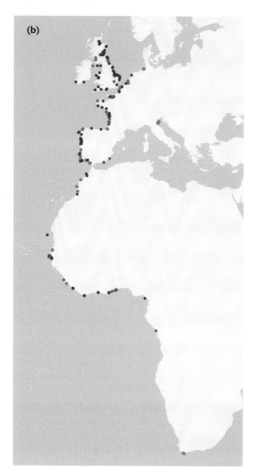
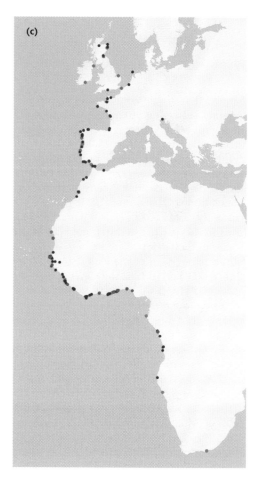

together generating over half of these recoveries; Angola, Ivory Coast, Liberia and Sierra Leone account for an additional 30%, and European countries a further 11%. The trapping and killing of terns in West Africa is carried out by children setting noose traps baited with dead fish on the shore (Mead 1978), and is more prevalent in years when sardines are also abundant (Dunn & Mead 1982). There may be temporal differences in trapping activities in different countries and, in recent years, the proportion of recoveries coming from Angola has decreased but that from Senegal has increased. Although the trapping of terns may, overall,

be less common today than it was in the 1960s, it is still widespread in parts of West Africa (A Jonard pers comm) and has implications for the interpretation of recovery patterns.

Sandwich Terns breeding in Britain & Ireland begin post-fledging dispersal around the coasts of Britain and Ireland and across the North Sea to the Netherlands and Denmark in late June (Smith 1975) and, during July and August, there is post-fledging dispersal in both directions between Britain and the Netherlands (Møller 1981a). Dispersal can be rapid, with juveniles being recorded 65 km from the natal colony only three days after fledging (Smith 1975). Within three to four months of ringing, juveniles head rapidly south to the wintering areas off the West African coast (Fig 4), often travelling in family parties and remaining dependent on their parents even in the winter quarters (*BWP*). All but a few stragglers have left British & Irish waters by late October. The median changes in latitude for birds recovered as adults and juveniles from August to December indicate that the speed and distance of autumn migration is similar for the two age classes (Fig 5).

The non-breeding-season recovery locations for adult and immature birds are almost exclusively coastal (Figs 4, 6 & 7); in Britain at least, the Sandwich Tern is a rare bird inland. There appears to be no difference in non-breeding range in relation to the region of origin within Britain & Ireland. However, the lack of recoveries along the coast of Belgium and Channel coast of France suggests that birds from the northwest and southwest of Britain & Ireland rarely enter the English Channel during their southward migration.

The wintering range of first-winter birds remains largely centred on the West African coast from Senegal to Ghana but ranging from Morocco and the Iberian Peninsula south to South Africa (Fig 6). Most young birds remain in these areas during the following summer (Figs 5 & 7). Winter

Fig 5. Monthly variation in the differences in latitude between ringing and recovery locations of Sandwich Terns present in Britain & Ireland during the breeding season. Monthly medians (points) and interquartile ranges (bars) are shown.

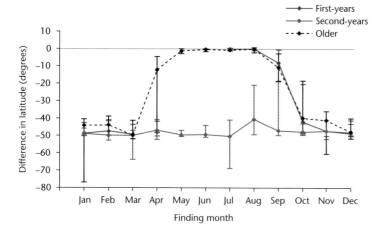

Fig 6. Locations during midwinter (November–February) of (a) 553 first-year and (b) 319 older Sandwich Terns ringed as pulli in Britain & Ireland.

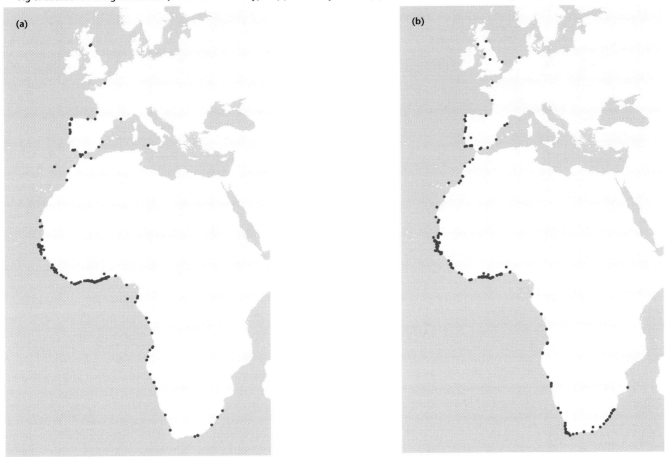

Fig 7. Locations in (a) March–April (167:39:135) and (b) May–July (99:48:552) of Sandwich Terns ringed as pulli in Britain & Ireland. Those recovered as first-years (red) and second-years (blue) are differentiated from those recovered as older birds (grey). Sample sizes of the age classes at recovery (first-years:second-years:older birds) are shown.

Fig 8. Movements of over 20 km and recovery locations of Sandwich Terns ringed as pulli in Britain & Ireland and recovered in a subsequent breeding season when of breeding age. There were 99:567 movements under:over 20 km but only those over 20 km are plotted. The 35 recoveries in Africa are not shown because they are unlikely to represent birds at breeding colonies.

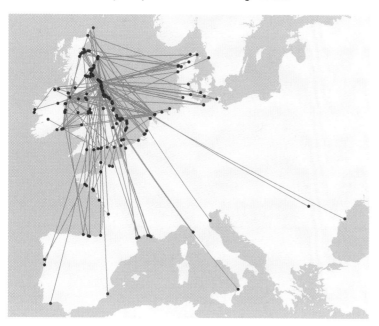

recoveries of older Sandwich Terns are distributed predominantly from around the Iberian Peninsula to the coast of South Africa, extending northeast to a single recovery in Mozambique (Fig 6). The distribution of recoveries along the coast will be determined not only by the numbers of wintering birds but also by social, cultural and political factors including the prevalence of trapping, density of local people, and the ease of reporting. The scarcity of recoveries along the coast of southern Morocco must be due, at least in part, to a low human population density. Further south, upwellings of nutrient-rich water, driven by the Canary and Guinea ocean currents, support important stocks of pelagic fish, particularly off Senegal and Ghana, that are exploited by Sandwich Terns and other tern species. Climate-driven changes in the locations and strength of these upwellings, and hence associated fish stocks (Binet 1997), may affect the distribution of wintering birds and the number of recoveries from year to year. Upwellings due to the Benguela Current, particularly off Angola, may also provide important feeding areas for wintering birds. That recoveries are relatively few from Nigeria south to Gabon may reflect the absence of upwelling systems. There is little variation in the overall pattern of recoveries in the wintering quarters of birds from different regions of Britain & Ireland, and the wintering grounds along the coast of West Africa are used by birds from all areas of northwest Europe (Møller 1981b).

Starting in March, adults of three years or more make a rapid return journey to the breeding grounds by May (Figs 5 & 7), although early arrivals regularly reach Britain in late March, whilst young birds remain in Africa for most of their second year (Fig 5). Not all birds return to breed in their third year (BWP) and breeding-season recoveries of adults

(three years old or more) occur throughout the wintering range (Figs 7 & 8). Birds returning to Europe for the first time as breeding adults normally breed within 500 km of their natal colonies (Møller 1981b). Sandwich Terns ringed as nestlings in Britain & Ireland have been recovered in subsequent breeding seasons in Denmark, the Netherlands, Belgium and France, providing evidence of considerable interchange between west European breeding populations. Natal dispersal to countries bordering the North and Baltic Seas is not confined to Sandwich Terns ringed on the east coasts of Britain, and there is also interchange between different regions within Britain & Ireland. The breeding-season recoveries of adults along the northern Mediterranean coastline and east to the Danube Delta (Fig 8) may be the result of birds from Britain & Ireland mixing with wintering terns from the Black Sea populations and subsequently moving back with them. Too few adults of breeding age have been ringed or resighted to allow the extent of breeding dispersal to be assessed but breeding Sandwich Terns are well known for abandoning breeding colonies (BWP, Lloyd et al 1991), in response to predation, habitat changes, the encroachment of colonies by gulls and, sometimes, for no apparent reason.

The small numbers of recoveries of foreign-ringed Sandwich Terns within Britain & Ireland have largely come from birds ringed in Belgium, Denmark, Germany and the Netherlands. One notable recovery was an acuflavida ringed as a nestling in North Carolina, USA, and recovered dead, in its first winter, in southwest England in November. This complements an earlier recovery of a North Carolina acuflavida in the Netherlands (BWP).

Although we now know a great deal about Sandwich Tern migration, there is much that can be learned from the existing data, especially from detailed analytical and modelling studies of recovery patterns in the wintering quarters. There is a continued need to maintain a consistent ringing effort for this species in the long term. Although the mortality due to trapping in their wintering quarters was identified many years ago, this remains a problem and could have significant consequences for European populations of Sandwich Terns, particularly if breeding colonies and wintering birds come under pressure from future reductions in food availability. The ringing of nestlings should be maintained, in order to monitor changes in wintering distribution, pre-breeding mortality and colony recruitment from year to year, but the ringing (or resighting) of adult birds at breeding colonies also needs to be encouraged to improve mortality estimates from mark–recapture data and to assess the breeding site-fidelity of adults. More-detailed quantitative studies of the annual recruitment of first-time breeders into colonies and the extent of interchange between different populations will be important for understanding the population dynamics of the species. A high profile needs to be given to educating the public in areas where trapping takes place; the reduction of mortality is important not just to safeguard breeding populations, in Britain & Ireland and elsewhere, but also because feeding concentrations of these birds are useful markers of fish concentrations for local fishermen. Similarly, the removal of rings from birds released back into the wild by trappers (Becker & Wendeln 1996) must be discouraged. These problems can only be tackled by obtaining the cooperation of local communities.

David Noble-Rollin & Chris Redfern

Roseate Tern

Sterna dougallii

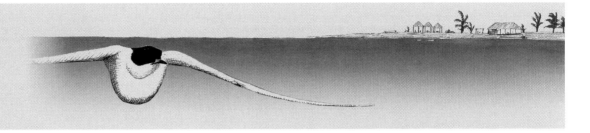

Roseate Terns rank among the most beautiful seabirds, and their immaculate plumage, elegant build and dashing flight may be observed in many parts of the world. Although their patchy breeding distribution is mainly tropical, the ranges of some populations extend well into the temperate zone (Gochfeld 1983). There are five distinct subspecies, with the nominate *dougallii* breeding in Britain, Ireland, France, the Azores, the eastern coast of the USA, the Caribbean and Africa (Gochfeld 1983). The race *bangsi* breeds from the Malayan Peninsula eastward into China, Japan, the Philippines, New Guinea and New Caledonia; *korustes* is found breeding in Sri Lanka and Myanmar, *arideensis* in the Seychelles and Madagascar, and *gracilis* in Australia (Gochfeld 1983). The European populations migrate south along the Atlantic seaboard to winter in the Gulf of Guinea (*BWP*, Monteiro *et al* 1996), while the American populations migrate through the West Indies and Trinidad to winter on the Brazilian coast (Nisbet 1984, Hays *et al* 1997). The migration routes and wintering areas of the populations outside the North Atlantic are unknown.

Roseate Terns are among the most marine of terns, and inland records are extremely rare (*BWP*). The species' stronghold in northwest Europe is in the Irish Sea, with large colonies having occurred in Anglesey and Counties Down, Antrim, Dublin and Wexford, the relative importance of these changing radically between 1969 and the 1990s (Cabot 1995). Regular breeding also occurs at colonies in Northumberland, Lothian and Brittany (Cabot 1995). Roseate Terns breed on offshore islands or islets in coastal lagoons that are within foraging range of concentrations of sand-eels or Sprat (*BWP*). During winter in West Africa, Roseate Terns feed in

The analysis of the data for this species was supported by Ian Forsyth & Pamela Allen

areas with high densities of Anchovy and juvenile sardines in shallow, inshore waters and return each night to roost with huge flocks of other terns on saltpans, breakwaters and wrecks (Dunn & Mead 1982, Ntiamoa-Baidu 1992).

The distribution of ringing effort for birds later recovered closely reflects that of the breeding colonies (Fig 1). Most has occurred in the Irish Sea, particularly at Rockabill, Tern Island, Lady's Island Lake, Anglesey and the Northern Irish sea-loughs. Large numbers have also been ringed in the Northumbrian colonies at the Farnes and Coquet Island and at three colonies in the Firth of Forth. Roseate Terns have been ringed almost exclusively as chicks in June, July and August (Fig 2).

Of 873 ring-recoveries, 49% were found dead, 49% resighted and 2% were recaptured. The majority of the dead recoveries were immature birds during winter, whereas resightings comprise adult birds at their breeding colonies.

The cause of death was known for 71% of the 430 dead recoveries (Fig 3), and of these 75% were due to deliberate capture by humans. Trapping occurs mainly in winter, with boys in Ghana and Senegal using baited hooks or nooses to catch terns for sport, food and income (Dunn & Mead 1982, Ntiamoa-Baidu *et al* 1992, Stientien *et al* 1998). Ring-recoveries are more likely to be reported from countries where trapping occurs, particularly if its inhabitants are literate in English,

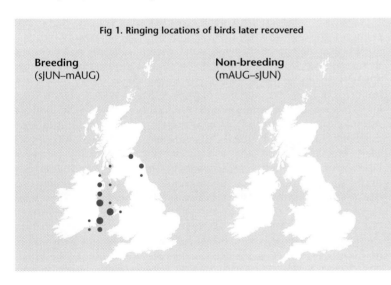

Fig 1. Ringing locations of birds later recovered

Breeding (sJUN–mAUG)

Non-breeding (mAUG–sJUN)

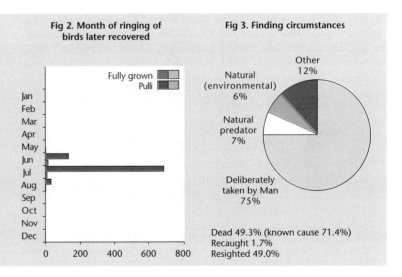

Fig 2. Month of ringing of birds later recovered

Fully grown
Pulli

Jan, Feb, Mar, Apr, May, Jun, Jul, Aug, Sep, Oct, Nov, Dec

0 200 400 600 800

Fig 3. Finding circumstances

Other 12%

Natural (environmental) 6%

Natural predator 7%

Deliberately taken by Man 75%

Dead 49.3% (known cause 71.4%)
Recaught 1.7%
Resighted 49.0%

Ringing and recovery data

	<1960	60–69	70–79	80–89	90–97	Total
RINGING						
BTO ringing totals (%)	14	35	18	14	18	28,905
RECOVERIES						
BTO-ringed (%)	3	21	11	8	56	873
Foreign-ringed (%)	0	0	0	0	0	0

Statistical analyses

	Breeding population (sJUN–mAUG)	Wintering population (mOCT–mAPR)
Status	LONG-DISTANCE MIGRANT (4)	NONE
Age differences[NT]	Not significant*	—
Sex differences	Not tested	—
Regional differences	Not tested	—
Finding circumstances	Significant	—

Fig 4. Recovery locations during the breeding season of Roseate Terns ringed in Britain & Ireland. Those recovered in the year of hatching (18, blue squares), as first-years (27, blue circles) and as second-years (57, red circles) are differentiated from those recovered as adults (376, grey circles). The recovery of a second-year bird in the USA is not shown.

Fig 5. Recovery locations in (a) September–October (45) and (b) April–May (57) of Roseate Terns ringed in Britain & Ireland.

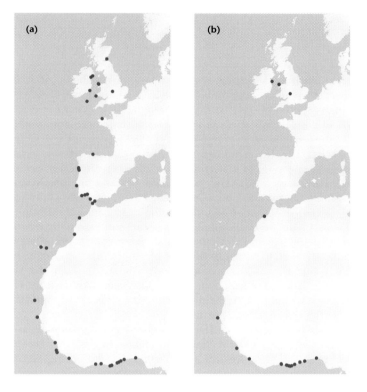

creating spatial bias in the distribution of recoveries. The likelihood of recovery also varies according to age because immature terns are more prone to trapping than adults (Dunn & Mead 1982), resulting in 94% of winter recoveries being of first-year birds. In contrast, most dead adults are recovered at their colonies during the breeding season, with the main finding circumstance being natural predation. These sources of variation in recovery rates require careful consideration when interpretations of spatial and age-specific migration patterns are made from recovery data.

Roseate Terns fledge their chicks in July and pre-migratory dispersal occurs during August. Most ring-recoveries of juveniles during July and August are close to the colony of origin (median distance between ringing and recovery 31–60 days after ringing as pulli = 32 km, n=15). Adults and juveniles leave the Irish Sea colonies and move to Dublin Bay, where roosts of over a thousand Roseate Terns have been recorded (Cabot 1995). During this period, juveniles practise fishing but are still dependent on their parents for food (Shealer & Kress 1994). This period is probably important for the adults and juveniles to lay down fat reserves in preparation for the long migration ahead.

During September and October, the number of recoveries in the breeding grounds declines steeply and recoveries are dispersed along the entire western Iberian and West African coastlines, suggesting a rapid migration to the wintering grounds with no discrete staging areas en route (Fig 5). Radar studies during autumn in Ghana show that terns migrate close inshore in large flocks during both day and night (Grimes 1977). Between November and May, virtually all recoveries are between the Equator and 10°N, mostly in Ghana, Togo and Ivory Coast (Fig 6). Most recoveries from this region are of immature birds but adults have also been reported there in January, suggesting that the wintering areas of different age classes are similar. Roseate Terns from all regions of Britain and Ireland appear to follow a similar migration route and share the same wintering grounds (Fig 6). Furthermore, all recoveries of Azorean-ringed birds come from Ghana (Monteiro et al 1996, L R Monteiro pers comm), suggesting that it is the principal wintering area for all European Roseate Terns. The

fact that other tern species are trapped and reported from a wider area of the West African coastline (this volume) suggests that the concentration of European Roseate Terns in Ghana is real rather than an artefact of the high trapping effort there.

Counts of roost sites in Ghana confirm that it is a very important country for wintering terns, but that numbers vary seasonally. Terns are present all year but the first migrants arrive during July and numbers increase rapidly to a peak of 40,000 birds in October (Ntiamoa-Baidu 1992), with counts of Roseate Terns at individual roosts numbering hundreds of birds. The numbers of terns in Ghana decline steeply from late November to December and reach summer levels by January (Ntiamoa-Baidu 1992), this being associated with a reduction in food availability as prey fish move eastwards and into deeper water (Kwei 1964, Mendelssohn & Cury 1987, Cury & Fontana 1988). However, numbers of Roseate Tern ring-recoveries in Ghana do not decline sharply until March, suggesting that the reduction in roosting tern numbers is due to the egress of more abundant species and that Roseate Terns remain in Ghana throughout the winter. Although the majority of Roseate Terns breeding in Europe migrate to the Gulf of Guinea, there are two recent records of a chick ringed at Rockabill and recovered in Brazil, and an adult ringed in Brazil and recovered breeding in the Azores (H Hays pers comm). This shows that some European Roseate Terns may make a transatlantic migration and spend the winter alongside the USA population.

The majority of first-year birds remain in West Africa during the summer (Fig 4), although there is some evidence of northward movement along the West African coastline in June and July. Resightings of first-year birds at the breeding colonies are rare and tend to be in July. Only 23 individuals have been resighted at Rockabill over nine years, these being mostly of birds hatched there, although two were from Lady's Island Lake and one from Lothian.

Breeding adults return to the colonies in Britain, Ireland and France during summer, with the first birds arriving in May. Many second-year

Fig 6. Recovery locations in West Africa during November–March of Roseate Terns ringed in Britain & Ireland. Those recovered as immatures, *ie* at less than three years of age (154, red), are differentiated from those recovered as adults (10, blue). The recovery of an immature in eastern England during February is not shown.

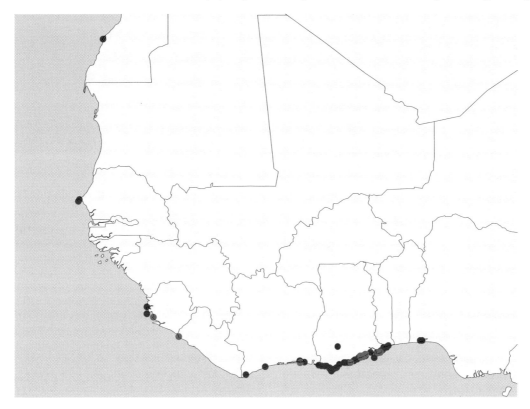

birds also return to Europe in late June and July to prospect at different colonies (Fig 4), but these seldom breed (*BWP*). Recoveries of Roseate Terns during the spring migration to the breeding grounds are extremely scarce compared to autumn. Those available hint that the general migration route in spring is similar to that followed during the autumn (Fig 5), this being supported by sightings of Roseate Terns migrating north in April off Senegal and in early May off Mauritania (*BWP*). However, radar studies in Ghana have failed to detect large flocks of terns migrating westward during spring, suggesting that they could be migrating further offshore (Grimes 1977).

Resightings of adults that were ringed as chicks show that natal dispersal occurs among all colonies in northwest Europe, and so the colonies within this region can be regarded as components of a metapopulation. Dispersal beyond this metapopulation to those in the Azores or USA appears to be extremely rare. Only one transatlantic recovery has been reported during the breeding season; a bird ringed as a chick on Rockabill Island, County Dublin, was seen at a breeding colony on Bird Island, Massachusetts, two years later (Nisbet & Cabot 1995).

Roseate Terns have an unfavourable conservation status in Britain & Ireland (Batten *et al* 1990, Gibbons *et al* 1996a) due to a catastrophic decline from 3,812 pairs in 1968 to 561 pairs in 1987 (Cabot 1995, Lloyd *et al* 1991). Ring-recoveries suggest that a reduction in juvenile survival

rates, perhaps due to increased trapping in the wintering grounds, was the most likely explanation for this decline (Mead 1978, Cabot 1995, Green 1995a). The Roseate Tern population has increased steadily to 787 pairs in 1999 following conservation efforts at the breeding colonies (Avery *et al* 1995, Casey *et al* 1995) and in the wintering grounds (Ntiamoa-Baidu 1991). The population recovery has been slow, however, and studies show that survival rates are still low compared to other terns (N Ratcliffe 1997). Winter trapping is still a source of ring-recoveries and may be a factor limiting population growth.

Ring-recoveries have demonstrated that large numbers of Roseate Terns winter in Ghana but the importance of adjacent countries may be under-represented by low reporting rates. For example, large flocks of Roseate Terns have been seen in Lagos Harbour, Nigeria (Wallace 1972), despite the fact that only two recoveries have ever been reported from there. Monthly counts and constant effort mist-netting at tern roosts along the Gulf of Guinea coastline are required to delimit the boundaries of the Roseate Tern's wintering range and to describe seasonal movements within it. Such work is being conducted in Ghana and could be extended to adjacent countries, although there are political and logistical barriers to achieving this.

Norman Ratcliffe & Oscar Merne

Common Tern
Sterna hirundo

Common Terns are gregarious seabirds, often drawing attention to themselves with strident calls, and with a dainty flight that gave rise to their old name of 'sea swallows'. Although they are mainly coastal, they also nest widely inland, especially in central and eastern England, making this the tern most familiar to people in Britain.

The nominate race *hirundo* breeds from the Canadian Rockies eastwards to the Yenisei Valley and Kazakhstan. It breeds all along the coast of Norway to Lapland, and extensively inland in the rest of Fennoscandia and in a broad swathe across Russia to Kamchatka, between about 40° and 65°N. Common Terns just reach Iceland as vagrants, and only sporadically breed in the Faeroes (*European Atlas, BWP*). They breed on Madeira (*HBW*), in the Azores (Hume 1993) and there are a few scattered breeding colonies on offshore islands in western tropical Africa, often erratically occupied, in the wintering range of European breeders. There are some colonies in Bermuda and the Caribbean, including islands off Venezuela. To date, only birds of the nominate race are believed to have occurred in Britain & Ireland.

Western European birds migrate down the western seaboard of Europe and Africa. A few probably winter off Portugal and southern Spain but the majority winters along the west coast of Africa. This is a 'leap-frog' migration; Fennoscandian birds go to South Africa, while the highest winter concentrations of British and Dutch birds are along the Gulf of Guinea coast between Sierra Leone and Ghana. Birds from eastern Europe migrate through the eastern Mediterranean and Red Sea to winter in east coast Africa. Exceptionally, breeding Common Terns ringed in the Azores have been recovered exclusively in Brazil (H Hays

The analysis of the data for this species was supported by the Merseyside Ringing Group in memory of Ron Birch

& N Ratcliffe pers comm), alongside Nearctic birds that winter as far south as Argentina.

A montane race *tibetana*, resembling a shorter-billed *hirundo*, breeds from the Himalayas to Mongolia and China, with these birds wintering from east India to Malaysia, and a few reaching South Africa. Those of the black-billed northeast Asian race *longipennis* move through Japan and the Philippines to winter in New Guinea, Indonesia and Australia.

Common Terns breed in a wide range of habitats from the arctic fringe to the tropics, both along coasts and on inland fresh waters. Outside the breeding season, they occur mainly in coastal waters, being found mostly on inlets and estuaries, often resting on jetties and beaches. They favour flat areas for breeding, mainly in lowlands but at altitudes up to 300 m or more in Scotland, and higher elsewhere, even up to 4,500 m. In Britain & Ireland, Common Terns breed wherever there are sufficient small fish and nesting areas safe from ground predators, on coasts, shingle banks in rivers and islands in lakes and gravel-pits; they take readily to artificial nesting platforms. Elsewhere in western Europe they are mostly confined to the coasts and major rivers, whilst in eastern Europe they are widespread.

Over 91% of the British & Irish Common Tern recoveries are from birds ringed as chicks (Figs 1 & 2). Occasionally, it can be difficult to distinguish Common Tern from Arctic Tern chicks when ringing in

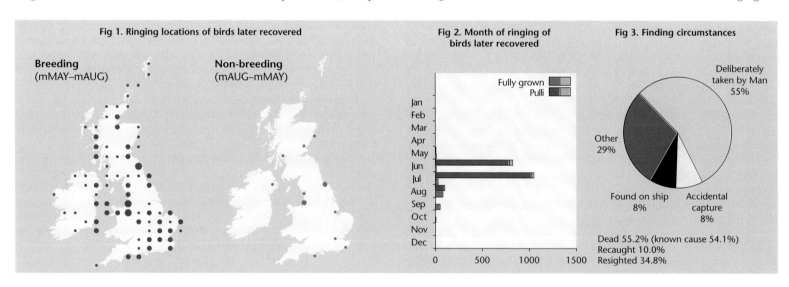

Fig 1. Ringing locations of birds later recovered

Breeding (mMAY–mAUG)

Non-breeding (mAUG–mMAY)

Fig 2. Month of ringing of birds later recovered

Fully grown
Pulli

Jan
Feb
Mar
Apr
May
Jun
Jul
Aug
Sep
Oct
Nov
Dec

0   500   1000   1500

Fig 3. Finding circumstances

Deliberately taken by Man 55%

Other 29%

Found on ship 8%

Accidental capture 8%

Dead 55.2% (known cause 54.1%)
Recaught 10.0%
Resighted 34.8%

Ringing and recovery data

	<1960	60–69	70–79	80–89	90–97	Total
RINGING						
BTO ringing totals (%)	24	18	11	23	24	127,216
RECOVERIES						
BTO-ringed (%)	8	13	13	17	49	2,102
Foreign-ringed (%)	←	46	→	21	33	112

Statistical analyses

	Breeding population (mMAY–mAUG)	Wintering population (mOCT–mMAR)
Status	[LONG-DISTANCE MIGRANT] (2)	NONE
Age differences[NT]	Not significant*	—
Sex differences	Not tested	—
Regional differences	Significant[3]*	—
Finding circumstances	Not significant	

Fig 4. Seasonally accurate locations in (a) August–October (342:16:274),
(b) November–February (100:15:25), (c) March–April (39:5:21) and (d) May–July (36:250:452) of Common Terns ringed as pulli in Britain & Ireland. For the period August–October, those recovered as juveniles (red) and one-year-olds (grey) are differentiated from older birds (blue). For the remaining periods, those recovered as one-year-olds (red) and two-year-olds (grey) are differentiated from older birds (blue). Recoveries in the year of hatching are excluded from (d). Sample sizes of the classes juveniles:one-year-olds:older birds (for August–October) and one-year-olds:two-year-olds:older birds (for other periods) are shown.

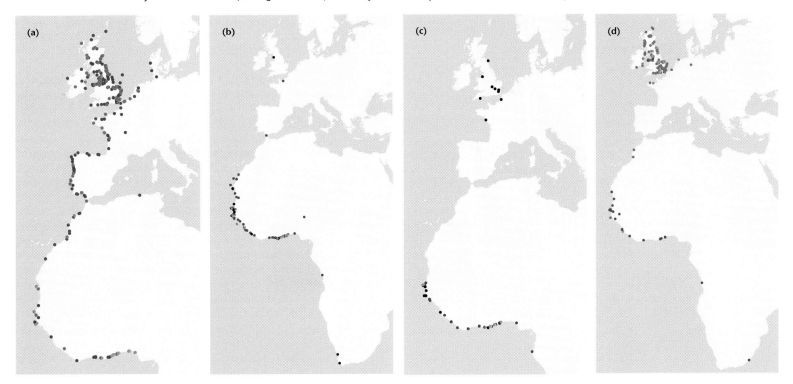

mixed colonies. All of the extreme recoveries of Common Terns have been carefully scrutinized because of this risk, although most of the colonies where they have been ringed contain only Common Terns. The ringing of Common Terns has been biased towards English inland breeding sites (Fig 1), many of which have been specially provided for the terns, and many of the remote Scottish and Irish sites have not been targeted. The records of natal dispersal and migration routes show much mixing between the coastal and inland breeders, so there is unlikely to be any serious misinterpretation of the species' migration from this ringing bias. Most of the Common Terns ringed when fully grown have been caught by cannon-nets or tape-lured into mist-nets at night in Merseyside or Cleveland (Fig 1), in increased numbers from 1977 onwards.

Of 646 birds recovered dead from known causes, as many as 71% were directly attributable to Man (Fig 3), almost all in Africa. Deaths due to pollution, predation or illness were mostly in Europe, as were almost all recoveries from birds recaught or resighted. Thus, one of the substantial biases in the recoveries data comes from the incidence of African trapping, which varies greatly between countries, as does the likelihood of a trapped bird's ring being reported. Many locals used not to inform the ringing centres, and often kept or killed the bird. Nowadays, they are reported more frequently, and birds caught accidentally by fishermen are likely to be released. There has, however, been a recent increase in 'trophy hunting' rings, of which perhaps only one in 12 are reported (Wendeln & Becker 1999). There are also large variations in the numbers of West African recoveries between years, more when high sardine numbers keep birds inshore throughout the day (Dunn & Mead 1982).

Undirected post-fledging dispersal starts as early as July and continues into October but, for the first two months after ringing, most birds stay close to their natal site. Much of the movement of these coastal birds within Britain may be overland: there is strong evidence for departures at dusk from Teesmouth in a southwesterly direction, taking birds to Liverpool Bay (Ward 2000). Some travel quickly to West Africa, where Common Terns have been recovered in Ghana as early as the end of August. Adults begin the annual moult of their flight feathers straight after breeding, suspend it during the southward migration and complete the moult in the winter quarters, differing from Arctic Terns, which rarely start to moult before they reach their wintering areas. Southward movement is most marked from August to October (Fig 4a), juveniles often accompanying adults and being fed by them.

Juvenile birds may gather at coastal sites, including Seaforth, Teesmouth and Dublin Bay, before starting the southward migration (S J White pers comm). British birds appear to move south somewhat earlier than those from Norway, with those from the Baltic colonies later still (Ward 2000). By late August and early September, several chicks from Norfolk had reached Durham, 300 km northwest, mingling with others including a Belgian-ringed chick that had dispersed 470 km to the northwest.

During September, and especially October, a strong southward movement occurs along the coast of southwest Europe (Fig 4a). In the third month after ringing, the median distance moved by British & Irish pulli recovered dead is 1,327 km (n=57), with a typical recovery site somewhere between Britain and Iberia or Morocco. The fastest movement takes place in the fourth month after ringing (usually October–November), when the median distance travelled increases to 4,430 km (n=21), the distance to the western tip of Africa.

Away from Britain & Ireland, migration follows the coasts. Common Terns keep mainly to the inner continental shelf, although they have been seen regularly 600 km offshore from Ghana (Urban et al 1986). Adult Common Terns occupy the same winter quarters, with the same routes and similar timing of passage, as the first-year birds (Fig 4). The winter distribution is determined mainly by the distribution of shoals of fish, especially sardines and anchovies (Dunn & Mead 1982). In the autumn, upwelling occurs along the west coast of Africa and the Gulf of Guinea, where large shoals of sardines are moving in from deeper water towards the Ivory Coast and Ghana to spawn. During the rainy season,

Fig 5. Movements of over 20 km and recovery locations of Common Terns ringed as pulli in Britain & Ireland and recovered in a subsequent breeding season when of breeding age. There were 115:354 movements under:over 20 km but only those over 20 km are plotted.

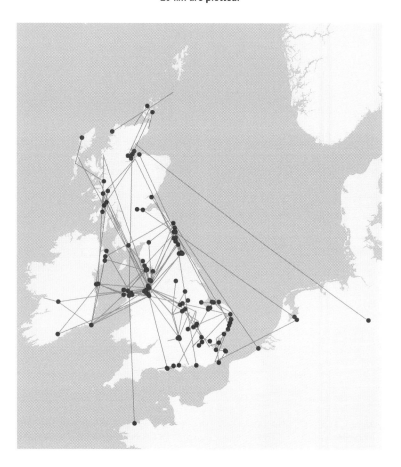

the rivers transport large quantities of food out to the Gulf, where the fish flourish, providing ideal conditions for the terns.

In December and January, most recoveries of British- or Irish-ringed birds, of all ages, come from the coast from southern Morocco to Nigeria, although few are found east of Ghana (Fig 4b). From February to May, as the adults start to move north, the centre of gravity of the first-year population remains farther south, with most first-years concentrated along the coast from Senegal to Nigeria (Fig 4c). In June and July, many first-year birds tend to move farther west and north, and there are few recoveries east of Sierra Leone, but one individual was caught at a sardine-processing factory near Accra, Ghana, on 19 June and again a month later. Another first-year bird was caught on a fishing boat off Guinea-Bissau on 14 December and again eight months later in Togo, a further 2,000 km east. Most birds stay off Africa during their first summer (Fig 4d) but, occasionally, one-year-old Common Terns return to Britain, although many of them are indistinguishable in plumage from two-year-old birds (S J White pers comm).

Recoveries suggest that the main wintering areas for British & Irish birds are Ghana and Senegal (Fig 4b) but, because trapping for food and recreation has been particularly prevalent there, the consequent high recovery rate might overstate the importance of these countries (BWP). The next most important countries are Sierra Leone, Liberia and Ivory Coast. Fewer recoveries come from Mauritania, Gambia, Guinea-Bissau and Guinea, and fewer still from east or south of Ghana. There is a similar distribution of birds from the Netherlands, France, Switzerland, western Germany, Spain, and probably Belgium (BWP). There is no evidence of any differences in wintering areas within the British & Irish population. The recovery rate from all countries from Sierra Leone to

Ghana is declining following extensive education programmes, while that along the west coast from Morocco to Guinea is increasing, but there is no suggestion that this reflects a real change in the birds' distribution. Small numbers of British- & Irish-bred Common Terns travel much farther south, to Angola and South Africa (Fig 4b), although movement into the Indian Ocean is much less common than for Sandwich or Arctic Terns. Only two British-ringed pulli have been found in South Africa east of the Cape, one of which was almost 1,000 km into the Indian Ocean in Transkei.

In Africa, adult birds part company with the immatures from February onwards. They skirt the northwest African coast at an average speed of 80–120 km/day (Urban *et al* 1986). Many are back in British & Irish breeding areas by April (Fig 4c). The paucity of records at west coast observatories implies that there is little movement through the Irish Sea to the Scottish colonies, and the frequency of inland sightings suggests that much of the spring passage takes place directly overland to the breeding sites. In fact, the only British observatories to record substantial numbers in spring are Dungeness and Portland Bill. At both sites, the passage peaks in late April and early May and is mainly eastward, hinting that these birds are mostly on their way to breeding areas elsewhere in northern Europe (R & F).

Sightings of marked birds show that most two-year-old birds return to breeding areas (S J White pers comm). The second-year birds return later than established breeders, from late May onwards, with most arriving by late June. A second-summer German bird, seen at Seaforth on 29 May, was recorded back in its north German natal colony 11 days later. Many breed at three years old (Cramp *et al* 1974) and some not until four.

Many Common Terns ringed as pulli have been recovered when at least three years old in a subsequent breeding season at considerable distances from their birthplace (Fig 5), although not all are cases of natal dispersal because first breeding may be delayed beyond the third year of life. Nevertheless, considerable interchange between natal and breeding colonies is likely, particularly amongst first-time breeders; chicks are known to settle often to breed in another colony (HBW), and a four-year-old Belgian chick was found nesting in Merseyside. In contrast, adults are highly faithful to their breeding colony (BWP). Indeed, they tend to return to the same section of a colony where they have previously been successful (HBW). There are only 12 cases in the recoveries database of apparent breeding dispersal, seven of over 20 km. Three of these are to continental Europe (Belgium, Netherlands and Spain), with two crossing the Irish Sea and two movements within Ireland.

Ring-recoveries show that many Common Terns from the northern European populations occur on passage through Britain. For instance, all 13 of the British-ringed birds recovered in Norway, Sweden or Finland were ringed as fully grown birds on autumn passage. Many of these records are from the western parts of Britain, suggesting a substantial passage directly across the country; none involve Ireland (Fig 6). Overall, there have been 101 recoveries to or from countries to the north and east, with 23 involving Belgium and the Netherlands, 14 involving Germany, Poland and the Baltic States, and 64 exchanges with Fennoscandia; these indicate the spread of origins of the Common Terns that pass through Britain & Ireland. They do not yet include birds from any southern or eastern populations. Common Terns from different European origins share the same migration route southward, at least to some extent. Baltic juveniles disperse southwest towards southern Sweden, Denmark and the southern Baltic before joining birds from the Netherlands and Britain & Ireland along the West African seaboard. Birds from both Austria and Germany have been recovered in Tanzania and a Norwegian bird has been found in Sudan, so some must take an easterly route, however (Urban *et al* 1986). Some birds from the Black Sea population are reported to travel through the Strait of Gibraltar, joining the southward route of most other European Common Terns, and going as far as the tip of South Africa (BWP), but ringing results indicate that birds reach South Africa via the Indian Ocean (Williams & Underhill

Fig 6. Recovery locations in (a) autumn (51, red) and winter (1, blue) and (b) the breeding season (24, red) and spring (2, blue), and movements of over 20 km, of Common Terns either ringed abroad and recovered in Britain & Ireland or ringed in Britain & Ireland outside the breeding season as fully grown birds and recovered abroad.

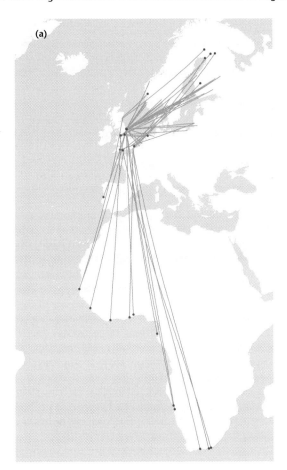

1997). Southerly and westerly populations within Europe, including Britain & Ireland, tend to winter north of the Equator, while the more northerly and easterly ones winter farther south, in Angola, South Africa, and, to a lesser extent, Mozambique; those in South Africa in winter are mainly from around the Baltic (Morant *et al* 1983, Williams & Underhill 1997). Half the British- & Irish-ringed birds recovered in South Africa had been ringed in Britain on autumn passage, probably from the Baltic. An exceptional recovery involved a bird ringed as an adult in Northern Ireland on 17 May 1959 and found dead on 26 October 1968 some 300 km inland in Victoria, Australia. From the ringing date, it could have been a Fennoscandian bird caught on spring passage. Birds ringed as chicks in Sweden (*BWP*) and Finland (Phillipps 1997) have also reached Australia.

It is very unusual for European Common Terns to mix with their American conspecifics, with the exception of birds breeding in the Azores (above). Arctic Terns from North America normally migrate down the eastern side of the Atlantic but nearctic Common Terns cross it only rarely: from more than one million ringed in the USA, just four records are considered acceptable (Nisbet & Safina 1996). All were birds in their first autumn or winter and were found in France (October), the mid-Atlantic (November), at sea off the Ivory Coast (December) and in Togo (February). Occasional Common Terns of unknown origin have wintered in European waters (*eg* Hudson 1973).

Conservation problems for Common Terns include marine pollution, overfishing and trapping, with the last of these being by far the biggest avoidable cause of death. However, most of those trapped are juveniles and, since Common Terns are amongst the longest-lived birds, the biggest threat to the species comes from hazards that jeopardize the survival of adults. It seems that they encounter their principal risks on migration and in their winter quarters, and greater knowledge of the birds' movements, especially within winter, would assist their conservation.

David Norman

Arctic Tern
Sterna paradisaea

The Arctic Tern moves on a global scale, performing the most remarkable and extensive migratory journeys undertaken by any bird. This small bird literally crosses the world, travelling between the polar regions and experiencing more daylight than any other living organism. Its breeding grounds lie in the north in an essentially circumpolar distribution, with the populations breeding in Britain and Ireland being at the southern edge of its breeding range. It breeds north to higher latitudes than any other tern, mainly in coastal areas and offshore islands on flat grass or shingle areas and on beaches. In the non-breeding season, it heads south to the Antarctic seas, spreading along the food-rich area at the edge of the pack ice, involving a return, straight-line journey of up to 20,000 km. The same broad migratory pattern occurs throughout its extensive distribution. Two main routes south are used. Birds from the Bering Sea and eastern Siberia areas appear to move south along the American Pacific coast; many from the Nearctic make a wind-assisted transatlantic crossing, joining those from northern Europe and western Siberia moving down the west coast of Europe and Africa (Salomonsen 1967b, *BWP*, Lee & Cardiff 1993). Unlike the closely related Common Tern, there are no distinct races of Arctic Terns, probably a reflection of the relatively high degree of population mixing that appears to occur.

The distribution of the Arctic Tern inevitably means that neither ring-recoveries nor observations will reveal the full extent of its movements. Its breeding grounds are sparsely populated, its wintering grounds largely uninhabited, and much of its movements occur in small groups of a dozen or so individuals at high altitude across open oceans.

The analysis of the data for this species was supported by Geoff Randall

What we know of the routes taken and the areas occupied is a composite picture built up from ring-recoveries, observations and radar-based studies.

In Britain & Ireland, its breeding stronghold is in Orkney and Shetland, with colonies also along the west coast of Scotland, in western Ireland and to a lesser extent eastern Ireland, and relatively small numbers breeding in northern England (*1988–91 Atlas*). There has been bias in both ringing and recoveries towards the northeast of England due to a number of detailed studies that have taken place at Coquet Island (Fig 1). Nonetheless, movement patterns are likely to be similar throughout Britain & Ireland. Over 90% of the recoveries relate to birds ringed as pulli (Fig 2). The pattern of recoveries partly reflects the relatively high post-breeding mortality of juveniles, probably largely due to predation and starvation close to the breeding colony. In addition, the practice of trapping terns on beaches in West Africa, particularly Ghana and Liberia, is evident in the data on finding circumstances (Fig 3). This introduces a further bias into the assessment of migration routes, though Arctic Terns appear to be taken in smaller numbers than the other terns involved (Mead 1978).

At the end of the breeding season, the main post-breeding movement of adult birds is southwards, and there are no known sex differences (Figs 4a & b). Movements through Britain & Ireland are

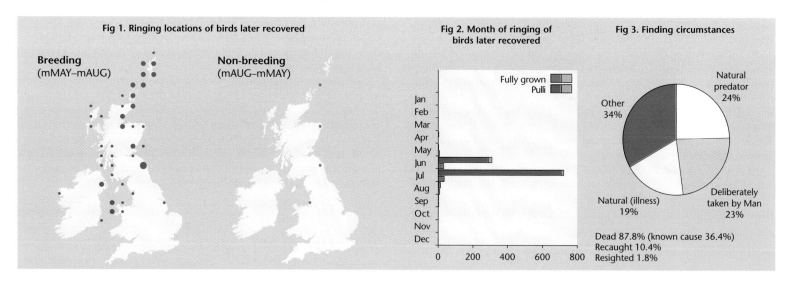

Fig 1. Ringing locations of birds later recovered

Breeding (mMAY–mAUG)   Non-breeding (mAUG–mMAY)

Fig 2. Month of ringing of birds later recovered

Fully grown / Pulli

Fig 3. Finding circumstances

- Natural predator 24%
- Other 34%
- Deliberately taken by Man 23%
- Natural (illness) 19%

Dead 87.8% (known cause 36.4%)
Recaught 10.4%
Resighted 1.8%

Ringing and recovery data

	<1960	60–69	70–79	80–89	90–97	Total
RINGING						
BTO ringing totals (%)	10	18	15	31	26	158,442
RECOVERIES						
BTO-ringed (%)	5	26	21	27	21	1,098
Foreign-ringed (%)	←	55	→	21	25	73

Statistical analyses

	Breeding population (mMAY–mAUG)	Wintering population (sNOV–mMAR)
Status	LONG-DISTANCE MIGRANT (3)	NONE
Age differences	Not tested	—
Sex differences	Not tested	—
Regional differences	Not tested	—
Finding circumstances	(Not significant)	—

Fig 4. Locations during (a) August–September (143:62), (b) October–November (33:18), (c) December–March (22:6) and (d) April–June (2:368) of Arctic Terns ringed in Britain & Ireland. Those recovered as first-years (red) are differentiated from those recovered as older birds (blue). Three first-years (Australia: Oct–Nov, Dec–Mar, South Atlantic: Dec–Mar) and two older birds (Australia: Aug–Sep, Russia: Apr–Jun) are not shown. Sample sizes of the age classes (first-years:older birds) are given.

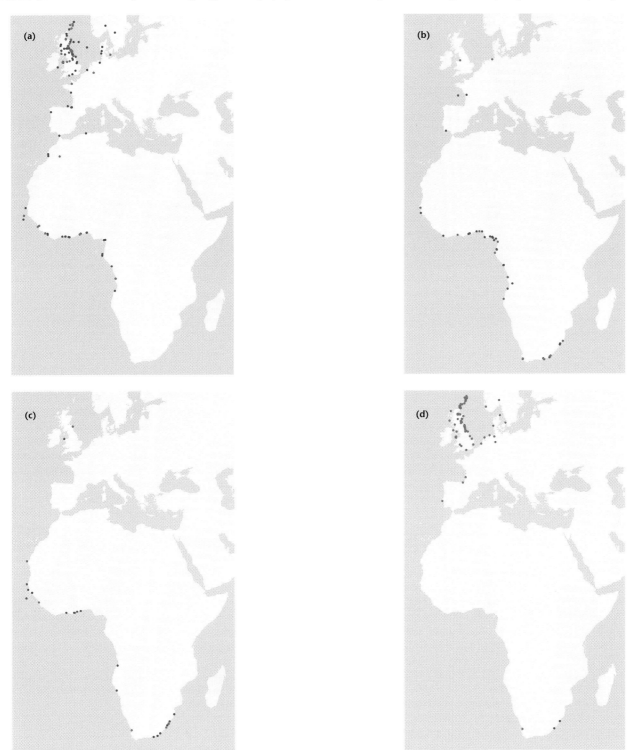

thought to occur mainly offshore. The migration continues southwards along the West African coast, apparently further offshore than the Common Tern (*BWP*). Movement continues to South Africa, then on to the edge of the pack ice in early winter (Fig 4c). The birds then appear to spread out along the edge of the pack ice, with the greatest concentration occurring to the south of the Indian Ocean at 30–150°E (Salomonsen 1967b, *BWP*, Gudmundsson *et al* 1992). After the completion of moult, return passage begins in March, with those birds heading for European colonies apparently moving northwards through the eastern Atlantic, approximately retracing the autumn route. There is

a suggestion, however, that some cross the Indian Ocean and return overland, possibly at altitudes of thousands of metres, and this route may account for occasional recoveries in the Urals (Bourne *et al* 1996). Analysis of US sightings and specimens suggests that the spring migration is more protracted than previously thought (Lee & Cardiff 1993). In Britain, overland northward movements of Arctic Terns are indicated by observations of hundreds or even thousands of birds some springs at reservoirs in central England; such observations are perhaps a consequence of poor flying conditions at sea or at high altitudes over land (Kramer 1995).

Fig 5. Movements of over 20 km and recovery locations of Arctic Terns ringed as pulli in Britain & Ireland and recovered in a subsequent breeding season when of breeding age. There were 305:153 movements under:over 20 km but only those over 20 km are plotted. Three recoveries (Spain, Portugal and Liberia) are not shown.

Fig 6. Movements since 1979 of foreign-ringed Arctic Terns recovered in Britain & Ireland. Those recovered as first-years (12, red) are differentiated from those recovered as older birds (19, blue). The movements of a first-year bird ringed in Greenland and an older bird ringed in South Africa are not shown.

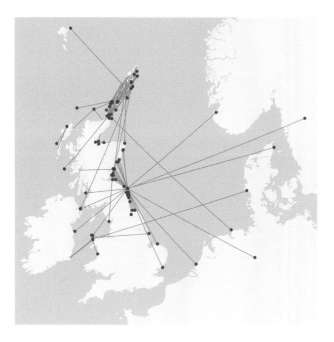

After fledging, there appears to be some slight northward and eastward movement of some juveniles towards the Baltic area before moving south, but the main post-breeding movement appears similar to that of the adults, southwards along the West African coast (Figs 4a & b). The subsequent movements of immatures are poorly known but, despite the presence of occasional first-summer birds on the breeding grounds, the limited recoveries of birds ringed in Britain & Ireland suggest that the majority remain south of the breeding colonies (Fig 4d), with some one-year-old birds possibly remaining in equatorial areas, some wintering in South Africa and others moving to the pack ice with the adults (*BWP*). Thereafter some young birds appear to circumnavigate the Antarctic, possibly for two years, then gradually penetrate further north to the breeding colonies. Some birds breed in their third year but the majority not until four years old. Intercolony exchanges are generally common in Arctic Terns, and birds ringed in Britain & Ireland have been recovered in colonies mainly to the south of where they were ringed but occasionally also to the east and slightly north in other European countries bordering the North Sea (Fig 5). However, 67% of the natal dispersal movements apparent from the ring-recovery data were less than 20 km (total *n*=458). Little information is available on breeding colony fidelity from individually marked birds. It is evident from the ephemeral nature of colonies that birds move about even when of breeding age but over what range and whether abstinence from breeding is involved remains unclear.

There have been a relatively small number of recoveries of foreign-ringed Arctic Terns in Britain & Ireland. This is partly a consequence of the absence of large-scale ringing of the species in more northern areas, making it difficult to build up a picture of movements through British & Irish waters. Those foreign-ringed birds that have been recovered originate almost entirely from colonies in Scandinavia and the Baltic (Fig 6); the vast majority were ringed as pulli and recovered during the breeding season, again reflecting the colony exchange that occurs. It is not known to what extent American-breeding Arctic Terns might occur in Britain & Ireland on passage; Nearctic breeders migrate south along the west coast of Europe and Siberian breeders may pass Britain & Ireland as well, at least during the autumn.

Clearly, there are major gaps in our understanding of the movement of Arctic Terns. The degree of population mixing in the wintering grounds, development of movement patterns with age, movements within the Antarctic, and the composition and stability of the small migratory parties that are seen are all largely unknown. Only the broad range of movements is well documented. The Man-induced mortality that occurs in West Africa is a cause for concern, as in several other tern species. For obvious reasons, it seems unlikely that sufficient information on the species' movements in the Antarctic and in the open ocean will ever come from ring-recoveries. On the other hand, ringing is likely to assist us in further detailing parts of the routes taken, and patterns of intercolony exchange. That the Arctic Tern's wintering and breeding grounds are sparsely populated, while inhibiting our full understanding of its migration pattern, undoubtedly provides some safeguard for the future of this most impressive of migrants.

Pat Monaghan

Little Tern
Sterna albifrons

The Little Tern is one of the smallest of the world's terns. Its rapid wingbeats and headlong flight are familiar to coastal observers in southern Britain & Ireland in the breeding season, but its spring and autumn movements are less conspicuous than those of the other terns.

Little Terns breeding in Britain & Ireland are of the nominate race, which breeds from Ireland eastward to central Asia and southward to northern India and North Africa. Further races occur in central Africa, Australia and eastern Asia. The nominate race winters to the south of the breeding range on the coasts of Africa and off the Arabian Peninsula. Its total population size is probably between 70,000 and 100,000 pairs with around 2,800 of these breeding in Britain & Ireland, mainly in southeast England (Lloyd *et al* 1991). The species uses shallow inshore marine and estuarine habitats for feeding throughout the year. It is rare to see them far out at sea (Stone *et al* 1995). Little Terns are present on British & Irish coasts from April to September. They nest in small loose groups on sand, gravel or shingle beaches on undisturbed coasts or on islands.

All ring-recoveries for Britain & Ireland have stemmed from ringing in or immediately after the breeding season, between May and August inclusive, at or close to colonies (Fig 1), and 87% of these have been of pulli (Fig 2). The spatial distribution of the origins of recovered birds from Britain & Ireland does not reflect that of Little Tern abundance; the east coast of Britain was the origin for more recoveries than expected, while Norfolk and Suffolk produced far fewer, and the west coasts of Scotland and Ireland none at all. Just over a half (55%) of the ring-recoveries were of dead birds, and these formed the great majority of records to the south of Britain. Nearly half of the dead birds with a cause

The analysis of the data for this species was supported by the Rye Bay Ringing Group and the Wetland Trust

of death attributed were deliberately taken by humans (Fig 3). This may introduce bias towards areas where terns are or were hunted, in the same way as there is a bias towards sites where ringing occurs for the 42% of records that are recaptures.

The general pattern of movements is typical of a bird migrating to spend the winter in nearshore areas off western Africa, and showing a dispersive phase when immature. Already, in August, there are recoveries as far south as northern Portugal, and one record (a bird ringed as an adult) from the northern Adriatic. Large flocks of Little Terns have been recorded in the Netherlands at this time of year (Keijl & Koopman 1991), suggesting that it may be a staging point for birds from a wide area. Some movement is particularly rapid: one bird was ringed in Essex on 21 August and recovered in Portugal six days later. There were no recoveries in Britain & Ireland after September, and all recoveries in western Africa are between October and February (Fig 4), with the exception of one immature in Morocco in May. There were no other recoveries to indicate return passage, which is relatively rapid (*BWP*). The southernmost recovery from Britain & Ireland is from Guinea-Bissau, whereas Little Terns ringed elsewhere in western Europe have been recovered further south in the Ivory Coast and Ghana (Urban *et al* 1986).

There are a number of breeding-season recoveries from northern continental Europe, particularly in the Netherlands and Denmark. The

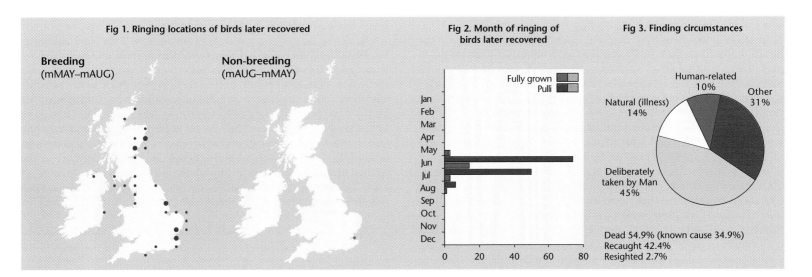

Fig 1. Ringing locations of birds later recovered

Breeding (mMAY–mAUG)

Non-breeding (mAUG–mMAY)

Fig 2. Month of ringing of birds later recovered

Fully grown
Pulli

Fig 3. Finding circumstances

Human-related 10%
Other 31%
Natural (illness) 14%
Deliberately taken by Man 45%

Dead 54.9% (known cause 34.9%)
Recaught 42.4%
Resighted 2.7%

Ringing and recovery data

	<1960	60–69	70–79	80–89	90–97	Total
RINGING						
BTO ringing totals (%)	16	9	24	25	26	12,210
RECOVERIES						
BTO-ringed (%)	16	9	23	27	25	150
Foreign-ringed (%)	←	67	→	0	33	3

Statistical analyses

	Breeding population (mMAY–mAUG)	Wintering population (mOCT–sAPR)
Status	[LONG-DISTANCE MIGRANT]	NONE
Age differences	Not tested	—
Sex differences	Not tested	—
Regional differences	Not tested	—
Finding circumstances	Not tested	—

Fig 4. Locations in August–September (29, red) and October–February (9, blue) of Little Terns that were present in Britain & Ireland during the breeding season, with seasonally accurate locations (points) differentiated from seasonally inaccurate locations (asterisks).

Fig 5. Movements of over 20 km and recovery locations of Little Terns ringed as pulli in Britain & Ireland and recovered in a subsequent breeding season when of breeding age. There were 11:50 movements under:over 20 km but only those over 20 km are plotted.

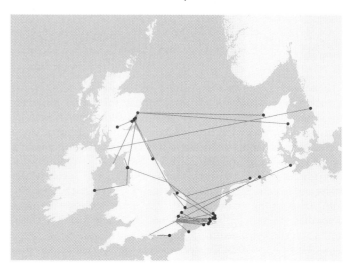

majority of these birds were ringed as pulli in Britain or Ireland and recovered when of breeding age (Fig 5). This appears to indicate some natal dispersal but, without further information on retraps, it is impossible to determine the degree to which this species returns to its natal colony or moves elsewhere. This factor, and the small sample size of birds ringed and recovered as adults, makes it difficult to reach firm conclusions about breeding site-fidelity. However, there appear to be proportionately as many birds ringed as adults recovered elsewhere in the breeding season (from a total sample of seven birds) as birds ringed as pulli. This hints that adults may not be particularly site-faithful between years, a fact borne out by the variability of counts at individual colonies between years (Sears & Avery 1993). There is a distinct tendency for birds ringed further north in Britain to be recovered further north on the Continent, with European recoveries of birds ringed in southeast England tending to be from the Netherlands (Fig 5). There have been four recoveries in Europe away from the northern and western seaboards, two from Italy and two from France, and all originating from southeast England. Little Terns do not breed until they are at least two years old, and it has been assumed that they spend their first year in their African winter quarters (*BWP*), but there is no supporting evidence from recoveries of British & Irish birds. There has been only one recovery in the breeding

season of a first-year bird; this was ringed as a pullus in Essex and recovered inland in northeast France in July of the following year.

There are no known major conservation threats to these birds at sea. Tern trapping in West Africa has been identified as a problem for some time, especially for Roseate and Sandwich Terns, and education programmes, for example in Ghana, have been implemented to address the problem. Little Terns may winter mostly north of the principal trapping areas, and are considered more wary of baited snare-traps than other species (Avery 1991). The low site-fidelity possibly shown by this species has advantages and disadvantages. If a site is unsuitable in one year, birds will readily nest elsewhere; however, the mobility of colonies may make planning for colony protection difficult. The degree of movement between Britain and continental Europe indicates that censuses at least at the scale of northern Europe would be necessary if we are to monitor population changes realistically.

As can be seen, our knowledge of this species is far from complete. We know little about actual migration routes, movements during the winter period, location of first-year birds throughout the year, or whether there is a passage through British & Irish waters of birds breeding elsewhere. There appears to be little information on the origins of the Little Terns gathering in the Netherlands; perhaps the next steps in understanding this species will be to examine ringing and breeding information on a Europe-wide basis. In view of the low recovery rates for dead birds, live recaptures of birds at large roosts (such as those in the Netherlands) could generate important information. The ringing of Little Tern chicks at a more representative spread of colonies throughout Britain and Ireland would also be beneficial.

Mark L Tasker & the late Maurice Adcock

Common Guillemot (Guillemot)

Uria aalge

The Guillemot is one of the most common seabirds in the temperate and colder parts of the North Atlantic and North Pacific Oceans. In the east Atlantic, it breeds from Svalbard south to Portugal (though numbers are small at the extremes of this range), including the Baltic. The latest census in 1986–87 suggested a British & Irish population of about 1.2 million birds (Lloyd *et al* 1991), and numbers have increased since (Upton *et al* 2000). It is particularly sensitive to chemical pollution and is usually the most common species involved in oiling incidents. A walk along any beach will usually find a dead Guillemot or two. Throughout its range the species is used as an indicator of marine conditions and its numbers, both at colonies and washed up dead, and breeding success are widely monitored. Two subspecies breed in Britain & Ireland. The chocolate-brown-mantled *albionis* is found in England, Wales, Ireland, and also in Helgoland, France and Iberia, and the blacker and slightly larger nominate *aalge* in Scotland and at all other Atlantic colonies, except those north of about 69°N where it is replaced by *hyperborea* (*BWP*).

This is a dispersive rather than a migratory species with many adults, even from the northernmost colonies, present in neighbouring seas throughout the year (*BWP*). Adults can be seen ashore at some northeastern colonies at any season except from early August to the end of September, which coincides with the main moult period, when they are flightless. Small numbers of Guillemots from Scandinavian and Faeroese colonies reach northern Britain and some enter the North Sea. Birds from Helgoland remain within the North Sea and individuals

The analysis of the data for this species was supported by Andrew Harris

from the small Baltic population tend to winter within that area, where they are joined by a few birds from elsewhere (Mead 1974a). Unlike the Puffin and Razorbill, the Guillemot is rarely seen in the Mediterranean.

Guillemots breed on sheer cliffs and isolated islands. Ringing them is not for the faint-hearted and it is possible to ring large numbers at only a few colonies. These colonies are well dispersed geographically (Fig 1) and, except for the large colonies in the Outer Hebrides and west Ireland being under-represented, ringing effort generally reflects the species' distribution in Britain & Ireland. Two colonies, Canna and Great Saltee, have each provided over a thousand recoveries. Most Guillemots are ringed as chicks over just a few weeks each year (Fig 2). The last previous national analysis (Mead 1974a) was based on about 500 recoveries. The total number of recoveries now stands at over 6,000.

Over half (55%) of all recoveries have details of the cause of death (Fig 3); these include birds drowned in fishing nets usually set in relatively shallow inshore waters (43% of this total), oiled (35%), and fleyged (flight-netted) or snared at colonies or shot in winter for human consumption (13%). Those without specific details were mainly washed up dead or dying on beaches. The distribution of recoveries is therefore

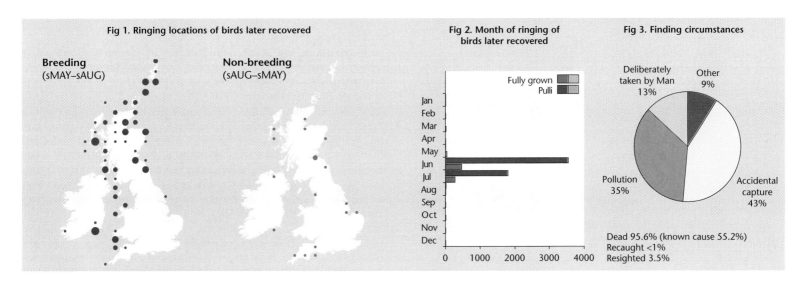

Fig 1. Ringing locations of birds later recovered

Breeding (sMAY–sAUG)

Non-breeding (sAUG–sMAY)

Fig 2. Month of ringing of birds later recovered

Fully grown
Pulli

Fig 3. Finding circumstances

Deliberately taken by Man 13%

Other 9%

Pollution 35%

Accidental capture 43%

Dead 95.6% (known cause 55.2%)
Recaught <1%
Resighted 3.5%

Ringing and recovery data

	<1960	60–69	70–79	80–89	90–97	Total
RINGING						
BTO ringing totals (%)	3	2	11	43	40	223,065
RECOVERIES						
BTO-ringed (%)	4	4	7	47	37	6,162
Foreign-ringed (%)	←	67	→	20	13	69

Statistical analyses

	Breeding population (sMAY–sAUG)	Wintering population (sNOV–sFEB)
Status	SHORT-DISTANCE MIGRANT* (2)	?
Age differences[NT]	Significant	—
Sex differences[(NS)*]	Not significant*	—
Regional differences	Significant[4]	—
Finding circumstances	Significant	—

Fig 4. Locations outside the breeding season of (a) 530 adult and (b) 3,391 immature Guillemots that were ringed in Britain & Ireland during the breeding season.

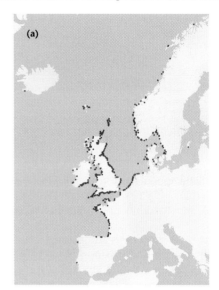

heavily biased towards areas of high fishing activity (notably southern Scandinavia and Ireland where 74% of all known-circumstance recoveries were in nets), pollution (the Netherlands, Germany and Channel Islands, 91%) and human predation (Faeroe Islands, 99%). The proportions have changed over the years. In the 1960s, 49% of all recoveries of Guillemots ringed in Shetland were shot in Norway, while 18% were in fishing nets and a further 11% were oiled; in the 1980s the

Fig 5. Monthly variation in the differences in (a) latitude and (b) longitude between ringing and recovery locations of Guillemots present in Britain & Ireland during the breeding season. Monthly medians (points) and interquartile ranges (bars) are shown.

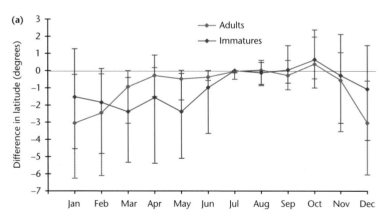

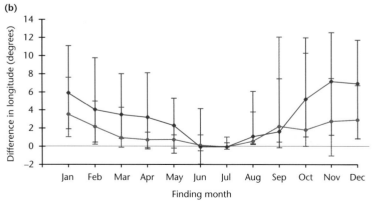

corresponding figures were 6%, 44% and 14% (Heubeck *et al* 1991). This change followed a ban on the shooting of auks in southern Norway in 1979 and an increase in Guillemots drowned in the Kattegat, possibly in response to increased Herring stocks attracting more auks to the area rather than to a change in fishing practices (Peterz & Olden 1987). A further complication is that naive birds in their first year of life are much more likely to be shot or caught in nets than adults (Birkhead 1974). Ring-recoveries exaggerate the coastal range and underestimate the true marine range of all seabirds. This is of little consequence in relatively enclosed areas such as the North and Irish Seas but Guillemots are much more numerous off west Britain & Ireland than the recoveries suggest (Stone *et al* 1995), and many of these are likely to be British or Irish birds. However, the Guillemot does avoid deep oceanic water and rarely strays off the continental shelf.

Recoveries outside the breeding season are spread from the North Cape in Norway to Gibraltar, and from southwest Iceland to the Baltic, but the main concentrations outside Britain & Ireland have been in southwest Scandinavia, the Netherlands, France and northern Spain (Fig 4). In general Guillemots were recovered to the south and east of where they had been ringed (Fig 5), but to a considerable extent this was due to so many of the recoveries coming from Canna and Great Saltee and the rather limited chances of birds being found to the north and west of these colonies. Immatures, here taken to be Guillemots less than five years old, the age when most birds start to breed, were reported from substantially further away from the ringing locations (median recovery distance 587 km, $n=3,751$) than were adults (357 km, $n=340$), and the formal statistical analyses for the winter period confirm that immatures are recovered significantly further from the colonies than adults. The rather few recoveries of birds of known sex give no indication of a marked difference in movements between the sexes.

A young Guillemot leaves the colony when still only partly grown and unable to fly, accompanied by the male parent who continues to feed it for several more weeks. During this time the male undergoes its main moult when it too is flightless. Male and chick immediately move out to the open sea to traditional areas where food is presumably predictable and abundant. One chick travelled 356 km from Shetland to off southern Scandinavia in 15 days and another from Grampian was off Northumberland (244 km) nine days after being ringed. The maximum median recovery distance by month of chicks occurs 4–5 months after fledging (693 km).

Fig 6. Recovery locations of British & Irish-ringed Guillemots in (a) August (143), (b) October (415), (c) December (563) and (d) February (830).

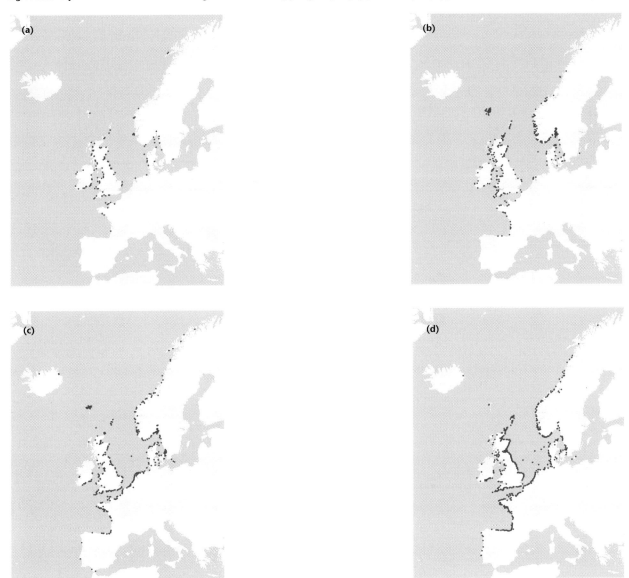

Relatively few Guillemots of any age are recovered outside Britain during August (Fig 6) but by October many birds have reached the Faeroe Islands, southwest Norway, the Kattegat and the Skagerrak, and a few from colonies in west Britain and Ireland are in the Bay of Biscay. Birds continue to move further away during the winter so that by December many recoveries come from the southern North Sea, an area which has been increasingly used by Guillemots during the last few decades (Mead 1974a, Harris *et al* 1997). February is the peak month for Guillemots to be recovered and by then many more are reported from east Britain, presumably as adults from the northeast move back towards their colonies. There is also a concentration in the Bay of Biscay of birds from western colonies, which return to their colonies much later in the winter than do east-coast Guillemots.

Mead (1974a) wondered whether birds from separate colonies might have discrete wintering areas. The present evidence is hardly compelling but the idea deserves further attention since Guillemots from the different regions do have somewhat different recovery areas (Fig 7). Birds from the north scatter most and have relatively long movements (median distance moved for birds ringed in the breeding season and recovered in winter=718 km, n=925) including most of the recoveries in north Norway, while those from the southwest move mainly southwards

into the Bay of Biscay and travel least (median=346 km, n=318). Birds from the northwest also move considerable distances (median=761 km, n=421) with recoveries of first-year birds tending to come from the North Sea whereas numbers of older individuals are reported from the English Channel or further south (Swann & Ramsay 1983). Guillemots from the northeast mostly remain within the North Sea (median= 639 km, n=166), although small numbers pass into the English Channel. Still, during the winter there is much mixing of birds from different populations, notably in the North Sea and English Channel. Any disaster at this time is likely to affect birds from many populations, and ringing can help identify the areas of origin of birds killed in oiling incidents or natural wrecks (*eg* Fig 8, see also Baillie & Mead 1982, Hudson & Mead 1984, Baillie *et al* 1994).

Since 1909, 69 foreign-ringed Guillemots have been recovered in Britain & Ireland, from the Netherlands (eight), Germany (29), the Faeroe Islands (23), Norway (five), France (three) and Russia (one). Probably all of the Dutch and some of the German birds had been oiled, cleaned and rehabilitated. Three such individuals were found breeding in a single northeast colony (Harris & Wanless 1997). The Russian bird had been ringed as a breeding adult at a colony in Murmansk and found dead in northeast England, and was presumably of the northern race *hyperborea*.

Fig 7. Locations outside the breeding season of Guillemots present in the (a) north (1,940), (b) northeast (408), (c) northwest (963) and (d) southwest (855) of Britain & Ireland during the breeding season.

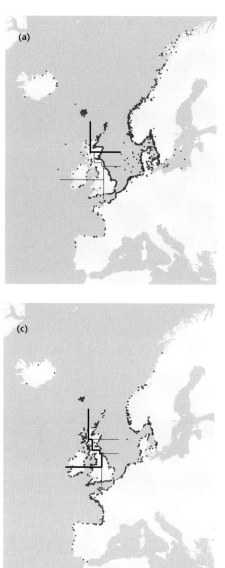

(a)

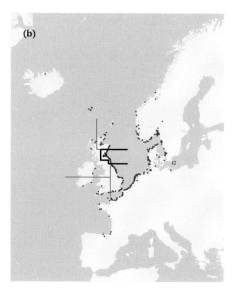

(b)

(c)

(d)

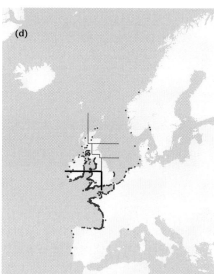

Fig 8. Ringing locations of Guillemots recovered along the south coast of England (including all of Kent and Cornwall) between January and March, summarized into squares of 0.5° latitude and 1° longitude. (Sample sizes: small circles 1–9 ringed, large circles 10–99 ringed.) A single French-ringed bird is included.

Like most seabirds, the Guillemot is highly philopatric but many in their third and fourth years of life visit other colonies. Systematic checks in one season at the Isle of May found 51 such visitors originating from most of the British and Irish colonies where substantial numbers of young had been ringed (Halley & Harris 1993). Most of these visitors were not seen again and appeared to have moved on, but other studies at this colony suggest that at least 25% of young reared there may have bred elsewhere (Harris *et al* 1996). Two chicks ringed at British colonies have been found at Hornøya (1,897 km away at 70°N in Norway) when old enough to be breeding, and singles at two Baltic colonies, while a chick ringed in the Baltic bred on Skomer in the Irish Sea. These colony interchanges span the ranges of all three Atlantic subspecies.

The usefulness of Guillemot ringing to conservation has been recognized by JNCC which has made a substantial contribution towards the cost of rings since 1981. The annual ringing total currently exceeds the numbers ringed during the first 60 years of the Ringing Scheme. We are fast approaching the time when we will be able to use ring-recoveries to monitor the movements, and even the survival, of British & Irish Guillemots on an annual basis.

Mike P Harris & Bob Swann

Razorbill
Alca torda

Razorbills are one of the four species of auks that breed on the rocky coasts of Britain and Ireland. Although they are less obvious than the noisy and gregarious Guillemot or the comical and colourful Puffin, a very significant proportion of the total world population occurs on these islands.

Globally the Razorbill is restricted to the North Atlantic and adjacent waters of the Arctic. Two races are recognized: the nominate *torda* breeds in eastern Canada, northeast USA, south and southwest Greenland, Bear Island, Jan Mayen, Norway, Sweden, Finland, Denmark and northwest Russia (around Murmansk and the White Sea). The other race, *islandica*, breeds in Iceland, the Faeroes, Britain, Ireland, northwest France, the Channel Islands and Helgoland (Germany) (*BWP*, *HBW*, Lloyd *et al* 1991). Of a total world population of approximately 500,000–700,000 birds, Britain & Ireland holds around 182,000 birds (Lloyd *et al* 1991), second in importance only to Iceland (*European Atlas*).

After the breeding season and the post-breeding moult, there is a gradual movement of Razorbills southwards. In the eastern Atlantic, the species winters south to Iberia and Morocco, and also penetrates into the western Mediterranean as far as Italy and Tunisia (*BWP*). Occasional birds reach the Canary Islands, the Azores and Western Sahara. No defined migration routes are known and it seems likely that there is a general southward movement in autumn and a northward movement in spring, which may be concentrated at such locations as the Straits of Dover and Gibraltar, or in certain weather conditions at prominent headlands. In the western Atlantic, the species winters mainly in the shallower shelf waters south to New York, occasionally to South Carolina and Florida.

The analysis of the data for this species was supported by Dúchas The Heritage Service — National Parks & Wildlife

In the breeding season, adult Razorbills concentrate in shallow coastal waters at or near the breeding colonies. The small Baltic population occurs in brackish waters but otherwise the species is fully marine. The colonies themselves are usually on high rocky cliffs, both on the mainland and islands. Nest sites are on rock or earthen ledges, in crevices, under boulders or in talus, occasionally in rabbit or Puffin burrows. In winter, the species is generally found in relatively shallow waters fairly close to shore, usually where water temperatures are 4–15°C, as in the breeding range (*BWP*).

The vast majority of Razorbills that have been recovered have been ringed at breeding colonies in Britain & Ireland (Fig 1), mainly between the second half of May and the end of July (Fig 2). Over 72% of these have been ringed as unfledged young, and the remainder as breeding adults or immatures (Fig 2). In general, there is a good correspondence between the ringing locations (Fig 1) and the main breeding areas, as indicated in the *1988–91 Atlas* and by Lloyd *et al* (1991). This is particularly so in relation to southwest England, Wales, the Isle of Man, western Scotland, Shetland and southern Ireland. Relatively few Razorbills have been ringed, however, at major breeding colonies in Orkney and eastern Scotland, or at Flamborough Head, the Cliffs of Moher, Horn Head, Rathlin Island and Lambay Island.

Over half (53%) of the recoveries from British & Irish Razorbill ringing have a known cause of death (Fig 3). Of these, pollution (mainly

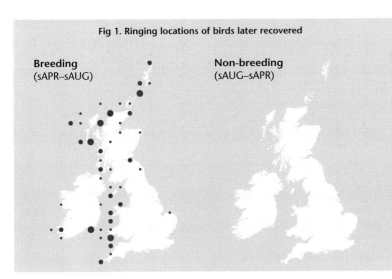

Fig 1. Ringing locations of birds later recovered

Breeding (sAPR–sAUG) Non-breeding (sAUG–sAPR)

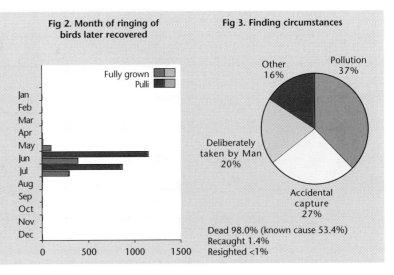

Fig 2. Month of ringing of birds later recovered

Fully grown
Pulli

Jan Feb Mar Apr May Jun Jul Aug Sep Oct Nov Dec

0 500 1000 1500

Fig 3. Finding circumstances

Other 16%
Pollution 37%
Deliberately taken by Man 20%
Accidental capture 27%

Dead 98.0% (known cause 53.4%)
Recaught 1.4%
Resighted <1%

Ringing and recovery data

	<1960	60–69	70–79	80–89	90–97	Total
RINGING						
BTO ringing totals (%)	12	10	28	30	20	86,657
RECOVERIES						
BTO-ringed (%)	9	11	24	38	19	2,824
Foreign-ringed (%)	←	31	→	62	8	26

Statistical analyses

	Breeding population (sAPR–sAUG)	Wintering population (sNOV–sFEB)
Status	LONG-DISTANCE MIGRANT* (2)	?
Age differences[NT]	Significant	—
Sex differences	Not tested	—
Regional differences	Significant[3]	—
Finding circumstances	Significant	

Fig 4. Recovery locations of Razorbills ringed in Britain & Ireland as pulli or known breeders and recovered (a) as immatures outside the breeding season (1,025), (b) as adults outside the breeding season (263), (c) as immatures during the breeding season (excluding the year of hatching, 207) and (d) as adults during the breeding season (129). Two recoveries of immatures outside the breeding season (one each from Greenland and the Azores) are not shown.

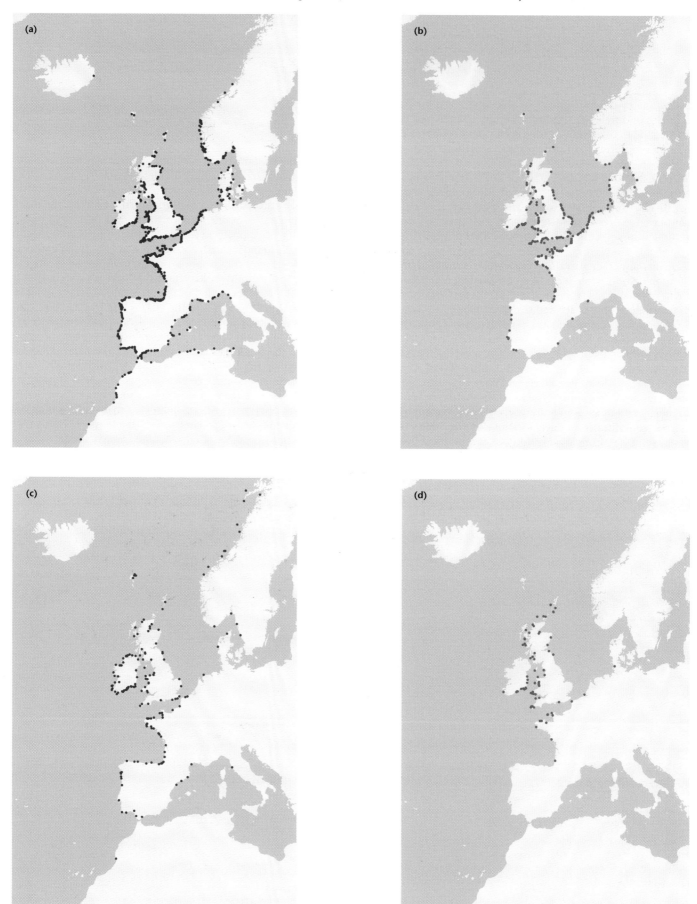

Fig 5. Movements of over 20 km and recovery locations during November–February of Razorbills ringed as pulli or known breeders in (a) southwest (505), (b) northwest (257) and (c) northern (121) Britain & Ireland.

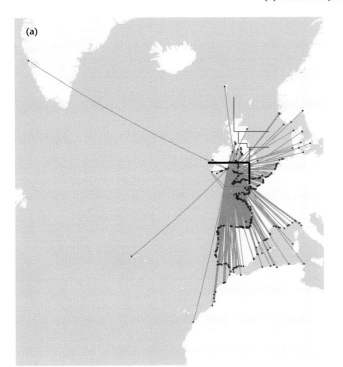
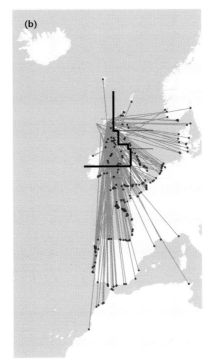
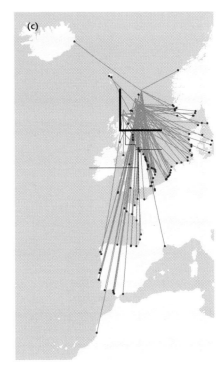

marine oil spills — both chronic and major incidents) has been the single most important cause of recovery (37%). Accidental capture (mainly entanglement and drowning in fishing nets) has also been important (27%), and deliberate taking by Man (mainly shooting in Spain, Norway, France and Denmark) accounts for a further 20% of recoveries. These recovery circumstances introduce a number of biases, so that the recovery patterns must be interpreted with caution (North 1980). For example, 119 of the 158 recoveries in Ireland (75%) and 82 of the 98 recoveries in Portugal (84%) were due to accidental capture in fishing nets. Similarly, all 17 recoveries from the Faeroes, 120 of the 206 recoveries in Spain (58%) and 75 of the 99 recoveries in Norway (76%) were of birds deliberately killed by Man. Hence, birds frequenting geographical areas free from these causes of death will be less likely to be reported if they die. It should also be borne in mind that the immature age classes may be more susceptible to some causes of death, such as accidental capture in nets or hunting (Lloyd 1974); recoveries of these age classes in areas where such mortality causes occur may overemphasize the proportion of the population that frequents that area. Previous analyses of the national ring-recovery data for Razorbill were based on around 700 recoveries up to the early 1970s (Lloyd 1974, Mead 1974a); there are now almost 3,000 recoveries available.

British & Irish Razorbills have been recovered throughout the species' range in the eastern Atlantic and western Mediterranean (Fig 4). Recoveries extend right around the coasts of Britain and Ireland, north to the Faeroes and the southwest coast of Norway (and as far north as the Lofoten Islands), and south to the Mediterranean coasts of Africa from Morocco to Tunisia, and the Atlantic coasts of northwest Africa to the Western Sahara. Outside this range there are isolated recoveries in Iceland, western Greenland and the Azores. Many of the recoveries most distant from Britain & Ireland have been of immature birds. As with most seabirds, recoveries may not indicate accurately the true marine range for Razorbills because birds that die at sea are either washed ashore at the coast (possibly at an appreciable distance from their place of death), or sink to the bottom and are never recovered (Hope Jones et al 1970). British & Irish Razorbills are likely to be more numerous off the

remote west coasts of Britain and Ireland than is suggested from recoveries (Stone et al 1995).

During late summer and early autumn, when the flightless young are completing their growth at sea (July and August) and adults are undertaking their post-breeding moult (August to October, BWP), most recoveries of British & Irish Razorbills are local to the area of ringing; the 40 or so recoveries from further afield at this time have involved mainly immature birds. By October, increasing numbers of recoveries are reported along the Atlantic coasts, mostly from southwest Norway to Iberia, and this trend increases between November and February but with fewer recoveries in the north and more in the western Mediterranean and northwest Africa. From March to June, a reverse trend is evident, though by now reduced numbers of recoveries are indicative of heavy mortality of young birds during the winter months.

There are age-related differences in the seasonal movements of Razorbills (Fig 4). The great majority of adult recoveries during the breeding season are in Britain & Ireland, with most of the remainder on adjacent coasts of mainland Europe. By contrast, immatures recovered during the breeding season have a distribution spanning all coasts from northwest Africa to northern Norway, and the western Mediterranean. Outside the breeding season, rather few adults are recovered in Iberia, Mediterranean France or further south. Immatures, on the other hand, have been recovered throughout the east Atlantic range of the species, and account for the isolated recoveries in Iceland, western Greenland and the Azores. On average, immature Razorbills have been recovered significantly further south (by 4° latitude) and west (by 2° longitude) in winter than adults. The median distance moved by immature birds between breeding and wintering locations is 974 km ($P5$–$95 = 170$–$2,305$ km, $n = 488$) but is significantly less, 684 km, for adults ($P5$–$95 = 91$–$1,514$ km, $n = 158$).

Not all British & Irish Razorbills behave in the same way during post-breeding dispersal and migration (Fig 5). The great majority of those ringed in the southwest region (mainly on Great Saltee and the Pembrokeshire islands) are recovered in western France, Iberia, the western Mediterranean and northwest Africa, with rather small numbers

Fig 6. Movements of over 20 km and recovery locations of Razorbills ringed as pulli in Britain & Ireland and recovered in a subsequent breeding season when of breeding age. There were 30:75 movements under:over 20 km but only those over 20 km are plotted.

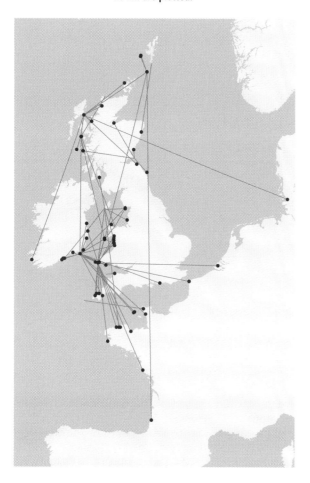

Fig 7. Movements of Razorbills ringed abroad as pulli (11, red) or other birds (7, black) and recovered in Britain & Ireland. The 8 pre-1979 foreign-ringed Razorbills (Russia 4, France 2, Finland 1 and the Netherlands 1) are not shown.

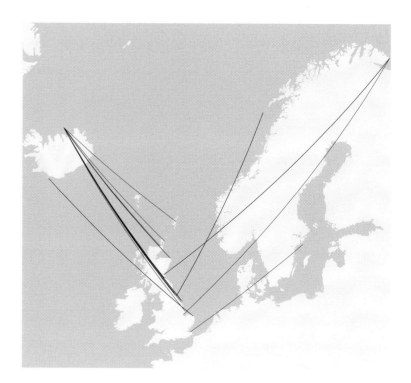

penetrating the Strait of Dover to produce diminishing numbers of recoveries from Belgium to Norway. Razorbills from the northwest region tend not to move far south, and a larger proportion occurs in the North Sea and western Norway. The birds from the north region have a strong tendency to move east to southwest Norway and Denmark, with relatively few moving south to the English Channel and the Atlantic coasts of France and Iberia. The existence of differences between breeding regions in the average wintering locations of birds were confirmed by the formal statistical analyses. Numbers of recoveries from the northeast and southeast regions (where Razorbill colonies are few and far between) are small (less than 30).

While there is much evidence that the majority of breeding adults return to the same colony, or even nest site, year after year (Lloyd 1976), and that many young birds return to their natal colony to breed, there is some indication from the ring-recoveries that a small number of breeding adults may move to other colonies (eg between Great Saltee and Skomer). For 28 birds ringed as adults of breeding age and recovered dead in a subsequent breeding season, the median distance moved was 2 km (P5–95=0–355 km). A rather large number of birds ringed as pulli have been recovered at breeding age (here defined as four years of age) at or near other breeding colonies during the breeding season (Fig 6). For 78 such recoveries of dead birds, the median distance moved was 97 km (P5–95=0–625 km).

Only 26 Razorbills ringed abroad (14 in Iceland, four in Russia, three in Norway, two in France and one each in Finland, the Netherlands and Sweden) have been recovered in Britain & Ireland (Fig 7). Most of these were ringed as pulli and recovered in Britain & Ireland outside the

breeding season (many in February). Biometric measurement of tideline corpses has confirmed the presence of nominate *torda* in Britain & Ireland; 3.9% of 228 dead Razorbills washed up in east Cork in January and February 1983 were *torda* (*Birds in Ireland*). Given the overall proportion of *torda* in the world population of about 9–12%, this suggests that the seas off Britain & Ireland might be an important wintering area for birds of the nominate race.

Many Razorbill recoveries are attributed to accidental capture, mostly as by-catch in fishing nets, and to shooting in the North Sea and the Baltic. If these anthropogenic factors, individually or collectively, are causing excessive mortality in adult Razorbills, or significantly reducing recruitment of young birds to the breeding population, there are conservation implications for either the whole population or parts of it. The advent of monofilament nets appears to have increased significantly the by-catch of diving seabirds, including Razorbills, but little is known about the overall impact of this by-catch at the population level; Mead (1989) considers that entanglement in fishing nets may be the most important artificial mortality factor for Razorbills, however.

Relatively little is known of the movements of Razorbills away from the breeding colonies. Information on the distribution of Razorbills at sea is incomplete, although much systematic survey work has been carried out on this recently, particularly in the North Sea, the Irish Sea and the Western Approaches (Stone *et al* 1995). When adult Razorbills are undergoing their post-breeding moult and chicks are completing their growth at sea they are particularly vulnerable to oil spills, and perhaps in some areas to entanglement in fishing nets. More precise identification of their moulting sites and the 'nursery' areas where young are nurtured while completing their growth in British and Irish waters will be important for the species' conservation, though it is likely that ringing can make only a minor contribution to this. New remote-tracking technologies may have a larger part to play in the future.

Oscar J Merne

Black Guillemot
Cepphus grylle

The Black Guillemot or Tystie is a distinctive seabird, especially in summer plumage, with its unmistakable white wing-patches, vermilion gape and bright red legs and feet. Its breeding range is almost circumpolar. It nests around the coasts of northeastern Canada and the USA eastwards through Greenland, Iceland, northern Europe and along the arctic coast of Russia to northernmost Alaska; it is absent only from western arctic Canada. In the northern Pacific, it overlaps marginally with a congener, the Pigeon Guillemot. Several races have been recognized. Those in Britain & Ireland are *arcticus*, which also breeds in North America, southern Greenland, western Sweden, Denmark, Murmansk and the White Sea; the nominate *grylle* breeds in the Baltic, *mandtii* in arctic North America and Canada south to *c* 58°N, northern Greenland (north of *arcticus*), Jan Mayen, Bear Island and Svalbard to eastern Siberia and northern Alaska, *faeroeensis* in the Faeroes and *islandicus* in Iceland.

The Black Guillemot is sedentary through most of its range, although northerly birds are often forced to move south by encroaching ice and to gain increased daylight hours for foraging in midwinter (*BWP*). Some individuals remain in the far north, feeding along the edges of the pack ice. A few ringed birds from Scandinavia have been recovered in winter hundreds of kilometres south of their breeding areas (Myrberget 1973). As Britain and Ireland are at the southerly limit of the species' range and not exposed to arctic winters, populations here are more sedentary than those further north.

In Britain, the Black Guillemot is a bird of rocky coasts in the north and west, breeding most commonly around Orkney and Shetland; it is

The analysis of the data for this species was supported by the Copeland Bird Observatory

also frequent on the north and west coasts of Scotland and in the Western Isles. Smaller numbers are found along the Scottish northeast coast and south on the west coast as far as Kirkcudbright. It is present in small numbers all around the rocky coasts of Ireland and the Isle of Man, and a handful of pairs breed in northwest England and northwest Wales. The species is coastal throughout the year, rarely being seen more than 2 km from land or in water greater than 40 m deep (Ewins & Kirk 1988). In winter, most birds stay within the breeding range but a few individuals are recorded annually scattered around the coasts of southern and eastern England. Generally the nest is among crevices in cliffs, boulders or coastal scree, usually well hidden in a hole. Black Guillemots do not form huge colonies like most other auks but, where there is suitable habitat, several pairs will nest in proximity.

The low ringing total for Black Guillemots relative to the other species of auks reflects not only the species' scattered distribution but also the difficulty of access to many nest sites. Most birds have been ringed in Shetland, especially Fair Isle, and Orkney, with smaller numbers at other sites in the north and west of Scotland and in northeast Ireland (Fig 1). All recoveries have been from birds ringed during the breeding season (mainly as nestlings), between May and September (Fig 2). Of about a quarter of ring-recoveries that are of known cause, a third have been due to oiling (Fig 3). Predation is also a

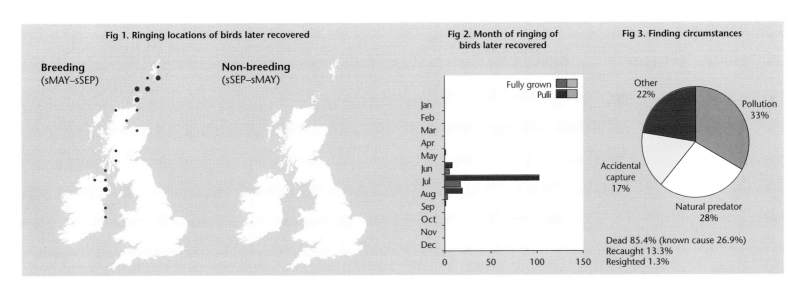

Fig 1. Ringing locations of birds later recovered

Breeding (sMAY–sSEP)   Non-breeding (sSEP–sMAY)

Fig 2. Month of ringing of birds later recovered

Fully grown
Pulli

Fig 3. Finding circumstances

Other 22%
Pollution 33%
Accidental capture 17%
Natural predator 28%

Dead 85.4% (known cause 26.9%)
Recaught 13.3%
Resighted 1.3%

Ringing and recovery data

	<1960	60–69	70–79	80–89	90–97	Total
RINGING						
BTO ringing totals (%)	5	10	20	39	26	9,370
RECOVERIES						
BTO-ringed (%)	3	8	19	36	34	157
Foreign-ringed (%)	0	50	50	0	0	2

Statistical analyses

	Breeding population (sMAY–sSEP)	Wintering population (sDEC–sMAR)
Status	SEDENTARY* (0)	?
Age differences	Not tested	—
Sex differences	Not tested	—
Regional differences	Not tested	—
Finding circumstances	Not tested	—

Fig 4. Recovery locations and movements of over 20 km for the 157 included recoveries of Black Guillemots ringed or recovered in Britain & Ireland.

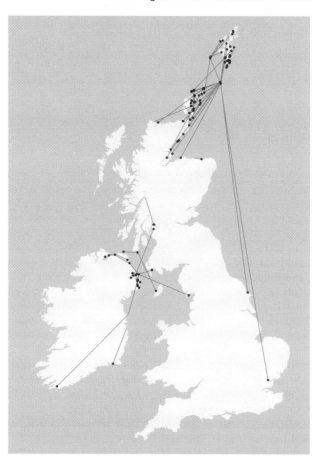

common cause of recovery (28% of recoveries of known cause); Black Guillemots are especially vulnerable to mammalian predators, such as feral cats, rats, otters and mink, during the breeding season. Great Skuas and Great Black-backed Gulls regularly take Black Guillemots in some areas. The third most important cause of recovery is drowning in nets. Being a bird of shallow inshore waters the Black Guillemot comes into contact with a range of nets set for a variety of fish species. The expansion of the fish-farming industry in much of the species' British range has led to increased mortality from this cause in the last 20 years.

After the chicks fledge, the adults gather into autumn moulting flocks, sometimes in excess of 600 birds, and remain flightless for a period of four to five weeks, mostly in September (Ewins 1988a, Ewins & Kirk 1988). After the moult, the flocks break up and the birds disperse around the coast. During the winter, many seek sheltered waters and there are only small numbers left on very exposed coasts. Black Guillemots come ashore only rarely during the winter months (Greenwood 1991).

Based on only a small number of recoveries, Mead (1974a) found no clear evidence for regular long-distance movements of British or Irish Black Guillemots. With a considerably greater number of recoveries now available, this statement still remains true and all movements of both British and Irish birds can be described as dispersive (Fig 4). Most individuals do not move far from their natal colony; for all recoveries of dead birds, the median distance moved is only 10.5 km ($P5-95=0-186$ km, $n=134$). Some birds do disperse more widely, especially juveniles in their first autumn and winter; these movements are generally in a southerly direction (Fig 4) but, from those colonies that have been studied, there are very few recorded movements longer than 50 km.

Ewins (1988b) pointed out that the proportions of birds dispersing from Fair Isle and Foula were higher than from other colonies. These two isolated islands are subject to frequent gales in the winter and, because of their relatively small size, provide little shelter in storm conditions. Birds from colonies in archipelagos such as Orkney and Shetland or from deeply indented coasts rarely need to move far to find areas of calm shallow water suitable for feeding, even in the worst conditions. Birds from Foula disperse mainly in an easterly direction to mainland Shetland, while most Fair Isle birds disperse southwards to Orkney and the northeast of mainland Scotland (Fig 4). Exceptionally, an adult from Fair Isle was recovered in Yorkshire in February and an immature in Essex in November.

No British- or Irish-ringed Black Guillemots have been recovered abroad and the only recoveries from abroad have been two immature birds ringed in Sweden and found on the east coast of England. Both were ringed on the Kattegat coast, southwest Sweden; one was a chick ringed in June and recovered, less than four weeks later, in Norfolk, and the other was also ringed in June and recovered on the Northumberland coast in the following February. These recoveries indicate that both Scottish and Scandinavian birds contribute to the reports, mainly in winter, of birds along the English east coast.

Recovery circumstances (Fig 3) probably do not reflect fully the importance to this species of oiling as a cause of mortality, as major pollution incidents have occurred in areas where few Black Guillemots have been ringed. For example, after the *Esso Bernicia* oil spill in Shetland in December 1978, 670 corpses were recovered but none of these were ringed (Heubeck & Richardson 1980); at that time, little ringing of this species had been carried out on Mainland Shetland. As a result of the *Braer* oil spill (also in Shetland, in 1993), 209 corpses were recovered, of which two were ringed. One was a local movement within the Scalloway islands and the other bird had moved 56 km southwards into the polluted area (Okill 1993). The species remains vulnerable to oil pollution throughout its range and, when high mortality of sedentary, locally breeding adults occurs, it can be some years before the local population re-establishes itself. The introduction of mammalian predators to breeding islands can have a devastating effect on breeding success, and the range expansion of predatory species like the Great Skua will bring previously unaffected breeding areas within the range of these predators. The loss of birds in fishing nets can reduce local numbers and any expansion of inshore or unregulated fisheries could seriously affect nearby populations.

The Tystie remains the least ringed of our breeding auks and, whilst studies continue on islands such as Fair Isle, most ringing effort has taken place in very restricted areas. The ringing of this species throughout a greater part of its range would add much information on birds breeding away from the regularly visited colonies and would give an insight into the pressures on populations in different areas.

David Okill

Atlantic Puffin (Puffin)

Fratercula arctica

The Puffin is well known and loved as a breeding species but, despite much recent research, very little is known of its ecology away from the breeding colonies. The species nests on some of the most spectacular islands in the colder parts of the North Atlantic and the adjacent Arctic Ocean but during the winter it is rarely seen. It then probably occurs at very low densities over vast areas of sea rarely visited by ornithologists, stretching from the Barents Sea south to the Azores and Canary Islands and from Newfoundland east to the western Mediterranean (Harris 1984a). The centre of the species' distribution is Iceland and chicks ringed on the Westman Islands have been recovered in their first winter off Newfoundland, as have similarly aged birds from Greenland, Iceland and Scotland; in contrast, older birds from the Westman Islands remain further north and east in the seas between Iceland, Greenland and Canada (Harris 1984b, Petersen 1998). Puffins from north and northeast Iceland move eastwards outside the breeding season. Puffins ringed in northern Europe have been reported off Norway and at sea west to Iceland and Greenland and in the northern North Sea (T Anker-Nilssen pers comm).

Traditionally the Puffin has been divided into three subspecies – the small southern *grabae* which breeds in the Faeroes, Britain, Ireland and southwest Norway, the larger nominate *arctica* in Iceland, the rest of Norway, east Canada, and most of Greenland, and the rare, large and massive-billed *naumanni* in the far north of Greenland and in Svalbard. There is, however, considerable doubt as to the distinctness of *grabae* and *arctica* (Moen 1991).

The bulk of recoveries come from long-term population studies, notably at the Isle of May, Farne Islands, Skokholm, Skomer and St

The analysis of the data for this species was supported by the Isle of May Bird Observatory

Kilda, and from ringing groups that have returned regularly to a few large colonies, notably the Shiant Islands and Sule Skerry (Fig 1). There is thus a good geographic spread of ringing locations apart from a lack of coverage of southwest Irish colonies. Fully grown Puffins are easily caught in large numbers using mist-nets or, along with chicks, extracted from burrows. Unfortunately birds netted in June and July (when most Puffins are ringed; Fig 2) include substantial numbers of immatures; unless a bird was caught brooding a chick or carrying fish, it cannot be assumed that it belonged to the colony where it was ringed.

Most recoveries are of birds found dead on beaches. In 26% of cases where the circumstances were reported, pollution has been stated as the cause of death, mainly oil (Fig 3). A further 24% of recoveries were due to natural environmental factors such as severe weather, 9% were shot or trapped, 6% were drowned in fishing nets and 32% were killed by natural predators (mainly by gulls at the colonies where they had been ringed). There are several biases in the recovery data. All birds reported in the Faeroes and Iceland and 76% of those in Norway were shot at sea or fleyged (flight-netted) for food at colonies during the breeding season, 63% of Irish birds (mainly immatures) were caught in fishing nets, whereas 68% of recoveries from the western shores of continental Europe between Sweden and Morocco and in the Mediterranean were due to pollution mainly outside the breeding season. Given these biases,

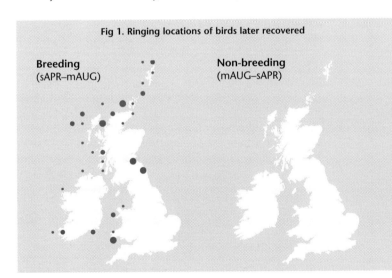

Fig 1. Ringing locations of birds later recovered

Breeding (sAPR–mAUG)

Non-breeding (mAUG–sAPR)

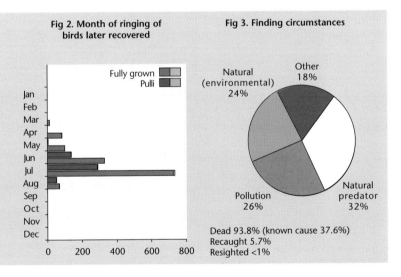

Fig 2. Month of ringing of birds later recovered

Fig 3. Finding circumstances

Dead 93.8% (known cause 37.6%)
Recaught 5.7%
Resighted <1%

Ringing and recovery data

	<1960	60–69	70–79	80–89	90–97	Total
RINGING						
BTO ringing totals (%)	7	6	31	39	18	199,248
RECOVERIES						
BTO-ringed (%)	4	9	24	44	19	1,785
Foreign-ringed (%)	←	38	→	29	33	21

Statistical analyses

	Breeding population (sAPR–mAUG)	Wintering population (sNOV–sFEB)
Status	SHORT-DISTANCE MIGRANT* (2)	?
Age differences[NT]	Significant	—
Sex differences[NT]	Not tested	—
Regional differences	Significant[4]*	—
Finding circumstances	(Not significant)	—

Fig 4. Locations outside the breeding season of Puffins that were ringed in the (a) north (37), (b) northeast (306), (c) northwest (48) and (d) southwest (38) of Britain & Ireland during the breeding season. A single bird in Greenland (from 'north') and three birds in Newfoundland (two from 'northwest' and one from 'north') are not shown.

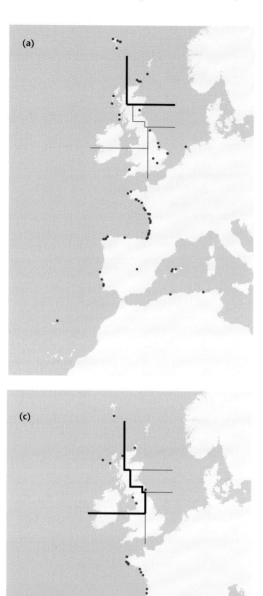

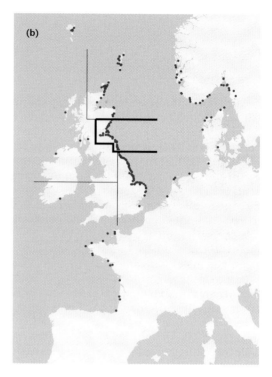

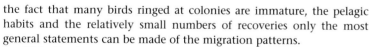

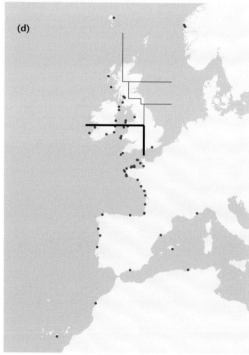

the fact that many birds ringed at colonies are immature, the pelagic habits and the relatively small numbers of recoveries only the most general statements can be made of the migration patterns.

All Puffins leave the colonies and adjacent seas by the end of August. Unlike other Atlantic auks, the Puffin has only a partial post-breeding moult and the replacement of the primaries, during which birds are flightless, is delayed until the late winter (Harris & Yule 1977). Presumably birds migrate quickly to the wintering areas but there are few relevant observations or recoveries; by winter recoveries are well dispersed. In southeast Scotland, birds return to land in late February or March but elsewhere they are not normally seen at colonies until late March or April.

Most British & Irish Puffins breed in north and west Scotland and Ireland. Individuals from colonies in the north and west disperse extremely widely with recoveries coming from central Norway south to the Canary Islands and from Newfoundland east to Italy (Fig 4). We must presume that Puffins also winter in the central North Atlantic, although there are relatively few sightings and only the remotest chance of getting a ring-recovery. Many Puffins ringed in Iceland, Norway and Greenland have been recovered in the winter off eastern Canada but it is unclear how many birds from Britain & Ireland join them. The four Scottish-ringed birds recovered off eastern Canada were spread over 50 years. All were birds in their first year of life and British & Irish adults appear not to cross the Atlantic. None of the 34 British- & Irish-ringed Puffins

Fig 5. Movements of 13 Puffins ringed abroad and later recovered in Britain & Ireland. The 8 pre-1979 foreign-ringed Puffins (France 5 and Norway 3) are not shown.

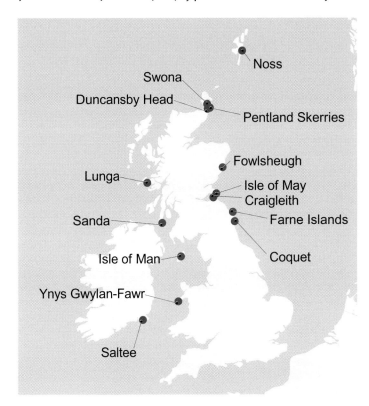

Fig 6. Colonies where Puffins colour-ringed as chicks on the Isle of May were subsequently resighted when four or more years old.
(*Source*: Harris & Wanless 1991, © Oxford University Press, 1991. Reprinted from Bird Population Studies: Relevance to Conservation and Management by C.M. Perrins, J.-D. Lebreton & G.J.M. Hirons (1991) by permission of Oxford University Press.

recovered in the Mediterranean were under a year old when reported but this might be due to chance since Carboneras (1988) saw a few first-year individuals in the Mediterranean between March and April. Puffins from colonies in northeast Britain mostly remain within the North Sea and the Skagerrak. A few do pass through the Strait of Dover and get reported from France but this appears to be a fairly recent phenomenon, perhaps associated with the increase in the numbers of Puffins breeding in eastern Britain (Harris 1984b). On average birds move further in their first winter than during subsequent winters (Harris 1984a). However the longest recorded movement, from St Kilda to northern Italy (4,100 km) was of a bird recovered in its third year of life. Analysis of the current data set for all breeding regions combined demonstrates that immatures winter significantly further south and west than adults.

A total of 21 birds ringed abroad have been reported from Britain & Ireland — 15 from Norway (including one from north of the Arctic Circle), one from the Faeroes and five from France (Fig 5).

During the second and third years of life Puffins often, perhaps even normally, visit several colonies, sometimes hundreds of kilometres apart, presumably to assess their relative merits as breeding sites. The most extreme record was a Puffin ringed on the Treshnish Isles in late June and fleyged while visiting the Westman Islands (1,087 km away) 21 days later. Once a bird has bred, usually when aged 4–6 years (Harris 1984a), it remains very faithful to its selected colony. Many seabirds are

extremely philopatric. However, a study of colour-ringed Puffin chicks marked on the Isle of May showed that, of young which survived, some 50% bred away from their natal colony (Harris & Wanless 1991). Some of these had moved considerable distances (Fig 6). A chick colour-ringed on the Farne Islands has bred on Kjør in southwest Norway, still within the accepted range of *grabae*.

A previous review of recoveries of Puffins, including those ringed in Britain & Ireland, used information up until the end of 1982 (Harris 1984b). The BTO database now has three times as many recoveries, resulting from 200,000 Puffins ringed, yet little progress has been made in elucidating the migration of this truly pelagic bird. There will doubtless be more exciting Puffin recoveries in the future but little chance that ringing will be able to add much to the understanding of Puffin migration. Recoveries have proved useful in determining the origins of Puffins killed in major oil spills and severe winter wrecks (Greenwood *et al* 1971, Harris *et al* 1991), but the available evidence suggests that Puffins rarely congregate away from the colonies so that any oil spill in the open sea is unlikely to kill more than a few individuals. The most productive use of ringing of Puffins is probably the systematic collection and analysis of long-term retrap data to monitor mortality and recruitment rates.

Mike P Harris

Rock Pigeon (Rock Dove) and Feral Pigeon
Columba livia

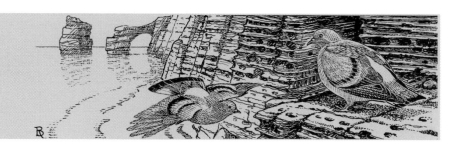

The analysis of the data for this species was supported by Brian and Pat Martin

The Rock Dove has been domesticated since at least 4500 BC (Simms 1979). Its natural range originally extended from the western Palearctic and northern Afrotropical regions to the Indian subcontinent, between 7°N and 62°N, although the exact limits are somewhat obscure due to the presence of domesticated birds (*European Atlas*). Dovecote birds were probably first brought to Britain by the Romans (Simms 1979). Hybridization between dovecote birds living wild and true Rock Doves took place freely and, by the early 1970s, wild-type Rock Doves were believed to be restricted to the Atlantic coasts of Ireland and Scotland (*1968–72 Atlas*). These wild populations have been further diluted by birds showing characters of feral forms, and the genetic integrity of Rock Doves in all but the most isolated colonies is in doubt (*1988–91 Atlas*). Large populations of Feral Pigeons (domesticated forms having reverted to life in the wild) breed in all the major urban and industrial areas of Britain and Ireland. These are often indistinguishable from semicaptive dovecote birds or racing pigeons, however, and the presence of colour-ringed racing pigeons in Feral Pigeon flocks indicates a continuing genetic input from domesticated birds. World-wide, the Feral Pigeon now occurs almost everywhere Man has penetrated, except the polar regions (*BWP*). The race of the original Rock Dove which bred in western and southern Europe is the nominate *livia*, while at least eight other races have been described from elsewhere.

The homing ability of domesticated birds is well recognized, and they have been used in many orientation experiments (*eg* Holland *et al* 2000). However, free-living populations of both the Rock Dove and Feral Pigeon are remarkably sedentary throughout their range. Local movements do take place and are said to be most marked in seasonally arid regions (*BWP*). An apparent small passage has been detected at bird observatories on Fair Isle (*Birds in Scotland*) and at Cape Clear (Sharrock 1973, *Birds in Ireland*), although these may be no more than local movements. In the wild, Rock Doves live mainly on coastal cliffs and islands throughout the year, where they nest and roost in caves. Coastal breeders forage in a narrow belt of often marginally cultivated land behind clifftops (Murton & Westwood 1966). Feral Pigeons nest and roost communally in buildings and other man-made structures but many also live on inland and coastal cliffs.

There are no foreign recoveries of wild Rock Doves ringed in Britain & Ireland, and no recoveries in Britain or Ireland from ringing abroad. The distribution of the ringing sites of birds recovered largely reflects the distribution of the wild form in Britain, although Ireland is under-represented (Fig 1). There, only 18 birds were ringed during 1975–97 (Forsyth 1998). Nearly two-thirds of Rock Dove recoveries have been of birds ringed as nestlings, and most of the fully grown birds were ringed between May and July (Fig 2). Feral Pigeons are not normally ringed because many are indistinguishable from semicaptive dovecote birds and racing pigeons. A total of 42% of all recoveries (which may include some Feral Pigeons) had a known cause of death and 53% of these were of birds deliberately taken by Man, while predators took another 40% (Fig 3).

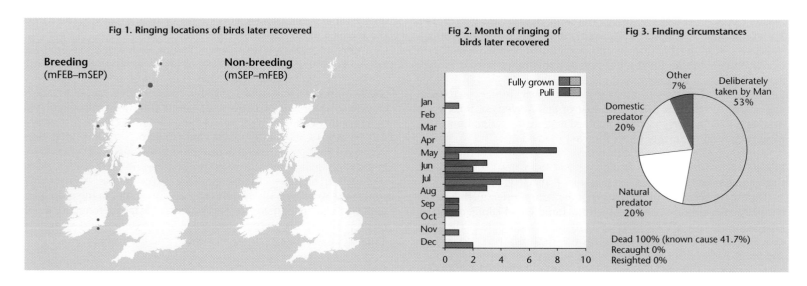

Fig 1. Ringing locations of birds later recovered

Breeding (mFEB–mSEP)

Non-breeding (mSEP–mFEB)

Fig 2. Month of ringing of birds later recovered

Fully grown
Pulli

Fig 3. Finding circumstances

Other 7%
Deliberately taken by Man 53%
Domestic predator 20%
Natural predator 20%

Dead 100% (known cause 41.7%)
Recaught 0%
Resighted 0%

Ringing and recovery data

	<1960	60–69	70–79	80–89	90–97	Total
RINGING						
BTO ringing totals (%)	10	2	13	29	46	1,208
RECOVERIES						
BTO-ringed (%)	14	3	19	28	36	36
Foreign-ringed (%)	0	0	0	0	0	0

Statistical analyses

	Breeding population (mFEB–mSEP)	Wintering population (sNOV–sJAN)
Status	[SEDENTARY]	[SEDENTARY]
Age differences	Not tested	Not tested
Sex differences	Not tested	Not tested
Regional differences	Not tested	Not tested
Finding circumstances	Not tested	Not tested

Fig 4. Recovery locations and movements of over 20 km for the 36 included recoveries of Rock Doves ringed or recovered in Britain & Ireland.

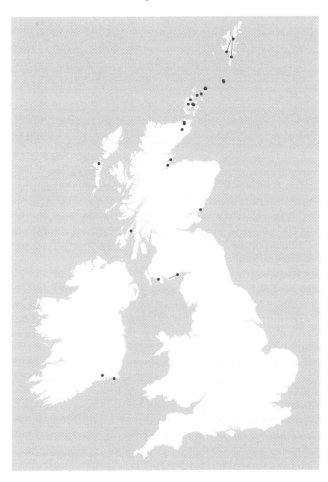

Nearly 87% of all recoveries were of birds ringed in the breeding season and 55% of these were recovered during the breeding season.

Despite the small sample of recoveries, it is clear that Rock Doves in Britain & Ireland are highly sedentary (Fig 4). The median distance between ringing and recovery of all Rock Doves found dead was only 500 m. However, two birds ringed in the breeding season and recovered in the winter had moved 1 km and 28 km and another two recovered in the spring had moved 3 km and 11 km. A single bird ringed in spring and recovered in autumn travelled 19 km while one ringed in winter and recovered in spring had travelled 11 km. Seven recoveries show a median natal dispersal of less than 1 km, while three recoveries show a median breeding dispersal of 17 km. There are too few data to discuss seasonal or regional patterns of recovery.

Feral Pigeons living in Salford Dock, Manchester, remained throughout the year, often in the same building, with juveniles showing a slightly greater tendency to disperse than adults. Sightings of wing-tagged birds showed that most (86%), of all ages, were found within 90 m of the ringing site and nearly all within 1 km. The longest distance recorded was 6.4 km (Murton *et al* 1972, 1974). In the Czech Republic, a feral population roosted in Brno and fed by day on surrounding farmland with regular movements of 6–8 km. Birds rarely moved over 18 km and only exceptionally up to 30 km (Havlin 1979).

Very little is known about the biology of the Rock Dove in Britain or Ireland and, following hybridization with domesticated forms, it may be too late to study genetically pure birds. On the other hand, the Feral Pigeon is very common, yet despite its familiarity there is still much to be learned about many aspects of its biology in Britain & Ireland, although there are more studies from abroad (Haag-Wackernagel 1995, Johnson & Janiga 1995). It is a serious pest (Feare 1990) with an apparently growing population in urban and industrial areas, accompanied by a spread to more rural areas (*1968–72 Atlas, 1988–91 Atlas*). There is much scope for research on population dynamics and movements using marking techniques other than ringing, particularly in Ireland, where less is known about the species than elsewhere.

Patrick Smiddy

Stock Pigeon (Stock Dove)

Columba oenas

The Stock Dove in Britain & Ireland is a sedentary bird, although this feature is not typical of the species elsewhere. The breeding range of the nominate race *oenas* extends from Morocco north and east across Europe to the Caspian Sea and into western Siberia. Birds in western Europe, around the Mediterranean Sea and in Asia Minor are largely resident, but those breeding elsewhere are migratory, to an extent dependent on the severity of winter conditions (*BWP*). Stock Doves from Fennoscandia and eastern Europe are totally migratory; they and others from the partially migratory populations in central Europe follow a southwesterly route to their wintering quarters, which are located around the western Mediterranean, especially in central Spain (*European Atlas*). One Ukrainian bird was recovered from Greece in December but most migrants from the former Soviet Union winter south of the Caucasus; those wintering in Asia Minor may occur alongside eastern European breeders in addition to local breeders (*BWP*). The only other race, *yarkandensis*, breeds in central Asia and is thought to move southwest for the winter.

Stock Doves occur throughout Britain except in the far north, and in Ireland are concentrated mainly in the southeast (*1988–91 Atlas*). Their current distribution represents an almost complete recovery following a 1960s ban on organochlorine seed dressings, which caused a widespread decline in numbers and a westward range contraction during the 1950s (O'Connor & Mead 1984). Because they nest mainly in tree-holes, they are found primarily in parkland, forest edges and wooded farmland during the breeding season. In winter, they can occur on any suitable foraging area, especially cereal stubbles and weedy arable fields, with

The analysis of the data for this species was supported by Peter Wilkinson

the greatest density on mixed farmland (*Winter Atlas*). They also occur in coastal areas, where they nest on cliffs and in rabbit burrows; however, many such areas were abandoned between the two Atlas surveys (*1988–91 Atlas*), possibly as a consequence of the expansion of the Peregrine (O'Connor & Mead 1984), or maybe competition from Feral Pigeons, whose population increased between the *1968–72 Atlas* and the *1988–91 Atlas*.

The distribution of ringing locations for Stock Doves subsequently recovered broadly reflects the breeding distribution in Britain & Ireland (Fig 1). Only 17 recoveries were of Stock Doves ringed in Ireland, however, where they occur at relatively low density; all except one were ringed in Northern Ireland. Four-fifths of the recoveries were from birds ringed as chicks. Over three-quarters of the remaining fully grown Stock Doves were caught during the main breeding period April–September (Fig 2), implying either that ringing effort is concentrated on this time, or that the doves are more difficult to catch in winter.

Traditionally, the Stock Dove has been a quarry species in the same way as the Woodpigeon. Its status changed under the Wildlife & Countryside Act (1981), and it has been protected since the Act came into force on 1 October 1982. This change is reflected in the causes of recovery: between 1965 and 1982, 70% of ring-recoveries were from birds reported as shot, whereas after 1982 the proportion of dead birds

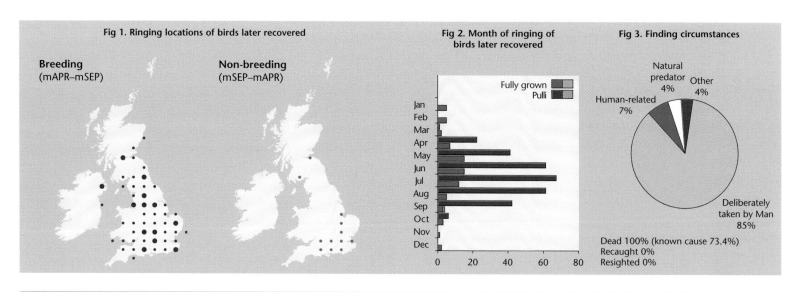

Fig 1. Ringing locations of birds later recovered

Breeding (mAPR–mSEP)

Non-breeding (mSEP–mAPR)

Fig 2. Month of ringing of birds later recovered

Fully grown
Pulli

Fig 3. Finding circumstances

Natural predator 4%
Other 4%
Human-related 7%
Deliberately taken by Man 85%

Dead 100% (known cause 73.4%)
Recaught 0%
Resighted 0%

Ringing and recovery data

	<1960	60–69	70–79	80–89	90–97	Total
RINGING						
BTO ringing totals (%)	15	7	16	28	34	12,999
RECOVERIES						
BTO-ringed (%)	34	16	19	18	13	376
Foreign-ringed (%)	←	67	→	33	0	3

Statistical analyses

	Breeding population (mAPR–mSEP)	Wintering population (mNOV–sMAR)
Status	SEDENTARY (0)	[SEDENTARY]
Age differences[NT]	Not significant*	Not tested
Sex differences	Not tested	Not tested
Regional differences	Not tested	Not tested
Finding circumstances	Not significant*	Not tested

Fig 4. Recovery locations and movements of over 20 km for the 377 included recoveries of Stock Doves ringed or recovered in Britain & Ireland. The two pre-1979 foreign-ringed Stock Doves (from Finland and the Netherlands) are not shown.

have dropped after 1982, by about a third, so that the data may not give a good indication of recent changes. All three recoveries of British-ringed Stock Doves abroad were taken by Man.

The recoveries demonstrate the short distances moved by Stock Doves; for all dead recoveries, the median distance moved is just 6 km ($P5$–95=0–48 km). As observed by Murton (1966) and O'Connor & Mead (1984), Stock Doves in Britain & Ireland are very sedentary. The same authors also pointed out that there was little difference between the average distances moved by young birds and by adults. There is no evidence of a directional component in any of the movements at different times of year, so that the movements are typical of dispersal rather than migration. Only four recoveries of Stock Doves ringed in Britain indicate movements of over 200 km: one within Britain, two to France and one to Spain (Fig 4). All were birds ringed as nestlings, and all but one were recovered in their first autumn.

In the past, large flights of Stock Doves have been reported through England in the autumn, probably as drift movements from the normal migratory routes from Fennoscandia and other countries east of Britain (Denby Wilkinson 1950, des Forges & Harber 1963, Murton 1966). The flights involved flocks of 20–150 birds, and were often associated with Woodpigeon movements. More recently, evidence of immigration has been sparser (Crawley 1996), suggesting that the passage is now much reduced. For instance, although regular diurnal movements have been noted in northeast Hampshire (Clark & Eyre 1993) and along the Norfolk coast (Taylor *et al* 1999) in late autumn and in spring, such movements rarely exceed 50 birds a day. The reduction in numbers of passage birds may be explained by marked declines in numbers of Stock Doves breeding in Fennoscandian countries (Koskimies 1989, Bergström *et al* 1992, Viker 1994, Anon 1997). Only three foreign-ringed nestlings have been recovered in Britain: one from Utrecht, the Netherlands, recovered near Bletchley, Buckinghamshire, in February; one from Tyrväntö, Finland, recovered at Ormesby, Norfolk, in March; and one from Schoten, Belgium, recovered at Alkham, Kent, in January (Fig 4). The small number, origins and timings are all consistent with drift migration. Curiously, Stock Doves in North Norfolk, common in the summer, appear to be fairly sparse in winter before a noticeable reappearance of flocks in February–April (Bloomfield & McCallum 1999). Where Norfolk Stock Doves spend the winter and to what extent the spring passage consists of continental birds remain unknown.

Following the recovery in numbers since the 1960s, densities of Stock Doves in Britain are still increasing slowly, and the species' conservation status is good (Aebischer 1995b). The situation in Ireland is of greater concern, given that the Stock Dove's Irish range contracted by a third between the *1968–72 Atlas* and 1988–91 (*1988–91 Atlas*). More ringing of Stock Doves in the southeast of Ireland would greatly improve the representativeness of the Irish ring-recovery data and, eventually, allow the population dynamics of Irish Stock Doves to be investigated. Likewise, targeted ringing of Norfolk Stock Doves in the spring and summer would help elucidate the movements of local breeders and the origins of passage birds.

Nicholas J Aebischer

reported as shot (probably in mistake for Woodpigeons) fell to 34% (Aebischer 1995b). The remaining recoveries for which there was a known cause were largely human-related (Fig 3). As a result of the change in legislation, it is likely therefore that the recovery rate would

Common Wood Pigeon (Woodpigeon)

Columba palumbus

The Woodpigeon is common throughout Britain & Ireland but reaches its highest densities in regions of productive arable land. For British farmers, it is a major bird pest feeding on a wide range of arable crops; in particular it has been an important cause of farmers ceasing to grow oilseed rape (Lane 1984). While coastal movements occur, especially in late autumn and spring, and Woodpigeons gather into large flocks to roost or feed, this species is essentially sedentary in Britain & Ireland. This is in contrast to the larger migratory movements shown by some continental Woodpigeons (Murton & Ridpath 1962). The sedentary nature of the British & Irish population increases the agricultural problems created by this species, since their all-year presence renders many crops vulnerable.

The Woodpigeon's breeding range is large; extending from western Siberia, eastern Turkey and Iraq in the east to the Faeroes in the west, and from North Africa in the south to Fennoscandia in the north. The species is largely migratory in western Siberia and in northern and eastern Europe. The scale of movements declines towards the west and south of the range, such that Woodpigeons are partially migratory in most of Europe and resident in countries such as Britain, Ireland and Morocco (*BWP*). During October, Scandinavian and Baltic birds move through Denmark, the Netherlands and France (*eg* Lebreton 1969), some continuing southwest through the western end of the Pyrenees where they have been commercially trapped in large numbers for food. For many, their goal is the acorn harvest in the forests of northwest Spain. Similar Woodpigeon movements have been described through the Swiss Alps into central Italy (*eg* Gatter *et al* 1990). Ring-recoveries have shown

The analysis of the data for this species was supported by the Central Science Laboratory

that some of the Woodpigeons of Denmark, the Netherlands, north Germany, Poland and western Russia also move southwest in autumn but that a greater proportion of these populations is sedentary, travelling large distances only in response to bad weather. Short-distance ('commuting') movements from nests in predator-free urban areas to fields have been recorded in Poland (Tomiałojć 1999).

The major ringing locations of recoveries of Woodpigeons reflect the distribution of the species, at least in Britain (Fig 1). The majority of Woodpigeon ringing is of pulli during summer; most of those birds ringed as adults are caught during the winter months (Fig 2). Ninety-seven percent of all farmers shoot Woodpigeons to protect crops (Smith *et al* 1995), and it is not surprising, therefore, that most Woodpigeon recoveries are of shot birds (Fig 3). The likelihood of ring-recovery from shot birds may be higher than that from Woodpigeons dying from, for example, predation or disease. However, Inglis *et al* (1997) found no significant differences between survival rates estimated from shot birds and those from birds that had died from all other known causes.

As the Woodpigeon is dependent upon a number of crops for its winter food supply, its movements and numbers have varied markedly with changes in agricultural practice (Murton *et al* 1963, 1964b, Inglis *et al* 1990, 1997). In the 1960s, in the good arable regions of Britain, spring-sown barley was the major crop with autumn-sown wheat

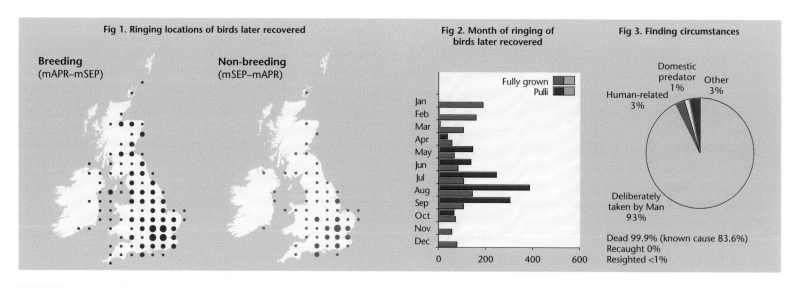

Fig 1. Ringing locations of birds later recovered

Breeding (mAPR–mSEP)

Non-breeding (mSEP–mAPR)

Fig 2. Month of ringing of birds later recovered

Fully grown
Pulli

Fig 3. Finding circumstances

Domestic predator 1%
Other 3%
Human-related 3%
Deliberately taken by Man 93%

Dead 99.9% (known cause 83.6%)
Recaught 0%
Resighted <1%

Ringing and recovery data

	<1960	60–69	70–79	80–89	90–97	Total
RINGING						
BTO ringing totals (%)	21	22	17	20	19	34,372
RECOVERIES						
BTO-ringed (%)	21	38	18	16	8	2,543
Foreign-ringed (%)	←	88	→	12	0	8

Statistical analyses

	Breeding population (mAPR–mSEP)	Wintering population (mNOV–sMAR)
Status	SEDENTARY (0)	SEDENTARY
Age differences[NT]	Significant*	Not significant*
Sex differences	Not tested	Not tested
Regional differences	Significant[4]	Not tested
Finding circumstances	Not significant	Not significant*

414

Fig 4. Variation in the distances moved by juvenile Woodpigeons with time after ringing as pulli. Medians for 30-day periods (points) and interquartile ranges (bars) are shown.

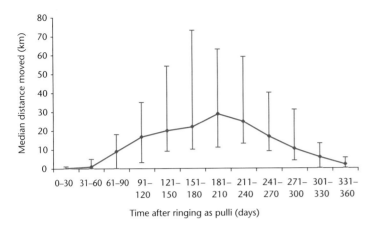

Fig 5. Recovery locations and movements of over 20 km for the 2,544 included recoveries of Woodpigeons ringed or recovered in Britain & Ireland.

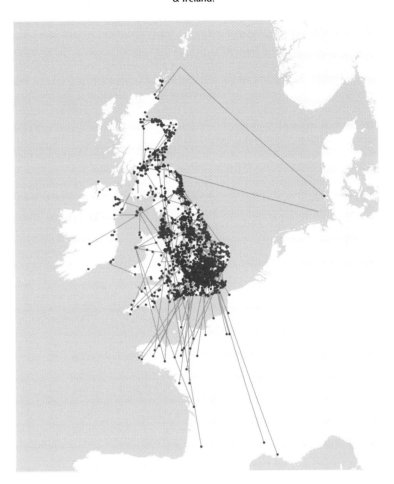

occupying most of the remaining area. Throughout the 1970s, winter wheat was increasingly grown and autumn-sown barley replaced spring-sown varieties. Also, the area of clover ley was reduced markedly. During the mid-1970s, oilseed rape was introduced and the area devoted to this crop in Britain increased steeply throughout the 1980s, before levelling off at around 400,000 ha. Prior to the introduction of oilseed rape, the number of Woodpigeons wintering in a given locality was largely controlled by two crops. The area of cereal sowings determined how many Woodpigeons stayed in the area through December, while the population size over the remaining winter months was correlated with the availability of clover (Murton *et al* 1963, Inglis *et al* 1990). As clover leys were increasingly ploughed to increase the area of autumn-sown cereals, the numbers of Woodpigeons fell markedly. The introduction of oilseed rape provided the species with a winter food that was more abundant than clover had been, as easy to forage upon, and was seldom covered by snow. The area of oilseed rape, therefore, came to determine the size and movement patterns of Woodpigeon populations throughout the winter: as the area devoted to this crop increased, so did the numbers of Woodpigeons (Inglis *et al* 1990, 1997).

The sedentary nature of the British & Irish Woodpigeon is clearly shown by the fact that the median distance between ringing and recovery (for all birds recovered dead) is just 5 km. However, this simple statistic hides a more complex pattern of movement determined by agricultural practice rather than geographical location. Inglis *et al* (1997) analysed the relationship between arable crops and Woodpigeon movements in Britain. They allocated birds to poor or good arable counties dependent upon their initial ringing location: information from the MAFF Agricultural Census Surveys was used to categorize counties into poor and good areas for oilseed rape and cereal production. Records were also divided into pre-1970, before the introduction of oilseed rape into Britain, and post-1980, after the spread of this crop. After the introduction of oilseed rape, the mean distance between ringing and recovery sites increased by 55% for birds ringed in poor arable areas but fell by 37% for birds ringed in the good areas. Inglis *et al* (1997) suggest that after the introduction of this highly attractive crop, the birds in poor arable areas moved further afield in order to feed on the few oilseed rape fields present. In the good arable areas before the growing of oilseed rape, Woodpigeons fed throughout the winter on food sources that became depleted (*eg* cereal stubbles and sowings) and this necessitated frequent movement between suitable fields. After the advent of oilseed rape, Woodpigeons in these good arable areas had an abundant and reliable source of food which enabled a more sedentary behaviour pattern to be adopted.

The ring-recoveries also reveal differences in movement patterns between birds ringed as immatures and as adults. The median distance between ringing and recovery sites is 11 km for birds both ringed and

recovered as immatures, and 5 km for those ringed as immatures and recovered as adults, but only 2 km for birds both ringed and recovered as adults. Over a 12-month period, the median dispersal distances for birds ringed as pulli are initially small but then show a marked increase before falling again towards the end of the period (Fig 4). These data support the finding from a study involving radio-tagged Woodpigeons that newly fledged birds initially remain in their natal area but then depart over the winter before returning the following spring to breed (Inglis *et al* pers comm). This scale of winter movement is not seen in subsequent years, with the birds overwintering in the general locality of their first breeding attempts.

There has been much debate concerning the arrival of foreign Woodpigeons in Britain (*eg* Denby Wilkinson 1950) and the emigration of British birds to the Continent (*eg* Lack & Ridpath 1955). The evidence has largely been based upon direct sightings of birds either coming in from the sea onto the east coast of England (*eg* Lack 1954a), or leaving the south coast of England and departing southwards over the English Channel (*eg* Lack & Ridpath 1955). Murton & Ridpath (1962) argued that most of these observations resulted from Woodpigeons 'coasting and occasionally making sallies for short distances out to sea and then returning'. They concluded that only a small number of British Woodpigeons actually emigrate to the Continent and, similarly, that very few foreign birds reach these shores during their autumn migration. Murton (1965) makes the point that while it would be impossible to stand in the Pyrenees in autumn and not see migrating flocks of Woodpigeons, 'in contrast it is possible to stand on the English coast for a month and not see a Woodpigeon, whereas migrating flocks of Starlings, Chaffinches and Skylarks will be almost a daily occurrence'.

More systematic watching of the coast in recent decades has revealed annual movements in late autumn, westward along the North Norfolk coast, but southward along the coasts of Yorkshire and Suffolk (Mather 1986, Taylor *et al* 1999). The numbers involved vary greatly from year to year. In 1994, an exceptional total of 88,397 birds was logged flying south at Landguard Point in Suffolk between 10 October and 25 November, with 30,610 birds on 2 November alone (Rafe 1996). Apparently exhausted birds roost diurnally on cranes and gantries at this site during passage times. It is likely that the majority of these birds are from Fennoscandia and heading for France or Iberia, and are not in Britain long enough either to be ringed or for any rings they are carrying to be recovered. If on the other hand they are British, then the ringing data are greatly underestimating the scale of movement of British-bred birds.

Certainly the ring-recovery data contain no evidence of widespread immigration of Woodpigeon into Britain: indeed, despite many long-distance recoveries on the Continent, just eight foreign birds, ringed in the Netherlands (three), Germany (two), Denmark, Norway and Belgium, have been recovered here. Similarly these data provide no evidence of large-scale emigration of Woodpigeons to the Continent. Of 2,543 recoveries of Woodpigeons ringed in Britain & Ireland only 1% was recovered overseas: 28 were recovered in France and one in Germany (Fig 5).

The importance of the Woodpigeon as an agricultural pest has resulted in a number of studies of this species, some involving analyses of movement patterns. However, an emphasis stemming from concerns over levels of crop damage has left gaps in our knowledge. The current ringing data do not allow us to interpret the large-scale coastal movements that have recently been observed: this may require new approaches to ringing programmes in Fennoscandia. Furthermore, we need additional ringing of British and particularly Irish birds if we are to understand the movements of Woodpigeons in the upland areas and urban habitats of Britain & Ireland.

Ian R Inglis

Eurasian Collared Dove (Collared Dove)

Streptopelia decaocto

The identity of the small pinkish-coloured doves that had suddenly started visiting chicken runs in Norfolk did not become common knowledge until James Fisher broadcast a radio programme about Collared Doves, which included recordings of their distinctive calls, in the late 1950s. The first Collared Dove recorded in Britain was seen in Lincolnshire in 1952 (May & Fisher 1953). Others quickly followed and in 1955 at least one pair bred at West Runton in Norfolk (Richardson *et al* 1957). By 1963, the Collared Dove was firmly established as a common addition to the British avifauna. Its establishment in Ireland followed rapidly, with single pairs first breeding in 1959 near Dublin and close to Galway City. By 1964, the species was breeding in 15 of the 18 counties in which it had been recorded (*Birds in Ireland*).

The nominate race of the Collared Dove *decaocto* was originally centred on northern India. It was introduced to China, Korea and Japan (*BWP*). Three races have been described around the fringes of the original core area: *stolickzae* in southeast Kazakhstan and eastwards to western China, *intercedens* in southern India and Sri Lanka, and *xanthocyclus* in northwest Myanmar. The range expansion performed by *decaocto* across Europe from the Balkans has been extraordinary (*European Atlas*), proceeding at *c* 44 km/year (Hengeveld & van den Bosch 1991).

In southwest Europe, it is now occupying the Iberian Peninsula and spreading into North Africa, while in the east it has crossed the Urals and is moving into Siberia (Nowak 1989). Elsewhere it has expanded into Kazakhstan and Turkmenistan and south into Egypt and northern Saudi Arabia. Although they bred in Iceland in 1971, only 24 birds had been recorded there up to the end of 1996 and the species has failed to

The analysis of the data for this species is dedicated to the memory of Leslie Kent, who loved birds

become established there (Petursson & Thrainsson 1999, O K Nielsen pers comm). Ship-assistance has taken individuals close to the North American continent (P W Smith 1987), and a Collared Dove was recorded at Cape May in 1987 (Lehman 1988), but the colonization of North America that is now taking place appears to result from the release of around 50 birds of Dutch origin in the Bahamas in 1974 (P W Smith 1987). A release in the French Antilles in 1976 has not so far spread as far north as the Bahamas birds (Barre *et al* 1997) and is not thought to be involved in the spread into Florida. North American Collared Doves have since spread in a northwesterly direction and have already been recorded in North Carolina (Le Grand & Brinkley 1996) and Alabama (Drennan 1997).

While its abundance within Britain almost exactly mirrors that of the human population (*1988–91 Atlas*) the Collared Dove is as familiar in remote locations such as Benbecula, where there are few trees, as it is in North Norfolk, one of its earliest breeding areas. Although closely associated with human habitation and activity, its prime habitat appears to be the well-treed suburban areas rather than city centres, which are the province of Feral Pigeons. It is also present at lower densities in rural areas, although always near to habitation or farms. It has occupied a niche apparently close to that used by House Sparrows, although its requirement for nest sites is entirely different. Large concentrations of

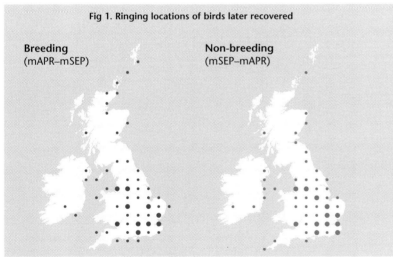

Fig 1. Ringing locations of birds later recovered

Breeding (mAPR–mSEP)

Non-breeding (mSEP–mAPR)

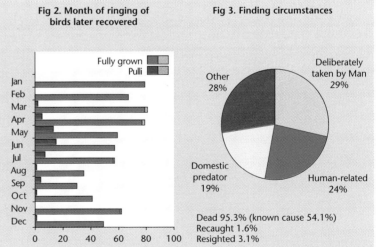

Fig 2. Month of ringing of birds later recovered

Fig 3. Finding circumstances

Dead 95.3% (known cause 54.1%)
Recaught 1.6%
Resighted 3.1%

Ringing and recovery data

	<1960	60–69	70–79	80–89	90–97	Total
RINGING						
BTO ringing totals (%)	0	10	37	27	26	24,022
RECOVERIES						
BTO-ringed (%)	0	17	39	28	16	739
Foreign-ringed (%)	←	88	→	10	2	50

Statistical analyses

	Breeding population (mAPR–mSEP)	Wintering population (mNOV–sMAR)
Status	SEDENTARY* (0)	SEDENTARY
Age differences[NT]	Not tested	Not significant*
Sex differences	Not tested	Not tested
Regional differences	Not tested	Not tested
Finding circumstances	Not tested	Not significant*

Table 1. Summary movement statistics for all seasonally accurate dead recoveries of Collared Doves ringed in Britain & Ireland by five-year periods with all ages combined.

	Sample	Median distance (km)	P5–95 (km)	Mean direction for movements of >20km only (degrees)	Standard error (degrees)
1960–64	28	4	0–419	221.7	18.4
1965–69	136	7	0–610	285.3	10.6
1970–74	152	7.5	0–400	305.4	12.6
1975–79	132	1.5	0–275	264.5	32.6
1980–84	100	2	0–163	309.6	26.3
1985–89	60	2	0–216.5	270.5	30.9
1990–94	61	0	0–233	301.4	25.6
1995–97	35	0	0–13	*	*

* Indicates no movements of greater than 20 km.

Collared Doves are associated with farming activities which involve the handling and spillage of animal feedstuffs, especially grain, such as at grain stores, feed mills and large-scale chicken units. In the early days of its arrival in Britain, large numbers gathered in late summer and autumn on harvested fields near to urban areas. This habit is less commonly seen now, possibly as a result of more efficient harvesting resulting in less spillage.

Ringing effort within Britain & Ireland has been neither constant nor evenly spread (Fig 1). Although easily cage-trapped in large numbers at sites where it concentrates, it is not easily mist-netted, the preferred catching method for most ringers. A high proportion of those ringed have been caught in the southern half of England, by Dungeness Bird Observatory and a few specialist groups at Manea in Cambridgeshire, Avonmouth near Bristol, and Twyford in Hampshire, and by Ministry of Agriculture researchers at Ellesmere Port in Cheshire, Old Trafford in Manchester and Soham in Cambridgeshire. Elsewhere, infrequent ringing reflects the lower density of ringers and the opportunistic nature of their trapping of the species.

Collared Doves have been recorded breeding in all months, but most birds are in reproductive condition from March until September (Coombs *et al* 1981). This is reflected in Fig 2, which shows recoveries of Collared Doves ringed as pulli in all months except November, January and February. Fewer fully grown Collared Doves have been ringed in August, September and October, when many move out of the suburbs to exploit spilled grain in harvested cereal fields and around farms (*BWP*).

There are fewer recoveries of Collared Doves than might be expected for what is a relatively large bird which is commensal with people. Finding circumstances have been reported for over half of those found dead, and of these, nearly three-quarters were directly related to human activity (Fig 3). It is noteworthy that, although the species was legally protected in Scotland until 1967, and in England and Wales until 1977, almost a third of recoveries of known circumstance were of birds shot or hunted. A further 19% of recoveries of known circumstance were the result of domestic predators, usually cats, again reflecting the species' association with human habitation.

Fig 4. Recovery locations and movements of over 20 km of Collared Doves ringed in Britain & Ireland and recovered (a) before 1980 (416) and (b) 1980–97 (323). Birds ringed and recovered in all seasons, and of all age classes, are included.

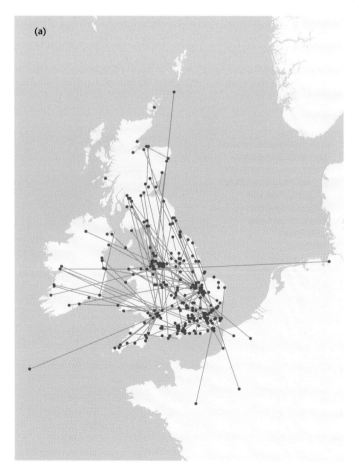

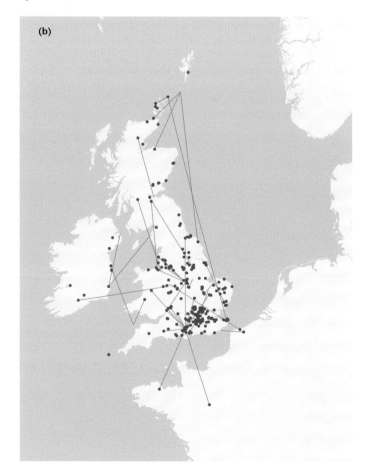

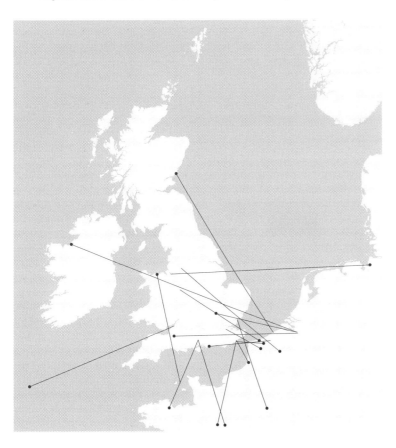

Analysis of all recoveries from Collared Doves ringed in Britain & Ireland shows that their dispersal distances have reduced since the mid-1970s (Table 1); the median distance moved between 1965 and 1979 was significantly greater at 6 km ($P5$–95=0–419 km, n=420) than that of 1 km ($P5$–95=0–203 km, n=284) for the periods 1960–64 and 1980–97 combined. While Collared Doves have been recorded dispersing in all compass directions, the mean vector has consistently been in a northwesterly or westerly direction (Fig 4); as shown by the standard errors, however, this tendency was most focused in the period 1965–74 (Table 1). This pattern mirrors that found in Europe as a whole (Kasparek 1996). During the period 1960–79, birds aged as adults were consistently moving greater distances than those aged as first-year but, since 1980, there has been no consistent pattern. However, this conclusion should be treated with caution since clear guidelines to ringers on ageing Collared Doves were not published until 1979 (Insley & Young 1979). Analysis of movement between the ringing and recovery locations shows that northwesterly movements are evident primarily in August with some tendency for opposing movements in late autumn and winter. With the exception of August, there was no clear evidence of seasonality in the movements of Collared Doves. This contrasts with observations elsewhere where, for example on the island of Helgoland, there is a marked peak in spring and early summer, with the great majority of birds being recorded in May and June (Kasparek 1996). A similar spring and early summer passage is also found in the Scottish Hebrides (Daw 1998, Rabbitts 1999).

All of the overseas ring-recoveries have involved movements to and from locations on or near the English Channel or North Sea coasts (Fig 5). The absence of any really long-distance movements lends weight to the suggestions that Collared Doves in Iceland, and those on, or near, the North American coastline, have been ship-assisted (P W Smith 1987, O K Nielsen pers comm).

At the time of the *1988–91 Atlas,* it was estimated that there were some 230,000 Collared Dove territories in Britain & Ireland. Comparison of the number of 10-km squares in which the species was found between the two atlas projects suggested that there had been a 6.7% spread in Britain and a 2.8% contraction in Ireland. Steady population growth seems to be continuing in Britain with BBS figures showing a statistically significant 16% increase between 1994 and 1998 (Noble *et al* 1999).

There has been little recent evidence of Collared Doves in Britain & Ireland making the kind of long-distance dispersals which assisted their irruption. Continued ringing of the species should now be focused on integrated population monitoring and studying mortality rates. Although less directly dependent on farmland than many of the common species that appear to have been badly affected by changes in agricultural practice, it is nevertheless a species whose population might ultimately be affected by changes in either farming or related activity.

Hugh Insley

European Turtle Dove (Turtle Dove)

Streptopelia turtur

The Turtle Dove is exceptional in two ways (Jarry 1995): it is the world's only member of the pigeon family to undertake long-distance migrations exceeding 4,000 km, and it is the only trans-Saharan migrant to be almost exclusively granivorous throughout the year.

Four subspecies are recognized. The one breeding in Britain & Ireland is the nominate race *turtur*, whose summer range extends across the whole of Europe except Fennoscandia, eastward through Asia Minor and the former Soviet Union to Kazakhstan and western Siberia (*European Atlas*). The entire breeding population winters in the Sahelian zone of Africa, from Senegal and the Gambia to Ethiopia. Autumn migration generally follows a southwesterly direction. Most doves from western Europe pass through southwest France and Iberia into Africa via Morocco (*BWP*). Depending on their origin, doves breeding further east enter Africa by crossing the Mediterranean from Italy or the Balkans, or pass through the Middle East and Arabia (*BWP*). The race *arenicola* breeds in the Balearic Islands, northwest Africa and from the Levant east to Iran and northwest China. It shares the same wintering area as *turtur*, as do the remaining two races: *hoggara*, which breeds in the mountains of the central Sahara, and *rufescens*, in Egypt and northern Sudan; these last two races appear to be resident in the southern parts of their ranges.

Turtle Doves in Britain & Ireland are restricted largely to southern, eastern and central England. This pattern has been emphasized by an eastward and southward range contraction between the two breeding atlas surveys (*1988–91 Atlas*), corresponding to a decline in abundance of 72% (R J Fuller *et al* 1995). Declines have also been observed elsewhere in Europe, particularly western Europe and the Balkans (Jarry 1994). British Turtle Doves are closely associated with lowland arable farmland.

The analysis of the data for this species was supported by the Rye Bay Ringing Group and the Wetland Trust

They require a mixture of hedgerows, shrubby woodland margins or bushy scrub for nesting, and open weedy patches of ground where they can forage for seeds. During autumn migration, they appear to favour fields of ripe or newly harvested peas, wheat and sunflowers for feeding (Murton *et al* 1964a, Dias & Fontoura 1996). In winter, they congregate in open savanna where both wild and cultivated seeds are abundant (Morel 1987). Birds roost communally in groups of up to several thousand, mainly in dense *Acacia* woodland close to sources of fresh water (Morel 1987, Jarry & Baillon 1991).

The distribution of ringing sites where Turtle Doves later recovered have been ringed during the breeding season (Fig 1) broadly parallels the breeding distribution of the species in Britain. Anomalous locations in Ireland, Scotland and coastal Wales are likely to be birds on spring passage, the latest one being ringed on 6 June. Outside the main breeding season, many of the ringing locations are coastal ringing stations well placed to sample the passage of migrant birds. Of more than 200 recoveries of British-ringed Turtle Doves, 31% were marked as nestlings, the rest as fully grown birds (Fig 2). Most fully grown birds were ringed over the three months May–July, most nestlings also over a three-month period starting a month later.

Although protected in Britain and in Ireland, the Turtle Dove is a major quarry species in nearly all countries bordering the Mediterranean. The proportion of ringed doves recovered is therefore relatively high, but

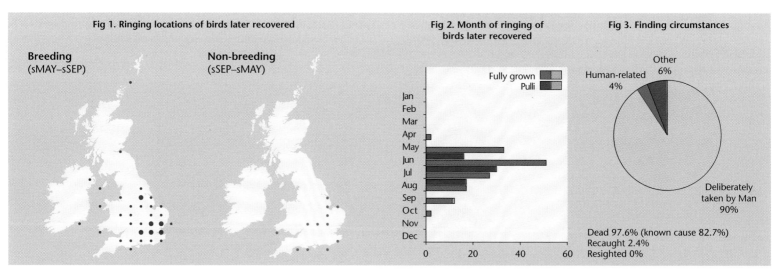

Fig 1. Ringing locations of birds later recovered

Breeding (sMAY–sSEP)

Non-breeding (sSEP–sMAY)

Fig 2. Month of ringing of birds later recovered

Fully grown / Pulli

Fig 3. Finding circumstances

Other 6%
Human-related 4%
Deliberately taken by Man 90%

Dead 97.6% (known cause 82.7%)
Recaught 2.4%
Resighted 0%

Ringing and recovery data

	<1960	60–69	70–79	80–89	90–97	Total
RINGING						
BTO ringing totals (%)	22	23	24	20	10	6,823
RECOVERIES						
BTO-ringed (%)	26	34	25	13	2	206
Foreign-ringed (%)	←	80	→	0	20	5

Statistical analyses

	Breeding population (sMAY–sSEP)	Wintering population (mNOV–sMAR)
Status	[LONG-DISTANCE MIGRANT]	NONE
Age differences	Not tested	—
Sex differences	Not tested	—
Regional differences	Not tested	—
Finding circumstances	Not tested	—

Fig 4. Recovery locations during August–October of Turtles Doves ringed in Britain & Ireland. Those ringed as pulli or juveniles and recovered during the same calendar year (35, red) are differentiated from other or unknown age classes (76, blue) and those known to be seasonally inaccurate (18, grey). The recovery of an 'other' age class bird in the Ukraine is not shown.

Fig 5. Recovery locations during March–May of Turtles Doves ringed in Britain & Ireland. Those ringed as pulli or juveniles and recovered by the end of May the following year (5, red) are differentiated from other or unknown age classes (36, blue) and those known to be seasonally inaccurate (10, grey).

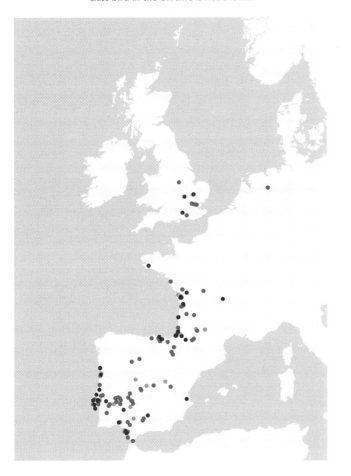

the distribution of recoveries will reflect the intensity of shooting and trapping during migration. This must be borne in mind when interpreting recovery locations in terms of migration routes. In the 83% of cases where the cause of death was reported, 90% of recoveries were of doves deliberately taken by Man (Fig 3). Only four recoveries were of birds that had been recaught by ringers, three in England and one in Portugal. One of the English recaptures, the only foreign-ringed recovery, was of a bird ringed as a September juvenile in Portugal and caught in Nottinghamshire the following July.

British adults start their post-nuptial moult some time in late July or early August. As a result, many late clutches and broods are deserted by parents overtaken by the migratory urge (Murton 1968). Moult is suspended during the migration period itself. Most Turtle Doves leave Britain in August or September (R & F). The recoveries give no indication that the departure dates of adults and juveniles differ. The doves follow a route through western France and central and western Iberia (Fig 4). For centuries, the concentrations of migrating Turtle Doves along the coast of southwest France (Gironde) and northern Portugal have been exploited by hunters and trappers (eg Dias et al 1996), who consider that the fattened migrants are a gastronomic delicacy. The main migratory wave passes through between mid-August and the end of September (dos Santos Júnior 1979, Devort et al 1988), as it does in the Balkans (Nankinov 1994) and the Levant (Shirihai 1996). Most birds travel in flocks of five to 30, with occasional flocks of over a hundred; congregations of up to a thousand have been observed feeding in fields of ripe sunflowers. Murton (1968) noted

that the pattern of recoveries in Iberia was further west than expected given the winter destination. He suggested that most Turtle Doves actually take a direct route, flying too high to be seen (or hunted), and that the observed movements and recoveries correspond primarily to inexperienced young birds being drifted west in unfavourable weather conditions; night flights may explain why redirected or coasting movements are most evident in the early morning. Although the subject of some debate (Marchant 1969, Ash 1977, Bourne & Beaman 1980), it seems that Turtle Doves are indeed mainly night migrants (Devort et al 1988, Jarry 1995), with a strong diurnal component at times. A recent study of captive birds found that most of them showed signs of nocturnal restlessness as they accumulated fat, with a high degree of individual variability (Guyomarc'h 1998). In addition, the age ratio of doves coasting diurnally is strongly biased towards juveniles, the proportion of young birds being 82% in the Gironde, and 97% in northern Portugal (dos Santos Júnior 1979, Devort et al 1988). On a broader scale, looking at the recoveries of doves ringed in Britain & Ireland, the proportion of juveniles within 100 km of the Atlantic coast is almost five times as high as that further inland: 37% compared with 8%. These observations are consistent with Murton's hypothesis.

From Iberia, the doves cross into Morocco and give rise to spectacular movements along the Atlantic coast (Morel 1985). Passage through Morocco starts at the end of August and continues into October; the first definite turtur have been recorded passing through Senegal and the Gambia at the end of September although some individuals probably arrive much earlier (Morel 1985). The strongest autumn passage in Senegal, the Gambia and Mali is in October. The presence of both *turtur* and *arenicola* over winter is confirmed for Mauritania and Senegal (Morel 1985, 1987). In West Africa from November onwards, Turtle Doves have also been recorded in the Gambia, northern Guinea, southern Mali, Burkina Faso, southern Niger, northern Ivory Coast, northern Ghana, northern Nigeria, and northern Cameroon (Morel 1987, Morel & Morel 1988). The birds resume their moult upon arrival in the wintering quarters, and most complete it by March, when pre-migratory fattening is already under way (Morel & Morel 1988).

There is a mass return from the south into Mali, Senegal and the Gambia in February and March, when dense concentrations of hundreds of thousands occur (Mountfort 1981, Morel 1987). Three recoveries of British-ringed Turtle Doves from Mali indicate that British birds are involved in these movements. Some *turtur* are still present south of the Sahara in May (Morel 1985), but most disappear in March and the first half of April (*BWP*). The first ones reach Morocco in mid-March, and the main northward passage through the Mediterranean region is during April and the first half of May (Morel 1985, Nankinov 1994, Shirihai 1996). British-ringed birds on return migration have been recovered predominantly in Spain and southwestern France (Fig 5), with only one recovery in Portugal. The more easterly migration route that this represents compared with the autumn pattern (Fig 4) may give a truer picture of the route followed in autumn (Murton 1968). Turtle Doves first arrive back in Britain in mid-April. The main arrival takes place during May, and movements extend through into June (Davis 1963, *R & F*). In Denmark and Sweden, spring passage takes place mainly between mid-May and mid-June (Møller 1976, Cederwall 1978).

One dove ringed as a chick in England was recovered in May in southeast France, possibly on the Italian flyway, and another was recovered a year later in Ukraine in August. This implies that some mixing occurs between the western and eastern flyway populations, although the amount must be very small since it represents less than 1% of the recoveries. Five doves ringed in England as chicks were recovered during subsequent breeding seasons (June–July) at an average distance of 7 km from where they hatched (range 0–22 km). For 16 doves ringed as breeding adults, recovery locations in subsequent summers were on average 11 km away from the ringing site (range 0–107 km). These limited data suggest that the patterns of natal and breeding dispersal are similar; half the birds remained within 3 km from one year to the next, and only 15% of them moved more than 20 km.

Within western Europe, agricultural intensification is considered at least partly responsible for the decline in Turtle Dove numbers, both through loss of hedgerows used for nesting, and the widespread use of herbicides in arable areas (Jarry 1995). By eliminating arable weeds, herbicides have much reduced the abundance of weed seeds that provide most of the doves' food, especially when they return in the spring. Breeding success in East Anglia has almost halved over the last 30 years (Calladine *et al* 1997, Aebischer *et al* 2001). Another factor considered to be at least as important is the deterioration of the wintering habitat through drought, particularly in West Africa (Jarry 1994). The dense *Acacia* woodland used for roosting is also being seriously degraded by cutting for charcoal (Jarry & Baillon 1991). An estimated two to four million Turtle Doves are shot or trapped during autumn migration in France, Spain, Portugal, Italy, Greece and Malta, with a further 50,000 killed in the spring, in Morocco and (illegally) in southwest France (Boutin 2001). Additional unquantified hunting losses take place on the wintering grounds (Morel 1987, Jarry 1994). These losses may have contributed to the decline of western European Turtle Dove populations but are not considered its main cause (Jarry 1994).

It is difficult to evaluate the full effect of shooting and trapping on Turtle Dove abundance in the absence of detailed bag statistics from the countries concerned. As highlighted by the EU Management Plan for this species (Boutin 2001), collections of such data should become a priority, and be accompanied by national monitoring of breeding abundance and success. Radar studies could provide more precise information on the migration route through Iberia, and on the relative importance of nocturnal versus diurnal migration. An international ringing programme involving the marking of adult and young birds on the breeding grounds, and expeditions to the savannas south of Senegal and the Niger Inundation Zone, could clarify the location of wintering areas for western European breeders. Such a programme would also provide useful data on winter habitat requirements and winter threats.

Nicholas J Aebischer

Common Cuckoo (Cuckoo)

Cuculus canorus

Few birds evoke more public interest than the Cuckoo. It is a harbinger of spring as it moves north into its Palearctic breeding grounds. There are many people with more than a passing interest in birds who know the male's 'cuckoo' call well but have never knowingly seen the species. Its parasitic habits have proved endlessly fascinating and a source of new insights into the relationship between brood parasites and their hosts. And, because those habits mean that a young Cuckoo never encounters its parents, it is possible to be confident that the juveniles' first southward migration is undertaken without any guidance whatsoever from older birds.

The Cuckoo, represented by various races, has an extensive Palearctic breeding range, from Ireland and Spain in the west to Kamchatka and Japan in the east. Throughout this range, the species is a summer visitor. All the western Palearctic birds winter in Africa, as do those from a large part of western Asia. The African winter distribution covers most of the continent south of the Sahara. Eastern Asian birds winter in southeast Asia but the position of the migratory divide is not known (*BWP*).

The Cuckoo is catholic in its choice of habitat throughout the year, probably occurring in most areas where its favoured food, large hairy caterpillars, can be found. Indeed it is absent only from montane and tundra habitats, extensive dense forest, and major urban areas. Within Britain & Ireland, it occurs in farmland of all types (although only sparsely in tracts of intensive arable farming), in open moorland, in parkland and light woodland, and in the suburban fringes of larger towns. Different species play host to its eggs and young in these various

The analysis of the data for this species was supported by the Rye Bay Ringing Group and the Wetland Trust

habitats. The Meadow Pipit is the major host in the moorlands of the northwest while the Dunnock and, to a lesser extent, the Robin are the main hosts in lowland farmland. In areas of reedbed in the southeast of Britain, Reed Warblers are also extensively parasitized by the Cuckoo (Brooke & Davies 1987).

Despite this extensive distribution, the Cuckoo is not a particularly numerous bird. The *1988–91 Atlas* puts the British and Irish populations at 13,000–26,000 and 3,000–6,000 respectively. Given the species' low density and the fact that no British ringers have developed successful techniques for catching free-flying Cuckoos, it is no surprise that the number ringed in Britain & Ireland is not great and the number of those recovered is correspondingly low.

The majority of the Cuckoos whose rings were recovered were ringed as either chicks or juveniles, mostly in the southeast of Britain (Figs 1 & 2). This doubtless partly reflects the distribution of ringers. It is probably also a reflection of the fact that Cuckoo chicks in the nests of Reed Warblers, a host of the southeast, are easier to find than those in the nests of other hosts. In contrast, the paucity of recoveries from birds ringed in northwest Scotland and Ireland, areas of high Cuckoo density (*1988–91 Atlas*), is probably related to the difficulty of finding young Cuckoos to ring in Meadow Pipit nests. However, the recovery data do not suggest any regional variation in the migration patterns of British &

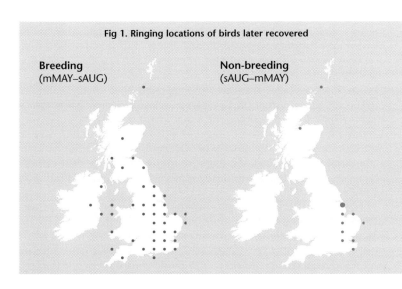

Fig 1. Ringing locations of birds later recovered

Breeding (mMAY–sAUG)

Non-breeding (sAUG–mMAY)

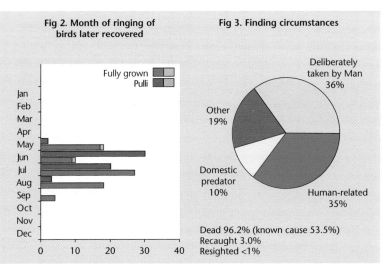

Fig 2. Month of ringing of birds later recovered

Fully grown
Pulli

Fig 3. Finding circumstances

Deliberately taken by Man 36%

Other 19%

Domestic predator 10%

Human-related 35%

Dead 96.2% (known cause 53.5%)
Recaught 3.0%
Resighted <1%

Ringing and recovery data

	<1960	60–69	70–79	80–89	90–97	Total
RINGING						
BTO ringing totals (%)	32	16	19	23	10	5,894
RECOVERIES						
BTO-ringed (%)	26	31	21	13	9	130
Foreign-ringed (%)	←	75	→	25	0	8

Statistical analyses

	Breeding population (mMAY–sAUG)	Wintering population (sNOV–mMAR)
Status	[LONG-DISTANCE MIGRANT]	NONE
Age differences	Not tested	—
Sex differences	Not tested	—
Regional differences	Not tested	—
Finding circumstances	Not tested	—

Fig 4. Recovery locations in the breeding season (39, large red squares), autumn (51, red points), winter (4, large blue squares) and spring (11, blue points) of Cuckoos ringed in Britain & Ireland, together with movements of over 20 km for birds recovered in autumn and spring. The movements of foreign-ringed individuals (2, black broken lines and points) are also shown. A recovery in Cameroon during winter is not shown.

Irish Cuckoos. Just over half of the recoveries of dead Cuckoos have a cause attached and, of those, over 80% are associated with the activities or proximity of Man or his pets (Fig 3).

The seasonal pattern of occurrence of the Cuckoo in Great Britain is summarized well by the famous traditional rhyme, which exists in various regional versions. Armstrong (1958) reported the Sussex variant as:

> In April come he will;
> In May he sings all day;
> In June he changes his tune;
> In July he prepares to fly;
> In August, go he must.
> If he stay until September,
> 'Tis as much as the oldest man can remember.

In more humdrum prose, adult Cuckoos leave their breeding grounds decidedly early, and indeed some observatories record influxes of adults in late June (R & F). While this raises the possibility that the adults embark on southward migration ahead of the juveniles, the limited ring-recovery data offer support that is both meagre and tantalizing. There is a single overseas recovery in July, in northeast Italy, of a Cuckoo of uncertain age. In August, however, there are two recoveries of British-ringed adult Cuckoos, as compared to 29 juvenile recoveries (both in Britain and abroad). The two adults had reached southern France and northern Italy, and provided two of the three southernmost recoveries in this month.

While the adult Cuckoo is preparing to fly, the young Cuckoo remains dependent on its foster parents for two weeks after fledging (Wyllie 1981). There follows a period of dispersal that is random in direction (Seel 1977). Such dispersal is typically over short distances but it has taken British juveniles as far afield as Fyn (Denmark) and Schleswig-Holstein (Germany). Then the southward migration starts and Cuckoos have largely left Britain & Ireland by mid-September.

Using various methods, Seel (1977) estimated that young birds moved south across Europe at about 20 km/day, while the progress for all age groups combined was 20–70 km/day. The track is southeasterly towards Italy (Fig 4). Scandinavian birds presumably follow a similar track, and therefore rarely deviate west to Britain. Because of their southeasterly course, very few British & Irish Cuckoos are recovered in Iberia, and then only in the east of the peninsula (Fig 4).

The total absence of any recoveries of British & Irish Cuckoos in North Africa in the autumn is remarkable. It accords with Moreau's (1972) comment that fewer Cuckoos are seen in North Africa in autumn than spring and hints that the birds, having reached the northern shores of the Mediterranean Sea, fatten and then overfly that sea, North Africa and the Sahara in a single flight of at least 3,500 km.

It is not known where in Africa British & Irish birds spend the winter. The single recovery is of a bird ringed as a nestling and found in Cameroon in January (Fig 4). The only other recovery of a western European bird is of a Dutch juvenile found in Togo in January (BWP). With the exception of the race bangsi breeding in Iberia and northwest Africa and wintering in West Africa, Moreau (1972) considered that most Cuckoos wintered in Africa south of the Equator.

At the start of the spring migration, Cuckoos may make a continuous flight to the southern shores of the Mediterranean (Moreau 1972), and indeed the recoveries of British-ringed birds in Malta and Tunisia were in spring (Fig 4). The suggestion of rapid northward movement in spring is also supported by observations of large numbers of migrating Cuckoos in Tanzania, still south of the Equator, in late April (Prins 1986), at the very time that numbers in Europe are increasing fast.

The first Cuckoos begin to arrive in southern Europe in March. To assess their progress thereafter, De Smet (1970) collated records of when the first Cuckoo was heard in various latitudinal bands. He estimated a northward advance of 50 km/day. The sparse ringing data, namely the Maltese and Tunisian birds mentioned above, plus a March bird from northeast France and an April bird from southeast France, suggest that the British birds approach from the southeast, a straightforward reversal of their autumn route. This was also supported by a recent analysis of Cuckoo arrival dates from the Royal Meteorological Society phenological reports (Huin & Sparks 2000). The main arrival (first heard) is between 17 and 23 April in southern England and between 1 and 7 May in northern Scotland (Wyllie 1981). Of course, given the national enthusiasm for early Cuckoos, there are earlier records, and the earliest-ever record accepted by Hudson (1973) was of a bird seen in Yorkshire on 15 February 1945.

If continental Cuckoos are also arriving at their breeding grounds from the southeast, they would only infrequently pass through Britain in spring. This picture is supported by the scarcity of Scandinavian recoveries. In fact there is just one, of a May-ringed Fair Isle bird that was killed six days later in Norway (Fig 4). However, the considerable number of Cuckoos recorded at some east-coast observatories in late May has been interpreted as a passage of continental Cuckoos (R & F) and the few exchanges between Britain & Ireland and Denmark are also suggestive (Fig 4).

A fascinating aspect of Cuckoo biology is the tendency of females to lay eggs that match, more or less closely, the eggs of the host (Brooke & Davies 1988). Although not yet convincingly demonstrated in the wild, it seems likely that this system is maintained because, first, females inherit egg colour from their mothers and, second, females tend to exploit the same host species that reared them. For the second of these to apply, one would expect no great degree of natal dispersal, since any substantial dispersal would take the first-year females outside the natal region into others where the spectrum of available hosts could differ. The British data on this point are too few to be informative but a recent analysis of European data by Lindholm (1999) showed that 75% of 16 birds ringed as nestlings and recovered in subsequent breeding seasons were recovered within 40 km of the natal site. She estimated mean natal dispersal as 27 km. Once Cuckoos have started to breed, philopatry is strong and there are records of females returning to the same site for up to eight years and males for up to ten years (Wyllie 1981).

A decrease in Cuckoo numbers has been indicated by the *1968–72* and *1988–91 Atlases*. The extent of this decrease is uncertain, however, especially as the CBC has not confirmed the decrease (Marchant *et al* 1990, Crick *et al* 1998). It is therefore worth mentioning that the number of fully grown Cuckoos ringed each year in Britain & Ireland was fairly steady at an annual rate equivalent to 120 per million birds ringed overall during the period 1961–90 but declined significantly to 68 per million in the period 1991–96. These proportions deliberately exclude Cuckoo chicks, for which the numbers ringed may fluctuate as particular studies come and go. However, the figures for fully grown birds suggest a recent but nonetheless significant reduction in Cuckoo numbers. Whether this is due to deterioration of the habitat and food supply in Britain & Ireland, to a reduction in host numbers, or to problems on migration and in the winter quarters, is unknown. Further research on the extent of the wintering area used by British & Irish birds is required.

M de L Brooke

Barn Owl
Tyto alba

Although the Barn Owl is globally one of the most widespread terrestrial bird species, it is essentially a bird of the tropics and subtropics (*BWP*); only in North America, southern Argentina and Europe does the species form part of the temperate avifauna. The nominate race *alba* is found in western and southern parts of Europe, from Britain & Ireland south to the Mediterranean, and across into North Africa (Taylor 1994, Shawyer 1998). The dark-breasted race *guttata*, which is a scarce vagrant to both Britain and Ireland, is found in central Europe to the east of the 3°C January isotherm (*European Atlas*), occurring from Germany eastward to the Ukraine and Bulgaria. That none of the races so far studied shows regular migrations suggests that the species is largely sedentary, although populations in Australia and parts of North America may be partly nomadic (Stewart 1952, Taylor 1994). Dispersal in continental Europe is more pronounced than in Britain and has been linked with fluctuations in prey availability and climatic events (von Sauter 1956, Honer 1963, Bairlein 1985c).

Within Britain & Ireland, the Barn Owl is most abundant within a number of strongholds in southwestern and eastern England, Wales and southwest Scotland (*1988–91 Atlas*). The species exploits a range of habitat types but is usually associated with open grassland, woodland edge and young conifer plantations, both in the breeding season and in winter.

Some 90% of Barn Owl recoveries have been of birds ringed as pulli, typically at nestbox sites established as part of local conservation efforts. The distribution of the ringing sites of birds recovered broadly reflects the distribution of the species in Britain & Ireland (*1988–91 Atlas*),

The analysis of the data for this species was supported by the Rye Bay Ringing Group and the Wetland Trust

except that southwestern Wales and Ireland are under-represented (Fig 1). Most ringing takes place between May and August (91%), with some second broods ringed between September and mid-November (Fig 2). Little ringing takes place outside the breeding season. Many captive-bred birds have also been ringed prior to release but data from such birds are not included in the current analysis. There are marked short-term fluctuations in Barn Owl productivity, especially in Scotland (Taylor 1994), and these have a direct influence on the numbers ringed each year (Toms & Clark 1998, Toms *et al* 2000). The numbers ringed have increased year-on-year since the mid-1980s, a reflection of the increasing conservation efforts directed towards this species (Toms *et al* 2000).

Two-thirds of all Barn Owl recoveries have been attributed to a cause of death and the vast majority of these (82%) are human-related, involving suspected collision with road or rail traffic (Fig 3). The causes of recovery for birds ringed in Britain & Ireland are similar to those reported elsewhere (Fajardo 1990, de Bruijn 1994). The reporting rate for birds killed on the roads is likely to be significantly higher than that for birds that die from other causes (Illner 1992). This introduces bias, since owls that are killed on the roads are not necessarily representative of the population as a whole. In addition, some individuals killed on roads may be transported for some distance before falling from the vehicle

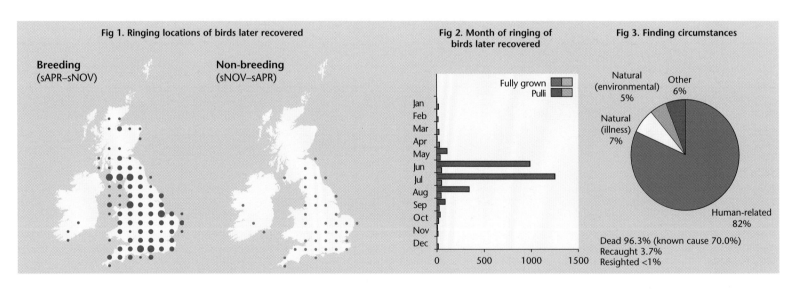

Fig 1. Ringing locations of birds later recovered

Breeding (sAPR–sNOV) Non-breeding (sNOV–sAPR)

Fig 2. Month of ringing of birds later recovered

Fully grown / Pulli

Fig 3. Finding circumstances

Natural (environmental) 5%
Other 6%
Natural (illness) 7%
Human-related 82%

Dead 96.3% (known cause 70.0%)
Recaught 3.7%
Resighted <1%

Ringing and recovery data

	<1960	60–69	70–79	80–89	90–97	Total
RINGING						
BTO ringing totals (%)	5	4	10	24	57	24,264
RECOVERIES						
BTO-ringed (%)	5	6	13	25	51	3,146
Foreign-ringed (%)	←	25	→	13	63	8

Statistical analyses

	Breeding population (sAPR–sNOV)	Wintering population (sJAN–sMAR)
Status	SEDENTARY (0)	SEDENTARY*
Age differences[NS]	Significant*	Not tested
Sex differences[NS]	Not significant*	Not tested
Regional differences	Significant[4]	Not tested
Finding circumstances	(Not significant)	Not significant*

Fig 4. Recovery locations and movements of over 20 km for the included recoveries of Barn Owls ringed or recovered in Britain & Ireland, with those ringed in Britain & Ireland (3,146, red) differentiated from those ringed abroad (6, black). The two pre-1979 foreign-ringed Barn Owls (Belgium 1 and the Netherlands 1) are not shown.

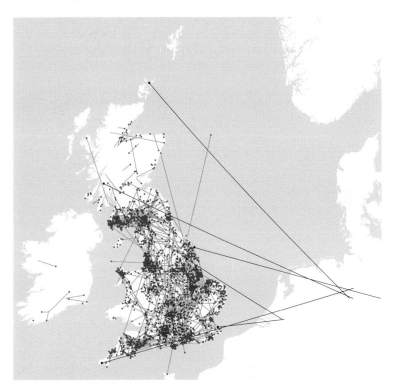

Table 1. Dispersal distances of European Barn Owls, showing the percentages of recoveries within specific distance bands.

Country	Age	Recovery distance (km)			Source
		0–50	51–100	>100	
Denmark & Sweden	All ages	73.6	17.4	9.0	Frylestam 1972
Britain & Ireland	Under 1 year old	88.9	6.7	4.4	British & Irish Ringing Scheme
	Over 1 year old	88.7	6.7	4.6	
France	All ages	71.8	8.9	19.3	Baudvin 1986
Netherlands	All ages	86.8		13.2	Braaksma & de Bruijn 1976
Spain	All ages	66.7	6.0	27.3	Martínez & López 1995
Germany	Under 1 year old	45.9	32.0	22.1	Bairlein 1985c
	Over 1 year old	37.6	32.2	30.2	

with which they had collided (Percival 1990, Taylor 1994). This often leads to an overestimation of the dispersal distances for such birds; Taylor (1994) found that road-killed Barn Owls had travelled significantly further than those reported from other mortality causes. Despite these biases, it is still possible to make comparisons across classes of recoveries showing similar patterns of recovery circumstances.

Young Barn Owls ringed in Britain & Ireland disperse from their natal sites during the first few weeks after fledging. Bunn *et al* (1982) showed that 37% of birds ringed as pulli had moved more than 3 km from their nest sites within two weeks of fledging. This had risen to 59% three to four weeks later. Analysis of the present recovery data shows that the median dispersal distance for recoveries made in the second month after ringing as pulli was 3 km, rising to 7.5 km and 12 km in the third and fourth months respectively. Recoveries suggest that dispersal of young birds is largely completed within the first four or five months post-fledging and that there is little additional movement after this period. The median distance of natal dispersal derived from the complete set of British & Irish data is 12 km ($P5–95=0–103$, $n=384$). In a detailed population study in southwest Scotland, the natal dispersal distances of females were found to be significantly greater than those of males (Taylor 1994), and this finding is similar to that reported from a North American study (Marti 1999). Too few British & Irish Barn Owls have been sexed to allow examination of sex-related differences in dispersal patterns at the national level. Percival (1990) found no significant regional or temporal variation in the dispersal patterns of Barn Owls ringed as pulli, and the current data support this.

There are few data available on the movements of birds of breeding age but those that exist strongly suggest that these birds are largely sedentary. Movements between the breeding and non-breeding season of birds ringed as adults (median=4 km, $P5–95=0–50$ km, $n=121$) are far shorter than those of birds ringed during their first year of life and recovered before reaching breeding age (median=10 km, $P5–95= 0–100$ km, $n=1,417$). Radio-tracking has shown that foraging ranges can increase from the 1–2 km seen during the breeding season to 4–5 km during the winter months (Cayford 1992) but pairs appear to be

remarkably site-faithful throughout their lives (Taylor 1994). The median distance for breeding dispersal is 3 km ($P5–95=0–84$, $n=23$).

The sedentary nature of the population within Britain & Ireland is in contrast to published data on populations in some parts of continental Europe (Fig 4). In southern Germany, Bairlein (1985c) found that during the second month after fledging only 27% of individuals were recovered within 10 km of their natal sites, with almost 40% recovered more than 50 km away. Table 1 shows the different dispersal distances found for various European countries. Those of France and the Netherlands are intermediate between those of Britain & Ireland and Germany, while those of southern Sweden (where Barn Owls seemingly no longer breed; *European Atlas*) and Denmark are closest to the pattern seen in Britain & Ireland. Such differences in dispersal could relate to a number of factors including prey availability, climatic events and geographical features (Schneider 1937, von Sauter 1956, Honer 1963).

In mainland Europe, the distance moved by young Barn Owls varies from year to year and the term '*Wanderjahren*' has been applied to years with increased dispersal (von Sauter 1956). In such years, pronounced dispersal of young birds takes place in late summer and is usually completed by mid-November. Increased mortality is also a characteristic feature of these years. The most recent *Wanderjahr*, in 1990, saw the mass arrival of young Barn Owls in Denmark (Laursen 1997) and single birds from Germany and the Netherlands recovered in Britain during the following winter (Mead & Clark 1993, Mead *et al* 1995). The most likely explanation for this phenomenon is the combination of a particularly successful breeding season followed by a sudden crash in continental vole populations (Honer 1963, van der Hut *et al* 1992). Schönfeld (1974) demonstrated that Barn Owl movements were shorter in years of high vole abundance than in years when vole abundance was low.

Large waterbodies and areas of high ground appear to limit the movement of dispersing Barn Owls (Frylestam 1972, Bairlein 1985c) and the presence of these features can influence both the orientation of movement and the distance travelled. Marti (1999) showed that the direction of dispersal for young Barn Owls was influenced by local topography, with those individuals moving beyond local topographic features seemingly dispersing in all directions. There have been only a handful of recoveries involving movements of Barn Owls between Britain and continental Europe. Four birds from northern Germany, three from the Netherlands and one from Belgium have been recovered in Britain, while a bird from the Isle of Wight was recovered on the French coast and one ringed on Humberside was found dead on an oil rig in the North Sea. Individuals of the race *guttata* have occasionally been recorded in Britain, mainly along the east coast as far north as Shetland (*Birds in Scotland*) and even in Ireland (*Birds in Ireland*). Some of these individuals were ringed, confirming the origins of the birds concerned. Dispersal movements within Britain & Ireland show no directional pattern and this is in agreement with other published studies (de Bruijn 1994, Martínez & López 1995). In Britain, young birds may disperse along linear habitats associated with rivers and coastal margins (Shawyer 1998).

The fragmented nature of the Barn Owl population within Britain & Ireland, coupled with the relatively sedentary nature of this species, suggests that conservation efforts should be aimed at expanding existing populations and linking them through the establishment of corridors of suitable habitat (Toms et al 2001). Additional research

needs to be carried out on the nature of dispersal movements during the first few months after fledging using radio-tagging rather than ringing. This will help to quantify the potential biases associated with the dominance of road deaths as a cause of recovery and the possible variation in reporting rates between recovery types. Ringing also needs to be targeted towards the trapping of adult birds at the nest, together with greater efforts to sex both adults and young, thus increasing our understanding of mortality and movement patterns in relation to age and sex.

Mike Toms

Little Owl

Athene noctua

The Little Owl's plump, flat-headed shape, with striking white eyebrows and long-legged stance, presents a familiar sight over much of lowland Britain. Affinities for sunbathing, perching at conspicuous look-out posts in all seasons and hunting during daylight hours, as well as at dusk, make it generally easier to locate than other owls. It presents the appearance of an indigenous and sedentary feature of the British avifauna but the historical literature reveals it to be non-native, and ring-recoveries show that it exhibits a degree of mobility.

The Little Owl breeds across Eurasia from Britain and the Mediterranean eastward to the Yellow Sea. It is also found over much of North Africa and Arabia south into the central Sahara, Somalia and Ethiopia (*BWP*). The same range is occupied all year. The northern limit of breeding, at around 55°N, is governed by mean winter temperatures, birds avoiding areas subject to long spells of snow-cover. Marked population decreases have followed cold winters in central Europe (*European Atlas*).

In Britain, the Little Owl owes its origin to crate-loads of birds shipped from the nearby Continent and released, in Yorkshire as early as 1842. These birds, and those from subsequent releases, are considered to belong to the darkest of seven subspecies frequenting the Western Palearctic, *vidalii*, which breeds from the southern Baltic through the Low Countries to Iberia. The most extensive and successful introductions were made in the 1870s, with breeding well established in Bedfordshire, Northamptonshire, Rutland and Kent by the end of the 19th century. The population expanded rapidly during 1910–30 (chronicled in the *Handbook*), subsequently extending more slowly but

The analysis of the data for this species was supported by A B Wassell

with periodic reversals (*1988–91 Atlas*). When, in 1930, a pair bred on the Great Orme, Caernarfonshire (*Birds in Wales*), breeding had finally been confirmed in all the historic counties of England and Wales. Little Owls have been reported in Scotland since 1925 but successful nesting was unproven until 1958 when a pair bred near Eldrom, Berwick (*Birds in Scotland*). There have been just four confirmed sightings of single Little Owls in Ireland, the first killed at Kilmorony, Kildare, in June 1903, and the most recent at Dunlavin, Wicklow, in December 1981 (*Birds in Ireland*).

Little Owls in Britain currently occupy a broad range of lowland agricultural landscapes, especially where well timbered with hedgerow trees, shelter belts, copses or orchards, and also man-made habitats such as parks, cemeteries and quarries (Glue & Scott 1980). They breed over much of southern and central England and the Welsh Marches, more sparingly in many eastern counties, southwest England, northern England and western Wales, and very thinly in southern Scotland (*1988–91 Atlas*). The distribution in winter broadly accords with that shown for breeding birds (*Winter Atlas*).

The distribution of ringing sites of birds subsequently recovered matches the breeding range fairly closely (Fig 1). Populations in the Thames corridor are strongly represented but nesting strongholds elsewhere in southeast England and on the Welsh border are somewhat

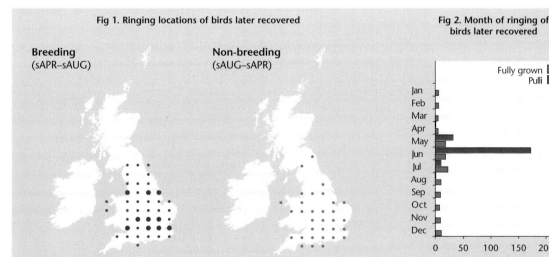

Fig 1. Ringing locations of birds later recovered

Breeding (sAPR–sAUG)

Non-breeding (sAUG–sAPR)

Fig 2. Month of ringing of birds later recovered

Fully grown
Pulli

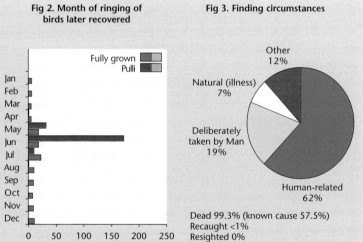

Fig 3. Finding circumstances

Other 12%

Natural (illness) 7%

Deliberately taken by Man 19%

Human-related 62%

Dead 99.3% (known cause 57.5%)
Recaught <1%
Resighted 0%

Ringing and recovery data

	<1960	60–69	70–79	80–89	90–97	Total
RINGING						
BTO ringing totals (%)	20	11	16	31	23	7,854
RECOVERIES						
BTO-ringed (%)	32	20	16	23	9	410
Foreign-ringed (%)	0	0	0	0	0	0

Statistical analyses

	Breeding population (sAPR–sAUG)	Wintering population (sNOV–sFEB)
Status	SEDENTARY (0)	[SEDENTARY]
Age differences[NT]	Significant*	Not tested
Sex differences	Not tested	Not tested
Regional differences	Not tested	Not tested
Finding circumstances	Not tested*	Not tested

Fig 4. Locations in (a) autumn (12,48,17), (b) winter (9,20,5) and (c) spring (8,11,10), and movements of over 20 km between the breeding and non-breeding season, of Little Owls present in Britain & Ireland during the breeding season. Locations and movements are shown for birds ringed as adults (blue), birds ringed as pulli and recovered in their first year (red), and birds ringed as pulli and recovered in subsequent years (black). Sample sizes (adults, pulli first year, pulli subsequent years) are given.

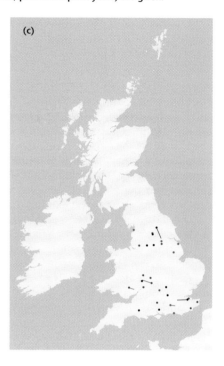

under-represented. The temporal distribution of ring-recoveries, though influenced by changes in ringing effort over time, shows that all phases of colonization during the 20th century are represented: there were 44 recoveries of dead birds during 1909–39, 156 in 1940–69, and 207 in 1970–97. Almost two-thirds of recoveries are from birds ringed as nestlings, nearly all between May and July (Fig 2). This reflects the highly synchronized breeding season of the Little Owl. Those pulli ringed as early as April and as late as August are from the occasional early clutch laid in warm springs, or from repeat clutches; true second broods are rare (Glue & Scott 1980). Of recoveries from birds ringed as adults (26%), most were marked at or close to the nest in May or June, or in November or December while raiding roosts of small passerines.

Helpfully, more than half of all recoveries have been ascribed a known cause of death (Fig 3). Of these, 62% were attributed to human-related activities and most of these to road or rail traffic. Great care is needed when attempting to interpret these data because ringed birds colliding with traffic are much more likely to be reported than birds dying from other causes (Illner 1992). People finding ringed owls are generally unable to diagnose poisoning, parasitic infection, viruses or fungal diseases, which normally require a full post-mortem. Nor, unless the bird is emaciated, are observers able to suggest starvation as the main cause of death. Nonetheless, Jennings (1961) concluded, from an extensive examination of bird corpses, that the largest single cause of mortality in wild birds was some form of injury. Trauma may be the cause of death even where illness or starvation has contributed.

Moving traffic clearly presents a substantial hazard for the Little Owl. Interestingly, when recoveries of Little Owls ringed in Britain were divided into two periods, 1910–54 and 1955–69, they showed a sixfold increase in the proportion of owls killed on roads (Glue 1971), reflecting the increased speed and density of traffic. Intriguingly, the proportion killed on railways over the same 60-year spell had changed relatively little (Glue 1971). Studies of Little Owls ringed on the Continent, in Germany and the Netherlands (Exo & Hennes 1980) and in Spain (Hernandez 1988), also pointed to road losses as the most significant non-natural factor. There are instances of Little Owl corpses found dead on the front of cars or railway locomotives, also in a goods shed,

indicating that traffic victims are sometimes transported. These cases could lead to an overestimation of dispersal distances. This bias has to be borne in mind when examining movements but need not preclude comparisons across classes of birds showing similar patterns of recovery circumstances.

A further 19% of known causes of death relate to birds deliberately taken by Man, whether shot, trapped, killed or poisoned. Little Owls were once widely deemed undesirable because of alleged sustained attacks on poultry and gamebirds, although early work by Hibbert-Ware (1937–38) had demonstrated a spectrum of prey dominated by insects, earthworms, small rodents and fewer small birds. Encouragingly, the proportion of ringed Little Owls reported as killed by Man has fallen fivefold since the legal protection afforded them in 1954 (Glue 1971). Frequenting farmland with gaming interests, however, and hunting more often by day than the other British owls, the Little Owl remains a vulnerable, if illegal, target for the unscrupulous gamekeeper or casual rough shot, with individuals occasionally taken in tunnel traps set for other species (Hewson 1972).

The timing and scale of dispersal movements undertaken by the Little Owl in Britain (Figs 4 & 5) revolve around the highly synchronized breeding season during May–July (Glue & Scott 1980). Upon leaving the nest chamber, most young are fairly proficient at flying within a week. The parents continue to feed their young for a further four or five weeks (Haverschmidt 1946), the family unit generally staying together throughout August, and often into September. Ringing data confirm field observations that juvenile owls stay close to their natal site during their first 90 days of life. From July to September, many inexperienced first-year owls are recovered emaciated, dead on road or rail, beneath wires, or killed by Man or natural predators (Glue 1973). In late autumn, juveniles disperse over relatively short distances, median movements in the fourth and fifth months being just 6 km and 3.5 km respectively. Birds disperse on average further than the sympatric Tawny Owl and, in contrast, there is some indication that movement does not cease in late autumn. The median natal dispersal distance is 7 km ($P5$–$95 = 0$–92 km, $n = 57$).

Young show no clear-cut directional preferences. However, those few recoveries available suggest that Little Owls ringed in the breeding

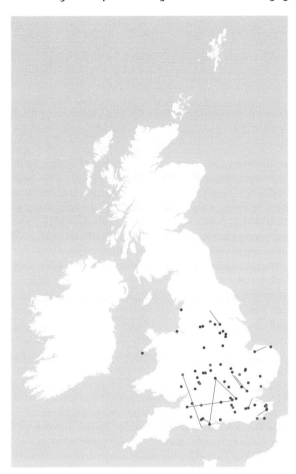

The sedentary nature of the Little Owl within Britain tallies with that of the source populations in continental Europe. Median dispersal distances from November to March of first-year birds were 15 km in western Germany, and within the distance band 10–19 km in the Netherlands (Exo & Hennes 1980). For those having achieved breeding age (April onwards), the equivalent median distances were 7.5 km and 0–9 km respectively.

Little Owls ringed as nestlings in Britain have been found incubating eggs in the following breeding season, confirming that birds may reach sexual maturity in their first year. Relatively few data exist to show the movements of birds of breeding age. Those available confirm field observations that the great majority stay within territories through the autumn and winter, but reveal that a few travel up to 45 km and that longer movements occur rarely. One exceptional female, having been ringed in May in Dorset, was found 182 km north-northwest in Hereford 13 months later, a remarkable movement, posing the question of human agency (Fig 5). A median dispersal distance of just 2 km for Little Owls ringed and recovered, including all age classes, provides factual evidence for a strongly sedentary species, generally site-faithful but undertaking limited post-natal movements spanning autumn and winter. This strategy is intermediate between the highly sedentary Tawny Owl and the somewhat more mobile Barn Owl and Long-eared Owl, whereas Short-eared Owl is more migratory and nomadic.

Ringing studies on the Continent show that populations are primarily resident, though first-year birds disperse somewhat randomly, the great majority settling within 20 km of the birthplace, a few undertaking extensive displacements (Exo & Hennes 1978, 1980). Long-distance movements are an occasional feature, rarely exceeding 200 km, but one of 600 km has been recorded in Poland (*BWP*). There is no firm evidence that any dispersing continental birds have ever reached Britain, although intriguingly the *Handbook* suggests that a number of British records may be of genuine vagrants.

Despite initial worries following its introduction, accompanied by heavy persecution on a local scale, the non-native Little Owl has successfully exploited a vacant niche among the avifauna of lowland Britain. As with other introductions, however, this harmonious status is not to be taken for granted in the longer term. Ringing of Little Owls in the 20th century revealed much of its annual cycle. Additional ringing, especially concentrated in the western and northern fringes of its current range, could help to elucidate the factors restricting population expansion. Radio-tagging, especially of adults, could provide welcome extra detail on size of home ranges, foraging needs, and dispersal. Research directed at the heavy losses attributed to traffic could help resolve the biases associated with the dominance of such incidents among ring-recoveries, assess any overall impact on population sizes, and suggest management practices that could reduce mortality. In Britain today, as in much of central Europe, Little Owls breed at low density and in declining numbers, attributed variously to loss of breeding and hunting habitat and safe nest holes, traffic casualties and severe winter weather, aggravated by a sedentary life style. Carefully targeted research could help unravel the relative importance of these factors.

David E Glue

season in northern parts of the range may travel further than those from southern sites. Median recovery distances for birds ringed in the northwest (15 km, *n*=4) and northeast (7.5 km, *n*=6) exceed those of the southwest (2 km, *n*=111) and southeast (1 km, *n*=171) regions. Some recoveries of long-distance travellers may relate to pioneer colonists. For example, a Little Owl found dead at Musselburgh, Lothian, in 1962 had been marked as a chick in Northumberland earlier that year. Another, ringed (when of unknown age) at Rhydycroesau, Denbigh, in December 1981, was recovered 60 km south-southwest at Pantydwr, Radnor, in the following year. Water undoubtedly presents the dispersing Little Owl with a considerable obstacle. There have been no recoveries involving Little Owl movements to continental Europe. Of the four confirmed records of birds reaching Ireland, one was washed ashore, still alive, near Larne, Antrim, in autumn 1945, and another seen on Great Saltee, Wexford, in May 1960 (*Birds in Ireland*).

Tawny Owl
Strix aluco

The Tawny Owl is the most familiar, widespread and common British owl but is absent from Ireland, the Isle of Man and the more remote islands in Scotland. It is very much a sedentary species, rarely moving more than a few kilometres from its natal site throughout its life. There are few other species that show such a high degree of site-fidelity.

It is found across most of Europe, from Scotland and southern Scandinavia to the Mediterranean and into northwest Africa. Eastwards its range extends to the east coast of China, though the species is absent from most of central Asia, separating the Asian populations from those in Europe and western Russia. Tawny Owls are generally absent from more isolated islands because of their limited dispersal ability, and even seem unable to maintain a population on the Isle of Wight. They do, however, occur on most of the inshore Scottish islands including Islay, Jura, Mull, Skye and Raasay. Six races have been recognized within the Western Palearctic: *sylvatica* found in Britain and southwest Europe, *aluco* found in northern and eastern Europe, *siberiae* in the Ural Mountains and western Siberia, *wilkonskii* in the Caucasus, Transcaucasia, northeast Turkey, and northwest Iran, *sanctinicolai* in western Iran, and *mauritanica* in northwest Africa. A further five races have been described in Asia (*BWP*).

Most Tawny Owls are associated with some form of wooded habitat, occurring most abundantly in broad-leaved woodland but they are also common in conifer forests and even lightly wooded gardens and parks, including urban areas. They also occur widely in more open habitats, such as farmland where there is at least some tree cover in the form of hedges and small copses (Hardy 1992, Redpath 1995). The species is strongly territorial, remaining in territories throughout the year.

The analysis of the data for this species was supported by the late Michael Bickmore

There has been a long history of Tawny Owl ringing in Britain. The first recovery was made in 1912, of a bird ringed as a chick two years previously. This pioneering individual moved a distance of 5 km – beginning a pattern of short-distance movements that was to continue to the present day. It was not, however, until the 1960s and 1970s that large-scale ringing across the country was undertaken. Birds have been ringed throughout Britain (Fig 1), though with many fewer ringed outside the breeding season. There are no major biases in the geographical extent of ringing activity; this broadly reflects the species' overall distribution (*1988–91 Atlas*). Most birds are ringed as pulli in April–June (Fig 2), with relatively small numbers trapped and ringed as fully grown birds throughout the year. Much of the ringing has been done by specialist owl enthusiasts, often using extensive nestbox schemes. Our current knowledge of the dispersal and survival patterns of this species across the country has been heavily dependent on such work. There have been a number of professional studies too, most notably by Oxford University (Southern 1970, Hirons 1976), Forestry Commission (Petty 1992) and the BTO (Percival 1990).

The Tawny Owl ring-recovery data do have a number of important biases that need to be considered. A large proportion of the recoveries are from birds that have died through human-related causes (Fig 3), with a particularly high proportion killed on roads. Illner (1992) has shown

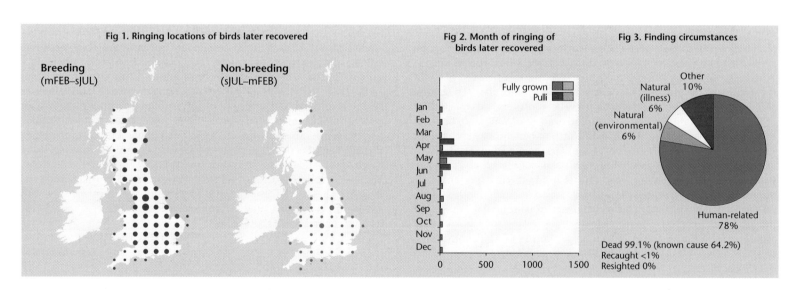

Fig 1. Ringing locations of birds later recovered

Breeding (mFEB–sJUL)

Non-breeding (sJUL–mFEB)

Fig 2. Month of ringing of birds later recovered

Fig 3. Finding circumstances

Dead 99.1% (known cause 64.2%)
Recaught <1%
Resighted 0%

Ringing and recovery data

	<1960	60–69	70–79	80–89	90–97	Total
RINGING						
BTO ringing totals (%)	9	6	13	33	39	27,979
RECOVERIES						
BTO-ringed (%)	10	10	23	35	21	1,776
Foreign-ringed (%)	0	0	0	0	0	0

Statistical analyses

	Breeding population (mFEB–sJUL)	Wintering population (sOCT–sJAN)
Status	SEDENTARY (0)	SEDENTARY
Age differences[NT]	Not significant	Not tested
Sex differences	Not tested	Not tested
Regional differences	Significant[4*]	Not tested
Finding circumstances	Not significant	Not significant*

Fig 4. Locations in winter (283) and movements of over 20 km between the breeding season and winter, of Tawny Owls present in Britain during the breeding season.

Fig 5. Movements of over 20 km and recovery locations of Tawny Owls ringed as pulli in Britain and recovered in a subsequent breeding season when of breeding age. There were 278:22 movements under:over 20 km but only those over 20 km are plotted.

that recoveries of owls can overestimate the actual proportion killed on roads by as much as threefold. Dead birds may also be transported by traffic after they have collided, inflating estimates of dispersal distance. Ringing returns thus give us a biased picture of how owls die.

There is little evidence of any significant mobile component of the population. Though the maximum distance moved was 687 km, this was very much exceptional. This individual was ringed as a chick in Highland Region and recovered in Dyfed. It is probable that such a movement was assisted; it was found dead on a road, so may have been transported by a vehicle after collision. No other Tawny Owls in Britain have moved more than 205 km. Generally this species moves only very short distances between seasons. Fig 4 shows the very small scale of movement between the breeding and winter periods. Movements between breeding and spring/autumn locations are similarly short.

Young Tawny Owls generally establish territories in close proximity to their natal site. The median distance moved of birds ringed as chicks and recovered in a subsequent breeding season when of breeding age is only 4 km ($P5$–95=0–29 km, n=291) and only 7% of natal dispersal movements (for birds found dead) have been of more than 20 km (Fig 5). This is in broad agreement with a more detailed study in Northumberland, where the median natal dispersal distance of both males and females was 3.05 km (Petty 1992). The main period of dispersal away from the parental territory occurs from 90 days after ringing: the median distance moved up to this time is less than 1 km, and thereafter it is 3–6 km. This finding is consistent with more detailed local studies that have reported juvenile dispersal around three months after fledging, during August–November (Southern *et al* 1954, Petty & Thirgood 1989, Coles & Petty 1997). Percival (1990) found three distinct dispersal peaks; these are in the autumn or early winter following fledging, when birds might be establishing their own territories, in the May–June after that, when the next year's young would be starting to become independent, and in their second March–April period when, since Tawny Owls usually breed first at two years old (Southern 1970), birds would be establishing their own breeding territories. The age of first breeding used for the current analysis was set to one since some Tawny Owls begin breeding at one year of age, although others may not begin breeding until they are three years old (Delmée *et al* 1978, Petty 1992). Percival (1990) found longer juvenile dispersal distances in Scotland and northern England than further south, a latitudinal trend that agrees with

Mikkola (1983) who found dispersal distances in Scandinavia to be greater than in studies further south.

There are many fewer data available on adult movements (including breeding dispersal), as many fewer birds have been ringed as adults. The pattern does appear still to be quite clear. Once the birds obtain a territory there is very little movement outside that. The median distance moved by adult Tawny Owls between ringing and recovery is less than 1 km ($P5$–95=0–11, n=102).

No major regional differences are apparent in movement patterns of Tawny Owls using Britain during the breeding season, though the median distance moved was greater in the northwest (5 km) and the northeast (4 km) than in southern regions (2 km). Only a small number of birds from the ring-recovery data set have been sexed, with movements of these birds suggesting that there is no real difference between males and females in the median distance moved: males 2 km ($P5$–95=0–23, n=23) and females 1.5 km ($P5$–95=0–16.5, n=40). An earlier analysis of the ring-recovery data (Percival 1990) showed that the slightly greater median distance moved by males was not statistically significant. No long-term temporal trends in dispersal have been found either (Percival 1990).

There have been no foreign Tawny Owl recoveries to date, either of birds ringed abroad moving to Britain or birds ringed in Britain moving elsewhere. It is clear that the British population is isolated with probably no interchange with other populations.

The very low dispersal rate is characteristic of most Tawny Owl populations that have been studied, with the only exception being birds on the northern fringe of their geographical range in Scandinavia, where rather greater movements have been recorded. Even so, there were still very few birds moving more than 100 km, with a median of 10–15 km (Mikkola 1983).

From a conservation perspective, species with a low dispersal rate are often thought to be more vulnerable to local changes such as habitat loss. However, as far as Tawny Owls are concerned, their low-dispersal strategy appears to be highly successful. They are one of our most abundant predatory birds, have a markedly stable population trend and are continuing to thrive in Britain. Continued ringing of this species across the country, particularly of adults, should help ensure that we have the data to check that this trend is sustained.

Steve Percival

Long-eared Owl
Asio otus

The Long-eared Owl is a widespread specialist predator of microtine rodents in open habitats and one of the few owl species to undertake long-distance movements. In Britain it is both an uncommon, but widespread resident breeding species and a regular and semi-irruptive winter visitor from more northerly and easterly breeding grounds; in Ireland it is a more common breeding species and probably a less frequent migrant. The Long-eared Owl has a circumpolar holarctic distribution with the northern limit approximating to the July 15°C isotherm (Mikkola 1983), the nominate race *otus* being distributed throughout the boreal and temperate Old World. The seasonal movements of the species remain relatively little understood, with the number of birds moving varying from year to year in response to fluctuating rodent abundance (Korpimäki 1992). The Nearctic race *wilsonianus* (here including the doubtfully valid *tuftsi*) is also partially migratory (Marks *et al* 1994), while the other subspecies *canariensis* is a resident and endemic in the Canary Islands.

In Britain, the Long-eared Owl is associated mainly with coniferous and scrub habitats but also breeds in deciduous woodland. The main habitat requirement for breeding is large areas of rough grassland or moorland with abundant populations of small mammals near the nest. There is historical evidence that the species may previously have been more widespread and more associated with woodland (Holloway 1996); the changes may perhaps be due to interspecific competition with the Tawny Owl. In Ireland, the Isle of Man and the Isle of Wight, where there are no Tawny Owls, the Long-eared Owl is also found in wooded habitats and even in suburban environments. In winter, communal

The analysis of the data for this species was supported by Russell McAndrew

roosts form, often in scrub near water, and always in proximity to open habitat suitable for hunting (*Winter Atlas*).

It is evident from Fig 1 that the distribution of ringing locations of birds subsequently recovered does not entirely reflect the breeding and wintering distributions of this species within Britain & Ireland. Comparison with the *1988–91 Atlas* shows populations within southern England, Wales and Ireland to be under-represented in the ring-recovery data and this may introduce bias into any interpretation of movement patterns based purely on these data. Most Long-eared Owls that have been ringed in Britain & Ireland are ringed either as pulli (47.1%) or as adults on migration or in winter (38.4%); relatively few breeding adults have been ringed (Fig 2).

Some 94% of the ring-recoveries refer to birds found dead and the cause of death was known for approximately half of these. Human-related mortality, mostly mediated through collision with vehicles, accounted for 77% of the ring-recoveries for which the cause of death was known, while a further 9% were deliberately taken by Man (Fig 3). This is similar to the pattern seen elsewhere in Europe (Williams 1996). The reporting rate for birds killed on the road is likely to be significantly higher than that for birds dying elsewhere, and is therefore not necessarily representative of the population as a whole. There is a notable seasonal variation in recoveries, with a marked peak in the late

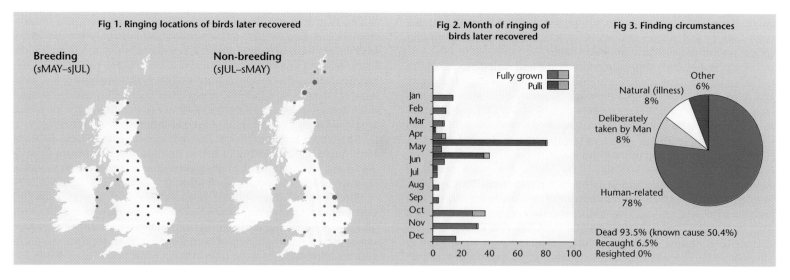

Fig 1. Ringing locations of birds later recovered

Breeding (sMAY–sJUL)

Non-breeding (sJUL–sMAY)

Fig 2. Month of ringing of birds later recovered

Fully grown
Pulli

Fig 3. Finding circumstances

Other 6%
Natural (illness) 8%
Deliberately taken by Man 8%
Human-related 78%

Dead 93.5% (known cause 50.4%)
Recaught 6.5%
Resighted 0%

Ringing and recovery data

	<1960	60–69	70–79	80–89	90–97	Total
RINGING						
BTO ringing totals (%)	14	9	24	28	26	3,738
RECOVERIES						
BTO-ringed (%)	9	14	24	30	23	255
Foreign-ringed (%)	←	53	→	25	23	40

Statistical analyses

	Breeding population (sMAY–sJUL)	Wintering population (mNOV–mMAR)
Status	SEDENTARY* (0)	[LONG-DISTANCE MIGRANT]
Age differences[NT]	Significant*	Not tested
Sex differences	Not tested	Not tested
Regional differences	Not tested*	Not tested
Finding circumstances	Not significant*	Not tested

Fig 4. Locations outside the breeding season and movements of over 20 km between the breeding and non-breeding season of 74 Long-eared Owls present in Britain & Ireland during the breeding season.

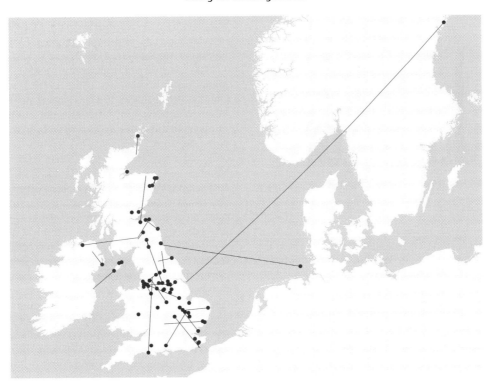

Fig 5. Movements and recovery locations of 18 Long-eared Owls present in Britain & Ireland outside the breeding season and abroad during the breeding season.

winter and spring, a post-fledging peak in August and then a slight increase in mortality during October and November, presumably related to migration. This general pattern has also been found in a larger analysis of European data (Williams 1996), with the notable difference of the lack of the August post-fledging peak in the European data (presumably fledging dates are more dispersed across Europe and so hide this seasonal mortality).

The somewhat limited ring-recovery data suggest that young Long-eared Owls begin to disperse from their natal sites between 31 and 60 days after fledging, but seemingly do not undertake long-distance movements until two to three months after fledging when their flight feathers are fully grown (Ulmschneider 1990). Natal philopatry appears to be relatively low, with a median natal dispersal distance of 42 km based on 12 recoveries. Studies in North America suggest that some males, unlike females, return

Fig 6. Numbers of Long-eared Owls arriving at Spurn and Fair Isle Bird Observatories, 1963–94. (*Source*: Williams 1996.)

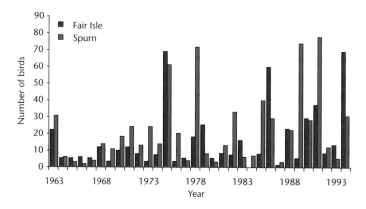

to breed less than 2 km from their natal territories (Marks 1985). There are few records of birds from the British & Irish breeding population being recovered outside Britain & Ireland, which suggests a largely resident breeding population (Fig 4).

Ring-recoveries suggest that the vast majority of the birds arriving in Britain & Ireland for the winter originate from Fennoscandia, with smaller numbers from Russia and elsewhere in eastern Europe, though this pattern may reflect greater ringing effort in Fennoscandia. There are fewer movements between eastern Britain and the Low Countries (Fig 5). Differential migration occurs between the sexes, with males apparently remaining further north than females, at least in some parts of the range. Uneven sex ratios in favour of females have been found in autumn migrants passing through Fair Isle (male:female ratio 16:56; Harvey & Riddiford 1990) and also at Landguard Bird Observatory (7:32; Williams 1996). A similarly biased sex ratio has been found in dead birds wintering in Britain (male:female ratio 8:42; Wyllie *et al* 1996) and in skins collected during winter, lodged at the British Museum (2:13; Williams 1996). Long-eared Owls wintering in southern Norway have been found to show a significant sex bias in favour of males (23:13; Overskaug & Kristiansen 1994), while wintering populations in eastern Denmark, Sweden and southern Germany approach parity (Erritzoe & Fuller 1999). A female-biased sex ratio has also been found in Long-eared Owls wintering in the Netherlands (10:27; Erritzoe & Fuller 1999) and in northern India (10:34; Williams 1998). It appears that there is also a biased age ratio, towards first-winter birds, certainly evident in males arriving in Britain (pers obs). However, this is difficult to document because so few birds have been accurately aged.

Autumn migration is spread across the whole autumn, and arrival dates vary widely from year to year, presumably in relation to fluctuations in food supply and breeding success, with birds arriving from July to December but generally showing a peak in October. Migration seems to occur mostly at night but birds can be seen arriving after sea-crossings until late in the morning. Immigrants seem to be scattered in small numbers throughout Britain to Scilly and across into Ireland. It is possible that some of the westerly and southern migrants are continuing further south in Europe, since wintering birds from northern breeding areas have been recorded as far south as Spain. Many birds are seen singly but there is evidence that birds may migrate in flocks, especially in years of invasions (see Slack *et al* 1987).

The Long-eared Owl is semi-irruptive, with vastly increased numbers migrating in some years (Glue 1976, Davenport 1982, Mikkola 1983, Glue & Whittington 1987). Cyclical peaks have been documented in numbers arriving at mid-latitudes within Europe. On Helgoland, numbers of autumn migrants have been found to peak every two to five years (Schmidt & Vauk 1981), while on Fair Isle peaks have been observed every three to four years (Harvey & Riddiford 1990; Fig 6). Numbers recorded at Fair Isle have been found to be significantly correlated with numbers recorded at other east coast sites with long data sets (Norfolk and Spurn Point). The numbers recorded on the Norfolk coast were also found to be correlated with the numbers at two other sites with shorter runs of data (Gibraltar Point and Sandwich Bay).

Spring migration is also spread out, with birds moving north between February and June. Numbers recorded on Fair Isle and on the North Sea oil platforms in spring have both been found to be correlated with the numbers observed there on autumn migration the previous year (Williams 1996). The number of migrants recorded in autumn is significantly correlated with the number of winter roosts subsequently reported in county bird reports (Williams 1996). This correlation suggests that winter roosts, especially the large ones, may be largely composed of winter immigrants; it is not known if immigrant and British breeding birds form joint roosts. Elsewhere, winter roosts have been shown to contain resident owls and their offspring (Wijnandts 1984, Ulmschneider 1993). The distribution of roosts in Britain implies that winter immigrants reach all areas but are concentrated in the east (Williams 1996) and this is where the larger roosts tend to be found. Roosts are often in traditional sites, suggesting that there may be at least some degree of winter site-fidelity between years (Smith 1981). The ring-recovery data show a median between-winter recovery distance of 223 km, but this is based on only four recoveries and therefore cannot provide any information on the degree of fidelity to wintering sites. Roost sites tend to be located in areas where they are not susceptible to disturbance.

It is unknown whether any of the winter visitors ever remain to breed, as there has never been a recovery of a foreign-ringed bird at a confirmed breeding locality, but few breeding adults are caught. Likewise, there is little evidence of British-bred birds moving overseas; two birds ringed in Britain during the breeding season and subsequently recovered on the Continent are considered to have been late migrants (Fig 4). The relatively high recovery rate makes ringing of this species valuable. Our lack of knowledge of the undoubtedly interesting and complex movements of this species is a reflection of the small numbers ringed, and studies that catch and ring breeding adults should be encouraged, together with greater use of radio-tracking techniques.

Rob Williams

Short-eared Owl
Asio flammeus

Among terrestrial birds, the Short-eared Owl is often perceived as the classic example of an opportunistic wanderer, seeking out unpredictably volatile and often cyclical populations of microtine rodents. Géroudet (1965) described them succinctly as: 'nomads who camp where the table is laid'. Is this the complete story, however? Structurally, these owls are ideally suited to long-distance travel. Long, narrow wings and a relatively light wing-loading enable them to cruise for long periods with little expenditure of energy (Mikkola 1983). Some populations are capable of establishing a relatively settled existence, however, and regulate their clutch sizes to some extent to match their prospective food supplies (Roberts & Bowman 1986).

The Short-eared Owl has a wide circumpolar range, and a discontinuous distribution in America, extending south to Patagonia and the Falklands (BWP). In Europe, the species nests in Britain & Ireland and Iceland, and is widespread on the Continent, breeding patchily and erratically from Spain north to Scandinavia but possibly more extensively eastwards from Finland and the Ukraine (European Atlas). Those owls breeding within Eurasia and North America belong to the nominate race flammeus. At least seven other subspecies occur elsewhere. This owl is tolerant of a wide range of climates but nests chiefly in tundra, boreal and temperate zones. Large tracts of Fennoscandia and Russia can be vacated when there is a collapse in populations of microtine rodents, which is typically a cyclical occurrence with a periodicity of three to four years (Hölzinger et al 1973, Hanski et al 1991, Korpimäki & Norrdahl 1991). Those populations that occur on remote islands, such as the Caroline, Hawaiian and Galápagos groups, probably result from the spectacular long-distance movements occasionally undertaken by wandering birds.

The analysis of the data for this species was supported by Philip Ellis

Not surprisingly, individuals may be found, if only for part of the year, on all continents, with the exception of Australia.

To breed successfully, Short-eared Owls require a relatively extensive and undisturbed tract of open ground harbouring adequate supplies of small mammals. Within Britain, these basic requirements are met most frequently across stretches of grass–heather moorland, bogs and recently afforested parts of the Scottish uplands, foothills and Borders, the Pennines and Staffordshire moors of England, sections of the Cambrian Mountains and parts of North Wales. Pairs breed more erratically on coastal rough grazing and marshland in southeast England, and also more consistently on outlying islands, notably Orkney, the Inner Hebrides, the Isle of Man and Skomer (*1988–91 Atlas*). Breeding numbers may vary substantially between years, and site occupation is often tenuous in many parts; territory size and hunting ranges may vary widely in relation to rodent abundance (Lockie 1955, Mikkola 1983, Village 1987). Ireland supports only a small breeding population; first noted in Galway in 1959, this was initially confined to the southwest but has spread north (Jones 1979, *Birds in Ireland*), reaching Antrim in 1997. The Short-eared Owl is largely a winter visitor to Ireland, occupying mainly east-coast estuarine habitats, though individuals wander widely. In Britain, in winter, many birds move from upland moors, forested areas and bogs to coastal marshes and dunes, farmland and downland (*Winter Atlas*). In winter, Short-eared Owls generally roost communally, regularly on the ground at favoured

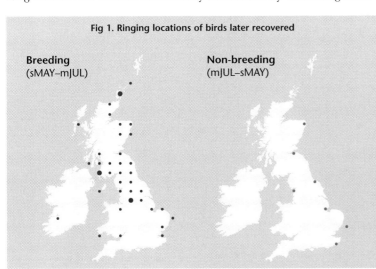

Fig 1. Ringing locations of birds later recovered

Breeding
(sMAY–mJUL)

Non-breeding
(mJUL–sMAY)

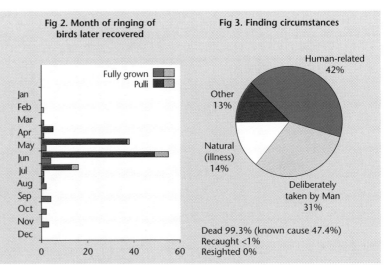

Fig 2. Month of ringing of birds later recovered

Fig 3. Finding circumstances

Human-related 42%

Other 13%

Natural (illness) 14%

Deliberately taken by Man 31%

Dead 99.3% (known cause 47.4%)
Recaught <1%
Resighted 0%

Ringing and recovery data

	<1960	60–69	70–79	80–89	90–97	Total
RINGING						
BTO ringing totals (%)	16	9	20	32	24	2,335
RECOVERIES						
BTO-ringed (%)	21	14	22	26	18	125
Foreign-ringed (%)	←	47	→	32	21	19

Statistical analyses

	Breeding population (sMAY–mJUL)	Wintering population (mNOV–sMAR)
Status	SEDENTARY*	[LONG-DISTANCE MIGRANT]
Age differences	Not tested	Not tested
Sex differences	Not tested	Not tested
Regional differences	Not tested	Not tested
Finding circumstances	Not tested	Not tested

Fig 4. Locations in (a) the breeding season (7:5), (b) autumn (32:11), (c) winter (8:5) and (d) spring (2:3), and movements of over 20 km of Short-eared Owls ringed in Britain & Ireland as pulli. Birds recovered in their first year (red) are differentiated from birds recovered in later years (blue). Sample sizes (first years:older birds) are given. The 32 seasonally inaccurate movements are shown in (a) in grey.

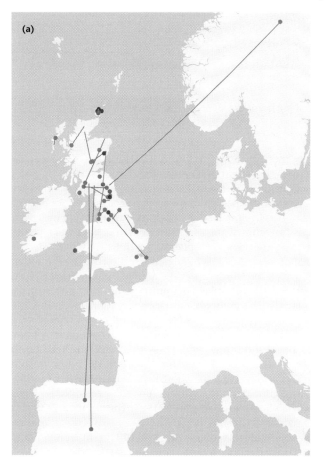

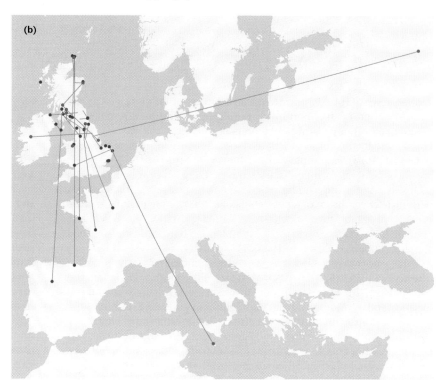

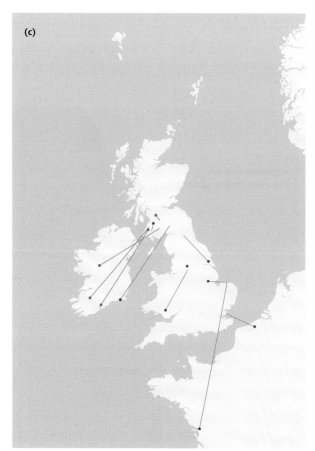

Fig 5. Exchanges of Short-eared Owls between Britain & Ireland and abroad for birds present in Britain & Ireland in (a) the breeding season (0:2), (b) autumn (1:2), (c) winter (3:0) and (d) spring (1:0). Birds recovered in their first year (red) are differentiated from birds recovered in later years (blue), with six seasonally inaccurate exchanges shown in grey. Those ringed as pulli in Britain & Ireland (shown in Fig 4) are excluded from this figure, as are those ringed abroad pre-1979 in Finland (3), Iceland (1), Norway (1), Sweden (1), Germany (1) and Belgium (1). Sample sizes (first years:older birds) are given.

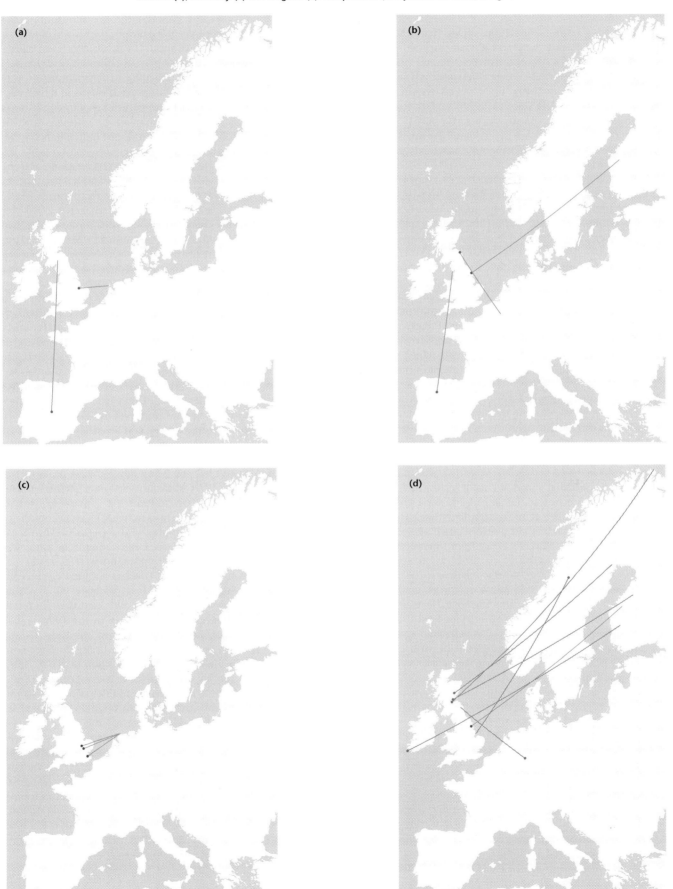

settling places among tall grasses, heather, sedges and scrub. Roosts may hold a dozen or more owls but comings and goings reflect the mobility of the population in winter (Glue 1977, *Winter Atlas*).

The distribution of ringing sites of those owls subsequently recovered (Fig 1) matches closely the breeding range of the Short-eared Owl in Britain & Ireland (*1988–91 Atlas*). Populations on the Staffordshire moors and in Dumfries & Galloway and Orkney are especially strongly represented but central Wales, the Scottish Borders and much of the western Highlands are somewhat under-represented. Overall, of the Short-eared Owl recoveries involving birds ringed within Britain & Ireland, and those of foreign origin since 1979, 84% and 91% respectively relate to owls ringed as nestlings, mostly during May–July (Fig 2). These provide a rich sample of birds of known natal origin. The small number of pulli ringed as early as April very probably involved owls raised in years of Field Vole abundance (Lockie 1955).

Usefully, almost half of all Short-eared Owl recoveries have been attributed a cause of death (Fig 3). Of these, 42% are human-related, the great majority through collision with a moving vehicle on road or rail (almost all within Britain). The main hunting technique employed by this owl, alternate flapping and gliding 0.3–2 m above the vegetation, and rarely above 3 m (Clark 1975), increases their vulnerability to traffic. Caution is required when interpreting this aspect of the ringing data, however, since the reporting rate for Short-eared Owls killed on road and rail is likely to be greater than for those birds recovered in other ways, especially in habitats more remote from Man, and may not be representative of the population at large. In addition, studies for other owl species (*eg* Barn Owl, Taylor 1994), have demonstrated that corpses may be transported for some distance by the vehicle with which they have collided. Small samples preclude an accurate assessment of this potential bias.

Some 31% of those confirmed causes of death involve Short-eared Owls deliberately taken by Man (whether shot, trapped or poisoned) but this factor is of unknown overall significance to the population. Cases include nine birds recovered in Britain, five in Ireland, four in Spain and single instances in Russia and Malta. This owl's year-round affinity with moorland, and a strong winter association with coastal habitats and downland, make it a potential target for gamekeepers and foreshore guns. Short-eared Owls are not at the top of the food chain, a fact emphasized by a small number of recoveries (8%) that describe birds killed by larger avian and mammalian predators such as Rough-legged Buzzard and Red Fox. A few owls (14%) died from starvation, either as migrants exhausted after sea-crossings or as birds prevented from hunting by high winds, driving rain or snow-cover.

Young Short-eared Owls reared in Britain & Ireland generally stay near the breeding site for several weeks after fledging, learning hunting techniques and gradually relying less on parents for food (Lockie 1955, Village 1987). For most nesting attempts, this behaviour spans May to July. The median dispersal distance for recoveries made within the second month after ringing is just 9 km (*n*=13), rising strongly to 61 (*n*=8), 228 (*n*=5), 418 (*n*=5) and 490 km (*n*=6) in subsequent monthly periods. Young birds disperse in all directions, with the strongest movements undertaken between August and November, though individuals continue to wander throughout their first winter of life (Fig 4).

Recovery samples are too small to detect regional differences in dispersal. Many ring-recoveries suggest a movement away from upland moors and hills to coastal localities from July to October, and some movement westward to Ireland (notably in November). Movements within Britain, and those to the Continent, exhibit progressively greater distances along a southerly axis, most strikingly from breeding strongholds in southwest Scotland and northern England (Fig 4). Water is no barrier to this owl, unlike both Tawny and Little Owls. Ringing shows how Britain exports home-bred birds to France and Iberia, and even Malta: a Norfolk nestling was found on Gozo in October. Recoveries in central England and along the east coast in April and May endorse an observed return spring passage to breeding haunts within Britain and on the near Continent at this time. The ring-recovery data contain only four natal dispersal movements, an insufficient number from which to determine the degree of natal site-fidelity. Similarly there is no information on breeding dispersal. Information from published sources suggests that this species is strongly opportunistic in nature, in contrast to other British & Irish owl species. Historically, Short-eared Owls have responded rapidly to the vole plagues periodically witnessed in Scotland (Adair 1892, Lockie 1955), breeding in larger numbers and producing bigger broods in areas where vole populations were at high densities. More recent work has shown that numbers of breeding Short-eared Owls were positively correlated with vole numbers on southern Scottish study sites (Village 1987). Resightings of wing-tagged individuals demonstrated that individuals seemed less likely to breed in the study area in successive years when vole numbers were in decline than when numbers were increasing. Two wing-tagged owls were located 420–500 km away in the following year, one of which was definitely breeding. Furthermore, of all Short-eared Owls ringed in Britain & Ireland and later recovered, a strikingly high 14% had moved to other countries: six to Spain, four to France, two to Sweden and singles to Belgium, the Faeroes, Germany, Malta and European Russia (Figs 4 & 5), providing further evidence of long-distance travel.

On the Continent, the Short-eared Owl is strongly migratory in the north, broadly a partial migrant in other parts of its breeding range, and nomadic at times throughout. In autumn, owls usually withdraw from Fennoscandia (except Scania) and much of Russia, to winter in central and southern parts of Europe (*BWP*). Owls ringed in Fennoscandia have provided a broad scatter of recoveries but with most moving southwest to warmer climes (*BWP*). Britain receives a substantial influx of Short-eared Owls in late autumn, primarily from late August through to November, chiefly to the east coast and to a lesser extent the southern counties (Davenport 1982, *Winter Atlas*). Clues to the origins of these birds are provided by seven recoveries from Finland, four from the Netherlands, two each from Belgium, Norway and Sweden, and singles from Iceland and Germany, including owls ringed at the nest. Breeding numbers, productivity and survival can increase sharply over small and large areas of the Short-eared Owl's breeding range during peaks of the vole cycle (Picozzi & Hewson 1970, Mikkola 1983, Shaw 1995). Progeny from such events no doubt contribute towards the considerable variability of the winter influx. Some summer ring-recoveries are far from the natal ringing site. For example, a Finnish-bred bird travelled west to Scotland in the subsequent summer, while an English-ringed nestling was found in September, two years later, in Vologda, Russia (Figs 4 & 5).

Worryingly, the Short-eared Owl has declined as a breeding bird over wide parts of Europe, chiefly it is perceived as a result of habitat degradation (*European Atlas*). The owl increased in Britain at times during the 20th century, most recently in the 1970s, reflecting short-term provision of favourable nesting grounds through upland afforestation. More recent surveys show a highly fragmented breeding population and a slight population reduction (*1988–91 Atlas*). Increased ringing of this species, which is of conservation concern and on the Amber List (Gibbons *et al* 1996a), could help throw welcome extra light on the reasons behind such trends through an improved knowledge of the bird's annual cycle. Additional research is required to determine the nature of dispersal movements during the first few months of life, the scale of interchange between pockets of breeding birds within Britain & Ireland, and the extent and degree of nomadism on a wider scale. Radio-tagging and wing-tagging of adults and juveniles could greatly improve our appreciation of breeding ecology and seasonal movement patterns. Nesting perhaps amid deep heather, on remote moorland, the Short-eared Owl poses a testing challenge to ringers but it is a bird that richly deserves closer scrutiny and offers rich rewards by way of exciting research prospects and intriguing recoveries.

David E Glue

European Nightjar (Nightjar)

Caprimulgus europaeus

Nightjars are enchanting and mysterious birds of the night, known best by their churring song. They are summer visitors to Britain & Ireland and feed on flying insects, mostly moths and beetles. Protected by their wonderfully cryptic plumage, they will often sit unseen on the ground at their roost or nest site until approached to within a few metres.

Nightjars breed throughout the Palearctic. The nominate race *europaeus* occurs throughout northern Europe as far east as Mongolia. Up to five other races are recognized, though there is some debate over two or three of these, and there seems to be much clinal intergradation (Cleere 1998). The stronghold of the species is Russia, Belarus and some other former Soviet states, whose Nightjar population estimates comprise between one-third and two-thirds of the European total of between 300,000 and 800,000 pairs (*European Atlas*). Within western Europe, the bulk of the population breeds in Spain, where there are thought to be between 80,000 and 100,000 pairs. The British population of about 3,400 pairs is a very small proportion of the whole, and Ireland holds only about 25 pairs. British Nightjar sites are widely spread but there is a skew towards East Anglia and southern England, where more than 80% of birds are found (Morris *et al* 1994).

Eastern and southern Africa probably hold most of the world population of the nominate race in winter, though there are some records from West Africa, and a few as far north as Morocco. A small population, thought to be of the race *unwini*, overwinters in northwest India and Pakistan. The autumn migration seems to be on a broad southerly front across western Europe and North Africa, while the more easterly populations migrate southeast across the Middle East. Ring-recoveries are

The analysis of the data for this species was supported by Stour Ringing Group

few, however, and insufficient to reveal clear migration routes and differential wintering areas if they exist. Furthermore, the nocturnal nature of the species at all times, and its cryptic plumage, make it unlikely to be seen on migration.

In Britain, 54% of Nightjars breed in plantation woodlands (Morris *et al* 1994). Most of the rest (38% of the total) occupy lowland heath, and the remaining 8% nest on the periphery of raised bogs, or on commons, sand-dunes, shingle, industrial tips or chalk downland. At least in some areas of Britain, however, Nightjars may depend on different habitats for feeding. Radio-tracking of birds nesting on clearfell and heath in Dorset and the New Forest, Hampshire, has revealed that they make nocturnal excursions, almost certainly solely for feeding, to habitats not used for breeding such as deciduous woodland, open farmland and wet meadow (Alexander & Cresswell 1990). In the African wintering areas, Nightjars use all types of wooded habitats, including mopane and miombo woodland, riparian formations and savanna. They are found also in open sandy country, clearings in wet evergreen forest and in dry acacia scrub near coasts, occurring in highlands at altitudes up to 5,000 m (Cleere 1998).

Most ringing of Nightjars in Britain & Ireland has been at breeding sites in southern England (Fig 1). No ring-recoveries involve Ireland. There are 75 recoveries of British-ringed Nightjars available for analysis,

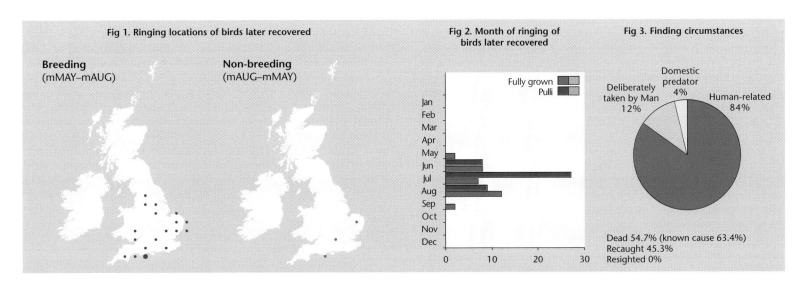

Fig 1. Ringing locations of birds later recovered

Breeding (mMAY–mAUG) Non-breeding (mAUG–mMAY)

Fig 2. Month of ringing of birds later recovered

Fully grown
Pulli

Jan, Feb, Mar, Apr, May, Jun, Jul, Aug, Sep, Oct, Nov, Dec

0 10 20 30

Fig 3. Finding circumstances

Deliberately taken by Man 12%
Domestic predator 4%
Human-related 84%

Dead 54.7% (known cause 63.4%)
Recaught 45.3%
Resighted 0%

Ringing and recovery data

	<1960	60–69	70–79	80–89	90–97	Total
RINGING						
BTO ringing totals (%)	12	5	10	37	36	3,651
RECOVERIES						
BTO-ringed (%)	11	7	9	49	24	75
Foreign-ringed (%)	0	0	0	0	0	0

Statistical analyses

	Breeding population (mMAY–mAUG)	Wintering population (mNOV–mMAR)
Status	[LONG-DISTANCE MIGRANT]	NONE
Age differences	Not tested	—
Sex differences	Not tested	—
Regional differences	Not tested	—
Finding circumstances	Not tested	—

Fig 4. Recovery locations and movements of over 20 km for the 75 included recoveries of Nightjars ringed or recovered in Britain & Ireland.

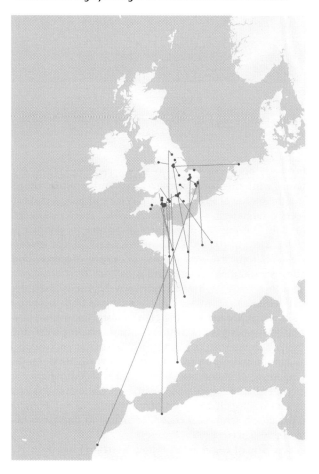

of which 84% have been in Britain. The recoveries are mainly from birds ringed as pulli although breeding adults and fledged juveniles, many attracted to mist-nets using tape-lures, have also been ringed and recovered (Fig 2). Around half of the birds recovered in Britain were caught and released by ringers. There are very few records to indicate the causes of death but human-related causes are greatly in the majority (Fig 3). In Britain, half the birds recovered dead were killed on the road. Of the 10 birds recovered elsewhere in Europe, all were dead — six were shot, two were killed on roads and two collided with man-made structures such as power lines. Two birds in Morocco were trapped and killed, probably for food.

Observations have revealed only the basics of the species' seasonal movements. Nightjars start to leave their breeding grounds from late July onwards, though most depart in late August or September, and some late birds are recorded in Britain in October or even November (*BWP*). The winter quarters are occupied from late September to early April; birds head north or northeast again from March onwards to arrive on the breeding grounds in late April and May (*BWP*). Ringing adds little to this picture. Within Britain, the pattern of recoveries is heavily influenced by the distribution of specialist ringing activity. Of recoveries from abroad, eight birds were in France, two in Morocco, and one each in the Netherlands and Spain (Fig 4). The dates of finding, where reliably known, suggest that all the birds recovered abroad were on passage.

Ringing and radio-tracking have provided insights into movements on the breeding grounds, however, both within and between breeding seasons. Two males radio-tracked in the New Forest took short foraging trips to a nearby farm with pasture and deciduous woodland, though they were also seen feeding over heath. In the week before autumn departure, one of these birds moved into oak woodland and the other to Blackthorn

scrub (Andy Welch pers comm). Birds in Dorset travelled up to 6 km (median=3 km, *n*=36) to feeding sites outside the breeding areas (Alexander & Cresswell 1990). Nightjars radio-tracked in Thetford Forest, Norfolk/Suffolk, travelled no further than 2 km and mostly their activity was within 1 km of their nest site. These birds selected grass heathland and young plantations, though their choice was limited because other habitats such as deciduous woodland are scarce in Thetford Forest (Bowden & Green 1991). A study of birds breeding in Clipstone Forest, Nottinghamshire, recorded only short foraging excursions averaging less than 400 m. Nonetheless, these Nightjars also visited atypical habitats such as deciduous woodland (Carl Larsen pers comm).

Patterns of natal and breeding dispersal are difficult to assess because the data are so sparse. Both are certain to be influenced by the patchy distribution of Nightjar breeding habitat. In the national ring-recovery database, three of 13 birds ringed as pulli and recovered as adults in a subsequent breeding season were more than 20 km distant (maximum 61 km).

In the Dorset study of Nightjars breeding in forestry plantation clearings and on heathland, birds ringed as juveniles and retrapped in subsequent years had moved further (median=4.4 km, *n*=44) than birds ringed as adults (median=0.4 km, *n*=81); this difference was significant for both sexes. The medians quoted will underestimate the real values, however, because trapping effort was confined to particular sites within Dorset, and long-distance movements will not have been detected. Birds moved significantly further after their first breeding season than in subsequent breeding seasons but no difference was detectable between the sexes. Birds ringed during their first breeding season and recaught a year or more later had moved a median distance of 1.6 km (*n*=15), whereas birds known to be at least two years old when first ringed had moved a median of only 0.2 km (*n*=16) when caught again a year or more later. Breeding site-fidelity among adult male Nightjars in the New Forest was apparently very high: of 15 birds retrapped between years, none had moved from the site where it was originally ringed (Andy Welch pers comm).

While Nightjars breed throughout the near Continent and in southern Norway, and some through passage of continental birds is therefore likely, there is no clear evidence that birds from foreign breeding populations occur in Britain either in spring or in autumn. Ring-recoveries show no suggestion of British-ringed birds breeding abroad, and no Nightjars ringed abroad have been recovered in Britain.

After a decline lasting for most of the 20th century, the British population in the 1990s seemed at least to be stable, and maybe even rising, probably due to the increase in the area of suitable breeding habitat (Gribble 1983, Morris *et al* 1994, Scott *et al* 1998). The increasing amount of clear-fell from forestry plantations now maturing, having been planted after World War II, is thought to account for the welcome increase in the population shown by the national survey in 1992. Although this suggests that breeding sites are the key to population growth, the importance of feeding habitats such as deciduous woodland and wetlands should not be overlooked. These locations are visited at the time of night that Nightjars catch most of their food, as shown by increases in body-weight and activity patterns of radio-tagged birds in Dorset (Cresswell & Alexander 1992).

It is possible that birds breeding in different regions of Europe have distinct wintering areas but it seems unlikely that ringing alone will ever yield sufficient data to show this. Perhaps analysis of song structure or genetic material, or advances in radio-tracking technology, may one day shed light on the global movements of this and other elusive migratory birds. Research to quantify the importance of feeding habitats would also be useful for assessing the best way to conserve Nightjar populations.

Brian Cresswell

Common Swift (Swift)

Apus apus

The Common Swift (hereafter Swift) is the most aerial of all our birds. Uniquely for a British & Irish bird, some of the non-breeders do not come to ground at night but 'roost' on the wing; some birds may not even touch down at all during the whole summer. It is even possible that most Swifts spend the whole of the winter in Africa on the wing, since roosting sites have not been reported (Moreau 1972). When 'roosting' in this way they ascend to 600 m or more at dusk (Lack 1958a), possibly to avoid collisions; some head out over the sea, possibly for the same reason, returning at dawn (Lack 1958b). A special 'gliding' flight may be involved (Wright *et al* 2000).

It breeds throughout most of the Palearctic, from Morocco, Ireland and Norway in the west to China in the east, avoiding the higher latitudes. Those populations breeding from Iraq/Iran eastwards through Mongolia to China belong to a separate subspecies, *pekinensis*, which is paler than the nominate race.

Historically, the Swift nested in holes high in large trees, often those made by woodpeckers; it still does so in a few places. However, in most areas it nowadays nests almost exclusively in buildings, usually those where the nest sites can be above about 6 m from the ground, allowing the bird easy access to the site. This restricts the breeding habitat to towns or villages, but the birds forage over much wider areas. In fine weather, they often forage quite high in the sky though they concentrate in places where their prey accumulate, such as along weather fronts. In wet or windy weather, they tend to forage in sheltered areas, such as the lee of a wood or the embankment of a reservoir.

The analysis of the data for this species was supported by Jake Allsop & Chris Mead for 'Concern for Swifts'

Almost all Swifts winter in Africa, south of the Sahara, with larger numbers in tropical areas than in southern Africa. Small numbers of Swifts may winter in northern India and in Arabia, though these are presumably not from Britain & Ireland. The main wintering grounds of the nominate race are probably largely south of 4°S in the Congo Basin, Tanzania and from Malawi to the Cape (Fry *et al* 1988, Herroelen 1998). Although the majority of birds seem to winter well south of the Equator, it is possible that a small number may spend much of the northern winter no further south than 10–15°N, since there are apparent wintering records in the Gambia, Ivory Coast, Liberia, Nigeria, Cameroon and even Mali, with a few others further to the east in Ethiopia (Moreau 1972). However, general observations suggest that these areas do not hold many Swifts in winter and many of the sightings to the north of the main wintering range may be of birds en route to or from their breeding quarters (Fry *et al* 1988) or forced to move northwards by food shortages or northeastern harmattan winds (Herroelen 1998). There is potential for confusion with the African Black Swift through much of the wintering range. Because they are long-lived (Perrins 1971), many Swifts make the return journey to Africa many times.

Being so aerial, the Swift is entirely dependent on airborne prey. Since these are only plentiful in fine weather, the behaviour of the birds is

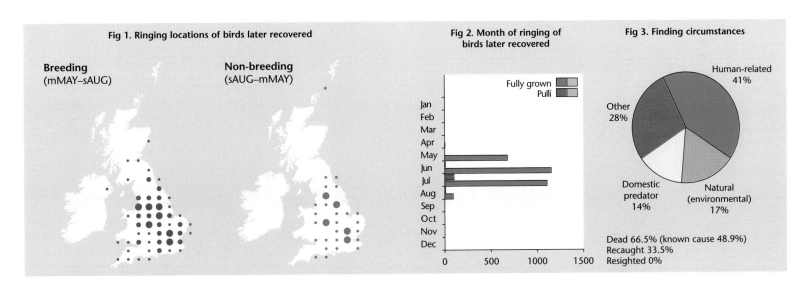

Ringing and recovery data

	<1960	60–69	70–79	80–89	90–97	Total
RINGING						
BTO ringing totals (%)	5	34	26	25	9	168,618
RECOVERIES						
BTO-ringed (%)	5	34	28	26	6	3,147
Foreign-ringed (%)	←	86	→	14	0	7

Statistical analyses

	Breeding population (mMAY–sAUG)	Wintering population (mOCT–mMAR)
Status	LONG-DISTANCE MIGRANT* (4)	NONE
Age differences	Not tested	—
Sex differences	Not tested	—
Regional differences	Not tested	—
Finding circumstances	Not tested*	—

Fig 4. Recovery locations in (a) autumn (138:12:98), (b) winter (20:1:43), (c) spring (228:27:36) and (d) the breeding season (2188:1:255) of Swifts ringed in Britain & Ireland. Those ringed during the breeding season (red) and outside the breeding season (blue) are differentiated from those of uncertain seasonality (grey). Sample sizes of the three classes (ringed breeding season: ringed outside the breeding season: uncertain seasonality) are shown.

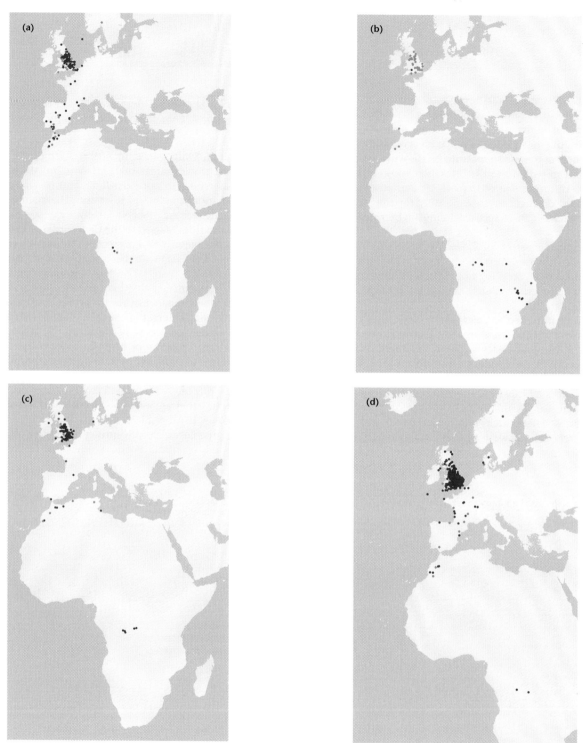

strongly weather dependent. They return from wintering in Africa in late April or early May, when spring is already well under way and flying insects are available; hence they are one of the last migrants to return in spring. They are also one of the first birds to leave on their southward migration. Indeed, Lack (1958c) pointed out that the Swift was the only British species whose autumn migration date was fixed by the date at which breeding started. While this is an oversimplification, it is true that the birds migrate soon after the young have left the nest. In accordance with this, birds from further south in Europe, although having a food supply that extends later into the summer than British and Irish birds,

depart earlier, again very soon after their young have fledged (Lack 1956). In Britain & Ireland, departures start as early as mid-July, though in years when bad weather delays the start of breeding or, in the case of individuals which have lost a clutch and relaid, adults may be present into early September or even later, though such late birds are exceptional. Stragglers in October and November may well be continental migrants rather than departing British or Irish birds. Very exceptionally, Swifts have been recorded as being apparently trapped in Europe, perhaps because they could not build up sufficient reserves to migrate; in one case these remained into early November before dying (Kolunen & Peiponen 1991).

The extreme aerial habit of Swifts means that they are not easily killed by hunters or recaptured by ringers so that there are relatively few ring-recoveries on which to base our knowledge. Figure 1 shows largely what one might expect with a species centred on the urban areas. The large majority of birds subsequently recovered have been ringed as fully grown during the four summer months, with small numbers of pulli ringed in July and August (Fig 2). Figure 3 shows that more than half of the known causes of recovery are associated with Man or his pets. The close association of nesting Swifts with Man may mean that these circumstances bias Swift recovery patterns less than those of many other species. However, almost 70% of the 43 recoveries of known cause in Africa, and seven of the nine in Iberia, have been due to hunting, which will influence overall recovery patterns.

Although few nestlings have been ringed, we have learned something of their movements from ringing. Most depart from the nesting site almost immediately and do not return to the nest to roost, though there have been a (very) few reports of young birds roosting nearby. Late summer catches by ringers contain very few juveniles, suggesting that most young leave the country fairly quickly (Hutson *et al* 1970). It seems likely that they receive no further parental care from the moment that they leave the nest. Observations at a colony in Oxford (pers obs) have shown that the fledglings often leave the nest when the parents are absent and that the parents may continue to roost in the nest site for three or four days after the young have departed, so that no post-fledging care is possible. In one case, a chick left the nest on 31 July and was killed in Madrid (*c* 1,300 km south) on 3 August; that night its parents were still roosting in the nest. This is also the fastest recorded movement of a fledgling Swift from its nesting site. The migration habits of these young birds are not well known, though it appears that, unlike the adults, they do not moult their flight feathers in winter in Africa. Since they do not normally breed in their first year, and may not start until the age of four, it is generally assumed that the Swifts that are seen in Africa throughout the northern summer are immatures. Some first-year birds do return to Britain but numbers seem low (Hutson *et al* 1970). There are three recoveries of British-ringed birds in central Africa in the northern summer, one in each of May, June and July. At least one of these was an adult but, since there is often an inaccuracy in the reported finding dates of African recoveries, it is probably unwise to draw any conclusions until more records are available.

Their dependence on aerial insects means that, in bad weather, Swifts may be very mobile within Europe. The most common pattern is for them to head into the wind; by doing this they tend to skirt round depressions, so reaching better weather sooner. In bad weather, their search for airborne insect food may take them on journeys of perhaps 2,000 km (Koskimies 1950, Svärdson 1951). At such times, movements between England and continental Europe are quite frequent (Hurrell 1951, Harber 1952). These movements are, to some extent, borne out by the records from the bird observatories, where few Swifts breed. Observations show almost no signs of spring and autumn peaks but, rather, constant levels throughout most of the period of May to August. R & F report that 'Large flocks can appear at any location at any time during the summer. Feeding birds are attracted to sea-breeze fronts where insects are carried upwards to the inversion level, they move in the van of thunderstorms where updrafts similarly sweep insects to higher levels, and they fly round the southern edge of depressions to reach a warmer sector.'

These lengthy movements must, of course, be undertaken mainly by non-breeding birds, since breeders tend to return to the nest with food at least three times a day even in bad weather. Normally, breeding birds tend to feed close to the nesting site, as in fine weather they return with meals up to 8–10 times per day. Nevertheless, nesting birds may be involved in such movements on occasions (Koskimies 1950). This means that the location of a recovery far distant from a bird's breeding site or birthplace, especially in the first two or three years of life, does not necessarily mean that it has dispersed that distance; it may have been searching for better feeding. Since most Swifts are mist-netted when flying low in bad weather,

this means that the place of origin cannot be known with any degree of accuracy. Similar large-scale weather movements have been reported from their wintering quarters (Moreau 1972), where of course the birds are not constrained by having to return to a nest site.

British & Irish ring-recoveries of Swifts are in line with the general observations of their winter quarters, with recoveries in the Congo Basin (18), Malawi (11), Tanzania (two) and one each from Zambia, Zimbabwe, Mozambique and South Africa (Fig 4). Bearing in mind the low probability of obtaining recoveries from some of these areas, it seems likely that the centre of gravity of the distribution is the Congo Basin but many Swifts, ringed in a number of European countries, have been recovered in Malawi (Oatley 1999). This relatively small number of recoveries differs a little from the overall winter distribution in that there is a dearth of ring-recoveries of British-ringed birds in the west, especially Angola and Namibia, and the south, from Zambia southwards. Swifts are regularly observed in these areas; whether the absence of British-ringed recoveries from these areas is due to the fact the British & Irish birds have a more easterly and more northerly distribution within the general wintering area is not yet clear. There is some evidence that *pekinensis* may occupy the arid western areas in winter (*BWP*, Fry *et al* 1988); if so, the races must cross over during migration.

Little is known also of the routes followed or times taken, though presumably the birds face fewer constraints than most other migrants since they are able to continue feeding on the wing during the day. There are more British-ringed birds recovered in Iberia in autumn than in spring (Fig 4) and therefore it has been suggested that the spring migration occurs on a more easterly front than the autumn one (*BWP*). This seems unconvincing; there are actually eight recoveries in northwest Africa in April–June compared with only six in August and September, though the only other North African recovery, in Tunisia, was in spring. In autumn, on leaving Morocco, they must head in a southeasterly direction since there are no recoveries in West Africa and indeed the species is not common there. Also, extremely large numbers of Swifts have been noted on passage in Mali in autumn (Curry & Sayer 1979) but not farther west. Hence, presumably, birds passing through Spain in the autumn head southwards to Mali and then southeastwards to reach the main wintering grounds.

It is noticeable that there are no recoveries between the south side of the Sahara and the northern edge of the Congo Basin (Fig 4), suggesting that, despite the low probabilities of being found in these areas, the Swifts may pass through fairly fast in both spring and autumn. The speed of their movement may be judged by the fact that they are seen from as early as 13 July in Mali, where a juvenile was collected on 1 August (Curry & Sayer 1979). Given that a British juvenile can reach Madrid in four days from leaving the nest, it would take only a further eight days for it to reach Mali at that speed.

Swifts cannot be sexed in the hand, so nothing is known about differences, if any, in the timing and extent of migration between the sexes. Lack (1958c) reported that failed breeders left first, followed by successful breeders and lastly non-breeders, but the differences between the groups were small and there was a large overlap. On return in spring, non-breeders arrive at the same time as breeders, except that the one-year-olds do not return until the middle of June (E Kaiser 1992).

Swifts are hard to census and little is known about their status, though some reports indicate that they may be declining. Their current dependence on buildings for nest sites may make them vulnerable to changes, especially those such as increased weather-proofing or insulation, which reduce the number of available nest sites. There is some indication that the aerial plankton on which they are dependent may be becoming less plentiful; a study using suction traps in Stirling has shown that 15 major groups of prey have declined by an average of 49% between 1973 and 1997 (T Benton pers comm). This could present serious problems for the Swift, especially if the decline continues.

Chris Perrins

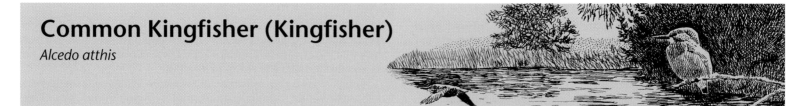

Common Kingfisher (Kingfisher)
Alcedo atthis

Kingfishers are most commonly seen as an electric blue flash darting low along waterways or over bodies of fresh water, where they may be found all year. While rare at migration watch-points in Britain & Ireland, some Kingfishers move to winter in coastal habitats and occasionally cross the English Channel or the North Sea.

The Common Kingfisher is one of the most northerly and widespread members of a mainly tropical family; several of its relatives are confined to remote islands, mainly in the Pacific (Fry *et al* 1992). The race *ispida* occupies much of Europe from Ireland, central Scotland and southernmost Fennoscandia east to the Urals and the Caspian, but is replaced in the Mediterranean Basin by the nominate *atthis*, which also breeds in central Asia. Five other races breed from India and China through Indonesia to the Solomon Islands (Fry *et al* 1992). In winter, the species withdraws completely from the northern parts of its range, from Poland and the Ukraine eastwards to China and Sakhalin Island, and becomes more widespread in western Europe, North Africa, the Middle East and on islands between Java and the Philippines (*BWP*). Movement is mainly at night (Fry *et al* 1992). Birds from northern and central Europe may make long migrations into milder parts of the range for the winter, on headings between west and south, while those in western maritime countries and the Mediterranean Basin may be mainly resident (*BWP*), although birds in some Mediterranean areas may move to the coast as fresh water dries up in late summer; Spanish birds are reported as mainly sedentary (Martín & Pérez 1990).

Kingfishers require waters that are clear, ice-free and rich in fish prey shorter than 10 cm (*European Atlas*). For breeding, they also require a

The analysis of the data for this species was supported by David Milne QC

suitable, undisturbed soft earth cliff, vertical or overhanging, usually but not always close to water, in which to excavate a nest-tunnel (Morgan & Glue 1977). Breeding birds are aggressively territorial but may be very mobile along rivers; in Belgium, one nesting male that was radio-tracked had a home range 13.8 km long (*European Atlas*). Kingfishers are frequent in coastal waters in winter, when freshwater sites, especially in more northerly and upland sites and in continental climates, are likely to be frozen. Pairs or groups of immatures wintering together may represent family bonds persisting after breeding, as is common among kingfishers world-wide (Keller *et al* 1989). Mortality may be severe in harsh winter weather but, with breeders rearing two to three broods of up to six young in each, local populations are capable of rapid recovery (Marchant *et al* 1990).

The breeding and non-breeding ringing locations of British & Irish Kingfisher ring-recoveries are similar, and largely reflect the distribution of the species in Britain, although there are few data for Scottish and very few data for Irish birds (Fig 1). Most recoveries have been from birds ringed during the breeding season, when most have been ringed as fully grown juveniles and, due to the inaccessibility of nests, only 7% have been ringed whilst nestlings (Fig 2). The advent of mist-nets had a large effect on the numbers of Kingfishers caught for ringing, and over 80% of recoveries in Britain & Ireland have been made since 1970.

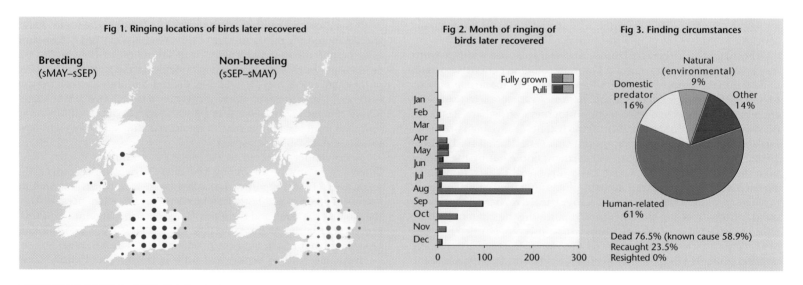

Fig 1. Ringing locations of birds later recovered

Breeding (sMAY–sSEP)   **Non-breeding** (sSEP–sMAY)

Fig 2. Month of ringing of birds later recovered

Fully grown / Pulli

Fig 3. Finding circumstances

Natural (environmental) 9%
Domestic predator 16%
Other 14%
Human-related 61%

Dead 76.5% (known cause 58.9%)
Recaught 23.5%
Resighted 0%

Ringing and recovery data

	<1960	60–69	70–79	80–89	90–97	Total
RINGING						
BTO ringing totals (%)	5	11	30	31	23	19,966
RECOVERIES						
BTO-ringed (%)	5	9	36	35	15	731
Foreign-ringed (%)	←	33	→	33	33	6

Statistical analyses

	Breeding population (sMAY–sSEP)	Wintering population (mNOV–mMAR)
Status	SEDENTARY (0)	?
Age differences[NS*]	Not significant*	—
Sex differences	Not tested	—
Regional differences	Not tested	—
Finding circumstances	Not significant*	—

Fig 4. Locations outside the breeding season, and movements of over 20 km between the breeding and non-breeding season, of 299 Kingfishers present in Britain & Ireland during the breeding season. Movements of over 20 km of birds ringed as known first-years (58, red) are differentiated from those birds not ringed as known first-years (17, grey).

Fig 5. Recovery locations and movements of over 20 km of 163 Kingfishers present in Britain & Ireland outside the breeding season. Movements of over 20 km of birds ringed as known first-years (19, red) are differentiated from those birds not ringed as known first-years (9, grey).

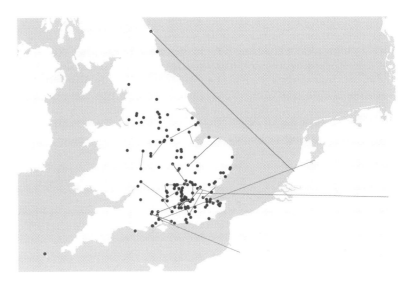

Almost a quarter of Kingfisher recoveries have been recaptured by ringers; the rest were found dead, with 59% of these having a known cause of recovery (Fig 3). Since many lowland waterways used by Kingfishers are close to dense human populations, it is not surprising that as many as 61% of these recoveries were attributed directly to humans, most resulting from collisions with windows or cars, and a further 16% to domestic predators, mainly cats. Birds dying of more natural causes are less likely to be found.

Juvenile Kingfishers begin to disperse from the natal territory within days of reaching independence, and there follows a long period of apparently random dispersal that is most pronounced between July and October (BWP). Of birds ringed as pulli in Britain & Ireland and recovered in their first year of life, however, the median distance moved was only 9 km (P5–95=0–92 km, n=33). During dispersal, birds may be seen crossing watersheds or dry habitats in the lowlands, and sometimes appear at garden ponds or other unexpected localities. As early as July, birds may reach remote locations such as the Isles of Scilly, although most records there have been between mid-August and October (Gantlett 1991). There had been 11 records at Cape Clear Island up to 1986, all in August or September (Birds in Ireland).

This period of dispersal merges into an autumn migration which, although performed by probably a small minority of British & Irish birds, takes birds away from harsher climates and towards the lowlands and the coast, where new winter territories are established. Movements of up to 250 km have been recorded, mostly in the autumn (Fig 4). Sample sizes for northern Britain are small but median movement distances of 12.5 km

and 7.5 km, for the northeast and northwest respectively, compare with a median of 5 km for southern Britain and, although the difference is not significant, this may possibly reflect a greater mobility of northern birds. A small number of birds ringed in Britain in the breeding season have been recovered on the Continent, with one exceptional movement of an immature ringed in Pembrokeshire on 14 August that was caught again by a ringer on the north coast of Spain only 19 days later. Another, ringed as an adult female in Hertfordshire on 4 July, was found on the south coast of Brittany in mid-October. There have also been single recoveries of British-ringed birds in Belgium, the Channel Islands and Normandy that were ringed in July or August and may well have been hatched in Britain. A juvenile ringed in Finistère, northern France, in July, but of unknown and possibly British origin, was found in Gwynedd in March almost two years later. One ringed in December in the Netherlands and recovered in Northumberland on 1 April may also have been British-bred.

Kingfishers are very susceptible to severe weather. Many die in harsh winters but some are believed to undertake cold-weather movements, with the extent of movement during the winter varying between years according to the severity of the weather (Morgan & Glue 1977). Evidence for this in the ring-recovery data is very limited however.

Return movements in the spring are not generally observed in Britain & Ireland. Relevant ring-recoveries are few but show some movement inland from the coast between spring and the breeding season (n=3). Winter immigrants to a river in central Poland, which had arrived in October or November, departed in March or April (Keller et al 1989). An exceptional occurrence at the Skerries, 3 km off Anglesey (which itself holds no regular breeding pairs), was recorded in March 1936 (Birds in Wales).

Due to the lack of nestlings ringed, and the concentration of ringing in the late summer and autumn, little is known of natal dispersal, breeding dispersal or between-winter movements. Of six pulli recovered in the breeding season, the most distant was 23 km from its natal site. Relatively few longer movements have been recorded for birds both ringed and recovered as adults (Fig 4); for recoveries of birds found dead, the median distance travelled was 3 km for adults (P5–95=0–85 km, n=61), and 6 km for birds ringed and recovered as immatures (P5–95=0–66 km, n=248). It appears that many adults are sedentary in Britain, and that most birds of all ages are site-faithful in both winter and summer. Of eight recoveries indicating breeding dispersal, however, one was longer than 20 km and had certainly shifted its home range. Keller *et al* (1989) retrapped winter adults, of both sexes, at or close to sites they had occupied in an earlier winter.

Both movement distances and the distributions of British & Irish ring-recoveries are very similar between the sexes. More generally across the range, females, both immature and adult, move more than males, which show greater attachment to the nesting territory (*BWP, HVM*).

The longer distances travelled by migrant Kingfishers on the Continent bring occasional passage or winter visitors to Britain. In Scotland, the occasional birds seen in the Northern Isles, Western Isles and northern Highlands, out of the normal range, are perhaps more likely to be of continental than British origin (*Birds in Scotland*). During 1979–97, birds ringed in Germany (a pullus), the Netherlands and northern France between June and September have been recovered in Britain, all during September–October in the year of ringing (Fig 5).

The Kingfisher's restricted requirements for breeding mean that it is highly vulnerable to pollution and disturbance at this season. The species is also threatened by drainage and increasing drought. A more detailed knowledge of the movements of breeding adults throughout the year would help to indicate how local populations might be affected by pollution incidents, and more information on the recruitment patterns of juveniles into the breeding population would enable the longer-term effects of such events to be predicted. The extent of interchange between Irish and British, and between British and continental populations, remains to be quantified.

Jez Blackburn & John H Marchant

Eurasian Wryneck (Wryneck)

Jynx torquilla

The analysis of the data for this species was supported by Brian H Bailey

The Wryneck is a most unusual species, being the only representative of its subfamily (Jynginae) in the Palearctic region, and sharing it with only one other: the Afrotropical Red-breasted Wryneck *J. ruficollis*. Those birds that occur in Britain & Ireland follow a true trans-Saharan migration reminiscent of their many passerine fellow-travellers, in marked contrast to the much more sedentary woodpeckers to which Wrynecks are closely related.

Wrynecks breed continuously across Europe and Asia from Britain to Japan in a broad range of climatic zones stretching in the West Palearctic from Lapland to Algeria. The nominate *torquilla* is the only race recorded in Britain & Ireland, and breeds east to the Urals and south to the Pyrenees, Alps, Bulgaria and the Caucasus, and is probably also that occurring in northern Portugal, Spain and the Balearic Islands. Neighbouring races include *tschusii* which breeds in the northern Mediterranean coastal region, and the northwest African *mauretanica*; these are much less migratory than *torquilla*, *tschusii* being partially resident though regular in Malta and coastal North Africa outside the breeding season, and *mauretanica* mainly resident. A very few nominate *torquilla* also winter in the Mediterranean Basin but this race predominantly winters in Africa south of the Sahara, across the northern tropics from Senegal to Ethiopia. There is a suggestion of a migratory divide, the western and northwestern European population tending to move via Iberia, with more easterly European breeders more likely to move through Italy and the Balkans (*BWP*). A number of eastern races perform similar migrations, wintering from Pakistan to China and southern Japan. There are no breeding records from Ireland where it occurs almost annually on migration,

predominantly recorded in autumn and, in the south, a rare vagrant in the spring (*Birds in Ireland*). It is argued that these birds derive from Scandinavian or central European populations (Hutchinson 1980).

The preferred breeding habitat is open deciduous woodland, adjacent to bare ground or short vegetation on which to forage for ants, its primary food. Such areas as orchards, parks, fragmented woodland, woodland fringes and large gardens are eminently suitable. Maritime climates are less favoured as are intensive agriculture, steppe, desert, mountains and wetlands. Migrants have been observed in a wide variety of habitats, in Britain often at coastal locations, but also in urban gardens. In the West African wintering grounds they can be found in the acacia savanna and the fragmented woodland and cultivated areas that are typical of the region, up to 2,500 m or more asl (Fry *et al* 1988, pers obs).

Recovery information from birds ringed in Britain & Ireland is sparse (Figs 1 & 2), and the picture is complicated by the contraction of the species' range southwards and eastwards in northwest Europe, including its extinction as a breeding bird in England. The decline in Britain has taken place over more than a century, with a steady contraction of its range from being widely distributed in England and Wales pre-1900 to a last breeding stronghold in Kent by the late 1960s (Parslow 1973). For the years 1986–97, an annual average of 269 Wrynecks has been

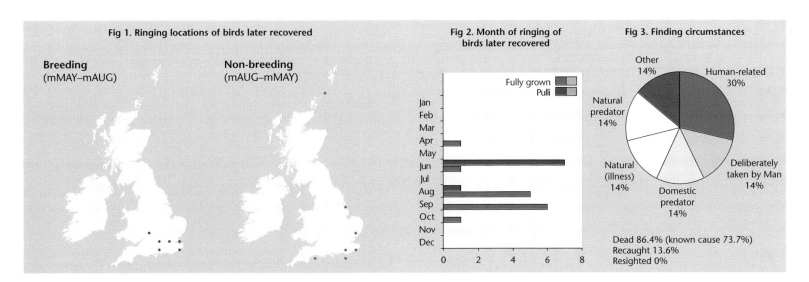

Fig 1. Ringing locations of birds later recovered

Breeding (mMAY–mAUG)

Non-breeding (mAUG–mMAY)

Fig 2. Month of ringing of birds later recovered

Fig 3. Finding circumstances

Dead 86.4% (known cause 73.7%)
Recaught 13.6%
Resighted 0%

Ringing and recovery data

	<1960	60–69	70–79	80–89	90–97	Total
RINGING						
BTO ringing totals (%)	27	22	28	14	8	2,028
RECOVERIES						
BTO-ringed (%)	41	9	14	32	5	22
Foreign-ringed (%)	0	0	0	100	0	2

Statistical analyses

	Breeding population (mMAY–mAUG)	Wintering population (mOCT–mMAR)
Status	PASSAGE ONLY	PASSAGE ONLY
Age differences	—	—
Sex differences	—	—
Regional differences	—	—
Finding circumstances	—	—

Fig 4. Recovery locations and movements of over 20 km for the 22 included recoveries of Wrynecks ringed or recovered in Britain & Ireland. Two individuals ringed as pulli in Norway and recovered in Yorkshire and Berkshire are not shown.

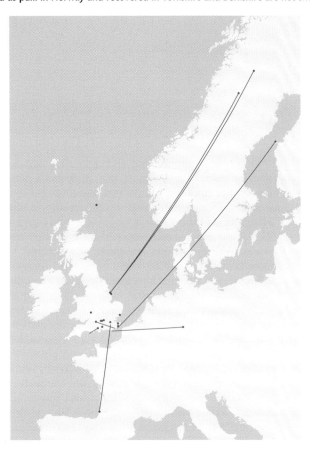

recorded in Britain, these almost entirely during migration of the continental European population (Fraser *et al* 1999b). It is thought most likely that the small breeding population established in the Scottish Highlands in the late 1960s (Burton *et al* 1970) was derived from this population, with increased numbers of pairs coinciding with above-average numbers of spring records at British bird observatories the same year (*1988–91 Atlas*). The last reported confirmed breeding in Britain was in 1993 (Ogilvie *et al* 1999a). Reported causes of death for ring-recoveries are mostly connected with human activity (Fig 3).

An analysis of all European ringing data (Peal 1972) has shown some post-fledging dispersal with a gradual transition into autumn migration at or near the end of the post-juvenile moult, but there is almost no information from British-ringed pulli. Birds migrating through Britain start appearing in mid-August, and the earlier birds may include juveniles as indicated by two Norwegian-ringed nestlings, each found in late August in Yorkshire and Berkshire in the year of ringing. In Orkney, adults comprise about 10% of autumn migrants of known age (pers obs). The peak migration period shows a movement towards the south and west over time across the British observatories, being late August on Fair Isle and mid- or late September in the Irish Sea (R & F). Generally, the main passage occurs in September and most birds have left by mid-October.

In Orkney and Shetland, migrant Wrynecks are well known to move on rapidly after making a landfall, often vanishing by midday when relatively numerous at first light (pers obs). Of 209 birds ringed on Fair Isle, only two have been retrapped 24 hours or more after ringing, both showing weight loss. Similarly, on North Ronaldsay, of 43 ringed only one has been retrapped, this two days after ringing and also showing weight loss. A remarkable series of 14 autumn birds found dead after

ringing on Fair Isle between 1958 and 1983 includes 10 found within four days of ringing including one 'emaciated', three up to two weeks after and one predated by a cat after one day (Deryk Shaw pers comm). These data contrast strongly with reports from observatories further south. On the Isle of May, five individuals retrapped three to six days after first capture showed an average weight gain of nearly 30% (Langslow 1977b), and on Bardsey Island three autumn juveniles gained 6–34% over three to seven days, and one gained approximately 30% over 43 days (Loxton *et al* 1999). Similar weight gains also occur on the Calf of Man (T Bagworth pers comm). These differences seem likely to be related to the availability of ants in the different locations: Fair Isle only holds one species *Myrmica ruginodis* (N Riddiford pers comm), and none have been recorded for North Ronaldsay. However, an 'ample' supply is available on the Isle of May, and at least 10 species from four genera have been recorded on Bardsey (Hoy & Loxton 1987). Though no direct evidence about staging is available, these substantial weight gains at favourable sites might suggest that a long flight, possibly reaching Iberia in one hop, takes place after departure from Britain. One bird ringed in Kent in late April 1981 was recovered 815 km away in coastal France in late August 1983. This supports other indications that western European birds take a westerly route through Iberia, showing a movement slightly west of due south (Fig 4).

The migration continues onwards to the northern tropics via the Mediterranean, where ring-recoveries suggest that the shortest sea-crossings are used, and Wrynecks are quite common along the North African coast on migration (*BWP*). The first birds appear in the West African wintering grounds from early September. Evidence of site-fidelity in winter comes from two individuals that have been retrapped at Ginak in the Gambia one year after ringing (J M B King pers comm) and from one bird caught in three different winters at the same site in Senegal (Sauvage *et al* 1998). Winter site-fidelity has also been demonstrated in the race *tschusii* wintering on the southern Italian island of Vivara (Scebba & Lövei 1985).

The spring return from the tropics starts in early March with some birds still present there in April. The first arrivals are seen in Britain in April, occasionally in March. Passage peaks in early May and is heavily weighted to the east coast and Northern Isles (R & F). All four autumn migrants ringed in eastern and southern England and recovered were found in Germany and Fennoscandia in the subsequent summer (Fig 4), also compatible with a more easterly track being taken in the spring, but there are no relevant data from spring ringing.

There is strong evidence from English birds during 1915–30 that juveniles return to their natal area to breed, with three birds ringed as nestlings recovered in subsequent years at or close (8 and 32 km) to their natal site, and one adult retrapped 2 km from its ringing site two years later. One Scottish site was utilized in three consecutive years (*Birds in Scotland*). Using extensive European data, Peal (1972) found that 75% of young birds return to within 25 km and 90% to within 70 km of their natal site, and nearly all adults return to the immediate vicinity of their previous breeding place. Exceptions to this include four Fennoscandian birds recovered in spring between 160 and 480 km from their ringing site (*BWP*).

This account is based on rather scant information about Wryneck movements in Britain & Ireland. The effective loss of the species as a breeding bird is of considerable concern but no clear causal factor has been identified. Further studies of its prey species on migration may help retrospective analyses of its decline, and continued ringing of migrants with particular attention to fat status and retrap condition might further elucidate its staging strategy, movements and habitat requirements. A new analysis of observatory data, updating R & F, with reference to changes attributable to its breeding decline, might prove fruitful.

Kevin Woodbridge

Green Woodpecker
Picus viridis

In contrast to its loud exhilarating call, large size and striking appearance, the movements of the Green Woodpecker are surprisingly subtle, yet they give an insight into the ecology and behaviour of this specialized species.

Woodpeckers are typically poor dispersers, with breeding adults showing extreme site-fidelity, enhanced by the patchiness of resources and a high degree of specialization. This in turn has assisted the evolution of many taxa due to genetic isolation between populations. The Green Woodpecker, with five races restricted almost entirely to the Western Palearctic, is a typical member of this group. Generally it is a common species found throughout most of continental Europe, extending to Norway, Sweden and east into Russia, Turkey and Iran (Winkler *et al* 1995).

During the 20th century the species expanded its range in Britain, colonizing the Isle of Wight in 1910, extending throughout northern England, finally colonizing southern Scotland in 1951 and is continuing to spread northwards (*1988–91 Atlas*, Holloway 1996). The species is absent from Ireland, although three 19th century records are listed from Counties Donegal, Kildare and Longford (*Birds in Ireland*).

The Green Woodpecker is typically associated with semi-open habitats such as parkland and, although arboreal, is not particularly a forest species (*BWP*). Its distribution covers a wide altitudinal breadth from coastal areas to subalpine forests (Winkler *et al* 1995). Territory size is dependent upon the quality of the habitat, with up to 6–12 pairs being found per square km of deciduous woodland (*BWP*). Due to the specialized diet of this species, habitat quality is greatly influenced by

The analysis of the data for this species was supported by Brian and Pat A Martin

the desired ant populations, with smaller ant species being taken preferentially during the summer from forest gaps, woodland glades and grassland. During the winter, the Green Woodpecker may be found gleaning larger more conspicuous ant species in habitats such as residential gardens, golf courses and orchards. In severe winter weather, when frozen ground prevents access to its chosen prey, individuals have been recorded foraging for larger invertebrates on dead wood.

The distribution of ringing locations of recoveries of Green Woodpeckers (Fig 1) is mainly consistent with the breeding distribution (*1988–91 Atlas*), although South Wales is under-represented and the recent colonizations of the Isle of Wight and Scotland have yet to produce recoveries. The vast majority of recoveries are of birds ringed when fully grown (Fig 2). The ringing of pulli accounts for only 3% of the birds recovered — a direct consequence of the inaccessibility of nests.

Less than half of all Green Woodpecker recoveries have been attributed to a known cause of death (Fig 3). The most frequent are human-related (54%), often involving suspected collision with a road vehicle, train or window. Hence recovery locations will be biased towards areas with dense human populations. Individuals 'taken by Man' account for 11% of the known causes of birds recovered, although this is largely a relic of this species' past popularity amongst collectors and taxidermists and would therefore constitute a much smaller

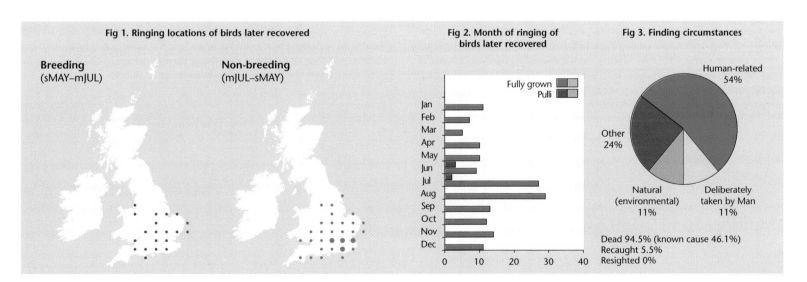

Fig 1. Ringing locations of birds later recovered

Breeding (sMAY–mJUL)

Non-breeding (mJUL–sMAY)

Fig 2. Month of ringing of birds later recovered

Fig 3. Finding circumstances

Human-related 54%
Other 24%
Natural (environmental) 11%
Deliberately taken by Man 11%

Dead 94.5% (known cause 46.1%)
Recaught 5.5%
Resighted 0%

Ringing and recovery data

	<1960	60–69	70–79	80–89	90–97	Total
RINGING						
BTO ringing totals (%)	10	10	17	28	36	4,388
RECOVERIES						
BTO-ringed (%)	8	20	20	24	28	164
Foreign-ringed (%)	0	0	0	0	0	0

Statistical analyses

	Breeding population (sMAY–mJUL)	Wintering population (mOCT–sMAR)
Status	[SEDENTARY]	SEDENTARY
Age differences	Not tested	Not tested
Sex differences	Not tested	Not tested
Regional differences	Not tested	Not tested
Finding circumstances	Not tested	Not tested

Fig 4. Recovery locations and movements of over 20 km for the 164 included recoveries of Green Woodpeckers ringed or recovered in Britain & Ireland.

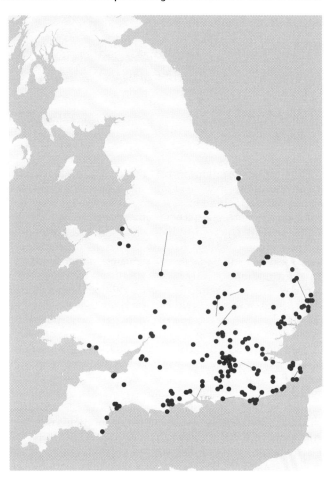

Dispersal of this species is very localized, characterized largely by apparently random post-fledging and winter movements. Individual movements over 20 km are unusual, only 11 British recoveries having been recorded beyond this distance (overall median=2 km, P5–95= 0–23 km, n=155 — recoveries of dead birds only) (Fig 4). Such movements can often be attributed to severe weather conditions. This is illustrated by the recovery of a Green Woodpecker ringed as an adult on 23 July 1961 in Whaley Bridge, Derbyshire, and recovered 71 km away at Cannock, Staffordshire, on 30 January 1963. Maximum recovery distances of 82 km and 170 km have been recorded in Germany (HVM). In Russia, seasonal movements are reported to be much more defined with a pronounced southward autumn displacement pre-empting the predictably severe winter (Dement'ev & Gladkov 1966). The existence of records for western islands such as Scilly, Mull and Bardsey, where there have been 15 records up to 1985 (Birds in Wales), is further evidence of longer movements by some individuals.

In Britain, greatest activity occurs during the autumn and winter, when some individuals (mainly immatures) leave wooded areas in favour of more open habitats (BWP). In contrast, adults typically demonstrate extreme site-fidelity throughout the year, following the establishment of their breeding territories. This is a reflection of the monogamous mating system of this species, which may involve the establishment of lifelong pair bonds (BWP). The median movement from recoveries of dead Green Woodpeckers ringed as adults is only 1 km (P5–95=0–9.5 km, n=40) whereas for juveniles the median distance is 3 km (P5–95=0–23 km, n=52).

Predictions of the future distribution of the Green Woodpecker have been modelled, using data from breeding bird censuses (Buckland & Elston 1993, Page et al 1999). Such models, however, cannot replicate the unpredictable effects of protracted cold weather. Ringing data offer the potential to fill such gaps in knowledge by providing estimates of mortality rates. Since recovery data are presently so limited, more ringing, especially of pulli and juveniles, is essential to provide data for survival estimates and to elucidate the movements of this species. The dependence of the Green Woodpecker upon ant populations means that it is very sensitive to changes in modern agricultural practices: in particular, the application of certain agrochemicals to 'improved' grasslands, and changes in grazing pressures, can prove detrimental (BWP). As a consequence, this species has the potential to be used as a visible indicator of changes in habitat quality, long before they may be detected within the invertebrate fauna itself.

Jacqueline King

proportion of the birds recovered today. Another major recorded cause of death is 'natural (environmental)' (11%). This reflects this species' vulnerability to severe weather, which was believed to be the major cause of Green Woodpecker decline following the harsh winter of 1962/63 (Dobinson & Richards 1964). During freezing weather feeding behaviour and habitat use may change and consequently distances individuals move may increase. Increased mortality in severe weather may therefore result in an upward bias to movement distances recorded by ringing.

Great Spotted Woodpecker
Dendrocopos major

Great Spotted Woodpeckers are year-round residents in Britain that can be found in any area with woodland or trees. Although none of the three British woodpeckers is truly migratory, the Great Spotted comes the closest, with eruptive movements of northern European populations bringing occasional migrants across the North Sea.

The species has an immense range, breeding across Eurasia from the Canary Islands and Britain to Kamchatka and Hainan. Around 14 races are currently recognized (Short 1982, Winkler *et al* 1995). The nominate race *major* occupies the north of the range from Scandinavia to the Amur River. In Britain *anglicus* is the endemic resident subspecies, with its numbers augmented in some winters by the arrival of members of the nominate race from Scandinavia. The two races can be distinguished only in the hand, *major* being longer-winged but with a shorter, thicker bill (*BWP*). Some authors (Short 1982, Winkler *et al* 1995) include *anglicus* with *pinetorum*, which is found across central Europe from the Netherlands to Romania, although this has not been finally resolved. Despite their presence on islands in the Canaries and Japan, there are no resident Great Spotted Woodpeckers in the Isle of Man or Ireland and they are also absent from the Northern and Western Isles. Remains of Great Spotted Woodpecker bones have been found in cave deposits in Ireland, suggesting that the species was once part of the resident avifauna, but the species now occurs only as an irregular passage and wintering bird (*Birds in Ireland*).

Woodland and trees of all types are favoured by Great Spotted Woodpeckers although they may sometimes be found in unlikely habitats such as coastal scrub and reedbeds, particularly during the autumn. In

The analysis of the data for this species was supported by Stephen & Shirley Ann Moores

southern England, where overall densities are highest (*1988–91 Atlas*), they can often be seen in isolated trees in farmland or making long flights across open country.

The distribution of the ringing sites of birds later recovered (Fig 1) shows a concentration in south and east England, which probably reflects the overlap of areas of high population density for Great Spotted Woodpeckers with the concentration of ringing activity. Outside the breeding season, there are additional records on the east coast of northern England and Scotland that probably reflect the occurrence of migrant birds. Great Spotted Woodpeckers tend to be trapped in the course of general ringing and there have been no particular efforts to ring large numbers. Birds have been ringed throughout the year with no major peak in any month (Fig 2). As is to be expected for a single-brooded species, ringing of pulli is over a short period mainly in May and June. Where finding circumstances were recorded for dead birds, 51% of deaths were related to human activities (usually collisions with vehicles or other man-made objects) and 17% to the activities of domestic animals, especially cats (Fig 3). Hunting is not significant for the Great Spotted Woodpecker in Britain; only 8% of recoveries with a known cause were due to hunting.

Great Spotted Woodpeckers show remarkably little tendency to undertake long-distance movements. Overall, the median distance for

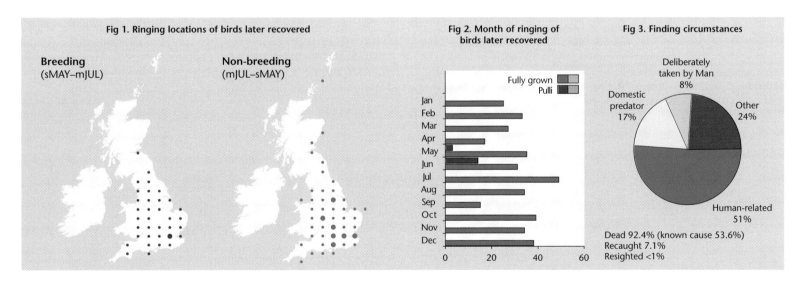

Fig 1. Ringing locations of birds later recovered

Breeding (sMAY–mJUL)

Non-breeding (mJUL–sMAY)

Fig 2. Month of ringing of birds later recovered

Fully grown
Pulli

Fig 3. Finding circumstances

Deliberately taken by Man 8%
Domestic predator 17%
Other 24%
Human-related 51%

Dead 92.4% (known cause 53.6%)
Recaught 7.1%
Resighted <1%

Ringing and recovery data

	<1960	60–69	70–79	80–89	90–97	Total
RINGING						
BTO ringing totals (%)	6	9	15	30	40	13,759
RECOVERIES						
BTO-ringed (%)	9	17	18	29	28	394
Foreign-ringed (%)	0	0	0	0	0	0

Statistical analyses

	Breeding population (sMAY–mJUL)	Wintering population (mOCT–sMAR)
Status	SEDENTARY*	SEDENTARY*
Age differences[NT]	Not tested	Not significant*
Sex differences[(NS)*]	Not tested	Not significant*
Regional differences	Not tested	Not tested
Finding circumstances	Not tested	Not significant*

Fig 4. Recovery locations and movements of over 20 km for the 394 included recoveries of Great Spotted Woodpeckers ringed or recovered in Britain & Ireland.

all recoveries of birds found dead is just 2 km from the ringing site and, although there are a few long-distance movements on record, 95% of all recoveries are within 40 km of the ringing site (Fig 4). Many of these long-distance movements involve birds ringed at coastal bird observatories. For example, a juvenile ringed at Spurn Point in October was recovered in Cambridgeshire in the following January and another juvenile, ringed at Sandwich Bay in August 1991, was controlled at Ickburgh, Norfolk, the next January. The latter bird then remained in the same area of Norfolk and was last retrapped in 1997 (Taylor *et al* 1999). The only overseas recovery so far is of a bird ringed at Dungeness Bird Observatory in September 1962 that was recovered in Belgium in November of the same year and seems likely to have been an immigrant returning home. There have been no recoveries of foreign-ringed birds in Britain & Ireland.

There is a suggestion from the ring-recoveries that young birds disperse from the nesting area after fledging. Only 17 birds ringed as pulli have subsequently been recovered and, of these, three (18%) had moved more than 20 km from the place of ringing (24, 52 and 54 km). In addition, 21 of 118 (18%) recoveries of birds ringed as juveniles were found more than 20 km from the place of ringing, compared with 13 of 259 (5%) of adults.

The nominate race *major* is known to perform eruptive movements in some years (*BWP*), when large numbers are trapped at Scandinavian bird observatories in autumn (Schildmacher 1963, Hildén 1969, 1971, 1974, Eriksson 1971). In Finland, there were 12 eruption years out of the 25 between 1949 and 1973 (Hildén 1974), although only in the biggest eruptions do significant numbers of birds reach Britain (Williamson 1963b). It is fascinating that the British irruption year of 1962 was when the bird trapped at Dungeness Bird Observatory was subsequently recovered in Belgium. Unfortunately it is not known to which race this particular bird belonged.

There is now considerable evidence from the biometrics of birds caught at east-coast and Scottish bird observatories that *major* occurs in small numbers in Britain in most autumns. As yet there are no ring-recoveries to prove this link. It has also been suggested that *pinetorum* has occurred in Kent (Taylor *et al* 1981) but, as it is difficult to distinguish *pinetorum* and *anglicus* on the basis of biometrics, this remains unproven.

The last big irruption year for *major* in eastern Britain was 1968 when large numbers arrived in the Northern Isles and eastern Scotland (*Birds in Scotland*); also in that year more than 17 birds were recorded at Spurn Point (Mather 1969) and considerable numbers in Norfolk (Taylor *et al* 1999). In Scotland, 1974 was also an irruption year (*Birds in Scotland*) but few were found then in England. Since then, small numbers of *major* have been identified each year but no big irruptions have been recorded.

Over the last few decades, Great Spotted Woodpecker numbers in Britain have been increasing and the range has expanded (*1988–91 Atlas*). This, together with the trend towards sympathetic woodland management and the widespread planting of trees in the lowlands and uplands, suggests a very positive future for the species in Britain.

Ken W Smith

Sky Lark (Skylark)
Alauda arvensis

The ethereal song of the Skylark is still common and widespread in Britain & Ireland, despite recent declines in breeding numbers. The population in lowland Britain is temporarily swelled by large numbers of presumed continental immigrants, perhaps especially during severe winters, yet there are few ring-recovery data that suggest the origins or destinations of such birds.

Skylarks breed in a broad band across the Palearctic from Morocco, the Faeroes and north Norway east to Kamchatka and Japan (*BWP*). During summer all European countries are occupied except Iceland. The nominate race *arvensis* is widespread across northern Europe but some authorities (*eg BWP*) separate a northwestern race *scotica*, found in Ireland, northwest England, Scotland and the Faeroes. Four further races are found in southern Europe and northwest Africa. In winter, the entire range shifts markedly southwards, except in western Europe where the species is found year-round in Britain & Ireland, southernmost Norway, Denmark, western Germany, the Low Countries and France. Within Britain & Ireland, most upland and northern Scottish breeding areas are vacated in winter (*Winter Atlas*). Autumn migration routes of European breeders lie largely between west and south, although these extremes are rarely recorded (*Der Zug*, Spaepen 1995). Breeders from Siberia eastwards winter in the Middle East, Pakistan, northwest India and China (*BWP*).

During the breeding season the Skylark is a species of open country, from sea-level to altitudes of 2,000 m in the Swiss Alps and 2,750 m in Armenia. Breeding habitats include open areas with grasses or low green herbage, especially agricultural land (*BWP*). During winter Skylarks, now typically in flocks, retain their preference for open countryside,

The analysis of the data for this species was supported by John Callion

particularly stubbles, fallow land and emerging cereal crops but also sand-dunes, saltmarsh and ungrazed grassland (*BWP*, Gillings & Fuller 2001).

Given that the Skylark is one of the most widespread breeding species in Britain & Ireland (*1988–91 Atlas*), surprisingly few have been ringed. Further, the recovery rate is low for a bird of its size; so far only 207 recoveries are available for birds ringed in Britain. In addition, a further 15 foreign-ringed birds have been recovered in Britain during the same period (10 of which were pre-1979). The locations of Skylarks ringed in Britain during the breeding season and later recovered are scattered thinly through southeastern England, northern England and Scotland, whereas non-breeding ringing locations were largely in southern Britain (Fig 1). This probably reflects the more southerly winter distribution of the species as well as the concentration of ringers. One-third of Skylark recoveries were from birds ringed as pulli; these pulli were ringed in small numbers between April and August, whilst fully grown birds have been ringed throughout the year (Fig 2). Of 207 British ring-recoveries, 194 (92%) of the birds were dead, 11 were recaught, and two were resighted. Since the main causes of recovery were human-related, including predation by cats, collisions with traffic or man-made structures, attraction to lights, and entering buildings (Fig 3), it is likely that the recovery locations are biased towards areas of high human population.

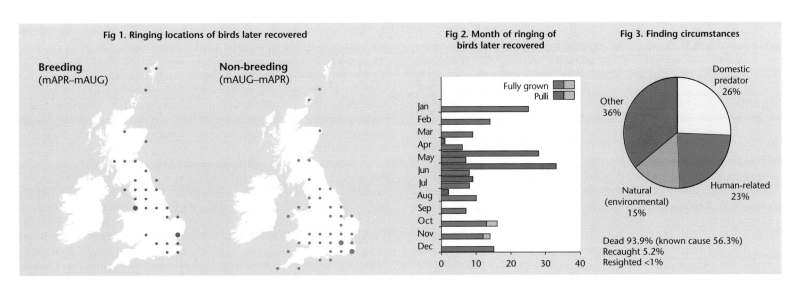

Fig 1. Ringing locations of birds later recovered

Breeding (mAPR–mAUG)   **Non-breeding** (mAUG–mAPR)

Fig 2. Month of ringing of birds later recovered

Fully grown / Pulli

Fig 3. Finding circumstances

Domestic predator 26%
Other 36%
Natural (environmental) 15%
Human-related 23%

Dead 93.9% (known cause 56.3%)
Recaught 5.2%
Resighted <1%

Ringing and recovery data

	<1960	60–69	70–79	80–89	90–97	Total
RINGING						
BTO ringing totals (%)	18	19	19	26	17	46,688
RECOVERIES						
BTO-ringed (%)	20	35	16	19	9	207
Foreign-ringed (%)	←	67	→	13	20	15

Statistical analyses

	Breeding population (mAPR–mAUG)	Wintering population (mNOV–mFEB)
Status	?	?
Age differences	—	—
Sex differences	—	—
Regional differences	—	—
Finding circumstances	—	—

Fig 4. Locations in autumn (16, red), winter (16, blue) and spring (14, grey), and movements of over 20 km between the breeding and non-breeding season, of Skylarks present in Britain & Ireland during the breeding season.

Fig 5. Recovery locations and movements of over 20 km of 110 Skylarks present in Britain & Ireland outside the breeding season. The 10 pre-1979 foreign-ringed Skylarks (Germany 4, the Netherlands 4, Sweden 1 & Belgium 1) are not shown.

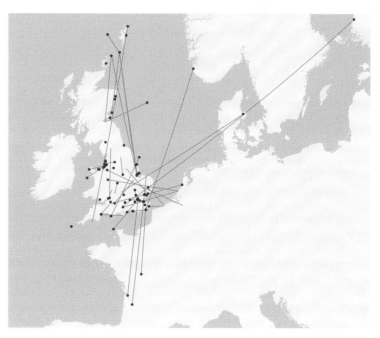

According to the *Handbook*, autumn migration of British birds involves southward movements that begin in Shetland and the Hebrides in late August. Movements continue along the east coast into November, where the birds may become mixed with continental immigrants. On the other side of the country, movements to Ireland occur from mid-September (*Handbook*), with pronounced movements noted from Wigtown in November (*Birds in Scotland*). During the same period, visible migration from Wales to Ireland is commonly noted. For instance, on 6 October 1962, 1,000 Skylarks passed south over Bardsey but passage is more typically 250–500 birds per day (*Birds in Wales*). In Ireland, heavy passage is noted in the northeast during October, from where Skylarks move south across the country, and large numbers are then seen departing south from southern headlands (*Birds in Ireland*). For example at Hook Head, Wexford, there are several sightings of 1,000 birds per day, and sometimes up to 6,000 (*Birds in Ireland*). Southerly departure, presumably to Iberia, normally takes place from southeast Ireland, and only occasionally are large movements witnessed off Cape Clear Island further west. As yet, there have been no recoveries of British-ringed Skylarks in Ireland and few recoveries of Scottish-ringed breeders, although one ringed as a chick in West Lothian was later recovered in Portugal (*Birds in Scotland*, Fig 4). Dougall (1996a) suggested that Skylarks from the Northern Isles may be obligate, partial migrants (Berthold 1993) with part of the population migrating annually to winter as far south as southern England. Return migration of British birds is thought to be along the same routes and takes place between late February and early April (*Handbook*).

These observations of migratory movements are difficult to reconcile with the recorded distances between ringing and recovery of British breeders (Fig 4). Dougall (1996a) found that two-thirds of British-ringed Skylarks were recovered within 10 km of the ringing site. Although sample sizes are small for seasonal comparisons (typically less than 10 recoveries), movements through the autumn and winter period tended to be longer than at other times, indicating that there is at least some migration during the non-breeding season.

Unfortunately, the difficulties in ageing Skylarks, small sample sizes and high skew towards zero distances preclude interpretation of summaries by region, age and sex. On the Continent, males tend to migrate later than females (Spaepen & van Cauteren 1968) by as much as eight days (Schekkerman 1999), and then return to breeding haunts sooner in the spring (Spaepen & van Cauteren 1968). The small numbers of appropriate recoveries of British Skylarks show no evidence of significant natal or breeding dispersal, and this agrees with an earlier analysis of ringing returns (Dougall 1996a) and two local studies: in Grampian (Duncan 1987) and in Lancashire (I H Wolfenden pers comm). Dougall (1997) summarized studies revealing strong site-fidelity between breeding seasons, between summer and winter sites, and between winters.

A small number of recoveries show Skylarks crossing the North Sea between mainland Britain and Scandinavia and the Low Countries, and crossing the Channel between southeast England and France (Fig 5). More details of Skylark movement can be gleaned from patterns of visible migration. There is a very apparent arrival of Skylarks from the Continent from mid-September to early November when 'vast numbers from central Europe arrive between the Tees and Kent' (*Handbook*). Many east-coast sites record large movements at such times. In Norfolk, peak numbers occur in late October, such as at Sheringham: 3,500 west, 2,000 east, 1,800 west on single days in 1978, 1979 and 1993 respectively (Taylor *et al* 1999). If such movements are associated with foggy or wet weather, Skylarks may be grounded on islands and attracted to lighthouses where they may suffer significant casualties. For instance, on 6 November 1868 a total of 15,000 larks was collected at the lantern and in nets on Helgoland (Nelson 1907) and on 2 December 1882 at Bell Rock Lighthouse 'they were striking hard for a couple of hours like a shower of hail' (Clarke in Nelson 1907).

It has been said that, owing to the large number of migrating Skylarks ringed in Belgium, there should be more recoveries if Britain is a regular destination (Dougall 1996a, Spaepen 1995). However, most authors suggest that these continental immigrants continue inland across the country, possibly to Ireland or further south and that this is probably the reason for the paucity of recoveries (eg Hardman 1974). Of the 15 recoveries of foreign-ringed Skylarks, six had been ringed in the Netherlands, four each in Belgium and Germany and one in Sweden (Fig 5). These ringing locations concur with the known migration routes of Fennoscandian breeders as defined by Spaepen (1995). Also, five recoveries involving birds ringed in Britain & Ireland were from on board ships: one in the Baltic Sea, one in the North Atlantic Ocean and three in the North Sea. After continental birds have arrived they presumably move south through Britain and depart via the south coast or continue west to Ireland. Moore (1969) notes that movements west along the Devon coast occur in some but not all autumns and, in Cornwall, birds closely follow both the south and north coasts, sometimes as many as 140 per hour. There, birds on the north coast depart in a northwesterly direction, presumably to Ireland, while from the south Cornish coast they depart south (Penhallurick 1978a). Passage over the Scilly Isles is usually in a northwesterly direction (Clark & Rodd in Penhallurick 1978a), presumably to Ireland.

Spring passage of continental birds is along similar routes to those used in autumn (Handbook), though passage records of large numbers are few (Birds in Ireland, Buckland et al 1990), due to either winter mortality reducing numbers, migration over a more protracted period, or a lack of the poor weather conditions that typically cause birds to build up and 'fall' during autumn migration. There has been little evidence of a significant spring passage, at least in Norfolk, in recent years and this may be related to the series of mild winters witnessed over the same period (Taylor et al 1999).

Cold-weather movements of Skylarks can be a major feature in some winters (BWP) and were known as 'rushes' in Yorkshire. There, Skylarks were seen to congregate in flocks a day or two prior to severe weather and depart upon its arrival (Nelson 1907). At such times, significant visible migration may be seen, for example in northeast Scotland 8,300 passed in two hours over Newtonhill on 24 January 1976, and in the same year 2,600 passed over Old Aberdeen on 4 December in just half an hour (Buckland et al 1990). Further south at the Axe Estuary in Devon 5,000 passed south-southwest on 13 January 1964 with 20,000 west or southwest there on 28 December 1964 (Moore 1969). Similar passage was noted in Norfolk during January and February 1979 when all birds were moving west (Taylor et al 1999). The first winter of fieldwork for the Winter Atlas coincided with a cold period in northwest Europe and a large-scale evacuation of Skylarks was apparent from most areas of Britain, except southeast England (Gillings 2001b). Birds in southeast England could have been on passage from areas to the east and north. During these cold spells both Sporne (1980) and Dougall (1997) made highly female-biased Skylark catches whereas during normal weather they made catches of equal sex ratio. This could indicate that cold-weather movements involve flocks of female Skylarks, probably immatures, although if females are subordinate to males they may be more likely to risk coming to baited sites and hence be caught (Dougall 1997).

An increased understanding of Skylark movements is urgently required against the current background of Skylark declines throughout northwestern Europe. The British breeding population of Skylarks declined by over 50% between the 1970s and 1990s and over 50% of European countries report declining populations (European Atlas). Given that winter survival may be a crucial factor in governing these recent trends, it is important that we discover the wintering grounds of different populations so that appropriate action can be taken to provide suitable habitat (such as weedy stubble fields, Gillings & Fuller 2001) for wintering larks. It is hard to believe that earlier studies were prompted by the fact that Skylarks were once considered a serious agricultural pest (eg Hardman 1974).

As is apparent from the anomaly between visible migration and recoveries, we still have much to learn about Skylark migration. To what degree British & Irish breeders are sedentary (apart from local altitudinal movements) is open to question. Neither is it clear how many continental Skylarks use Britain, either as a wintering ground or as a passage route; visible migration and 'at sea' recoveries suggest that there may be a large regular passage of birds across the North Sea that ringing is currently failing to detect. In order to clarify the status of Skylark movements in Britain & Ireland, we require much more ringing of Skylarks throughout Europe. It would be particularly useful to catch more adult Skylarks, perhaps by tape luring on the coast during autumn migration, and by drag netting in autumn and winter, both in Britain and countries north of Belgium and in Iberia, so as to provide a more uniform ringing effort throughout northwest Europe. Greater use of sexing techniques for sexing caught birds would help to clarify differences between sexes in movements in Britain & Ireland, for instance whether female or male Skylarks are more prone to move in response to cold weather (Dougall 1997, Schekkerman 1999). Increased autumn and winter effort should be coupled with more ringing of pulli and breeding adults throughout Britain & Ireland, which would help to define the extent of partial migration and benefit applied studies of survival rates.

Simon Gillings & Tom W Dougall

Sand Martin

Riparia riparia

Sand Martins are trans-Saharan migrants and are among the first of the summer visitors to return northward to Europe in the spring. The same species breeds across Asia and North America, and migrates south into parts of central Asia and South America. The birds breeding in western Europe migrate south into West Africa but winter no further south than the Sahel zone. Some central and many eastern European birds winter much further south in East Africa, with many beyond the Equator and some reaching Mozambique. The very extensive breeding range is patchy, depending on sub-soil type, as the birds usually need fresh vertical banks of a suitable substrate, generally sand, in which to dig their nest holes each year (*BWP*). In Europe colonies extend from 70°N, well beyond the Arctic Circle, to the very south of Spain but there are none in Iceland and there has not been even sporadic breeding in the Northern and Western Isles of Scotland for many decades (Mead 2000).

In densely populated areas of Britain & Ireland, most colonies are in man-made sites, generally at sand-pits and gravel workings but sometimes in drainage channels, railway embankments and even in drainpipes. Especially in more remote areas, natural sites in riverbanks and seacliffs are also used. Colonies may be very concentrated or extend over several hundred metres and may have a handful of nesting pairs or, in a few cases, many hundreds (*BWP*). Most are in river valleys and associated with waterbodies over which the birds feed, especially in colder weather. Even during the height of the breeding season some birds roost in reedbeds and other such sites, and these become very important in the late summer and autumn. Wandering juveniles and migrant birds use these sites, and unoccupied holes in the colonies, on

The analysis of the data for this species was supported by Rye Bay Ringing Group and the Wetland Trust

passage and visit occupied colonies in large numbers, particularly in late July and early August (Mead & Harrison 1979a). Large communal roosts, generally in vegetation over water, are also used on migration through Europe and in Africa in the winter.

Recoveries from ringing in the breeding season have come from almost all parts of the breeding range, whilst those from passage sites are mainly from the southeast, with the Sussex sites at Chichester and Icklesham predominating (Fig 1). The ringing of nestlings is forbidden, except in special circumstances, since the nesting tunnels are very vulnerable to subsidence. Specialist ringers developed means of trapping the nesting birds with tubes and bags but these were superseded, in the late 1950s, with the introduction of mist-nets. Trapping of the birds at colonies is allowed after they have settled to breed – mainly in June, July and early August (Fig 2). Since the birds are gregarious at all times of the year, they attracted the attention of ringers at roosts, feeding sites and on passage. The BTO ran a Sand Martin Enquiry from 1960 to 1968. Cheap or free rings led to over 400,000 birds being ringed, with a maximum 75,151 in 1966, and over 10,000 recoveries reported, mostly recaptures by ringers. The end of the Enquiry coincided with the start of a serious long-term drought in the winter area, which drastically reduced survival (Cowley 1979, Mead 1979a). Since then annual ringing totals have averaged about 16,000, dropping to barely 4,000 in some

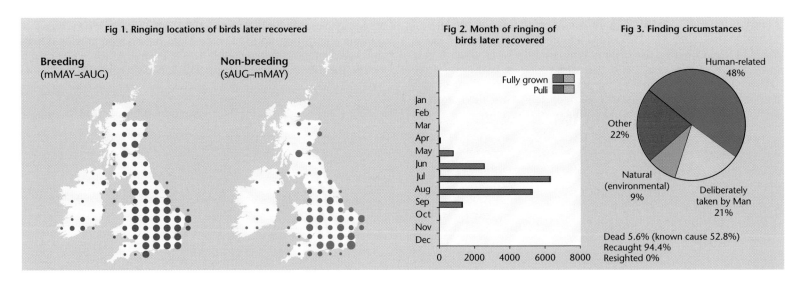

Fig 1. Ringing locations of birds later recovered

Breeding (mMAY–sAUG)

Non-breeding (sAUG–mMAY)

Fig 2. Month of ringing of birds later recovered

Fully grown / Pulli

Fig 3. Finding circumstances

Human-related 48%
Other 22%
Natural (environmental) 9%
Deliberately taken by Man 21%

Dead 5.6% (known cause 52.8%)
Recaught 94.4%
Resighted 0%

Ringing and recovery data

	<1960	60–69	70–79	80–89	90–97	Total
RINGING						
BTO ringing totals (%)	3	44	13	19	22	957,741
RECOVERIES						
BTO-ringed (%)	0	57	7	14	22	16,176
Foreign-ringed (%)	←	55	→	23	23	515

Statistical analyses

	Breeding population (mMAY–sAUG)	Wintering population (sNOV–mMAR)
Status	[LONG-DISTANCE MIGRANT]	NONE
Age differences	Not tested	—
Sex differences	Not tested	—
Regional differences	Not tested*	—
Finding circumstances	Not tested	—

Fig 4. Recovery locations and movements of over 20 km of Sand Martins ringed in Britain & Ireland during the breeding season and recovered as (a) first-year birds in July (909), (b) first-year birds in August (1,480), (c) first-year birds in September and October (230), (d) older birds in July (507), (e) older birds in August (674), and (f) older birds in September and October (209).

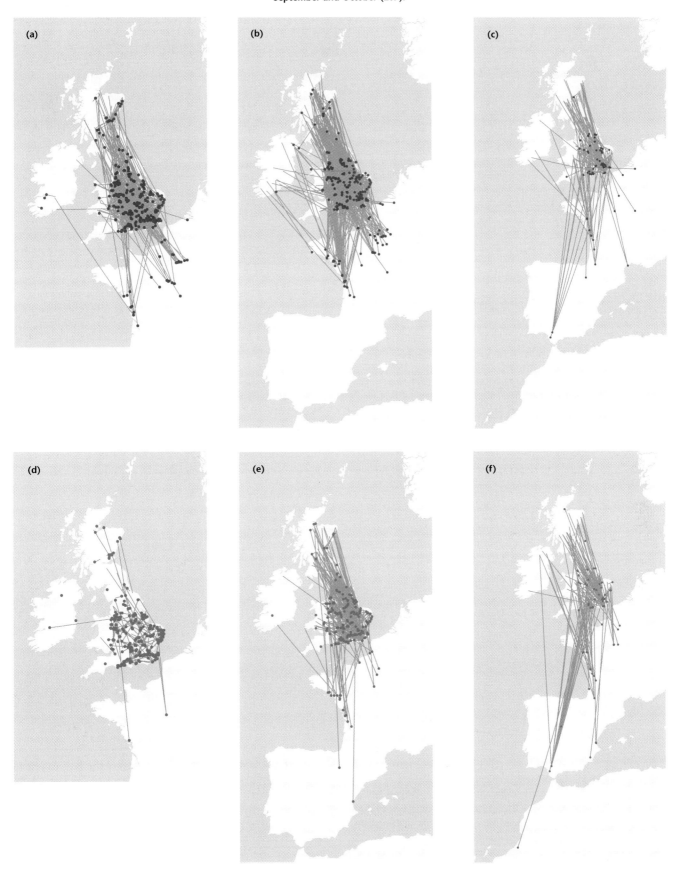

Fig 5. Locations in (a) July (3,409), (b) August (5,776), (c) September (1,426, red) & October (10, black), (d) November–February (93) and (e) March (127, grey), April (222, blue) & May (844, red) of Sand Martins present in Britain & Ireland during the breeding season.

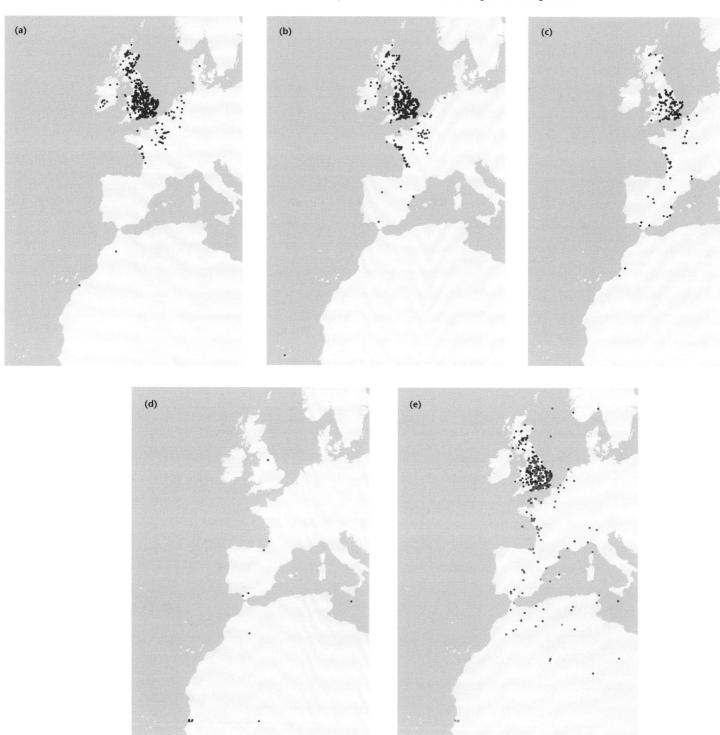

years but recovering to 40,000 in those years when the summer and autumn roost ringers at Icklesham were very active.

Some 94% of all reported recoveries are recaptures by ringers away from the ringing site. The recovery rate increased almost twentyfold due to the Enquiry and remains very high. Most of the birds deliberately taken by Man (Fig 3) were recovered abroad; human-related recoveries include a proportion destroyed during excavations at colonies although, generally, workers are very protective of *their* birds. Fly-fishermen caught more than a dozen, and birds were hit by cricket and golf balls. One old recovery was taken by a breeding Red-backed Shrike and a flying bird was taken by a Pike (Mead 1979a). There is no evidence that the patterns of

recoveries recorded at different times over the last 40 years have varied substantially, although ringing efforts in Britain & Ireland and elsewhere in Europe and Africa have differed.

Many newly fledged juveniles continue to roost in their natal holes (or adjacent ones) within the colony for several weeks or may use reedbeds close to the natal site. Gradually they disperse, faster with later broods, using other roosts and unoccupied holes at other colonies, mostly within 80 km of the natal site. This seems to be a familiarization period (Baker 1978, Mead & Harrison 1979a) helpful to the inexperienced birds when they return the following year. By the end of July, oriented movement, most often just east of south, is apparent and

Fig 6. Recovery locations and all included exchanges of Sand Martins between Britain & Ireland and abroad involving birds present in Britain & Ireland during autumn (438, red) and spring (10, black).

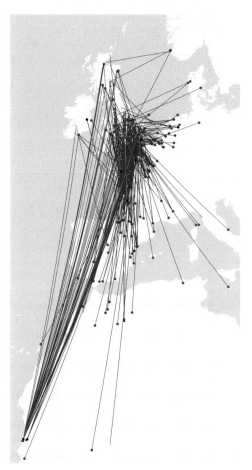

the birds are mostly in reedbed roosts; roosting at colonies still occurs, even many hundreds of kilometres from the breeding site (Mead & Harrison 1979a). Regular roosts may hold a few thousand birds but the biggest, on the Ouse Washes (Cambridgeshire and Norfolk), was estimated to hold two million in August 1968 (Mead & Harrison 1979a). This may have been because of extensive aphid infestations on crops in the adjacent fens. Passage by juveniles is very gradual, and the birds may spend about a week on average at one roost before travelling 100–300 km to the next. Adult movements appear to be later, more direct and faster (Fig 4). In most years, passage through Britain is concentrated during August and by the beginning of September it is diminishing, but with a higher proportion of adults.

The few recoveries of Irish-ringed birds in autumn show movements oriented east and southeast indicating, along with the British birds, a Channel crossing from Kent, Sussex or Hampshire (Fig 4). After crossing the English Channel, the birds move to the west coast of France, using roosts as they did in Britain, travelling an average of 22–40 km per day and still probably moving roosts every seven days or so (Mead & Harrison 1979a). There is little indication that birds from different British and Irish breeding areas are segregated. The birds mostly skirt the western end of the Pyrenees and then cross to the Ebro Valley and many then use the eastern coast of Spain (Fig 5), in contrast to most other migrants that use the Atlantic coast in autumn. There is good evidence that some cross Spain to the Coto Doñana and the short crossing at and near Gibraltar is used (Finlayson 1992). Passage through Europe is

virtually over by the first few days of October (Fig 5). The few onward recoveries in Africa indicate that the early wintering area, largely in Senegal, is probably reached via the western edge of the Sahara. There are very few winter recoveries, except controls by ringers, but the February and March recoveries in Mali suggest that the birds gradually spread east along the Sahel zone (Figs 5 & 6). Surviving birds may penetrate further east in years when the rainfall is poor, or has failed, in the west (Mead & Harrison 1979b, *BWP*).

The return passage starts in March and some birds are near their breeding colonies by the end of the month with others still reaching them in late May (Fig 5). Early records almost always involve the experienced second-year and older birds, with the first-year birds generally arriving in May. The Sahara is crossed on a broad front as far east as 10°E, and possibly further (Fig 5). This may be a very stressful crossing (Ash 1969, Moreau 1972). There are relatively many more recoveries in North Africa in spring than in autumn. Passage across the Mediterranean of both British and Irish birds takes place from Gibraltar east to Malta but it is not clear how many birds make the longer sea-crossings. Onward passage is much faster than in the autumn and is, on average, further to the east in France (Fig 5). Birds returning early may face cold weather conditions in late March and April and some have been found dead in their colonies after freezing weather (Mead & Harrison 1979b).

Many colony sites are transitory and rely on continuing sand-extraction or erosion of riverbanks. The birds are generally able to establish their colonies close to the site used in the previous year, however. Early arrivals are known to choose their nest sites to maximize their chance of breeding successfully (Jones 1987a). Detailed analyses for recoveries and recaptures at a group of colonies in Hampshire suggested that about 93% of adults and 87% of juveniles settle to breed in the next year within 10 km; most of the rest are within 99 km with only one in 200 (adults) and one in 50 (juveniles) at higher distances (Mead 1979b). These dispersal movements do not seem to be significantly directional but the irregular distribution of colonies makes this difficult to ascertain. Rather few Sand Martins are sexed by ringers or finders but there are clear indications that males, both adults and juveniles, are likely to settle to breed closer to the colonies where they were hatched, or bred previously, than females (Mead 1979b, Holmes *et al* 1987). Recoveries of dead Sand Martins show a median breeding dispersal distance of only 3.5 km ($P5–95=0–651$ km, $n=130$).

Some birds from adjacent North Sea countries pass through Britain, mainly the southeast, on passage in both spring and autumn (Fig 6) but there are so few recoveries for the numbers ringed that these are probably rather exceptional.

The conservation of Sand Martins in their breeding areas is very much dependent on the provision of banks or hard-holes for nesting in areas where there are opportunities for feeding. Populations are severely affected, however, by the weather conditions in the wintering area (Persson 1987, Szép 1995a). Detailed work by Jones (1987b) showed that the smaller birds from Scotland suffered lower mortality than larger birds during the 1983–84 population crash. Habitat provision in the breeding area is therefore not a guarantee of the species' well-being. Continued ringing in Britain & Ireland is needed to monitor, indirectly, the overwinter survival of the birds in the wintering quarters. Detailed ringing information from these wintering areas, each year, would be invaluable in showing how the birds utilize regions and habitats as the winter progresses and under differing environmental conditions. Such fieldwork would be difficult, however, given the current political and logistical situations in these wintering zones.

Chris Mead

Barn Swallow (Swallow)
Hirundo rustica

Swallows are the icon of the northern summer and migrate from Britain & Ireland to South Africa for the winter. This fact was established with the report, from Natal on 23 December 1912, of an adult female Swallow ringed at a nest in Staffordshire by James Masefield (the brother of the poet, John). Swallows breed all across Eurasia from Morocco to Ireland and Norway in the west to Kamchatka, Japan and southern China — and also very extensively in North America. In Europe they are missing only from Iceland, the Faeroes and the Arctic Ocean coast of Fennoscandia and northern Russia (*European Atlas*). In winter they are found widely in Africa south of the Sahara, from Pakistan to New Guinea and in northern and central South America (*BWP*). Until the introduction of ringing, there was no way of connecting particular breeding and wintering sites within this range but it is now known that, while some birds in southern Iberia are resident, all other European populations are trans-Saharan migrants to Africa and winter in distinct areas there (*BWP*). British & Irish birds, wintering in the Republic of South Africa and Namibia, share their wintering area with birds from the borders of Europe and Asia in the former USSR, and are probably outnumbered by them (Davis 1965, Mead 1970).

In Britain & Ireland, almost all breeding Swallows are associated with buildings, ranging from remote bothies, barns and pillboxes to porches, garages and garden sheds in suburbia. They are often semicolonial, particularly around farm buildings where animals are kept, but many pairs nest singly. Only the most built-up areas, the highest hills and parts of the remotest islands of the north and west of Scotland lack them. Throughout the year they feed aerially on insects over all sorts of terrain, especially among trees and shrubs and over open habitats, with wet ones particularly favoured in cold weather.

The analysis of the data for this species was supported by Martin & Kath George

Swallow nestlings, and breeding adults caught at the nest or in its immediate vicinity, have been ringed from the early years. It was only in the 1950s, with the introduction of mist-nets, that large numbers of free-flying birds could be caught for ringing, mostly at their communal overnight roosts in reedbeds. The Swallows that have been recovered have been ringed very widely in Britain but at only scattered locations in Ireland (Fig 1). Birds ringed in August, September and, to a lesser extent July (Fig 2), are mostly roosting juveniles. Nestlings are ringed in June, July and August with many fewer in September and a handful in May. Very few birds are caught in spring, on arrival, when the birds appear to settle at potential breeding sites immediately. Almost all females attempt to breed in the first summer of their return but up to 20% of first-year males may remain unpaired (*BWP*).

About half of the usable recoveries relate to birds recaught by ringers and in more than 80% of the rest, for which the finding circumstances were known, death was related to human activities (Fig 3). Those deliberately caught by Man (12%) mainly occurred on passage across Africa. In Britain & Ireland, around 70% of recoveries of dead birds have been 'human-related', including birds trapped in buildings, particularly by sash windows, when they are prospecting for breeding sites. Other

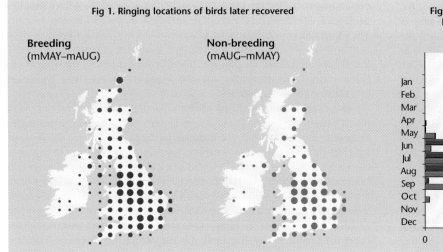

Fig 1. Ringing locations of birds later recovered

Breeding (mMAY–mAUG)

Non-breeding (mAUG–mMAY)

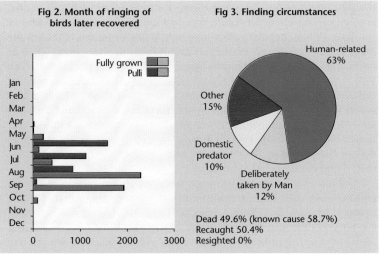

Fig 2. Month of ringing of birds later recovered

Fully grown
Pulli

Fig 3. Finding circumstances

Human-related 63%

Other 15%

Domestic predator 10%

Deliberately taken by Man 12%

Dead 49.6% (known cause 58.7%)
Recaught 50.4%
Resighted 0%

Ringing and recovery data

	<1960	60–69	70–79	80–89	90–97	Total
RINGING						
BTO ringing totals (%)	7	25	22	26	21	1,347,440
RECOVERIES						
BTO-ringed (%)	6	31	22	23	18	8,646
Foreign-ringed (%)	←	77	→	16	7	208

Statistical analyses

	Breeding population (mMAY–mAUG)	Wintering population (sDEC–mFEB)
Status	LONG-DISTANCE MIGRANT (4)	NONE
Age differences[NT]	Not significant*	—
Sex differences	Not tested	—
Regional differences	Not significant[2]*	—
Finding circumstances	Not tested	—

Fig 4. Locations in (a) August (1,889, blue), September (2,008, red) & October (138, grey), (b) November–February (111, red) and (c) March (19, grey), April (88, blue) & May (525, red), of Swallows present in Britain & Ireland during the breeding season.

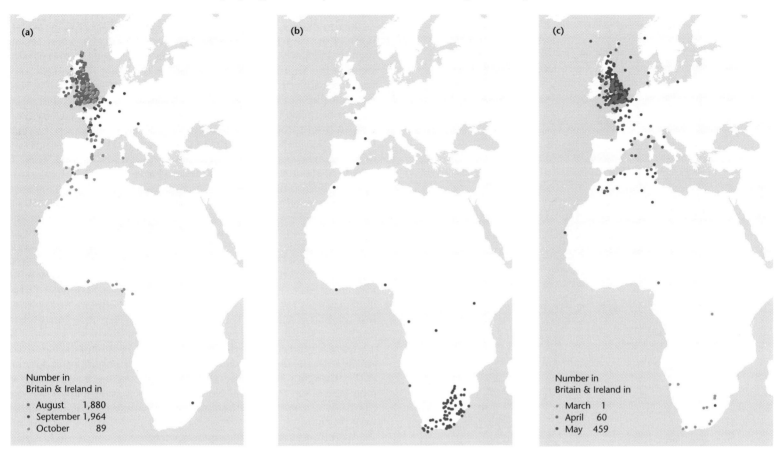

(a)

Number in
Britain & Ireland in

• August   1,880
• September 1,964
• October   89

(b)

(c)

Number in
Britain & Ireland in

• March   1
• April   60
• May   459

human-related recovery methods include road traffic accidents, whose prevalence appears to be age-related. In an unpublished analysis undertaken in the 1970s, 40% of recoveries reported with a cause of death within one month of fledging were from this cause, in the next 11 months it was about 13% and, in older birds, about 8% (pers obs). A further 11% of recoveries in Britain & Ireland have been due to domestic predators (mostly cats). Clearly these finding circumstances bias the reported recovery locations of dead birds towards the breeding season rather than other times of the year and other localities. In South Africa, the main winter area, more than a quarter of recoveries have been live recaptures by ringers; those recovered dead have also had largely human-related (44%) or natural, environmental (46%) finding circumstances but only 12% were reported as taken by hunters.

Newly fledged birds stay around the breeding site, being fed by their parents, for several days, and sometimes up to six weeks (*BWP*), and are then often expelled by the male. They then generally enter local communal roosts and may stay in these for several more weeks, presumably familiarizing themselves with the local area to which they will return the following summer (Baker 1978), whilst the adults are still raising further broods. Oriented movement southwards starts in late August, with the birds apparently moving short distances every few days to settle at more southerly roosts (Ormerod 1991). The mean body mass of the birds using such roosts gradually increases through the autumn and periods of wet and windy weather cause mean mass of the birds to fall (Ormerod 1989). Irish birds probably all move to Wales and southern England during the autumn. A very few cross the English Channel in late August but most Swallows leave Britain in September and early October (Fig 4). The birds do not necessarily seek a short crossing by moving through southeast England. Most then move along the French Biscay coast and a strip some 100 km wide to reach the

Pyrenees, where most switch to the Mediterranean coast of Spain, apparently using the northern edge of the mountains to make their crossing (Fig 4). Some then fly out into the Mediterranean and are recovered on the Balearics but many of the recoveries range across southern Spain. Recoveries in North Africa in autumn are mainly in October, and largely west of the Greenwich meridian. There are few from the coast of the Sahara, one from the fringe and none from the central desert area. Observations clearly indicate that the majority of birds overfly the desert having built up considerable fat reserves to the north. Such weight gains have been proved for the populations passing through Italy (Pilastro & Spina 1999) but not for British & Irish birds, which may gain weight in southern Spain or North Africa.

There are no recoveries from the Sahara or the Sahel zone and the next area where British & Irish birds are found is along the northern edge of the Gulf of Guinea, mostly in Nigeria and the Congo Basin in October (Fig 4). Here some British birds have been caught and eaten at the huge roost in elephant grass at Ebok Boje in the Cross River State, Nigeria, where efforts are being made (*Incredible Journeys*, BBC TV) to reduce the annual take of 100,000 Swallows (*European Atlas*). It is possible, from the few recoveries, that adult birds pass through this area more quickly than the juveniles and that the young birds are more widely dispersed. The few recoveries over the next 4,000 km may indicate a rapid onward journey through the equatorial forest belt. The majority of November records are in the wintering area of the Republic of South Africa but few have penetrated to the very south. From December through to February the recoveries come from the wintering area, including Namibia (Fig 4). At this time the birds undergo a complete moult (van den Brink *et al* 2000).

With the advent of mist-nets, ringers in South Africa have also been able to catch large numbers of Swallows. Ringing in southern Africa has

Fig 5. Recovery locations abroad of Swallows present in Britain & Ireland in autumn (504, red) and spring (17, black).

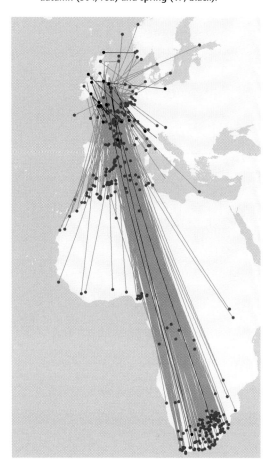

Fig 5. Recovery locations abroad of Swallows present in Britain & Ireland in autumn (504, red) and spring (17, black).

shown that most birds forage within 50 km of the night roost and that most, but not all, remain faithful to the roost at which they settle (Oatley 2000). Moister habitats are favoured. There is good evidence that, around the 1960s, wintering British & Irish birds spread to the very south from being centred on the area round Pretoria (Mead 1972). This was based only on dead recoveries of Swallows and efforts were made to allow for human ethnographic biases. Currently 20 of the 22 recoveries reported from the Western Cape have come from Britain & Ireland, and our birds may outnumber those from other parts of the breeding range (Oatley 2000). In northeastern South Africa, it is believed that birds from the former USSR, particularly around the Urals, outnumber our birds (*BWP*). There is no current evidence that adult birds differ from the juveniles in the timing of their arrival in the winter quarters, nor that birds of different ages or sexes, nor from different breeding areas within

Britain & Ireland, migrate through or winter in different areas. However, with the volume of ring-recovery data now becoming available, more detailed analyses to address these questions would be worthwhile.

Return passage starts in late February (*BWP*) but the first recoveries north of the wintering area have been reported in March, when arrivals begin in England (Fig 4). There are very few spring recoveries on passage south of the Sahara and the passage across the desert is physically very stressful, with many fatalities (*BWP*). In North Africa, records spread much further east than in autumn and crossings of the Mediterranean seem to be spread between the Balearics and Italy. Onward passage is on a broad front through France. In April and May, the only reports from the winter quarters are from the Johannesburg and Pretoria area (Fig 4). In spring, experienced birds may be able to return in about five weeks at a speed of about 300 km per day (Mead 1970).

Most birds settle to breed at or close to the sites where they were hatched, or where they bred the previous year. Many studies have shown that males are rather more site-faithful than females (*BWP*) but the differences are only a few kilometres. In Germany, returning adults were 230 m away (males) and 610 m (females), on average, and nestlings were 740 m and 2,500 m away respectively. The median natal dispersal distance for British & Irish birds is 7 km (P5–95=0–261 km, n=435); the median for males is less than 1 km (n=12) but is rather higher at 11 km for females (n=14). The median breeding dispersal distance for British & Irish birds is less than 1 km for both sexes (overall P5–95=0–45 km, n=67).

There is good evidence that passage birds from around the North Sea and as far as the Baltic are present in Britain both in spring and autumn (R & F, Fig 5) but no evidence, from the few recoveries, that either sex is more common. The coastal Norwegian birds may regularly cross the North Sea but the records from further away may represent birds that went off course.

Apart from worries about persecution for food at some roosts in Africa, conservation concern for this species is concentrated on the extensive loss of birds from some parts of its breeding range (Mead 2000). Census data indicate a loss of 16% in the UK breeding population between 1970 and 1998 (Gregory *et al* 2000), although more recent analyses suggest an increase during the 1990s (*eg* Baillie *et al* 2001). Ringing results suggest that the reasons for local declines should be sought locally: the intensity of modern farming, loss of livestock and scarcity of nest sites have been implicated. Further detailed studies are in progress – not least the EURING Swallow Project (Spina 1998a) with over 115,000 Swallows ringed in 1997, the pilot year – which are seeking to investigate the detailed population dynamics and dispersal patterns shown by the species. A more detailed knowledge of Swallow migration, which could be obtained in future from highly miniaturized satellite-transmitters, would pinpoint problems on migration that, otherwise, are likely to remain unknown – and perhaps reveal more details of the journey across the Sahara.

Chris Mead

House Martin
Delichon urbica

Despite House Martins being common, widespread and universally well known in their breeding range due to their commensal relationship with Man, they remain, to some extent, birds of mystery. It is still uncertain whether they roost terrestrially or aerially, both in their breeding range (when not in their nests), and in their wintering areas south of the Sahara Desert; also unknown are the locations of the various European populations in these areas. Like the other two common hirundines, Swallow and Sand Martin, they are long-distance trans-Saharan migrants, but whereas Swallows and Sand Martins roost in huge concentrations in reedbeds on migration and in their winter quarters, there would appear to be no authentic records of House Martins doing so (*BWP*).

The nominate race breeds from western Europe east to western Siberia, and from Fennoscandia south to the western Mediterranean coast of North Africa; other races, *lagopoda* and *dasypus*, breed further east in Asia as far as Japan (*BWP*). The nominate race winters in Africa south of the Sahara, crossing the Mediterranean along its length from Gibraltar to Israel. It is common throughout Britain & Ireland, though thinly distributed over much of northern and western Scotland and western Ireland; it is also very local on moors and upland areas, where scattered human dwellings provide only limited nesting sites, and sparse cultivation limits the availability of insect food (*1988–91 Atlas*).

In their breeding range, House Martins are almost always associated with human habitations, building their mud nests under protective overhangs such as the eaves of houses and under bridges; a small proportion, less than 1% of the population, nests on cliffs (Clark & McNeil 1980). They are aerial feeders, feeding on insects at a higher

The analysis of the data for this species was supported by Chris Whittles

altitude than Swallows but lower than Swifts, and favour agricultural areas (*1988–91 Atlas*). Nesting is colonial, with some colonies, particularly in southern Europe, numbering several hundred nests on a single structure (Philippona 1992); in central and northern Europe the nests in each colony tend to be more widely scattered.

House Martins have been ringed widely over Britain & Ireland during the breeding season, limited perhaps only by the distribution of those ringers interested in the species (Fig 1). Outside the breeding season, greater numbers have been ringed in the south and east, reflecting those caught by tape-luring, often at observatories, during autumn migration; virtually all caught by this method are juveniles. Few House Martin pulli have been ringed (Fig 2), since these can be extracted only from special artificial nests, and not through the small entrance holes of the natural mud nests. A quarter of the recoveries were recaught by ringers. The remainder were found dead, 41% of these having the cause of death documented (Fig 3). Around 70% of these had recovery circumstances associated with humans or their pets.

Over 90% of the recoveries were in Britain & Ireland and are of little significance with regard to migration routes but some 70 recoveries from central and southern Europe and North Africa show a broad front of passage, from eastern Spain to Italy (Fig 4). There has been only one recovery from south of the Sahara, in Nigeria, from over 290,000 House

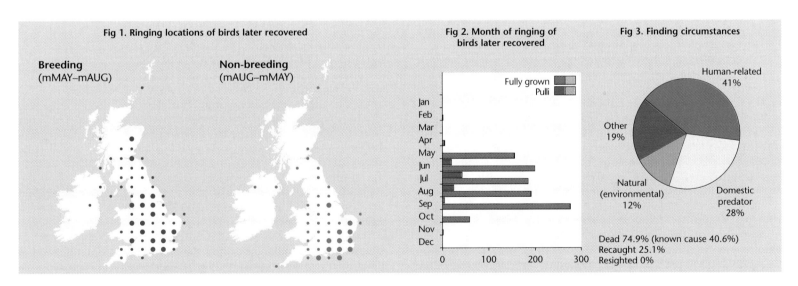

Fig 1. Ringing locations of birds later recovered

Breeding (mMAY–mAUG) Non-breeding (mAUG–mMAY)

Fig 2. Month of ringing of birds later recovered

Fully grown / Pulli

Fig 3. Finding circumstances

Human-related 41%
Other 19%
Natural (environmental) 12%
Domestic predator 28%

Dead 74.9% (known cause 40.6%)
Recaught 25.1%
Resighted 0%

Ringing and recovery data

	<1960	60–69	70–79	80–89	90–97	Total
RINGING						
BTO ringing totals (%)	7	11	18	42	21	292,875
RECOVERIES						
BTO-ringed (%)	8	17	25	38	12	1,155
Foreign-ringed (%)	←	81	→	19	0	16

Statistical analyses

	Breeding population (mMAY–mAUG)	Wintering population (sDEC–sMAR)
Status	[LONG-DISTANCE MIGRANT]	NONE
Age differences	Not tested	—
Sex differences	Not tested	—
Regional differences	Not tested	—
Finding circumstances	Not tested	—

Fig 4. Locations in (a) August–September (9, blue) and October–November (25, red) and (b) February–May (20, blue), June–July (3, red) and those of uncertain seasonality (17, grey) of all included exchanges between Britain & Ireland and abroad. There are no recoveries in December or January.

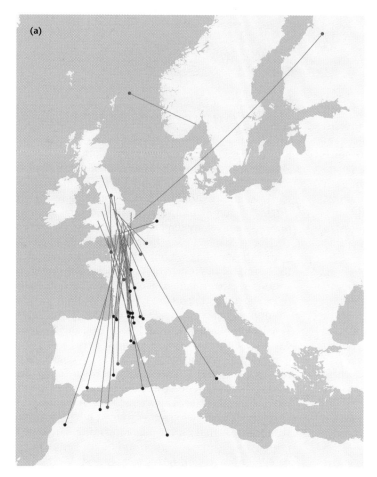

Martins ringed in Britain & Ireland. A few recoveries from northern Europe indicate that some Fennoscandian birds pass through Britain.

In central England, House Martins start to arrive at their breeding colonies at the end of April and depart between late August and early October; in southern Spain they start to arrive at the end of February and depart between the end of August and mid-October (Hill 1992, Pajuelo *et al* 1992). Post-breeding flocks are seen from late August onwards, often on overhead wires in company with Swallows. Records at the east-coast observatories of Sandwich Bay, Spurn and Fair Isle show heavy passages northwards in mid-May, probably including some birds of Fennoscandian origin. The observatories also record peak autumn southward passage in September, with large numbers building up during the second half of the month at Sandwich Bay; again, some of these are probably from northern continental countries, having crossed the North Sea (R & F).

By the end of 1994, over a million House Martins had been ringed in Europe and North Africa (Hill 1997). Of these, just 20 have been recovered south of the Sahara, while from only 300 ringed south of the Sahara, there has been one trans-Saharan recovery (Fig 5). The recovery rate for Swallows is much higher; of the 1.3 million ringed in Britain & Ireland by the end of 1996, 482 have been recovered south of the Sahara. One of the main sources of European Swallow recoveries south of the Sahara is from birds caught and released by ringers, particularly in southern Africa, where these birds are netted in very large numbers at their communal reedbed roosts. Also, many Swallows ringed at these roosts have been recovered in Europe, resulting in much exchange of information. Such exchange has not been possible for House Martins, since no terrestrial roosts have yet been located (*BWP*), and aerial roosting must be suspected. Although the sample of trans-Saharan

recoveries is small, there is some suggestion of longitudinal separation of European House Martins in Africa, with eastern populations wintering in East Africa, central populations in the south around Zambia, Zimbabwe and South Africa, and western populations in countries bordering the Bight of Benin (Fig 5).

House Martins migrating from northern and central European countries normally delay moult until arrival in their winter quarters (Jenni & Winkler 1994). In Spain, however, recent studies have shown that both post-breeding and post-juvenile moult start at the breeding colonies (Hill 2000). Pre-migratory fattening was not noted in a study in Lincolnshire (pers obs), though some fat deposition at the posterior end of the sternum was observed on birds in southwest Spain in autumn (Hill 1992). In general, it must be assumed that birds continue feeding aerially throughout migration.

The habitat of the birds in their winter quarters is poorly known; in spite of some 90 million crossing the Sahara every autumn (Moreau 1972), they are seen comparatively rarely. They have been observed feeding low down in company with other hirundines at bush fires, in front of tropical storms, and at sewage-farms in inclement weather but they are more usually seen in small parties, flying very high and often only just within range of binoculars (D Aspinwall pers comm). The Zambian Ornithological Society newsletters report many such winter sightings over the whole country, and it would appear that the birds are not restricted to mountainous regions as has previously been suggested. 'Wrecks' due to adverse weather conditions sometimes occur. Grobler (2000) describes a recent one in South Africa in January in which local farmers reported that large numbers, seeking shelter from unseasonal rain and cold, had huddled on top of each other up to five deep on

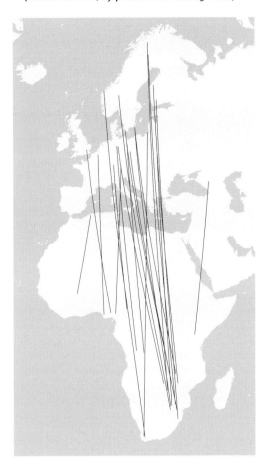

Fig 5. Trans-Saharan ring-recoveries of House Martins: all were ringed north of the Sahara except for one ringed in Kenya and recovered by the Black Sea. (*Source*: Hill 1997, by permission of *Safring News*.)

mainly Palearctic hirundines, dying over the whole of Rhodesia (now Zimbabwe) during a cold spell in November; they estimated that 20% of the country's wintering population of Swallows had perished, as well as many House Martins.

While data are lacking regarding site-fidelity in winter, the birds show a high degree of fidelity to their breeding sites. In a seven-year study (Hill 2002) at 28 colonies in an area of 220 km² in Lincolnshire (in which a colony was defined as a whole village or small town, a separate suburb in a large town, or an isolated farmhouse or bridge), recaptures of birds ringed as adults showed that 86% of the males retrapped ($n=311$) and 76% of the females ($n=246$) had returned to the colony where they were ringed, and that 98% of the males and 97% of the females were at the same colony or at one within 5 km of their ringing site. The British & Irish recoveries of dead birds show a median breeding dispersal distance of less than 1 km (P5–95=0–41 km, $n=147$), and a median natal dispersal distance of 4 km (P5–95=0–123 km) for the small available sample of 24 birds. A previous study in Germany showed that 58% of 125 first-year males, but only 16% of 68 females, settled to breed in the village where they were hatched; for females, late-hatched birds settled further from their natal sites than those hatched early (Hund & Prinzinger 1979). Turner & Rose (1989) refer to an adult mortality rate of 40–60% but the Lincolnshire study suggested that it could be as high as 75% (Hill 2002).

Despite being one of Europe's common trans-Saharan migrants, almost nothing is known about the House Martin's wintering areas in Africa. Until a method is devised for catching large numbers of House Martins in countries south of the Sahara or for remote tracking of small passerines, it is unlikely that recovery rates will ever be high enough to establish with certainty the ranges of the various European populations in their winter quarters. Existing ring-recoveries also tell us little about the importance of Britain & Ireland for passage migrants from Fennoscandia. Long-term monitoring in the Netherlands since 1990 has shown a steady decline in numbers there; declining numbers have long been suspected in Britain but no overall trend has yet been proven. It would seem unlikely that any continuing decrease in numbers could be attributed to conditions in their African winter quarters; more likely it would be due to a reduction in supplies of insect food in their breeding areas, because of changes in agriculture and farming methods.

L A (Sandy) Hill

window sills and in farm buildings. He estimated that *c* 20,000 died that night from cold and hunger in the area; a sample ($n=272$) was found to be in an emaciated condition, the mean weight being 8.6 g, less than half the norm. Steyn & Brooke (1971) refer to vast numbers of migrants,

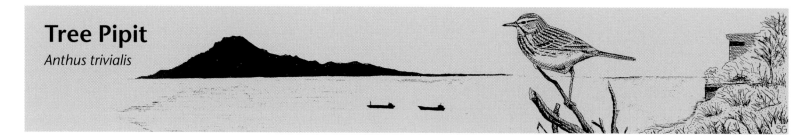

Tree Pipit
Anthus trivialis

It is the incisive, high-pitched flight call of the Tree Pipit that normally alerts the migration watcher to this long-distance traveller, as it passes overhead *en route* to or from its African wintering grounds. The species is seldom seen in large numbers on passage despite being a relatively common breeding bird in Britain, suggesting that significant numbers migrate by night. It breeds almost throughout Britain, though not in the Outer Hebrides and Northern Isles (*1988–91 Atlas*). Remarkably, the species is absent from Ireland apart from passage birds and the occasional territory holder; *Birds in Ireland* suggests that Tree Pipits may be rare breeders but are overlooked.

The remainder of the breeding range covers most of continental Europe, and extends east across Siberia past Lake Baikal, and south to the Caspian Sea and Himalayas (*European Atlas*). Tree Pipits are notably absent as a breeding bird from southern Spain and islands in the Mediterranean, and are scarce breeders in Portugal. British birds spend the winter south of the Sahara, along with the majority of birds from the continental European breeding population. The African wintering range stretches from Guinea on the west coast to Ethiopia in the east and from there southward into South Africa, though the distribution of British birds within this range is poorly known (*BWP*). Birds from the eastern part of the breeding range winter in India and neighbouring countries. The migratory divide between birds wintering in Africa and India is not known, though the populations of the two eastern races, breeding in Afghanistan and the northwest Himalayas, winter entirely in India. A few birds also winter in the Middle East and on Crete and other Greek islands. Ringing data suggest that most European birds, and some birds

The analysis of the data for this species was supported by Heather & Tony Coats

from northwest Russia and the Baltic States, probably migrate in a southwesterly direction into Portugal or the western Mediterranean before moving on to Africa (*Der Zug*).

Typical breeding habitat consists of open country with scattered trees and bushes for song-posts, with the highest densities in upland areas. This includes heathlands and grasslands but intensively farmed agricultural areas are avoided. Conifer plantations and coppiced woodlands in the first few years of growth provide additional breeding habitat. Migrating Tree Pipits will occupy areas of coastal scrub, and can be found in dense ground vegetation where no bushes or trees are available. In the African wintering quarters savanna-type habitats are preferred, though cultivated areas and forest clearings are also occupied (*BWP*).

The small number of Tree Pipit recoveries involving Britain mean that only tentative conclusions can be drawn from the ringing data. The ringing sites of Tree Pipits subsequently recovered are scattered throughout the species' range in Britain with perhaps a slight bias towards the southeast (Fig 1). There are no recoveries of birds ringed in Ireland. The majority of recoveries are of birds ringed during the breeding season, and about half are birds ringed as pulli (Fig 2).

The geographical distribution of recoveries is potentially biased by hunting pressure, as 35% of recoveries found dead with a known cause of death refer to birds deliberately taken by Man. The majority of the

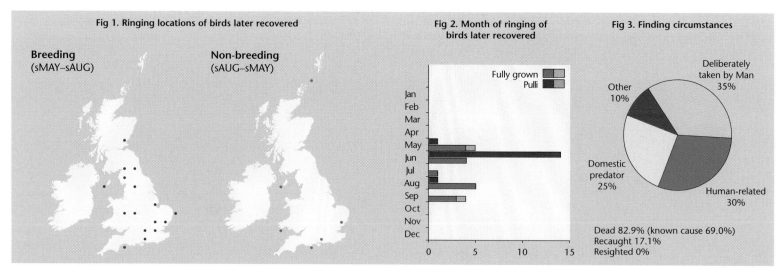

Fig 1. Ringing locations of birds later recovered

Breeding (sMAY–sAUG)   Non-breeding (sAUG–sMAY)

Fig 2. Month of ringing of birds later recovered

Fully grown
Pulli

Fig 3. Finding circumstances

Deliberately taken by Man 35%
Other 10%
Domestic predator 25%
Human-related 30%

Dead 82.9% (known cause 69.0%)
Recaught 17.1%
Resighted 0%

Ringing and recovery data

	<1960	60–69	70–79	80–89	90–97	Total
RINGING						
BTO ringing totals (%)	22	16	19	25	18	16,460
RECOVERIES						
BTO-ringed (%)	24	15	21	27	12	33
Foreign-ringed (%)	←	33	→	33	33	3

Statistical analyses

	Breeding population (sMAY–sAUG)	Wintering population (mNOV–sMAR)
Status	[LONG-DISTANCE MIGRANT]	NONE
Age differences	Not tested	—
Sex differences	Not tested	—
Regional differences	Not tested	—
Finding circumstances	Not tested	—

Fig 4. Recovery locations and movements of over 20 km of Tree Pipits present in Britain & Ireland in autumn (16, blue), spring (1, black) and the breeding season (16, red). The two seasonally inaccurate recoveries are shown in grey. A single pre-1979 movement involving a bird ringed in Italy is not shown.

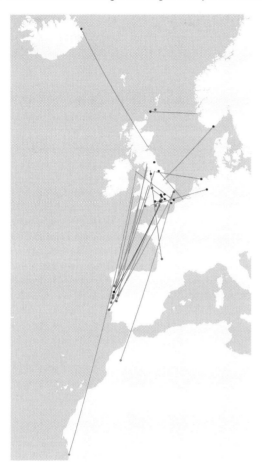

remaining birds found dead are the result of unintentional human-related deaths or were killed by domestic predators (Fig 3). Ringing effort is unlikely to have greatly biased the pattern of recoveries of birds ringed in Britain as only four recoveries refer to birds retrapped by ringers (11%).

Tree Pipits occur throughout Britain on passage, particularly on coasts in autumn (*BWP*). They are scarce migrants in Ireland, occurring mainly on the Wexford coast or at Cape Clear but more widely in autumn than in spring (*Birds in Ireland*). Autumn movements occur mainly in August and September, with a peak in late August, but continue into October. However, ring-recoveries show that pre-migratory dispersal can take place as early as July. Data from bird observatories indicate that Tree Pipits move across the country in a southwesterly direction in the autumn with the strongest passage of birds recorded through observatories in southwest Britain (*R & F*). On departing Britain, the majority of birds appear to continue in a southwesterly direction and make their first landfall in Portugal. All but one of the foreign recoveries of British-breeding birds in autumn are from Portugal, the only other being from the southwest coast of France (Fig 4). The cluster of recoveries from Portugal is mainly of birds that have been shot, and so may simply reflect the intensity of hunting pressure encountered. However, there are no recoveries from northern Spain and only the one recovery from southern France, despite both areas having similar levels of hunting to that in Portugal. All but one of the seasonally accurate recoveries in Portugal, together with the recovery in France, were in September (the other in Portugal being in October). The sole recovery of a passage bird further south than Portugal comes from Morocco, which suggests that North Africa may provide additional stopover sites for British birds, though the date of this recovery is not known.

The African wintering grounds are occupied from September to May (*BWP*). However, there is no evidence to indicate the timing of arrival and departure of British birds and the only clue to their distribution within the African wintering range comes from a single recovery in Mauritania (Fig 4). Tree Pipits are not known to be particularly gregarious in winter though they can occur at high density in preferred habitats and occasionally in small groups, and some communal roosting occurs. A certain degree of winter site-fidelity is indicated from a study in Nigeria where two birds were recorded returning to the same site in subsequent years (*BWP*). There is also evidence from a ringing study in Senegal of pre-migratory fattening in spring prior to crossing the Sahara (Loske 1990).

Spring migration begins in late February, when the first birds reappear in North Africa, but the peak passage through southern Europe occurs in April (*BWP*). The first arrivals in Britain can occur in late March with the greatest numbers arriving in late April and early May. What little evidence there is seems to suggest that spring migrants retrace the route taken in autumn. Arrivals are concentrated in southwest Britain (*R & F*) and a single recovery in Portugal suggests that it is again used as a staging post. However, exchanges with Belgium and the Netherlands suggest that spring movements to Britain may also be via the Low Countries. A bird ringed in Belgium on 3 May was controlled near York 10 days later, while a juvenile ringed in Yorkshire in July, and another bird ringed in Dorset in September were recovered in the Netherlands the following May (Fig 4). Recovery data provide little or no information regarding natal and breeding dispersal or breeding site-fidelity.

A significant proportion of the Tree Pipits occurring on the east coast of Britain in spring and autumn are likely to be from continental breeding populations. The slightly later timing of peak passages at east-coast bird observatories, such as Spurn Point and Fair Isle, and their association with southeasterly winds suggest that such birds are drift migrants on their way to or from northern Europe (*R & F*). Evidence from ring-recoveries shows that at least some Norwegian birds pass through eastern Britain in spring. A bird ringed in Lincolnshire on 9 May was recovered just over a year later in Norway, while a bird ringed in Norway was retrapped on North Ronaldsay in May (Fig 4). A bird ringed in Fife on 21 May and recovered eight days later in Iceland (where Tree Pipit is only a vagrant) was presumably also a displaced migrant en route to breeding grounds in northern Europe. In addition to the recoveries mapped in Fig 4, a bird ringed in northwest Italy on 26 September 1976 was found dead at Sheringham, Norfolk, the following May.

The main threats to the British population of Tree Pipits during migration periods come from the hunting pressure they suffer in southern Europe and the ongoing expansion of the Sahara Desert (Biber & Salathé 1991). Potential threats south of the Sahara will remain largely unknown until we have more information regarding the precise wintering quarters of British birds.

Michael Shepherd

Meadow Pipit

Anthus pratensis

The Meadow Pipit is the most common pipit in western Europe. It is a familiar sight in the uplands and marginal lands of northwest Europe during the breeding season, and even to city dwellers in spring and autumn, when migrating individuals or small flocks pass overhead, calling. The species is less conspicuous during winter when it occurs at low altitudes inland and along the coastal fringe (*Winter Atlas*).

The Meadow Pipit breeds in southeast Greenland, Iceland, the Faeroes, and through the middle to northern latitudes of continental Europe and western Asia as far east as the Ob River. Two subspecies are recognized: the nominate race *pratensis* occupies most of the range, while *whistleri* breeds in Ireland and western Scotland (*CBWP*). In Britain & Ireland, the Meadow Pipit nests from sea-level to altitudes of over 1,000 m and it is the most common nesting passerine above 500 m. The breeding population has been estimated at 1.9 million territories in Britain and 900,000 territories in Ireland (*1988–91 Atlas*). The winter population in Britain & Ireland could be between 1 million and 2.5 million birds (*Winter Atlas*).

The northern limits of the winter range vary with the severity of the season but wintering normally occurs throughout the lowlands of both Britain and Ireland and in western continental Europe north to Denmark and east to western Germany. Otherwise, wintering is centred on the Mediterranean Basin, including Italy, the Balkans, Turkey, the Nile Delta and northwest Africa (Spaepen 1988, *CBWP*). Morocco is a favoured wintering area, where Smith (1965) noted that Meadow Pipits occurred in enormous numbers in the lowlands, including the Sous Plains; they are also found on the Middle Atlas plateaux and at altitudes

The analysis of the data for this species was supported by Stuart Craig & Tom Dougall

up to around 2,500 m in the High Atlas (Simms 1992). Although most British & Irish Meadow Pipits winter in the Iberian Peninsula, many remain within Britain & Ireland all year.

A very visible, mainly diurnal, autumn passage occurs between mid-July and late October, predominantly in a southwesterly direction in western Europe (Helbig *et al* 1987, *CBWP*). The first month or so involves local dispersal of birds moving down from the higher uplands and beginning their moult. Post-juvenile moult can result in some juveniles remaining at a site for up to seven weeks before embarking on their southerly autumn passage (Dougall 1993, Dougall & Craig 1997, pers obs). In southern Europe, migration peaks at Gibraltar between mid-October and early November (*CBWP*). Spring passage of western populations peaks in March and April and follows the same route as in autumn. Movement is close to northeast in direction across much of continental western Europe and the most northerly breeding sites are occupied by mid-May (Helbig *et al* 1987, Spaepen 1989, *CBWP*). Occasional unseasonal snowy weather in spring can result in altitudinal return movements from upland areas to adjacent lower ground (Turnbull 1984).

The ringing locations of Meadow Pipits ringed during the breeding season and subsequently recovered are scattered throughout much of Britain but are confined largely to the east coast in Ireland (Fig 1). In the

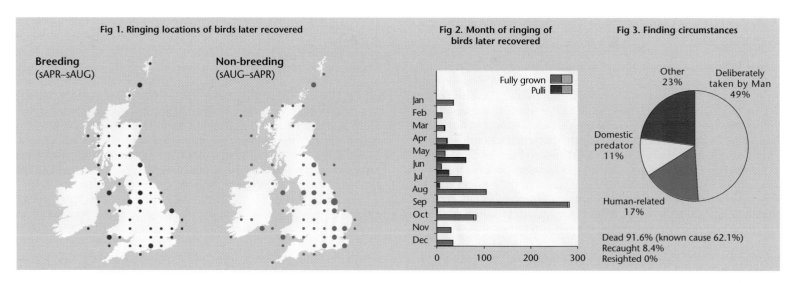

Fig 1. Ringing locations of birds later recovered

Breeding (sAPR–sAUG)

Non-breeding (sAUG–sAPR)

Fig 2. Month of ringing of birds later recovered

Fully grown / Pulli

Fig 3. Finding circumstances

Other 23%
Deliberately taken by Man 49%
Domestic predator 11%
Human-related 17%

Dead 91.6% (known cause 62.1%)
Recaught 8.4%
Resighted 0%

Ringing and recovery data

	<1960	60–69	70–79	80–89	90–97	Total
RINGING						
BTO ringing totals (%)	12	16	17	26	28	183,617
RECOVERIES						
BTO-ringed (%)	20	32	20	20	9	857
Foreign-ringed (%)	←	41	→	18	41	22

Statistical analyses

	Breeding population (sAPR–sAUG)	Wintering population (sDEC–sMAR)
Status	LONG-DISTANCE MIGRANT (4)	[SHORT-DISTANCE MIGRANT]
Age differences[NT]	Not significant*	Not tested
Sex differences	Not tested	Not tested
Regional differences	Significant[3]*	Not tested
Finding circumstances	Significant	Not tested

Fig 4. Locations in autumn and movements of over 20 km between the breeding season and autumn, of 120 Meadow Pipits present in Britain & Ireland during the breeding season.

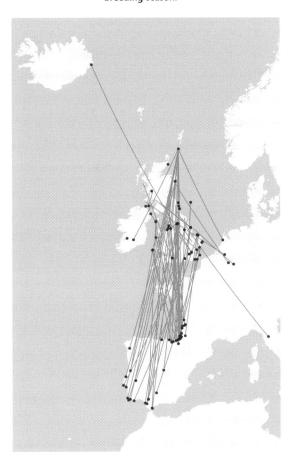

Fig 5. Locations in winter and movements of over 20 km between the breeding season and winter, of 67 Meadow Pipits present in Britain & Ireland during the breeding season.

non-breeding season, Meadow Pipits have been ringed more extensively in Ireland and on offshore islands but in Scotland largely at coastal sites, where autumn passage can be heavy and birds easy to trap (Davis 1981, Maguire 1985, Dougall 1993). Although ringing locations in England and Wales are as widespread as in the breeding season, more birds are ringed at coastal sites, especially along the east and southeast coasts of England. The vast majority of Meadow Pipit recoveries have involved fully fledged birds ringed in the autumn, with only 19% ringed as pulli (Fig 2).

Almost two-thirds of all Meadow Pipits recovered dead have had their demise attributed to a cause. Almost half of these deaths were due to hunting with a further 17% through traffic accidents, collisions with static objects, entering buildings or other human agency (Fig 3). To a large degree, the geographical distribution of recoveries of dead birds reflects hunting pressure along the species' migration routes, whereas the distribution of live controls reflects the locations of ringers catching the species at scattered coastal observatories, and in central and eastern England, Belgium and the Netherlands.

For Meadow Pipits ringed in the breeding season in Britain & Ireland, autumn recoveries are scattered around the British coast, with a few inland, in Ireland and the Low Countries, and many along the Bay of Biscay and in the Iberian Peninsula (Fig 4). The concentration of recoveries from the southwest coast of France of birds ringed in many parts of Britain suggests a coastal route followed by a westerly shift in direction to enter the Iberian Peninsula, as has been shown for Dutch-ringed Meadow Pipits (Speek & Speek 1984).

Populations nesting elsewhere in continental Europe are able to take a more direct northeast–southwest route to and from their breeding and wintering areas (Helbig et al 1987, Spaepen 1989). There are five autumn recoveries east of the main flyway, and one in winter; these may be

continental birds taking a more easterly route on subsequent migrations. The Icelandic bird may have been ringed in Britain while still on passage.

Although there are some recoveries inland in the south of England in winter, the vast majority are from France, the northern Spanish coast, Portugal, inland southern Spain, and Morocco (Fig 5). Birds are furthest to the south between November and January, after which return movement northward from the winter quarters begins but does not reach Britain & Ireland until March (Fig 6).

Fig 6. Monthly variation in the differences in latitude between ringing and recovery locations of Meadow Pipits present in Britain & Ireland during the breeding season. Monthly medians (points) and interquartile ranges (bars) are shown.

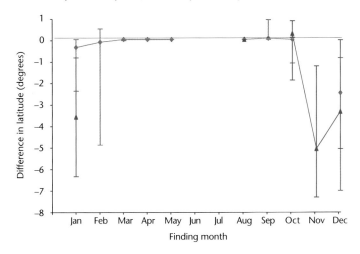

Fig 7. Locations in (a) the breeding season (78), (b) autumn (207), (c) winter (135) and (d) spring (16), of Meadow Pipits present in Britain & Ireland during autumn.

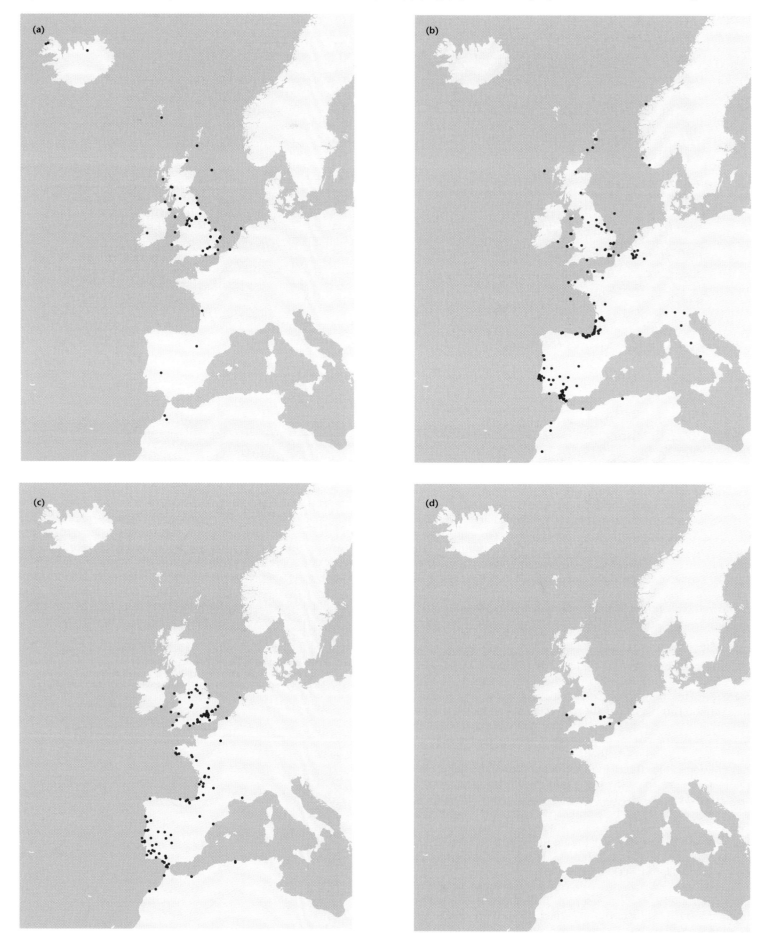

Of 39 ringed Meadow Pipits recovered in subsequent breeding seasons, all of which except one were found dead, none was outside Britain & Ireland and 95% were within 13 km of their ringing site. This accords with the findings of Hötker (1982) in Saxony who found, in a colour-marked population, that adults returned to their previous year's territories, or nearby, irrespective of whether they had been successful, and that first-time breeders usually returned to within 5 km of their natal site (although some could be over 20 km away).

Although there have been 163 recoveries involving Meadow Pipits ringed as pulli, only 15 of these involve recovery during a subsequent breeding season. This means that little is known about natal dispersal in the British population; the median natal dispersal distance is less than a kilometre ($P5$–$95=0$–13 km). Retraps indicate some degree of winter site-fidelity. Severe weather, especially with snow-cover, has been known to generate cold-weather movements, although the present analysis has been unable to confirm that these can extend to Brittany and Spain as reported in the *Winter Atlas*.

Since few recoveries of Meadow Pipits ringed in Britain & Ireland, or in Belgium (Spaepen 1988), have been of birds likely to have been aged accurately, it is not possible to look for age differences in migration patterns with any degree of confidence. Although in recent years it has become easier to age the species (Svensson 1992) there are still pitfalls (Dougall & Craig 1993). However, there are no obvious differences in movements at any season between those aged as adults and those aged as immatures.

Alongside the movement of British & Irish birds, there is a substantial through passage, under-represented in the ringing data, of Icelandic and Scandinavian birds. Williamson (1959) felt that there was strong evidence from both the observation of migration, through St Kilda, North Rona, Fair Isle and western Ireland, and from detectable plumage differences, that the origins of Meadow Pipits on west-coast passage lay in southeast Greenland, Iceland and the Faeroes, whereas east-coast passage probably involved continental birds. Although there are few recoveries on breeding grounds abroad, it is likely that many of the Meadow Pipits ringed in autumn in Britain & Ireland have originated in Iceland, the Faeroes or the southwest of Norway. There have been 22 recoveries in Britain & Ireland of birds ringed abroad; nine in Belgium, six in the Netherlands, three each in Iceland and Norway and one in France. The majority of these birds were ringed on passage, rather than as pulli or adults from known breeding populations, again making it impossible to determine the origins of birds passing through Britain & Ireland.

Recoveries of birds ringed in autumn in Britain & Ireland (Fig 7) follow the same general distribution as for those ringed during the breeding season, involving the Low Countries, France, the Iberian Peninsula and northwest Africa. Exceptions are birds recovered in the regions of the Rhône Delta, Po Valley and northwest Italy in autumn, and around the Rhône Delta, northern Italy and the Algerian coast in winter. Many of these recoveries will have involved birds from more northerly and easterly populations on passage through Britain & Ireland, although some may be British or Irish breeders. It may be that Britain & Ireland is important, from a conservation viewpoint, as a stopover area for the species.

There are some major gaps in our knowledge of the winter ecology of the Meadow Pipit. From Meadow Pipits ringed in Britain & Ireland in winter almost all of 82 recoveries have been within Britain & Ireland, at all seasons, with the exception of three in autumn (two in the Low Countries and one in Iceland). Of the 20 recoveries of foreign-ringed birds made since 1909, none involved the winter period. There is thus no evidence that foreign Meadow Pipits winter in Britain & Ireland. This suggests that the winter population is composed mainly of birds of British or Irish origin. Also, there is little evidence from ring-recoveries of cold-weather movements to the Continent. Indeed, the only three recorded movements of over 20 km within or between winters were all between-winter movements within the south of England. This further suggests that within Britain & Ireland in winter the Meadow Pipit may be rather site-faithful, although more work on this aspect would also be welcome.

Tom Dougall

Rock Pipit
Anthus petrosus

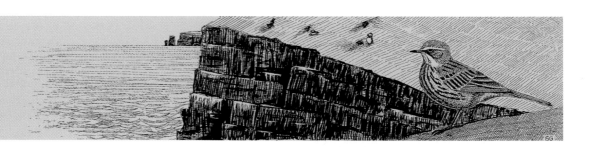

As its name implies, the Rock Pipit is found in rocky habitats, at least during the breeding season, when it inhabits the rocky coastline of northwestern Europe, rarely nesting above 100 m asl. Two races breed within this area, the nominate *petrosus* in Britain, Ireland, the Channel Islands and northwest France, and *littoralis* in Fennoscandia and the Baltic countries (Knox 1988). Along ice-free shores, the species is mainly sedentary but the more northerly populations of *littoralis* migrate southwards in autumn, reaching as far south as Portugal, Sicily and Malta (*Der Zug*). The species is also recorded in northwest Africa. Ring-recoveries suggest birds of the race *littoralis* almost certainly account for the vast majority of those recorded along the coasts of southeast England in winter.

Rock Pipits are found breeding around virtually the entire west and north coasts of Scotland, on most islands and around the whole coastline of Ireland, except where sandy bays and coastal resorts predominate in the east (*1988–91 Atlas*). The only major gaps in the distribution are along the English & Welsh coasts from north Humberside around to the Isle of Wight (apart from isolated pockets on the chalk cliffs of Kent and Sussex) and from the Wirral north to mid-Cumbria. In winter, Rock Pipits are found around the whole of the coastlines of Britain and Ireland (*Winter Atlas*). They feed mainly in the intertidal zone, on sandy beaches, saltmarshes and the foreshore, as well as along sea walls and promenades. The few that are found away from the coast in winter have generally followed the inland courses of rivers. At other times of the year, most inland records refer to birds on passage.

The analysis of the data for this species was supported by Ian & Kate Darling

In 1986, the BOURC decided to treat the Rock/Water Pipit group as a superspecies composed of three species *A. petrosus*, *A. spinoletta* and *A. rubescens*, whereas previously they were regarded as one polytypic species (Knox 1988). Consequently, Rock and Water Pipits have been coded separately in the BTO ring-recovery database only since then. However, all four recoveries of Rock/Water Pipits ringed inland were identified at the time of ringing as being Water Pipits and it is unlikely that the coastal recoveries used in the following analyses include any Water Pipits.

Relatively few Rock Pipits have been ringed in Britain & Ireland and the recovery rate is only about 0.5%; there are fewer than 150 recoveries available for analysis. The ringing locations of Rock Pipits marked during the breeding season and subsequently recovered are concentrated in northeast Scotland, the Irish Sea coasts and the southwest, with almost half from the Fife region or Fair Isle. Non-breeding season ringing localities reflect the wider distribution of the species during the winter months (Fig 1). About 35% of the Rock Pipits recovered were ringed during the breeding season, nearly half whilst nestlings, and 52% were ringed in autumn. Only 8% of those recovered had been ringed in winter (Fig 2).

Just under half of the recoveries of Rock Pipits found dead have a known cause, of which 38% are human-related. Of these the majority

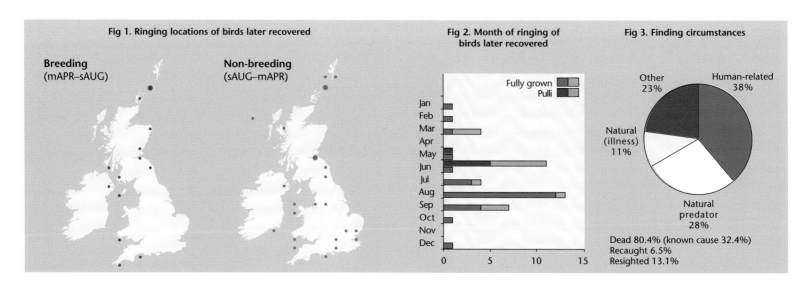

Fig 1. Ringing locations of birds later recovered

Breeding (mAPR–sAUG)

Non-breeding (sAUG–mAPR)

Fig 2. Month of ringing of birds later recovered

Fully grown
Pulli

Jan, Feb, Mar, Apr, May, Jun, Jul, Aug, Sep, Oct, Nov, Dec

0 5 10 15

Fig 3. Finding circumstances

Other 23%
Human-related 38%
Natural (illness) 11%
Natural predator 28%

Dead 80.4% (known cause 32.4%)
Recaught 6.5%
Resighted 13.1%

Ringing and recovery data

	<1960	60–69	70–79	80–89	90–97	Total
RINGING						
BTO ringing totals (%)	29	21	20	18	13	24,869
RECOVERIES						
BTO-ringed (%)	28	30	21	12	9	128
Foreign-ringed (%)	←	30	→	45	25	20

Statistical analyses

	Breeding population (mAPR–sAUG)	Wintering population (mNOV–mMAR)
Status	[SEDENTARY]	[LONG-DISTANCE MIGRANT]
Age differences	Not tested	Not tested
Sex differences	Not tested	Not tested
Regional differences	Not tested	Not tested
Finding circumstances	Not tested	Not tested

Fig 4. Movements of over 20 km and recovery locations of Rock Pipits ringed in Britain & Ireland and probably of the race *petrosus* (87:39). Sample sizes of movements under:over 20 km are given but only those over 20 km are plotted.

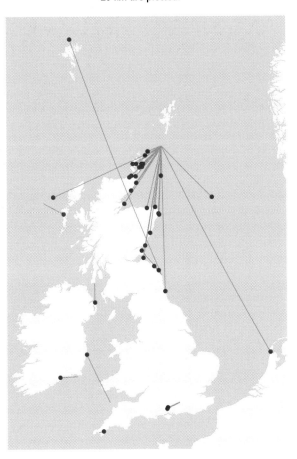

Fig 4. Movements of over 20 km and recovery locations of Rock Pipits ringed in Britain & Ireland and probably of the race *petrosus* (87:39). Sample sizes of movements under:over 20 km are given but only those over 20 km are plotted.

are as a result of the bird having been intentionally taken or having entered a man-made structure, such as a building. Natural predation accounts for a further 28% (Fig 3).

Populations of the race *petrosus* in Britain & Ireland, as well as in the Faeroes, are basically resident with generally just local dispersive movements taking place. However, some birds make short journeys away from their breeding grounds from September onwards (*Der Zug*). Autumn movements away from Fair Isle were noted by Williamson (1965) who thought the birds involved were probably juveniles. The timing of this autumn departure is supported by two recoveries from Fair Isle — a nestling ringed in June and recovered in Orkney in late September, and an adult ringed in late August and recovered over 300 km away in Tayside region in mid-September; although this latter bird had not necessarily bred on Fair Isle. Of Rock Pipits ringed on Fair Isle between June and September, 22 have been recovered at a distance of over 100 km, the majority of which were found on Orkney or the Scottish mainland in autumn or winter (Fig 4). Movements of greater than 100 km are still exceptional, however, and there have been only three others from Rock Pipits ringed in Britain & Ireland, two of them from birds ringed in the winter. Of 2,000 ringed on Skokholm off the Pembrokeshire coast, not a single long-distance recovery was reported (Evans 1966c).

In Ireland, Sharrock (1973) showed that the largest numbers on Cape Clear were present in late September and suggested that these were mainly migrants. However, Hutchinson (*Birds in Ireland*) believed that the autumn peaks are post-breeding aggregations and that there is a very limited movement of Rock Pipits. There have been only three recoveries of over 20 km involving Ireland (Fig 4).

There is a southerly passage of Rock Pipits every autumn at Spurn from September to November, involving birds of both races (Mather 1986). Further south, in Norfolk, birds of the race *petrosus* are possibly annual visitors but only in small numbers (Taylor *et al* 1999). Although no Rock Pipits ringed on Fair Isle have been recovered further south in Britain than Tyne & Wear, one marked in July was found long dead in the

Fig 5. All included exchanges of Rock Pipits between Britain & Ireland and abroad. Those ringed abroad (14, red) are differentiated from those ringed in Britain & Ireland (1, black). The 6 pre-1979 foreign-ringed Rock Pipits (Norway 2, Sweden 2, Germany 1 and France 1) are not shown.

Netherlands two years later. Another, almost certainly *petrosus*, ringed in Northumberland in January was found dead the following spring at sea, north of the Faeroes. Thus some birds from the more northern part of the range of *petrosus* may move a considerable distance south in autumn.

It has been known for many years that Scandinavian birds of the race *littoralis* are passage migrants and winter visitors to the coasts of eastern and southern England, and Wales. However, the extent to which it is involved has become clearer in recent years. In East Anglia, for example, Rock Pipits are regular autumn migrants along the North Norfolk coast, invariably flying westward, with the peak passage in October. Daily counts at any one site rarely exceed about 20, but 350 passed Sheringham during one day in early October 1990. This direction of passage suggests an eastern or northeastern origin, which is supported by the fact that the heaviest movements of Rock Pipits often coincide with arrivals of Scandinavian migrants such as Chaffinches and Bramblings (Taylor 1997).

Birds of the race *littoralis* undergo a partial late-winter body moult that results in a distinctive spring plumage, making them separable from birds of the race *petrosus*. The appearance of these spring-plumaged birds in March and early April was thought to indicate that *littoralis* was only a spring passage migrant. However, it now seems likely that they are the same birds that have been present throughout the winter. On the saltmarsh at Wells and Warham in North Norfolk, for example, of 200 Rock Pipits that were still present in mid-March 1998, all 40 that were examined critically in the field showed strong characteristics of the race *littoralis* (McCallum 1998). In the Netherlands, concentrations of wintering *littoralis* have been recorded in the southwest, also on saltmarsh, where they feed almost exclusively on the mollusc *Asiminea grayana* (Bourgonje 1994). However, apart from the Dutch recovery mentioned earlier and four recoveries in the North Sea, the only other foreign recovery of a British-ringed Rock Pipit involved one ringed in Essex in December which was recovered three years later in October at Kaliningrad in Baltic Russia and was presumably of the race *littoralis*.

The recoveries of foreign-ringed Rock Pipits in Britain & Ireland (all found between September and April) also indicate that many of the wintering birds in southern and eastern England are from Fennoscandia and the Baltic region (Fig 5). Eight from Fennoscandia were ringed as nestlings and, as the remainder from that area were ringed between March and September, all were almost certainly of the race *littoralis*.

Colour-ringed birds were still present at the site of ringing in Sweden in August and one ringed on the west coast of Norway on 9 September was found at sea, about 40 km off the Suffolk coast, the following day. This is about a week earlier than the first Rock Pipit of the autumn is generally recorded in East Anglia, where the passage peaks in Norfolk during the second half of October (Taylor *et al* 1999). One particularly interesting multiple recovery involved a nestling colour-ringed on Malon Island in southern Sweden in June, where it was still present on 23 August; it was reported on the Norfolk coast in February, before being found back again on Malon Island on 26 March.

Winter site-fidelity was demonstrated by two Swedish colour-ringed Rock Pipits that were present at localities in Hampshire for two and three consecutive winters respectively. Breeding site-fidelity among migrant *littoralis* was shown by an adult also ringed on Malon Island, subsequently seen in Suffolk during the winter, and recorded back on Malon Island in June.

Seven of the Swedish-ringed Rock Pipits were sexed as males, and none of the others specifically as females. However, this almost certainly reflects the comparative ease with which colour-ringed birds can be sexed as males after ringing, as a result of subsequently being observed while singing, rather than indicating a difference in migratory patterns between the sexes.

Future ringing of the species in Britain & Ireland should concentrate on winter trapping and colour-ringing, in order to explore the distribution and movement of *littoralis*.

Moss Taylor

Yellow Wagtail
Motacilla flava

The Yellow Wagtail is a widespread, conspicuous and often abundant migrant whose flight calls draw attention to birds making diurnal movements. Because this species uses communal roosts extensively for much of the year, ringers have been able to catch it in large numbers in both breeding and wintering areas. Moreover, the considerable racial variation in head pattern and coloration make it especially amenable to the study of movements, even in the absence of ringing returns.

Its breeding range extends from Britain across Europe and Asia to include western Alaska, and from north of latitude 70°N in arctic Norway south to Banc d'Arguin in Mauritania, the Nile Valley, Kashmir and the Yellow River in China (*BWP*). The breeding range of the yellow-headed British race *flavissima* is now largely restricted to England and the Welsh Marches, with a few pairs in the central lowlands of Scotland. It is only a scarce visitor to Ireland, where there were formerly several isolated breeding colonies. However, it also breeds in several coastal regions of mainland Europe, from southern Norway to northern France, where it can be found nesting alongside the blue-headed central European race *flava*. Each year several pairs of *flava* also nest in England (*1988–91 Atlas*).

Most races of Yellow Wagtail are long-distance migrants, which winter in Africa south of the Sahara, India or Southeast Asia. However, some southern breeding populations are resident and remain in Morocco, Egypt or elsewhere in North Africa during the winter. Some birds also overwinter in regions lying between the Black Sea and Caspian Sea (*BWP*). The most northerly breeding populations tend to winter furthest south, so that a leap-frog migration pattern exists in this species (Bell 1996). It has also been shown that, in the West African winter quarters, male Yellow

The analysis of the data for this species was supported by Andrew Harris

Wagtails tend to winter further to the north than females: in northern Nigeria up to 63% of wintering birds may be males while, just 5° further south, only 37% are males. Many birds also seem to move gradually south to less arid areas, as the dry season progresses (Wood 1992).

Populations of Yellow Wagtails breeding in Europe migrate to African winter quarters that lie predominantly to the west of due south from their breeding ranges (*Der Zug*). They largely appear to follow great-circle routes between breeding and wintering sites but considerable latitudinal displacement can occur, particularly within the Mediterranean Basin in spring, following a difficult crossing of the Sahara (Wood 1982b). Birds that breed north of the Caspian Sea may winter either in East Africa or in India (to the southeast). It is not known if this migratory divide involves entirely separate populations or if, alternatively, siblings may winter in different continents. Once they have discovered a suitable wintering site, Yellow Wagtails appear to return to it in successive winters. One bird that was ringed at a communal roost in central Nigeria was twice recaptured in the same roost over seven years later (Wood 1976). There are many other instances of recurrence in winter, both in East and West Africa.

Within their British breeding range, Yellow Wagtails frequent damp grassland in river valleys, marshes and coastal areas. They will also use other low herbage and crops as feeding and breeding sites. In winter, they

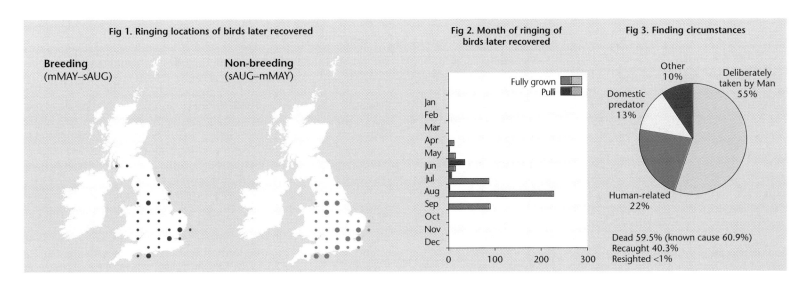

Fig 1. Ringing locations of birds later recovered

Breeding (mMAY–sAUG)

Non-breeding (sAUG–mMAY)

Fig 2. Month of ringing of birds later recovered

Fully grown
Pulli

Jan Feb Mar Apr May Jun Jul Aug Sep Oct Nov Dec

0   100   200   300

Fig 3. Finding circumstances

Other 10%
Deliberately taken by Man 55%
Domestic predator 13%
Human-related 22%

Dead 59.5% (known cause 60.9%)
Recaught 40.3%
Resighted <1%

Ringing and recovery data

	<1960	60–69	70–79	80–89	90–97	Total
RINGING						
BTO ringing totals (%)	12	25	35	21	7	70,275
RECOVERIES						
BTO-ringed (%)	13	34	38	13	1	483
Foreign-ringed (%)	←	92	→	8	0	13

Statistical analyses

	Breeding population (mMAY–sAUG)	Wintering population (mOCT–sMAR)
Status	[LONG-DISTANCE MIGRANT]	NONE
Age differences	Not tested	—
Sex differences	Not tested	—
Regional differences	Not tested	—
Finding circumstances	Not tested	—

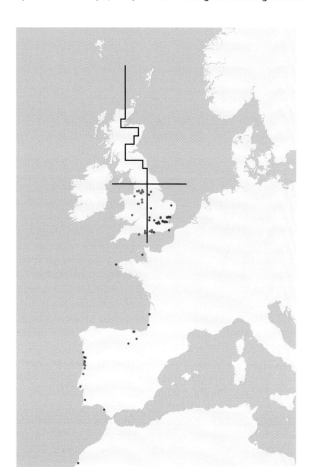

Fig 4. Locations in autumn of Yellow Wagtails that were ringed in the southeast (65, red) and southwest (38, blue) of Britain during the breeding season.

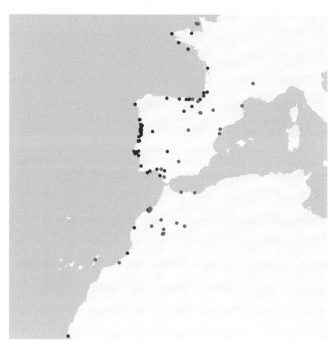

Fig 5. Locations of Yellow Wagtails in southern Europe during autumn migration (September–November) (151, red), and spring migration (March–April) (72, blue), for birds ringed in Britain & Ireland.

are particularly associated with domestic livestock or wild herbivores, feeding on the insects that are disturbed from vegetation as these animals walk through it. Some male Yellow Wagtails defend exclusive winter territories in the most favourable feeding sites, often along watercourses or lake margins. Although they will sometimes perch in trees and bushes, they feed almost entirely on insects captured on or close to the ground. Their food supply is thus closely constrained by soil moisture levels and can be extremely scarce in the African Sahel towards the end of the dry season (Wood 1979). Many migrant warblers that also overwinter in this region commonly consume fruits during this difficult time of year. However, there is only one record of fruit-eating by Yellow Wagtails (Fry et al 1972) and it is still something of a mystery how they are able to fatten for northward migration, immediately south of the Sahara, on a predominantly insectivorous diet (Fry 1992).

The majority of recoveries of British-ringed Yellow Wagtails are of birds that were initially caught at post-breeding roost assemblages. Nevertheless, the distribution of ringing sites is broadly representative of the predominantly English breeding range of this species (Figs 1 & 2). Fewer than 500 have subsequently been recovered and almost 60% of recoveries are from localities within Britain. Hunting and other human-related causes of death predominate in the ring-recovery data (Fig 3). Many overseas recoveries have come from Spain and Portugal, especially for the 1960s. Since 1970, most overseas recoveries have been from Morocco and recently there have been very few from Iberia. This is probably because of the changing pattern of human predation on songbirds in these regions, rather than changes in movement patterns.

In Britain, most Yellow Wagtails have only one brood, starting in late May (Smith 1950, Mason & Lyczynski 1980). By July, a high proportion of

juveniles and adult birds resort to communal roosts, often in reedbeds or other tall vegetation along water margins. Roosts situated along the south coast of England are well away from the principal breeding areas and may attract birds from a wide catchment. Here, adult birds undergo a quite rapid complete post-nuptial moult. The number of birds captured by ringers at these roosts reaches a peak in August and autumn roosts are abandoned before the end of September, with some birds leaving before they have completed their moult (Hereward 1979). By August, a few British-ringed birds are found along the west coast of France or in northern Spain, and in September there are many recoveries from localities along the coast of Portugal and from the north and southwest coasts of Spain (Fig 4). Few are recovered from inland Iberia during autumn migration.

There may be regional differences in the initial route taken by migrants from Britain (Fig 4). Birds ringed in southeast England have been recovered along the coast of the Bay of Biscay, as well as from the Portuguese coast. Those originating in southwest Britain show recoveries exclusively from coastal Portugal. It is possible that the latter make direct flights from England to western Portugal, whilst Yellow Wagtails from southeast England follow the western coast of France into the Iberian Peninsula.

Some birds have reached the western coast of Morocco by September and a few are already in winter quarters in Senegal and the Gambia before the end of October. Because little ringing has been undertaken in these countries, compared with the extensive ringing of Yellow Wagtails that has occurred in Nigeria and Ghana (Smith & Ebbutt 1965, Fry et al 1972), there is little information available about midwinter distribution and behaviour of the British race flavissima. There is no reason to believe, however, that their behaviour differs significantly from that of birds wintering further east in West Africa, although there, the dominant races are nominate flava, the Scandinavian *thunbergi* and the Mediterranean race *cinereocapilla*. Northward passage from the wintering areas of British breeding birds begins as early as February and, by March and early April, there are many recoveries from Morocco and Spain. Because the northward journey seems initially to follow the coast of West Africa, it is possible that British Yellow Wagtails do not face conditions that are quite so inhospitable as those encountered by north and central European breeders, which must traverse the central Sahara Desert. Even so, much of northern Mauritania and Western Sahara are quite inhospitable in the spring but there are extensive coastal wetlands to be found in Morocco. However, many spring recoveries from Morocco are inland, in the Atlas Mountains (Fig 5), where spring rains create many temporary pools and, presumably, a flush of insect prey.

The inland passage of birds through North Africa is continued in Spain, where northward recoveries all lie east of a line from Cadiz to Bilbao, with a few as far to the east as the Camargue in southern France (Fig 5). There are no recoveries at all from Portugal of birds moving north towards Britain. Again, this may in part reflect the greater availability of temporary wetlands and associated insects throughout eastern Spain in the spring.

More easterly breeding Yellow Wagtails also appear to migrate further to the east during spring migration than when on southward migration in the autumn (*BWP*). Nevertheless, continental races are frequently recorded at British coastal observatories during the spring. On Fair Isle, *flava* and *thunbergi* are both more commonly recorded than the British *flavissima*, and spring passage continues strongly into early June (*R & F*). Birds belonging to several continental races are also quite common on passage in Britain during the southward migration, although racial identification is often difficult in the autumn (*R & F*). Migrants appearing at the coast in late September and through October are very likely to be of continental origin.

Yellow Wagtails of the nominate race, captured on northward passage along the Mediterranean coast of Spain, were considerably heavier than birds in Africa during midwinter (Wood 1982b). This presumably means that birds are able to re-fatten after crossing the inhospitable Sahara but also indicates the advantage to be gained by birds that arrive on breeding grounds with a significant reserve of fat. This may tide them over periods of cold weather, when insects may be scarce, and enable them to devote more time to territorial establishment and nesting activities.

The Yellow Wagtail has declined as a breeding bird in Britain during the past two decades (*1988–91 Atlas*, Crick *et al* 1998). In part, this may be due to drainage of wetlands, but it is more commonly associated with changing agricultural practices. The switch from hay to silage crops within moist valley grasslands may have been particularly significant. On passage and in winter quarters there have also been important losses of natural and seminatural wetland areas. However, these losses may have been balanced by the widespread development of irrigated agriculture, which often affords a suitable habitat for this species. Nevertheless, use of insecticides in such areas may have had harmful effects.

Our understanding of the movements of British breeding populations of Yellow Wagtail would be considerably augmented by ringing and behavioural studies in their West African winter quarters and at migration sites in Morocco in the spring. It would be helpful to know whether the race *flavissima* fattens to the same extent as other races before attempting a desert crossing and what is its condition upon arrival in the foothills of the Atlas Mountains. More extensive studies of British breeding populations may also reveal the effect on breeding success of body-weight and fat reserves, when the birds arrive on the breeding grounds.

Brian Wood

Grey Wagtail
Motacilla cinerea

Grey Wagtails are small, graceful insectivorous birds of fast-flowing streams and rivers. In Britain & Ireland they are partial migrants, or possibly altitudinal migrants in some areas. Some, especially those in southern Britain and in Ireland, may remain on their breeding grounds; others from upland Scotland, northern England and Wales move to lower altitudes or fly south, southeast or southwest in autumn. Populations in central Europe and northern Asia are migratory.

Grey Wagtails breed mainly in mountainous areas across the Palearctic from Ireland and Britain south to Morocco and Algeria and eastwards to Kamchatka, Japan, Gansu and Sichuan. Resident races occur in the Atlantic islands (Canaries, Madeira and Azores) and in the Atlas Mountains of Morocco, while migratory or partially migratory populations occur elsewhere. Grey Wagtails migrate through Europe, the Mediterranean and Iranian regions, and central and eastern Asia including Japan. On migration, Grey Wagtails associate in small flocks but at other times are largely territorial. They winter in Britain & Ireland and in the Mediterranean area, in Iberia, Italy and along the Rhine, while other European populations winter in northwest Africa (*Der Zug*). Birds from central Europe may fly directly across the Mediterranean, rather than across the narrow Strait of Gibraltar, to the North African coast. Passage birds are regularly recorded on Mediterranean islands such as Malta and Sicily, where some Grey Wagtails overwinter. Grey Wagtails from central Europe may cross the Bosphorus into Turkey and the Middle East in the autumn (Porter 1993). Some populations winter as far south in Africa as the Gambia in the west, the Congo Basin in central Africa and, in the east, Malawi, occasionally reaching southern

The analysis of the data for this species was supported by Stephanie J Tyler

Africa. Others from further east winter in the Himalayan foothills, to 2,000 m, and south throughout the Indian subcontinent, as well as in southern China and Taiwan, and across southeast Asia to western New Guinea and surrounding islands.

In the breeding season, Grey Wagtails favour upland fast-flowing streams and rivers with abundant rocks or exposed shoals and with a riparian fringe of broad-leaved trees. They also breed on lowland watercourses, including canals, where there are mill races or mill streams, weirs, artificial waterfalls as at lake outflows, or lock gates. On migration and during the winter months, Grey Wagtails may occur in a much wider variety of habitats. These include both upland and lowland watercourses, even slow-moving lowland rivers, streams and ditches, lake shores, isolated rocky pools in dry rivers, coastal marshes, rocky shores, watercress beds, sewage-farms, farmyards, desert oases and wells.

Grey Wagtails are difficult to catch in large numbers. With their excellent eyesight and aerial manoeuvrability, they are usually able to avoid mist-nets. As they are largely territorial, both during the breeding season and in the winter months, they are well spaced along watercourses, and roosts tend to be smaller than those of other wagtails. Most birds have therefore been ringed as nestlings (Figs 1 & 2). Ringing locations of recoveries of birds that had been ringed during the breeding season and in the winter cover much of the species' breeding and

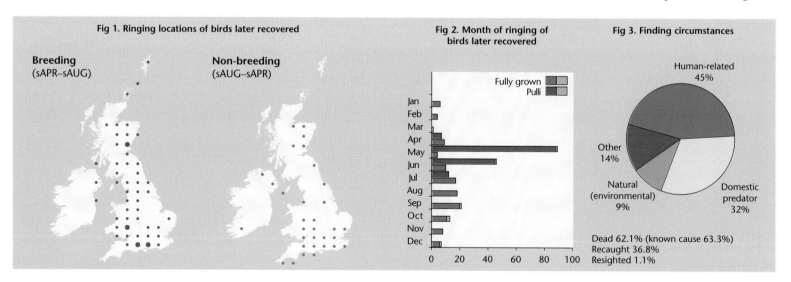

Fig 1. Ringing locations of birds later recovered

Breeding (sAPR–sAUG)

Non-breeding (sAUG–sAPR)

Fig 2. Month of ringing of birds later recovered

Fully grown
Pulli

Fig 3. Finding circumstances

Human-related 45%

Other 14%

Natural (environmental) 9%

Domestic predator 32%

Dead 62.1% (known cause 63.3%)
Recaught 36.8%
Resighted 1.1%

Ringing and recovery data

	<1960	60–69	70–79	80–89	90–97	Total
RINGING						
BTO ringing totals (%)	7	8	25	37	23	34,584
RECOVERIES						
BTO-ringed (%)	4	13	31	36	16	266
Foreign-ringed (%)	←	40	→	50	10	10

Statistical analyses

	Breeding population (sAPR–sAUG)	Wintering population (sNOV–sMAR)
Status	SHORT-DISTANCE MIGRANT (3)	?
Age differences[NT]	Not significant*	—
Sex differences	Not tested	—
Regional differences	Not tested	
Finding circumstances	Not tested*	

Fig 4. Locations in (a) autumn (52) and (b) winter (52), and movements of over 20 km between the breeding and non-breeding season, of Grey Wagtails present in Britain & Ireland during the breeding season.

wintering range in Britain (*Winter Atlas, 1988–91 Atlas*). Ireland, however, is poorly represented. The abundance of recoveries originating from birds ringed in Hampshire, Mid and South Wales and Angus in northeast Scotland result from particular studies of Grey Wagtails. Apparent absences from some areas, such as northwest Wales and parts of eastern Scotland, only reflect a paucity of ringers and of Grey Wagtails ringed. Apart from nestlings (57%), most recoveries came from birds ringed as juveniles (23%), mostly from June to September (Fig 2).

Some 62% of recoveries were of birds found dead. Three recoveries were from resightings of marked individuals, the rest being controls by ringers. Most causes of recovery for birds found dead and for which the cause of recovery was known were human-related (45%), with domestic predators, notably cats, accounting for a further 32% of recoveries (Fig 3). Most recoveries involved distances of less, often considerably less, than 100 km. Fewer than 20 birds moved further than 500 km. For all Grey Wagtails recovered dead, the median distance moved was 21 km (P5–95=0–591 km, *n*=169).

Juveniles in their first 10–12 weeks after fledging move only short distances but thereafter they undertake much longer flights as they move southwards in the autumn. Most of the autumn and winter recoveries of birds breeding in Britain & Ireland were in the south, southwest or southeast of Britain (Fig 4). Both young and adult Scottish birds and those from northern England moved to southern Britain or to Ireland for the winter. Birds from the northwest and northeast of Britain therefore moved longer distances than birds breeding further south. Median movements (all recoveries) of Grey Wagtails from the northeast and northwest were, respectively, 103 km and 182 km, compared with 15 km for Irish birds, 7 km for birds from the southeast and 22 km for birds from the southwest. Too few individuals have been sexed to determine whether the patterns of movement for males and females are similar.

Individuals ringed and recovered as adults (median=1 km, P5–95= 0–546 km, *n*=12) showed a similar median distance moved to individuals ringed and recovered as immatures (median=27 km, P5–95=0–556 km, *n*=57), although the number of birds ringed as adults is quite small.

There is no evidence for marked annual differences in recovery patterns, although severe winter weather may result in hard-weather movements and much-increased mortality (Tyler 1979, Gopfert 1986a). It is of interest though that five of the six recoveries of birds that had crossed the English Channel to France were in the late autumn or winter of years prior to 1977. These were years with cold winters. Two of the French recoveries originated from nestlings ringed in the New Forest, Hampshire, and the other three were of Scottish origin (Tyler 1979). Since then there has been just one more foreign recovery, of a nestling ringed on a tributary of the River Wye in South Wales and found the following January in France. Two Grey Wagtails ringed on the Channel Islands (Fig 5) and recovered in Britain may have been British-breeding birds that had wintered on the islands or were passing through from France or from further south. It is likely that some Grey Wagtails breeding in Britain reach Spain or Portugal as do some continental Grey Wagtails (*Der Zug*). There are two recoveries of birds ringed in Portugal (Fig 5). These were ringed in their winter quarters and may have returned to Britain to breed. Alternatively, they might have been passage birds that were moving through Britain to Scandinavia or elsewhere in northwest Europe. One had been ringed in Portugal in October 1954 and was recovered two years later in mid-April near Sheffield, Yorkshire. The other was a female ringed in December 1984 and killed on a road in Leicestershire on 1 July the following year.

It seems surprising that there have been so few French recoveries given the regular observations of birds on diurnal passage along the

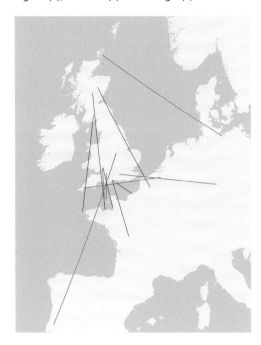

south coasts of England and Wales during the autumn, and of many heading out to sea. During the late summer, singles or small flocks of Grey Wagtails pass south through mainland Britain or down the coasts. Small flocks may comprise siblings, which may remain together after leaving their natal site. Concentrations then occur along the south coasts of Britain. In Sussex, autumn passage at coastal sites has been recorded between late August and late October (James 1996). Sharrock (1969) found maximum passage at extreme southerly headlands on the south coast of England. Other observers have noted an early morning passage west or southwest from coastal headlands such as Prawle Point in South Devon (Norman 1970). Maximum passage occurred in fine, sunny weather and was greatly influenced by winds, passage ceasing altogether when winds were greater than force 5. Peak passage occurred on 11–12 September in 1968 when about 25 birds flew west on both mornings. Many birds passing along the coast appear to leave Britain via Portland Bill (M Rogers pers comm). At Port Eynon in South Wales, flocks of up to 17 Grey Wagtails have been noted in September heading out to sea (*Birds in Wales*). Migrating birds also turn up on Welsh islands such as Bardsey, where they have been recorded nocturnally at the lighthouse (Roberts 1986).

Natal dispersal appears to involve random movements. From 31 recoveries of birds ringed as nestlings and recovered in the breeding season a year or more later, 15 birds had moved less than 20 km from their natal site. There is some evidence from personal observation of fidelity by adults to breeding sites, although there are insufficient ring-recoveries to test this further.

Populations of Grey Wagtails in other parts of Europe are partial or full migrants, depending on how far north and east they breed (Jorgensen 1976, *Der Zug*). Flocks of Grey Wagtails from northwest, west and central Europe move southwest in the summer and autumn. A westerly passage is noted annually along the North Norfolk coast from late June to early November, peaking in September and October, with a maximum daily count of 20 heading west on 18 September 1993 (Taylor *et al* 1999). The direction of this passage suggests the arrival of Scandinavian or continental birds.

A few may winter in Britain, as shown by a recovery in Norfolk of a bird from Belgium, and of two birds from Germany, one of these found near Rochester, Kent. Others continue south, many crossing the Strait of Gibraltar in the autumn (Tellería 1981, Finlayson 1992) to winter in northwest Africa, along the coast and in Saharan oases (Smith 1968) but notably in the mountains of Morocco. Some winter in Algeria, where two birds were found that had been ringed in the former Czechoslovakia (Jorgensen 1976). Small numbers also winter in Tunisia from October to late March (Thomsen & Jacobsen 1979). A small proportion of birds passing across the Strait of Gibraltar cross the Sahara to winter in tropical West Africa (Moreau 1972), notably in Senegal and the Gambia (Serle *et al* 1977) and in northeast Congo (Moreau 1972). Recoveries of German-ringed Grey Wagtails have been reported in Algeria, Morocco and Tunisia, as well as in Mauritania, Mali, Senegal and Ghana (Schloss 1982).

The way in which Grey Wagtails migrate is little known. Diurnal movements seem to be normal and it is likely that birds do not fly very long distances before pausing to feed. Herremans (1988a), who caught Grey Wagtails migrating in central Belgium, found a mean weight of only 16.9 g (*n*=153) but he noted that a few caught during peak migration were heavy (up to 21.3 g) and showed evidence of pre-migratory restlessness when kept overnight. These birds, however, are likely to have been making only short migrations with plenty of opportunities to stop and feed on the way. The trans-Saharan migrants might be expected to lay down fat reserves before undertaking long-distance movements but as yet there is no real evidence for this. Grey Wagtails have often been recorded at desert oases and along the Red Sea coast. If they do make frequent stops by water to feed, they do not need to lay down large fat reserves.

When on passage, or during the winter months, Grey Wagtails may roost communally. Roosts are generally small but occasionally contain a hundred or more birds. While winter roosts of Grey Wagtails may contain the same individuals for several weeks or months, autumn roosts may have a high turnover of migrants, presumably of birds that stop for a day or two and then fly further south (*eg* Gopfert 1986b). Variation in numbers at a roost in a Cheshire quarry between late summer and mid-November suggested a turnover of passage migrants (T Ford & D Elphick pers comm).

As Grey Wagtails are catholic in their diet (Ormerod & Tyler 1991) and in their choice of habitats during migration and during the winter months, they may not be especially vulnerable to habitat changes. However, migrating flocks favour extensive gravel shoals on rivers (pers obs). River management that involves the removal of gravel shoals may therefore be detrimental within Britain & Ireland, and elsewhere in Europe. In Africa, loss of wetlands within and near the Sahara as well as loss of forest cover and of permanent streams in highland areas might also have adverse impacts on long-distance migrants and wintering birds. Possible climate changes, including milder winters in parts of Europe, may be beneficial in encouraging Grey Wagtails to avoid migrating south.

Little has been learnt in recent decades about Grey Wagtail movements. Larger numbers of wagtails need to be ringed to show, for example, differences between the sexes and between young and adult birds in the pattern of movements, and the extent of wintering areas of different populations. More data are also required to show breeding and wintering site-fidelity.

Stephanie J Tyler

Pied Wagtail
Motacilla alba

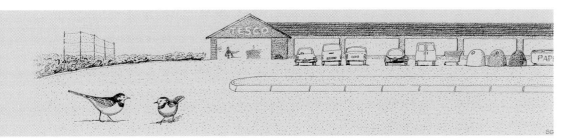

The sharp calls and distinctive plumage of the Pied Wagtail are familiar year-round throughout much of Britain & Ireland. However, most upland and northern breeding areas are vacated in late summer and autumn, as the species moves to lower altitudes and extends to more southerly latitudes for the winter. The species is found across the Palearctic from east Greenland, Iceland and Morocco to south China and far eastern Siberia, and also across the Bering Strait in western Alaska. The two European races are the partially migrant *yarrellii* and the White Wagtail, nominate *alba*, which in the north and east of its range is completely migratory (*CBWP*).

The race *yarrellii* is largely confined as a breeder to Britain & Ireland, with a few pairs on the near Continent in France, the Netherlands, and southwest Norway; it winters within Britain & Ireland, along the Atlantic coast of France, in the Iberian Peninsula and in northwest Africa. A few White Wagtails nest in east Greenland and there are large populations in Iceland and throughout continental Europe. Occasional White Wagtails breed in Britain, either as pure pairs or mixed with *yarrellii*. In winter, they are found in the Mediterranean Basin and southwards into tropical Africa.

In Britain & Ireland, breeding occurs at altitudes from sea-level up to 700 m in a variety of habitats from remote rural areas to inner cities but usually near water (Mason & Lyczynski 1980, Simms 1992). The species often associates with man-made structures for breeding and roosting (Broom *et al* 1976, Dougall & Appleton 1989, Mackay & Sellers 1989, Simms 1992), and on passage it is regularly encountered in some numbers feeding on areas of mud or shingle at sewage-works, reservoirs

The analysis of the data for this species was supported by Peter & Janet Wood

and gravel-pits or on areas of short vegetation, such as playing fields, where its insect prey can be easily located. With its propensity to associate with humans, it remains a conspicuous bird in winter, feeding along water margins, on roadsides in cold weather and on wet farmland, and roosting in rural reedbeds and in urban buildings and parks.

Pied Wagtails have been widely ringed in Britain during the breeding season but there have been no recoveries of birds from Shetland, the Inner Hebrides or most of Ireland (Fig 1). In the non-breeding season, the distribution of ringing data reflects the bird's southward population shift but Ireland is again under-represented. Most Pied Wagtails recovered have been ringed as immatures in autumn and winter, reflecting the relative ease of catching them at roosts (Fig 2). The cause of death is known in just over half (51%) of all recoveries from dead birds. Of these, 69% involved human activities or those of domestic animals, especially cats (Fig 3), and a further 10% were deliberately taken by Man. The geographical distribution of recoveries reflects human population density but, in addition, mirrors the location of traditional hunting areas along the species' migration routes and in its winter range.

The ringing results reveal major latitudinal differences in migration patterns within Britain, for both adults and immatures. Juvenile *yarrellii* disperse locally and randomly while undertaking their post-juvenile moult. In an analysis which included 246 controls of live birds, Dougall

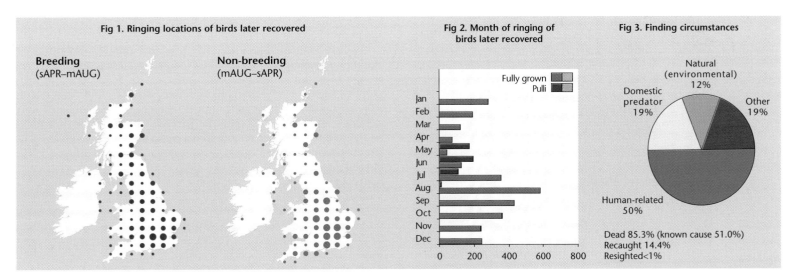

Fig 1. Ringing locations of birds later recovered

Breeding (sAPR–mAUG)

Non-breeding (mAUG–sAPR)

Fig 2. Month of ringing of birds later recovered

Fully grown / Pulli

Fig 3. Finding circumstances

Natural (environmental) 12%

Domestic predator 19%

Other 19%

Human-related 50%

Dead 85.3% (known cause 51.0%)
Recaught 14.4%
Resighted<1%

Ringing and recovery data

	<1960	60–69	70–79	80–89	90–97	Total
RINGING						
BTO ringing totals (%)	9	16	29	30	17	222,538
RECOVERIES						
BTO-ringed (%)	8	23	30	29	9	3,528
Foreign-ringed (%)	←	52	→	31	17	29

Statistical analyses

	Breeding population (sAPR–mAUG)	Wintering population (sNOV–sMAR)
Status	LONG-DISTANCE MIGRANT* (2)	SHORT-DISTANCE MIGRANT*
Age differences[NS]*	Significant	Significant*
Sex differences[NS]*	Significant*	Not significant
Regional differences	Significant[4]	Not tested
Finding circumstances	(Not significant)	(Not significant)

Fig 4. Locations in autumn, and movements of over 20 km between the breeding season and autumn, of Pied Wagtails present in (a) Ireland & northern Britain (109) and (b) southern Britain (296) during the breeding season.

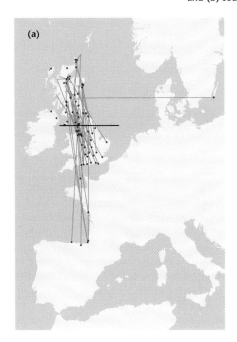

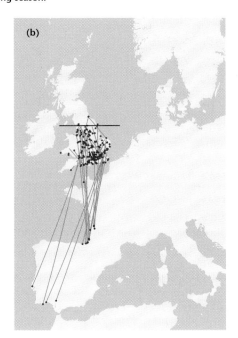

(1992) established that, during their first autumn and winter, some 'northern' British birds (hatched north of 54°N) had moved up to 50 km within a month of ringing. 'Southern' birds (hatched south of 52°N) started to move later, and even four months after ringing few had taken part in distant movements. 'Southern' fledglings dispersed widely and over a longer period than 'northern' ones. 'Northern' wagtails dispersed randomly until the fourth month after ringing, when their dispersal tended to become oriented between south and southeast. These two periods correspond to post-juvenile dispersal and to migration proper once post-juvenile moult nears completion or is complete (Ginn & Melville 1983). By three months after hatching the median recovery distance for birds found dead is 11 km and by nine months after ringing (late winter), the median distance moved is 630 km from their natal sites. For birds hatched north of 55°N, Dougall (1991) found no evidence of any difference in migratory behaviour between northern and southern elements. Within the group hatched south of 52°N, Dougall (1992) reported that birds in their first autumn moved less far than immatures from elsewhere in Britain, and that the proportion that migrated seemed to be smaller. As adults complete their post-nuptial moult, they too commence southward migration, 'northern' populations especially from late September.

In autumn, there are four recoveries of birds from southern Britain already as far south as southern Spain and Portugal, whereas birds from elsewhere in Britain & Ireland have been recovered only as far south as the coast of northern Spain (Fig 4). Birds from all regions (except Ireland) have been recovered throughout the winter range but regional differences nevertheless emerge in the winter distribution of recoveries (Fig 5). In general, it would appear that most *yarrellii* that migrate from northern Britain winter in southern England or the western French and Spanish Atlantic fringes, whereas those from southern Britain winter further south, in Portugal especially, and in southern Spain. This confirms the earlier findings of Davis (1966a). Surprisingly, perhaps, there are no ring-recoveries of southern British birds in North Africa, whereas there are three of northern birds.

Davies (1976) and Bailey & Rowan (1987) showed that adult male *yarrellii* were dominant and defended feeding territories in winter, tolerating the presence of females and immature males until food became scarce during colder conditions when these birds would be expelled to join flock-feeding wagtails nearby. Fleming (1981) found two

classes of feeding birds in winter near Oxford, one site-faithful and one mobile. Mackay & Sellers (1989) found that those birds wintering farthest north in Britain (in Caithness and around the Moray Firth) were mainly adults and males, and therefore dominant, whereas Dougall & Appleton (1989) found a ratio of adults to immatures of 1:3 at a winter roost further south in Scotland. A ratio of one adult to 4.55 immatures was reported from Bath, Avon (Bailey & Rowan 1987).

The main difference in the distribution of recoveries of adults and immatures in the non-breeding season is the apparent excess of immatures in southern France, and in Portugal and southern Spain (Fig 6). No sex-related differences in the distribution of recoveries are apparent.

Dougall (1996b) was unable to show any difference in timing of autumn migration between Scottish adults and immatures, both age groups being on the move particularly in late September and early October. Baggott (1969) found that southern English adults were mainly sedentary and that their post-nuptial moult was not completed until well into the autumn. Galbraith (1977) found little difference in the rate and duration of adult moult between a migratory population in Strathclyde and a largely non-migratory one in Somerset (Baggott 1970), but the southern population had a mean starting date 11 days later than the Scottish one and this is no doubt linked to the sedentary nature of southern adults.

Movements on the British & Irish wintering grounds are generally short, except for journeys between feeding areas and roosts, which may be of several kilometres. For 166 birds reported dead within the same winter as ringing, the median recovery distance was 4 km and 95% were recovered within 24 km. Neither Davis (1966a) for Britain & Ireland as a whole, nor Dougall (1991) for northern Britain, found any direct evidence from ring-recoveries of hard-weather movements; no such movements involving this species were observed during the severe 1962/63 winter (Dobinson & Richards 1964). There is limited evidence of changes in wintering location between winters; 12% of the 153 recoveries show a difference of over 20 km, of which three are long-distance.

Some *yarrellii* are still in their winter quarters in April, at least in northern Spain and Brittany, but most have returned north to breed, those in Scotland arriving from early March. There has been a scattering of April recoveries in the North Sea, Northern Isles and southwest

Fig 5. Locations in winter, and movements of over 20 km between the breeding season and winter, of Pied Wagtails present in (a) Ireland & northern Britain (159) and (b) southern Britain (529) during the breeding season.

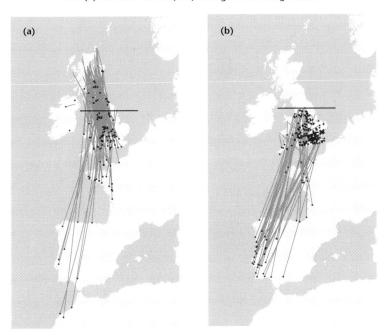

Fig 7. Locations in spring, and movements of over 20 km between the breeding season and spring, of Pied Wagtails present in (a) Ireland & northern Britain (22) and (b) southern Britain (109) during the breeding season.

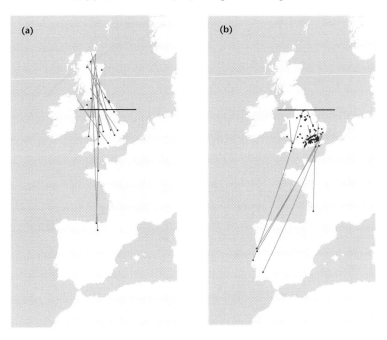

Fig 6. Locations outside the breeding season of (a) 278 adult and (b) 365 immature Pied Wagtails that were present in Britain & Ireland during the breeding season.

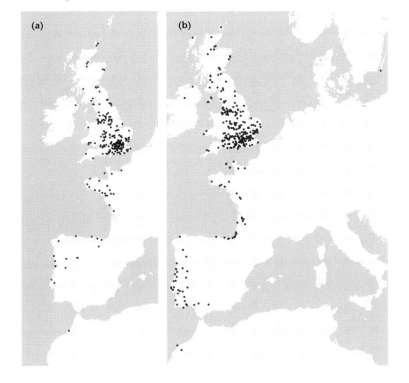

Norway, reflecting passage, but by June all recoveries have been of birds on their breeding grounds in Britain & Ireland, except for four recoveries in Iceland and one near Calais in France.

The distribution of spring recoveries mirrors that of autumn with birds from the south of Britain still being reported from further south than birds from the north of Britain (Fig 7). There is one particularly interesting recovery of an Irish breeding-season bird in Hampshire in spring. It could be that northern British birds migrate later in autumn and return earlier in spring than their southern counterparts but this requires further investigation.

Natal dispersal is difficult to assess; 68% of breeding-season recoveries of birds ringed as pulli were within 20 km of their hatching site. Of the longer-distance movements (Fig 8) most may still have been on migration when recovered but the one to southwest Norway is of particular interest in view of the small breeding population of *yarrellii* there (*CBWP*).

Breeding site-fidelity is apparently high; 42 of 49 recoveries of birds ringed when of breeding age and in the breeding season, and recovered in a subsequent breeding season, were within 20 km of the ringing site. The seven others may have been ringed or recovered on spring passage, which overlaps with the breeding season in April and May. Recoveries between breeding seasons are confined to Britain for birds ringed and recovered as immatures but there is a scattering of recoveries of adult birds on the Continent, in the North Sea, the Northern Isles and in Norway. It may well be that most, if not all, of these recoveries are of White Wagtails.

Fortunately, the two European races are usually separable by plumage characteristics while on passage through Britain & Ireland, especially in spring. In autumn, the first arrivals of White Wagtails are difficult to detect because the two races are very similar before and during the post-juvenile moult. Observations suggest, however, that autumn passage occurs on both east and, particularly, west coasts and widely inland, until at least October. It is likely that the entire population from Greenland, Iceland and the Faeroes passes through Britain & Ireland at this time, although many birds will go unrecognized. Bowley (1996) reported that heaviest passage was noted on northern and western offshore islands (probably reflecting the sources of the birds to the northwest), with passage being recorded at Fair Isle from early August, reaching a huge peak later that month, before tailing off to mid-October, with only stragglers into November. Further south in Britain, the migration peak comes a week or so later; on Scilly, for example, White Wagtails are abundant from late August to mid-September. There have been few systematic studies inland, although passage was observed in Hertfordshire in 1961 from the end of July to mid-October, peaking in early September. Recent work in north Lanarkshire (I Livingstone pers comm) has revealed that in a roost of up to 600 wagtails, White Wagtails were present from 20 August to 14 October, peaking in late September and early October. In the early period, most were immatures, whereas in

Fig 8. Movements of over 20 km and recovery locations of Pied Wagtails ringed as pulli in Britain & Ireland and recovered in a subsequent breeding season when of breeding age. There were 53:25 movements under:over 20 km but only those over 20 km are plotted.

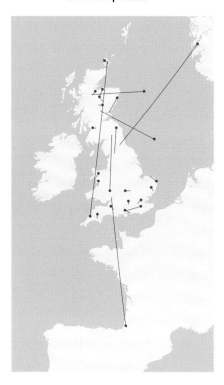

Fig 9. Movements of Pied Wagtails ringed abroad and recovered in Britain & Ireland (14, blue) and ringed in Britain & Ireland outside the breeding season and recovered abroad during the breeding season (10, red). The 15 pre-1979 foreign-ringed Pied Wagtails (from Iceland 9, France 4 and Belgium 2) are not shown.

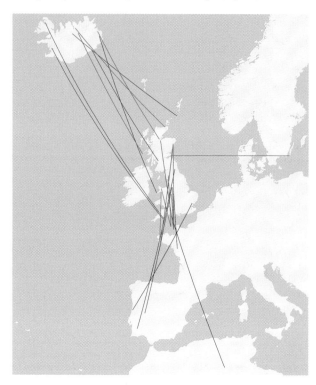

October most were adults on passage, presumably having completed their moult. The proportion of White Wagtails in the roost increased through the autumn as *yarrellii* moved out.

Ring-recoveries confirm that many White Wagtails passing through Britain & Ireland are from Iceland. Only a single movement, from Sweden to Scotland, has involved mainland Europe (Fig 9). Alerstam (1990a) reported that most Swedish White Wagtails migrate southeast for the winter. Finlayson (1992) remarked how suddenly White Wagtails arrived at the Strait of Gibraltar in autumn, with peak numbers in October. It would seem likely that these birds are from the northwest European populations, many of which will have passed through Britain & Ireland earlier in the autumn. There are few records, if any, of White Wagtails in Britain & Ireland in the winter. In spring, it is one of the earliest returning migrants, appearing on a broad front across Britain & Ireland (Bowley 1996) from as early as mid-March and with peak numbers during April. Finlayson (1992) recorded northward movement in spring at the Strait of Gibraltar from late February to early April.

Britain & Ireland has a special conservation responsibility for this species, holding almost all breeders of the distinctive *yarrellii* race and playing host to a large proportion of the populations of White Wagtail from Greenland, Iceland and the Faeroes as passage migrants. Future investigations could concentrate on establishing the movements of Irish birds, looking at differences in timing of autumn movements in terms of age and regional origin of the birds, and assessing the winter distribution of the sexes and ages within the wintering populations, both within Britain & Ireland and elsewhere. On the wintering grounds, it would be interesting to know how the two subspecies interact where they occur together.

Tom Dougall

The author dedicates this account to the memory of Alan Hilton for stimulating his interest in Pied Wagtails.

Bohemian Waxwing (Waxwing)

Bombycilla garrulus

The analysis of the data for this species was supported by Chris & Mike Evans

There is an almost mystical unpredictability about the movements of Waxwings. This, combined with the species' beautiful plumage, confiding nature and inextricable association with berries and human habitations, makes the Waxwing a bird that few people will ever tire of seeing. Waxwings breed in boreal forests from northeastern Fennoscandia east across Russia to Kamchatka, and from central Alaska and British Columbia east to Hudson Bay (*BWP*). The nominate race *garrulus* occupies Fennoscandia and west Siberia, with *centralasiae* in central and eastern Siberia and *pallidiceps* in North America. All but the southwestern fringes of these areas are deserted in winter. The normal extent of the winter range is difficult to define but in the Palearctic includes the Low Countries, the Balkans and Caucasus, central China and Japan. It is as an irregular irruptive winter visitor that it is found in Britain & Ireland. Numbers arriving vary considerably from winter to winter. Some years only small numbers are seen while in others many thousands arrive; in Ireland, Waxwings are recorded less than annually. The size and timing of irruptions are influenced by post-breeding population size and by the abundance of its favourite food, Rowan berries, during autumn dispersal.

Large-scale invasions in 'Waxwing years' attract attention and have been well documented (*eg* Cornwallis 1961, Everett 1967, Cornwallis & Townsend 1968, Lyster 1971, Murray 1998, Taylor *et al* 1999). In the past, Waxwing invasions into Britain & Ireland were believed to occur in 10-year cycles (*Winter Atlas*). This was probably suggested by the large invasions of 1937, 1946 and 1957. Since then, however, invasions have gradually become more frequent. More recently, considerable invasions

occurred in 1988, 1990, 1991, 1995, 1996 (January and November) and 1999.

Although birds have been recorded arriving in Britain & Ireland as early as the end of August (a single in Orkney) (*Birds in Scotland*) and more often in September, and influxes can occur at almost any time during the winter; invasions occur most commonly during October and November: 12 of the 18 large invasions recorded since 1937 have occurred during this period. Most birds depart during March or April but small groups are not unusual in early May. June records are exceptional but there have been two invasions in July (*BWP*).

Waxwing ringing in Britain & Ireland has chiefly been carried out opportunistically. The distribution of ringing sites for ring-recoveries (Fig 1) is broadly typical of the areas where Waxwings most regularly appear. There is an eastern bias in Scotland and England with a scattering of inland records across mainly central Scotland and the Midlands of England with a few penetrating to Ireland. Largest numbers have been ringed in November (Fig 2), which reflects both the most common arrival period and the fact that flocks are at their largest early on as widespread scattered groups amalgamate and become concentrated at good food sources. The Waxwing has a relatively high recovery rate for a passerine. This is partly due to large numbers of resightings (half the total recoveries) of colour-marked birds, mainly

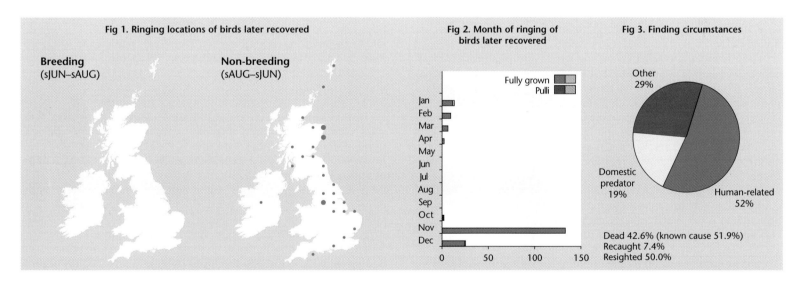

Fig 1. Ringing locations of birds later recovered

Breeding (sJUN–sAUG)

Non-breeding (sAUG–sJUN)

Fig 2. Month of ringing of birds later recovered

Fully grown
Pulli

Fig 3. Finding circumstances

Other 29%

Domestic predator 19%

Human-related 52%

Dead 42.6% (known cause 51.9%)
Recaught 7.4%
Resighted 50.0%

Ringing and recovery data

	<1960	60–69	70–79	80–89	90–97	Total
RINGING						
BTO ringing totals (%)	5	10	18	9	58	2,368
RECOVERIES						
BTO-ringed (%)	2	6	13	6	72	186
Foreign-ringed (%)	←	76	→	0	24	17

Statistical analyses

	Breeding population (sJUN–sAUG)	Wintering population (sOCT–sMAR)
Status	NONE	[LONG-DISTANCE MIGRANT]
Age differences	—	Not tested
Sex differences	—	Not tested
Regional differences	—	Not tested
Finding circumstances	—	Not tested

Fig 4. Recovery locations and all 16 included exchanges of Waxwings between Britain & Ireland and abroad. The 13 pre-1979 foreign-ringed Waxwings (Finland 6, Norway 4, Sweden 2 and the Netherlands 1) are not shown.

from a study in Aberdeen, but is also a result of the species' close association with human habitations. Of the 52% of recoveries of dead birds with known causes, 71% are related to human factors such as hitting windows or traffic or falling prey to domestic pets (Fig 3).

Exchanges of Waxwings between Britain & Ireland and abroad are shown in Fig 4. Of the birds ringed abroad, one ringed in Norway in October 1990 was part of an invasion and was recorded in Grampian just 28 days later. The others, one ringed in Norway in mid-December 1995 and two in late January 1996 in Denmark and Belgium, were all recovered during the late winter invasion of 1995/96 when large numbers arrived during January and February. A bird ringed near Helsinki on 25 October 1970 was found dead 18 days later in Stranraer, a distance of 1,800 km and minimum speed of 100 km per day, while another Finnish bird ringed on Åland on 10 October 1970 was caught by ringers in Fife on 14 November 1970, a distance of over 1,400 km and minimum speed of 40 km per day. Ringing dates show that these birds were already on migration when ringed and so their actual origins are unknown.

Each invasion into Britain & Ireland has its own peculiarities but all appear to follow a similar general pattern of events. Initial scattered records of individuals and small flocks are often followed by a build-up of numbers in areas where food is abundant. These areas are often in the centres of busy towns where favoured berries such as Rowan (often ornamental types), Whitebeam and Hawthorn have remained uneaten by thrushes and Starlings. Flocks can quickly reach several hundred birds and repeatedly return to feed, regardless of the presence of humans and traffic.

This initial phase of dispersed groups amalgamating when good food sources are available was well illustrated by colour-ringing in northeast Scotland in 1990 when a very large Waxwing invasion during late October and November coincided with a good berry crop. Ringing was carried out in early November at three rural towns 15–20 km outside Aberdeen and at one site in the city suburbs. Flocks of 30 to 80 birds were counted at these sites and 113 birds colour-ringed over a two-week period. By the second half of November, the rural flocks had dispersed as food sources diminished and a large flock of almost 300 birds had converged onto Whitebeams near Aberdeen city centre. This flock contained at least 42 marked birds from the rural and suburban sites.

As favoured food sources become depleted, flocks fragment and begin to disperse locally or continue onward migration (Fig 5). Smaller flocks settle in areas for the winter but remain highly mobile in response to local food availability. The large flock in Aberdeen dispersed towards the end of November and resulted in subsequent widespread sightings throughout Scotland and England during the remainder of the winter

(Fig 5). Birds had reached central Scotland and northeast England by the end of December and as far south as Yorkshire by mid-January. Some birds continued south during February into the Midlands while others appeared to settle in northeast England and remained there throughout March. Similar movements of Scottish-ringed birds from previous invasions suggest this southward migration is a regular feature of Waxwing dispersal in Britain & Ireland. In November 1970, two Waxwings from a flock of seven ringed in Aberdeen (R L Swann pers comm) were both recovered the following spring, one in March in Liverpool and the other in Sheffield in April while another bird ringed in Ayr in January during that same invasion was recovered in Wales at the end of March.

Local dispersal was also apparent. Of 17 birds colour-ringed at one of the rural sites near Aberdeen in early November 1990 and resighted during the winter, 13 were reported over 100 km away while the other four remained locally until the end of the winter. Similarly in 1988, 18 birds were colour-ringed at three sites in and around Aberdeen between mid-November and early December. Three birds had moved 570 km by early January when they were sighted in Lowestoft, Suffolk (Duncan 1989b). They were then regularly seen around the Lowestoft area until mid-March. Meanwhile at least three other birds from these same catches remained in Aberdeen for the rest of the winter.

Further south, ringing and distribution maps (eg Cornwallis 1961) show continued southward migration with some westward dispersal, possibly of birds that have arrived in eastern England from across the North Sea. A bird ringed in Hartlepool on 3 November 1974 was found in Antrim on 16 April 1975.

It is intriguing that birds within the same flocks in early winter disperse in such an erratic manner and can be found hundreds of kilometres apart as winter progresses. Cornwallis & Townsend (1968) suggested that Waxwings begin their migration in a southwesterly 'preferred direction', stimulated by some internal hormonal change. On finding abundant food this directional impulse fades and birds begin to search randomly. This impulse must vary between individuals which perhaps explains why some birds continue their migration while others remain within an area where initial food supplies were found.

First-winter birds outnumber adults during invasions but ratios can vary. In 1988 and 1990, over 75% of birds caught and counted in flocks were juveniles, while in 1991 96% of birds were juveniles. No detailed analysis has been made of differences in movements between age and sex classes, but a higher proportion of adult females appear to winter in Aberdeen than other age and sex categories (pers obs).

Waxwings in Britain & Ireland are often associated with traditional sites where birds habitually appear in invasion years, but this may be as

Fig 5. Locations in (a) October–December (79:1) and (b) January–February (46:0), and movements of over 20 km, of Waxwings ringed during October–December. Movements within a winter (red) are differentiated from those made between winters (blue). Sample sizes for within-winter:between-winters are given. A single between-winters movement of a bird from Norfolk to eastern European Russia is not shown on map (a).

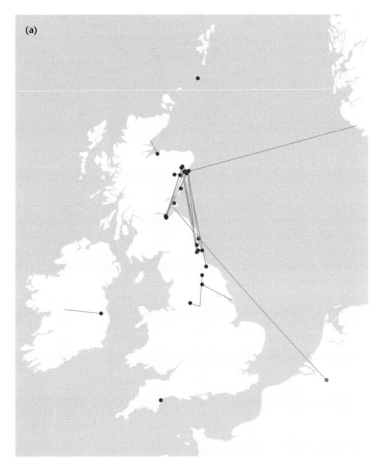

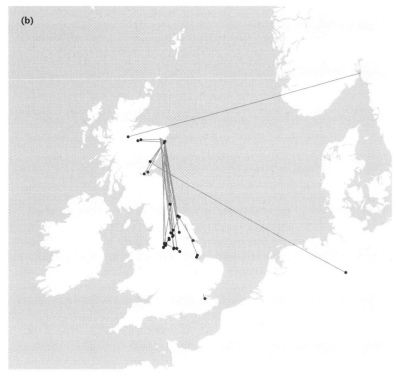

much to do with the species' highly specialized winter diet as with site-fidelity, with birds attracted to sites meeting their specific food requirements. Indeed, only two ringed Waxwings have been recorded returning to Britain in subsequent winters. A bird ringed in Aberdeen city centre on 29 November 1990 was resighted at the same place on 9 November 1993, while another ringed in Aberdeen on 28 January 1996 was resighted there on 22 November 1996.

Generally Waxwings are regarded as being rather nomadic in winter. Of two birds ringed together at Heacham, Norfolk, on 3 November 1974, one was recovered in Sweden on 6 December 1975 and the other at Kirov, 700 km east of Moscow, on 27 October 1977; the Swedish recovery, however, lacks confirmatory details and has been excluded from the analyses. Recoveries from ringing elsewhere in Europe also demonstrate the rather unpredictable nature of movements. A Polish bird recovered 5,500 km away the following winter in eastern Siberia (presumably within the range of *centralasiae*) shows the extreme distances which Waxwings are capable of travelling, while a bird ringed in winter in Budapest was recovered there five years later (*BWP*).

Of Waxwings ringed in Britain & Ireland and found abroad (Fig 4), only four have been ringed and recovered during the same irruptions. Two

Waxwings, one ringed in Norfolk in November 1965 and the other in Fife in November 1974, were recovered in March 1966 in France and February 1975 in Germany respectively, suggesting that some birds may return to the Continent during winter. A bird ringed in Grampian in November 1990 was found in the Netherlands the following May and another ringed in Grampian in November 1991 was in Denmark the next April, possibly suggesting return passage through the Low Countries.

There is little evidence from ringing to suggest a northward return passage of Waxwings in Britain & Ireland later in the winter. Flocks appearing at new sites during spring may be thought to be passage migrants when really they are just wandering locals exploiting different food sources. Many Waxwings probably depart for the Continent direct from their wintering sites.

The origins of Waxwings visiting Britain & Ireland therefore remain uncertain. This, coupled with the variable timing, numbers involved and onward movements during each invasion, is worthy of further ringing studies.

Raymond Duncan

White-throated Dipper (Dipper)

Cinclus cinclus

All five of the world's dipper species are notable for their remarkable adaptations to flowing waters, living almost exclusively along cascading rivers and streams (Tyler & Ormerod 1994). In the case of our own familiar Dipper *Cinclus cinclus*, ringing has revealed a range of intraspecific variations in migratory behaviour, and has shown both classical and novel elements in their movements.

Dippers occur across upland areas of the Palearctic from Norway, Ireland and Morocco eastwards to Turkey, Iran, the Urals, and to the northern slopes of the Himalayas. About 13 races are recognized across this range (*BWP*), although as yet their separation is not supported by genetic evidence, and there can be much colour variation within supposed races (Spitznagel 1995). Those recognized on plumage characteristics include *hibernicus* in Ireland, the Outer Hebrides and the west coast of Scotland, and *gularis* in the rest of Britain. The nominate race *cinclus* occurs in Fennoscandia, central France and northwest Iberia, and *aquaticus* from Belgium and eastern France eastwards into central Europe. Among this set of races, true inter-regional migrants occur in the Urals and in northern Fennoscandia, from where some birds fly each winter across the Gulf of Bothnia southeastwards into Finland, Estonia or Latvia (Tyler & Ormerod 1994). Others fly southwest into Denmark and the Low Countries, and even to Britain. These migrant Dippers have an annual cycle of weight change that contrasts with the largely non-migratory birds in Britain & Ireland, for example gaining weight in spring prior to their northward crossing of the Baltic Sea (Lehikoinen & Hakala 1988). Fattening strategies therefore vary within this species in ways that match variations in annual life cycle.

The analysis of the data for this species was supported by Northumbrian Water

In Britain & Ireland, the majority of Dippers are sedentary save for some altitudinal movements in mountain regions. Dippers vacate some high-altitude streams during harsh winter weather, or perhaps as part of regular winter movements, in favour of estuaries, larger rivers, or even coastal areas (Tyler & Ormerod 1994). Conversely, high flows probably cause birds to make short-term movements that allow them to feed in small tributaries adjacent to their territory. Otherwise, the major lifetime movements involve the various elements of dispersal, and daily flights between feeding areas and roosts.

The British & Irish ring-recovery data on Dippers comprise nearly 500 recoveries, of which only 2% are from Ireland. Ringing sites predominantly follow the upland distribution of Dippers along hill streams, though ringing coverage is clearly more extensive during the breeding season than the non-breeding season (Fig 1). The northwest Highlands and Ireland are under-represented among recoveries, the latter despite some active Dipper research programmes.

About 77% of the recoveries have been from birds ringed initially as nestlings. Overwhelmingly, these are from the peak breeding periods of April and May, when post-fledging survival is greatest (Ormerod & Tyler 1993), with smaller numbers from March and June (Fig 2). By contrast, fully grown birds are ringed throughout the year, reflecting their year-round residency. Ringing fully grown Dippers requires specialized

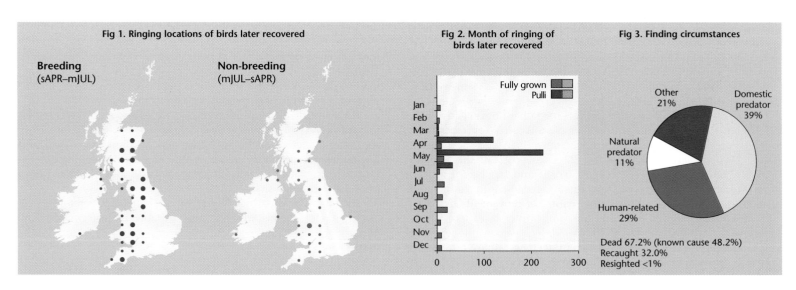

Fig 1. Ringing locations of birds later recovered

Breeding (sAPR–mJUL)

Non-breeding (mJUL–sAPR)

Fig 2. Month of ringing of birds later recovered

Fully grown
Pulli

Fig 3. Finding circumstances

Other 21%
Domestic predator 39%
Natural predator 11%
Human-related 29%

Dead 67.2% (known cause 48.2%)
Recaught 32.0%
Resighted <1%

Ringing and recovery data

	<1960	60–69	70–79	80–89	90–97	Total
RINGING						
BTO ringing totals (%)	8	6	15	41	30	55,265
RECOVERIES						
BTO-ringed (%)	9	7	16	45	23	493
Foreign-ringed (%)	←	0	→	100	0	1

Statistical analyses

	Breeding population (sAPR–mJUL)	Wintering population (sOCT–sJAN)
Status	SEDENTARY* (0)	?
Age differences[NT]	Not significant*	—
Sex differences	Not tested	—
Regional differences	Not tested	—
Finding circumstances	Not tested	—

Fig 4. Recovery locations and movements of over 20 km for the included recoveries of Dippers ringed or recovered in Britain & Ireland, with those present in Britain & Ireland during the breeding season (74, red) differentiated from those from other or uncertain breeding populations (419, grey).

Table 1. (a) Breeding and (b) natal dispersal in Dippers.

(a)		Median (km)	P95 (km)	n
All BTO data (dead)		0	11	5
Ireland	males	< 1	< 2.5	174*
	females	< 1	< 2.5	
Wales	males	< 1	< 2.5	138*
	females	< 1	< 2.5	

* Total of males and females combined.

(b)		Median (km)	P95 or max (km)	n
All BTO data (dead)		5	43	33
Ireland	males	5	< 15	64
	females	8	< 25	44
Wales	males	3	7	103
	females	5	15	63

(*Sources*: O'Halloran *et al* 2000, Tyler *et al* 1990.)

Note: Some of the birds in the samples from Ireland and Wales may also be included in the 'All BTO data (dead)' category.

techniques either at roost by torchlight or using mist-nets set across rivers into which birds are driven. An annual population census using these methods has operated in Mid Wales since 1985, and is revealed by the expanded number of Welsh ring-recoveries from birds outside the breeding season (Ormerod *et al* 1988).

Recovery circumstances are known for nearly half of 332 ringed birds found dead. Among these, 40% were due to domestic predators and 36% were in some other way human-related (Fig 3). These data clearly reveal more about the hunting habits of cats, in taking this riverine species, than about Dippers! There are natural predators, too: Dipper rings have been found in owl pellets and, perhaps more surprisingly, at Peregrine eyries.

The lack of any widespread seasonal movement in Dippers breeding in Britain & Ireland is confirmed by the geographical distribution of ring-recoveries (Fig 4). The median distance for 220 such recoveries of dead birds was just 2 km, and 95% were within 35 km. Also apparent from the lack of movement is the geographical isolation of Dipper subpopulations at a scale smaller than the divisions associated with currently recognized races.

With respect to breeding and natal dispersal, ring-recoveries from dead birds can be compared with published data from 373 Dippers ringed and recaptured during intensive studies in Ireland (O'Halloran *et al* 2000), and 314 during studies in Wales (Tyler & Ormerod 1994). Many of these involved movements too small to qualify for inclusion in the Ringing Scheme dataset but they augment our knowledge of Dipper movement and survival.

Breeding dispersal is infrequent in Dippers, and only seven of 138 adults in Wales and 18 of 174 in Ireland changed between sites after becoming established in a given territory (Tyler *et al* 1990, O'Halloran *et*

al 2000). The distances involved were mostly less than 5 km (Table 1) but one bird in Ireland travelled 15.9 km.

Upon reaching independence at about two weeks after fledging (Yoerg 1994), dispersing juveniles start to move upstream or downstream from parental territories. These movements can begin as early as April, and continue through into September or October by which time most dispersal movements appear to be complete (Galbraith & Tyler 1982). In keeping with general patterns in passerines, natal dispersal in Dippers is significantly further in females (median 5–8 km between sites of hatching and first breeding) than males (3–5 km, Table 1). Ring-recoveries from dead birds suggest that only a small proportion of these movements exceed 40 km, and the 95th percentiles from intensive Irish and Welsh studies are even shorter. Roughly 15% of dispersing young birds cross into different river catchments, but females (21% in Wales and 23% in Ireland) are significantly more likely than males (8.5% and 10%) to cross watersheds in this way. Differences between the sexes in natal dispersal distances are highly consistent from year to year (see Tyler & Ormerod 1994). They also involve greater distances than would be expected from birds simply replacing likely adult mortality, implying that young birds either actively seek good habitat or explore (Tyler *et al* 1990).

In species like the Dipper, which are caught sometimes during daylight and sometimes at roost, ringing allows an assessment of diurnal movement. Although the majority of birds roost within 3 km (95% of birds) or even 1 km (73%) of their breeding territories, small numbers travel 5–8 km between feeding and roosting sites (Tyler & Ormerod 1994). These birds clearly fly through or over the territories of others. In addition, these birds must have discovered these roost sites previously — either by following adult birds as juveniles, or by 'discovery dispersal' during their own development. Young birds, still in juvenile plumage, can sometimes be observed making quizzical investigations of potential roosts even in daylight (pers obs).

The occasional Dippers that are recorded in most years well outside the normal range, in the Northern Isles or in southeast England, confirm that longer-distance migrants sometimes reach Britain. Most such individuals are 'Black-bellied Dippers' of the nominate race *cinclus*, but some appear to be *gularis* or similarly coloured birds of continental origin. The occurrence of birds from the range occupied by *aquaticus* has been suspected but has yet to be confirmed. A single recovery of an adult

Black-bellied Dipper ringed in southwest Sweden on 4 March 1985 and recaptured in Fife on 3 April 1987 confirms Scandinavia as a source of Dippers visiting Britain. However, the true number and distribution of these visitors in Britain is incompletely known because they are unlikely to be detected among the regular residents. Out-of-range Dippers have occurred in Norfolk mostly between October and April, with a peak in December–February, but some apparently aberrant individuals have stayed for over a year (Taylor *et al* 1999). In Shetland, a peak of sightings occurs in late March or early April and may indicate return passage towards Scandinavia (*BWP*).

The status and abundance of Dippers strongly reflect the water quality and habitat structure of rivers, and of all bird species they are among the most widely recognized indicator of environmental quality (*eg* Logie *et al* 1996, Buckton & Ormerod 1997, Buckton *et al* 1998). The effects of adverse water quality are shown in impaired breeding, subtle changes in survival, or territory selection. However, 'pollution' has been a reported cause of death in 3% of Dipper recoveries, showing that water quality in extreme circumstances can cause direct mortality. By contrast, effects on survival from persistent pollutants such as PCBs appear now to be negligible or non-existent (Ormerod *et al* 2000), although effects in the past might have been larger (Ormerod & Tyler 1992). Current conservation issues revolve around the population response of Dippers along rivers that continue to suffer from problems of acidification, or are recovering from the past problems of sewage and industrial pollution. In these cases, movement data illustrate some of the dispersal dynamics that will be required between or within catchments to regain lost populations (Buckton *et al* 1998). Additionally, the very pronounced site-fidelity and generally low dispersal reveal why Dippers are such effective monitors of environmental contamination and river health — for example in pinpointing polluting discharges even before traditional chemical monitoring (Ormerod *et al* 2000).

The remarkably resilient and amenable Dipper has proved a highly effective model species in addressing a wide range of basic and applied ecological questions. Future developments are therefore likely to be many and varied. In Europe, work is ongoing to assess their response to climatic change (Sæther *et al* 2000), and to examine how their naturally fragmented population structure is reflected in gene-flow and genetic diversity (F D'Amico pers comm). Closer to home, the developing Waterways Breeding Bird Survey will chart their responses to changing habitat quality, pollution and recovery in rivers. For the volunteer ringer, resolving the true extent of winter altitudinal movements, and the true origins of winter visits from the Continent, will provide a fruitful challenge.

Steve Ormerod

Winter Wren (Wren)
Troglodytes troglodytes

Even this tiny bird is capable of remarkably long migrations. Its standard vernacular name, Winter Wren, derives from experience in the USA where it is a winter visitor, mainly from Canada, to most of the eastern states. Long-distance seasonal movements also occur from the northern parts of its European and east Asian ranges; individuals from Sweden can move up to 2,500 km (*BWP*). Many populations are resident, however, or even entirely sedentary.

The breeding range extends from Iceland and Morocco to western Russia and Iran, and separately from Kazakhstan across China to Taiwan and Kamchatka and from the Aleutians and California across North America to Newfoundland (*BWP*). Aside from Iceland and the Faeroes, where the indigenous races are resident, the northernmost parts of this range are deserted in winter. Only the southernmost parts of the Scandinavian range are occupied all year and Wren is a summer visitor to Finland, the Baltic States and northwest Russia. Much of southeasternmost Europe, from Bulgaria to the Volga Basin, and parts of the Middle East are occupied only in winter.

Wrens are abundant in Britain & Ireland throughout the year. Breeding occurs in an extensive range of habitats affording low dense vegetation, especially damp woodland with dense ground cover and watercourses with well-vegetated margins, from the coast to high mountains. In winter, an even wider range of habitats is used (*BWP*). Breeding densities are relatively low in the uplands, and in Scotland are high only in scattered pockets, mainly near the coast (*1988–91 Atlas*). In winter, Wrens vacate some upland areas in Britain where the climate may be too harsh (*Winter Atlas*). Overwinter survival is highly variable

The analysis of the data for this species was supported by Dr D A Rose, Newcastle-upon-Tyne

but, after heavy mortality in severe winters, a high reproductive potential may allow the population to recover after as few as two breeding seasons (Garson 1980, Marchant *et al* 1990).

The race *indigenus* is present throughout most of Britain & Ireland but, across southern and central England, it intergrades with nominate *troglodytes*, the race that occurs across nearly all of continental Europe. Four further races are unique to Britain. Those endemic to Shetland (*zetlandicus*), Fair Isle (*fridariensis*) and St Kilda (*hirtensis*) are believed to be sedentary, whereas some of the birds resident in the Outer Hebrides (race *hebridensis*) probably move to the coast in winter (Hawthorn *et al* 1976). Nominate *troglodytes* is known to occur in Britain as a passage migrant and winter visitor. A further 30–40 races are described from elsewhere in the range.

Ireland and Scotland, and to a lesser extent Wales and southwest England, are poorly represented as ringing locations within the recovery data at all seasons (Fig 1). Fully grown Wrens are ringed throughout the year (Fig 2), with large numbers of juveniles trapped between July and October. Few nestlings are accessible to ringers, because of the risk of damage to the fragile, domed nest.

The overall recovery rate is very low, because the species' small size and skulking habits mean that few Wrens are ever found dead. Most recoveries (91%) are from dead birds, however, with only 9% recaptured

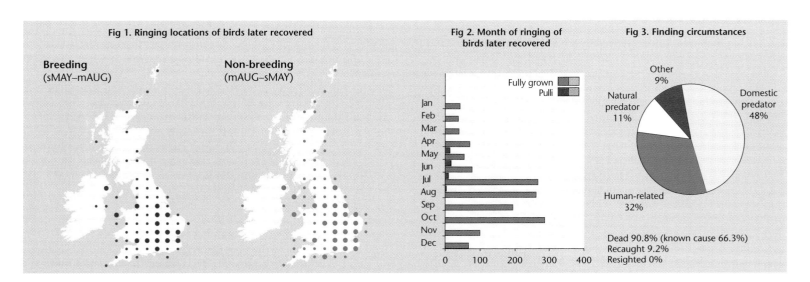

Fig 1. Ringing locations of birds later recovered

Breeding (sMAY–mAUG)

Non-breeding (mAUG–sMAY)

Fig 2. Month of ringing of birds later recovered

Fully grown
Pulli

Fig 3. Finding circumstances

Other 9%
Natural predator 11%
Domestic predator 48%
Human-related 32%

Dead 90.8% (known cause 66.3%)
Recaught 9.2%
Resighted 0%

Ringing and recovery data

	<1960	60–69	70–79	80–89	90–97	Total
RINGING						
BTO ringing totals (%)	3	8	25	33	30	397,052
RECOVERIES						
BTO-ringed (%)	4	14	31	31	20	1,538
Foreign-ringed (%)	←	0	→	100	0	1

Statistical analyses

	Breeding population (sMAY–mAUG)	Wintering population (sDEC–sMAR)
Status	SEDENTARY (0)	SEDENTARY*
Age differences[NT]	Not significant*	Not tested
Sex differences	Not tested	Not tested
Regional differences	Not significant[3]*	Not tested
Finding circumstances	Not significant	Not tested

Fig 4. Locations outside the breeding season and movements of over 20 km between the breeding and non-breeding season of 484 Wrens present in Britain & Ireland during the breeding season.

Fig 5. All 13 included exchanges of Wrens between Britain & Ireland and abroad.

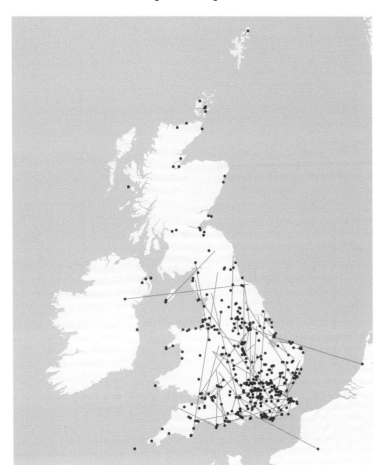

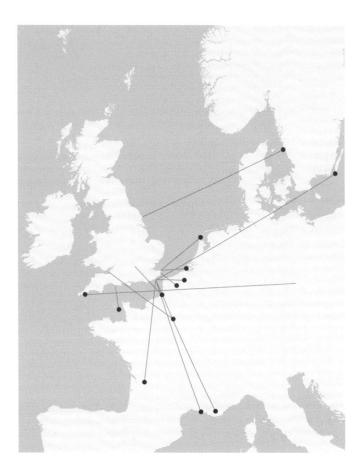

away from the site of ringing. In those cases where the cause of recovery was known, domestic predators accounted for 48%, and other human-related factors, such as colliding with windows and entering buildings, a further 32% (Fig 3); more-natural deaths must be greatly under-recorded.

As a whole, the ring-recovery data show that British & Irish Wrens are mostly sedentary, with a median distance moved of less than 1 km for all recoveries from dead birds (P5–95=0–130 km, n=1,398). Restricting the analysis to movements between the breeding season and other seasons, however, reveals that 21% of breeding adults had moved more than 20 km from the ringing site.

Juvenile Wrens may complete their post-juvenile moult close to the natal site in favourable areas but many individuals then disperse (Armstrong 1955, Hawthorn 1974). The birds that appear in reedbeds between October and early December show a slight excess of females over males, and may be those birds that have lost out in the renewed territorial competition that occurs after moulting; entering this habitat, which is not used for breeding, reduces the expenditure of valuable resources in territorial conflict (Hawthorn 1975). Many birds remain in these reedbeds until the end of March.

Hawthorn & Mead (1975) suggested two types of movement between breeding and wintering areas for British Wrens. First, movements of random direction of up to 50 km occur in October, associated with the completion of moult and increased territorial activity at that time (Hawthorn 1975). Because so few Wrens had been aged by the ringers, Hawthorn & Mead (1975) were unable to equate these movements directly to the major dispersal of juveniles earlier referred to by Armstrong (1955). Second, longer movements occur less commonly and appear to have a southerly bias.

Mapping the recoveries between the breeding season and other times of year (Fig 4) reveals a number of movements from higher ground (eg the Pennines and Cheviots) southwards to coastal areas. It is not yet known whether such relatively long seasonal movements may be general among upland breeders. In a wood in lowland Kent (less than 60 m asl), retrapping showed that many Wrens were resident throughout the year; at a woodland site in the Chilterns (about 200 m asl), however, only a small proportion of the breeding population appeared to be present in winter (Hawthorn & Mead 1975). With ringing samples so small, there are no distant winter recoveries of Wrens from the higher ground in Scotland, although the Winter Atlas data suggest these might be the birds most likely to move to lower altitudes or coastal areas outside the breeding season.

Most autumn movements away from breeding areas occur in September and October, although they may begin in August (Armstrong 1955). The majority of the long-distance movements are in a southerly direction but single recoveries in Ireland in autumn, and the Netherlands and France in winter, indicate that some British Wrens may also travel long distances east or west. There was no evidence of increased movement during the severe winter of 1962/63; maintaining a winter territory, where local knowledge can be employed in finding food, is probably of high survival value (Hawthorn & Mead 1975).

Recoveries provide little information on natal or breeding site-fidelity, although the median distance among 19 recoveries appropriate for indicating breeding dispersal movements was less than 1 km, and breeding adults are commonly retrapped by ringers at the same site in successive breeding seasons (pers obs). Male Wrens gain a selective advantage by building a large number of nests within the defended territory and by maintaining their occupation of patches of dense vegetation where nests remain in place longest (Evans & Burn 1996). These factors would tend to promote breeding site-fidelity, at least among males.

Fidelity to wintering areas also appears to be high. In a reedbed in Berkshire, 40% of Wrens caught in one winter were also caught the following winter (Hawthorn *et al* 1971). Given the likely annual mortality of around 60% (*BWP*), this suggests very high, if not complete, winter site-fidelity. Hawthorn (1975) speculated that the majority of Wrens that winter in reedbeds are forced to occupy marginal territories upon their return to the breeding area, such that they must then return to the reedbed in the following winter. Such traditional wintering areas probably exist for Wrens breeding in any habitat that does not provide resources for overwintering, such as many upland areas. Wrens reappear in their breeding areas by the end of April.

Those Wrens that do migrate generally do so at night, and sometimes become involved in lighthouse attractions. Most bird observatories around the British & Irish coast detect elevated numbers in late autumn, mainly in October, and occasionally to a lesser degree in spring. In Ireland, seasonal movements are observed at headlands and lighthouses, especially in October–November (*Birds in Ireland*).

Many coastal migrants are undoubtedly British or Irish birds that are dispersing or moving southward or coastward for the winter. Ring-recovery data show, however, that at least some of the coastal migration observed in southern and eastern England involves immigrants or passage migrants from continental Europe (Fig 5). Most of the 15 ringing exchanges between Britain & Ireland and abroad have resulted from birds ringed in southeast England during autumn. The birds involved in exchanges with Sweden and Germany were surely nominate *troglodytes*, of continental origin, moving south and west from their breeding areas for the winter. The German bird was ringed there in June, as a nestling, and found in Cornwall the following November. Both Swedish recoveries were made in April, presumably as the birds returned towards their breeding areas in spring. Too recently to include in the maps and statistics, details have been received of a bird ringed at the Russian Baltic ringing station of Rybachy on 3 September 1996 and recovered long dead in West Sussex the following March, at a distance of 1,524 km (Toms *et al* 1999). The three birds found in southern France were likely also to have been continental *troglodytes*, caught at Dungeness en route to their winter destination, but may have originated in Britain. The remaining movements in Fig 5 were also by birds of uncertain origin.

The regular migrants on Fair Isle in autumn are thought to be nominate *troglodytes*, probably from Norway (Williamson 1965), although there is no evidence of this as yet from ring-recoveries.

More Wrens need to be ringed in marginal habitats, especially in the uplands, to determine the origins of birds that constitute the passage movements around the coasts of Britain & Ireland and to help differentiate British & Irish breeders from possible continental immigrants. Ringing especially needs boosting in Ireland, where we know almost nothing about local movements or the origins of any winter immigrants. Ageing techniques now available to ringers should eventually permit a more comprehensive examination of age-related movements.

The wide spread of compass directions of Wren movements in autumn and spring may be an important adaptive mechanism for recolonizing areas where the population has been reduced by severe weather (Hawthorn & Mead 1975). Dispersal beyond the existing breeding range is thought to have contributed to the rapid spread of the species across Eurasia (Armstrong 1955). Many coastal habitats for Wrens, including reedbeds, are continually under threat from drainage and other development. It would be desirable, from a conservation perspective, to clarify the links between such winter refuges and the breeding populations that use them, so that the full implications of the loss of such coastal habitats are known and can be taken into account when development is planned.

Greg Conway

Hedge Accentor (Dunnock)
Prunella modularis

In Britain & Ireland, birdwatchers are unlikely to see a Dunnock that is more than a kilometre from where it was hatched. Despite this, Dunnocks are migrants over much of the rest of their range.

The Dunnock's world distribution is virtually limited to the West Palearctic apart from a small breeding population in northern Iran and an introduced one in New Zealand (*BWP*). The species is resident in Britain & Ireland, northwestern Europe and northern Iberia as well as some regions of Turkey and, in these areas, movements are mostly limited to short-distance post-juvenile dispersal. Populations in Ireland and western Scotland are of the race *hebridium* and are generally sedentary (*BWP*). The race *occidentalis*, which is found in the rest of Britain and western France, generally makes only short movements limited to post-natal dispersal (*BWP*). The nominate race *modularis* breeds in Fennoscandia, the former USSR and northeast Europe, and migrates southwest to winter in southern Iberia, the northern Mediterranean countries, including its islands, and the northern coast of the Black Sea (*European Atlas*).

In Britain & Ireland, the Dunnock is a widespread and common breeding bird, although it is rare in the Scottish Highlands, the Hebrides and Orkney, and generally absent as a breeder in Shetland (*1988–91 Atlas*). The highest breeding densities in Britain & Ireland tend to be in areas below 300 m above sea-level, although over much of the rest of the Dunnock's world range it is a bird of all altitudes, including up to the treeline in montane regions. This distribution is probably a reflection of the Dunnock's habitat preference which, in all seasons, is open scrub and similarly structured habitat such as gardens, open woodland and

The analysis of the data for this species was supported by Mary Waller

farmland with hedges (Davies 1992). In Britain & Ireland, the wintering range is much the same as the breeding range (*Winter Atlas*), although in continental Europe birds from higher altitudes tend to move to lower areas in response to colder weather (*BWP*).

The distribution of ringing locations of recoveries in Britain largely reflects the breeding and wintering distribution of the Dunnock (Fig 1), although this is not so for Ireland, where Dunnocks are widespread and common but ringers are not. Approximately 97% of all Dunnocks ringed in Britain & Ireland are fully grown (fledged juveniles or adults), and the recoveries generally reflect this bias in age of ringing as only 6% come from birds ringed as nestlings (Fig 2). For birds ringed when fully grown, there is a relatively uniform spread of recoveries in relation to month of ringing, with a peak for the juveniles in late summer and autumn, which is when most birds of this age are ringed (*eg* Taylor 1984).

Approximately 95% of all recoveries were due to birds being found dead rather than through recaptures by ringers; the cause of death was known in 58% of cases. Predation by domestic pets accounted for the majority of cases, followed by human-related causes such as traffic collisions and a small proportion due to natural predation (Fig 3). This may not represent the true picture as Dunnocks dying away from human habitation are much less likely to be found.

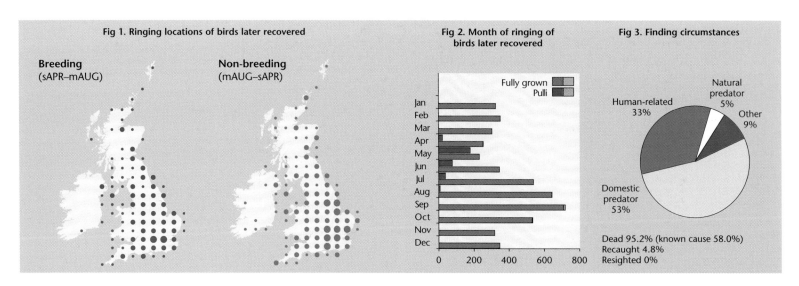

Fig 1. Ringing locations of birds later recovered

Breeding (sAPR–mAUG)

Non-breeding (mAUG–sAPR)

Fig 2. Month of ringing of birds later recovered

Fully grown / Pulli

Fig 3. Finding circumstances

Human-related 33%

Natural predator 5%

Other 9%

Domestic predator 53%

Dead 95.2% (known cause 58.0%)
Recaught 4.8%
Resighted 0%

Ringing and recovery data

	<1960	60–69	70–79	80–89	90–97	Total
RINGING						
BTO ringing totals (%)	8	19	26	27	20	603,201
RECOVERIES						
BTO-ringed (%)	12	26	26	22	13	5,198
Foreign-ringed (%)	←	36	→	23	41	22

Statistical analyses

	Breeding population (sAPR–mAUG)	Wintering population (sNOV–sMAR)
Status	SEDENTARY (0)	SEDENTARY
Age differences[NT]	Not significant	Not significant
Sex differences[NS]	Not significant*	Not tested
Regional differences	Not significant⁴*	Not tested
Finding circumstances	(Not significant)	(Not significant)

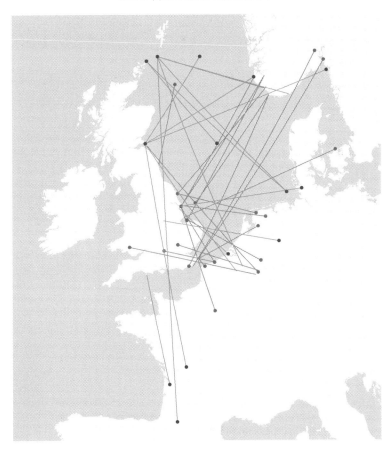

Fig 4. All 37 included exchanges of Dunnocks between Britain & Ireland and abroad, with those present in Britain & Ireland during the breeding season (22, red) differentiated from those present outside the breeding season (15, grey). Eight pre-1979 foreign-ringed birds are not shown: Germany (3), Norway (2), Belgium (1), France (1) and the Netherlands (1).

In an intensive study of the Dunnock's breeding system, Davies (1992) found that post-natal dispersal of young Dunnocks occurs shortly after they reach independence but movements are generally very short, in the region of a few hundred metres rather than kilometres. Recoveries of nestlings ringed in Britain & Ireland confirm the short dispersal distances found by Davies; 107 birds were recovered dead in the first 90 days after ringing and had a median movement of less than 1 km. The median movement of the 198 Dunnocks which were ringed as nestlings and recovered dead within a year was less than 1 km, with 95% of these birds moving less than 5 km.

There is, however, evidence from some east-coast ringing stations in England which suggests that there may be some autumn eruptions involving British-bred Dunnocks (Williamson 1962b, Boddy 1983, Taylor 1984). These eruptions usually involve large numbers of birds being observed or captured in a small area between late August and early September. Apparent eruptions in July and early August appear to be due to increased captures of locally bred juveniles which subsequently stay in the same area over the next few months, but from late August to mid-October further peaks in capture rates tend to comprise juveniles that are recaptured at a lower frequency than those from the earlier capture peak (Boddy 1983). These patterns of captures and recaptures have been interpreted to suggest that Dunnocks undergo sporadic partial migrations in late autumn (Boddy 1983, Taylor 1984) but the evidence is equivocal. Little is known about the relative dispersal and subsequent survival of juveniles from first and second broods; so a double peak in autumn captures could, therefore, be interpreted as the products of first and second broods, but with lower recapture rates of second-peak birds due to lower survival of those juveniles. Further work is needed, preferably in conjunction with detailed nest monitoring and ringing and retrapping of nestlings, although if these eruptions were regularly of more than just a few kilometres they would surely be detected in the ring-recovery data. Of 2,704 recoveries of Dunnocks from the British & Irish breeding population, however, the median movement is less than 1 km ($P5–95=0–7$ km).

Recoveries of adult Dunnocks ringed in Britain & Ireland during the breeding season suggest that post-breeding movements are as short as the post-natal dispersal of young birds, if not shorter. Of 266 adult Dunnocks ringed during the breeding season and recovered in a following autumn, winter or spring, 94% showed movements of less than 20 km, with an overall median movement of less than 1 km ($P5–95=0–24$ km). Movements of adult Dunnocks between breeding seasons show a similar distribution of distances. These data are supported by the more detailed observations of colour-ringed birds by Davies (1992) who found that the mean movement of breeding adults between years was less than 30 m, with no difference between the sexes.

Although the Dunnock is highly sedentary in Britain & Ireland, it is a very different story in northern Europe, where the nominate race *modularis* migrates southwest in the autumn and northeast in the spring. Although most of these migrating Dunnocks remain on the Continent, there can be noticeable movements down the east coast of Britain in spring and autumn when the weather conditions are right for arrivals of Scandinavian migrants. Most migrants are likely to go unnoticed amongst the resident Dunnocks but at Fair Isle, where the species is largely absent as a breeder, nearly all the birds are nominate-race migrants. Peak migration periods of Dunnocks on Fair Isle tend to fall mostly from the end of March through to the end of April in spring, and late September to October in the autumn, with no consistent differences between seasons. The number of birds involved in these movements varies greatly between years, however, with peak daily counts generally in the region of a few tens of birds rising to 100 in exceptional years. Annual ringing totals of Dunnocks on Fair Isle for 1994 to 1998 ranged between seven and 161 due to an exceptional passage in 1998; usual totals are between 10 and 20 birds, so nominate-race Dunnocks are not passing through in large numbers. The few foreign exchanges of ringed Dunnocks mostly involve the east coasts of England and Scotland, and the Northern Isles, with exchanges with Norway (12), Belgium (seven), France (five), the Netherlands (five), Germany (four), the North Sea (three) and Denmark (one) accounting for all records (Fig 4).

The British & Irish Dunnock breeding population has shown a steady but shallow decline in recent decades (Crick *et al* 1998) and is of conservation interest. Along with the necessity for continued ringing to gather demographic information, there are still unanswered questions about the species' local movements. For example, more research is needed to understand the post-juvenile eruptions which seem to occur in early autumn in some years and whether they are caused by changes in food supply or social factors such as young birds being forced out of natal territories.

Ian R Hartley

European Robin (Robin)

Erithacus rubecula

European Robins are familiar birds throughout most of Britain & Ireland. Ironically, given how much Robins have taught us about how birds orient during migration (*eg* Wiltschko *et al* 1998), there are surprising gaps in our knowledge of their movements in Britain & Ireland.

Robins breed from the Azores east to the Ob River in Russia, and from northern Norway south to the Canaries. Most winter from Britain & Ireland south to Morocco and east to a line from Denmark to Turkey. Racial variation is subtle and few individuals can be identified to subspecies. This makes ringing an essential tool for studying Robin movements. The nominate race *rubecula* breeds in continental Europe south to Spain and Greece, and east to the Ural Mountains, as well as in Asia Minor, Madeira and the Azores. It varies from being almost totally migratory in Fennoscandia and eastern Europe to being virtually sedentary in southern Europe. Most populations are partially migratory, however, with females more likely to migrate than males and immatures more likely to migrate than adults. Migrants move west and south into western Europe and the Mediterranean, including North Africa. Most of the peripheral races, including *melophilus* of Britain & Ireland, are largely sedentary but *tartaricus*, breeding to the east of the Urals, is fully migratory, wintering mainly within the range of *hyrcanus* (*BWP*).

Robins inhabit scrub and woodland in boreal, temperate and Mediterranean zones. They prefer moist, shady areas with access to low perches and open ground for foraging, and cover for refuge especially while singing (*BWP*).

The analysis of the data for this species was supported in memory of Dr June Rosalind Wilkie

The distribution of ringing locations in Britain & Ireland of Robin ring-recoveries (Fig 1) is similar to their breeding distribution (*1988–91 Atlas*). The large populations of Ireland and southwest Britain are under-represented, however, especially among birds ringed during the breeding season. Only 34% of the Robins ringed in Britain & Ireland and subsequently recovered had been ringed during the main breeding season (April–July) and only 9% were ringed as nestlings (Fig 2).

Of over 8,700 Robin recoveries, 95% were found dead. Of these, 61% have a cause of death recorded. Half were attributed to domestic predators and a further 32% to human-related causes (mainly collisions with traffic) (Fig 3). The pattern of recoveries is thus likely to be heavily influenced by the distributions of cars and cats. The bias of recoveries towards domestic predators, and cats in particular, is not surprising given the bird's feeding behaviour and abundance in gardens.

Colour-ringing shows that juvenile Robins begin to disperse from their natal territory about three weeks after leaving the nest, by which time they have become independent of their parents (*BWP*). Ring-recoveries reveal that some individuals travel several kilometres during the first few days of this dispersal. The few movements of over 100 km are not detected until at least nine weeks later, which would typically be after completion of the post-juvenile moult (*BWP*).

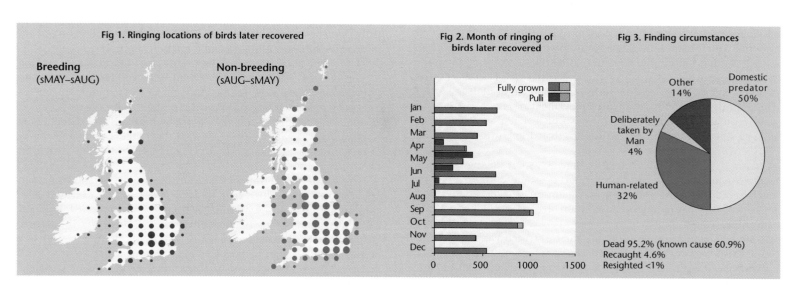

Fig 1. Ringing locations of birds later recovered

Breeding (sMAY–sAUG)

Non-breeding (sAUG–sMAY)

Fig 2. Month of ringing of birds later recovered

Fully grown / Pulli

Fig 3. Finding circumstances

Other 14%
Domestic predator 50%
Deliberately taken by Man 4%
Human-related 32%

Dead 95.2% (known cause 60.9%)
Recaught 4.6%
Resighted <1%

Ringing and recovery data

	<1960	60–69	70–79	80–89	90–97	Total
RINGING						
BTO ringing totals (%)	10	14	21	29	25	677,246
RECOVERIES						
BTO-ringed (%)	16	23	22	24	15	8,590
Foreign-ringed (%)	←	41	→	33	26	206

Statistical analyses

	Breeding population (sMAY–sAUG)	Wintering population (sNOV–sMAR)
Status	SEDENTARY (0)	SEDENTARY
Age differences[NT]	Not significant*	(Significant)
Sex differences[(NS)]	Not significant*	Not tested
Regional differences	Significant[5*]	Not tested
Finding circumstances	Not significant	(Not significant)

Fig 4. Movements of over 20 km between the breeding season and (a) autumn (767:125), (b) winter (979:79) and (c) spring (460:44) and locations outside the breeding season of Robins present in Britain & Ireland during the breeding season. Sample sizes of movements under:over 20 km are given but only those over 20 km are plotted.

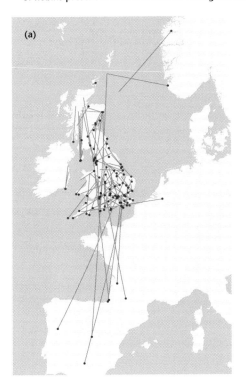 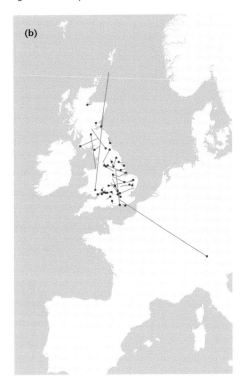 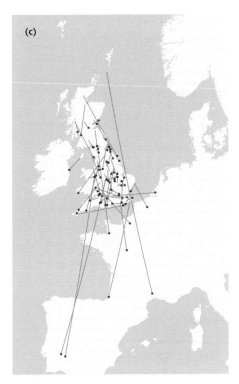

Many Robins hatched in Britain & Ireland spend their lives within sight of their birthplace, but a few winter as far south as Spain. The number wintering abroad appears to be a small fraction of those leaving their breeding sites in the autumn. As was demonstrated by Burkitt (1926), in the first colour-ringing study of a wild passerine, many of these departing birds return the following spring.

Juveniles soon establish individual territories, as do adults of both sexes when they finish moulting. Most males and some females winter on part of their past or future breeding territory. The remainder leave the breeding site, although many return in the following spring. Colour-ringing studies show that some adults leave before their post-breeding moult (Harper 1986) but that others leave after moulting (Burkitt 1926). Indeed, some adults and many juveniles depart as late as October, exceptionally November, after defending a territory for several weeks (BWP). These 'migrants' return to their breeding sites from late December until April, exceptionally May (Harper 1986).

We do not know where 'migrants' winter, although seasonal changes in Robin density suggest that many move into habitats that are unsuitable for breeding such as reedbeds and urban areas with little vegetation (Winter Atlas). At two suburban sites, their pairing dates were no later than those of strictly resident females, with most pairing in January or February (Jackson 1958, Harper 1985). This is consistent with 'migrants' having wintered nearby. In six rural populations, however, they paired several weeks later on average than residents, often not returning until March or April (Burkitt 1926, Lack 1943, Harper 1986). That colour-ringing studies based on thorough coverage of small sites have failed to locate wintering 'migrants' suggests that most move over 1 km. General ringing on the other hand suggests that few move far; of Robins present in Britain & Ireland during the breeding season (May–July) and located elsewhere at other times of year only 10% (n=2,454) had moved more than 20 km. Twenty of these were found abroad: two in Norway and the remainder from the Netherlands south to Iberia (Fig 4). Some of these birds were probably continental breeders ringed while still on spring passage; for example, one of the Norwegian

recoveries was ringed on Fair Isle where Robins do not breed (Birds in Scotland). Another exceptional recovery was that of a Robin ringed as a juvenile in Shetland in October 1992, and found dead the following summer, having travelled 1,200 km to the remote arctic island of Jan Mayen. Four birds recovered abroad (two in France, one in Spain and one in Portugal) were ringed in Britain & Ireland as adults during the breeding season. Eight were ringed as nestlings and so definitely belonged to the British & Irish population. One from Montgomeryshire was shot over 1,600 km away in southwest Spain during its first winter (Mead 1984). Ringing showed that many Robins, of unknown origin, return to the same territory in Spain or Gibraltar in successive winters (Herrera & Rodriguez 1979, Finlayson 1980), although some birds move within Iberia during the winter (Finlayson 1992). It is thus possible that some Robins spend their lives alternating between two territories, one in Britain or Ireland and the other in Iberia. A striking example of an adult wintering abroad was a bird ringed as a juvenile in Surrey in July, a most unlikely date for an immigrant, and found in Switzerland in the April after its third winter (Mead 1984).

However far some Robins travel, most are much less adventurous. Most Robins breed close to their birthplace, with the distance of natal dispersal exceeding 20 km in only 3% of cases (n=68). Breeding dispersal is similarly limited, with less than 5% of distances exceeding 20 km (n=66). Colour-ringing has revealed that most individuals, including 'migrants', breed on a territory which overlaps with the site of a previous one (even if defended only briefly as a juvenile) (Harper 1985). Site-fidelity is similarly strong in Britain & Ireland in the winter. Less than 2% of Robins recovered in the same November–February period were more than 20 km from the ringing site (n=405), and only 7% of those recovered in a subsequent winter (n=396). Several of these records are likely to involve migrants from Fennoscandia or elsewhere in northern Europe.

Falls of the nominate race rubecula occur on the east coast of Britain from August to November, peaking in October. Most of these birds appear to be from Fennoscandia, and heading for wintering grounds from the Low Countries south to Iberia and North Africa (BWP).

Fig 5. Locations abroad during (a) the breeding season (21), (b) autumn (137), (c) winter (103) and (d) spring (77) of Robins that were present in Britain & Ireland outside the breeding season.

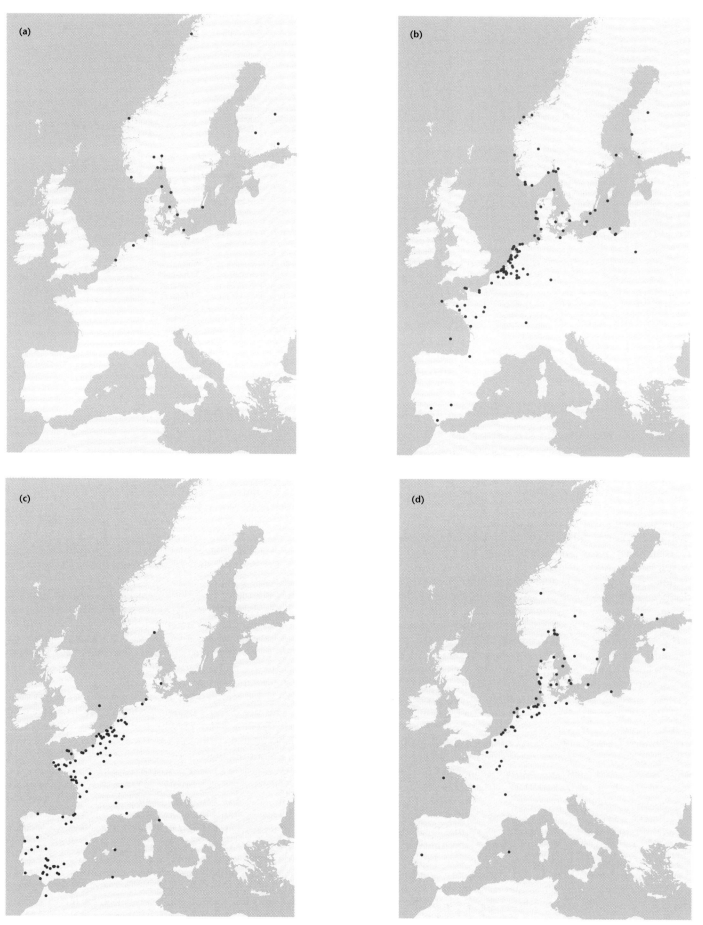

Ring-recoveries (Fig 5) suggest that others come from the Baltic States, Poland, and eastern Germany west to Belgium.

The only Irish-ringed Robins to be recovered abroad were both marked in County Down and recovered in Spain and Norway (Fig 5). Like the vast majority of recoveries between Britain and the Continent, these birds were almost certainly Fennoscandian breeders (see below). The bird recovered in Spain (in January) had been ringed in the previous March, presumably while on return passage (*Birds in Ireland*).

Few Robins on passage are likely to spend long in Britain & Ireland. They typically travel by night, resting and foraging by day. Although many continue their migration on the next night, some stay at stopover sites for several days or even weeks (Davis 1962, Szulc-Olech 1965, Bottoni *et al* 1991). During stopovers of more than a day or so, individuals usually establish temporary territories. Most of the territorial individuals initially lose weight before fattening up considerably (*eg* Szulc-Olech 1965), although at one Norwegian site most lost weight throughout their stay (Mehlum 1983). Ring-recoveries support the idea that a few *rubecula* winter in Britain & Ireland (*BWP*), with records for 17 birds that were abroad at other times of the year. Most of these birds were ringed or recovered in countries from Sweden southwest to Belgium. Three were recovered farther south, however, in the Bay of Biscay, Spain and Algeria, suggesting that at least some were on passage rather than wintering here. Return passage of *rubecula* peaks across most of its range in March, with most breeding sites occupied by late April (*BWP*). The passage of *rubecula*, particularly through southeast Britain, makes any movement by the native *melophilus* hard to detect (Fig 5).

Most movements by Robins in Britain & Ireland are too long to be monitored by colour-ringing and yet are not detected by ring-recoveries. This means either that biases in the recovery data are unexpectedly large or, more likely, that most movements are missed owing to the coarse resolution of ringing and recovery locations. That a small number of Robins from the British breeding population have been recovered on the Continent is a tantalizing result, even though the numbers are small. More ringing of nestlings would provide interesting information, since only this reliably excludes passage migrants. No Robin ringed as a nestling in Britain has been recovered abroad since 1967, despite two such records in the first five years of the Ringing Scheme (Lack 1943); there is no example from Ireland. Ringers should pay particular attention to Irish nestlings since *rubecula* appears to be rare there on passage and most of the major coastal movements in the autumn are believed to involve *melophilus* (*Birds in Ireland*). If we had to search for British & Irish Robins wintering abroad, analogy with the wintering distributions of Finnish and Belgian birds (Mead 1984, Adriansen 1988) would lead us to northwestern Iberia. Ringing there (and elsewhere in southwest Europe) might be rewarding since no Robin ringed south of the Channel Islands has yet been recovered in Britain & Ireland. We suspect, however, that few *melophilus* leave our shores. If so, it is striking that all of the colour-ringing studies in Britain & Ireland, from a variety of rural and suburban habitats, have reported male-biased sex ratios in the winter and the return of 'migrants' in the spring (Burkitt 1926, Lack 1943, Jackson 1958, Harper 1986, Tobias 1997, D Harper pers obs). Consequently, information about the ecology and behaviour of wintering Robins, especially females, is probably unrepresentative. This would be dangerous if Robins were of conservation concern, and we wonder how many rare species believed to be sedentary make similar movements that as yet are undetected. Resolving the problem of where 'migrants' go in this and other small, mainly sedentary species will probably require new methods suitable for studying movements of a few kilometres, such as radio-telemetry.

Gavin Fennessy & David Harper

Common Nightingale (Nightingale)

Luscinia megarhynchos

With its drab plumage and skulking habits, the Nightingale is inconspicuous except when singing and, for most people, it is only the loud and attractive song, given by night and day, that draws attention to the species. With a fairly small British population, and none in Ireland, limited numbers of Nightingales are ringed each year and recoveries have been reported of only 66 British-ringed birds. Consequently, much of what we know about the movements of this trans-Saharan migrant comes from observations rather than ring-recoveries.

In Britain, most Nightingales are found southeast of a line from the Humber to the Severn, with few in Devon and none in Cornwall (*1988–91 Atlas*). They are most abundant in the coastal counties from Norfolk to Sussex, which together held 78% of the 4,430 singing males located in a national survey in 1999 (Wilson *et al* 2002). The Nightingale has recently been lost as a breeding species in Wales (*Birds in Wales*) and is only an annual passage migrant in small numbers in Scotland (*Birds in Scotland*). No ring-recoveries affect Ireland where it is a rare migrant (*Birds in Ireland*). In continental Europe, it is much more numerous, especially to the south. The nominate race *megarhynchos* breeds in Europe, western Turkey and northwest Africa. The races *africana* and *hafizi* occur from eastern Turkey and the Caucasus east to Mongolia. The closely related Thrush Nightingale *L. luscinia* is largely allopatric to the north and east, extending from Denmark to northeast Mongolia (*BWP*). In Britain, Nightingales breed in scrub and in the early successional stages of woodland, including coppices and conifer plantations. A crucial factor is the presence of very dense, low cover (Fuller *et al* 1999).

The analysis of the data for this species was supported by Jan Pritchard & Audrey Thompson

The wintering range of the Nightingale is a belt from Kenya to Senegal. In contrast, the Thrush Nightingale winters only in eastern Africa, south to South Africa. Nightingale wintering habitats include savanna woodland, scrub, forest edges and secondary growth (*BWP*). As in the breeding season, the presence of dense cover seems essential.

The ringing locations for ring-recoveries are all broadly within the Nightingale's breeding range (Fig 1). The two exceptions relate to birds ringed as autumn migrants in Shetland and the Channel Islands. The latter is the only recovery of a foreign-ringed bird in Britain. Over half (55%) of the British-ringed Nightingales that have been recovered subsequently have been ringed during May–June (Fig 2), many as nestlings in June.

Exactly half of the 66 recoveries have arisen from birds being caught or resighted by ringers. Of the 33 recoveries found dead, 70% have a known cause, over half of which (57%) have been attributed to human-related causes or being deliberately or accidentally taken by Man and a further 39% to domestic predators (Fig 3). Instances of deliberate capture have been restricted to continental Europe, accounting for four of the seven foreign recoveries.

The Nightingale is single-brooded in Britain and moult is started in late June (Morgan 1982, Ginn & Melville 1983). Little is known about

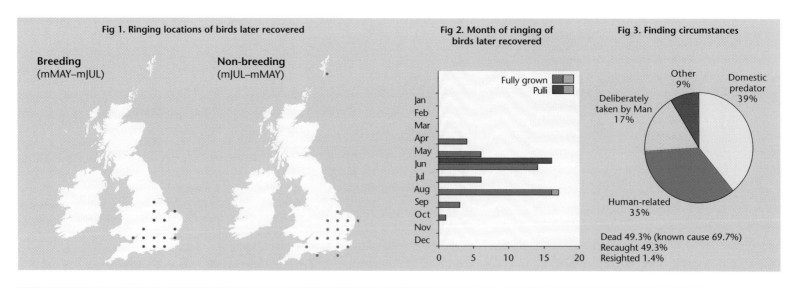

Fig 1. Ringing locations of birds later recovered

Breeding (mMAY–mJUL)

Non-breeding (mJUL–mMAY)

Fig 2. Month of ringing of birds later recovered

Fully grown / Pulli

Fig 3. Finding circumstances

Other 9%
Domestic predator 39%
Deliberately taken by Man 17%
Human-related 35%

Dead 49.3% (known cause 69.7%)
Recaught 49.3%
Resighted 1.4%

Ringing and recovery data

	<1960	60–69	70–79	80–89	90–97	Total
RINGING						
BTO ringing totals (%)	35	12	13	24	16	9,803
RECOVERIES						
BTO-ringed (%)	14	11	21	32	23	66
Foreign-ringed (%)	←	0	→	100	0	1

Statistical analyses

	Breeding population (mMAY–mJUL)	Wintering population (mSEP–sAPR)
Status	[LONG-DISTANCE MIGRANT]	NONE
Age differences	Not tested	—
Sex differences	Not tested	—
Regional differences	Not tested	—
Finding circumstances	Not tested	—

Fig 4. Locations of Nightingales in (a) the breeding season (16), (b) autumn (22), (c) winter (4) and (d) spring (18).

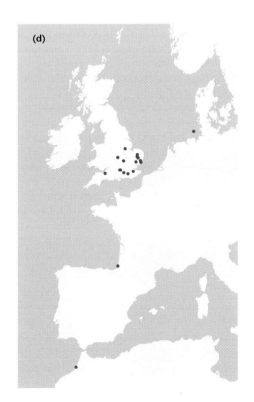

Nightingale behaviour between breeding and migration. Some may disperse from breeding sites to other areas where pre-migratory feeding is better. However, many are believed to remain in breeding areas where they become highly elusive. The trapping, together, on 11 August 1998 at a breeding site near Canterbury, Kent, of two adults and three juveniles belonging to at least two broods was highly unusual (J Pritchard pers comm). Substantial pre-migratory fattening has been recorded in southern Britain, both at a breeding site in Kent, where a juvenile in September weighed 34.8 g, about 50% above typical values for adults or juveniles (Woodcock 1992) and at Portland Bill, where one gained 53%, also reaching 34.8 g, in two weeks (Clafton 1971).

Because the Nightingale's migration periods overlap entirely with the short breeding season, it is not possible to separate with certainty those recoveries relating to British-breeding birds from those of other populations. Most recoveries shown in Fig 4 are likely to involve the British population, but some may relate to either the autumn or spring passage of continental birds.

Autumn passage starts in mid-July, with the bulk of records at coastal observatories in August and early September (R & F). Breeding-season recoveries are scattered through the breeding range but autumn recoveries show a distinct bias towards the English east and south coasts (Fig 4). Autumn passage is directed south-southwest through western France and Iberia (BWP). The westerly tendency is shown by the occurrence of birds at observatories such as Bardsey and Skokholm, which are to the west of the breeding range.

Three of the four recoveries after mid-September were well to the southwest of Britain. The exception was the October recovery in Shetland of a bird that had been ringed 9 km away, a day earlier. Other than this, there have been no recoveries after the end of September. Observations and recoveries of birds ringed in continental Europe (BWP, Der Zug) support the interpretation of the few recoveries of British-ringed Nightingales, and indicate a southwesterly movement, with concentrations of records in southwest France and southwest Iberia. There are few records in North Africa in autumn (BWP) and it is assumed that the Sahara is crossed in one continuous flight.

No British-ringed Nightingales have been recovered in the Afrotropics and it is not known precisely where the British breeding population winters but, by analogy with other passerine migrants (such as Sedge Warbler), it is probably towards the west. The first arrivals south of the Sahara are in August, but the main arrival is from late October to early December (Keith et al 1992). In early winter, some onward southerly movement may occur, but birds are mostly sedentary, occupying small territories, with daytime song frequent (Keith et al 1992). There is no information on winter site-fidelity.

Northward passage occurs mainly between mid-March and early April, but some birds remain south of the Sahara into May (Keith et al 1992). The first arrivals in Europe are in March but the peak arrival time in Britain is in late April and early May (R & F). Most ring-recoveries in spring are of birds that have returned to breeding grounds (Fig 4). However, there are two, in northwest Morocco and southwest France, that indicate that birds may follow a similar route to that used in autumn. The temporal pattern of northward movement is not known but is assumed to be fairly rapid.

There is strong breeding season site-fidelity by adult Nightingales, especially males. Grüll (1981) found that, on average, nearly half of males and a quarter of females returned to his Austrian study area from year to year. At Eccles in Kent, 19 of 47 ringed males (40%) and seven of 36 females (19%) were retrapped in the area in at least one subsequent year during 1979–92 (Woodcock 1992). Birds returned to the same territory in six cases for the males but only one case for the females. At two sites near Canterbury, however, seven of 41 ringed males (17%) and three of 19 ringed females (16%) were retrapped in at least one subsequent year during 1988–98, implying either lower male site-fidelity or lower survival in this area (J Pritchard pers comm). Return rates of juveniles appear always to be lower (though within these, fidelity and survival are confounded). At the Eccles site, only three of 21 ringed juveniles (14%) returned to the area; all three proved to be males. At Canterbury, none of 17 juveniles has been retrapped in subsequent years.

With few ring-recoveries, there is little evidence of passage of continental Nightingales through Britain but it seems likely that some occur in spring and autumn. A June recovery on Helgoland of a bird ringed in August in Dorset implies that some autumn passage occurs. Overshooting by birds on spring passage sometimes occurs and small numbers are recorded at observatories to the north of the breeding range, such as the Calf of Man and Fair Isle (R & F). Although many of these are probably of the British population, some may be continental breeding birds. Some birds from further afield occasionally occur in Britain. Two examples considered to be of the *hafizi* race have been recorded, on Fair Isle in October 1971 and at Spurn Point in October 1991 (Rogers et al 1998, T Melling pers comm).

The Nightingale's British breeding range is contracting and the population is declining, although this trend is tempered by the apparent stability of numbers in the core areas, especially in Kent (Fuller et al 1999). The reasons for the decline are not known but could include land-use and habitat changes, changing predation levels, or pressures during migration or in the wintering range. There is little information on the scale of hunting or trapping but most foreign recoveries arise from this cause. Liming has accounted for some birds, eg 112 presumably east European birds were caught in Cyprus in this way in one spring (Flint & Stewart 1983). In the 19th century, many Nightingales were trapped in Britain for sale as cagebirds (Holloway 1996); it is not known whether this practice continues elsewhere. Similarly, little is known of pressures that might arise from hunting or habitat change in the wintering quarters.

The contraction of the British population is at variance with trends elsewhere in Europe, where numbers are believed to be largely stable, and it is perhaps more likely that factors closer to home are responsible for the decline here. More detailed investigation of the distribution of Nightingales during post-breeding dispersal, on migration and in winter might elucidate whether they are affected by factors operating outside the breeding range, but the British population may be too small to generate sufficient recoveries to distinguish their routes and destinations from those of continental birds.

Andrew Henderson

Black Redstart

Phoenicurus ochruros

First recorded as a breeding bird in Britain in 1845 and next in 1923 in Sussex (*BWP*), the Black Redstart became a familiar sight around London on derelict bombsites in the late 1940s. Small numbers continue to breed in Britain, mainly in the southeastern quarter of the country, with numbers varying between 80 and 120 pairs or territory-holding males (*1988–91 Atlas*). Black Redstarts have not been known to breed in Ireland. Typical breeding sites include derelict buildings, power stations and town centres. Some birds probably remain in these areas throughout the year but it is mainly as a passage migrant that the species is seen throughout much of both Britain and Ireland. Passage occurs mainly on the south and east coasts of both countries, peaking in late March and early April and again in late October and early November (Langslow 1977a, *R & F, Birds in Ireland*). Numbers seen are generally small but much larger arrivals occur occasionally, usually following southeasterly winds in spring or northeasterly winds in autumn, and frequently associated with poor weather. For example, an arrival of at least 305 birds occurred on the Kent coast on 28 March 1998 (pers obs, Braggs 2000).

Whereas the Black Redstart is rare as a breeding species in Britain, it is widespread and common throughout the middle latitudes of the Continent and also nests in smaller numbers further north in southern Scandinavia. It occurs in a wide range of built-up areas and also in rocky and broken terrain, including cliffs and up to the snowline. The birds breeding in Britain and western continental Europe are of the race *gibraltariensis*, except those in Iberia which are of the race *aterrimus*. Eastern races, including the nominate *ochruros* and *phoenicuroides*, are

The analysis of the data for this species was supported by Kathleen & Ivor Bace

believed to occur occasionally as vagrants to western Europe on autumn passage. Most European breeders winter in similar habitats in the Mediterranean Basin, being common on the coasts of the western Mediterranean and extending as far south as the northern limit of the Sahara. Birds breeding in eastern Europe are more likely to winter in the eastern Mediterranean (*BWP*). It has been estimated that a population of about 500 birds may winter in Britain & Ireland, mainly around the southern and western coasts (*Winter Atlas*).

Up to the end of 1997, a total of 4,105 birds had been ringed in Britain & Ireland. The breeding-season ringing locations of Black Redstarts subsequently recovered reflect the southeasterly distribution of the breeding population. Recoveries of birds ringed in other seasons, probably all passage migrants, stem from a wider range of mostly coastal sites (Fig 1). Most Black Redstarts that have been ringed in Britain & Ireland and subsequently recovered have been ringed in March–April (29%) or in September–October (42%) (Fig 2). It is not possible to say how many birds ringed when fully grown were breeding birds and how many were passage migrants but at Dungeness Bird Observatory, where both breeding and passage birds occur, around 24% of birds ringed were judged to be either breeding adults or locally bred juveniles (pers obs).

Relatively few pulli are ringed; birds ringed as pulli comprise only 13% of those recoveries and juveniles 42%. There have been 46

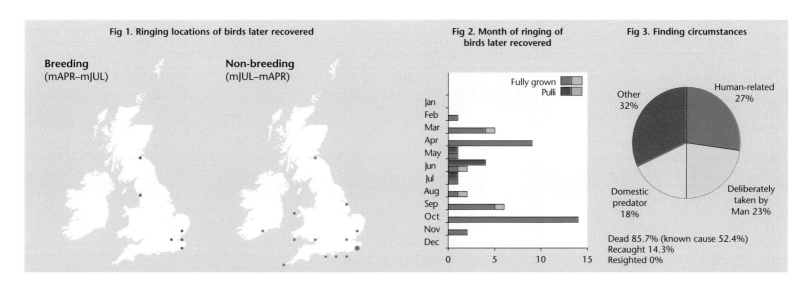

Fig 1. Ringing locations of birds later recovered

Breeding (mAPR–mJUL)

Non-breeding (mJUL–mAPR)

Fig 2. Month of ringing of birds later recovered

Fig 3. Finding circumstances

Dead 85.7% (known cause 52.4%)
Recaught 14.3%
Resighted 0%

Ringing and recovery data

	<1960	60–69	70–79	80–89	90–97	Total
RINGING						
BTO ringing totals (%)	14	12	20	32	22	4,105
RECOVERIES						
BTO-ringed (%)	22	22	18	27	11	45
Foreign-ringed (%)	←	43	→	43	14	7

Statistical analyses

	Breeding population (mAPR–mJUL)	Wintering population (sNOV–sMAR)
Status	?	?
Age differences	—	—
Sex differences	—	—
Regional differences	—	—
Finding circumstances	—	—

Fig 4. Recovery locations and movements of over 20 km for the 49 included recoveries of Black Redstarts ringed or recovered in Britain & Ireland, with those present in Britain & Ireland during the breeding season (12, red) differentiated from those from other or uncertain breeding populations (37, grey).

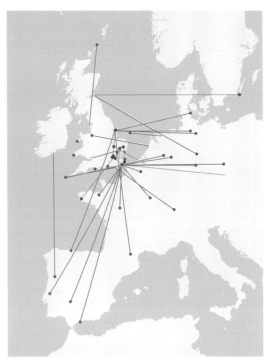

recoveries of birds ringed in Britain & Ireland, just over 1% of those ringed, a typically low proportion for a small passerine species. In addition there have been four recoveries of birds ringed abroad.

Of recoveries of dead birds with a known cause, 68% were related to human activity or taken by domestic predators, probably reflecting the tendency of Black Redstarts to breed in buildings. This 68% includes 23% deliberately taken by Man, mainly in Iberia (Fig 3).

Juveniles are the first to leave the breeding areas, having departed mainly by early September (*BWP*), although the largest autumn numbers occur at British bird observatories in October (*R & F*). This suggests that autumn southerly movement is relatively slow, which is supported by one autumn-ringed bird recovered in southern France in November (Fig 4). Autumn birds probably originate from the western Continent, since there are recoveries from the Netherlands in August, Belgium in September and central France in October but none from further east. Central and eastern European birds are presumably not likely to pass through Britain & Ireland in autumn in large numbers as they are moving south to southeast at the start of their migration (*BWP*). Birds are likely to arrive in their wintering areas in December but the only winter recoveries are two in Spain and one in Portugal, all in January. It is possible that the British & Irish wintering population includes some birds escaping harsh continental conditions by travelling west rather than south (*Winter Atlas*) but the ringing data show no real evidence of this.

Bird observatory records show spring passage with two peaks, the first in March involving mainly adult males and the second in April (Langslow 1977a, *R & F*). It is assumed that birds move in a roughly northerly direction from their wintering areas to Britain but there is only one recovery, of a bird in March on the coast of Brittany, to support this. There is a strong suggestion that spring arrivals in Britain include a considerable proportion of birds that have drifted west from their normal route, as there are eight exchanges of probable breeding birds involving central Europe (Germany, Switzerland, the Czech Republic and Sweden) (Fig 4).

There are many gaps in our knowledge. The absence of recoveries from North Africa may indicate that few birds breeding in or passing through Britain & Ireland leave Europe to winter there, or simply may reflect the lower reporting rates there. Recovery data do not indicate when birds arrive in their wintering area. There is a high proportion of recoveries involving birds from western continental Europe but it is not known whether these are simply on passage, arriving to winter, or even recruiting to the British breeding population. More recoveries would help answer these questions but it is unlikely that the numbers of birds ringed can be increased greatly and the recovery rate is always likely to be low.

David Walker

Common Redstart (Redstart)

Phoenicurus phoenicurus

To British birdwatchers, the Redstart conjures up a dual image. First, as a characteristic breeding species of northern and western oakwoods, it is often associated with Wood Warblers and Pied Flycatchers, with which it forms a distinctive summer woodland bird community (*1988–91 Atlas*). Second, as a passage migrant in spring and autumn, it is seen most frequently in September along the east and south coasts of Britain, en route south to African winter quarters. In Ireland, the species is chiefly a scarce passage migrant (*Birds in Ireland*). Like other small, trans-Saharan migrants, the Redstart commands respect for its marathon journey each spring and autumn.

The Redstart has an extensive breeding range, inhabiting boreal, temperate, steppe and Mediterranean zones, where it breeds between the July 10°C and 24°C isotherms in Europe and Siberia as far east as Lake Baikal (*BWP, European Atlas*). There are two distinct races. The nominate race *phoenicurus* breeds throughout Europe and Siberia, and sparingly in northwest Africa, while *samamisicus* breeds around the Black and Caspian Seas, and in the northern Middle East (*BWP*).

The main wintering area is the scrub-savanna belt lying immediately south of the Sahara, at approximately 9°30´–15°30´N, with a southward extension to around 2°N in eastern Congo and Uganda (*BWP*). However, ring-recoveries between December and February from the western Mediterranean Basin, from Iberia and Morocco east to Italy (*Der Zug*), together with occasional observations in winter north to the latitudes of Britain and eastern Germany (*BWP*), suggest that some individuals (probably a minority) winter north of the Sahara.

The analysis of the data for this species was supported by the Sinnott family

The main migration route in autumn of western and central European populations is southwest, many staging in Iberia before continuing south to African winter quarters. Some northern Scandinavian breeders use a more easterly route via the Balkans or Italy and Algeria, while those ringed in Poland and the former USSR have produced more recoveries in northern Italy than elsewhere (*Der Zug*). A similar route is followed during the return migration in spring, although there is some suggestion that a slightly more easterly route is favoured (Hope Jones 1975).

During the breeding season, Redstarts frequent open forests, clearings and woodland edge, preferably where the understorey is not too dense. In southern and central Europe, the species prefers mainly broad-leaved forests, and in northern Europe barren pine forests (*European Atlas*). It also inhabits gardens and parkland with scattered trees. The availability of secure, dry nest cavities in trees, rocks, banks, or indeed nestboxes, is an important habitat requirement.

In winter, it is found in a variety of habitats in Africa, including dry acacia steppe, lusher thickets, the edges of cultivated ground, and woodland of various types, with an overall preference for arid or semi-arid landscapes (*BWP*). In midwinter, in northern Nigeria, Jones *et al* (1996) found that the density of Redstarts increased with tree cover (up to a peak of 0.6 birds per hectare) and suggested that it is likely that

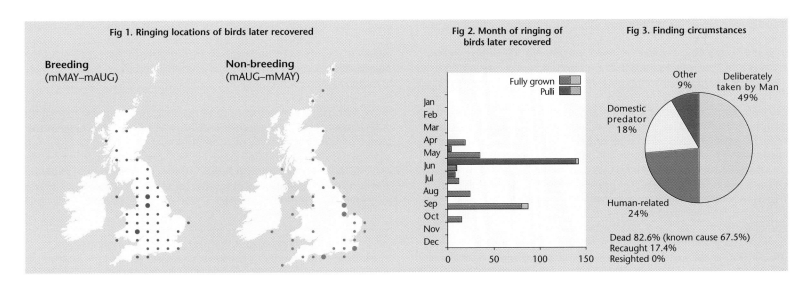

Fig 1. Ringing locations of birds later recovered

Breeding (mMAY–mAUG)

Non-breeding (mAUG–mMAY)

Fig 2. Month of ringing of birds later recovered

Fully grown / Pulli

Fig 3. Finding circumstances

Other 9%
Deliberately taken by Man 49%
Domestic predator 18%
Human-related 24%

Dead 82.6% (known cause 67.5%)
Recaught 17.4%
Resighted 0%

Ringing and recovery data

	<1960	60–69	70–79	80–89	90–97	Total
RINGING						
BTO ringing totals (%)	13	21	15	26	25	83,811
RECOVERIES						
BTO-ringed (%)	12	34	17	23	15	343
Foreign-ringed (%)	←	65	→	13	23	31

Statistical analyses

	Breeding population (mMAY–mAUG)	Wintering population (sNOV–mMAR)
Status	[LONG-DISTANCE MIGRANT]	NONE
Age differences	Not tested	—
Sex differences	Not tested	—
Regional differences	Not tested	—
Finding circumstances	Not tested	—

Fig 4. Locations of Redstarts in (a) September (36:38) and (b) April (17:15), with known British & Irish breeders (red) differentiated from those of uncertain breeding populations (grey). Sample sizes of British & Irish:uncertain breeding populations are given.

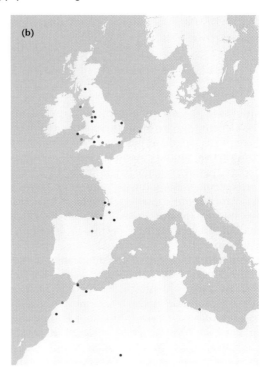

invertebrate prey is more abundant in areas with more trees. Fleshy fruits are sought out for fattening prior to spring migration (Jones *et al* 1996).

In Britain, the Redstart is widespread in the north and west, particularly in upland areas, but is uncommon or absent throughout lowland southern and eastern Britain. It is scarce or lacking in Ireland and on most islands. The Welsh population is perhaps the largest in Britain, followed by those in the northern Pennines and the Lake District. This is broadly reflected in the distribution of birds ringed during the breeding season that later provided recoveries, although the Scottish population is under-represented because of fewer ringers (Fig 1). During passage seasons, birds have been ringed in numbers along the east and south coasts of Scotland and England, notably at observatories.

Many recoveries (41%) come from pulli ringed during June, predominantly from nestbox schemes (Fig 2). The next most important months have been May, August and September, when migrants have been ringed at coastal sites. The ring-recovery information therefore encompasses both breeding birds and those on active migration.

Of the 356 recoveries included, 62 were of birds trapped by ringers. Of the remainder found dead, the cause of death is known for two-thirds (Fig 3). About half of these were deliberately killed by humans, while a further 24% of deaths were human-related. Domestic predators accounted for an additional 18% of the total.

Most Redstarts in Britain fledge between mid-June and early July (*BWP*). During the first few weeks of life, the young move only a short distance from their natal area. The median distance moved within 60 days of being ringed as pulli was less than 25 km (*n*=19). Berthold (1985) showed that, typically for a long-distance migrant, post-juvenile moult starts early and proceeds rapidly in the Redstart, and that fat deposition and migratory restlessness begin before the post-juvenile moult is complete. During the latter half of August, both young and adults leave the breeding grounds, mostly in directions between southeast and south-southwest (Hope Jones 1975), and start to appear at coastal sites by the end of August. There are no foreign recoveries of Redstarts during August, and September is clearly the key month for autumn departure. The map of September recoveries shows a cluster of records in southeast England and along the south coast, together with records from the

western seaboard of France, throughout the Iberian Peninsula, and in North Africa (Fig 4a). For most, these locations reflect staging posts en route to winter quarters, and suggest that many use Iberia as their main stepping stone on the way south.

September is also the peak month for passage of foreign-breeding Redstarts through Britain. Hope Jones (1975) compared recoveries of British-bred Redstarts with those ringed on passage in Britain, and found some evidence to suggest that British breeders used a more westerly route. Recoveries of birds ringed on passage in Britain were clustered in south-central Iberia, as are most British & Irish breeders, but also included records from southeast France, northern Italy and northern Algeria. This suggests that autumn-passage migrants in Britain involve Scandinavian breeders (Fig 5).

Observations show that the first arrivals south of the Sahara appear in the first half of September but the species is not common there until mid-October (*BWP*). Ring-recoveries add little to our knowledge of this species in midwinter, and a precise definition of the wintering area is still an important gap in our knowledge. Fig 5d shows British & Irish breeders in Iberia in winter, but none in Africa, seemingly a reflection of variation in reporting rates and the small sample size available. There are only two recoveries from south of the Sahara, one from the Gambia in October and a midwinter recovery from Senegal in January. The only other recoveries during the midwinter period December to February are from the southern part of Spain and Portugal, and from North Africa.

Northward migration in spring may be evident during March, although most birds begin pre-migratory fattening in late March or early April (*BWP*). Ringing data support observations that passage through North Africa is more conspicuous in spring than in autumn; more individuals of this species (like many other passerines) stage in North Africa on their spring migration. Correspondingly there are fewer recoveries in southern and western Iberia in spring but more from northeast Spain and France. April is the main month for spring migration, and the map of ring-recoveries shows two main concentrations, one in North Africa, and another in northeast Spain and southwest France (Fig 4b).

Most British Redstarts return to their breeding grounds during late April (Southern 1939, *BWP*). Peak passage at British bird observatories occurs in late April for southern Britain, and in early May further north

Fig 5. Movements between Britain & Ireland and abroad of Redstarts abroad in (a) autumn (45), (b) the breeding season (5), (c) winter (5) and (d) spring (17), excluding those involving known British & Irish breeders.

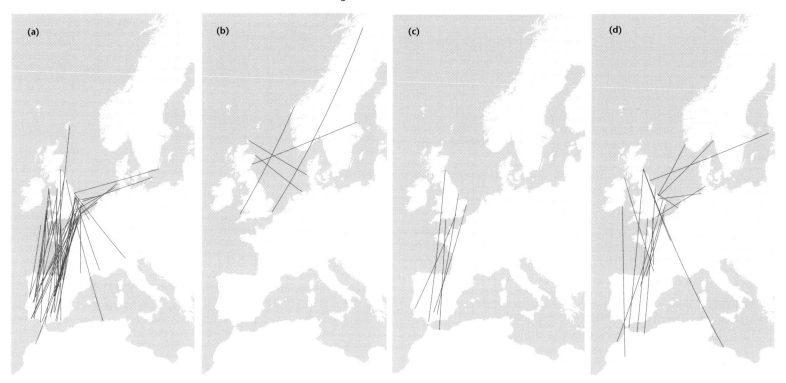

(R & F). Blondel (1967) showed significant differences in wing length between breeding populations of Redstarts in different areas. By analysing measurements taken at bird observatories in spring, Hope Jones (1975) suggested that the smaller spring migration (compared to autumn) is composed mainly of British-breeding Redstarts. The Northern Isles are the exception to this finding; for males measured in April and May on Fair Isle, the mean wing length was close to that expected for Redstarts breeding in southern Scandinavia and northern Germany. The largest spring arrivals on Fair Isle coincide with winds from the east or southeast, and consist predominantly of birds drifted across the North Sea (R & F). Exchanges of ringed birds between Britain & Ireland and abroad — involving Sweden, Denmark, Germany, the Netherlands and the Channel Islands — suggest the most likely source areas of migrants through Britain (Fig 5).

There is little evidence to suggest any differences between males and females, or between first-years and adults, in the timing of migration, migration routes, staging areas or final destinations. There are more long-distance ring-recoveries from dead birds for females than for males (median distances 1,117 km and 735 km respectively, sample sizes 78 and 82, all seasons combined), although this perhaps occurs by chance. There is no known difference in the pattern of movements of birds ringed in different regions of Britain.

Little information about natal and breeding dispersal of Redstarts can be gleaned from ring-recovery information. Data on natal dispersal suggest that just over half of a sample of 19 recoveries moved more than 20 km to their first breeding site. There were only two adults from which information on breeding dispersal could be judged in Britain, and both moved more than 20 km. More work needs to be done to establish the level of site-fidelity among both first-years and adults.

In common with other trans-Saharan passerine migrants, Redstarts are potentially threatened by changes in climate and habitat in Africa that result in desertification of parts of the Sahel. In particular, the need for habitat of sufficient quality to provide adequate pre-migratory fattening may be crucial.

Roger Riddington

Whinchat
Saxicola rubetra

A colourful bird of open country, the Whinchat is primarily a long-distance migrant overflying the Sahara to winter in tropical Africa. In this, it differs from its close relative, the Stonechat, the British & Irish population of which is only partially migrant over short distances.

The Whinchat breeds very widely in Europe, but is absent from Iceland, from arctic coasts of northernmost Fennoscandia and Russia, and from Atlantic and Mediterranean lowlands in France, Iberia, Italy and the Balkans (*BWP, European Atlas*). The breeding range extends a short distance into Russia, east of the Urals. Birds from the whole of this area move to Africa for the winter. Although it has been recorded as a non-breeder in most African countries, the main winter concentration appears to lie in a fairly narrow band from Senegal to Uganda, with smaller numbers from Kenya south to Zambia (*BWP*, Dejaifve 1994).

Breeding Whinchats were formerly widespread in Britain & Ireland but contracted markedly in range in the 1970s and 1980s, and are now rare south of a line from the Humber to the Severn and in most parts of Ireland (*1988–91 Atlas*). In its now-preferred upland areas in the north and west, the Whinchat still breeds commonly in some areas of Britain. In Ireland, it nests rather sparsely, mainly in the north and centre. Its breeding habitats include various types of farmland and young conifer plantations with grassy ground cover, at up to 500 m above sea-level (Fuller 1982). It favours moister and less rough habitats than the Stonechat and makes greater use of seasonal growth of green vegetation such as bracken and tall rank grass, rather than perennial shrubs such as gorse and heather, thus reducing interaction with the Stonechat. Where both species occur,

The analysis of the data for this species was supported by John Webber

Stonechat pairs vigorously chase invading Whinchats from their territories. In Africa, Whinchats occur in savanna in the Sahel zone and also further south in cultivated land, gardens, and forest clearings (*BWP*).

Given that over 30,000 individuals have been ringed, the British & Irish recovery total is remarkably small. The ringing localities of recovered birds show a wide scatter in the breeding season, and a distinctly southeasterly distribution at passage times (Fig 1). Of 103 recoveries, 43% were from birds ringed as nestlings, almost entirely in June (Fig 2). Fully grown birds, which are difficult to catch on the breeding territory, have been ringed mainly in autumn at coastal passage sites. The collapse of the lowland population in Britain has meant that fewer Whinchats have been ringed in recent years, and probably the recovery rates in Britain & Ireland and abroad are also changing. Since 1990, there have been only two foreign recoveries, compared to an average 14 per decade in the previous 40 years. Of 63 recoveries with a known cause of death, 55% were deliberately taken by Man and a further 24% were road casualties or otherwise human-related; another 10% were due to domestic predators (Fig 3).

June and July records at British bird observatories of adult non-breeders or failed breeders merge into autumn passage, which begins in earnest in late July (*R & F*). Early migrants are sometimes observed as family parties. Most observatories record a broad peak of passage in late

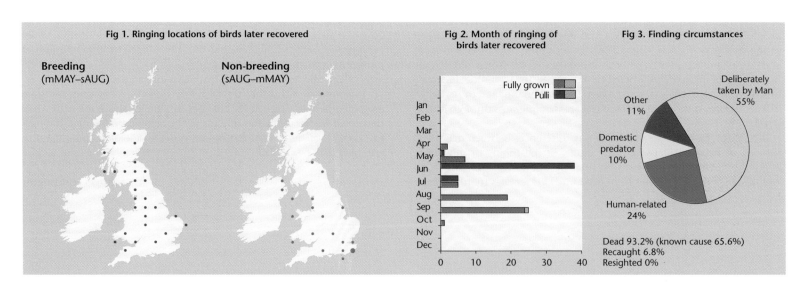

Fig 1. Ringing locations of birds later recovered

Breeding (mMAY–sAUG)

Non-breeding (sAUG–mMAY)

Fig 2. Month of ringing of birds later recovered

Fully grown
Pulli

Fig 3. Finding circumstances

Deliberately taken by Man 55%

Other 11%

Domestic predator 10%

Human-related 24%

Dead 93.2% (known cause 65.6%)
Recaught 6.8%
Resighted 0%

Ringing and recovery data

	<1960	60–69	70–79	80–89	90–97	Total
RINGING						
BTO ringing totals (%)	17	18	20	26	19	32,872
RECOVERIES						
BTO-ringed (%)	29	26	22	18	5	102
Foreign-ringed (%)	←	67	→	33	0	3

Statistical analyses

	Breeding population (mMAY–sAUG)	Wintering population (mNOV–mMAR)
Status	[LONG-DISTANCE MIGRANT]	NONE
Age differences	Not tested	—
Sex differences	Not tested	—
Regional differences	Not tested	—
Finding circumstances	Not tested	—

Fig 4. Locations in (a) September–November and (b) April–May of Whinchats present in Britain & Ireland during the breeding season (red) or from other or uncertain breeding populations (grey), the latter being divided into seasonally accurate (solid lines and symbols) and not seasonally accurate (broken lines and open symbols).

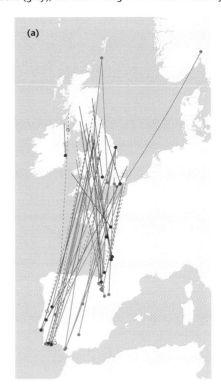

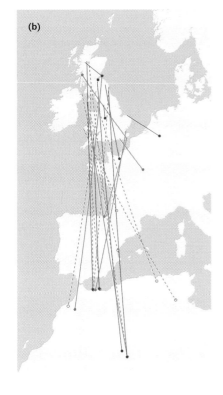

August or early September. Migrant Whinchats are also relatively frequent inland. Passage continues through October and occasional stragglers are seen into early November.

There are no foreign recoveries from British & Irish ringing before September, when a grouping appears in southwest France and southward into northern Spain, an area that may be the first stopover for migrants leaving British coasts (Fig 4a). Some birds have already reached southwest Iberia by September. In October, while recovery locations are distributed northwards to Sussex, most are in Portugal or southwest Spain.

After November, when there have been two recoveries of British- & Irish-ringed birds in Portugal, nothing is known of these birds until April. In the absence of any winter recoveries, it can only be guessed that the winter quarters of British & Irish Whinchats lie towards the west of the African range. In the grasslands north of the Congo River, Whinchats are present from late October to early April and hold individual territories averaging about 0.4 ha (Dejaifve 1994). Birds remain on territory after the grass-fires that are regular in midwinter, and may benefit from the greater accessibility of insect prey on burnt ground. After the first rains, normally in mid-February, an abundance of winged termites and other food enables Whinchats to fatten for spring migration.

That no autumn recoveries are known from North Africa suggests that Whinchats may overfly the Sahara non-stop from Iberia on the southward journey. The six dated recoveries from North Africa, four of them ringed in Britain during the breeding season are all from April and May (Fig 4b). The pattern of spring recoveries, with no confirmed British & Irish breeders in Iberia at this season, points to a more easterly spring migration route than in autumn; most returning birds may perhaps overfly or move rapidly through Spain and France, having fattened in Africa north of the Sahara.

Whinchats start arriving in Britain & Ireland in mid- or late April. Arrivals on the breeding grounds in Ayrshire were generally between 25 April and 10 May, with males preceding females by three to eight days (Gray 1974). Colour-ringing and retrapping in Gwent (S J Smith 1996) and a colour-ringing study in Cumbria (pers obs) have found, from

relatively modest numbers, that there is good measure of natal site-fidelity. In a pioneering colour-ringing study in Germany, Schmidt & Hantge (1954) found that 6.5% of marked nestlings, 47% of adult males and 27% of adult females returned to the study area in the following spring. Subsequent workers have found mostly similar figures (Bastian 1992).

A continental origin is likely for many autumn migrants, especially those arriving in south and east Britain during easterly winds. Coastal falls of up to a thousand birds occasionally occur in such circumstances. A single recovery from Oslo in the breeding season, and four others to and from Norway and Sweden, indicate Scandinavia as the most likely origin for passage migrants, but some from further east may also occur. In spring, passage at Fair Isle and Spurn Point throughout May and early June implies a northerly destination for many east-coast spring migrants (R & F). A migrant in North Norfolk on 18 May 1995 that was found dead almost exactly a year later in the Netherlands may have been bound for Scandinavia on both occasions. Three recoveries in Algeria and Tunisia of birds ringed in western Britain on passage (two of which are shown in Fig 4) were further east than all North African recoveries known to be of British origin; these birds are also likely to have been continental breeders.

The contraction of range in Britain & Ireland during the 1970s and 1980s (*1988–91 Atlas*) is likely to have involved a large reduction in breeding numbers, although numerical assessments of trends have become available only more recently. The causes of decline may include habitat change on British & Irish farmland and in Africa, and the perhaps more temporary effects of Sahelian drought. New information on the distribution of British & Irish Whinchats within the observed winter range of the species would help to distinguish these factors. The current lack of any information specifically on British & Irish Whinchats from the winter quarters hampers any conservation measures that may become desirable.

John Callion

Stonechat
Saxicola torquata

Predominantly insectivorous at all times of the year, the colourful Stonechat finds benefit in territorial behaviour but is potentially vulnerable to the British & Irish winter. Many territories are occupied year-round while others, on more exposed ground, are deserted in the winter months, with some birds appearing on passage or spending the winter well away from nesting areas. Some British Stonechats winter as far afield as Iberia or North Africa.

The Stonechat breeds in a zone of the West Palearctic extending from Ireland, Scotland, Denmark and Morocco east to Iran, and in a well-separated area that covers most of northern Asia, including European Russia and, recently, Finland (*BWP, European Atlas*). The race *hibernans* breeds in Britain & Ireland, and also in western Brittany and on the west coast of the Iberian Peninsula; *rubicola* breeds widely in western and southern Europe, east to Turkey and the Caucasus, intergrading with *hibernans* in northwest France, western Belgium and the Netherlands. During winter, the range of both *rubicola* and *hibernans* extends southwards as far as the desert fringes in North Africa. Whereas these races are partially migratory, Asian birds are wholly so. The two Siberian races are long-distance migrants to southern Asia; western Siberian *maura*, and possibly the eastern race *stejnegeri* too, are annual vagrants to Britain & Ireland, sighted mainly on the eastern seaboard of Scotland and England. A further 15 apparently sedentary races in Africa and Madagascar complete a remarkable world distribution.

Stonechats have a northwesterly bias to their breeding range within Britain & Ireland, with their highest level of abundance in northwestern

The analysis of the data for this species was supported by D J Montier

Scotland and western Ireland; in England, breeding Stonechats are now scarce away from the far west and south (*1988–91 Atlas*). Most pairs select low-lying vegetation for nest sites, favouring gorse, grass and heather. Remarkably, many Stonechats are strongly territorial in pairs throughout the winter, either enlarging the breeding territory by a factor of two or three to ensure the availability of sufficient food, or establishing new winter territories, many of which are coastal. Pair bonds often break down with the advancement of spring, when returning migrants and first-summer birds are seeking territories (Johnson 1961, 1971). Although often used for a succession of years, winter territories can be totally unsuitable as nesting habitat, often including damp areas of sedge, sewage-works or urban fringe. Golf courses also provide good winter habitat, with short vegetation for perching and close-cropped grass for feeding. In Iberia, wintering Stonechats occupy similar habitats to those in Britain & Ireland, sometimes in pairs or in loose flocks; some birds find food by following cows and horses (pers obs).

Ringing has concentrated on several sections of the British & Irish population (Figs 1 & 2). The majority of birds ringed in the breeding season and subsequently recovered are nestlings, often ringed as part of an intensive study, whereas those marked at other seasons have been trapped at predominantly coastal locations, with an emphasis towards

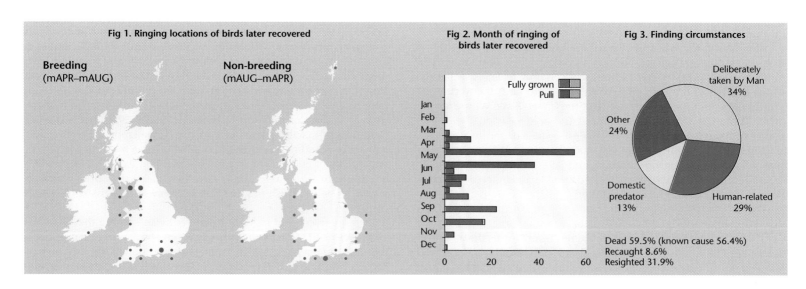

Fig 1. Ringing locations of birds later recovered

Breeding (mAPR–mAUG)

Non-breeding (mAUG–mAPR)

Fig 2. Month of ringing of birds later recovered

Fully grown / Pulli

Fig 3. Finding circumstances

Deliberately taken by Man 34%
Other 24%
Domestic predator 13%
Human-related 29%

Dead 59.5% (known cause 56.4%)
Recaught 8.6%
Resighted 31.9%

Ringing and recovery data

	<1960	60–69	70–79	80–89	90–97	Total
RINGING						
BTO ringing totals (%)	10	14	29	19	27	24,696
RECOVERIES						
BTO-ringed (%)	7	16	26	15	35	184
Foreign-ringed (%)	←	0	→	100	0	1

Statistical analyses

	Breeding population (mAPR–mAUG)	Wintering population (sNOV–sMAR)
Status	LONG-DISTANCE MIGRANT*	?
Age differences	Not tested	—
Sex differences	Not tested	—
Regional differences	Not tested	—
Finding circumstances	Not tested	—

Fig 4. Locations of Stonechats in (a) autumn (51), (b) winter (71) and (c) spring (14), and movements of over 20 km between the breeding and non-breeding season. Those present in Britain & Ireland during the breeding season (red) are differentiated from those of other or uncertain breeding populations (grey), the latter being divided into seasonally accurate (solid lines and dots) and not seasonally accurate (broken lines and dots).

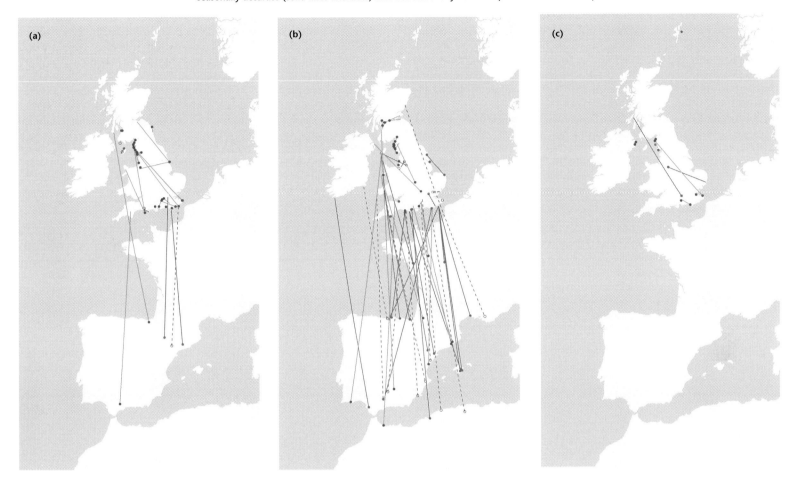

southeast England, and may include many migrants. Rather few fully grown birds have been trapped by ringers, territorial Stonechats being notoriously difficult to catch.

Since the Stonechat is a partial migrant in Britain & Ireland, its migratory behaviour would be expected to differ regionally. The *c* 2,000 pulli ringed in Cumbria during the 1990s represent about 8% of the grand total ringed in Britain & Ireland; these birds have produced almost half of all recoveries within Britain & Ireland at more than 100 km from their place of ringing but none of the foreign recoveries as yet. Large-scale ringing elsewhere, for example in northwestern Britain or in western Ireland, might well produce different influences on the overall pattern of recoveries. Recovery locations, too, are strongly influenced by human activity; over 75% of recoveries have recorded a human-related cause, and a third were deliberately taken (Fig 3). Of the 38 foreign recoveries recorded so far, at least half were from birds killed by Man, mostly in Spain or Algeria.

The Stonechat has a long breeding season and, with often three broods in a year, a high breeding potential (Fuller & Glue 1977). Early-brood youngsters may begin to disperse from June onwards, with larger numbers in August and early September (Clark & Eyre 1993).

True autumn migration commences in September following the completion of post-breeding moult and the weakening of the pair bond. Sandwich Bay, Dungeness and other south-coast observatories record migrant Stonechats between mid-September and early November, often in double figures. Some of these birds may winter within Britain, while others emigrate (Fig 4). Recoveries show that some pulli hatched in southern England and in western Scotland emigrate, largely to southern

Iberia. Movements within Britain & Ireland, mostly from Cumbria, show a mainly southeasterly orientation (Fig 4), apparently towards the shortest sea-crossing to the Continent, by the Strait of Dover. The dates of ringing and recovery for longer movements indicate that some British birds are already in Spain by 15 October, while others destined for the Mediterranean are still in Britain as late as 18 October. A further recovery in Morocco, three in Algeria, three in Majorca and many others in Mediterranean France and Spain had been ringed at passage seasons but were probably of British- or Irish-bred birds (Fig 4).

During the winter, most birds are either in southern Iberia or close to where they were ringed in Britain (Fig 4b). Emigrants may be mostly first-winter birds but some older birds are also involved. Two siblings ringed in Cumbria in 1990 were both recovered at Sandwich Bay in October, one in 1991 and the other in 1993. Another duo of Cumbrian siblings showed differing winter strategies, one residing close to its natal area and the other recovered at Sandwich Bay in November of its first year.

Once winter territories are established, these tend to remain until late winter or until birds succumb to severe weather (pers obs). There is no evidence from ringing of cold-weather movements. Pair territoriality has also been described for Stonechats wintering in Israel (Rödl 1994).

Spring passage and the reoccupation of nesting territories occur early in the year. In Norfolk, passage is noted from late February onwards, peaking in March, while wintering birds depart by mid-April (Taylor *et al* 1999). On Skomer, where Stonechats occur only as non-breeders, a strong spring passage is noted in March, in some years with peaks early and late in the month (S J Sutcliffe pers comm). A bird ringed in northern Spain in late October and found near London in early March is the only foreign-ringed Stonechat so far recovered in Britain & Ireland.

There are no ring-recoveries to indicate that any long-distance migrants show site-fidelity in winter. While Cumbrian nestlings have shown little evidence of natal site-fidelity (pers obs), there has been a remarkable record of a nestling ringed in northeast Ireland, seen in Buckinghamshire the following winter, and then back at the same Irish site to breed the next summer (Lack & Ferguson 1993). There are few observations of breeding site-fidelity, although some adults occupy the same territory throughout the whole year.

A tiny population of Norwegian Stonechats has been established since 1974, perhaps originating from Scottish birds (Ree 1977). Possibly these or other continental birds may winter in Britain or occur on passage. Siberian Stonechats certainly occur but in very small numbers. The records fall mainly between late September and early November, with up to five together in North Norfolk on 29 September 1991 (Taylor *et al* 1999).

The winter destinations of these birds are unknown. Smaller numbers occur in spring, between late April and early June, and occasional individuals have overwintered.

Ringing has given some remarkable insights into the Stonechat's partial migration strategy. We do not yet understand, however, the importance of factors such as population pressure, age, previous experience and genetic make-up in determining whether a bird will migrate or not in a particular season. With the large populations in northwestern Britain and in Ireland little studied by ringing, there are many gaps in our understanding of the pattern of migration in Britain & Ireland as a whole. The conservation implications of further habitat or climatic change are therefore impossible to predict although, as with other partial migrants, it could be that global warming is swinging the balance in favour of sedentary behaviour.

John Callion

Northern Wheatear
(Wheatear)

Oenanthe oenanthe

Wheatears are large bold chats, highly distinctive and obvious on migration but less so among the boulders and scree of their upland breeding grounds. They are usually the first spring migrant to return to British & Irish shores in early March, thus heralding the start of spring. Birds of the race *leucorhoa* undergo what is probably the longest transoceanic migration of any passerine (Snow 1953).

The breeding range is the broadest of any chat and is covered by four subspecies; the nominate *oenanthe* breeds from the Faeroes and Ireland in the west to the Pyrenees in the south, east across Europe and northern Siberia as far as Alaska, while birds of the larger 'Greenland' race *leucorhoa* breed from Labrador and eastern arctic Canada to Greenland and Iceland. The southern European subspecies *libanotica* is found in Spain south of the Pyrenees and eastwards into Asia as far as Mongolia, and the distinctive *seebohmi* is confined to northwest Africa (*BWP, European Atlas*).

Apart from a few in Iraq, and a small number of stragglers that remain on the eastern seaboard of the United States and the West Indies, the entire world population winters in Africa, south of the Sahara (although probably some birds of the North African race *seebohmi* are resident) (*BWP*). Wheatears worldwide therefore take very different routes to their winter quarters in Africa. They winter in a broad belt south of the Sahara from Mauritania and Sierra Leone to the Indian Ocean (though not in northern Somalia), and south in eastern Africa to northern Zambia and, rarely, as far as 18°S (*BWP*). Migration is on a broad front in a southwesterly to south-southwesterly direction across Europe, the Mediterranean and the North African coast (*Der Zug*; see also Fig 3.1a in Chapter 3), though birds from Canada and Greenland initially migrate

The analysis of the data for this species was supported by Dungeness Bird Observatory

southeastwards to reach Britain, Ireland and continental Europe before moving south-southwest into West Africa. These winter from Senegal and Sierra Leone to Mali (*BWP*).

In Britain & Ireland (as in other parts of Europe), there has been a marked retraction of the breeding range from lowland areas in the southern half of England and inland counties of Ireland, mainly due to habitat change (*BWP, 1988–91 Atlas*). Breeding is now chiefly at altitudes above 300 m in Scotland, northwest and southwest England, Wales and western Ireland. Only on the islands of Scotland and in coastal Caithness do Wheatears commonly breed below this contour (*Birds in Scotland, 1988–91 Atlas*). Favoured habitat is open, well-drained grassland and moorland closely cropped by sheep or rabbits, with numerous boulders, rocky outcrops and scree in which to find holes to nest. Lowland Wheatears nest chiefly in old rabbit burrows and frequent close-grazed swards. Saturated wet areas such as blanket bog are avoided, as are enclosed or wooded habitats (*BWP*). On migration, coastal lowlands and managed grasslands are preferred, but any open habitat (such as arable farmland) will be used. On their drier African wintering grounds, birds are mainly found on bare soil, favouring hillsides and rocky outcrops, from sea-level to over 3,000 m (Keith *et al* 1992).

The details of birds ringed during the breeding season and recovered (Fig 1) show that most were ringed in an area that corresponds roughly

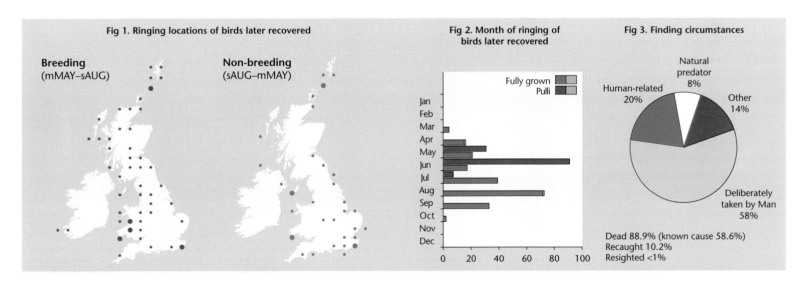

Fig 1. Ringing locations of birds later recovered

Breeding (mMAY–sAUG) Non-breeding (sAUG–mMAY)

Fig 2. Month of ringing of birds later recovered

Fully grown / Pulli

Fig 3. Finding circumstances

Natural predator 8%
Human-related 20%
Other 14%
Deliberately taken by Man 58%

Dead 88.9% (known cause 58.6%)
Recaught 10.2%
Resighted <1%

Ringing and recovery data

	<1960	60–69	70–79	80–89	90–97	Total
RINGING						
BTO ringing totals (%)	20	16	17	29	18	71,399
RECOVERIES						
BTO-ringed (%)	21	21	17	19	13	331
Foreign-ringed (%)	←	70	→	10	20	10

Statistical analyses

	Breeding population (mMAY–sAUG)	Wintering population (sNOV–mFEB)
Status	[LONG-DISTANCE MIGRANT]	NONE
Age differences	Not tested	—
Sex differences	Not tested	—
Regional differences	Not tested	—
Finding circumstances	Not tested	—

Fig 4. Locations in (a) August & September (53:41), (b) October–February (12:20), (c) March & April (25:21) and (d) May–July (61:10), and movements of over 20 km between the periods specified below of Wheatears. Those present in Britain & Ireland during the breeding season (red) are differentiated from those of other or uncertain breeding populations (grey). Sample sizes of British & Irish:other or uncertain breeding populations are given. An individual ringed in Greenland during August and recovered in Wales during May is not shown.

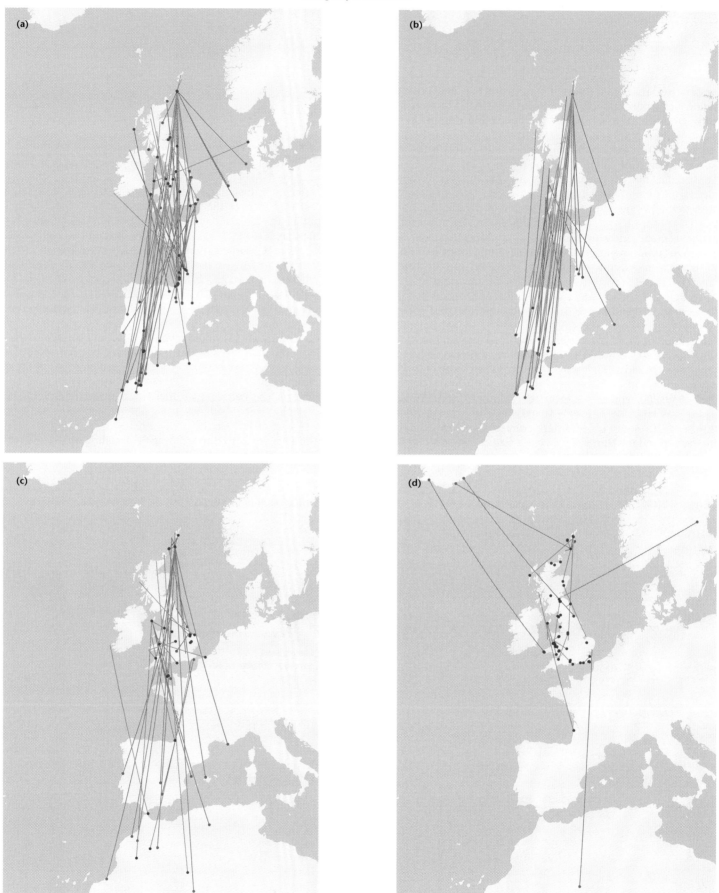

to the breeding range in Britain, including lowland areas such as Breckland and Dungeness. Outside the breeding season, birds are ringed on passage in the Northern Isles and at ringing stations along the east, west and south coasts of Britain (Fig 1). Relatively few recoveries are from Irish-ringed birds. Foreign-ringed birds recovered in Britain, all ringed in autumn and recovered in spring, have come from Iceland (two), France (one), the Channel Islands (one), and Greenland (four). Most recoveries are of birds ringed as pulli or juveniles (Fig 2).

Of the 174 dead birds whose death can be attributed to a known cause, 58% were deliberately taken by Man and a further 20% were human-related, mostly involving collisions with cars, windows or lighthouses (Fig 3). Birds are deliberately killed on passage by hunters in the south of France (eg Les Landes region along the Bay of Biscay), Spain and Morocco, these three countries together providing 86% of 100 such recoveries. The number and distribution of recoveries is thus heavily influenced by the distribution of hunting pressure. Temporal changes in recovery location show that whereas in the 1950s and 1960s France, Spain and Portugal accounted for 62% of all recoveries (the rest mainly from Britain), in the last 30 years these countries have only supplied 11%. In recent years, Morocco has provided the lion's share, with 42% of ring-recoveries (compared to just 3.6% in the 1950s and 1960s). Of the 35 recoveries with other human-related causes, 28 were in Britain.

Autumn migration of British & Irish breeders may begin as early as mid-July and most breeders have moved away by early September (Fig 4a). Ring-recoveries, and radar-tracking (BWP) show that British & Irish birds appear to migrate through France, Spain and Portugal, into Morocco and Algeria (Figs 4a & b), before crossing the Sahara to winter presumably south of the desert in West Africa. Passage through Britain & Ireland continues until near the end of October with stragglers into November, December, or even through the winter. Passage peaks through France from mid-August to mid-September and across the Mediterranean and North African coast chiefly through September and early October (Figs 4a & b), arriving on the wintering grounds in September and October (BWP). Later passage through Britain & Ireland from late September and October also involves birds of the race leucorhoa, which do not start migrating from their Nearctic breeding grounds until late August (BWP) and arrive on their wintering grounds from October. Large falls of this race have occurred in Britain & Ireland following certain weather patterns; a period of southwesterly winds over the North Atlantic, which was thought to have created a build-up of migrants in Greenland and northeast Canada, and a switch to more favourable northwesterly winds on the late date of 18 October 1986, allowed a huge number of birds to migrate southeastwards. Gale-force northwesterly winds then grounded 10,000–20,000 Wheatears on the Isle of Man (Thorpe & Spencer 1992). Large falls of Greenland birds, and drift migrants from the Continent, have occurred on Fair Isle (eg 1,000 on 21 September 1959, 500 on 11 September 1977, and 500 on 7 September 1980; Dymond 1991) and on the Suffolk coast (8,000 in September 1965; Davis 1966b). The sightings of Greenland Wheatears flying southeast far out in the North Atlantic between the end of August and late September have led to the belief that many migrate direct from Greenland to mainland Europe (some therefore bypassing Britain & Ireland) — a distance of some 2,500 km (Snow 1953).

Wheatears are highly territorial on their wintering grounds. Aggressive behaviour has been observed in Kenya, where individuals held separate feeding territories although occasionally a pseudo-pair would defend an area (Leisler et al 1983), and similar behaviour has been noted over much of the wintering range (Moreau 1972). Such territories are also defended against other wheatear species (Moreau 1972). Likewise, if numbers of birds are grounded for any length of time on migration, in spring or autumn, then individuals will set up temporary feeding territories (Conder 1989). A recent study on Helgoland (Delingat & Dierschke 2000) has revealed differences between nominate oenanthe and leucorhoa in the lengths of migration stopovers. While nominate oenanthe feed up for one day before moving on, birds of the larger race spend considerably longer (up to 10–17 days) building up fat reserves, and put on considerable amounts of weight (up to 20 g), before continuing migration. Post-breeding territoriality has been noted from individual juveniles as well as adults (Tye 1982, Conder 1989).

Spring migration is a protracted affair, with the first migrants (of nominate oenanthe) leaving their wintering grounds in January; passage is recorded from mid-February to May in Algeria (BWP). Males migrate, on average, a week or two before females. Birds may stop off on the northern edge of the Sahara Desert to rest and feed, and birds have been noted defending feeding territories in northern Morocco in early spring (BWP). The first arrivals to British & Irish shores are in early March on the south coast (exceptionally late February) and first returns to the Northern Isles are at the end of March. The main passage of nominate oenanthe through Britain & Ireland occurs in late March and early April. A second peak between late April and mid-May is mainly due to the later-migrating leucorhoa race which evidence suggests (eg Snow 1953) takes a more overland route in spring than in autumn, passing through western Europe and Britain & Ireland before heading out across the sea towards Iceland and Greenland (Figs 4c & d). The four Greenland-ringed birds recovered in Britain have all been birds ringed in the autumn and controlled in the spring. There are no favourable winds for the northward journey, which may explain why they choose to travel overland for as much of the journey as possible rather than risk the more hazardous sea-crossing (Snow 1953).

Breeding site-fidelity is apparently very high for established breeders but much less so amongst first-time breeders (BWP). However, the ring-recovery data show that of 10 birds ringed as pulli and returning to breed, only two had moved further than 20 km from their natal site.

Conservation efforts should mainly be concentrated on improving breeding habitat in the south by reducing arable land and increasing short-sward pasture, and possibly by providing nest sites, following the decline in rabbit numbers. Further north, efforts should be made to keep the uplands from being forested. Further work needs to be carried out to ascertain the exact wintering grounds of British & Irish breeders (there have been no midwinter, December or January, recoveries to date) and more ringing and colour-ringing studies to assess natal dispersal and site-fidelity.

Deryk N Shaw

Ring Ouzel
Turdus torquatus

Of the six species of thrush that breed in Britain & Ireland, the Ring Ouzel is unique in having a wholly migratory population that winters around the Mediterranean Basin. It is one of the earliest returning spring migrants, and by late March is frequently back on its upland breeding grounds, where its melancholy piping song is one of the most evocative sounds. In southwest England, the Ring Ouzel has long been known as the Michaelmas Blackbird on account of its appearance there in late September and October (Swaysland 1903).

The nominate race *torquatus* breeds discontinuously in Britain, Ireland, Scandinavia and the Kola Peninsula of western Russia, birds migrating to southern Spain and northwest Africa in winter (*BWP*). The central and southern European race *alpestris* breeds in montane areas from northern Spain east to the Carpathians; some birds migrate short distances to winter at lower elevations in the south of their breeding range, while others overwinter on Mediterranean islands or in North Africa (*European Atlas*). A third race *amicorum* breeds and winters in Asia Minor.

British & Irish Ring Ouzels inhabit their breeding areas in open heather moorland habitats in upland regions from March to August. Nesting territories frequently contain crags, gullies, scree, boulders and scattered bushes or trees (*BWP*), and birds often forage in areas of short-grazed turf and bracken for invertebrates. On passage, ouzels are frequently gregarious and sometimes migrate in relatively large flocks (*BWP*), making use of chalk downland and other open habitats, often close to the sea (Leverton 1990). Berries are a vital food source from late summer onwards, and are exploited by ouzels at regular stopover sites as the birds migrate south (Leverton 1993). On the wintering grounds,

The analysis of the data for this species was supported by Kevin B Briggs & Colin Ryall

ouzels congregate in dry, mountainous areas and form nomadic flocks, feeding largely on juniper berries in montane scrub (*BWP*).

Within Britain & Ireland, breeding Ring Ouzels are most abundant in the Pennines, northwest England, the Southern Uplands, the Grampians and the Highlands (*1988–91 Atlas*). This pattern is broadly reflected in the distribution of ringing sites of birds later recovered (Fig 1), though the Highlands are under-represented. No Irish-ringed ouzel has yet been recovered. Most birds recovered after ringing during the non-breeding season were ringed on the east coast of Britain, reflecting passage movements of Fennoscandian migrants. Birds ringed as nestlings during May and June provided 36% of recoveries (Fig 2). Recoveries of fully grown birds largely refer to ouzels ringed on passage, especially in autumn. Only one foreign-ringed ouzel has ever been recovered in Britain: a Belgian-ringed bird was found here in 1968 (Toms & Clark 1998).

Of 107 recoveries with known cause, 97% were from birds found dead. No sex or age differences in recovery patterns were apparent. Where the cause of death was ascertained (Fig 3), 77% had been killed deliberately by hunters, mostly in France. The distribution of ouzel recoveries is heavily biased towards those areas where trapping and shooting are most intense (Durman 1976b).

Pre-migratory dispersal of British ouzels begins in late July. Birds remain in the general vicinity of their territory but become more elusive and probably move into food-rich areas at slightly higher altitudes

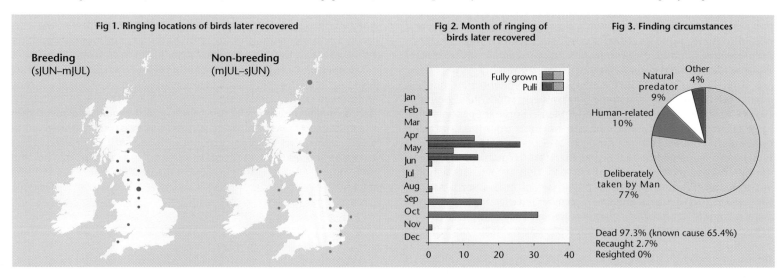

Fig 1. Ringing locations of birds later recovered

Breeding (sJUN–mJUL)

Non-breeding (mJUL–sJUN)

Fig 2. Month of ringing of birds later recovered

Fully grown
Pulli

Jan, Feb, Mar, Apr, May, Jun, Jul, Aug, Sep, Oct, Nov, Dec

0 10 20 30 40

Fig 3. Finding circumstances

Other 4%
Natural predator 9%
Human-related 10%
Deliberately taken by Man 77%

Dead 97.3% (known cause 65.4%)
Recaught 2.7%
Resighted 0%

Ringing and recovery data

	<1960	60–69	70–79	80–89	90–97	Total
RINGING						
BTO ringing totals (%)	17	18	24	25	15	9,089
RECOVERIES						
BTO-ringed (%)	19	32	25	15	9	110
Foreign-ringed (%)	0	100	0	0	0	1

Statistical analyses

	Breeding population (sJUN–mJUL)	Wintering population (sNOV–sAPR)
Status	LONG-DISTANCE MIGRANT*	NONE
Age differences	Not tested	—
Sex differences	Not tested	—
Regional differences	Not tested	—
Finding circumstances	Not tested	—

Fig 4. Locations in (a) autumn (39), (b) winter (11), (c) spring (4) and (d) the breeding season (6), and movements of over 20 km between the breeding season and the season indicated, of Ring Ouzels present in Britain & Ireland during the breeding season.

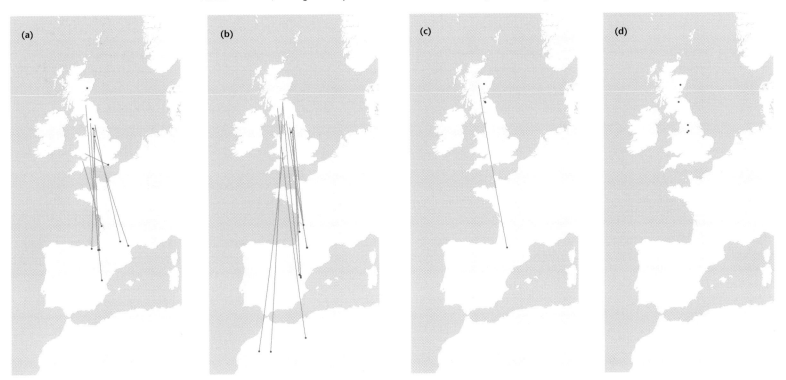

containing berries such as Bilberry (Appleyard 1994, pers obs). All individuals undergo moult, complete in adults and partial in juveniles, from July to August (*BWP*), after which birds may congregate to feed on Rowan and other berries as they descend to lower altitudes and prepare to migrate (*1968–72 Atlas*).

Southward migration of British ouzels starts in late August and continues into October (Durman 1976b), with most birds arriving in northwest Africa from late October onwards (*BWP*). A small peak in the number of ouzels recorded at some observatories in late September probably represents the main departure period for British birds (*R & F*). No birds ringed in Britain during the breeding season have yet been found farther east than the Pyrenees (Fig 4). Although sample sizes are small, most have been recovered from three distinct areas: southwest France and northern Spain, east-central Spain, and the Atlas Mountains of central Morocco and northwestern Algeria.

Most recoveries in southwest France and northern Spain were found either in September–October when the birds are migrating south, or in March–April as they return north (Fig 4). East-central Spanish recoveries were found later in the autumn, in November–December, reflecting the onward passage of some British ouzels. The lack of recoveries outside this period suggests that birds may continue their migration southwards once food supplies in Spain have been depleted or covered by snow (C Ryall pers comm). The limited information from northwest Africa supports this hypothesis, the few British birds recovered there having all been found between November and March. The majority of the nominate race winter at high altitude in the Atlas Saharien from Morocco eastwards (*BWP*). Information regarding winter site-fidelity is currently lacking; an ouzel ringed in Cambridgeshire in November 1964 and recovered in the French Alps in December 1969 (Bircham & Bibby 1978) was almost certainly a Fennoscandian bird still on migration when ringed, and not one of the occasional individuals that overwinters in Britain.

Ouzels start to leave northwest Africa and migrate back north during late February and March, and some British males arrive back on their breeding grounds as early as mid-March (*BWP*). March arrivals are expected at all observatories on the south and west coasts and at Fair Isle, where a peak late in the month probably denotes the main wave of

immigration by British breeders (Durman 1976b, *R & F*). Except for Fair Isle, none of the east-coast observatories experience this early peak, suggesting that most British migrants arrive from the southwest and then rapidly move inland to their breeding grounds (*R & F*). Migrants at Fair Isle in March and early April are probably overshooting British birds, since Fennoscandian ouzels do not return to their breeding grounds until April or May (*Der Zug*). During late April and early May, a second, larger wave of ouzels is recorded at British observatories, especially those on the east coast. With most British birds already on their breeding grounds, this peak largely comprises later-returning Fennoscandian ouzels (Durman 1976b). Four ouzels ringed in Britain have been recovered in or en route to Fennoscandia. All were ringed on the east or southeast coast of Britain in spring or autumn and recovered in Norway or northern Germany between May and October (Fig 5).

General ring-recoveries have so far shed little light on natal dispersal or breeding site-fidelity but valuable data have come from intensive colour-marking schemes. Durman (1977) found that both members of a breeding pair near Edinburgh had been ringed as chicks in neighbouring nests the previous year; they bred successfully at a site *c* 1.8–2.0 km away from their natal territories. In Tayside, 27 male ouzels were found breeding 0.8–4.5 km from their natal sites, and 20 females nested 0.8–4.0 km from theirs (D S C Arthur pers comm). In Grampian, four males moved 1.8–4.6 km from their natal sites to breed, while six females moved 0.4–6.0 km (I Sim pers comm). Such results suggest that some ouzels are broadly philopatric and return to their natal area to breed. However, one colour-ringed female found breeding in Ross-shire was almost certainly ringed as a nestling 225 km to the south (Durman 1977).

Breeding ouzels are widely assumed to be site-faithful from year to year but evidence is scant. In the Borders, one male returned to the same territory, four males moved 0.7–0.9 km and three females moved 0.7–3.3 km between years (pers obs). Durman (1977) recorded a male breeding in the same territory in consecutive years, while in Tayside four males moved 0.2–3.1 km and four females moved 0.2–1.0 km between years (pers obs). In Shropshire, a returning female nested 250 m from the previous year's site and then moved a further 700 m to nest the following year (Smith 2001). In Grampian, three females returned to the same

Fig 5. Recovery locations and movements of over 20 km of Ring Ouzels ringed in Britain & Ireland during (a) February–May (19) and (b) mid-July–November (39).

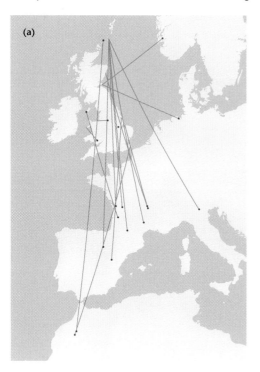
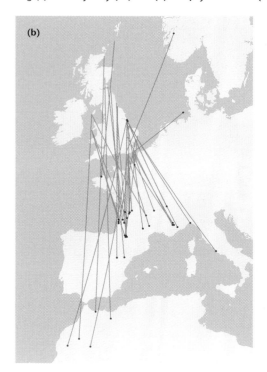

territories, four females moved 0.2–4.9 km and one male moved 1.0 km between years. Within a season, one female moved 5.2 km between nesting attempts and bred with different males, while another pair moved 4.2 km between nesting attempts (I Sim pers comm). Clearly, more information is required to establish the true extent of breeding site-fidelity.

Fennoscandian birds start to leave their breeding grounds in September and head south-southwest towards southern France (*BWP*). Following the small September peak, presumably denoting the emigration of British birds (*R & F*), most British observatories show a substantial passage from mid-October until early November (Durman 1976b). This is most obvious on the east coast, but a similar pattern occurs elsewhere suggesting a widespread autumn passage of Fennoscandian birds through Britain (*R & F*).

Since ouzels are no longer occasional breeders in southeast Britain (Holloway 1996), all recoveries from this region relate to birds ringed on passage. Numerous ouzels ringed in the southeast have been recovered abroad in similar areas to those from other regions of Britain (Fig 5), but significant numbers have been recovered much farther east, as far as central Italy. Most of these birds were ringed at coastal observatories in southeast Britain during the autumn and subsequently recovered during the autumn or winter. Durman (1976b) divided such recoveries into those ringed and recovered during the same migration period and those recovered in a subsequent migration period. The latter showed a more easterly distribution, suggesting that Fennoscandian birds normally migrate through Europe on a more easterly route and that their occurrence in Britain in both spring and autumn is mainly a result of wind-drifted passage (Durman 1976b).

No significant numbers of Ring Ouzels were recovered until the 1950s but the 1960s saw a peak, which still accounts for one-third of all recoveries. Only three ouzels were recovered abroad during the period 1990–97, compared with 28 in the 1960s. The number of ouzels recorded at observatories on the west coast of Britain in spring has also declined

significantly since the early 1970s, but there has been no significant change on the east coast (pers obs). These trends may be due to spatial and temporal changes in mortality or recovery factors, breeding success or migration routes.

The Ring Ouzel has continued to decline as a breeding bird in many parts of Britain & Ireland while Fennoscandian populations have apparently remained stable (*European Atlas*). The fact that winter recoveries of British birds have come mainly from montane areas in southern Spain and northwest Africa (Fig 4) has potential conservation implications because these areas have reportedly suffered widespread losses of Juniper forests to agriculture, forestry, development, overgrazing and cutting for firewood (Tyler & Green 1994, C Ryall pers comm). Juniper berries form a large part of the ouzel's winter diet (Zamora 1990) but as yet the impact of these habitat changes on wintering ouzels is unknown (Arthur *et al* 2000).

Many more recoveries are required before confident interpretations can be made. There is an urgent need for more birds to be ringed throughout the species' breeding range, especially in the Highlands, Wales, Ireland and southwest England. The resulting information on dispersal, survival and breeding site-fidelity would be extremely valuable. Winter ringing expeditions to the Atlas Mountains and Spain would help increase the number of recoveries and may reveal whether British & Irish and Fennoscandian populations winter together or separately. More promisingly, DNA-based studies should be considered as a method for investigating the relatedness of birds wintering in different areas. This dearth of basic information must be addressed now because of the Ring Ouzel's continued decline in Britain & Ireland. Factors operating on its migration routes or wintering grounds may well be responsible for the species' plight but a clearer picture of its movements is needed to help direct research and conservation efforts.

Ian Burfield

Common Blackbird (Blackbird)

Turdus merula

The Blackbird is one of the most abundant breeding birds over much of Europe, and is found in a very wide variety of habitats. Although probably originating as a bird of woodland or woodland edge, it is now closely associated with man-made habitats, particularly parks and gardens. The nominate race *merula* occupies most of the European range, from Spain and the Faeroes east to the Urals. About another 14 races occur in more southerly pockets of distribution from the Azores and the Canaries eastward to China and Sri Lanka. Flourishing introduced populations are found in New Zealand and southeast Australia.

Over much of its range the species is largely sedentary, but northern populations migrate to southern or western Europe, as do various proportions of Blackbirds breeding in areas further south, such as southern Scandinavia, Poland, Germany or the Low Countries. These movements take place almost entirely within the breeding range (*BWP*).

Its abundance, and the relative ease with which large numbers can be trapped on autumn migration or in winter roosts, have made the Blackbird one of the most commonly ringed species throughout Britain where the pattern of ringing locations of recovered birds (Fig 1) closely matches their distribution (*Winter Atlas, 1988–91 Atlas*). There are many Irish recoveries too, particularly of birds ringed in the east and south, although Blackbirds from the rest of Ireland are under-represented in the recoveries. The numbers of Blackbirds passing through eastern Britain on migration typically peak in mid-October, a pattern that is fairly consistent from year to year (Taylor 1984). Roosting behaviour may be weather dependent but there is some evidence to suggest that the largest roosts occur in mid-November (Swann 1975, Jackson & Jackson 1976,

The analysis of the data for this species was supported by Lailan and Robin Young

Batten 1977). As a result, the greatest numbers of free-flying Blackbirds are ringed during the months October to December (Fig 2).

Just over half of all recoveries from dead birds have a known cause of death, three-quarters of those deaths being human-related or due to domestic predators (Fig 3), reflecting the Blackbird's abundance in suburbs and the high mortality caused by cars and cats in these areas. Thus there is likely to be a bias in the recovery data towards suburban populations, which differ from rural populations in a number of demographic parameters (Snow 1958).

The recovery data from Blackbirds breeding in Britain & Ireland reveal a largely sedentary population. Juvenile, natal and breeding dispersal are all over short distances. Recoveries of birds ringed as pulli and later found dead show median distances of less than 1 km for all monthly periods during their first year of life, with a 95% limit that does not exceed 13 km in the first four months. Only 3% had moved more than 20 km when recovered as adults in the breeding season. Of adults ringed in the breeding season, only 1% had moved more than 20 km when recovered in a subsequent breeding season. Long-distance seasonal movements do occur but are few in number. Of 13,385 recoveries outside the breeding season of birds ringed in the breeding season, only 4% occurred more than 20 km from the ringing site. The proportion varies markedly with breeding area, however, being largest

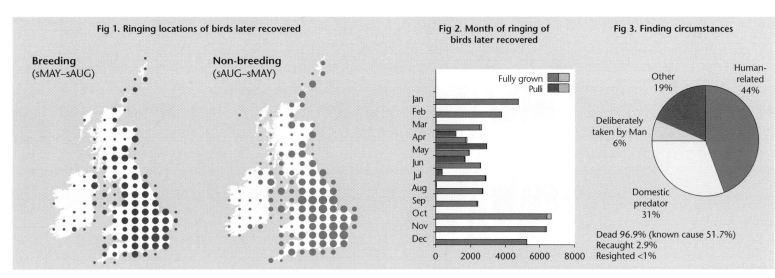

Fig 1. Ringing locations of birds later recovered

Breeding (sMAY–sAUG)   **Non-breeding** (sAUG–sMAY)

Fig 2. Month of ringing of birds later recovered

Fully grown / Pulli

Jan Feb Mar Apr May Jun Jul Aug Sep Oct Nov Dec

0 2000 4000 6000 8000

Fig 3. Finding circumstances

Other 19%   Human-related 44%

Deliberately taken by Man 6%

Domestic predator 31%

Dead 96.9% (known cause 51.7%)
Recaught 2.9%
Resighted <1%

Ringing and recovery data

	<1960	60–69	70–79	80–89	90–97	Total
RINGING						
BTO ringing totals (%)	11	22	24	26	16	1,520,344
RECOVERIES						
BTO-ringed (%)	11	27	29	23	10	49,480
Foreign-ringed (%)	←	53	→	28	18	1,465

Statistical analyses

	Breeding population (sMAY–sAUG)	Wintering population (sDEC–sMAR)
Status	SHORT-DISTANCE MIGRANT (1)	SHORT-DISTANCE MIGRANT*
Age differences[S]	Significant*	Significant*
Sex differences[S]	Not significant	Significant
Regional differences	Significant[S]	Significant[S]
Finding circumstances	(Not significant)	(Not significant)

Table 1. Summary of distances moved by Blackbirds between ringing and recovery by region, for movements of over 20 km and involving dead recoveries.

Region	Sample	Median (km)	P5 (km)	P95 (km)
Northwest	83	195	23	497
Northeast	91	115	22	861
Southeast	272	57	23	480
Southwest	91	107	22	598
Ireland	19	64	22	579

for the northwest region (11%) and smallest in the two southern regions (each 3%). The median distances moved (Table 1) show a similar regional dependence, birds from the northwest moving further than birds from other regions and birds from the southeast moving the shortest distances. The majority of movements between the breeding and non-breeding seasons are in a southerly or westerly direction (Fig 4). There is some evidence of a 'migratory divide' (Snow 1966, 1978) in the British Blackbird population, whereby migrant individuals from the north and west of Britain tend to cross to Ireland, while some Blackbirds from the south and east travel south to France, although the numbers doing so are small.

Lack (1944) found no age differences in the proportions of British birds migrating to Ireland. This was true also of some other partial

Fig 4. Locations in winter, and movements of over 20 km between the breeding season and winter, of Blackbirds present in the (a) northwest (264), (b) northeast (460), (c) southeast (2,719) and (d) southwest (1,327) of Britain and in (e) Ireland (68) during the breeding season.

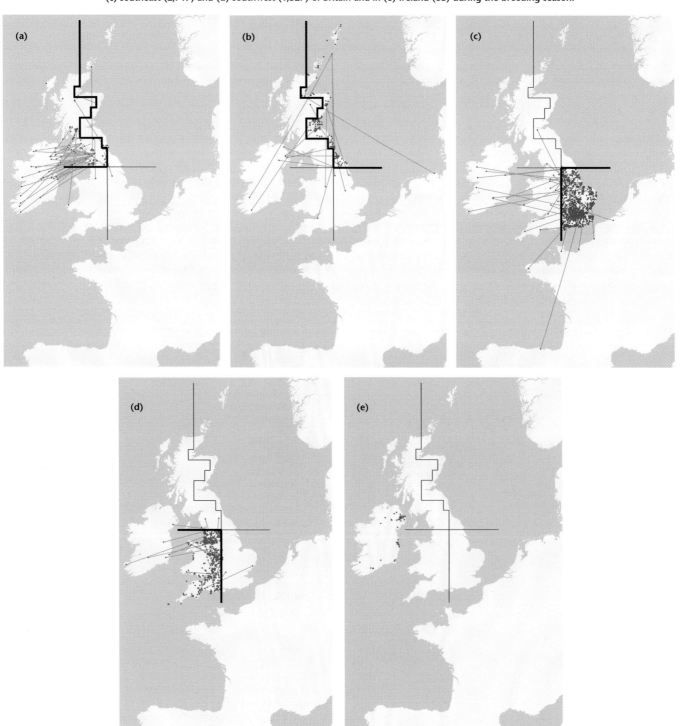

Table 2. Total numbers of recoveries, and numbers of overseas recoveries, of Blackbirds from the British breeding population (classified as birds ringed in Britain as pulli, adults ringed during the breeding season or juveniles before 1 September).

Years ringed	Totals	Ireland	Continent
1909–59	3,274	61	6
1960–68	3,717	23	12
1969–79	4,085	15	11
1980–97*	4,143	1	6

*1980–94 for adults

Table 3. The estimated percentages of Blackbirds of continental origin amongst different age and sex classes wintering in Britain & Ireland (percentages recovered abroad of birds ringed in Britain & Ireland outside the breeding season). Only birds of known sex are included.

Age	Male % (n)	Female % (n)	Both sexes % (n)
Immature	10.5 (8,724)	12.8 (5,107)	11.4 (13,831)
Adult	11.6 (4,324)	16.5 (3,044)	13.6 (7,368)
All	10.9 (13,048)	14.2 (8,151)	12.2 (21,199)

migrants that travelled to Ireland and to the Continent. For species moving more to the Continent than the Blackbird, younger birds were generally in the majority. On this observation, Lack based a suggestion that adoption of the migration route to Ireland might have been relatively recent, possibly originating in westerly hard-weather movements, and under different physiological control from that to the Continent. This hypothesis may have gained retrospective support from the gradual abandonment since then of the Irish route (Main 2000b; Table 2), most probably as a consequence of milder winters accompanied by a move into more hospitable suburban habitats.

Ringing reveals considerable movement between Britain & Ireland and countries in northern Europe. Most of the 4,017 British- or Irish-ringed birds recovered abroad were from Norway (24%), Sweden (18%), Germany (17%) and Denmark (13%). There have been 693 recoveries in Britain or Ireland of Blackbirds ringed abroad, with Norway, Germany and the Netherlands contributing approximately 20% each. Recoveries in autumn of birds present in Britain & Ireland in the autumn were widely spread, mainly to the northeast as far as Finland, but with some reaching the Iberian Peninsula in the south. In winter the northern and eastern distribution is more restricted, with no recoveries in Finland and a reduction of the spread in Sweden and Norway. There are, however, more recoveries in France and the Iberian Peninsula in winter and even two in Iceland, where the Blackbird is almost exclusively a winter visitor

(Fig 5). The recoveries in France, Spain and Portugal suggest that some of the birds merely pass through Britain to more southerly wintering areas. Regional movement patterns suggest that few birds ringed in the northwest region, and none ringed in Ireland, move on to countries further south (Fig 6). Most birds recovered in southern Europe were ringed in southeast England, many probably being coastal migrants. Foreign locations in the breeding season of birds present in Britain & Ireland outside the breeding season show a more northerly distribution (Fig 7), with none breeding further south than northern France. Thus, foreign Blackbirds ringed in Britain & Ireland in the autumn belong to both the wholly migratory northern populations and partially migrant populations in the Netherlands, Germany and southern Scandinavia.

Of Blackbirds ringed in Britain & Ireland outside the breeding season, 24,330 were recovered in Britain & Ireland and 3,291 abroad. Although it is not known what fraction of the birds recovered in Britain & Ireland are from continental Europe, virtually all of those recovered abroad are likely to be continental, since very few natives of Britain & Ireland move abroad. On this assumption, the figures may be used to derive a lower limit (which would apply if no continental birds were recovered in Britain & Ireland) of 12% for the proportion of birds present in Britain & Ireland outside the breeding season that are of continental origin.

Table 3 compares the percentage of Blackbirds recovered abroad with those recovered in Britain & Ireland, for birds of known age and sex ringed outside the breeding season. As mentioned above, these may be

Fig 5. Locations in (a) autumn (2,657) and (b) winter (3,347) of Blackbirds present in Britain & Ireland during autumn.

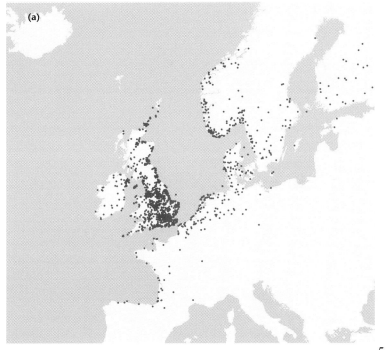

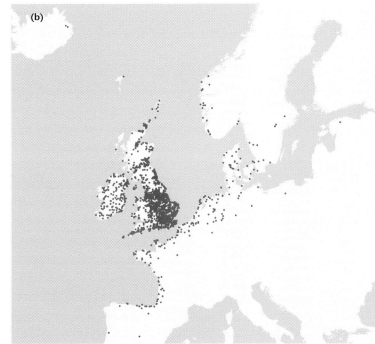

Fig 6. Locations abroad of Blackbirds that were present in the (a) northwest (259), (b) northeast (949), (c) southeast (2,460) and (d) southwest (731) of Britain and in (e) Ireland (104) outside the breeding season.

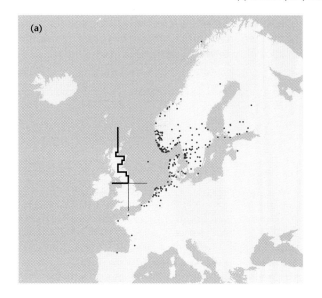

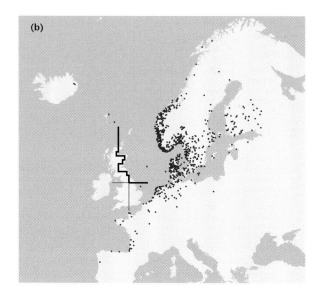

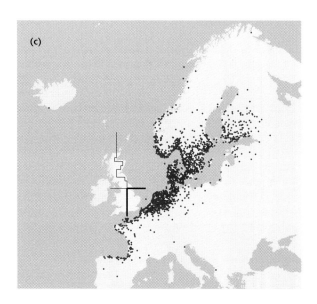

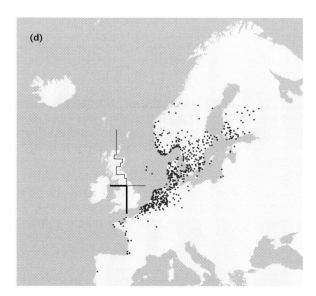

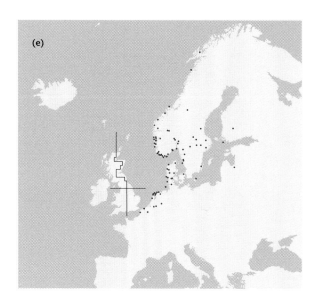

Fig 7. Locations in the breeding season of 8,893 Blackbirds present in Britain & Ireland outside the breeding season.

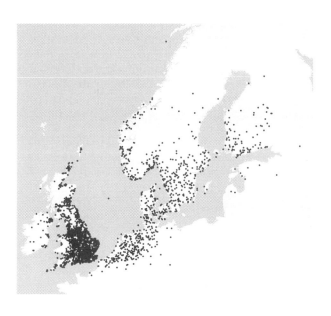

Fig 8. Movements of over 20 km and recovery locations of Blackbirds ringed in winter and recovered in a subsequent winter. There were 1,295:347 movements under:over 20 km but only those over 20 km are plotted.

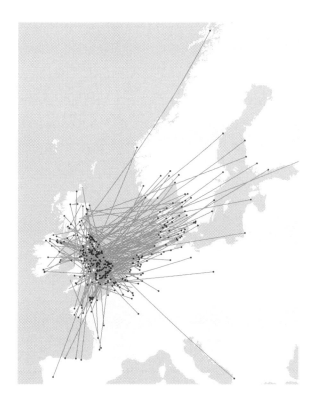

Fig 9. Proportions of Blackbirds ringed in Britain & Ireland and recovered dead in different periods between 1909 and 1997 in the countries indicated.

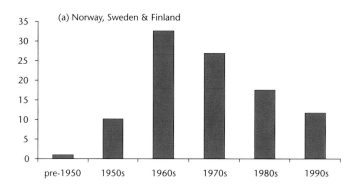

(a) Norway, Sweden & Finland

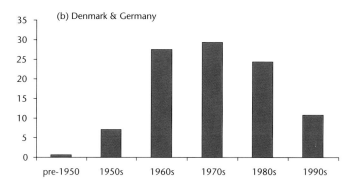

(b) Denmark & Germany

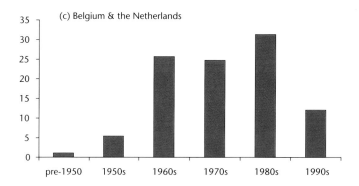

(c) Belgium & the Netherlands

(both adults and immatures) than amongst males. Schwabl (1983) found that, in a population in southwestern Germany, the tendency to migrate increased with age in females but decreased with age in males. It should be noted that Table 3 cannot be precise, being derived from data for a number of different wholly and partially migratory populations, which may show different patterns. Details of age and sex effects are still unclear and further research is required to determine whether patterns are consistent in different populations.

Unlike other thrush species, Blackbirds do not undertake significant hard-weather movements (Snow 1966). Of 793 recoveries in the same winter as ringing, only 37 were more than 20 km from the ringing site, and only eight of these involved exchanges with abroad. By contrast, many birds are found in Britain & Ireland and abroad in different winters (Fig 8). There is, however, a distinct southerly bias. It is known that virtually all of the Norwegian Blackbirds that move to Britain & Ireland do so every year (Main 2000b), and this is reflected by a paucity of between-winter movements involving Norway (*ie* Blackbirds ringed in Britain & Ireland in winter are not generally recovered in Norway in subsequent winters). For the partially migratory populations further south, however, a North Sea crossing appears to be an occasional or less than annual event in the life of some individuals.

taken as lower limits to the proportions of continental natives present; they may then be used to indicate the tendency to migrate of the different classes of continental birds. The differences are small but suggest that there are more continental immigrants amongst females

The Blackbird has spread northwards in Fennoscandia over the past half-century or so (*BWP*) and Spencer (1975), making due allowance for variations in ringing effort, suggested that increasing numbers of migrants, particularly from Finland, were wintering in Britain & Ireland. The proportions of recoveries over different periods show a very similar pattern in the seven different countries that had a minimum of 50 recoveries. Fig 9 illustrates this, showing the typical peaked pattern of recoveries. In the earliest period, the relatively small numbers probably reflect the lower ringing effort, and in the 1990s recoveries up to 1997 only are included, which would be expected to depress the number of recoveries for this decade by about 20%. Even when these effects are taken into account, however, there are clear peaks in recoveries in the 1960s (Norway, Sweden & Finland), the 1960s and 1970s (Denmark & Germany) and the 1960s to the 1980s (Belgium & the Netherlands). Although firm conclusions should not be drawn without detailed knowledge of temporal changes in the ringing effort and recovery chances in each country, the evidence suggests that recoveries from northeastern Europe have decreased in recent years. This could arise through population declines in the source areas, although there is no evidence for recent declines in European countries other than Britain (Tucker & Heath 1994). Alternatively, such movements may be the result of harsh winter weather conditions in a partially migratory species such as the Blackbird. It is tempting to speculate that the decline in overseas recoveries is the result of less severe winters in recent years, either because birds do not have to move in response to severe weather periods, or because the generally milder climate allows more birds to remain near their breeding grounds year-round, instead of migrating south and west for the winter.

The British Blackbird population has declined by approximately 30% since the early 1970s and is listed as of medium conservation concern by Crick *et al* (1998). The cause of the decline may lie in agricultural intensification as decreases have been greater on farmland. Future ringing studies should be targeted at obtaining recovery data from constant effort sites, particularly in rural habitats, so survival and productivity can be monitored.

Dan Chamberlain & Iain Main

Fieldfare
Turdus pilaris

The '*chack-chack*' calls of Fieldfares gathered in berry-bearing hedgerows, open fields, or on fallen apples in orchards, and the noisy flocks moving from roost to food source and back in the morning or evening are a midwinter delight for many birders. The species is monotypic and breeds over a vast range from central France to Lake Baikal and the Lena River in eastern Siberia (*BWP*). The entire population is migratory. Those breeding in France, Switzerland and southwest Germany migrate the shortest distances, from their breeding areas to the Rhône Delta and nearby areas of southern France and northern Italy. Scandinavian birds migrate mainly on a broad front to the southwest, so that those from Norway usually winter in Britain, Ireland, northwest France and northwest Iberia; those from Sweden go to southeast Britain, Belgium and France; and those from Finland mainly to southeast Britain, Belgium, southern France and northern Italy. Some Russian and Siberian birds winter in the Levant and the Transcaucasus but most from these breeding areas are recovered in southern France and northern Italy. Thus, these Fieldfares, along with Siberian Redwings, are among the greatest east–west passerine migrants on earth, with round-trip migrations often exceeding 12,000 km (Milwright 1994).

Wintering Fieldfares favour the low-lying floodplains of western Europe which are warmed by the Gulf Stream or the Mediterranean. Within these areas, they forage for soil invertebrates, berries and fruit, mainly in open farmland with mature hedges. At the same time, their roosting behaviour also requires scrubby woodland, often associated with water in the form of lakes, ponds or gravel-pits (*BWP*, Milwright 1994).

Isolated pairs of Fieldfares have bred sporadically in several areas of England and Scotland since 1960, building by 1991 to an estimated

The analysis of the data for this species was supported by Mary Milwright

British population of up to 25 pairs (*1988–91 Atlas*). These birds are considered to derive from Scandinavian stock. The very slow expansion into Britain is probably not part of the strong southwest expansion of the central European breeding stock which has quickly covered about a third of France (*European Atlas*), where they first bred in 1953 and by 1976 had a population estimate of 'not above 10,000 pairs' (*BWP*). Nothing is known of the migratory movements of the tiny British population but it seems likely they would be similar to the movements of Norwegian Fieldfares.

The wintering population in Britain & Ireland is in the region of a million birds. Many are ringed at winter roosts and feeding areas in southeast and central England. However, the ringing places of birds later recovered (Fig 1) seriously under-represents the real distribution in Ireland, south Scotland, and north and southwest England (*Winter Atlas*). Only 8% of Fieldfares ringed in Britain & Ireland and subsequently recovered were ringed in October (compared with 26% for Redwing), while over half were ringed in January or February (Fig 2). Of 799 Fieldfare recoveries involving Britain & Ireland, only 6% were recaught by ringers. However, Fieldfares are hunted and trapped in large numbers over much of their continental autumn and winter ranges, as well as some parts of their breeding range. As a result, 58% of all deaths of known cause were of birds deliberately taken by Man (Fig 3). The principal countries involved have been France (where 93% of 111

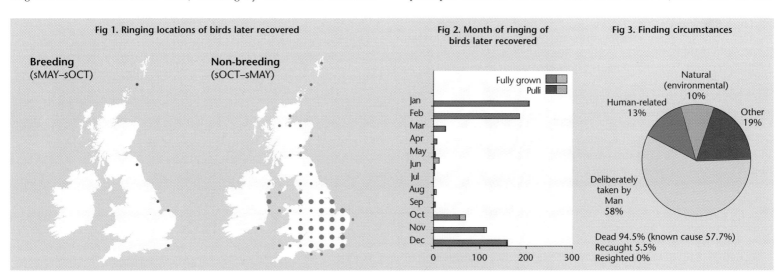

Fig 1. Ringing locations of birds later recovered

Breeding
(sMAY–sOCT)

Non-breeding
(sOCT–sMAY)

Fig 2. Month of ringing of birds later recovered

Fully grown
Pulli

Fig 3. Finding circumstances

Natural (environmental) 10%
Human-related 13%
Other 19%
Deliberately taken by Man 58%

Dead 94.5% (known cause 57.7%)
Recaught 5.5%
Resighted 0%

Ringing and recovery data

	<1960	60–69	70–79	80–89	90–97	Total
RINGING						
BTO ringing totals (%)	2	20	27	33	18	52,046
RECOVERIES						
BTO-ringed (%)	3	27	32	27	9	750
Foreign-ringed (%)	←	69	→	23	8	160

Statistical analyses

	Breeding population (sMAY–sOCT)	Wintering population (sDEC–sMAR)
Status	NONE	LONG-DISTANCE MIGRANT
Age differences	—	Not significant
Sex differences	—	Not significant*
Regional differences	—	Not significant[2]
Finding circumstances	—	(Not significant)

Fig 4. Locations of Fieldfares in (a) May (75, red), June (72, blue) and July (36, grey), (b) August (27, red) and September (13, blue) and (c) October (31, red) and November (64, blue).

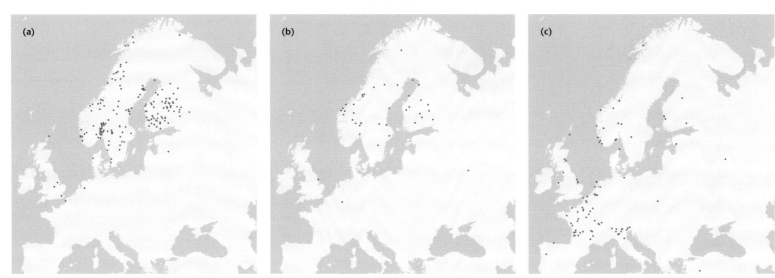

recoveries of known cause were deliberately taken), Italy (100% of 43) and Finland (72% of 54).

During May–July, Fieldfares that migrate to Britain & Ireland are in Fennoscandia or Russian Karelia, with the exception of a few late migrants still in eastern Britain, the near Continent, and one juvenile male in Estonia (Fig 4a). Several winter-ringed Fieldfares from the western Continent have been recovered in the breeding season in central Siberia east to 87°E. A few recoveries of birds ringed in Britain & Ireland have occurred in non-Karelian Russia (mainly around Moscow) but none east of 40°E; most of these were recovered at passage times (Milwright 1994).

Few Fieldfares leave their breeding areas early in the autumn (Fig 4b), with less than 1% having moved more than 50 km from the nest site before the end of September (Sæther 1979). Adults tend to migrate earlier and to more distant destinations than juveniles. The main month for migratory departure is October but in some years many, mainly first-winters, stay in Fennoscandia through November and December particularly if there are good crops of Rowan berries (Tyrväinen 1970, 1975). Some birds ringed in Britain & Ireland move on to western France and northwest Iberia (Figs 4c & 5). Fieldfares ringed in the breeding season in Norway have been recovered in northwest Iberia (where half of the recoveries of Fieldfares ringed in the breeding season are from Norway) and northwest Britain & Ireland (where the majority of recoveries of Fieldfares ringed in the breeding season are from Norway). In east and southeast England, however, 74% of recoveries of Fieldfares ringed in the breeding season were from Sweden and Finland and were recovered in their first winter (Milwright 1994). The geographical bias of British & Irish Fieldfare ringing sites to southeast and central England (Fig 1) will therefore probably lead to an under-representation of Norwegian birds and an over-representation of Swedish and Finnish birds in the national ringing sample.

Ringing has detected very few long-distance within-winter movements after December, when the weather is at its most challenging (Fig 5). In the western European wintering area as a whole, less than a quarter (15/72) of movements of over 200 km were of birds ringed after 20 December but more than three-quarters (122/155) of short movements (up to 20 km) were started after that date (Milwright 1994). Although this could be partly an artefact of the shorter available time in which to detect the rarer longer movements, it is likely that the large numbers that may be seen moving in January and February are birds engaged in short movements (up to 20 km) in search of food. In severe winters, when food resources available without penetrating frost-hardened ground have been exhausted, the failure of these large flocks

to move on to more distant frost-free areas can lead to very high mortality (von Lübcke 1980, Swann 1980, Milwright 1994).

No birds ringed in Britain & Ireland have been recovered in the same winter in southeastern France or northern Italy but many have been recovered in both these areas in later winters, mostly on the floodplains of the Rivers Rhône and Po (Fig 6). In these two areas, 9% of recoveries of Fieldfares ringed in the breeding season are from Norway, compared with 31% from Sweden or Finland, so it is likely that British- or Irish-ringed birds found there are from the Swedish and Finnish populations, which favour southeast Britain as first-winter birds, and not from the Norwegian stock which probably makes up the bulk of the British & Irish wintering birds. It would not be expected that a species whose subsequent winter destinations can be as far apart as Ireland and Italy would have much winter site-fidelity, but 18% of 119 birds recovered dead in subsequent winters were within 20 km of their ringing site, and

Fig 5. Movements of over 20 km and recovery locations of Fieldfares ringed and recovered in the same autumn/winter period. Birds ringed during October–December (red, 25:25) are differentiated from those ringed in January–February (blue, 45:12). Sample sizes of movements under:over 20 km are given but only those over 20 km are plotted.

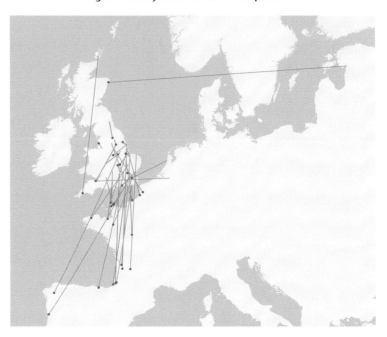

Fig 6. Locations in subsequent winters in October–December (red, 144) and January–February (blue, 84) of Fieldfares present in Britain & Ireland during winter (October–February).

there is some evidence to suggest these were mainly of Norwegian origin (Milwright 1994). If those British- & Irish-ringed birds of Swedish and Finnish origin could be excluded from the analysis, we might discover that winter site-fidelity is an important part of the migratory strategy of Norwegian birds.

Spring return migration takes place from late March through to early June, with adults making up the bulk of the early movers. Some birds ringed in Britain & Ireland are recovered in Fennoscandia in April and many more in May, although a few birds still linger then in eastern England, the Netherlands and Denmark. Flocks seen in Britain in May are probably late-returning first-year birds. Very few spring recoveries are found between the main western European wintering range and the breeding areas. This may indicate that the return movement, at least as far as Fennoscandia (though probably not Siberia), is usually made in a single flight. However, it should be noted that the hunting and trapping which produces most of the winter recoveries is not usually carried out in April, leading to a major bias in the spring records.

There has been a temporal change in the recovery locations of British- & Irish-ringed Fieldfares since 1960. The proportion recovered in Britain or Ireland has shown a continuous decline, while the proportions recovered in Finland, France and Sweden have all risen. Three possible reasons for these changes could be: a relative increase in Fieldfare ringing in southeast England compared to the rest of Britain & Ireland (first-winter Swedish and Finnish birds in Britain are mainly found in southeast England, and many are likely to spend subsequent winters in southern France where their recovery potential is considerably increased); an increase in hunting pressure (particularly in France); and a decline in the Norwegian Fieldfare breeding population (British & Irish recoveries in Norway have also declined since 1970).

Fieldfares have survived hunting and trapping pressures over much of their range for very many years. Reports of 600,000 being trapped in a single season in East Prussia in the 17th century, and of Norwegian trappers exporting 150,000 in a good year from Stavanger in the 19th century (Norman 1994a), show that this is not a new challenge for the species. Most of the vast breeding range contains a low human population so direct human activity probably has little to do with the success or failure of a particular breeding season for the species as a whole. The major factor involved in Fieldfare population fluctuations is likely to be the highly variable spring and summer weather in the breeding areas. However, since this cold-weather species has been expanding its range in a southwesterly direction during the initial stages of global warming, it is, at present, impossible to predict the effect of future climate change on Fieldfares.

The major unknown factors in Fieldfare migration are the winter destinations and routes of those birds that breed in the northern half of the Siberian range. This area represents about 40% of the species' world breeding range but has a human population that is too sparse to produce many ring-recoveries. However, on the basis of present information, it is unlikely that these birds will be involved in movements to or from Britain & Ireland. Within the context of British & Irish wintering birds, more ringing in central and southwest Ireland would be useful to better establish the probable connection between birds from those areas and northern Norway.

Digby Milwright

Song Thrush
Turdus philomelos

The analysis of the data for this species was supported by Lailan and Robin Young

The mellifluous song and widespread (although declining) distribution of Song Thrush have made it a widely recognized and appreciated species in Britain & Ireland. The majority of British & Irish Song Thrushes are strikingly sedentary but others make interesting large-scale movements. Appreciable numbers of birds from the Low Countries winter in Britain. Some British breeders are shot by hunters while wintering in France, Spain or Portugal. Other British breeders winter in Ireland, and a small number of recoveries from Norway and Sweden suggest that the large numbers of Song Thrushes in Britain during autumn may include Scandinavian birds on passage through the country. Young Song Thrushes appear more migratory than adults, and birds from northern Britain seem more likely to move than those from further south.

Song Thrushes breed across most of Europe, from northern Spain, Ireland and northern Norway eastward across Russia to Lake Baikal, and southeast around the Black Sea towards the Caspian (*BWP*). Three European subspecies have been described: *clarkei* in Ireland, most of Britain, the Low Countries, and northwest France, *hebridensis* in the Western Isles and the Isle of Skye, and *philomelos* throughout the rest of Europe (*BWP*). In summer, Song Thrushes are absent from Iceland, the Faeroes and Shetland, and scarce or absent on the Mediterranean fringes of Europe, though in winter they reach North Africa and parts of the Middle East, some penetrating to Senegal and Arabia. Birds from central and eastern parts of Europe, including some from Russia, appear to migrate southwest to France and Iberia. The most northerly populations tend to move furthest south, reaching North Africa, while the most

easterly populations remain furthest east and winter around the northeastern Mediterranean (*BWP*).

The Song Thrush seems capable of living in a broad range of habitats, with a combination of open ground and bushes or trees. No marked seasonal shift in habitat use is evident (*BWP*).

For Song Thrushes, ring-recovery data are abundant, with over 11,000 records available. Within Britain, many of the Song Thrushes that have been recovered were ringed in the southeast; very few were ringed in Ireland (Fig 1). This may partly reflect the distribution of Song Thrushes (*1988–91 Atlas*) but it is undoubtedly also influenced by the distribution of ringers. Good numbers of both nestlings and free-flying birds have been ringed (Fig 2). However, because Song Thrushes can normally be sexed only as breeding adults, there is little information on whether the migratory habits of males and females differ. Where the cause of recovery is known, many are the result of collisions with traffic and other human-related processes (Fig 3). Caution must be exercised when inferring migration patterns directly from the patterns of ring-recoveries. The large number of winter immigrants from the Netherlands may be accentuated by the particularly active ringing scheme in that country, but perhaps a more serious bias stems from the high levels of hunting in France and Iberia. Indeed 94% of the recoveries

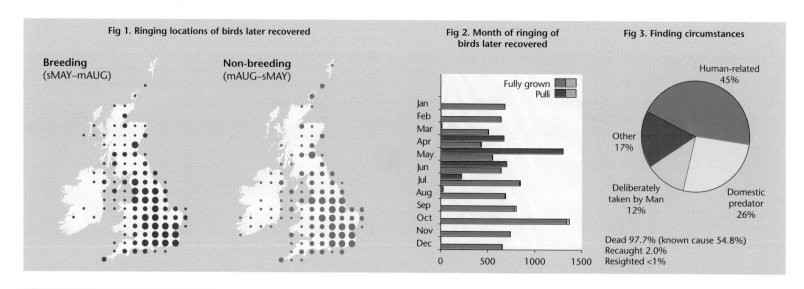

Fig 1. Ringing locations of birds later recovered

Breeding (sMAY–mAUG)

Non-breeding (mAUG–sMAY)

Fig 2. Month of ringing of birds later recovered

Fully grown
Pulli

Jan Feb Mar Apr May Jun Jul Aug Sep Oct Nov Dec
0 500 1000 1500

Fig 3. Finding circumstances

Human-related 45%
Other 17%
Deliberately taken by Man 12%
Domestic predator 26%

Dead 97.7% (known cause 54.8%)
Recaught 2.0%
Resighted <1%

Ringing and recovery data

	<1960	60–69	70–79	80–89	90–97	Total
RINGING						
BTO ringing totals (%)	22	21	23	22	12	534,362
RECOVERIES						
BTO-ringed (%)	22	30	27	16	5	11,445
Foreign-ringed (%)	←	58	→	22	19	192

Statistical analyses

	Breeding population (sMAY–mAUG)	Wintering population (sNOV–mMAR)
Status	SHORT-DISTANCE MIGRANT* (1)	SEDENTARY
Age differences[NT]	Significant	Not significant
Sex differences[NS]	Not significant*	Not tested
Regional differences	Significant[4]	Not tested
Finding circumstances	(Not significant)	(Not significant)

Fig 4. Movements of over 20 km between the breeding season and winter and locations in winter of Song Thrushes present in the (a) northwest (47:79), (b) northeast (80:52), (c) southeast (901:273) and (d) southwest (332:82) of Britain during the breeding season. The 21 movements involving birds present in Ireland during the breeding season are not shown, only one of which involved a movement of over 20 km. Sample sizes of movements under:over 20 km are given but only those over 20 km are plotted.

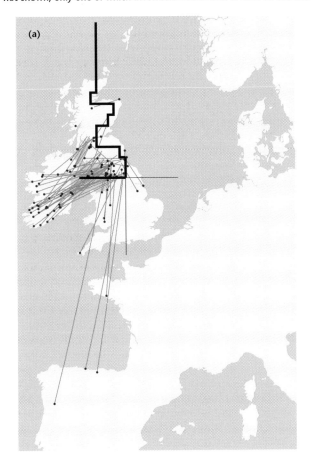

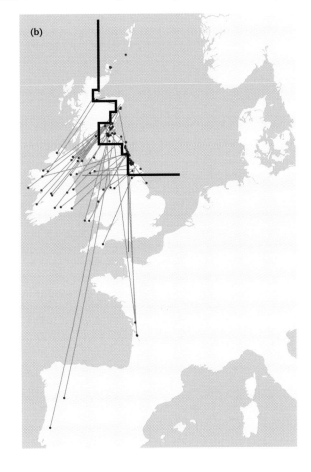

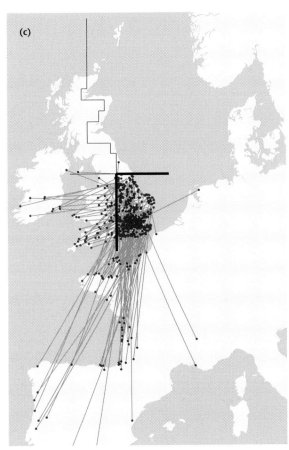

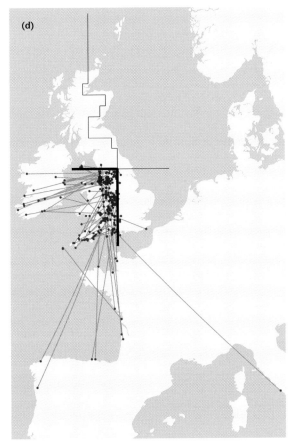

Fig 5. Movements of over 20 km and recovery locations of Song Thrushes ringed as pulli in Britain & Ireland and recovered in a subsequent breeding season when of breeding age. There were 311:32 movements under:over 20 km but only those over 20 km are plotted.

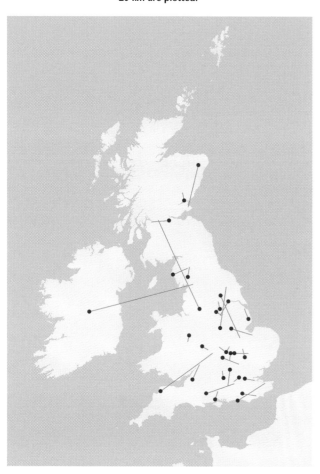

of the data refer, only 23% (360/1,593) moved more than 20 km. Further, of those that do move, most remain in Britain or move to Ireland. It is only a smaller number that move to western France or to Iberia, and many fewer such recoveries would be received were it not for hunting activities in these countries.

Given their rather limited movement, it is no surprise that Song Thrushes tend to be faithful to both their breeding and wintering areas. There have been no ring-recoveries of British-bred nestlings in continental Europe during subsequent breeding seasons (Fig 5) and the median distance for natal dispersal is less than 1 km ($P5–95=0–36$ km, $n=342$). Breeding dispersal is similarly limited with the median distance moved also being less than 1 km ($P5–95=0–35$ km, $n=190$). Particularly for first-year birds, what displacement there is from breeding areas appears to increase then decrease right through the winter rather than showing short pulses in autumn and spring.

Ring-recoveries of Song Thrushes in winter show that most winter movements are local. Within a winter the median distance moved is less than 1 km ($P5–95=0–174$ km, $n=136$) and between winters it is 1 km ($P5–95=0–638$ km, $n=701$). There is evidence that during the cold winters of 1962/63 (Dobinson & Richards 1964) and 1978/79 (Cawthorne & Marchant 1980), more birds moved south and west with more recoveries being reported from France. Indeed it may be that residency interrupted sometimes by cold-weather movements describes the typical winter behaviour of Song Thrushes better than regular seasonal movements. Recoveries between winters indicate more frequent movement than recoveries between breeding and wintering areas, although this may be influenced by the movements of foreign-breeding birds.

Despite the sedentary nature of many British & Irish Song Thrushes, migration is readily observed, especially on the British east coast in autumn, and large falls can occur. While the scale of migration is smaller than for other migrant thrushes, counts on Fair Isle rarely exceeding 500, there were about 3,000 on the Isle of May in October 1966 (*Birds in Scotland*). In Norfolk, autumn arrival is noted between mid-September and early November, and a smaller spring passage occurs from March to early May (Taylor *et al* 1999). Autumn passage is also noted in Wexford and at Cape Clear (*Birds in Ireland*). The median distance moved for birds ringed in autumn and recovered in winter is 38 km ($P5–95=0–1,775$ km, $n=773$), in contrast to 5 km or less between all other combinations of seasons, suggesting that significant passage is occurring. The small number of records of Fennoscandian breeding Song Thrushes support this; nearly all of them were in Britain in autumn, mainly at coastal sites (Fig 6). It has been suggested that some southern-Fennoscandian breeding Song Thrushes may remain in Britain in winter (Goodacre 1960) but there is only one winter recovery to support this. Ringing data may not give a clear picture of the final destination of passage migrants, however, because their movements may be swamped by those of the much larger numbers of residents. However, the small numbers of birds reaching northern Iberia and the Mediterranean may include these passage migrants. Appreciable numbers from the Netherlands and Belgium also spend the winter in Britain (Fig 6b), but again these represent a small fraction of the wintering population; the vast majority of birds ringed in Britain & Ireland in winter also breed in Britain & Ireland. Like those of British & Irish Song Thrushes, the winter movements of these continental birds may be prompted by weather conditions; a bird ringed in the Netherlands as late as December was recovered dead 12 days later in Norfolk.

The Song Thrush is currently a species of serious concern to British conservationists, on account of substantial widespread declines since the mid-1970s (Thomson *et al* 1997). An understanding of the environmental processes responsible is still lacking and there is still no clear course of remedial conservation action. In efforts to narrow the list of possible causes, ringing data have contributed greatly to our understanding of the population processes responsible (Thomson *et al* 1997, Thomson & Cotton 2000). An understanding of migratory

from Iberia were birds taken deliberately by Man and a very different picture of wintering areas emerges if these are excluded. Despite the high number of birds ringed in October amongst the recoveries, there are relatively few foreign recoveries to confirm that this peak is caused partly by foreign migrants on passage through Britain.

Although there are many interesting movements, it is clear that Song Thrushes breeding in Britain are largely sedentary. For almost all groups of the data, regardless of how they are pooled or split according to age group, sex, season or region, the median distance moved is small, usually less than 1 km. Some breeders do move, many within Britain or to Ireland, and some to France or to Spain and Portugal. However, only about a quarter of birds that were ringed during the breeding season and then recovered in winter had moved more than 20 km (492 out of 1,872 recoveries). Early estimates based on the limited data available at the time suggested that two-thirds of first-year birds and half of adult birds wintered away from the natal area (Lack 1944). These figures have since been interpreted to mean that most British-bred Song Thrushes are migratory (*BWP*), but the much larger data set now available suggests that this is not the case, particularly if the potential bias due to hunting in France and Iberia is taken into account. The race of ringed Song Thrushes is generally unknown, but most records presumably refer to *clarkei*, though birds ringed on the Western Isles may be *hebridensis*, and there is evidence that these individuals sometimes winter in Ireland (*BWP*). Within Britain, birds from the north appear more migratory than those from the south (Fig 4), indeed 63% (79/126) of winter recoveries of birds ringed in the breeding season in the northwest travelled more than 20 km, and 39% (52/132) from the northeast did so too. In the southwest and southeast combined, the area to which the great majority

Fig 6. Locations during the breeding season of Song Thrushes present in Britain & Ireland in (a) autumn (510), (b) winter (906) and (c) spring (211).

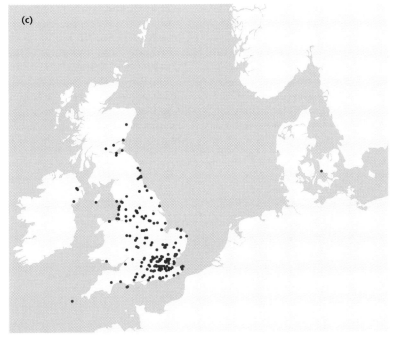

processes is also important in this respect. Firstly, because most of the British breeding population remains in the country during winter, it is more likely to be changes here than changes abroad that are responsible. Secondly, the fidelity of birds to their natal and breeding areas suggests that any environmental change driving a widespread decline must itself be widespread. It has been suggested that hunting pressure in France and Iberia could contribute to the decline of our breeding population, but Baillie (1990a) could find no evidence that the proportion of recoveries from this source had increased as the population went into decline.

The main unknowns concern the numbers and ultimate destinations of passage migrants through Britain in autumn. It is not clear how many Scandinavian birds pass through Britain. It would also be good to be able to quantify the numbers moving, and to correct for the different numbers ringed and different chances of recovery in different regions over time. More research on the routes taken by the birds which move would add to our information about their destinations, and a better understanding about the role played by weather conditions could allow us to better understand not just the timing of movements but also the differences between years and between populations.

David L Thomson
(Netherlands Institute of Ecology, NIOO-CTO Publication 2625)

Redwing
Turdus iliacus

The sibilant calls of Redwings overhead on a still night are perhaps the most evocative sounds of the approach and departure of winter. The breeding range of this small thrush covers a vast range from Iceland to the Kolyma Basin in eastern Siberia (*BWP*). The nominate race (*iliacus*) breeds from Scotland eastwards. The race *coburni*, which nests in Iceland and the Faeroes, differs markedly in several aspects of its migration.

Fennoscandian Redwings winter over most of western Europe and large numbers move as far as southwest Iberia and some into northwest Africa. Some second-winter and older birds from Fennoscandia winter in the Aegean, the Levant and the Transcaucasus as far as the Caspian coast of Iran, but it is likely that Russian and Siberian birds make up the bulk of the mainly adult population that winters in these eastern areas. Ring-recoveries indicate that most of the first-winter birds and many of the adults from Russia and Siberia winter in the same western European areas as the Fennoscandian birds. The race *coburni* winters mainly in Ireland and northwest Iberia, although many late-autumn *coburni* recoveries are from Scotland or western France.

Redwings of the nominate race have bred sporadically since 1925 in Britain, as far south as Kent, and have maintained a small breeding population in northern Scotland since about 1967 (*BWP, 1988–91 Atlas*). The breeding habitat of the Scottish population is usually associated with scrubby woodland close to water or damp meadows. This population is considered to derive from Scandinavian stock (*BWP*). Wintering Redwings in Britain & Ireland share the low-lying open farmland habitat of the Fieldfare in their search for soil invertebrates, berries and fruit. However, unlike Fieldfares, they regularly forage in colder weather on the ground in woodland in the same manner as Blackbirds (*BWP*).

The analysis of the data for this species was supported by Iain William Livingstone

The distribution of British & Irish ringing sites of birds that have been recovered is biased strongly to the centre and southeast of England (Fig 1). Thus ringing seriously under-represents the large wintering numbers in southwest England, Wales, southwest Scotland and particularly Ireland (*Winter Atlas*). The peak month for Redwing ringing is October (Fig 2), when many are caught at coastal ringing stations on the east coast and the Scottish Northern Isles during autumn migration. However, few stay to winter in these coastal areas. Even the non-coastal central counties of East Anglia hold few midwinter Redwings, in contrast to their large flocks of overwintering Fieldfares (Milwright 1984).

Remarkably, more than half of the recoveries of Redwings ringed in Britain & Ireland have come from overseas. Where the cause of recovery was known, 83% of this overseas sample was deliberately taken by Man (Fig 3). Hunting was the cause for the majority of recoveries in southern and southwest Europe, especially France (95%, *n*=294), Greece (92%, *n*=13), Italy (100%, *n*=75), Portugal (100%, *n*=105) and Spain (99%, *n*=80), and also accounted for recoveries in some northern European countries, *eg* Norway (50%, *n*=16) and Belgium (88%, *n*=17).

British- & Irish-ringed Redwings that move east to breed have been recovered in May to July from Norway to Russia just east of the Urals (Fig 4a). Over 60% of these recoveries are in Finland compared to only 5% from Norway and 14% from Sweden. In Russia, the extremely sparse human population is such that few recoveries can be expected, so the

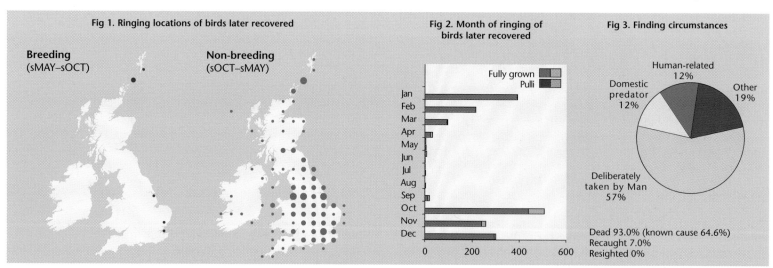

Fig 1. Ringing locations of birds later recovered

Breeding (sMAY–sOCT)

Non-breeding (sOCT–sMAY)

Fig 2. Month of ringing of birds later recovered

Fully grown
Pulli

Jan
Feb
Mar
Apr
May
Jun
Jul
Aug
Sep
Oct
Nov
Dec

0   200   400   600

Fig 3. Finding circumstances

Human-related 12%
Domestic predator 12%
Other 19%
Deliberately taken by Man 57%

Dead 93.0% (known cause 64.6%)
Recaught 7.0%
Resighted 0%

Ringing and recovery data

	<1960	60–69	70–79	80–89	90–97	Total
RINGING						
BTO ringing totals (%)	3	16	33	29	19	215,488
RECOVERIES						
BTO-ringed (%)	4	27	37	23	9	1,725
Foreign-ringed (%)	←	55	→	33	12	288

Statistical analyses

	Breeding population (sMAY–sOCT)	Wintering population (mNOV–sMAR)
Status	NONE	LONG-DISTANCE MIGRANT
Age differences	—	Not significant*
Sex differences	—	Not tested
Regional differences	—	Not significant[2]*
Finding circumstances	—	(Not significant)

Fig 4. Locations of Redwings in (a) May (52, red), June (24, blue) and July (21, grey), (b) August (20, red) and September (28, blue) and (c) October (168, red).

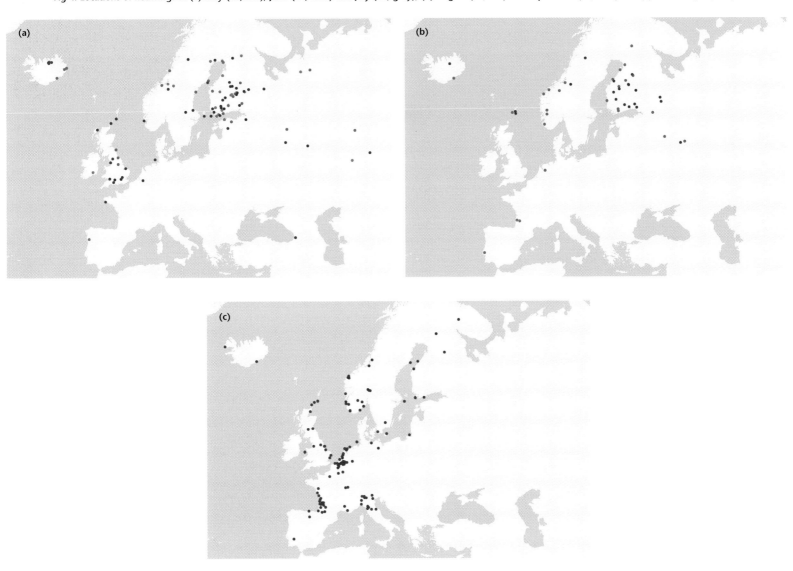

15% actually found there is a surprisingly high figure. Thus, it seems likely that the majority of the nominate Redwings that come to Britain & Ireland are from Finland and the huge unringed populations further east.

Recoveries of British & Irish-ringed Redwings outside the breeding area in August and September are uncommon (Fig 4b). Autumn migration peaks in October when many move into southern Norway and the southern North Sea coasts of eastern Britain, Belgium and the Netherlands (Fig 4c); from November onwards the numbers in these areas diminish as the birds move into western Britain, Ireland, and particularly southwest France and Iberia (Ashmole 1962, da Prato *et al* 1980, Milwright 2002). Over half of all nominate Redwings ringed in the breeding season in any part of the breeding area were recovered in southwest France (Gironde) or Iberia (*cf* 12% of similar Fieldfare recoveries in the same areas). Within-winter movements appear to reduce in distance in the coldest months of January and February (Fig 5). Less than a quarter (54/227) of such movements of those ringed in October and November were short distance (under 20 km) but the proportion rose to more than three-quarters (114/149) for those ringed in January and February (Milwright 2002). This could be partly due to the shorter time period available for recording the rarer longer movements of birds ringed in January and February, however. The mean distance from breeding to wintering areas of nominate Redwings is less in their first winter than in later winters, and the most distant destinations, such as western Iberia, are occupied mainly

by older birds (Milwright 2002). Nothing is known of the movements of the small British breeding population.

Records of Redwings ringed in winter and recovered in a subsequent winter are concentrated in England, southern France, western Iberia and western Italy (Fig 6), although smaller numbers are also recovered in Cyprus, the Levant, and the Transcaucasus as far as the Caspian coast of Iran. Winter recoveries so far east suggest a link between Britain & Ireland and breeding grounds towards the eastern end of the range, and add weight to the theory that most British- & Irish-wintering nominate Redwings breed in unpopulated areas unvisited by bird ringers.

Spring departure from Iberia and southwest France appears to start in March and this area empties of Redwings by early April. The presence of large spring flocks indicates that eastern England and the Netherlands are used as refuelling stops by many returning birds from late March to early May. First-winter birds tend to leave later than adults (Milwright 2002).

The Icelandic race *coburni* has a relatively small population of 100,000 to 300,000 breeding pairs (*European Atlas*) but the movements of this race are better understood than those of the nominate race. Icelandic ringing has produced 150 overseas Redwing recoveries; all except five were in Scotland, Ireland, western France or Iberia (Milwright 2002). In winter (December to February), 58% of recoveries of Icelandic-ringed Redwings were in Scotland or Ireland and the remainder were in western France or

Fig 5. Movements of over 20 km and recovery locations of Redwings ringed in (a) October–November (54:173), (b) December (51:30) and (c) January–February (114:35) and recovered in the same winter (October to February). Sample sizes of movements under:over 20 km are given but only those over 20 km are plotted. Movements involving Iceland and the Faeroes are not shown.

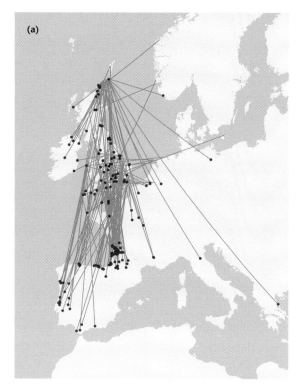

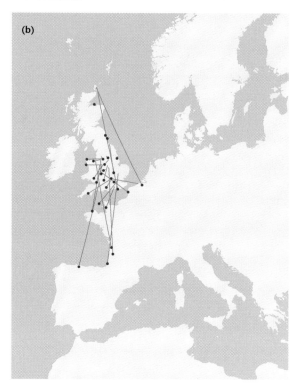

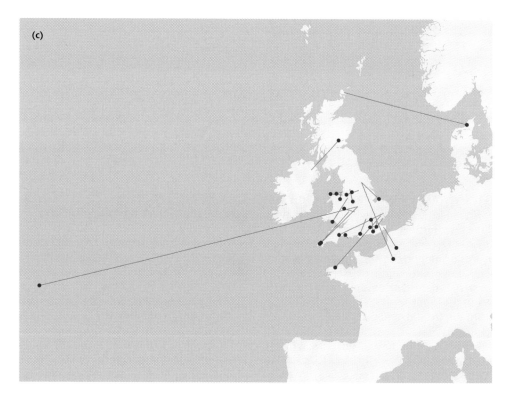

Iberia. Redwings from the eastern half of Iceland are more likely to winter in Scotland and Ireland than those from the western half (Milwright 2002). No Icelandic-ringed individual has been recovered anywhere in England or Wales.

Autumn departure from Iceland, which is almost complete, appears to be highly synchronized in October. As the autumn and winter progresses, the density of recoveries in Scotland decreases and there are

two recoveries in western Ireland (Fig 7). Ring-recoveries prior to 1979 suggest that the density of recoveries in western Ireland increased as winter progressed. Similarly, most late-autumn Icelandic birds in France probably relocate to northwest Iberia for the winter (Milwright 2002). There is no evidence that birds use Scotland or Ireland as a staging post on the way to France or Iberia, and some very short ringing–recovery intervals between Iceland and France or Iberia suggest that direct flights

Fig 6. Locations in subsequent winters in October (78, black), November–December (213, blue) and January–February (296, red) of Redwings present in Britain & Ireland in winter (October–February).

Fig 7. All included exchanges of Redwings between Britain & Ireland and the Faeroes and Iceland, split by season in Britain & Ireland: October–November (12, black), December–March (4, red), April (8, blue) and seasonally inaccurate (8, grey). A further 45 Icelandic-ringed birds were recovered in Britain & Ireland prior to 1979, and 3 Icelandic-ringed birds have been recovered in the Faeroes.

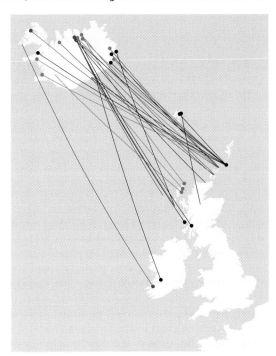

are normal (Milwright 2002). Irish wintering flocks contain a high proportion of adult birds, whereas those in northwest Iberia appear to include more first-winter birds. It seems therefore that, among Icelandic *coburni*, the first-winter birds tend to migrate further than the adults, whereas for the nominate race the reverse appears to be true. Movements within the same autumn and winter of birds identified as *coburni* when ringed in the Scottish Northern Isles show three of the four recoveries relocating southwest to mainland Scotland and Ireland later in the winter; the fourth bird moved to southern Norway in November.

Spring migration is concentrated in April, when three of the four British recoveries of Icelandic-ringed birds were from the Outer Hebrides (Fig 7). Two Scottish-ringed birds have also been recovered in March and April in the Faeroes. Most British- & Irish-ringed birds returning to Iceland are recovered there in April but some birds do make the journey earlier — as shown by a bird ringed on Fair Isle in April and recovered in Iceland on the following 17 March.

There can be little doubt that Icelandic Redwings are derived from the nominate stock, and as Iceland would have been uninhabitable during the last ice age it seems likely that the two races have separated since then. It is very unlikely that the birds that established the Icelandic subspecies had already established a southeast migratory pattern before arrival in Iceland, since all known populations of the presumed parent stock have a well-established west to southwest migration. Thus, it is

remarkable that this separation must have led almost immediately to a race with a novel and highly focused migratory direction.

Hunting and trapping are the main causes of recovery of ringed Redwings and almost the exclusive cause in southern Europe (Peirò & Candela 1995). There is no doubt that these factors represent a major controlling factor to the population size of both races. The relative hunting and trapping pressure may currently be increasing in France and Portugal, since the proportion of British- & Irish-ringed birds taken there has risen sharply, from 22% before 1970 to 46% during the 1990s. However, these activities seem to be diminishing in other parts of the winter range, notably in Italy and Belgium. Nonetheless, the huge population fluctuations which this species undergoes are much more likely to be due to annual weather differences in the breeding season in the breeding area, and the biggest long-term challenge to the species may be the effect of global warming on its breeding biology.

Much more could be learnt of the migratory movements of nominate Redwings if large-scale ringing were carried out over a number of years in the Yenisei, Lena and Kolyma river basins of central and eastern Siberia. In addition, more ringing in the west of Ireland and Portugal would fill in some gaps in our knowledge of the movements of both races of Redwing.

Digby Milwright

Mistle Thrush

Turdus viscivorus

Mistle Thrushes are familiar year-round in Britain & Ireland and might be thought of by many observers as an entirely sedentary species. Across much of continental Europe, however, they are strongly migratory and in Britain & Ireland the species can best be described as a partial migrant. They have a surprising history of dynamic colonization in Britain & Ireland during the 19th century, being initially rare in northern England and Scotland, and unknown in Ireland before 1800 (*Birds in Ireland*, Holloway 1996). There has been a decline in Britain & Ireland in the range and numbers of Mistle Thrushes in the last 25 years (*1988–91 Atlas*), the cause of which is unknown.

The breeding range presently extends from Morocco, Ireland and southeast Norway, east across Eurasia to the western Himalayas and almost to Lake Baikal (*BWP*). The nominate race *viscivorus* occupies most of this area but is replaced by *deichleri* in northwest Africa, Corsica and Sardinia, and by *bonapartei* in central Siberia and the mountains of Central Asia. The entire northeast European and central Asian parts of the range are completely deserted in winter, most birds wintering within more southerly or westerly parts of the breeding range (*BWP*). Further south and west, the species is more sedentary or dispersive. The main winter range of central European and Scandinavian birds is from Belgium through western and southern France to northeast Spain, though small numbers may reach the range of *deichleri* in Morocco and Tunisia.

In Britain & Ireland, Mistle Thrushes are now found almost everywhere, although they are absent from Shetland and Orkney and have a very local distribution in the Outer Hebrides (*1988–91 Atlas*). They breed in open woodland and in areas of grassland, provided there

The analysis of the data for this species was supported by Gerry & Enid Burman

are enough mature trees to provide song-posts and nest sites, although occurrence in some treeless areas suggests that nests may be built in walls or on the ground (*BWP*). Family parties can be seen feeding in open grassland in May and June, and by early autumn small flocks of a few dozen may gather, sometimes in areas where they do not breed, feeding on fruit later as it ripens. In winter, some individuals vigorously defend supplies of berries against conspecifics and other thrushes (Snow & Snow 1984). The winter distribution is broadly similar to that in the breeding season, although less widespread in parts of northern and upland Scotland (*Winter Atlas*).

Migrant Mistle Thrushes are noted occasionally at bird observatories and other coastal watch-points, generally in small numbers. At Fair Isle, there is a small and irregular autumn passage, mainly in September–October, and a slightly larger one during February–May, but peak counts rarely exceed 10 birds (*Birds in Scotland*). An exceptional movement of more than 300 Mistle Thrushes, accompanied by large movements of other thrushes and finches, occurred at Cape Clear Island in October 1959 (Sharrock 1973). On 22 October 1961, about 600 Mistle Thrushes are reported to have arrived over the sea at Malin Head, Donegal (*Birds in Ireland*).

Most Mistle Thrush ring-recoveries are from birds ringed in England, with major concentrations in the south and east; there are few data from

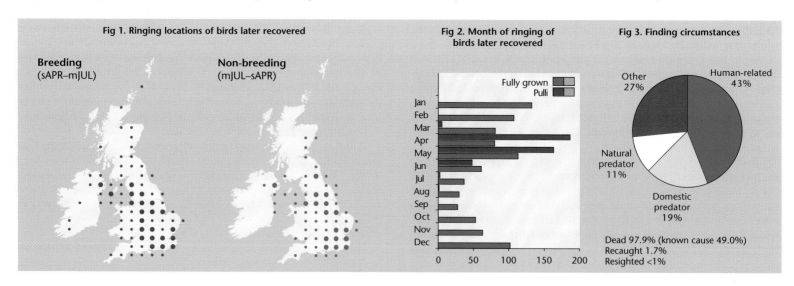

Fig 1. Ringing locations of birds later recovered

Breeding (sAPR–mJUL)

Non-breeding (mJUL–sAPR)

Fig 2. Month of ringing of birds later recovered

Fig 3. Finding circumstances

Dead 97.9% (known cause 49.0%)
Recaught 1.7%
Resighted <1%

Ringing and recovery data

	<1960	60–69	70–79	80–89	90–97	Total
RINGING						
BTO ringing totals (%)	23	18	22	23	13	42,628
RECOVERIES						
BTO-ringed (%)	23	28	23	20	6	1,277
Foreign-ringed (%)	0	0	100	0	0	1

Statistical analyses

	Breeding population (sAPR–mJUL)	Wintering population (sNOV–sMAR)
Status	SHORT-DISTANCE MIGRANT (1)	SEDENTARY
Age differences[NT]	Significant	Not significant*
Sex differences	Not tested	Not tested
Regional differences	Not tested	Not tested
Finding circumstances	(Not significant)	Not significant

Fig 4. Locations outside the breeding season and movements of over 20 km between the breeding and non-breeding season of 444 Mistle Thrushes present in Britain & Ireland during the breeding season.

Fig 5. Movements of over 20 km and recovery locations of Mistle Thrushes ringed in winter and recovered in the same winter (27:4, red) or (b) a subsequent winter (37:7, blue). Sample sizes of movements under:over 20 km are given, but only those over 20 km are plotted.

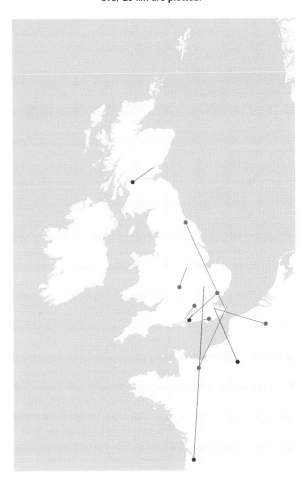

Wales, Scotland or Ireland (Fig 1). Irish ringing reports record that only 883 birds were ringed in Ireland during 1975–92, in contrast to almost 20,000 in Britain for the same period. Most birds were ringed either as pulli during March–June or between December and May when fully grown (Fig 2). Almost 98% of recoveries involved birds found dead, of which half had a known cause of death. Over half of these were related to human activity or to domestic cats (Fig 3); these recovery causes will be over-represented as birds dying in proximity to Man are more likely to be reported.

The vast majority of Mistle Thrushes in Britain & Ireland are sedentary. Over 98% of Mistle Thrush ring-recoveries are for birds both ringed and recovered in Britain & Ireland and the median distance travelled is less than 1 km ($P5–95=0–41$ km). The longest movements are of birds breeding in Britain and recovered in France or Belgium (Fig 4). Birds from all parts of Britain have been found in France but most were ringed in southeast England. A small number of birds ringed in Scotland and northern England have been found to the west in Ireland. The small number of movements among Scottish birds lends little support to Snow's (1969) suggestion that these birds are highly migratory. There have been 44 recoveries of Mistle Thrushes between winters and 31 within winters of which small numbers, seven and four respectively, had moved further than 20 km, suggesting that seasonal migrations are not always regular (Fig 5).

Sightings indicate that birds from the Continent arrive in Britain in small numbers in autumn. Taylor *et al* (1999) have summarized reports of arrivals of Mistle Thrushes from over the sea in Norfolk, especially in October. These observations, coupled with recoveries such as those from Fair Isle and Fife to eastern and southern France (Fig 4), and another of a Dutch-ringed bird, a pullus ringed on Texel in June 1978, in Kent seven months later (Spencer & Hudson 1980), indicate that there is a small-scale movement. However, it seems likely that these represent the exceptions rather than the rule. Perhaps cold-weather movements may account for some of these observations. It is not known what proportion of the small number of autumn arrivals remain in Britain for the winter and how many move on, perhaps to Ireland or to France. Both ringing and observations therefore suggest that there is little movement of Mistle Thrushes from continental Europe and that, as suggested by Snow (*Winter Atlas*), the high winter population in southeast and central England simply reflects the high breeding density there (*1988–91 Atlas*). Given the scale of movement on the Continent on a southwest–northeast axis, it is perhaps surprising that so few continental Mistle Thrushes visit Britain for the winter.

Clearly current uncertainty in the proportion of the population that migrates and how this may differ regionally is a major limitation in our knowledge of this species.

John O'Halloran

Cetti's Warbler

Cettia cetti

The explosive song of the Cetti's Warbler can be heard at any time of year and many individuals are probably sedentary. However, its developing range and status in Britain since the first record in 1961 provide evidence of continental immigration and of the dispersive ability of the species.

Cetti's Warblers occur in more southern regions of the West Palearctic from Britain and Morocco east through Turkey to central Asia, where they are replaced by a greater variety of congeners ranging eastwards through the Himalayas and China to Japan and Southeast Asia. Much of the Asian range is vacated in winter where the species is a short-distance or altitudinal migrant. In western Europe, the species markedly expanded its range in the course of the 20th century from a primarily Iberian and Mediterranean distribution. It first bred in Britain in 1972 where it is at the northern limit of its global range. From observation, the species is sedentary or a partial migrant in western Europe though there may be regular altitudinal movements in Iberia where it can breed as high as 1,450 m. As a small insectivore, the species suffers high losses in cold winters.

In Britain, the distribution has primarily been south of a line from South Wales to the Wash but numbers have come and gone in response to cold winters. Most notably, the stronghold has shifted from East Anglia and Kent to a more westerly pattern in places with the mildest of British winters. There were up to 574 pairs in 1996; the highest yet recorded (Wotton *et al* 1998). The species has occurred only as a vagrant in Ireland. Cetti's Warblers live in dense tangled scrub on the margins of wetlands, lakes and rivers. They forage quite extensively on bare muddy

The analysis of the data for this species was supported by
The Slapton Ringers

ground kept free of low vegetation by the shading scrub above (Bibby 1982). In reed swamps, they primarily occur round the damp scrubby margins and avoid inundated areas, though in winter pure reedbeds can be a sufficient habitat.

The habitat of the Cetti's Warbler is thus quite rare and fragmented in Britain and it is clear that the species would have to be quite dispersive to be able to find and colonize new areas. Wetland sites, especially those with reed swamps, are attractive to ringers in the summer when *Acrocephalus* warblers and other species can be caught in numbers. Sites spread throughout the British range have contributed to the ring-recoveries (Fig 1). Winter ringing in these habitats is less productive and the catching patterns of Cetti's Warblers undoubtedly reflect this bias (Fig 2). Of those recovered, very few were ringed as pulli — the nests are surprisingly hard to find. As might be expected for a skulking bird of thick habitats much frequented by ringers, the majority of movements were reported as live captures by ringers, with only four found dead (Fig 3).

No ringed Cetti's Warblers have yet been known to leave Britain and all the movements of British-ringed birds are between sites within the known breeding range (Fig 4). Yet there have been quite a few movements over 5 km. The distribution of movement distances is biased by non-reporting of the shorter ones (retraps) and there are too few dead

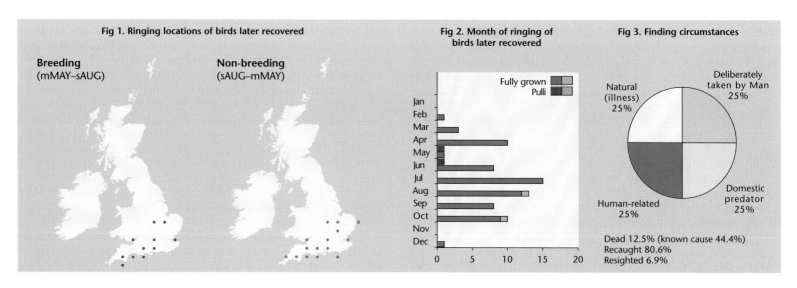

Ringing and recovery data

	<1960	60–69	70–79	80–89	90–97	Total
RINGING						
BTO ringing totals (%)	0	0	11	43	47	3,382
RECOVERIES						
BTO-ringed (%)	0	0	3	53	44	70
Foreign-ringed (%)	←	50	→	0	50	4

Statistical analyses

	Breeding population (mMAY–sAUG)	Wintering population (sNOV–mFEB)
Status	[SEDENTARY]	?
Age differences	Not tested	—
Sex differences	Not tested	—
Regional differences	Not tested	—
Finding circumstances	Not tested	—

Fig 4. Recovery locations and movements of over 20 km for the 72 included recoveries of Cetti's Warblers ringed or recovered in Britain & Ireland.

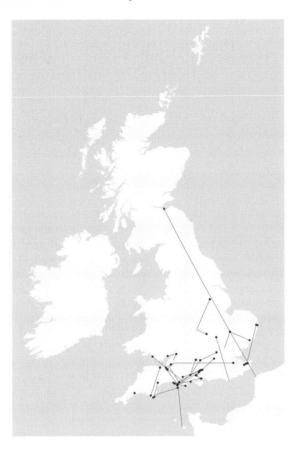

birds to allow analysis. Three of the four reported dead had moved but they are probably a biased sample dying close to humans and their pets.

Four foreign-ringed individuals have arrived in Britain; one each from Belgium and France, and two from Jersey. Three at least were ringed as juveniles and suggest that northerly moving juveniles were probably the source of colonization. The French individual ringed on 24 August 1993 near Calais was probably near its birthplace. It died six weeks later on 5 October well to the north of the breeding range having reached Edinburgh. It became a first record of the species for Scotland and made the longest recorded movement of 649 km.

Do adult Cetti's Warblers move? There are only five recoveries of adult Cetti's Warblers ringed in May to August inclusive when they would almost certainly have been at their breeding sites. One was found

dead at the site of ringing, the others had moved short distances (6–26 km). At least two, and possibly four, of these were changes of likely breeding place rather than movements outside the breeding season. This suggests that few Cetti's Warblers move after their first breeding season at one year old. There are 10 recoveries of fully grown birds ringed in April: three were found at the site of ringing but four had moved 25 km or more. Four of the movements were in the same year. Given the rare and short movements of established adults, it seems likely that these were first-summer birds not yet established at their first breeding places. Two of the same-year movements occurred after capture in the last 10 days of April, which is quite late given that first clutches are often laid in April.

Of young birds that moved onwards in the same year, only two were found in August, both having moved 10 km. This suggests that those ringed as juveniles were at, or very close to, their natal areas and that post-juvenile movements mainly take place after August. Later in their first year, nine individuals were recovered 0–72 km from their site of ringing. There was no clear orientation to movements but more females than males were involved. Thirteen birds of unknown age were first caught in late autumn, 12 in September or October and one in December: again, there were more females. These unaged birds were unusual in that five moved more than 100 km. Since it has previously been argued that British birds do not generally move this far, it may be that there are more mobile birds of southern origin arriving in Britain in the period September to October.

Overall, the data suggest that Cetti's Warblers move very little once established as breeders. Juveniles may move in their first autumn starting in September and sometimes continuing into April the next year before they first settle. The movements are not obviously oriented. Females seem to be rather more mobile than males, as had previously been suggested by direct observation. Some continental birds reach Britain in the period September to October. This is a pattern that accords with features of a generally sedentary species, though the dispersive movements in the first year are relatively extensive compared with the most sedentary of species. This is probably because of the scarce and dispersed nature of the Cetti's Warbler's habitat.

Although breeding sites will always be fairly scarce, Cetti's Warblers probably have a secure future in Britain because of the considerable conservation effort that goes into maintaining wetlands. Cold winters are a big enemy but populations are now well established in the south and west and the species clearly has the dispersive ability to locate and colonize fragments of suitable habitat in a patchy environment. It will be interesting to learn more about how dispersal works in an essentially sedentary species with a very fragmented pattern of suitable habitat.

Colin J Bibby

Common Grasshopper Warbler (Grasshopper Warbler)

Locustella naevia

Grasshopper Warblers are small, secretive and well-camouflaged birds that spend most of their lives on or near the ground in tall thick grasslands and reedbeds, and are probably the most inconspicuous species in the Western Palearctic. The nominate race *naevia* breeds throughout Britain & Ireland, but rather patchily, and also somewhat unevenly, across central Europe from the north of Spain and Romania northwards to Norway and Finland, and eastwards across the former USSR to about 47°E. It seems to be most abundant in Germany, Latvia and France (*European Atlas*). This race seems to overwinter principally, or maybe exclusively, in the western half of West Africa, but there are winter records also from north of the Sahara (Urban *et al* 1997). In the Caucasus, a larger race *obscurior* breeds but its winter range is not known. Two smaller races, *straminea* and *mongolica*, breed from southern Russia to Mongolia and overwinter mainly in India, with a few records from northeast Africa (*BWP*, Urban *et al* 1997).

In Britain & Ireland, Grasshopper Warblers breed in rough grassland, downland scrub, upland bog and damp moorland, but rarely at altitudes above 300 m (*1988–91 Atlas*). Reedbeds are used more frequently on passage and in the winter range, and at these times the species is also recorded from dry upland grassland (*BWP*, Urban *et al* 1997).

The ringing information for the few ring-recoveries that have involved Britain & Ireland is illustrated in Figs 1 & 2. A cause of death has been reported for only a handful of recoveries (Fig 3). This species is relatively rarely ringed and probably has the lowest ring-recovery rate of any British & Irish breeding bird. Special measures of capture, even at the best sites, are required if bird ringers are to catch very many. Most bird

The analysis of the data for this species was supported by Terry Robinson

ringers operating in reedbeds set their mist-nets too high to catch Grasshopper Warblers; usually 85–90% of birds are captured when flying less than 50 cm above the ground – *ie* in the lowest shelf of mist-nets, with this lowest shelf-string set no more than 15 cm above the ground (Rumsey 1975). A technique that has proved extremely useful to assist in the capture of this species is playing continuous recordings of the reeling song. At dawn, the birds respond by approaching the sound and many are captured in mist-nets within 15 m of the speaker. Of 4,500 birds ringed on autumn passage in Sussex by the Rye Bay Ringing Group during 1987–99, only four were subsequently recovered dead, only four were retrapped in subsequent autumns, and no birds were caught that had been ringed elsewhere (pers obs).

In an effort to increase the reporting rate of ringed Grasshopper Warblers, 112 birds in Senegal were fitted with red colour-rings in addition to the metal ring. Of these, two were recovered in Britain, while there was one further recovery from a further 239 birds ringed in Senegal and the Gambia without colour rings; neither of the two colour-ringed birds would have been reported by their finders had they not been colour-ringed (pers obs). These are very small sample sizes but they do suggest that a larger study using colour rings in Africa would be useful.

Very few Grasshopper Warblers have been ringed in Britain as pulli or breeding adults, and scarcely any at all in Ireland despite a major part

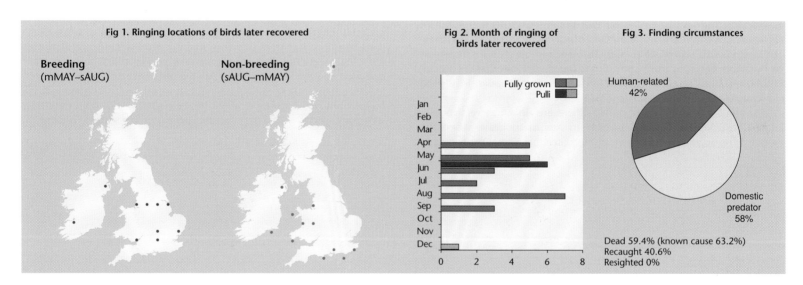

Fig 1. Ringing locations of birds later recovered

Breeding (mMAY–sAUG)   Non-breeding (sAUG–mMAY)

Fig 2. Month of ringing of birds later recovered

Fully grown / Pulli

Fig 3. Finding circumstances

Human-related 42%

Domestic predator 58%

Dead 59.4% (known cause 63.2%)
Recaught 40.6%
Resighted 0%

Ringing and recovery data

	<1960	60–69	70–79	80–89	90–97	Total
RINGING						
BTO ringing totals (%)	4	15	21	18	42	16,829
RECOVERIES						
BTO-ringed (%)	3	16	32	26	23	31
Foreign-ringed (%)	←	0	→	0	100	1

Statistical analyses

	Breeding population (mMAY–sAUG)	Wintering population (sNOV–sMAR)
Status	[LONG-DISTANCE MIGRANT]	NONE
Age differences	Not tested	—
Sex differences	Not tested	—
Regional differences	Not tested	—
Finding circumstances	Not tested	—

Fig 4. Recovery locations and movements of over 20 km for the 32 included recoveries of Grasshopper Warblers ringed or recovered in Britain & Ireland. A further recovery, in Cumbria, of a bird ringed in Senegal was excluded from the data because it was transported on a car grille before recovery. It was thought to be a local breeder, however, because it had invertebrate prey in its bill.

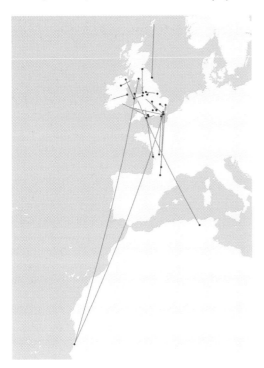

of the British & Irish population breeding there (Forsyth 1993, *1988–91 Atlas*). As a result little can be deduced about juvenile dispersal or post-breeding movements from the few ring-recoveries. Migrants first appear on the south coast of England in early July. Significant autumn numbers occur in reedbeds in East Sussex and Dorset, as suggested by annual catches of *c* 500 birds at Icklesham (pers obs) and *c* 100 birds at Keysworth (A Martin pers comm). The phenology of autumn migration of juvenile birds through southeast England shows three clear peaks, representing the passage of three broods roughly in late July, late August and late September; the first and third of these are quite variable while the second consistently contains the largest numbers (pers obs). Adults are caught in much smaller numbers, mostly in late August and September, while some juveniles pass through during the first half of October. The large numbers of migrants in southeast England in autumn may include some continental European birds but there is no evidence of this yet from ring-recoveries.

A small cluster of recoveries in southwest France suggests that this may be an important stopover site (Fig 4). Mist-netting indicates that significant numbers of birds are present in Portuguese reedbeds in autumn (C J Mead pers comm). The relevance of Morocco and elsewhere in North Africa to the autumn migration of Grasshopper Warblers is unknown, as is the timing of arrival in West Africa. The birds moult completely in early winter (pers obs) but the proportion of moult that is undertaken in Iberia and North Africa compared with West Africa is also unknown.

Recoveries south of the Sahara suggest a coastal bias to the winter distribution. This may be a result of most of the African ringing activity being conducted at the coast but there may be more significance than this implies. Ringing at Djoudj National Park in northern Senegal, a major centre of abundance for wintering Grasshopper Warblers (Rodwell *et al* 1996), has resulted in all three of the trans-Saharan recoveries involving Britain & Ireland. A bird ringed at Rye Bay was controlled at Djoudj and birds ringed at Djoudj have been recovered in Cumbria and in Dumfries & Galloway. Two other recoveries of Grasshopper Warblers in westernmost Africa involve Germany and Sweden, implying that birds visit this area from a relatively wide zone of northern Europe; a Swedish-ringed bird was recovered in coastal Mauritania in October and one ringed on the Gambian coast was recovered in northwest Germany. By contrast, for Sedge Warbler, recoveries from Djoudj suggest that a high proportion of birds of this species there are from Ireland and western Britain, with many British and most continental European birds wintering further east.

The West African winter range of Grasshopper Warblers is surprisingly little known. Aside from the ringing and recovery locations already mentioned, the species has been reliably recorded only in Mali, in the inland delta of the River Niger, in a small wetland in northern Ghana and in grassland at higher altitudes on the Guinean slopes of Mount Nimba (*BWP*, G Jarry pers comm). A thorough search of the Lake Chad region would be most valuable and might reveal whether any birds of the nominate *naevia* occur in winter east of Ghana.

Recurrence of a ringed bird in a subsequent winter has been recorded only once at Djoudj, a much lower rate than for the congeneric Savi's Warbler (Sauvage *et al* 1998). There is a suggestion that the Grasshopper Warbler shows much less site-fidelity than other warbler species (*BWP*) and this seems to be borne out by British & Irish ringing data. The majority of Grasshopper Warblers seem to have left Djoudj by early February, with only small numbers remaining in March and April (pers obs), and consequently the one recovery in February in Algeria may have been a northbound migrant. It would appear that the ephemeral wetlands of northwest Africa may have great importance for this species during February to May, in contrast to some other wetland specialists, such as Savi's Warbler and Bluethroat, that stay later at Djoudj (pers obs) and presumably largely overfly North Africa.

Bird observatory data suggest a particularly strong spring migration on Irish Sea coasts (*R & F*). This is consistent with the historically large numbers of birds killed at Bardsey lighthouse (Durman 1976a) and an apparent concentration of the population around the Irish Sea during the 19th century (Holloway 1996). Most birds return to Britain & Ireland during the second half of April and during May (*R & F*).

Grasshopper Warblers have undergone a substantial population decline in Britain since the early 1970s (Crick *et al* 1998), and the British & Irish range contracted markedly between the *1968–72* and *1988–91 Atlases*. However, the species has increased and spread in parts of northern and central Europe (*European Atlas*). The species is well known for large population fluctuations from year to year, which are likely to be linked to unknown factors outside the breeding season (*1988–91 Atlas*). Certainly the species winters in environments that change dramatically from year to year. A large vibrant wetland one year may be totally desiccated at the same season during the next year. If Grasshopper Warblers place less reliance on regular winter site-fidelity than do their close relatives, as seems to be the case, they may have a better strategy to make use of transient wetlands and to avoid the severe population depletion that might follow localized drought. The erratically fluctuating breeding populations may be explained by the species having a relatively low fidelity also to breeding areas.

In breeding areas, a thinly dispersed species that is not very site-faithful is especially difficult to monitor. Monitoring may be easier in Africa because the birds appear to be more concentrated into relatively few locations there, and perhaps the time is near when it may be possible to establish a sustained programme of population monitoring in Africa. For the Grasshopper Warbler, one of the most private of British and Irish breeding birds, this can only be achieved by targeted ringing or aural surveys.

Stephen Rumsey

Sedge Warbler
Acrocephalus schoenobaenus

Sedge Warblers are long-distance trans-Saharan migrants that lay down extensive fat reserves in northern Europe in preparation for long-haul flights to the African wintering grounds. Their relatively large breeding range extends southwards from arctic Fennoscandia to Greece and Turkey, and from Ireland in the west to central Siberia in the east (*European Atlas*). The entire breeding population winters south of the Sahara, from Senegal east to Ethiopia and south to northern Namibia and South Africa (*BWP*). Most British and Dutch birds probably leave Europe between southwest Iberia and Italy, while Fennoscandian birds head more directly on a north-south axis over central Europe, Italy and east as far as the Aegean (*Der Zug*). Those Sedge Warblers breeding further east, as far as central Siberia, may use both the eastern Mediterranean and Middle-Eastern migration routes but probably most pass through the Mediterranean (*BWP*). Most wintering and passage birds in East Africa are thought to breed in Russia and elsewhere in the former USSR (Pearson 1982).

Sedge Warblers breed extensively within both Britain and Ireland, with strongholds in the fens and coastal levels of eastern England and in lowland areas of Scotland and east-central Ireland (*1988–91 Atlas*). Preferred breeding habitats are lowland marshes and waterways, although dry scrub, young conifers and even crops are sometimes used. Although knowledge is scant, Sedge Warblers seem to utilize a range of habitats in the African winter quarters but most commonly those associated with fresh water, such as reedbeds, papyrus and the marshy fringes of lakes (*BWP*).

The breeding-season ringing places of birds later recovered broadly parallel the breeding distribution of the species in Britain but under-

The analysis of the data for this species was supported by Joan Carson

represent the Irish population. In addition, relatively large numbers of Sedge Warblers have been ringed along the south coast of England and in Tayside, mainly in autumn (Fig 1). Most Sedge Warblers that have been ringed in Britain & Ireland and subsequently recovered have been ringed as birds of the year in July and August (more than 70%). Only 3.5% have been ringed as nestlings (Fig 2).

Of more than 4,000 Sedge Warbler recoveries, 84% have been recaught by ringers. The pattern of live recoveries is therefore greatly influenced by the distribution of ringers. Of the 16% of recoveries found dead, 63% have a cause of recovery documented. Of these, almost half (45%) have been attributed to human-related causes, such as collisions with cars and windows, and a further 36% to domestic predators (Fig 3).

Pre-migratory movements of Sedge Warblers begin in late July with birds apparently searching for sites with high densities of Plum-reed Aphids, an important but ephemeral and unpredictable food source (Bibby & Green 1981). Autumn migration occurs mainly during August to October, with most birds having left Britain & Ireland by the end of September (*R & F*), and a slight tendency for adult Sedge Warblers to leave earlier than juveniles (*BWP*). Many British & Irish birds lay down fat reserves in the reedbeds of southern England, South Wales (Ormerod 1990) and northwest France. Along the south coast of England, ringing has shown that Sedge Warblers may move both east and west in

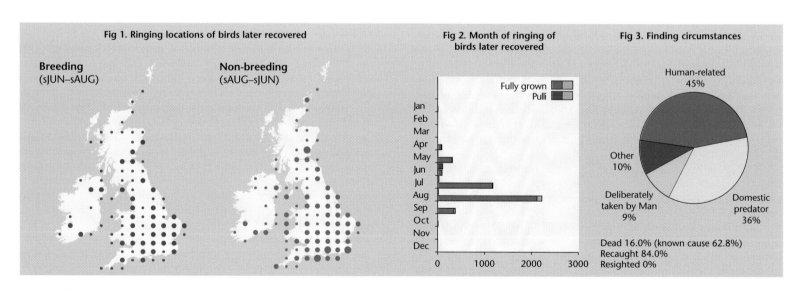

Fig 1. Ringing locations of birds later recovered

Breeding (sJUN–sAUG)

Non-breeding (sAUG–sJUN)

Fig 2. Month of ringing of birds later recovered

Fully grown
Pulli

Fig 3. Finding circumstances

Human-related 45%

Other 10%

Deliberately taken by Man 9%

Domestic predator 36%

Dead 16.0% (known cause 62.8%)
Recaught 84.0%
Resighted 0%

Ringing and recovery data

	<1960	60–69	70–79	80–89	90–97	Total
RINGING						
BTO ringing totals (%)	2	11	22	25	40	603,858
RECOVERIES						
BTO-ringed (%)	1	5	18	23	53	4,277
Foreign-ringed (%)	←	18	→	29	52	214

Statistical analyses

	Breeding population (sJUN–sAUG)	Wintering population (sNOV–sMAR)
Status	[LONG-DISTANCE MIGRANT]	NONE
Age differences	Not tested	—
Sex differences	Not tested	—
Regional differences	Not tested	—
Finding circumstances	Not tested	—

Fig 4. Locations in (a) autumn (1,087), (b) winter (24) and (c) spring (378), and movements of over 20 km between the breeding and non-breeding season, of Sedge Warblers present in Britain & Ireland during the breeding season. Seasonally accurate movements (red) are differentiated from seasonally inaccurate movements (grey).

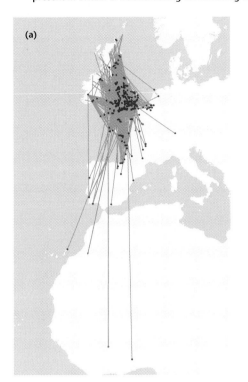
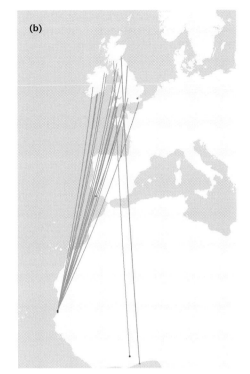
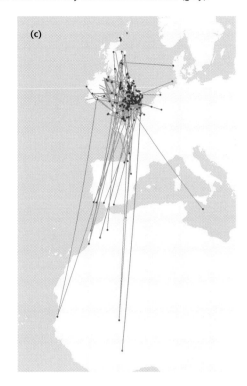

autumn, and they may need to cross to France to find sufficient food to accumulate fat reserves (Insley & Boswell 1978, Bibby & Green 1981). After fattening, most Sedge Warblers undertake rapid long-haul flights across Iberia, North Africa and the Sahara Desert without significant further fattening; in contrast to Reed Warblers, relatively few Sedge Warblers have been recovered in Iberia during autumn migration (Fig 4a). Scandinavian ring-recoveries show that Sedge Warblers migrate faster in autumn than do Reed Warblers (Bensch & Nielsen 1999). The British & Irish recoveries also suggest that first-year birds are more likely to be recovered inland in France and Belgium than are adults (Fig 5), and, curiously, only males have been recovered in southern Spain.

Sedge Warblers are most abundant in North Africa during mid-September to mid-October, and are common on the southern edge of the Sahara by September (*BWP*). Passage south of the desert can be prolonged (*eg* August to December in Chad) and, in West Africa, arrival on the main winter quarters begins in September and peaks in October (*BWP*). Both passage movement and arrival in the main winter quarters occur later in eastern Africa than in the west.

The recoveries show that the winter quarters for British & Irish Sedge Warblers lie south of 17°N and west of 2°E (Fig 4). Most exchanges of British & Irish Sedge Warblers reported from countries south of the Sahara have involved Senegal (92), Mali (11) and Ghana (eight), with smaller numbers from Burkina Faso (two), Liberia (one) and Sierra Leone

(one). However, nearly all of the recoveries from Senegal and Mali have been retraps from intensive expeditionary work, and British & Irish Sedge Warblers are undoubtedly more widely distributed within the wintering range. It is notable that 10 of the 12 recoveries from south of the Sahara with known cause of death were of birds deliberately taken by Man. Despite their limitations, the African recoveries reveal remarkable differences in wintering quarters for birds ringed in different parts of Britain & Ireland. All trans-Saharan recoveries of Irish-ringed Sedge Warblers have occurred in western Senegal (mainly in the Parc National du Djoudj), along with most from southwest Britain, while most of the birds recovered further east in West Africa were ringed in eastern Britain (Table 1).

Territorial behaviour has been reported for Sedge Warblers in several wintering countries (*BWP*). In Kenya and Uganda, local movements occurred to exploit swarms of flies but many birds remained on their winter territories for several weeks (Pearson 1972, 1982). Ringing studies in Nigeria and Uganda indicate fidelity to wintering sites between years (Pearson 1972, Elgood 1982). In Uganda, up to 50% of wintering Sedge Warblers were estimated to return to the same site in the following year (Pearson 1972). Lower retrap rates in northern Senegal (Sauvage *et al* 1998) may reflect a relatively high prevalence of passage birds in that area.

In West Africa, spring migration begins in late February, and the first birds reach their breeding grounds in France by late March and Britain by early April. Pre-migratory fattening often takes place at wetland sites south of the Sahara (Fig 4) and can involve passage birds remaining for two to three weeks in one location (*BWP*). Having crossed the desert, Sedge Warblers probably need to replenish fat reserves in either North Africa or Iberia in order to reach breeding grounds further north (Ash 1969). Most birds have passed through North Africa by mid-April and most have crossed the Mediterranean by early May (*BWP*).

Overall, there is little information within the ring-recovery database on juvenile, natal and breeding dispersal. The small numbers of recoveries of dead birds suggest that site-fidelity may be high, however. Three Sedge Warblers ringed as nestlings were recovered dead 0–4 km

Table 1. Exchanges between African countries south of the Sahara and regions of Britain & Ireland. Recoveries from abroad before 1979 are excluded.

Area of Africa	Area of Britain & Ireland				
	Ireland	Southwest	Northwest	Southeast	Northeast
Senegal	25	37	2	18	1
Further east	0	8	1	14	3

Fig 5. Locations in autumn of (a) 2,021 first-year and (b) 580 older Sedge Warblers present in Britain & Ireland during part of the year.

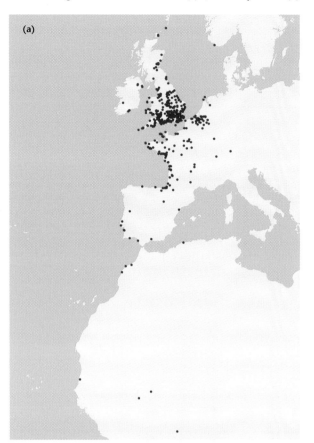

Fig 6. Recovery locations and all included exchanges between Britain & Ireland and abroad of Sedge Warblers not confirmed as being British & Irish breeders. Those birds present in Britain & Ireland during (a) autumn (702) and (b) spring (133) are shown separately from (c) those known to be seasonally inaccurate (64).

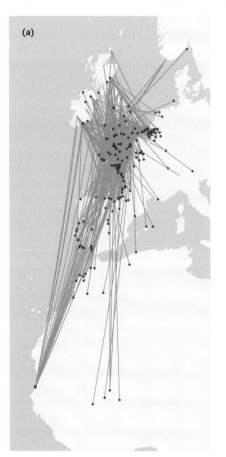

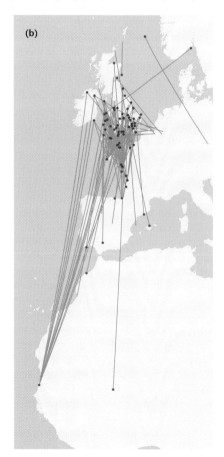

from their ringing site in a subsequent breeding season and three ringed as breeding adults were recovered dead 0–12 km from the ringing site during a subsequent breeding season. Intensive studies suggest that males show a high degree of fidelity to breeding sites but females less so; in Nottinghamshire, a third of returning males bred on or within 50 m of their previous territory and only 14% moved more than 400 m (Catchpole 1972). Similarly, in Oxfordshire, most returning males used their previous territory or an adjacent one but females moved further (Christmas 1978). At the Nottinghamshire study site, there was no evidence of fidelity to the natal area by birds breeding for the first time (Catchpole 1970, 1972), although in Lancashire a proportion of first-time breeders were from local nests (Kennedy 1978).

A small number of exchanges of Sedge Warblers between Norway and England suggest that an unknown proportion of Scandinavian birds may pass through Britain during autumn and spring passage (Fig 6).

British & Irish Sedge Warblers appear to depend for pre-migratory fattening in autumn on a relatively small number of wetland (particularly reedbed) sites scattered across southern Britain and France and depend, in spring, on similar sites south of the Sahara and probably in North Africa and Iberia. Many wetland sites in Europe and Africa are threatened with drainage and degradation, and the continued loss of such sites could limit breeding populations in future. The availability of freshwater habitats over the extensive floodplains of the Senegal and Niger Rivers, where many birds are thought to winter, is dependent upon abundant summer rainfall over large catchment areas. The extent of wetland habitats south of the Sahara in West Africa has fluctuated enormously since the late 1960s in response to a series of devastating droughts. This probably accounts for the highly variable (and sometimes high) mortality rates and fluctuating population levels of Sedge Warblers in Britain & Ireland (Peach *et al* 1991). Another potential threat to many trans-Saharan migrants is the continued expansion of the Sahara Desert due to drought and increased land drainage and grazing (Biber & Salathé 1991).

More ringing would help to establish the true extent of Sedge Warbler wintering areas and differentiate those areas used by birds from different regions of Britain & Ireland. It is unlikely that reporting rates from West Africa will increase enough to produce this information via recoveries, and therefore more ringing in the wintering area would be valuable. Such ringing could also provide more information on fidelity to wintering sites, winter habitat use and related threats to populations.

Will Peach

Eurasian Reed Warbler
(Reed Warbler)
Acrocephalus scirpaceus

This brown unstreaked warbler enlivens reedbeds during the summer with its repetitive song. While identification of the Reed Warbler in Britain & Ireland is not a great problem, in winter quarters south of the Sahara the difficulty of distinguishing it from similar species highlights the importance of ringing studies as the primary tool for understanding its migrations and population biology.

The two subspecies, nominate *scirpaceus,* which occurs from Ireland and Morocco east to the Volga, and *fuscus* from the Caucasus and north Caspian through Iran to Kazakhstan (*European Atlas*), are predominantly birds of mid-latitude lowlands between 60°N and 40°N, but extending south to 30°N in Morocco, Israel and Iran (*BWP*). In Britain & Ireland, the breeding population is estimated to be 40,000–80,000 pairs, *c* 1–3% of the European population (*1988–91 Atlas, European Atlas*). Although stands of the Common Reed are found widely throughout Britain, they occurs more commonly in low-lying southern and eastern England (Perring & Walters 1976), where its distribution by 10-km squares correlates closely with both the abundance and distribution of breeding Reed Warblers. The range of the species has spread markedly north and west in recent decades, and now includes eastern Ireland. Southwest Scotland was colonized in 1993 but, elsewhere in Scotland, Reed Warblers breed sporadically (Murray 1999), and the Irish population is represented by only 40–50 singing males (*1988–91 Atlas*).

Reed Warblers are trans-Saharan migrants but the extent of their wintering range has been difficult to determine since both subspecies are morphologically and genetically closely related to the African Reed Warbler (Helbig & Seibold 1999), and can only reliably be distinguished

The analysis of the data for this species was supported by Malcolm Calvert

in the hand (van den Brink & Loske 1990). Ringing has shown that western populations of nominate *scirpaceus* migrate southwest, entering North Africa via Morocco. Central and eastern European populations of *scirpaceus* (including some German birds), together with *fuscus* from further east, depart south or southeastwards, entering Africa via the eastern end of the Mediterranean (Dowsett-Lemaire & Dowsett 1987). The wintering distribution reflects these two separate routes into Africa: Reed Warblers occur in West Africa from Senegal to Nigeria (*scirpaceus*), and in the east from Sudan south to Zambia (*fuscus*) (Dowsett-Lemaire & Dowsett 1987), with both races occurring in the Congo Basin and records from Botswana and Namibia of mainly *fuscus* but also *scirpaceus* (van den Brink & Loske 1990). Despite their strong association with reedbed and wetland habitats for breeding and on passage (Cantos & Tellería 1994, Honza & Literak 1997), Reed Warblers are found in a variety of African habitats, predominantly those with low trees and rank vegetation, but ranging from dry grassland or scrub and bushes in gardens, to marshland with papyrus, reedmace and reedbeds (Dowsett-Lemaire & Dowsett 1987).

The ringing locations in Britain & Ireland for birds later recovered are broadly similar to the breeding distribution (Fig 1). Most recoveries have been of birds ringed as juveniles, typically in July to September; only 7% of recoveries have been from birds ringed as nestlings (Fig 2). Recaptures

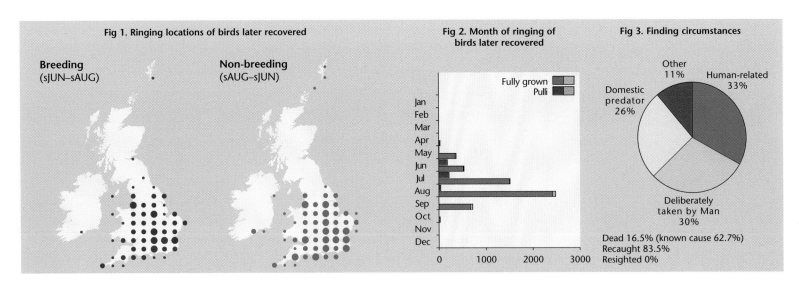

Fig 1. Ringing locations of birds later recovered

Breeding
(sJUN–sAUG)

Non-breeding
(sAUG–sJUN)

Fig 2. Month of ringing of birds later recovered

Fully grown
Pulli

Fig 3. Finding circumstances

Other 11%
Human-related 33%
Domestic predator 26%
Deliberately taken by Man 30%

Dead 16.5% (known cause 62.7%)
Recaught 83.5%
Resighted 0%

Ringing and recovery data

	<1960	60–69	70–79	80–89	90–97	Total
RINGING						
BTO ringing totals (%)	1	9	24	30	37	509,082
RECOVERIES						
BTO-ringed (%)	0	7	23	31	38	5,927
Foreign-ringed (%)	←	18	→	32	51	209

Statistical analyses

	Breeding population (sJUN–sAUG)	Wintering population (sNOV–mMAR)
Status	[LONG-DISTANCE MIGRANT]	NONE
Age differences	Not tested	—
Sex differences	Not tested	—
Regional differences	Not tested	—
Finding circumstances	Not tested	—

Fig 4. Dispersal of juvenile Reed Warblers and Sedge Warblers. Points show the median distance moved (km) with time after ringing as pulli, and bars show the interquartile range.

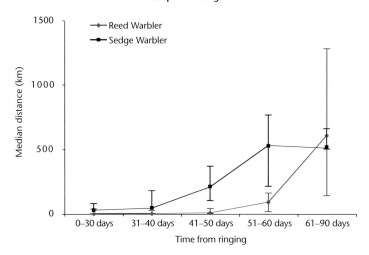

last third of August (*BWP*). Up to 30% of Reed Warbler pairs in England are double-brooded and the passage of juveniles extends into October (*BWP*). Juveniles ringed in June and July are similar to adults with respect to their timing and speed of migration and this implies that the later departure of juveniles overall (Insley & Boswell 1978) is caused by the spread of hatching dates rather than by behavioural differences.

Recoveries of Reed Warblers ringed as nestlings (usually 6–7 days before fledging) provide useful information on the speed and timing of post-fledging dispersal. Although the majority of these recoveries were controls, the results are unlikely to be substantially biased within Britain & Ireland as long as the time-scale and dispersal distances are small. Median distances may be progressively underestimated as a result of lower trapping effort abroad but data from the smaller samples of dead recoveries were similar to those for all recoveries up to 90 days after ringing. Juvenile Reed Warblers initiate a partial post-juvenile moult before migration (Ginn & Melville 1983) and tend not to disperse far from their natal areas until 51–60 days after ringing (Fig 4). In contrast, Sedge Warblers have very little post-juvenile moult on their breeding grounds (Redfern & Alker 1996) and begin dispersal 31–40 days after being ringed as nestlings (Fig 4).

During their southward migration in autumn, Reed Warblers move both east and west along the south coast of England, as do Sedge Warblers (Insley & Boswell 1978). The distribution of autumn recoveries of adults and juveniles ringed in Britain & Ireland in the breeding season suggests that Reed Warblers then cross the Channel, perhaps in a broad front, to the Low Countries and northern France, generally avoiding the higher ground of Brittany, and converge on coastal wetlands of southwest France (Fig 5). Unlike the Sedge Warbler, there are no indications for differences between adults and juveniles in the distribution of recoveries during their migration south. Recoveries of Reed Warblers were particularly numerous in Belgium, and practically all of these were controls by ringers. Many Belgian controls have resulted from the use of high-powered tape-lures to attract birds down during nocturnal migration (Herremans 1990a, b), a capture technique that may give a biased picture of Reed Warbler migration (Schaub *et al* 1999). The scattering of recoveries in north-

by ringers represent over 80% of recoveries of British- & Irish-ringed birds and over 90% of foreign-ringed birds in Britain & Ireland. Consequently, our understanding of Reed Warbler movements based on the total recoveries may be biased by the distribution and activities of ringers in reedbeds. However, recoveries abroad were mainly of dead birds and the few live retraps have had a qualitatively similar distribution.

The cause of death is known for 63% of the recoveries of dead birds, and domestic predators, deliberate taking by Man, and other human-related causes have figured in approximately equal measure (Fig 3). Beyond Britain & Ireland, known deaths were largely a result of being deliberately taken by Man, particularly in Spain, Portugal and Morocco, which between them accounted for over 90% of deaths by hunting.

Adult Reed Warblers start to leave their breeding grounds in Britain & Ireland in late July, with the peak passage across the south coast in the

Fig 5. Locations in (a) August–September (2,084), (b) November (5), (c) December–February (9) and (d) April–May (583) and movements of over 20 km between the breeding season and the period indicated, of Reed Warblers present in Britain & Ireland during the breeding season. Seasonally accurate recoveries (red) are differentiated from those of uncertain seasonality (grey).

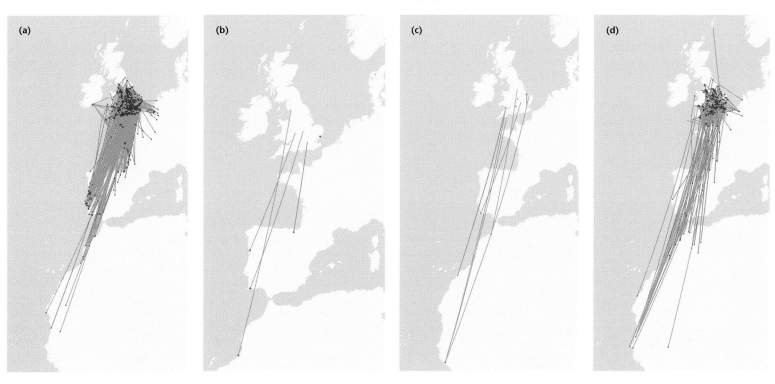

Fig 6. Exchanges with abroad of Reed Warblers not known to be British & Irish breeders and present in Britain & Ireland during (a) autumn (510) and (b) spring (35), or (c) of uncertain seasonality (149).

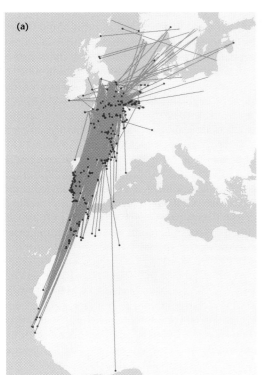

central Spain suggests that the birds make an overland crossing from southwest France to the coast of Portugal. Reed Warblers then cross to Morocco and move down the West African coast, arriving south of 8°N from early or mid-October onwards (Dowsett-Lemaire & Dowsett 1987). The virtual absence of autumn recoveries from the Mediterranean coasts of France and Spain suggests that British & Irish Reed Warblers take an almost exclusively western route south to their wintering grounds. Conversely, nominate *scirpaceus* from further north and east in western Europe pass mostly through Switzerland and the Mediterranean coast of France (*BWP*).

In contrast to the higher migration speeds of the Sedge Warbler (Bensch & Nielsen 1999), Reed Warblers are thought to migrate in short stages (*BWP*). Estimates based on fat deposits suggest a flight range of only 150 km for those passing through Lake Constance in Germany (A Kaiser 1992). With the exception of Belgian recoveries resulting from the use of high-powered tape-lures, recoveries of British & Irish Reed Warblers in France and the Iberian Peninsula may often be at regular stopover sites for migratory fattening (Bibby & Green 1983, Cantos & Tellería 1994). Since juvenile and adult Reed Warblers may start migration while still in body moult (Herremans 1990a), migration in short stages may allow completion of body moult during the journey south. There are no indications of any differences in migration routes between the sexes, nor any apparent differences for birds originating in different regions of Britain & Ireland, in contrast to the results for Sedge Warbler.

Once birds have passed through Morocco, the likelihood of recovery decreases further, so that November recoveries have been mainly distributed along the Portuguese and Moroccan coasts as the last birds move through. Although there have been good numbers of recoveries from West Africa between Mauritania and Guinea-Bissau, most of these were controls from Senegal of birds on passage (Fig 5). For December to February there have been only six recoveries of British- & Irish-ringed Reed Warblers in Africa: these were in Ghana, Morocco, the Gambia and Guinea-Bissau. With so few winter recoveries, it is impossible to determine the precise wintering range of British & Irish Reed Warblers. However, intensive

ringing and retrapping of Reed Warblers in Senegal suggests that some birds winter there, returning to the same area in subsequent winters, but that some also move through on passage (Sauvage *et al* 1998). Ringing studies further east have also shown that Reed Warblers (of unknown origin) may return to the same wintering areas regularly (Aidley & Wilkinson 1987, Dowsett-Lemaire & Dowsett 1987, *BWP*), and mostly undergo a complete moult during November to early March (Pearson 1973).

In March, recoveries indicate that British & Irish Reed Warblers may be passing through West Africa in preparation for a rapid movement north to their breeding grounds. By April, recoveries were scattered from Morocco north to breeding areas in south and east England (Fig 5); the similarity in the distribution of spring and autumn recoveries suggests that the outward and return migrations are along similar routes (Dowsett-Lemaire & Dowsett 1987). However, in contrast to autumn migration, Moroccan recoveries south of the Atlas Mountains in spring indicate that birds return from North Africa on a broader front, possibly taking more direct overland routes and using drier habitats when necessary (Dowsett-Lemaire & Dowsett 1987). Furthermore, Reed Warblers make the return journey more quickly, as shown by the relative paucity of spring recoveries in Iberia and southern France. Although Reed Warblers start to arrive back in southern Britain from mid-April, the main arrivals are not until May (*R & F*). Despite the rapid return journey, the spring migration is protracted and some do not leave Africa until early June; these late birds are unlikely to return to breeding grounds in western Europe until mid-June (Dowsett-Lemaire & Dowsett 1987).

The majority of foreign-ringed Reed Warblers recovered in Britain & Ireland were ringed along the main migration route of birds breeding in Britain & Ireland. However, nearly 25% of foreign recoveries originated from further north and east in Europe and Scandinavia and these were mainly autumn-ringed juveniles subsequently recovered along the south and east coasts of Britain & Ireland (Fig 6). The population of Reed Warblers in Scandinavia and the Baltic States is five to ten times greater than that in Britain & Ireland (*European Atlas*), and it is likely that birds from continental Europe and Scandinavia reach these shores as a result of juvenile dispersal and drift migration, brought in on easterly winds (*R & F*). The few breeding-season recoveries in Scandinavia and the Baltic States of birds ringed in Britain & Ireland in autumn support this view. In addition, the lack of breeding-season recoveries in these areas of birds ringed in Britain & Ireland in spring suggests that Reed Warblers do not pass through Britain & Ireland on their way to breeding grounds further north.

In many species of birds, adults are more faithful to their breeding grounds than juveniles, which disperse from their natal areas (Paradis *et al* 1998). In the Reed Warbler, the availability of suitable reedbed habitat is likely to be a major factor influencing dispersal distances. Juvenile Reed Warblers are markedly site-faithful (*BWP*) and there is no evidence from the recovery data for a marked difference in natal and breeding dispersal. From retrap data for Wicken Fen in Cambridgeshire, estimates of annual return rates for adults between 1970 and 1978 ranged from 49% for males to 63% for females (Redfern 1979); whether this apparent sex difference is a consistent feature of Reed Warbler populations, perhaps resulting from a polygynous breeding system, requires further study. However, the same study found no evidence for sex differences in natal dispersal distances.

The concentration of Reed Warbler recoveries in discrete stopover areas, particularly coastal wetlands of southwest France and Portugal, highlights the importance of maintaining suitable habitat in these areas for migrating birds. Many important sites, however, particularly in popular coastal regions such as the Algarve, are under continuing pressure from development for tourism. Reedbed and wetland habitats are important for breeding and migration but little is known about the habitat requirements and distribution of Reed Warblers in their winter quarters. A much greater understanding of wintering distribution is required to assess the effects of habitat changes in these areas on west European population levels. In view of the morphological similarities of Reed and African Reed Warblers, and the paucity of winter recoveries, ringing studies in the winter range will have a major role in revealing these aspects of Reed Warbler biology. Closer to home, a quantitative understanding of dispersal is important for assessing the contribution of movements to population processes in this species but, as yet, there are insufficient data to compare natal and breeding dispersal and how these might relate to the availability of suitable habitat. Addressing these issues will require more effort to collect and analyse retrap data across networks of sites. Furthermore, studies are needed to quantify the relative importance of domestic predators and other human-related causes (including hunting) for the mortality rates and population levels of the Reed Warblers breeding in Britain & Ireland.

Chris Redfern & Peter Alker

Lesser Whitethroat
Sylvia curruca

The strange rattling song of the Lesser Whitethroat, heard in spring from hedgerows and scrubland mainly in south and east Britain, sets it apart from its British & Irish congeners, as do the routes it follows on migration.

The species is a common summer migrant to the West Palearctic, and to south-central and central Asia. Its breeding range extends from Britain and northern France to southern and central Scandinavia in the north to as far south as Iran, and as far east as Mongolia and the Lena River in Siberia. None nest southwest of a line from England to Israel. Nine subspecies are currently recognized (*BWP*), though several are considered by some authorities to be separate species. The nominate *curruca* is widespread across Europe from England to west Siberia, where it intergrades with the 'Siberian Lesser Whitethroat' *blythi*, which occupies the northeast of the range. All populations are migratory, with eastern races wintering mainly in Arabia, Pakistan or India, while European populations winter just south of the Sahara in northeast and central Africa (*BWP*).

The Lesser Whitethroat breeds extensively across England, eastern Wales and parts of southeast Scotland, and has clearly extended its breeding range since the *1968–72 Atlas*, especially in southern Wales, Anglesey, northern England and southern Scotland (*1988–91 Atlas*). In Ireland, it is a rare but annual spring and autumn migrant, most numerous in October (*Birds in Ireland*). Lesser Whitethroats favour habitats that include tall hedgerows on farmland and along grassy verges by country roads, scrubby patches in open fields, and regrowth in clearings or young plantations, often of conifers (*BWP*). On migration,

The analysis of the data for this species was supported by Roger Taylor

the species becomes extremely skulking, preferring to keep to thorny scrub and dense bushes, often close to water, but is also found in reedbeds, olive groves and in arid open country with low thorny scrub. In the African wintering grounds, Lesser Whitethroats largely inhabit semi-open woodland and dry savannas, as well as scrub thickets by wadis and pools (Moreau 1972, Urban *et al* 1997).

The breeding season ringing locations of birds later recovered (Fig 1) broadly parallel the denser breeding distribution of the species in Britain, lying southeast of a line from the Humber to the Severn Estuary (*1988–91 Atlas*), but probably under-represent the Welsh population. During migration periods there is a strong ringing bias towards southeast England. Most ring-recoveries have come from birds ringed as fully grown juveniles, with only 2% from birds ringed as pulli (Fig 2).

There have been over 400 recoveries of Lesser Whitethroats, of which 42% have been live recaptures by ringers. Of the dead birds, 67% have a documented cause of recovery (Fig 3), with 44% of these directly attributed to human-related accidents such as hitting traffic or overhead wires. The many recoveries (32%) of birds deliberately taken by Man, such as by shooting, snaring or trapping, come mainly from Italy and other countries where hunting is widespread. The legal status of hunting in some countries has changed and this may well influence recovery rates over time.

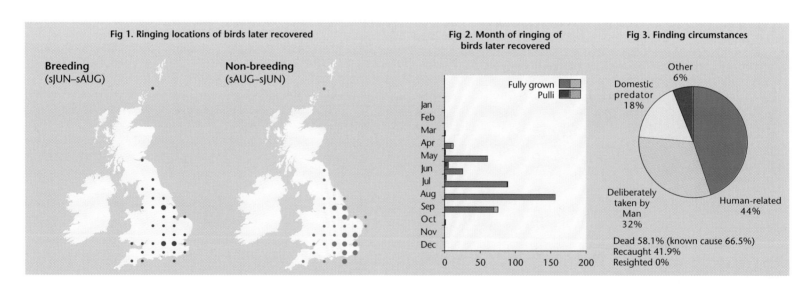

Fig 1. Ringing locations of birds later recovered

Breeding (sJUN–sAUG)

Non-breeding (sAUG–sJUN)

Fig 2. Month of ringing of birds later recovered

Fully grown / Pulli

Jan, Feb, Mar, Apr, May, Jun, Jul, Aug, Sep, Oct, Nov, Dec — 0 50 100 150 200

Fig 3. Finding circumstances

Other 6%
Domestic predator 18%
Deliberately taken by Man 32%
Human-related 44%

Dead 58.1% (known cause 66.5%)
Recaught 41.9%
Resighted 0%

Ringing and recovery data

	<1960	60–69	70–79	80–89	90–97	Total
RINGING						
BTO ringing totals (%)	3	12	24	35	26	93,513
RECOVERIES						
BTO-ringed (%)	3	14	21	37	25	414
Foreign-ringed (%)	←	33	→	28	39	18

Statistical analyses

	Breeding population (sJUN–sAUG)	Wintering population (mOCT–sMAR)
Status	[LONG-DISTANCE MIGRANT]	NONE
Age differences	Not tested	—
Sex differences	Not tested	—
Regional differences	Not tested	—
Finding circumstances	Not tested	—

Fig 4. Locations in (a) August–October (146), (b) March–April (43) and (c) May–July (173), and movements of over 20 km of Lesser Whitethroats. Birds present in Britain & Ireland during the breeding season (red) are differentiated from those present during other seasons (grey). Two birds ringed outside the breeding season and recovered in Egypt during November–December are not shown. There are no January–February recoveries.

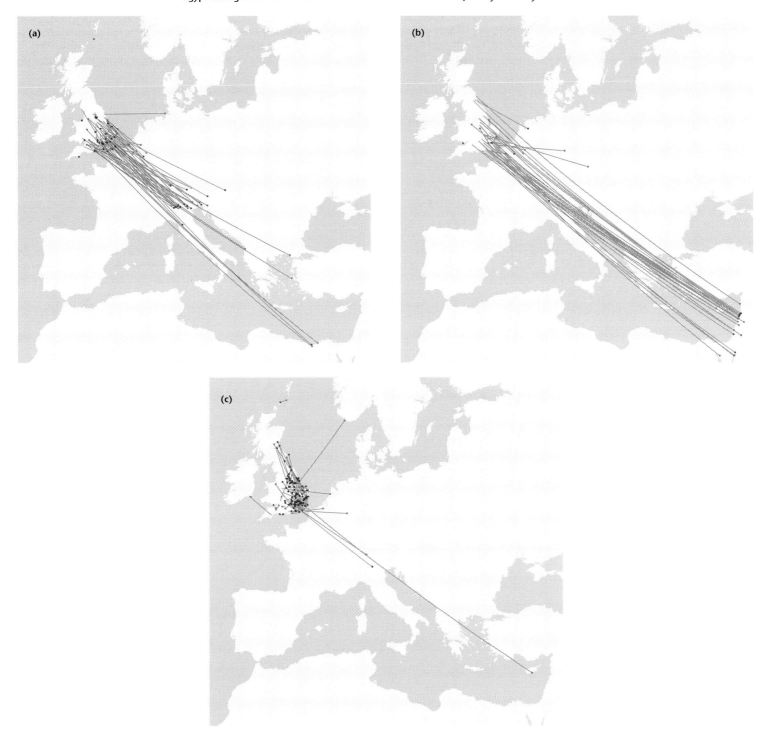

Dispersal from the breeding grounds appears to coincide with the near completion of moult, in both juvenile and adult birds (Norman 1992). These movements usually start in mid-July in Britain, in a mainly southward direction, though many juveniles appear to be more random in their direction over the autumn period before eventually moving southeast (Rabøl 1973). The weights of birds caught during this period suggest that only short-stage overnight flights, for example to staging areas on the south coast of England, are possible. Peak departures of birds from the south coast occur at the end of August and beginning of September, with a second wave of passage in September, possibly involving reorientating birds both from Britain and the near Continent

(R & F). Fat-loads of departing migrants from the British coastline are generally less in this species than in other British *Sylvia* warblers, and it is estimated that the average flight-range for departing Lesser Whitethroats is about 770 km (Ellegren & Fransson 1992). The numerous autumn recoveries from northern Italy of birds ringed on the British breeding grounds fit well with this estimated flight-range (Fig 4a); this area appears to be a main stopover area in which birds refuel before continuing their migration. Interestingly, there are few recoveries of British-ringed breeding birds further east than northern Italy (Fig 4a), suggesting perhaps that British birds cross the eastern Mediterranean from Italy or Greece. Autumn recoveries of birds reported in the Aegean and northern

Sinai areas were mostly ringed as autumn passage birds (Fig 4a). These more easterly recoveries indicate that some birds make a second stopover before heading south to cross the Mediterranean into northern Egypt and then onward to the main wintering grounds of Sudan, Chad, Eritrea and north and central Ethiopia. There are no ring-recoveries of birds from the wintering grounds, however. A heavy passage occurs through northern Sudan in early October with birds reaching western Sudan and Chad from mid-October (Newby 1980). Numbers of birds wintering further west than this are small but regular; sites include northern Nigeria and Mali, and even northern Senegal (Lamarche 1981, Newby *et al* 1987, Urban *et al* 1997).

Little is known about the ecology of Lesser Whitethroats in their wintering grounds. Birds do not appear to hold firm winter territories but move around within wide but delimited areas for short periods (*BWP*). However, there is evidence of winter site-fidelity from five birds ringed in Ethiopia and retrapped there two years later (Ash 1981).

The spring migration from wintering areas starts as early as late January, continuing until late April or early May. Passage birds have been recorded in Ethiopia and Israel in January but departures of birds wintering further west are much later, most leaving northern Nigeria and Chad in March or early April, and central Ethiopia mainly by mid-March (Urban *et al* 1997). Northward migration to the Levant coastline is much in evidence by March (Fig 4b), perhaps skipping northeast Egypt altogether, suggesting that birds pass further east in the spring than they do in the autumn, as do several other species from further south. The passage of birds at Eilat in Israel, for example, is far greater in the spring than it is in the autumn (Shirihai 1996). Birds then take a northwesterly heading to cross continental Europe on a line very similar to that taken in the autumn (Fig 4b), reaching southern Britain by late April (Fig 4b, *R & F*). More northerly breeding populations in continental Europe return much later, from mid-May and into June (*BWP*).

Evidence from long-term ringing studies suggests that site-fidelity to the breeding area is very strong in this species (Boddy 1994). One long-term study at a site in northeast England has shown the average return rate of adult birds to be 23%, with 88% of recaptures of returning birds occurring at the original ringing site rather than at alternate sites (Norman 1992).

The extraordinary concentrations that are apparent on both autumn and spring migration may mean that Lesser Whitethroats are more susceptible than many Palearctic–African migrants to ecological change (Shirihai 1996). Few studies have been undertaken on the habitat, or indeed food requirements, of Lesser Whitethroats during migration. Even less is known about this species on its wintering grounds in Africa. Additional ringing of the species within Britain and Africa may perhaps identify the chief wintering areas and movements within these important regions. More detailed studies of the species on the wintering grounds are certainly required in order to understand its needs in an environment of fast ecological change.

Jeff Baker

Common Whitethroat (Whitethroat)
Sylvia communis

The Whitethroat is one of the characteristic breeding birds of open scrub, hedgerow and young woodland throughout Britain and much of Ireland, except for the highest uplands (*1988–91 Atlas*). Though not as common as it once was, its darting display flights, obvious white throat, and scratchy song render it conspicuous.

All Whitethroat populations are totally migratory. The nominate race breeds in western Europe and northwest Africa, east to Scandinavia, Poland, Austria and northern Greece (*BWP*), wintering in the northern tropics from West Africa east to Sudan (Urban *et al* 1997). Three other races, *volgensis* (breeding in eastern Europe and west Siberia), *icterops* (Turkey, Near East, and west and north Iran), and *rubicola* (east Iran and Afghanistan, to northwest China and western Mongolia) winter farther east and south in Africa than *communis*, with some birds reaching northern South Africa (*BWP*, Urban *et al* 1997). Nominate *communis* remain throughout the winter mainly in the semi-arid northern Sahel zone, at 12–18°N, unlike most other small insectivorous migrants (*BWP*). Vegetation there is largely grassy steppe with patches of *Acacia* and evergreen and semi-evergreen trees and scrub, where the birds forage.

Breeding Whitethroats are more abundant in east and south-central England than elsewhere in Britain & Ireland. To the north and west, concentrations tend to be in coastal areas where scrubby woodland and hedgerows are common (*1988–91 Atlas*). Whitethroats are caught at *c* 70% of Constant Effort Sites each year (Peach *et al* 1998). Nevertheless, birds from the southeast of Britain are over-represented in the sample of recoveries available (Fig 1). Many Whitethroats are ringed while on autumn passage, increasing the proportion of recoveries from more southerly regions (Figs 1 & 2).

The analysis of the data for this species was supported by Mike & Frances Boddy

A quarter of Whitethroat recoveries have been live recaptures. The vast majority of these (96%) were in Britain & Ireland, with just nine birds recaptured abroad. Nearly two-thirds of Whitethroat ring-recoveries from dead birds had a known cause of death (Fig 3). The numbers of recoveries (dead) abroad of birds ringed in Britain & Ireland declined from 52% of all dead recoveries in the 1950s, and 43% in the 1960s, to only 12% during 1980–97. This may be because recoveries of birds deliberately taken by humans, mostly in southern Europe, have become less frequent in recent years. Of all the recoveries of dead birds that had a cause of death attributed, fewer than 2% within Britain & Ireland fell into this category, compared with 92% of those in Spain and Portugal.

Southward migration of Whitethroats begins in late July, with the peak movement during mid- to late August (*R & F*). Numbers leaving throughout September steadily decline, and a few stragglers remain as late as the third week of October. The migration of first-year birds appears to begin just before that of adults (da Prato & da Prato 1983), probably because of the earlier start and completion of body moult by some juveniles; most adults do not complete moult until at least mid-August (Boddy 1992). The British & Irish ring-recovery data show that four juvenile Whitethroats recovered in June had made only local movements (5 km or less). During July, 24% of juveniles had moved 6–25 km, none had moved 26–100 km and 8% had moved over 100 km

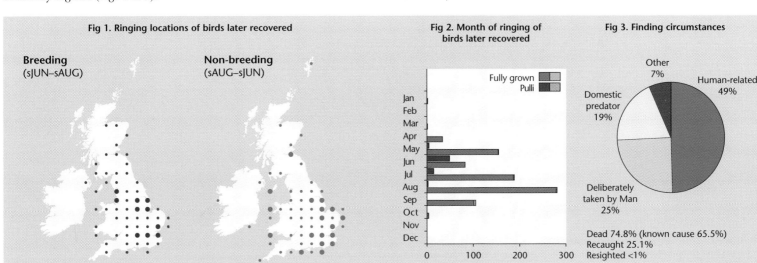

Fig 1. Ringing locations of birds later recovered

Breeding (sJUN–sAUG)

Non-breeding (sAUG–sJUN)

Fig 2. Month of ringing of birds later recovered

Fully grown
Pulli

Jan
Feb
Mar
Apr
May
Jun
Jul
Aug
Sep
Oct
Nov
Dec

0   100   200   300

Fig 3. Finding circumstances

Other 7%
Human-related 49%
Domestic predator 19%
Deliberately taken by Man 25%

Dead 74.8% (known cause 65.5%)
Recaught 25.1%
Resighted <1%

Ringing and recovery data

	<1960	60–69	70–79	80–89	90–97	Total
RINGING						
BTO ringing totals (%)	15	23	14	20	28	276,010
RECOVERIES						
BTO-ringed (%)	17	31	12	18	22	907
Foreign-ringed (%)	←	50	→	15	35	20

Statistical analyses

	Breeding population (sJUN–sAUG)	Wintering population (sNOV–sAPR)
Status	[LONG-DISTANCE MIGRANT]	NONE
Age differences	Not tested	—
Sex differences	Not tested	—
Regional differences	Not tested*	—
Finding circumstances	Not tested	—

Table 1. Percentages of adult and first-year Whitethroats capable of flights from Lincolnshire to northern France (up to 425 km) or northern Iberia (1,200 km) in still air, without further refuelling. Estimates are based on calculations using Program 1 from Pennycuick (1989), wingspan from Baggott (1986), and fat-free body mass during migration from Ellegren & Fransson (1992). Data from 1981–91 at Theddlethorpe, Saltfleetby–Theddlethorpe Dunes NNR (pers obs).

	Flight range	Aug 1–15	Aug 16–31	Sep 1–15	Sep 16–30
Adults	N France (>15 g)	0	16	33	100
	N Spain (>19 g)	0	2	5	42
	Sample size	76	64	21	12
First-years	N France (>15 g)	7	15	26	45
	N Spain (>19 g)	0	0	1	6
	Sample size	942	809	245	62

(*n*=25). In August and September, 13% of movements were of 26–100 km, with 41% over 100 km (*n*=155). Recoveries under 25 km showed undirected post-juvenile dispersal. Longer movements in Britain were generally between southeast and southwest, apart from one bird that moved east from Devon to Kent.

Whitethroats in southeast Scotland appear to leave the area shortly after breeding, without a noticeable gain in body-weight (da Prato & da Prato 1983). Farther south, on the Lincolnshire coast, mean weights of both adult and first-year Whitethroats, including birds known to be of local origin, rise considerably as the migration period progresses (pers obs). An increasing proportion of the birds caught later in the season, especially adults, are thus capable of a long unbroken southward flight (Table 1). Ellegren & Fransson (1992) also reported a significant positive correlation between fat-load, hence increasing flight range, and the progress of autumn for migrant Whitethroats in southeast Sweden. Flight ranges calculated for Whitethroats caught on Bardsey Island in autumn indicated that most could have reached northern France, but not Iberia, in a single flight (Baggott 1986). There are far fewer recoveries of adults in Britain & Ireland during autumn than in spring, which may suggest a strategy of flights direct to France or Iberia, as originally proposed by da Prato & da Prato (1983).

The majority of Whitethroats probably take the shorter south or southeast route across the English Channel, perhaps landing in northern France, before subsequently heading south-southwest towards Iberia. Of birds ringed in autumn on the south coast, and recovered abroad in the same autumn, 86% were from Kent or Sussex and all recovery directions lay between south-southeast and southwest. There are relatively few recoveries from northern France, and none from Brittany. Concentrations further south in France, and especially northern Spain and Portugal (Fig 4a) may have been caused by the distribution of hunting pressure, especially in earlier years. Whitethroats appear to overfly northern France regularly *en route* to Iberia; biometrics show that some birds are capable of doing so late in the migration period (Table 1). Autumn recoveries show a pronounced southwestern orientation along the Atlantic coasts of France and Iberia (Fig 4a). No British- or Irish-ringed Whitethroats have

Fig 4. Locations of Whitethroats in (a) autumn (78:38:265), (b) winter (2:1:18) and (c) spring (31:51:187). Birds known to be British & Irish breeders and recovered as first-years (red) or older birds (blue) are differentiated from those of uncertain seasonality, age or breeding population (grey). Sample sizes of the three classes (first years:older birds:uncertain) are shown.

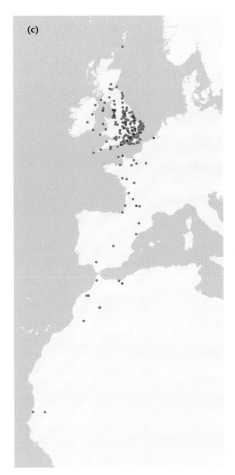

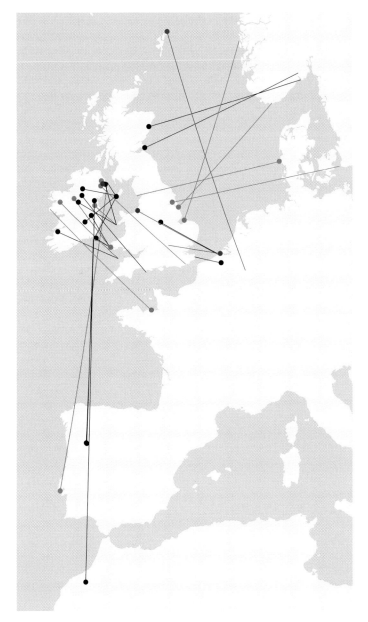

Fig 5. Recovery locations and all included exchanges of Whitethroats involving Ireland, and involving countries north of France. Birds present in Britain (or Ireland) in the breeding season (4, red), autumn (7, blue) and spring (18, black) are differentiated from those of uncertain seasonality (6, grey). The 2 pre-1979 foreign-ringed Whitethroats (from Germany and the Netherlands) are not shown.

are high (Alerstam 1990a, Biebach 1992). Autumn passage of Whitethroats in northwest Africa commences in late August and lasts to early November but stopovers in the region are rare (*Der Zug*, Urban *et al* 1997). There have been just four autumn recoveries of British-ringed birds in northwest Africa, all on or close to the Atlantic coast of Morocco during September and October (Fig 4a). The main arrival in the Sahel region is in late September and early October, though a few birds arrive at the end of August (*BWP*). Passage through northern Senegal during October and November suggests that some birds winter farther south. The species is common in Nigeria from early October, and in northern Ghana from November (Urban *et al* 1997), though these birds may not include any from Britain or Ireland. Six British-ringed Whitethroats have been reported from south of the Sahara, five in Senegal and one in Burkina Faso, between mid-September and April. A bird ringed in Belgium was recovered in Senegal, with one each from Germany to Ghana, Sweden to Chad, and Finland to western Sudan (*BWP*). These limited data suggest that birds breeding in northwest Europe (including Britain & Ireland) winter further west in Africa than those from farther east. Birds ringed in Nigeria have been found on passage in Libya (two) and Egypt (Urban *et al* 1997).

It is likely that at least some Whitethroats spend the northern winter at the same sites in Africa in successive years, though there is only limited published evidence for this (Ash 1980, 1981, Stoate 1995, Sauvage *et al* 1998). Wintering densities of the species in the Sahel appear to follow invertebrate abundance associated with different tree species (Jones *et al* 1996, Stoate 1997), and in Senegal are higher in woodland than savanna (Morel & Betlem 1992). Very small numbers of Whitethroats may attempt to overwinter north of the Sahara (Fig 4b). Just seven birds, probably late migrants, were recorded in the second half of November, and another was seen in late December, during three winters of intensive fieldwork for the *Winter Atlas*. There are no December or February, and just two January, recoveries from Iberia. A late March recovery in London may have been an exceptionally early migrant.

Northward migration through Africa normally commences in March (*BWP*), with a strong passage in northern Senegal from late March to mid-April. One Whitethroat ringed in Senegal in mid-March had reached Lancashire by 1 May. Few birds remain in West Africa by early May (*BWP*, Urban *et al* 1997). Whitethroats showed significant increases in body-mass from ringing to recapture in northern Senegal in mid-March (Stoate & Moreby 1995). Many Whitethroats stop to fatten at Lake Chad where they put on as much as 30–40% of body-mass, probably in order to overfly the Sahara at its widest point (Fry *et al* 1970); their weights are then similar to the highest weights recorded in autumn in Lincolnshire (pers obs). Due to the prevailing northerly winds, the flight to North Africa is especially hazardous, requiring precise timing to take advantage of any temporarily clement weather conditions (Alerstam 1990a). Following winter rains in North Africa, Whitethroats can readily refuel there in spring before crossing the Mediterranean. Spring passage in North Africa is much more conspicuous and on a broader front than in autumn, with more sightings in the Sahara (*BWP*, Urban *et al* 1997). The main passage in Morocco and Algeria is from late March to mid-May (Urban *et al* 1997). Movement of Whitethroats through Gibraltar commences in March, peaking in late April, with males preceding females (Finlayson 1992).

The migration route used from West Africa to Britain & Ireland in spring appears to be more direct than that used in autumn (Fig 4c). All recoveries of British & Irish Whitethroats from northern Africa in spring have been in Morocco, commencing in April. The reporting sites there were more widely spread than for the autumn recoveries, and were mainly inland. The northward movement progresses mostly over eastern Spain and then through western France. There are no recoveries in spring in western Iberia. Arrivals in Britain appear to be on a broad front, but possibly somewhat earlier in the southwest (R & F). The first Whitethroats are seen at Portland in early April, with the largest numbers recorded there in the first half of May. Earliest arrivals elsewhere usually begin in mid-April, with the main immigration occurring in mid-May (Davis 1967, R & F). Considerable annual variations in arrival dates may occur, because

been recovered farther east than northern France during autumn, and only 10 have occurred east of the Greenwich meridian. Just one recovery was reported from southern Iberia before September, and none in Morocco until October. Most birds had reached Iberia by the end of September, and the majority appeared to have moved on by November. Both adult and first-year Whitethroats occurred in Coto Doñana, southwest Spain, throughout August–October, with over 80% of the total birds present during September (Herrera 1974). Many birds refuel in Iberia, with stopovers of up to three weeks recorded (*BWP*). Whitethroats increased body mass by over 0.4 g per day in northeast Portugal during August and early September (Ferns 1975).

Some migrating Whitethroats may attempt to cross both the Mediterranean, at or near its narrowest point, and the Sahara in a direct flight from Iberia, while others may fly as far as possible over hospitable terrain, along the Moroccan coastline, before crossing the Sahara. At this time of year, the prospects of locating good tail-winds to boost travel speed of the influence of the weather along the migration route. Passage probably continues into early June but is difficult to assess because of the presence of birds already on territory. Males arrive in Britain, on average, earlier than females by seven or eight days (da Prato & da Prato 1983, Boddy 1992). Also, adults of known age were caught earlier on their second or later return from Africa than on their first return, males by six days and females by four days (Boddy 1992). British & Irish ringing data show that the median recovery distance for Whitethroats ringed in one breeding season, and recovered (dead) in a later one, is only 3 km ($P5-95=0-26$ km, $n=8$). More male Whitethroats than females returned to a previous breeding site (da Prato & da Prato 1983, Boddy 1993). For birds ringed as juveniles, twice as many males as females returned to their ringing site in the following year, with almost all breeding dispersal of females occurring on their first or second return from Africa (Boddy 1993).

Few Whitethroats breeding abroad seem to be involved in passage through Britain & Ireland. Birds from continental Europe show a weak migratory divide at about 10°E. To the west of this, Whitethroats head west of south to Iberia, and to the east towards the central or eastern Mediterranean (*Der Zug*). Five birds ringed in Sweden and Norway have been recovered near the British east coast, two in spring and three in autumn, and clearly do not belong to the British breeding population (Fig 5). Whitethroats that arrive on Fair Isle in September and early October, during east or southeast winds, may also be from northern parts of the species' continental breeding range (Davis 1967, *R & F*). Six birds exchanged with Belgium and the Netherlands were mainly, if not entirely, British breeders on passage. The only other recoveries from north or east of France involved a British-bred bird reported in Denmark, and a Whitethroat of unknown origin ringed in Germany.

Rather little is currently known about where British & Irish Whitethroats spend the winter months, or the routes they take through Africa to get there. Ringing expeditions in Africa, on the scale of that undertaken in Senegal in the 1990s, are necessary to obtain sufficient ring-recovery data. Such studies in West Africa have begun to provide an understanding of the problems facing Whitethroats in the Sahel (Stoate & Moreby 1995, Jones *et al* 1996, Stoate 1997). The British and western European breeding populations are almost certainly being limited by lack of rainfall there, together with increased desertification caused partially by human pressures (Winstanley *et al* 1974, Baillie & Peach 1992, Peach *et al* 1998). Scientifically directed ringing and related studies in the Sahel should be encouraged and supported. Within Britain, hedgerow management and scrub destruction have greatly reduced potential breeding habitat since the 1960s or earlier. Where suitable habitat remains, Whitethroat densities can still be high (Boddy 1993). Ireland is extremely under-represented in the British & Irish ring-recovery data for Whitethroats (Figs 1 & 5), and would merit some concentrated effort. To assess any future changes in migration routes or wintering areas, it is important that ringing continues to provide adequate samples of Whitethroats, especially as only one bird in every 300 ringed is recovered (Toms *et al* 1999).

Mike Boddy

Garden Warbler
Sylvia borin

The Garden Warbler, though unexceptional in appearance, appears supremely adapted to the life style of a trans-Saharan migrant passerine. Through a concerted programme of field and laboratory studies of this species (*eg* Bairlein 1987, 1991, Berthold 1991, 1993, 1996), a great deal has been learnt about how this and other long-distance migrants complete their remarkable annual cycles. For example, hand-reared captive birds exhibited gonadal growth and regression, moult and migratory restlessness at appropriate seasons, and all in the absence of external cues such as changing day-length, thus demonstrating an innate circannual rhythm (Berthold 1996, Gwinner 1996).

Garden Warblers nest throughout the middle and northern latitudes of the West Palearctic from southern Spain, Ireland and northern Norway east to the Caucasus, and beyond the Urals into western Siberia, a range lying mainly between the July isotherms of 12°C and 28°C (*BWP*). The nominate race *borin* occurs in western Europe and throughout Fennoscandia, intergrading with the Russian race *woodwardi* over a broad zone of central Europe. In winter, the entire population shifts to Africa, where it is found from Senegal east to Kenya and south to Angola and Kwazulu-Natal. Nominate *borin* is common in West Africa and in central Africa, though its winter quarters overlap considerably with *woodwardi*, which is the more common race in eastern and southern Africa; in the drier areas of western southern Africa, *woodwardi* may perhaps occur exclusively (*BWP*).

The Garden Warbler's breeding range extends into cooler regions than are occupied by most other *Sylvia* warblers (*European Atlas*). At high latitudes or in montane woodlands, birds may arrive in mid-May or later and depart as early as late July. With such a relatively short breeding

The analysis of the data for this species was supported by the Dartford Ringing Group

season, these populations are particularly vulnerable to adverse weather (Widmer 1996). Young develop faster in the nest than those of the closely related Blackcap (Berthold *et al* 1970).

Garden Warblers are widely distributed in Britain in suitable woodland, although most abundant in Wales and the southern half of England, and mostly absent from the Isle of Man and from Scotland to the north and west of the Great Glen (*1988–91 Atlas*). In Ireland, breeding is highly localized (Herbert 1991). The *1988–91 Atlas* estimated that there were 200,000 breeding territories in Britain and just 180–300 pairs in Ireland. Breeding pairs favour glades, edges and regrowth in deciduous woodland and tall scrub. Winter habitats are similar, including savanna woodlands and bush, gardens, secondary growth and clearings in forests and riverine thickets, in places at altitudes over 2,000 m (*BWP*).

The ring-recoveries from ringing in the breeding season originate from most parts of Britain & Ireland where the species is common but with a bias towards eastern England (Fig 1). Since Garden Warblers do not nest in Shetland, birds ringed there in the breeding season are likely to be late spring migrants. During passage seasons, many Garden Warblers have been ringed on Fair Isle and at English bird observatories between Spurn Point and Portland Bill, as well as on the breeding grounds. Relatively few recoveries have come from birds ringed as nestlings (Fig 2). As for most small migrant passerines, ring-recovery rates for Garden

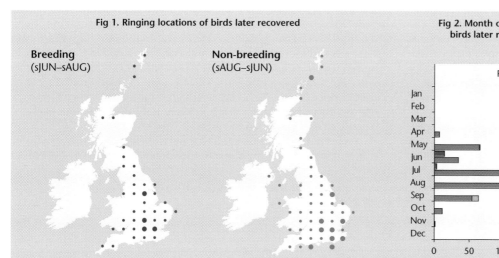

Fig 1. Ringing locations of birds later recovered

Breeding (sJUN–sAUG)

Non-breeding (sAUG–sJUN)

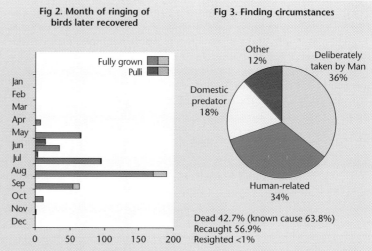

Fig 2. Month of ringing of birds later recovered

Fully grown
Pulli

Fig 3. Finding circumstances

Other 12%

Deliberately taken by Man 36%

Domestic predator 18%

Human-related 34%

Dead 42.7% (known cause 63.8%)
Recaught 56.9%
Resighted <1%

Ringing and recovery data

	<1960	60–69	70–79	80–89	90–97	Total
RINGING						
BTO ringing totals (%)	4	13	18	33	33	120,860
RECOVERIES						
BTO-ringed (%)	1	9	16	36	37	454
Foreign-ringed (%)	←	40	→	34	26	47

Statistical analyses

	Breeding population (sJUN–sAUG)	Wintering population (mNOV–mMAR)
Status	[LONG-DISTANCE MIGRANT]	NONE
Age differences	Not tested	—
Sex differences	Not tested	—
Regional differences	Not tested	—
Finding circumstances	Not tested	—

Fig 4. Locations in autumn, and movements of over 20 km between the breeding and autumn, of 92 Garden Warblers present in Britain & Ireland during the breeding season.

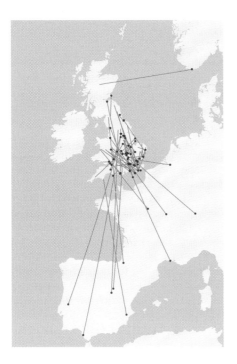

Fig 5. Locations of Garden Warblers in September (65, red) and October (17, blue). Known British & Irish breeders (bold) are differentiated from other or unknown breeding populations (halftone). Note that there are no locations for known British & Irish breeders in October.

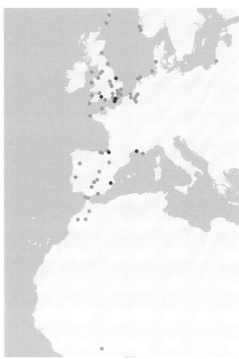

Warblers are very low. Known causes of death are predominantly through hunting or are related to other human activities or artefacts (Fig 3).

The autumn passage of this species is evident at British bird observatories during a long period from late July to early November, within which two peaks are apparent (*R & F*). The first of these, in late August or early September, predominates on the east and south coasts, where the species occurs in higher numbers than are observed later in the autumn. It is likely that a high proportion of these birds are departing adults and young from the British & Irish population. The later peak in late September or early October is stronger at the west coast observatories, Spurn and Fair Isle, and probably originates mainly from the Continent (*R & F*).

Ring-recoveries suggest a convergence of departing British birds in August and September onto the Sussex coast, involving birds from points as diverse as West Wales, the Borders and East Anglia (Fig 4). To some extent, this pattern reflects the high ringing effort in Sussex that is directed each autumn to warblers, but counts at Beachy Head confirm that Garden Warblers are exceptionally abundant there as autumn migrants. Quinn &

Clement (1971) estimated that twice as many Garden Warblers pass through Beachy Head in the autumn as the combined total from seven British bird observatories. The peak of passage is regularly in mid-August (R D M Edgar pers comm), although the highest day-totals, perhaps influenced by influxes of continental birds, have been in the first eight days of September (James 1996). Some individuals may spend several days fattening on elderberries there before departure but most move through rapidly (R D M Edgar pers comm). At a Buckinghamshire site, Garden Warblers were found to move on more quickly than Blackcaps in autumn (Phillips 1994). Four birds ringed in Britain in the breeding season have been recovered in Spain, two in mid-France and one in Switzerland by August (Fig 4). Adults, which delay moult until after arrival in the winter quarters, depart especially early. There is some evidence from ringing on the Continent that Garden Warblers migrate more quickly than Blackcaps: one Swedish-ringed bird was recovered in Italy after only four days and one ringed near Leningrad was in Italy 10 days later (*BWP*).

Recoveries in September and October from British & Irish ringing are scattered widely from the Baltic to the wintering grounds in West Africa

Fig 6. Recovery locations of Garden Warblers south of the Sahara (in any month). Known British & Irish breeders (2, red) are differentiated from those of other or unknown breeding populations (5, grey).

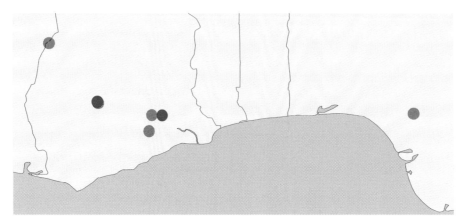

Fig 7. Locations in spring, and movements of over 20 km between the breeding season and spring, of 60 Garden Warblers present in Britain & Ireland during the breeding season.

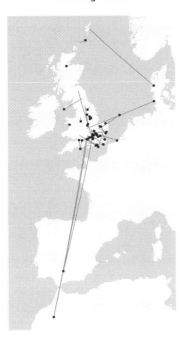

Fig 8. Movements within the same autumn and associated recovery locations of Garden Warblers using Britain & Ireland (17:94). Sample sizes of movements under:over 20 km are given but only those over 20 km are plotted.

fruiting trees or shrubs, particularly *Lantana* which, having been introduced from Mexico, is found in many parts of the African range. Recaptures in several parts of the winter range indicate a degree of wintering site-fidelity, for example in Malawi up to five years after ringing (Hanmer 1986). Garden Warblers begin to move north from Transvaal and Zimbabwe in late February and have left Gabon by mid-March (Urban *et al* 1997). In Nigeria, peak passage is recorded in the second half of April, with some still passing in the last week of May (Smith 1966).

Spring recoveries in Morocco and Spain of birds bound for Britain suggest that the routes followed in autumn and spring are likely to be broadly similar (Fig 7). Garden Warblers are one of the later summer migrants to arrive in Britain & Ireland in spring. Numbers peak in early or mid-May on the Kent coast (*R & F*). A study of BTO nest record cards showed a later peak of egg-laying than for other *Sylvia* warblers, with an overall mean date of 25 May (Mason 1976). While many adults return to former breeding sites, too few British data are available to estimate the extent of natal or true breeding site-fidelity. In the Swiss Alps, Widmer (1996) recorded remarkably high annual return rates of 48% for adults and 6% for pulli.

Observations and ringing returns indicate a substantial through passage of continental Garden Warblers in Britain in both autumn and spring. The second peak of autumn passage at British & Irish coastal sites, believed to consist mainly of continental birds, occurs in early September at Fair Isle, and in late September or early October further south in Britain and in Ireland, although Irish numbers are relatively small (Sharrock 1973, *R & F*, *Birds in Ireland*). This late peak is more evident than the early one at British west-coast sites, such as the Calf of Man and Skokholm that lie beyond the northwest edge of the species' main breeding range (*R & F*). Easterly winds can bring substantial falls of Garden Warblers to British North Sea coasts (*eg* Taylor *et al* 1999). Autumn movements occur in both directions across the North Sea; for example, one ringed in Norfolk on 21 August 1977 was retrapped on Helgoland a month later, and an exceptional bird was ringed in Austria on 22 August 1992 and caught again at Icklesham, East Sussex, on 28 September the same year (Fig 8). In spring, a marked passage at Fair Isle and at Spurn Point in late May and early June is likely to consist largely of displaced continental migrants (*R & F*).

Owing to the field studies undertaken at points along the migration route, the movements of Garden Warblers are, among warblers in general, relatively well understood. However, as with most trans-Saharan migrants, the specific migration routes and wintering areas of the populations breeding in Britain & Ireland are still poorly delineated. More information on seasonal distribution within Britain & Ireland, and more ringing during the breeding season, would help to establish the timings of departure from the breeding grounds and of coastal migration for the British & Irish population, and to disentangle the data for migrants of different origins.

(Fig 5). Most overseas recoveries at this time are from Spain, however. Recoveries further east, from Norway and the east Baltic to the Camargue, are likely to include some from birds originating in Scandinavia or elsewhere on the Continent that were trapped in Britain or Ireland on passage. A small group of recoveries in Morocco suggests that Garden Warblers may begin their Saharan crossing from North Africa rather than southern Europe. Only a limited degree of fattening is found among migrants in Iberia (Cantos & Tellería 1994).

The strategy by which Garden Warblers cross the Sahara is the subject of some controversy. Bairlein (1987) argued that Garden Warblers typically make regular stopovers at desert oases, to avoid the risk of dehydration that would arise during a long flight through the heat of the day. This and other migrants occur in substantial numbers at oases, sometimes gaining weight over a period of a few days. These birds may be the exceptions, however, and an unbroken trans-Saharan flight may be more typical (B Wood 1989). Biebach (1992) found that Garden Warblers in autumn at two North African sites carried enough fat to cross the Sahara in an unbroken flight with the help of the tail-winds that are common at that season. A rapid crossing by at least some Garden Warblers is indicated by arrivals in central Nigeria as early as 19 September for adults and 20 September for an exceptional first-winter bird (Smith 1963). Birds in Nigeria in September carried some fat but many of these had probably arrived south of the Sahara several days earlier (Smith 1963, 1966).

In all, there have been seven recoveries south of the Sahara of Garden Warblers ringed in Britain, of which six were from Ghana and one from Nigeria (Fig 6). Two of these recoveries were from birds ringed in the breeding season, and therefore likely to have been British-bred, whereas the origin of those ringed at passage seasons is less certain. The cluster of recoveries in the range of hills running northwest from Accra, spanning a period from late September into February, suggests that Ghana, and this small area in particular, may be especially important as a wintering area for birds migrating from Britain.

Little is known of the wintering strategy of the species but there is evidence of movements within East Africa in response to rain (*BWP*). Ring-recoveries indicate that Garden Warblers from further east in Europe are found further to the east in the winter range (*Der Zug*, *BWP*, Urban *et al* 1997). Also, there is some evidence that northern breeding populations winter further south than those that breed in southern and central Europe (Berthold 1988). Single Garden Warblers or small parties are attracted to

John H Marchant & Stan da Prato

Blackcap
Sylvia atricapilla

Increasing numbers of Blackcaps have been seen in gardens in winter over the past 40 years and their rich spring song has been heard more often throughout their range. Studies on them have contributed greatly to our knowledge of the control of migration as well as helping to explain changes in their habits. Within England & Wales, breeding Blackcaps are most abundant southeast of a line drawn from the Gower to the Wash. While they occur at widespread localities further north and west, and have been increasing in recent years, their distribution remains patchy. The range in Ireland contracted early in the 20th century but expansion since the 1940s has now led to breeding in every county.

Within the Palearctic, Blackcaps breed between 35°N and 63°N. The population is largely migratory, although there are resident populations in Iberia, parts of France and in northwest Africa (*BWP*). Blackcaps are common migrants along the eastern and southern coasts of Britain and their numbers have risen, especially in autumn (Langslow 1978). Spring and autumn migrants in Britain & Ireland include birds originating in Scandinavia and west-central Europe. There is a migratory divide at about 12°E. To the west of this longitude, populations move south or southwest while those to the east move southeast. Leap-frog migration occurs for Blackcaps and they are common in winter in East Africa (*BWP*).

Migration into Britain begins in early April (Mason 1995) and continues until at least the end of May. Eggs are laid mostly in May (Mason 1976). Breeding Blackcaps inhabit a wide range of woodland and shrubby habitats. Dense low vegetation in which to build their

The analysis of the data for this species was supported by Gordano Valley Ringing Group

nests is a prerequisite and they dislike coniferous woodlands. Otherwise, a tree that is tall enough to sing from and a suitable nesting site gives them a wide range of options. Within Britain & Ireland in winter, Blackcaps use various kinds of woody and shrubby habitats but are mostly seen in gardens feeding on berries and at bird tables. In Africa and Iberia, a wide range of scrub and forest habitats are used by Blackcaps feeding on seasonal fruits and insects (*BWP*).

Blackcap movements based on ring-recoveries to and from Britain & Ireland were examined by Langslow (1979). Since then, the number of recoveries available for analysis has increased more than fivefold although the patterns recognized remain similar. The distribution of ringing locations during the breeding season for birds later recovered is similar to the distribution in the *1988–91 Atlas*. Birds have been ringed in the non-breeding season mainly within the breeding area, or at the main coastal observatories throughout Britain & Ireland (Fig 1). Around three-quarters of the Blackcaps that have been recovered have been ringed in Britain & Ireland between July and September, with very few ringed in the winter months (Fig 2).

Just over half of all recoveries are of birds found dead, while around 40% have been recaptured by ringers. For foreign-ringed birds found in Britain & Ireland, about 40% have been found dead and 60% recaptured. A third of all recoveries with known finding circumstances

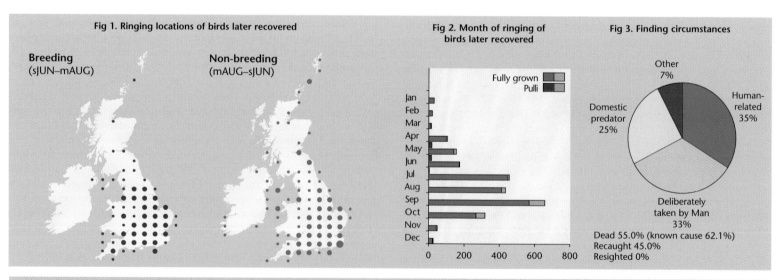

Fig 1. Ringing locations of birds later recovered

Breeding (sJUN–mAUG)

Non-breeding (mAUG–sJUN)

Fig 2. Month of ringing of birds later recovered

Fully grown
Pulli

Fig 3. Finding circumstances

Other 7%
Domestic predator 25%
Human-related 35%
Deliberately taken by Man 33%

Dead 55.0% (known cause 62.1%)
Recaught 45.0%
Resighted 0%

Ringing and recovery data

	<1960	60–69	70–79	80–89	90–97	Total
RINGING						
BTO ringing totals (%)	1	7	19	35	38	404,841
RECOVERIES						
BTO-ringed (%)	1	7	17	36	39	2,272
Foreign-ringed (%)	←	18	→	27	56	248

Statistical analyses

	Breeding population (sJUN–mAUG)	Wintering population (sNOV–mFEB)
Status	LONG-DISTANCE MIGRANT* (4)	[LONG-DISTANCE MIGRANT]
Age differences	Not tested	Not tested
Sex differences	Not tested	Not tested
Regional differences	Not tested	Not tested
Finding circumstances	Not tested*	Not tested

Fig 4. Locations during (a) June–August (507:80), (b) September–October (238:405), (c) December–February (37:169) and (d) April (71:154) of Blackcaps using Britain & Ireland during the year. Known British & Irish breeders (red) are differentiated from those of uncertain breeding population (grey). Sample sizes of the classes (known British & Irish breeders:uncertain breeding population) are shown. Birds of uncertain breeding population in the Lebanon in October (1) and April (3) are not shown.

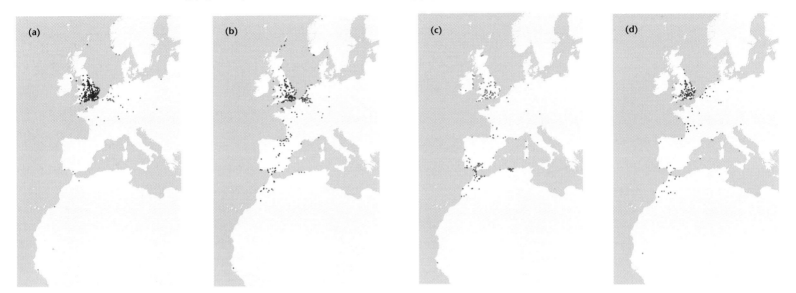

are of birds deliberately taken by humans (Fig 3) but the proportion rises to around 90% for recoveries from Iberia and northwest Africa. By contrast, in Britain & Ireland, domestic predators account for 40% of the birds found dead. Furthermore, human activity seems to take a greater toll on Blackcaps in France and Britain than elsewhere, with half the recoveries the consequence of collisions with traffic or with man-made structures. All these factors will potentially bias the relationship between the actual and real patterns of distribution. Nevertheless the relatively large number of recoveries gives some confidence in their reliability especially when compared with recovery patterns in other small migrants.

Almost all the recoveries in June, July and August of known British & Irish breeders are within the main breeding areas in England (Fig 4a), although there are a few cases where a breeding bird has been caught one year in Britain and then recaptured during the breeding season in continental Europe in a later year. Recoveries for September and October give a clear pattern of migration routes, as birds are found throughout western France, Iberia and North Africa (Fig 4b). Blackcap migration peaks in late September inland in England (Phillips 1994), and in mid-October in Spain (Cuadrado 1992). The smaller numbers of direct movements (Fig 5) (ie birds recovered in the same summer/autumn as that in which they were ringed) support this and show southerly movements of known British breeders in July–August, with many more evident in September. The weights of Blackcaps in Britain prior to migration suggest the capability of a non-stop flight to Iberia (Langslow 1976, Phillips 1994).

There were no clear differences in recovery patterns between the sexes or between age classes. However, while recoveries in September of British & Irish birds remain predominantly within Britain, by October the median change in latitude is 3°S for adults but 14°S for immatures. This is consistent with adult Blackcaps moulting in Britain & Ireland before departing. Furthermore, the main coastal passage at Beachy Head (likely to be British birds) peaks in September (Edgar 1996) and is almost exclusively immatures.

Movement is still apparent through November but by December the winter pattern is in place (Fig 4c). While many western birds winter in southern Iberia and northwest Africa, some cross the Sahara (BWP). Evidence for trans-Saharan migration comes from studies of the weights of Blackcaps in the migratory seasons together with five recoveries of British-ringed birds. In addition, by the mid-1980s there had been only three recoveries south of the Sahara from ringing in continental Europe (two in Senegal and one in Nigeria; Der Zug). The rate and scale of weight gained,

and the low arrival weights of Blackcaps at spring passage sites in Tunisia, support the conclusion that many cross the Sahara on migration (Wood 1982a). There is insufficient information from birds recovered after ringing to determine which populations migrate south of the Sahara and which do not. All the British & Irish breeding adults recovered in winter had moved substantial distances, mainly to southern Spain and northwest Africa (Fig 4c). There are five recoveries south of the Sahara although none were ringed in Britain & Ireland as adults during the breeding season. It remains possible, therefore, that some of the British & Irish population crosses the Sahara along with birds from continental populations.

There are also a number of winter recoveries within Britain & Ireland (Fig 4c) and the British wintering population has been increasing over recent years (Leach 1981, Winter Atlas). The majority of records occur in gardens (95%; Leach 1981) and there is some evidence that more are found during periods of hard weather. This contrasts with the pattern of Chiffchaffs in winter where birds were concentrated in southern parts of Britain and Ireland, especially near water (Winter Atlas). Of particular interest are the origins of the birds present in Britain & Ireland during winter. Fig 4c shows a single bird confirmed as a British & Irish breeder still present in Britain during the winter along with a substantial number of birds of unknown breeding population. The direct movements (Figs 5b & c) show a pattern of northwesterly movements during September and October of birds from some of the continental breeding populations. These are coming into Britain & Ireland slightly after the time that known British & Irish breeders are leaving, with most of such autumn recoveries occurring at coastal locations.

The ring-recovery data support two important conclusions. First, the vast majority of the breeding population in Britain winters mainly in southern Iberia and northwest Africa (Fig 4c). Second, the recoveries in winter in Britain & Ireland are predominantly of birds from populations from the near Continent (Fig 4c), which arrive from September (Fig 5b) and are still present in the spring, but gone by the following breeding season (Fig 6). Taken together, this is good evidence that the British wintering population is distinct from the breeding population and largely originates in west-central Europe. Why a new west-northwest migration direction should have originated in the last 30 years remains unanswered, although Berthold (1995) explores the possible mechanisms. Around 35% of birds ringed in Belgium in autumn are recovered north of the ringing site (Fouarge 1981). Autumn locations suggest that British wintering birds breed in the Low Countries and Germany (Fig 6).

Fig 5. Movements of over 20 km and locations during (a) July–August (127:6), (b) September (177:126) and (c) October (21:193) of Blackcaps ringed in June–October or of confirmed breeding status and recovered during the same July–October. Known British & Irish breeders (red) are differentiated from those of uncertain breeding population (grey). Sample sizes of the classes (known British & Irish breeders:uncertain breeding population) are shown.

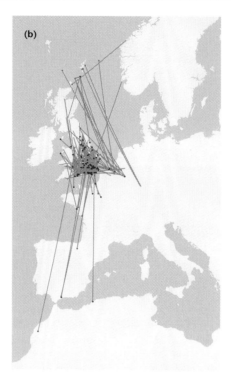
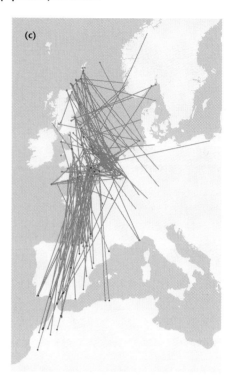

Fig 6. Locations during the breeding season (4, red), autumn (36, blue) and spring (38, grey) of Blackcaps present in Britain & Ireland during the winter.

The spring passage is apparent during April (Fig 4d), although some of the birds remain in northwest Africa. The breeding-season pattern is established by May.

There have been 49 breeding-season recoveries of birds that had been ringed as adults in a previous breeding season within Britain & Ireland. Half of them had moved more than 20 km which suggests that fidelity to breeding sites may be weak (median of the 25 dead recoveries = 15 km, P5–95=0–437). Samples of ringed pulli are too small to draw any conclusions about natal dispersal. However, evidence that the annual survival rate calculated from capture–recapture studies is similar to that from ring-recoveries suggests strong breeding site-fidelity (Peach 1993).

Across winters, about half the recoveries are found more than 20 km away from the original ringing site, with about two-thirds of them in a south or southwesterly direction. The proportion of movements over 20 km is similar to that for breeding birds between breeding seasons. Although the median distance for between-winter movements of Blackcaps found dead is 50 km, the sample size (n=12) is too small for any conclusions to be drawn about site-fidelity; however, evidence from Spain suggests strong winter site-fidelity (Cuadrado 1992, Cuadrado et al 1995). The median distance moved within a winter is 6.5 km (P5–95=0–791, n=24).

Whilst the overall patterns of movements and their timing are now understood, much detail remains uncertain over the routes of movement and where the bulk of the population spends the winter. Perhaps Blackcaps will give more surprises with their changes in habits and perhaps they might even become a marker for changes in mean winter temperatures.

Derek R Langslow

Wood Warbler
Phylloscopus sibilatrix

The Wood Warbler is one of the most enigmatic of Britain's summer visitors. Its penetrating song and spectacular courtship chases enliven the mature woods that it favours but, away from its breeding haunts, this is one of the least-known birds, being seldom found on migration, in spring or in autumn, and there are few records in its wintering areas.

It breeds from Britain and France eastwards to the Altai Mountains in southern Siberia at about 90°E. A small Irish population was believed to number about 30 pairs at the time of the *1988–91 Atlas*. Its range extends north to the Arctic Circle in Fennoscandia and Russia, with odd birds in Lapland, and as far south as the tip of southern Italy and northern Greece (*European Atlas*). The entire breeding population winters in equatorial Africa, from about 9°N to 5°S. It spreads between about 10°W in the Guinea highlands and Sierra Leone and 35°E in western Kenya (Moreau 1972, *BWP*, Urban *et al* 1997). All birds appear to enter Africa through the central and eastern Mediterranean, so that those of British & Irish stock head southeast while those from Siberia may fly mostly west for over 4,000 km before turning to a more southerly direction. The front of the return, spring journey is much broader, and British birds apparently take a more westerly route over the western Mediterranean.

Wood Warblers breed in Britain mainly in deciduous woods, with a strong bias to the west of the country. They prefer closed-canopy woods with sparse understorey and little ground vegetation, although it appears to be important that there are some low branches near to the nest. In continental Europe, they also occupy mixed woodland. They winter in humid lowland habitats; many are closely associated with evergreen forest, especially edges and clearings, and they also frequent

The analysis of the data for this species was supported by Dave Hanford

more scattered trees with open, spreading foliage. In Africa, they may occur on passage in more open savanna but generally little is known of their habitat preferences on migration.

Relatively few Wood Warblers have been ringed, and the recovery rate of rings, at less than 0.25%, is among the lowest for any British & Irish bird. Ringers seldom encounter them, and fewer than two per season are seen at most observatories (*R & F*). Although there are only 40 ring-recoveries in the BTO database, 38 of them are from birds marked in the breeding season, 29 as pulli and nine as adults in the normal months of breeding, and most have been ringed in the species' breeding stronghold in western Britain (Figs 1 & 2). This means that the ringing information, although sparse, is more informative than for most other species (for which many birds are of unknown origin). The data so far do not allow any deductions to be made about differences between ages and sexes. Although over half of the recoveries have come from recaptures by ringers within Britain & Ireland, this does not appear to have introduced any significant bias into their geographical distribution. Of the 65% of recoveries reported dead for which a cause was reported, about half were deliberately taken by hunters (Fig 3); the recovery rate from hunting has dropped, however, with none reported from this cause since 1956.

In autumn, many British Wood Warblers probably embark on their migratory journey direct from their breeding areas, or nearby, and

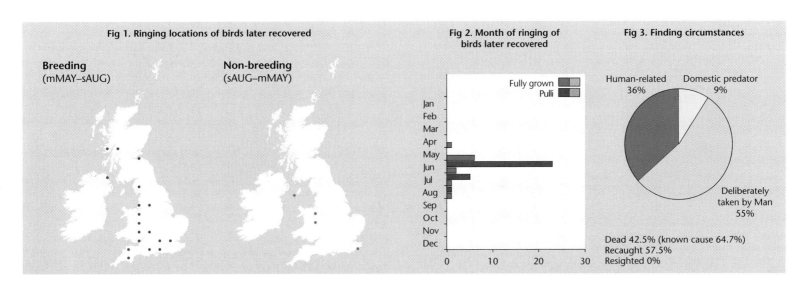

Fig 1. Ringing locations of birds later recovered

Breeding (mMAY–sAUG)

Non-breeding (sAUG–mMAY)

Fig 2. Month of ringing of birds later recovered

Fully grown / Pulli

Fig 3. Finding circumstances

Human-related 36% / Domestic predator 9% / Deliberately taken by Man 55%

Dead 42.5% (known cause 64.7%)
Recaught 57.5%
Resighted 0%

Ringing and recovery data

	<1960	60–69	70–79	80–89	90–97	Total
RINGING						
BTO ringing totals (%)	12	10	14	45	20	17,510
RECOVERIES						
BTO-ringed (%)	18	8	5	50	20	40
Foreign-ringed (%)	0	0	0	0	0	0

Statistical analyses

	Breeding population (mMAY–sAUG)	Wintering population (mNOV–sAPR)
Status	[LONG-DISTANCE MIGRANT]	NONE
Age differences	Not tested	—
Sex differences	Not tested	—
Regional differences	Not tested	—
Finding circumstances	Not tested	—

Fig 4. Recovery locations and movements of over 20 km for the 21 included recoveries of Wood Warblers ringed or recovered in Britain & Ireland. Those birds that appear in Fig 5 are not shown.

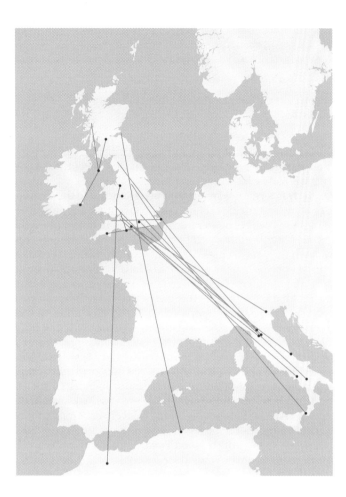

Fig 5. Movements of over 20 km and recovery locations of Wood Warblers ringed during the breeding season in Britain & Ireland as pulli (6:4, red) and adults (2:2, blue) and recovered in a subsequent breeding season when of breeding age. Sample sizes of movements under:over 20 km are given but only those over 20 km are plotted.

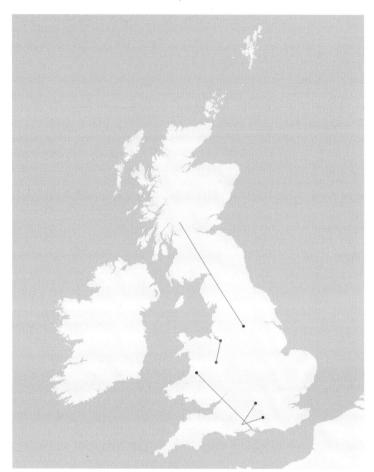

relatively few are seen or caught at the migration 'hot spots'. Scattered individuals occur at inland and coastal sites across England, mostly in August, and the three ring-recoveries in Britain in August are all at well-studied English south-coastal locations. Two other birds ringed at such sites in that month produced recoveries in following years. Subsequent autumn recoveries (Fig 4) show that they migrate to the southeast to pass through Italy, with eight records scattered along the peninsula from mid-August to early October. Since there are no ring-recoveries *en route* between Britain and Italy, it seems quite likely that birds undertake that journey in one flight. Other populations pass a little farther east, and Wood Warbler is amongst the 10 species most frequently taken by the Eleonora's Falcons that breed in autumn on the islands in the Aegean Sea (Alerstam 1990a).

Wood Warblers probably cross the Sahara directly from Europe, as there are very few autumn observations of the species on the African side of the Mediterranean (Moreau 1972). This is one of the few small birds that generally flies over the central Saharan region rather than around the edges. Birds seem to touch down soon after crossing the desert (Moreau 1972) and passage south of the Sahara, from Burkina Faso to western Sudan, is noted from September to November (Urban *et al* 1997). They arrive in the main wintering areas, from the Ivory Coast to the Congo Basin, in October–November, and stay until late March or April, undergoing their main moult during this time. No British-ringed birds have been found south of the Sahara, and there is no information on winter movements or year-to-year site-fidelity. There are November recoveries from France to Cameroon and from the former Yugoslavia to the Democratic Republic of Congo, with a bird ringed in August in Nigeria recovered in Greece and another from Germany being found in Burkina Faso in April (*BWP*).

Wood Warblers appear to follow a clockwise loop migration route, with the northward return journey in spring taking them somewhat farther to the west than their autumn passage. They are seldom found in the Sahel but are very conspicuous in North Africa in April and early May. This implies that birds gain weight for a trans-Saharan flight and depart from near to their wintering areas, then land soon after clearing the Sahara, just as they do in autumn. The British-ringed bird in Algeria (Fig 4) was found there in April, and the one reported from Morocco (but not reliably dated) emphasizes just how far west British birds occur. The spring pattern is amplified by birds found in Algeria in April that had been ringed in Belgium and Russia, with one from Germany found in May in Morocco; one ringed in Tunisia in April was recovered in France (Urban *et al* 1997). In spring, Wood Warbler has been the seventh most frequently ringed passerine over the 10 years of a migration project covering the Mediterranean islands, with most birds making landfall on the islands of the Tyrrhenian Sea, and far fewer in the western Mediterranean (Pilastro *et al* 1998b). The first birds reach western and central Europe in mid-April, with some flying into Britain during April, but most arrive in early May, as the first birds are reaching Fennoscandia and Russia (Fouarge 1968, R & F).

Movement into Britain & Ireland goes largely unnoticed at the main migration watch-points, birds presumably usually overflying the coast and arriving directly in their breeding areas. The speed of spring passage is graphically illustrated by one male that did land at an observatory, being ringed on the Calf of Man on 8 May: the following morning, less than 24 hours after ringing, it had established a territory 205 km away in Scotland, and by that evening had attracted a mate and started nest-building (Morton 1986).

There have been no recoveries in Britain or Ireland of Wood Warblers ringed overseas but a few presumed continental drift migrants are encountered at the observatories. At Fair Isle, well north of the British breeding range, spring passage peaks in late May and autumn passage is heavier than at more southerly locations, continuing into September, with stragglers in October, as at Spurn, long after birds have deserted their British breeding grounds (R & F). At Cape Clear and on Scilly, autumn passage is also late, mainly in September (Sharrock 1973, Gantlett 1991). These observations suggest that most of the birds recorded away from the main migration routes are of continental origin.

Four of the ringing records suggest substantial natal dispersal, with birds ringed as pulli recovered in a subsequent breeding season at distances up to 350 km, although it has to be questioned whether some were late migrants (Fig 5). Six recoveries were close to the natal site, and there must be other recaptures of such birds by ringers, not normally entered into the national database. Most adult birds appear to be faithful to breeding areas from one year to another, even if they have not bred successfully (Norman 1994b), but there are records of territory-holding males being caught on territory 19 and 66 km away in a subsequent breeding season (Fig 5).

There is so much that we do not know about the Wood Warbler. It is the most common trans-Saharan migrant for which there are no recoveries of British-ringed birds in the winter quarters. It has not been established where they fatten up to prepare for their migrations, or how they manage to make much longer unbroken flights than other *Phylloscopus* warblers. Their habitat requirements in winter and on passage are unknown, as are their population dynamics and annual survival rates. There can be very large local fluctuations in numbers (*European Atlas*) but the total population appears to be reasonably stable, although there are suggestions that it varies in parallel with that of other trans-Saharan migrants that are sensitive to African rainfall (Marchant *et al* 1990). The species is considered to have a favourable conservation status (Tucker & Heath 1994) although, with many gaps in our knowledge of the main factors affecting their life cycle, there must be an element of vulnerability to unforeseen and poorly understood influences.

These gaps are not likely to be filled by observation or by random ringing. Some aspects of their annual cycle can be probed by captures of adults on territory, allied with colour-ringing (Norman 1994b), as in the BTO's Retrapping Adults for Survival project, and by systematic nest recording and ringing of chicks. For more insight into their migration, perhaps we shall have to await the advance of technology to the state where remote-tracking becomes possible for birds of this size.

David Norman

Common Chiffchaff (Chiffchaff)

Phylloscopus collybita

The Chiffchaff's repetitive song is one of the classic harbingers of spring; over much of lowland Britain & Ireland it may be expected to be heard as early as mid-March. The unprepossessing nature of the song and of the small olive-brown bird that produces it suggest an unremarkable species but, in one aspect at least, this impression is misleading, for the Chiffchaff has a complex and dynamic migration pattern.

The nominate race breeds over most of west and central Europe as far north as Denmark and southern Sweden. The race *abietinus* breeds in Fennoscandia east to the Urals and south to northern Turkey, and *tristis* through most of Siberia to 155°E. All three occur regularly in Britain & Ireland (*BWP*, Clement *et al* 1998). Three other races, *brevirostris*, *caucasicus* and *menzbieri* breed from Turkey to Iran but have not been recorded in Britain or Ireland. In most of Spain and Portugal, the Chiffchaff is replaced as a breeding bird by the Iberian Chiffchaff *Phylloscopus brehmii* (formerly a race of *collybita*), which has occurred as a vagrant in southern Britain. The winter range of *collybita* includes western Europe, the Mediterranean region, North and northern tropical Africa, Arabia, Iraq and northern India.

The Chiffchaff breeds commonly in mature lowland woodland with good undergrowth. Most types of woodland are occupied, although most territories have at least some tall trees, and ground cover is essential. Outside the breeding season, it may be found in wet and dry scrub, marshes and reedbeds. Since the species is insectivorous throughout the year, birds wintering in the northernmost parts of the range are particularly attracted to favourable microclimates, supporting

The analysis of the data for this species was supported by the Rye Bay Ringing Group and the Wetland Trust

good numbers of invertebrates such as at sewage-works, in wet woodland and along well-vegetated borders of lakes and streams.

Within Britain & Ireland, the breeding range is heavily biased towards the south (*1988–91 Atlas*), and it is here that most of the birds recovered from British & Irish ringing have been caught; Ireland is distinctly under-represented (Fig 1). Very few recoveries have been generated from birds ringed as pulli (2%), with 65% resulting from the capture of juveniles or fully grown birds in July–September (Fig 2). Many recoveries have been the result of recaptures (64%), and so are strongly influenced by the distribution of ringers. Of the 35% of recoveries found dead, 61% have the causes of recovery documented (Fig 3). Of these, by far the most common are human-related: collisions with traffic or man-made structures (33%), domestic predators (29%) and deliberate taking by Man (26%).

In Britain & Ireland, most Chiffchaffs fledge between late May and mid-July (Rodrigues & Crick 1997). Seemingly random short-distance dispersive movements commence in July and continue into September (Norman 1991). These merge into a more definite migratory movement that commences in late August and peaks in the second half of September. The migratory strategy is characterized by a series of comparatively short hops. Movements of departing birds orientate towards southeast England as migrants take advantage of the short

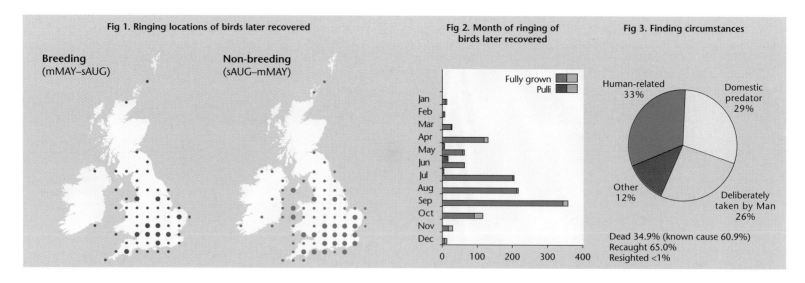

Fig 1. Ringing locations of birds later recovered

Breeding (mMAY–sAUG) Non-breeding (sAUG–mMAY)

Fig 2. Month of ringing of birds later recovered

Fully grown / Pulli

Fig 3. Finding circumstances

Human-related 33%
Domestic predator 29%
Other 12%
Deliberately taken by Man 26%

Dead 34.9% (known cause 60.9%)
Recaught 65.0%
Resighted <1%

Ringing and recovery data

	<1960	60–69	70–79	80–89	90–97	Total
RINGING						
BTO ringing totals (%)	3	12	19	32	34	327,554
RECOVERIES						
BTO-ringed (%)	2	10	15	34	39	1,178
Foreign-ringed (%)	←	19	→	30	51	108

Statistical analyses

	Breeding population (mMAY–sAUG)	Wintering population (mNOV–sMAR)
Status	[LONG-DISTANCE MIGRANT]	[LONG-DISTANCE MIGRANT]
Age differences	Not tested	Not tested
Sex differences	Not tested	Not tested
Regional differences	Not tested	Not tested
Finding circumstances	Not tested	Not tested

Fig 4. Locations during (a) autumn (209:387), (b) winter (25:122) and (c) spring (108:205) of Chiffchaffs using Britain & Ireland, with known British & Irish breeders (red) differentiated from those from other or uncertain breeding populations (grey). Sample sizes of British & Irish:other or uncertain breeding populations are given.

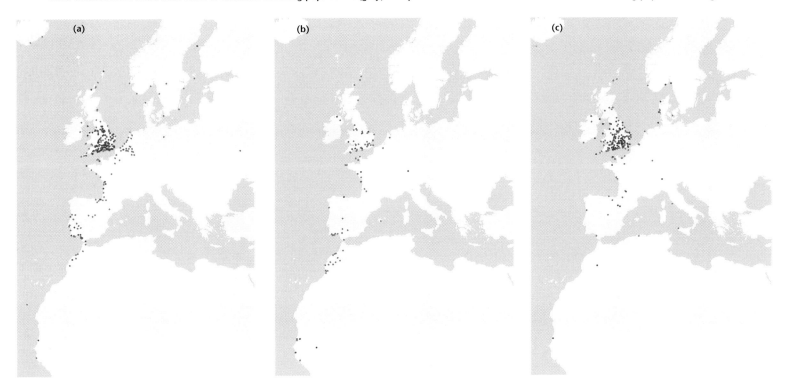

sea-crossing to the Continent (*R & F*). There is a tendency for females to commence their migration a few days earlier than males, although whether this has an influence on the route taken or the wintering destination is unknown (Geen 1988).

Having reached northern France and the Low Countries, birds head southwestward to reach southwest France by late September and the Atlantic coast of Spain, Portugal and Morocco from early October onwards (Fig 4a). Many birds cross the Sahara in October and early November to occupy wintering grounds that extend from Mauritania south to Guinea-Bissau (Fig 4b). There are wintering records of Chiffchaffs, ringed in Britain & Ireland, along most of the migration route from southern Britain southwards but particularly in southern Portugal, Spain and Morocco. The small number of winter recoveries of known British & Irish breeders is consistent with this pattern, extending over a range of more than 40° of latitude (Fig 4b). An earlier analysis of British & Irish ring-recoveries demonstrated that the proportion of Chiffchaffs wintering around the Mediterranean is lower than for Blackcap, with a greater proportion of Chiffchaffs seemingly wintering south of the Sahara (Lack 1989).

Ringing expeditions to the Parc National du Djoudj have confirmed Senegal as a major wintering area for Chiffchaffs of British & Irish origin. Recoveries generated from this work have been distributed evenly throughout the breeding range in Britain & Ireland, and do not show the bias towards western Britain and Ireland displayed by the Sedge Warbler (this volume).

Spring migration commences in February, with the main movements in March and April. Birds have reached all observatories on the south coast of England by early March (*R & F*). The route taken largely reverses that used in autumn, although there are few recoveries in North Africa for the spring period (Fig 4c). The approach to Britain is from a more westerly direction, with more birds observed at south- and west-coast observatories than further east, and a lack of spring recoveries in the Low Countries. Onward movements within Britain are often rapid, with distances of more than 100 km being covered in a single 24-hour period. During spring migration, males precede females by two or three weeks

(Reynolds 1978). Birds arriving to breed in Ireland appear to cross the English Channel and Irish Sea in two flights rather than make a direct approach from France through the western approaches.

Both Britain and Ireland are also used by birds originating elsewhere in Europe and Siberia. Birds of the races *abietinus* and *tristis* (along with *collybita* presumed to be from the Continent) are regularly identified in late autumn, particularly at east-coast sites (Williamson 1954a; Fig 5). Here the passage of continental birds in the second half of October is usually larger than the wave of departing British birds earlier in the autumn. This movement is also observed along the south and west coasts of Britain and south coast of Ireland but is rather smaller and later, continuing into early November (*R & F, Birds in Ireland*). Birds have been recovered in Britain at this time, having been ringed during the breeding season or earlier in the autumn in the Netherlands, Germany, Denmark, Norway, Sweden and Estonia.

Continental birds are also found in Britain in spring, although their appearance is decidedly later than the arriving British & Irish breeders. Passage is noted at all coastal observatories from April through May and into June, but is most obvious on the east coast of England in May. Birds ringed in Britain at this time have been recovered later in spring or in the breeding season in the Channel Isles, Belgium, Germany, Denmark and Sweden. There is a migratory divide between the Scandinavian populations of *abietinus*, which migrate southwestwards in autumn, and the Finnish and more easterly birds, which migrate southeastwards (*BWP*). A proportion of Scandinavian birds probably use Britain as part of their normal migration route in both spring and autumn, whereas birds from further east usually arrive only after being displaced by easterly winds.

From a domestic viewpoint, perhaps the most interesting aspect of the Chiffchaff's biology is the development of its habit of wintering in Britain & Ireland. Birds are recorded in winter throughout Britain & Ireland but most records are in Britain south of a line from the Mersey to the Humber, particularly in southwest England (*Winter Atlas*). Wintering in Britain & Ireland is by no means a recent phenomenon, being recorded in Worcestershire in 1846 (Tomes 1901), but the scale has

Fig 5. Exchanges of 48 Chiffchaffs between Britain & Ireland and continental Europe east of 2°E. The 21 pre-1979 foreign-ringed Chiffchaffs (France 9, Germany 2, Belgium 2, Spain 2, the Netherlands 2, Senegal 2, Gambia 1 and Estonia 1) are not shown.

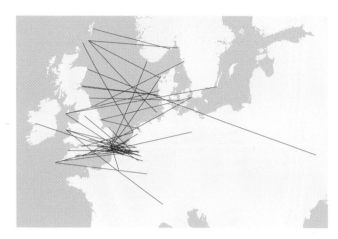

undoubtedly increased greatly since the 1940s (Dennis 1992). With numbers approaching three figures now present at favoured southwestern sites, the estimate of a thousand wintering birds in Britain & Ireland less than 20 years ago (*Winter Atlas*) must now be revised significantly upwards.

What, therefore, are the origins of these pioneering birds? Unfortunately, this cannot be answered precisely because there are no winter recoveries in Britain or Ireland of birds ringed as pulli. However, there is a body of information that will assist in reaching reasonable conclusions. First, birds of the races *collybita*, *abietinus* and *tristis* are all found regularly in Britain & Ireland in winter (Penhallurick 1978b, *BWP*, Dennis 1992), although *tristis* is certainly the least common. Our wintering birds therefore undoubtedly have a wide area of origin. Second, a small number of recoveries are of Chiffchaffs present in Britain & Ireland both in the breeding season and in the winter. However, considering the large number of Chiffchaffs ringed, the relative scarcity of these recoveries suggests that only a small proportion of the wintering birds of the race *collybita* are British or Irish in origin. Third, there are overseas movements of birds present in Britain in winter involving the Netherlands (in spring), Belgium (in the breeding season) and the

Channel Isles, Belgium, Netherlands and the Ukraine (in autumn). All lines of evidence therefore suggest that wintering birds in Britain & Ireland originate from many parts of the Palearctic range.

Wintering birds usually first appear in late October or November, and may remain faithful to a site through the winter, and even between winters (Long & Long 1982), but there are many observations of previously occupied sites being depopulated following a spell of hard weather (*Winter Atlas*). Undoubtedly, increased mortality is to be expected at such times but whether birds are able to make hard-weather movements to aid survival is unknown. Both males and females are recorded as wintering in southern England, without an obvious sexual bias, although the numbers involved are small (Reynolds 1978, A J Beasley pers comm).

The timing of departure of wintering birds is difficult to determine but Reynolds (1978) records last dates of recapture from mid-March to early April of three birds ringed at a Hertfordshire site in winter. Whether wintering birds are displaced by incoming migrant males is unknown.

The Chiffchaff is an adaptable species, and is particularly worthy of study as a good example of a bird apparently able to respond to climatic change. It does not appear to be prone to the population crashes shown by some other passerines wintering in the Sahel region of West Africa but, with a significant proportion of British & Irish birds undoubtedly wintering in this area, expansion of the Sahara through drought and habitat degradation must pose a threat. Breeding habitat is plentiful, and the species will have benefited from modern, more enlightened forestry practices of avoiding large blocks of evergreen monocultures.

Despite the comparatively large number of birds ringed overall, there are aspects of the Chiffchaff's movements that remain poorly understood. In particular, since rather few birds are ringed as breeding adults or pulli, little is known of breeding site-fidelity and juvenile dispersal in Britain & Ireland. Much more needs to be learned of the origins of birds wintering in Britain & Ireland, the composition of this population in terms of age and sex, the extent and nature of hard weather movements, and the timing of spring departure. Similarly, large numbers of Chiffchaffs were caught during the ringing expeditions to Senegal in the early 1990s; full analysis of these data should provide real insight into the origins, constitution and site-fidelity of the birds wintering south of the Sahara.

Graham Geen

Willow Warbler
Phylloscopus trochilus

The Willow Warbler is one of the earliest and most common summer visitors to arrive in Britain & Ireland from its African wintering grounds. The species is considered to be the most numerous passerine summer migrant to the West Palearctic, and the British breeding population alone is in the region of 2.3 million pairs (*1988–91 Atlas*). However, during the early 1990s, Peach *et al* (1995a) found a large decline in numbers had occurred over southern Britain, and northern populations seem to have been similarly affected in the late 1990s (pers obs). In Sweden, the race *trochilus* has also shown a decline during the same decade but *acredula* appears to be stable (A Lindström pers comm). The moult strategy of the species is unique among West Palearctic warblers. Adults undergo a complete moult of plumage on the breeding grounds and another in Africa prior to autumn and spring migrations (Underhill *et al* 1992), while young of the year undertake their first full moult in Africa when natal primary and tail feathers are only about six months old.

The nominate *trochilus* breeds throughout the middle latitudes of western Europe north to southern Sweden, and eastwards to southern Poland and northern Romania. The race *acredula* breeds from Fennoscandia and eastern Europe, east of the nominate, to Siberia, where it intergrades with *yakutensis*. While *trochilus* migrates south or southwest in autumn, *acredula* moves south to southeast, with the Swedish population showing a migratory divide at 60–63°N, the northern birds taking the eastern route and the southern birds migrating southwestwards (Hedenström & Pettersson 1987, *BWP*). Both *trochilus* and *acredula* migrants occur regularly on the east coast of Britain in autumn and to a lesser extent in spring (*R & F*).

The analysis of the data for this species was supported by the Rye Bay Ringing Group and the Wetland Trust

The breeding habitat of Willow Warblers in Britain & Ireland is broadly defined but damp ground with Alder and willow is favoured (*1968–72 Atlas*). The species is also common in forest clearings, along paths, railway banks, in rough pastures (Cramp 1955), and in birch woodland (Mason 1997).

The ringing sites within Britain & Ireland of those birds ringed during the breeding season and later recovered generally represent the extensive breeding distribution of the species, although there are few data for the Irish populations. During the autumn, birds are more numerous on Fair Isle, and at many ringing stations in southern England and on the eastern seaboard (Fig 1). Many birds recovered were ringed in Britain & Ireland either as juveniles in July and August (almost 50%) or as fully grown birds in April and May (a further 20%); only 8% were ringed as nestlings (Fig 2).

The highest proportion of fatalities of known cause (45%) was due to human-related factors, such as collision with windows, with a further 26% due to domestic predators, and a substantial 19% of birds deliberately taken by humans (Fig 3). Of the recoveries available for analysis, 59% resulted from recaptures of birds by ringers. Recovery patterns are thus strongly influenced by the distribution of ringers.

Intensive studies on juvenile Willow Warblers have shown that migration begins in northern England in the second half of July

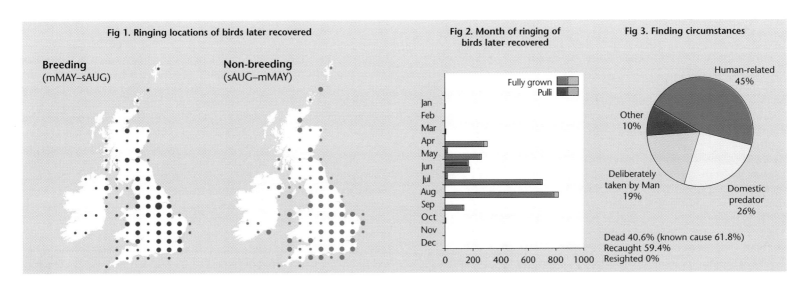

Fig 1. Ringing locations of birds later recovered

Breeding (mMAY–sAUG)

Non-breeding (sAUG–mMAY)

Fig 2. Month of ringing of birds later recovered

Fully grown
Pulli

Fig 3. Finding circumstances

Human-related 45%

Other 10%

Deliberately taken by Man 19%

Domestic predator 26%

Dead 40.6% (known cause 61.8%)
Recaught 59.4%
Resighted 0%

Ringing and recovery data

	<1960	60–69	70–79	80–89	90–97	Total
RINGING						
BTO ringing totals (%)	5	11	20	37	27	1,004,200
RECOVERIES						
BTO-ringed (%)	3	10	17	42	28	2,554
Foreign-ringed (%)	←	29	→	47	24	111

Statistical analyses

	Breeding population (mMAY–sAUG)	Wintering population (mNOV–mMAR)
Status	[LONG-DISTANCE MIGRANT]	NONE
Age differences	Not tested	—
Sex differences	Not tested	—
Regional differences	Not tested*	—
Finding circumstances	Not tested	—

Fig 4. Locations in (a) July (12:6), (b) August (5:18) and (c) September–October (3:11) of Willow Warblers ringed as adults in Britain & Ireland from mid-May to the end of October and recovered during autumn in the same year. Birds ringed from mid-May to the end of June (red) are differentiated from birds ringed from July to the end of October (grey). Sample sizes of the classes (mid-May–June:July–October) are given.

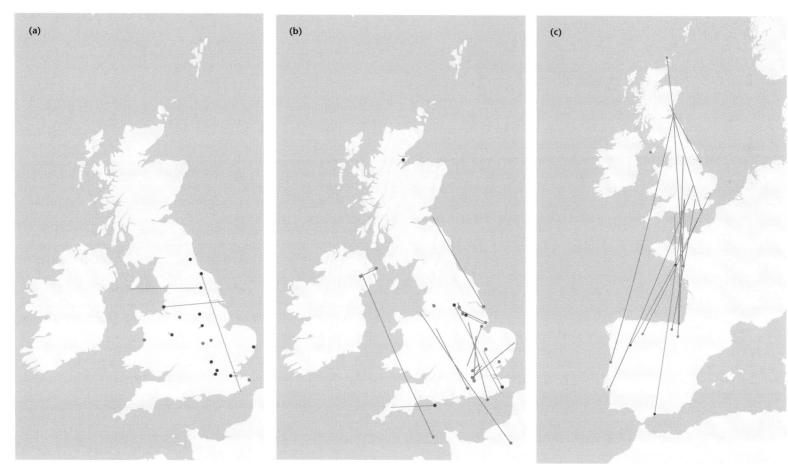

(Norman 1987), after post-fledging dispersal movements that are usually of a local nature (S C Norman 1994). Many birds begin orientated migration in the late stages of post-juvenile moult at around 41–60 days of age, as established for birds on active migration at Bardsey Island (Norman 1987), and for *trochilus* in Sweden, but *acredula* commences migration earlier at 35–40 days of age (Lindström *et al* 1996). Birds in southern Britain initiate orientated migration only when post-juvenile moult is completed at more than 60 days of age (Lawn 1984). It is now known that other first-year trans-Saharan passerine migrants, such as Bluethroat and Lesser Whitethroat, start migration at a similar point in the moult cycle (Boddy 1983, Lindström *et al* 1985, Ellegren & Fransson 1992, Norman 1992). Some partial migrant species, for example Grey Wagtail (Herremans 1988a) and Goldcrest (Pettersson & Hasselquist 1985, Norman 1999) also employ this strategy.

Adults appear to begin their autumn passage a week or two later than first-autumn birds, in early August (compare Figs 4 & 5). The delay is probably due to the physiological demands of post-nuptial moult. Many female Willow Warblers do not start moulting until mid-July and finish in late August (Norman 1997). As with first-autumn birds, some adults also begin migration before autumn moult is completed (Norman 1987, Lapshin 1988, Hedenström *et al* 1995).

Initial migration flights of first-autumn birds are in the range of 25–200 km (Fig 5), as is the case in several other trans-Saharan species (Berthold 1993). Studies of fat reserves in young Willow Warblers in Britain and Sweden have revealed that sufficient fat is deposited to fuel short-distance flights only (Baggott 1986, Norman 1987, Lindström *et al*

1996). Adults have more pointed wings than juveniles and thus are better equipped for longer migratory flight (Norman 1997), and those which commence migration later than young birds may compensate by making longer initial flights. Following fledging, young birds may, for a period of time, be less proficient at foraging than experienced adults and may need more daylight search time to obtain equivalent amounts of food. Juveniles therefore, in the early stages of autumn migration, may only manage weight increases sufficient to fuel shorter-distance movements than adults. As the migration season progresses, improved foraging techniques may lead to more fat deposition to support longer migratory flights. However, as Willow Warblers do not require a specialist food resource and are able to exploit a wide range of invertebrate prey across a broad spectrum of habitat types on passage, they could migrate through Britain using a diurnal 'feed-on-the-move' technique, as southerly movements of 25–100 km need not necessarily involve individuals in overnight flights or significant weight gains. Adults, however, may use knowledge gained from previous autumn migrations to head directly for particularly favoured staging posts. These may lie mainly across the Channel, as very few adults are controlled within Britain or on the south coast of England in the same autumn (Fig 4).

Autumn movements of juveniles through Britain are generally on a south to southeast bearing (Fig 5). As the season progresses, longer-distance flights are more in evidence, most numerous in August, with more northern birds heading for the southeast of England, where the south coast between Dorset and Kent appears to serve as a staging post

Fig 5. Locations in (a) July (45:101), (b) August (46:355) and (c) September–October (5:111) of first-year Willow Warblers ringed in Britain & Ireland and recovered during the same autumn. Birds ringed as pulli (red) are differentiated from birds ringed as juveniles (grey). Sample sizes of the age classes (pulli:juveniles) are given.

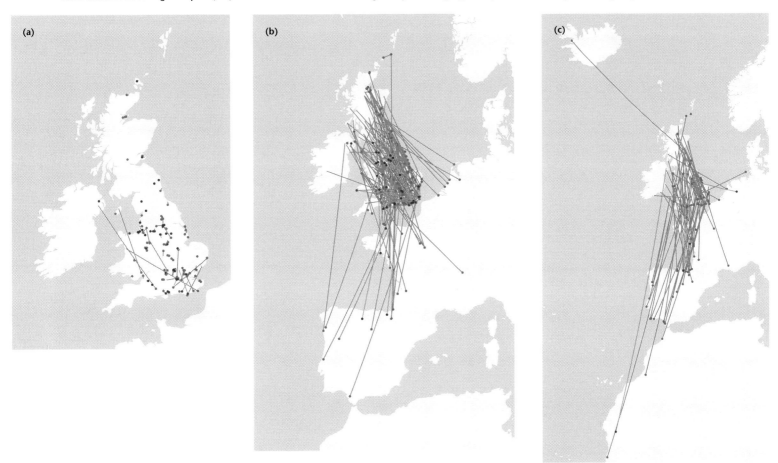

for many British-bred Willow Warblers (Fig 5). These figures also show that many Irish birds, and probably a proportion from northwest Britain, use the Channel Islands rather than the south coast of England as a staging post. This would accord with all British & Irish Willow Warblers starting migration on a southeast heading.

Recoveries of first-autumn birds show that there is a change of direction to a south or southwest orientation on departure from England, with recoveries in western France (where Bibby & Green (1983) found that body-mass was similar to that of birds in England), southwest France, northern Spain and western Iberia (Fig 5). Recoveries in southern Spain and Morocco have been mainly in September and October. Fat deposition in preparation for trans-Saharan flight probably takes place in Iberia (Mead & Watmough 1976).

Adults have been recovered abroad only from late August, later in the autumn than first-winter birds, but their direction of movement was also to the south or southwest (Fig 4). The number of adults recovered abroad in September and October, although small, suggests they take a similar route to first-winter birds across Europe.

The main wintering areas for British & Irish Willow Warblers appear to be countries in the Gulf of Guinea region, principally the Ivory Coast and Ghana (Fig 6), in contrast to the wintering grounds established for *acredula*, which lie further east in Africa and south to the Cape (*Der Zug*). The species is very adaptable in its winter quarters and exploits a wide range of habitats, including wooded savannas and ravines, dry evergreen forests, and even tree heath and gardens (*BWP*). Despite intensive expeditionary ringing in Senegal since the late 1980s, only three Willow Warblers from Britain & Ireland have been recaptured there.

Most Willow Warblers, whether ringed as nestlings or breeding adults in Britain, subsequently return in spring to the general vicinity of their birth (Lawn 1984), although sex differences in the return rates of juveniles from wintering areas to natal areas are also evident (Norman 1994). The spring migration of *trochilus* begins in late February in Africa and is both faster and more direct than autumn passage, birds mostly bypassing western Iberia (Fig 7), with immigration into Britain occurring mainly across south and southwest coasts (*R & F*). Males are known to arrive on breeding territories around two weeks in advance of females (Durman 1967, Lawn 1982). Males have been recovered during March and early April both on passage in southern Europe and in Britain. Females, however, have not been recovered until late April, and most were then already in Britain. They may, therefore, undertake longer flights to their breeding grounds than males.

A mix of British and continental birds occurs in the autumn, and to a lesser extent spring, mainly on the east coast of Britain, individuals from Fennoscandia featuring principally (Fig 7), probably as a result of adverse winds deflecting them from their intended route (*BWP*). Late August peaks on the east coast of Britain are considered to originate from different populations to those forming earlier peaks at west and south coast sites, and continental drift migrants are thought to be involved (*R & F*). Hogstedt & Persson (1982) found that the peak migration period for the species in southern Sweden is from mid- to late August, when east-coast numbers are highest in Britain. Norman & Norman (1985) calculated from the consideration of known moult time-spans in continental Willow Warblers that birds from these populations should not occur in Britain before 4 August. May (and a few June) recoveries in

Fig 6. Locations during November–February of Willow Warblers ringed or recovered in Britain & Ireland. Those birds present in Britain & Ireland during the breeding season (6, red) are differentiated from those present outside the breeding season (15, grey) and those of uncertain seasonality (4, open symbols).

Fig 7. Locations during March–May of Willow Warblers ringed or recovered in Britain & Ireland. Those birds present in Britain & Ireland during the breeding season (488, red) are differentiated from those present outside the breeding season (587, grey) and those of uncertain seasonality (78, open symbols).

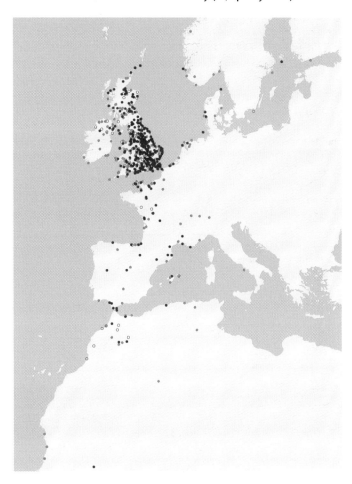

the Netherlands and Fennoscandia (Fig 7) seem to confirm that a proportion of east-coast birds in autumn and spring are displaced migrants travelling from or to the Continent.

As relatively large numbers of Willow Warblers have been ringed in Britain & Ireland, we have a reasonable understanding of their seasonal movements relative to that for a number of other trans-Saharan migrants. There is still much to learn about the wintering range of

British & Irish breeders and the ecology of the species away from the breeding areas, however, which wider-scale expeditionary work could address. An increased understanding of the passage use of Britain & Ireland by populations breeding further north and east in Europe would also be beneficial.

Steve C Norman & Wilf Norman

Goldcrest
Regulus regulus

Despite being the smallest European bird, the Goldcrest is able both to overwinter in severe cold and 18-hour darkness north of the Arctic Circle in coastal Norway, and to migrate the breadth of Europe to escape even worse winter conditions. It is one of the lightest birds anywhere in the world that makes regular sea crossings, and the frequency of encounters with birds visibly exhausted by their exertions suggests that migrating Goldcrests habitually operate close to their physiological limits.

Goldcrests both breed and winter widely across Europe, but are only vagrants to Iceland and in southern Europe are confined as nesting birds to mountain forests (*BWP*). The breeding range continues eastward across Asia to Lake Baikal, and there are further Asian populations east to Sakhalin Island and Japan and south to Tibet. Isolated races are found in the Azores and the Canaries. The northern fringe of the breeding range, which reaches the limit of boreal forest in Fennoscandia and western Russia, is generally deserted in winter, and birds then appear south of the breeding range in Mediterranean Europe. In Finland, Goldcrests are completely migratory in the north but there is an increasing proportion of resident birds further south; the population is more migratory when autumn numbers are high (Hildén 1982).

The species is a common nesting bird throughout Britain & Ireland, being absent only from the Fens and other reclaimed farmland, high mountains, moorland and other areas where suitable woods are lacking (*1988–91 Atlas*). Even the least hospitable British & Irish breeding sites may be occupied all year, but birds occur more widely outside the breeding season, in hedgerows, gardens and coastal scrub as well as in

The analysis of the data for this species was supported by the Steyning Ringing Group

woodland. Migrants are regular at coastal promontories and islands during spring and autumn, and large falls can occur.

The ring-recovery data for Britain & Ireland are skewed very heavily towards coastal sites and away from the breeding season (Figs 1 & 2). Well-placed nets and traps can intercept large numbers of coastal migrants concentrated by lines of bushes or trees, whereas few ringers operate in the preferred forest breeding habitats where, in any case, Goldcrests stay mainly out of reach in the canopy. Only exceptionally are pulli ringed, because of the delicate and enclosed nature of the nest. With 88% of all recoveries being from birds ringed during the main passage seasons, March–April and September–November (Fig 2), sedentary behaviour and non-coastal migration are under-represented in the data. There were no recoveries from birds ringed in the breeding season in Ireland, despite breeding densities being generally higher there than in Britain (*1988–91 Atlas*).

Goldcrests are short-lived birds, with a high turnover of individuals in the population, but because of their tiny size and dense habitat they are rarely found dead, even in human-related circumstances. Dead birds accounted for only 58% of returns, the remaining 42% being recaught by ringers. Predation, mostly by cats, accounted for two-thirds of recoveries of known cause; a further 20% were human-related, mostly through hitting windows or falling victim to road traffic (Fig 3).

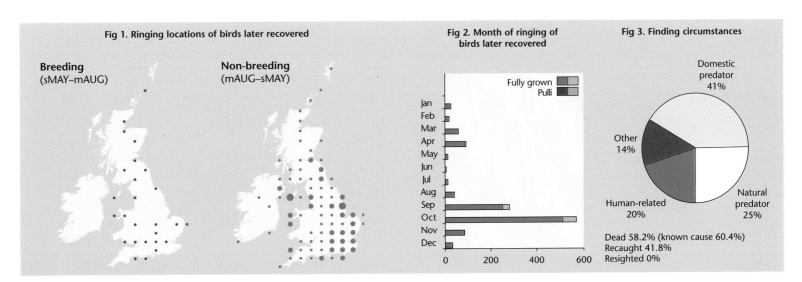

Fig 1. Ringing locations of birds later recovered

Breeding (sMAY–mAUG)

Non-breeding (mAUG–sMAY)

Fig 2. Month of ringing of birds later recovered

Fully grown / Pulli

Fig 3. Finding circumstances

Domestic predator 41%
Other 14%
Natural predator 25%
Human-related 20%

Dead 58.2% (known cause 60.4%)
Recaught 41.8%
Resighted 0%

Ringing and recovery data

	<1960	60–69	70–79	80–89	90–97	Total
RINGING						
BTO ringing totals (%)	1	6	21	39	32	336,461
RECOVERIES						
BTO-ringed (%)	1	4	25	43	27	1,115
Foreign-ringed (%)	←	26	→	32	41	133

Statistical analyses

	Breeding population (sMAY–mAUG)	Wintering population (sNOV–sAPR)
Status	SEDENTARY*	SEDENTARY*
Age differences	Not tested	Not tested
Sex differences	Not tested	Not tested
Regional differences	Not tested	Not tested
Finding circumstances	Not tested	Not tested

Fig 4. Locations in (a) autumn (20), (b) winter (32) and (c) spring (19), and movements of over 20 km between the breeding and non-breeding season, of Goldcrests present in Britain & Ireland during the breeding season.

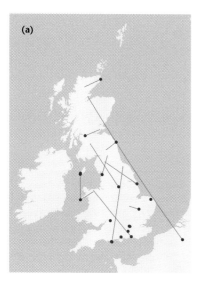
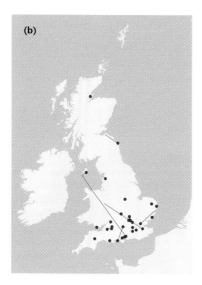
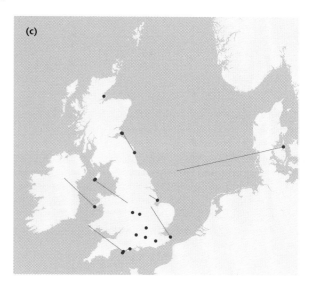

Fig 5a. Recovery locations in winter, and movements of over 20 km between autumn and winter, of Goldcrests ringed in Britain & Ireland during autumn and recovered during the following winter. Known females (73, red) and males (119, blue) are differentiated from birds of unknown sex (8, grey).

Fig 5b. Recovery locations in spring, and movements of over 20 km between winter and spring, of Goldcrests ringed in Britain & Ireland during winter and recovered during the following spring. Known females (17, red) and males (12, blue) are differentiated from birds of unknown sex (1, grey).

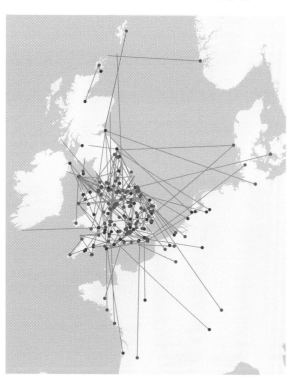
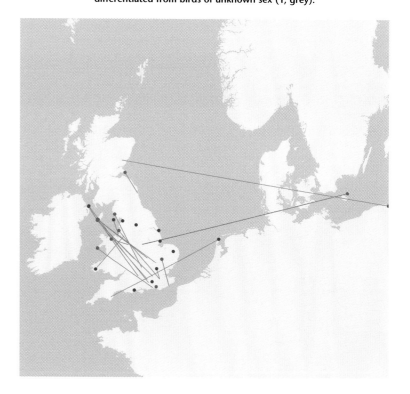

Remarkably little information is available about the movements of British & Irish breeding Goldcrests. Just 81 recoveries (7% of the total) were from birds either ringed or recovered in the breeding season. Almost two-thirds of the movements between breeding and non-breeding seasons were within 20 km, suggesting sedentary behaviour, especially in southern and central England (Fig 4). Retrap data held by ringers indicate that some of our breeding adults are indeed truly sedentary all year, at least in southeast England (pers obs), as some are in Norway (Hogstad 1984) and Belgium (Vercauteren 1991). The longer movements suggest a generally southerly or southeasterly movement of British Goldcrests across southern Britain in autumn and a northwesterly return in spring. At the Calf of Man, strong passages are noted between

mid-July and early November, peaking in September, and between mid-March and mid-May; since the main autumn movement at the Calf is about a month earlier than at Scandinavian observatories, a largely British origin for these birds may be inferred (Thorpe & Sapsford 1992). The BTO's Garden BirdWatch survey has revealed regular October and March peaks of occurrence in gardens (Cannon 2000), which suggest that movement occurs on broad fronts across Britain at these seasons. Although a notable element of the ring-recoveries is the large proportion (15%) that are international, there is no confirmed case of a British- or Irish-breeding Goldcrest wintering abroad. Single recoveries linking the western North Sea in the breeding season with Denmark in the spring, and coastal northeast Scotland with Belgium in the autumn (Fig 4),

Fig 6. Locations abroad during (a) autumn (43:69:4) and (b) spring and the breeding season (10:8:3), and movements of over 20 km, of Goldcrests that were present in Britain & Ireland outside the breeding season. Females (red) and males (blue) are differentiated from those of unknown sex (grey). Sample sizes of the classes (female:male:unsexed) are shown.

(a)

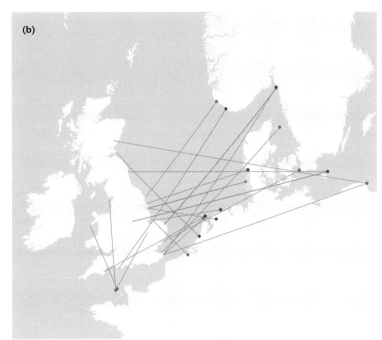

(b)

might refer to early-arriving or late-departing immigrants rather than to British birds.

When recoveries from birds trapped in Britain & Ireland at passage seasons are plotted (Fig 5), sample sizes are much enhanced but the movements of native British & Irish birds become confounded with those of continental migrants. Many such recoveries amplify the northwest–southeast axis suggested by the breeding-season recoveries,

Fig 7. Movements of over 20 km and recovery locations of Goldcrests ringed in winter and recovered in the same winter (66:26, red) or a subsequent winter (12:14, blue). Sample sizes of movements under:over 20 km are given but only those over 20 km are plotted.

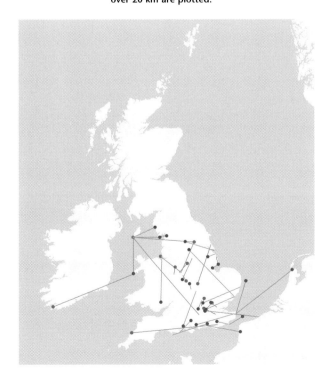

however, with a few birds from the northwest crossing the English Channel (Fig 5a). Winter recoveries of birds ringed at passage seasons therefore provide indirect evidence that some British & Irish breeders may leave Britain via the south or southeast coasts to winter on the near Continent.

Although some of the movements plotted undoubtedly refer to immigration or onward passage of birds originating on the Continent, it is striking that most of the longer-distance spring movements of birds wintering in south-central England are towards the northwest, suggesting a British or Irish rather than continental breeding destination (Fig 5b). Both the movements of individual birds and the volume of recorded passage emphasize the importance of the Calf of Man as a passage site (Thorpe & Sapsford 1992). Its pre-eminence may indicate that birds originating in Scotland, Northern Ireland or the Isle of Man are more likely to move south for the winter than those from regions further south. The Goldcrest therefore appears to be a partial migrant in Britain & Ireland and perhaps, like those in Finland (Hildén 1982), more migratory in the north. These conclusions must remain tentative, however, since they are heavily influenced by the large numbers of Goldcrests ringed on the Calf of Man.

Most ringing exchanges between Britain and the Continent are of birds visiting Britain for the winter. The breeding distribution of these birds across Europe is poorly known, because virtually all the recoveries link Britain with coastal migration hotspots such as the Baltic observatories, rather than with likely breeding sites (Fig 6). Some come from as far away as western Russia, but the relative importance of the source countries is unknown. Hanssen (1981) considered that Britain & Ireland was probably not a major wintering area for Scandinavian Goldcrests, many of which move southward into continental Europe (Grenmyr 1997). Immigrants arrive in Britain from late August to early November, and depart mostly in March and April. Numbers appear to vary widely between winters, but the large falls that occur in some autumns on the British east coast may owe more to immediate weather conditions than to a particularly strong annual influx. As many as 15,000 Goldcrests were present on the Isle of May on 11 October 1982 (Ellis 1983). While the east coast provides most of the records, many immigrants penetrate the English eastern counties, and some reach Irish

Sea observatories (Fig 6). There is no clear evidence yet that any continental immigrants occur as far west as Ireland, although this is very likely. In Britain, immigrants are probably greatly outnumbered by the resident population of around 560,000 breeding pairs (*1988–91 Atlas*).

Immigrants reaching northern Britain have a strong east–west component to their movements; as yet, there are no recoveries linking Scotland with the northernmost Baltic stations (Fig 6). Headings involving the English east coast are more northeast–southwest, with many recoveries from Norway and some from northern Finland and Sweden. Some birds on this heading apparently penetrate to Dorset and Devon. It is not yet known whether any migrants originating on the Continent are among those birds that depart from Britain in autumn towards France and the Low Countries (Fig 5).

Recoveries in the same winter as ringing show a number of movements from the east coast that probably refer to continental immigrants, and in western Britain some southerly and easterly movements that are more likely to relate to home-bred migrants (Fig 7). Movements between different winters include one from Bardsey to County Cork but none between Britain and the Continent. There are too few such recoveries, however, to indicate whether continental immigrants tend to return to Britain & Ireland in later winters.

A fascinating aspect of Goldcrest migration is the extent to which ages and sexes may differ in their behaviour. Little can be said about differences between first-winter birds and adults, however. Birds recorded as first-winters make up 96% of recoveries from British & Irish ringing in September–November, more than would be expected even from the species' high productivity; this may arise perhaps because older birds are more sedentary, or less likely on migration to be grounded at coastal sites. In Sweden (Grenmyr 2000), however, and probably in

Britain & Ireland too, up to one-third of autumn adults are wrongly aged as first-winter, based on the shape of their tail-feathers.

There is an overall skew towards males among recoveries from British & Irish ringing (58% of birds that were sexed) and among foreign-ringed birds recovered here (62%). At the Calf of Man, in contrast, males comprised only 47% of first-winters that were sexed and 39% of adults; in spring, the sex ratio was equal (Thorpe & Sapsford 1992).

Males predominate at passage or wintering sites in the Baltic, Belgium and France (Hildén 1982, *BWP*, Vercauteren 1991). Grenmyr (1997, 2000) suggests that the bias towards males at Swedish observatories in autumn results from the two sexes following differing routes. Males appear to show a greater tendency to cross the open water of the Baltic and North Seas, whereas females may be more likely to follow coastlines. Autumn British birds found abroad in winter support this, with all recoveries suggesting short sea-crossings to or from the Netherlands being of females, and all birds found in Denmark and Norway being males (Fig 5a). The sex ratio among immigrants from Norway is about equal but most that have reached Britain from Sweden and the east Baltic have been males (Grenmyr 1997; Fig 6).

Despite its wide population fluctuations and a recent overall decrease in British breeding numbers, the Goldcrest's status is not of immediate conservation concern (Crick *et al* 1998). We know little, however, about the partial migration of British & Irish breeders and have little understanding of how important Britain might be as a winter refuge for birds from northern Europe. These unknowns could best be studied by increasing the amount of ringing at breeding sites, although data would inevitably be very slow to accumulate.

John H Marchant

Firecrest

Regulus ignicapillus

The Firecrest is Britain & Ireland's second-smallest bird; only Goldcrests are slightly smaller on average. Although tiny, the Firecrest is a most beautiful species whose fiery crest shines brilliant orange when displaying. Firecrests were discovered breeding in the New Forest in 1962 (Adams 1966) and are now localized breeding birds in England and Wales. They have long been regular double passage migrants and scarce winter visitors but are much rarer in Scotland and Ireland and have not been found to breed there.

The entire range of Firecrests is confined to parts of the West Palearctic. The nominate race *ignicapillus* breeds in south and west Europe north to Britain, Denmark and the Baltic Sea and east to Belarus, Latvia, the Ukraine, Georgia and Turkey. Birds of the race *balearicus*, which breed in the Balearic Islands, Tunisia, Algeria and a small area of Morocco, are greyer on the underparts. The race *madeirensis* is resident on Madeira and has a duller orange crown, a shorter supercilium and a slightly longer bill. Southern populations of Firecrests are mainly resident. The eastern and more northerly populations tend to be migratory and winter in the Mediterranean and the extreme west of Europe from Portugal to Britain, with a few in Ireland.

Firecrests in Britain are typically found breeding in conifer plantations, particularly Norway Spruce and to a lesser extent Douglas Fir, Scots Pine and Western Hemlock, but may also be found in mixed woodland or even broad-leaved woodland dominated by Oak and Beech with some Holly (Batten 1973). On passage, a variety of wood and scrub habitats are used, particularly near the coast. They are generally less

The analysis of the data for this species was supported in memory of Bill Woodford

closely associated with conifers than Goldcrests at any time of the year, and are less likely to winter in their breeding sites.

By the end of 1997, 6,618 Firecrests had been ringed in Britain & Ireland. There have been no recoveries of Firecrests ringed in the breeding season (Figs 1 & 2). The coastal distribution of ringing sites of recovered birds largely reflects the predominance of passage migrants in the ringing totals (Fig 1). There have been just 29 recoveries, all of fully grown birds; there is therefore limited information from ring-recoveries on the movements of this species.

Over half of the ringed birds found dead have known causes of death, of which 60% were human-related (Fig 3). This reflects the low likelihood of such a small bird being found dead via other causes, rather than the full range of causes of death.

Nine foreign-ringed birds have been found in Britain, seven from Belgium and one each from the Netherlands and the Channel Islands; and four British-ringed birds have been found, two in the Netherlands and one each in Belgium and Spain (Fig 4). The median distance moved by the 19 British-ringed birds that have been found dead was 198 km. A bird ringed at Dungeness and recovered in Spain had moved 870 km. One bird was found dead at Wick, Caithness, on 11 February 1976 having been ringed at Holme, Norfolk, 645 km to the southeast on 13 October the previous year.

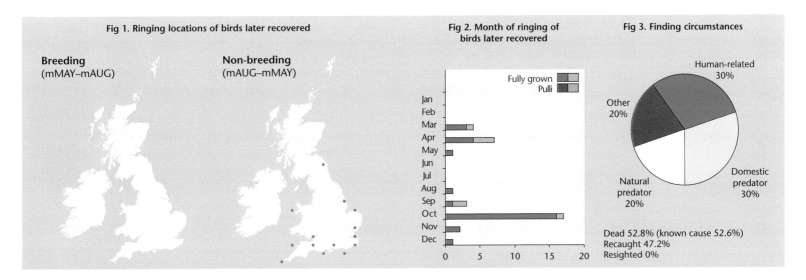

Fig 1. Ringing locations of birds later recovered

Breeding (mMAY–mAUG)

Non-breeding (mAUG–mMAY)

Fig 2. Month of ringing of birds later recovered

Fully grown / Pulli

Fig 3. Finding circumstances

Human-related 30%

Other 20%

Natural predator 20%

Domestic predator 30%

Dead 52.8% (known cause 52.6%)
Recaught 47.2%
Resighted 0%

Ringing and recovery data

	<1960	60–69	70–79	80–89	90–97	Total
RINGING						
BTO ringing totals (%)	2	9	22	36	30	6,618
RECOVERIES						
BTO-ringed (%)	0	3	14	52	31	29
Foreign-ringed (%)	←	22	→	22	56	9

Statistical analyses

	Breeding population (mMAY–mAUG)	Wintering population (sDEC–sMAR)
Status	?	?
Age differences	—	—
Sex differences	—	—
Regional differences	—	—
Finding circumstances	—	—

Fig 4. Recovery locations and movements of over 20 km for the included recoveries of Firecrests ringed or recovered in Britain & Ireland, with dead recoveries (19, red) differentiated from live recaptures (17, blue). The two pre-1979 foreign-ringed Firecrests (both from Belgium) are not shown.

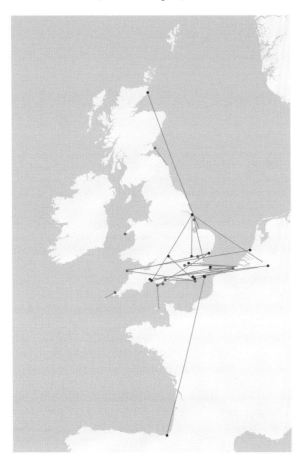

Firecrests have eight main breeding centres in southern England, where birds are present every year (*1988–91 Atlas*, J Ferguson-Lees pers comm). There are a variable number (8–41) of smaller sites that are only occupied in some years; national breeding populations fluctuate markedly from year to year (Batten *et al* 1990, Ogilvie *et al* 1999b).

The main arrival of birds on breeding grounds in Britain occurs between late April and early May (Batten 1973) but birds have occasionally been recorded singing on the breeding grounds in March and early April (Adams 1966, J H Marchant pers comm). The breeding grounds appear to be deserted by late July or early August, but the lack of song at that time makes location of the birds difficult.

Firecrests migrating to and from Britain appear to avoid wide stretches of sea and instead focus on narrow stretches of the English Channel. In autumn, the first birds arrive in early September and the passage may continue into November. There may be two peaks, the first on the east coast from mid-September to early October probably involving continental birds, some perhaps deflected from their intended southwest heading. A later more widespread peak occurs in the second half of October, coinciding with anticyclones (Redman & Hooke 1954) and may be due to an exodus from central Europe following the onset of cold weather (*R & F*).

In winter, the distribution of Firecrests is mainly coastal and the species can occur as far north as Cumbria and the Borders. The best areas are in sheltered scrub and woodland edge habitats near coasts, particularly between Devon and West Sussex, where birds most regularly winter. They show a preference for woodland adjacent to rivers or other water. Most inland sites are not occupied in successive winters (*Winter Atlas*). Only a few are found in winter in Ireland, where it is still a scarce but increasing double passage migrant (*Birds in Ireland*). Firecrests are very rare in Scotland north of the Borders.

In spring, the return movement is evident mainly in the south and southeast of Britain between early March and early May, with the majority moving in late March or early April.

Although the Firecrest is less dependent on conifer plantations than the Goldcrest, the largest colonies have been in mature spruce plantations, and can be severely affected by clear-felling. Felling should be avoided from April to August. If and when it does take place, blocks of 3 ha or more should be left so there are always some stands of trees at least 30 years old remaining in the area (Batten *et al* 1990).

There are far too few ring-recoveries of Firecrests to give much information on the movements of individual birds. We do not know if the British breeders are purely summer visitors and whether they leave the country in winter. Related to this there is no information on either winter or breeding site-fidelity. It would also be valuable to know the origins of winter immigrants and if any of the passage migrants in spring and autumn have destinations beyond Britain & Ireland. It is unlikely these questions will be answered for many years, unless a special effort is made in the areas where these birds are most regular in Britain.

Leo Batten

Spotted Flycatcher
Muscicapa striata

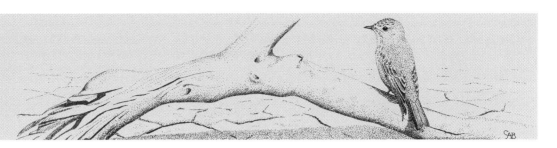

Catching sight of the fleeting flash of a Spotted Flycatcher, as it darts into the air to snatch an insect, is usually our first sign that this long-distance trans-Saharan migrant has returned once again to breed in the gardens and woodlands around us. It is one of the latest breeding migrants to return to Britain & Ireland each spring, seldom appearing in good numbers until the second week of May, with peak passage in southern England during the last two weeks of May (*R & F*).

The species is distributed across most of the western and central Palearctic. The nominate race *striata* breeds from Ireland and northwest Africa eastwards across the Urals to the Irtysh River where it intergrades with *neumanni,* which continues eastwards to western Transbaikalia. The race *neumanni* is found also in Asia Minor, northern Turkey and northwestern Iran, while in the Balkans the population appears to be intermediate between *neumanni* and *striata*. The Crimea, Balearics, Corsica and Sardinia have their own races, and in southern Asia two more races are found through Iran, the Himalayas, Kentai, Altai, and Mongolia north to southeastern Transbaikalia (*BWP*). In Britain & Ireland, the Spotted Flycatcher is absent only from Shetland as a breeding species, with irregular or small populations breeding in Orkney and the Outer Hebrides (*1988–91 Atlas*). The British breeding population was estimated at 120,000 pairs in 1988–91 (Stone *et al* 1997).

All populations winter in Africa south of the Sahara, with most crossing the Equator. They are locally common in southern West Africa, Cameroon, and East Africa, and common and widespread from the southern Congo Basin and Zambia throughout southern Africa (*BWP*).

The analysis of the data for this species was supported by Dr C S Townsend

Spotted Flycatchers use a variety of breeding habitats from sea-level to *c* 900 m and occasionally up to 1,500 m elevation. Common components of preferred habitats include raised perches, often in mature trees and shrubs, telephone wires, fences and buildings. They require open woodland with clearings or glades, and are often found near open water, rivers or streams, and along the edges of dense woodland. Dry deciduous woodland is preferred but they are also found in native pinewoods. In suburban and urban environments, they are found around gardens, orchards, and parks. However, they are absent from open habitats such as grasslands lacking shrubs, arid areas, exposed mountainous areas, and also from dense forests (*BWP*).

In the wintering quarters, the habitats chosen are often similar to those used when breeding. Secondary woodland, disturbed land, and suburban areas are preferred but they will utilize habitat along logging tracks in forest. They are often associated with trees and shrubs in parks and gardens, often near open water (*BWP*). In South Africa, Spotted Flycatchers roost in blue gum, poplar, and willow (Kok *et al* 1991).

The ringing locations during the breeding season of Spotted Flycatchers that have been recovered (Fig 1) are a good indicator of the general breeding distribution of the species within England and Wales but greatly under-represent the Scottish and Irish populations. Most

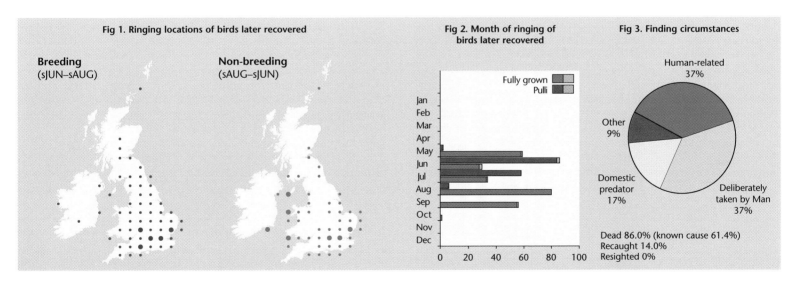

Fig 1. Ringing locations of birds later recovered

Breeding (sJUN–sAUG)　　Non-breeding (sAUG–sJUN)

Fig 2. Month of ringing of birds later recovered

Fig 3. Finding circumstances

Dead 86.0% (known cause 61.4%)
Recaught 14.0%
Resighted 0%

Ringing and recovery data

	<1960	60–69	70–79	80–89	90–97	Total
RINGING						
BTO ringing totals (%)	13	19	22	30	16	86,666
RECOVERIES						
BTO-ringed (%)	14	28	19	26	14	406
Foreign-ringed (%)	←	61	→	33	6	18

Statistical analyses

	Breeding population (sJUN–sAUG)	Wintering population (mNOV–sAPR)
Status	[LONG-DISTANCE MIGRANT]	NONE
Age differences	Not tested	—
Sex differences	Not tested	—
Regional differences	Not tested	—
Finding circumstances	Not tested	—

Fig 4. Locations in (a) autumn (August–October, 93), (b) winter (4) and (c) spring (36), and movements of over 20 km between the breeding and non-breeding season, of Spotted Flycatchers present in Britain & Ireland during the breeding season.

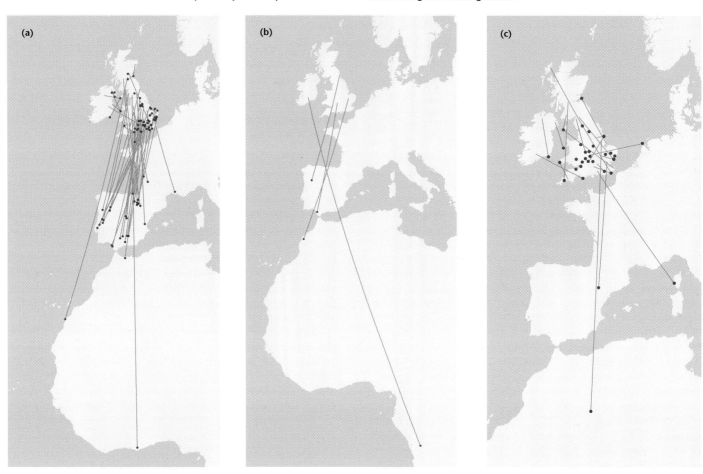

Spotted Flycatchers ringed on passage and later recovered were ringed in southeastern England or in Wales, with few ringed in Scotland or Ireland (Fig 1). More than a third of ring-recoveries were from birds ringed as nestlings, reflecting the generally easy accessibility of the nests (Fig 2).

Of 413 Spotted Flycatcher recoveries, only 14% were recaptured by ringers. Therefore, the distribution of ringers has only a small influence on the distribution of recoveries. Of the remainder found dead, the causes of death are known for 61% (Fig 3). While the proportions are subject to some bias, the regional differences in causes of recovery are nevertheless revealing. In Britain, 60% of 111 recoveries were due to human-related causes and a further 30% to domestic predators. In Spain, 86% of 42 recoveries were due to birds being deliberately taken by Man, and so were all of the 23 deaths in Portugal and Morocco.

Spotted Flycatchers breeding in Britain & Ireland begin to migrate south in late July. The first peak of migration is between mid-August and early September, followed by a second from mid-September to early October (BWP). Observatories on the east coast of Britain tend to record a single peak in late August or early September that probably involves continental drift migrants (R & F). The great majority of birds follow a southwest to south-southwest heading on migration that takes them through western France and Iberia during August–October (Fig 4a). Evidence from a few recoveries suggests that birds breeding in eastern Ireland cross to western Britain before continuing south. Recoveries start to occur in North Africa during September, and in West Africa during October (passage through these areas tends to be September–November). Whilst many Spotted Flycatchers winter in coastal West Africa from the Gambia to Nigeria, others continue their migration southeast into the Congo Basin and Angola (BWP). There are no recovery data to indicate

that birds caught during the breeding season in Britain & Ireland continue their migration beyond Angola, to winter in South Africa (though one bird ringed as a juvenile at the end of August in Gwynedd was recovered in South Africa in the following March). There is little evidence to indicate fattening up and overflying during autumn migration, and the race striata appears to be opportunistic, feeding as it gradually moves south during migration. Spotted Flycatchers are nocturnal migrants (BWP). Site-fidelity between winters has been identified in West Africa (Salewski et al 2000) and southern Africa (BWP). A study in the Ivory Coast revealed that Spotted Flycatchers were non-territorial during the winter months, and over 23% of ringed birds returned to winter in the same area from one year to the next (Salewski et al 2000).

The return migration, in spring, of birds that breed in Britain & Ireland probably begins in April but little is known of the strategy adopted. The general migration route may be more directly north in the spring as birds are less commonly reported in western West Africa, with passage over the Mediterranean being over a broader front (BWP). However, the fact that spring passage is more rapid than that seen in the autumn may give the appearance that the birds are less common in this area at this time. The few spring recoveries of birds using Britain & Ireland during a previous breeding season suggest that migration may occur over a broad front, or that some birds subsequently breed elsewhere in Europe (Fig 4c). Two adult birds ringed in Britain & Ireland during the breeding season and recovered in western Germany and Denmark during a subsequent breeding season might suggest that the latter is true. However, fidelity to a breeding area by breeding adults may actually be high as suggested by a median breeding dispersal distance of just 3 km, although this is based on only 15 recoveries. A moderate degree of fidelity to natal sites is also suggested from a median natal dispersal distance of 9 km (24 recoveries of dead birds only). With the inclusion of retrapped birds, there were 22 recoveries of breeding birds of less than 20 km, and 10 recoveries of over 20 km from the natal site.

The majority of birds breeding west of 12°E in continental Europe migrate southwest into Iberia and West Africa, in a similar pattern to that of British & Irish breeders (Creutz 1941, *Der Zug*). Autumn migrants, including those originating from Britain & Ireland, occur in France and Spain in August–September, southern Europe and North Africa in September–October, and are in wintering areas throughout West Africa by October (as Fig 4b). Some continental birds, probably mainly from Norway, Sweden and the Low Countries, pass through Britain en route to Africa. The single August-ringed bird recovered in South Africa may suggest that some winter beyond the known wintering grounds of British birds, or that some birds from eastern Europe may drift as far west as Britain during their autumn migration but still continue on to winter in their usual areas. Those breeding east of longitude 12°E (eastern Europe) move in a south to southeast direction passing through southern Europe on a broad front but with pronounced passage through Italy and Greece (*BWP*, *Der Zug*). Birds are commonly seen in Sudan and Chad during the autumn migration, suggesting a broader migration front through the northern half of Africa for eastern European birds (*BWP*). Autumn passage through East Africa peaks between October and mid-November (*BWP*). Winter destinations of eastern European birds include the Congo Basin, Angola and South Africa, with birds reaching South Africa in November and December (*BWP*, *Der Zug*).

Spring migration northwards for Spotted Flycatchers wintering in South Africa begins in late February or early March, and most birds have left by the third week of March (*BWP*). Latest departure dates are recorded as 17–26 March (Kok *et al* 1991). There is insufficient information to know whether these birds migrate northwards solely along the east coast of Africa, or whether some head to West Africa.

Passage across the Equator, through Gabon in the west and Kenya in the east, of all birds wintering to the south, peaks in early April. Birds reach Nigeria between early April and late May (peak passage mid-May), and trapping shows that these spring passage birds have much more body fat than birds trapped during autumn passage (*BWP*). Few birds are recorded in Chad and Sudan during spring migration suggesting that a more concentrated passage occurs from Nigeria northward and along the east coast of Africa, or that birds overfly these central countries (*BWP*). From Nigeria, birds rapidly move northwards, rather than west into Ghana and the Gambia, crossing the Sahara directly, and passing through North Africa and the Mediterranean mostly between mid-April and the end of May (*BWP*). They may, however, stop off in North Africa to improve their condition before continuing north (*BWP*).

The breeding productivity of Spotted Flycatchers in Britain & Ireland is currently increasing (Crick *et al* 1998), yet the breeding population has undergone a long-term decline in all habitats (Marchant *et al* 1990, Crick *et al* 1998). As an opportunistic, gradual migrant, the availability of suitable foraging areas along migration routes is likely to be an important factor in the survival of the birds. For this reason, Spotted Flycatchers are likely to be susceptible to habitat loss and degradation in Europe and Africa, and droughts in Africa and elsewhere. Habitat loss and degradation through changes in land use in southern England and in continental Europe, especially in southern Iberia, are of concern. Such changes have included intensification of agriculture and subsequent increased use of pesticides, which may be detrimental by reducing the availability of airborne invertebrates.

There is relatively little specific information on movements abroad, especially in Africa, so increased effort in ringing both in Britain & Ireland and in wintering areas in Africa would be valuable. This would help determine which countries and sites are of conservation importance to the species, and where avoidable mortality is most common, thus enabling appropriate conservation measures to be implemented.

Paul E Baker & Helen Baker

Pied Flycatcher
Ficedula hypoleuca

As a summer migrant to the western Palearctic, this flycatcher is widely distributed in Europe and northwest Asia. Its taxonomy is complicated by clines of paler, browner morphs in males but four subspecies are generally recognized. The nominate *hypoleuca* occurs from Norway and eastern France across Europe to the Urals, with apparently rather isolated populations further west in France and in Britain; *sibirica* breeds east of the Urals, *iberiae* in parts of north and central Iberia and *speculigerus* in the Atlas foothills and uplands from Morocco to northwest Tunisia. Winter quarters for all races comprise those regions of western Africa between the Sahara and the Gulf of Guinea (*BWP*). The Pied Flycatcher overlaps broadly with a sibling species, the Collared Flycatcher *Ficedula albicollis*, in central and eastern Europe, and both are replaced around the Balkans and the Caucasus by the Semi-collared Flycatcher *F. semitorquata*; these two species winter mainly in east-central Africa (*BWP*).

Pied Flycatchers are essentially forest and forest-edge birds in the breeding season. British populations are concentrated in the hilly west and north, where Sessile Oak is a dominant tree, often in association with birches and sometimes with Alder and Rowan; continental European populations additionally use woods where Norway Spruce and Aspen are frequent. In many areas of Britain and elsewhere in Europe, the birds also breed on woodland edges and in areas of scattered trees, though the British plantations of exotic conifers are almost invariably shunned. Winter habitats range from closed forest, through savanna woodland to garden trees (*BWP*).

The analysis of the data for this species was supported by David Boddington

Breeding density may be determined by the availability of nest holes, and a feature of Pied Flycatcher biology is the willingness of this species to take to artificial nestboxes, and to breed very productively in them. Local increases in breeding density and in range have resulted from this behavioural trait, and over recent decades the 34% increase in breeding range within Britain (and start-up, as a rarity, in eastern Ireland in 1985) may be a direct consequence of the numbers of nestboxes available (*Birds in Ireland, 1988–91 Atlas*).

The breeding distribution is well paralleled by the distribution of ringing locations of birds later recovered (Fig 1). The birds' liking for nestboxes make them good subjects for studies of breeding productivity and for the easy and rapid ringing of large numbers of nestlings. Pulli in nestboxes form a high proportion of all Pied Flycatchers ringed in Britain, though smaller numbers of fully grown migrant birds have also been ringed at bird observatories and at coastal ringing stations (Figs 1 & 2). One major study has shown that birds in natural nesting cavities suffer a much higher predation rate than those in nestboxes, with consequently lower fledging success (Lundberg & Alatalo 1992). With a high percentage of British birds now breeding in nestboxes, it is assumed that any resulting bias (in comparison with natural-cavity breeders) will be reflected purely in an increased ratio of survival of

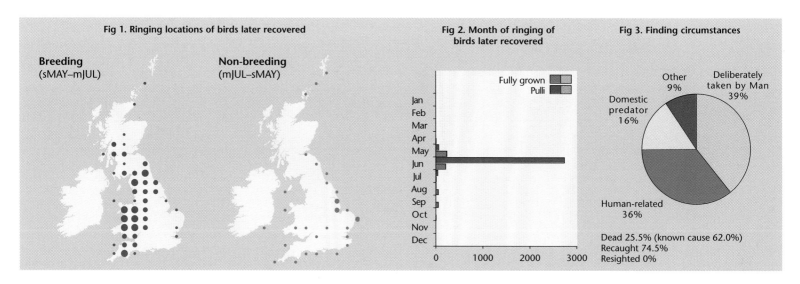

Fig 1. Ringing locations of birds later recovered

Breeding (sMAY–mJUL)

Non-breeding (mJUL–sMAY)

Fig 2. Month of ringing of birds later recovered

Fully grown
Pulli

Fig 3. Finding circumstances

Other 9%
Deliberately taken by Man 39%
Domestic predator 16%
Human-related 36%

Dead 25.5% (known cause 62.0%)
Recaught 74.5%
Resighted 0%

Ringing and recovery data

	<1960	60–69	70–79	80–89	90–97	Total
RINGING						
BTO ringing totals (%)	3	5	11	37	44	452,924
RECOVERIES						
BTO-ringed (%)	1	3	8	40	48	3,424
Foreign-ringed (%)	←	50	→	38	12	26

Statistical analyses

	Breeding population (sMAY–mJUL)	Wintering population (sNOV–mMAR)
Status	LONG-DISTANCE MIGRANT*	NONE
Age differences	Not tested	—
Sex differences	Not tested	—
Regional differences	Not tested	—
Finding circumstances	Not tested	—

Fig 4. Locations in (a) autumn (237), (b) winter (13) and (c) spring (144), and movements of over 20 km between the breeding and non-breeding season, of Pied Flycatchers present in Britain & Ireland during the breeding season.

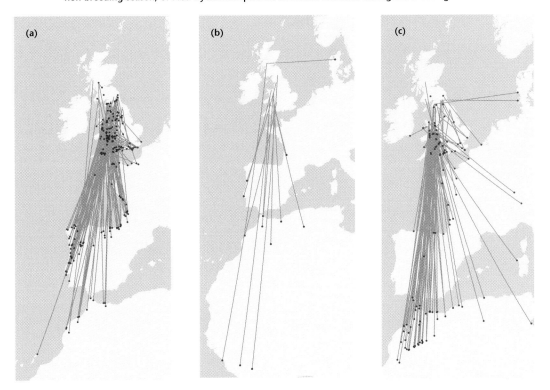

fledged young to eggs laid, but whether there is any other effect, for example on overwintering survival, is not known. It seems unlikely that the nestbox boom will have contributed to any bias in the dispersal or migration patterns shown by ringing.

The circumstances of finding for birds recovered dead are known for 62% of the recoveries (Fig 3). The 'hunting' category accounts for 93% of

Fig 5. Locations outside the breeding season of (a) 108 adult and (b) 279 first-year Pied Flycatchers that were present in Britain & Ireland during the breeding season.

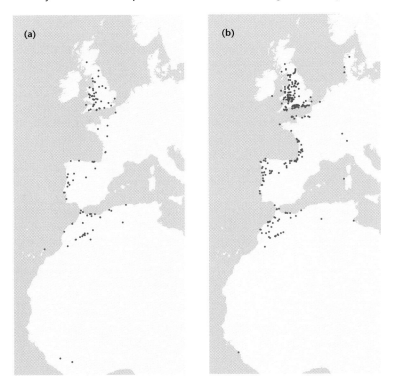

the 118 recoveries of dead birds in Africa and 82% of the 84 in Iberia. However, overall, recoveries of dead birds constitute only a quarter of the records, the remaining three-quarters relating to birds recaptured; of these, the great majority have been found at or in nestboxes and released alive. In Britain, this category of ringing 'controls' constitutes 85% of the recoveries; in six other countries of northwest Europe it comprises 56% of the 32 recoveries of British-ringed birds. Thus there are indications of two types of recovery bias operating through the Pied Flycatcher's year: the higher chances of being caught at a nestbox and released alive in Britain and elsewhere in northwest Europe, and the higher chances of being caught or shot and killed while on passage in Iberia and Africa, or while wintering in Africa.

Pied Flycatchers are purely summer migrants to Britain & Ireland, and normally there are no records after the end of October. The dispersal of birds within and around the breeding areas is likely to take place in July, though the species is elusive during that month and the pattern is very poorly known. From the beginning of August, birds turn up at coastal bird observatories, with a passage peaking during August for sites in the south and west of Britain, during August and September for sites in eastern England, and in September at Fair Isle (R & F). In Ireland, where the species is predominantly an autumn migrant, there is a marked passage that peaks in early September (*Birds in Ireland*). British breeders and their fledged young appear to leave the country by moving to the south coasts of England or Ireland or, perhaps more frequently, by flying directly to northern and western Iberia. Recoveries in autumn of British-ringed birds are concentrated in coastal southwest France, in northwest Spain and in northern Portugal, with several records from coastal north and northwest Morocco (Fig 4). The importance of northwest Iberia as a fattening area for migrant Pied Flycatchers has been emphasized in several studies (*eg* Ferns 1975, Bibby & Green 1980, Veiga 1986).

Onward passage to wintering quarters is indicated by a mere three recoveries in Africa south of the Sahara (Fig 4). Recoveries in Iberia and Morocco at this season may relate to late migrants rather than to birds genuinely wintering but the true extent of the normal wintering range

Fig 6. All included exchanges of Pied Flycatchers between Britain & Ireland and abroad, with those present in Britain & Ireland during the breeding season excluded. Those present in Britain & Ireland in autumn (104, red) are differentiated from those of uncertain seasonality (176, grey). There are no foreign recoveries involving birds present in Britain & Ireland during spring.

There is no obvious difference in long-distance recovery patterns between 12 males and 17 females but this sample is rather small, since Pied Flycatchers cannot be sexed when they are ringed as chicks. Several studies have enabled much to be learned about the biology and social life of Pied Flycatchers (summarized in *BWP*, Lundberg & Alatalo 1992); in particular, ringing has indicated that males show a higher breeding site-fidelity than females, and that up to 14% of nestlings return to breed in their natal area. These results are supported by the British & Irish ring-recovery data. The median distance moved by 157 Pied Flycatchers ringed as nestlings and recovered dead in a subsequent breeding season was only 10 km (P5–95=0–179 km) and the median breeding dispersal distance was 3 km (P5–95=0–110 km, n=37).

Interpretation of the pattern of movements made by British & Irish birds is complicated by arrivals, particularly in autumn but also in spring, of Pied Flycatchers of presumed continental European origin. A prolonged passage well into October at observatories and other coastal sites, and a second peak at some sites in the second half of September when most British breeders have already departed (R & F), are likely to indicate a strong through passage of continental birds. Ring-recoveries link birds arriving in late August and September with Scandinavia, northern Germany and Russia (R & F, Fig 6). Recoveries of birds ringed in eastern England indicate that their autumn onward passage takes them also to much the same regions of northwest Iberia and northwest coastal Africa as those used by British-bred birds (Fig 6). There is one recovery of a bird in winter quarters in central Africa: a first-winter bird ringed on the coast of Lincolnshire in September, and found in the Central African Republic the following February. This hints at a more easterly wintering area for continental birds (reorienting after autumn arrival in Britain) compared with a westerly one for British birds but this facile interpretation is compromised by three recoveries of Fennoscandian Pied Flycatchers well into the western end of the overall wintering range (Lundberg & Alatalo 1992). However, the general pattern seems to be that all the Pied Flycatchers that leave Britain in autumn undertake a dog-leg on their journey to the winter quarters: south-southwest to northwest Iberia, then south to Africa south of the Sahara. There is also the possibility that some birds could take a straight route south or marginally west of south, along the Biscay coasts of France and Spain, and onward through northeast Morocco. There is no evidence from the ring-recoveries for the passage through Britain & Ireland of Scandinavian breeders during the spring migration.

As a mainly forest or woodland species, the Pied Flycatcher is obviously highly dependent on this type of habitat at all times of year. The conservation implications are acute in the breeding season, especially if standing old or rotting timber (with available nest holes) is 'tidied' away in the interests of human safety or fuel provision. Forest and savanna areas of native trees, with their associated invertebrates, are essential to birds on passage, especially in fattening areas such as northern Portugal, and perhaps the Atlas foothills. The winter ecology of Pied Flycatchers in west-central Africa is at present little known, although a study in the Ivory Coast has been recently completed (Salewski *et al* 2000), but any significant reduction in tree cover in that zone must eventually have dire consequences for the species. There are few data currently available on habitat use and population density at that season; if augmented, those would prove extremely valuable in understanding and interpreting any future changes in the status of the species at all stages of its migrant life. Meanwhile, in Britain, populations are at present possibly at an unnaturally high level because of the ample provision of nextboxes; long may this situation continue — to the benefit of the birds and the people who study and watch them — but the birds' future well-being is critically dependent upon conservation of their woodland habitat.

Peter Hope Jones

remains to be determined. There are no data to indicate directly the nature of any movement of British Pied Flycatchers within their winter quarters. A recent colour-ringing study in the Ivory Coast has indicated, however, that in good-quality habitat Pied Flycatchers defend, for a long period in the winter months, a well-defined feeding territory, to which they often return in subsequent winters. One bird remained on winter territory for 188 days, and another was recorded in at least four winters (Salewski *et al* 2000).

Return to Britain in spring appears to be effected by a route to the east of the autumn path (Fig 4). This spring migration takes birds through much of northwest Africa from the Atlas Mountains and northwards, and across central Spain, to arrive at British breeding grounds from mid-April to mid-May; passage at coastal bird observatories is, with the sole exception of Fair Isle, very considerably less obvious than in autumn (Hope Jones *et al* 1977, R & F), indicative perhaps of an extended flight direct from Africa or southwest Europe to inland Britain. It is possible that spring immigration of breeders entering Britain could be from the south to southeast, in contrast to the autumn departure of south to southwest. Only very few birds reach Ireland in spring (*Birds in Ireland*). Autumn movements of home-bred juveniles and breeding adults begin in August, and most have already left Britain by September.

There is only a slight difference between the long-distance recovery patterns shown by adults and first-year birds ringed in Britain & Ireland: a wider scatter of headings in the younger cohort, with a few recoveries to the east of the main adult flight-lines, as illustrated by a series of seven recoveries between Denmark and Tunisia (Fig 5). It has already been suggested from experimental evidence (Sandberg *et al* 1991) that adult Pied Flycatchers orient — on autumn migration — with higher precision than do young migrants.

Bearded Tit
Panurus biarmicus

Usually classified with the parrotbills of eastern and southern Asia, the Bearded Tit is the sole representative of the family Timaliidae in temperate parts of the Palearctic. A locally numerous reedbed specialist, it is mainly sedentary in Britain and western Europe but periodically makes pronounced diurnal eruptive movements.

Breeding numbers have increased enormously in Britain from just a few pairs in the late 1940s. The species spread from its East Anglian refuge to form new colonies in southern and western England and in Yorkshire during the 1960s and early 1970s (Axell 1966, O'Sullivan 1976), and more recently in Lancashire (Wilson 1993) and the Tay reedbeds in Scotland (S Moyes pers comm). There was a marked expansion on the Continent at the same time. Eruptive movements have spread the species to a number of countries, with particularly notable increases to thousands of pairs in the Netherlands and Sweden (Bibby 1983, *BWP*). In Britain, after a series of recent mild winters, numbers are now close to the peaks reached in the late 1970s and early 1980s. The species was more widespread in the 1990s than at any other time in the 20th century, with over 60% breeding outside East Anglia (Campbell *et al* 1996). The species is rare in Ireland, but has nested in County Wicklow (*Birds in Ireland*).

The nominate race *biarmicus* breeds in Europe west to Britain and Spain, north to the southern Baltic and east to Poland, Switzerland and the Balkans. The paler *russicus* breeds from the Carpathian Basin, Ukraine and Asia Minor through central Asia to northern China. In northern and western Europe, birds are dispersive but winter broadly within the breeding range. In eastern Europe and Asia, the northern

The analysis of the data for this species was supported by Arthur Bowles, Kevan Brett & Dave Parsons

populations are more distinctly migratory, and some birds winter south of the breeding range (*BWP*).

Bearded Tits are confined in the breeding season to lowland reedbeds, typically extensive areas of Common Reed growing in fresh or brackish water. They depend on reeds in winter also but are then found more often in small reedy patches, along ditches and around estuaries, and may feed with other small seed-eating birds among nettles and willowherbs. Apart from a thriving colony in Lancashire, the main British breeding sites, and most of the minor ones, are near the coasts of eastern and southern England. In winter, distribution is rather more dispersed, and more inland sites are occupied.

The distribution of the ringing sites of birds that were recovered broadly reflects the distribution of Bearded Tits in Britain in both the breeding and non-breeding seasons (Fig 1). Most birds recovered have been ringed at breeding sites, as fully grown birds from June to October (Fig 2). There are very few recoveries of Bearded Tits ringed as nestlings. Of 938 recoveries, the great majority (94%) were recaught by ringers, and the pattern of these controls may have been influenced by a concentration of ringers at wintering sites in southern England. Of 53 recoveries of birds found dead, most were attributable to known causes, the most common of these being natural predation (Fig 3).

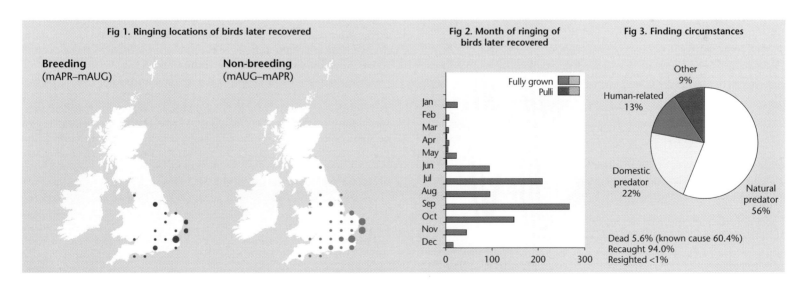

Fig 1. Ringing locations of birds later recovered

Breeding (mAPR–mAUG)

Non-breeding (mAUG–mAPR)

Fig 2. Month of ringing of birds later recovered

Fully grown / Pulli

Fig 3. Finding circumstances

Other 9%
Human-related 13%
Domestic predator 22%
Natural predator 56%

Dead 5.6% (known cause 60.4%)
Recaught 94.0%
Resighted <1%

Ringing and recovery data

	<1960	60–69	70–79	80–89	90–97	Total
RINGING						
BTO ringing totals (%)	1	16	43	19	22	29,114
RECOVERIES						
BTO-ringed (%)	0	17	48	17	18	938
Foreign-ringed (%)	←	87	→	13	0	23

Statistical analyses

	Breeding population (mAPR–mAUG)	Wintering population (sNOV–sMAR)
Status	[SHORT-DISTANCE MIGRANT]	[SHORT-DISTANCE MIGRANT]
Age differences	Not tested	Not tested
Sex differences	Not tested	Not tested
Regional differences	Not tested	Not tested
Finding circumstances	Not tested	Not tested

Fig 4. Locations in (a) April–September (228) and (b) October–February (684) of Bearded Tits ringed or recovered in Britain & Ireland.

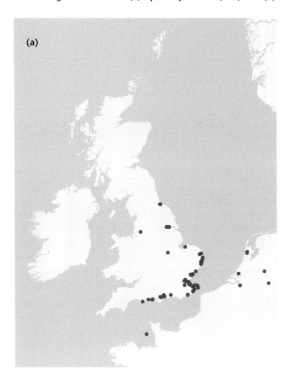

Fig 5. Locations outside the breeding season and movements of over 20 km between the breeding and non-breeding season of 424 Bearded Tits present in Britain & Ireland during the breeding season.

Bearded Tits of all ages form autumn flocks immediately after moult, from mid-September onward, and on still mornings form noisy high-flying parties above the reedbeds. From late September, groups of birds may break away and leave the breeding marsh, calling continuously as they go (Axell 1966). October is the main month of autumn movement, but visible migration continues to mid-November. Although a substantial proportion of the population may thus depart from the main breeding marshes, other parties typically remain sedentary at these sites throughout winter.

Monthly recovery patterns are similar from April to September, with records confined mainly to the coastal breeding sites (Fig 4a). By October, recovery sites are more numerous, scattered along the east and south coasts and extending inland to the Midlands and the London area and southwest to Devon, and a dispersed recovery pattern is seen throughout winter (Fig 4b). In a Suffolk study, exchange of ringed birds between two nearby breeding marshes began in late September, and birds were controlled up to 30 km away from early October onwards; there were, however, very few long-distance movements from these sites until late October (Pearson 1975).

Autumn movements seem to be determined largely by reedbed availability and influenced by competition with birds from other marshes (Pearson 1975). As a whole, the British population undergoes a westward shift in winter of over half a degree of longitude, according to ring-recoveries; there is no overall latitude shift. Most movements of birds ringed in the breeding season and recaught away from the ringing site in the non-breeding season have been over 20 km, and many have been in the range 100–395 km (Fig 5). No bird ringed in Britain in the breeding season has been recovered on the Continent. When recoveries of dead birds are considered, half were found within 3 km of the ringing site, suggesting that the proportion of birds wintering away from breeding marshes may be less than 50%. Movements of birds of known age ringed in summer before moult indicate that adults are as prone to migrate as first-year birds. Recovery patterns reveal no difference between the sexes. There are many recorded instances of Bearded Tits migrating in pairs, some of them ringed together as juveniles (Axell 1966).

Controls from birds ringed at wintering sites have shown that many birds that migrated in autumn returned in spring to their breeding marshes (*eg* Axell 1966). One classic example demonstrated a succession of migrations between wintering and breeding sites: a pair ringed at Farlington, Hampshire, in December 1966 were controlled together at Minsmere, Suffolk, the following July, then back at Farlington the next November; the female was caught yet again at Minsmere in July 1968 and finally back at Farlington the following December. Most between-winter controls involve birds at the same site but some had changed wintering site, in some cases by up to 130 km. The same wintering site may be used by birds from different breeding areas (O'Sullivan 1976). Many of the wintering sites of the 1960s were subsequently colonized, presumbly by birds which did not migrate in spring.

Return to the breeding marshes takes place mainly in late March and April. While March recoveries show a dispersed pattern similar to that in winter, April recoveries are practically confined to breeding areas. A bird ringed as a pullus in Lancashire was found in a subsequent breeding season 111 km east in Cleveland, but most one-year-old birds appear to return to the natal marsh. In a Suffolk study, many colour-ringed Walberswick birds wintered in nearby reedbeds at Minsmere and Benacre but few remained to the breeding season. Breeding-season exchanges between Walberswick and Minsmere, 5 km apart, were minimal (Pearson 1975). There are few examples of breeding dispersal from the recovery data but they include some large displacements. Of 31 birds ringed as breeding adults and recovered over 20 km away, only four were in the breeding season but these included birds from Hampshire and Somerset subsequently found breeding in Kent.

Bearded Tits occasionally reach Britain from the Continent. Ringing has revealed two main periods of influx, coinciding with population explosions in large new reedbeds in the Netherlands and expansion in western Europe. Nine Dutch birds were controlled in Britain during 1965–66 and another 11 during 1970–73, all in late autumn or winter at scattered sites in southern and western England and North Wales. Birds ringed during these periods at British wintering sites and recovered in the Netherlands (four), Belgium (five), Germany (three) and France (one) were presumably surviving immigrants which returned to the Continent. There have since been only four recoveries involving Britain and the Continent; there were two Dutch birds to Essex in 1986–87, a Swiss bird to Kent in 1989 and an October Sussex bird to France in 1990. Continental immigration may have helped the species recover in Britain from its precarious situation in the 1940s but appears to have played little part in the subsequent breeding expansion which was clearly shown by ringing to be fuelled by the East Anglian population.

The Bearded Tit remains vulnerable in winter to hard weather and coastal floods. Otherwise its fortunes in Britain will be largely determined by the availability of suitable breeding habitat. Changes in migratory behaviour may occur in future and ringing will be necessary to monitor these. Ring–retrap data will be valuable in studies of breeding productivity and survival, and will continue to provide useful autumn population estimates at some of the large reedbeds where breeding numbers are difficult to census in spring.

David Pearson

Long-tailed Tit
Aegithalos caudatus

The Long-tailed Tit is one of Europe's most distinctive birds, their noisy and hyperactive family flocks being particularly conspicuous outside the breeding season as they travel around their large ranges. They are among the smallest of British & Irish bird species and are unusual in being one of our few residents that is insectivorous throughout the year. They also have a remarkable cooperative breeding system in which birds whose own breeding attempt has failed may redirect their parental care by becoming helpers at the nests of their close relatives (Gaston 1973, Glen & Perrins 1988). The species' distribution extends from Ireland across Europe and Asia to Japan, and there is considerable geographic variation across this wide range, with 19 recognized races, split into four groups. The race *rosaceus* found in both Britain and Ireland is a member of the western European *europaeus* group, and is distinct from the white-headed nominate race which is found in northern Europe and Asia. Long-tailed Tits are sedentary over much of their range, including Britain & Ireland, but periodic eruptive movements of nominate *caudatus* occur from northern Europe (Ehrenroth 1976), and more regular migratory movements in Asia (*BWP*).

Within Britain & Ireland, the Long-tailed Tit is typically found in deciduous or mixed woodland with a substantial shrub layer. However, they tend to favour edge habitats and so are also found in scrub, farm hedges and gardens. Population density declines northwards and westwards, and they are usually absent from upland areas (*1988–91 Atlas*). The ringing locations of Long-tailed Tit ring-recoveries generally reflect this pattern of abundance, although Ireland is under-represented

The analysis of the data for this species was supported by Moss Taylor

(Fig 1). There is a marked peak in recoveries of birds ringed in October (Fig 2) but this does not appear to be associated with a peak in dispersal or any other obvious movements of Long-tailed Tits in Britain & Ireland (*BWP*, Harrap & Quinn 1996). Of more than a thousand Long-tailed Tit recoveries, 55% were found dead and of these 61% had the cause of recovery documented. Domestic predators accounted for 35% of these recoveries and 53% were attributed to other human-related causes (Fig 3).

The sedentary nature of the population within Britain & Ireland is evident from ring-recoveries (Fig 4) and from detailed population studies. There has been just a single ring-recovery abroad (ringed in Norfolk in October 1983, recovered in Belgium in September 1984) from birds ringed in Britain & Ireland, and within Britain & Ireland the median distance moved between ringing and recovery for birds found dead was just 2 km, 95% of recoveries being made at distances less than 60 km. There is no consistent directional pattern of movement and no evidence for altitudinal movements from ring-recoveries. No regional variation is apparent in the number or distance of movements before recovery, although in Ireland withdrawal from the extreme western breeding areas has been reported (*Birds in Ireland*). Intensive population studies have revealed a survival rate of breeders between seasons of 57% (Hatchwell 1999), indicating that breeding dispersal is low. This contention is supported by the ring-recovery data which show that all

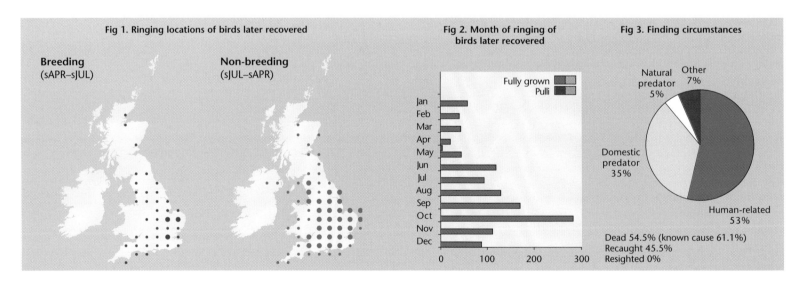

Fig 1. Ringing locations of birds later recovered

Breeding (sAPR–sJUL)

Non-breeding (sJUL–sAPR)

Fig 2. Month of ringing of birds later recovered

Fully grown / Pulli

Fig 3. Finding circumstances

Natural predator 5% / Other 7%

Domestic predator 35%

Human-related 53%

Dead 54.5% (known cause 61.1%)
Recaught 45.5%
Resighted 0%

Ringing and recovery data

	<1960	60–69	70–79	80–89	90–97	Total
RINGING						
BTO ringing totals (%)	1	7	23	30	40	231,795
RECOVERIES						
BTO-ringed (%)	1	11	21	33	33	1,194
Foreign-ringed (%)	0	0	0	0	0	0

Statistical analyses

	Breeding population (sAPR–sJUL)	Wintering population (sDEC–mFEB)
Status	SEDENTARY*	SEDENTARY*
Age differences	Not tested	Not tested
Sex differences	Not tested	Not tested
Regional differences	Not tested	Not tested
Finding circumstances	Not tested	Not tested*

breeding-season recoveries of birds ringed as breeders involved movements of less than 20 km from the ringing site. The difficulty of sexing this species in the hand (except by the presence of a brood patch) means that ring-recovery data cannot be used to investigate whether a sex bias in adult movements exists. However, in the population study described above, survival rates of adult males and females were the same, indicating no sex difference in adult breeding dispersal (Hatchwell 1999).

Limited information is available from ring-recovery data concerning movements of Long-tailed Tits in relation to age. Because of the potential for damage to nests, pulli are not routinely ringed (Fig 2). Furthermore, although juveniles ringed in the first few weeks after fledging are easily distinguished from adults, following their post-juvenile moult it is not possible to separate adults from juveniles using plumage characteristics. One consequence of this is that it is difficult to determine whether the longer distances moved by a few individuals are made by immatures or by adults. Nevertheless, ring-recoveries do suggest that immatures moved further before recovery (either as immatures or adults) than did birds ringed as adults; although median distances were similar for the age classes (2 km), 95% of birds ringed as known adults were recovered less than 20 km from where they were ringed, while the equivalent distance was about 60 km for birds ringed as immatures. If some immatures are misrecorded as adults then the movements of adults may be overestimated in these data.

In the absence of routine ringing of pulli, it is impossible to evaluate natal dispersal from the general ringing data. However, a small number of studies in which large numbers of pulli have been ringed have shown that natal dispersal is strongly female-biased (Glen & Perrins 1988, Russell 1999, pers obs). Flocks comprising juveniles, their parents and any helpers from the previous breeding season typically remain in the natal area during the non-breeding season. Recruitment of first-year males from these flocks into the local breeding population is relatively high, while that of females is low: 30% of male fledglings and just 11% of female fledglings ringed as pulli subsequently bred in one intensively studied area (pers obs). It seems likely, therefore, that first-year females are responsible for many of the longer movements detected from ring-recoveries. However, there are also a few instances of parties (of three to seven individuals) of unknown composition moving more than 100 km (Perrins 1979, *BWP*). This high natal philopatry and local recruitment of males may provide the preconditions for the evolution of the Long-tailed Tit's cooperative breeding system (Glen & Perrins 1988).

Despite the periodic large-scale eruptive movements of Fennoscandian Long-tailed Tits (Ehrenroth 1976), there have been no recoveries in Britain & Ireland of birds ringed abroad, and there have been just a few records of the distinctive white-headed birds of the *caudatus* race in southern and eastern coastal counties of Britain (Perrins 1979, Harrap & Quinn 1996). The relatively weak flight of Long-tailed Tits probably restricts their ability to cross large waterbodies. Indeed, within Britain & Ireland, detailed population studies have shown that

Fig 4. Locations outside the breeding season and movements of over 20 km between the breeding and non-breeding season of 319 Long-tailed Tits present in Britain & Ireland during the breeding season.

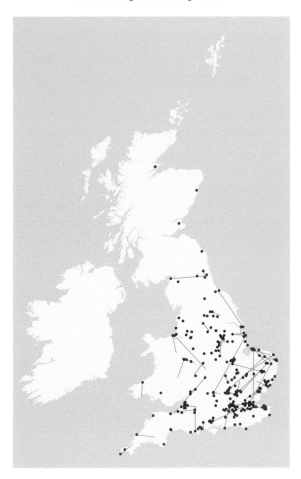

the degree of isolation of woodland habitat influences the rates of extinction and recolonization (Hinsley *et al* 1995) and also the extent of natal dispersal (Russell 1999). Variation in natal dispersal has predictable consequences for the prevalence of helping behaviour in this cooperatively breeding species (Russell 1999), but there is no evidence that habitat fragmentation is a matter of conservation concern for this species (*1988–91 Atlas*). It may be that Long-tailed Tits are buffered from any detrimental effect of habitat fragmentation by their ability to exploit edge habitats. However, dramatic crashes in populations may be caused by harsh winters; 80% decreases and local extinctions have been reported following exceptionally hard winters (*1988–91 Atlas*).

Ben Hatchwell

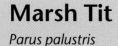

Marsh Tit
Parus palustris

Despite their name, Marsh Tits are primarily woodland birds. Most individuals spend their entire lives within a short distance of where they hatch. Although not uncommon, Marsh Tits and their close relatives Willow Tits remain the least studied of the more common British tits, and this applies particularly to their movements.

Marsh Tits have a disjunct world distribution, with an eastern group centred on China and a western one, found exclusively within the West Palearctic, extending from northern Spain, Britain and southern Scandinavia eastward to the Black Sea and western Russia. Within Britain, Marsh Tits breed in England though rather more patchily in the north than the south, in most of Wales but not in Anglesey, and in southeast Scotland, where numbers have gradually increased since the first known nesting in 1921 (*Birds in Scotland*). They are absent from Ireland and the Isle of Man. Five races are recognized in the West Palearctic, two of which are found in Britain. The race *dresseri* breeds in Wales, England south from Lancashire and Yorkshire, and western France and the nominate *palustris* breeds in northern England and Scotland, as well as southern Scandinavia and central Europe. The three other races are *italicus* (French Alps and Italy), *stagnatilis* (eastern Europe) and *kabardensis* (the Caucasus) (*BWP*).

The non-breeding range in the West Palearctic is very similar to that in the breeding season. The high degree of similarity is particularly evident when the 10-km square distributions of the two in Britain are compared, the non-breeding distribution faithfully reproducing all the principal features of the breeding distribution, a clear sign that the species is highly sedentary (*Winter Atlas, 1988–91 Atlas*). Occasionally

The analysis of the data for this species was supported by John Wood

Marsh Tits appear beyond their normal British range but rarely at any great distance. There is one record for Ireland and at least one record for the Isle of Man together with several of 'black-capped' tits which may be Willow Tits rather than Marsh Tits (Cullen & Jennings 1986), and one each for Skomer and Skokholm (*Birds in Wales*), but such records are quite exceptional. Marsh Tits are very unusual at continental migration watch-points and apparently show virtually no tendency towards the occasional irruptions recorded for other tits. Even during the large-scale irruption of tits in 1957 only a small passage was reported in the Netherlands and Germany, while in Britain there were just a few reports from coastal areas or of increases inland but nothing to suggest that any birds arrived here from the Continent (Cramp *et al* 1960). There is, however, some evidence for regular movements in the Russian part of the range (*BWP*).

In Britain, Marsh Tits are birds of broad-leaved woodland, especially oak and beech, with a preference for larger woods which have a well-developed shrub layer. They are sometimes associated with damper areas such as alder carr and trees along riverbanks but can equally well be found in dry situations. Occasionally in Britain, and more commonly elsewhere in their range, they also breed in birch scrub. They avoid conifers and are very unusual in built-up areas. Territories average 2.5 ha in Britain, relatively large for such a small bird, and they usually remain within these

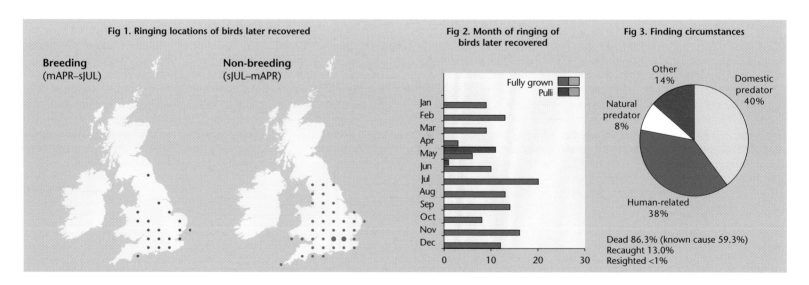

Fig 1. Ringing locations of birds later recovered

Breeding (mAPR–sJUL)

Non-breeding (sJUL–mAPR)

Fig 2. Month of ringing of birds later recovered

Fully grown
Pulli

Fig 3. Finding circumstances

Other 14%
Natural predator 8%
Domestic predator 40%
Human-related 38%

Dead 86.3% (known cause 59.3%)
Recaught 13.0%
Resighted <1%

Ringing and recovery data

	<1960	60–69	70–79	80–89	90–97	Total
RINGING						
BTO ringing totals (%)	7	19	23	28	23	32,582
RECOVERIES						
BTO-ringed (%)	12	31	23	24	10	146
Foreign-ringed (%)	0	0	0	0	0	0

Statistical analyses

	Breeding population (mAPR–sJUL)	Wintering population (mNOV–mFEB)
Status	[SEDENTARY]	[SEDENTARY]
Age differences	Not tested	Not tested
Sex differences	Not tested	Not tested
Regional differences	Not tested	Not tested
Finding circumstances	Not tested	Not tested

Fig 4. Recovery locations and movements of over 20 km for the 146 included recoveries of Marsh Tits ringed or recovered in Britain & Ireland.

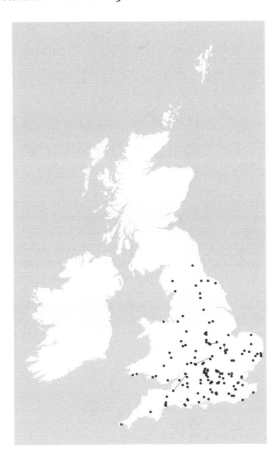

even when the weather is severe enough to drive out other tits (Perrins 1979). Nests are made in natural cavities but they use nestboxes to a certain extent; use of artificial sites has allowed around 200 nestlings a year to be ringed in Britain, about 20% of the annual total.

Ring-recoveries come from birds ringed throughout the main part of the British range with rather more in central, eastern and southern England than elsewhere (Fig 1). Almost half were of birds ringed during the immediate post-breeding period, in June–September (Fig 2), and, of these, a little over half were ringed as juveniles. For many birds, the circumstances of recovery are simply recorded as 'found dead'; of the 59% for which the circumstances are known, the most significant categories are predation by cats and collision with motor vehicles (Fig 3, Sellers 1984). This pattern follows closely that for the Willow Tit and may contain similar biases that tend to exaggerate the amount of movement.

The small number of ring-recoveries preclude detailed analysis of movements but they do serve to emphasize the essentially sedentary nature of British Marsh Tits (Fig 4). An analysis of 108 recoveries by Sellers (1984), found that 85% of recoveries were less than 5 km from the place of ringing, 11% between 5 km and 10 km, 3% between 10 km and 20 km, and just 1% above 20 km, the longest being 79 km. The movements do not show any obvious orientation, and there is no evidence that they are of an out-and-back nature (Sellers 1984). Ageing and sexing of Marsh Tits in the hand presents some difficulties and many of the recoveries are of birds of unknown age or sex. Nevertheless, it is clear that some at least of the individuals that move more than 5 km are young birds, and that such movements as there are take place in late summer or autumn. Although the evidence from ringing is weak, it appears that the movements are primarily associated with post-juvenile dispersal. However, there are some movements of more than 5 km that involve birds marked as adults, and they include, for instance, the longest on record; there is the possibility, however, that these birds were incorrectly aged. The extremely sedentary nature of Marsh Tits and Willow Tits contrasts with that of the more common tits and is presumably, in part at least, a reflection of these two species' food-hoarding habits.

The British ring-recoveries give no clear picture of either natal or breeding dispersal. A project in Bourton Woods, Gloucestershire, found that individual nestboxes were only occupied by Marsh Tits in successive years about 20% of the time. Whether these were the same birds was generally unknown. There were only five cases of adult females being handled at successive breeding attempts and these had moved to a nearby box, the distances involved being 20, 60, 110, 120 and 150 m (Sells 1998 & pers comm). By contrast, a female ringed as a nestling moved 825 m between its hatching and breeding boxes. These results accord with those from elsewhere in the Marsh Tit's European range, where the distances moved between hatching and breeding were typically 800–1,000 m (Nilsson 1989).

Although the picture which emerges from the available information is of a very sedentary bird, further characterization of the species' movements, and the factors which influence them, would be valuable. The principal requirements are to improve ageing and sexing criteria, applying the new methods proposed by King & Muddeman (1995), and to encourage more ringing of Marsh Tits, so that ring-recovery information, especially for birds of known age and sex, is gathered at a faster rate. Given the Marsh Tit's conservation status as an Amber List species, the best way forward would appear to be integrated ringing and population biology studies covering in particular breeding productivity, natal and breeding dispersal and overwinter mortality, with the emphasis on the factors that influence any changes.

Robin M Sellers

Willow Tit
Parus montanus

The Willow Tit was recognized as a distinct species in Britain only a century ago and, like the Marsh Tit with which it was originally confused, many aspects of its biology remain comparatively poorly known. It is, like the Marsh Tit, a woodland species with a very sedentary lifestyle.

Willow Tits are found across the whole Palearctic Region, from Britain to Kamchatka and in Europe from the Alps and the Carpathian Mountains northwards into arctic Norway and Finland. This range is appreciably further north than the Marsh Tit's and is largely defined by the distribution of conifers. Willow Tits are found in all the counties of England and Wales, although rather patchily in places, while in Scotland they occur in southern Strathclyde, Dumfries & Galloway and much more sparingly in the Borders and Lothian. In addition, there are isolated breeding records further north in Scotland, possibly relics of the species' former more extensive breeding range which once extended as far north as Ross-shire (*Birds in Scotland*, Holloway 1996). They do not breed in Ireland or the Isle of Man. British birds are recognized as a separate race *kleinschmidti*, distinct from the many forms of mainland Europe, the most relevant of which to Britain are *rhenanus* of the near Continent and the northern race *borealis* (*BWP*). In North America, Willow Tits are replaced by the very similar Black-capped Chickadee, with which they were originally considered to be conspecific.

A close correspondence between the non-breeding distribution and that in the breeding season, both in Britain (*Winter Atlas, 1988–91 Atlas*), and elsewhere in the Palearctic is strong evidence that Willow Tits are extremely sedentary. There are a number of records beyond the normal range in Britain but these are very unusual. On the Isle of Man,

The analysis of the data for this species was supported by Robin Cole & Tom Kittle

there are no fully authenticated records, though there are a number of sightings of 'black-capped' tits that almost certainly refer to Willow rather than Marsh Tits (Cullen & Jennings 1986). No records of Willow Tits are listed in *Birds in Ireland*, and *Birds in Scotland* lists only one from outside the former range in Scotland, a bird found on Fair Isle in November 1935 that may have been of the northern race *borealis*. There have been several other claims of *borealis*, especially in Yorkshire, and at least one of *rhenanus*, but few have been properly documented (Limbert 1984). Willow Tits were not involved in the large irruption of tits and other species in Britain in 1957 (Cramp *et al* 1960) and there is no firm evidence that *rhenanus* has ever occurred in Britain. Elsewhere in their European range, but particularly in the north, Willow Tits occasionally show irruptive movements apparently initiated in response to acute food shortages (Helle & Mikkola 1969, Ehrenroth 1973, Tiainen 1980, *BWP*). Further south in mainland Europe, the evidence from ringing and from observations at well-watched bird migration sites, such as the Col de Bretolet in Switzerland, is of annual small-scale movements over distances up to about 200 km, which seem to be associated principally with post-juvenile dispersal (*BWP*).

The Willow Tit's distribution in the Palearctic is largely determined by its preference for coniferous or mixed woodland. In Britain, the species is also found in scrubby and generally damper areas of alder,

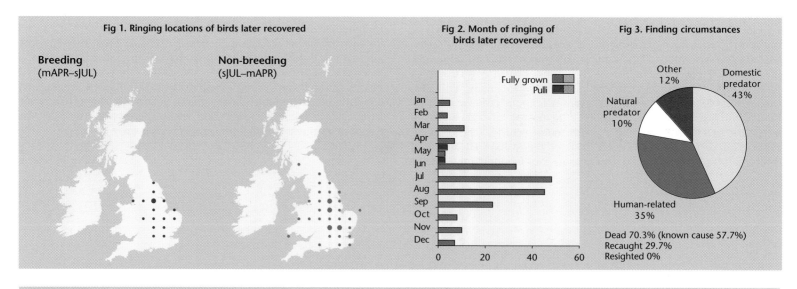

Fig 1. Ringing locations of birds later recovered

Breeding (mAPR–sJUL)

Non-breeding (sJUL–mAPR)

Fig 2. Month of ringing of birds later recovered

Fully grown / Pulli

Fig 3. Finding circumstances

Other 12%
Domestic predator 43%
Natural predator 10%
Human-related 35%

Dead 70.3% (known cause 57.7%)
Recaught 29.7%
Resighted 0%

Ringing and recovery data

	<1960	60–69	70–79	80–89	90–97	Total
RINGING						
BTO ringing totals (%)	1	15	31	34	20	43,395
RECOVERIES						
BTO-ringed (%)	1	19	34	33	12	212
Foreign-ringed (%)	0	0	0	0	0	0

Statistical analyses

	Breeding population (mAPR–sJUL)	Wintering population (mNOV–mFEB)
Status	[SEDENTARY]	[SEDENTARY]
Age differences	Not tested	Not tested
Sex differences	Not tested	Not tested
Regional differences	Not tested	Not tested
Finding circumstances	Not tested	Not tested

Fig 4. Recovery locations and movements of over 20 km for the 212 included recoveries of Willow Tits ringed or recovered in Britain & Ireland.

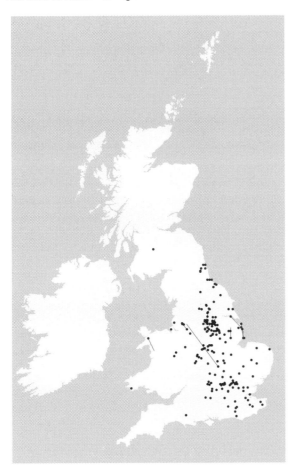

years but has declined somewhat in recent years; in 1996 and 1997 the totals fell below 1,000 birds for the first time since 1968. The majority of recoveries have been of birds found dead but for only a little over half of these were the circumstances of death known. Predation by cats and collision with motor vehicles are the most common causes recorded (Fig 3, Sellers 1984). It seems unlikely that this accurately reflects the true pattern of mortality in the species and in all probability there is a bias towards birds away from their preferred woodland habitats. Thus, the ring-recoveries may disproportionately reflect the behaviour of birds which have already begun to move and, if anything, will exaggerate the frequency of such movements.

With such a small number of recoveries available, only the main features of the Willow Tit's movements can be identified. They show the Willow Tit, like the Marsh Tit, to be a very sedentary bird. Thus, the majority of recoveries are a short distance from the place of ringing (Fig 4). Of 114 recoveries for all age groups combined described by Sellers (1984), 78% were within 5 km, 12% between 5 km and 10 km, 6% between 10 km and 20 km and 4% above 20 km. The longest on record is 167 km. Many movements over 5 km involve birds marked as juveniles and in the main these seem to take place in late summer or autumn. An earlier analysis of the British Willow Tit recoveries noted that all the movements over 5 km were of birds marked in eastern England, east of a line from the Pennines to the Isle of Wight (Sellers 1984). It was tentatively suggested that this might be a result of differences in breeding density between eastern and western England but further information on breeding densities from the *1988–91 Atlas* does not fully support such an interpretation. Movements are not concentrated in any particular direction and appear to be randomly orientated (Sellers 1984). Although the evidence is not conclusive, the nature of the movements in terms of the ages of the birds concerned, their orientation, timing and the distribution of distances moved suggest that they are primarily dispersive in nature and are probably best interpreted as post-fledging dispersals. There is no evidence that any of these are return movements, though further information on this point would be valuable.

The Willow Tit is clearly a highly sedentary species yet some individuals do occasionally undertake substantial movements. Further information about the nature, timing and causes of these would be useful and the immediate need is to increase the number of birds ringed, especially during the summer months when ageing is reasonably straightforward. Improved methods for ageing at other times of the year and for sexing would also be a great boon. Given the species' Amber List status, there is a strong need to develop models of Willow Tit populations and to understand what factors influence or control their numbers. Integrated population monitoring and ringing studies appear to be the optimum approach but the problems posed by the hole-nesting habits of Willow Tits for studying breeding biology and ringing nestlings are formidable.

Robin M Sellers

elder, birch and willow, and will use copses and other small woodland areas that Marsh Tits shun. Willow Tits maintain large territories throughout the year and do not readily vacate them (Perrins 1979). They excavate their own nests in decaying timber, and this in part explains their liking for damper areas. They do occasionally use nestboxes if they are filled with wood chippings or similar material that the birds then remove. Nests are rarely accessible to ringers, however, and as a result the number of nestlings ringed in Britain in a year rarely exceeds 40. Ringing locations of ring-recoveries are concentrated in the eastern half of Britain (Fig 1). There is only one recovery of a bird ringed in southwest England, one from Scotland and just a handful from Wales. Most recoveries have been of birds ringed in the summer months (Fig 2) and include a substantial proportion of juveniles but there are some from birds ringed in all other months of the year. The annual total of fully grown birds ringed has typically ranged between 1,000 and 1,500 during the past 20

Coal Tit
Parus ater

The analysis of the data for this species was supported by David Francis

The Coal Tit is the smallest of the true or parine tits in Europe, a fact that has shaped many aspects of its ecology, including its patterns of movement. It is one of the most widely distributed passerines of the Palearctic region, occurring from the Atlantic to the Pacific and from boreal forests north of the Arctic Circle to the montane forests of the Himalayas, China and Taiwan. Across this great range some 20 races are recognized, of which half occur within the western Palearctic. In general, Coal Tits move little in the west and south of Europe, but may be irruptive, sometimes in very large numbers, further east and when food becomes scarce in winter. Hence, the *1988–91* and *Winter Atlases* have described the Coal Tit as one of the most sedentary species in Britain & Ireland and, although the present account will not modify this view substantially, ring-recoveries have provided further insight.

In Europe, the Coal Tit is chiefly a bird of coniferous forest, and shows a number of adaptations for exploiting this habitat, which give it an edge here over its principal competitors, the Blue Tit and Great Tit. Hence, in coniferous forest it may be much more abundant than those species. In broad-leaved woodland, the tables are turned: Coal Tits tend to be scarcer here than other tits, and, largely because of their smaller size, are socially subordinate to them. The results of this subordination are seen both in summer when Coal Tits may nest in a range of inadequate nest sites including mouse holes in the ground, and in winter, when they may suffer from reduced access to food. Coal Tits can offset this latter disadvantage somewhat by hoarding food to be eaten later when not watched by other tits. In northern parts of its range, food hoarding in late summer and autumn provides the birds with a supply

of food in the depths of winter when it would otherwise be difficult to find. The presence of Coal Tits throughout their Fennoscandian breeding range in winter reflects the effectiveness of this strategy. Despite this, food availability is still a major factor driving the movements of this species.

The Coal Tit is found across most of Britain & Ireland, but because of its preference for conifers, is most abundant in Ireland and the British uplands. As in continental Europe (*European Atlas*), where the species occurs as the nominate race *ater*, the *1988–91 Atlas* showed that the British Coal Tit *britannicus* (found also in northeast Ireland), and Irish Coal Tit *hibernicus* have recently expanded their ranges, especially into the Western Isles of Scotland, and along the Atlantic coast of Ireland respectively. These expansions have largely followed the extensive planting of conifers for commercial forestry in these areas.

Coal Tits that have been recovered had been ringed throughout Britain & Ireland, but only sparsely in Scotland, Wales and Ireland (Fig 1). This has biased the distribution of recoveries towards England in general and the southeast in particular, especially with respect to birds ringed during the breeding season. This is unfortunate given the distribution of the species in these islands. Because of their disadvantage in competition with other tits, they are less frequently encountered in nestboxes than those species. Therefore, in contrast to the Blue Tit and Great Tit, in which pulli constitute about a third to a half of all

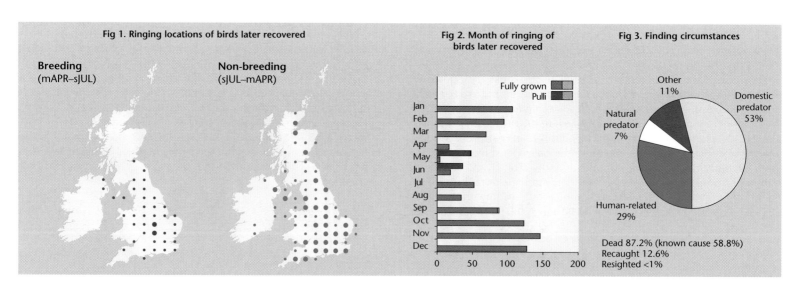

Fig 1. Ringing locations of birds later recovered

Breeding (mAPR–sJUL)

Non-breeding (sJUL–mAPR)

Fig 2. Month of ringing of birds later recovered

Fully grown / Pulli

Fig 3. Finding circumstances

Other 11%
Natural predator 7%
Domestic predator 53%
Human-related 29%

Dead 87.2% (known cause 58.8%)
Recaught 12.6%
Resighted <1%

Ringing and recovery data

	<1960	60–69	70–79	80–89	90–97	Total
RINGING						
BTO ringing totals (%)	4	7	24	31	34	174,432
RECOVERIES						
BTO-ringed (%)	8	11	26	31	24	964
Foreign-ringed (%)	0	0	0	0	100	3

Statistical analyses

	Breeding population (mAPR–sJUL)	Wintering population (mNOV–mFEB)
Status	SEDENTARY*	SEDENTARY
Age differences[NT]	Not tested	Not significant*
Sex differences	Not tested	Not tested
Regional differences	Not tested	Not tested
Finding circumstances	Not tested	Not significant*

Fig 4. Locations outside the breeding season and movements of over 20 km between the breeding and non-breeding season of 227 Coal Tits present in Britain & Ireland during the breeding season.

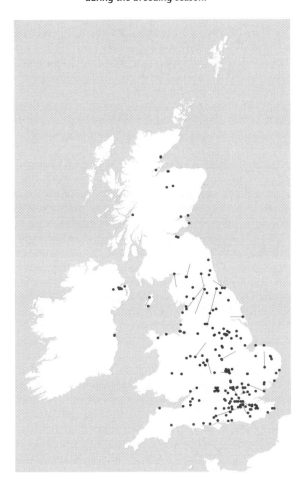

Table 1. Post-fledging dispersal in the Coal Tit. The table shows the numbers and median distances of recoveries within each 30-day period after ringing as pulli. Note that pulli will have remained in the nest for up to ten days after ringing, during which period they would not be available for recovery. Thus the recovery period for the first group is less than 30 days.

Days	Approx. month equivalent	Sample	Median distance (km)	Distance (km) containing 95% of observations
0–30	June	6	0	7
31–60	July	5	0	4
61–90	August	1	6	6
91–120	September	4	7.5	13
121–150	October	5	7	11
151–180	November	2	7	8
181–210	December	3	11	39
211–240	January	1	11	11
241–270	February	4	5.5	15
271–300	March	3	6	51

Table 2. Percentage of Coal Tit movements of over 20 km between the breeding season and other seasons, by breeding region.

Ringing region	Finding season: percentage over 20 km			Overall percentage over 20 km (number of recoveries)
	Autumn	Winter	Spring	
Ireland	0	0	0	0 (11)
Northeast	0	0	0	0 (17)
Northwest	40	40	0	35 (17)
Southeast	12	3	7	7 (140)
Southwest	11	13	0	10 (42)

individuals ringed in Britain & Ireland, most Coal Tits are ringed as fully grown birds trapped outside the breeding season, and less than one-tenth are ringed as pulli (Fig 2). In common with most small passerines, the reported circumstances of recovery are heavily biased towards situations in which members of the public will find them. Hence more than 80% are recovered by domestic predators or in other human-related circumstances (Fig 3), and how much this might have distorted our understanding of the birds' movements is unclear.

The Coal Tit is less strictly territorial during the breeding season than other tit species (BWP), presumably because of the low densities at which it generally breeds. Outside the breeding season, they join flocks of other small birds, especially other tits. Little is known about the proportion of time that Coal Tits spend with mixed-species flocks. Ring-recoveries between the breeding season and other times of the year are shown in Fig 4; a small proportion of the movements are of greater than 20 km. The ringing data suggest that they move little during winter because all recoveries made within the same winter as that in which they were ringed were within 20 km of the ringing site (n=14). Even between winters, Coal Tits do not seem to be any more likely to move any great distance because, of 89 such recoveries, only three were further than 20 km from the ringing site.

A limitation on the uses to which the greater part of the overall ringing data set can be put is the fact that, until recently (Gosler & King 1989), it was not possible to distinguish the sexes on plumage. Hence although about 9% of recoveries of Coal Tits ringed in Britain & Ireland in the breeding season were more than 20 km from the ringing site, we cannot tell whether a majority of these were female, as might be expected from our knowledge of other tit species (Greenwood et al 1979). There is some evidence, however, that long-distance movements are

most likely to be undertaken by birds in their first year of life, as indicated by Sellers (1984): the median distance to recovery for 30 adults was less than 1 km (P5–95=0–59 km) while that for 43 birds recovered while still immature was 6 km (P5–95=0–15 km). However, the median recovery distance for 70 immature Coal Tits recovered when adult was less than 1 km (P5–95=0–35 km), which might suggest an overall movement back towards the natal area after winter. Such a return trend is also suggested by the recoveries of birds ringed as pulli, typically in nestboxes in woodland.

Table 1 shows the median distances from natal sites to recovery locations for Coal Tits ringed as pulli. For the first 60 days after ringing, a period that includes the chicks' development to independence from their parents, and during which we should expect the greatest mortality to occur, the median distance is less than 1 km. The lack of a peak in recoveries (which would indicate a peak in mortality) at this time probably reflects a recovery bias rather than a real biological pattern. This would arise because, as few Coal Tit broods are ringed in garden nestboxes, the peak of post-fledging mortality occurs largely unseen in the woods where the broods were ringed. This contrasts with the Great Tit and Blue Tit, which frequently nest in gardens, and which show a considerable peak in ring-recoveries in the first 60 days. An increase in movements occurs over the next month, with the median recovery

Fig 5. Recovery locations and all 6 included exchanges of Coal Tits between Britain & Ireland and abroad.

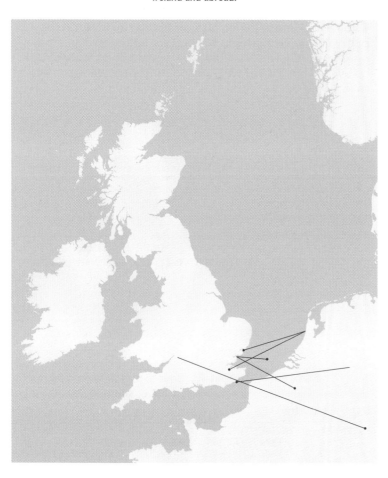

distance increasing to 6 km (Table 1). The median distance remains at around 7 km until midwinter, when a further increase occurs, presumably in response to food shortage. As mentioned above, some evidence for a return to the natal area is suggested by a halving in the median recovery distance after this, although the number of recoveries for analysis is small.

Although Coal Tits clearly occupy small home ranges, to which they are largely faithful, movements occur within this area in response to changing conditions. Hence, Glue (1982) described how numbers increased in gardens in winters when the beechmast crop was poor, and Sellers (1984) showed that numbers in gardens were especially high in years when the average recovery distance (ranging between 10 and 30 km) of Coal Tits was greater. Together, these observations suggest that food shortage in their preferred woodland habitats causes Coal Tits to travel further in search of food, moving into new habitats such as gardens, where Coal Tit numbers generally increase dramatically from July onwards each year (Cannon 2000). Analysis of the overall ringing data set gives further insight. Table 2 shows the percentage of recoveries, in each region, of Coal Tits ringed as fully grown birds during the breeding season but recovered in a subsequent season. In the northwest, the proportion moving more than 20 km is significantly greater than that in any other region despite the small number of recoveries available for analysis from this region. This table also shows the reduction in median recovery distance between autumn and spring in several regions. The greater mobility of Coal Tits in the northwest, a pattern described in other tit species in this volume, probably reflects a difference in the distribution of suitable habitats between this region and others.

The quality of the beechmast crop is known to be important in determining both the survival and movements of other tit species (*eg cf* Great Tit). It is not clear, however, whether the apparent relationship between beechmast abundance and Coal Tit movements described above is driven by the shortage of beechmast *per se*, or of winter seed in general: this might be the case if Beech crops tend to be good in years when crops of other species such as Spruce, Oak, Hazel or Yew are also good.

On the Continent, eruptions of Coal Tits occur from time to time, and although these may coincide with those of other tits (Cramp 1963), whose own eruptions are closely associated with beechmast abundance (Perrins 1966), they are also often quite independent (Ulfstrand *et al* 1974). As is the case for Great Tits and Blue Tits, the eruptive behaviour of continental Coal Tits may bring them to Britain, typically to southern and eastern coasts (Cramp *et al* 1960), but as far north as the Isle of May (*Birds in Scotland*). The independence of Coal Tit movements from those of other tits is implied by the fact that while invasions of Great and Blue Tits to Britain have become rare since 1960, irruptions of continental Coal Tits still occur. Thus, Gantlett (1991) describes an invasion of 30 continental Coal Tits on St Agnes, Scilly, in 1975, and Sellers (1984) mentions that a bird ringed in Essex in April and found dead on the Noord Hinder Lightship the following May was of the continental form; there was also an influx into south and east Britain starting in September 1996 (Taylor *et al* 1999). One German- and two Dutch-ringed Coal Tits were recovered in Britain in this invasion (Fig 5). The timing of continental eruptions coincides broadly with the periods in late summer and autumn, during which juveniles are dispersing (Table 1). The difference in the extent of dispersal behaviour between the British & Irish birds and those of the continental *ater* race is graphically demonstrated by the fact that it is birds of this latter form, and not of *britannicus* which occur periodically, and even bred between 1976 and 1989, on the Isles of Scilly (Gantlett 1991).

It is interesting that while the numbers of ring-recoveries in continental Europe of British-ringed Great and Blue Tits have declined since the 1950s, and none has occurred for many years, coincident with the reduction in the extent of irruption in these species, continental recoveries of British-ringed Coal Tits, which might indicate continental birds returning there, have occurred largely since 1990. Perhaps these birds are not all continental immigrants, but indicate an increasing mobility of the British population in response to the steady increase in the Coal Tit population described above. Although more than 170,000 Coal Tits had been ringed in Britain & Ireland by the end of 1997 (Toms *et al* 1999), many more will need to be ringed before we have a complete picture of the movements of this species, especially with respect to its upland population strongholds, and know if movement patterns are indeed changing in response to population growth.

Andrew G Gosler

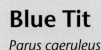

Blue Tit
Parus caeruleus

The Blue Tit is common and familiar more or less throughout Europe. In southern Europe it is often the most common tit species, and in the very north of its range, where it is a relatively recent colonist, numbers have grown to a point where it may be one of the most abundant species (Hildén 1990). It is chiefly a bird of broad-leaved woodland, and especially oakwoods, where it is largely sedentary. It is nevertheless abundant in a wide range of other woodland, garden and scrub habitats. As with the Great Tit and Coal Tit, while our own Blue Tits (race *obscurus*) are strictly resident, in northern Europe the species is a partial migrant, and this, coupled with the periodic occurrence of eruptions, brings members of the larger nominate race to Britain's east and south coasts.

Being readily attracted to garden feeders in winter and nestboxes in spring, Blue Tits are easily trapped for ringing throughout the year; indeed this was the first species of which one million birds (1981) had been ringed in Britain & Ireland. Today more than 2.5 million Blue Tits have been ringed here. The pattern of ringing sites of birds recovered, both in the breeding and non-breeding seasons, largely reflects their distribution in Britain but birds in Ireland are under-represented (Fig 1). Blue Tits are ringed in all months of the year, many as pulli in nestboxes, with large numbers of fully grown birds being caught at feeding stations in winter (Fig 2).

The principal causes of mortality in Blue Tits are likely to be starvation and predation by natural predators (McCleery & Perrins 1991). Starvation may also cause young Blue Tits, even if still dependent on their parents, to enter situations where the likelihood of reporting is

The analysis of the data for this species was supported by Margaret Smith

very high, because some 87% of recoveries for which the cause of death was known were associated with humans, either directly or through their domestic predators (Fig 3).

Some 21% of ringed fledglings are found dead in the first 30 days after ringing (Table 1). This more-or-less halves in the next 30 days and drops further to around 6.5% in the next 60 days. Recovery rates are approximately constant from then onwards. Small increases in recovery rate in about November, February and March might reflect a greater tendency to move into gardens then, so bringing them into greater risk of capture by cats, and thence being reported. The high but declining mortality in the first three months after fledging, suggested by these figures, accords with intensive observations that have been made on the related Great Tit.

Despite the facility that the Blue Tit obviously offers for study, less attention has been paid to it by professional ornithologists than has been attracted by the Great Tit. One reason for this is that competition for nest sites between it and the larger Great Tit often means that a proportion of the Blue Tits have to use natural nest sites, in which they go unobserved, rather than nestboxes. Perhaps also related to this competition is the fact that Blue Tits are less strongly territorial than Great Tits outside the breeding season. Blue Tits tend to be more mobile and form flocks which often act as the focus for other species of *Parus*,

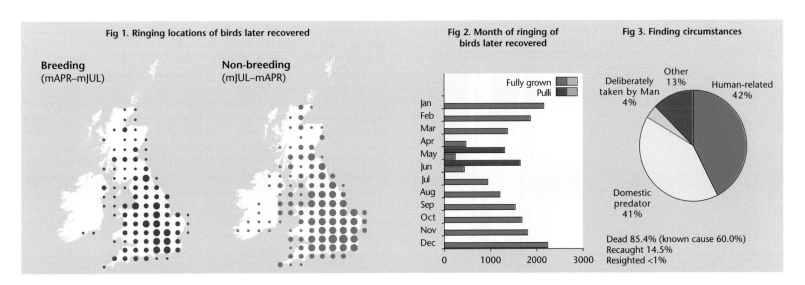

Fig 1. Ringing locations of birds later recovered

Breeding (mAPR–mJUL)

Non-breeding (mJUL–mAPR)

Fig 2. Month of ringing of birds later recovered

Fully grown / Pulli

Fig 3. Finding circumstances

Deliberately taken by Man 4%
Other 13%
Human-related 42%
Domestic predator 41%

Dead 85.4% (known cause 60.0%)
Recaught 14.5%
Resighted <1%

Ringing and recovery data

	<1960	60–69	70–79	80–89	90–97	Total
RINGING						
BTO ringing totals (%)	4	9	22	35	29	2,469,170
RECOVERIES						
BTO-ringed (%)	10	16	26	32	16	18,767
Foreign-ringed (%)	←	44	→	22	33	9

Statistical analyses

	Breeding population (mAPR–mJUL)	Wintering population (mNOV–mFEB)
Status	SEDENTARY (0)	SEDENTARY
Age differences[S*]	Significant	Not significant
Sex differences[S*]	Not significant*	Not significant
Regional differences	Significant[4]	Not tested
Finding circumstances	Not significant	(Not significant)

Table 1. Post-fledging dispersal in the Blue Tit. The table shows the percentages and median distances of recoveries within each 30-day period after ringing as pulli. Note that pulli will have remained in the nest for up to ten days after ringing, during which period they would not be available for recovery. Thus the recovery period for the first group is less than 30 days.

Days	Approx. month equivalent	Percentage of 1372 observations	Median distance (km)	Distance (km) containing 95% of observations
0–30	June	20.6	0	6
31–60	July	9.2	0	10
61–90	August	6.4	0	11
91–120	September	6.5	2	28
121–150	October	7.5	4	52
151–180	November	8.5	3	46
181–210	December	6.8	2	68
211–240	January	6.9	3	41
241–270	February	8.5	3	40
271–300	March	8.2	2	31
301–330	April	6.3	1	26
331–360	May	4.7	2	15

Table 2. Percentage of Blue Tit movements of over 20 km between the breeding season and other seasons, by breeding region. Too few data are available from Ireland to include in this analysis.

Ringing region	Recovery season	n	Percentage over 20 km	Overall percentage over 20 km
Northeast	Autumn	141	10.6	
	Winter	122	16.4	12.0
	Spring	70	7.1	
Northwest	Autumn	112	24.1	
	Winter	134	19.4	20.4
	Spring	98	17.4	
Southeast	Autumn	1,160	9.4	
	Winter	1,420	11.1	9.7
	Spring	784	7.8	
Southwest	Autumn	547	10.4	
	Winter	646	10.2	10.0
	Spring	321	8.7	

Fig 4. Movements of over 20 km and recovery locations of Blue Tits ringed in winter and recovered in the same winter (649:8, red) or a subsequent winter (777:77, blue). Sample sizes of movements under:over 20 km are given but only those over 20 km are plotted.

Long-tailed Tits, Nuthatches, Treecreepers and migrant warblers. The breakdown of territoriality means that Blue Tits tend to be more dispersive than the socially dominant Great Tits (Lack 1966, Burgess 1982). Blue Tit flocks typically consist of a core number of resident (though not necessarily territorial) birds and a variable number of nomadic individuals that spend time with the flocks (*BWP*). Although Blue Tit flocks are highly mobile, they nevertheless remain within a small area, so that almost 90% of all British & Irish recoveries come from within 20 km of the ringing site, and 95% are within 26 km. Blackwell & Dowdeswell (1951) described how a playing field just 130 m wide presented a complete barrier to local movements of Blue Tits so that their ringed study population, which was otherwise stable in composition through the winter, was completely divided in two.

In one of the earliest studies of its kind, Kenrick (1940), using colour-ringing, identified four broad categories of Blue Tit in his local population. About 38% were fully resident, bred in local nestboxes and visited bird tables in the winter. Another 12% were summer residents, which although seen in successive years were only ever seen at the nestbox. A further 25% were winter visitors, seen in successive winters but never in the breeding season, while the final 25% were described as passage migrants as they were caught particularly in February and March and never seen again. Given the problems of resighting birds within a prescribed area, it is possible that the 75% making up the first three categories were actually full residents, but the occurrence of 'single-encounter' birds just in the spring-passage period is interesting.

Natal dispersal occurs within the first month after fledging for some broods but 95% of recoveries at 0–30 days after ringing are within 6 km of the nest site (Table 1). Little changes until about the fourth month after ringing (*c* September) when the median distance widens to 2 km, and the 95% limit to 28 km. The recovery data show a gradual expansion thereafter until *c* December (181–210 days after ringing) when 5% of recoveries were more than 68 km from the nest. The range then contracts month by month so that for those recruited to the breeding population 95% of birds are within just 15 km of the natal site, and half are within 2 km. The large numbers of birds available for this analysis give a high degree of confidence in this description of events.

The composition of winter flocks of Blue Tits is highly stable, and the flocks appear to behave in an integrated, coordinated way. This is reflected in the ring-recovery data. Only 1.2% of 657 ringed birds moved more than 20 km within a winter (Fig 4), while distant movements between winters (Fig 4) are more frequent (9.0% of 854 Blue Tits

Fig 5. Locations outside the breeding season and movements of over 20 km between the breeding and non-breeding season of 5,588 Blue Tits present in Britain & Ireland during the breeding season.

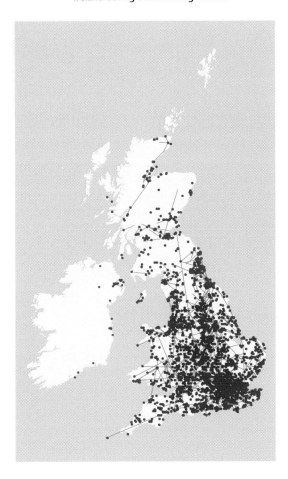

Fig 6. Recovery locations and all 14 included exchanges of Blue Tits between Britain & Ireland and abroad. Four pre-1979 birds ringed in Germany, Belgium, France and the Netherlands are not shown.

recovered in a subsequent winter were more than 20 km from the ringing site). However, Table 2 shows that, as in the Great Tit, Blue Tits in the northwest region of Britain were about twice as likely (20.4% of recoveries) to move more than 20 km than those in any other region (9.7%–12.0% in other regions). This probably indicates a basic difference in Blue Tit dispersal in upland and lowland Britain, and reflects the availability of suitable habitat for the species in these regions (Fig 5).

Although the median recovery distance did not differ between sexes (less than 1 km for both), 95% of females (960 observations) were found within 35 km of the ringing site, while 95% of males (899 observations) were within just 15 km. This supports Burgess' (1982) and Dhondt's (1989) reports that female Blue Tits dispersed further than males, as might be expected for a gregarious species, in which males are dominant over females.

In northern continental Europe, the Blue Tit is a partial migrant. Typically, it is the young of the year that move south out of Fennoscandia in autumn. From observations at the Swedish observatory of Falsterbo, Smith & Nilsson (1987) estimated that about 40% of first-year females migrated and that, while most migrants were of this age class, virtually all the adults that migrated were female. Furthermore, young migrants tended to come from late broods rather than early ones. These observations suggested that such migrations were a response to

competition: the dominant males and early young were mostly resident while the females and late young tended to move. This therefore suggested an environmental cause of Blue Tit migration. However, Hellmann (1985) reported that hand-reared German Blue Tits (therefore free from the stresses of competition) exhibited true migratory restlessness, which increased through the summer. In September, restlessness was greatest in the mornings, which was consistent with the observation that migratory movements occurred mostly between the hours of 8 and 11 am through September and October. This therefore suggests strongly that at least some of these birds have a genetic predisposition to migrate.

In southern Sweden, autumn movements show a southwesterly orientation, with northeasterly return movements in the spring (Källander 1983). There is no doubt that some of these Scandinavian migrants reach eastern Britain, since these larger, brighter-plumaged individuals are not uncommon at east-coast observatories. There have, however, been remarkably few movements to or from Britain confirmed by ringing (Fig 6).

In addition to the more-or-less regular migrations of Scandinavian Blue Tits, the species is, from time to time, strongly eruptive in continental Europe. In some years, such as 1957, this has brought huge influxes to the east and south coasts of England, with birds then proceeding north and west (Cramp *et al* 1960, Cramp 1963). With the ameliorating winter climate and greater provision by humans of food for birds, such massive, almost continent-wide movements have become rare, and will probably remain so.

Andrew G Gosler

Great Tit
Parus major

Occurring more or less throughout the Palearctic and Orient, the Great Tit has the widest geographical range of any tit species, and one of the largest of any palearctic passerine. Across this vast area, the 30 or so races show a wide range of movement patterns from resident to largely migratory (*BWP*, Gosler 1993). Thus, while British & Irish populations (race *newtoni*) of this common and familiar bird are fully resident, and individuals largely sedentary, eruptions occur of nominate continental Great Tits that bring them to our shores from time to time.

Great Tits have been ringed throughout most of their range in Britain, but ring locations of recovered birds under-represent their distribution in Ireland (Fig 1). Because it is largely sedentary in Britain & Ireland, the geographical spread of ring-recoveries reflects this pattern (Fig 4) but is likely to be biased by the distribution of human population. Great Tits are ringed throughout the year (Fig 2), typically either as pulli in nestboxes, or as fully grown birds captured in mist-nets, often at feeding stations. There are known causes for over 60% of Great Tit recoveries. Of these, nearly half are attributed to domestic predators (usually cats) and over a third to other human-related factors (Fig 3). These finding circumstances have clearly been strongly influenced by birds dying in proximity to Man and do not reflect the full picture. Notwithstanding biases that these factors might produce, the Great Tit's strong association with human habitats such as gardens, and the widespread provision of nestboxes mean that it is highly accessible to study by ringing and, as indicated by intensive studies, the British data are generally of sufficient quality to allow meaningful interpretation.

The analysis of the data for this species was supported by the Edward Grey Institute of Field Ornithology

To understand the movements of British & Irish Great Tits we must appreciate something of the bird's annual cycle. Adults occupy breeding territories and, males especially, remain on these throughout the year if conditions permit. Non-breeding Great Tits generally form flocks that are more-or-less mobile, and which are joined by the adults if resources are inadequate to sustain them on their territories. This results in a seasonal cycle, from static territoriality to roaming flocks, which coincides with a shift from a chiefly insectivorous diet in summer to a chiefly herbivorous one (especially tree seeds such as beechmast) in winter.

The nature of Great Tit flocks as aggregations of independent individuals, rather than as integrated associations of birds, is reflected in the national ring-recovery data. There are more than three times as many movements of Great Tits reported between winters as within: 5% of 163 birds recovered within the winter in which they were ringed had moved more than 20 km, while 17.7% of 231 birds recovered in a subsequent winter had moved more than 20 km.

Much of the success of this species can be attributed to this behavioural and ecological flexibility, and this is reflected in the nature of its movements. Rather than being rigidly prescribed, therefore, these are responsive to changing local conditions. The Great Tit's adaptability is reflected also in the range of habitats that it occupies. Globally it occurs in a very diverse set of woodland and scrub situations, from

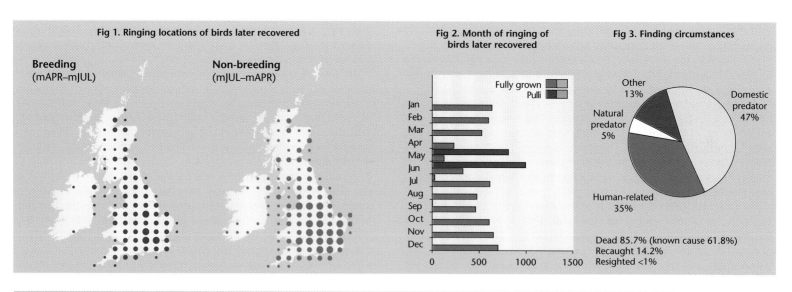

Fig 1. Ringing locations of birds later recovered

Breeding (mAPR–mJUL)

Non-breeding (mJUL–mAPR)

Fig 2. Month of ringing of birds later recovered

Fully grown / Pulli

Fig 3. Finding circumstances

Other 13%
Natural predator 5%
Domestic predator 47%
Human-related 35%

Dead 85.7% (known cause 61.8%)
Recaught 14.2%
Resighted <1%

Ringing and recovery data

	<1960	60–69	70–79	80–89	90–97	Total
RINGING						
BTO ringing totals (%)	5	9	18	36	32	1,097,681
RECOVERIES						
BTO-ringed (%)	10	16	23	32	19	7,765
Foreign-ringed (%)	←	81	→	13	6	16

Statistical analyses

	Breeding population (mAPR–mJUL)	Wintering population (mNOV–mFEB)
Status	SEDENTARY (0)	SEDENTARY
Age differences[NS*]	Not significant*	Significant
Sex differences[NS*]	Not significant*	Not significant
Regional differences	Significant[4*]	Not tested
Finding circumstances	Not significant	Not significant

Fig 4. Recovery locations of Great Tits ringed or recovered in Britain & Ireland, with (a) dead recoveries (6,655, red) differentiated from (b) recaptures (1,106, grey) and live resightings (7, black).

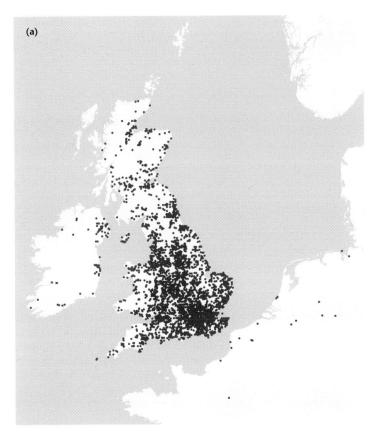

(a)

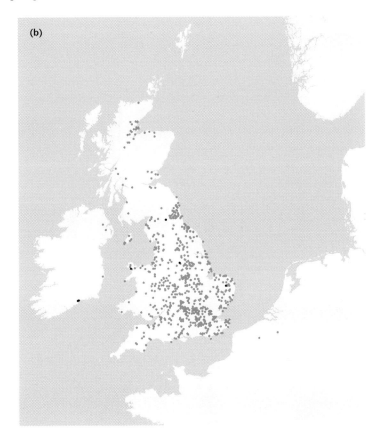

(b)

broad-leaved forests and gardens of Europe, to the boreal taiga of Siberia and mangrove forests in Malaysia. In Britain & Ireland it can be found in most woodland, scrub and garden habitats throughout the year, although during the breeding season the favoured habitat, and that in which breeding success is greatest, is broad-leaved (especially oak) woodland.

The Great Tit has been the focus for a series of significant population studies across Europe, but especially in the Low Countries, Scandinavia and Britain (particularly in Wytham Woods near Oxford), and much of our knowledge about its movements comes from these. Although there are no regular national movements, local ones occur in response to changes in food availability, and consequently habitat quality and population density, and therefore the availability of suitable territories. Like other tits (Sellers 1984), they show no particular orientation.

Table 1. Post-fledging dispersal in the Great Tit. The table shows the percentages and median distances of recoveries within each 30-day period after ringing as pulli. Note that pulli will have remained in the nest for up to ten days after ringing, during which period they would not be available for recovery. Thus the recovery period for the first group is less than 30 days.

Days	Approx. month equivalent	Percentage of 848 observations	Median distance (km)	Distance (km) containing 95% of observations
0–30	June	18.8	0	5
31–60	July	14.0	0	11
61–90	August	7.4	2	8
91–120	September	5.8	2	33
121–150	October	7.4	4	52
151–180	November	6.4	4	42
181–210	December	6.0	4	62
211–240	January	5.2	4	39
241–270	February	7.0	3	61
271–300	March	7.6	3.5	29
301–330	April	6.5	3	19
331–360	May	8.0	2	27

Table 2. Percentage of Great Tit movements of over 20 km between the breeding season and other seasons, by breeding region. Too few data are available from Ireland to include in this analysis.

Ringing region	Recovery season	n	Percentage over 20 km	Overall percentage over 20 km
Northeast	Autumn	82	13.4	
	Winter	65	13.8	13.5
	Spring	53	13.2	
Northwest	Autumn	61	18.0	
	Winter	80	20.0	17.0
	Spring	64	12.5	
Southeast	Autumn	660	7.7	
	Winter	597	11.9	10.9
	Spring	410	14.6	
Southwest	Autumn	289	10.0	
	Winter	259	16.6	11.3
	Spring	178	5.6	

Fig 5. Locations in spring, and movements of over 20 km between the breeding season and spring, of 715 Great Tits present in Britain & Ireland during the breeding season.

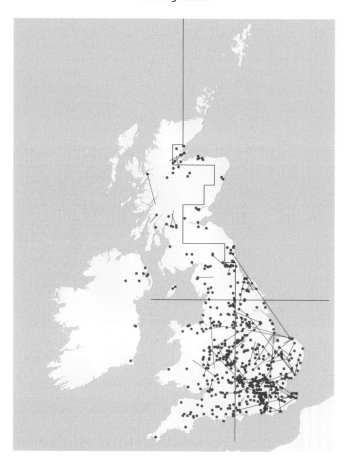

Fig 6. All included exchanges of Great Tits between Britain & Ireland and abroad, with those present in Britain & Ireland during the breeding season (1, red) differentiated from those present in Britain & Ireland outside the breeding season (24, blue).

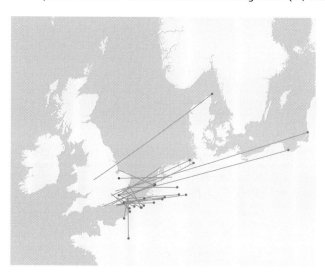

showed that Great Tits fledging from later nests were less likely to survive to breed than those from earlier nests. This is partly because of a reduction in the quantity and quality of food available to these late young, both in the nest and once fledged, but their higher mortality also results from competition with earlier-fledged broods (Kluyver 1971).

In Wytham, the median natal dispersal distance of Great Tits is 562 m (range 0–3,246 m) for males and 835 m (range 0–3,498 m) for females (Delestrade *et al* 1996), and the birds are more likely to move if hatched, or breeding, in poorer habitat (Krebs 1971, Delestrade *et al* 1996). As suggested by Dhondt (1979), considering recovery data from southern Sweden, the greater dispersal distance of females may occur simply because males settle earlier than females. Valuable though these statistics are, they are biased by the fact that natal movements beyond the boundaries of the study plot go largely undetected (van Noordwijk 1984). Verhulst *et al* (1997) reported that, while Wytham-hatched females travelled further to nest *within* Wytham, there was no such sex difference in the recovery distances of birds that left the wood. There was no sex bias in either immigration or emigration rate, and, although in any year about half the breeding population were immigrants (McCleery & Clobert 1990), only 6% of these came from within 2 km of Wytham, suggesting that immigrants travelled further than this to enter the wood.

Here, the overall British & Irish ring-recovery data are enlightening (Table 1). The median dispersal distance during the first 60 days after ringing, during which mortality is highest, is less than 1 km and most movements are less than 11 km. However, this increases to 2 km at 61–90 days (after which mortality rates are constant) and to 4 km at 121–150 days (about five months), at which point 95% of movements are within 52 km. Curiously, after about eight months (around February/March) the median recovery distance declines again: at 271–300 days (about nine months), 95% of recoveries are within 30 km, which is about half the distance for this statistic in the previous six months. This then seems to reflect a movement back towards natal sites. However, it may also indicate that, although late summer and autumn are the peak periods for dispersal (Taylor 1984), there may be a further pulse of more-or-less local dispersal, perhaps in response to increased territorial activity, by birds which have hitherto remained within their natal areas. Unfortunately, we do not know the sexes of the birds ringed as pulli. Nevertheless, there is a suggestion from the overall data set that the greatest movements are undertaken by females. Although the median distances for recoveries of sexed birds were zero for both males and females, 95% of female movements were within 36 km, while 95% of male movements lay within just 20 km.

Broods are largely dependent on their father for two weeks after fledging, and thus remain close to the natal territory. Drent (1984) suggests that males may take their broods to the area in which they survived their own formative months. Recoveries of three dependent fledglings from the same Wytham brood, killed by a cat in a garden 2 km from their natal nestbox, and within 10 days of ringing during the poor summer of 1998, show that Great Tits will take their broods some distance if food is scarce. Great Tit populations suffer their greatest mortality at this time, as shown by the numbers of recoveries by months after ringing for Great Tits ringed as pulli and recovered after fledging (Table 1). While 18.8% were recovered within 30 days of ringing, and a further 14.0% in the next 30 days, from about three months after ringing, approximately equal numbers of recoveries occur in each month (median: 6.5%, range: 5.2–8.0%). Indeed, since these birds will have been in the nest for up to 10 days after ringing, during which time they could not contribute to this data set, the period of risk for recovery is less for the first than for the later periods. This means that the losses during the first 30 days should be proportionally even greater still. Dhondt (1979) estimated that in southern Sweden only 22% of young survived to September, with a roughly constant 13% mortality rate per week through the summer. Much the same pattern was found by Riddington (1992) in Wytham, although losses were greater around the time that fledglings achieved independence. These figures indicate that, as for most small birds, the greatest cause of death of Great Tits is starvation.

Dhondt & Hublé (1968) found that Great Tit fledglings from late nests in their Belgian study population were more likely to emigrate, and to travel further from the natal site, than early ones. This was confirmed by an analysis of the Dutch national ringing data by Kluyver (1971) and of the Belgian national data by Dhondt & Olaerts (1981). Perrins (1965)

The overall ring-recovery data not only reinforce the findings of the intensive population studies, and support the view of a highly sedentary species in which most movement is related to natal dispersal, they also provide new insights at the larger geographical scale. For example, Table 2 reveals differences between four regions of Britain. In the southeast, only 10.9% of movements between the breeding season and other seasons were greater than 20 km, while in the northwest 17.0% were. This may reflect a fundamental difference in the nature of Great Tit movements in upland and lowland Britain. In a study on the North York Moors, Norman (1986) found that Great Tits regularly moved between feeding sites more than 5 km distant, especially when sites were linked by valleys. A comparison between regions of recovery distances between breeding and other seasons is also interesting. In the northeast, the proportion of movements greater than 20 km is remarkably constant across seasons. In the northwest and southwest, around half as many movements were recorded greater than 20 km between breeding and spring, as there were between breeding and either autumn or winter. This accords with the suggestion of a return towards natal or previous breeding sites in the spring. However, in the southeast the number of longer movements was higher between breeding and spring compared with other seasons, and was nearly doubled (14.6% versus 7.7%) compared with movements between breeding and autumn. This difference in spring movements between the east and west of Britain is plainly evident from a map of movements (Fig 5). It may have several causes but two are worth mentioning. First, the onset of breeding behaviour may be earlier in the west, especially the southwest, so that birds may be more likely to have settled on territory there by the spring. Second, the presence of large conurbations in the southeast may enhance overwinter survival, resulting in greater competition for territories there, and the presence of unsettled (floating) birds into the spring. In support of this second idea, an earlier analysis of BTO ringing data by O'Connor (1980) found that Great Tit dispersal distance increased with increasing population density.

The importance of beechmast as a winter food for Great Tits, and the effect of variation in this crop on their survival and population densities, are well established from many intensive studies in northern Europe (Perrins 1966, van Balen 1980). Gosler (1987) found that as the Beech crop of 1983 became exhausted through the winter, Great Tits left Wytham Woods in the order of increasing social dominance: first-year females, adult females, first-year males and adult males. Perrins (1966) also showed that the occurrence of eruptive movements of Great Tits in Europe, many of which resulted in irruptions into Britain (Cramp et al 1960, Cramp 1963), was linked to a failure in continental beech crops. Cramp et al (1960) and Cramp (1963) showed that the autumn eruptions of 1957 and 1959, which resulted in invasions to southeast England in those years, had broadly two or three centres of movement, but that those entering Britain generally came from the Low Countries. The importance of eruptions appears to be waning. Between 1950 and 1959, nine British-ringed Great Tits were recovered in continental Europe, followed by six recoveries during the 1960s and two in the 1970s (Fig 6). None has occurred since then. A reduction in occurrence of long-distance movements by Dutch Great Tits was reported by van Balen & Hage (1989), who suggested that this might reflect the greater provision of winter food at bird tables. Such winter feeding has been responsible for making a sedentary population out of a migratory one in the Finnish city of Oulu near the Arctic Circle (Orell & Ojanen 1979). Nevertheless, although Hansen (1978) considered autumn movements of the Great Tit in Denmark to represent dispersal rather than migration, the species is truly a partial migrant in many countries around the Baltic, where southwest-oriented movements occur in autumn and northeasterly return movements are seen in the spring (Källander 1983, Rymkevich & Bojarinova 1996). Dhondt (1979) found two periods of movement in southern Sweden: dispersal within the first six weeks after fledging, and a second period, which began in September and included longer, more directed movements. Further changes in the dispersal patterns of this species are likely to occur with further widespread changes in human land use and development. The trend appears to be towards a reduction in migratory behaviour, perhaps with increased dispersal where population densities increase. Continued ringing is likely to chart these changes as they occur.

Andrew G Gosler

Wood Nuthatch (Nuthatch)

Sitta europaea

The Nuthatch is a small woodland bird noted for its sedentary nature rather than for any spectacular feats of migration or dispersal. The species breeds in Britain but not in Ireland, and so far there have been no sightings or recoveries of British-ringed Nuthatches outside Britain. Similarly, although the species breeds in all continental countries adjacent to Britain, no foreign-ringed Nuthatch has yet been recovered in Britain. Of the four European species of nuthatch, only *Sitta europaea* is widespread (Matthysen 1998). It is a polytypic species, but authorities disagree on the number of races (*eg BWP*, Matthysen 1998). The race present in Britain and much of central and southern Europe is *caesia* which is characterized by buffish underparts and whitish cheeks and ear-coverts. The race *caesia* merges with *europaea*, which occurs from Fennoscandia eastwards, along a gradation zone from Denmark and the eastern Baltic south to the Black Sea. Further east in the western Urals, *europaea* merges with *asiatica,* which is also white-breasted but smaller. Another buff-breasted subspecies, *levantina,* is recognized in Spain and the Mediterranean region by some authorities (see Matthysen 1998 for details).

None of the world's 24 species of nuthatches is truly migratory. Some northern populations or those at altitude may show seasonal movements and some Eurasian populations are sporadically irruptive. The best-documented irruptions are those of the Siberian race *asiatica,* individuals of which are regularly recorded in Finland and less often in Sweden and the Baltic States. The Red-breasted Nuthatch of North America is the only nuthatch which shows more-or-less regular large-scale movements (Matthysen 1998). Every two or three years, birds,

The analysis of the data for this species was supported by John & Rosalind Matthews

mostly juveniles, move south of the usual breeding range, and a return passage is evident in the following spring. Such movements may involve large numbers of birds, some of which have also been recorded further afield. One individual, the first and currently the only record for Britain & Ireland, was present in a Norfolk coastal pinewood for several months from October 1989 (Aley & Aley 1995).

Nuthatches are not social birds. Once settled on a breeding territory, birds seldom move and most such movements are short, perhaps involving the occupation of an adjacent or nearby territory. In general, and specifically for British Nuthatches, males and females are both highly territorial and pairs usually remain together and defend their territories in winter as well as during the breeding season. Such strict territoriality by both sexes may have arisen as a consequence of the birds' food-hoarding behaviour (Enoksson 1990, Pravosudov 1993). Nuthatches are woodland birds and occur in a range of habitat types including coniferous and deciduous woodland, parkland and gardens with large trees.

It is unlikely that the ring-recovery data for Britain are unduly biased (but see later concerning recoveries in winter). Indeed, the ringing locations of birds later recovered in both the breeding and non-breeding seasons more-or-less coincide with the species' distribution in Britain (Fig 1). The relatively short duration of the breeding season is highlighted by the concentration of the ringing of pulli in May and June (Fig 2) and

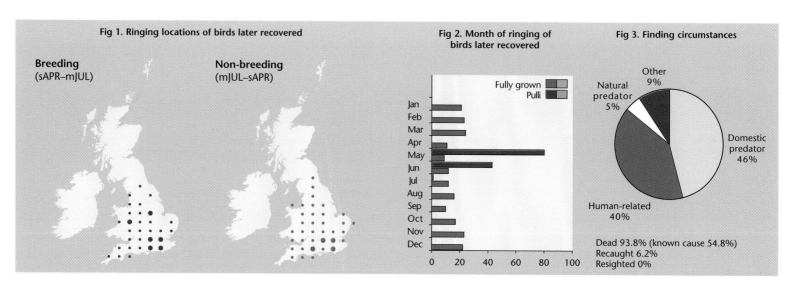

Fig 1. Ringing locations of birds later recovered

Breeding (sAPR–mJUL) Non-breeding (mJUL–sAPR)

Fig 2. Month of ringing of birds later recovered

Fully grown / Pulli

Fig 3. Finding circumstances

Other 9%
Natural predator 5%
Domestic predator 46%
Human-related 40%

Dead 93.8% (known cause 54.8%)
Recaught 6.2%
Resighted 0%

Ringing and recovery data

	<1960	60–69	70–79	80–89	90–97	Total
RINGING						
BTO ringing totals (%)	6	8	12	37	37	33,013
RECOVERIES						
BTO-ringed (%)	16	16	18	29	21	324
Foreign-ringed (%)	0	0	0	0	0	0

Statistical analyses

	Breeding population (sAPR–mJUL)	Wintering population (mNOV–mFEB)
Status	SEDENTARY* (0)	SEDENTARY*
Age differences	Not tested	Not tested
Sex differences	Not tested	Not tested
Regional differences	Not tested	Not tested
Finding circumstances	Not tested	Not significant*

Fig 4. Recovery locations and movements of over 20 km for the 324 included recoveries of Nuthatches ringed or recovered in Britain & Ireland.

reflects the fact that Nuthatches generally make only one breeding attempt per year (Schmidt *et al* 1992, Matthysen 1998). Of the known causes of death, those relating to human activity, including ownership of cats and other potential predators, comprise 86% of recoveries (Fig 3). This is unlikely to reflect the true picture as Nuthatches dying from other causes remote from human activity are unlikely to be found.

Movements by British-ringed Nuthatches are generally short (Fig 4). For 95% of 304 birds (ages and sexes combined) found dead, the maximum distance from the place of ringing was only 15 km and most were found within 1 km of the site where they were ringed. Apart from one surprisingly long movement (of 246 km between Shropshire and Essex), the longest recorded distances moved by British-ringed Nuthatches are 87 km and 52 km, but given the sedentary habits of most ringed Nuthatches, even these movements are exceptional. To 1996, only 33 Nuthatches had been recorded more than 10 km from their place of ringing (Toms & Clark 1998). Sedentary behaviour also appears to be the norm for continental birds; in an analysis of Nuthatches ringed in Belgium and the Netherlands, only 15 of 222 birds moved more than 20 km, the maximum distance being 102 km (Matthysen & Adriaensen 1989). Similarly, of 200 recoveries of birds in western Germany, only eight were found more than 100 km from their place of ringing (*BWP*). However, more examples of longer movements have also been recorded. Matthysen (1998), using data from *Der Zug*, listed 17 cases in central Europe and southern Scandinavia of Nuthatches moving more than 100 km, the longest distance being 460 km between the upper Rhine and southeast France. He also cited a number of other studies recording movements in excess of 100 km.

In Britain, the median distances between ringing and recovery for both males and females were less than 1 km (*P*5–95 all males=0–41 km, breeding males=0–52 km; all females=0–6 km, breeding females= 0–7 km). Studies elsewhere in Europe have found that males and females disperse similar distances; Matthysen (1998) suggests that this is due to the strong territorial behaviour shown by both sexes.

Minor differences in movement distances between adults and juveniles are apparent for British Nuthatches. For birds ringed and recovered as adults, median recovery distance was less than 1 km, whereas for birds ringed as juveniles and recovered as juveniles or later as adults, the median recovery distances were 2 km and 3 km respectively. The data are the same both for all birds and for breeding birds only. This age-related pattern is as expected for a strongly territorial and sedentary species where most movement is related to juvenile dispersal. Studies outside Britain have also found juvenile dispersal distances to be relatively short. For example, in Germany, the median and maximum distances were 1.1 km and 6.1 km respectively for males and 0.8 km and 11.3 km for females, the difference between the sexes not being significant (Matthysen & Schmidt 1987). However, these figures referred to birds resighted within the study area and thus did not include longer-distance movements beyond its borders.

Studies of Nuthatches in Belgium, Sweden, Germany and Siberia have shown a range of post-fledging dispersal behaviour related, at least in part, to different methods of territory acquisition but all agreed that dispersal occurs very rapidly after fledging. Currie & Matthysen (1998) noted the onset of dispersal at about 10 days post-fledging and most juvenile summer territories appear to be established within a month of the first observed fledging date (Matthysen 1998). Such rapid initial dispersal may be another aspect of the importance of territory ownership in Nuthatches, the process being driven by competition between juveniles for territories. A second peak in dispersal activity was also noted in late summer around August and September and appears to involve birds making longer movements than those typical of the initial dispersal. Such birds may have failed to obtain a territory or may be moving on from an initial settlement. These autumn movements are sometimes at a sufficient scale by some Nuthatch populations to be classed as minor irruptive movements and are probably promoted by locally high population densities. It has also been noted that such movements may favour a westerly or southwesterly direction but the reason for this tendency, if genuine, is unknown. Dispersal activity is low in the winter but shows a resurgence in spring with a peak around March or April in Belgium (Matthysen 1998) and a little later in April in Sweden (Enoksson 1987). There is some evidence of post-breeding dispersal around June to October and, in Belgium, these movements were most likely to involve second-year females and may have been related to breeding failure or poor breeding success (Matthysen 1998). Recoveries of Nuthatch nestlings ringed in Britain show an increase in distance moved between ringing and recovery up to about five months post-fledging. These results are generally consistent with the results of the continental studies, although derived from fewer than a hundred birds. Better knowledge of the post-fledging dispersal of British Nuthatches will have to await further study.

As befits a woodland bird, most studies of Nuthatches have been conducted in relatively large tracts of woodland or forest. However, in many parts of Europe, and most of Britain, woodland is now highly fragmented, often occurring as small isolated patches in landscapes dominated by agriculture, industry or urban sprawl. In addition to the effects of habitat loss alone, the division of woodland into scattered patches may pose problems of access and dispersal even for organisms as mobile as birds, and especially for sedentary species like Nuthatches. Studies in the Netherlands have shown that small, isolated woods in agricultural landscapes are less likely to be colonized by Nuthatches (Verboom *et al* 1991). In Sweden, such isolation effects have also been shown for Nuthatches using remnant deciduous woodland patches isolated in coniferous forest managed for timber production (Enoksson *et al* 1995). In Belgium, wood size and isolation did not affect breeding success (Matthysen & Adriaensen 1998), local survival (Matthysen 1999) or the timing of post-fledging dispersal (Currie & Matthysen 1998). Fewer territories in isolated woods were occupied, more birds remained unpaired and territory occupation was not related to territory quality, however, despite the fact that dispersers moved several times as far as was usual for birds in large forests (Matthysen *et al* 1995, Matthysen & Currie 1996). Thus woodland fragmentation reduced the ability of dispersers to find mates and territories, and to find the best territories; the latter effect was related to a reduction in the incidence of movement between territories in fragmented woods following initial settlement.

In Britain, the distribution of Nuthatches (*1988–91 Atlas*) has a gap in eastern England where landscapes are dominated by intensive arable agriculture and a low density of woodland. Analysis of landscape structure within part of this gap suggested that, although the woodland appeared adequate for Nuthatches, if not top quality, it was sufficiently isolated from surrounding breeding Nuthatch populations for the number of arriving dispersers to be too low to establish a local breeding population (Bellamy *et al* 1998). Matthysen (1998, 1999) has suggested that fragmented woodland in his study area in Belgium depends on emigration from adjacent large forests to maintain its Nuthatch population. The situation in eastern England may therefore be similar, with some areas lacking sufficient sources of colonists to maintain local populations.

The Nuthatch population in Britain is currently increasing (Marchant *et al* 1990, Crick *et al* 1998), and the species' range is extending northwards (*1988–91 Atlas*). It will be interesting to note if occupation of isolated woodlands increases during the course of this expansion. The expansion of the British Nuthatch population testifies to its current health but given the species' sedentary nature, it remains vulnerable to increases in woodland fragmentation and isolation and to factors which reduce woodland habitat quality, such as the loss of large old trees which provide nest sites and food supplies throughout the year.

Shelley A Hinsley

Eurasian Treecreeper (Treecreeper)

Certhia familiaris

The analysis of the data for this species was supported by Treswell Wood IPM Group

The Treecreeper is widely distributed through the middle northern latitudes of Europe and Asia, extending as far north as 70° in more temperate coastal areas. It is replaced in North America by the very similar Brown Creeper. It is almost exclusively arboreal, and rarely observed feeding on anything other than invertebrates extracted from crevices in the bark of trees. The preferred nesting site is behind loose bark on ageing trees and populations in managed coniferous woodlands may be limited by lack of such nesting sites (*1968–72 Atlas*).

Although most races of Treecreeper are sedentary, the northern nominate race, *familiaris*, is a partial migrant and makes occasional eruptive movements from the north of its range. Some Asian races exhibit altitudinal migration (*BWP*). The British & Irish race, *britannica*, is sedentary. There is no evidence for altitudinal migration and, apart from an unexplained paucity of records in Cornwall, any apparent local scarcity in Britain & Ireland in winter is probably best explained by uneven observer effort (*Winter Atlas*) rather than migration.

In Britain & Ireland, broad-leaved woodland is the Treecreeper's preferred habitat. Secondary habitats all have reasonable numbers of trees and include conifer plantations, parkland, gardens and even farmland with well-treed hedgerows. In parts of Europe where Short-toed Treecreepers are present, Treecreepers tend to inhabit conifers whereas Short-toed Treecreepers use broad-leaved trees. The few areas where Treecreepers are absent are those with intensive arable farmland or treeless moorland.

As is expected for such a small bird, the ring-recovery rate is among the lowest of all British & Irish birds. Their cryptic colouration and

avoidance of many human habitats further reduce the chances of finding dead birds. Most recoveries are recaptures by ringers, and the distribution of ringing sites of recoveries, with very few in Ireland or Scotland (Fig 1), reflects ringing effort more than the distribution of the species. Most Treecreepers ringed are fully grown birds that have been trapped with mist-nets. About 5% are currently ringed as nestlings in May and June (Fig 2), and small numbers can be trapped at their roost sites (Davis 1981). There are typically just under 2,000 individuals ringed annually.

Nearly 60% of the ring-recoveries for birds found dead have been attributed to a known cause (Fig 3); by far the largest category is predation by cats (29 recoveries) but this will be exaggerated because of cats' habit of bringing in their prey (Flegg 1973). Of the 11 recoveries attributed to natural predation, seven are from Tawny Owl pellets and only one recovery is attributed to a Sparrowhawk. Their cryptic plumage together with their habit of associating with tit flocks for protection from predators (Arévalo & Gosler 1994) may explain why Treecreepers do not form a major part of the Sparrowhawk diet (*BWP*).

Only 15% of ring-recoveries from 111 dead birds were more than 5 km from the place of ringing. The low numbers of recoveries and the extremely local nature of the movements of Treecreepers do not allow us to determine any overall patterns of direction, time of movements or

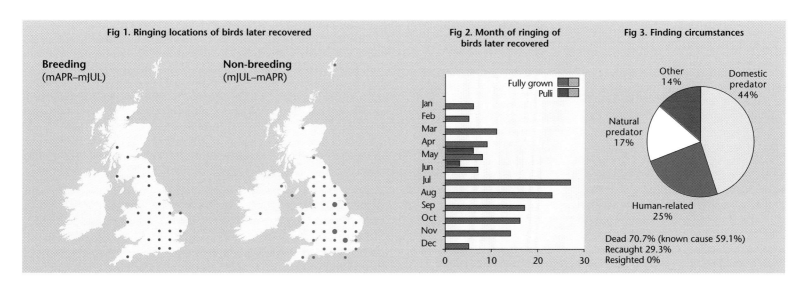

Fig 1. Ringing locations of birds later recovered

Breeding (mAPR–mJUL) Non-breeding (mJUL–mAPR)

Fig 2. Month of ringing of birds later recovered

Fully grown
Pulli

Fig 3. Finding circumstances

Other 14%
Domestic predator 44%
Natural predator 17%
Human-related 25%

Dead 70.7% (known cause 59.1%)
Recaught 29.3%
Resighted 0%

Ringing and recovery data

	<1960	60–69	70–79	80–89	90–97	Total
RINGING						
BTO ringing totals (%)	3	10	23	35	29	55,726
RECOVERIES						
BTO-ringed (%)	3	21	31	27	18	157
Foreign-ringed (%)	0	0	0	0	0	0

Statistical analyses

	Breeding population (mAPR–mJUL)	Wintering population (mNOV–mFEB)
Status	[SEDENTARY]	[SEDENTARY]
Age differences	Not tested	Not tested
Sex differences	Not tested	Not tested
Regional differences	Not tested	Not tested
Finding circumstances	Not tested	Not tested

Fig 4. Recovery locations and movements of over 20 km for the 157 included recoveries of Treecreepers ringed or recovered in Britain & Ireland.

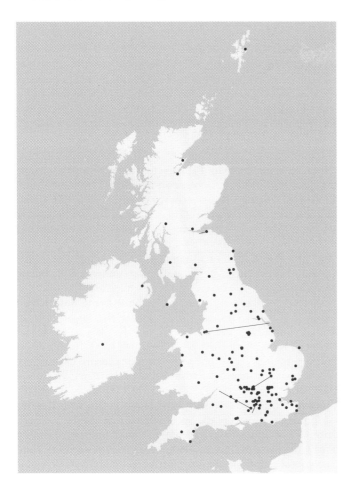

Fig 5. Numbers of new Treecreepers ringed in Treswell Wood 1972–99 by month of ringing, and retrap rates of monthly cohorts for birds retrapped during the subsequent breeding season. A ringed bird was considered as a retrap if it was recaptured in or after the June of the year of that breeding season. Birds ringed in any monthly cohort known to be over one year old have been excluded from the retrap rate calculations. (*Source*: Treswell Wood IPM Group.)

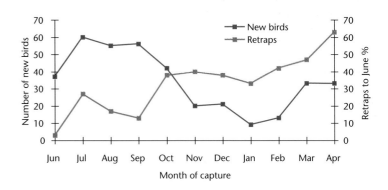

differences between sexes. There is, however, evidence to suggest that juvenile Treecreepers may move a little further than adults, although the sample sizes are too small to demonstrate statistical significance (Table 1). There is no unequivocal evidence for the timing of post-natal dispersal. The 'adult' category includes birds of unknown age ringed from January onwards, and so may include some birds which are still engaged in (late) post-natal dispersal. These data, drawn from both live and dead birds, support the idea that a movement of as much as 5 km is exceptional for a Treecreeper of any age class; indeed, there are only five recoveries of more than 20 km (Fig 4). Studies of Treecreepers give a size range of Treecreeper territories from 1 ha (Ptushenko & Inozemtsev 1968) to 15 ha (pers obs), depending on habitat, which is large for such a small bird. Natal dispersal distances recorded in particular studies have typically been well under 1 km (*BWP*).

Local studies where recaptures are recorded are more likely to give an idea of typical movements. In Treswell Wood, Nottinghamshire, the median distances between first capture of birds and their last-ever capture (including recoveries elsewhere) are 250 m for birds ringed as juveniles and 170 m for birds ringed as known adults. These include data for birds which have lived to be up to seven years old. Adults are almost never found more than 500 m from a previous capture position. These data suggest that birds remain in their relatively large territories once they have secured them.

Some recapture rates and dates of first capture of Treecreepers in Treswell Wood are presented in Fig 5. These data run from 1972 to 1999 and are drawn from a mist-netting regime which is more-or-less constant effort throughout the year and time period (du Feu & McMeeking 1991). The large number of new birds ringed in the summer and autumn is composed mainly of known juveniles, presumably reared very locally.

There is a fall in new captures during the winter months followed by an increase in the spring. This points to more movement of birds occurring just prior to the breeding season. Mackenzie (1956) noted that Treecreepers in his Scottish study site formed micro-populations of 8–12 birds, which reduced to a single pair by the breeding season. This is consistent with the observation of an increase in captures of new birds prior to the breeding season, if some local redistribution occurs in which birds without territories move to adjacent areas where breeding sites are available. The recapture rates indicate both a generally high survival for a small bird and low rates of dispersal. The probability of later recapture rises through the year (as is expected because birds ringed later do not have to survive as long in order to be available to be recaptured at the end of the breeding season) with the exception of lower rates in August and September. This is consistent with post-natal dispersal taking place during August and September, the birds captured then including a higher proportion of transients. Higher immediate post-fledging mortality is likely to be an additional cause of the low recapture rate for June-ringed birds.

Although there have been no recoveries in Britain or Ireland of foreign-ringed Treecreepers, there are occasional British sightings of *familiaris* from Scandinavia or eastern Europe. These are generally in years of irruptive movements on the Continent. The one recovery in Shetland, which has no resident Treecreepers, was of a bird ringed there a month earlier in the autumn of 1976 at a time when foreign-ringed passerines occurred in large numbers (Spencer & Hudson 1978). There is one exceptional movement of a bird ringed at Spurn in September 1983 and recovered 15 days later in Merseyside, 200 km westwards (Fig 4). It is

Table 1. Distances moved by Treecreepers between ringing and recovery, by age at ringing. Birds in adult plumage have been recorded in 'Age unknown' class if caught in autumn. Birds caught from 1 January onwards have been counted in the 'Adult' class.

Distance (km)	0	1–4	5–20	21–200
Ringed as nestling	3 (33%)	3 (33%)	3 (33%)	0 (0%)
Ringed as juvenile	26 (55%)	4 (9%)	15 (32%)	2 (4%)
Ringed as adult	34 (72%)	3 (6%)	9 (19%)	1 (2%)
Age unknown	36 (67%)	6 (11%)	10 (19%)	2 (4%)

possible this may have been a continental bird for there was also strong immigration of Goldcrests to the east coast from Scandinavia at the same time (Mead & Hudson 1984).

Although the CBC population trend for Treecreepers is relatively stable, there are year-to-year fluctuations that are associated with wet winters (Peach *et al* 1995b). The restricted movement shown by these birds and their reluctance to cross open areas (*BWP*) will make it difficult for them to recolonize an isolated area which has lost its population after a natural or man-made catastrophe.

New developments in the computerization of the BTO's ringing data may allow future interpretation of the movement patterns within the present 5 km limit. Even so, there remain unknowns that may only be resolved through more intensive local studies. In one study, which mapped habitats with a 50 m resolution, Treecreepers were shown to have a preference for areas with dense foliage cover, foraging opportunities and potential nesting sites (Haila *et al* 1996). It is not known how these preferences might vary through the year. The species does not lend itself easily to intensive studies, however. Colour-ringing, effective in many species, is not likely to be useful for Treecreepers because their short legs are usually kept out of sight.

Treecreepers are notoriously difficult to attract to nestboxes, and even the special wedge-shaped design (Mackenzie 1956) is rarely used. A new design is needed which is reliably attractive to them and would allow many more nestlings to be ringed annually. If this were to be coupled with mist-netting studies, the real extent of natal dispersal could be assessed.

Chris du Feu

Eurasian Jay (Jay)
Garrulus glandarius

As with most corvids, the Jay is essentially a highly sedentary bird, although some northern populations can be migratory. Acorns are a staple food but oaks fruit with great irregularity. All populations, but especially those in higher latitudes, are prone to periodic eruptions, probably due to failures of the acorn crop. The Jay is found throughout Europe, with the exception of Iceland and northern Scandinavia, in North Africa, and in a band extending eastward across Asia to Japan. Geographical variation is marked with between 30 and 60 subspecies described, nine of which occur in Europe. The nominate race occupies Scandinavia and most of temperate Europe but is replaced by *rufitergum* in the Netherlands, Belgium and Britain and by *hibernicus* in Ireland. Six other races occur in southern and eastern Europe.

Jays breed throughout England and Wales, being absent only from the treeless expanses of the Fens and upland areas such as the Pennines, but are more locally distributed in Scotland and Ireland (*1988–91 Atlas*). Although a quintessential species of woodland, Jays have adapted to man-made environments including leafy suburbs and parks, conifer plantations and wooded farmland. This adaptability and the reduction in the number of gamekeepers contributed to the steady rise in Jay numbers during the 20th century and a corresponding range expansion in Scotland and Ireland (*1988–91 Atlas*, Holloway 1996). However, there has been a steady decrease in numbers on CBC plots since the mid 1980s (Baillie *et al* 2001).

The locations of breeding-season ringing sites for Jay ring-recoveries reflects both the species' distribution in Britain & Ireland, with the great majority in England, and the distribution of active ringers, resulting in

The analysis of the data for this species was supported by Peter J Cobb

concentrations in the southeast and in the industrial belt of northern England. The distribution of ringing locations is slightly more dispersed during the non-breeding season (Fig 1). Just over half of all ring-recoveries were of birds ringed during the months May to August; a quarter of these were ringed as pulli (Fig 2).

The Jay is one of only 13 bird species that can legally be subjected to population control in Britain at any time. As with other corvids, the Jay's opportunistic nature and fondness for taking the eggs of other birds has led to it coming into conflict with game interests, and large numbers are shot or trapped each year. It is therefore not surprising that most of the ring-recoveries are of dead birds and, of those with a known cause, 74% have been deliberately taken by Man (Fig 3).

In common with Jays in other temperate areas, British & Irish birds are on the whole highly sedentary (Fig 4). The median distance from ringing to recovery site for birds recovered dead is less than 1 km, with only 5% moving more than 40 km. Not even juveniles move far from their natal area; the median distance for natal dispersal (dead birds only) is less than 1 km ($P5–95=0–10$ km, $n=16$) and all were under 20 km (Fig 4).

Only one bird ringed in Britain has been recovered abroad; ringed at Dungeness, Kent, on 12 October 1955, it was recovered in Zeeland, the Netherlands, on 2 June the following year. The ringing and recovery

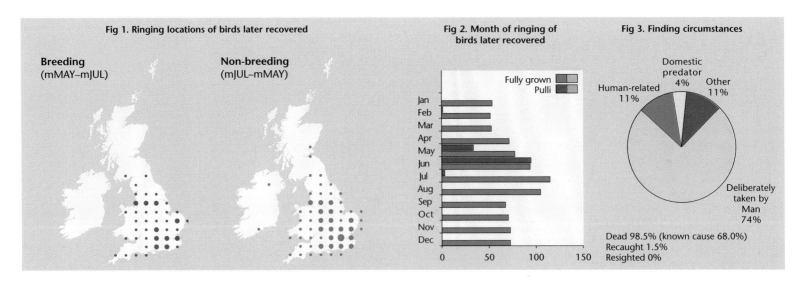

Fig 1. Ringing locations of birds later recovered

Breeding (mMAY–mJUL)

Non-breeding (mJUL–mMAY)

Fig 2. Month of ringing of birds later recovered

Fully grown
Pulli

Fig 3. Finding circumstances

Domestic predator 4%
Human-related 11%
Other 11%
Deliberately taken by Man 74%

Dead 98.5% (known cause 68.0%)
Recaught 1.5%
Resighted 0%

Ringing and recovery data

	<1960	60–69	70–79	80–89	90–97	Total
RINGING						
BTO ringing totals (%)	10	13	20	33	24	17,704
RECOVERIES						
BTO-ringed (%)	13	20	24	27	16	1,029
Foreign-ringed (%)	0	0	0	0	0	0

Statistical analyses

	Breeding population (mMAY–mJUL)	Wintering population (mOCT–mAPR)
Status	SEDENTARY (0)	SEDENTARY
Age differences[NT]	Significant*	Not significant*
Sex differences	Not tested	Not tested
Regional differences	Not tested	Not tested
Finding circumstances	Significant	Not significant*

Fig 4. Recovery locations and movements of over 20 km for the 1,029 included recoveries of Jays ringed or recovered in Britain & Ireland.

dates suggest that this bird was probably of continental origin, having returned to its natal area following a movement to Britain in the previous autumn.

Given the eruptive nature of Jays in northern and eastern Europe, it is somewhat surprising that no foreign-ringed birds have ever been recovered in Britain or Ireland. Continental Jays are known to occur in Britain, in varying but generally very small numbers. However, the most eruptive Jay populations are those from the north of their range, including areas such as northern Scandinavia and Russia (*BWP*), where there are very few ringers. Irruptions of Jays usually occur when there has been a failure of the acorn crop — a staple winter food source in many areas. At such times, an exodus from breeding areas occurs during September and October and large diurnal movements have been noted. Westward movements along the coasts of the southern Baltic Sea can be enormous, for example 35,000 were counted moving over Gdańsk between 19 September and 17 October 1964 (*European Atlas*).

The most recent large irruption into Britain was in 1983 when large flocks were noted across the southern half of Britain (John & Roskell 1985). Movements were first noted on the coastline between East Anglia and Hampshire in late September, with a continued, mainly westward movement through to the middle of October. Large numbers were also noted at many inland sites at this time. During mid-October unprecedented numbers were noted in southwest England, peaking at an estimate of 6,000 migrant Jays in Cornwall on 17 October, including flocks several hundred strong. The flocks dispersed rapidly in late October, although numbers were noted as being higher than normal throughout the following winter in many areas, and a small return movement was noted on the east coast of England in the spring of 1984.

Surprisingly, not a single bird was noted on the Isles of Scilly at the time of the 1983 influx, despite the fact that they lie just 40 km from the Cornish mainland where flocks of up to 800 were seen. This illustrates the reluctance of Jays to cross open seas and may explain why influxes into Britain are rare. Jays are seen arriving in over the sea at east-coast sites almost annually but never in large numbers and, even in the 1983 influx, the number of birds seen flying in from the North Sea or English Channel was small. It was thought that the 1983 movements undoubtedly contained some birds of continental origin but that their numbers were greatly swollen by movements of British birds. Of two birds shot in Cornwall at this time, one was identical to Scandinavian birds of the nominate race and the other was typical of the British race (John & Roskell 1985). In Britain, as well as on the Continent, the failure in the acorn crop was estimated at 90% in 1983.

Smaller influxes have occurred in subsequent years, notably October 1993, when up to 135 Jays per day were noted moving west at St Margaret's, Kent (Hodge 1995), and October 1996 when daily counts included up to 131 moving west on the Norfolk coast (Taylor *et al* 1999) and up to 79 in Kent (Hodge 1998). These influxes were confined to southeast England with no significant counts made in the southwest. The return movement in the spring of 1997 was, however, one of the largest ever noted at that time of year. Numbers of Jays recorded during April and May 1997 at Spurn Point were higher than at any time since 1983 (Bell *et al* 1997), while there were daily counts of up to 49 moving along the Norfolk coast (Taylor *et al* 1999). Most of the spring movement in Norfolk is westerly but birds have also been noted flying in-off and out to sea (Taylor *et al* 1999). Four birds ringed at Weybourne in Norfolk during the autumn of 1993 showed characteristics of the nominate continental race. Interestingly, one was retrapped at the same site on 1 January 1994, the first evidence of continental birds overwintering in Norfolk (Young-Powell 1994).

The lack of ring-recoveries of foreign-ringed birds in Britain & Ireland (Fig 4) and the difficulty of identifying continental races in the field, leave many gaps in our knowledge about the scale of influxes of continental Jays. Although there is evidence that Jays do arrive in Britain from the Continent, it is impossible to gauge how many birds are involved and to assess whether this may be a relatively unusual occurrence, with none at all in some years. The large movements of Jays are almost certainly related to food shortages due to failures in the acorn crop but the exact mechanisms of these eruptions are still little understood. It is not known what influence the age of the bird has on its eruptive tendencies. It could be that young birds make long movements more readily than adults. If so, there could be an influence of population density on eruptive movement, with eruptions more likely at times of high numbers following good breeding seasons.

Andy Wilson

Black-billed Magpie (Magpie)

Pica pica

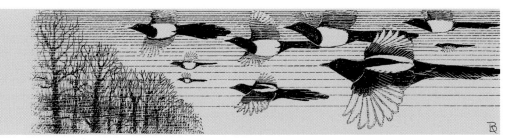

The analysis of the data for this species was supported by Ian Forsyth and Pamela Allen

Magpies are fascinating creatures of great character, exotic colouring and unusual structure. They are relatively large, well armed, and notoriously trap-shy, making them a considerable challenge to the catching and handling skills of ringers. In his fascinating monograph Birkhead (1991) writes: 'In most areas breeding Magpies are remarkably sedentary and no populations are known to undertake migration'. Nothing to contradict this assessment can be found in the British & Irish ring-recovery data. However, there are interesting aspects of Magpie movements, one of which is their relatively recent and large-scale colonization of suburban and even urban habitats.

Confined to the northern hemisphere, Magpies are widely spread across Europe and much of Asia from the Atlantic to China. Isolated populations occur in parts of northwest Africa and Saudi Arabia but they are otherwise absent from Africa and the Middle East. They do not occur in the Indian subcontinent but breed fairly commonly across the western half of North America (*BWP*). The British & Irish race is the nominate *pica*, which occurs in most of Europe, intergrading with *fennorum* in northern Fennoscandia and *melanotos* in Iberia. The two other West Palearctic races are *bactriana*, occurring across the former USSR south of *fennorum*, and *mauritanica*, which occurs in northwest Africa (*CBWP*). However, these variations are clinal (albeit quite marked at their extremes) and of scant interest to ringers and birdwatchers in Britain & Ireland due to the absence of long-distance movements, even in winter. Although Magpies are adaptable, versatile and competitive birds, their range is limited by their sedentary nature and minimal dispersal, their apparent reluctance to cross the sea and above all their

requirement for a mixed habitat with trees for cover, roosting and nesting and open ground for feeding (Birkhead 1991). The latter explains their absence from both treeless habitats such as semi-desert or wetland and from continuous forest.

In Britain & Ireland, Magpies are fairly ubiquitous and have generally increased, in some areas very markedly, although they remain uncommon in the Highlands and the Borders of Scotland. Open moorland is not favoured, but Magpies respond well to patchy afforestation as long as there is access to adjacent fields or grassland. Mosaic habitats provided by mixed farming are ideal for this species. The parks and gardens of suburbia are also very productive Magpie habitats. In fact, the Magpie population has recently expanded into suburban and urban areas on a scale that alarms many members of the public. Interestingly, this phenomenon is not confined to Britain & Ireland (eg Askokova *et al* 1997, Schwarz & Flade 2000) but may reflect universal features of modern urban environments including abundant food (Vodoladzskaya 1997) and the increased availability of tall trees for nesting as recent urban plantings mature (Tatner 1982).

Population control by trapping and shooting, mainly linked to traditional gamekeeping practices, undoubtedly affects the distribution of British & Irish Magpies. However, with the decline in keepering witnessed over the 20th century, there has been a general range

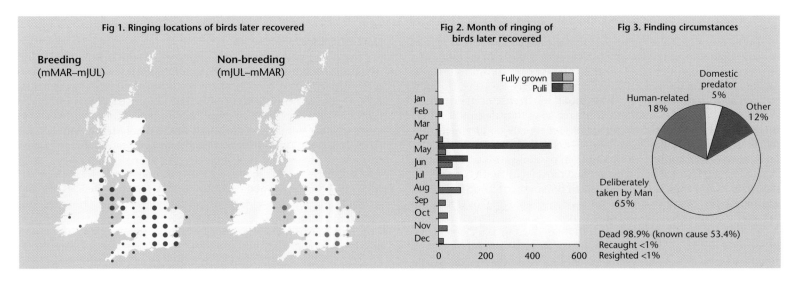

Fig 1. Ringing locations of birds later recovered

Breeding (mMAR–mJUL)

Non-breeding (mJUL–mMAR)

Fig 2. Month of ringing of birds later recovered

Fully grown / Pulli

Fig 3. Finding circumstances

Domestic predator 5%
Human-related 18%
Other 12%
Deliberately taken by Man 65%

Dead 98.9% (known cause 53.4%)
Recaught <1%
Resighted <1%

Ringing and recovery data

	<1960	60–69	70–79	80–89	90–97	Total
RINGING						
BTO ringing totals (%)	14	8	14	40	24	21,889
RECOVERIES						
BTO-ringed (%)	11	12	13	37	27	1,102
Foreign-ringed (%)	0	0	0	0	0	0

Statistical analyses

	Breeding population (mMAR–mJUL)	Wintering population (mOCT–mJAN)
Status	SEDENTARY (0)	SEDENTARY
Age differences[NT]	Not significant*	Not tested
Sex differences	Not tested	Not tested
Regional differences	Not tested	Not tested
Finding circumstances	Significant	Not significant*

Fig 4. Recovery locations and movements of over 20 km for the 1,102 included recoveries of Magpies ringed or recovered in Britain & Ireland.

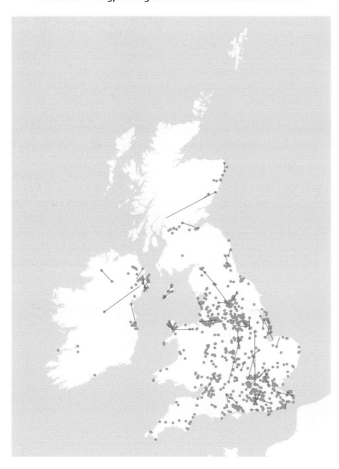

also significantly influence recovery distribution; some gamekeepers scrupulously report all rings, others simply bury them with their wearers. The distribution of recoveries is probably determined more by the incidence of artificial control than by population density, movement or other natural factors.

Although Magpie control compromises our ability to interpret ring-recovery data, information about natural population processes can still be obtained from systematic ringing within defined study areas. For example, in an urban environment, where only one of 15 birds recovered had been shot, Tatner (1986) was able to model survival rates and make useful predictions of demographic parameters from quite a small sample. Care must be taken in estimating post-fledging survival rates from ringing Magpie pulli because, unlike many smaller passerines, Magpies hatch asynchronously and runt nestlings often die in poor years (Birkhead 1991).

Magpie populations have essentially two post-juvenile components: highly territorial breeding pairs and a pool of adult non-breeders. Winter flocking and the recruitment of non-breeders into vacant territories are the only significant dispersal mechanisms but even these movements are extremely localized (Eden 1987). For birds ringed as pulli, the median recovery distance peaks in the tenth month after ringing at only 5 km, although the sample is small (n=25). Subsequently, the median returns to less than 1 km. The median natal dispersal distance calculated from the ring-recovery data is just 1.5 km ($P5$–95=0–26, n=88). Hence, local movements, by which gradual dispersion could take place, may occur but are impossible to demonstrate from the ring-recovery data. Winter flocks are generally of a dozen or so birds but have increased in size in recent years, with groups of up to 200 now regular in some areas (Dennis 1996). Møller (1985) found that urban roosts were larger than rural ones, presumably a result of the higher population densities seen in urban areas. In some places, territorial birds also join communal winter roosts (Møller 1985). These short winter movements show as a median movement of 1 km ($P5$–95=0–23) for the 88 birds ringed as immatures in the breeding season and recovered dead in winter, compared to a median of less than 1 km ($P5$–95=0–13) for 109 birds of the same class but recovered earlier, in autumn. These distances are shorter, however, than many daily journeys to winter roosts (Birkhead 1991). Clearly we would expect greater movement than this if the winter flocks were actually parties of migrating birds, something that was still widely believed by observers until as recently as the early 1900s (Stubbs 1910).

To date, British & Irish ring-recovery data shed no light on sex differences in movement patterns or survival as most non-specialist ringers find Magpies impossible to sex in the hand. Again, it is worth noting that more systematic ringing could in fact elucidate such differences as methods have been developed that allow over 90% of Magpies to be sexed from combinations of measurements (Birkhead 1991). There is no conclusive evidence that females disperse further than males, although Birkhead et al (1986) found that a significantly higher proportion of females bred in more than one territory during their life than did males, presumably because females who lost mates also lost their territory, while males who lost mates simply replaced them while retaining their territory.

Despite the absence of long-distance ring-recoveries in the British & Irish data (Fig 4), there are records of much longer movements within western Europe and in North America, as well as tantalizing reports of coastal movements in Britain & Ireland that may indicate occasional sea-crossings. Hutchinson's observation (Birds in Ireland) that flocks of Magpies are not unusual on headlands in autumn is reflected in bird observatory logs, which note small gatherings at coastal sites such as Sandwich Bay and the Calf of Man in October (Briggs et al 1998, Bagworth 1999). Are these birds that have crossed, or are about to cross the sea, or just groups of juveniles, displaced from inland breeding areas and hemmed in by the water? On Scottish islands, vagrants have appeared on Islay and North Ronaldsay but not yet in Shetland (Birds in Scotland). At the opposite end of Britain, at least four single birds have appeared on Scilly between October and April (Gantlett 1991). Further afield, Magpies have been observed on the island of Lesvos, and are

expansion in many rural habitats (Tapper 1992). Recent slow distribution changes in Scotland are linked to the subsequent partial recolonization of areas cleared of Magpies by persecution in the 19th century, although Valerie Thom comments that 'there is clearly scope for further study' of the Magpie's mysterious absence from most of highland Scotland (Birds in Scotland). Magpies were increasing in Ireland in 1895 (Dixon 1895) and are still doing so more than a century later (Birds in Ireland), again a situation worthy of further study, particularly as their means of arrival in Ireland is unclear. Tradition holds that they were introduced (Dixon 1895), so an important question concerning the distribution and movements of British & Irish Magpies remains open — do they ever cross the sea?

The ringing locations of recovered birds (Fig 1) reflect the population densities of both Magpies and their ringers, with very few from Scotland or Ireland and, interestingly, East Anglia. East Anglia is the one area of England where Magpies have shown a range expansion in the period between the 1968–72 and 1988–91 Atlases, and it is also an area where keepering has been maintained at a level above the national average (Tapper 1992). Apart from this, the small sample of recoveries available is quite evenly and widely spread; hence it is hard to observe any significant patterns. Furthermore, large numbers of Magpies are deliberately killed under 'general licences', which are subject to renewal but unlikely to be revoked after a threefold population increase in the last 30 years (Crick et al 1998). The majority (57%) of Magpie ring-recoveries come from birds ringed as pulli (Fig 2). As expected, some 65% of ring-recoveries for which the finding circumstances are known are of birds deliberately taken by Man, with another 18% human-related (Fig 3). As Magpies are sedentary and hard to catch by non-lethal methods, it is likely that a far lower proportion of ringed birds will be recovered in uncontrolled areas. The attitude of gamekeepers towards ringing will assumed to be of Turkish origin (D Balmer pers comm). There are records in the literature of suspected coastal migratory movements by small numbers of Magpies. For example, Moss Taylor has recently provided an intriguing summary of such observations on the Norfolk coast (Taylor *et al* 1999) and *BWP* notes apparent pre-migratory movements observed at Falsterbo. In addition, there are a few long-distance recoveries in the literature. Holyoak (1971) cites a Finnish recovery of 450 km, *BWP* a French recovery of 330 km and there have been a small number of continental-scale movements in the USA (Linsdale in Bent 1946).

If Magpies do move across the North Sea, we might expect them to take the shortest crossings and perhaps to follow the well-known migration corridor of Finnish and Swedish Jackdaws (Alerstam 1990a). This would suggest Denmark as a likely place to come across some of northern Europe's more mobile Magpies. The pattern of Magpie ring-recoveries from the Danish ringing scheme is generally very similar to those from Britain & Ireland, with few movements of over 10 km and the vast majority very local (K T Pedersen pers comm). However, there are 10 Danish ring-recoveries (5.4% compared with our 0.4%) involving movements of over 100 km, including a pullus ringed in May 1962 that was subsequently recovered in Norway, 471 km from its natal site, in February 1964.

Short sea-crossings are clearly possible but only more systematic ringing and observation will elucidate the degree of exchange between Britain & Ireland and the Continent. This would require remarkable patience as interesting movements are very elusive; for example, the Magpie colour-ringing project on Bardsey has been largely abandoned due to the absence of off-island sightings after several years of hard effort (D Anning pers comm). Regular migration watches on the East Pennines have recorded occasional high-altitude Magpies but nothing that can be described as a regular or significant migratory movement (K Clarkson pers comm). Perhaps the anecdotes, rumours and scant continental evidence are irrelevant to our 'stay-at-home' island birds. Or does the prize of our first overseas Magpie recovery remain to be grasped by an enterprising ringer? Either way, the problem remains that Magpies are hard to catch in any numbers by ringers' usual methods. New methods of capture may have to be devised if the Ringing Scheme is to obtain the volume of data needed to answer interesting and important questions about Magpie range expansion and population change, and in the process to seek out that elusive long-distance movement.

Andrew Cannon

Red-billed Chough (Chough)

Pyrrhocorax pyrrhocorax

The Chough is a highly gregarious member of the crow family that was formerly found along much of the western seaboard of Britain, as well as on Irish coasts, where it typically inhabited rocky coastal cliffs and offshore islands. The species is essentially sedentary and, as a result of persecution during the mid-19th century, followed by more recent changes in agricultural practices, declines and local extinction have occurred throughout much of its former British & Irish range. Eight races are recognized (*BWP*). While the species is widespread, it is locally restricted and geographically fragmented, particularly within the west European populations of Ireland, the Isle of Man, Wales, west Scotland, Brittany, southern France, Spain and Portugal. Relict populations remain in the Swiss Alps, the Italian Apennines, Greece, Sicily, Sardinia and Crete (*European Atlas*). There are isolated populations in the Canary Islands and within the African continent, in the Atlas Mountains and Ethiopia. The species is much more widespread in Asia, occurring from central Turkey and the Caucasus eastwards across northern Iran and Afghanistan, throughout the Himalayas and central Asian mountains as well as the northern and central mountain ranges of China.

British & Irish Choughs are of the nominate race *pyrrhocorax*, which is found nowhere else, and breed almost exclusively on rocky coastlines, typically placing their nest within the dark recess of a cave or rock fissure. Old buildings and ruins have been readily utilized, particularly on the Isle of Islay and more recently on the Isle of Man. Where suitable nesting and feeding habitats exist, the species may frequent inland areas, with pairs known to be breeding up to 5–6 km from the coast in the Isle of Man (pers obs), 19 km in Ireland (Whilde 1989) and 28 km in

The analysis of the data for this species was supported by Tony Cross & Ian M Spence

Wales, where slate quarries in Snowdonia are traditional sites (Roberts 1989).

The Chough is a highly specialized feeder and unlike the other crows, which are commonly found throughout much of Britain & Ireland, is almost exclusively insectivorous. Although there is considerable seasonal, and perhaps geographical, variation in habitats used for feeding, short-grazed pasture is utilized throughout the year, and it is in this habitat that the Chough's long curved bill is best suited to probe for its principal food, insect larvae. The dung of livestock is also an important source of invertebrate food particularly during autumn and winter with both the adult and larvae of various beetles being favoured. Many other soil-living invertebrates are taken opportunistically, particularly during the breeding season, and include ants, earwigs, millipedes, moth caterpillars and spiders. These are usually foraged for around rocky outcrops, field boundary walls, semi-vegetated cliff faces and areas of recently burnt heather moorland. During the autumn and winter, cereal grains on stubble fields can form an important food source and are often foraged for in the hours just before going to roost (A S Moore pers comm). Some birds also use the strandline, foraging among wrack beds for kelp flies and beetle larvae.

Until recent years, there have been relatively few Choughs ringed in Britain & Ireland, probably as a result of the small population size and restricted geographical range, but this is further exacerbated by the

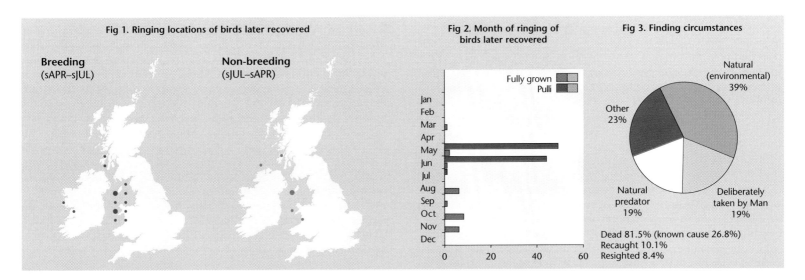

Fig 1. Ringing locations of birds later recovered

Breeding (sAPR–sJUL)

Non-breeding (sJUL–sAPR)

Fig 2. Month of ringing of birds later recovered

Fully grown / Pulli

Fig 3. Finding circumstances

Natural (environmental) 39%

Other 23%

Natural predator 19%

Deliberately taken by Man 19%

Dead 81.5% (known cause 26.8%)
Recaught 10.1%
Resighted 8.4%

Ringing and recovery data

	<1960	60–69	70–79	80–89	90–97	Total
RINGING						
BTO ringing totals (%)	9	5	6	26	54	2,664
RECOVERIES						
BTO-ringed (%)	8	14	7	30	40	119
Foreign-ringed (%)	0	0	0	0	0	0

Statistical analyses

	Breeding population (sAPR–sJUL)	Wintering population (sOCT–sJAN)
Status	SEDENTARY*	[SEDENTARY]
Age differences	Not tested	Not tested
Sex differences	Not tested	Not tested
Regional differences	Not tested	Not tested
Finding circumstances	Not tested	Not tested

Fig 4. Recovery locations and movements of over 20 km for the 119 included recoveries of Choughs ringed or recovered in Britain & Ireland.

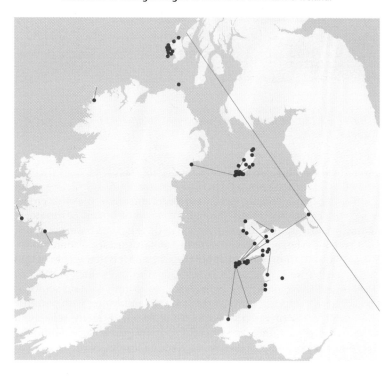

habitats they frequent. Consequently, there have been few recoveries. However, the distribution of ringing sites of birds later recovered reflects the species' current range as shown in the *1988–91 Atlas*, except for relatively small samples from both Islay and Ireland (Fig 1). The majority (79%) of ring-recoveries are from Choughs ringed as nestlings (Fig 2) and most involve dead birds; it has only been in the late 1990s that adult birds have been caught with any frequency.

Just over a quarter of recoveries from dead birds are attributable to a known cause of death. Of these, 19% were a result of natural predation and over a third were attributed to other natural causes, a further 19% were deliberately taken by Man (Fig 3). It has been suggested that increased predator pressure, in particular from Peregrines, may depress the numbers of Choughs. Such predation may pose a considerable threat to some populations, particularly those that are already limited by other factors.

Breeding Choughs tend to remain close to their nest sites throughout the year, although some local movements occur, particularly during winter, depending on food availability. Pairs are thought to bond for life and the same nest site or location is used annually; many traditional sites have been in use for considerably longer than the expected lifespan of an individual. Young remain dependent on their parents for several weeks following fledging, remaining as a family unit and often returning to the nest area to roost. Within two months, the young join post-breeding flocks, which may include extended family groups. Such flocks, which can sometimes contain over 100 birds, may range widely in search of suitable feeding and roosting sites. Many movements of up to 45 km from natal areas have been recorded in Wales, the Isle of Man and

Ireland (Holyoak 1971, Roberts 1985) and there is at least one record of an individual moving *c* 80 km during winter in North Wales (Stratford & Cross pers comm). Juvenile birds are likely to remain in these flocks until old enough to breed, usually about three or four years, but sometimes longer. Density of populations and availability of suitable nest sites are likely to be influencing factors (Bignal & Curtis 1989) in determining the age of first breeding.

There have been only three recoveries well away from their strongholds of birds ringed as nestlings (Fig 4). These involved a bird ringed in Wales and found dead 143 km to the northeast in Liverpool, another ringed on the Calf of Man and found freshly dead in Newcastle, County Down, 71 km to the west, and one from Islay reported as a road casualty in Buckinghamshire 604 km to the southeast. This last recovery must be viewed with some caution, given its location so far inland and such a distance away from known areas of occurrence. Furthermore, the finding circumstances suggest it may have been transported some distance by the vehicle with which it collided or by other human agency; the record is not accepted locally (Lack & Ferguson 1993). Sight records away from known breeding areas imply that other long-distance movements occasionally occur. Chough have been reported in Cornwall (Meyer 1990), on Barra (*Birds in Scotland*), on Orkney (360 km from the nearest breeding area), in eastern England (210 km) and in Devon (100 km) (*BWP*). As a result of the Scottish and Manx populations being confined to relatively small islands and very few birds having been ringed in Ireland, it is only within Wales that recorded movements have exceeded 50 km (Fig 4). Ringing studies in North Wales during the 1990s have shown birds moving up to 75 km from their natal areas to sites of first breeding (Stratford & Cross pers comm), with females showing greater dispersal (maximum 75 km, mean=24 km) than males (maximum 45 km, mean=17 km).

Analysis of recoveries by month of reporting shows two peaks. There is a period of high post-fledging mortality in July and August, indeed 92% of recoveries received during the non-breeding season of birds ringed during the breeding season involved juveniles. There is also an increase in recoveries during October to November, possibly as a result of juvenile birds succumbing to the rigours of the onset of winter.

The Chough has been the subject of considerable research throughout its British & Irish range. There are three long-term colour-ringing programmes in existence, which are providing important information that is assisting the implementation of species survival plans. Such information is also crucial in those areas attempting to restore suitable habitat, such as in Cornwall, in the hope of natural recolonization (Meyer 2000). There are still many unanswered questions, however, and further detailed study, involving the ringing of both adults and pulli, as well as radio-tagging, would assist in understanding the complexities of the species' family structure and the use of specific habitats at certain times of year. In particular, although colour-ringing studies in North Wales are providing information on wintering areas used in Snowdonia, little is known about the wintering areas used in west Wales, and on the Isle of Man many birds disappear from the regular coastal haunts during late autumn. The use of satellite-tracking, combined with more conventional ringing studies, might be beneficial in identifying these areas.

Aron Sapsford

Eurasian Jackdaw (Jackdaw)

Corvus monedula

The Jackdaw is a relatively small but remarkably lively and gregarious member of the crow family. Although essentially catholic in diet, its distribution and movements are partly governed by a strong preference for grassland invertebrates, particularly during the breeding season. Thus, within the relatively mild climate of Britain & Ireland, breeding Jackdaws are mainly sedentary, in sharp contrast to northern and eastern populations from continental Europe.

Of the four most clearly recognized subspecies, which range throughout the western Palearctic from Norway and North Africa, east to the Himalayas, the nominate *monedula* (Fennoscandia) and the eastern European race *soemmerringii* (which intergrades with *monedula*) are the most migratory. These populations move south and west in autumn to avoid severe winter weather. Birds from Algeria (*collaris*) and those from Britain, Ireland and western continental Europe (*spermologus*) are less migratory. Short-distance dispersive movements do occur among British & Irish birds but even Scottish winter flocks tend to remain within 40 km of their natal areas (Buckland *et al* 1990). Following an expansion of breeding range in northern latitudes (*European Atlas*), extreme movements may have included vagrancy as far afield as North America (K J McGowan pers comm). More typically, birds from Scandinavia occur in Belgium, France, the Netherlands and to an unknown extent in Britain & Ireland.

Jackdaws breed semicolonially; highest breeding densities occur in rural areas comprising a mixture of pastoral and arable farmland for foraging, with suitable nest cavities in close proximity. In winter, they forage across farmland and roost in woods in large mixed-species flocks

The analysis of the data for this species was supported by Academic Press

with Rooks and Carrion Crows. These flocks can often comprise many thousands of birds, of which Jackdaws are a significant proportion. Jackdaws from continental Europe might add substantially to the resident population, although few authors have attempted to quantify the continental influx.

The distribution of ringing places of birds later recovered largely reflects the species' breeding range in England and Scotland (Fig 1). There may be slight over-representation in southeast England, and under-representation from Wales and Ireland, where high breeding densities occur. Birds ringed outside the breeding season also closely match the breeding distribution, indicating that resident birds occupy similar habitats and localities in winter and summer. Unfortunately, few individuals have been ringed in east-coast localities in either Britain or Ireland, where migrant birds from continental Europe or Britain, respectively, are most likely to occur. Although Jackdaws are ringed throughout the year, over 70% of all recoveries were from birds ringed during the breeding season (Fig 2). Over a third (40%) of the Jackdaws recovered were ringed whilst chicks.

Throughout Britain & Ireland, Jackdaws are still perceived as a pest species and therefore are subject to legal control for the protection of gamebirds or arable crops. Consequently, two-thirds of all ring-recoveries of dead birds that had known finding circumstances were deliberately

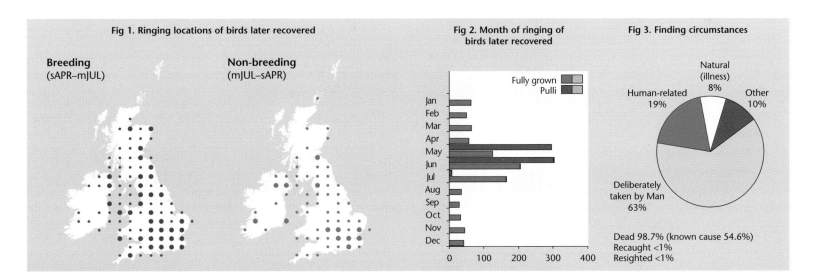

Ringing and recovery data

	<1960	60–69	70–79	80–89	90–97	Total
RINGING						
BTO ringing totals (%)	26	11	14	26	24	36,948
RECOVERIES						
BTO-ringed (%)	33	18	15	22	12	1,508
Foreign-ringed (%)	←	83	→	13	4	23

Statistical analyses

	Breeding population (sAPR–mJUL)	Wintering population (sNOV–sMAR)
Status	SEDENTARY (0)	SEDENTARY
Age differences[NT]	Significant*	Not significant*
Sex differences	Not tested	Not tested
Regional differences	Not significant[S]*	Not tested
Finding circumstances	(Not significant)	Not significant

Fig 4. Locations in winter, and movements of over 20 km between the breeding season and winter, of Jackdaws present in Britain & Ireland during the breeding season. Jackdaws ringed as breeding adults (13, black) are differentiated from all other birds (180, red).

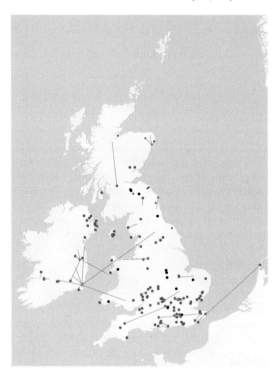

Fig 4. Locations in winter, and movements of over 20 km between the breeding season and winter, of Jackdaws present in Britain & Ireland during the breeding season. Jackdaws ringed as breeding adults (13, black) are differentiated from all other birds (180, red).

Fig 5. All 10 included exchanges of Jackdaws between Britain & Ireland and abroad. The 19 pre-1979 foreign-ringed Jackdaws (the Netherlands 8, Denmark 5, Belgium 3, Germany 1, Sweden 1 and Norway 1) are not shown.

taken by Man (Fig 3). Sixty-three percent of recoveries were found during the breeding season when the movements and whereabouts of birds are relatively predictable, so that both ringed and recovered birds reflect the distribution of the resident breeding population.

Partly because ringers do not target roving winter flocks, median distances between ringing and recovery are short. The median movement between ringing and recovery is less than 1 km for females (P5–95=

0–11 km, $n=35$) and 2 km (P5–95=0–9 km, $n=22$) for males. Breeding adults, in particular, remain close to the breeding colonies and revisit their nest site at frequent intervals throughout the winter months (pers obs) (Fig 4). Even during the most active phase of post-natal dispersal (that is, between about 100 and 300 days after fledging) the distance between ringing location and recovery location is normally less than 30 km. In fact, young Jackdaws also tend to be strongly philopatric with many birds eventually returning to their natal areas to breed (pers obs). There are a few longer movements, made mainly by immature birds moving between summer and winter quarters (Fig 4). Certainly, there appears to be a small seasonal drift to milder conditions, but only averaging around 30 km south and 10 km west in midwinter. Jackdaws have also been ringed in winter in Ireland and recovered later in Cumbria or southwest Scotland, showing that such seasonal movements can involve a sea-crossing.

Ringing evidence for movements of birds to the Continent includes only six recoveries of Jackdaws ringed in Britain & Ireland since 1909: these come from Denmark, Sweden, the Netherlands (three) and Belgium. All four foreign-ringed Jackdaws (from Denmark, Sweden and two from the Netherlands) that have been recovered in Britain & Ireland (all in southern England) since 1979 were ringed either as chicks or as immatures and, therefore, are truly representative of foreign populations (Fig 5).

The ringing locations of foreign-ringed recoveries are probably fairly representative of the origins of a much larger flux of birds between Britain & Ireland and colder climates on the Continent. The arrival of continental birds to Britain & Ireland (*Winter Atlas*, Buckland *et al* 1990) has some foundation, based on annual but variable numbers of autumn and spring records along the eastern coast of Britain (*eg* Taylor *et al* 1999). In Norfolk, autumn passage, from September to November, has included counts of up to 193 Jackdaws in 1993, and 251 in 1997; return passage peaks between March and April, and has resulted in daily counts of up to 105 birds flying out to sea from a single locality (Taylor *et al* 1999). Individuals showing characteristics closest to the eastern European subpopulation *soemmerringii*, although rare, are also recorded annually in very small numbers from well-watched parts of the east coast and occasionally further inland (Taylor *et al* 1999). Elsewhere within Britain & Ireland, extremely large movements of Jackdaws have been recorded, although the source of these flocks is uncertain. For example, in October 1983 a passage of over 20,000 Jackdaws was recorded flying north over Cornwall (Christophers 1984), with unprecedented numbers of around 4,000 birds visiting the Isles of Scilly in the same autumn (Rogers 1984). These movements coincided with anticyclonic weather and the arrival of large numbers of Redwings and Fieldfares into Cornwall, clearly indicating that, at least on occasion, Jackdaws may arrive *en masse* from continental Europe.

The greatest uncertainties in respect of Jackdaw movements concern the frequency and magnitude of arrivals in Britain & Ireland from the Continent. A clearer account of their movements is likely to emerge from further ringing of adults outside the breeding season, and especially around the coasts of Britain & Ireland.

Unlike many other species associated with farmland, the Jackdaw currently fares well, with the population either stable or increasing throughout much of Britain, Ireland and northern Europe (*European Atlas*). Although possibly limited by the availability of nest sites, this highly adaptable species, like its frequent companion the Rook, appears to have benefited from intensive cereal production and stock-feeding, and possibly also from a lower intensity of predator control and direct persecution during the last 20 years or so.

Ian Henderson

Rook
Corvus frugilegus

The Rook is one of the most widespread, common and familiar resident birds of farmland throughout Britain & Ireland. Its gregarious, noisy and sometimes mysterious habits have made it the subject of folklore and of many country tales and sayings.

The nominate race *frugilegus* is found across most of the middle latitudes of the temperate and boreal West Palearctic region, at altitudes up to 600 m in Europe and Asia but more often below 350 m in Britain & Ireland; it is most abundant in the northwest of its range. The range extends from Europe and Asia Minor eastward to the Yenisei River, northwest Altai and northwest Sinkiang. There it is replaced by the race *pastinator*, which occurs in eastern Asia including eastern Siberia, Japan, Korea and eastern China (*BWP*). Many of the Eurasian populations are seasonal migrants, moving in a generally southwesterly direction to winter (Busse 1969), but in Britain & Ireland the Rook is a resident and primarily sedentary species that rarely moves more than 50 km from its natal site.

Rooks breed colonially, in rookeries, typically in tall trees in small woods, copses and hedgerows surrounded by open farmland that is preferably a mixture of pasture and arable crops (Brenchley 1984). While both density and distribution correspond very closely between the breeding season and the winter (*Winter Atlas, 1988–91 Atlas*), Rooks are more mobile in autumn and winter as they search for an abundant but more patchily distributed food supply. In winter Rooks roost communally, often at traditional sites which are usually themselves large rookeries to which birds from neighbouring rookeries may commute from up to 20 km away each day (Patterson *et al* 1971, Coombs 1978). The

The analysis of the data for this species was supported by Anne Brenchley

size of winter roosts varies geographically, with roost size generally increasing northwards. Roosts in northeast Scotland have recorded in excess of 65,000 individuals. Roost size is usually in proportion to the local breeding density but in some areas of low breeding density (such as Derbyshire, Hampshire, Lincolnshire, Perthshire and South Yorkshire) roosts of 10,000 or more birds indicate that the distance travelled to feed and roost may exceed 20 km (*Winter Atlas*).

Only a few hundred Rooks are ringed in Britain & Ireland each year, mostly pulli and juveniles between the months of March and June, and of these only 4% have been subsequently recovered, recaptured or resighted (Figs 1 & 2). Rooks have been caught throughout Britain & Ireland but peaks in ringing effort are noticeable when specific research projects are undertaken, particularly in Scotland and Ireland in the 1970s and 1980s (Patterson *et al* 1971, Feare *et al* 1974, Green 1981, Macdonald & Whelan 1986).

The Rook suffers from an image problem. The often very large and conspicuous flocks are accused, rightly or wrongly, by farmers of doing damage to crops. Rooks can cause localized and sporadic damage to crops, and while this damage is small in comparison to that caused by various invertebrates, some of which Rooks eat, farmers are often keen to attempt local population control. Overall, for 58% of Rook recoveries found dead, the cause of death is known, and of these 77% were taken

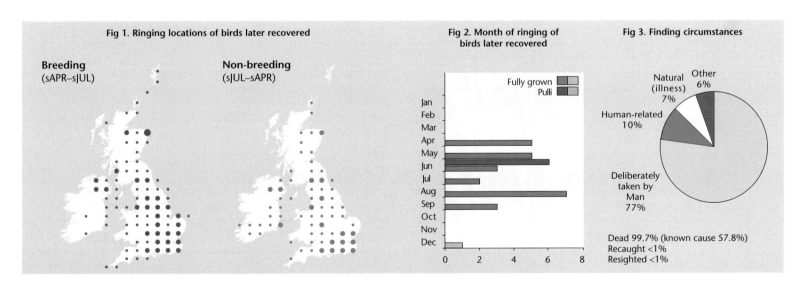

Fig 1. Ringing locations of birds later recovered

Breeding (sAPR–sJUL)   **Non-breeding** (sJUL–sAPR)

Fig 2. Month of ringing of birds later recovered

Fully grown / Pulli

Fig 3. Finding circumstances

Natural (illness) 7%   Other 6%
Human-related 10%
Deliberately taken by Man 77%

Dead 99.7% (known cause 57.8%)
Recaught <1%
Resighted <1%

Ringing and recovery data

	<1960	60–69	70–79	80–89	90–97	Total
RINGING						
BTO ringing totals (%)	26	24	20	20	9	36,075
RECOVERIES						
BTO-ringed (%)	26	26	22	19	7	1,596
Foreign-ringed (%)	←	84	→	13	3	63

Statistical analyses

	Breeding population (sAPR–sJUL)	Wintering population (mNOV–sMAR)
Status	SEDENTARY (0)	SEDENTARY
Age differences[NT]	Significant*	Significant*
Sex differences	Not tested	Not tested
Regional differences	Not Significant[3]*	Not tested
Finding circumstances	Not significant	Not significant*

Fig 4. Variation in the distances moved by juvenile Rooks with time after ringing as pulli. Medians for 30-day periods (points) and interquartile ranges (bars) are shown.

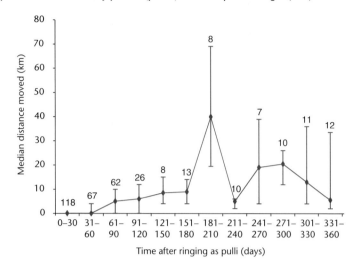

Fig 5. Recovery locations and movements of over 20 km for the 1,607 included recoveries of Rooks ringed or recovered in Britain & Ireland.

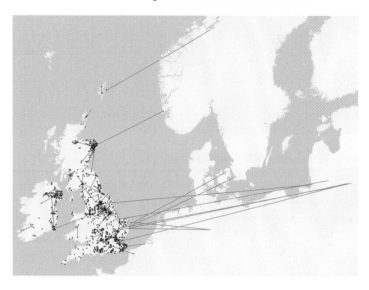

Table 1. Distances moved by Rooks between ringing and recovery, by region of ringing and breeding population.

| | British and Irish breeders | | | Birds from unknown breeding populations | | |
	Median (km)	P95 (km)	n	Median (km)	P95 (km)	n
Northwest	6	56	66	6.5	59	56
Northeast	5.5	75	196	7.5	48	132
Ireland	4	43	107	7	73	102
Southeast	0	38	415	4	70	227
Southwest	0	28	214	2	21	87

by Man and were mainly shot (Fig 3). Young Rooks are at their most vulnerable from human predation in the breeding season and are often shot in or near the nest. Studies in northeast Scotland, and elsewhere across Britain, have shown that mortality due to food shortage is most likely to occur in the post-fledging period, in June to August, when there is a bottleneck in the availability of food (Feare *et al* 1974, pers obs). Therefore, shooting juveniles at the nest does little to influence population size and may even allow those that fledge to increase their chances of further survival.

Young Rooks stay in the vicinity of the rookery until autumn, when there is a tendency to move further afield to forage and to roost in non-natal rookeries, but it is exceptional for these movements to be beyond 50 km (Fig 4). In both northeast Scotland and eastern Ireland, Rooks from different rookeries feed together more often in winter than in other seasons and this could be related to the more scattered nature of the winter food supply (Feare *et al* 1974, Macdonald & Whelan 1986). Seasonal movements in search of food are more marked in the northern latitudes and McKilligan (1980) noted the winter exodus from a Scottish Highland valley as food shortages became apparent. In the milder climes of southeast and southwest Britain, Rooks are less likely to change their distribution seasonally and again this is probably related to food supply.

For all recoveries of dead Rooks involving Britain & Ireland up to 1997, the median distance moved from the place of ringing was only 4 km (P5–95=0–51 km, n=1,602). Southern birds, especially those ringed in the breeding season, showed even less inclination to move from the place of ringing than those in northern Britain and Ireland (Table 1). Of recoveries of birds ringed in the breeding season and found in winter, 21% were over 20 km. Whilst the British & Irish Rook populations are resident (only two British Rooks have been recorded abroad; Fig 5), there is an irregular influx of Rooks from continental Europe, recorded from visual observations and count data (*eg* Dunnet & Patterson 1968), on the east coast of Britain in winter (*Winter Atlas*). This is also evident from the foreign-ringed birds that have been recovered in Britain (over 60 in total to 1997), from more than 10 different European countries. The majority of these recoveries were in eastern England and primarily from the Netherlands (23), Germany (15) and the Baltic States (11). The *European Atlas* suggests that this winter immigration has become less predictable in recent years and certainly in the last two decades of the century only 13 foreign recoveries were recorded in Britain (Fig 5). The significance of this figure is hard to assess in the absence of recent information about ringing effort across the source areas but may be related to declines on the Continent. The vast majority of foreign-ringed birds were ringed as either breeding adults or pulli between March and June and recovered between October and May the following year in Britain, most recoveries being in the winter months of November to February.

The ecology of the Rook is closely bound up with agricultural practices and, unlike its corvid cousins, the Carrion Crow and Magpie, it has not been able to adapt to areas of high human population and exploit the variety of food sources found in cities, towns, and suburban gardens. Rook populations declined after the 1940s as agricultural intensification and the use of pesticides increased but they have been increasing slightly throughout the United Kingdom in recent decades (Marchant & Gregory 1999). Future changes will be dependent on trends and patterns in agricultural practice. Whatever the future holds, the Rook will still be a common sight in the countryside for many decades to come.

Anne Brenchley

Carrion Crow
Corvus corone

Although the Carrion Crow occurs as two distinct colour forms in Britain & Ireland, it is traditionally viewed as a single species (Goodwin 1986, *BWP*). The all-black form *corone* is found in England, Wales and southern Scotland, while the grey-and-black Hooded Crow *cornix* is found in Ireland, northern Scotland and the Isle of Man. The two forms are believed to have evolved distinctive plumage patterns during isolation in separate glacial refuges (*1968–72 Atlas*). In regions of post-glacial secondary contact, such as Scotland (*Winter Atlas, 1988–91 Atlas*) and the Italian Alps (Saino & Villa 1992), the two forms hybridize to produce fertile offspring, an example of allopatric hybridization.

The Carrion Crow occurs widely across Europe and Asia. The two all-black forms *corone* and *orientalis* are thought to have evolved independently in the wetter maritime climes at opposite ends of Eurasia; *corone* in western Europe and *orientalis* in central and eastern Asia (Madge & Burn 1994). These are geographically replaced in the rest of the Palearctic by three grey-and-black races, *cornix, sharpii* and *pallescens*, with which they intergrade or freely hybridize (*BWP*). Apart from *pallescens*, which seems to be largely sedentary, all Carrion Crow races include both sedentary and migratory populations (*BWP*). A fourth hooded form from lowland Iraq, *capellanus* (Mesopotamian Crow), may be sufficiently different from neighbouring hooded races as to warrant specific status.

Taking both races together, the Carrion Crow is the most widely distributed corvid species in Britain & Ireland (*1988–91 Atlas, BWP*). Its adaptability and catholic diet allow it to exploit a wide range of habitats, including open farmland, open woodland and forest clearings, coastal

The analysis of the data for this species was supported by Chris & Mike Evans

areas (where it frequently forages along tidal estuaries), parks, gardens and upland moors (*BWP*, Madge & Burn 1994). Non-breeders often form large aggregations at good feeding sites, especially in the intertidal zone of estuaries, at rubbish dumps and intensive animal units (*BWP*); Berrow *et al* (1991) recorded larger numbers of birds on intertidal feeding grounds during the winter months. Afforestation has provided new and secure nesting sites in many upland areas. The species has also spread into towns, cities and even major conurbations such as London (Prestt 1965).

Like other corvids, the Carrion Crow has traditionally been considered a pest by gamekeepers and by farmers (O'Connor & Shrubb 1986, Tapper 1992). Persecution, however, is believed to have lessened in recent years due to a substantial reduction in the level of gamekeeping activities, especially in Britain (Tapper 1992). Likewise, as a consequence of the modernization of stock-rearing practices and an increase in arable farming, the Carrion Crow has been perceived less as a pest by farmers and persecution has decreased (Marchant *et al* 1990).

With the exception of parts of northwest Scotland, the distribution of ringing sites for birds that were recovered reflects broadly the distribution of the Carrion Crow in Britain (*Winter Atlas, 1988–91 Atlas*); in Ireland, ringing sites were largely in the northeast of the island (Fig 1). Some 85% of recoveries have been of birds ringed as nestlings,

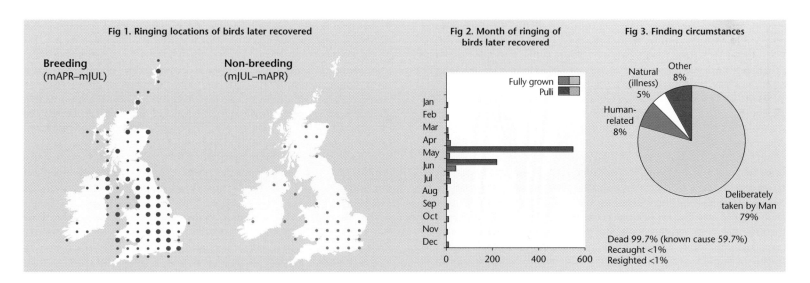

Fig 1. Ringing locations of birds later recovered

Breeding (mAPR–mJUL)

Non-breeding (mJUL–mAPR)

Fig 2. Month of ringing of birds later recovered

Fully grown / Pulli

Fig 3. Finding circumstances

Other 8%
Natural (illness) 5%
Human-related 8%
Deliberately taken by Man 79%

Dead 99.7% (known cause 59.7%)
Recaught <1%
Resighted <1%

Ringing and recovery data

	<1960	60–69	70–79	80–89	90–97	Total
RINGING						
BTO ringing totals (%)	23	14	21	27	15	15,911
RECOVERIES						
BTO-ringed (%)	21	19	20	24	17	929
Foreign-ringed (%)	88	0	0	12	0	8

Statistical analyses

	Breeding population (mAPR–mJUL)	Wintering population (sNOV–mMAR)
Status	SEDENTARY (0)	?
Age differences[NT]	Not significant*	—
Sex differences	Not tested	—
Regional differences	Not significant[5]*	—
Finding circumstances	Not significant	—

Fig 4. Locations outside the breeding season and movements of over 20 km between the breeding and non-breeding season of 359 Carrion Crows present in Britain & Ireland during the breeding season.

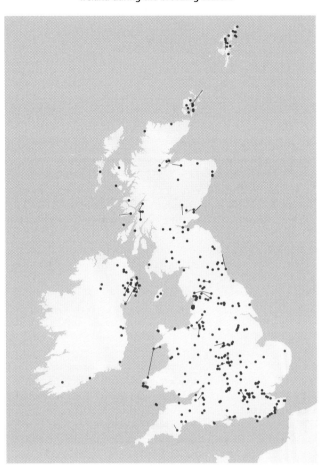

Fig 5. Movements of over 20 km and recovery locations of 82 Carrion Crows ringed as pulli in Britain & Ireland and recovered in a subsequent breeding season when of breeding age.

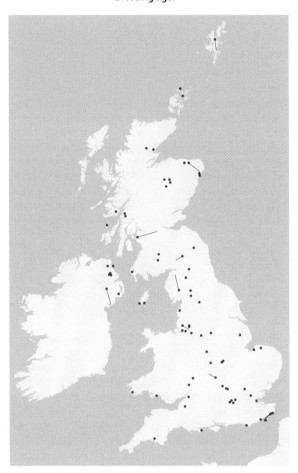

predominantly in the months of May (59%) and June (23%). Little ringing takes place outside the breeding season (Fig 2). The distribution of recoveries largely mirrors that of the ringing locations. No British- or Irish-ringed birds have been recovered abroad. While recoveries were not assigned to *corone* or *cornix*, their distribution is such that the majority of birds are likely to have been the black form *corone*.

Over 99% of ring-recoveries were from dead birds, with less than 1% recaught or resighted in the field. This is consistent with the fact that, while the level of persecution of the Carrion Crow may have decreased in recent years, large numbers of birds are still shot or trapped each year (Tapper 1992). Approximately 60% of all recoveries were attributed to a known cause of death and a large majority of these (79%) were deliberately taken by Man (Fig 3). A further 8% of deaths were also human-related, for example through collision with motor vehicles. The recovery rate for birds shot, trapped, or killed on the road is likely to be significantly higher than for birds that die of natural causes. This could introduce bias if birds shot or trapped are not representative of the population as a whole; a common feature of hunted species is the greater vulnerability of first-year birds to shooting. Proportionately more birds were deliberately taken by Man in Ireland (c 93%) than in Britain (c 77%). This may be an artefact of small sample size in Ireland, or it may reflect geographical variation in hunting pressure. Most recoveries have been made between March and July, just before and during the breeding season.

Both forms of Carrion Crow nesting in Britain & Ireland are highly sedentary. There appears to be no obvious seasonal shift in the distribution of recoveries for either immature or adult birds and no evidence of cold-weather movements. Seasonal changes in the proportion of hybrid birds on the western seaboard and islands of Argyll during the winter have been explained by winter movement of upland birds to the

coast (*1968–72 Atlas*); a winter movement to the coast has also been recorded in Sussex (*BWP*). However, the ringing data provide no direct evidence of such movements (Fig 4).

Recoveries indicate that the median distance travelled for all birds recovered dead was 3 km (*P5–95*=0–25 km, *n*=926). There appears to be no seasonal pattern in the distribution of the few recoveries of over 20 km. The median distances travelled by birds in each of five geographical regions varied between 2 km and 6 km; this is within the range of daily flights between communal roosts and feeding areas (*BWP*). Distances appeared to be shorter in southern Britain, and especially the southeast, than elsewhere. Holyoak (1971) also found a statistically significant difference in median dispersal distances between northern England and Scotland (7.9 km) and southern England and Wales (4.2 km).

Based upon a small number of recoveries of birds of known sex, there is a tentative suggestion that females (6; median 13 km) may move longer distances than males (8; median 0 km). In Norway, Slagsvold (1979) found that more females and first-winter birds disperse than males, both locally and over long distances.

Local populations comprise breeding pairs, which hold a territory, and flocks of other birds (Loman 1985). Flocks are usually composed of juveniles and non-breeding adults, and are often concentrated around aggregated food resources, such as refuse dumps (Slagsvold 1980). Following fledging, young birds generally remain in their natal territory for several weeks before joining the non-breeding flock (Loman 1985). The recovery data indicate that for birds ringed during the breeding season, most of which were ringed as nestlings, the median dispersal distances for the breeding season, autumn and winter/spring were 0 km, 1 km and 5 km, respectively, suggesting a progressive dispersal of young birds away from their natal area. For birds ringed as pulli, the median dispersal distance for recoveries made in the first two months after ringing was less than 1 km, rising to 4 km by the sixth month and 8.5 km by the eighth. The recovery data indicate that the median natal dispersal distance was 6 km (*n*=82) but a few longer movements have occurred (Fig 5); this compares to a median of 8 km in eastern Germany (Siefke 1994). Loman (1985) suggested that difficulties in obtaining a territory appear to ensure at least local dispersal in many cases. Charles' (1972) finding that flock birds will pair and breed when new nest sites are provided supports the idea that suitable territories are limiting. There are too few data to measure breeding dispersal but this is clearly also on a very local scale. Dispersal movements within Britain & Ireland show no obvious directional trend.

Like *corone* and *cornix* populations in Britain & Ireland, birds of the black form *corone* occupying northern France, Belgium and the Netherlands are also largely sedentary. In Switzerland, alpine *corone* migrate in a southwesterly direction and display more accentuated migratory habits than neighbouring lowland populations; the harsh mountain climate may be the main reason for this (Busse 1969). A small number of *corone* have been observed on Fair Isle and other northern Scottish islands, possibly originating from Denmark, while several dozen hybrid birds observed on Fair Isle may also have originated from mainland Europe (*Winter Atlas*).

Fennoscandian Hooded Crows migrate in a southwesterly direction over an area encompassing Norway, Sweden, Denmark, the Netherlands, Belgium, and northern France, with those from further north and east tending to travel greater distances than populations from further west and south (Busse 1969, *BWP*). Birds migrate in a narrow front, the orientation of which is strongly influenced by the sea. Some birds from Norway and mountainous areas of western Sweden winter in the southwestern corner of Norway, in the vicinity of Stavanger; a tendency which may result from a marked reluctance to cross the open sea. Birds from western Finland migrate along two fronts which show a strong tendency to follow the Baltic coastline; those from further west migrate along the western shore, while birds from southeastern Finland migrate along the southern shore.

In the past, Hooded Crows were recorded regularly down the eastern seaboard of England, mainly from October to March. Four Norwegian-ringed birds and three Swedish-ringed birds were recovered in Britain prior to 1951, and a single Danish-ringed bird in 1986. Hooded Crows, most likely Scandinavian immigrants, were also recorded in bag returns from the east coast of England (Tapper 1992). A reduction in the number of Hooded Crows wintering in England has been attributed to a change in the migratory behaviour of Scandinavian birds, with a greater proportion wintering further north due to climatic amelioration (Busse 1969, Holyoak 1971). Winter recoveries of Finnish nestlings and juveniles have shown a reduction since the 1940s in both the proportion migrating and the distances moved (*BWP*). A study in Skåne, southern Sweden, showed that many local birds left the area in winter; migrants included immature and adult birds, though territory-holding adults remained (Loman 1985). Eastern Germany has resident populations of *corone* and wintering *cornix* from Finland and the Baltic countries. Ring-recoveries, and a decrease in numbers of *cornix* in western parts of the winter range, indicate that these Hooded Crow populations have also contracted their winter range in recent decades; improved food availability in winter, due to human activity, and climatic factors have been proposed as explanations (Siefke 1994).

During the 20th century, both *corone* and *cornix* populations in Britain & Ireland underwent significant changes in numbers and range. CBC data indicate that *corone* numbers in Britain doubled between 1964 and 1977 (Gregory & Marchant 1996), while between the *1968–72* and *1988–91 Atlases* the *corone* range in Britain extended by about 30 km into regions previously occupied exclusively by the Hooded Crow. A progressive reduction in gamekeeping pressure and in the level of persecution by farmers has been implicated (Marchant *et al* 1990, Tapper 1992). The increase in numbers of *corone* has not been reflected in an increase in bag returns (Tapper 1992). The zone of hybridization between *corone* and *cornix* that exists within Scotland has moved northwards throughout the century. Until at least 1975, the degree of northward movement had been greatest in the east of the region, with little northward shift at the western end of the zone (Cook 1975). During the next 15 years, however, northward movement was evident along the whole length of the zone (*1988–91 Atlas*). Interestingly, the width of the hybrid zone has remained relatively constant over this period, possibly suggesting that hybrids show a reduced fitness.

Carrion Crows are now also observed regularly in Ireland, mainly in the north and east, where they are also breeding in small numbers (*1988–91 Atlas*, O'Donoghue *et al* 1996). Moore & Lenehan (1976) suggested that the late winter or early spring peak of *corone* records in eastern Ireland reflected a winter influx from Britain. This is not yet confirmed by the recovery data.

The picture to emerge from the ringing data of highly sedentary British & Irish populations is to some extent at odds with the field observations of *corone* in Ireland and the dynamic changes in the distribution of *corone*, *cornix* and hybrid forms in the 20th century. Additional research into breeding success and the nature of dispersal in the two races, and among hybrid birds, would aid the understanding of the dynamics of the hybrid zone and the expansion of the *corone* population. Of particular interest in this regard is the expansion of *corone*, and possibly the hybrid zone, into Ireland. Additional research on the movements of young birds using radio-telemetry, rather than ringing, would help to disentangle dispersal from roosting movements and to quantify the potential biases of a data set largely derived from birds killed by hunters.

Paul D O'Donoghue

Common Raven (Raven)
Corvus corax

The Raven has many credits to its name. As well as being the largest member of the largest order of birds in the world (passerines), it is also one of the most widely dispersed of all terrestrial birds, able to live and breed in a remarkable range of habitats and climates, ranging from the arctic slopes of Alaska in midwinter where temperatures reach −50°C or colder, to the searing heat of California's Death Valley where air temperatures may be in excess of 50°C (Schwan & Williams 1978). It must also be the best represented of all birds in folklore, myth and legend and is immortalized in a great many British place names (D A Ratcliffe 1997).

Holarctic in range, with at least 10 subspecies, the Raven occurs almost throughout Europe and Asia from Greenland (mainly coastal), Iceland and northern Scandinavia east to the Pacific, and from the Arctic Ocean south to the Canaries, northwest Africa, Pakistan, the Himalayas and northern Manchuria. An area from eastern Britain and southern France east to southeast Germany is largely unoccupied (*European Atlas*). The range in North and Central America extends from the Arctic to Nicaragua (*BWP*). The nominate race *corax*, which breeds from Ireland and Britain across northwest Eurasia, is largely sedentary in the south, with dispersive movements chiefly in the first autumn and winter (*BWP*). In the north of its range, it is more prone to make medium-distance movements. In Fennoscandia, for instance, northern birds make seasonal southerly movements of over 200 km. The east Asian race *kamtschaticus* is apparently dispersive and is a winter visitor to northeast China and northern Japan, especially in severe winters (*BWP*). Other populations are essentially sedentary although breeding

The analysis of the data for this species was supported by Tony Cross & Ian M Spence

birds in Iceland, Greenland and Canada tend to move to coastal areas in winter and those in the Alps and Himalayas make altitudinal movements in response to cold weather (*BWP*).

Its range in Britain is much reduced from that of 200 years ago, when it bred in almost every county (Holloway 1996). During the 19th century, relentless persecution by farmers and gamekeepers effectively eliminated it from most areas of lowland England (and elsewhere in lowland western Europe). Parts of Wales, always one of the species' strongholds in Britain & Ireland, hold some of the highest recorded breeding densities anywhere in its extensive global range, reflecting the abundance of suitable nest sites and the high availability of carrion on which to feed (Newton *et al* 1982, Cross & Davis 1986).

The Raven is generally associated with rugged coasts and mountainous terrain but, in the absence of persecution, it is equally at home in lowland farmland, parkland and open forest. It is an omnivore and an opportunist, with large numbers aggregating at regular food sources such as rubbish-tips and abattoirs. In Wales, Red Kite feeding stations have become important for some local Raven populations (pers obs).

A few dedicated enthusiasts have made a major contribution to the overall numbers of Ravens ringed. The maps of ringing locations (Fig 1) owe as much to the distribution of these specialist ringers as to that of

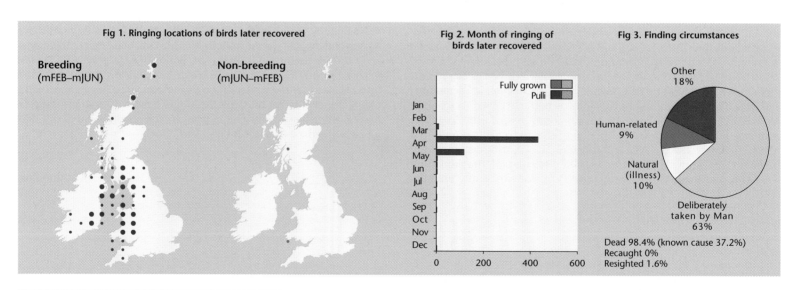

Fig 1. Ringing locations of birds later recovered

Breeding (mFEB–mJUN)

Non-breeding (mJUN–mFEB)

Fig 2. Month of ringing of birds later recovered

Fully grown
Pulli

Fig 3. Finding circumstances

Other 18%
Human-related 9%
Natural (illness) 10%
Deliberately taken by Man 63%

Dead 98.4% (known cause 37.2%)
Recaught 0%
Resighted 1.6%

Ringing and recovery data

	<1960	60–69	70–79	80–89	90–97	Total
RINGING						
BTO ringing totals (%)	8	10	16	30	36	9,669
RECOVERIES						
BTO-ringed (%)	13	17	21	31	17	568
Foreign-ringed (%)	0	0	0	0	0	0

Statistical analyses

	Breeding population (mFEB–mJUN)	Wintering population (mSEP–sJAN)
Status	SEDENTARY (0)	[SEDENTARY]
Age differences[NT]	Not significant*	Not tested
Sex differences	Not tested	Not tested
Regional differences	Not tested	Not tested
Finding circumstances	(Not significant)	Not tested

Fig 4. Recovery locations and movements of over 20 km for the 568 included recoveries of Ravens ringed or recovered in Britain & Ireland.

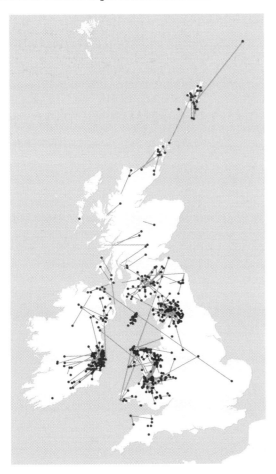

Table 1. Post-fledging dispersal in the Raven. The table shows the median distances of recoveries within each 30-day period after ringing as pulli.

Days	n	Median distance (km)	P5 (km)	P95 (km)
0–30	21	0.0	0	4
31–60	27	0.0	0	21
61–90	16	6.0	0	25
91–120	18	11.5	0	229
121–150	21	35.0	1	133
151–180	16	50.5	0	110
181–360	88	33.0	4	105

the Raven itself. Study areas have included Mid and North Wales, Shropshire, Cumbria, eastern Ireland, Shetland, Orkney and parts of southern Scotland. Sizeable populations of Ravens in Devon and Cornwall, western Ireland, the west coast of Scotland and the Western Isles are under-represented. Over 98% of all Ravens ringed and recovered in Britain & Ireland were ringed as nestlings (Fig 2), the adults being remarkably trap-shy. An evaluation of trapping techniques used in North America showed that capture rates could be as low as one Raven per 27 days (Engel & Young 1989).

Although the Raven has long been a protected species, the finding circumstances indicate that persecution is still substantial. Of all recoveries with known cause, 63% were listed as deliberately taken by Man (Fig 3). This compares with 79% for the Carrion Crow, which can be killed legally. It is certain that other ringed Ravens that are deliberately killed are not reported, or the cause of death is withheld, through fear of prosecution (pers obs, D Hayward pers comm). In some areas the level of non-reporting may be substantial, thereby biasing the recovery data.

The map of recoveries (Fig 4) illustrates the relatively sedentary nature of British & Irish Ravens. There have been no international movements involving Britain or Ireland, although a Raven raised on Shetland in 1993 was recovered in its first August, 229 km away in the North Sea. An exceptional recovery of a pullus ringed in Antrim in 1987 and recovered in Suffolk, 551 km to the southeast, the following January was the longest movement so far recorded under the British and Irish Ringing Scheme and one of only a handful of recorded sea-crossings within Britain & Ireland.

Juvenile Ravens remain on or around their natal territory for between one and two months after fledging (pers obs). The median distance travelled by pulli recovered dead during the first two months

after ringing was less than 1 km, but this distance increases up to the sixth month (Table 1). After this time there is some indication that birds may exhibit a partial return towards where they were reared. In the USA, radio-tagging studies have shown that Ravens may undertake daily movements of more than 50 km between communal roost sites and daytime feeding areas (Engel & Young 1992, Heinrich et al 1994). Few equivalent data exist for Britain & Ireland but colour-ringed Ravens have been noted making regular movements of 47 km between rubbish tips in England and Wales (pers obs). An exceptional roost of Ravens in Newborough Forest, Anglesey, estimated at c 2,000 individuals during winter 1998/99, must have been drawing birds from a considerable distance (D Brown pers comm).

For 50 nestlings recovered during the breeding season after three years or more, the median distance moved was 27 km (P5–95 = 3–153 km, n=50); some of these birds may not yet have been breeding so this may be a poor indication of the real natal dispersal. Colour-ringing in Shropshire (Shropshire Raven Study Group) has shown that, although Ravens can breed successfully at two years old, most do not breed until three or four years old, and one Raven on Orkney definitely did not breed until it was six (Booth 1986). Of a sample of 20 colour-ringed breeding adults in Shropshire and Mid Wales, the median natal dispersal distance was 9 km. The median distance travelled by eight females (13 km) was significantly greater than that for 12 males (7 km) (Shropshire Raven Study Group unpublished data). This pattern of females dispersing further than males follows that shown in several other corvid species, and in many other bird species (Greenwood 1980). These dispersal distances are very heavily biased towards areas checked by those involved in the project and are almost certainly underestimates of the true figures. Two unsexed birds nested at much greater distances in Derbyshire (114 km and 120 km) (M Lacey pers comm) and were reported only because they nested in another study area.

Very little information exists on breeding dispersal but most anecdotal evidence and colour-ringing results suggest that adult Ravens are strongly faithful to their territory from year to year. In Shropshire, two of 21 identifiable breeding adults moved territory, one by 1.2 km between nests and the other by 2.5 km. Both movements were after a successful first nesting and were probably both made by females (one was definitely a female).

A regular presence of continental Ravens in Britain & Ireland is not suspected, although a larger number of isolated individuals have been wintering in southeast England during the 1990s. The successful reintroduction program in the Netherlands (Renssen & Vogel 1993) may account for some of these birds.

Ravens have declined in areas of southern Scotland and northern England in association with habitat loss due to afforestation (Marquiss et al 1978, D A Ratcliffe 1997). In Wales, however, where afforestation has been on the whole somewhat more patchy in nature, plantations may have boosted some local populations by providing additional or secure nest sites (pers obs, Newton *et al* 1982) and in many other areas tree-nesting is again becoming more common (D Hayward pers comm, D A Ratcliffe 1997). Persecution, perhaps the main limiting factor to Raven distribution in Britain & Ireland, appears to be in decline. A comparison of finding circumstances before and after the 1981 Wildlife and Countryside Act shows that the proportion of all recoveries of known cause that were reported as taken by Man decreased from 74% to 48%. This Act, alongside government anti-poisoning campaigns, has made the indiscriminate use of poisoned baits far less common. Indoor lambing and better husbandry have perhaps also meant that the Raven is now perceived as less of a threat to young lambs than it once was and wildlife programmes, revealing the bird's intelligence and character, may have helped to change attitudes among farmers and gamekeepers. This climate of greater tolerance is allowing the Raven population to increase

and it is slowly regaining some of its former haunts in lowland Britain, thereby helping to balance local declines in the north (D Hayward pers comm, Roberts & Jones 1999). Signs of this recovery are nowhere more apparent than along the Welsh border and in the West Midlands. The Shropshire Raven Study Group found more than 115 pairs breeding within the county in 1999, representing a considerable recent increase in numbers fuelled by high breeding success.

Clear opportunities exist for non-ringing birdwatchers to assist in the collection of much needed extra data by checking breeding adults for colour-rings and reporting them to the BTO and by documenting local recolonization.

Tony Cross

Common Starling (Starling)

Sturnus vulgaris

The Starling is one of our most familiar and widely distributed birds (*1988–91 Atlas*). It is at home in towns, gardens and the wider countryside, and yet the numbers of this highly adaptable species have declined markedly over the last two decades (Crick *et al* 1998, Dolton & Brooke 1999). Our resident breeding population is augmented in winter by immigrants from northwest continental Europe, the arrival of which can present a moving sight to watchers on the east coast of Britain in late October and early November. Once here, their aerial manoeuvres as they prepare to alight in their night roost present one of the most exciting spectacles of ornithology.

The breeding range of the Starling extends from the Atlantic seaboard of Europe east to Lake Baikal in Russia, possibly even to the Pacific coast in eastern Asia (Feare & Craig 1998). Most of this breeding range is occupied by two subspecies, the western of which, nominate *vulgaris*, occurs in Britain & Ireland and breeds east to the Ural Mountains. Within Europe, the decline of populations in the north has been accompanied by range contraction in some areas, while the breeding range in the south is extending. As a result, Starlings now breed commonly in Italy, and in northeastern Spain their range now overlaps with that of their close relative, the Spotless Starling, with which there is some hybridization. Ten other subspecies occur around the western and southern periphery of this enormous breeding area but only one of these, *zetlandicus* of the Shetland Islands, nests in Britain & Ireland (*BWP*). Another subspecies on the northwest of the Starling's range, *faroensis* of the Faeroes, has not yet been recorded in Britain & Ireland. In southern and western Europe, some populations are resident (including British & Irish breeding birds), while

The analysis of the data for this species is dedicated to the memory of Bill, Luke and Eleanor Woodford

elsewhere Starlings are migrants. Asian migrants winter to the south, while more western populations migrate progressively more to the southwest and west, reaching North Africa and the Canary Islands, and also Iceland (Feare 1984, Fliege 1984). In addition to this natural range, Starlings have become successfully established, after introduction by Man, in southern Australia, New Zealand, South Africa and North America.

Although Starlings are omnivorous, and will visit garden bird feeding stations almost all year, they have seasonal shifts in diet and hence also in habitat use. Invertebrates are important to them throughout the year but in April–May they predominate in the diet, both of adults and nestlings (Feare & McGinnity 1986). Most invertebrates are obtained from grassland, which thus represents an important habitat at all seasons. Adults and recently fledged young also obtain invertebrates from woodland. Through summer and autumn the proportion of plant food in the diet increases, with a sequence of ripening soft fruits taken from trees and bushes. Seeds are also eaten, and the consumption of large quantities of cereals, especially from feeding areas for cattle, sheep and pigs in winter, represents an area of conflict with farming (Feare 1984). In summer, adults tend to remain near their breeding areas, but large flocks of juveniles are found feeding on coastal saltmarshes, moorland and in cherry orchards, suggesting a divergence in the habitats used by adults and young at this time of year.

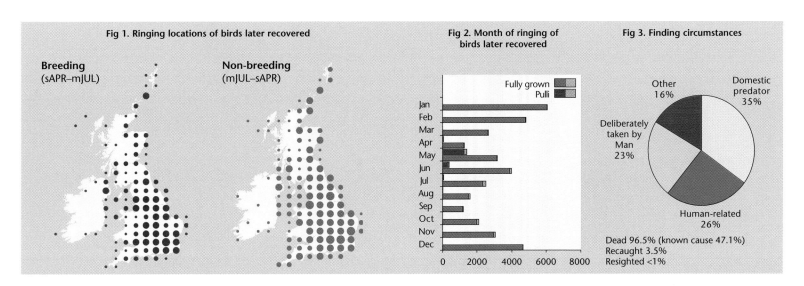

Fig 1. Ringing locations of birds later recovered

Breeding (sAPR–mJUL)

Non-breeding (mJUL–sAPR)

Fig 2. Month of ringing of birds later recovered

Fully grown
Pulli

Fig 3. Finding circumstances

Other 16%
Domestic predator 35%
Deliberately taken by Man 23%
Human-related 26%

Dead 96.5% (known cause 47.1%)
Recaught 3.5%
Resighted <1%

Ringing and recovery data

	<1960	60–69	70–79	80–89	90–97	Total
RINGING						
BTO ringing totals (%)	21	24	18	24	12	1,226,267
RECOVERIES						
BTO-ringed (%)	31	30	16	18	5	37,618
Foreign-ringed (%)	←	78	→	17	5	4,053

Statistical analyses

	Breeding population (sAPR–mJUL)	Wintering population (sNOV–sMAR)
Status	SEDENTARY (0)	[LONG-DISTANCE MIGRANT]
Age differences[S]	Significant	Significant
Sex differences[S]	Not significant	(Significant)
Regional differences	Significant[S*]	Significant[S]
Finding circumstances	(Not significant)	(Not significant)

Fig 4. Locations outside the breeding season and movements of over 20 km between the breeding and non-breeding season of 227 adult Starlings present in Britain & Ireland during the breeding season.

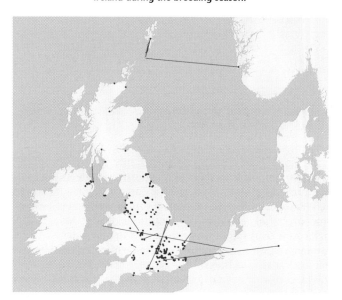

The ringing of Starlings in Britain & Ireland has been widespread, reflecting their overall distribution, in both the breeding and non-breeding season, although with some concentration in eastern England, and relatively few birds ringed in Ireland (Fig 1). The huge number of birds ringed, and the propensity of Starlings to inhabit human settlements, has produced a sample of almost 40,000 recoveries for analysis. Large numbers have also been ringed on continental Europe (Fliege 1984). Ring-recoveries have been generated from the ringing of all age groups, with the ringing of adults most concentrated in November–March, although some have also been caught on the nest during nestbox studies (Fig 2).

The circumstances of finding are known for almost half of the recoveries of dead birds and of these, over 80% are a consequence of Man's activities or those of domestic pets (Fig 3). Most of these recoveries are therefore associated with human dwellings, and although this may not bias long-distance movements to a significant extent, it may well lead to underestimation of the occurrence of Starlings in remote areas, a factor which applies especially to juveniles in summer. In some countries, Starlings are regarded as agricultural pests and are killed in order to reduce damage, while in other countries they are hunted. Over half of the recoveries from Belarus, Belgium, Denmark and France were of birds deliberately taken by Man, and the few recoveries from Italy and Spain all fell into this category. In the absence of this human intervention, it is

Fig 5. Movements of over 20 km between the breeding and non-breeding season and locations outside the breeding season of Starlings present in the (a) northwest (515:165), (b) northeast (968:259), (c) southeast (7,292:1,609) and (d) southwest (2,984:692) of Britain and in (e) Ireland (288:31) during the breeding season. Sample sizes of movements under:over 20 km are given but only those over 20 km are plotted. Confirmed adult birds are excluded.

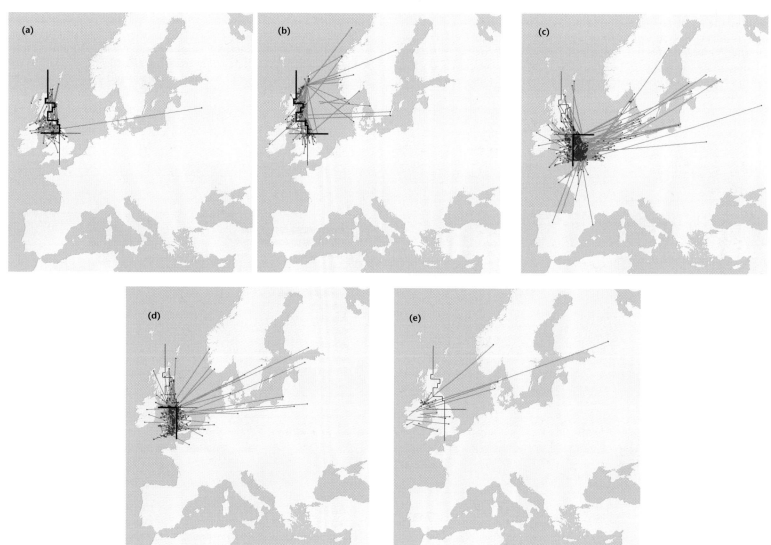

Fig 6. Monthly proportions of recoveries of Starlings ringed as fully grown birds in Britain & Ireland that have occurred abroad. The total number of recoveries for each ringing month is shown above each bar.

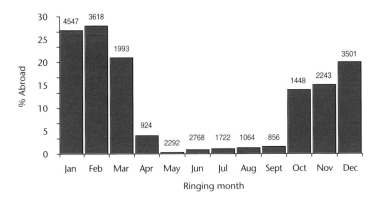

likely that the numbers of birds reported from these countries would be lower.

The recovery data confirm that Britain & Ireland hosts Starling populations of two origins, a resident breeding population and a large number of birds that migrate to Britain & Ireland for the winter. None of the 128 recoveries of birds ringed as pulli in Britain & Ireland and recovered in a subsequent breeding season has been recovered abroad; the median natal dispersal distance was 2 km ($P5–95=0–33$ km). However, birds in their first winter show a tendency for dispersal within Britain & Ireland, with the median distance moved reaching 19.5 km in the eighth 30-day period (around January) after ringing as pulli, but returning to zero in spring. As mentioned previously, however, the extent of movement during summer may be underestimated, as large numbers of juveniles inhabit saltmarshes and moorlands, where ringed

birds are less likely to be found than those that remain close to human habitation. There is no indication of directional summer dispersal of juveniles as seen in some European populations (Studer-Thiersch 1969).

Of 227 adults ringed in Britain & Ireland during the breeding season and recovered at other seasons, only three have been recovered abroad, one each in Norway, Germany and the Netherlands (Fig 4). A further three birds, ringed as adults in eastern Britain during the breeding season, have been recovered during a subsequent breeding season in Norway and Finland (2), from a total of 275 breeding dispersal movements. Some or all of these birds may have been unseasonal migrants in Britain & Ireland, rather than breeding birds. Thus British & Irish breeding adults remain almost entirely within the confines of Britain & Ireland and many individuals are apparently sedentary.

Birds ringed during the breeding season (but not confirmed as adults of breeding age, and including immatures) and recovered during other seasons also indicate that the British & Irish population is largely sedentary throughout the year. The median distance moved, from a sample of over 10,000 recoveries of dead birds covering all seasons, was less than 1 km, and just under 80% of movements were less than 20 km. There were no apparent sex differences revealed by either the mapping or the statistical analyses. Some of the birds that did move longer distances reached the Continent (Fig 5) and, although less than 1% of birds did so, around twice as many birds from the southeast reached Europe than from all other regions combined. Most of these overseas recoveries were in autumn and winter, with very few in spring. Some of these could represent migrants from elsewhere moving through the southeast at the beginning or end of the defined breeding season, however.

The main period of autumn migration into Britain & Ireland is October–November (Fig 6). However, birds from different breeding populations in Europe migrate at different times and use different routes. Starlings from parts of western Europe migrate along a flyway through

Fig 7. Locations abroad of Starlings that were present in the (a) northwest (229), (b) northeast (709), (c) southeast (3,578) and (d) southwest (1,682) of Britain and in (e) Ireland (75).

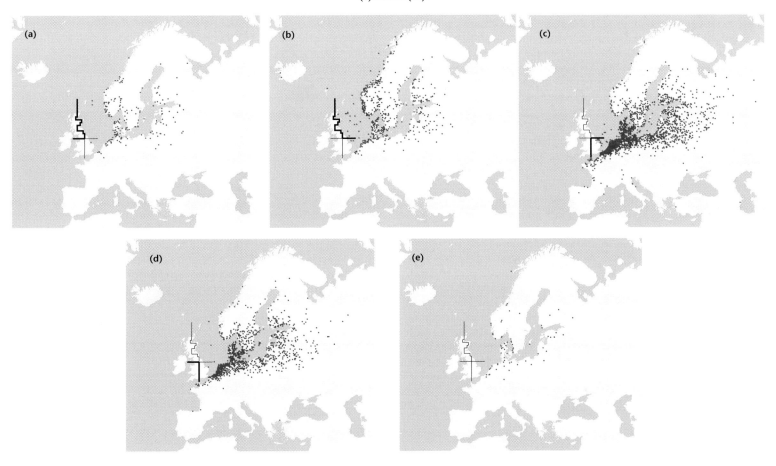

Fig 8. Movements of over 20 km and recovery locations of Starlings ringed in winter and recovered in a subsequent winter. There were 1,203:1,463 movements under:over 20 km but only those over 20 km are plotted.

Generally, birds from the two northern regions of Britain originate from further north than birds from the southern regions, with the smaller sample of birds from Ireland originating from a broader arc, but possibly not extending eastwards as far as many birds from Britain. These regional differences broadly confirm those reported by Goodacre (1959).

Recoveries between winters suggest that there is no marked fidelity to wintering areas (Fig 8), a conclusion also reached by Spaans (1977) for birds ringed in the Netherlands and by Feare (1984) in Hampshire. The birds to the east are apparently outside the normal wintering range (*BWP*) but were present in those areas in midwinter. The median distance moved by birds between winters was only 23 km (*P5–95*=0–600 km, *n*=2,361), and Spaans (1977) found that older birds tended to winter closer to the areas they used in the previous winter. In-depth studies of wing-tagged wintering Starlings in different parts of England have illustrated different patterns of within-winter site-fidelity. At a dairy farm in Hampshire, Feare (1980) found that birds caught in mist-nets at the cattle feedlot were faithful to localized feeding sites, and to daytime roosting sites, throughout the winter. By contrast, Summers & Cross (1987), who trapped birds at a pig farm in Norfolk, recorded much more extensive movements. These two sites differed in habitat and in the ages of the birds. The Hampshire farm was mixed grass and arable, and the birds that fed in the cattle feeding areas were predominantly adults, while the Norfolk farm was in a predominantly arable area and the birds caught in the traps were mainly in their first winter. Both Peach & Fowler (1989) and Summers & Feare (1995) found that both immatures and adults, and males and females, commuted the same distance from the winter roost to feeding areas each day, but the former authors recorded males and females using different parts of their study area, which they attributed to avoidance of competition within the agricultural habitat.

Continental Starlings leave Britain & Ireland in spring from March to April (Fig 6). Radar studies indicate that they depart in the morning directly from their night roosts (Harper 1959, Lack 1960), although Lack thought that some may also leave at night.

The decline by about half in the British breeding population, as demonstrated by the CBC (Crick *et al* 1998), has been matched, or possibly exceeded (Feare 1994), by a decline in the number of continental immigrants in winter. As a result, the Starling has been placed on the Amber List (Gibbons *et al* 1996a). The reasons for the declines in Britain and northern Europe are not entirely clear, but agricultural changes, including intensification and a reduction in mixed farming, as is the case in Finland (Tiainen *et al* 1989), are likely to be involved. As the declines have affected both the resident and immigrant populations, migration does not appear to be a factor in population decrease, and causes must be sought on the breeding and wintering areas. The large samples of birds recovered abroad, having been ringed in Britain & Ireland, do not show any marked temporal changes in distribution. The smaller samples of foreign-ringed birds recovered in Britain & Ireland do show some patterns, however: in the 1990s, the proportion of recoveries from Belgium and the Netherlands dropped by about a third compared with the previous two decades; and the proportion of recoveries of birds ringed in Lithuania has increased since the 1970s, to the extent that in the 1990s they comprised over a third of all recoveries of foreign-ringed Starlings. Whether these patterns reflect real changes in the origins of wintering birds remains to be seen but further monitoring, and perhaps a greater targeted ringing effort, might throw light on the underlying causes of the declines and illustrate the responses of this adaptable species to its changing environment.

northern Germany and the Low Countries (Fliege 1984), birds breeding in the Netherlands passing in September and early October, birds from Germany and Scandinavia in mid-October, and birds from Poland, Finland and Russia in late October and November (Perdeck 1967). Many birds cross the North Sea from the Netherlands to reach Britain, but radar studies showed that others make the longer crossing from Denmark (Lack 1963). In late October and early November large numbers of Starlings, often with Lapwings, can be seen arriving on the Lincolnshire coast in flocks. Arrival begins soon after dawn and lasts until early afternoon (pers obs), indicating that most of this migration is diurnal. Most flocks do not land at the coast but continue inland, although Lack (1963) noted departures on radar, typical of Starlings, to the west from coastal Norfolk in the morning and he thought that these were birds that had arrived the previous day and had stopped overnight on the coast. At Hunstanton, Norfolk, a total of 409,000 passed in autumn 1997, including 87,000 on 16 October (Taylor *et al* 1999). At the same time of year, westerly-flying flocks can be seen over Surrey and Hampshire in the mornings, again suggesting that many flocks continue their migration inland after the oversea crossing (pers obs).

The geographical origins of migrant Starlings that visit Britain & Ireland are shown for each region in Fig 7. In all regions, the centre of origin lies approximately east-northeast, but within an arc extending from the Norwegian coast to the Low Countries, north Germany, north Poland and into northern Russia almost as far east as the Urals. Outliers have reached Iceland, Iberia, the Mediterranean and the Caspian.

Chris Feare

House Sparrow
Passer domesticus

The House Sparrow, with its unique association with Man, must be one of the most familiar of all wild birds. Its distribution in Britain & Ireland follows closely that of Man, being common in built-up areas from urban centres to suburbs, villages and farms. The distribution in winter is almost identical to that in the breeding season (*Winter Atlas, 1988–91 Atlas*).

The House Sparrow has a world-wide distribution. Its natural range extends from North Africa throughout Europe and Asia, with the exception of Southeast Asia, China and Japan; it extends north to about 70°N in Norway but only to 53°N at 140°E, the eastern limit of its distribution. The natural range has been augmented by introductions, mainly in the second half of the 19th century, to most other inhabited parts of the world. The nominate race, which occurs throughout Europe and northern Asia, is mainly resident with some limited dispersal of juveniles before they settle down to breed. A southward withdrawal is evident from parts of the range with extreme winters, such as northern Siberia, though even here some birds are able to overwinter by moving into cattle byres where there is warmth and food (Summers-Smith 1988). Eleven subspecies have been described; nine of these, including the nominate race, are essentially sedentary. Two subspecies are full or partial migrants. The race *bactrianus* (considered by Russian workers to be a separate species *Passer indicus*; Gavrilov & Korelov 1968) breeds in southern Siberia, the former Soviet Asian republics and Afghanistan, and moves south to the plains of northwestern India and Pakistan in the winter. The race *parkini* breeds at high altitudes from Kashmir in the west to southern Tibet and Nepal

The analysis of the data for this species was supported in memory of Joan Coker, a very special wife and mother

in the east, and is largely migratory, moving to lower altitudes in the winter (Summers-Smith 1988).

Ringing and recovery locations in Britain & Ireland reflect both the distribution of the human population and that of the bird (Fig 1). The great majority of House Sparrows ringed have been fully grown birds, with a more-or-less uniform seasonal distribution apart from a slight peak in the breeding season, involving not only the naive juveniles but also the breeding adults that are less cautious and easier to catch at this time of year (Fig 2). Although the House Sparrow is one of the most common breeding birds in Britain & Ireland (Stone *et al* 1997), comparatively small numbers have been ringed and recovered. This is largely because, from 1970, ringers were actively discouraged from putting rings on a bird considered to be largely sedentary and of little interest, though this restriction was subsequently relaxed and was removed in 1993. Recoveries are mainly human-related or associated with domestic pets, principally cats (Fig 3; Churcher & Lawton 1987). It should be noted, however, that human-related causes of recovery are likely to be over-reported and this may lead to biases in the data. About 10% of recoveries are taken by Man; House Sparrows are sometimes considered to be a pest, especially in food stores, and can be killed by appropriate people under licence.

The movements undergone by House Sparrows, as shown by the median value of less than 1 km for all the 5,963 ring-recoveries of dead

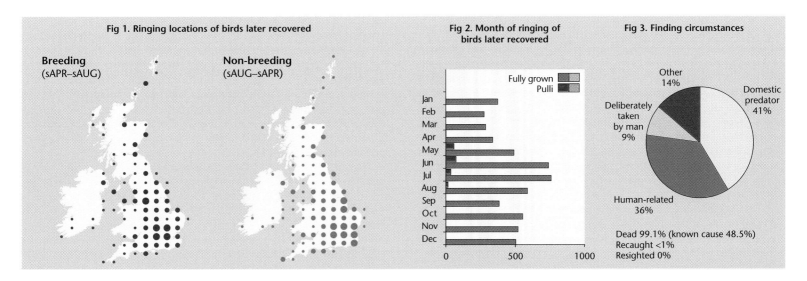

Fig 1. Ringing locations of birds later recovered

Breeding (sAPR–sAUG)   **Non-breeding** (sAUG–sAPR)

Fig 2. Month of ringing of birds later recovered

Fully grown / Pulli

Fig 3. Finding circumstances

Other 14%
Domestic predator 41%
Deliberately taken by man 9%
Human-related 36%

Dead 99.1% (known cause 48.5%)
Recaught <1%
Resighted 0%

Ringing and recovery data

	<1960	60–69	70–79	80–89	90–97	Total
RINGING						
BTO ringing totals (%)	21	48	10	11	10	411,478
RECOVERIES						
BTO-ringed (%)	28	55	7	6	3	6,019
Foreign-ringed (%)	0	0	0	0	0	0

Statistical analyses

	Breeding population (sAPR–sAUG)	Wintering population (sNOV–sMAR)
Status	SEDENTARY (0)	SEDENTARY
Age differences[NS*]	Not significant*	Significant*
Sex differences[NS*]	Not significant	Not significant
Regional differences	Not significant[4*]	Not tested
Finding circumstances	(Not significant)	(Not significant)

Fig 4. Locations outside the breeding season and movements of over 20 km between the breeding and non-breeding season of 2,238 House Sparrows present in Britain & Ireland during the breeding season.

Fig 5. Movements of over 20 km and recovery locations of House Sparrows ringed during the breeding season in Britain & Ireland as adults and recovered in a subsequent breeding season (359:4, red) or ringed in winter and recovered in a subsequent winter (175:6, blue). Sample sizes of movements under:over 20 km are given but only those over 20 km are plotted.

birds, are very limited. Movements greater than 20 km from the place of ringing appear to occur year-round, except in the breeding season, though only a small proportion (c 3%) of the population is involved. For birds ringed during the breeding season, there are no significant differences between the different regions of Britain & Ireland, nor in the season when the recoveries were made. All the recoveries over 20 km in autumn, winter and spring of birds ringed in the breeding season are shown in Fig 4. The distances are very modest and there have been only three recoveries abroad of birds ringed in Britain (Figs 4 & 5) and none in Britain or Ireland of foreign-ringed birds. No exchange between Britain and Ireland has been identified.

Colour-ringing studies have shown that once birds have bred they remain faithful to the breeding colony for life, with village and suburban birds making only a short movement of up to 2 km to ripening grain fields in early autumn. The young make similar movements but disperse around neighbouring breeding colonies and do not necessarily return to their natal site (Summers-Smith 1963). No sightings or recoveries of these colour-ringed birds were made further afield, but it seems reasonable to assume that the birds involved in the movements greater than 20 km revealed by the full ring-recovery data are juveniles or adults that have not yet bred. There have been only four such recoveries of adults ringed in the breeding season and only six of birds ringed in winter and recovered in a subsequent winter (Fig 5). These birds may have been part of a 'floating' population, the existence of which is revealed by the observation that unringed birds of either sex can appear in the breeding season in colonies where all the breeders are ringed, and fill vacancies in the breeding colony when a breeding bird disappears. Colour-ringing results suggest that the movements are more akin to a dispersal than a directional migration.

The House Sparrow must rank as one of the most sedentary species of wild bird. It is also a very successful one. One measure of its success is its extensive distribution, a testament to its capacity for dispersal. For example, it spread from the Urals to the Amur Delta in eastern Siberia between the beginning of the 19th century and 1929, some 5,500 km in a little over 100 years (c 40 km/year) and there have been remarkable colonizations of North America, South America, South Africa and Australia by introduced birds, where 14 separate estimates of rates of

range expansion lie between 15 and 80 km/year (Summers-Smith 1956, *BWP*). Some of this spread was certainly assisted by Man, but not all. The fact that such expansions have occurred bears witness to the importance of dispersive movements in the life of the House Sparrow.

There is a significant number of published reports of House Sparrows apparently crossing the North Sea and of movements along the east coast of England from Yorkshire to Kent, especially involving Spurn and Lincolnshire, from July to December and a return from February to May (Summers-Smith 1956). Ring-recoveries have failed to demonstrate movements between Britain and the Continent and suggest that the sightings were most probably coastal movements of British birds. These reports date as far back as 1880, but oddly are not continued after the 1950s. Considering the amount of birdwatching that now takes place on the east coast, this would seem to indicate a change in House Sparrow behaviour. However, although House Sparrows are considered generally sedentary, limited autumn passage of birds of the nominate race has been reported from Sweden, the west coast of Germany and through Swiss alpine passes, but the numbers involved are small (*BWP*). Jenni & Schaffner (1984) found that 91% of the birds trapped in the Swiss movements were juveniles.

Since the 1970s, the House Sparrow has decreased significantly in Britain & Ireland (Balmer & Marchant 1993). This decline is continuing and has occurred in all habitats, though it has been more acute in rural areas and large cities, such as London, than in suburbs and small towns (Summers-Smith 1999). This pattern is consistent with the hypothesis by Heij (1985), based on a study in Rotterdam, the Netherlands, that showed that populations in rural areas and town centres acted as 'sinks', depending on the suburban populations acting as 'sources'. Further, targeted, ringing studies are needed to investigate this idea in Britain & Ireland and establish whether survival rates differ in the different habitats. In Britain & Ireland, however, the real situation may be even more complex, with some evidence to suggest that the decrease has been greater in the south than the north. More data are needed to determine what, if any, conservation measures should be considered.

J Denis Summers-Smith & Derek K Thomas

Eurasian Tree Sparrow (Tree Sparrow)

Passer montanus

The Tree Sparrow has had a chequered history in Britain & Ireland, and is well known for its fluctuations in numbers, both locally and nationally. There was a fivefold increase in the British population in the 1960s and 1970s that was followed by an equally rapid decline to the level of the early 1950s (Marchant *et al* 1990, Summers-Smith 1995). There is some local movement, including apparent arrivals on the east coast of England but little evidence to suggest that the recent peak in numbers was a consequence of immigration from the Continent (Summers-Smith 1995). In fact, these movements appear to be more akin to a dispersal than to a directed migration, and are of only limited extent.

The Tree Sparrow has an extensive distribution in Europe and Asia, broadly similar to that of the House Sparrow, but differing in that it is absent from eastern Turkey to India and present from Thailand south to Java and east to China and Japan, where the House Sparrow does not occur, except for recent introductions. There are six subspecies, although there is little indication of extensive movements in any of these populations. There is some withdrawal from high latitudes in the winter and evidence of a limited southward autumn movement in western continental Europe and also through the high Swiss alpine passes in a southwesterly direction; numbers involved are small, though movements of 500–600 km have been recorded (*BWP*). Jenni & Schaffner (1984) found that 96% of the birds trapped in the Swiss movements were juveniles.

In Britain & Ireland, the Tree Sparrow is largely a bird of farmland. Eastwards across Eurasia, however, it becomes more a bird of built-up

The analysis of the data for this species was supported by Mark R Fletcher

areas so that in the Far East, where the House Sparrow is absent, it is a prominent urban species, equally at home in towns and villages.

Ringing locations of birds recovered reflect the largely eastern distribution of the species in Britain & Ireland, biased by the distribution of ringers in the more populous south and Midlands of England (Fig 1). There have been just over 700 recoveries of Tree Sparrows, with a distribution that largely matches the distribution of the ringing locations, emphasizing the sedentary nature of the bird and the limited movements undertaken. There is little variation in the seasonal frequency of ringing; the recoveries include many birds ringed as pulli or juveniles (Fig 2). The finding circumstances for ring-recoveries may suggest the significant role played by domestic predators, largely cats but this and the percentage of human-related recovery causes are likely to have been exaggerated as birds that die in proximity to Man are more likely to be found and reported (Fig 3).

Although the median distance moved by birds recovered dead is less than 1 km (P5–95=0–91 km, *n*=608), movements of greater than 20 km do occur. Such movements made by birds ringed in the breeding season are most pronounced during the autumn and winter (Fig 4). This figure indicates that, while most Tree Sparrows can be regarded as sedentary, a proportion of the British & Irish breeding population shows a generally

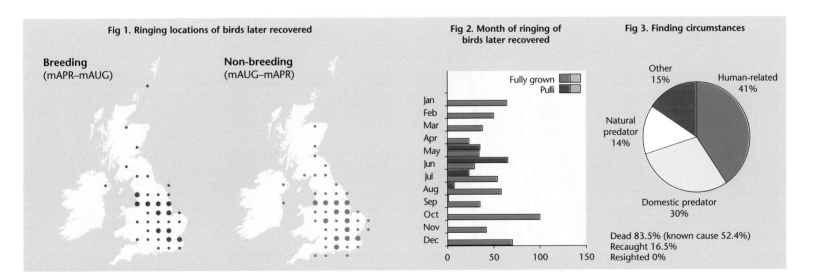

Fig 1. Ringing locations of birds later recovered

Breeding (mAPR–mAUG) Non-breeding (mAUG–mAPR)

Fig 2. Month of ringing of birds later recovered

Fully grown
Pulli

Fig 3. Finding circumstances

Other 15%
Human-related 41%
Natural predator 14%
Domestic predator 30%

Dead 83.5% (known cause 52.4%)
Recaught 16.5%
Resighted 0%

Ringing and recovery data

	<1960	60–69	70–79	80–89	90–97	Total
RINGING						
BTO ringing totals (%)	5	30	37	17	10	217,074
RECOVERIES						
BTO-ringed (%)	6	38	34	15	6	728
Foreign-ringed (%)	86	0	14	0	0	7

Statistical analyses

	Breeding population (mAPR–mAUG)	Wintering population (mNOV–mMAR)
Status	SEDENTARY* (0)	SEDENTARY
Age differences[NT]	Not significant*	Not tested
Sex differences	Not tested	Not tested
Regional differences	Not tested	Not tested
Finding circumstances	Not tested	Not significant*

Fig 4. Locations in (a) autumn (104), (b) winter (128) and (c) spring (37), and movements of over 20 km between the breeding and non-breeding season, of Tree Sparrows present in Britain & Ireland during the breeding season.

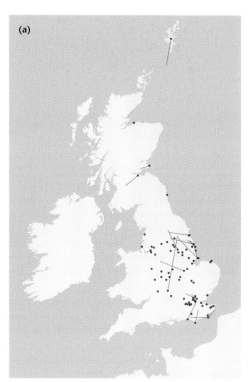
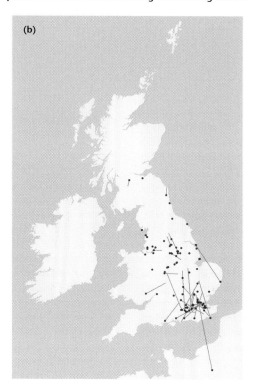

southerly dispersal during the autumn and winter. The numbers involved are small but suggest that Tree Sparrows in Britain are less sedentary than House Sparrows: 23% of Tree Sparrow movements between the breeding and non-breeding seasons are greater than 20 km, while for House Sparrow this figure is just 3%.

There have been seven recoveries of British- & Irish-ringed birds on the Continent, and a further seven of birds ringed on the Continent and recovered in Britain: one from the Netherlands and three each from Belgium and France. These give evidence of some exchange between Britain and the Continent. This occurred in the period 1955–80, as did the four exchanges between Britain and Ireland. This was a time when the British population was at a high level, suggesting that the movements could have been a response to population pressure. However, this was also the period from which the majority of Tree Sparrow ring-recoveries originate, with 71% of dead recoveries coming from 1960–79, and the increased exchanges could simply reflect increased ringing effort. It is perhaps relevant that the recolonization of Ireland, where the Tree Sparrow was thought to have become extinct in 1959, was coincident with the population explosion in Britain.

There have been numerous reports of movements in both autumn and spring on the east coast of England from as far north as Northumberland and extending along the south coast to Hampshire (Clark & Eyre 1993, Taylor et al 1999). The autumn movements were matched by records of Tree Sparrows landing on ships off the coasts of East Anglia and Kent. It is not clear whether these involved birds from continental Europe or were merely local movements, though the ring-recoveries given above suggest some limited exchange with the Continent. It may be relevant that these reports largely dried up after the population decline in Britain in the 1980s.

The ring-recovery data show both median breeding and natal dispersal distances to be less than 1 km (breeding dispersal $P5–95=0–20$ km, $n=27$; natal dispersal $P5–95=0–53$ km, $n=24$), although the small sample sizes should be noted. Dispersal has been extensively investigated in Poland (Pinowski 1965), where movements of juveniles into new areas or areas where there are unoccupied sites tend to be limited. Within Britain & Ireland, Tree Sparrow colonies can appear and disappear rapidly, suggesting that dispersive movements may enable the species to respond to changing conditions.

According to the CBC, Tree Sparrow numbers in Britain fell by 87% between 1972 and 1996 (Crick et al 1998). Based on this evidence, the species was Red-listed as a bird of high national conservation concern. The intensive study of remaining Tree Sparrow colonies, ideally using colour-rings, must be considered an important component of any conservation strategy. We need to increase our understanding of the nature of movements away from and between colonies, together with the collection of more information on population parameters.

Mike Netherwood & J Denis Summers-Smith

Chaffinch
Fringilla coelebs

The Chaffinch is one of the most familiar birds of Britain & Ireland, breeding commonly throughout the area. Their numbers are greatly increased in winter by immigrants from Fennoscandia and at all times of year it is one of our most numerous species.

Their breeding range extends from Britain & Ireland across all of Europe (except for Iceland, the Faeroes and arctic Russia) and North Africa, the Middle East as far as Iran and almost to Lake Baikal in central Siberia (*BWP, European Atlas*). The species has evolved to noticeably different forms where birds are resident on islands such as the Azores and Madeira. Many races are recognized but the only ones known to have occurred in Britain & Ireland are *gengleri*, which breeds only in these islands, and the nominate race, which covers the rest of Europe north of the Mediterranean Sea and the Pyrenees. The British & Irish birds tend to be more brightly coloured and are, on average, significantly smaller than the immigrants from continental Europe, although there is overlap in individual measurements.

The species winters entirely within the Palearctic region but nearly all the birds from the northeast of the range migrate for the winter, augmenting those in the southwest (including Britain & Ireland) where they are resident (Newton 1972). Thus, the enormous wintering population in Britain & Ireland consists of roughly equal numbers of local birds, mostly on or close to their breeding territories, and immigrants, mainly from Fennoscandia (*Winter Atlas*). The females tend to move further, so that males predominate in winter in the Netherlands, Belgium and Britain but females are in the majority in Ireland (*BWP*). This differential migration has been noted since the

The analysis of the data for this species was supported by the Fylde Ringing Group

earliest days of bird observation, and Linnaeus named the Chaffinch *coelebs* (bachelor) because the few individuals that remained to winter in his Swedish homeland were mostly males.

Chaffinches breed in boreal, temperate and Mediterranean zones, in all types of woody habitats, from extensive forests and woods to tall hedgerows, orchards, parks and gardens, including those in the centres of some towns and cities (*European Atlas*). During the breeding season, the adults eat seeds but feed their young on arthropods. At other times Chaffinches feed mainly on seeds on the ground, foraging in almost any habitat in Britain & Ireland in winter.

The maps of ringing locations of Chaffinches that have been recovered (Fig 1) reasonably replicate their English and Welsh breeding and wintering distributions as shown by the *1968–72 Atlas*, the *1988–91 Atlas* and the *Winter Atlas*, but the Scottish and, especially, the Irish populations are under-represented. There is no significant bias introduced by ringing at observatories or other migration 'hot-spots'. The ringing dates for recoveries are spread well throughout the year (Fig 2) although only 3% were ringed as nestlings. Of the birds that had been sexed, 59% were males, reflecting their excess in the southern English winter population. The Chaffinch is one of the 10 most-ringed species in Britain & Ireland, with a recovery rate typical of a small passerine at 0.7%. Of the recoveries of birds found dead, 59% have a documented

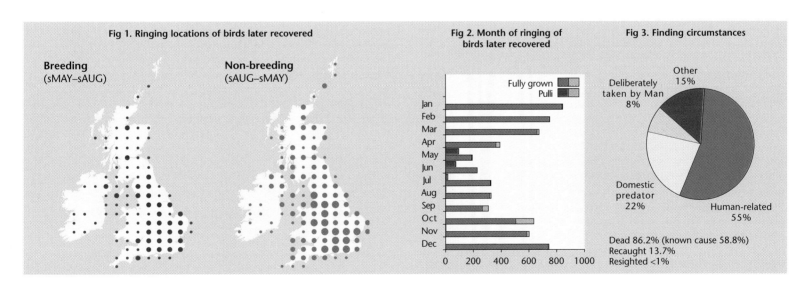

Fig 1. Ringing locations of birds later recovered

Breeding (sMAY–sAUG) Non-breeding (sAUG–sMAY)

Fig 2. Month of ringing of birds later recovered

Fully grown / Pulli

Fig 3. Finding circumstances

Other 15%
Deliberately taken by Man 8%
Domestic predator 22%
Human-related 55%

Dead 86.2% (known cause 58.8%)
Recaught 13.7%
Resighted <1%

Ringing and recovery data

	<1960	60–69	70–79	80–89	90–97	Total
RINGING						
BTO ringing totals (%)	9	12	18	32	29	844,552
RECOVERIES						
BTO-ringed (%)	14	19	19	28	12	5,900
Foreign-ringed (%)	←	65	→	26	9	779

Statistical analyses

	Breeding population (sMAY–sAUG)	Wintering population (sNOV–mMAR)
Status	SEDENTARY (0)	[SHORT-DISTANCE MIGRANT]*
Age differences[NS*]	Not significant*	Significant
Sex differences[NS*]	Not significant*	Not significant*
Regional differences	Not significant[4*]	Significant[2]
Finding circumstances	Not significant	Significant

Fig 4. Locations abroad of (a) 420 female and (b) 632 male Chaffinches using Britain & Ireland.

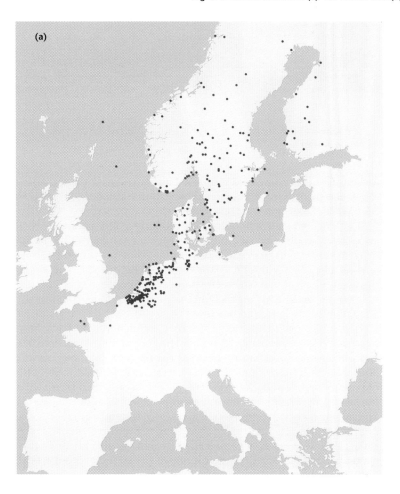 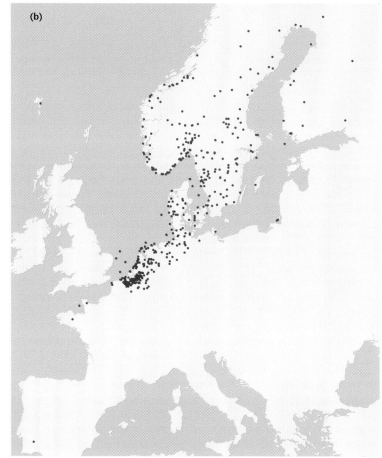

cause (Fig 3), with over half (55%) of them human-related and another 22% attributed to domestic predators.

British & Irish Chaffinches are very sedentary. Previous analyses showed that 90% move no more than 5 km from their natal site, and the rest – almost entirely first-year birds – less than 50 km (Newton 1972). The present study of a larger data set reinforces this finding, confirming that, for birds ringed in Britain & Ireland during May, June and July, the median distance of movement is less than 1 km at all seasons.

After breeding, the adult birds moult in their territories and most young birds stay locally for the first two or three months after fledging, although occasional individuals have been found over 20 km distant. Later in the year, most birds remain close to their breeding area but some move away. The proportion of British & Irish birds making distant movements decreases from autumn to winter to spring, suggesting that they tend to move back towards their natal area, or that more of the distant movers die. For birds ringed as breeding-age adults, 15% of recoveries in autumn (August–October) were over 20 km, as were 9% of recoveries in winter (November–February) and 5% in spring (March–April). These figures mask regional differences, however, and the movements of British birds ringed in the two northern regions in the breeding season differ significantly from those ringed in the south. In autumn, 32% of movements of those in the north were over 20 km, compared to only 10% of those in the south; in winter, 16% of movements of those in the north were over 20 km, compared with 9% of those in the south, while by spring there was little difference, with 8% of movements of those in the north over 20 km, and 6% of those in the south (considering all age classes combined). This highlights the dangers of generalizing from data collected mainly in southeastern England. Based on the work of Marler (1956) around Cambridge and of Newton (1967a) in the Oxford area, it has been widely reported that the large

flocks of Chaffinches are mainly composed of continental birds, while British & Irish birds tend to remain in smaller groups close to their territories (Winter Atlas, Birds in Scotland, Birds in Ireland). However, most local birds in northern Scotland leave their territories and form large feeding and roosting flocks in winter with few, if any, continental birds present (Swann 1988).

Despite their autumnal wanderings, no bird ringed as a chick and found dead in a subsequent breeding season has moved as much as 20 km. For 35 such recoveries of dead birds the median distance moved was 2 km (P5–95=0–14 km). Similarly, breeding birds in Britain & Ireland are very site-faithful. There are only seven records of movements over 20 km of adults ringed from May to July and recovered in a

Fig 5. Half-month of recording in Britain & Ireland of Chaffinches ringed or recovered abroad.

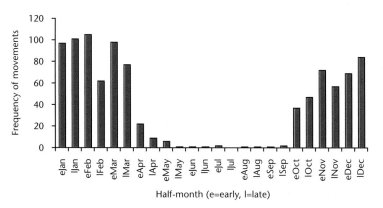

Fig 6. Movements of over 20 km and recovery locations of Chaffinches ringed in winter and recovered in a subsequent winter. There were 403:238 movements under:over 20 km but only those over 20 km are plotted.

subsequent breeding season. Some of these could have been late returning migrants, however, and certainly two of them were ringed at observatories. In contrast, there are 109 recorded breeding-dispersal movements of less than 20 km.

In winter, the Chaffinch population in Britain & Ireland is roughly doubled by the immigration of continental birds (*Winter Atlas*), mostly of Scandinavian origin, with smaller numbers from Finland and a few from northwest Russia. They migrate by day in flocks, most actively in the morning hours, although occasionally they arrive during the night (Durman 1976a). The autumn migration spans August–December but is chiefly in September–November, with the main arrival in southeast England peaking in the second half of October (Newton 1972). The females migrate before the males, and first-years before adults (*BWP*). A detailed study of many years of autumn passage at Col de Bretolet, Switzerland, showed that the mean date of first-year females occurred first, followed four days later by adult females, with first-year males a further seven days later, while the peak passage of adult males, on average, was another 11–12 days after that. The passage of adult males tended to be concentrated into a shorter period than that of the females (Schifferli 1963).

By contrast with Bramblings, which migrate at night directly across the North Sea, Fennoscandian Chaffinches seldom cross the North Sea direct to Britain, but migrate on a narrow front through Denmark, northwest Germany, the Netherlands, Belgium and the northeast of France (Fig 4). This route involves exceptional changes of direction, especially for Norwegian birds, many of which head east of south initially. The mean direction of movement at various points along the route gradually shifts: Denmark 180° (due south), Helgoland 200°, East Friesian coast 224°, mid-Holland 236°, South Holland 248°, and finally Calais 282° (west–northwest) (Perdeck 1970). Birds heading for Britain hug the coast of the Netherlands and Belgium, seldom flying more than a few tens of kilometres inland. This is shown vividly by a geographical analysis of recoveries of birds ringed in the Low Countries. Of those ringed in autumn in the coastal region within 52–53°N and 4–5°E, 90% were found in Britain & Ireland and only 10% in France or Iberia; of

those ringed inland within 51–52°N and 4–5°E, 26% reached Britain & Ireland; while for those ringed farther south still (within 50–51°N and 4–5°E), only one (5%) was found in Britain (*Der Zug*). Observations of visible migration and radar evidence (Eastwood 1967) show that their strategy for crossing the North Sea or the English Channel appears to depend on the wind direction (Elkins 1988a), so that arrival on these shores can be from the east, southeast or even south, to make landfall along the east or south coast, even as far west as Portland Bill (Newton 1972).

Small numbers of Chaffinches do directly cross the North Sea in autumn. Passage through the Northern Isles is most marked in late September and October, although numbers are usually low, with the Fair Isle daily maxima often under 50 birds (*Birds in Scotland*). A fall of over 300 Chaffinches on the Isle of May in autumn 2000 had wing lengths suggesting Fennoscandian origin and were in the company of a smaller number of Bramblings (M Martin pers comm). Further indications of North Sea passage come from three ringed birds, one from southwest Norway on 1 October that was found on a ship 350 km southwest the same day (*Der Zug*), one ringed on Fair Isle on 23 October that was recovered in Ireland in December, and one ringed in the Netherlands on 2 November that was recaptured on Shetland 25 days later.

The immigrants winter mainly in southern and central Britain (south of 54°N) and in Ireland (*BWP*). After arrival in southern and eastern England, some, especially the females, subsequently move northwards through Britain and some head for Ireland. Westward movement is very clear along the north coast of Wales, and huge numbers — with a maximum of 20,000 in a day — pass through Bardsey in October (*Birds in Wales*). Many Chaffinches, especially single-sex flocks of females, can be found on occasions in immense numbers in the headland fields of west Wales, awaiting the right weather conditions to make the short sea-crossings (*Birds in Wales*). They arrive in Ireland mainly in late October and early November, with the largest numbers seen in Wexford, where flocks of 1,000 occur at times (*Birds in Ireland*). An extreme autumn movement was shown by a Belgian-ringed bird that turned up in a later winter in Iceland, where occurrence is only accidental (*BWP*). Some indication of the seasonal pattern of exchanges between Britain & Ireland and abroad can be seen from Fig 5.

In Britain, several ringed, continental Chaffinches have returned to the same area in successive winters (Newton 1972), providing direct evidence of winter site-fidelity for some of the immigrant birds. Others, however, have been found away from their ringing site, and 37% of the movements of ringed birds between winters have been over 20 km, as depicted in Fig 6. Many of those in continental Europe have been recorded in the depths of winter, with 11 in December, 16 in January and 14 in February. Some of the extreme changes of wintering area include birds from Wicklow to Cornwall, from western Ireland to Denmark, and four that switched between England and France or the Channel Islands from one winter to another. One ringed in February in Berkshire was reported dead in Portugal in April of the following year, an unprecedented movement and the only recovery of a British- or Irish-ringed Chaffinch south of 49°N.

Hard weather movements may occur (*Winter Atlas*) but, by contrast with Bramblings, the recovery data suggest that movements of Chaffinches within a winter are uncommon: only 10% of the movements of ringed birds within a winter have been over 20 km (n=371). Even this figure is likely to overstate the extent of within-winter movements, as 'winter' is defined from the beginning of November to mid-March. These dates include part of both migration seasons, and some examples of apparent movement will be birds caught at different points on the same migration route, and not really changes of wintering area.

The winter visitors depart from Ireland in mid-March (*Birds in Ireland*), and passage through the Scottish Northern Isles is most marked in March and April (*Birds in Scotland*). Spring departures from southeast England are mostly in March but can span mid-February to mid-May. Reversing the autumn pattern, males and adults tend to migrate a few days before females and first-year birds. Their spring return migration is usually faster than autumn, and more birds than in autumn cross the North Sea on a broad front, especially between Norfolk and the Netherlands (*BWP*). There are nine spring recoveries from widely scattered localities in the North Sea, on ships, oil or gas installations (two in March, five in April and two in May), compared with only two in autumn, both in October on the line from the Netherlands to Norfolk. The migration across the sea is accomplished in less than a day of non-stop flying, and there are no examples of ringed birds found so quickly, but some idea of the timing of spring return is given by ringed birds moving from Lincolnshire on 16 March to Denmark (818 km) on 4 April, from Fair Isle (15 April) to Helgoland (829 km) seven days later and from the Isle of May on 18 April to Stockholm (1,280 km) on 4 May. Britain's only Chaffinch movement involving the Faeroes was ringed there on 6 April and recaptured on North Ronaldsay (375 km) a week later.

Returning birds often arrive in Scandinavia in March or the first few days of April but, at the other extreme, several presumed continental immigrants have been recorded still in Britain in June, such as one ringed at Dungeness on 7 June, found in a later year in the Netherlands on 23 October. There are rare instances of presumed continental birds that appear to have settled to breed here. An intriguing example was a female ringed in the Netherlands on 26 September that was caught in a later year in Lincolnshire on 18 June, when it had an active brood patch, and retrapped three months later.

It is interesting to examine the sex differences in immigrant Chaffinches, although here the ringing bias to south and east England tends to obscure the effects. Gilbert White, in letters dated January 1768 and December 1770, commented on the vast preponderance of females — 'at least fifty to one' — in the wintering Chaffinch flocks around Selborne in Hampshire (White 1789). This does not accord with more modern observations, however, so perhaps there has been a shift in migration and wintering habits. By 1949 it was reported that males were in the majority in winter in the Netherlands, Belgium and Britain but females were predominant in Ireland (Deelder 1949). The high proportion of males in the ring-recoveries database — half as many again as females — reflects their present-day excess in the southern English winter population, where much ringing is concentrated. Farther north in England, over 2,000 birds ringed in a variety of feeding flocks and roosts in north Cheshire during winters from 1980–99 showed only a slight majority of males (pers obs).

The Chaffinch has a favourable conservation status, and there are no particular conservation implications of its migration routes. Bird-trappers in Belgium used to take large numbers but this habit has declined and poses no threat to the species.

Some of the main gaps in knowledge are the true differences in behaviour between local birds and immigrants and between males and females, especially flocking, dispersal and migration. Ideally, more ringing in Scotland and Ireland is needed to shed light on these questions.

David Norman

Brambling
Fringilla montifringilla

Bramblings, larger, more attractive relatives of the Chaffinch, are winter visitors to Britain & Ireland from their northern breeding grounds. Their nasal calls often signal the end of autumn. In Britain & Ireland four-figure flocks may be met with but, elsewhere in Europe, huge flocks of two to three million birds may congregate in a small area when sufficient food is available, and roosting flocks of up to 20 million birds have been recorded in central Europe (Jenni 1987).

Bramblings breed in a broad band between approximately 55°N and 70°N, stretching from Norway in the west right through Russia to the shores of the Bering Sea at as far as 170°E. Breeding is irregular or sporadic in Iceland, the Faeroes and northern Britain and on the Continent as far south as Italy (*BWP*). No subspecies are described, despite the vast size of the breeding range.

During the breeding season birds are found predominantly in open upland, birch, mixed birch and conifer forests, feeding on seeds, caterpillars and other insects. After breeding, the birds switch to a mainly seed diet with a strong preference for beechmast, and large numbers of birds will halt their movement south when good crops of beechmast are encountered. The Brambling is much less of a farmland bird than its close relative, the Chaffinch, although, in parts of Britain & Ireland where Bramblings occur, mixed flocks of the two species are the norm.

Ringing localities for the British & Irish ring-recoveries show concentrations across southeast England, the Midlands and east Wales that fit well with the winter distribution described in the *Winter Atlas* (Fig 1). Eastern Ireland, northeast England and Scotland, especially the central lowlands, are under-represented. In addition, large numbers of

The analysis of the data for this species was supported by Chris Whittles

migrants have been ringed in the Northern Isles, where relatively few winter. Ringing dates span October–May, with large peaks in January and February (Fig 2). Of the included recoveries, 53% have been of dead birds and 47% were recaught by ringers. Of the dead birds recovered, 55% were from a known cause and, of these, approximately a third were deliberately taken by Man (Fig 3). For example, of 11 recoveries from Italy, 10 were within this category, suggesting that hunting is likely to influence the distribution of recoveries.

The Fennoscandian population begins to move south and southwest in early September and large flocks of birds form where there is a plentiful supply of beechmast; this often results in huge flocks of birds gathering in southern Sweden in early winter (*BWP*). Jenni (1987) showed that birds stayed as far north as the availability of beechmast allowed and that, as increasing snow-cover prevented the birds from reaching the beechmast, they moved further south. Heavy snow-cover and a poor beechmast crop can lead to huge influxes of birds into southern Germany and Switzerland. Despite this overall picture, Bramblings regularly begin to make landfall along the full length of the British east coast in about mid-September. Unlike Chaffinch, which migrates mainly by day, Brambling movements are often nocturnal and may leave exhausted stragglers grounded at the coast during the day. The main arrival period continues until early November in Norfolk (Taylor *et al* 1999). Again unlike

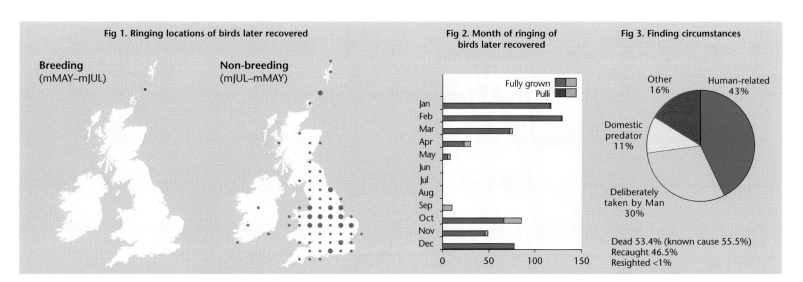

Ringing and recovery data

	<1960	60–69	70–79	80–89	90–97	Total
RINGING						
BTO ringing totals (%)	4	23	32	26	15	86,923
RECOVERIES						
BTO-ringed (%)	4	24	33	31	8	534
Foreign-ringed (%)	←	65	→	26	9	134

Statistical analyses

	Breeding population (mMAY–mJUL)	Wintering population (mNOV–sMAR)
Status	NONE	LONG-DISTANCE MIGRANT*
Age differences	—	Not tested
Sex differences	—	Not tested
Regional differences	—	Not tested
Finding circumstances	—	Not tested

Fig 4. Recovery locations in the same autumn or the following winter and movements of over 20 km of 62 Bramblings ringed during autumn in Britain & Ireland or abroad.

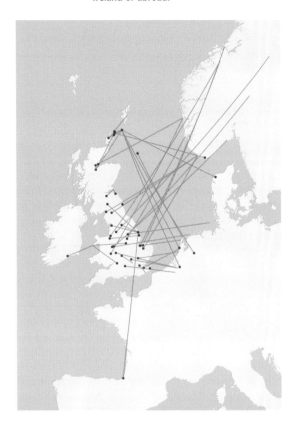

Fig 5. Garden BirdWatch reporting rate for Brambling (1995–99). The reporting rate is simply the proportion of gardens recording Brambling during a given week. (*Source*: Cannon 2000.)

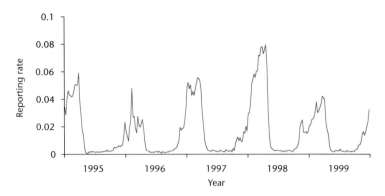

Chaffinches, many Bramblings appear to make direct crossings of the North Sea in autumn, rather than taking a circuitous approach via the Low Countries (Fig 4). Flocks also arrive at southwestern watch-points, such as the Isles of Scilly, especially in October; these may perhaps be birds arriving from the Continent, having approached along the English Channel, but more likely they and other south-coast migrants are on a rapid through passage and departing for France or Iberia. Recoveries provide some evidence of this passage but suggest that relatively small numbers pass through Britain to winter in Ireland (Fig 4).

In some years, weather conditions may bring new arrivals from the Continent in midwinter, often in substantial numbers (Taylor *et al* 1999). Single birds or small flocks visiting peanut feeders in gardens are

Fig 6. Movements of over 20 km and recovery locations of Bramblings ringed in winter and recovered in (a) the same winter (39:26, red) or (b) a subsequent winter (1:72, blue). Sample sizes of movements under:over 20 km are given but only those over 20 km are plotted.

Fig 7. Recovery locations in the same spring and movements of over 20 km of 141 Bramblings ringed during winter or spring in Britain & Ireland or abroad.

a regular feature of late winter and early spring, perhaps at a time when beechmast and other natural foods have become depleted. The Garden BirdWatch survey reporting rate for Bramblings (Fig 5) shows consistent reporting of birds beginning in October and building to a maximum in March and April before falling away steeply in May (Cannon 2000). Although Britain & Ireland is on the western periphery of the main wintering areas, large influxes of birds do occur, coinciding with those of central Europe, causing winter numbers in Britain & Ireland to vary between 50,000 and two million birds (*BWP*). Only one bird ringed in Britain & Ireland has been recovered further south in the same winter (Fig 6a), suggesting that once the birds arrive they generally stay until beginning the return journey to their breeding areas.

Swiss ringing data, analysed by Jenni (1982, 1985), show that males winter further north than females, with the proportion of males decreasing from north to south over the winter range; also adults probably winter further north than juveniles. Although ring-recoveries have shown that many birds show winter site-fidelity (Verheyen 1954, *BWP*), others have been recovered in widely differing areas, with British-ringed birds recovered in subsequent years in the Low Countries, France and Italy (Fig 6b). These extreme changes of wintering quarters may be caused simply by the birds' natural migration, or through birds being caught up by mass movements and pulled away from their original direction and destination (Verheyen 1954).

Large wintering flocks have typically dispersed or returned to the Continent by mid-April. A small spring passage is apparent across England in late April and early May, often of birds hunting insects in the treetops at sites that had not held Bramblings during the winter. It is not known, however, whether these are just late-departing British & Irish winterers, or whether some may be passage migrants from southwest Europe (Fig 7). Apart from the occasional nesting attempt, only occasional stragglers or early autumn migrants are seen in Britain & Ireland during June–August.

With few areas of beechmast in Britain & Ireland, and influxes coinciding with harsher winter weather when beechmast may be inaccessible because of snow, garden feeders of peanuts and sunflower seeds are important food sources for Bramblings. Conversely with milder winters being experienced in central and northern Europe we may find that the numbers of Bramblings wintering in Britain & Ireland will begin to diminish as birds become able to find enough food further north.

Ray Marsh

European Greenfinch (Greenfinch)

Carduelis chloris

The Greenfinch breeds in most of temperate Europe, parts of North Africa and western Asia. In most areas, it is a diurnal partial migrant restricted almost entirely to the breeding range (*BWP*). Most British Greenfinches are known to spend their entire lives close to their birthplaces but some make extensive seasonal movements (Boddy & Sellers 1983, Main 1996). There are small numbers of winter visitors to Britain from continental Europe, mainly Norway.

Nesting semicolonially where there are mature trees and shrubs and access to its seed diet, the Greenfinch is nowadays a familiar bird of parks and gardens in Britain & Ireland. Outside the breeding season, feeding flocks may be found in more open areas such as farm fields and saltmarshes.

The ringing site distributions of birds later recovered (Fig 1) broadly mirror the breeding distribution (*1988–91 Atlas*), except that Ireland is seriously under-represented and there are local biases towards the centres of human population and some coastal and island ringing stations. Results derived from ring-recoveries are therefore likely to be dominated by the behaviour of Greenfinches in southeastern Britain. Most recovered Greenfinches have been ringed in winter and spring, when they are relatively easy to trap at communal roosts or garden feeders. Relatively few have been ringed during the breeding season, and very few as pulli (Fig 2).

A substantial proportion of Greenfinch recoveries (24%) are recaptures by other ringers, away from the ringing site, of live ringed birds. This has the effect of biasing the seasonal distribution of recoveries towards winter and spring when the ringers are expending

The analysis of the data for this species was supported by Iain and Jill Main

most effort. Recoveries of dead birds, however, are most frequent in April and early May, and extend throughout the breeding season (Mead 1974b, Main 1996). Of those of known cause, at least 86% have been attributed to circumstances associated with human populations (Fig 3).

The similarity of the ringing site distributions of birds later recovered for the breeding and non-breeding seasons (Fig 1), and the small median values of distances moved, reflect the fact that the majority of British & Irish Greenfinches make no seasonal movements at all. Of 7,607 Greenfinches ringed in the breeding season and recovered (dead or alive) outside the breeding season, 5,490 (72%) had moved no further than 20 km. These could have been daily foraging or roosting movements but journeys greater than 20 km are probably seasonal. Most of these are short in migration terms but they include some measured in hundreds of kilometres. For movements greater than 20 km, the median distance between ringing and dead recovery is 57 km, with 5% moving further than 253 km. Boddy & Sellers (1983) pointed out that the way in which the number of such recoveries varies with distance is consistent with a picture in which birds stop at random rather than on reaching a particular destination.

The domination of the data by recoveries of birds ringed in southeastern Britain makes longitude a more sensitive indicator of seasonal movement than latitude (Fig 4). The clearest autumn (generally

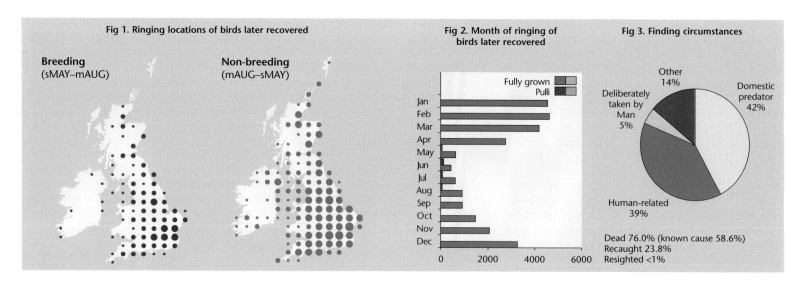

Fig 1. Ringing locations of birds later recovered

Breeding (sMAY–mAUG)

Non-breeding (mAUG–sMAY)

Fig 2. Month of ringing of birds later recovered

Fully grown
Pulli

Fig 3. Finding circumstances

Other 14%
Domestic predator 42%
Deliberately taken by Man 5%
Human-related 39%

Dead 76.0% (known cause 58.6%)
Recaught 23.8%
Resighted <1%

Ringing and recovery data

	<1960	60–69	70–79	80–89	90–97	Total
RINGING						
BTO ringing totals (%)	5	15	22	30	28	1,481,219
RECOVERIES						
BTO-ringed (%)	5	21	25	30	17	26,663
Foreign-ringed (%)	←	33	→	30	37	141

Statistical analyses

	Breeding population (sMAY–mAUG)	Wintering population (mNOV–mMAR)
Status	SEDENTARY* (0)	SHORT-DISTANCE MIGRANT*
Age differences[NS]	Not significant*	Significant
Sex differences[NS]	Not significant	Not significant
Regional differences	Significant[4*]	Not tested
Finding circumstances	(Not significant)	(Not significant)

Fig 4. Monthly variation in the differences in longitude between ringing and recovery locations of Greenfinches present in Britain & Ireland during the breeding season. Monthly medians (points) and interquartile ranges (bars) are shown. Only movements of greater than 20 km are included.

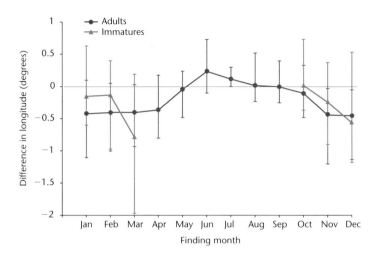

Fig 5. Movements of over 20 km and recovery locations of Greenfinches ringed in winter and recovered in (a) the same winter (1,897:375, red) or (b) a subsequent winter (1,439:893, blue). Sample sizes of movements under:over 20 km are given but only those over 20 km are plotted.

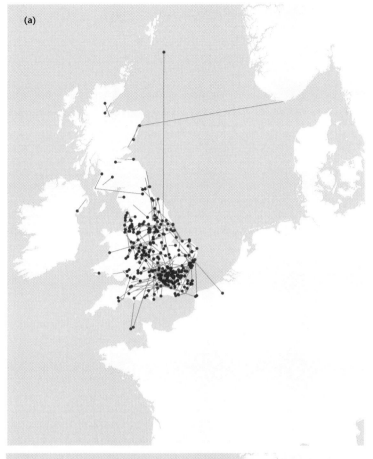

southwestward) and spring (northeastward) movements are evident for recoveries in November and May respectively. Thus many birds are still on spring passage after the start of the breeding season. These observations are consistent with the results of examining the *directions* of movement month by month (Main 1996). That study was also able to show that return movements may be established as early as February and that, in midwinter, movements in either direction might occur, perhaps dependent on weather conditions. Over 10% of movements within a winter exceed 20 km (Fig 5a). Winter site-fidelity does not appear to be strong: over a third of displacements between different winters exceed 20 km, almost 5% of these being across the sea (Fig 5b). It is not possible to correlate the winter movements with weather.

In spring, the birds return rapidly (Main 1996) to their natal or previous breeding locations, to which they seem faithful. Only one out of 58 birds ringed as nestlings and recovered in a subsequent breeding season had moved more than 20 km. There are 23 records (out of 301) of adults moving more than 20 km between breeding seasons but the overlap between spring migration and breeding season means that not all of these birds will necessarily have been back in their breeding areas when caught (19 of the 23 movements greater than 20 km involved birds ringed or recovered in May). Although the small number of recoveries (261) of Greenfinches ringed as nestlings precludes any detailed study of juvenile dispersal, it appears to be small: of 66 birds found dead within four months of ringing, none had moved more than 20 km.

For British Greenfinches, significantly more females than males move further than 20 km (Main 1996). This is reflected in Table 1. Similar results have been found for Greenfinches migrating from Fennoscandia, and in that case it has also been possible to demonstrate that immature birds travel further than adults, leading to a significantly larger proportion of young birds in the south of the range outside the breeding season (Main 2000a).

Table 1. Distances moved by Greenfinches ringed in Britain & Ireland during the breeding season and recovered outside the breeding season. Only movements of over 20 km by birds recovered dead are included.

	Median (km)	P5 (km)	P95 (km)	*n*
Male	72	23	284	169
Female	83.5	23	322	150
Unknown	81.5	22	399	40

Fig 6. Movements of over 20 km between the breeding and non-breeding season and locations outside the breeding season of Greenfinches present in the (a) northwest (162:92), (b) northeast (405:88), (c) southeast (3,512:1,595) and (d) southwest (1,329:299) of Britain and in (e) Ireland (82:13) during the breeding season. Sample sizes of movements under:over 20 km are given but only those over 20 km are plotted.

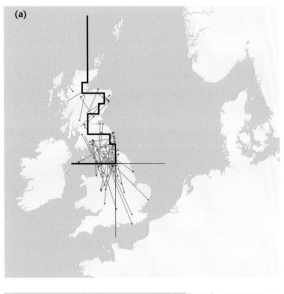
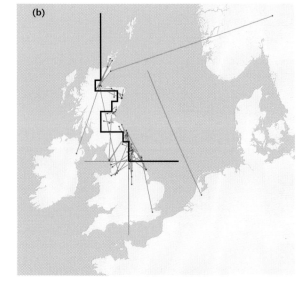
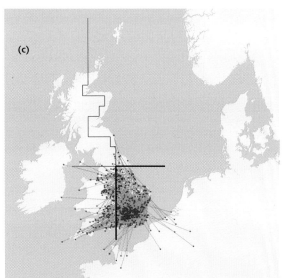
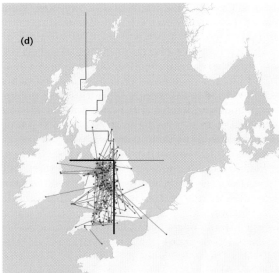
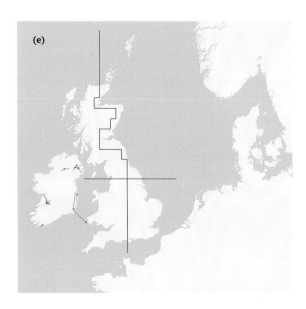

Fig 7. Movements overseas of Greenfinches present in Britain & Ireland in (a) autumn (88), (b) winter (118) and (c) spring (70). Birds ringed in Britain (solid red lines) are differentiated from those ringed in Ireland or abroad (broken black lines). There are no records of Greenfinch movements between Ireland and countries other than Britain.

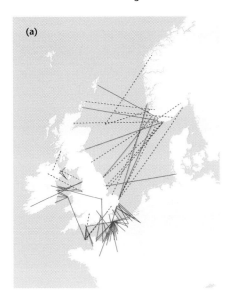 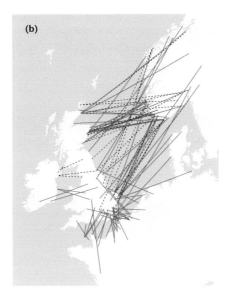 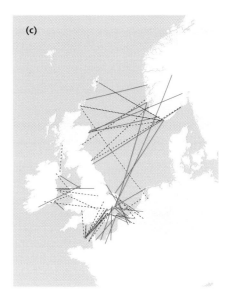

Movements between the breeding and non-breeding seasons for the five breeding regions are illustrated in Fig 6. A detailed analysis (Main 1996) has shown that, in Britain south of York and Lancaster, both the proportion of movements exceeding 20 km and the median distance moved exhibit increasing trends from west to east but are low in the extreme southeast. The same study analysed the directions of the seasonal movements, which had earlier been investigated by Boddy & Sellers (1983). For Greenfinches breeding in southern Britain, significant trends towards the south or west were found for all areas except the extreme southwest, where very few movements exceed 20 km. In all cases, the individual directions of movement were spread widely about the trend direction.

A few Greenfinches present in Britain in the breeding season (Fig 6) or later (Fig 7) move to Ireland, and a rather larger number to the Channel Islands or continental Europe. It has been estimated (Main 1999) that approximately 0.1% of all British Greenfinches cross the Irish Sea, while at least 2% of the birds breeding in southeast England cross the English Channel. That those sea-crossings are not annual events is indicated by the fact that individual birds can be found on different sides of the sea in different winters (Fig 5b). It is likely that the movements are triggered by high breeding density or food shortage in Britain, rather than severe weather, since most occur promptly in autumn (Main 1999) and there are few records of sea-crossings *during* the winter (Fig 5a).

Although southern England is host to small numbers of Greenfinches from the near Continent, most winter visitors to Britain are from Norway (Fig 7). Like emigration from Britain, immigration from the Continent appears to be occasional rather than annual (Fig 5). It has been proposed (Main 1999) that the birds reaching northern Britain from Norway consist of part (not more than 1%) of a population that normally winters at the Norwegian coast, whereas those found in the southeast comprise a wind-drifted fraction (not more than a few percent) of a separate population making a regular migration by way of continental countries bordering the North Sea. The increasing frequency with which exchanges with Norway have been recorded since 1985, and fluctuations in the numbers of captures in Britain from one winter to the next (Duncan 1996), suggest the recent development of irruptive immigration to Britain accompanying a growth of the Norwegian

Greenfinch population. This may not be the whole story, however, since the annual numbers of ringing or recovery events in Norway associated with movements to Britain have kept pace with a progressive shift during the same period of Norwegian Greenfinch-ringing activity towards the southwest of the country, where most of the visitors to Britain originate (Main 1999). It has become apparent that there may be sufficient morphological differences between Norwegian and British Greenfinches to allow their separation in the hand (Duncan 1989a). The systematic recording of such properties as weight, wing length and fat score, particularly by ringers in eastern Britain, might enable unringed Norwegian birds to be recognized, and the nature of the movements between Norway and Britain to be clarified.

While changing farming practices in Britain have led to observable changes in Greenfinch behaviour, such as reduced winter feeding in stubble fields, there is no firm evidence that seasonal movements have been directly affected. Marchant *et al* (1990) noted an increase in the proportion of long-distance recoveries between 1977 and 1986, and suggested that this might reflect increased mobility of British Greenfinches outside the breeding season in response to man-made environmental changes. The phenomenon appears, however, to be confined mainly to southeastern England, and to be correlated with increasing breeding density in that region (Main 1996).

In spite of the fairly detailed information available, for Greenfinches in southern Britain at least, the intriguing question remains whether their autumn movements are controlled by an in-built migratory urge, as suggested by the non-random directional trends, or whether they are at least partially dispersive, as suggested by the distance distributions and the wide spreads about the mean directions. The post-fledging or post-breeding dispersal preceding any migration may limit the capacity of ring-recovery data to separate the two mechanisms. The rapid return to the breeding grounds in spring, by contrast, is clearly migratory. Whatever the autumn mechanism, this will lend an apparently out-and-back character to any movement which is sampled at two points only.

Iain Main

European Goldfinch (Goldfinch)

Carduelis carduelis

In their native range, Goldfinches are quintessential partial migrants. This range extends eastward from the Azores and Ireland across mainland Europe and Africa north of the Sahara, as far as the Himalayas and western China (*BWP*). The northern limit of the range falls in northern Scotland, through southern Fennoscandia and into Asia approximately along the line of 60° latitude. Within the breeding range, black-crowned races occur to the west of the Urals (the populations considered here) and grey-crowned ones occur to the east. In only the very north of this range in Asia is the species entirely migratory (*BWP*). Elsewhere, a variable proportion of the breeding population remains, forming roving winter flocks and, depending on local conditions, undertaking altitudinal or cold-weather movements (Newton 1972, Lack 1988). British breeding Goldfinches are classified as a race (*britannica*) separate from the very similar nominate *carduelis* (found across northern mainland Europe and east to the Urals: Clement *et al* 1993), and up to 80% of the former population winters overseas (Newton 1972). The wintering range of black-crowned Goldfinches extends only a little further south than the breeding area, incorporating more of northern Africa, Sinai and the Middle East (*BWP*): birds from more southerly European populations (five more races very like the nominate: Clement *et al* 1993) presumably, therefore, undertake shorter migratory movements than northern individuals.

Goldfinches have been introduced successfully into areas such as parts of Australasia, and are popular cagebirds. Changes in the scale of trapping for the cagebird trade caused large changes in Goldfinch abundance until its cessation in the 1980s, after which food availability, and ultimately, the intensity of weed control, have been the likely causes

The analysis of the data for this species was supported by Chris Whittles

of 20th century population change (Holloway 1996). Although the British population has fluctuated since the 1960s, it has not declined severely like those of other species with similar ecologies (Siriwardena *et al* 1998a). This may reflect the specialization of Goldfinches on the seeds of plants (*eg* Compositae: Wilson *et al* 1999) that have been affected little by agricultural intensification. Goldfinches are common wherever these plants occur: in Britain & Ireland chiefly on farmland, but reaching their highest densities around rural human habitation (Gregory 1999).

The ringing of Goldfinches has clearly been concentrated in southern Britain (Fig 1). Although the British population is at its densest in the south, both in summer and in winter, other concentrations are found in northern England and lowland Scotland (*Winter Atlas, 1988–91 Atlas*). These birds and those in Ireland may therefore not be sampled well by ringing, so their patterns of movement cannot be assessed. However, the recovery sample should not be seriously biased with respect to the population using Britain & Ireland at different times. Most Goldfinch recoveries are of birds ringed between July and October, with fewer birds ringed in winter and spring (Fig 2) when abundance in Britain & Ireland is lower.

Half of the 704 recoveries of ringed Goldfinches of known cause have occurred in Britain & Ireland, and half overseas. Over 300 of the former (76% of which were road casualties) occurred either in human-

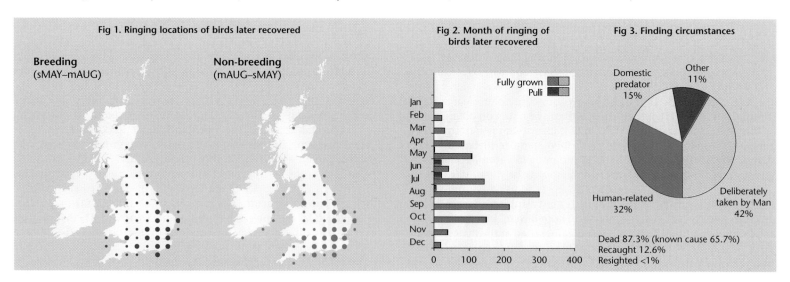

Fig 1. Ringing locations of birds later recovered

Breeding (sMAY–mAUG)

Non-breeding (mAUG–sMAY)

Fig 2. Month of ringing of birds later recovered

Fully grown
Pulli

Jan, Feb, Mar, Apr, May, Jun, Jul, Aug, Sep, Oct, Nov, Dec

0 100 200 300 400

Fig 3. Finding circumstances

Domestic predator 15%

Other 11%

Human-related 32%

Deliberately taken by Man 42%

Dead 87.3% (known cause 65.7%)
Recaught 12.6%
Resighted <1%

Ringing and recovery data

	<1960	60–69	70–79	80–89	90–97	Total
RINGING						
BTO ringing totals (%)	2	18	32	24	24	153,166
RECOVERIES						
BTO-ringed (%)	2	31	34	20	12	1,215
Foreign-ringed (%)	←	84	→	8	8	77

Statistical analyses

	Breeding population (sMAY–mAUG)	Wintering population (sNOV–sAPR)
Status	LONG-DISTANCE MIGRANT* (3)	SEDENTARY*
Age differences[NS*]	Not significant*	Significant*
Sex differences[NS*]	Not significant*	Not tested
Regional differences	Not tested	Not tested
Finding circumstances	Significant	Not significant*

Fig 4. Locations in winter, and movements of over 20 km between the breeding and winter, of 161 Goldfinches present in Britain & Ireland during the breeding season.

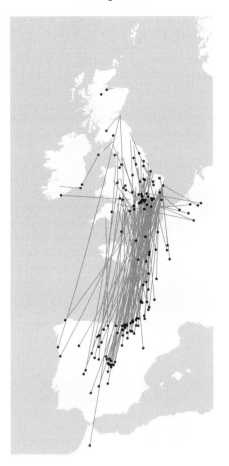

Fig 5. Movements of over 20 km and recovery locations of Goldfinches ringed in winter and recovered in a subsequent winter. There were 8:9 movements under:over 20 km but only those over 20 km are plotted.

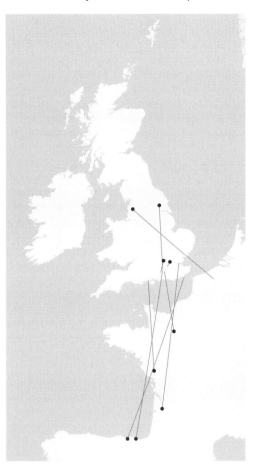

related circumstances or when caught by domestic cats (Fig 3). There could therefore be a bias towards individuals from near human habitation, although this may be relatively unimportant for a species that is commonly found on roadside verges and waste ground. In addition, almost all of the foreign recoveries of Goldfinches (219 in Spain, the remainder mostly in Belgium and France) have been the victims of hunting. Despite the importance of overwinter mortality in the species' demography (Siriwardena *et al* 1999), it is impossible, from recovery data alone, to say whether hunting pressure in continental Europe has had significant impacts on Goldfinch abundance in Britain. Nevertheless, variation in hunting effort could have introduced spatial and temporal biases into the pattern of recoveries, perhaps reducing the extent to which they are representative of the population as a whole.

A further potential bias could result from the domination of the recovery data set by birds ringed while they were immature, which form around 65% of the sample. Such birds are likely to move further, both as a result of natal dispersal behaviour and because they are likely to be subordinate relative to adults and at a competitive disadvantage. It is also possible that juveniles are more susceptible to trapping or other hunting methods and are thus more likely to be recovered than adults. As a result, the pattern of recoveries may overestimate the extent to which the British & Irish Goldfinch population is migratory.

Notwithstanding the potential quantitative biases in the data set, the pattern of ring-recoveries shows that several different movement strategies are undertaken by British & Irish breeding Goldfinches. First, many birds clearly winter within Britain & Ireland (*Winter Atlas*), some remaining close to their breeding areas and others undertaking predominantly southerly movements (Fig 4). The principal overseas

migration is south-southwesterly through western France into Iberia, wherein British and Irish birds join other European Goldfinches (Glück 1982, Asensio 1986, Finlayson 1992, Deán 1998), while another common movement, perhaps unrelated, sees birds move to the southeast, primarily into Belgium (Fig 4). Sex ratios in winter in Britain and in Spain suggest that more females migrate than males (Newton 1972) and that females tend to winter further south (Asensio 1986). However, there are no significant differences in British & Irish ringing data between the locations of, or distances moved by, males and females, or, indeed, adults and juveniles. Forty recoveries of dead Goldfinches provide information on breeding dispersal, giving a median distance of less than 1 km (P5–95=0–338 km), suggesting that such movements do not make a large contribution to the long-distance patterns. Too few relevant recoveries have occurred (four only) to provide reliable information on natal dispersal.

Overseas recoveries of migrant birds have been most common between October and February inclusive (367/453) but a few have occurred in every month except June. This suggests that breeding birds have not all returned until May, and that autumn migration can begin as early as July, the latter perhaps showing the movements of failed breeders and juveniles from early nests.

Although recoveries have occurred more frequently in Iberia than in France, the geographical spread of winter recoveries (Fig 4) suggests that migratory British & Irish Goldfinches do not travel to a specific wintering area. Rather, it seems that birds stop wherever conditions are suitable. Dividing the recovery data by month shows no progressive movement southward in autumn or northward in spring, probably because the birds can complete their migration in only a few days. There is also no indication that different routes are taken in spring and autumn. It is important to recall here that the numerical distribution of overseas recoveries may be seriously biased by geographical variation in hunting pressure. In this context, it may be significant that recoveries have occurred in Morocco (one is shown in Fig 4, and two more have occurred after having been ringed outside the breeding season). Reporting rates of dead, ringed birds are probably relatively low in Africa, so the migration of British & Irish Goldfinches across the Strait of Gibraltar may be more common than recoveries suggest. Significant numbers of European Goldfinches cross into Africa throughout the winter of every year but it is unknown how many of these birds are of northern European origin (Asensio 1986, Finlayson 1992).

Recoveries of British & Irish breeders in Belgium and the Netherlands have mostly occurred in October and November (46/67), the remainder being spread throughout the year. This concentration in autumn is highly statistically significant, and consists of significantly more birds ringed in southeast than in southwest Britain. However, it could principally reflect the old Belgian bird-catching season, which ran for six weeks from the beginning of October (Newton 1972). Trapping ceased across much of the country in 1972 but continued until 1991 in Wallonia. The temporal pattern of recoveries could, therefore, easily be misleading, and it is unclear whether Goldfinches entering Belgium in autumn remain there or move on towards southwest Europe (or elsewhere). This movement may represent birds taking the shortest crossing of the English Channel before they fly towards Iberia (*BWP*), but it is clear from the visible passage in Ireland and western Britain (*Birds in Ireland*, *Birds in Wales*) that many individuals also take longer routes over water.

An interesting question in respect of all partial migration is whether an individual's migratory strategy is obligate or facultative, *ie* whether an individual can be flexible and migrate in some years but not in others. Most research to date suggests that the migratory tendency is genetically controlled (Berthold 1993), but at least some birds clearly winter in Britain and overseas in different years (Fig 5). The ring-recovery evidence for Goldfinch suggests, therefore, that individuals do not have 'hard-wired' strategies that generate unchanging migratory behaviour throughout their lives.

Most published material on the migration of British & Irish Goldfinches has drawn on the results of ringing and so, unsurprisingly, has reached similar conclusions to those described above (*eg* Newton 1972). The only available evidence for the regions not covered well by ringing comes from observations of migrating flocks and of birds remaining in Britain & Ireland in winter. Irish, Scottish and Welsh Goldfinches are believed to follow a predominantly southwesterly migratory path similar to those from southern England. A heavy autumn passage of Goldfinches occurs through Ireland (*Birds in Ireland*) and some of these birds are probably those seen heading out to sea from western Wales (*Birds in Wales*) and Scotland (*Birds in Scotland*). Two ring-recoveries show movements between Britain and Ireland (Fig 4), both involving British breeders recovered in midwinter, showing that some individuals overwinter in Ireland.

It has been suggested that some Goldfinches from continental Europe or Scandinavia winter in Britain (Newton 1972, *Birds in Scotland*). It is perhaps more likely that any movements across the North Sea (involving the nominate race rather than the British race *britannica*) are by birds on passage towards southwest Europe. Only three recoveries provide evidence for such movements: one German-ringed bird recovered in Cambridgeshire, one Swedish-ringed bird recovered in Kent and one bird ringed in Suffolk and recovered in Malta. The Swedish bird supports the passage hypothesis because it was ringed in September and recovered just three weeks later. Similarly, the recovery in Malta could have been a bird ringed while on passage through Britain. The German bird, however, was ringed only 80 km from the Belgian border in late August and was recovered the following May. Despite the speculation to the contrary (Spencer & Hudson 1978, *BWP*), therefore, this was probably a British-breeding bird. Notwithstanding the foregoing discussion, it is more than possible that significant influxes of nominate-race birds to northern Britain occur, remaining undetected as yet because of the similarity of the two races in the field and the comparatively low ringing effort in the north. Biometric data from the ringing of Goldfinches in Fife suggest strongly that winter flocks consist of both *britannica* and nominate birds (although reliable quantitative estimates of the proportion of each cannot be made); no recoveries confirm this as yet (Robertson 1997). The nominate race has yet to be accepted onto the British List (BOU 1992).

Our current understanding of Goldfinch demography indicates that changes in annual survival have been critical in determining breeding abundance in Britain (Siriwardena *et al* 1999). Conditions in the non-breeding season are probably the key influence on survival, and the results of ringing reported here show that many key habitats have been and will probably continue to be found overseas. Therefore, although the British & Irish Goldfinch population is not in decline, consideration of the causes of past population changes and any future conservation problems should encompass conditions in the key areas of continental Europe. Further, any changes in the proportion of the population leaving Britain & Ireland in winter could have important implications for population stability, and such changes could lead to significant but unpredictable interactions with hunting pressure. The future conservation of British & Irish Goldfinches, and of those other species with similar migratory strategies (*eg* Linnet), would therefore benefit from the monitoring of overseas hunting activity.

Several key factors in Goldfinch migratory patterns remain unknown: first, the extent to which the distribution of recoveries from hunting reflects the real distribution of wintering birds; second, whether any changes in movement patterns over time have been influenced by population fluctuations in Britain & Ireland; third, whether Irish and northern British birds have different migratory strategies from southern birds; fourth, whether significant influxes of nominate *carduelis* birds occur to northern Britain; and, fifth, how the selection of migratory strategy is controlled in individual birds.

Gavin Siriwardena

Eurasian Siskin (Siskin)
Carduelis spinus

Although a familiar and widespread breeding species in the conifer forests of Britain & Ireland, to many, the Siskin is most commonly known as a late winter visitor to gardens, especially in central and southern Britain. Ringing has shown that while many of these wintering birds are of native origin, birds from continental Europe also visit and pass through Britain & Ireland in large, but varying numbers.

Siskins have a discontinuous breeding distribution across much of Europe and Russia as far as about 100°E, with a separate population breeding and wintering in the Far East. Despite the several apparently discrete breeding areas, no subspecies have been described. In the west, the main breeding range extends from Ireland and Norway through Finland and Russia and westwards through central Europe, locally on mountains into Spain and through the Balkans and northern Turkey to the Caucasus. The *European Atlas* estimates that 90% of the European breeding population of 3–15 million breeding pairs occurs within the forests of Fennoscandia, the Baltic States and Russia. Like other species that feed on tree seeds, Siskins have an unpredictable main food supply and may make irregular movements in search of food. During the winter months in irruption years, Siskins can be found almost anywhere in Europe, with southern limits along the north coast of Africa, and in Sinai, Israel, Iraq, northern Iran and southern Kazakhstan.

The *1988–91 Atlas* showed that the breeding distribution of Siskins in Britain & Ireland had expanded greatly over the previous two decades, with an 85% increase in the number of 10-km squares recording their presence in Britain and a 20% increase in Ireland. Estimates of the breeding population have increased from 20–40,000

The analysis of the data for this species was supported by the Sinnott family

pairs in 1968–72 to 360,000 pairs in 1988–91. Although the Siskin is still primarily a bird of the coniferous forests of the north and west, it can now be found almost anywhere in Britain with suitable breeding habitat, and in Ireland it remains a well-distributed but localized breeder. In Britain, this huge population expansion is thought to reflect changes in the age structure of the conifer forests, the maturing plantations of the middle decades of the 20th century providing new breeding habitat and sources of food.

Siskins are more widespread in Britain & Ireland during the winter months, although their numbers and distribution vary greatly from year to year. The *Winter Atlas* suggests concentrations from southeast Wales through the West Midlands and in southeast England, which coincide with lowland areas of high human population density. Although Siskins can still be found in coniferous and birch forest, their favoured winter habitat is riverside alder, where flocks of several hundred can occur.

Siskins have now become common visitors to garden peanut feeders throughout late winter and spring, a habit first recorded in 1963 in Surrey (Spencer & Gush 1973). The BTO's Garden BirdWatch showed that in the winters of 1994/95 and 1997/98 almost 40% of participating gardens recorded Siskins, compared with about 15% in the intervening years (Cannon 1998). Rather than reflecting breeding performance, the number of birds visiting suburban gardens in winter appears to be

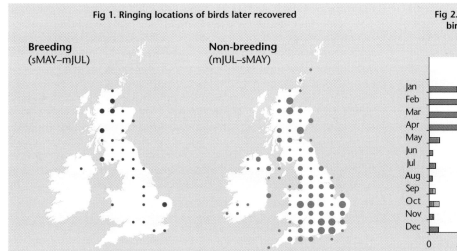

Fig 1. Ringing locations of birds later recovered

Breeding (sMAY–mJUL)

Non-breeding (mJUL–sMAY)

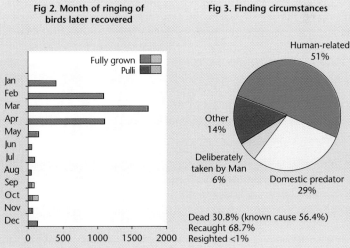

Fig 2. Month of ringing of birds later recovered

Fig 3. Finding circumstances

Human-related 51%
Other 14%
Deliberately taken by Man 6%
Domestic predator 29%

Dead 30.8% (known cause 56.4%)
Recaught 68.7%
Resighted <1%

Ringing and recovery data

	<1960	60–69	70–79	80–89	90–97	Total
RINGING						
BTO ringing totals (%)	0	1	9	34	56	212,266
RECOVERIES						
BTO-ringed (%)	0	1	7	39	54	4,903
Foreign-ringed (%)	←	32	→	31	37	280

Statistical analyses

	Breeding population (sMAY–mJUL)	Wintering population (sNOV–sMAR)
Status	SHORT-DISTANCE MIGRANT*	SHORT-DISTANCE MIGRANT*
Age differences[NT]	Not tested	Significant
Sex differences[(NS)*]	Not tested	Not significant*
Regional differences	Not tested	Not tested
Finding circumstances	Not tested	(Not significant)

Fig 4. Locations in winter and movements of over 20 km between the breeding season and winter of 182 Siskins present in Britain & Ireland during the breeding season.

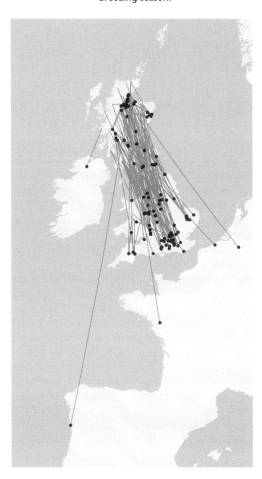

Fig 5. Exchanges of Siskins between Britain & Ireland and abroad, with those abroad during the breeding season (60, red) differentiated from those abroad at other seasons or of uncertain seasonality (616, grey). Points show locations abroad during the breeding season.

influenced by the relative success of the season's cone crop, high numbers coinciding with poor cone crops and vice versa (D Jardine pers comm). Garden feeding provides a valuable supplement to natural food, especially in the early mornings or on wet and overcast days, as Siskins are unable to feed on unopened cones.

The increase in range and breeding numbers coupled with their recently acquired habit of visiting gardens has led to a dramatic increase in the number of Siskins ringed in Britain & Ireland. During 1909–97, 212,000 had been ringed, 42% of which were in the period 1993–97. Although relatively few are ringed in breeding areas (Fig 1), and hardly any pulli have been ringed (Fig 2), Siskins can easily be caught in winter and spring with mist-nets or traps baited with peanuts, and ringers have also exploited their familiarity with feeders as they arrive back at forest breeding sites (Shaw 1990). The ease of capture during the late winter and spring is reflected in the seasonal distribution of ringing for birds subsequently recovered (Fig 2); 87% of recoveries are from birds that were ringed during January–April, and 77% of recoveries occurred in the same months. A very high proportion of recoveries (69%) are from recaptures by ringers, mainly during the first four months of the year, and the cause of recovery is only known for about half of the remaining birds, recovered dead (Fig 3). The most common causes of reported death are from collisions with windows (35%), predation by cats (28%) and traffic accidents (10%); clearly these are unrepresentative of the hazards facing Siskins for most of the year. Because so many of the data come from retraps, the distribution of recoveries both geographically and seasonally is heavily influenced by that of Siskin ringers.

Breeding birds are always closely associated with conifers. In Britain & Ireland, Siskins typically start nesting in early April and once the chicks hatch they are fed seeds from ripening spruce and pine cones,

supplemented with insects and seeds from other plants. Shaw (1990) showed that the onset of breeding varies with the success of the previous year's cone crop. In a year following a very heavy cone crop, birds were trapped in the forest as early as the beginning of February and females were thought to have started laying by mid-March. However, in a year following a very poor cone crop the first birds were not trapped until mid-April, and even in the second half of May many of the birds caught were still not breeding. In these poor years, breeding can be delayed until seeds of annual plants are available to supplement cones but such delays preclude the opportunity to raise a second brood.

Although some Siskins remain in their breeding areas throughout the year if food is available, most have deserted the conifer forests by the end of July or early August, when the supply of cone seeds is exhausted. From then until their return to the forests between February and early April, their staple natural diet becomes the seeds of birch and alder. As many northern British birds move south to winter in central and southern Britain (Fig 4) they are joined by continental birds arriving on the east coast from mid-September. Large numbers of birds enter the country by the southeast via Belgium and the Netherlands but others cross the North Sea on a more direct route from Scandinavia to make landfall almost anywhere from Shetland to East Anglia (Buckland et al 1990, Taylor et al 1999). The distinctive calls of small groups of Siskins as they pass overhead are a characteristic feature of east-coast birdwatching in the autumn months.

Over half of the foreign movements recorded are to or from Belgium and the Netherlands, and while the majority of these birds probably originate from Fennoscandia and the Baltic States, others migrate to Britain from central and eastern Europe and even from as far east as the Ukraine (Fig 5). However, as these continental birds are arriving to mix with British & Irish birds wintering in central and southern England, others are leaving the country to the south. Small numbers of birds ringed in Britain have been found in winter in Iberia (14) and North Africa (four), and others have been found to the southeast in Italy (11) with individuals even reaching the former Yugoslavia and Greece. Some

Fig 6. Movements of over 20 km and recovery locations of Siskins ringed in winter and recovered in a subsequent winter. There were 30:162 movements under:over 20 km but only those over 20 km are plotted.

over 10 days, giving a fat-load of 19% of body-weight. He calculated that this amount of fat would give a potential flight range of 400–500 km and so enable the birds to reach southern Scotland or to cross the North Sea and make landfall in the Netherlands, while those individuals that showed fat-loads of 35% could reach northeast Germany in one flight. Sellers (1986), studying Siskins in Gloucestershire in the same year, estimated a similar fat-load before departure but, using a different formula, calculated a potential flight range of 500–1,000 km. Weight gains are not only recorded in the south of England. Chesney (1987) found that 25% of his Tayside birds had gained weight between captures in April and some individuals had enough fat to reach Norway. However although retraps can show significant weight gains, less than 8% of the birds trapped in late March or April in northwest Surrey over a 13-year period were more than 1.5 g heavier on first capture than the average winter weights, and less than 10% of these birds were retrapped more than once (pers obs). While some birds may fly direct, the absence of fat and evidence from multiple ring-recoveries of individual birds suggest that an alternative strategy of a slower and stepped journey is adopted by many birds returning to breed in northern England and Scotland.

There are only a few recoveries that give valuable clues to the speed of migration. An autumn movement from Latvia to Staffordshire of about 1,600 km took a maximum of 14 days at an average of 114 km/day, and there are two other movements of an equivalent speed but over shorter distances. By far the fastest movement recorded, however, is from Shropshire to the Highland Region in three days at an average of 189 km/day.

Most Siskin studies seem to record an imbalance in the ratio of males to females trapped, with more males in both adult and immature classes (eg Jardine et al 1994, R Denyer pers comm), and the recovery data reflect this imbalance. However Payevsky (1994) analysed the recoveries from nearly 150,000 Siskins trapped near Rybachy in Baltic Russia and found no significant differences in the distances between ringing and recovery location nor in the direction of migration between the ages or sexes. Nor did he find any differences in annual survival rates either between males and females or between adults and immatures, although he did find that, on average, adults migrate earlier in spring and later in autumn. While the distribution maps for recoveries involving Britain & Ireland show no obvious difference in pattern between the sexes, there is an interesting absence of immature birds recovered southwest of a line from Brittany to northern Italy. There are insufficient data to test for age- or sex-related differences in the movements of British & Irish breeders. However, statistical analyses based on recoveries of birds ringed in Britain & Ireland in winter show that immatures (n=41) have been recovered significantly further west (by more than 5° of longitude) than adults (n=34). This suggestion of some kind of differential migration, albeit based on a small sample, deserves further investigation.

At a time when many common birds are facing long-term population declines, the Siskin has benefited both from afforestation of the uplands and from the increased provision of food in gardens. Although much is already known about its behaviour and movements during the late winter and spring months, the Siskin remains a relatively difficult species to study during the breeding and post-breeding dispersal periods. Increased ringing activity at breeding sites, especially in more southern and western areas, and studies that improve our understanding of the factors that drive variability from year to year should be encouraged in order to provide a more balanced understanding of the movements of this delightful bird.

Alan Martin

of these southern recoveries are from the British breeding population but most are probably from birds ringed on passage through Britain (for example a bird ringed on Fair Isle in September was recovered a few months later in Portugal).

Ringing has shown that at least some birds return to the same wintering areas in subsequent years. In a study in northwest Surrey, 3% of the birds ringed over a 12-year period were recaptured in later years (133 birds), of which five were trapped in three different years and two birds returned for four successive years (Martin 1997). Similar results have been obtained in other parts of the country but there are also numerous records of birds changing locations during the course of a winter, and changing countries in successive years (Fig 6). Clearly, weather conditions and food availability are important factors determining the extent of winter movements. Senar et al (1992) studying site-fidelity in the Siskin found, however, that even when excess food was continually available only 8% of the birds captured became 'resident' for the winter whereas the majority (which he called 'transients') stayed for short periods, often only being caught on one occasion. The resident birds became sedentary as soon as they arrived, making short-range movements of less than 3 km, whereas the transients were very mobile making movements of 10–40 km in a single day. Further studies have even suggested that differences in wing shape have evolved to suit the nomadic or winter-resident lifestyles (Senar et al 1994).

The return migration to breeding areas in spring seems to follow the same routes as the autumn movements, with birds moving north towards Scotland or east through Belgium and the Netherlands (Buckland et al 1990). The timing of the birds' departure varies between years but most have left southern gardens by mid-April. Prior to departure, Siskins can increase their body-weight significantly. Cooper (1985) observed that birds retrapped in his study area in north Sussex gained on average 2.5 g

Common Linnet (Linnet)

Carduelis cannabina

Linnets are classic partial migrants. In Britain & Ireland, some remain in winter, while others move south or southwest to winter in a narrow longitudinal band from western France, through central Spain to Morocco. The species has a large western Palearctic breeding range extending from the Atlantic seaboard of Europe to Russia and the Caucasus, and from North Africa to southern Fennoscandia (*BWP*). Only Iceland, northwest Scotland, and northern Fennoscandia are unoccupied. Linnets winter largely within their breeding range, although parts of northern Italy, North Africa, the Middle East and Russia bordering the Black and Caspian Seas have wintering populations but few or no breeding birds. Fennoscandia, alpine regions of Italy and Switzerland, and much of Poland, Russia and the Baltic States are largely vacated in winter. A southerly or southwesterly orientation during autumn migration is usual. For example, birds wintering in Mediterranean France are from Germany, the former Czechoslovakia and Switzerland; those in central France and eastern Spain are from Belgium, and birds from eastern Germany move to Italy (*BWP*).

The *1988–91 Atlas* shows that Linnets breed throughout both Britain and Ireland, excepting only northwest Scotland, the Shetland Islands and a few other areas of higher ground, where they are often replaced by Twite. Inland breeding densities are highest in southern and eastern England, but coastal areas around most of Britain tend to hold high breeding densities relative to the neighbouring hinterland. Throughout their range, Linnets favour areas of heathland, scrub, thickets and hedgerows, wherever dense shrubs provide adequate nesting cover. Unusually for a passerine, but typically for the genus *Carduelis*, Linnets

The analysis of the data for this species was supported by Landguard Bird Observatory

rely largely on a diet of seeds, even when feeding their young (Newton 1967a, Eybert & Constant 1992, 1998, Moorcroft *et al* 1997). Open ground is thus also needed to provide the seed-bearing weeds and other ruderal plants that are their main food sources. Elsewhere in Europe, orchards, vineyards, young plantations, forest edges and clearings all provide suitable habitats, and Linnets can be found breeding up to 2,300 m above sea-level in alpine meadows, moorland and scree, wherever low-growing woody vegetation provides nesting cover (Frey 1989a, b). Outside the breeding season, Linnets retain a need for shrubby vegetation to provide safe communal roost sites, and for seeds, which may be collected either in low-growing shrubs, herbaceous vegetation, or on the ground. In Britain & Ireland, this means that the winter distribution is very similar to the breeding distribution, despite the southerly departure of many birds to winter in France and Spain. Locally, however, Linnets congregate in large flocks in seed-rich habitats such as saltmarshes, and stubble fields on farmland (*eg* Wilson *et al* 1996). The dependence of Linnets on seeds (and especially those of agricultural weeds such as Polygonaceae, Brassicaceae, Caryophyllaceae and Asteraceae) has left them vulnerable to the effects of agricultural intensification, especially increased herbicide use, and population declines in Finland and in Britain have been attributed to the effects of agricultural change on seed availability (Tast 1968, O'Connor & Shrubb

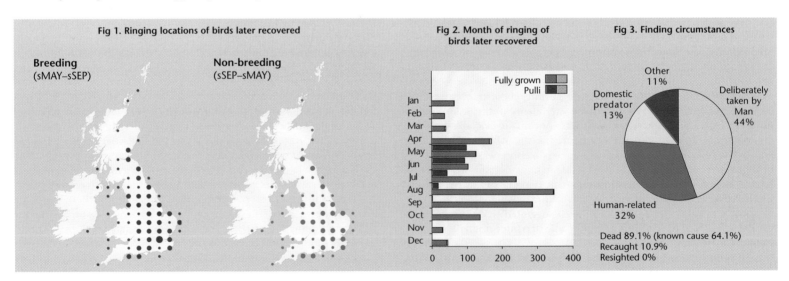

Fig 1. Ringing locations of birds later recovered

Breeding (sMAY–sSEP)

Non-breeding (sSEP–sMAY)

Fig 2. Month of ringing of birds later recovered

Fully grown
Pulli

Fig 3. Finding circumstances

Other 11%
Domestic predator 13%
Deliberately taken by Man 44%
Human-related 32%

Dead 89.1% (known cause 64.1%)
Recaught 10.9%
Resighted 0%

Ringing and recovery data

	<1960	60–69	70–79	80–89	90–97	Total
RINGING						
BTO ringing totals (%)	9	30	27	20	14	351,835
RECOVERIES						
BTO-ringed (%)	10	45	23	14	8	1,869
Foreign-ringed (%)	←	74	→	13	13	76

Statistical analyses

	Breeding population (sMAY–sSEP)	Wintering population (sNOV–sAPR)
Status	LONG-DISTANCE MIGRANT* (3)	SEDENTARY
Age differences[NS]	Not significant*	Significant*
Sex differences[NS]	Not significant	Not significant*
Regional differences	Significant[3]*	Not tested
Finding circumstances	Significant	Not significant*

Fig 4. Movements of over 20 km between the breeding season and winter, and locations in winter, of Linnets present in the (a) northeast (28), (b) northwest (10), (c) southeast (186) and (d) southwest (71) of Britain during the breeding season. A single movement of a Linnet present in Ireland is not shown.

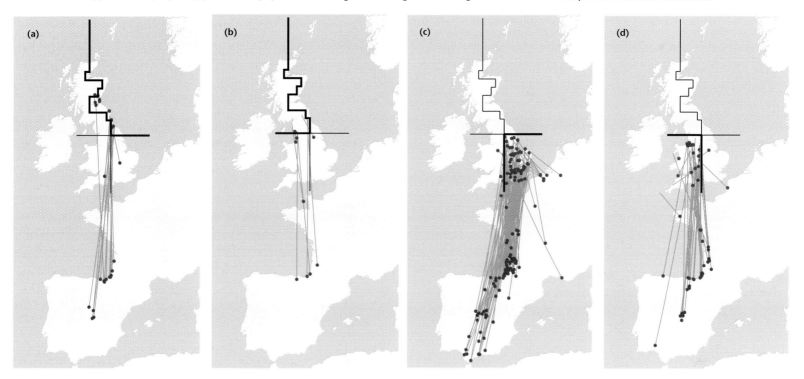

1986). In Finland, this has led to a redistribution of the breeding population to alternative habitats, such as parks, gardens and industrial sites (Tast 1968). The same shift has not been as apparent in Britain, where a recent population recovery may be attributable to the increased sowing of oilseed rape, and its exploitation by Linnets as a food source for both adults and nestlings (Moorcroft *et al* 1997, Moorcroft & Wilson 2000).

The ringing places of Linnets that have been recovered mainly reflect lowland English populations. Populations in Ireland, Wales, southwest and northwest England, and southwest Scotland are all under-represented (Fig 1). The great majority of Linnets ringed in Britain & Ireland, and later recovered, were ringed between April and October (89%). These comprise a mixture of breeding adults, fledged birds of the year and the 14% of birds ringed as nestlings (Fig 2). The remaining 11% of recoveries reflect birds ringed during the winter months, when flocking in open habitats makes Linnets more difficult to capture than during the breeding season. The 74 recoveries in Britain & Ireland of foreign-ringed Linnets come from France (31), Belgium (23), Spain (16), the Netherlands (two), Germany (one) and Norway (one). Historically, recapture by ringers has played only a small part in the generation of recovery data for Linnets. Of the total ring-recoveries, 89% were of dead birds, although recovery circumstances vary markedly between Britain & Ireland and elsewhere in Europe. Britain (62%), France (25%) and Spain (10%) dominate the distribution of recovery locations of dead birds, with very small numbers recovered in Belgium, Holland, Ireland, Italy, Morocco, Portugal and Scandinavia. Circumstances for birds recovered dead are shown in Fig 3. In Britain, the great majority of recoveries relate either to non-deliberate human causes such as collision with vehicles or buildings (56%), or to domestic predators such as cats (22%); only 5% were reported as being deliberately taken by humans. In contrast, 89% of all recoveries in France, and 95% of those in Spain, reflect birds taken by hunting, in the latter country mostly by use of nets and limesticks (Santos *et al* 1988). The geographical pattern of recovery abroad is therefore likely to be heavily influenced by the distribution of hunting activity.

In Britain & Ireland, Linnets have a long breeding season extending from April to the end of August. Post-breeding dispersal and migratory movement is therefore spread over a long period, with most birds remaining close to their natal area until their fourth month after fledging. Movement at coastal observatories is noted from August (Newton 1972, Durman 1976a, *BWP*), by which time the first British & Irish breeding birds have moved to the Low Countries and France. Significant numbers of wintering birds have reached the Aquitaine region of southwestern France, and a strip of central Spain a few hundred kilometres wide from the western Pyrenees south to Gibraltar, by October, and recoveries from these regions remain frequent through to January (Fig 4). Some birds may cross to northern Africa, as shown by a November recovery in Morocco, and some wander outside the usual wintering 'corridor', with single winter recoveries from the Mediterranean coast of France, northern Italy and Sardinia.

In contrast, Fig 4 also shows that many British breeders remain to winter even in Scotland, where flocks of over a thousand birds have been recorded as far north as Montrose and Inverness (*Birds in Scotland*). In Ireland, there are believed to be few wintering Linnets relative to the breeding population (*Birds in Ireland*), which implies that any influx of wintering birds from Britain is small relative to the exodus of the Irish population to winter in France and Spain. Throughout their winter range, Linnets remain associated with seed-rich habitats, such as stubbles and fallow fields (*eg* Tellería & Santos 1985). Seven Linnets have been ringed in Britain in winter and recovered in France or Spain in a subsequent winter (Fig 5), suggesting that the same individuals may winter at different latitudes in different years. Two birds ringed on the English east coast in winter, and recovered in eastern Belgium and northern Italy in a subsequent winter, perhaps imply a reorientation of Scandinavian or central European birds that had drifted west of their usual wintering range in the winter in which they were ringed. Within a single winter, by contrast, 28 of 39 recoveries were within 20 km of the site of ringing. One bird ringed in winter on Merseyside and recovered in the same winter in Ireland confirms some exchange of Linnets between Britain and Ireland, but the paucity of ringing and recovery

Fig 5. Movements of over 20 km and recovery locations of Linnets ringed in winter and recovered in the same winter (28:11, red) or a subsequent winter (7:20, blue). Sample sizes of movements under:over 20 km are given but only those over 20 km are plotted.

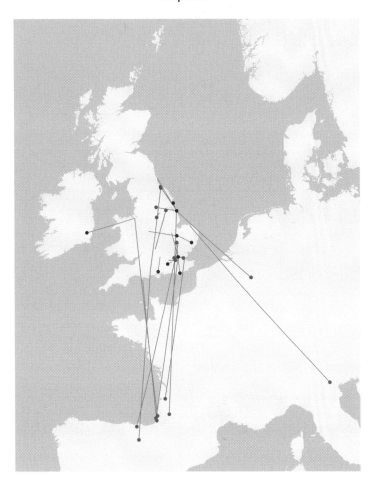

involve birds found in the southeast region during the breeding season (Fig 4). Such exchanges include birds leaving Britain in the autumn, returning in the spring, and found in midwinter in the Low Countries. This implies that this region might represent a discrete wintering area for a proportion of the Linnet population breeding in eastern England, although the concentration of recoveries in Belgium is almost certainly partly due to the impact of autumn hunting in Belgium, which also has an effect on the recovery maps for Goldfinch and Redpoll. In addition, movements mapped as straight lines in Fig 4 also conceal the fact that many Linnets wintering in France and Spain make a more circuitous return to Britain via a sea-crossing from Belgium or Holland, to cross the east coast of England, reversing this route in autumn. Regular westward migration in spring, and southerly or southeasterly migration in autumn, at east-coast observatories such as Holme and Spurn corroborate this (Durman 1976a), and show that many Linnets breeding in Britain migrate to and from the Continent via the North Sea rather than moving directly south over the English Channel. There are few ringing data from Ireland but observations at coastal watch-points reveal a heavy autumn passage (August–October) of birds heading south or southeast, perhaps reaching France via the coast of South Wales and southwest England. The return passage is also detectable along the south coast from Wexford to Cape Clear Island, suggesting that Irish breeding Linnets return via a similar route (*Birds in Ireland*).

Four recoveries involve birds ringed in southeast Britain as breeding birds, and recovered in the Low Countries in a subsequent breeding season, thus confirming that breeding populations in these two regions are connected by dispersal. Overall, however, Linnets breeding in Britain & Ireland tend to remain faithful to the area in which they first breed, with 55 of 63 (87%) recoveries of breeding adults in subsequent breeding seasons being within 20 km of the place of ringing.

Natal dispersal of Linnets is poorly understood. There are only 40 recoveries of Linnets ringed as pulli and recovered in a subsequent breeding season. Of these, only one is more than 20 km from the place of ringing, suggesting that fidelity to the natal region may be high. At a more local level, however, of several hundred Linnets colour-ringed as pulli on Oxfordshire farmland between 1995 and 1998, not one has yet been resighted as a breeding adult on the same farms (D Moorcroft pers comm). Even after accounting for high levels of post-fledging mortality, this suggests that dispersal from the immediate vicinity of the natal site may be considerable.

Given that Linnets depend primarily on the seeds of ruderal plants as a food source, agricultural change has the potential to influence population movements as well as trends in abundance. Although the recent population trends in Britain are not correlated with changes in survival rate, as estimated from ring-recovery data (Siriwardena *et al* 1999), reductions in the availability of seed-rich stubbles could nevertheless have altered the movement patterns of Linnets and caused increases in the proportion of birds emigrating during the winter in recent decades.

Overall, the movement patterns of most English Linnet populations are well understood. The wintering areas of those birds that leave England during the winter are reasonably well known, although the extent to which this picture is biased by the generation of recoveries from hunting is unknown. Ring-recovery data for southwest England, Wales, Ireland and parts of Scotland are much sparser, and any future increase in Linnet ringing effort would best be concentrated in these regions. In southern and eastern England, further ringing will help to clarify the extent and timing of flow of individuals between breeding and wintering populations there and on the near Continent.

Jeremy Wilson

data from Ireland renders generalizations difficult. The very small number of exchanges of Linnets between Britain and Scandinavia (two with Norway and one with Denmark) all involve breeding birds from Scandinavia occurring in Britain in autumn and winter. Whether this reflects the regular wintering of some Scandinavian breeders in Britain, or simply that Scandinavian birds moving to their normal wintering quarters in Belgium, France and Spain are occasionally drifted westwards by weather conditions, is unclear.

The return movement north is reported as beginning as early as February in the Gibraltar area (*BWP*), and British & Irish ring-recoveries support this view; the centre of gravity of recoveries has shifted to northern Spain, western France and the Low Countries by March and April, with only a few late-returners in the Low Countries by May. This picture is corroborated by the observation of a strong spring passage of Linnets at both British and Irish observatories in March and April, and the return of breeding birds to a long-term study area on Oxfordshire farmland in the last week of March and first week of April (Newton 1972, D Moorcroft pers comm).

There is very little evidence that these geographical patterns of movement differ substantially between the sexes or between age classes. Differences are apparent, however, in relation to the British & Irish region in which birds occur during the breeding season. Most notably, exchanges between Britain and the Low Countries almost exclusively

Twite
Carduelis flavirostris

Despite its rather drab plumage, the Twite has a special charm. At all seasons, it frequents some of the wildest and most remote tracts of our countryside: rain-soaked moorlands and mountains in the breeding season and storm-lashed Atlantic coastal farmlands and the vast grey expanses of North Sea saltmarshes in winter. The noisy antics of foraging parties impart a special character to such places and the birds' rich, rasping calls never fail to bring cheer to an otherwise sombre landscape.

The Twite has a curiously disjunct world distribution, with two widely separated centres of population. At least six races inhabit the hills and mountains of central Asia, from eastern Turkey eastward to central China, between the Himalayas in the south and the Kirghiz Steppes in the north, and make poorly documented, apparently nomadic but essentially altitudinal seasonal movements. Two races breed in northwest Europe. Birds of the nominate race breed principally along the western and northern coasts of Norway and the Kola Peninsula and winter in the coastal lowlands around the North and Baltic Seas and inland in central and eastern Europe where sometimes large numbers roost in urban areas. Birds of the race *pipilans* breed in Britain & Ireland (*BWP*). They tend to nest amongst tall vegetation, notably bracken and heather on open moorlands and mountain slopes from sea-level to the highest mountain summits, feeding in a diversity of places including flower-rich meadows and lightly grazed pastures, newly sown arable land, close-cropped or salt-singed turf and amongst tideline detritus. In winter, they also forage on saltmarshes, particularly those rich in glassworts, Sea Lavender, Annual Seablite or Sea Aster and amongst coastal stubbles and weedy fields (Orford 1973, Davies 1988, Reed 1995, Brown & Atkinson 1996).

The analysis of the data for this species was supported by Pat & Ann French

Relatively few Twite have been ringed in Britain & Ireland (Fig 1), and just seven foreign-ringed birds have been recovered here. Overall, 24% of recoveries have been from birds ringed as pulli. Nearly all those recoveries with ringing dates between May and July were ringed as pulli or juveniles, whilst recoveries with ringing dates between July and April were from birds ringed when fully grown (Fig 2). Though these data are few, there is no indication that movements differ between sexes or age classes. We know the finding circumstances for just 30 dead birds (Fig 3), most of which were found in Britain.

The bulk of the race *pipilans* breeds along the west and north coast of Scotland and on the Northern and Western Isles. Although breeding birds are also widely scattered elsewhere in upland Scotland, in Ireland, along the Pennines of northern England and very locally in Wales, the bird is only numerous in the south Pennines, approximately between Skipton, North Yorkshire, and the moorlands of Cheshire and Staffordshire (*1988–91 Atlas*). While this geographic spread is broadly represented in the ring-recovery data, the bulk of these data relate to the south Pennines and to the known wintering haunts of the south Pennines population on North Sea coasts between the Wash and the Thames, and between Boulogne and The Hague. This probably reflects the greater number of ringers and observers active in these areas, relative to northern and western Scotland, but as a consequence, we have a

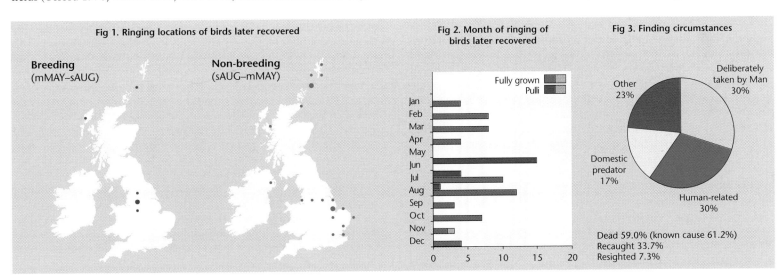

Fig 1. Ringing locations of birds later recovered

Breeding (mMAY–sAUG)

Non-breeding (sAUG–mMAY)

Fig 2. Month of ringing of birds later recovered

Fully grown
Pulli

Jan, Feb, Mar, Apr, May, Jun, Jul, Aug, Sep, Oct, Nov, Dec

0   5   10   15   20

Fig 3. Finding circumstances

Other 23%
Deliberately taken by Man 30%
Domestic predator 17%
Human-related 30%

Dead 59.0% (known cause 61.2%)
Recaught 33.7%
Resighted 7.3%

Ringing and recovery data

	<1960	60–69	70–79	80–89	90–97	Total
RINGING						
BTO ringing totals (%)	11	13	39	22	15	16,726
RECOVERIES						
BTO-ringed (%)	6	22	39	18	15	82
Foreign-ringed (%)	←	86	→	14	0	7

Statistical analyses

	Breeding population (mMAY–sAUG)	Wintering population (mNOV–sMAR)
Status	[SHORT-DISTANCE MIGRANT]	[LONG-DISTANCE MIGRANT]
Age differences	Not tested	Not tested
Sex differences	Not tested	Not tested
Regional differences	Not tested	Not tested
Finding circumstances	Not tested	Not tested

Fig 4. Locations outside the breeding season and movements of over 20 km between the breeding and non-breeding season of Twite present in Britain & Ireland during the breeding season, with birds from the Pennines (26, red) differentiated from those from other breeding areas (8, blue).

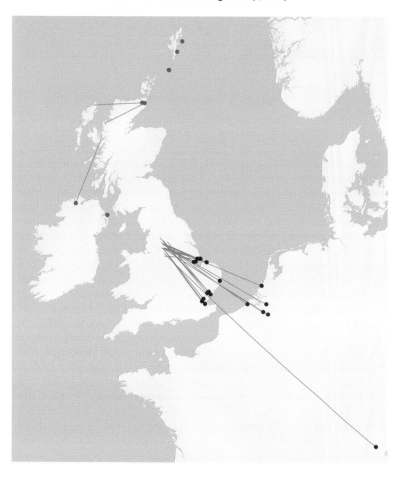

same heading between these areas. This is a most unusual recovery, however, as Twite are only very occasionally reported in Italy, mainly in the northeast, and records usually involve birds of the nominate race. Of the 26 recorded movements of Pennine birds between breeding and non-breeding areas, all involved distances in excess of 20 km (median 277 km). Definite spring and autumn movements are not discernible and this may, in part, reflect the paucity of recovery data overall and the lack of targeted ringing of the species at intermediate points. It may, however, indicate that the movements between breeding and wintering areas do not involve intermediate staging areas, or that stopovers are brief. The fact that inland gatherings of Twite are not reported away from the breeding areas lends strength to the argument that the movements are direct and uninterrupted. The timing of arrivals and departures in coastal areas documented by county bird reports ties in well with the ringing data: along the Norfolk coast, for example, birds are very rarely reported before the last week of September and few linger beyond mid-April. Certainly, not all birds move to the coast in winter and small foraging parties, presumably from the local population, are reported in the south Pennines in most winters. However, the factors that might determine the fraction of the population that remains inland are unknown. Overall, the evidence points to a large-scale movement of birds away from the south Pennines. Small numbers of birds also winter in the northwest of England (*Winter Atlas*) and, although the source of these birds is unknown, a Pennine connection seems likely, especially given the recovery of a Pennine bird from the Ribble Estuary in March.

Ring-recovery data suggest that birds breeding elsewhere in Britain & Ireland are much more sedentary: four of eight movements of such birds were of less than 20 km (median 7.5 km). The *Winter Atlas* supports such a contention, clearly indicating that large numbers of Twite are found in these areas in winter. These have probably moved downhill to food-rich areas such as coastal farmland where they occur in large flocks in weedy fields (Clark & Sellers 1997). There is also some evidence of interchange between Orkney and Shetland and between southwest Scotland and Northern Ireland.

Our own study of the movements of birds colour-ringed in North Norfolk in winter suggests that, while individual birds made many movements between patches of suitable habitat during the winter, they remained faithful to the general stretch of coast. Resightings of 45 colour-ringed birds showed that birds made movements of up to 25 km during the winter and movements of up to 10 km were made regularly, sometimes on a daily basis (Atkinson 1998). No resightings were made outside Norfolk but two birds returned the following year, and one the year after, suggesting some site-fidelity between winters. However, unless a particularly large number died between winters, the low return rate suggests that they are not particularly site-faithful. In fact, there are several instances amongst the BTO data of birds wintering on different sides of the North Sea in successive years. In contrast, recaptures of birds of the nominate race appear to indicate marked fidelity to wintering areas between years (*BWP*).

Rather little information is available on fidelity to breeding areas. Just one of the 63 birds colour-ringed by us as pulli in the south Pennines in 1995 was found in a subsequent year, nesting just 6 km from its natal area.

In total, seven foreign-ringed Twite have been recovered in Britain & Ireland, five from the Netherlands, and two from France. These are birds ringed in winter and recovered in the same or a subsequent winter in southeast England or in the breeding season in the south Pennines. Interestingly, and despite a huge ringing effort, there have been no recoveries in Britain & Ireland of birds that breed in Norway, many of which have been found in Germany, the Netherlands and Belgium, in areas overlapping the wintering range of Pennines-bred birds. While there may, in fact, be little or no interchange between the two populations, it is likely that at least a part of the Norwegian population winters in southeastern Britain. The arrival of such birds could account for the easterly movements of small numbers of Twite annually observed

more detailed understanding of the movements of birds between the Pennines and the coast than of movements in the northern part of the range. The movements of the Welsh- and Irish-breeding birds are totally unknown.

Between April and September, recoveries of British & Irish birds come from the south Pennines, the Northern and Western Isles, the west coast of Scotland and adjacent northeastern Ireland, clearly reflecting the broad distribution of breeding birds (*1988–91 Atlas*). Twite remain for a relatively long period in their breeding areas and have an extended laying season (*BWP*, Brown *et al* 1995). Some recoveries involve birds ringed as pulli in August and none of the five juvenile birds recovered within 90 days of ringing had moved further than 7 km from their natal area. Our own studies in the south Pennines (pers obs, H A McGhie pers comm) indicate that young and adults gather in large foraging flocks after breeding and remain near the nesting areas well into August at least: 15 birds colour-ringed as pulli near Halifax in 1995 were subsequently resighted up to 74 days after hatching (mean 47 days) during which time they had moved only as far as 8.2 km from the nest (mean 2.4 km).

Between October and March, the distribution of recoveries is markedly different. Whilst there are still recoveries from the Northern Isles of Scotland and Northern Ireland, there are no recoveries from the south Pennines. Additionally, there are a large number of recoveries from the southern North Sea coasts between the Wash and the Thames and again in northeastern France, Belgium and the southwest of the Netherlands. These data clearly describe a movement of birds between breeding areas in the south Pennines and wintering areas around the shores of the southern North Sea (Fig 4). The one unusually long-distance recovery from northern Italy in November is further along the along the Norfolk coast for example, and overwintering by a significant fraction of the population could have accounted for the remarkable estimates, in the tens of thousands, of wintering Twite in the Wash during the 1970s and early 1980s (Taylor *et al* 1999). An alternative explanation, however, is that there has been a massive decline in the size of the Pennines breeding population, a possibility supported by evidence of marked declines since the mid-1970s on two Pennine CBC plots (Fuller *et al* 2002).

Twite associate strongly at all seasons with relatively small areas of vulnerable habitat: with tall upland vegetation and with flower-rich swards in the breeding season and with seed-rich stubbles or saltmarsh vegetation in winter. The retention and appropriate management of both types of habitat is likely to be crucial to their conservation. Clearly, a more detailed understanding of the habitats that are used by particular populations will assist this. Future studies should focus on further elucidation of the movements of Pennine birds, to determine whether any staging areas are used in spring or autumn between the breeding areas and the coast, on the movements of birds in Scotland, and on determining whether there is any exchange or interaction between the two main populations in northwestern Europe. Much still remains to be learnt about this enigmatic bird.

Andy Brown & Phil Atkinson

Lesser Redpoll
Carduelis cabaret

Common Redpoll
Carduelis flammea

These small finches, in common with several other species that breed at higher latitudes in the northern hemisphere and feed chiefly on tree seeds, are much more conspicuous as migrants in some years than others. During 'eruption' autumns, large numbers migrate much further south than usual, a consequence of high populations, and/or poor crops of their preferred seed foods.

The taxonomy of Redpolls is complicated, but three distinct forms are generally acknowledged. The smallest form, *cabaret*, has recently been elevated to the level of a separate species (BOU 2001). It breeds in Britain, chiefly in the north, west and southeast, and throughout Ireland except for parts of the south and east (*1988–91 Atlas*); some also occur along the western fringes of the Low Countries and in isolated mountainous areas of central Europe, including the Alps. Its wintering range lies chiefly in southern Britain, central and southern Ireland, Belgium and France, though the mountain populations move only locally, to lower altitudes, in winter. The nominate race of *flammea* breeds further north than *cabaret*, right across Europe, Asia and North America. Birds from Finland and northern European Russia move southeastwards into central Russia in winter and those from Scandinavia travel to central Europe, though variable numbers remain in Fennoscandia (Eriksson 1970). Much less detailed information from further east indicates that birds from the subarctic Asian breeding areas also move southeast or south in winter, reaching the central Asian republics, such as Kazakhstan and Mongolia, and Japan (*BWP*). Alaskan and Canadian breeding birds winter chiefly in the northern USA (Troy 1983). Birds of the third form *rostrata* (a race of *Carduelis flammea*) breed in Iceland, where they are mostly resident, and

The analysis of the data for these species was supported by the late Geoffrey Gush

around the fringes of southern Greenland, from which they migrate to Iceland in autumn. The Icelandic breeders are sometimes classed as a separate race *islandica* (*eg* European Atlas).

In the Arctic, Redpolls breed chiefly in areas of shrubs, such as Dwarf Birch and willows, but will occupy treeless tundra. In subarctic zones, more extensive tree cover, especially birch, is preferred, but nesting in Juniper is often recorded. In Britain, scrub woodland and young conifer plantations are the favoured habitats, while in the mountainous areas of central Europe subalpine conifer woods, especially larch, are used in summer. Winter habitats are predominantly birch and Alder woods, but also open ground, especially where seeds of *Compositae* and *Chenopodiaceae* are available.

Most Redpolls ringed in Britain & Ireland have been caught during the non-breeding season and very few nestlings have been marked (yielding only 16 recoveries so far). The distribution of breeding-season ringing effort (Fig 1), when compared with the breeding distributions recorded in the *1968–72* and *1988–91* Atlases, shows that the large populations in Scotland, Wales and Ireland are seriously under-represented. Populations have declined since the late 1970s and the range has contracted slightly (*1988–91 Atlas*). Of the total of more than 1,500 juveniles and adults yielding recoveries, about half were ringed in August to October inclusive, *ie* just before and during autumn migration

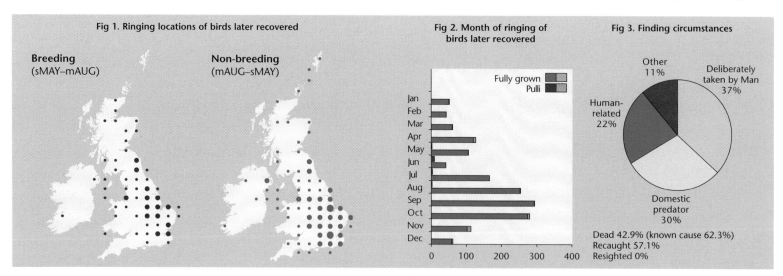

Fig 1. Ringing locations of birds later recovered

Breeding (sMAY–mAUG)   Non-breeding (mAUG–sMAY)

Fig 2. Month of ringing of birds later recovered

Fully grown / Pulli

Fig 3. Finding circumstances

Other 11%
Deliberately taken by Man 37%
Human-related 22%
Domestic predator 30%

Dead 42.9% (known cause 62.3%)
Recaught 57.1%
Resighted 0%

Ringing and recovery data

	<1960	60–69	70–79	80–89	90–97	Total
RINGING						
BTO ringing totals (%)	1	10	48	25	16	183,331
RECOVERIES						
BTO-ringed (%)	1	16	51	22	9	1,583
Foreign-ringed (%)	←	69	→	16	15	81

Statistical analyses

	Breeding population (sMAY–mAUG)	Wintering population (mNOV–sMAR)
Status	[SHORT-DISTANCE MIGRANT**]	[LONG-DISTANCE MIGRANT*]
Age differences	Not tested	Not tested
Sex differences	Not tested	Not tested
Regional differences	Not tested	Not tested
Finding circumstances	Not tested	Not tested

Fig 4. Locations in (a) autumn (365), (b) winter (123) and (c) spring (119), and movements of over 20 km between the breeding and non-breeding season, of Redpolls present in Britain & Ireland during the breeding season.

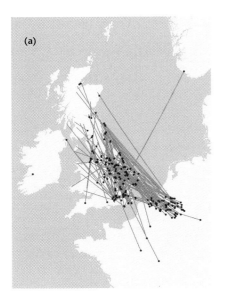 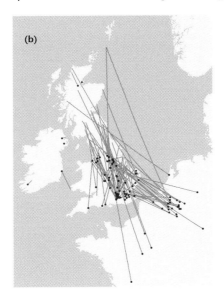 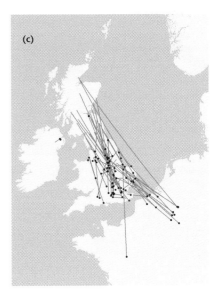

(Fig 2). Of the recoveries analysed, 43% were reported as dead, two-thirds of these from known causes (Fig 3). The other 57% were birds recaught by ringers. While in Britain 'domestic predators' were responsible for half of the known causes of death, almost all of the 123 recoveries from Belgium were taken by Man for the (former) cagebird industry. Legislation restricting this practice was introduced in 1979 by the European Directive on the Conservation of Wild Birds, so information on the frequency and extent of movements from Britain to continental Europe has declined in recent decades.

After breeding ends, usually in early August, Redpolls often gather in flocks of some tens, occasionally hundreds, of adults and juveniles in a few favoured feeding sites, where adults moult, before beginning southward migration. Very few recoveries of ringed birds have come from Scotland after August and from anywhere in Britain north of the Humber after September. Departures from Northumberland and active southward passage have been recorded in the second half of September (Evans 1966b, 1969). Arrivals of birds on passage and at potential wintering sites in central and southern England occur chiefly in October. In years in which birch seed crops in central and southern England are poor, many birds cross the Channel in October and early November, to Belgium, the Netherlands and France. By the latter month in years of large eruptions, such as 1977 (Boddy 1984), a few individuals have travelled as far as northern Italy and, by midwinter, reached the Mediterranean coast of France. Autumn movements of birds using Britain & Ireland during the breeding season follow a predominantly south-southeasterly direction within Britain, turning more to the southeast after the Channel is crossed (Fig 4). This picture may be biased somewhat, however, by the concentration of recoveries attributable to bird-catching in Belgium in the 1960s and 1970s. Mapping provides no clear evidence of differences in autumn and winter recovery areas between adults and juveniles, or between males and females, although juveniles tended to be recovered further to the east of their ringing localities than did adults (Fig 5). No differences between the age classes or sexes were detected in the statistical analyses. Most of the recoveries in central and southern France have been of birds ringed in the southeast region of England (chiefly the eastern Midlands) but, as most of these refer to birds ringed during the non-breeding season (Fig 6), they may have come from further north. The possibility remains that some southern English breeding birds move south in autumn, only to be replaced by northern British birds in winter. The few (12) movements of ringed individuals between winters support the supposition that winter site-fidelity is not the norm, (10 had moved more than 20 km), though some ringed Redpolls have returned to a

Fig 5. Monthly variation in the differences in (a) latitude and (b) longitude between ringing and recovery locations of Redpolls present in Britain & Ireland during the breeding season. Monthly medians (points) and interquartile ranges (bars) are shown.

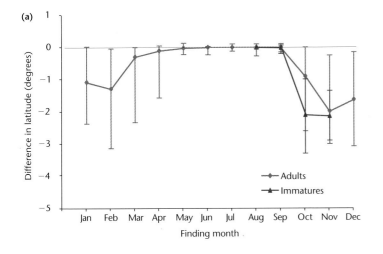 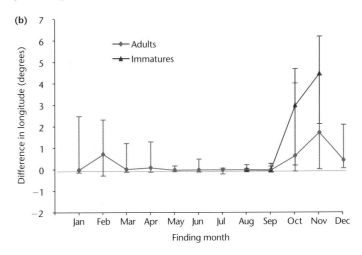

Fig 6. Movements overseas of Redpolls present in Britain & Ireland in (a) autumn (209), (b) winter (23) and (c) spring (35).

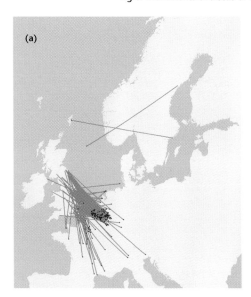 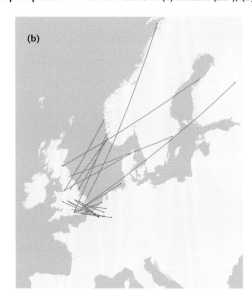 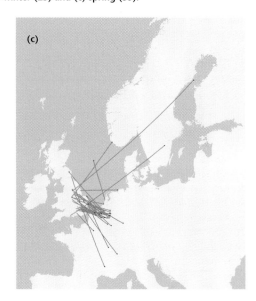

wintering site in western Germany (Mohr 1967). An alternative explanation of the variable proportion of birds moving across the Channel in different autumns would be that the emigrants were chiefly juveniles searching for a suitable wintering site, with sufficient food, to which they would return in subsequent years as adults. Thus in autumns with good birch seed crops in southern England, juveniles would not need to emigrate but the adult survivors from previous emigrations would continue to do so.

Return movements in spring from southern to northern England have begun by early April, and passage of birds returning from the Continent has been noted in Kent in mid-April, but often continues further north into early May (Evans 1966b, Newton 1967b). Movements from southern England follow predominantly a north-northwesterly direction (Fig 4), reversing the autumn migration route. A few recoveries suggest lack of fidelity to breeding areas by some individuals, notably two that had been present in one breeding season in central England but were recovered in May in a later year in Belgium. Although these could have been late-returning migrants, the establishment and spread of breeding *cabaret* in Belgium and the Netherlands may have arisen not only by colonization by young birds but also by such adults. At least some, perhaps the majority, of adult Redpolls return to the same breeding areas between years (22 recoveries of dead birds between breeding seasons indicated a median movement of only 11 km, P5–95=0–75 km) even though the distribution and particularly the abundance of the species have decreased significantly over the decades between the *1968–72* and *1988–91 Atlases*. This decline has continued during the 1990s (Crick *et al* 1998).

Although most nominate *flammea* from Scandinavia move to the east of south in autumn (Peiponen 1967), a few ringed birds have been recovered after movements between south and south-southwest (Eriksson 1970). Some reach eastern Britain in most years. Large-scale eruptions of many thousands of birds into western central Europe occur

in some autumns, notably 1972 (Ernst 1983) but rarely into Britain, where 1910 was the last major influx (Evans 1911). The few recoveries in Norway, Sweden and Finland, of birds ringed in Britain during the non-breeding season, and the slightly greater number of Redpolls ringed in Fennoscandia and recovered in Britain (Fig 6), concur with the general picture for this species of change in wintering area by some individuals from year to year.

A few *rostrata* from Greenland reach northwest Scotland in most years and large influxes have reached western Scotland and Northern Ireland, notably in 1925, 1955 and 1959 (Williamson 1963a). These may be the result not only of successful breeding in some years, leading to eruptions, but also of displacement of birds from their normal sea-crossing to Iceland, causing them to reach northern Britain by 'cyclonic approach' (Williamson 1961). No recoveries of ringed *rostrata* are available to shed further light on these movements at present.

Major uncertainties in present knowledge relate to the extent of preparation for migration in autumn by different ages of Redpolls in different years. Indications of substantial fat deposition in September in Northumberland (Evans 1969) and Kent (Boddy 1984) in years of eruptions to continental Europe, but not in other autumns, need confirmation. Further information is also needed to check whether juveniles move further than adults and whether the proportion of adults amongst the emigrants from southern England is affected by the size of the birch seed crop there. The decline in abundance of Redpolls breeding in Britain & Ireland is associated with a decline in abundance and seed production of birch in southern England (*1988–91 Atlas*). Ringing of birds in autumn and throughout the winter might indicate how nomadic the species has become in its non-breeding areas, and hence provide guidance for a 'species action plan' for its conservation in the future.

P R Evans

Common Crossbill Scottish Crossbill

Loxia curvirostra *Loxia scotica*

Parrot Crossbill

Loxia pytyopsittacus

Crossbills are specialist feeders on the seeds of conifers and are renowned for their irruptive patterns of movement. At any one location, their population size fluctuates markedly, correlated with food abundance (Reinikainen 1937, Petty *et al* 1995). When high numbers coincide with a failure in food supply over a wide area, the subsequent exodus regularly results in large-scale movements to areas distant from the large coniferous forests of their core breeding range (Newton 1972). Crossbills often breed in these areas, some returning to their core range the following year. The size, scale, direction and timing of crossbill movements thus vary from year to year, and are largely determined by the availability of the seeds of coniferous trees.

Crossbills inhabit coniferous forests across the northern hemisphere and some 25 forms of the genus have been described, 10 in North America and 15 in the Palearctic (Newton 1972, Groth 1993). The Common Crossbill has a holarctic distribution and some 20 forms. The nominate race *curvirostra* breeds in the boreal forests of Europe west to Japan, four subspecies breed in the Mediterranean Basin, and others in southern Asia. Nominate *curvirostra* may include further forms, as two bill sizes (Herremans 1988b) and three call types (Summers *et al* 2002) have been distinguished. At least one form breeds annually in coniferous woodland throughout Britain & Ireland and the other two probably breed following irruptions. In irruption years, Common Crossbills also often reach areas outside the known breeding range (*eg* Iceland).

Parrot Crossbills have a much smaller breeding range, restricted to Fennoscandia and European Russia, an area within which the birds

The analysis of the data for these species was supported by the Highland Crossbill Study Group

move about from year to year. In some years population irruptions to the south and west are followed by breeding, which has occurred in Scotland, Denmark, the Netherlands, Belgium and England (*European Atlas*). The Scottish Crossbill is endemic, restricted to the north and east of Scotland.

The various forms of crossbill are superficially similar and vary mainly in size and bill morphology associated with variation in the robustness of the cones that protect their principal foods. Each form of crossbill has a bill morphology so well suited to extract seed from a specific conifer, that it is largely dependent on that food source for breeding (Benkman 1993a). This in turn means that the seasonal patterns in reproduction, moult and movements of different types of crossbill are determined by the patterns of seed production in the conifers to which they are adapted.

Of the three species, the Common Crossbill has the smallest bill, well adapted to remove seeds from Norway Spruce cones and the Parrot Crossbill has the largest and most powerful bill to open the hard cones of Scots Pine. The Scottish Crossbill has an intermediate bill adapted to prising apart the cone scales of Scots Pine, the only native cone-bearing conifer in Scotland. Although each crossbill specializes on one conifer species, they also use other foods. Common Crossbills switch between foods in mixed conifer plantations, using spruce or larch in winter and

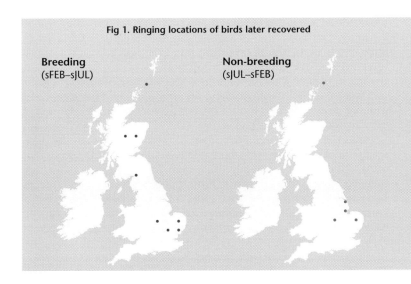

Fig 1. Ringing locations of birds later recovered

Breeding (sFEB–sJUL) Non-breeding (sJUL–sFEB)

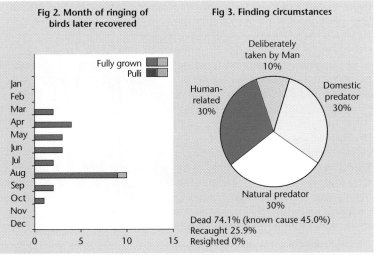

Fig 2. Month of ringing of birds later recovered

Fully grown
Pulli

Fig 3. Finding circumstances

Deliberately taken by Man 10%
Human-related 30%
Domestic predator 30%
Natural predator 30%

Dead 74.1% (known cause 45.0%)
Recaught 25.9%
Resighted 0%

Ringing and recovery data

	<1960	60–69	70–79	80–89	90–97	Total
RINGING						
BTO ringing totals (%)	6	11	11	12	60	3,566
RECOVERIES						
BTO-ringed (%)	3	14	3	14	66	29
Foreign-ringed (%)	←	0	→	0	100	1

Statistical analyses

	Breeding population (sFEB–sJUL)	Wintering population (sOCT–sJAN)
Status	[LONG-DISTANCE MIGRANT]*	[LONG-DISTANCE MIGRANT]*
Age differences	—	Not tested
Sex differences	—	Not tested
Regional differences	—	Not tested
Finding circumstances	—	Not tested

Fig 4. Recovery locations and movements of over 20 km for the 30 included recoveries of Crossbills ringed or recovered in Britain & Ireland.

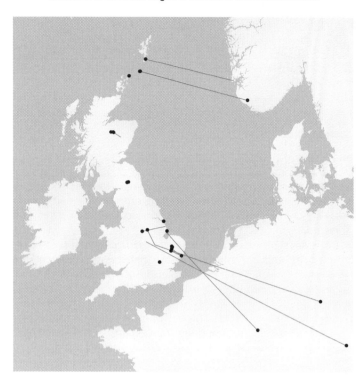

Fig 4. Recovery locations and movements of over 20 km for the 30 included recoveries of Crossbills ringed or recovered in Britain & Ireland.

Scots Pine in spring, as the cones ripen to release seeds (Marquiss & Rae 1994). Scottish Crossbills also use non-native conifers outside the breeding season (Nethersole-Thompson 1975).

Common Crossbills breed mainly from November to April, when spruce seed is most available, whereas Scottish and Parrot Crossbills breed from March to June, the period when Scots Pine seed is most available. As the current year's conifer seed is eaten or shed, crossbills move to find a new seed-crop. Norway Spruce produces seed prolifically but periodically, often synchronized over large areas. Common Crossbills therefore experience regular depletion of their food and must either switch to other foods or move to an area where spruce seed is available, prior to their next breeding season. They make their greatest movements in summer, laying down fat stores while feeding on Scots Pine prior to their migration to find new spruce crops (Newton 1972).

Unlike spruce, Scots Pine produces seed most years and the seeds take a year to ripen, the cones staying on the tree for two years. As the last of the ripe pine seed is consumed or shed in summer, the new seed-crop becomes available. Crossbills that can prise open the hard cones of Scots Pine thus only occasionally need to move large distances, when the pine crop fails or birds are very abundant. Parrot Crossbills make irruptive movements in continental Europe less frequently than do Common Crossbills (Newton 1972), and Scottish Crossbills are assumed to be resident, because no population has been recorded outside the Scottish breeding range.

The movements of Common Crossbills have been deduced mainly from spatial and temporal patterns of abundance, but also from observations of the directions of flights and from the recoveries of ringed birds. The sample of crossbills ringed is relatively small and few are ringed as nestlings. This is because they are not easy to catch and their nests not easily found or reached. The recovery rate is also low and only 30 recoveries are recorded here; 29 from birds ringed in Britain and one from Norway.

Most crossbills have been caught in the same few places — either at drinking sites in coniferous woodland or at migration stations (Fig 1). It is therefore possible that the northwest–southeast orientation of movements involving Britain (Fig 4) is the result of spatial bias. The far

greater numbers of recorded movements within continental Europe suggest a different pattern (Gatter 1993, summarized below). None of these birds had been ringed in the nest (Fig 2). Most had been ringed as fully grown birds in spring or summer — the seasons of greatest movement when most crossbills are caught at bird migration stations, such as Fair Isle and the Col de Bretolet, western Switzerland. The recovery circumstance is known for 10 birds and only one had been deliberately taken by Man (Fig 3), so there is also likely bias towards individuals in poor condition.

Despite the paucity of data from Britain & Ireland and its potential bias, it contributes to the wider picture of crossbill movements. Newton (1972) reviewed the evidence from the Palearctic, suggesting that crossbills differed from other migrant birds in making only one main movement each year. In most years this involves relatively short distances from areas where spruce seed is exhausted to those where it is plentiful, but in irruption years the birds move large distances (up to 4,000 km) into southern and western Europe, including Britain & Ireland. Between 1800 and 1965, 67 such invasions occurred irregularly, at intervals of one to 11 years, and the birds came from the boreal forests of northern Europe in Fennoscandia and in Russia west of the Urals. Irruptions occurred when spruce crops were poor, but not always, so it is thought that high population density is a major predisposing factor.

The European ring-recoveries are mostly of birds ringed as they migrated but they show onward movements further south and west, and return movements in subsequent years to specific regions in the far north and east. This suggests that irruptions are not random dispersal movements but resemble conventional migrations, with populations of a specific provenance having strong orientation and a return phase, albeit delayed (see also Knox 1992). Invading crossbills usually breed but it is unknown whether the subsequent juveniles disperse randomly, have an inherent tendency to migrate in a specific direction, or merely accompany adults returning to the area of their provenance.

Since Newton's review, there have been 11 further irruptions and more recoveries, largely endorsing existing interpretations. However, on the basis of long-term records of birds flying over a bird observatory in southern Germany, Gatter (1993) suggested that Common Crossbills move not once but two or three times each year. The main movements are to the south and west in summer but, following moult in autumn, birds return north and eastwards in winter to new breeding grounds. After breeding, the birds then move again in the same direction towards the area of their original provenance. Gatter argued that such movement patterns are shown in all years but are over much greater distances in irruption years. The idea is plausible but requires evidence from ringing or laboratory orientation studies.

Amongst recent irruptions, that of 1990 was by far the most spectacular as the birds were more numerous and travelled further than usual (*BWP*). They apparently came from northern Russia, with large numbers passing through Latvia, Estonia and southern Sweden, though fewer were reported in Finland. Large influxes occurred over most of Europe, with exceptional numbers reported for Iceland, the Faeroes, Britain and Ireland, the Netherlands, Belgium, Germany, Switzerland, France and Hungary. Migrants may well have reached the Mediterranean, as there were unusual numbers in Malta and Gibraltar. The records spanned May to September and the greatest numbers in most places were in late July and August. In Britain, the invasion was most obvious in the north, with large numbers arriving in late May. By the second week of June, birds were common in southern England and in Ireland. Substantial numbers were involved, with midwinter estimates of half a million in Scotland and forty thousand in Kielder Forest (Borders).

Relatively few Parrot Crossbills are ringed and there is less information on their movements. Irruptions occur with less than half the frequency and the birds do not move so far as Common Crossbills. Most invasions from Scandinavia reach Denmark but numbers are small and only occasionally do birds travel further. Exceptional were the irruptions of 1982 and 1990, when large numbers of birds reached far south (Germany) and west (Britain) of their normal range. In Britain, there were about a hundred records in 1982 and twice that number in 1990. Consistent with the seasonal availability of Scots Pine seed, Parrot Crossbills disperse from breeding areas in July and August and irruptive movements south take place from September through to November. The birds then winter in pine woodland where some breed the following spring, though many disappear, apparently to return north.

There is only one ring-recovery of a Scottish Crossbill, ringed as a nestling in Strathspey and captured as a breeding male two years later in upper Deeside (Fig 4).

All three species of crossbill bred in northeast Scotland during the 1990s, and studies of individually colour-marked birds there have provided some new information (Marquiss & Rae 1996). Dispersal of juvenile Scottish and Parrot Crossbills started in June, though most moved in July. After fledging, young were fed by their parents for a further seven weeks so that movements in July included some cohesive family parties from late broods. By August, all juveniles were independent and had started body moult; adults had begun both wing moult and body moult. Parrot Crossbills used seminatural Scots Pine forest, where colour-ringed birds that were seen in October or November had apparently settled, because most were still in the same areas the following spring. In contrast, Scottish Crossbills dispersed from their Scots Pine breeding areas into nearby larch or spruce for the winter, moving back into Scots Pine woodland in February or March.

On a larger scale, there was indirect evidence of the greater residency of Scottish and Parrot compared with Common Crossbills from resightings of 327 colour-ringed, fully grown individuals of measured bill size (Marquiss & Rae 2002). Small-billed crossbills (depth less than 11.1 mm) were not seen within 5 km of the capture site after six months whereas those with intermediate and large bills (up to 14 mm) were seen often, and for up to four years. Moreover there was no evidence of larger-billed birds preparing for long-distance movements. The only birds netted that had pre-migratory fat were small-billed birds feeding on Scots Pine in late spring and early summer prior to their departure.

The main factor currently influencing the conservation of crossbills is commercial forestry. The exploitation of boreal forests world-wide has substantially reduced the average age of trees and thus the amount and distribution of conifer seed (Benkman 1993b). This is said to have reduced the abundance of Parrot Crossbills in Fennoscandia (*European Atlas*); large-billed crossbills prefer to feed on old Scots Pine trees, which have rounded canopies with high densities of small cones (Summers & Proctor 1999). Conversely, at lower latitudes, reforestation using both native and exotic tree species has increased the abundance and diversity of conifers, enabling the establishment of new populations of Common Crossbills.

In Britain & Ireland, aspects that will influence the abundance and movements of all three crossbills are the extension of seminatural Scots Pine forests and the retention of a high proportion of 'old growth' trees in mixed-species commercial woodlands. A key question now is how much old forest is required to sustain viable populations of the larger-billed crossbills. To resolve this we need unbiased estimates of the scale of crossbill movements in non-irruption years.

Mick Marquiss

Common Bullfinch (Bullfinch)

Pyrrhula pyrrhula

The Bullfinch is one of the most attractive of the European finches. It has a wide geographical range, extending in forest and scrub from Ireland across Eurasia to Japan, in boreal, temperate and montane areas. Bullfinches of high and mid-latitudes (in Europe the races *pyrrhula* and *europea*) are partially migratory and irruptive, their movements varying from year to year depending on winter seed-crops. The most northerly birds from Fennoscandia and Russia move the longest distances (sometimes more than 2,000 km), while the mid-latitude birds mostly move less than 400 km. In mountain areas, they make altitudinal movements (*BWP*). Bullfinches that breed in Britain and Ireland (race *pileata*) and Iberia (race *iberiae*) are non-migratory. Birds of the British & Irish race are smaller and duller in colour than the nominate 'northern' Bullfinches that breed across northern Eurasia and occur occasionally in eastern Britain as scarce migrants.

In Britain & Ireland, Bullfinches are found mainly in dense woodland and scrub but they are also seen in thick hedgerows on farmland and in shrubby parks and gardens. Although resident, they move around locally in response to changes in the availability of their favourite foods (mainly seeds of certain trees and herbaceous plants), and in spring, when buds begin to swell, they are frequent visitors to gardens and orchards. In the breeding season, Bullfinches are seen mostly as singletons or pairs but in autumn and winter they form parties of up to a dozen or more. While feeding, the birds usually remain within a few metres of cover, darting into hiding when disturbed.

Most of the British & Irish ring-recoveries of Bullfinches relate to England, especially to the fruit-growing areas of the southeast (Fig 1),

The analysis of the data for this species was supported in memory of Ben Mercer

with relatively few from Wales, Scotland and Ireland. Only a small proportion of recoveries relates to birds ringed as nestlings, and most recoveries refer to birds ringed when fully grown, many as juveniles in the autumn (Fig 2). About two-thirds of all recoveries were attributed to a known cause of death, and most of these were human-related, as many individuals were killed by domestic cats or as pests in commercial orchards (Fig 3). Many more males than females have been recovered, especially in the breeding season when females remain at their nests for most of the time and so are less likely to fall into human hands.

The results of the present analysis reflect the sedentary habits of Bullfinches in Britain, as found by earlier studies (Summers 1979). Regardless of season, most British-ringed birds were recovered within 20 km of where they were ringed, and very few at more than 100 km, with the longest recorded movement within Britain being 178 km. For British & Irish breeders, the median distance between ringing and recovery (in any season) was less than 1 km (P5–95=0–22 km, n=1,538). Movements from the site of ringing can evidently occur in any compass direction, and at no time of year are any directional preferences apparent. There are therefore no significant latitudinal or longitudinal shifts in distribution through the year. Only one foreign-ringed Bullfinch has been recovered in Britain, moving from the Netherlands to Essex, and only four Bullfinches ringed in Britain have been recovered

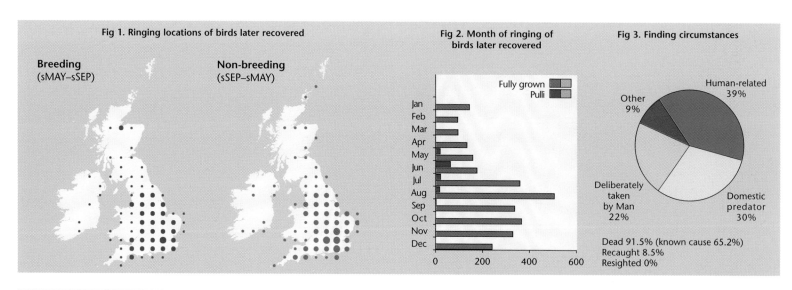

Fig 1. Ringing locations of birds later recovered

Breeding (sMAY–sSEP)

Non-breeding (sSEP–sMAY)

Fig 2. Month of ringing of birds later recovered

Fig 3. Finding circumstances

Dead 91.5% (known cause 65.2%)
Recaught 8.5%
Resighted 0%

Ringing and recovery data

	<1960	60–69	70–79	80–89	90–97	Total
RINGING						
BTO ringing totals (%)	2	18	32	30	18	256,856
RECOVERIES						
BTO-ringed (%)	4	29	34	24	9	3,075
Foreign-ringed (%)	0	100	0	0	0	1

Statistical analyses

	Breeding population (sMAY–sSEP)	Wintering population (sNOV–mMAR)
Status	SEDENTARY (0)	SEDENTARY
Age differences[S]	Not significant*	Not significant
Sex differences[S]	Not significant*	Not significant*
Regional differences	Not tested	Not tested
Finding circumstances	Significant	Not significant*

Fig 4. Dispersal distances for Bullfinches (a) ringed in one breeding season (May–August) and recovered in a later breeding season and (b) ringed in one mid-winter period (December–February) and recovered in a later midwinter period.

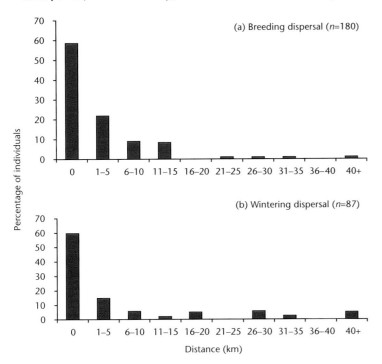

Fig 5. Movements of over 20 km and recovery locations of Bullfinches ringed in winter and recovered in a subsequent winter. There were 98:20 movements under:over 20 km but only those over 20 km are plotted.

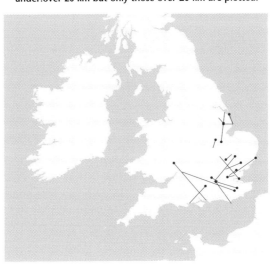

abroad. Of these, three, one in Belgium and two in France, were females in autumn or winter and were recovered at longer distances (305–392 km) than the maximum recorded within Britain. However, the fourth foreign recovery referred to a male, ringed one winter on the coast of southeast Scotland and recovered in a later winter 1,600 km to the northeast in northern Sweden. Almost certainly this was a 'northern' Bullfinch which was caught as it visited Britain in the invasion year of 1994 but which stayed nearer its breeding area in another year. To judge from sight records, mainly from Fair Isle, a handful of northern Bullfinches reach northeast Britain in most years. Invasions involving much larger numbers than usual occurred in 1910 and 1994 (Riddington & Ward 1998). Other long-distance ring-recoveries of Fennoscandian Bullfinches have been obtained in the mid-latitudes of continental Europe, from Belgium eastwards to southern Russia (*BWP*).

Bullfinches have a long breeding season, in which each pair has time to raise two or three broods. In consequence, young are produced throughout the period May–August, and occasionally into September (Newton 1966). After they have become independent, the juveniles wander around and some were recovered more than 1 km from the natal site between two and four weeks after ringing, and at more than 5 km three months after ringing. Little information is available on natal dispersal because only 26 birds ringed as nestlings were recovered in later breeding seasons (taken as May–August): of these birds, 22 had moved less than 5 km, another three had moved 6–11 km, with a single individual at 46 km (median distance less than 1 km).

Much more information is available on breeding dispersal, for 180 individuals of breeding age were ringed one breeding season (taken as May–August) and recovered in a later one (Fig 4). Some 80% of these individuals had moved less than 5 km between years, another 17% had moved 6–20 km, and less than 3% had moved greater distances (maximum 51 km). The median distance was less than 1 km, and there was no obvious difference in breeding dispersal between the sexes. It seems, therefore, that most British Bullfinches breed in the same locality in successive years.

More surprisingly, perhaps, some Bullfinches of breeding age made movements within a breeding season that were longer than expected of

normal foraging flights. In total, 102 birds were both ringed and recovered within the same breeding season (again taken as May–August inclusive). Nineteen of these birds had moved more than 5 km between ringing and recovery site, and three had moved more than 20 km. From the dates involved, it is not impossible that some of these birds could have made substantial moves between successive breeding attempts in the same season. They involved both sexes (Newton 2000).

Turning to wintering dispersal, of 118 movements of individuals between different winters, only 20 moved further than 20 km (Fig 5; median=0 km, P5–95=0–104 km). Using a more restricted definition of midwinter (December-February), 87 individuals were ringed in one midwinter period and recovered in a later one. Again some 75% of these birds had moved less than 5 km between years, another 11% had moved 6–20 km, and 12% had moved greater distances (Fig 4). The median distance was less than 1 km and again there was no obvious difference in dispersal distances between the sexes. Yet other individuals made movements of similar lengths within the same winter. Repeated trapping and ringing at particular sites, together with studies of radio-tagged birds, have revealed that the majority of Bullfinches spend most of their time in a relatively small area, with occasional excursions elsewhere, and periodic shifts from one location to another, in line with changes in food supplies (Greig-Smith & Wilson 1984). This explains why large numbers can be caught at particular sites over a period of months, when no more than a small number are present at one time.

After a period of great abundance in southern Britain from the 1950s to the mid-1970s, Bullfinches declined greatly in numbers (Siriwardena *et al* 1998a). As is clear from ringing, British Bullfinches are generally so sedentary that the causal factors of any population changes must lie within Britain. When their numbers were high, from the 1950s to the mid-1970s, many thousands of Bullfinches were killed as pests each year in the fruit orchards of the southeast and the western Midlands of England. As similar numbers were killed year after year, the culling seems to have had no long-term effects on population trends. The more recent decline, which has occurred over much of the country, is clearly due to different factors. As in several other seed-eaters, changes in agricultural practice have been suspected, notably the decline in farmland weeds, the seeds of which are important to Bullfinches, especially in years when native tree seeds are scarce (Newton 1967c, 1972). The Bullfinch is no longer a significant pest in commercial orchards and culling has virtually stopped. Further ringing may help to answer one of the main unknowns about Bullfinch movements, namely the extent of penetration of Britain by continental (northern) birds.

Ian Newton

Hawfinch
Coccothraustes coccothraustes

The Hawfinch in Britain is normally restricted to mature forest, where it is typically a shy and wary bird; rarely and irregularly, however, it appears outside its breeding range or at coastal watch-points in circumstances suggesting migratory or irruptive movements. In Ireland, Hawfinches occur only as rare migrants (*Birds in Ireland*).

The species is found across the Palearctic from Morocco and Britain to Japan and Kamchatka (*BWP*). In Europe, the nominate race *coccothraustes* is widespread but breeds patchily in western Europe and rarely north of the southern fringe of Fennoscandia; it appears to grade into *nigricans* in the Balkans and the Ukraine. Numbers in Britain are small everywhere, but there are a number of isolated localities where breeding density is relatively high; these occur west into Wales and north to southeast Scotland, but mostly in southeast England (*1988–91 Atlas*). The total British population is only 3,000–6,500 pairs, and appears to be in long-term decline (*1988–91 Atlas*). In contrast, the species is a familiar one in Dutch woodlands and town parks, and has increased in the Netherlands at least fourfold since the 1970s (Bijlsma 1987, *European Atlas*).

The entire Russian population deserts its breeding range in winter, and at this season the species' range includes the whole of Spain and Italy, western Turkey, parts of central Asia, and easternmost Asia from Japan to Taiwan. Elsewhere in its European range the species is found year-round but is not necessarily sedentary; local and altitudinal movements are known and some birds make longer movements, especially in their first winter (Mountfort 1957). Females predominate among winter visitors to Spain (Asensio & Antón 1990), and in eastern

The analysis of the data for this species was supported by Bernard Pattenden

Germany it was found that females were more likely than males to travel more than 50 km (Krüger 1979). Diurnal migration is observed in central Europe mostly from September to November and in spring from February to April (*BWP*).

When breeding, Hawfinches favour mixed mature broad-leaved forests or parkland including oak and hornbeam. Their winter distribution is governed largely by the availability of suitably large tree seeds, such as those of hornbeam and cherry. Feeding flocks, of over a hundred in the past but in recent decades a few dozen at most, gather at favoured British localities in winter. That most if not all such sites are in areas where many Hawfinches breed suggests that most seasonal movements within Britain may be of only a few kilometres, although a less likely explanation would be that birds depart after breeding and are replaced by others from elsewhere. Some previously favoured winter locations are no longer used, for example in Oxfordshire (*1988–91 Atlas*) and at East Wretham Heath in Norfolk, where large gatherings were reported from 1973–85, peaking at 183 in January 1975 (Taylor *et al* 1999). Changes in flock distribution from year to year may be associated with fluctuations in the seed-crop of trees such as hornbeam (Axelsson *et al* 1977).

Some British and Irish observations indicate longer movements within Britain & Ireland, and also continental immigration. There is

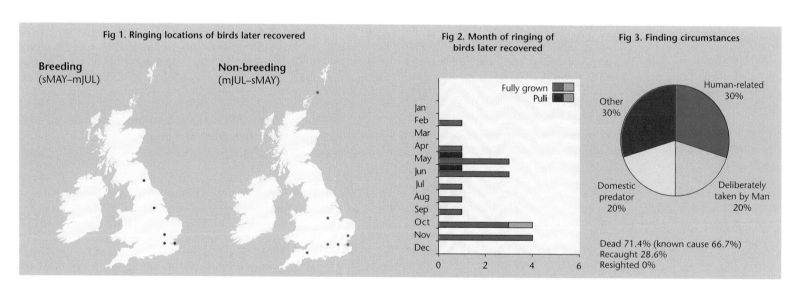

Fig 1. Ringing locations of birds later recovered

Breeding (sMAY–mJUL)

Non-breeding (mJUL–sMAY)

Fig 2. Month of ringing of birds later recovered

Fully grown
Pulli

Jan, Feb, Mar, Apr, May, Jun, Jul, Aug, Sep, Oct, Nov, Dec

Fig 3. Finding circumstances

Human-related 30%
Other 30%
Domestic predator 20%
Deliberately taken by Man 20%

Dead 71.4% (known cause 66.7%)
Recaught 28.6%
Resighted 0%

Ringing and recovery data

	<1960	60–69	70–79	80–89	90–97	Total
RINGING						
BTO ringing totals (%)	14	19	26	32	10	1,331
RECOVERIES						
BTO-ringed (%)	5	15	30	40	10	20
Foreign-ringed (%)	←	50	→	0	50	2

Statistical analyses

	Breeding population (sMAY–mJUL)	Wintering population (sNOV–sMAR)
Status	[SEDENTARY]	?
Age differences	Not tested	—
Sex differences	Not tested	—
Regional differences	Not tested	—
Finding circumstances	Not tested	—

Fig 4. Recovery locations and movements of over 20 km for the 21 included recoveries of Hawfinches ringed or recovered in Britain & Ireland. A bird ringed in Germany in 1962 and recovered in Shetland in 1967 is not shown.

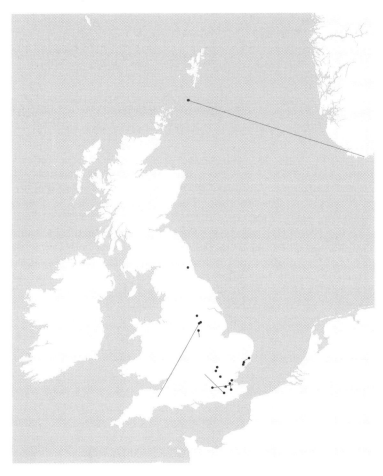

historical evidence of sporadic large-scale winter influxes into Norfolk, mostly during 1859–90 (Taylor *et al* 1999). More recent records, from the east coast north to Shetland, suggest a minor late-autumn arrival in late October and early November, and spring returns in April or early May.

On the Isles of Scilly, occasional birds appear, especially in October–November, but not annually; in 1978, however, up to 40 birds were present for a month from 6 October (Gantlett 1991).

The shy and elusive behaviour of the Hawfinch makes it a very difficult bird to catch. Few have been ringed in Britain and there is only a small sample of recoveries, in which many breeding and wintering localities are not represented (Fig 1). A few birds are ringed as pulli, and fully grown birds are ringed mostly in the breeding season or in October and November (Fig 2). Circumstances of recovery, most of which were related to human activity or to cats, were reported for only 10 recoveries (Fig 3).

The results of ringing have so far added little to our understanding of Hawfinch movements in Britain & Ireland (Fig 4) but there is little evidence of long-distance movements. Of the 10 recoveries of dead Hawfinches that were present in Britain & Ireland in the breeding season the median distance moved is just 12.5 km (P5–95=0–96 km). There are four breeding dispersal movements, all of which are of less than 20 km. Three of these movements were recaptures by ringers; the one bird found dead had moved 14 km. Three shorter-distance recoveries between the breeding season and other times of year suggest that some westward movement in winter might occur in southern England. An adult male ringed in Somerset in October 1977 was later found dead in a Nottinghamshire breeding area. Ringing has also indicated links between Britain and some northern parts of the Hawfinch's European range: a female ringed near the Czech border in Germany on 27 March 1962 was killed by a cat at Haroldswick, Shetland, on 7 May 1967 (Hudson 1969) and a male ringed in southernmost Norway on 11 October 1990 was found dead on Fair Isle on 10 April 1994 (Fig 4).

At present, therefore, there are major gaps in our knowledge of Hawfinch movements. It is not known whether birds from any of the British breeding concentrations perform regular seasonal migrations, or how much dispersal may occur between them. While connections with the Continent have been established by ringing, the origins, frequency and scale of continental immigrations are not known, nor whether it is these rather than British birds that occur sporadically in Ireland and on Scilly. This lack of knowledge will hamper any conservation efforts that may become necessary if the species' British decline continues.

John H Marchant & Jonathan Simons

Snow Bunting
Plectrophenax nivalis

Black-and-white flocks of tinkling Snow Buntings are a thrilling winter sight in coastal habitats in northern and eastern Britain as they wheel between sand-dunes or flush at the approach of a lone walker. Counts of this enigmatic species show great variation between and within winters, giving it a nomadic reputation as flocks move between abundant, but often transient, seed supplies uncovered by tides or shifting sand. This wandering nature is also typical of the substantial but less well-known inland wintering populations that exist in northern Britain. The Snow Bunting exhibits the greatest altitudinal and climatic range of all Britain & Ireland's birds, wintering in a spectrum of open habitats from benign stubbles in lowland farmland to the hostile expanses around snow and ice fields on top of our highest mountains, clinging to these in all but the most severe of winter storms.

The Snow Bunting's circumpolar breeding range is the most northerly of all songbirds, stretching throughout the arctic tundra of northern Europe, Asia and North America, and the islands of the Arctic Ocean and Bering Sea (*BWP*). Populations in the southern extensions of its range, such as those in southern Norway and Scotland, are restricted to expanses of tundra at higher altitudes. The breeding grounds are mostly abandoned before the onset of winter, but small numbers remain in some southern or oceanic areas, notably in Iceland, during winter. A protracted migration occurs on a wide front to temperate coastal regions and inland steppes and plains of Europe, Asia and America. In Europe, wintering Snow Buntings are concentrated along the North Sea and southwest Baltic coasts and lowlands, and on the central European plains. Two races occur commonly in Britain & Ireland in winter,

The analysis of the data for this species was supported by Carol Wilkinson

namely the nominate *nivalis* (breeding from Alaska east to northwest Russia) and the darker and more sedentary Icelandic race *insulae*. The Scottish breeding population of 70–100 pairs (*1988–91 Atlas*) is at least 90% composed of birds showing characteristics of *insulae* (R D Smith 1996).

Snow Bunting ringing in Britain & Ireland increased significantly from the early 1980s after Rae (1986) discovered that birds were easily caught with spring-nets at seed baits. A number of specialist studies of local wintering populations resulted, with much initial emphasis placed on identifying their origins. Better techniques were subsequently developed to assign age, sex and race to trapped birds (see Jukema & Fokkema 1992, R D Smith 1992, 1996), and these, together with the many foreign recoveries, have helped to give us a better understanding of which birds come to Britain & Ireland, and how they distribute over the wintering area.

Specialist ringing effort has produced the majority of ring-recoveries of British & Irish Snow Buntings. It is likely, however, that ringing sites generally reflect the distribution of wintering Snow Buntings (Fig 1, *Winter Atlas*), although few birds have yet been ringed on western British coasts or in Ireland. Although Snow Buntings are reported to leave the northernmost parts of their breeding range by early September, only a minority appear in Britain & Ireland before mid-October, and few

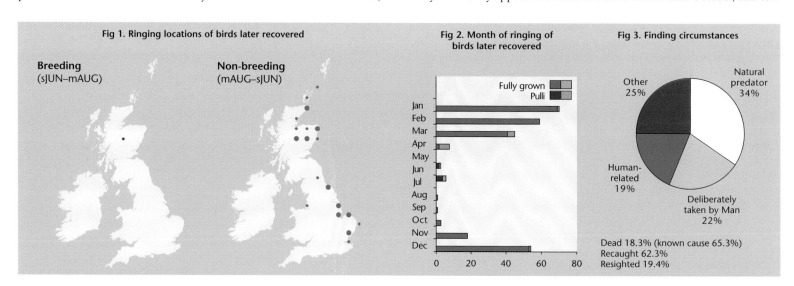

Fig 1. Ringing locations of birds later recovered

Breeding (sJUN–mAUG)

Non-breeding (mAUG–sJUN)

Fig 2. Month of ringing of birds later recovered

Fully grown
Pulli

Fig 3. Finding circumstances

Natural predator 34%
Other 25%
Human-related 19%
Deliberately taken by Man 22%

Dead 18.3% (known cause 65.3%)
Recaught 62.3%
Resighted 19.4%

Ringing and recovery data

	<1960	60–69	70–79	80–89	90–97	Total
RINGING						
BTO ringing totals (%)	12	6	9	48	26	18,030
RECOVERIES						
BTO-ringed (%)	4	6	1	50	39	253
Foreign-ringed (%)	←	6	→	81	12	16

Statistical analyses

	Breeding population (sJUN–mAUG)	Wintering population (sDEC–mMAR)
Status	[SHORT-DISTANCE MIGRANT]	[LONG-DISTANCE MIGRANT]
Age differences	Not tested	Not tested
Sex differences	Not tested	Not tested
Regional differences	Not tested	Not tested
Finding circumstances	Not tested	Not tested

Fig 4. Exchanges with Britain & Ireland of Snow Buntings abroad in (a) the breeding season (4, red), autumn (6, blue) and of unknown seasonality (1, black broken line) and in (b) winter (12, blue) and spring (33, red, one in Canada is not shown). Pre-1979 exchanges with Belgium (1) and Greenland (1) are not shown.

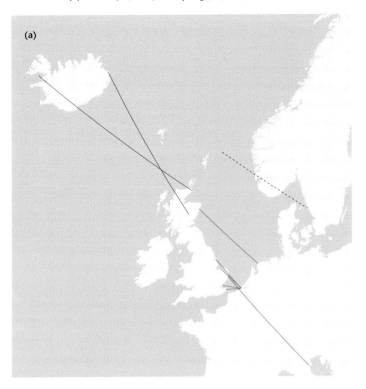

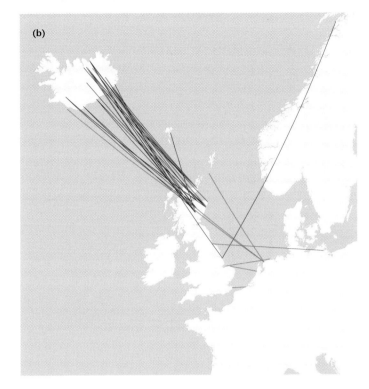

are trapped before mid-November (Fig 2). Only a small number of birds (*n*=32) have been reported dead (Fig 3), and only three British-wintering birds were found dead in countries where they could have been breeding. All three involved human intervention, reflecting the low likelihood of finding corpses of Snow Buntings suffering natural deaths in the Arctic.

In total, there have been 60 recoveries of British- & Irish-wintering Snow Buntings moving to or from abroad (Fig 4). A total of 12 of these were birds moving to or from the Low Countries. Some involved short-distance movements to or from southeast Britain in the same or subsequent winters, but others were birds moving north through Britain on spring migration. Exceptional recoveries have connected Britain with northern Italy and northern Germany.

Despite their proximity, there have been only single recoveries of Snow Buntings from Norway and Sweden, suggesting Britain & Ireland is not a major wintering site for birds of Scandinavian origin. Instead, the majority of movements towards possible breeding areas have been to the northwest, especially Iceland (40 movements). There are also single movements to or from the Faeroes, Greenland and Canada, the last of these a bird possibly choosing to winter on opposite sides of the Atlantic in different winters. Until recently, the Icelandic race *insulae* was thought to be sedentary, and movements involving Iceland were considered to involve birds originating further north. However, Banks *et al* (1991) documented the capture in Scotland of three birds ringed in Iceland as nestlings or newly fledged young, supporting their contention (based on plumage characteristics) that about 80% of the birds wintering in northern Scotland were *insulae*. Similar conclusions have been drawn by ringers trapping Snow Buntings in upland Scotland (60–100% *insulae*, differing between sexes, R D Smith 1996), Norfolk (50–87% in different winters, P W Atkinson pers comm), Suffolk (89%, Odin 1997), Kent (85%, P W J Findley pers comm) and the Netherlands (64%, Jukema & Fokkema 1992). This accords with a partial migration from Iceland, predominantly of females and of young birds of both sexes, and is supported by the capture in Iceland in January of a second-year female that had been ringed the previous spring in Scotland.

However, up to 50% of Snow Buntings at some sites in some years show characteristics of nominate *nivalis*. As yet, there are insufficient

recoveries from within the breeding range of *nivalis* to indicate where these birds originate. Three birds showing characteristics of the nominate race have been recorded moving between Iceland and Scotland but these birds were recovered on spring migration and could have been refuelling in Iceland prior to further migration. There is ample evidence of birds from northeast Greenland moving into central European wintering grounds via Scandinavia (*Der Zug*). Although there is as yet no direct proof, these recoveries, along with the Greenland and Canadian recoveries, suggest that some *nivalis* Snow Buntings reaching Britain & Ireland may hail from southern or eastern Greenland.

Little information is available on autumn arrival to suggest whether birds arrive directly at their wintering sites, or gradually filter southwards through the country. It is clear, however, that Snow Buntings can wander widely after their arrival in a wintering area: 62% of 92 within-winter recoveries were from birds that had moved more than 20 km (Fig 5). Some of these movements will reflect early spring migration (most notably a bird seen in Scotland on 11 March 1990 and retrapped in Iceland four days later), but others involve multiple recoveries and return movements, indicating use of a number of well-dispersed sites, possibly influenced by prevailing weather conditions (Smith 1994a).

However, despite the nomadic tendencies of Snow Buntings, the recovery data provide some evidence of fidelity to wintering areas, since 13% of 53 between-winter recoveries were within 20 km of the original ringing site. Recapture studies have indicated rates of return of only 2–5% to the actual site where birds were ringed (Fokkema *et al* 1978, Banks *et al* 1991). In contrast, a six-winter study of colour-ringed birds at an upland Scottish site recorded rates of return of established wintering birds of 28–45% the following winter, with males returning almost twice as often as females (Smith 1994a). Only 5–15% of the transient birds marked at that site were recorded in a subsequent winter however. Transient individuals probably make up a substantial proportion of the population present at most sites at any one time (Banks *et al* 1991, Smith 1994a), especially when numbers at the site are high.

There is also evidence that age and sex affect Snow Bunting winter settlement patterns. The proportion of adults and males trapped at 10 sites in northeast Scotland increased with altitude and distance from the

Fig 5. Movements of over 20 km and recovery locations of Snow Buntings ringed in winter and recovered in the same winter. There were 35:57 movements under:over 20 km but only those over 20 km are plotted (with one movement from Scotland to Iceland not shown).

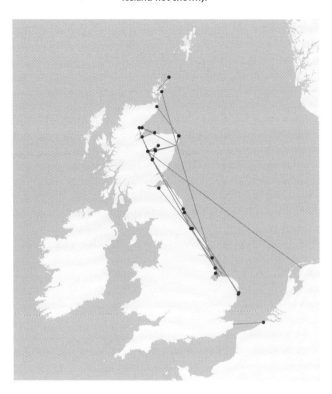

sea (Smith *et al* 1993). Juvenile females made up 60% of catches at coastal sites but only 20–30% at montane sites, while adult males increased from 3% at coastal sites to 20% at montane sites. Indeed, females make up the majority of winter-trapped individuals at most coastal sites (averaging 71% across nine studies of more than 100 trapped individuals from Orkney to Kent, including Friesland; Banks *et al* 1991, Jukema & Fokkema 1992, Odin 1997, P W Atkinson, R Duncan, P W J Findley, B Proctor, R Rae, J Williams & E Wood pers comm) and most of these are in their first winter (81%, four studies). Moreover, data from these nine studies indicate that the proportion of females increases from north to south (pers obs), reflecting the tendency for more males to winter near their breeding areas (see Banks *et al* 1991). Smith (1994a) found that females, which are smaller and subordinate to males, were more likely to leave an upland site following snowfalls, perhaps because they were less able to compete for food. Such competitive differences may predispose females to a more transient nature, causing them to depart sites where food is scarce more quickly than males, despite the risks involved in finding and learning about alternative sites.

Spring passage through Britain is well documented by patterns of weight-gain and the timing of ring-recoveries. Banks *et al* (1991) noted birds gaining weight from mid-February, and at least 10 birds wintering in England or the Netherlands have been trapped in Scotland in the same spring between 4 March and 13 April. Most winter-resident adult males studied at a Scottish upland site showed large weight-gains and departures during late February and March (Smith 1994a). Females showed similar but later weight-gains and departures, as did birds showing characteristics of the *nivalis* race (pers obs), suggesting a later return, in April and early May, to the more hostile northern breeding areas.

Scotland also hosts a small but thriving population of breeding Snow Buntings (*1988–91 Atlas*), which were first ringed in large numbers in 1988 and have been studied intensively (Smith 1994a, b, Smith & Marquiss 1994). Scottish Snow Buntings breed on montane areas and are seldom seen at altitudes below 1,000 m until the first substantial snowfalls in October. Colour-ringed, post-breeding adults moved up to 30 km between mountain massifs before, during and after the moult period in August–September. Independent young are seldom seen away from their natal massif before September, but then movements of up to 56 km become commonplace. On average, 23% of birds returning to breed the next summer had been seen on high ground within 10 km of their breeding site during the previous winter and early spring, but males predominated and were seen more frequently, especially in midwinter, suggesting partial migration of females and young away from the breeding areas when climatic conditions deteriorated (Smith 1994b). There was some indication, however, that departing birds did not travel far from their breeding areas, as they sometimes reappeared during very mild midwinter spells. Three breeding adults and two birds ringed as nestlings were found at wintering sites 20 30 km distant (at altitudes of approximately 600 m) but another individual ringed as a nestling was the only bird known to go further, wintering on the coast 108 km northeast of its natal site.

Breeding adults were seen on their future breeding territories (and often with their future mate) during milder weather from early March onwards. Both sexes were largely site-faithful, rarely moving more than 1 km from the previous summer's territory, although one male was found to have moved 30 km between summers, and others were known to move up to 5 km to find new territories or mates within summers. Natal site-fidelity was much lower: only 12% of ringed nestlings were found breeding within 10 km of where they were reared. In contrast, at least nine birds ringed as nestlings were discovered at breeding sites 28–118 km distant (Smith 1994b).

At present, it is thought that Scottish Snow Buntings are largely self-sustaining and that immigration from other populations is rare (Smith 1994b). The degree of natal dispersal is probably sufficient to ensure that chance extinctions on isolated mountains will be replaced periodically. However, as it is still a rare breeding species in Britain, the Snow Bunting could come under increasing pressure should climatic conditions become warmer or more extreme. Away from the Scottish breeding areas, the winter status of the species in Britain & Ireland is heavily dependent on the degree of partial migration. If global warming allowed more birds to overwinter in Iceland, for example, the wintering range might retreat northwards. It would be useful to compare the breeding success and survival rates of Icelandic birds that follow different migratory strategies. However, the most obvious major challenge awaiting future Snow Bunting enthusiasts perhaps awaits a well-directed ringing expedition: who will provide the first direct evidence of where British-wintering *nivalis* birds originate?

Rik Smith

Yellowhammer

Emberiza citrinella

The Yellowhammer is one of the best known and most attractive buntings in Europe. For many, its characteristic song is a familiar sound of the countryside during the summer months. It has a wide geographical range, breeding across the upper and middle latitudes of the West and central Palearctic; in Europe it is absent only from Arctic Ocean coasts, Iceland, most of the Iberian Peninsula and the coasts and islands of the Mediterranean (*European Atlas*).

Outside Britain & Ireland, the Yellowhammer is a partial short-distance migrant in most of its range. The northern and easternmost part of its range is vacated in winter; otherwise it winters mainly in the breeding range, especially in milder winters. It is a winter visitor to northern Spain, much of Italy and the Balkans, western Turkey and northern Israel. Migration is largely influenced by weather conditions, so migration patterns vary between years. In cold winters, Yellowhammers are regularly found in small numbers as far south as North Africa and parts of the Middle East. Southward migration begins in September and continues until late autumn, with birds arriving in the winter range in October or November, and return movements beginning in February or March (Byers *et al* 1995).

The *1988–91 Atlas* shows that the Yellowhammer is widely distributed across lowland Britain & Ireland, with the population concentrated in eastern Britain and the Midlands and generally lower densities in the west. High breeding densities are also found at scattered coastal localities. The species is less common on the higher ground of Wales and northern England, and in the uplands and islands of Scotland. In Ireland, the Yellowhammer has disappeared from large areas of the west and is now found mainly in the east, south, and in eastern Donegal.

The analysis of the data for this species was supported by Ken Capps

Three races are recognized. Birds in Ireland, Scotland, Wales and the Isle of Man belong to an endemic race *caliginosa*. This grades into nominate *citrinella* in northern and western England; *citrinella* is also found throughout the range in western Europe. A further race, *erythrogenys*, extends from Russia east to Siberia (*BWP*). The variation is largely clinal and many individuals cannot be assigned a race.

In Britain & Ireland, Yellowhammers are found in open country, cultivated areas with hedges, plantations, scrub, rough grassland and parkland. In the breeding season, Yellowhammers are strongly associated with hedgerows (Morgan & O'Connor 1980) and their density on farmland is strongly correlated with the area of cultivated cereal crops, hedgerow availability and altitude (Kyrkos *et al* 1998). In the autumn and winter period, local movements to new feeding areas are typical. At this time of year, stubble fields are the preferred foraging habitat (Wilson *et al* 1996), although other agricultural land and saltmarshes are used. In some areas, Yellowhammers may leave forestry plantations for nearby farmland (pers obs).

The ringing locations of Yellowhammers that have been recovered largely reflect lowland agricultural areas of central, southwestern and eastern England and eastern Scotland (Fig 1). Populations in Ireland, Wales and northwest England are all under-represented. Over half of the recoveries refer to birds of unknown age, with only 6% ringed as

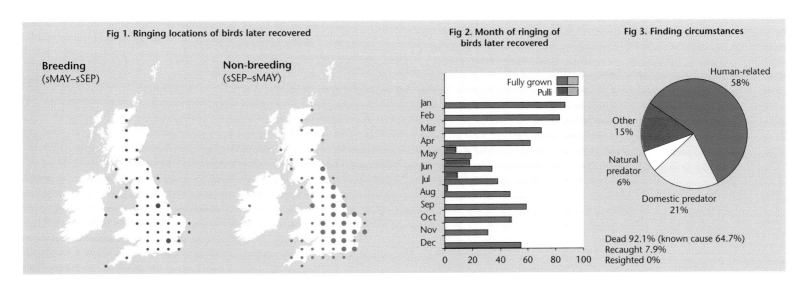

Fig 1. Ringing locations of birds later recovered

Breeding (sMAY–sSEP)

Non-breeding (sSEP–sMAY)

Fig 2. Month of ringing of birds later recovered

Fully grown
Pulli

Jan, Feb, Mar, Apr, May, Jun, Jul, Aug, Sep, Oct, Nov, Dec

0 20 40 60 80 100

Fig 3. Finding circumstances

Human-related 58%
Other 15%
Natural predator 6%
Domestic predator 21%

Dead 92.1% (known cause 64.7%)
Recaught 7.9%
Resighted 0%

Ringing and recovery data

	<1960	60–69	70–79	80–89	90–97	Total
RINGING						
BTO ringing totals (%)	10	17	23	31	19	132,523
RECOVERIES						
BTO-ringed (%)	15	23	25	23	13	669
Foreign-ringed (%)	←	0	→	100	0	1

Statistical analyses

	Breeding population (sMAY–sSEP)	Wintering population (sNOV–sAPR)
Status	SEDENTARY (0)	SEDENTARY
Age differences[NT]	Significant*	Not significant
Sex differences[(NS)]*	Not tested	Not significant*
Regional differences	Not tested	Not tested
Finding circumstances	Not tested	Not significant

Fig 4. Locations in winter and movements of over 20 km between the breeding and non-breeding season of 161 Yellowhammers present in Britain & Ireland during the breeding season.

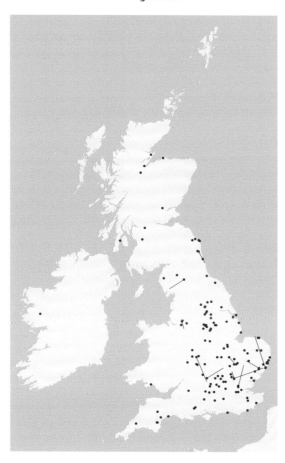

nestlings. Many recoveries (53%) stem from ringing between December and April, perhaps because winter flocks are easier to catch than territorial birds during the breeding season (Fig 2).

About 65% of all recoveries were attributed to a known cause of death. The majority of these were human-related, such as collisions with buildings or vehicles (58%), or were due to domestic predators such as cats (21%) (Fig 3). Of the Yellowhammers recovered, over three-quarters were recovered as adults and 65% of known-sex birds were males. Over two-thirds of all the recoveries were between March and August, when birds are most likely to be in their breeding areas.

The sedentary nature of the Yellowhammers that breed in Britain & Ireland is clearly evident from the recoveries (Fig 4). Lack (1988) showed almost no differences in the distribution of Yellowhammers between different winters or within winters of the fieldwork period for the *Winter Atlas* (1981/82–1983/84). Regardless of season, 95% of birds were recovered within 25 km of where they were ringed, and the median distance is less than 1 km. There was no evidence of a preferred direction of movement with regard to location of ringing site, time of year, age or sex. The *Winter Atlas*, however, suggests a minor change in distribution between the breeding season and winter range, with a tendency in winter to withdraw from upland areas. In Wales, birds leave the higher altitudes in autumn to congregate in small flocks on the lower ground; flocks tend to be small but groups as large as 100 are occasionally recorded (*Birds in Wales*). Some longer-distance ring-recoveries suggest a winter movement towards the coast or lower ground (Fig 4), although there are no significant latitudinal or longitudinal shifts in distribution of British & Irish breeding birds through the year.

Only one foreign-ringed Yellowhammer has been recovered in Britain & Ireland, a juvenile ringed in Norway in October and recovered in Kent 13 months later. There have also been three Yellowhammers ringed in Britain & Ireland recovered abroad, one in France and two in the Netherlands, all adults ringed and recovered in the autumn/winter period. All three were ringed in coastal eastern England, between Suffolk and Lincolnshire, and it is possible that these were continental birds, which are known to pass down the east coast of Britain in small numbers (Payn 1978, Taylor *et al* 1999). Small numbers are recorded on passage through the Northern Isles in most years, in both spring and autumn. A few birds occasionally winter in Shetland, Orkney and the Outer Hebrides, and it is possible that these birds are of Scandinavian origin (*Birds in Scotland*). In Ireland, Yellowhammers have been recorded in spring at migration points such as Great Saltee, at Copeland and at Tory Island. Occasionally larger numbers of birds are noted in autumn, such as 100 in September and October on Cape Clear Island and an amazing 500 at Malin Head, Donegal, on 28 September 1963 (*Birds in Ireland*). The Yellowhammer remains a scarce spring and autumn visitor to Lundy (Dymond 1980) and the Isles of Scilly (Gantlett 1991) in southwest England and to most of the Pembrokeshire islands (*Birds in Wales*).

The breeding season of Yellowhammers in Britain & Ireland extends from the end of April to mid-August. Two, occasionally three broods are raised, and young are produced throughout May–August (*BWP*). Post-fledging dispersal is therefore spread over a long period, with most birds remaining close to their natal area until their third month after fledging (when the median distance moved is less than 5 km, *n*=14). Little information is available on natal dispersal because only five birds ringed as nestlings have been recovered in later breeding seasons; all of these birds had moved less than 20 km (median 2 km). This does suggest that fidelity to the natal area may be high. There is only slightly more information available on breeding dispersal, but all 23 birds of breeding age ringed during a breeding season were recovered within 20 km in a subsequent one.

Of 55 birds ringed in one winter and recovered in a later one, 93% had moved less than 20 km and the median distance was less than 1 km. Of 33 movements within the same winter 88% had moved less than 20 km. The small number of movements beyond 20 km of the ringing site, both during a single winter period and between different winters, suggests that the majority of Yellowhammers spend most of their time in a relatively small area. Variation in winter food supply may explain why some birds move from the local area and why some move greater distances than others.

Many species of farmland bird began long-term declines in the early 1970s, coinciding with a period of change in agricultural practice (Marchant *et al* 1990). The Yellowhammer is unique in that, after a period of long-term stability, it has declined steadily since the late 1980s (Siriwardena *et al* 1998a). It is clear from ringing that Yellowhammers in Britain & Ireland are largely sedentary, so the causal factors responsible for the population decline must lie within Britain & Ireland. There is some evidence that adult survival, estimated from ring-recovery data, has declined since the late 1980s (Kyrkos 1997, Siriwardena *et al* 1998b). Given that Yellowhammers depend on seed as a winter food source it is important that good winter foraging habitat (particularly stubbles) is available close to breeding areas. At a local scale, the distribution of winter food sources may influence local population movements.

Future understanding of the movement patterns of Yellowhammers would benefit enormously from increases in Yellowhammer ringing effort, particularly in southwest England, Ireland, Wales and parts of Scotland and during the breeding season.

Dawn Balmer

Reed Bunting
Emberiza schoeniclus

Reed Buntings are small omnivorous passerines which, although conspicuous during the breeding season when males sing their repetitive songs from protruding vegetation in marshy areas, can be far less easy to find in winter. As a result, historically there has been much disagreement about the migratory status of the breeding population in Britain & Ireland, with opinions, even for the same county, varying from resident to almost entirely migratory! More recently, ringing data have been used to show conclusively that almost all individuals from the British breeding population winter within Britain, at which time they are joined by very small numbers of predominantly Scandinavian breeding birds (Prŷs-Jones 1977, 1984). Irish birds are likewise almost certainly resident within Ireland, although ringing data are inadequate to confirm this.

The distribution of Reed Buntings covers much of the Palearctic, with numerous subspecies that different authorities have divided into between two and four groups based, in particular, on beak size (*BWP*). In Europe, populations of medium-billed birds breed in marshlands from southern Iberia east across southern Europe, where they appear to be sedentary (*BWP*). Elsewhere, small-billed birds, largely of the nominate race, breed across almost the whole of central and northern Europe. In the northeast, they are totally migratory, moving south and west to winter in countries bordering the Atlantic and Mediterranean, mainly within Europe but with a few reaching northwest Africa; further to the southwest, breeding birds become increasingly sedentary (Prŷs-Jones 1984, *Der Zug*). A relationship between temperature and winter distribution becomes strikingly apparent when January isotherms are

The analysis of the data for this species was supported by R Burridge

examined. Most birds breeding in areas with a mean January temperature below 0°C migrate; in milder areas, the proportion of birds moving away decreases rapidly with increasing temperature, with populations becoming essentially sedentary at the 5°C January isotherm. However, midwinter temperature is not in itself the key factor controlling the winter distribution of small-billed Reed Buntings. Instead, the cause is almost certainly the much increased probability of prolonged snow-cover when temperatures average below freezing for any extended period. Snow cuts off access to the fallen grass and herb seeds on which the birds largely depend in winter (Prŷs-Jones 1984). Further east, around the Black Sea and in central Asia, where winter precipitation averages much less, small-billed Reed Buntings regularly winter in areas averaging far below freezing for long periods.

Within Britain & Ireland, Reed Buntings are widespread throughout the year, although largely absent from the higher upland areas of north and west Britain in the breeding season (*1988–91 Atlas*) and almost entirely so in winter (*Winter Atlas*). They breed at greatest density in marshy and wetland areas but, especially when population levels are high, are also scattered widely through drier agricultural land and some young conifer plantations. In winter, they spread out much more extensively to feed across the non-forested landscape, although usually congregating to roost at night in wetland areas.

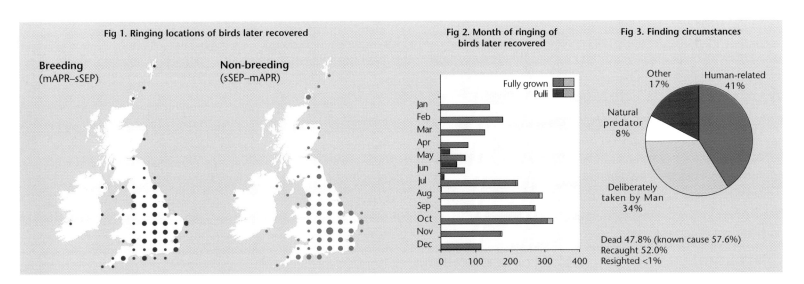

Fig 1. Ringing locations of birds later recovered

Breeding (mAPR–sSEP) Non-breeding (sSEP–mAPR)

Fig 2. Month of ringing of birds later recovered

Fully grown
Pulli

Fig 3. Finding circumstances

Other 17%
Human-related 41%
Natural predator 8%
Deliberately taken by Man 34%

Dead 47.8% (known cause 57.6%)
Recaught 52.0%
Resighted <1%

Ringing and recovery data

	<1960	60–69	70–79	80–89	90–97	Total
RINGING						
BTO ringing totals (%)	4	16	34	27	19	328,177
RECOVERIES						
BTO-ringed (%)	2	16	31	30	21	2,089
Foreign-ringed (%)	←	27	→	29	45	56

Statistical analyses

	Breeding population (mAPR–sSEP)	Wintering population (mNOV–mFEB)
Status	SEDENTARY (0)	SEDENTARY
Age differences[NS*]	Not significant	Not significant
Sex differences[NS*]	Not significant*	Significant*
Regional differences	Not tested	Not tested
Finding circumstances	Not significant*	Not significant*

Fig 4. Movements of over 50 km between the breeding season and (a) autumn (237:52), (b) winter (187:89) and (c) spring (199:35) and locations outside the breeding season of Reed Buntings present in Britain & Ireland during the breeding season. Sample sizes of movements under:over 50 km are given but only those over 50 km are plotted.

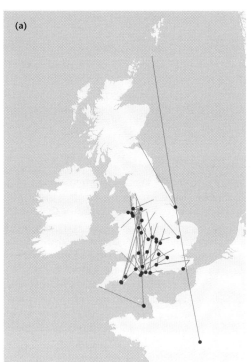
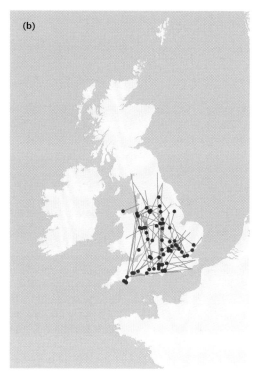
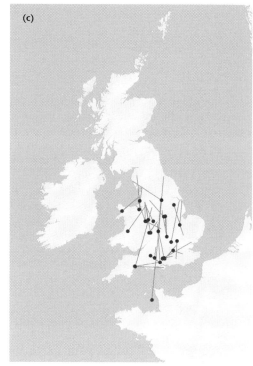

Ringing of Reed Buntings that were subsequently recovered has been largely concentrated into central and southern Britain, with particularly few Irish-ringed birds being recovered (Fig 1). About half of all ring-recoveries were from birds aged as juvenile when ringed, largely during the late summer and autumn months, with less than 5% ringed as nestlings during the summer; the remainder had ringing dates spread more evenly through the year, although with distinct peaks in autumn and in late winter or early spring (Fig 2). Roughly half of all Reed Bunting recoveries have been from birds found dead, with the other half comprising individuals recaught alive by ringers. Of birds found dead, over half had a cause of death ascribed, of which three-quarters were in some way human-related (Fig 3). Given that, in common with other small passerines, Reed Buntings are in fact likely to die from starvation or natural predation, these recoveries clearly comprise a sample biased in some degree towards areas of higher human population density.

During the breeding period, Reed Buntings are almost entirely insectivorous, but independent young and post-breeding adults rapidly become increasingly granivorous in late summer (Prŷs-Jones 1977). At this time, they begin to disperse from their immediate breeding area over the surrounding countryside. Movements during this period have been studied in most detail in Finland and have shown that birds may roam over a radius of at least 5 km at this time (Haukioja 1971); the situation in Britain & Ireland is probably similar.

An analysis of movement distances between summer and winter was carried out by Prŷs-Jones (1977, 1984). The larger sample of recoveries of all types up to 1997 shows that 53% of movements between the breeding season and winter were of more than 20 km and 32% were greater than 50 km (n=276). The median distance moved from recoveries of dead birds was only 4 km (P5–95=0–156 km, n=100), however, suggesting some possible bias in the distances recorded through recaptures by ringers. The relatively small numbers of movements exceeding 50 km predominantly resulted in birds wintering in a southerly or southwesterly direction from their breeding grounds (Glue 1982; Fig 4). The autumn movements take place mainly in September and October. In spring, some males can be found on mild days singing on territory by the start of March and most birds may be paired by early April.

It thus seems reasonable to consider British Reed Buntings as predominantly fairly sedentary, but with a directional autumn dispersal to milder areas by a minority of individuals which, in extreme cases, results in wintering over 300 km from the breeding area. Movement abroad by British breeding birds is minimal, involving under 2% of the usable ring-recoveries, and extends only as far as the Channel Islands and, possibly, the continental coast bordering the English Channel (Fig 4). The single recovery in mainland France relates to a female that was ringed on Fair Isle on 5 May, which might well have been a late-returning Scandinavian breeder (see later). As most of lowland Britain lies between the 2°C and 5°C January isotherms, these results accord with expectations based on the species' wider European movement patterns.

Contained within these overall statistics, however, is intriguing evidence of sexual differences in seasonal movement patterns. Previous analysis showed that under one-third of male Reed Buntings, but nearer two-thirds of females, wintered more than 5 km from their breeding areas, although this difference was only marginally significant on the sample size of 43 relevant recoveries available up to 1973 (Prŷs-Jones 1977). In the larger sample of birds present in Britain & Ireland during the breeding season and located in winter up to 1997, the median distances moved were 2 km for males (P5–95=0–120 km, n=50) and 6 km for females (P5–95=0–239 km, n=26) but the formal statistical analyses, using only birds ringed during the breeding season and recovered dead in winter, found no significant difference between the sexes in the distances moved. The trapping of Reed Buntings at winter roosts in central and southern England reveals sex ratios markedly biased in favour of males (Bell & Hornby 1968, Fennell & Stone 1976, Prŷs-Jones 1977). Analysis of data from two sites with records spanning a number of winters further showed that the preponderance of males was negatively correlated with winter temperature at both sites, ranging from under 1.5 males per female in the warmest to nearly three males per female in the coldest (Prŷs-Jones 1977). However, comprehending the extent to which differential movement of the sexes may be involved in producing this is complicated because female Reed Buntings also experience significantly higher annual mortality than males, averaging

Fig 5. Included exchanges of 72 Reed Buntings between Britain & Ireland and abroad, excluding those birds present in Britain & Ireland during the breeding season.

52% and 39% respectively (*n*=242, Prŷs-Jones 1977). Given that Reed Buntings suffer greatly in prolonged periods of snow-cover, with exceptionally severe winters such as that in 1962/63 producing population crashes, it is probable that there are complex interactions between winter severity, degree of movement and level of mortality, which in turn are likely to differ between the sexes. Although available data reveal no obvious age-related movement patterns, it remains unclear whether this may to some extent reflect the difficulties that ringers have in accurately ageing fully grown Reed Buntings.

The ring-recoveries of Reed Buntings found dead suggest that the majority of individuals remain in a fairly small wintering area within any one winter, with a median distance moved of less than 1 km (*P*5–95=0–36, *n*=21). Ring-recoveries suggest that movements between winters are also relatively localized, with a median distance moved of 4 km (*P*5–95=0–124, *n*=17), although some individuals do make much longer movements.

Adult Reed Buntings show a high degree of breeding site-fidelity, with most males moving no more than 50 m between breeding seasons and females seldom more than 200 m; by contrast, first-time breeders tend to settle in the general vicinity of where they were reared, but with much less precision (Bell & Hornby 1968). Although the sample size is small, the ring-recovery data support a high degree of breeding site-fidelity, with a median breeding dispersal of less than 1 km (*P*5–95=0–13, *n*=39) from recoveries of dead birds.

Ring-recoveries show that a very small number of Scandinavian-breeding Reed Buntings, and even fewer from Finland, winter in Britain (Fig 5). Rather more appear to move from Scandinavia down the east coast of Britain in autumn to winter in France and, probably, the Low Countries. In addition to recovery evidence, small-scale movement has been noted at many places along the east coast from Fair Isle in the north to Sussex in the south (Prŷs-Jones 1984). Much the major proportion of Scandinavian birds, however, must migrate south through the Low Countries and Germany into France. In spring, there is little evidence for return migration to Scandinavia via Britain, whereas in Belgium there is a marked passage lasting from late February to early April (Collette 1972).

This analysis of Reed Bunting movements has shown that the British and, probably, Irish populations are essentially self-contained, so monitoring at any time of year should provide information of direct relevance to the conservation of the breeding populations. These have undergone a major decline since the mid-1970s, which is almost certainly linked to declines in winter seed availability as a result of agricultural changes. Reed Buntings are known to be making increasing use of gardens for feeding in times of winter hardship (Thompson 1988, Cannon 2000), and links between population levels, severe weather and numbers frequenting gardens deserve further study. More generally, a co-ordinated long-term programme of regular ringing at an array of roost sites could shed much light on the complex subject of the interaction between movements and mortality in producing the observed unbalanced winter sex ratios.

Robert Prŷs-Jones

Corn Bunting
Miliaria calandra

The feeble flight, rotund profile and dangling legs of the Corn Bunting in summer do not suggest a strong flyer, yet this species has at one time or another managed to colonize the remotest fringes of Britain & Ireland. This open-country specialist probably evolved on the steppes of central Asia (Duncker 1912). Its current world range, which extends from the lower and middle latitudes of Europe and the Mediterranean eastwards to Afghanistan and western China, owes much to Man's alteration of the environment. The spread of cereal agriculture across Europe that began around 6000 BC (reaching Britain around 5000 BC) resulted in the clearance of vast areas of woodland, creating open habitats suitable for Corn Buntings and other steppe species. During the breeding season, the Corn Bunting occupies many types of open-country habitat but is largely confined to arable farmland in the north of its range, including Britain & Ireland (Donald & Evans 1995). In winter, birds feed largely on cereal stubbles (Donald & Evans 1994), a habitat which has declined greatly in availability in recent years. Roosting flocks utilize reedbeds and rank grassland.

The changing fortunes of the Corn Bunting in Britain during the 20th century have been charted by Donald *et al* (1994), who found evidence of declines during the 1930s and recovery during the 1950s and 1960s before the well-documented declines of the 1980s and 1990s. The Corn Bunting is now probably extinct in Ireland, although a few pairs may still survive on the west coast (pers obs).

Corn Buntings are at least partially migratory in central and northern parts of their European range and apparently sedentary in other areas. Some populations breeding in northeastern Europe are

The analysis of the data for this species was supported by Ralph Rettke-Grover

wholly migratory and appear to move southwest in autumn to winter in Iberia and North Africa. Wintering tends to take place largely within the breeding range but records from Africa as far south as Mauritania and Senegal (Farnsworth 1994) suggest that longer-distance movements can occur. There is some evidence of autumn and spring passage across the Strait of Gibraltar (Finlayson 1992).

Although British breeding birds appear to be largely resident, their migratory status is uncertain, due largely to the paucity of ring-recovery data (Figs 1–3). Very few Corn Buntings are ringed annually in Britain due to their recent scarcity, to the difficulty of finding their nests and to the fact that they tend to occupy fairly intensively managed farmland, a habitat generally under-worked by ringers. At the time of writing, the British & Irish Ringing Scheme has generated just 84 ring-recoveries (Fig 4). Most of the few ringing data available stem from a small number of ringing studies at communal winter roosts (*eg* Boddy & Blackburn 1978) or from parts of intensive ecological studies (*eg* Shepherd *et al* 1997). Of the 70% of recoveries for which the cause of death was established, 43% were human-related and 32% were due to natural predation (Fig 3).

British & Irish Corn Buntings appear to be largely resident: for 53 recoveries of dead birds, the median distance moved was only 4 km ($P5$–$95=0$–56 km). Reports around 1900 of large autumn and spring flocks at coastal sites now recognized as migration points are intriguing,

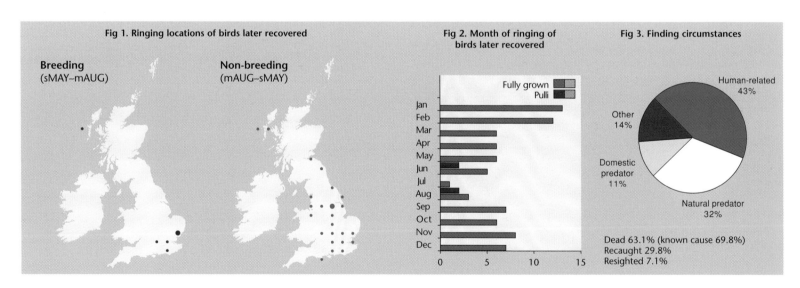

Fig 1. Ringing locations of birds later recovered

Breeding (sMAY–mAUG)

Non-breeding (mAUG–sMAY)

Fig 2. Month of ringing of birds later recovered

Fully grown
Pulli

Jan Feb Mar Apr May Jun Jul Aug Sep Oct Nov Dec
0 5 10 15

Fig 3. Finding circumstances

Human-related 43%
Other 14%
Domestic predator 11%
Natural predator 32%

Dead 63.1% (known cause 69.8%)
Recaught 29.8%
Resighted 7.1%

Ringing and recovery data

	<1960	60–69	70–79	80–89	90–97	Total
RINGING						
BTO ringing totals (%)	6	13	28	36	17	13,149
RECOVERIES						
BTO-ringed (%)	18	14	26	35	7	84
Foreign-ringed (%)	0	0	0	0	0	0

Statistical analyses

	Breeding population (sMAY–mAUG)	Wintering population (sNOV–sMAR)
Status	[SEDENTARY]	SEDENTARY*
Age differences	Not tested	Not tested
Sex differences	Not tested	Not tested
Regional differences	Not tested	Not tested
Finding circumstances	Not tested	Not tested

Fig 4. Recovery locations and movements of over 20 km for the 84 included recoveries of Corn Buntings ringed or recovered in Britain & Ireland.

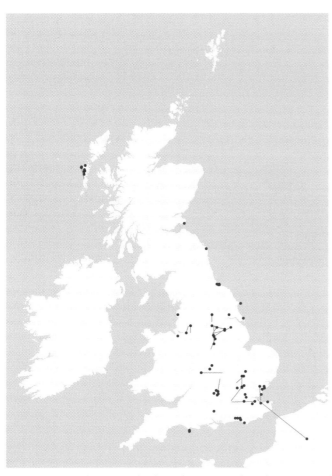

site in the four years of their study. The longest movement they recorded was of 35 km, and the authors concluded that recolonization of any parts of the former range in western Scotland was unlikely at present due the species' sedentary habits. Harper (1995) also found very low dispersal rates and recorded the furthest distance moved by any of his birds as 20 km. However, Hustings (1997) found that suitable habitat newly created in the Netherlands was very quickly occupied, suggesting some movement from natal areas. Donald (1997) analysed British ring-recovery data and found that the distance between ringing and recovery averaged just 2.4 km (with a maximum of 13 km) for birds both ringed and recovered in summer, whereas birds ringed in summer and recovered in winter (or vice versa) moved an average of around 21 km (the maximum distance moved being 205 km). There was no significant difference in the distances moved by males and females, although sample sizes were very small. The movements shown in Fig 4 suggest that long-distance movements of British birds are rare, while other evidence suggests that there is some short-distance dispersal in winter, with birds returning to their natal areas the following summer (Harper 1995). There is only one record of a British-ringed bird moving outside Britain, that being recovered in France. No Corn Bunting ringed abroad has been recovered in Britain or Ireland.

The paucity of ring-recovery data for Corn Bunting is unfortunate, since ringing has the potential to answer many interesting questions about this species. In view of the recent population decline, it would be useful to identify regions of net immigration or emigration, which would help to identify the most productive areas. Also, as there is some evidence that winter food supplies may be limiting populations, it would be useful to examine changes in survival rates. Ringing studies have shown that recent population declines of the closely related Reed Bunting can be explained entirely by observed declines in annual survival (Peach *et al* 1999).

The lack of data for Corn Buntings places great limitations on our ability to assess movements of this species. However, another method exists for tracking the movements of individual Corn Buntings. This species exhibits microgeographic variation in the song, birds from different areas singing different 'dialects'. McGregor *et al* (1997) and Holland & McGregor (1997) recorded songs in different areas and identified local dialects using sonograms. They then used variation in these dialects to detect movements of individual males away from their own dialect boundaries, and could identify from the patterns of dialect which populations were long established in the area and which had recently colonized. While not likely to be as powerful a tool as ringing to track long-distance movements, this work, which does not require that birds are caught, may shed more light on the movements of this species, at least on local scales (McGregor *et al* 1997).

although it is not known whether these records relate to resident wintering birds or to true migrants (Donald *et al* 1994). Probably because of severe declines in most northern and central European populations, such flocks are not observed today. Also intriguing are old and more recent reports of British-breeding birds being migratory, and odd birds still turn up on islands far from the nearest breeding populations. Comparison of the breeding and wintering distributions from the *1988–91 Atlas* and the *Winter Atlas* suggests that some breeding areas are abandoned in winter as birds move to coastal areas, although such movements are likely to be fairly short-distance. Intensive studies of colour-ringed birds have shown little seasonal movement and little dispersal from natal sites. Shepherd *et al* (1997), in a study in the Outer Hebrides, found that most birds settled very close to their natal sites and recorded only five movements of birds into or out of their 7,000 ha study

Paul F Donald

Minor Species Accounts

This section has been supported by Geoff Rogers, Alan Woodcock, Sandwich Bay Bird Observatory and Spurn Bird Observatory

Black-throated Diver
Gavia arctica

The Eurasian breeding range of the Black-throated Diver extends from northern Siberia in the east across to the Scottish Hebrides in the west, with the bulk of the population (*c*100,000–200,000 pairs) breeding in Russia. The small population of *c*150 pairs breeding in the United Kingdom is joined by winter immigrants that increase the wintering population to *c*1,400–1,800 individuals (*Winter Atlas*).

Very little is known about the movements of Black-throated Divers breeding within the United Kingdom: there have only been five individuals ringed in Britain & Ireland and no recoveries (Toms & Clark 1998). More is known about the populations breeding in Fennoscandia and Russia, where long-term ringing has revealed patterns of seasonal movement. Birds from the Russian breeding population (from northeast Russia and northern Siberia) perform a loop migration, leaving their breeding sites for the Kara and Barents Seas before cutting south across the Continent (possibly via the White Sea) to reach their Baltic wintering grounds (Schütz 1974). Other individuals winter on the Black and Caspian Seas, in the Mediterranean and on a number of larger lakes within Europe and Asia (*European Atlas*).

Black-throated Divers desert their Scottish breeding sites by August, with small parties occasionally gathering on inland lochs before moving to the coast (*Birds in Scotland*), which they reach during September and October. Studies of seabird distribution off northwest Europe have demonstrated that during the winter most individuals remain quite close inshore, with concentrations of birds recorded along the coasts of Denmark, Germany, the Netherlands and Belgium (Stone *et al* 1995). Smaller numbers occur around the coasts of Britain (and to a lesser extent Ireland), notably in the Moray Firth, the Firth of Forth and at the northeast end of the English Channel. It seems likely that these include birds from the Scottish lochs, together with birds from Norway, Sweden and possibly Finland. Around the British & Irish coastline the species is less gregarious than the Red-throated Diver, with rarely more than two to three individuals occurring together. However, larger groups are sometimes recorded during periods of passage (*Birds in Scotland*, Voipio 1990) or as a result of cold-weather movements (*Birds in Wales*).

Gatherings of Black-throated Divers have been reported during the pre-breeding period on sea lochs and amongst the islands off Argyll, Wester Ross and Sutherland. Individuals return to their Scottish breeding sites during April with the earliest eggs being laid at the end of April (Mudge & Talbot 1993). The timing of movements made by continental birds seems to be dependent upon the thawing of fresh waters, with birds leaving their winter quarters from mid-April to mid-May and arriving back on their breeding sites in late May or early June. It has also been noted that some non-breeders occasionally summer far south of the breeding range (*BWP*).

The Black-throated Diver faces a number of threats on its breeding grounds (Campbell & Mudge 1989), together with the risk of a major oil spill in one of the areas where individuals gather during the winter (Stone *et al* 1995) or during the pre-breeding period. An oil spill would have a particularly devastating effect were it to involve a moulting flock. Increased effort needs to be directed towards the ringing of breeding individuals in an attempt to determine where UK birds spend the winter.

Mike Toms

Great Northern Diver

Gavia immer

The breeding distribution of the Great Northern Diver is largely nearctic in nature, extending from the Aleutians across Canada and the northern United States to Greenland. The only regular European breeding occurs in Iceland, where there are estimated to be 300 breeding pairs (*European Atlas*). The waters off Britain and Ireland hold an internationally important wintering population of *c*3,500–4,500 individuals (*Winter Atlas*), thought to originate from Iceland, Greenland and possibly Canada. The almost complete absence of European ring-recoveries makes it impossible to be certain of the origins of wintering individuals: only eight individuals have been ringed in Britain & Ireland resulting in a single local recovery (Toms & Clark 1998).

Most individuals leave their Icelandic and Greenland breeding sites between September and October, although some immatures and failed breeders almost certainly leave earlier (*CBWP*). Small numbers arrive off north and northwest Scotland and Ireland during August but the main influx of birds occurs in October and November, presumably having come direct from the breeding grounds (*Birds in Scotland, Birds in Ireland*). Far smaller numbers overwinter along the eastern coast of Britain, where the species is the scarcest of the three diver species to regularly occur in the North Sea (Stone *et al* 1995). Great Northern Divers remain farther offshore than the smaller divers (Powers & Cherry 1983, Barrett & Barrett 1985, Webb *et al* 1990), although they come closer inshore to sheltered bays and harbours during periods of bad weather (*Birds in Wales*).

Spring departures begin during late April and early May, after birds have undergone moult. During this period loose parties of up to 50 individuals may be seen together (*Birds in Ireland*). Birds in summer plumage are often recorded in northern Scottish waters during May and June (*Birds in Scotland*), although most individuals have departed for their breeding grounds by this time. A small number of birds remain here throughout the summer and, although many of these are immatures, breeding has been recorded in Scotland on a small number of occasions (Hunter 1970, Hunter & Dennis 1972, Batten *et al* 1990). As with the other diver species, the Great Northern Diver is susceptible to the effects of oil spills (Heubeck & Richardson 1980) and more general pollution of the wintering areas (Mason & Macdonald 1988).

Mike Toms

Red-necked Grebe

Podiceps grisegena

Although the Red-necked Grebe is essentially a winter visitor to the United Kingdom, small numbers are present throughout the summer and breeding has been recorded on more than one occasion (Anon 1989, Parslow-Otsu & Elliott 1991). The true breeding range of this species lies east of a line extending from Sweden in the north, through Denmark, Germany and Hungary to Turkey in the south (*European Atlas*). A separate subspecies *holbollii* breeds in eastern Asia and northwest North America: an individual of this race was shot in Wester Ross in September 1920 (*Birds in Scotland*).

The European population winters mainly in coastal regions of the Baltic and North Seas, with North Sea concentrations in the Danish Straits and along the west coast of Norway (Piersma 1988a, Stone *et al* 1995). Departures from the breeding sites seemingly begin in August and continue through into early November (*CBWP*), with individuals moving singly, or in small parties. Andersson (1954), monitoring a small passage of Red-necked Grebes during 1949–53, concluded that many individuals undertake nocturnal flights, with some individuals settling on the sea at dawn and continuing on their journey by swimming during daylight hours.

Small numbers of individuals are present in British waters typically from September to March, with most birds along the east coast in sheltered localities and a smaller number on larger inland waters in south and central England. Chandler (1981) suggests a wintering population of *c*50 individuals, while the *Winter Atlas* puts the figure closer to 100 individuals. Reports of Red-necked Grebes wintering along the west coast are more sporadic (*Birds in Scotland*) and very few winter off Ireland or Wales (*Birds in Ireland, Birds in Wales*). Occasional influxes occur as birds are forced west by bad weather further east and this can greatly increase the numbers of individuals within Britain and, to a lesser extent, Ireland (Chandler 1981). Most individuals depart for their breeding grounds during March and April, although an increasing number have oversummered during recent years (Batten *et al* 1990).

Little is known about the movements of this species within Europe because of the paucity of ringing and recovery data: there have been two local recoveries from 15 individuals ringed within Britain & Ireland (Toms & Clark 1998). There have been a small number of long-distance recoveries involving birds ringed and recovered outside our region but even these shed little light on the movement patterns of this species. As with the other grebes, this species is susceptible to oil spills and entanglement in gill nets (Piersma 1988a).

Mike Toms

Slavonian Grebe

Podiceps auritus

The Slavonian Grebe has an almost continuous holarctic distribution, with a number of recognized subspecies (Parkes 1952, Fjeldså 1973), two of which are known to occur in Britain & Ireland. The species was first recorded breeding in Scotland in 1908 and now numbers about 60 pairs (*Birds in Scotland*, Ogilvie *et al* 1999b), with *c*400 individuals wintering around Britain's coasts and a further 30–40 off Ireland (*Winter Atlas*).

Birds breeding in Scotland show characteristics of the race *arcticus*, which also breeds in Iceland and northern Norway. Individuals of this race appear to winter predominantly off northwest Scotland and Ireland, Iceland, Greenland and northwest Norway (although see Piersma 1988a). Slavonian Grebes often remain on their Scottish breeding lochs or on other inland waters into late October but by November most have moved to the coast. Some individuals, presumably on passage, reach Fair Isle during August (*Birds in Scotland*). The numbers wintering at sheltered sites along the Scottish coast reach a peak in midwinter with one or two favoured sites holding significant concentrations (*eg* up to or exceeding 100 individuals in the Firth of Forth and 50–100 individuals off Shetland and Orkney). Numbers begin to decline in March, by which time the Scottish breeding sites are typically reoccupied (*Birds in Scotland*). Small numbers of individuals arrive off the west and north coasts of Ireland from October, reaching a peak from mid-December to the end of January (*Birds in Ireland*), with most having left by the end of April.

It has been suggested, with some supporting evidence, that individuals of the race *auritus* winter predominantly off the east coast of Britain, along the Dutch coast and off Denmark (Fjeldså 1973), with smaller numbers wintering further south and east along the eastern Mediterranean coast, the Caspian Sea and the Adriatic (Fig 1). This race breeds east from Sweden, Finland and the Baltic States and begins leaving the breeding grounds in late August (failed breeders leave first) with peak movements taking place during October and November (*BWP*). Wintering Slavonian Grebes often remain at favoured sites for extended periods, with numbers remaining relatively constant throughout the winter period. Weather-induced movements are occasionally seen, although these are typically of smaller magnitude than those observed for Red-necked Grebe (Chandler 1981). Spring departures are initiated in March and April but breeding sites to the east may not be reoccupied until late May.

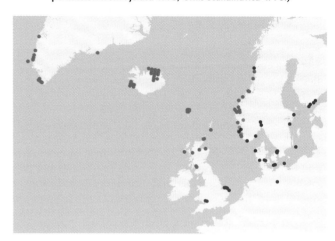

Fig 1. Distribution of Slavonian Grebes taken in northwest Europe and Greenland outside the breeding season. Those assigned to the race *arcticus* (blue) and the race *auritus* (red) are differentiated from those of unknown race. (Redrawn by kind permission from Fjeldså 1973, *Ornis Scandinavica* 4: 76.)

The lack of recovery data for Slavonian Grebes ringed in Britain & Ireland hinders any examination of the routes used for movement and the determination of breeding areas. There have been three recoveries from 19 individuals, one of which was a local movement: a bird ringed during the breeding season near Inverness was found long dead in Italy the following year, presumably on passage to or from its winter quarters (Clark *et al* 1996). A second individual, ringed during the breeding season on Lake Molotovskoye, northern Russia, was found injured in North Yorkshire in March the following year (Hudson 1964).

The use of favoured wintering sites over long periods makes this species susceptible to oil spills. Between 8% and 16% of the Shetland wintering population died as a result of the Esso Bernicia spill in the late 1970s (Heubeck & Richardson 1980).

Mike Toms

Black-necked Grebe

Podiceps nigricollis

The Black-necked Grebe is a rare but regular breeding bird in Britain, with an estimated population of less than 50 pairs (Stone *et al* 1997). Significant populations, composing three distinct races, occur elsewhere in Europe, Asia, southern Africa and North America (*European Atlas*, *HBW*). Outside the breeding season, Britain & Ireland is used by passage and overwintering individuals, many of which are thought to originate from the Continent (*Birds in Wales*).

Dispersal away from breeding sites begins in mid-August, reaching a peak during October, with most birds on their largely coastal winter quarters from November (Leibl & Zach 1992, *CBWP*). Failed breeders may leave as early as mid-July and these are presumably the birds reported from Britain & Ireland during the early part of the autumn passage period (*BWP*). Within North America, several hundred thousand individuals migrate to Mono Lake in central California where the adults and sub-adults undergo a complete moult, the juveniles only

undergoing a partial moult. The birds remain at the lake through into late autumn when the brine shrimp population collapses, before moving to the coast for the winter (Storer & Jehl 1985, Winkler & Cooper 1986). With a combined European, Russian and Turkish population of considerably less than 200,000 breeding pairs, movements within Europe are not on the scale of those seen in North America (*European Atlas*). The adults undergo a post-breeding moult from mid-June (failed or non-breeders) or July (birds with young) and winter-plumage birds are recorded in Britain & Ireland from September (*BWP*). Birds reported from Norfolk during autumn are usually in breeding plumage (Taylor *et al* 1999).

The West Palearctic wintering areas extend eastwards from the coasts of Britain, Ireland and Iberia across to the Mediterranean, Adriatic and Black Seas (Iborra *et al* 1991, *European Atlas*). Black-necked Grebes also make use of large, ice-free lakes in France, Switzerland and Turkey

(*CBWP*) and to a lesser extent the larger London reservoirs. Much larger concentrations occur across the eastern end of the wintering range, with hundreds of thousands of individuals thought to winter off Iran in the south Caspian Sea and many tens of thousands wintering on the Turkish lakes (*European Atlas*). Most of the British & Irish wintering population is present by mid-November, the birds seemingly remaining faithful to sites until the spring departures except during periods of severe weather (Clark & Eyre 1993). In Ireland, winter numbers peak in early December, also tending to remain constant from January through to early March, when the birds leave (*Birds in Ireland*).

The wintering distribution within Britain & Ireland is more southerly and westerly than that of the other grebes, with a suggested wintering population of *c*120 birds (*Winter Atlas*, Stone *et al* 1997), although this may be something of an underestimate. The general pattern of movements across Europe suggests that the species winters within the breeding range, with movements to the coast where freezing of inland waters occurs. Both diurnal and nocturnal movements are thought to occur within Europe, while movements in North America appear to be predominantly nocturnal in nature (Jehl 1996). Although there have been no recoveries from British- & Irish-ringed individuals (only nine individuals had been ringed up to the end of 1997), nor of foreign-ringed birds recovered within Britain & Ireland, there have been a handful of recoveries of birds ringed and recovered elsewhere in Europe. These suggest that the autumn movements have a strong southeasterly to southwesterly component, supporting the belief that birds wintering in sheltered estuaries in southeast England may originate from elsewhere in Europe (*CBWP*).

A small passage occurs in Britain & Ireland between March and May. While a few individuals begin to arrive on their breeding grounds during March, the main arrivals occur during April (Leibl & Zach 1992). During this period individuals appear to be quite mobile, visiting other waterbodies in addition to those on which they will eventually nest (*BWP*). Similarly, the numbers of birds present at individual breeding sites during this period may be significantly greater than the number remaining to breed, again suggesting mobility and the presence of birds on passage (*Birds in Scotland*).

Mike Toms

Cory's Shearwater
Calonectris diomedea

Late summer movements of Cory's Shearwaters within the North Atlantic result in varying numbers of sightings annually from southwest Britain & Ireland: while only 75 individuals were reported in 1996, some 1,731 were reported in 1997 (Fraser *et al* 1999b). This is unsurprising given the breeding distribution of this species, its known migration routes and the distribution of non-breeders (Thibault *et al* 1997). Cory's Shearwaters breed in burrows and crevices at colonies throughout the Mediterranean (race *diomedea*), and into the Atlantic (race *borealis*), where colonies exist on the Berlenga, Madeira, Selvagem and Canary Islands and the Azores (Rabouam *et al* 2000). The race *edwardsi*, which occurs on the Cape Verde Islands, is now generally regarded as a full species (Granadeiro 1993, Thibault *et al* 1997). There is little exchange between breeding colonies (Ristow *et al* 1990, Granadeiro 1991, Thibault 1993, Rabouam *et al* 2000) also demonstrated by the high degree of natal philopatry, more strongly evident amongst males than females (D Ristow pers comm).

Immature Cory's Shearwaters first attend breeding colonies when they are between four and seven years of age, although they do not breed until they are five to 13 years of age (Mougin *et al* 1986, Ristow *et al* 1990). Some non-breeders are therefore present at the breeding colonies during the breeding season. These prospectors show a high degree of fidelity to particular sites, both within a breeding season and between years (D Ristow pers comm). Failed breeders leave their breeding colonies somewhat earlier than the successful breeders and their young, the latter (successful breeders and young) tending to vacate breeding colonies from mid-October (Mediterranean colonies) to late October (Atlantic colonies) through into the first half of November (Round & Swann 1977, Zino *et al* 1987). Passage through the Strait of Gibraltar, some of which may be nocturnal, occurs largely between mid-October and mid-November (Tellería 1980). From here, birds are thought to winter in the southern hemisphere, off both South America (predominantly *borealis*) and South Africa, with some reaching the Indian Ocean (Mougin *et al* 1988, Thibault *et al* 1997). This winter distribution is based on observations at sea and a small number of ring-recoveries. More recently, satellite-transmitters have been fitted to a small number of birds (all adult males from the eastern end of the Mediterranean) demonstrating that at least some *diomedea* winter off West Africa, north of the Equator, and along the North Africa shelf (Ristow *et al* 2000).

Non-breeding individuals are present in the Gulf of Mexico from June to October (Pulich 1982, Haney & McGillivary 1985), with others summering off South America (Monteiro *et al* 1996). In some years substantial numbers are present in the Bay of Biscay between July and October, the timing again suggesting that these are non-breeders (Stone *et al* 1995). Records from the southwest of Britain & Ireland come predominantly from the late summer period (August–September), slightly before the main departures from colonies in the Mediterranean and the Atlantic. While the origins of the birds reaching Britain & Ireland are unknown, they most probably involve those non-breeders present in the Bay of Biscay, with a more northerly distribution in some years bringing greater numbers past the coasts of southwest Britain & Ireland. Non-breeders do move south to join the wintering breeders and their young (Thibault *et al* 1997).

An exceptional influx of Cory's Shearwaters into Britain & Ireland occurred during August 1980, when 2,851 were reported from England and 14,396 from Ireland, including 1,202 past Porthgwarra on 13 August and 10,939 past Cape Clear on 16 August (Dymond *et al* 1989). Other large influxes have occurred since but not on the same scale (Fraser *et al* 1999b). A small number of the annual records come from the eastern coast of Britain (Wallace & Bourne 1981, *Birds in Scotland*). Cory's Shearwaters are occasionally reported at other times of year, such records coming from a wider scatter of localities than those from late summer (Dymond *et al* 1989).

A progressive departure from the wintering areas begins in February with passage through the Strait of Gibraltar from mid-February to late March, as Mediterranean birds return to their breeding colonies (Finlayson 1992), and colonies are reoccupied over the same period (Thibault *et al* 1997). While some colonies show stable numbers (*European Atlas*) others have shown substantial declines (Tucker & Heath 1994). With uncertainties over exact wintering ranges and migration routes, monitoring of colonies and increased use of satellite tracking will be important for the future conservation of this species.

Mike Toms

Great Shearwater

Puffinus gravis

The Great Shearwater is a remarkable seabird; breeding on a handful of islands in the South Atlantic, yet with a population of nearly three million breeding pairs and an annual migration that takes it in a clockwise loop around the Atlantic Ocean (Voous & Wattel 1963, *BWP*; see Fig 3.6b). During late summer, Great Shearwaters occur in varying numbers off the coasts of western Britain & Ireland, although under certain conditions large numbers may be pushed inshore: 5,118 were seen off Cape Clear on 15 September 1965 and 4,487 on 3 September 1973, yet the totals seen in other years are a fraction of these numbers (Newell 1968, *Birds in Ireland*).

Great Shearwaters breed at three main sites, two (Nightingale Island and Inaccessible Island) in the Tristan da Cunha group and one (Gough Island) some 350 km further southeast. Since at least 1961, small numbers have been reported breeding on the Falkland Islands (*CBWP*). Adults have generally left these breeding sites by mid-April, followed shortly after by young birds, with migration evidently occurring on a narrow front taking them past the horn of Brazil (Metcalfe 1966, *BWP*). The northward progress of these birds is rapid and they arrive off the Atlantic coasts of North America in May and June, where the adults undertake moult (Bourne 1990). Large numbers gather off Nova Scotia, over the Newfoundland Grand Banks, and off Greenland (Warham 1996). This is supported by a small number of ring-recoveries from some 811 individuals ringed on Nightingale Island in 1938, which were reported from off the east coast of Newfoundland and the west coast of Greenland in June and August (Hagen 1952). Peak numbers in the northernmost latitudes occur in early August.

During the summer months there is a gradual dispersal eastwards and by early autumn numbers on the eastern side of the Atlantic have built up, typically well offshore (Newell 1968). The timing of the movement through British & Irish waters strongly suggests that these birds are non-breeders (Voous & Wattel 1963, Newell 1968, Warham 1996). Records along the Atlantic frontier, north and west of Scotland, peak in August, with sightings from the continental slope and over the Wyville-Thomson and Ymir Ridges (Pollock *et al* 2000). Sea-watching from the coast of Ireland shows Great Shearwaters to be regular visitors in small numbers off the south and west coasts, although birds remain far offshore unless pushed in by poor weather conditions (*Birds in Ireland*). The species is less commonly reported from the coasts of Scotland and Wales (*Birds in Scotland*, *Birds in Wales*), and is more likely to be encountered through pelagic trips than from the shore. Records from the east coast of England are rare (Wilson & Slack 1996, Taylor *et al* 1999).

From August the adults begin a rapid return passage, thought to occur on a broad front across the whole Atlantic, though clearly less pronounced along the eastern side (Warham 1996). Significant numbers are still present in the North Atlantic and in the Bay of Biscay during October and November (Voous & Wattel 1963), a time when breeding has already commenced, indicating that these late birds are non-breeders (Warham 1996). Only stragglers remain north of the Equator between December and April (*BWP*).

There is still much to learn about the movements of Great Shearwaters and they would appear to be a suitable species for satellite tracking, given the huge distances covered and the success of satellite tracking on the related Cory's Shearwater (Ristow *et al* 2000). A limited study of the avian by-catch in demersal longline fisheries off Brazil found Great Shearwaters to be the most commonly taken species (Neves & Olmos 1998). The impact of such fisheries-related mortality on this species has yet to be assessed.

Mike Toms

Sooty Shearwater

Puffinus griseus

Sooty Shearwaters are southern hemisphere breeders that undertake rapid transequatorial migrations outside the breeding season. These movements bring a relatively small, but variable, passage into the coastal waters of Britain & Ireland during late summer (Phillips 1963a). Sooty Shearwaters breed at high densities at both island and mainland sites in southeast Australia, New Zealand and Chile (*HBW*, Warham 1990) and in far smaller numbers on the Falkland Islands (Woods & Woods 1997). The movement patterns of this species have been studied in both the Pacific and Atlantic Oceans (Phillips 1963b, Cooper *et al* 1991, Minami & Ogi 1997, Spear & Ainley 1999) and appear to be more complex than the simple loop migrations originally proposed by Phillips (1963b).

Departures of successful breeders begin in mid-April (New Zealand), with chicks remaining at the colonies for up to a further four weeks (Richdale 1963). Most birds move into the northern Pacific on a broad front passing rapidly across the warmer tropical and subtropical seas to reach waters as far north as the Gulf of Alaska by June (Spear & Ainley 1999). Earlier arrivals off British Columbia are likely to be non-breeding birds or failed breeders (Phillips 1963b, Warham 1996). Numerous winter records from off South Africa (Cooper *et al* 1991) and Australia (Marchant & Higgins 1991) demonstrate that some birds remain within the southern hemisphere, while others move up the east coast of South America to winter in the North Atlantic. However, numbers wintering within the North Atlantic are thought to be considerably less than in the Pacific (Phillips 1963b).

Sooty Shearwaters appear off the northeast American coast from the second half of May, with a northward shift in distribution through into July. During this period there are few mid- or eastern Atlantic records, but by July birds are present off the Scottish continental shelf break and at features such as the Rockall bank (Webb *et al* 1990). By August records from the mid-Atlantic have increased, matched by a decline in records from the northwest Atlantic and by an increase in records from British waters (Phillips 1963a, b, Webb *et al* 1990, Pollock *et al* 2000). This suggests a fairly rapid crossing of the Atlantic, thought to occur between 45° and 60°N, resulting in peak concentrations in inshore British waters during September. Most records of feeding birds come from the continental shelf between the Faeroes and the west coast of Ireland, although September records of small groups of Sooty Shearwaters also come from North Sea coasts, the southwest and the English Channel (Phillips 1963a, Oliver 1971). Sightings in the Irish Sea are rare (*Birds in Ireland*, *Birds in Wales*, Webb *et al* 1990). Sooty Shearwaters are frequently reported from around the Northern Isles, the Hebrides and from Cape Clear, with 6,569 Sooty Shearwaters reported from Cape Clear in 1980, together with 1,360 that were reported to have flown past Papa Westray in just three hours on 30 August 1983 (*Birds in Scotland*). There are occasional years when major movements are witnessed elsewhere (Gibbs *et al* 1965), for example on 9 October 1987 some 406 were observed from Dungeness (Davenport 1989). On the same date 160 flew past Langney Point, Sussex — an unprecedented movement set against a previous annual maximum of seven birds (James 1996). Exceptionally high densities were also recorded during shipboard surveys off southwest Ireland in September and October 1980 (Webb *et al* 1990). It is worth noting that there is some debate on the nature of movements through the English Channel. Phillips (1963a) dismissed such movements, maintaining that Sooty Shearwaters enter and leave the North Sea via the Scottish north coast. However, it is certain that some Sooty Shearwaters do leave the North Sea via the English Channel, mainly along the French side, although much of this movement is probably linked to meteorological conditions at the time (Bourne 1971, Jones 1971, Oliver 1971, Davenport 1989).

By October, numbers in British & Irish waters begin to decline and small concentrations are reported off Spain and Portugal, suggesting a return movement south. Because of the distances involved, those birds present in northeast Atlantic waters during September and October are unlikely to be able to make the return to the breeding colonies in time for successful breeding; the main return passage off South America occurs during late August (*BWP*), while most birds return to New Zealand breeding colonies during mid-September (Warham *et al* 1982). Consequently, it has been suggested that those birds present in the northeast Atlantic during autumn are non-breeders (*BWP*).

Although the species is exploited commercially in New Zealand, where up to 250,000 are taken annually, it is not thought to be globally threatened (*HBW*). However, the presence of introduced predators on breeding islands, together with mortality attributed to birds drowning in gill-nets and the decline in numbers recorded off North America (Veit *et al* 1996, Lyver *et al* 1999), would suggest that efforts should be made to monitor breeding populations and to develop our understanding of the movements made by this species.

Mike Toms

Balearic Shearwater
Puffinus mauretanicus

The Balearic Shearwater is a regular visitor to British and Irish waters during the summer months, with around 1,000 individuals currently reported annually (Fraser *et al* 2000). The species was separated from the Manx Shearwater *Puffinus puffinus* in 1991 and treated as a race of the Mediterranean Shearwater *P. yelkouan* (BOU 1991). A further split has resulted in the two 'races' of Mediterranean Shearwater being separated into the Balearic Shearwater *P. mauretanicus* and the Levantine Shearwater *P. yelkouan* (BOU 2001), the latter species breeding in the eastern Mediterranean.

A complete understanding of the movements of the Balearic Shearwater is lacking. In part this reflects the difficulties in separating individuals in the field from both Levantine Shearwater and other short-winged species that can wander north from southern oceans (Yésou *et al* 1990). Although there have been claims of Levantine Shearwaters from British waters (Cade 1983, Curtis *et al* 1985, McCartney 1986), and much discussion on the overlap in appearance between Levantine and Balearic Shearwaters (Witherby 1921, Rees 1986, Yésou 1986, Yésou *et al* 1990), only the Balearic form is included on the British list (BOU 2001).

The Balearic Shearwater is thought to be largely restricted to the Balearic archipelago, with some 3,301 ± 1,174 pairs (Aguilar 1991) reported to breed at 25 different sites; about 70% of pairs are located on Formentera. Counts of birds at sea suggest that the total population is somewhat larger and that the species' breeding grounds may not be confined to the Balearic archipelago. Breeding takes place early in the year, beginning as early as January, and during the breeding period birds may range widely, taking them several hundred kilometres away from their breeding colonies (*European Atlas*).

Post-breeding, from May onwards, the bulk of the breeding population appears to leave the Mediterranean and peak passage counts are witnessed from Gibraltar during late June (Tellería 1981). The birds passing into the Atlantic gather together and undergo moult at sites in the Bay of Biscay with smaller numbers further north to the southern North Sea (*CBWP*) and off the southeast coast of Spain (de Juana & Paterson 1986). The main period of moult appears to begin in June, but it is not clear when it ends (*BWP*). The presence in the Bay of Biscay of individuals from Formentera has been confirmed by ringing (Yésou 1985b, Bourne *et al* 1988). Other moulting birds have been collected off the south coast of England, the Channel Islands, from within the Strait of Gibraltar and in southwest Portugal (Witherby 1921, Bourne *et al* 1988, Yésou *et al* 1990). Many moulting birds appear to associate with a marine front within the Bay of Biscay and movement of this front may displace birds from their usual moulting areas (see Yésou *et al* 1990). Some moulting birds reportedly also accumulate along a marine front off Northumberland (Bourne *et al* 1988). There may also be some movement into the southern hemisphere, with two moulting birds reported to have been collected from False Bay, South Africa (Mackrill 1988). The wintering area is not fully known, although birds appear to use the English Channel, the southern North Sea and the North Atlantic south to northwest Africa. Other individuals, most probably immatures, appear to winter off West Africa utilizing an area of upwelling also used by Audouin's Gulls from the Mediterranean (Yésou *et al* 1990).

Generally, records from southern coasts of Britain begin in mid-May, with peak numbers reported during July, August and September (Fraser *et al* 1999b, 2000). Although most records come from the southwest of Britain, significant numbers also come from eastern and northeastern coasts, with a handful of records from northern and northwestern coasts. National collation of records for Britain only began in 1986, since when there has been an increasing trend in the number of Balearic Shearwaters reported annually. This almost certainly reflects the increasing popularity of sea-watching, together with a general improvement in the ability of birdwatchers to identify these birds.

Return movements to the breeding grounds begin in September, with large numbers seen leaving the Bay of Biscay during September and October (Huyskens & Maes 1971). Movements through the Strait of Gibraltar have been witnessed from mid-October and birds are reported from the breeding grounds as early as November. The continuation of passage through the Strait of Gibraltar until March is likely to involve immature birds wintering off West Africa.

The taking of eggs and birds from breeding colonies has, until recently, been a problem throughout the Balearics (Mayol 1986). Additionally the birds may be at risk to pollution incidents during the period of moult, a time when they may become more dependent on fishery discards (Yésou 1985b). More information is needed about the size and location of breeding colonies, movements of different populations and age classes, and about the general ecology of this species.

Mike Toms

Great Bittern (Bittern)
Botaurus stellaris

The breeding range of this species extends from western Europe, where it has a patchy distribution, through its strongholds in central Russia and the Ukraine across to the Pacific coast. With 28 booming males in 2001 (G Gilbert pers comm), Britain holds about 1% of the EU breeding population. In winter, numbers increase to an average of 120 individuals (a range of 55 to 250 from UK winter sightings between 1980 and 1997; G Gilbert pers comm) with the arrival of birds from the Continent.

The skulking and secretive habits of this species make it difficult to detect movements outside the breeding season, and consequently relatively little is known about patterns of dispersal, partial migration or cold-weather movements. Recent radio-tracking studies (RSPB/English Nature Bittern Ecology Project) of young Bitterns have shown that they do disperse from natal sites. There have been 15 recoveries from the 98 Bitterns to have been ringed in Britain & Ireland since 1909, with a further eight foreign-ringed individuals also recovered here (Toms & Clark 1998). No British- or Irish-ringed Bitterns have been recovered overseas. In Britain, most ring-recoveries during winter have been from Bitterns fledged from East Anglia, with the pattern of recoveries not demonstrating any one direction of movement (G Gilbert pers comm). An analysis of European-wide recoveries was carried out by Zink (1958) and this demonstrated a general southwesterly movement of birds during the winter period.

Sightings of Bitterns away from known breeding sites within Britain & Ireland are relatively consistent from September through into November. However, numbers increase sharply in December and reach a peak in January (Bibby 1981a). This seems to point to an influx of birds (suggested by ring-recoveries to come from northwest Europe: the Netherlands, Belgium, Sweden and Germany) following hard weather on the Continent. Small variations between years in the timing of the peak in sightings have been shown to correlate with the severity of winter weather conditions. This also has an effect on mortality rates and, to a lesser extent breeding populations in subsequent years, demonstrating how susceptible the species is to severe winter weather (Underhill-Day &

Wilson 1978, Bibby 1981a, Underhill-Day 1981). A study of annual local survival of adult male breeding Bitterns in Britain, carried out between 1990 and 2000, showed that low spring rainfall had the greatest negative effect on adult overwintering survival, possibly due to relatively mild winters during the study period (Gilbert *et al* 2002).

The late autumn sightings of birds away from known breeding areas may be of dispersing youngsters, some of which are likely to be of British origin, and this would explain the low level of sightings throughout August to October before the first heavy frosts of the winter. Bibby (1981a) stated that the ringing evidence suggests that there may be rapid post-breeding movements, as found in the case of Grey Heron (Rydzewski 1956), although there are insufficient recoveries of birds ringed as nestlings and recovered during the autumn to be certain about this. The small amount of recovery data for birds ringed as adults and recovered during the winter months suggests that birds remain on or near their breeding areas despite the fact that casual sightings may be low over this period (particularly at eastern sites). Radio-tracking studies of adult male Bitterns through the winter have shown them to be resident, although their home ranges change (G Tyler pers comm). The *Winter Atlas* indicates that the winter distribution of Bitterns is predominantly southeastern, although there are concentrations of records on the south coast of Wales, the Humber and the Severn. The species is a scarce winter visitor to Scotland and Ireland (*Birds in Scotland, Birds in Ireland*).

The presence of booming males throughout the late winter, with booming beginning as early as January, suggests that adult birds might remain on their breeding areas throughout the winter, only moving if weather conditions force them to do so. The recognition of individual males from their booms has, over the last 10 years, identified a high level of site-fidelity among males (Gilbert *et al* 2002). With the possibility of milder winters over the coming decades, breeding populations may benefit from reduced overwinter mortality. However, milder winters may also reduce the number of Bitterns moving to Britain & Ireland.

Mike Toms

Little Egret
Egretta garzetta

The Little Egret has a more southerly breeding distribution within Europe than most of the other heron species of the region, being most abundant in the low-lying lagoon areas of southern Spain and France, and northern Italy (*European Atlas*). The species is widely distributed across the temperate and tropical latitudes eastwards from Iberia and Africa, through central and southern Asia, southeast to Australia (*CBWP*).

Within Britain & Ireland, the status of this species has changed dramatically over recent years following a northwards expansion of the range within France. The Spanish and Italian populations have also increased, although those in eastern Europe have tended to decrease over the same period (*European Atlas*). A strong northwesterly component to the post-breeding dispersal of birds from established French colonies is thought to have increased the number of overwintering birds remaining to breed in new areas (Combridge & Parr 1992, Lock & Cook 1998). The establishment of breeding colonies at new sites along the northwest coast of France has undoubtedly led to the colonization of sites in England and Wales (Lock & Cook 1998, Ogilvie *et al* 1999b).

Until 1989, the species was a rare vagrant to Britain & Ireland but during that summer the first of a series of influxes occurred, with about 50 birds present (Combridge & Parr 1992). Similar influxes occurred during the following summers, although the 1993 influx involved about 200 birds and during summer 1995 over 650 birds were recorded by WeBS (A J Musgrove pers comm). Similar numbers were recorded each autumn from then until the summer of 1999, when over 1,000 birds were recorded by WeBS, although the true figure may have been closer to 1,500 (A J Musgrove pers comm). The number of individuals arriving each year is presumably related to breeding success in French colonies (Hafner *et al* 1998). Birds predominantly make use of suitable estuarine sites as far north as a line between the Cleddau Estuary in Wales and the Medway Estuary on the east coast, although a handful of sites to the north of this line are used by small numbers of individuals (A J Musgrove pers comm).

Peak numbers of Little Egrets occur in Britain & Ireland in September and October, during the period of post-breeding dispersal

(Fraser *et al* 1997, Pollitt *et al* 2000). Numbers then decline, presumably as some birds return to France or perhaps migrate further south, but a substantial number remain throughout the winter months (*eg* over 500 were recorded by WeBS in January 2000).

Analyses of movements of birds from colonies in southern France and Spain show that Little Egrets from these colonies typically migrate south to southwest into Africa, with individuals reaching as far south as the Equator. Some egrets from eastern Spain and the Camargue region of France migrate northeast to overwinter in northern Italy, sometimes reaching Libya and Egypt (Voisin 1985, Bartolomé *et al* 1996). Individuals that remain within the breeding range throughout the winter months frequently suffer as a consequence of bad weather, and overwinter mortality can be substantial (Voisin 1991). The return migration from overwintering sites begins in March, with birds returning rapidly to their breeding colonies. Interestingly, in Britain & Ireland there is evidence of a small increase in numbers in early spring, the majority of birds then departing before the breeding season. This 'spring passage' is most likely to involve birds that have wintered further south overshooting as they return north before returning to the colonies in Brittany. However, given the establishment of British and Irish breeding colonies since 1996, these birds may well remain in Britain & Ireland in the future (Lock & Cook 1998, Ogilvie *et al* 1999b, A J Musgrove pers comm).

The susceptibility of overwintering individuals to severe winter weather could mean that the breeding range expansion in Britain may be only a temporary one. Global warming may greatly benefit this species, however, by reducing the risk of severe winter weather and by extending the amount of suitable habitat, particularly if schemes involving 'managed retreat' go ahead.

Mike Toms

Eurasian Spoonbill (Spoonbill)
Platalea leucorodia

Up to 75% of the world population of Spoonbills breeds at scattered sites across Europe, most notably in Russia, the Netherlands, Spain and from Hungary and Greece east to the Caspian (*European Atlas*). Although populations have been increasing in western Europe, doubling in Spain and the Netherlands, there has been an overall decline in the European breeding population. In 1998, a pair of Spoonbills nested in the United Kingdom for the first time in over 300 years (Ogilvie *et al* 2000).

Spoonbills are regular visitors to Britain & Ireland, almost all of them presumed to be of Dutch origin and arriving in small numbers during spring and autumn. Some dispersal of young birds away from the Dutch and Spanish breeding colonies normally takes place in July and August, with individuals reportedly only moving short distances (*CBWP*). However, recoveries from Britain & Ireland of Dutch-ringed birds show that a small number of these dispersing youngsters do move some distance, reaching Kent and Dyfed by the end of August. The main period of departure from the western European colonies takes place between August and the beginning of October, with departures from the Spanish colonies beginning several weeks earlier than those from the Dutch colonies. This period of departure is reflected in a peak in arrivals across Britain & Ireland during October as shown by ring-recoveries of Dutch-ringed birds and by data published in county bird reports. A small number of these birds may remain to overwinter, most notably during mild winters, but the majority presumably reorientate to follow their migration routes to the southwest (*Birds in Wales*, *Birds in Scotland*). Most of those overwintering in Britain do so in southwest England, often returning to traditional sites for many years.

During the migration period, Spoonbills remain dependent on coastal sites, many of which are under threat from land reclamation, disturbance and pollution: this is particularly so for stopover sites in France and Spain (Poorter 1990). Birds from the Dutch colonies will use some of the same stopover sites as used by Spanish birds, although by the time the Dutch birds arrive, those from Spain have usually departed (De la Court & Aguilera 1997). Both populations appear to follow a similar migration route along the west coast of Africa to the wintering grounds on the delta of the Senegal River and the Banc d'Arguin in Mauritania (Poorter 1990, De la Court & Aguilera 1997). Most immatures (one to two years of age) also oversummer at these sites (De la Court & Aguilera 1997), although two recoveries in Britain involve first-year birds that had either overwintered in Europe or returned as immatures the following spring. Populations from southeast Europe overwinter around the Mediterranean and North Africa, while some winter across the Middle East and into India (*CBWP*).

Individuals begin returning to their Spanish breeding grounds from early January and their Dutch breeding grounds from mid-February, although in both cases the main arrivals occur some weeks later. The older birds tend to arrive back at the breeding colonies earlier than younger individuals. The pattern of sightings and recoveries in Britain & Ireland shows a second peak in May, suggesting that many of these individuals may be failed breeders.

Mike Toms

Bean Goose
Anser fabalis

The Bean Goose has a large breeding range and is widely distributed across the northern Palearctic where it has been split into as many as five subspecies (*CBWP*). Two of these occur regularly in Europe: nominate *fabalis* — the Taiga Bean Goose, and the heavier-billed, shorter-necked *rossicus* — the Tundra Bean Goose (Coombes 1947, *European Atlas*, Madsen *et al* 1999). The *fabalis* population breeds across a zone extending from northern Fennoscandia, across north Russia to Siberian lowlands east of the Ural Mountains. The *rossicus* population breeds in northern Siberia (Madsen 1991, Madsen *et al* 1999).

Populations of both forms move south or southwest on their autumn migration, with birds from different breeding areas appearing to use a small number of more or less discrete wintering sites (Timmerman *et al* 1979, Fog 1982, Madsen *et al* 1999). Work in Fennoscandia using neck-collars (Nilsson 1984b, Nilsson & Pirkola 1991) shows that individuals of the race *fabalis* migrate to staging areas in southern Sweden, where they are joined by birds from further east, before many move further south through the Baltic to reach Denmark, the northern part of the Netherlands, coastal Germany and Poland. The remainder winter in southern Sweden, only moving further south with the onset of severe winter weather (Madsen *et al* 1999). Those *fabalis* reaching Britain are thought to largely originate from the Lapland breeding population (Parslow-Otsu 1991).

Individuals of the form *rossicus* coming from further northeast perform a 'leap-frog' migration to winter further south than those from *fabalis* breeding populations. This results in *fabalis*-dominated wintering populations in southern Sweden, Denmark, the northern part of the Netherlands, coastal Germany and Poland. *Rossicus*-dominated populations winter in the southern part of the Netherlands, western Germany, the Balkans, France, and Spain (Coombes 1947, Timmerman *et al* 1979, *European Atlas*), with interchange between those in the Balkans and elsewhere in Europe (van den Bergh 1984).

European wintering numbers are thought to consist of 80,000 *fabalis* and 300,000 *rossicus*, although only a tiny proportion of these actually use Britain (*Winter Atlas*). The majority of Bean Geese in Britain are of the form *fabalis*, with 300–350 wintering at sites along the Yare Valley in Norfolk and up to 130 wintering in the Carron Valley, Scotland. Numbers using a third site in the Dee Valley have declined since the 1950s and birds have only occasionally used this site in recent years. Historically, the numbers wintering in central Scotland were higher than they are today, although some early records in the literature almost certainly referred to other geese species (*Birds in Scotland*).

There appear to be three distinct phases of arrival for individuals using the Yare Valley sites. Failed breeders appear first, followed by a second group of arrivals containing many family groups. A third influx arrives during periods of pronounced cold weather. Although the 1927/28 winter saw over 5,000 Bean Geese arrive in Norfolk, such numbers are exceptional (Taylor *et al* 1999). Despite the statement in *CBWP* that the species '*rarely appears* [in Britain] *before early January*', recent first arrivals in Norfolk have mostly been in November. Birds leave again between mid-February and the end of the first week of March. The geese tend to leave earlier in mild winters than they do during cold winters. It was during the 1950s and 1960s, when just small numbers used to winter in East Anglia, that arrivals before New Year were unusual (Taylor *et al* 1999). *CBWP* stated that the late arrival of individuals suggests that movement into East Anglia is a secondary movement of birds moving from another wintering area. This seems to be the cause of the third influx of birds, those responding to cold-weather movements and pushing further southwest. Sightings of birds with neck-collars from the Västerbotten moulting flock support this idea, and also demonstrate a high degree of fidelity to the Yare Valley as a wintering site (Parslow-Otsu 1991).

Records of *rossicus* from outside the main Yare sites have continued to increase in recent years, with small parties regularly recorded in Norfolk. Movements of Bean Geese between breeding, moulting and wintering sites have been well studied across Fennoscandia (Lampio 1984, Nilsson 1984b, Tveit 1984, van Impe 1987) but there have only been four published recoveries of individuals found in Britain & Ireland, and very little information is published on colour-marked individuals seen wintering in Britain & Ireland.

Mike Toms

Egyptian Goose
Alopochen aegyptiacus

The Egyptian Goose has bred in the wild in Britain since the 18th century and there is now a well-established breeding population of *c*750–800 pairs, centred on Norfolk and slowly expanding south and west (Sutherland & Allport 1991). The species has also become firmly established in the Netherlands, where breeding was first reported in 1967 (Lensink 1999), and a smaller population exists in Belgium. However, the natural distribution of this species covers most of Africa south of the Sahara, as well as Egypt (*BWP*).

Egyptian Geese are thought to be partial migrants within the Afrotropical region, with ringing studies demonstrating seasonal movements of up to 1,000 km (Shewell 1959). Elsewhere, including the Nile Valley as well as European populations, the species is resident, only undertaking short-distance moult migration. Within Britain, the moult takes place during July and August, and family parties gather at a small number of sites across the breeding range. These aggregations are relatively loose affairs, with family groups and unaccompanied pairs clearly discernible. The main moulting concentrations are at Holkham Hall, Blickling Hall, Sennowe Park and Lynford, each site drawing birds from the local breeding population (Sutherland & Allport 1991, Seago 1997). There have been just five recoveries (from 80 ringed), all involving local movements of less than 5 km. Occasional records of individuals elsewhere in Britain & Ireland, away from the main breeding range, are likely to be escaped individuals from local collections.

Mike Toms

Long-tailed Duck
Clangula hyemalis

The Long-tailed Duck has a circumpolar breeding distribution almost entirely contained within the Arctic Circle (*CBWP*). The bulk of the European population, estimated at just over five million birds, breeds in northwest Russia, with smaller populations in Fennoscandia, Iceland and Svalbard, and on Bear Island (*European Atlas*). Most populations are migratory, wintering south of the breeding range between 55°N and 75°N, notably within the Baltic Sea where more than four million birds overwinter in three main areas: Hoburgs Bank, the Gulf of Riga and the Gulf of Pommern (*European Atlas*). Icelandic breeders are only partial migrants, remaining off the Icelandic coast or moving to Greenland. It has been suggested that some Icelandic birds may winter off Scotland but there is no evidence to support this.

Following breeding, the males undertake a moult migration to coasts or lakes close to the breeding grounds, where small flocks gather. More pronounced movements occur during July with females and young birds leaving the breeding areas. The main influx into the Baltic does not occur until November or even December. Individuals begin arriving off the coasts of Britain & Ireland during mid-October with peak numbers typically recorded during late December or early January (Ruttledge 1970, *Winter Atlas*, *Birds in Wales*). However, individuals often remain at some distance from the coast, making it difficult to estimate numbers and discover whether birds are present at a site (*Winter Atlas*). Large-scale movements take place at dusk as birds move to favoured roost sites in deeper water. During this time, more accurate assessments can be made of the numbers present. It is thought that the peak UK wintering population regularly exceeds 20,000 birds, with the majority of these favouring the shallow, sandy areas of the Moray Firth (Batten *et al* 1990). Other individuals winter off Shetland and Orkney, and far smaller numbers occur elsewhere around our shores (*Birds in Scotland*, *Birds in Ireland*, *Birds in Wales*, Cranswick *et al* 1999).

The lack of ring-recovery information greatly hinders our understanding of the origins of birds wintering in different areas and the migration routes taken. Those individuals wintering around Britain &

Ireland are thought to originate from northern Fennoscandia and northwest Russia. The one overseas recovery of a BTO-ringed bird was of an individual ringed on Fair Isle during October and shot inland in Finland, again during October, some 20 years later (Mead & Clark 1989). There is a pronounced overland passage between the White Sea and the Gulf of Finland and it appears that this individual was migrating to the Baltic when it was shot.

The numbers of Long-tailed Ducks wintering off Scotland remain high until mid-February after which a return movement to the breeding grounds begins. A major overland passage from the Gulf of Finland to the White Sea occurs in early May and breeding areas on the Russian tundra are reoccupied by the end of May or the middle of June, depending on the state of thaw. Breeding sites in Iceland tend to be reoccupied somewhat earlier (*CBWP*). The highly concentrated nature of the roosting flocks increases the risks to this species from an oil pollution incident (Hope Jones 1979).

Mike Toms

Black Scoter (Common Scoter)
Melanitta nigra

Common Scoters breed across the boreal and subarctic zones of Eurasia, and at scattered sites in the Nearctic from Alaska to Newfoundland (*CBWP*). The British & Irish breeding population is restricted to Scotland and Ireland and has been estimated at 195 pairs (Underhill *et al* 1998). Individuals from the Scandinavian and Icelandic breeding populations winter off our coasts, seemingly joining our own breeding birds: the only two recoveries in our region of individuals ringed abroad were from Iceland and the Gulf of Finland (Toms & Clark 1998).

With only eight BTO-ringed recoveries recorded, it is not clear how far British & Irish breeders move during the winter. However, the presence of moulting flocks soon after the breeding season, and of birds throughout the winter at coastal sites, suggests that the breeding population does indeed winter around our shores. Favoured moult sites may change over time, but moulting flocks of more than 1,000 birds are regularly reported at traditional sites off the eastern coast of Scotland (*Birds in Scotland*) and in Carmarthen Bay (*Birds in Wales*). The numbers involved indicate that these flocks include individuals from other breeding populations in addition to local breeders. An extensive moult migration takes place elsewhere in Europe, with large concentrations of birds gathering in the western Baltic, the eastern North Sea and off western France. During the early stages the moulting flocks are dominated by immatures and adult males, but from mid-August the females and juveniles join them, the passage continuing through into December (*CBWP*). After moulting is completed the flocks remain together and gather in sheltered, shallow

waters where they remain through the winter, feeding on a range of bivalve species (Durinck *et al* 1993b). The UK wintering population is thought to reach 37,500 individuals during this period (Stone *et al* 1997).

Breeders from the Russian Arctic are known to migrate along a west-southwesterly route via the White Sea, then overland to the Baltic. In contrast to Long-tailed Ducks, Common Scoters use the southwest Baltic largely as a staging area, with many moving rapidly southwest to the North Sea, the English Channel and the coasts of northern and western Iberia (Bräger *et al* 1995, Leopold *et al* 1995). Similar migration peaks are seen in the Dutch Wadden Sea (Camphuysen & van Dijk 1983), where very large numbers also winter (Stone *et al* 1995). Birds appear to follow a similar route on the return leg, which begins in late February or early April. Numbers in the western Baltic peak during March when the numbers present can greatly exceed the wintering population in some areas (Bräger *et al* 1995).

Breeding populations in Britain & Ireland are vulnerable to changes in water quality and predation by introduced American Mink, while the highly concentrated nature of the moulting and wintering flocks puts them at risk of oil spills. The immediate mortality of more than 4,500 Common Scoter was observed following the *Sea Empress* oil spill in Carmarthen Bay during February 1996 (Parr *et al* 1997), highlighting the risk to this species.

Mike Toms

Velvet Scoter
Melanitta fusca

Unlike the Common Scoter, the Velvet Scoter does not breed in Britain or Ireland, but it is a regular winter visitor with around 3,000 wintering over a number of east coast sites (Stone *et al* 1997). Breeding has been suspected on a number of occasions, most recently in 1945 on Shetland, but has never been proven (*Birds in Scotland*). The species has a holarctic breeding distribution and occurs widely from Fennoscandia, across northern Asia to the Pacific, and from Alaska through western Canada and the northern United States (*CBWP*). The species is migratory and winters along the Atlantic and Pacific coasts, extending as far south as northwest Africa, the southern United States and China.

During late summer, small numbers of Velvet Scoter moult among Common Scoter flocks at traditional sites along the east coast of Britain. The majority of these individuals are adult males, which are joined by females and young throughout August and September. Numbers continue to build up during the first half of the winter and normally reach a peak during February, before subsequently declining (*Winter Atlas*). Departures from northern Russia begin in late summer and increase throughout the autumn, while those from the Finnish skerries take place later in September (*CBWP*). During October and November there is a pronounced passage of birds through the southwest Baltic, followed by movement into the North Sea and the English Channel. The waters off eastern Denmark hold a significant proportion of the total northwest-European moulting population (Laursen 1989, Durinck *et al* 1994) and *c*20% of the northwest-European wintering population (*European Atlas*). Within the Baltic Sea, the Gulf of Pommern and the Gulf of Riga also have significant wintering populations (Svazas & Pareigis 1992, Durinck *et al* 1993a, 1994, *European Atlas*).

The main wintering site in Britain is the Moray Firth, where peak counts of several thousand individuals have been recorded (*Birds in Scotland*). Sites of secondary importance are St Andrews Bay and the Forth Estuary, although WeBS counts suggest roughly similar numbers at all three sites (Cranswick *et al* 1999). However, as with other sea ducks, WeBS counts may underestimate the number of individuals present at a site, and the situation is further complicated by pronounced annual variation in the numbers recorded. The origins of the birds wintering off the east coasts of Britain & Ireland are unclear. However, individuals ringed in Norway and Finland have been recovered in our region during the winter, and these may be joined by birds from northern Russia (Toms & Clark 1998).

A return movement begins in early March; the spring passage is somewhat later than that observed for Common Scoter, resulting in the presence of large flocks in Danish waters as late as early May (*CBWP*). The species is known to be a late breeder (*European Atlas*). Over-exploitation of shellfisheries (Durinck *et al* 1993b) and oil spills during the winter months remain the two main threats to this species (Batten *et al* 1990, Stroud *et al* 1990, Tucker & Heath 1994).

Mike Toms

Smew
Mergellus albellus

The Smew is a short-distance migrant with a boreal breeding range extending eastwards from northern Sweden and Finland, through Siberia to Kamchatka (*CBWP*). Most of the breeding population is found within Europe, predominantly in European Russia where there are estimated to be 7,000–15,000 breeding pairs. In recent decades the population has undergone a period of decline, most pronounced in the southern part of the breeding range. However, populations are now thought to be more stable (Tucker & Heath 1994).

Northwest Europe is thought to hold a wintering population of 15,000 individuals, with up to 10,000 of these concentrated in the Netherlands, notably on the IJsselmeer and along the Rhine (*Winter Atlas*). A further 50–60,000 birds winter in the Baltic Sea, with others gathering in the Black, Caspian and Azov Seas (Tucker & Heath 1994). Smaller numbers reach Britain & Ireland during the winter and the majority of these occur in the southeast of England and East Anglia. The species is a scarce visitor to Wales and Scotland and very scarce, but annual, in Ireland (*Birds in Scotland, Birds in Ireland, Birds in Wales*).

Individuals begin to depart from their breeding sites in September and these are usually deserted by the end of October (*CBWP*). A pronounced passage occurs through Sweden and the Baltic countries from mid-October to early November, with arrivals in countries around the North Sea usually peaking in December or even January as individuals respond to bad weather further east. Peak numbers of birds arrive in southeast England usually during January and are thought to originate from the Dutch wintering population. However, a complete absence of ring-recoveries prevents confirmation of this (Toms & Clark 1998).

The Winter Atlas suggests a wintering population of approximately 350 individuals, with periodic influxes in some years, *eg* 1978/79 (Chandler 1981). This is largely supported by published figures derived from WeBS counts (Cranswick *et al* 1999), which also demonstrate peak counts in January. Smew tend to use large lakes and are fairly mobile, making an assessment of the exact numbers present somewhat difficult. Females and juveniles tend to move further southwest than adult males and, within Britain & Ireland, males are clearly outnumbered by redhead females and juveniles (Chandler 1984). The wintering waters are usually vacated during late February or early March, although in some years numbers will not peak until as late as April. Occasional individuals remain well into the summer at sites far to the south of the breeding range, including Britain & Ireland.

Mike Toms

Red-breasted Merganser

Mergus serrator

The breeding range of the Red-breasted Merganser is largely holarctic, typically occurring beyond 50°N and extending across North America, Eurasia and Greenland (*European Atlas*). It has been suggested that within northern Eurasia and Greenland there are five discrete breeding populations (Scott & Rose 1996), although systematic counts and ring-recoveries seem to indicate a degree of interchange between these populations (Robinson 1999). A southwards expansion of the breeding range has substantially increased the British breeding population over the last 120–150 years (Parslow 1967), with the population for Britain & Ireland recently estimated at 2,850 pairs (*1988–91 Atlas*). Some 10,000 birds are thought to winter within Britain & Ireland (Stone *et al* 1997). While populations in Russia and Fennoscandia show no long-term trend, those in the Baltic countries show a pronounced decline (*European Atlas*).

Populations in the southern part of the breeding range (including Britain & Ireland) are thought to be partially migratory (*European Atlas*). Those in Finland, northwest Russia and the Baltic States are migratory and move to the Baltic Sea and other northwest European wintering areas, with smaller numbers reaching the Mediterranean (*CBWP*), while those from Norway, Sweden and Denmark appear to be largely sedentary, mixing with central European birds in the Baltic. A small number of ring-recoveries show that some of these birds winter further southwest along the Atlantic coast, as far south as Portugal (Robinson 1999). Although there have been no recoveries in Britain & Ireland of birds from central Europe, the directions and orientations of migratory flights of central European birds make it likely that those individuals wintering off the east coast of Britain & Ireland include both local breeders and birds from central Europe (Robinson 1999).

It is thought that most of the 4,000–8,000 birds of the Icelandic breeding population migrate south to winter off the coasts of Scotland, northern England and Ireland and this is supported by 10 Icelandic-ringed Red-breasted Mergansers that have been recovered in Britain & Ireland from October through to March (Scott & Rose 1996). It is also possible that a small number of birds from the east Greenland population, which move to winter in Iceland, reach Britain & Ireland (Robinson 1999).

Males and immatures gather in moulting flocks in coastal localities throughout June and July (*CBWP*), but true autumn migration does not begin until September. Numbers on the Scottish moulting sites generally peak in August, with important concentrations gathering in the Sound of Gigha, off the Kincardine/Angus coast and off Tentsmuir (*Birds in Scotland*). Individuals also moult at Lindisfarne, Northumberland, some of which have been fitted with wing-tags by Northumbria Ringing Group. The numbers of birds present at these moulting sites and their distribution suggest that birds from Iceland and Fennoscandia do not appear here before October at the earliest. Departures from the northern breeding grounds usually take place during late October and peak numbers are seen in the Baltic at this stage. Birds from Fennoscandia and Iceland probably reach Britain & Ireland during December, when numbers may peak at 10,000 individuals (*Winter Atlas*, Stone *et al* 1997). Females and their young move further than the males, a pattern seen in other diving ducks (Chandler 1984). There is evidence from southwest Canada of segregation of the sexes during winter, possibly linked to sexual dimorphism and use of food resources (Kahlert *et al* 1998).

Most of the British & Irish breeding population appears to be relatively sedentary, moving to nearby coasts to undergo moult and to overwinter. These local movements are supported by 16 ring-recoveries arising from 196 birds ringed in Britain & Ireland, as well as by 41 sightings of wing-tagged males, marked by Northumbria Ringing Group at the Lindisfarne moult site. Two autumn-ringed individuals fitted with BTO rings have, however, been recovered in Norway and Denmark at a later date, with a third individual recovered in the Netherlands (Toms & Clark 1998). Winter flocks are usually small, except for the large concentrations recorded on the Inner Moray Firth, the Forth Estuary and the Duddon Estuary (*Birds in Scotland*, Cranswick *et al* 1999). The use of sites, or particular parts of an estuary, is dependent upon a range of factors including state of the tidal cycle, season and time of day (Richner 1988). Disturbance may also prove to be an important factor. Red-breasted Mergansers do make cold-weather movements (Chandler 1981) and it is only during these that they are regularly recorded on inland waters (*Winter Atlas*).

Spring returns begin in late February and there is a clear influx of Scottish breeders onto freshwater rivers during April (Marquiss & Duncan 1993). Populations in the far north of the breeding range do not return until mid-May, their arrival dependent on the state of the thaw. Britain & Ireland are important for Red-breasted Mergansers from a number of breeding populations. In addition to the monitoring of our own breeding birds, greater ringing effort should be targeted towards those birds present here outside the breeding season, since our region clearly plays an important role in the movements made by Red-breasted Mergansers from across much of the breeding range.

Mike Toms

Ruddy Duck

Oxyura jamaicensis

The Ruddy Duck is native to the New World, breeding across North America, south through the West Indies and into South America as far south as Tierra del Fuego. Introduced into captive collections in Britain during the 1930s (Lever 1977), then escaping in 1953, Ruddy Ducks first bred successfully in the wild at Chew Valley Lake in 1960 (King 1976). By the early 1990s, the population in Britain had risen to 570 pairs while that in Ireland was estimated at 15–20 pairs (*1988–91 Atlas*). Captive individuals have also escaped from collections elsewhere in Europe and, together with birds moving from the British & Irish population, have continued the colonization of other European countries.

Within North America the Ruddy Duck is migratory, with birds making both short-distance moult migrations and much longer annual migrations to southern wintering grounds in Mexico, Belize and Guatemala (Palmer 1976b). It has been suggested that the British population is largely resident (*CBWP*), but more recent work suggests that the species may be developing a migratory strategy similar to its American relatives, with the limited seasonal migration of Ruddy Ducks from Britain & Ireland to winter in Europe (Hughes 1996). This would also explain the appearance of Ruddy Ducks in Norway, Finland and Sweden during the spring and early summer, together with the appearance of a small, migratory, breeding population in Iceland (*1988–91 Atlas*). The spread into Europe, indicated by over 900 records of 1,500 birds (Cranswick *et al* 1999), has serious implications for Spanish populations of the endangered White-headed Duck, with which Ruddy Ducks readily hybridize (Hughes & Grussu 1995).

Movements within Britain & Ireland take place during the autumn and flocks of several hundred may occur at favoured sites; notably Chew Valley Lake, Rutland Water and Blithfield Reservoir. Annual fluctuations

in the numbers occurring at individual sites are characteristic, although some of these seem to reflect the expansion of the population onto new wintering sites (Cranswick *et al* 1999). The eight recoveries derived from the 339 British-ringed individuals all involved local movements within Britain (Toms *et al* 1999). More information on its movements is needed to help understand how the species is likely to spread within Europe and whether suggested control measures are likely to be effective. Such control measures are essential if populations of the White-headed Duck are to be protected (Hughes 1996).

Mike Toms

European Honey-buzzard (Honey-buzzard)
Pernis apivorus

Honey-buzzards breed throughout the temperate and boreal regions of Europe, eastwards into the boreal regions of western Asia (*European Atlas*). The bulk of the 160,000 breeding pairs are found in Russia, eastern Fennoscandia, Germany and France, although smaller breeding populations occur elsewhere in Europe (*CBWP*). The British & Irish breeding population is thought to number 50–60 pairs (Roberts *et al* 1999), with a suspected expansion northwards and westwards from the traditional breeding areas of southeast and southern England. Away from traditional sites, evidence of breeding has now been reported from northeastern Scotland (*1988–91 Atlas*, Murray 1993), northern England and Wales (Roberts *et al* 1999). Neither the breeding status nor the movements of this species within Britain & Ireland are fully understood, largely because pairs are unobtrusive and occupy large home ranges. Additionally, some observers withhold information, fearing disturbance of breeding pairs (Ogilvie *et al* 1999b).

The Honey-buzzard is a long-distance migrant, arriving in Britain from mid- to late May (Batten *et al* 1990), presumably returning from tropical Africa via the Strait of Gibraltar. Populations from Sweden, Finland and elsewhere in central Europe also appear to use this route, as demonstrated by ring-recoveries (*CBWP*), while birds from further east use routes across the Sicilian Channel (Galea & Massa 1985) or through Israel (Bruderer *et al* 1994, Leshem & Yom-Tov 1998). It is not apparent from European ring-recoveries and migration watches whether sub-adult individuals remain in Africa for one or more breeding seasons before returning north to the breeding areas (Kjellén 1992). However, at least some yearling Honey-buzzards do return to the breeding grounds in their first summer, while others appear to remain in Africa (Bijlsma 1993).

The breeding season is relatively short and departures from the breeding grounds begin from mid-August (*CBWP*). Adult birds leave first

(Kjellén 1992, 1998), with the peak in young birds following some two weeks after the peak in adult movements (Kjellén 1992). The peak month for movements through Norfolk is September and in some years significant numbers are reported (Taylor *et al* 1999). Migrating Honey-buzzards move south to their wintering grounds by following routes around both the east and west ends of the Mediterranean Basin, and large concentrations may occur at particular crossing points as the birds utilize the thermals they need for their gliding/soaring flight (Bruderer *et al* 1994, Spaar 1997, Leshem & Yom-Tov 1996, 1998).

The full extent of the wintering range is unclear, but it certainly extends across the forest and wooded regions of tropical Africa, south of the Sahara, favouring open woodland to dense forests (*CBWP*). A small number of ring-recoveries involving birds ringed in the Netherlands show their presence in Ghana, Nigeria and Liberia during winter (Bijlsma 1993). The only recovery from a bird ringed in Britain was an individual ringed as a chick in the north of Scotland in August 1986 and found freshly dead in Guinea during February 1991 (BTO unpublished). The only two recoveries of foreign-ringed Honey-buzzards were a Swedish-ringed youngster found dead in Yorkshire on passage south, and a German-born bird, found alive in Kent during July, some six years after being ringed as a nestling (Toms & Clark 1998).

The concentration of Honey-buzzards at migration bottlenecks in southern Spain and the Middle East puts them at serious risk of persecution, with shooting a major threat. Despite the fact that hunting pressure in the Mediterranean is decreasing, juvenile mortality is high, partly because juveniles appear to be rather unwary of people and are readily shot.

Mike Toms

Rough-legged Buzzard
Buteo lagopus

This is the most northerly of Europe's breeding *Buteo* species, occupying a breeding range that extends across the arctic and subarctic zones (*European Atlas*). Beyond Europe, the species occurs in the same zones across Asia and North America (*CBWP*). Within Britain the Rough-legged Buzzard is a scarce but regular winter visitor, although it is only rarely reported from Ireland (*Winter Atlas*). In most years it occurs in small numbers along the East Coast, although there are periodic

influxes, which may result in the presence of up to 250 recorded birds during October or November (Scott 1968, 1978). With a European population estimated at 13,000–21,000 breeding pairs, and a Russian population estimated at 80,000–120,000 breeding pairs, the species is a relatively common raptor within its breeding range (*European Atlas*).

Departures from the breeding grounds typically begin in late August, although the timing of departure is dependent upon the availability of food and the amount of snowfall (*CBWP*). Individuals migrate mainly in a southeasterly direction to wintering grounds in central Europe or further east, explaining why only small numbers reach Britain & Ireland. Rough-legged Buzzard passage through Falsterbo, southern Sweden, is usually rapid and concentrated over a period of just a few days (Kjellén 1992), with Fennoscandian birds following a route along the Karelian Isthmus (*European Atlas*). Some individuals overwinter in central and southern Sweden (*European Atlas*).

In years when there is a large influx of Rough-legged Buzzards into Britain & Ireland, the main arrival takes place from mid- to late October (Scott 1968, 1978), with numbers dropping through November and December to leave a smaller number of overwintering birds. Very occasionally there may be a further influx in midwinter, possibly resulting from cold weather in the Netherlands, southern Sweden or elsewhere pushing the birds further south or west (Davenport 1982). The little evidence that is available suggests that the birds arriving in late October have come direct from breeding populations in Norway and Sweden, with winter recoveries in Britain & Ireland of two birds ringed in Sweden, and one in each of Norway and Denmark (Toms & Clark 1998). Scott (1978) suggested that food shortages in the northern breeding grounds might have forced some birds to breed further south and west than they would normally do, thus providing an increased source population from which the influx birds could come. This is supported by the fact that the species may make irregular movements during the pre-nesting period when food is scarce to search for areas with higher prey densities (*CBWP*). Most of the winter arrivals to Britain & Ireland remain along the east coast of England, notably in Norfolk, Suffolk and Kent, although some do move further west (Scott 1968, 1978, *Birds in Scotland*, *Birds in Ireland*, *Birds in Wales*).

Individuals remain in their winter quarters through into March, although during influx years, some birds have been reported in Britain & Ireland through into May, or exceptionally July (Scott 1978). The Fennoscandian breeding grounds are usually reoccupied during late April or May but this is again dependent upon food availability and snowfall (*CBWP*).

Mike Toms

Red Grouse
Lagopus lagopus

The Red Grouse *L. l. scoticus* is a subspecies of the Willow Ptarmigan, occurring within Britain & Ireland on moorland dominated by heather and with an estimated breeding population of *c* 250,000 pairs (Stone *et al* 1997). The world range of the Willow Ptarmigan extends across the arctic tundra south into alpine mountain regions and the edge of the boreal forest zone, from Ireland and Scandinavia across Russia and Siberia to Alaska and northern Canada (*HBW*).

Although some populations are at least partially migratory, those in Scotland and some parts of Scandinavia are largely sedentary, only making short-distance altitudinal movements in response to snowfall (Jenkins *et al* 1967, *Winter Atlas*). The movements of Scottish Red Grouse have been studied in some depth using birds either ringed as chicks or fitted with tabs (Jenkins *et al* 1967). This work on high-density populations has shown males to be almost entirely sedentary, with 94–98% moving less than 1.5 km, and females to be only slightly less so, with 79–83% moving less than 1.5 km. Some of those birds moving farther than 1.5 km may only have done so as a consequence of being driven during grouse shoots. Radio-tracking of birds in a lower-density population from their natal to breeding territories found that all males moved less than 1 km, while 40% of females moved over 2 km, up to a maximum of 10 km. Most female movements took place between August and December (Hudson 1992). It seems likely that natal dispersal distances are related to population density. The 175 ring-recoveries included in the analysis, from 1,554 birds ringed between 1909 and 1997, confirm the species' sedentary nature, with 95% moving less than 1 km and only six birds moving more than 5 km (overall range 0–35 km).

During the winter months, Scottish Red Grouse form flocks that move if heavy snow conditions prevent access to the heather. In such circumstances, the birds may descend to lower altitudes or occupy ridges where wind has drifted the snow off the heather (Jenkins *et al* 1967). Scandinavian populations also spend the winter in flocks and are largely resident, although there is some dispersal during spring with the onset of territory establishment. There is some evidence from ring-recoveries that Scandinavian birds may show greater movement in the second winter of life than the first, with females seemingly moving farther than males (*BWP*). Weeden (1964), working in Alaska, has suggested that there may be some segregation of the sexes during winter, although this needs to be examined more rigorously. Evidence of more pronounced movements comes from island populations of Willow Ptarmigan along the Norwegian coast, where birds leave small coastal islands in September and move up to 20 km to reach larger islands or the mainland itself (Myrberget 1972). Although established breeders typically return to their islands in March and April, some young do not return. Some populations exhibit altitudinal movements during the autumn of a similar nature to those seen in Rock Ptarmigan, where birds move to higher ground to exploit unused food resources (Watson 1965), before being forced back down by inclement weather conditions.

The most pronounced and regular movements are made by populations inhabiting the arctic tundra zones of northern Russia, Siberia, and North America. These populations move south in late autumn and winter, and in the harshest winters they may move up the river valleys of the taiga zone by as much as 250 km (*BWP*). These movements may be made through a series of short flights or, under other conditions, they may be more direct, with flocks of 200–300 birds reported from Russia.

Although Red Grouse populations undergo well-documented and much-studied population cycles (see Lawton 1990 for a review), the longer-term trend within Britain & Ireland has been one of decline. This decline appears to be linked to a combination of changes in heather management and quality, predation levels and the associated levels of keepering (Hudson 1992). Understanding of the limited movements of Red Grouse is an important component of determining how grouse populations can be managed to maintain population size at a sustainable level.

Mike Toms

THE MIGRATION ATLAS

Rock Ptarmigan (Ptarmigan)
Lagopus mutus

The Ptarmigan occurs throughout the subarctic and boreal zones across northern Europe, northern and northeastern Asia, Alaska, northern Canada, Greenland and Iceland (*BWP, HBW*). Relict populations are found in the Alps, the Pyrenees, Japan and in Scotland where the race *millaisi* occurs (*European Atlas*). The resident British breeding population is estimated to be 10,000 pairs (Stone *et al* 1997) located across the highlands of central and northern Scotland, on Mull, Skye and sporadically elsewhere (*Birds in Scotland, 1988–91 Atlas*).

Although there have been no ring-recoveries from the 32 Ptarmigan ringed in Britain, long-term studies have shown the species to be resident within Britain, generally only making altitudinal movements in response to severe weather conditions (Watson 1965). This pattern is repeated across the southern part of the Ptarmigan's world range, although the more northerly, high Arctic populations undertake long-distance, sometimes irruptive movements to avoid very difficult winter weather conditions. Ring-recoveries show that Icelandic Ptarmigan may make movements of up to 300 km, while individuals of the Greenland race *captus* have been taken at sea and in Iceland, suggesting that birds from these northerly populations can undertake significant migrations (*European Atlas*).

In Scotland, family parties break up throughout August to October and flocks are seen from this time onwards. These flocks move in response to worsening weather, often gathering together in corries. However, territorial behaviour and displaying by pairs may continue through into November, particularly on fine days. Watson (1965) and Gelting (1937) recorded some movements to higher ground made on fine days by flocks

of birds. Gelting (1937), working in Greenland, suggested that the birds were moving to exploit unused food resources and Watson (1965) felt that this was possibly the reason behind the movements he witnessed in Scotland. During the winter period small flocks of Ptarmigan frequent snow-free ridges and sheltered slopes, leaving these for lower ground only during periods of very deep snow (Watson 1965). During the winter Ptarmigan typically roost in snow hollows, and, even when the ground is virtually free of snow, birds will utilize the small amount that is available (Watson 1972). Across the Scottish Highlands severe weather can force Ptarmigan to desert ground above 1,200 m but on the more exposed western and northern slopes they will move down to 500 m or lower (Watson 1965). In most years, these flocks break up in March or April and the birds return to establish territories on their breeding grounds. Both males and females appear to make similar altitudinal movements in Scotland, although there is a suggestion that in Alaska the females may move to lower altitudes than the males (Weeden 1964).

Ptarmigan may be particularly sensitive to the effects of global climate change and it is important that information be gathered on any dispersive movements that the Scottish population might make. It is known that birds occasionally turn up far outside the normal breeding range and in 1977 Ptarmigan recolonized Arran (*Birds in Scotland*). Another important conservation issue is the effect of human use of the habitats in which Ptarmigan occur, either for walking, skiing or other forms of recreation (Watson 1982).

Mike Toms

Black Grouse
Tetrao tetrix

Black Grouse occur within the boreal, arctic-alpine and subarctic zones that are located across the high and middle latitudes of the Palearctic (*BWP*). Here they occupy a mosaic of vegetation types dominated by unimproved upland pasture, birch scrub, heather and bilberry (Parr & Watson 1988, Baines 1994). In Britain, and elsewhere in Europe, the Black Grouse is largely a sedentary species but further east in Russia seasonal migrations and periodic eruptions may take place. Black Grouse do not occur in Ireland even though there have been several attempts to introduce them there (*1988–91 Atlas*). The British breeding population has recently been estimated to be c5,000–8,100 displaying males (Hancock *et al* 1999), indicating a continued population decline (Baines & Hudson 1995).

As with the other grouse species occurring in Britain, Black Grouse show very little movement. Adult males have relatively small home ranges and associate with lekking sites throughout most months of the year even though attendance levels vary between birds and seasons (Baines 1996). Radio-tracking work in Scotland has revealed the home ranges of six adult males to be between 303 ha and 689 ha, with 75% of the total observations for each bird occurring within an area of between 62 ha and 151 ha (Robel 1969). This study also showed no major changes in the home ranges or mobility of the Black Grouse during the autumn and winter, although these results only relate to seven birds in one population over a single year. A separate Scottish study also supports the sedentary nature of Black Grouse, with only four study males recorded outside their home ranges: three first-winter males had moved

up to 5 km and one had moved some 17 km (Johnstone 1967). Lekking behaviour can also influence the distances travelled by males. While older males tend to remain faithful to one lek, young males may visit several as they attempt to gain access (Baines 1996). Three of the 14 British ring-recoveries involve movements of more than 5 km, the longest of these being a movement of 15 km, which took place over nearly four years.

Work on a Black Grouse population in the Alps has shown a similar pattern of movements, with sedentary males and slightly more mobile females and immature males (Pauli 1974). This tendency for females to wander farther than males has also been noted in Sweden, Finland and Norway. Analysis of Norwegian ring-recoveries produced a mean distance moved between ringing and recovery of 1.6 km for 29 males and 4.4 km for 18 females (*BWP*). During winter, the range of food taken and the habit of feeding in trees as well as on the ground potentially makes Black Grouse less susceptible than other grouse species to the amount of snow-cover. However, in some areas prolonged snow-cover over favoured food (*eg* bilberry) can displace Black Grouse by up to 2 km, as the birds respond to the localized availability of rowan, larch and pine (von Keller *et al* 1979). Food availability is likely to be more important in the far northern latitudes where conditions are harsher, and the effects of this can be seen from a comparison of weight changes in different populations through the winter months. Birds in the Alps manage to maintain their body-weight through the winter, while those in northern Finland lose weight, despite starting the autumn at the same weight as the Alpine birds (Marti & Pauli 1985). Under such conditions birds may be forced to move.

Indeed, it is within the higher latitudes that more pronounced movements can occur, occasionally involving hundreds of individuals, although they appear to be rare (*BWP*). Because these movements have occurred as early as the beginning of autumn, it seems likely that they are a response to population levels and food availability rather than to climatic conditions. Documented movements of up to 1,000 km are known from Sweden, with one male making a movement of 500 km that involved a 20-km sea-crossing from Gälveborg to Öland (*BWP*). Whilst this may appear surprising, it must be remembered that Black Grouse have a strong flight and are capable of sustaining this over some distance.

The sedentary nature of this species within Britain means that habitat fragmentation remains a serious threat to it (Batten *et al* 1990). Other threats include collisions with deer fences, habitat degradation due to overgrazing and increased rates of predation (Baines & Summers 1997).

Mike Toms

Western Capercaillie (Capercaillie)
Tetrao urogallus

The Capercaillie is largely confined to the Palearctic boreal coniferous forests, although smaller, isolated populations exist in central European mixed spruce and mountain spruce forests (*BWP, European Atlas*). The Scottish population originates from successful reintroductions that took place from 1837 onwards, the species having previously become extinct in the 1780s (*Birds in Scotland*). This population is now thought to number *c*2,200 adults but has been declining over recent decades (Catt *et al* 1998, Moss *et al* 2000).

Across its breeding range, the Capercaillie is generally regarded as being sedentary in nature, exhibiting a degree of local movements in winter and very occasional eruptive movements in some more northern areas (*BWP*). Capercaillie have been studied in some depth using radio-tags and such studies provide an insight into some, though not all, of the movements that may be made by this species. There have been 14 recoveries (including several resightings) from the 32 birds ringed in Britain, the sample sizes being too small to draw any conclusions about differences between age and sex classes.

Male Capercaillie are polygynous, only interacting with females during the early spring when they attend leks. Radio-tracking studies in southeast Norway (Wegge & Larsen 1987) and in the Alps (Storch 1997) show a similar pattern of male movements and spacing behaviour during the breeding season. Adult males associate with leks during the breeding season, occupying territories that radiate out from the centre of these leks. Wegge & Larsen (1987) found that 95% of daytime locations of older males (four years and older) were within 1 km of the lek centre and none of the birds studied visited more than one lek during the course of a single season. The territories are largely exclusive, although the older males will tolerate the presence of immature males within their territories (Wegge & Larsen 1987). Fidelity to these territories is strong and virtually every older male uses the same territory in subsequent years. Younger males, and in particular immatures, are more mobile, visiting two or more leks during the course of the short breeding season and rarely establishing fixed home ranges near the leks. Females are even more mobile during the breeding season, often visiting two or three leks, although some remain in the vicinity of a single lek (Storch 1997). With inter-lek distances typically approaching 2 km, the females have home ranges that cover an area of several square kilometres.

Once they have mated, the females withdraw to find a suitable nest site usually close to the display ground (*BWP*). Eggs hatch during early June, close to the peak in caterpillar populations on Bilberry (Baines *et al* 1996) and the young remain with the female through into autumn. There is little available information on the dispersal of wild young following the break-up of family parties, although some indication of the range of movements undertaken comes from the radio-tracking of released youngsters (Schroth 1991).

Several authors have suggested that in some years there is a net emigration of female young during autumn and have used this to explain how the pronounced skew to the sex ratio of chicks seen in years of low productivity is removed later in the year (Moss 1987, Moss & Weir 1987). Because of the pronounced size dimorphism and small egg-size in relation to adult body-size seen in this species, male chicks appear to experience higher mortality in years with poor summers or low productivity, thus producing a sex ratio biased towards females (Slagsvold & Grasaas 1979, Moss & Oswald 1985). In effect males have to work harder to attain their larger size. Since the sex ratio appears to approach unity later in the season there must either be a sudden increase in female mortality rates or some sex-related dispersal away from the productive areas in which these studies have been carried out. While there is some anecdotal evidence to support greater dispersal of females (Moss & Oswald 1985), specific radio-tracking work is needed to follow young females during this period, in much the same way as used by Schroth (1991) to study the movements of released birds.

The break-up of the leks at the end of the breeding season results in the abandonment of the territories held by the males. The males disperse and remain predominantly sedentary through the remainder of the year. During the winter months, local movements may occur in response to feeding requirements, with both males and females favouring areas with pine (Saniga 1998). In Scotland, shifts into woods containing pine have been noted (Zwickel 1966), and in Russia and the French Alps more regular movements occur from deciduous to coniferous woodland (*BWP*, Brenot *et al* 1996). Occasionally movements occur over much longer distances (up to 1,000 km or more are documented) and whilst some of these are described as eruptive, others are unexplained. The greatest distance between the ringing site and place of recovery for a Scottish Capercaillie is just 17 km, although the movement did occur within a single year.

Many populations continue to decline, seemingly a consequence of changes in the management of woodland habitats and fragmentation of suitable areas into smaller pockets. Changes in rainfall patterns may exert an influence on productivity and this will need to be monitored with respect to the potential implications of global climate change. Set against this background it is important to gather further information on Capercaillie movements to complete our understanding of this magnificent species.

Mike Toms

Red-legged Partridge

Alectoris rufa

While the native range of the Red-legged Partridge extends across Iberia, France, northwest Italy, Corsica and the Balearic Islands, the species was successfully introduced into Britain in 1790 and is now a familiar sight across much of southern and eastern England. The current population in Britain is estimated to be in the range of 90,000–250,000 territories (Stone *et al* 1997). Although recorded in Ireland, the populations there are not self-sustaining (*1988–91 Atlas*). The continued release of Red-legged Partridges on game-rearing estates makes it difficult to assess population levels accurately.

All populations can be described as being resident or sedentary, although, in Spain, those occupying land above 2,000 m may descend to lower altitudes to avoid poor weather conditions (*BWP*). The species has a weak flight and appears incapable of sustaining this over any distance (*1988–91 Atlas*). This strongly suggests that the tentative evidence put forward for immigration into Britain (*Handbook*) is incorrect. As with other gamebirds, ringing of Red-legged Partridges is prohibited in Britain & Ireland and this means that only relatively small numbers of individuals have been ringed and recovered. Such ring-recoveries reinforce impressions of a sedentary species, with most recoveries only involving local movements of less than 1 km.

In Britain, local dispersive movements take place during spring when the winter social groups break up, these social groups being based on family parties (Green 1983). Young males occupy home ranges close to their natal sites, with only 13–27% moving more than 0.5 km, while yearling females move farther, with between 69% and 79% moving more than 0.5 km (Green 1983). The distance of dispersive movements and subsequent recruitment into the breeding population may be determined by population density and habitat characteristics (Rands 1987).

Mike Toms

Common Quail (Quail)

Coturnix coturnix

The complex and variable movements of this secretive species are closely geared to maximize the production of young. In a remarkable sequential breeding strategy like those of some butterflies and moths, Quail breeding in Europe in summer include many young birds hatched at more southerly latitudes, or lower elevations, earlier the same year.

The Quail is one of very few members of its family that migrate seasonally and is the only migratory European gamebird. Its Palearctic distribution regularly extends from the Azores, Cape Verde Islands, Morocco and Ireland east to Lake Baikal and northern India; the winter range includes the Sahel Zone across Africa from Senegal to Sudan, and the whole of the Indian subcontinent (*BWP*). Probably most West Palearctic birds winter in North Africa or Mediterranean Europe, however, mainly south of 40°N, and some birds may be almost sedentary in these areas (Guyomarc'h *et al* 1998). Further populations breed widely in East and South Africa, and in Madagascar. Although the evidence of transequatorial migration is limited, the lack of clear differentiation between populations suggests that some genetic exchange is occurring, and therefore that separate African and island races (*eg BWP*) should no longer be recognized (Guyomarc'h *et al* 1998). The Japanese Quail *C. (c.) japonica*, which is native to eastern Asia from Lake Baikal to Japan, wintering mainly in southern China and southern Japan, and has slightly shorter wings and a different call, is best considered a well-marked race of *C. coturnix* (Guyomarc'h *et al* 1998).

In Europe, Quail are found mostly in crop-fields such as cereals and clover that are tall enough to conceal them, usually well away from trees and hedges, sometimes in grass leys, or in natural vegetation of similarly dense structure. Trans-Saharan migrants, perhaps affected by over-hunting, Sahelian droughts and agricultural intensification on the breeding grounds, have declined greatly since the 1960s or possibly earlier (Mendelssohn *et al* 1969, Guyomarc'h 1992, *European Atlas*). Larger numbers have been wintering in southernmost Europe, North Africa and Israel since the 1980s, however, indicating an expansion of the more sedentary sections of the population, perhaps in response to increases in the area of irrigated land (Aebischer & Potts 1994). Periodic large irruptions occur (*eg* Davis *et al* 1966, Murray 1991), often specific to certain parts of the range. The 'Quail-year' of 1989 in Britain and northeast France, and north to Denmark and Sweden, followed one in Spain in 1988 and another in France in 1987. High numbers and breeding success in North Africa, or adverse late-spring conditions there or in southern Europe, may contribute to later irruptions further north, as may southerly winds.

After breeding, migratory European Quail cross the Mediterranean on three main fronts, towards Morocco, Tunisia and Egypt, mostly between late August and October, with a peak in mid-September. Their habit of flying very low across the North African coast at dawn, after an overnight flight, has enabled hunters to trap enormous numbers for food, using lines of nets set parallel to the coast (Zuckerbrot *et al* 1980). In north Sinai, for example, birds arrive mostly singly or in loose parties of up to four birds; most that enter the nets do so within 30 cm of the ground. During darkness, flight altitude is likely to be much higher (Kane 1993). Since few are seen at Saharan oases, it appears that those Quail that cross from North Africa to the Sahel do so in a single nocturnal flight, although a number of shorter flights may be more usual in the west where the desert is more vegetated (*BWP*). First arrivals on the Sahelian wintering grounds are in late August, and some depart in late January, but most are present from October–November until February or March (Guyomarc'h *et al* 1998).

In spring, birds cross the Mediterranean using a similar strategy; many low-flying birds appear at dawn on north Mediterranean coasts between March and mid-May. Those that wintered in Iberia or North Africa may begin calling there in December and may then nest continuously from mid-February to mid-August, augmented by returning migrants in March and April. Following the first breeding attempt, there is a second migratory phase in April and May that may take a large proportion of the whole population to higher altitudes or to more northerly parts of Europe, where breeding activity continues until early August. First broods, which are capable of migrating just two months after hatching and mature sexually at the age of 12–15 weeks, join in strongly with the second phase of breeding as early as June (Guyomarc'h *et al* 1998). The proportion of breeding birds in the 1987 'Quail-year' in France that had been hatched earlier the same season was estimated at 50% (Hémon *et al* 1988). The pair-bond breaks while the female is incubating and males often begin onward migration earlier than successful females and their young.

The status of Quail in Britain & Ireland can only be assessed by the number of calling males reported. Males call only very occasionally while mated, however, and thus persistent calling may indicate a local shortage or absence of females (Moreau 1951, Guyomarc'h *et al* 1998). The true number of breeding pairs could therefore be either many fewer than indicated by the calling birds, if many remain unmated, or possibly many more, if there are large numbers of males that pair and stop calling before they are detected; also, the spatial and temporal distributions of calling and breeding males could be quite different. During 1988–98 an average of 532 calling males were found in the UK, with 1,655 in 1989 but only 107 in 1991; on average there were only nine cases of proven breeding per year (Ogilvie *et al* 2000). Often, groups may form in particular areas separated by large expanses of apparently similar but unoccupied habitat, perhaps as calling males attract others migrating overhead. Such areas may be occupied whenever there is an irruption, perhaps because their habitat or topography is especially suitable. In England, the light chalky soils from Dorset northeast to Cambridgeshire are well favoured (*eg* Moreau 1956, *1968–72 Atlas*, *1988–91 Atlas*), although there are probably no British or Irish localities where Quail are truly annual.

Arrivals of Quail in Britain & Ireland are rare before late April and, on sites monitored since April, often as late as June or July (Marchant *et al*

1990). Most are clearly associated with the onward wave of migration in early summer and may therefore include many young of the year. Nests and broods have at times been seen at locations throughout Britain & Ireland, north to Shetland. Possibly, in some years, an arrival of males is not followed by one of females and young, resulting in much calling but little nesting in Britain & Ireland. Calling generally stops in early August, often coinciding with harvest, and few Quail are detected subsequently (*eg* Murray 1991), although it is likely that they moult before departing southward about a month later. A few lone migrants are seen in September and October, especially on coasts and islands, and occasional individuals have been recorded in winter. Wintering was apparently regular in Ireland in the early 19th century (*Birds in Ireland*).

Little is known of the specifics of movements involving Britain & Ireland. An adult female ringed in Surrey on 3 May 1965 was shot in the Ebro Valley, near Zaragoza in Spain, on 15 September the same year. The only other ring-recovery so far was made locally in 1993. The few recoveries of British and Dutch birds are all from Spain or Morocco (*BWP*), suggesting a westerly route for northwest European breeders. Ring-recoveries indicate that some birds on this route return northwards through Tunisia and Italy but the strong spring movement through Spain indicates that this loop migration is not general (*BWP, European Atlas*).

A severe threat to the continued existence of migratory populations of Quail in western Europe is posed by the large-scale releases of captive-bred Japanese Quail that are currently made each September in France, Spain and Italy; these semi-domesticated aliens interbreed freely with native Quail and first-generation hybrids show a much reduced tendency to migrate (Guyomarc'h *et al* 1998).

John H Marchant

Common Pheasant (Pheasant)
Phasianus colchicus

Although the Pheasant is an introduced species, established feral populations have existed in Britain & Ireland since at least the 16th century and the species is now a widespread and familiar part of our avifauna (Holloway 1996, *Birds in Ireland*). The initial introductions involved birds of the race *colchicus* from the Caucasus but from the late 1700s most involved *torquatus* from China. The current population is predominantly managed for game shooting and many thousands of Pheasants are reared and released every year. This creates a somewhat artificial situation, influencing as it does the movements and general ecology of the species.

Within Britain & Ireland, and across most of its introduced range, the Pheasant is sedentary, each generally remaining within 5 km of where it was hatched or released (Gates & Hale 1974, Gill 1977, Hill & Robertson 1988). Local movements do occur, however, forming part of the annual cycle, and from October the birds form flocks that may remain together through into March or April (Hill & Ridley 1987). Research in Britain, both on sites where birds are released and on those where no releases take place, has shown a degree of sexual segregation during the late autumn and winter, with males spread through a wider range of habitats (Hill & Ridley 1987). Such groups contain regular members, which are mainly adult birds, together with more transitory individuals, predominantly immatures. The female immatures disperse further than adult females and females in general disperse further than males (Hill & Ridley 1987).

Similarly, previously territorial males move less far than males that have never held a territory, demonstrating that local movements are related to social organization as well as to food availability. At the end of the winter, the males disperse from the winter flocks to establish territories and this is matched by a break-up of the female-dominated flocks. It is during this period that differential dispersal distances for the age and sex classes are most pronounced.

Dispersal movements are small-scale, representing movements of several hundred metres as opposed to several kilometres. Although Pheasants are strong flyers over short distances, this cannot be sustained (*BWP*). Substantial movements, such as a flight of 6.5 km over water, are exceptional (*BWP*). The limited information available on movements within China, the native range, suggests that birds may undertake mass migrations in severe winters (*HBW*). This contrasts with information from Britain and Europe, which suggests that severe winter weather leads to increased mortality, rather than increased levels of movement (*BWP*).

Within Britain & Ireland the ringing of Pheasants is prohibited (Redfern & Clark 2001). Consequently, only 287 individuals have been fitted with rings since 1909, 17 of which have subsequently been recovered and only two of which have involved movements of more than 3 km.

Mike Toms

Golden Pheasant

Chrysolophus pictus

The Golden Pheasant is native to the mountains of central China, favouring low, dense scrub (Zheng & Zhang 1993). The species was first imported into Britain during the 18th century, although attempts were not made to naturalize it until the 1880s (*1968–72 Atlas*). Subsequent releases have resulted in small, established populations centred on Thetford Forest (Taylor *et al* 1999), the South Downs (Hampshire and into West Sussex), Galloway (*Birds in Scotland*) and Anglesey (*Birds in Wales*), totalling 1,000–2,000 birds (*1988–91 Atlas*). Other populations and reports of individuals appear from time to time, being derived from escapes and typically not self-sustaining. There are no self-sustaining populations outside China and Britain. All populations, including those in China (Ming 1994), appear to be in decline (Balmer *et al* 1996, Robertson 1996, *1988–91 Atlas*).

Golden Pheasants have been little studied and information on their behaviour and movements is generally lacking. Balmer *et al* (1996) fitted

radio-collars to a small number of birds in Thetford Forest and calculated home-range sizes over the course of a year. For one male, the calculated home range was 8.5 ha with 94% of its 152 locations within a circle 500 m in diameter. Two females had larger home ranges (23 ha and 45 ha) with approximately 90% of their locations within a circle 750 m in diameter. These results show the extremely sedentary nature typical of this species. All three recoveries arising from the six birds ringed have involved local movements within Thetford Forest. Only extreme events, such as forest clearance or fire, are likely to induce movement of established birds. No information is available on the dispersal behaviour of young birds. More information is needed on the ecology and movements of Golden Pheasants, if attempts are to be made to halt the population declines.

Mike Toms

Lady Amherst's Pheasant

Chrysolophus amherstiae

Like the closely related Golden Pheasant, Lady Amherst's Pheasant is an introduced species that has become naturalized within Britain but not in Ireland. The species is native to southwest China, southeast Tibet and northeast Myanmar, occurring in similar habitats to the Golden Pheasant but at higher altitudes. The total population in the native range is estimated in the tens of thousands (*HBW*).

Lady Amherst's Pheasants were first introduced into England in 1828 but the first releases did not take place until 1890 when birds were turned out in Woburn Park. Birds from subsequent releases have established a population of 100–200 pairs centred on Woburn and the surrounding area (Trodd & Kramer 1991). A small number of birds from Woburn were released at Halkyn Castle in Wales and spread to the neighbouring Gwynsaney estate. This population was estimated to have reached a maximum of 40–150 birds but has declined in recent years

(*Birds in Wales*). Both populations appear to be sedentary and reports of birds from elsewhere in the country are almost certain to be new escapes.

Within their native range, Lady Amherst's Pheasants are known to make substantial altitudinal movements, a reflection of the winter weather conditions affecting their high-altitude summer range (*HBW*). Although not listed as being globally threatened, populations in the Far East are subject to overexploitation for food and to habitat loss, while those in Britain have suffered through hybridization with Golden Pheasants. At the time of the *1968–72 Atlas*, it was suggested that the population in Britain was not completely pure and its value in conservation terms may be questionable.

Mike Toms

Spotted Crake

Porzana porzana

The Spotted Crake has a breeding distribution that extends from Britain and Iberia eastwards across Europe and into Russia, reaching as far east as central Siberia (100°E) and as far south as Iran. The European breeding population is estimated at 50,000–180,000 breeding pairs centred on eastern Europe and Russia. Breeding is more sporadic in western Europe (*European Atlas*). Spotted Crakes are migratory with the bulk of the population wintering in Africa, southern Europe, the Middle East and southern Asia (*CBWP*). The only two ring-recoveries involving Britain & Ireland are local movements of birds ringed on Fair Isle in September and October, both recovered within a few days of being ringed.

Although previously more numerous in Britain (Aplin 1890, 1891), the 1990s breeding population was put at only 20–30 pairs (Ogilvie *et al*

1999b, Francis & Thorpe 1999). More recent work gives a new and more reliable estimate of 75–80 pairs (Gilbert 2002). The centres of the breeding population changed between the two atlas surveys. While this could suggest sporadic breeding within Britain it could also reflect observer coverage and the generally elusive nature of this species (*1988–91 Atlas*).

During the autumn birds from Germany, Poland, the Netherlands and presumably Britain begin to move south or southwest towards their wintering grounds. These movements can start as early as July, although young from first and second broods may remain in the breeding area until September or October respectively (Becker 1995). Other individuals may begin movements in July, halting during August for a period of two to three weeks while they undergo moult (Taylor & van Perlo 1998). Some populations presumably take other routes around or across the Mediterranean, with individuals ringed in the Netherlands and Germany recovered in Italy (Taylor & van Perlo 1998), and large movements reported through Israel (Shirihai 1996), Egypt, Sudan and into Kenya (Urban *et al* 1986). Most of these migrants are south of the Mediterranean by November, from where they move to wintering grounds in central and eastern Africa. The difficulties in observing Spotted Crakes in Africa have restricted the number of wintering records, making it difficult to determine the full extent of the winter range (Urban *et al* 1986). Spotted Crakes appear to be quite mobile within Africa, following rain fronts to new areas where they remain until the habitat becomes too dry (Brooke 1974, Taylor 1987). Breeding populations from the eastern edge of the range are thought to migrate to India and Pakistan (Ali & Ripley 1980), while some individuals remain in temperate Europe (including Britain) and around the Mediterranean throughout the winter (*Winter Atlas, European Atlas*).

Spotted Crakes have left the southernmost wintering grounds by the end of April, with most East African records indicating a spring passage through April and May (Taylor & van Perlo 1998). However, other authors (*CBWP*) state that the species is rarely recorded south of the Sahara later than March and that individuals pass through Europe in March and April. What is certain is that the northern European breeding grounds are largely occupied by the end of May (*Birds in Scotland*). As for the autumn migration, the movements appear to be predominantly nocturnal. Habitat loss, particularly through agricultural intensification and the drainage of wet meadows, is thought to be responsible for the population decline seen in many parts of the breeding range (Alexander & Lack 1944, Tucker & Heath 1994). Any contraction in breeding range may reduce the number of individuals moving to Britain & Ireland during the spring.

Mike Toms

Corn Crake

Crex crex

The Corn Crake is rapidly declining throughout much of its breeding range, which extends from the western Palearctic east to southeastern Siberia and north-central Asia (*CBWP*) and the species is now listed as being globally threatened (Collar *et al* 1994, Heredia *et al* 1996). The long-term decline in the British & Irish breeding population has been well documented (Norris 1945, 1947, Cadbury 1980, Hudson *et al* 1990, Green 1995b, Sheppard & Green 1995, Casey 1998) and appears to be a consequence of the changes in grassland management that have followed a period of agricultural intensification (Green & Stowe 1993, Stowe *et al* 1993, Green 1996b). A similar pattern of decline has been seen in other European countries (Broyer 1991, Hashmi 1991, Stiefel 1991, Heredia *et al* 1996).

Within Britain & Ireland, breeding Corn Crakes are almost entirely restricted to northwest Scotland and a small number of core areas within Ireland (*1988–91 Atlas*). The population probably numbers 480 calling males in Britain, with a further 150 calling males in Ireland (Green 1995b, Casey 1998), although it should be noted that these figures do not necessarily equate to breeding pairs because of the way in which male calling behaviour changes through the breeding period (Stowe & Hudson 1988, Schäffer 1995, Tyler & Green 1996).

Although there are historical records of Corn Crakes wintering within Britain & Ireland (Baxter & Rintoul 1953), the species is largely migratory and is predominantly a summer visitor to our region. Corn Crakes leave their Scottish breeding sites between late July and September, heading south through France (10 recoveries of British- & Irish-ringed birds) and Iberia (one recovery), presumably then crossing into Africa via Morocco (Toms & Clark 1998, Toms *et al* 1999). The main passage across the Mediterranean takes place between early September and mid-November (*CBWP*), with pronounced autumn passage witnessed through Morocco, Tunisia, Egypt and Cyprus. It appears that birds from eastern populations enter Africa via the Red Sea and the Gulf of Aden (Urban *et al* 1986). Large numbers of Corn Crakes are trapped in Trammel & Eb nets or are shot on the Mediterranean coast of Egypt as a by-catch associated with the hunting of Quail (Stowe & Hudson 1991, Baha el Din *et al* 1996). It has been estimated that 9,000 may have been taken in 1993 and 14,000 in 1994, representing 0.5–2.7% of the European breeding population (Baha el Din *et al* 1996). Ringed individuals from Sweden and Finland have been recovered in Egypt (Baha el Din *et al* 1996).

The main wintering range is trans-Saharan Africa, across central Tanzania, Mozambique, Zambia, Malawi to northern Botswana and South Africa (Urban *et al* 1986). Observations are supported by a handful of ring-recoveries: single individuals from Germany, Sweden and Scotland to the Congo Basin, and another from France to Angola (Spencer & Hudson 1979).

The spring migration proceeds quickly, and is more pronounced through Tunisia than in the autumn, while being less pronounced through Egypt and Cyprus (*CBWP*). Spring movements begin as early as late February, with a pronounced passage across the Mediterranean during the second half of April. European breeding grounds become occupied from mid-April, while those in Scotland are typically occupied from early May (*Birds in Scotland*, Murray 1999) or occasionally late April (Murray 1998).

Mike Toms

Common Crane

Grus grus

Common Cranes breed from eastern Siberia, across the northern Palearctic and through into central Europe and Fennoscandia (*European Atlas*). The history of the Common Crane in Britain is a long one, with evidence of breeding extending back to Saxon times (Boisseau & Yalden 1998). However, breeding probably ceased during the 17th century in England and the 14th century in Ireland (BOU 1971), and it was not until 1981 that the species re-established itself as a breeding species by nesting in East Anglia, where one to three pairs now attempt to breed annually (Taylor *et al* 1999). This small British population is largely resident in one area but regular sightings of the species elsewhere in

Norfolk and Suffolk are mostly attributed to these birds making short excursions. Such movements are most frequently noted in spring, suggesting that they are the result of migratory urges that are suppressed by the barrier of the North Sea (Taylor et al 1999). However, the birds have been known to vacate the area in response to harsh winter weather.

The Common Crane is a migratory species, undertaking a somewhat protracted autumn migration to wintering grounds in France, Spain, Africa and the Middle East (Thevenot & Salvi 1987, Génard & Lanusse 1992, Alonso et al 1994, CBWP), although the Turkish population is reported to be sedentary (European Atlas). Birds from Sweden, northern Germany, and presumably Norway, migrate along a narrow western route that passes southwest from Germany through France to Spain (Salvi 1987, Swanberg 1987). Along this route are a number of traditional resting places; the most important of these being Lake Hornborga (Sweden), the Rügen-Bock region (Germany), the Lac du Der-Chantecoq (France) and the Laguna de Gallocanta (Spain) (European Atlas). The Finnish population uses an eastern flyway through Estonia and Hungary that ends along the Nile in Sudan (Karlin & Raivio 1987).

The relative scarcity of the species in Britain is noteworthy, given the large numbers migrating through the near Continent, and is due largely to the reluctance of large soaring birds to cross open water. Under certain weather conditions, however, migrating cranes may drift from the western route taking them north from France into the Netherlands, Belgium and across the English Channel into southern England (Wessels 1987). Small numbers of Common Cranes are regularly reported from Britain & Ireland in most years, with records from as far north as Orkney (Balfour 1956) and the Outer Hebrides (Campbell 1956). There are also occasional influxes involving substantial numbers of birds. One of the largest of these took place in October 1963, when an estimated 500 cranes came ashore between Beachy Head and the Isle of Wight, although they did not penetrate very far inland (Harber 1964). More recent influxes took place in October 1982, when up to 114 individuals arrived in Kent (McMinn 1983) and again in 1985, when a single flock

of 71 was noted over Folkestone and later Dungeness on 25 October (Rogers et al 1986, McMinn 1987). The 1982 influx appears to have been related to a period of light but variable winds, together with mist and drizzle over eastern Europe, the southern North Sea and southeast England. During this period (27–31 October) large numbers of cranes were also seen along the western continental seaboard (McMinn 1983). The dates of observed drift into Britain are consistent with the main departure dates from Germany in September/October.

Up until the 1950s, it appeared that the majority of Common Cranes using the western flyway would overwinter in Morocco (Thevenot & Salvi 1987, Alonso et al 1994). However, in recent decades Common Cranes appear to be wintering further north, closer to the breeding grounds (Alonso et al 1994). The numbers of Common Cranes wintering at the five or six Moroccan sites now only rarely exceed 800–1,000 (Thevenot & Salvi 1987). Instead, Common Cranes are increasingly using the Laguna de Gallocanta for overwintering, together with smaller numbers using marshlands in southwestern France (Génard & Lanusse 1992). It appears that the conversion of Holm Oak woodland in northern Spain to arable farmland has benefited the cranes, by providing winter food alongside secure roosting sites free from persecution (Alonso et al 1994). The number of cranes wintering at the Laguna de Gallocanta has been shown to be limited only by the availability of food in midwinter (Alonso et al 1994).

As the winter progresses, family parties of cranes break up as the juveniles become fully independent (Alonso et al 1984). The adult cranes leave the wintering sites before the juveniles and begin the spring migration back to their breeding grounds. Some 15,000–30,000 cranes pass through the Laguna de Gallocanta between mid-February and late March as they return north (Alonso et al 1990), reaching Sweden during April (CBWP). During the spring passage there are regular sightings of migrating cranes from Britain & Ireland, with a peak in these between April and May.

Mike Toms

Pied Avocet (Avocet)
Recurvirostra avosetta

Avocets recolonized Britain in 1947 and the breeding population now numbers c450 pairs, representing just over 1% of the European breeding population (Stone et al 1995, European Atlas). Breeding populations within Britain, as elsewhere in Europe, have shown a general increase in numbers (Engelmoer & Blomert 1985, Becker & Erdelen 1987, Hill 1988). The number of Avocets wintering in Britain has also increased over a similar period, with a winter maximum of 3,859 recorded in 1997/98 (Cranswick et al 1999).

While populations in the southern part of the range tend to be dispersive rather than migratory, those in northern regions migrate south to winter across a belt extending from West Africa, through the Mediterranean Basin and the Caspian, to as far south as India, Arabia and Sahelian Africa (CBWP). Increasing numbers from breeding sites within northwest Europe now winter near the breeding grounds, presumably a response to the run of mild winters observed in recent years.

Immatures typically leave the breeding areas before the adults, sometimes as early as mid-June, while the adults themselves leave from July (van Impe 1991). Many British breeders initially move to adjacent estuaries, while some individuals join moulting flocks in the Netherlands where they mix with breeding birds from Sweden, Denmark and Germany. These moulting flocks are a feature from August through

into early November, with numbers falling as birds either move further south to wintering sites or return to southern and southwestern Britain, where birds typically begin arriving from late October. There are a small number of important wintering sites in Portugal (Tagus Estuary), France (Vendée coast), Senegal (Guembeul) and Guinea (Blomert et al 1990, Triplet & Yésou 1998). Birds ringed in Britain & Ireland, including individuals ringed as chicks, have been recovered in Spain, Portugal and Morocco from late autumn through into midwinter (Fig 1). Regular overwintering within Britain started in 1947 and was largely restricted to the Tamar, Tavy and Exe Estuaries (Batten et al 1990, Glaves & Darlaston 1999), but many other sites in southern England and East Anglia are now used as the number overwintering has increased. Most of the birds using these sites are thought to come from the British breeding population, although there have been records of continental birds from estuaries in Devon (Prater 1981).

Departures from wintering areas begin in late February or early March (CBWP), although birds from northern breeding areas may not leave their wintering sites before mid-April (Blomert et al 1990). Some African sites are abandoned as water levels fall and this may mask departures for the breeding grounds. The return passage is more rapid than that seen in the autumn and birds returning from North African wintering grounds may stopover en route. Flocks have been reported

Fig 1. Recovery locations and movements of over 20 km for the 30 included recoveries of Avocets ringed or recovered in Britain & Ireland.

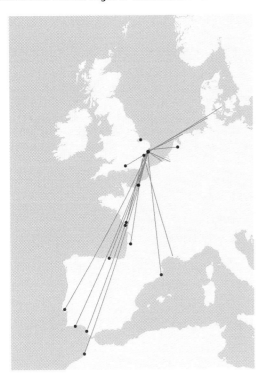

stopping at the Banc d'Arguin (Mauritania), seemingly to rest and readjust flock size rather than to feed, even though energetically they could have made the journey without stopping (Blomert *et al* 1990). Between 16,000 and 21,000 birds may pass through this site on spring passage, moving north up the Atlantic coast. Departures from British wintering sites begin in late February (*Winter Atlas*).

Breeding begins in early April in Spain (*HVM*) and France (Yésou 1985a), while birds arrive on British breeding grounds between mid-March and mid-April. Immatures (Avocets usually begin breeding in the second or third year) tend to arrive later than the breeding adults, unless they have overwintered locally (Cadbury & Olney 1978). Although Avocets do not show a strong fidelity to their natal site when they first begin breeding (Cadbury & Olney 1978), they will return to breed at the same site in subsequent years (*1988–91 Atlas*).

The importance of a small number of wintering and stopover areas, with 90% of the European wintering population gathering at just 10 sites, makes this species susceptible to damage to or development of its wintering sites. Although the British population is small and the species is included in the British Red Data book (Batten *et al* 1990), the species is not threatened globally. The general increase in the Avocet population within Britain & Ireland, coupled with continued ringing, should increase our understanding of the movements made by this species.

Mike Toms

Little Stint

Calidris minuta

The Little Stint primarily occurs as a passage migrant in Britain & Ireland, with only a small number of birds remaining to overwinter (Cranswick *et al* 1999). Breeding takes place on high Arctic coastal tundra from northern Sweden eastwards across Russia and northern Siberia to the New Siberia Islands: the bulk of the population (more than 100,000 pairs) breeds in Russia (*European Atlas*, *CBWP*, Schekkerman *et al* 1998). The wintering range extends across much of Africa (including Madagascar), the Mediterranean Basin and southern Asia (*CBWP*).

Adult Little Stints begin to leave their breeding grounds during late July and early August, with individuals reaching Britain, and to a lesser extent Ireland, from late July through into October (Prater 1981). The species is regarded as an uncommon passage migrant in western Britain & Ireland, with Scotland very much on the fringe of the migration route (*Birds in Scotland*). The numbers present in Britain & Ireland peak in September when larger numbers of juveniles begin to arrive, having departed from their breeding grounds some time after the adults. The number of Little Stints reaching Britain & Ireland can vary substantially from one year to the next (*Winter Atlas*, Cranswick *et al* 1999) and this most likely reflects annual fluctuations in productivity on the breeding grounds (Dement'ev & Gladkov 1969). Similar inter-annual fluctuations have been reported elsewhere (Fiala 1991). However, there have been several years in which exceptional passage numbers have been reported, seemingly the result of migrational drift following specific weather conditions over the North Sea and western Norway (Gibb & Tucker 1947, Nisbet & Vine 1956, Cranswick *et al* 1999).

By July, most adults will have crossed the North African coast where the species is mainly a passage migrant (Urban *et al* 1986), before reaching the tropical wintering areas from August or September. Most young birds do not reach the Equator until October, pushing as far south

Fig 1. Recovery locations and movements of over 20 km for the 23 included recoveries of Little Stints ringed or recovered in Britain & Ireland.

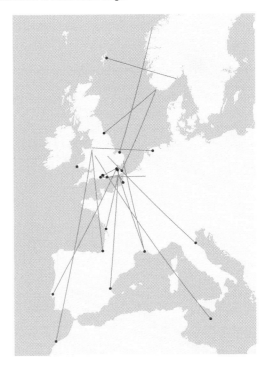

as southern Africa in November or December. The main arrival in Kenya is about two weeks behind that in Morocco and Tunisia, but similar to that in Senegal (Pearson 1987). Wintering takes place across Africa south of the Sahara with a substantial part of the wintering population located on inland sites; for example 50–70,000 winter on the Kenyan Rift Valley lakes, while only 4,000 winter on the Kenyan coast (Pearson 1987). The birds moult on the wintering grounds and this may take place over a protracted period as southward passage continues (Dean 1977, Pearson 1984, 1987).

Ring-recoveries link passage birds from Britain with the Mediterranean Basin in November and January and with North Africa during February (Fig 1). Birds ringed in southern Africa have been recovered on passage in Kazakhstan and the south Caspian, and on the breeding grounds in northeast Russia in June (Urban et al 1986, Toms & Clark 1998). There have been 19 recoveries from the 1,428 Little Stints ringed in Britain & Ireland, with a further 13 foreign-ringed birds recovered here (Toms & Clark 1998).

The spring return from the wintering grounds can begin in April, possibly peaking in early May (Pearson 1987, CBWP). In those years when heavy rainfall brings widespread flooding to central Kenya, sites are vacated during April, but in drier years birds may remain widespread inland to mid-May (Pearson 1987). The small spring passage through Britain & Ireland begins in late April, usually peaking in May, with a small number of individuals present through into June. This spring passage is largely restricted to the east coast of England but occasional birds are reported from Ireland (Birds in Ireland, Prater 1981). Both spring and autumn migration appear to take place on a broad front, with Britain & Ireland occupying the northwestern fringe, although the movements may take place along a large number of routes crossing Europe (CBWP).

Although it has been suggested that fidelity to natal sites is low (Tomkovich & Soloviev 1994), this may not be the case. The low return rates witnessed by Tomkovich & Soloviev may simply be a product of a small sample size and high mortality rates during migration. More work needs to be directed towards this species to understand the movement patterns and the risk posed by global climate change to both the breeding and wintering grounds.

Mike Toms

Temminck's Stint

Calidris temminckii

Temminck's Stints are uncommon but annual passage migrants to Britain, arriving in small parties at stopover sites on a wide range of inland and coastal waterbodies. Only open shorelines and sandy beaches tend to be avoided on migration, much as they are within the winter quarters. The species also maintains a tiny breeding population in Scotland (Ogilvie et al 1999a), this being at the extreme southwestern edge of the breeding range. The breeding range itself extends from Scotland across Norway, northern Finland and Sweden, and through northern Russia as far east as the Chukotskiy Peninsula, with Russia holding the bulk of the estimated 1–10 million breeding pairs (European Atlas, CBWP). The wintering range includes the Mediterranean Basin and North Africa, with small numbers wintering in Morocco, although the main wintering areas are further south, extending to Mali, Nigeria, Burundi and Kenya, and east across southern Asia to Japan (Urban et al 1986, CBWP).

Autumn migration takes place on a broad front, beginning in mid-July with the departure of adults from the breeding grounds. The adults leave before the young are fully fledged, and the young themselves do not depart until the first half of August (CBWP). Britain & Ireland is on the western edge of the migration route, hence the small numbers appearing annually in Britain and less than annually in Ireland (Birds in Ireland). The majority of records are reported during August and September, largely from the east coast and in particular from Norfolk, although small numbers are seen during July, with occasional records from as early as June (Dymond et al 1989). It is known that some birds leave the breeding grounds after nesting failure (Breiehagen 1989) and it is likely that the earliest birds seen on passage in Britain are these failed breeders. Unlike many other calidrid species, Temminck's Stints move overland during migration, making use of small, freshwater pools and the margins of other inland waterbodies (Fiala 1991, CBWP). Most individuals pass through quite quickly and autumn passage is largely completed by the end of September, although some late birds, almost certainly young of the year, are recorded through October and into November (Dymond et al 1989). There have been two recoveries during autumn passage through Britain of birds ringed in Fennoscandia: an individual ringed in Norway as a pullus was resighted in Suffolk just over two months later, and a bird ringed in Finland during August was recaptured nearly two years later in late July on the Medway Estuary,

Kent. The only other ring-recovery to involve Britain was an individual ringed in Spain during April 1987 and recorded breeding in July the same year at a site in the Scottish Highlands (Mead & Clark 1988).

Movements elsewhere in Europe, including Turkey, follow a similar pattern, with birds reaching Africa from early August and Pakistan from mid-August. Southward passage through Morocco occurs from late July, and Ethiopia from September to early October. Most reach the tropics during October, where they winter, usually in twos or threes, on lake margins and marshes (Urban et al 1986). Departures from these wintering grounds typically occur during March and April. Spring passage is more rapid than that seen in autumn, resulting in a more pronounced peak in the monthly pattern of records seen in Britain & Ireland. Small numbers of birds are reported from April but the main passage occurs from mid- to late May, with the number of reports falling rapidly through into June (Dymond et al 1989). This fits in well with the reoccupation of the European breeding areas from mid-May (Breiehagen 1989, CBWP), the Scottish breeding grounds being occupied over a similar period (Batten et al 1990). Birds arrive in small groups, seemingly unpaired (Breiehagen 1989).

There is a small amount of information on breeding and natal dispersal, derived from studies in Finland and Norway. Breiehagen (1989) reported a 53% return rate of colour-ringed adults from one year to the next, suggesting high site-fidelity. Although a proportion of the 47% that did not return would have died, the calculated survival rates of adults (Hildén 1975), together with an observed movement of individuals to and from study sites late in the breeding season, suggests that some birds do disperse to breed in other areas. Breeding populations tend to be patchily distributed and it is thought that a proportion of the female breeding population moves between separate breeding areas within the same season, laying a clutch in each area, the first being incubated by the male (Hildén 1975, Breiehagen 1989). In southern Norway, between 6% and 12% of birds ringed as pulli returned to the study area as yearlings (Breiehagen 1989).

As for other arctic breeding species, the number of Temminck's Stints reported on autumn migration, and more specifically the proportion of juveniles present, is likely to be correlated with breeding success (Roselaar 1979, Summers 1986, Dierschke 1994a). While fluctuations in productivity may produce year-to-year variations in passage numbers, this is set against the backdrop of a long-term decline in the numbers using some regular stopover sites (Fiala 1991). Although the loss of breeding habitat has resulted in a decline in breeding numbers and a contraction in range in some parts of the breeding range, little information is available on trends across the rest of Fennoscandia and Russia (Rönkä 1996, *European Atlas*). The number of reported Temminck's Stints in Britain & Ireland showed an increasing trend from the 1950s up until the 1980s and, although this may partly reflect the increase in observers, there are indications that the increase in spring records at least was genuine (Dymond *et al* 1989). However, the most recent figures suggest that this increase has halted, with annual numbers certainly involving fewer than 100 individuals (Fraser *et al* 1999b). The future status of this species as a breeding visitor and passage migrant remains uncertain.

Mike Toms

Pectoral Sandpiper
Calidris melanotos

Within Britain & Ireland, Pectoral Sandpipers are the most commonly recorded of the Nearctic-breeding waders, occurring annually in good numbers at sites across the region; the annual average for 1968–97 was 52 birds (Fraser *et al* 1999b). However, it seems likely that some Pectoral Sandpipers reaching Britain & Ireland arrive from the east, originating from Siberia where the species breeds eastwards from the Taimyr Peninsula (Sharrock 1971, *BWP*). The species also breeds in the coastal tundra regions of northwest Alaska, northern Canada and along the western shores of Hudson Bay (*BWP*).

The wintering range is largely restricted to South America, from northern Argentina and Bolivia to Paraguay (*BWP*) and it is thought that the majority of the Siberian population also uses this wintering area by crossing to Alaska and then joining the Nearctic population in a southerly migration. This is supported by the observation that the migration of juvenile Pectoral Sandpipers through North America occurs much later than that observed for other species, an unexpected occurrence for a species that winters so far south, but which could be explained by individuals first having to reach North America from breeding grounds in Siberia (Paulson 1993). In support of this route are two recoveries in Siberia of birds ringed in Saskatchewan and Kansas during autumn passage (*BWP*). Small numbers reach Australia and New Zealand from September (Higgins & Davies 1996), probably from the Siberian population, although an American origin cannot be ruled out for some of these birds (Paulson 1993). The handful of winter records from Africa almost certainly stems from autumn vagrants to Europe, which have reoriented south in parallel to the Nearctic migration route (Urban *et al* 1986).

Male Pectoral Sandpipers begin to leave their breeding territories in July while the females are still incubating and this produces a biased sex ratio in those flocks seen during the early part of the autumn migration (*BWP*). Passage through the United States runs from July to September and is largely centred inland, although an eastern component appears to take a direct route across the western Atlantic, with the species commonly recorded from the West Indies (*BWP*). It also seems likely that a proportion of the birds from Siberia, possibly the later-arriving juveniles, flies down the Pacific coast (Paulson 1993). Records from Europe typically come from late August to mid-October, with a peak in records from Britain & Ireland during the second half of September. These vagrants are believed to originate from birds undertaking a southeasterly movement across Canada, which then overshoot the Canadian coastline and become caught in Atlantic depressions (Nisbet 1959) or in the jet stream (Elkins 1988a). That the annual totals recorded in Britain & Ireland are relatively consistent could suggest that birds arrive via the jet stream rather than as a consequence of the variable Atlantic depressions.

Within Britain & Ireland, Pectoral Sandpipers are typically seen singly on both coastal or inland brackish and freshwater sites, although 11 were reported at Akeragh Lough (Kerry), six at Ballycotton (Cork) and four at Cantley Beet Factory (Norfolk), all in years when annual numbers reported were larger than normal (*Birds in Ireland*, Taylor *et al* 1999). Birds usually remain at sites for only a couple of days, fitting the pattern observed at spring stopover sites in North America (Farmer & Parent 1997), but there are some that have stayed for up to two weeks or more (*Birds in Wales*).

The distribution of autumn records within Britain & Ireland does not show the westerly bias that would perhaps be expected from a Nearctic vagrant. Sharrock (1971) examined this and showed that Pectoral Sandpipers on the east coast arrived earlier than those on the west coast. Again, this is unexpected for a potential Nearctic vagrant and could suggest that birds from the Siberian population arrive in Britain & Ireland from the east. It is also possible that some individuals arriving on the east coast may be birds that arrived the previous year and are undertaking the pattern of north–south migration, but on this side of the Atlantic.

Small numbers of Pectoral Sandpipers occur in Britain & Ireland during spring and, although Sharrock (1971) suggested that these were likely to be new transatlantic arrivals, the number of east-coast reports would support the hypothesis that at least some are birds that had arrived the previous year and wintered in Africa (James 1996, Taylor *et al* 1999). Birds arrive back on their tundra breeding grounds from late May (*BWP*). There has only been one ring-recovery involving Britain & Ireland: a bird ringed on 28 August 1989 in Lincolnshire was observed 12 days later, and for a further 10 days, in Hertfordshire.

Mike Toms

Spotted Redshank

Tringa erythropus

Spotted Redshanks occur in Britain & Ireland throughout the year, predominantly as passage migrants and winter visitors, although smaller numbers are present during the summer months (Clark 1978, Prater 1981, *Winter Atlas*). Their breeding range stretches from northern Fennoscandia eastwards across northern Siberia to the Chukotskiy Peninsula (*BWP*). Individuals migrate to a wintering range that extends from western Europe and equatorial Africa through the Middle East and across southeast Asia to southeastern China (*HBW*). Little is known about population trends, although a range expansion within Sweden has been documented (Mjelstad & Sætersdal 1986).

Female Spotted Redshanks spend only a few weeks on the breeding grounds before forming flocks and departing, leaving the males to continue with incubation (Hildén 1979). Females from the western end of the breeding range reach stopover sites, including the Wadden Sea, southern Hungary, southeastern Greece and central Turkey (*BWP*), from early June, with peak numbers on the Wadden Sea occurring in mid-June (Meltofte *et al* 1994). Passage of males and juveniles occurs during the second half of July and on into August (*BWP*). These autumn movements are probably typical of birds from across the breeding range, with long continuous overland movements between stopover sites taking place on a broad front (*BWP*). Many adults undergo moult while at these stopover sites, as well as refuelling for the next stage of their migration (*BWP*, Meltofte *et al* 1994). The number of birds at stopover sites declines through October, which fits the pattern of passage through North Africa and arrival on the wintering grounds (Urban *et al* 1986).

The first passage migrants pass through Britain & Ireland during late July but the main passage does not occur until mid-August, continuing to mid-September (Prater 1981, *Birds in Scotland, Birds in Ireland, Birds in Wales*). Most records relate to single birds or to small groups, although sizeable flocks can occur: a flock of 187 was recorded at Snettisham on 13 September 1977 (Taylor *et al* 1999). Although the bulk of the passage passes through eastern England, the species is regularly recorded at sites further west, with fairly regular inland records from sewage-farms, reservoirs and gravel-pits (Prater 1981). There have been 13 recoveries (from 374 ringed) involving birds ringed in Britain & Ireland, all of which were ringed during late July, August or September. Two were recovered in Morocco; five in France and singles were recovered in Italy, Malta and Denmark. The remaining three were recovered within Britain, including

one shot in Kent during October, some 5 km from where it was ringed 13 months earlier. Two of the recoveries in France come from the Mediterranean coast. Two birds from the Netherlands and one bird from Germany have been recovered here, two in January and one in September.

During the winter, some 100–200 individuals are thought to occur in Britain & Ireland using predominantly coastal sites (Prater 1981, Cayford & Waters 1996). Such numbers represent a significant proportion of the total northwest European wintering population (*CBWP*). The distribution of wintering birds within Britain & Ireland is more westerly than that seen during passage periods, and sites along the south and southwest coasts hold the bulk of the wintering population (Cranswick *et al* 1999). The bulk of the western Palearctic breeding population winters in Africa south to the Congo Basin and northern Tanzania, where birds utilize coastal saltpans and inland marshes (Urban *et al* 1986). In some parts of the wintering range Spotted Redshanks are abundant (Grimes 1969, Urban *et al* 1986), and even in North Africa, where the species is generally regarded as being a passage migrant, substantial numbers may winter. There are two recoveries in Morocco during winter of birds ringed in Britain, although one of these may conceivably have been on spring passage.

A return movement through North Africa is evident during late March and early May (Urban *et al* 1986) and migrants are already present on the Wadden Sea from late March, although the main passage does not occur until late April (Meltofte *et al* 1994). Spring passage through Britain & Ireland is less pronounced than that seen in the autumn and takes place during late April and early May (Prater 1981, *Birds in Ireland*). Small numbers of birds are present in Britain & Ireland during the summer months, a mixture of adults in breeding plumage and first-year birds (*BWP*).

Although 60 moulting birds were caught together at Terrington on 27 July 1975, numbers on the Wash at this time of year have now declined (N A Clark pers comm). It seems likely that these birds are predominantly non-breeders, since few oversummer in Africa (Urban *et al* 1986), although some may well be failed breeders beginning autumn migration. Breeding populations within Fennoscandia are back on territory from the start of May (Hildén 1979).

Mike Toms

Wood Sandpiper

Tringa glareola

While the Wood Sandpiper is often thought of as a passage migrant, it also manages to maintain a small breeding population in Scotland (Ogilvie *et al* 1999b). Birds from the Scottish population breed among tree-fringed mires, a similar habitat to that occupied within the main breeding grounds that stretch across the northern boreal and subarctic zones from Fennoscandia to Kamchatka and occasionally to the Aleutian Islands (*BWP*, Higgins & Davies 1996). With a European population estimated at 1,400,000 pairs, the Scottish population is insignificant in European terms.

Wood Sandpipers winter within a range of climatic zones across Africa, southeast Asia and to a lesser extent Australia (*BWP*, Higgins & Davies 1996). Migration to and from these wintering grounds brings a

component of the Scandinavian population through Britain & Ireland onto both coastal and inland waterbodies, with most records falling to the south and east of a line drawn from the Solent to the Wash (Nisbet 1956, *Birds in Scotland, Birds in Ireland, Birds in Wales*). However, the bulk of the migration takes place further east and this explains why only relatively small numbers occur on passage in Britain & Ireland. Scandinavian birds are thought to winter in West Africa, while populations from Russia probably winter in eastern and southern Africa. Recoveries of birds ringed during the winter in India suggest that birds from eastern Siberia winter there (*BWP*).

During late June, adult Wood Sandpipers breeding in Scandinavia and elsewhere in Europe begin to move south, seemingly making rapid movements to stopover sites lying to the north of the Mediterranean; an individual ringed in Sweden was recovered the following day in Italy, while another ringed in Denmark was found two days later, again in Italy (*BWP*). The southerly movement of Scandinavian breeders probably accounts for the southeasterly distribution of records in Britain & Ireland, with birds crossing from the Continent rather than making direct movements from Scandinavia (Nisbet 1956). Some stopover sites hold large concentrations of Wood Sandpipers, notably Italy and the Camargue where daily numbers can exceed 1,000 birds during autumn passage. Adult birds remain at the sites for up to four weeks and during this period they lay down fat reserves for the next stage of their migration south, gaining as much as 20–30% in body weight (*BWP*). It is at these sites that they also begin moult, although most arrest moult before departure south. Young birds arrive at these stopover sites several weeks behind the adults, reflecting the delay in their departure from the breeding grounds. The birds probably overfly the Mediterranean and the Sahara on a broad front and in a single flight to reach the main African wintering grounds that lie south of the Sahara.

Small numbers overwinter in North Africa and along the Nile Valley (Urban *et al* 1986, Higgins & Davies 1996), but the species is more commonly a passage migrant along the North African coast during July to October, with smaller numbers along the Red Sea coast (Urban *et al* 1986). Within Africa, Wood Sandpipers are the most widespread of the wintering Palearctic waders, occurring as far south as South Africa (Urban *et al* 1986).

Birds begin to leave the wintering grounds during April, although some individuals delay their departure and others remain to oversummer. The return passage in spring follows a similar pattern to that seen in autumn, though it may involve a more easterly route. Again, birds may overfly the Sahara and Mediterranean in a single flight and make use of stopovers to replenish their body reserves (Akriotis 1991, Scebba & Moschetti 1996), although the concentrations seen during the autumn are not repeated during the more rapid spring migration (*BWP*). The main period of spring migration through both Europe and the Middle East occurs from late April into May, with a small return passage witnessed in Britain & Ireland during May (Prater 1981). Birds have been recorded displaying at suitable sites in Scotland from late April (*1968–72 Atlas*). Breeding sites elsewhere in northern Europe are occupied from late April (Pulliainen & Saari 1991) with those in the northernmost regions not occupied until early June (*BWP*).

A bird ringed on the Shannon Estuary, Limerick, 23 August 1974 was recaptured in Belgium on 10 August 1982. The only other recoveries involved birds ringed in Lincolnshire during autumn: the first was recaptured at Wisbech Sewage Farm on 20 August 1960, having moved 84 km south in 10 days, while the other was found freshly dead on 1 November 1981, some 47 km from where it was ringed as a juvenile on 21 October 1978 (Toms *et al* 1999). This last recovery could suggest some degree of fidelity to its stopover site.

Mike Toms

Red-necked Phalarope
Phalaropus lobatus

Although up to 40 pairs of Red-necked Phalaropes may breed in Britain & Ireland in any one year, the species is a far more common breeder between 60° and 70°N where it nests within tundra and forest tundra across its circumpolar breeding range (Batten *et al* 1990, *CBWP*, M O'Brien pers comm). The bulk of the European population, some 65,000–95,000 pairs, occurs in Iceland, Sweden, Norway and Finland (*European Atlas*). The species winters pelagically, favouring areas of upwelling with abundant planktonic food (*BWP*). None of the 294 individuals ringed in Britain & Ireland up to the end of 1997 were recovered during 1909–97.

Red-necked Phalaropes leave their northern breeding areas from late June, with the females (the species shows sex role reversal — Hildén & Vuolanto 1972) departing first. On Fetlar females begin moult before leaving for their wintering grounds (M O'Brien pers comm), while records of birds in Norfolk in mid-June typically refer to females in breeding plumage (Taylor *et al* 1999). Males follow during late July, while juveniles move from August (*HBW*). Ring-recoveries, many of which are from the Ukraine, show that Fennoscandian birds migrate on a heading that takes them through the Gulf of Bothnia overland to the Black and Caspian Seas, where they stage before crossing into the Arabian Sea and the Gulf of Aden to winter. Mikkola *et al* (1990) report significant numbers staging on the Iranian salt lakes during April and it seems reasonable to assume that such sites are also used during autumn, possibly by populations breeding further east than Fennoscandia. This southeasterly movement takes them away from Britain & Ireland (*1968–72 Atlas*). None of the 3,058 Red-necked Phalaropes ringed in Iceland has been recovered outside Iceland (A Petersen pers comm), and so there is no information on where the Icelandic population winters or by which route it reaches its wintering range. While it is possible that they take an east Atlantic route (as suggested in *Birds in Wales*) in keeping with other Icelandic species, it seems more likely that

they migrate south via Greenland and Newfoundland in a similar way to Icelandic Purple Sandpipers. Huge numbers can gather in the Bay of Fundy during both spring and autumn passage, although the wintering grounds of these birds remain unknown. Colour-ringing of the Icelandic birds might increase the chances of discovering the migration routes used and whether any pass through Britain & Ireland.

Autumn passage through Britain & Ireland is more pronounced on the east coast than the west (Fraser *et al* 1997), with relatively few records from Wales (*Birds in Wales*), southwest England and the west coast of mainland Scotland (*Birds in Scotland*), again casting doubt on an east Atlantic route for Icelandic birds. Additionally, the species is extremely rare in Ireland outside the breeding season (*Birds in Ireland*). Inland reports within Britain & Ireland are not infrequent and birds have even been recorded from village ponds (Fraser *et al* 1997, Taylor *et al* 1999). It is not known where these passage migrants winter, nor where they breed, but some will almost certainly be those birds breeding in northern Scotland and in Ireland.

In North America, migration routes are far better known (Paulson 1993, *HBW*), with tens of thousands staging on Great Salt Lake and Mono Lake, before progressing to wintering grounds that lie off western South America. The eastern Siberian population is thought to winter in the East Indies (*HBW*).

Spring passage through Britain & Ireland is lighter than that seen during the autumn and most individuals are recorded between mid-May and early June, although arrivals in northern Scotland and Ireland are somewhat later (*Birds in Scotland*, *Birds in Ireland*, Fraser *et al* 1997, Taylor *et al* 1999). Again, most of the passage is via the east coast and involves single birds. Influxes of birds that stay to breed have been reported from Fetlar as late as 17 June (M O'Brien pers comm). Breeding site-fidelity is reported to be higher than for Grey Phalarope and has been estimated at 50% for both sexes from a study of marked individuals in Alaska

(Schamel & Tracey 1991). The same study also showed that males display greater fidelity to natal sites than females do, in keeping with the prediction for mate defence mating systems (Greenwood 1980). On Fetlar, adult survival rates of around 56% (from 29 colour-marked birds) were reported during the 1990s, while 28% of 43 colour-ringed chicks known to have fledged in 1993 and 1994 returned to Shetland in the following breeding season (M O'Brien pers comm).

The number of breeding pairs in Britain & Ireland has shown a marked decline since the turn of the 20th century when there were large populations in Ireland, the Outer Hebrides, Orkney and Shetland (M O'Brien pers comm). Some authors have suggested that there has been a similar decline in the number of birds recorded on passage in Britain & Ireland and that these two occurrences are linked, with the breeding

population being reliant on recruitment from passage birds from more northerly breeding populations (Everett 1971, *European Atlas*, Fraser *et al* 1999b, Ogilvie *et al* 1999b). While there are no long-term datasets with which to test this, examination of breeding and passage numbers for recent years does not show a positive correlation between the two (M O'Brien pers comm). This is something that requires further examination. The continued loss of suitable breeding habitat within Britain & Ireland, due to land drainage and vegetation succession (Batten *et al* 1990), may mean that the future of our breeding population is uncertain. However, it seems likely that the species will remain a scarce passage migrant.

Mike Toms

Grey Phalarope

Phalaropus fulicarius

Grey Phalaropes are regular passage visitors to Britain & Ireland that, in contrast to Red-necked Phalaropes, are most commonly reported from southwest coasts (Fraser *et al* 1999a). Their breeding range is circumpolar and restricted predominantly to arctic coasts, with a small Icelandic breeding population occurring on the southern edge of the breeding range (*BWP*). During the winter months Grey Phalaropes winter within zones of upwelling off western and southwestern Africa (Stanford 1953, Brown 1979), western South America and the southern United States (Haney 1985). None of the 79 Grey Phalaropes ringed in Britain & Ireland up to the end of 1997 have been recovered. This is unsurprising given the pelagic nature of this species.

In common with other phalaropes, the breeding grounds are vacated early, with adult females departing during July (Bengtson 1968, Ridley 1980). Males with eggs or chicks remain to late July and early August (*HBW*). Migration takes place pelagically with birds from northeast North America, Greenland, and Iceland thought to migrate southeast across the North Atlantic to winter off western Africa. This route is supported by the autumn passage seen off southwest Ireland and southwest England during September and October (*Birds in Ireland*, *Birds in Wales*) and by widespread pelagic records from across the Atlantic (*CBWP*). The number of birds reported in Britain & Ireland varies from year to year (Fraser *et al* 1999a), with larger numbers occurring following westerly gales. An unprecedented influx was reported in September 1960 when hundreds of birds were reported from Pembrokeshire, Scilly, Cornwall and Devon (Ferguson-Lees & Williamson 1960, Moore 1969, *Birds in Wales*). More typical numbers are considerably lower, with an annual average for 1986–97 of 212 individuals (Fraser *et al* 1999b). Inland records are rare.

Large numbers stage in the Bay of Fundy from July to September (Brown & Gaskin 1988). This gathering may involve birds that subsequently cross the Atlantic towards western Africa, although records of wintering phalaropes off the southeastern United States (Haney 1985) suggest that some may migrate south down the east coast of North America. Birds from the Alaskan and Siberian populations are thought to winter off western South America (Kistchinski 1975, *BWP*), although there is some evidence from Washington and Oregon that some winter off the west coast of North America (Paulson 1993). Most birds appear to reach their wintering grounds by the end of November, where they remain through into March and early April (*HBW*).

Return movements bring a small passage onto British & Irish coasts but the numbers during this period (April–May) are actually lower than records from the winter months (Fraser *et al* 1997). Breeding grounds are reoccupied from late May, the birds waiting at sea for the ground to thaw (Whitfield 1995). Breeding site-fidelity of males is thought to be low (Schamel & Tracey 1991), although where the availability of suitable breeding sites is restricted (as in Iceland) return rates are high (Whitfield 1995).

Population trends are generally unknown, due to the difficulties in assessing breeding and wintering populations, but the Icelandic population is known to have declined (*European Atlas*). The numbers reported annually in Britain & Ireland have also decreased in recent years (Fraser *et al* 1999b), although this could be the result of many different factors.

Mike Toms

Pomarine Skua

Stercorarius pomarinus

The slow, almost mechanical flight of the Pomarine Skua is a familiar sight to many sea-watchers during periods of autumn and spring passage. Although the numbers seen are typically small, there is a predictable pattern to the movements. Birds pass through within a fairly well-defined period and particular sites produce good counts on a regular basis (Davenport 1992). Local weather conditions can also influence the number of birds seen from individual sites and may result in counts of

more than 100 birds during a given day (Nightingale & Allsopp 1995, 1998, Wilson & Slack 1996). With just 10 individuals ringed within Britain & Ireland, it is unsurprising that there have been no recoveries.

Pomarine Skuas breed across the northern tundra regions of Russia, from the Kanin Peninsula eastwards through Siberia and across to Alaska and Canada (*BWP*, *HBW*). Breeding densities are linked to densities of lemmings, and in those breeding seasons when food is scarce some birds may appear to the south of the normal breeding range, though they rarely attempt to breed in these areas (Furness 1987, Olsen & Larsson 1997). Pomarine Skuas are migratory, wintering well to the south of the breeding grounds in the low-latitude tropical seas to the north of the Equator (Olsen & Larsson 1997), pushing as far south as Australia in the Pacific, and Argentina and southwest Africa in the Atlantic (Urban *et al* 1986, Higgins & Davies 1996).

Departures from the breeding areas can begin in July and August, immatures and unsuccessful breeders leaving first (Olsen & Larsson 1997). Autumn passage passes down both sides of Britain & Ireland, those birds using the northern route past Svalbard passing to the west of Ireland and those crossing overland to the Baltic passing through the North Sea and down through the English Channel (*BWP*). It is thought that the smaller numbers of birds passing through the Baltic include proportionally more juveniles than seen on the more northerly route (*BWP*). Passage through the North Sea begins in mid-August with immatures followed by a passage of adult birds, peaking in late September and early October. This is then followed by a passage of juveniles, with some birds still moving in early December, even though the main period of arrival on the wintering grounds occurs more than a month earlier. The timing of the autumn passage through British & Irish waters is some three to four weeks behind that of Arctic and Long-tailed Skuas. While on passage, and sometimes through into winter, some Pomarine Skuas may occasionally remain in Britain & Ireland for several weeks at localities where they can feed off local seabirds (R W Furness pers comm).

Although observations of Pomarine Skuas around the coasts of Britain & Ireland are more widespread during autumn passage, the numbers of birds reported at this time are much lower than those seen in spring (*Birds in Scotland*, *Birds in Wales*, James 1996, Taylor *et al* 1999). Passage numbers can vary greatly. The largest numbers along the west coast are often seen following depressions tracking from the west, while north or northeasterly gales within the North Sea can push birds onto the east coast (Wilson & Slack 1996, Taylor *et al* 1999). The effect of local weather conditions can be seen from the exceptional influx that took place in autumn 1985 when the collapse of previously stable high-pressure systems over the North Sea, and the ensuing strong northerly air flows, brought large numbers of Pomarine Skuas close inshore, with a number of inland records from Britain & Ireland (Fox & Aspinall 1987), and elsewhere in Europe (Camphuysen & van IJzendoorn 1988a, b).

Breeding success is also important in contributing to the passage numbers reported from western Europe, since peak years involve a larger passage and a greater proportion of juveniles (Breife 1989). In some years, juveniles account for between 75% and 85% of the total autumn passage passing southern Sweden and Denmark (Nyrup 1992). Years of peak passage show a strong correlation with large passage numbers of other tundra species such as Brent Goose, Little Stint and Long-tailed Skua, reflecting the abundance of lemmings on the tundra breeding grounds (Breife 1989).

Movements from breeding populations further east suggest a pronounced overland movement to the Red Sea, the Middle East and the Indian Ocean (Meininger & Sørensen 1986). Small numbers occur in the Mediterranean and probably include both overland migrants from Russia and birds entering via the Strait of Gibraltar. Movements have been reported across the width of the Pacific Ocean (King 1967, Tuck & Heinzel 1980) and it seems likely that a similar pattern may occur in the Atlantic, with some movement across the Atlantic as birds follow migrating terns (Escalante 1972). The scale of pelagic movement remains uncertain, however, since most of our understanding of passage movements comes from shore-based observation. It seems likely that passage through British & Irish waters occurs mainly along the continental shelf, matching movements made elsewhere in the range (Barton 1982), with birds only being pushed inshore by unfavourable weather conditions (Taylor *et al* 1999).

The wintering areas appear to be characterized by cool upwellings, often close to land, for example between the Caribbean and Sargasso Sea (north to Cape Hatteras) and off West Africa, between 8° and 20°N (Baillon & Dubois 1991). During the non-breeding season, birds move in response to local food availability and associate with fishing vessels in the search for discards. Records from the North Atlantic are scarce during the winter period, even though the species remains the most frequently recorded *Stercorarius* in this area during the winter (Olsen & Larsson 1997). During December 1994, over 50 were reported in Britain, with 12 reported from Ostend, Belgium, the following January, and up to five were reported between 8 February and 19 April 1995 overwintering in Norfolk (Taylor *et al* 1999).

Spring migration begins in March and birds arrive in the North Atlantic during April, although the peak passage in Britain & Ireland takes place in the last week of April and the first three weeks of May (Davenport 1992). At this time Pomarine Skuas are most abundant off northwest Scotland and southern Ireland, as revealed by observations from North Uist, Slyne Head, Cape Clear Island and Carnsore Point (Davenport 1981, 1992), with smaller numbers sighted from points along the English Channel coast (Taylor *et al* 1981, Clark & Eyre 1993). Again local weather events can greatly increase the number of birds reported, as was the case in May 1992 when an unprecedented 2,093 individuals passed Watsness, Shetland, on 9 May (Harrop *et al* 1993). Birds are typically seen in small groups when moving from west to east up the English Channel and into the North Sea. Combined observations from south-coast sites suggest a flight speed of between 35 and 56 km per hour (Davenport 1975). Local records show a dramatic increase in the numbers of Pomarine Skuas reported on spring passage and, while much of this increase must be down to an increasing interest in sea-watching, some authors have suggested that the greater numbers seen in recent years reflects a genuine increase in the size of the passage (Clark & Eyre 1993, James 1996).

Mike Toms

Long-tailed Skua
Stercorarius longicaudus

The Long-tailed Skua is the scarcest of the Palearctic *Stercorarius* skuas to occur in British and Irish coastal waters, yet it remains a regular passage visitor during both spring and autumn. Increasing interest in sea-watching, together with greater observer awareness has contributed to the increase in the number of records reported annually, although there remains some difficulty in distinguishing immatures and winter-plumage adults (*CBWP*).

The circumpolar breeding range extends across the arctic and subarctic regions of the northern hemisphere from Scandinavia east to arctic Greenland (Furness 1987, Olsen & Larsson 1997). Within this range, two subspecies are currently recognized (*longicaudus* and *pallescens*), although recent evidence suggests that differences in the morphological characters are '*clinal*' rather than '*absolute*' thus questioning the validity of *pallescens* (Olsen & Larsson 1997, *HBW*).

Breeding numbers fluctuate in response to the stage of the lemming cycle (Andersson 1971, 1976) and this appears to exert an influence on the numbers of birds seen on passage, although local weather conditions are also important (see later). Somewhat surprisingly breeding has been suspected in Scotland, although not proven, and in addition birds regularly occur at colonies of breeding Arctic Skuas on Shetland (*Birds in Scotland, European Atlas*).

Departures from the breeding grounds begin in August and appear to be largely complete by early September (Scandinavia, Andersson 1976), making the species the earliest of the three small palearctic skuas to undertake its autumn migration. Routes taken by birds during autumn passage remain unclear because of the strongly pelagic nature of the species. Some birds follow a route round the northwest of Britain & Ireland turning south towards the Equator. This southward passage is considered by some authors to be longitudinally restricted, mainly occurring between 25° and 28°W (*BWP*). Other birds filter south into the North Sea or enter it via the Swedish Lakes and the Baltic, a similar route to that used by Arctic Skuas but with relatively fewer birds reported from eastern Denmark. In most years, the autumn passage through Sweden and Denmark is small. An analysis of British & Irish records from 1958–95 showed a clear east coast bias to the records received for autumn, some 60% coming from the five counties from Norfolk to Northumberland (Dymond *et al* 1989). This highlights use of the North Sea during autumn passage (from mid-August to mid-September), either as a direct route south or for exploitation of available food. The paucity of records from the English Channel during autumn could suggest that birds using the North Sea subsequently pass into the North Atlantic via the Scottish north coast. Elsewhere, passage records have been noted from both the Atlantic and Pacific coasts of North America, from West Africa, eastern South America and from Japan (Vooren & Chiaradia 1989, Baillon & Dubois 1991, Higgins & Davies 1996). Long-tailed Skuas are usually seen singly or in small groups of three to five individuals; only occasionally are larger flocks witnessed. Overland movements are more commonly reported than for Arctic Skuas, with movements reported over the Greenland ice-cap and the Norwegian ranges, and with 269 Long-tailed Skua records noted from Lake Constance, Switzerland, between 1961 and 1981 (Olsen & Larsson 1997). There are also a number of inland records from Britain, at least some of which may involve deliberate overland passage (Fraser *et al* 1997). Records from the Mediterranean, Black Sea and Red Sea are rare during autumn (Meininger & Sørensen 1986, Shirihai 1996).

For a long while, very little was known about the wintering range and even now our knowledge is incomplete. The main wintering zone for those birds passing through British & Irish waters appears to be the zone of upwelling within the Benguela Current which lies off Namibia and western South Africa, south to the Subtropical Convergence (Urban *et al* 1986, Ryan 1989). Birds begin to arrive here from late September, with numbers building up to a peak in November. Groups of 100 or more mainly immature birds may gather at this time (Urban *et al* 1986). The other main wintering areas are situated along the convergent thermal front that lies between the Falkland Current and the Patagonian Shelf,

and in the southern Pacific Ocean (Veit 1985). Regular records for this period also come from eastern Australia (K A Wood 1989, Higgins & Davies 1996), reaching farther south to New Zealand only under exceptional conditions (Melville 1985). Long-tailed Skuas are only exceptionally found north of the Equator during the winter period (*CBWP*). Some birds reportedly oversummer within the wintering range.

From April, birds begin to reappear in the North Atlantic, the main passage occurring during May. This picture fits the departures from the wintering grounds off Africa, which begin in April following the completion of moult, and matches the pattern seen off Australia (Higgins & Davies 1996). Collectively, the observations from coastal watch-points suggest that spring passage is more concentrated than that seen in the autumn, taking place over a shorter period of time and with larger flock sizes often evident (Davenport 1991). Suitable weather conditions may occasionally push migrating Long-tailed Skuas close inshore to western coasts of Britain and Ireland. Observations from Balranald, North Uist, have shown that birds are not seen if winds remain offshore during the period of spring migration, which is 9–24 May (Davenport 1991, 1992). The spring passage through British & Irish waters peaks during May and early June, with the main passage occurring off the western coasts of Scotland and Ireland and only a small number of stragglers on eastern coasts (*Birds in Scotland, Birds in Ireland*). The number of Long-tailed Skuas seen on passage within British & Irish waters varies from year to year and massive influxes are occasionally noted, the most recent of which occurred in 1983, 1988, 1991 and 1994 (Dunn & Hirschfeld 1991, Davenport 1991, Olsen & Larsson 1997). The exceptional year in 1983 was mirrored by a significant passage at Eilat, Israel, a location where passage is normally very small (Shirihai 1996). The species is also rare and irregular on spring passage through southern Scandinavia and the Baltic (Olsen & Larsson 1997). Although there have been no recoveries from the four British- & Irish-ringed Long-tailed Skuas, a bird ringed on the German coast in June 1961 was recovered in northern Finland almost exactly six years later.

Arrivals on the breeding grounds begin in late May or early June (Andersson 1976, Hansen 1984) and, although the sample size is small (*n*=10), the ringing of adults by Andersson (1976) would suggest a high degree of site-fidelity, since nine of the birds were resighted at the study site in the following breeding season and seven occupied their previous territory. Sexual maturity is not reached until a bird is at least four years old and although the summer distribution of immature birds is unclear, some are present on the breeding grounds during the breeding season (Andersson 1976, Kampp 1982). Some are also present in the North Atlantic at this time, with others regularly reported from the Red Sea and with further scattered reports from off Ecuador and Tristan da Cunha (Olsen & Larsson 1997).

Although this species is not globally threatened, more information is needed on wintering ranges, population trends and migration patterns.

Mike Toms

Mediterranean Gull

Larus melanocephalus

When in breeding plumage, Mediterranean Gulls are undoubtedly the most striking *Larus* species to breed in Britain. While they were once scarce visitors to Britain & Ireland (Sharrock 1974), a steady increase in the northwest European breeding population since the late 1960s has resulted in Mediterranean Gulls now being a familiar sight to many birdwatchers in southern and eastern England, and to an extent at sites further north.

Globally, the species has a Palearctic breeding distribution with the main populations centred on the Ukrainian Black Sea coast (*HBW*). A rapid range expansion has coincided with one very strong peak in the almost cyclic population fluctuations witnessed in the Black Sea population. This has resulted in a discontinuous breeding distribution now spread across the Caspian, northeast Atlantic, North Sea and Black Sea coasts (Meininger & Bekhuis 1990, *European Atlas*). The first

Fig 1. Ringing locations and movements of over 20 km for the 29 included recoveries or first resightings of Mediterranean Gulls ringed or recovered in Britain & Ireland. Subsequent resightings of colour-ringed birds are not shown.

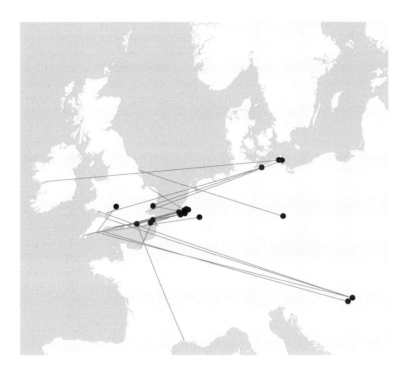

documented breeding attempt in Britain occurred in 1968 and was followed by regular breeding from 1976 (Taverner 1970). Breeding was confirmed at 24 British localities during 1997, although the habit of nesting within large colonies of Black-headed Gulls may mean that some breeding pairs are overlooked (Ogilvie et al 1999b).

The movements made by Mediterranean Gulls can be difficult to interpret, partly because of the range expansion but also because individuals may breed at widely separated sites in successive years.

Ring-recoveries resulting from birds ringed on the island of Orlov, Ukraine, during the late 1940s and early 1950s suggest that movements away from the Black Sea colonies begin in July, with individuals reaching the Adriatic and eastern Libya in August and September, and the central Mediterranean by October (Mayaud 1954). Some of these birds reach the western end of the Mediterranean, with a number passing through the Strait of Gibraltar and into the eastern Atlantic. These birds winter off Iberia and south along the northwest African coast to Mauritania, Senegal and the Gambia. Mayaud's intensive work also shows birds reaching northern France and the Baltic (Mayaud 1954). Some birds remain in the Black Sea, predominantly along the north and east coasts. Most movements are coastal, although some individuals move overland across Turkey, from early July through to November, or follow major river valleys, notably the Danube, across eastern Europe. It is movement up the Danube that appears to be responsible for the presence of large numbers in the Gulf of Venice (BWP).

While much important information has come from intensive ringing programmes, there is less information available from general ringing and even less relating to Britain & Ireland, where just 24 birds had been ringed up to the end of 1997. More information is available from the

coordinated colour-ringing of Mediterranean Gulls that has been taking place throughout Europe since the late 1980s, and this has increased our understanding of movement patterns and how new breeding populations have become established. Some of this information indicates the likely origins of birds present within Britain & Ireland. Each of the participatory countries uses its own coloured Darvic rings in conjunction with the standard metal rings of the ringing scheme concerned. The resulting rates of resighting have varied tremendously between countries, such that those for Belgium and the Netherlands have reached 53% for birds ringed as adults and 21% for those ringed as chicks, while those for Italy are just 2% (Boldreghini et al 1992).

The results of colour-ringing seem to indicate that most of the Hungarian population moves overland via the Danube and the Rhine to winter along the Atlantic coast, including Britain, with a small proportion moving south to winter in the Mediterranean and the Adriatic. Individuals ringed as pulli at Szeged-Feherto, Hungary, have been resighted at Copt Point, Kent, which is one of the most important sites for the species within Britain & Ireland. The scale of movements, and the value of using colour rings, can be seen from the multiple sightings of individual birds. For example, a Dutch bird ringed as a pullus in Zeeland during June 1993 was resighted at Calais during 1994, in Belgium and France in 1995 and in Kent, Belgium, France and the Netherlands during 1996, before being seen again at Folkestone during 1997. The origins of Mediterranean Gulls present in Britain & Ireland can be seen from Fig 1, which includes birds from the Netherlands (11), Germany (5), Hungary (3) and the former Yugoslavia (1).

Observations of Mediterranean Gulls from Britain & Ireland suggest a distinct arrival, peaking from July into early August but continuing into September and October. Birds are present throughout the winter months, with sites in the southwest of England used to a greater extent during winter than at other times of year (Winter Atlas). In the past, individual wintering sites within Britain have been shown to have a regular turnover of birds during the late winter and early spring period (Hume 1976) and this is matched by within-winter movements between sites as revealed by resightings of colour-ringed individuals. Hume (1976) also found that first-years move east much later than either adult or second-year birds: older birds begin return movements as early as late January or more commonly February. Given that many adults are back on their North Sea breeding grounds by late March or early April this is not unexpected. The return movement to Black Sea colonies of birds wintering at the western end of the Mediterranean occurs from early March to late May. Many immatures remain in the Mediterranean during the summer.

If the pattern of colonization witnessed within the Mediterranean is repeated along North Sea coasts, then we can expect the breeding population in Britain & Ireland to increase dramatically over coming years. Within the Mediterranean there has been a wave of colonization spreading westwards, characterized by large numbers of birds suddenly occupying a small number of sites. Such a pattern has been witnessed in Greece, Italy, and most recently France, where the number of breeding pairs has increased from 111 pairs in 1991 to 1,393 pairs in 1998 (Davies 2001). It seems likely that, across Europe, there is now sufficient information on colour-ringed Mediterranean Gulls to warrant a full review of the movements of this species, particularly in reference to potential increases in the number and distribution of breeding colonies.

Mike Toms

Little Gull
Larus minutus

This small, surface-feeding gull is primarily a passage migrant to Britain & Ireland, occurring in both autumn and spring (Stone *et al* 1995). However, small numbers of Little Gulls winter off the British and Irish coasts, particularly in the Irish Sea; birds regularly oversummer and breeding has been attempted on several occasions (Carson *et al* 1977, *Breeding Atlas*, Taylor *et al* 1999). Three discrete breeding populations occur within the middle to northern latitudes of the West Palearctic: in northwest Russia and the Baltic, in western Siberia between the Rivers Ob and Ural, and in eastern Siberia, east from the Lena Basin and Lake Baikal (*BWP*). Sporadic breeding occurs outside the main range, and small breeding populations have become established in Canada (first recorded 1962, Scott 1963) and the United States (first recorded 1975, Tessen 1975). The wintering areas of birds from the Russian northwest and the Baltic probably extend from the Irish Sea and the Baltic south to Morocco and the Mediterranean (Erard 1960). Those of the western Siberian population are imperfectly known but are thought to include the eastern Mediterranean, with winter records from the Nile Delta (Meininger & Sørensen 1993) and autumn records from the Bosporus (Thiede 1986) supporting this. Birds from eastern Siberia may well winter off China, where winter records extend from China south to Hong Kong (Leader 1999). Interestingly there are also winter records from the west coast of India (Bapat & Himmatsinhji 1992, Parasharya *et al* 1999).

The bulk of dispersal from breeding grounds in the Russian northwest and the Baltic appears to occur through the Baltic itself and along the coasts of the southern North Sea (Stone *et al* 1995). Numbers build up off eastern Scotland in late July and early August. Arrivals in Scotland are several weeks earlier than those in England and Wales (Hutchinson & Neath 1978). Bruun (1968), analysing published records, determined two different movements of birds through the Baltic, those moving along the southern Baltic doing so some four weeks earlier than the passage along the northern edge. Evidence of two waves of birds reaching Britain comes from Kent (Taylor *et al* 1981), Liverpool (P H Smith 1987) and from the general findings of Hutchinson & Neath (1978). The latter authors suggest that the two autumn peaks result from an initial post-breeding movement to sheltered sites for moult, followed by a general dispersal to the winter quarters. A small number of birds move overland to the Mediterranean and the Black Sea, either moving on a broad front or following the Rhine, Danube and other rivers. Numbers in the North Sea continue to increase and flocks of up to 1,000 birds have occurred in the past at Zeebrugge (van Impe 1966, Bruun 1968) and of up to 500 in the Firths of Tay and Forth, with many more in the Netherlands.

Hutchinson & Neath (1978) state that adults arrive off Britain some two to three weeks ahead of juveniles and this is supported by P H Smith (1987) who notes that the later arrival of juveniles coincides with the second wave of adults arriving in late September. However, the median passage date given by Garthe (1993) for adult Little Gulls past Helgoland Bight is some 10 days later than that for first-years, although first-years did not dominate the passage at any time during autumn. The size of the passage through Britain & Ireland, and that passing Helgoland Bight, has increased dramatically since the 1970s and to a greater degree than

could be accounted for by the increasing popularity of sea-watching (Hutchinson & Neath 1978, Dunn & Lassey 1985, P H Smith 1987, Garthe 1993). This increase matches a documented westward expansion in breeding range that has taken place over a similar time period (*European Atlas*).

Movements out of the North Sea take place in October, the birds moving to wintering areas in the western Mediterranean, with seemingly smaller numbers in the Irish Sea, the English Channel and off northwest Africa. Stragglers reach south to Gambia, Nigeria and Angola (*BWP*). Others remain in the southern North Sea. Birds from further east mix with those from western populations in the Mediterranean and this could explain the June recovery in Slavgorod, Siberia, of a bird ringed in Belgium during August (Roggeman 1977). British & Irish winter records are largely of adult and second-year birds, suggesting that immatures winter further south (*Winter Atlas*). Within the Irish Sea, the largest numbers are associated with the County Wicklow coast in an area extending some 30 miles south from Dublin. Particularly large counts have been reported from this area in some years, with over 600 present in January 1991, suggesting that a substantial number do winter within the Irish Sea (Ruttledge 1990, O'Sullivan & Smiddy 1992). The number of wintering records has also increased, matching the recent northerly extension to the wintering range (*European Atlas*).

As the numbers reported from Wicklow fall off during early spring, so the numbers reported from Seaforth, Merseyside, increase (Messenger 1993). This apparent spring passage occurs from April through into early May, the initial arrivals being predominantly first-year birds, although the main April peak itself is dominated by adults, mostly in breeding plumage (P H Smith 1987). The smaller numbers seen from late May are first-summer birds, which presumably do not return to the breeding grounds that year (P H Smith 1987). The birds at Seaforth make an overland crossing of northern England, spiralling at the coast to gain height before heading inland. Evidence of this cross-country movement towards the North Sea comes from records of small but regular numbers of birds at Pennington Flash, Audenshaw Reservoir and other inland sites, coupled with a lack of records from coastal sites to the north and south of Seaforth (Messenger 1993). There is also a well-documented spring passage through the English Channel and the southern North Sea over the same time period (Woutersen 1980, Ouden & Stougie 1990). Many of those wintering in the Mediterranean gather in the Camargue in April (adults) and May (immatures), before crossing overland to the breeding grounds, which are reoccupied in late May.

Some 507 Little Gulls have been ringed in Britain & Ireland generating 18 recoveries, including seven recovered overseas (France 3, Finland 2, Poland 1, Denmark 1). Recoveries in Britain & Ireland of foreign-ringed Little Gulls involve birds from Finland (7), Norway (1) and the Baltic States (3). Collectively, these confirm the presence of birds from the Baltic population (*ie* ringed as pulli) in Britain during autumn and spring passage, with at least two present in Britain during the winter months.

Mike Toms

Sabine's Gull

Larus sabini

The number of Sabine's Gulls seen annually from Britain & Ireland has remained relatively stable since 1989, although there are periodic influxes resulting from severe Atlantic gales during the autumn (Fraser *et al* 1997). Sabine's Gulls breed across Alaska, northern Canada, Greenland and northeast Siberia, wintering in the eastern Pacific off northwest South America and in the southeast Atlantic off southwest Africa (*HBW*, Quinn & Kokorev 1999). Populations from eastern Canada and Greenland migrate southeast in small flocks to the Atlantic wintering grounds, while those from western Canada, Alaska and eastern Siberia winter in the Pacific. The position of the migratory divide within Canada remains unclear.

Birds vacate breeding grounds in Canada and Greenland by the middle of September (*BWP*, Forchammer & Maagaard 1991), with adults seemingly leaving earlier than juveniles. While a small minority of Canadian breeders migrate overland in a southeasterly direction, most cross the Davis Strait to Greenland and from there move across the Atlantic towards southwest Europe (*BWP*). It is when this passage off western Europe encounters strong westerly gales that numbers get pushed onto the western coasts of Britain, Ireland and other parts of western Europe (*Birds in Scotland, Birds in Ireland, Birds in Wales*, Desmots & Yésou 1996). During September 1995, the tail of the tropical depression 'Iris' pushed large numbers onto the French coast, with some 850 birds taking refuge in the harbour of Les Sables d'Olonne, Vendée (Desmots & Yésou 1996). Similar recent influxes have been noted in Britain in 1983, 1987 and 1997 (Dymond *et al* 1989, Fraser *et al* 1999b).

Records from Britain & Ireland occur annually, typically from late August through to October. As with most seabird species, the number of records has increased in line with the increase in observers (Dymond *et al* 1989). Although there are records for all months of the year, there has been some discussion over the validity of the winter records given the potential for confusion with Kittiwake, particularly when birds are observed at distance or in poor weather (Dunn 1983, Alström 1984, Hume 1984, Grant 1987). Although records come from all coasts of Britain & Ireland, the largest numbers are reported from southwestern coasts, a result of large influxes in some years. Yorkshire and Norfolk are also well represented in the annual sightings and there

appears to be a degree of independence between the numbers reported on the east coast and those on the west coast (Fraser *et al* 1999b). There are also a small number of inland records (Vinicombe 1971, Taylor *et al* 1999). Examination of available passage records for 1958–67 (Sharrock 1971) supports the differential timing of departures of adults and immatures from the breeding grounds. Sharrock's analysis showed that up to 40% of adults had passed through by 10 September, while only 11% of immatures had done so. However, with 30% of adults also reported after mid-October, compared with only 14% of immatures, the pattern may be more complicated than it first appears, particularly since failed breeders must also be present, and because birds will be arriving from breeding grounds spread over a wide area.

Continued passage southwards takes the birds along the coast of West Africa throughout August to November, using a route that follows the Canary and Senegal Currents. Most of the birds then move rapidly south to winter in the Benguela Current off Namibia and off southern Africa where they arrive from the end of September (von Lambert 1967, Zoutendyk 1968, Furness & Furness 1982). During the winter months, the birds occur along the edge of the shelf, either singly or in flocks up to 50 strong. Occasional flocks may number 2,000 birds, particularly in association with fishing fleets (Urban *et al* 1986).

The return passage sees the birds pass West Africa from mid-March through to June, with a peak in early May (Urban *et al* 1986). Spring records from Britain & Ireland are far fewer than autumn ones, those that do occur peaking in May (Dymond *et al* 1989). Arrivals off eastern Canada and Greenland occur from the last week of May as the birds return to their breeding grounds. It is thought that immatures may remain in the south Atlantic, since they are seldom seen in the northwest Atlantic at this time and they have been recorded off West Africa during June (*BWP*, Urban *et al* 1986).

More information is needed on the age structure during passage, the degree to which immatures remain in the southern oceans during the northern summer, and the timing and routes of movements made by birds from different parts of the breeding range.

Mike Toms

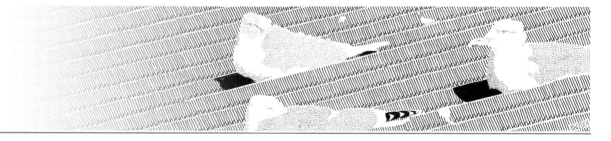

Iceland Gull

Larus glaucoides

Iceland Gulls are regular winter visitors to Britain & Ireland, typically occurring in relatively small numbers on northern and western coasts (*Winter Atlas*). Iceland Gulls breed on steep cliffs and offshore stacks along rocky coasts and fjords across northeast Canada, Baffin Island and east to Greenland, wintering south to New England, the eastern Great Lakes, Iceland and northwestern Europe (*HBW*).

Within Greenland, it appears that the well-studied western breeding populations are either resident or dispersive. Analysis of 557 ring-recoveries showed only seven movements outside the local breeding range, including two immatures that reached northern England (July) and northeast Scotland (January) (*BWP*). One of the remaining five ring-

recoveries demonstrates the potential for movements from Greenland to North America, with an individual recovered in Labrador (*BWP*). It is thought that the breeding populations in eastern Greenland exhibit a greater migratory tendency than those in the west, although there appear to be no ring-recoveries to substantiate this. During the winter months, the species is a common visitor to Iceland, supporting the notion that east Greenland populations are migratory, wintering southeast of the breeding range. It is also thought that northern populations are more migratory than those from further south (*HBW*).

Young Iceland Gulls fledge in late July in Greenland and move to coastal feeding areas along with post-breeding adults. From here, young from the eastern Greenland population appear to disperse quite widely over a period that extends from September through into November. Arrivals in Iceland occur from late September, with birds remaining through into early May. Some of these birds move further southeast, with individuals moving to the Faeroes and others reaching Britain & Ireland from October or November. However, the majority of reports in Britain & Ireland are from later in the winter, especially where they involve individuals on more southerly coasts (*Birds in Ireland*, *Birds in Wales*, *Birds in Scotland*). Most of the Welsh records come from the southern counties, especially Glamorgan, where 79% of records refer to the period 20 December–20 March (*Birds in Wales*). A very small number appear to reach Norway, Sweden and Denmark. Iceland Gulls are only vagrants to countries further east or south in Europe (*BWP*). Birds of the resident western Greenland population make local movements to the coast, where they winter.

The numbers wintering in Britain & Ireland are probably 100–200 annually, although there is variation from year to year. Periodic influxes have been reported, with a run of good years in the early 1980s. Large numbers were reported from Britain & Ireland during 1983 and 1984, matched by influxes elsewhere in Europe (Burneleau 1986). These influxes are likely to be linked to unfavourable weather conditions further north, which push birds south. It has also been suggested that they could be related to the continuing decline of the Icelandic fishing industry, which would again force birds to move further south. Most records refer to immatures. Inland records are few but Iceland Gulls have been reported from many inland sites in the Midlands and East Anglia (Dean & Dean 1976, Taylor *et al* 1999). A small number of reports involve long-staying individuals: one individual remained at St Stephen's Green, Dublin, from October 1968 until May 1970 (*Birds in Ireland*).

Although the vast majority of winter records from Britain & Ireland involve birds of the race *glaucoides*, which breeds in Greenland, there are also records of the race *kumlieni* (*Birds in Ireland*, Taylor *et al* 1999), which breeds further west into Canada. The two races appear to be part of an east–west cline, running from the pale-coloured *glaucoides* in the east, through the darker *kumlieni* to western populations of Thayer's Gull (Millington 1993). The degree of plumage variation is such that it is difficult to establish clear distinctions between *glaucoides* and *kumlieni*, and many birds, especially first-years, cannot be readily distinguished in the field. Consequently the British Birds Rarities Committee have taken a standpoint that records of birds showing characteristics associated with *kumlieni* should not be differentiated from those of *glaucoides* (Bradshaw 1999). Intriguingly, a 1983 influx of several hundred adult Iceland Gulls to the Faeroes appears to have been dominated by birds of the race *kumlieni* (Fjeldså & Jensen 1985).

Breeding colonies in Greenland are reoccupied during late April and early May, matching the decline in reports within Britain & Ireland during late March. Many immatures remain in flocks along the Greenland coast rather than moving up the fjords towards the breeding colonies. Others spend the breeding season further south, with individuals reported from Iceland, the Faeroes and from Britain & Ireland. Just six Iceland Gulls have been ringed in Britain & Ireland, none of which have been recovered. The two birds mentioned earlier that were ringed in Greenland remain the only foreign-ringed Iceland Gulls to be recovered here (Toms & Clark 1998).

Mike Toms

Glaucous Gull
Larus hyperboreus

This large gull is predominantly a winter visitor to Britain & Ireland and is always more numerous than the smaller Iceland Gull *L. glaucoides*. The four recognized races, that breed from high Arctic to subarctic coasts, vary in their degree of migratory behaviour, with some populations wintering largely within the breeding range and others wintering south to the northern United States, northern Europe and Japan (*HBW*). The origins of birds wintering in Britain & Ireland are not completely clear, though ring-recoveries of birds ringed as pulli in Iceland (3), Bear Island (1) and Norway (1) give some indication. In addition there have been three recoveries of birds ringed in Britain & Ireland: one a local movement, one from the Faeroes and one from the North Atlantic near the Faeroes. The presence of Iceland Gulls from Greenland within Britain & Ireland could also suggest that some of the Glaucous Gulls wintering in Britain & Ireland originate from eastern Greenland (Dean 1984).

Ring-recoveries elsewhere show that part of the European arctic population (race *hyperboreus*) migrates southwest through the Norwegian Sea to southwest Norway, the Faeroes and Iceland, reaching as far west as Greenland. Substantial ringing effort in western Greenland suggests that the local breeding population (race *leuceretes*) is sedentary, while that in eastern Greenland is thought to be migratory with birds moving to Iceland for the winter. Attempts to determine origin on the basis of plumage characteristics and proposed hybridization with Herring Gulls in southern Iceland have, quite correctly, been strongly questioned by some authors (Snell 1991). Although hybridization with *L. argentatus* and *L. glaucescens* does occur (Hume 1975), the complexities of plumage variability within the species groups makes it very difficult to draw conclusions about the origins of birds based purely on morphological characteristics (Strang 1977). Some authors state that the Icelandic population is sedentary (*BWP*) but the three Icelandic-ringed pulli recoveries in Britain & Ireland suggest otherwise. Interestingly, two of these involve birds present on Benbecula in the summer months (July, freshly dead; June, resighted), while the third relates to a bird found freshly dead at Ballycotton, County Cork, in March.

The peak in departures from the breeding colonies on Svalbard occurs from mid-September through to mid-October and it seems likely that the adults depart some time ahead of the immatures, as seen elsewhere; in Greenland, adults depart in October and immatures in December (*BWP*). The birds begin primary moult during the breeding season, often starting before the first egg is laid, and then continue replacement of flight feathers over a protracted period (Ingolfsson 1970).

As would be expected for a high Arctic breeding species, most of the records from Britain & Ireland are from northern regions. The main influx occurs in November and December in Scotland, although the timing is variable depending upon conditions further north, with birds present in the Northern Isles, the Outer Hebrides and at North Sea oil installations (*Birds in Scotland*). The main influx in Ireland, where birds favour fishing ports and refuse tips, occurs somewhat later between January and early March. Numbers on the south coast of England peak between January and March (James 1996), supporting the theory that Glaucous Gulls winter as far north as the weather conditions allow and move south only as conditions deteriorate. On 19 November 1952, 15 were present at Blakeney Point, Norfolk, while 80 were reported from Galway Docks, Ireland, during January and February 1981 (*Birds in Ireland*, Taylor *et al* 1999). Within Europe, vagrants have been recorded as far south as the Mediterranean, the Black Sea and the Caspian Sea.

The number of birds present within Britain & Ireland varies from year to year, with larger numbers occurring following persistent northerly gales during late winter. There has been a general increase in the number of individuals reported in recent decades, reflecting an increase in the number of people involved in sea-watching and greater interest in gulls (*Birds in Ireland*). This trend has been repeated elsewhere in Europe (Hirschfeld & Ullman 1985). Set against this increase, however, there have been years when exceptional numbers have been reported. These years typically match those in which large numbers of Iceland Gulls are also reported (James 1996). In 1969, there was a large influx into northern Scotland, with 300 on Fair Isle and 100 on Fetlar but with few further south. Although predominantly coastal, records also come from inland sites (Dean & Dean 1976).

Immatures appear to be generally more abundant in Britain & Ireland than adults, although earlier statements that adults are rare appear to be incorrect, given that adults are regularly reported. Most reports relate to individual birds, although there are cases where several birds have been seen together (Booth *et al* 1984) and in recent years Killybegs, Co Donegal, has developed a reputation for holding groups of Glaucous Gulls during the winter months (D E Balmer pers comm). It has been suggested that the deep-sea fishing vessels that land at Killybegs

after fishing the waters off Greenland probably encourage the movement of both Glaucous and Iceland Gulls back to Ireland (D E Balmer pers comm). Individuals frequently show a tendency to return to the same sites during subsequent years. Famously, a first-winter bird first seen in autumn 1963 at Cley, Norfolk, returned to winter annually until it was last seen in spring 1979 (Taylor *et al* 1999).

Spring departure dates are variable and appear to be governed by weather conditions, birds leaving later in years when spring is delayed and weather conditions are poor (*Birds in Scotland*). In mild winters, departures can begin as early as the last two weeks of January (*BWP*). Although the finding circumstances remain wholly unknown, a Glaucous Gull ringed on Fair Isle on 14 December 1951 was recovered at Porkere, the Faeroes, on 11 February the following year. As demonstrated by ring-recoveries, some birds may remain within Britain & Ireland throughout the summer months, and this matches other evidence suggesting that immature birds from the migratory populations summer to the south of their natal area, reaching as far south as the North Sea, the Baltic and the Irish Sea (*BWP*). Adult birds occupy the breeding grounds from late April (*BWP*).

Mike Toms

Black Tern

Chlidonias niger

The Black Tern is a spring and autumn passage migrant most commonly occurring in the southeast of Britain & Ireland, with only small numbers reaching Scotland in most years (*Birds in Scotland*). The species was formerly a common breeding bird in southern and eastern England but was effectively lost as a breeding species sometime before the mid-19th century, a consequence of extensive land drainage (Batten *et al* 1990, Gibbons *et al* 1996b). This pattern has been repeated elsewhere across the breeding range and the distribution within western Europe is now somewhat patchy. The main breeding populations are located in eastern Europe and Russia where colonies of 1,000–2,000 pairs can occur; elsewhere most colonies hold fewer than 20 pairs (Tucker & Heath 1994, *European Atlas*). Globally the breeding range stretches across Europe (north to southern Scandinavia and south to southern Spain), Asia and North America, with two subspecies, *niger* breeding in Europe and Asia and wintering in Africa, and *surinamensis* breeding in North America and wintering in Central and Southern America (*HBW*). At least two individuals thought to be of the race *surinamensis* have recently been reported in Britain & Ireland (Adriaens 1999, Andrews *et al* 1999).

Birds of the nominate race begin their autumn migration towards the end of June, the adults starting up to four weeks earlier than the juveniles. Juveniles appear to undertake dispersive movements initially, before they orientate towards their wintering grounds (*BWP*). Birds gather at traditional sites en route, with up to 80,000 using the IJsselmeer region of the Netherlands and up to 10,000 using the Elbe Estuary (Walters 1987, *BWP*). These stopover sites are typically extensive lakes, coastal bays, estuaries or lagoons (Tucker & Heath 1994). It is thought that the IJsselmeer acts as a stopover site for most of the Western Palearctic population, including some birds from western Siberia. Peak passage through the IJsselmeer occurs between July and August, continuing into September, at which stage the passage is largely composed of juveniles. The adult birds undergo a partial moult of their flight feathers whilst at the IJsselmeer (Walters 1987). Black Terns reach Britain & Ireland during autumn passage, although in smaller numbers than seen in the spring. Arrival dates appear to be somewhat variable, with the first birds reported from Norfolk as early as the beginning of

July and as late as the end of August (Taylor *et al* 1999). Passage numbers vary from year to year but peak passage on the east coast tends to occur from the last few days of August through into the middle of September, with late birds reported through into November (Nightingale & Allsopp 1998, Taylor *et al* 1999). Autumn influxes can occur under specific weather conditions, which result in a westwards deflection of Black Terns moving through the southern North Sea and northern part of the English Channel (Butterfield & Williamson 1955).

Very large numbers pass through the Mediterranean, using Italy and the Bosporus and some appear to cross into North Africa before making a direct crossing of the Sahara, the others presumably passing out of the Mediterranean and into the Atlantic (Urban *et al* 1986). Birds from the southern North Sea stopover sites pass through France and Spain and follow the Atlantic coastline south to the wintering grounds situated off the West African coastline. This route is supported by ring-recoveries in Spain of Black Terns from the former Czechoslovakia, Russia and Germany, as well as by ring-recoveries in Ghana, Ivory Coast, Angola and Nigeria of birds ringed in western Europe (*BWP*). Passage along the African coast, and to a lesser extent inland across the Sahara, takes place between July and November, with a heavy passage from Tunisia to the Ivory Coast and major concentrations at the Banc d'Arguin, Mauritania, in September and October (Urban *et al* 1986). Migration appears to be both diurnal and nocturnal (*BWP*). Black Terns are rare passage migrants to Israel, with a small passage in the middle of August and a somewhat larger passage during the second half of September (Shirihai 1996).

Concentrations of wintering Black Terns occur from Senegal and the Gambia to Namibia, with the majority located in an area stretching from the Gulf of Guinea to Namibia (Urban *et al* 1986). Significantly smaller numbers winter along the Nile Delta in Egypt and in the Black and Caspian Seas (*BWP*, Urban *et al* 1986). Within the wintering areas Black Terns will utilize estuaries, coastline and coastal lagoons. There have been no recoveries involving the 94 Black Terns ringed in Britain & Ireland, so no information is available on the wintering areas or routes taken by individuals using Britain & Ireland. A Dutch-ringed bird was recovered here in 1938.

The spring migration can begin as early as late March and the routes used are similar to those used in autumn, although the inland passage within Africa is reduced, particularly along the Nile Valley (Urban *et al* 1986). Many of the Black Terns passing up the Atlantic coast of Africa pass the Strait of Gibraltar and enter the Mediterranean before reaching the northwest coast of Italy. The pattern of ring-recoveries from birds ringed at Bologna, Italy, shows that these birds are from breeding populations spread across central Europe and Russia, extending as far east as central Siberia (*BWP*). This route, together with that along the Rhône Valley, has a heavier passage in spring than during the autumn, which could indicate that a loop migration takes place. There is a small passage in the eastern Mediterranean, peaking in Israel during the final days of May (Shirihai 1996). Others continue up the Atlantic coast to reach Britain & Ireland. The size of the passage reaching Britain & Ireland is variable and may be substantial in some years, with spring passage in Wales peaking in May and reported to be smaller than autumn passage in most years (*Birds in Wales*). Generally, however, the spring passage through Britain & Ireland is stronger than that seen in autumn, with particularly large numbers observed in some years (Hinde 1949, Goodbody 1951, Nightingale & Allsopp 1998, Taylor *et al* 1999). During such years, birds on spring migration may reach Norway, the Faeroes and even Iceland (*BWP*). In May 1997 a very large movement of Black Terns was witnessed, with 1,400 passing through the English Midlands on a single day and smaller numbers in Norfolk, Essex, Kent and further north at Leighton Moss and Spurn, demonstrating the potential for good numbers if the weather conditions are right (Nightingale & Allsopp 1998). Passage Black Tern numbers generally peak in May within Britain & Ireland (May/June in Scotland) and birds appear to pass through rapidly (*Birds in Scotland, Birds in Ireland, Birds in Wales*, Taylor *et al* 1999).

At least some first-years (race *niger*) remain in the winter quarters during the breeding season, *eg* 1,000–2,000 in Nigeria and other flocks in Algeria (Urban *et al* 1986), although others may move north without actually reaching the breeding grounds. Many more second- and third-years do return north and may visit the breeding colonies even if they do not breed. It has been reported that birds of the race *surinamensis* do attend colonies in their first year (*BWP*).

Although the Black Tern is not listed as being globally threatened, many populations are undergoing substantial declines due largely to wetland reclamation (Tucker & Heath 1994, Nisbet 1997, *European Atlas*). This decline has been particularly pronounced in the eastern United States in recent decades (Peterjohn & Sauer 1997).

Mike Toms

Little Auk
Alle alle

The Little Auk is the most northerly of the Atlantic Alcidae, breeding in huge colonies between 68° and 82°N. About 90% of the world population of Little Auks breeds in Svalbard and in the Thule district of northwest Greenland, with other colonies elsewhere in Greenland and from Franz Josef Land, Severnaya Zemlya and Bear Island across to Iceland, Jan Mayen and Baffin Island (*HBW*, Gaston & Jones 1998). Little Auks winter pelagically to the south of the breeding colonies and are scarce winter visitors to the coasts of Britain & Ireland. The northern North Sea is, however, a major wintering area (Stone *et al* 1995) and birds are seen off the coasts following gales that force the birds inshore (*Winter Atlas, Birds in Scotland*). In some years weather conditions may result in massive 'wrecks' along British and continental coasts, with occasional birds turning up far inland (Underwood & Stowe 1984, *Winter Atlas*, Camphuysen & Leopold 1996).

Breeding colonies are abandoned during the end of August and adult birds accompany their young offshore. Subsequent movements to the pelagic wintering areas vary in their duration, probably reflecting distances moved by birds from different breeding populations, such that numbers in the wintering areas build up from October through into December (Brown 1985, Stone *et al* 1995, Stenhouse & Montevecchi 1996). Little Auks from northwest Greenland winter mainly off northern Newfoundland, while birds from Svalbard populations move to winter off southwest and eastern Greenland (Isaksen & Bakken 1996). Despite intensive efforts, only a few ringed Little Auks have been found away from the breeding colonies (Salomonsen 1971, Isaksen & Bakken 1996), probably due to the offshore wintering distribution of the species.

At-sea distribution has not been mapped accurately throughout the wintering range of the species but appears to stretch from the Newfoundland Grand Banks south to the Gulf of Maine, and east across the North Atlantic to northern Norway and the northern North Sea (*HBW*, Stone *et al* 1995). At least some of the birds present in the northern North Sea originate from breeding colonies east of Svalbard on Franz Josef Land and Severnaya Zemlya. There has been no ringing of this population but individuals of the *polaris* race that breeds on Franz Josef Land have been found among beached birds in Shetland and the Firth of Forth (*Birds in Scotland*).

Stone *et al* (1995) describe the normal dispersion of Little Auks in British & Irish waters. The main concentrations in these waters are in the northern North Sea far to the east of Orkney and the Moray Firth, and over sandbanks east of Northumberland and North Yorkshire. Lower densities of birds occur off all coasts from Lincolnshire around to the northern Minch. Land-based reports are heavily influenced by weather conditions. Records around Britain & Ireland are more widespread following the periodic 'wrecks' that occur. The *Winter Atlas* illustrates one such wreck. During 1983, strong northeasterly winds resulted in flights of up to 3,500 individuals being witnessed along the British east coast. More than 1,200 corpses were collected from east-coast beaches and about 100 inland records were received (Underwood & Stowe 1984). Camphuysen & Leopold (1996) review all records of Little Auk wrecks from 1841 to 1997. Wrecks occur on both sides of the Atlantic, but not simultaneously. Influxes of Little Auks often occur during or immediately following severe storms, leading to the suggestion that they are simply blown ashore. However, there is also a suggestion that food shortages in 'normal' wintering areas may predispose such influxes.

The period of return to the breeding colonies is protracted, with birds arriving at Svalbard in early April and Greenland in early May. Arrivals at the Franz Josef Land colonies begin in late February, which suggests that some birds from these colonies, race *polaris*, winter locally; the majority of wintering birds leave the North Sea in February also. During the summer months, small numbers of immatures can be found on the Newfoundland Banks and elsewhere across the low Arctic Zone (*BWP*). The majority of immatures move north, however, reaching the summer drift ice of Baffin Bay, the Norwegian Sea and the Barents Sea.

The world population almost certainly numbers many millions of individuals but many of the estimates given for individual colonies have been based on conjecture and no complete information is available. Similarly, there is no information on population trends. Potential threats to populations could include oil spills and overexploitation of local colonies.

Mike Toms & Mark Tasker

Rose-ringed Parakeet

Psittacula krameri

The Rose-ringed Parakeet is one of several members of the parrot family that have been introduced to various sites in Britain & Ireland via the pet trade but, so far, it is the only one to have established a viable naturalized population.

This is also the only parrot that is widespread in both Africa and Asia (*HBW*). The natural range extends across the Sahel from Senegal and Mauritania east to Sudan and Somalia, and from Pakistan through India to Myanmar and Sri Lanka. Naturalized populations exist widely in Europe, Africa, Asia and, to a lesser extent, in North America, mainly in cities (*HBW*). The species is not migratory but, in Africa at least, makes minor seasonal movements in response to ripening crops and to rainfall (*BWP*).

Since colonies first arose in southeast England in the 1970s, a population now numbering over 4,000 birds has built up to the west of London, with smaller ones in southeast London and northeast Kent. Despite cagebird imports from the wild in both Africa and India, the English birds appear to originate wholly from the Indian part of the range (Morgan 1993, Pithon & Dytham 2001). Most birds occur in parkland or large gardens, eating a wide variety of foods but also feeding extensively on bird tables, and nesting in tree cavities (Ferguson 1992).

Throughout September to March, large roosts gather around sunset, with birds arriving in noisy, fast-flying flocks from many directions, and disperse in the early morning. A total count of all four known roosts found at least 1,508 birds in Britain on 9 October 1996, more than 1,100 of them at Walton-on-Thames in Surrey (Pithon & Dytham 1999). By the winter of 2000/01, the total UK population, still concentrated in these areas, was estimated to approach 4,500 birds (C Butler pers comm). The catchment areas of the roosts are not yet known but, since the West London population occupied about 10 10–km squares during the *1988–91 Atlas*, it seems likely that some birds may fly more than 20 km to roost each evening. The switch of the main West London roost from Wraysbury in Berkshire to Esher in Surrey, a distance of about 16 km, further demonstrates the local mobility of the population. Some birds may cease roosting communally as early as December to begin the breeding cycle (Pithon & Dytham 1999).

Rose-ringed Parakeets have been encountered at many locations in both Britain and Ireland that are far distant from any known breeding site. Beyond the regular range, however, it is impossible to distinguish wanderers belonging to the naturalized population from individuals that have recently escaped or been released from captivity. There has been just one local ring-recovery from the few dozen birds ringed (Clark *et al* 2001). So far, therefore, nothing is certain about the movements of the naturalized population other than the daily roosting flights. Since Rose-ringed Parakeets have extended their range rather slowly, despite population increase within the areas presently occupied, the mean distances of natal and breeding dispersal are probably rather short.

The alien presence of this species in Britain increases competition for nest sites among hole-nesting birds (*BWP*). If the population spreads to agricultural land, it could become, as it has in many other parts of its natural and introduced range, an economically important pest (Feare 1996). In these circumstances, support for control measures would undoubtedly grow, though by this time it may be too late to manage the population sufficiently to resolve these problems.

John H Marchant

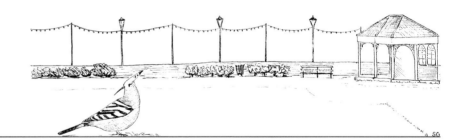

Hoopoe

Upupa epops

Hoopoes occur in Britain & Ireland mostly on spring migration, but have bred on at least 30 occasions (*BWP*). They also occur regularly in autumn and, rarely, have overwintered in both Britain and Ireland and at localities as far north as Cumbria.

The species is widespread across Eurasia to the Baltic States in the north and Sri Lanka and the Malay Peninsula in the southeast, but is absent from the far north and is patchily distributed or absent in areas of chilly maritime climate, high mountains, and parts of central Asia. It also breeds widely in Africa, although absent from forested zones and treeless desert. Parts of Spain and North Africa are occupied all year, but other West Palearctic populations are wholly migratory, most wintering alongside African residents in a zone from Senegal to Somalia and south to Uganda and Kenya (*BWP*). Vagrants have occurred in Iceland and on Svalbard.

The autumn migration is unusually long, with dispersal in Europe observed from mid-July into late October and even November. Continental ringing data suggest that birds migrate mainly southwest or south from western Europe, as far east as Germany and Austria, and mainly southeast or south from areas east of Poland and Hungary (*BWP*). Arrivals south of the Sahara begin in the second half of August, reaching their peak in September–October. Spring migration starts in early February in Morocco and Malta, and the main arrivals in Europe are from mid-March to late April (*BWP*).

There appears to be a shallow decrease in British sightings in recent decades, despite the growth in recording effort; during 1968–98, 124 were seen each year on average but the five highest year-totals were all before 1989 (Fraser *et al* 2000). This reflects the decline and range contraction that has been evident in Europe for a century or more and especially since the mid-1950s (*European Atlas*). Around 78% of recent British & Irish records have been in spring, and 22% in autumn (Dymond *et al* 1989). Records at both seasons have a marked southerly bias in both Britain and Ireland but occur north to Northern Ireland and the Western and Northern Isles, and are by no means restricted to coastal sites.

Autumn arrivals in Britain begin in early August and peak in early September (Dymond *et al* 1989). Records may continue into early

November and even through the winter. The origins and ages of these Hoopoes are unknown; early arrivals might be mainly first-winter birds dispersing from breeding areas on the near Continent, but late arrivals and those that stay the winter might have travelled longer distances, perhaps from eastern parts of the range. Of only two ring-recoveries so far that involve Britain & Ireland, one was from a bird ringed near Wick, Caithness, on 7 November 1989 that died on Orkney, 83 km further north, a few days later.

The first in spring are noted in late February in some years, but most appear in late April or early May. Birds are almost always seen singly and

it could be that the chance of finding a mate is a key factor limiting the number of breeding attempts. A pullus ringed in eastern Germany in June 1961 came aboard a fishing boat about 200 km southwest of Ireland on 30 April 1962, giving a slender clue to the nature of spring occurrences. Probably most individuals are overshoots from France or Iberia that reorient southwards later in the spring, or birds on passage to northern parts of the continental range.

John H Marchant

Lesser Spotted Woodpecker
Dendrocopos minor

The Lesser Spotted Woodpecker is mainly sedentary over much of its European range and is much less migratory in the north than its larger relative. At all seasons it is found from Portugal, Wales and Norway east across Eurasia to North Korea and Kamchatka (*BWP*). About 14 races are recognized, of which *comminutus* occurs only in England and Wales and nominate *minor* is found from Norway to the Urals.

In Britain, *comminutus* breeds widely in Wales and throughout England except northern Cumbria and Northumberland (*1988–91 Atlas*). Broad-leaved woodland, particularly with many snags and other dead wood, and also parkland and riverside alders are favoured all year. The species is very rarely observed out of typical habitat or at locations far from the nearest breeding pair, and appears to be extremely sedentary at all seasons, but periodic local absences and recolonizations show that some dispersal is occurring. The few ring-recoveries show movements mostly within 10 km, although one bird ringed as a juvenile in Hertfordshire on 2 July 1971 was found 40 km away in Oxford two years later.

In a marked Swedish population, adult birds showed very strong fidelity to their previous mate and to the breeding territory where they first settled (Wiktander 1998, Wiktander *et al* 2000). In the non-breeding season, they live solitary lives within a home range of several hundred hectares, usually with the breeding territory of 50–100 ha in the centre (Wiktander 1998). Fennoscandian nominate birds may be nomadic or

partially migratory, however. Small-scale eruptions occur, usually coincident with those of Great Spotteds; in autumn 1962, for example, at least 20 birds were seen at Revtangen in southwest Norway and about 250 at Falsterbo, southernmost Sweden, between September and November (*BWP*). Immigrants have reached the Netherlands (*HVM, BWP*). Finnish migrants have been recovered in southwest Sweden and in northern Norway.

No nominate *minor* have yet been recorded in Britain, nor any coastal or offshore sightings to indicate that continental immigration is occurring, but the occurrence of this race during Fennoscandian eruptions remains a possibility. The few Scottish sightings, of two birds in September 1968 and three in January 1970, all in the same area of Central Scotland, are suggestive of temporary residence, but the origin of the birds is unknown (Mitchell 1970). There are no records of this species from Ireland or the Isle of Man.

Since the 1970s, Lesser Spotted Woodpeckers have shown considerable decrease and range contraction, in Britain as in other parts of Europe (*European Atlas*). The shortage of ringing information, especially on natal and breeding dispersal, will be a drawback if the declines continue and the species becomes a high priority for conservation action.

John H Marchant

Wood Lark
Lullula arborea

Wood Larks are widespread across Europe but have only a small British population, and they no longer breed in Ireland. Their movements are of considerable conservation interest in the UK but are complex and not yet fully understood.

The breeding range extends from Morocco, England and Norway east to western Russia and Iran (*BWP*). Both races, the northern nominate and the southern *pallida*, are partially migratory; northeast Europe, including southern Fennoscandia, Poland, northern Ukraine and Russia, is deserted in winter, with birds wintering mostly within more southerly parts of the breeding range.

The *1968–72 Atlas* recorded breeding in many areas of England from Cornwall to Kent and north to Derbyshire, and in central and South Wales. In the early 1980s, the population became concentrated into five core areas, in South Devon, the New Forest in Hampshire, the Hampshire–

Surrey border, the Brecks in Norfolk and Suffolk, and the Suffolk coastal heaths (Sitters 1986, Sitters *et al* 1996). Wood Larks have since become re-established in Nottinghamshire and north Lincolnshire, and spread to Berkshire and West Sussex, and the population has risen from about 250 territories in 1986 to around 1,500 in 1997 (Wotton & Gillings 2000). Regular breeding ceased in Ireland in the 19th century and, although a pair bred in 1954, there have been few Irish sightings since 1900 (*Birds in Ireland*). Away from breeding areas, Wood Lark is recorded occasionally as a passage migrant or winter visitor as far north as Shetland and west to Scilly and Cape Clear Island.

The *Winter Atlas* map indicated that birds were present in winter in four of the five core breeding areas, but that the Brecks were deserted at that season. Also, total British wintering numbers were smaller than would be expected if the whole population were resident (Sitters 1986). It appears therefore that British-breeding Wood Larks are partially migratory, with some, especially in more southerly nesting areas, wintering close to the breeding grounds and others, particularly from the Brecks, moving long distances. In recent winters, small but significant numbers of Wood Larks have been found in stubble fields in and around Breckland (Atkinson 2001), suggesting perhaps that more birds are now sedentary there.

At least some British Wood Larks emigrate, as evidenced by a 1993 pullus from Breckland that was seen in the Netherlands on 9 October 1996 (Taylor *et al* 1999). Sightings indicate that occasional crossings of the English Channel also occur (Sitters 1986).

Among other sightings of colour-ringed pulli from Breckland, single birds were at Dungeness and on Scilly in their first October, while one was in Devon in its first February and back in the Brecks by May (Taylor *et al* 1999). Another, from 1986, was at Foreness Point in Kent on 12 March 1987 and nesting 4 km from its natal site in April 1988. These birds provide links between the British population and passage or winter records on the south coast. Some coastal records on passage or in winter

might well involve continental birds, however, especially those dated between mid-March and May, when British breeders are already back on territory, and those made at Fair Isle and other localities that lie well north of the British breeding range (Sitters 1986, Taylor *et al* 1999).

Breeding-season sightings of Breckland pulli, indicating natal or breeding dispersal, have mostly been local. There have been several in North Norfolk, Lincolnshire and Nottinghamshire (Taylor *et al* 1999), however, indicating that dispersal distances may be sufficient for some individuals to colonize pockets of suitable habitat at some distance from the birthplace.

Around 90% of the British population breeds on heathland or in young forestry plantations, and the future status of the species depends on sympathetic management of these habitats (Sitters *et al* 1996, Wotton & Gillings 2000). A better knowledge of the winter range of British breeding birds, and of the patterns of dispersal, would clearly aid its long-term conservation.

John H Marchant

Horned Lark (Shore Lark)
Eremophila alpestris

The Shore Lark has many guises but it is the race *flava* of Arctic Eurasia that visits Britain & Ireland, where it inhabits mainly the shoreline.

The world range is truly extraordinary. The species is almost ubiquitous in North America as a breeding bird, withdrawing from arctic zones during the winter; among about 25 races, nominate *alpestris* occupies Quebec, Labrador and Newfoundland (*BWP*). An isolated population is found in the Colombian Andes. In the southern Palearctic, it occurs in the Moroccan Atlas and from the Balkans and Turkey east to northern China. Finally, *flava* nests in the mountains of Scandinavia and eastwards along the Russian high Arctic to the Kolyma Delta, and also in southeast Russia eastwards from Lake Baikal. A pair nested successfully in Scotland in 1977 (Ellis 1990), and possibly also during 1972–76 (Batten *et al* 1990), while in 1997 a pair was again present in suitable habitat (Ogilvie *et al* 1999a). The wintering grounds of *flava* extend from Britain and continental North Sea coasts patchily through central Europe, with large numbers in southern Russia and across the steppes of Kazakhstan and Mongolia to northern China (*BWP*).

Regular wintering on the east coast of Britain dates only from about 1870 (*BWP*). The main range extends from Grampian to Kent but some also occur on west and south coasts. Much foraging time is spent on the tideline, or on sheltered saltmarsh or nearby fields. Numbers vary considerably between winters. The *Winter Atlas* estimated there to be a maximum of 300 birds in Britain during 1981–84. In Norfolk, the wintering total fell as low as only one or two birds in 1988/89 but a coordinated county survey on 5 December 1998 found 591, more than double the previous peaks there in the 1970s, and more birds than usual were also seen in other parts of Britain at this time (Lawton 1999). In Ireland, the species is very rare with, to the end of 1996, just 11 records of 16 individuals (Garner 1999).

After breeding, *flava* deserts its most northerly breeding grounds in August and September and departs from northern Norway mainly

between late September and mid-October (*BWP*). Records of visible migration suggest that the main route towards North Sea wintering grounds is through Sweden and Denmark. A few pass through Shetland during September–November, and arrivals in Norfolk also begin in September. Return passage is evident in May. Occasional birds have lingered on the coast into early June.

Ringing has so far provided little information about Shore Lark movements but there is recent colour-ringing evidence of winter site-fidelity and of northward spring movements along the east coast. A male ringed at Gibraltar Point in December 1996 was seen again there in April 1998 (Clark *et al* 2001). A female colour-ringed in Suffolk in March 1997 was reported in the same county the following March and November, and was thus known to be present in three successive winters (Clark *et al* 2000). Another female, ringed at Orfordness in Suffolk on 8 March 1998, was seen at Salthouse in North Norfolk on 6 May the same year. Five further birds from the same catch at Orfordness were all seen 35 km north along the coast later that month or in April. From a catch at Holkham Bay, Norfolk, on 31 December 1998, four birds were reported distantly the following year: a female was at Gibraltar Point on 29 April, a male in North Yorkshire on 2 May, another male on Fair Isle on 14 May, and a third male at Orfordness on 14 November (Clark *et al* 2001).

The origin of British wintering birds is presumably towards the western end of the breeding range in Scandinavia or western Russia, although the eastern limit of birds wintering in northwest Europe is not known. It is becoming clearer that the northeast American *alpestris* occurs occasionally; an old British record is now discredited but a 1998 record in County Down may have been of this form (Garner 1999) and one on Scilly in October 2001 is well documented (Small 2002).

John H Marchant

Richard's Pipit

Anthus novaeseelandiae

Richard's Pipit nests no closer to Britain & Ireland than West Siberia but is widespread in Europe as a scarce or rare passage migrant, apparently en route to western wintering grounds.

Migratory races of Richard's Pipit occur in central and eastern Asia, from eastern Kazakhstan across southern Russia and northern China to the Sea of Japan (*BWP*). Remarkably, the species is also resident in eastern and southern Africa, India, Southeast Asia and Australasia. The wintering grounds of migratory birds are incompletely known, but lie mostly between Pakistan and Malaysia, among local races. There have also been widespread winter observations in southern Spain and in North Africa, from Morocco to Egypt, that have been assigned to *richardi*, the westernmost of the migratory races (*BWP*); this may also be the race that winters in parts of Mauritania and Mali and occurs sporadically in countries further south in West Africa (Keith *et al* 1992). The extent of this western wintering area, well separated from the bulk of the population in southern Asia, is poorly known.

In the west of its range, *richardi* leaves its breeding grounds between the end of August and late September (*BWP*). There have been August arrivals in Britain & Ireland but the first are usually in early September, building to a broad peak from late September through October, and tailing off through November and December (Dymond *et al* 1989,

Chapter 1 Fig 1.2a). Occasional individuals, unlikely to be new arrivals, have been noted in January. Most birds appear at coastal sites in Norfolk, on Scilly or in Shetland, with smaller numbers at other east coast sites, in the south and north of Ireland, and in Wales, and occasional records in inland counties of southeast England (Dymond *et al* 1989, Fraser *et al* 2000, Chapter 1 Fig 1.2b). They feed typically in longish rough pasture, avoiding close-cropped areas, or on damp ground with plenty of low cover (*BWP*). The total numbers of autumn records are increasing long-term (Fraser *et al* 2000).

Spring occurrences in Britain & Ireland appear to be increasing faster than those in autumn. There were only 33 during 1958–85, less than 3% of all records (Dymond *et al* 1989), but 12 of 104 records in 1998 were in spring (Fraser *et al* 2000). Spring records are widely scattered but mostly near English coasts. The passage period spans early March to late June, with a small peak in late April and early May.

There are no ring-recoveries for this species that involve Britain or Ireland. Nothing yet links migrants in Britain & Ireland with particular breeding or wintering areas, therefore. On the western fringes of the range these areas have yet to be fully defined.

John H Marchant

Water Pipit

Anthus spinoletta

The Water Pipit breeds in the mountainous regions of southern Europe and south Asia, often above the treeline, descending to the lowlands in winter. Surprisingly, many European birds move north or northwest for the winter.

Water Pipit has recently been separated from Rock and Buff-bellied Pipits (Knox 1988). Its western nominate race nests from Spain to the Balkans and Carpathians, and possibly northwest Turkey, and two further races occur from Turkey to east of Lake Baikal (*BWP*). The winter range of nominate birds extends north to England, Denmark and Poland and south to Atlantic Morocco and Mediterranean North Africa. Eastern Water Pipits apparently winter in Egypt, Arabia and southwest Asia. Outside the breeding season the species occupies freshwater sites, both coastal and inland, as well as some brackish coastal sites.

Water Pipits leave their alpine breeding grounds from mid-September and return during March and April (de Crousaz 1966). Winter records in lowland Germany span a period from the second week of September to late May but there are relatively few before October or after mid-April (Witt 1982). Site-fidelity is known both on the breeding grounds in the Swiss Alps and at wintering localities at a range of distances (de Crousaz 1966, *Der Zug*).

During the winters of 1966/67 and 1967/68, the BTO organized a survey to establish the winter status of the species in Britain & Ireland. The results demonstrated that Water Pipits favoured the southern counties of England, in both coastal and inland areas, with watercress beds being particularly favoured (Johnson 1970). Fieldwork for the *Winter Atlas*, carried out 15 years later, confirmed the mainly southern distribution, with the highest concentrations in counties bordering the south coast of England, and smaller numbers in East Anglia, the Midlands and

northwest England. The *Winter Atlas* included only two records from Scotland and none from Ireland, where the species is rare, with only four individuals recorded up to 1986 (*Birds in Ireland*). The winter population in Britain may be as low as a hundred birds (*Winter Atlas*).

Birds have been noted in Norfolk as early as 17 September and as late as 22 May (Taylor *et al* 1999), but most British arrivals are from mid-October to late November and virtually all birds have left by the end of April (Johnson 1970). At Rye Meads sewage-works, Hertfordshire, where the species is regular, a peak is noted in January and another in April that might reflect birds on through passage (Roper 1995).

Between 1986 and 1996, a total of 66 Water Pipits had been ringed in Britain, those caught before 1986 having been included in the total for Rock Pipit. Fidelity to wintering sites, in some cases over three or four winters, has been shown by ringed birds returning to sites in Flintshire, Hampshire and Hertfordshire (Johnson 1970, Pain 1990, Roper 1995). Only two British-ringed Water Pipits have been recovered away from the site of ringing. One ringed in Surrey in February was recovered in Hampshire two years later in November, while the first foreign recovery concerned a first-winter bird ringed at Rye Meads on 2 December 1995 that was seen in the Netherlands on 17 October 1996.

Measurements of birds trapped for ringing suggest an excess of male birds at Rye Meads (Roper 1995), and a similar result has been obtained from each of six sites in Belgium, Luxembourg and Germany (Witt 1982). This raises questions about the winter behaviour of females and why it should be that males are apparently more likely to winter in distant lowland areas.

Moss Taylor & John H Marchant

Bluethroat

Luscinia svecica

The northern and southern forms of Bluethroats in western Europe are both scarce migrants in Britain & Ireland, with differing patterns of occurrence. These patterns have yet to be fully elucidated, however, because only the spring males can be readily distinguished.

The species as a whole nests widely across the Palearctic from Spain and Norway to Kashmir, northern China, and the Bering Sea in easternmost Siberia (*BWP*). A few pairs nest in northwest Alaska. Dense low woody vegetation in marshes or swamps is especially favoured for nesting. The nominate race *svecica*, the Red-spotted Bluethroat, breeds mainly north of the Baltic and across northern Russia to Alaska. Single pairs of Red-spotted Bluethroats nested successfully in northern Scotland in 1985 and 1995, and nesting was attempted in 1968 (Greenwood 1968, Murray 1987, Benn 1995). The southern European races *cyanecula* and *namnetum*, collectively the White-spotted Bluethroat, breed from Spain and the Netherlands eastward to Ukraine and the Baltic States, patchily across western and central Europe, with *namnetum* restricted to western France. There are isolated mountain populations of *svecica* within the range of *cyanecula* in central Europe. Six further races occur between Ukraine and China.

Some Bluethroats winter in Spain, or on Mediterranean coasts or islands, but many European birds of both forms winter in the Sahel zone of Africa, just south of the Sahara between Senegal and northern Somalia; White-spotted predominates in the western part of the African range (*BWP*). Birds are present in Senegal from mid-September to the end of March, and exceptionally to the end of May. Further east, birds winter in Arabia and at similar latitudes east to south China and Vietnam. Winter territories may be established, and both sexes sing at that season (*BWP*).

Scandinavian ring-recoveries suggest two main routes of autumn passage for European Red-spotted Bluethroats, south towards the central Sahel but mainly southeast, probably towards Pakistan and northwest India (Staav 1975, *BWP*). The main departure of both adult and first-winter birds from Scandinavia is in late August and early September, on completion of breeding and moult (Lindström *et al* 1985, Ellegren 1990, 1991). Autumn departure of White-spotted Bluethroats is later and is mainly southwesterly, towards West Africa; some winter in Spain, Italy and elsewhere in the Mediterranean Basin (*BWP*). White-spotted Bluethroats also return earlier to the breeding grounds in spring. Peak passage in the Alps and southern Germany occurs in early April. By contrast, some Scandinavian Red-spotteds are still in Kazakhstan in April, and arrivals in Sweden peak in mid-May (Staav 1975, *BWP*); in the very north of the breeding range, spring arrivals continue into mid-June.

On average, 133 Bluethroats were recorded per year in Britain during 1968–98 (Fraser *et al* 2000). Easterly winds may bring falls of migrants in both spring and autumn, however, leading to wide variation in the annual totals. In autumn, birds can occur all along the east and south coasts of Britain from Shetland to Scilly, with smaller numbers in inland and western counties. Most migrants choose ditches or swamp edges in preference to drier habitats (*BWP*). Over a hundred Bluethroats were observed on the east coast of Britain within a few days in early September 1965 (Davis 1966b); since the 1960s, however, autumn numbers appear to have been in decline (Dymond *et al* 1989). Most birds occur from late August to mid-October, but some have lingered into November.

Spring numbers are generally higher than in autumn and are distributed more to the north and east (Fraser *et al* 2000). Passage may begin with a small number of birds during late March and early April, mostly White-spotted males, but the main wave of passage, with birds that can be racially identified being almost exclusively Red-spotted, occurs during early May to early June. Spring passage periods of the two forms occasionally overlap, and they have occurred together, for example at Great Saltee on 18 May 1985 (*Birds in Ireland*), and on Fair Isle four days later (R Riddington pers comm), both during a major influx that brought 480 or more Bluethroats to Scotland alone during 8–20 May (Murray 1987). Perhaps especially after large spring falls, some birds linger into the summer and may attempt to breed.

Almost a thousand Bluethroats have been ringed in Britain & Ireland. A September juvenile in Dorset was found dead two months later just south of the Pyrenees. Of two first-summer birds ringed on Fair Isle on 24 May, in different years, a male was found on a boat west of Shetland 11 days later and a female was in Belgium four days later. Four other recoveries link spring migrants on the coast between Flamborough Head and Fair Isle with Sweden and Norway. Two recaptures at Slapton in Devon reveal that passage through Britain can be regular and is not simply the result of birds bound elsewhere encountering easterly winds; a first-winter male ringed on 21 September 1966 was retrapped at the same place on 14 September two years later, and an adult male ringed on 17 May 1958 was caught again on 5 May 1963 (*BWP*).

As a wetland species that winters largely in the African Sahel, Bluethroat would appear to be greatly at risk from the droughts that have occurred in that region in many years since the late 1960s. It is not known whether there might be a link between the autumn decline in Britain & Ireland since the 1960s and the contemporaneous series of droughts in the western Sahel, perhaps as Scandinavian birds increasingly take more easterly routes.

John H Marchant

Aquatic Warbler
Acrocephalus paludicola

The Aquatic Warbler is the only globally threatened bird species that occurs in Britain & Ireland as a regular passage migrant. Most records are of birds trapped by ringers, and not otherwise observed, so that ringing has been of great value in assessing the species' regional status as well as its movements.

Breeding formerly occurred west to France and Belgium but, following extinction in western Europe during the 20th century, is now confined to isolated fen mires in an area centred on Belarus and extending to the German–Polish border, Lithuania, Hungary, Ukraine and western Russia. Extensive surveys during 1995–98 put the total population at only 13,500–21,000 singing males; a further 2,000–11,000 singing males might occur in two isolated areas of Russia east of the Urals, but this remains to be confirmed (Aquatic Warbler Conservation Team 1999). Winter occurrence has been recorded in the wetlands of Senegal, Mauritania, Mali and Ghana but there are very few African records and important sites, habitats and movements within Africa have yet to be identified.

For breeding, Aquatic Warblers specialize in extensive wet fens with low vegetation, especially sedges and grasses. Suitable sites occur in river floodplains, as isolated mires, and by the Baltic coast. Breeding males occupy large home ranges but do not defend territories and take no part in nesting or parental care (Dyrcz & Zdunek 1993). Radio-tracking in Polish marshes has revealed that male home ranges may be up to 7.8 ha in extent and overlap by up to 74%; each contains a continually shifting core area in which the male spends most of his time (Schulze-Hagen *et al* 1999). Males maintain frequent song between the end of April and the end of August, singing most persistently in the evening. Breeding females forage close to the nest but typically shift sites between first and second broods.

Autumn migration begins in late June when some males leave the breeding grounds, but most adults and young depart in late July or early August. Migrants are noted regularly in Germany, Switzerland, the Rhine Delta, Belgium, southern England, France and Spain, and also in Bulgaria (de By 1990, Aquatic Warbler Conservation Team 1999). Records are scarcer in Fennoscandia, Ireland, and through the Mediterranean Basin.

Passage through Britain begins typically in the last days of July or in early August, although exceptional late June and early July records might relate to early autumn migrants. On average, 28 birds were recorded in Britain each year during 1958–98, with a peak of 102 in 1976 and only single figures in several years in the 1960s (Fraser *et al* 2000). During 1968–87, adults, which are readily identified by their faded plumage and worn primaries and tail feathers, comprised 7% of birds that were aged and had a median date of 17 August compared with 21 August for all British records (de By 1990). In most years, the last birds are seen in Britain in September. There are several October records, however, and two for early November (Dymond *et al* 1989).

The distribution of records is not as might be expected for a bird of eastern origin, with most birds in the Southwest Peninsula or along the central south coast and, although occurring from Shetland to Kent, east-coast sightings are surprisingly scarce. In Ireland, there had been only 11 autumn records by 1989, with a median date of 2 September (de By 1990).

In all, 685 birds were ringed in Britain & Ireland to 1997. Ringing sites at Radipole Lake in Dorset and Marazion in Cornwall have each provided many records. Within an hour of each other on 25 August 1990, two Polish nestlings with consecutive ring numbers were trapped in Britain, one at Chew Valley Lake, Avon, and the other near Helston in Cornwall (Mead & Clark 1991). The only recovery so far from British ringing was of a juvenile ringed at Rye Bay, Sussex, on 12 August 1995 that was caught again in North Kent 13 days later. Ringing studies still have much to contribute, therefore, to our knowledge of Aquatic Warbler movements.

It is intriguing that most of the birds trapped have been in tall *Phragmites* stands at dawn, and were not retrapped or seen subsequently, whereas other migrants are observed to select lower marshy vegetation such as sedges, grasses or *Spartina*, even when reedbeds are nearby, and sometimes to remain for subsequent days; this suggests that Aquatic Warblers making landfall overnight in reedbeds with other *Acrocephalus* warblers may move quickly to other habitats, and therefore that ringing may give a false idea of habitat preferences (Pattenden 1989, Lewis 1996, pers obs).

It is not known whether the birds that occur in Spain, with a median date of 17 September, include any that have passed through Britain. It seems likely, however, that onward passage from Britain and neighbouring countries continues through Iberia towards West African wintering grounds.

Spring records are rare in western Europe, especially in the west and north, and it appears that birds follow a more easterly route through Europe at that season (de By 1990). A relatively late passage is indicated by median dates for migrants of 23 April in Spain and 8 May in Germany. There are old spring records in County Mayo on 2 June 1906, in Norfolk on 12 May 1938, at Dungeness (a male in song) on 19 April 1949, in Cambridgeshire during 4–16 May 1953, and in Somerset on 13 May 1963, but none in the following 20 years at least (Naylor 1996, 1998). The species is clearly exceptional in Britain & Ireland at that season, especially since breeding ceased in neighbouring countries. Arrivals on the breeding grounds continue throughout May (Dyrcz & Zdunek 1993). In the same study about a third of ringed males returned to the site of ringing in the following year; one male was found 7 km distant, but the statistics of breeding dispersal are not yet known.

Recent breeding surveys have highlighted the continuing decline and range contraction of the species, and its vulnerability to habitat destruction, through drainage for agriculture or peat extraction, and to habitat change, for example through vegetation succession or changes in water levels (Aquatic Warbler Conservation Team 1999). Even in Belarus, a decline of more than 90% is believed to have occurred since the 1960s (Kozulin & Flade 1999). Drought and habitat change might also be problems for the species on the wintering grounds. The UK Biodiversity Action Plan emphasizes the need for protection of south-coast marshes to support the autumn migration (UK Biodiversity Group 1999). Further surveys are needed to identify conservation needs in Africa.

John H Marchant

Marsh Warbler

Acrocephalus palustris

The Marsh Warbler is noted for its remarkable mimetic song, which contains phrases learnt from a variety of African as well as European birds. It has a wide distribution across the middle latitudes of the West Palearctic from northeast France and southeast Norway to northeast Turkey and Kazakhstan, and winters in southeast Africa, mainly from Zambia and Malawi south to Natal and Cape Province (*BWP*).

Autumn departure from Belgium begins in the second week of July and is mostly complete by the end of August (Dowsett-Lemaire & Dowsett 1987). Birds from all parts of the breeding range migrate via the Middle East, entailing a southeasterly movement from western Europe, to enter Africa across the Red Sea between the end of July and mid-October. Little is then seen of them for two to four months, which they most probably spend during the rainy season somewhere in western or southwestern Ethiopia (Pearson *et al* 1988). First arrivals in Kenya are in late October, the forerunners of a large-scale onward nocturnal migration that peaks in November–December and is still evident in early or mid-January (Pearson 1982). Ring-recoveries from Ngulia in southeast Kenya are scattered widely across the breeding range and demonstrate the narrow front on which the whole population is believed to migrate at this time. Marsh Warblers are first recorded in Natal in late November but are not numerous there before late December or January. Southern arrivals again coincide with the start of the rainy season; birds of both sexes set up territories and sing during the annual primary moult, which in Zambia takes place between late January and early April (Kelsey 1989).

Winterers have left the south of the range by early April. Spring passage through Kenya is mainly in April but is much less evident than in autumn and concentrated nearer the coast. Arrivals on the breeding grounds are late in spring and continue to mid-June in western Europe (Dowsett-Lemaire & Dowsett 1987). Last records in Somalia and Arabia are in mid-May and a Belgian-ringed bird was still in Lebanon on 20 May.

In Britain, the species is both a passage migrant and a rare breeding bird but breeding numbers have been in decline since about 1950. During 1968–72, there were about 50–80 pairs breeding as far west as Somerset and Gwent, with about three-quarters of the total in a well-established population in Worcestershire (*1968–72 Atlas*). Breeding habitat there was mostly derelict riverside land with dense herbage and scattered shrubs or trees. The Worcestershire population crashed in the 1980s, however (Kelsey *et al* 1989), and is now extinct. A few dozen pairs of Marsh Warblers have continued to nest erratically at widespread locations, mostly in southeast England (Ogilvie *et al* 2000). A pair raised young on Orkney in 1993, in the first known breeding attempt in Scotland, and again nearby in 1997 (Meek *et al* 1998a). The species was first recognized as a rare visitor to Ireland in August 1991, and a singing male was present briefly in June 1996.

Excluding those at known breeding sites, about 50 Marsh Warblers are reported in Britain each year, mostly in spring in eastern counties between Sussex and Shetland (Fraser *et al* 2000). Spring records and breeding arrivals in Britain are mainly between 20 May and mid-June (Kelsey 1989, Kelsey *et al* 1989, Fraser *et al* 2000); there are probably no reliable reports earlier than the second week of May. In 1985, a Worcestershire pullus was found in Greece in its first October. A June bird in Hertfordshire had been ringed in Belgium almost three years earlier, and one in Orkney had been ringed in Denmark, as a juvenile, the previous August. Around four to 12 individuals are recorded in a typical autumn, between July and early November, but many more might pass unrecognized among the very similar Reed Warblers. Same-autumn recoveries from the Netherlands on 23 August to Lancashire on 19 October, and from Belgium on 29 August to Devon on 3 September, indicate the origins of some of these birds. A juvenile ringed in Sussex on 20 August was in western Germany on 7 August a year later.

Colour-ringing in Worcestershire and in Zambia demonstrated that site-fidelity in both summer and winter is high (Kelsey 1989), although the sporadic nature of recent breeding records in Britain suggests that some individuals may readily breed far from their natal areas. As an extreme example, a bird that was in Switzerland in June in both 1967 and 1968 was found, possibly breeding, in Iran in June 1970 (Dowsett-Lemaire & Dowsett 1987).

John H Marchant

Icterine Warbler

Hippolais icterina

The Icterine Warbler is a breeding visitor to much of northern, central and eastern Europe, occurring from Norway and eastern France eastward to the Black Sea and across the Urals into western Siberia. It inhabits open woodland or woodland edge with dense undergrowth and occurs also in orchards, parks and gardens (*BWP*). In winter, it has a southeasterly distribution in Africa, being found mainly between Tanzania and northern Cape Province. Overlap with its western counterpart Melodious Warbler is minimal at all seasons; where their breeding ranges meet in eastern France, the two species hold mutually exclusive territories (*BWP*).

Autumn migration has generally a southeasterly heading from the northwest of the range, and a southwesterly one from the northeast, so that most birds funnel through Italy or Greece and enter Africa on a front between Nigeria and Ethiopia (*BWP*). Departure begins in late July and in northern Europe is largely over by early September. Passage continues in the central Mediterranean region until October, presumably reflecting continuing arrivals of birds from the eastern part of the range (*BWP*). Within the main African winter range, birds arrive from mid-October to late November, and hold territory and sing through the winter (*BWP*).

In spring, northward movement from southern Africa begins in late February, but the peak of passage through Nigeria is not until late April, and return to the breeding grounds occurs during late April to early June (*BWP*). Icterine Warblers are abundant in Italy and the central Mediterranean between mid-April and mid-May, being replaced almost completely by Melodious Warblers at migration stations further west (Pilastro *et al* 1998b).

Fresh-plumaged first-winter birds begin to appear on British & Irish coasts in early August or sometimes at the end of July (Dymond *et al* 1989). Peak passage occurs around the end of August and tails off through September and early October, with late stragglers occurring to late November and even December. One ringed on Scilly on 2 September 1964 continued westwards and was found at sea south of Ireland the next day. Adults, recognizable by their abraded plumage, show a similar autumn peak; at Dungeness, four of 19 autumn birds trapped were adults (Riddiford 1991).

The British distribution of Icterine Warbler records is very similar to that of Barred Warblers, with most sightings along the east coast between Suffolk and Shetland and smaller numbers on the south coast west to Scilly and in the Irish Sea (Dymond *et al* 1989). In clear contrast, however, one in seven Icterine Warbler records are in spring but only one in about 280 Barred Warblers (Fraser *et al* 2000). Arrivals generally begin in mid-May, rarely as early as April, and continue to mid-June, and are perhaps more frequent inland than in autumn. Most are in Shetland or in eastern Britain south to Sussex. Spring records in particular are very variable from year to year, depending mainly on the prevalence of suitable easterly or southeasterly airstreams across the North Sea. Some spring migrants sing, and some have held territory into July. Breeding was successful in Highland Scotland in 1992, after an exceptionally strong spring passage, having been suspected elsewhere in Britain on earlier occasions in the century (Ogilvie *et al* 1995).

There have been no international ring-recoveries of this species for Britain & Ireland so far. Occurrences of Icterine Warblers might result from exploratory movements by juveniles from nearby breeding grounds, from oriented 'reverse migration' from western Europe, or from extended westerly movements by birds from the east of the range. These possibilities cannot presently be distinguished. Exploratory movements might be a forerunner to an extension of the breeding range across the North Sea. Those migrants that arrive in October and November, after most western birds have already departed for Africa, might be more likely to originate from the east of the range than from western Europe.

John H Marchant

Dartford Warbler

Sylvia undata

The Dartford Warbler, unusually for its genus, is mainly sedentary but some birds do migrate and, after local extinction at specific English breeding sites following hard winters, dispersal has proved sufficient to effect recolonization.

The global range extends from southern England locally through western France to Iberia, where it is widespread, and around western Mediterranean coastlines in northwest Africa, France and southern Italy; in winter, the range extends southward to include Atlantic Morocco, a strip of inland Algeria, and southern Sicily (*BWP*). Some European birds reach northwest Africa, with passage noted in the Strait of Gibraltar in autumn, especially October, and in March–April. The race *dartfordiensis* occupies the northwest of the range, including England, and there are two more southerly races (*BWP*). Vagrants have been recorded north to Ireland and Sweden, and east to Greece and Libya (*BWP*).

The British range has at times covered many parts of southeast England between Cornwall and Suffolk and some inland counties north to Shropshire. Within this area, the range and population size has varied greatly in recent decades in response to cold winters, which can cause severe mortality. Only 11 pairs were known following the 1962/63 winter, but the population in 1994 was estimated as 1,800–1,890 territories and substantial recolonization had then occurred of suitable sites in Devon, Surrey and Sussex (Gibbons & Wotton 1996). More recently, breeding has spread to Suffolk (Etheridge 2001). For breeding, British Dartford Warblers are largely restricted to lowland heath, a habitat that has become very limited in extent and is frequently under threat from development, degradation or fragmentation (Westerhoff & Tubbs 1991, Evans *et al* 1994).

Heathland breeding sites are frequently occupied year-round. Colour-ringing has shown that both members of a pair may remain on the same territory all year, and one bird was still on territory after a devastating fire (Bibby 1979).

Single birds or small groups sometimes appear in other bushy habitats, such as coastal gorse, often some distance from the nearest breeding site. Some 60% of all such records lay between 3 October and 6 November (Bibby 1979). Others occurred from late July to early April, but none during the breeding season. Of the five Irish records, all had been found during August to October (*Birds in Ireland*). Most such birds are likely to be juveniles displaced from the breeding grounds by renewed territorial activity after the autumn moult but, since some out-of-range birds occur even when breeding numbers are very low, Bibby (1979) considered it likely that a partial southward migration was also occurring. The origins and subsequent fate of such individuals are mostly unknown, but probably it is these that are instrumental in recolonizing distant breeding sites. Most are presumed to be dispersing birds from the English population. Ring-recoveries so far add little to this story. A Dartford Warbler killed by a cat in Barnes, London, on 1 November had been ringed the previous June as a juvenile in the New Forest, Hampshire, and a pullus from Surrey, ringed on 30 June, was in the New Forest by 11 August.

Immigration and emigration, if they occur, have still to be proven. The two Scottish records, at St Abb's Head on 18 May 1983 (*Birds in Scotland*) and on Fair Isle on 29–30 April 2000, might possibly, like the vagrants in Sweden in April and May, relate to spring overshooting from a continental population. A record on board ship in the English Channel, north of the Cherbourg Peninsula, on 4 November 1974 may indicate that some interchange occurs between England and France (Bibby 1979).

There remain many unknowns about the rates, distances and directions of dispersal. These could hamper conservation measures in the event of another severe setback to the population. While the population level is high, protection and management of heathland sites may promote further increase and range extension.

John H Marchant

Barred Warbler

Sylvia nisoria

The normal autumn migration of European Barred Warblers takes them directly away from Britain & Ireland, yet this species is a regular migrant on British and Irish coasts at that season.

As a breeding bird, the Barred Warbler occupies a broad swathe of central and eastern Europe and western Siberia from northern Italy and Germany eastward across the Urals to Mongolia (*BWP*). The winter range, in a limited area of East Africa from northeastern Tanzania to eastern and northern Kenya and probably southern Ethiopia, is geographically much smaller. A southeasterly departure is required from Europe and a southwesterly one from Kazakhstan and Mongolia. Thickets or thorny hedges, often admixed with trees, are favoured for nesting. In Africa, Barred Warblers are found in thickets and bush, often in dry country (*BWP*).

Barred Warblers arrive late on the breeding grounds and depart relatively early (*BWP*). The western fringes of the breeding range are deserted during August, with adults leaving on completion of their primary moult and generally earlier than the juveniles. The entire population funnels southward through the Middle East, entering Africa via Egypt or Arabia mostly during August to November.

After a stopover in Ethiopia or northern Kenya, first arrivals at Ngulia in southeast Kenya, in the southern part of the winter range, are not until late October (Pearson & Backhurst 1976, Lindström *et al* 1993). Nocturnal passage then continues until early January, with a peak from mid-November to early December. Both adults and first-winters have an extensive moult in Africa that includes the tail and many of the secondaries; this begins either just before or shortly after the final leg of the southward migration (Lindström *et al* 1993). Spring passage is evident in Kenya from late March to mid-April and the birds regain their breeding grounds between mid-April and late May (*BWP*).

During 1968–98, an average of 136 Barred Warblers occurred annually in Britain (Fraser *et al* 2000). Autumn occurrence begins in Britain & Ireland at the end of July or in early August, builds to a peak at the end of August, and has a long tail into mid-November and sometimes early December (Dymond *et al* 1989). More than a third of all records are in Shetland, with many more from the British east coast south to Norfolk and smaller numbers from Suffolk west to Scilly. Barred Warblers are relatively rare on the west coast of Britain. In Ireland, they have occurred in most coastal counties but most frequently in County Cork. Some adults have been reported, for example a female shot in Norfolk in 1897 (Taylor *et al* 1999), but autumn birds are overwhelmingly birds of the year.

There are isolated records for a handful of landlocked English counties (Dymond *et al* 1989) but almost all records are within sight of the sea. Many migrants take up residence in a relatively small area of bushy cover where they can be found regularly over a period of a week or more (Taylor *et al* 1999).

In remarkable contrast to its autumn status, Barred Warbler is an exceptional rarity in Britain & Ireland in spring. During 1968–98, there were just 15 spring records in Britain, all discovered between 10 May and 22 June (Fraser *et al* 2000). Most were on the east coast between Suffolk and Shetland. There have been no spring records in Ireland (*Birds in Ireland*).

By 1997, ringers had trapped 1,522 Barred Warblers in Britain & Ireland. Just three had been recovered, including a first-year bird ringed on Fair Isle on 8 September 1978 that was reported killed in Macedonia on 20 February 1979 (Spencer & Hudson 1980); this is a full two months before spring arrivals there would be expected. The authenticity of an earlier international report, of an adult ringed in Italy in July 1943 and reported captured in inland Hampshire three months later, has also been questioned (Spencer & Hudson 1980, Clark & Eyre 1993). One ringed at Sheringham, North Norfolk, on 5 September 1995 was trapped again 22 days later just 2 km away (Taylor *et al* 1999).

The arrival of juvenile Barred Warblers in northwest Europe in autumn has been ascribed to pre-migratory exploration, perhaps a forerunner to westward range expansion, or to reversed migration, on a heading directly opposite to that required to reach the wintering grounds. In the absence of reliable long-distance ring-recoveries and of any overwintering records, it is not known whether any Barred Warblers that reach Britain & Ireland in autumn reorient their migration in an appropriate direction and survive their first winter. Some might overwinter, perhaps, in unknown areas in southwest Europe or West Africa. Vagrancy to Sierra Leone has been recorded (*BWP*). The few spring records, being predominantly in northeast Britain, suggest overshooting from the breeding grounds to the east rather than the return of successful winterers from the south.

John H Marchant

Yellow-browed Warbler

Phylloscopus inornatus

This tiny leaf-warbler, with a breeding range that only just enters the West Palearctic in the northern Urals, is one of the most frequent Asian passerines in western Europe.

The breeding range occupies almost the whole of Russia east of the Urals, except for the far north and east, south to Kamchatka, and the West Siberian Plain. The races *humei* and *mandellii*, formerly regarded as the southern races of Yellow-browed, are now treated as a separate species, Hume's Leaf Warbler, which also occurs in northwest Europe but is much rarer (BOU 1997, Clement & Scott 1999). Yellow-browed Warblers winter mostly further east than Hume's, from central Nepal and Bangladesh east to Taiwan and Hainan and south to the Malay Peninsula (*BWP*).

Autumn migration begins in August or September. The available data suggest that most of the population migrates via northeast China, requiring an initial easterly heading from birds in the west of the range (*BWP*). From there, they filter south or southwest through China to the winter quarters, which are occupied from mid-October to mid-April. Northward movement in spring begins in late March and reverses the route followed in autumn, birds being abundant in northeast China from late April to mid- or late May. Sightings are annual in many European localities from the Faeroes to Portugal, and less regular in North Africa and the Middle East (*CBWP*). One was trapped in Senegal in September 1987 (Urban *et al* 1997).

British records totalled more than 7,000 during 1968–98, with numbers markedly higher in each recent year than in those before 1984 (Fraser *et al* 2000). Autumn arrivals may occur from early September to mid-November but there is a peak in the first half of October; most sightings are in the Northern Isles or Scilly, and many others elsewhere on the east or south coasts (Dymond *et al* 1989). Records well inland are not infrequent. In Ireland, most are seen at Cape Clear Island or other southern sites (*Birds in Ireland*). A few individuals have wintered in Britain, mainly on the south coast, departing by mid-April. Spring records totalled only four during 1958–85, all during late March to mid-May and along the British south coast, their distribution suggesting a return of successful winterers from the south rather than fresh arrivals from Asia (Dymond *et al* 1989). Shetland provided a spring record, its first, in 2001 (R Riddington pers comm).

The nature of the European passage of this species has generated much speculation and analysis (*eg* Rabøl 1969, van Impe & Derasse 1994, Thorup 1998, Phillips 2000). In 1985, when exceptional numbers of birds crossed northern Europe, arrivals in Finland were earlier than those in Sweden and Denmark, and about two weeks earlier than those in the Netherlands, Britain and Ireland; within Britain, arrivals were earliest in northeast Scotland and latest on the English south coast (Baker & Catley 1987). In Sweden, the mean date of arrival at a northerly location was 26 September, a week earlier than at a southerly one, reflecting the shorter great-circle distance from the breeding grounds and possibly a faster movement by more northerly birds (Ullman 1989). A bird carrying a

Norwegian ring, but whose ringing details are still unknown, was trapped on Fair Isle in 1990 (Dymond 1991). Another, ringed at Portland Bill on 21 October 1988, was recaptured on Guernsey the next day. These observations would all be consistent with a 180° reversal of the usual great-circle route towards Southeast Asia, bringing birds through northwest Europe on a southwesterly heading.

Adults cannot be separated reliably from young birds in autumn, even in the hand, and full confirmation of the occurrence of adults in Britain & Ireland is still awaited. Since winter records are so unusual in Britain, occupation of the same sites in consecutive winters, as happened in Hampshire in 1994–96 (Clark 1996, 1998), and in Cornwall in 2000–01 (K A Wilson pers comm), raises the notion that some winterers might be returning adults, but ringing has yet to demonstrate this.

The increasing numbers involved suggest that the birds that follow this western route may be contributing genetically to the population and might be pioneering new wintering areas for the species. At present, however, we do not know the origins or destination of the birds that pass through Britain & Ireland, nor whether any survive to breed in subsequent springs.

John H Marchant

Red-breasted Flycatcher

Ficedula parva

The Red-breasted Flycatcher is one of the few long-distance migrants nesting in Europe that winters mainly in the Indian subcontinent.

The species is usually treated as comprising a western, nominate race that breeds in central and eastern Europe, from Sweden, eastern Germany and Croatia east to the south Caspian and almost to the Urals, and an eastern one, *albicilla*, that breeds in the extreme east of European Russia and across the Urals to the Russian Far East (*BWP*). Support is growing, however, for treatment of *albicilla* as a separate species, 'Taiga Flycatcher' (Cederroth *et al* 1999). The winter range extends from Pakistan east to peninsular Thailand, Vietnam and southeast China. Nominate *parva* winters further west than *albicilla*, but both occur in a wide area of eastern India and Bangladesh (*BWP*). Tall forest with rich undergrowth is favoured at all seasons but more open wooded habitats are also used, perhaps especially outside the breeding season.

Departure from the European breeding grounds is protracted, extending from late July into September, and typically has a southeasterly heading (*BWP*). Major routes both north and south of the Black Sea take birds towards Iran and Afghanistan, which they reach mainly in October; some may winter in those places but most move on into Pakistan and India, where arrivals span a period from the end of August to November. In spring, return movements begin in mid-March but some birds are still in India or Pakistan in May. Passage through the Middle East is mainly from mid-April to mid-May. Central European forests are reoccupied from about mid-May and into June.

Records far to the west of the main range, reaching even the Canary Islands and Iceland, are relatively frequent (*BWP*). In autumn, passage birds occur in Britain & Ireland mostly between mid-August and mid-November, with a clear peak in early October (Dymond *et al* 1989). A few

birds seen in July, as far west as County Louth, might be unusually early autumn migrants, while the tiny number of December–February records appears to indicate rare attempts to overwinter. During 1968–98, an average 86 birds were seen in Britain each autumn, mostly on Scilly, in the Northern Isles, or along the east coast between Kent and Aberdeen (Fraser *et al* 2000). A first-winter bird on the Isle of May on 10 October had been ringed on 3 September at Lågskär in the Finnish Baltic. In Ireland, records have been mostly in the southern counties of Cork and Wexford (*Birds in Ireland*). A large majority are first-winter birds but a few adults have also been detected (*BWP*).

Around 6% of Red-breasted Flycatcher records in Britain are in spring (Fraser *et al* 2000). The passage period spans mid-April to late June, with a peak in the third week of May. Spring migrants appear mainly in Shetland and along the east coast of Britain; in Ireland and the west, records are very much rarer in spring than in autumn.

It is likely that most birds reach northwest Europe either by reversed migration (*eg* Nisbet 1962), or during a prolonged phase of post-juvenile exploration (Phillips 2000). Possibly, however, some are taking a deliberate heading towards southwestern wintering grounds that have yet to be identified; the sprinkling of autumn adults in Britain & Ireland may support this idea (Radford 1968), although an adult male ringed on Shetland on 6 September 1997 was trapped again in Norway 13 days later, suggesting that it had reoriented towards the east. The northeasterly distribution of spring records suggests overshooting from the east, rather than a return of winterers from the south or southwest.

John H Marchant

Crested Tit

Parus cristatus

The Crested Tit is a sedentary bird throughout its breeding range, which extends from Iberia and the Balkans north to Scotland, southern Fennoscandia and western Russia.

The race *scoticus* occurs almost exclusively in and around the Moray Basin catchment in northeast Scotland, where it is found mostly in native pinewoods, and Scots Pine plantations, with a tall heather understorey (Summers 2000, Summers & Canham 2001). By contrast, the species is widespread on the near Continent and inhabits a wider range of woodland types. The nominate race *cristatus* occupies the north of the range from Norway to the Urals, and south to Romania, and *mitratus* is found in western Europe between Spain, Denmark, eastern Germany and Serbia; four further races have been described (*BWP*).

The life-history of Crested Tit is geared towards high survival rates and low breeding productivity, in contrast to its congeners (Möckel 1992). Territories can be as large as 15.1 ha in Scotland, although with some overlap with neighbouring pairs (Summers 1998). Once fledged, juveniles disperse rapidly; by the second half of August, none of the first-year birds located in a 113 ha study area in Belgium had been hatched locally and, since none were seen nearby, dispersal distances might have been considerable (Lens & Wauters 1996). Between September and January, however, both adults and first-winters are firmly territorial, typically in groups of two to six birds that include the breeding pair and a small number of unrelated young; overwinter mortality in Belgian study sites is less than 8% (Lens & Dhondt 1992). Changes of territory boundaries or ownership may occur in January, in preparation for the breeding season, but most adults occupy the same territories all year. Outside the periods of post-fledging dispersal and spring territoriality, therefore, Crested Tits are extremely sedentary (Lens & Wauters 1996).

The normal sedentary behaviour and high winter survival may be disrupted by environmental disturbance, however. In eastern Germany, Möckel (1992) found that natal site-fidelity became rarer and adult mortality higher as spruce forests became degraded by airborne pollution. A severe storm in January 1990, that uprooted a quarter of all trees in the study area, displaced the Belgian birds by up to 5.5 km; they did not return to their original winter territories, which in many cases were already occupied by other birds (Lens & Dhondt 1992).

A few British observations indicate that birds occasionally venture well outside the breeding range. The Dee Valley, separated from the core of the Scottish range by the mainly treeless Cairngorm Mountains, was visited in 1950 and occupied sporadically in the 1970s and 1990s; also, there are old records for Lanark and Angus, and sightings in Stirling and Perth from the 1980s (*Birds in Scotland*, R W Summers pers comm). In England, the nominate race has been recorded on up to 10 occasions, at sites west to Devon and north to Yorkshire, but not since the 1870s; also, there is a record of *mitratus* on the Isle of Wight sometime before 1844 (*Handbook*). At least four of these old records were in winter. The lack of recent records strongly suggests that visits from continental birds have effectively ceased and that *scoticus* is firmly isolated.

The winter population size in Scotland is estimated to be 5,600–7,900 birds (Summers *et al* 1999). Ringing results for Crested Tit, demonstrating the large home ranges and year-round residency, have already helped to identify measures that are likely to aid its conservation.

John H Marchant

Eurasian Golden Oriole (Golden Oriole)

Oriolus oriolus

The Golden Oriole maintains a small breeding population in East Anglia and occurs widely in Britain & Ireland as a migrant, especially in spring.

The breeding range extends north from Morocco to eastern England and southern Norway, and eastward to Mongolia and the Himalayas (*BWP*, *European Atlas*). Breeding densities are low at the northwestern fringes in England, Norway, Denmark and Sweden. In winter, the more widespread nominate race shifts completely to tropical and southern Africa, from the Congo Basin and Tanzania south to the Cape, while *kundoo* from the southeastern part of the range is a partial migrant, with some birds reaching southern India (*BWP*).

Iberian and northwest African breeders may migrate west of south to reach wintering grounds in West Africa that are yet to be discovered. Autumn departure from other parts of Europe is generally southeasterly, crossing the Mediterranean from between Italy and Turkey to enter Africa via the northeast; main arrivals in East Africa are in October (*BWP*). Golden Orioles are relatively late migrants in spring, not arriving on the breeding grounds until trees are in leaf, and not reaching their northernmost breeding areas until June. In Kenya, the peak passage is in early April. Many birds perform a loop migration, moving north into Europe through Iberia or Italy and well to the west of their route into Africa (*BWP*). Occasional birds appear on the Cape Verde Islands in spring, but never in autumn (Feige 1986).

The species has long been a sporadic breeder in southeast England, for example in Sweet Chestnut coppice in Essex and Kent (Dagley 1994),

and has nested as far north as Fife (*Birds in Scotland*). In the mid-1960s, however, it established a breeding outpost in the Suffolk and Norfolk Fens; since the early 1980s, about 20–35 pairs have bred in this area in peak years (Milwright 1998). The Fenland population is largely confined to stands of hybrid Black Poplar, although many other woodland types, including conifers, are used elsewhere in Europe. Just two Fenland nests have been found in other species of tree but in each case the birds used poplars nearby for feeding (J Allsop & the Golden Oriole Group pers comm).

The earliest arrival in Fenland was 1 May; mean arrival dates are 14 May for males and 21 May for females (Milwright 1998). The mean fledging date is 3 July, but young from replacement clutches may still be in the nest in late July. The breeding areas are usually deserted by mid-August, the latest date on record being 30 August (Dagley 1994).

Golden Oriole is surprisingly rare in Britain & Ireland away from the breeding areas in autumn. Some are seen each year between late July and early November but with no peak timing during this period (Dymond *et al* 1989). Most are seen on the English south coast but others north to southern Ireland and the Western and Northern Isles of Scotland. Two Norfolk-ringed pulli recovered in their first autumn, on 10 and 30 August, were both found near the Suffolk coast, suggesting an easterly or southeasterly departure. In 1998, all four British records after mid-August were in Shetland (Fraser *et al* 2000). The dates and locations of autumn passage therefore suggest that British breeders mostly slip away unseen during August, and that later migrants are highly likely to be of continental origin.

In remarkable contrast to its autumn status in Britain & Ireland, Golden Oriole is regularly recorded away from its breeding areas in spring, mainly on the Isles of Scilly, in Kent and in Shetland, but also (as in autumn) at localities throughout Britain and southern Ireland. Some have occurred as early as mid-March, while records in early July also seem to relate to the spring peak that occurs from mid-May to early June (Dymond *et al* 1989). Of about 60 Irish records, all but five were spring sightings, mostly in May (*Birds in Ireland*). Spring sightings of migrants include some British breeding birds; a bird trapped at Gibraltar Point in Lincolnshire on 24 May 1986 was found breeding in Cambridgeshire in 1995 and 1996 (Clark *et al* 2000) and sexed as a male. Another spring

male, at Dungeness on 4 May 1984, had been ringed there, and identified as an adult female, on 14 July 1978. Since spring records may outnumber known British breeders, however, and occur in numbers well north and west of the breeding range, it is clear that most are from continental populations.

Breeding site-fidelity and similar longevity to the Gibraltar Point bird was shown by a ringed male that occupied the same territory in seven summers and was at least 11 years old when last seen (Milwright 1998). Further ringing studies may help to define the migration routes and dispersal patterns of British breeders and the breeding origins of spring and autumn migrants.

John H Marchant

Red-backed Shrike
Lanius collurio

The formerly widespread British breeding population of Red-backed Shrikes is now extinct, although less-than-annual breeding still occurs, and the species is now seen in Britain & Ireland mainly as a spring or autumn migrant.

The species has a wide breeding range across Europe and western Siberia, from northernmost Portugal, Israel and the Caucasus north to southern Fennoscandia and east to the upper Ob River (*BWP*). In the northern winter, the population shifts to a relatively small area of southern Africa, centred on Botswana and the Kalahari Basin, where it is one of the commonest Palearctic migrants, reaching highest densities in semi-arid Acacia savannas (Bruderer & Bruderer 1993). The migration routes are remarkable in that birds from all areas, including northern Iberia, concentrate around the eastern end of the Mediterranean in both spring and autumn, Iberian birds returning in spring via the Pyrenees (*BWP*, Pilastro *et al* 1998b).

Departure from the breeding grounds occurs from late July to September (*BWP*). Having rounded the eastern Mediterranean, birds pass through Egypt mostly between mid-August and early November to reach the southern African wintering grounds from late October onwards. Herremans (1997) reports that females winter in, on average, denser and taller bush than males, which are more often in more exposed, shrubbier Acacia. A high return rate of 23% to the final wintering destination suggests that occupation of the winter quarters is not opportunistic and therefore that Red-backed Shrikes may be rather vulnerable to habitat change or drought in southern Africa (Herremans *et al* 1995). Northward movement begins in late March (*BWP*). A more easterly route is taken than in autumn, through Kenya to Arabia, largely avoiding both Egypt and Sudan. Breeding grounds are reoccupied mainly in May.

Around 1850, the species bred widely in England and Wales, north to Cumbria and Yorkshire, but a progressive southward and then eastward contraction of range led to their extinction in about 1990 (*1968–72 Atlas*, Bibby 1973, *European Atlas*). During the final stages of this decline, sporadic breeding began in Scotland in 1977, possibly by birds from Norway where, in contrast to the rest of Europe, there has been some increase and spread in recent decades (*Birds in Scotland*, Tucker & Heath 1994).

An average of 246 migrant Red-backed Shrikes were seen in Britain annually during 1986–98, with highest numbers in years of occasional spring influxes (Fraser *et al* 2000). In Ireland, migrants are almost annual in autumn, but rare in spring (*Birds in Ireland*). First arrivals in autumn are sometimes in late July but more regularly in early August; passage peaks in late August or September (*R & F*). November sightings are occasional. It could be that birds arriving in early autumn are engaged in premigratory dispersal, and later ones in reversed migration from further afield. Spring numbers exceed those in autumn at Fair Isle but are progressively fewer at

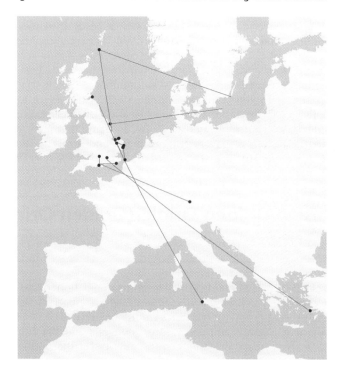

Fig 1. All 20 recoveries of Red-backed Shrikes involving Britain & Ireland.

more southerly and westerly observatories; the pattern suggests overshooting from the northwest of the range (*R & F*). The spring peak is in late May but there are records for April and through June to early July.

Ring-recoveries from the 1950s and 1960s link the previous English population with localities east to Kos in the Aegean Sea, where a pullus from Surrey was found on 25 September of its first year (Fig 1). More recently, two birds ringed as August juveniles in the Swedish and Danish Baltic have been recovered, at Flamborough Head on 22 May and at Fair Isle on 16 June. An adult male at Spurn Point on 9 June 1992 was on Fair Isle six days later.

In the absence of African recoveries, we do not know whether shrikes from Britain occupied a particular part of the winter range, or were distributed more widely. It is possible that factors operating in winter have contributed to their demise, although it is believed that the loss of summer habitat is sufficient to explain the declines in western Europe.

John H Marchant

Great Grey Shrike

Lanius excubitor

The *Winter Atlas* treated Great Grey Shrike as a regular winter visitor to Britain & Ireland and estimated its population during 1981–84 to be more than 150 individuals. Since then, however, numbers have declined; for 1986–92, Fraser & Ryan (1995) suggest a winter maximum of 75 birds.

The world range extends from central France and Norway eastward across Eurasia to the Bering Sea, and across Alaska and northern Canada to Labrador. There is a southward shift in winter, with migrants reaching western and central Europe and similar latitudes across Asia and North America. Some winter within the southern half of the breeding grounds, however, north to southern Scandinavia and the Baltic States (*BWP*). The southern group of races, breeding in Europe in Iberia and southern France and more widely across Africa and southern Asia, have recently been assigned to a separate species (Isenmann & Bouchet 1993) and are now called Southern Grey Shrikes *Lanius meridionalis*; these occur in Britain & Ireland only as rare vagrants (Clement 1995). Winter-visiting nominate *excubitor* from northern Europe apparently stop short of the range of *meridionalis* in southern France and Spain (*BWP*). In Ireland, Great Grey Shrikes are much less than annual, and most individuals have stayed for only a few days (*Birds in Ireland*).

Most Fennoscandian birds that leave the breeding areas winter in central and west-central Europe, but some Norwegian birds head towards Britain (Olsson 1981). Ring-recoveries link Britain with Norway, Denmark, the German Bight and Belgium. Autumn arrival in Britain begins in late September and peaks in October (Fraser *et al* 2000). Temporary territories may be established at the coast for a few days, before birds head off inland or resume their migration. One at Spurn on 8 October had reached the Lincolnshire Fens four weeks later, and another ringed on the Isle of May on 3 October was in Lanarkshire in mid-December. Numbers remain about stable from November onward, and fall off as birds return northward during April (Fraser & Ryan 1995). Occasional late migrants or birds attempting to oversummer may be noted during May–July.

Winter residents in Britain set up long-term territories in well-scattered traditional sites that may be occupied for many years. Winter site-fidelity has been documented in Europe (Boyd 1957, Olsson 1981) and North America (Rimmer & Darmstadt 1996). One ringed in Staffordshire in December 1971 was found dead in the same area a year later. There is also some ringing evidence, however, that individuals may winter progressively closer to the breeding grounds as they get older (*BWP*). Regular wintering sites are distributed from the north of Scotland to the south of England, with the highest density in Hampshire and Devon (Fraser & Ryan 1995). These authors classified British & Irish records during the six winters 1986–92 as winter residents (mean 37 birds per winter), autumn migrants (52), winter wanderers, seen for only a few days in the winter period (26), or spring migrants (13). The destination of autumn migrants is presumed to be France, or possibly northern Spain. It is not known whether spring passage birds include any that wintered further south than Britain.

The size of each autumn influx is variable; despite a general trend of decrease during the 1990s, passage numbers in 1998 were the highest on record, but few of these birds remained to winter (Fraser *et al* 2000). Migrant numbers in Sweden, which also fluctuate widely, are apparently highest when the abundance of small rodents promotes successful breeding (Olsson 1981).

Long-term changes in British wintering numbers appear to match the trends in breeding numbers in Finland and Sweden; wintering numbers in Finland have fluctuated without any clear trend since the 1950s (Hildén & Hildén 1996). Since lowland heathland is strongly favoured for winter territories, it is possible that the loss and fragmentation of this habitat that has occurred (Evans *et al* 1994), or increased disturbance, may also be implicated in the decline of wintering in Britain.

John H Marchant

Common Rosefinch

Carpodacus erythrinus

The Common Rosefinch has remarkable migrations that take it from southern Asia, where several more-sedentary members of its genus spend the whole year, to breeding grounds as distant as the far northwest and northeast of Eurasia.

The breeding range expanded north and west in eastern Europe during the 20th century, reaching Norway, Denmark and the Alps, and sporadic breeding has occurred in Britain since at least 1982 (Wallace 1999). From Finland and the Alps, the range occupies similar latitudes east to Kamchatka and northeast China, and there are more southerly races in mountainous areas between Turkey and the Caucasus and southwest China; the winter range extends from Pakistan and India narrowly across Southeast Asia to the coast of southeast China (*BWP*).

The species is noted for its rapid migrations that occur by day as well as by night (Bozhko 1980). Post-breeding departure occurs between late July and September, adults leaving before the juveniles (*BWP*). From Europe, most birds fly east as far as the northern Caspian Sea, then southeast across the southern Asian deserts, to reach Pakistan and India during August–October. In spring, return movements begin in April and are conspicuous morning and evening across the Kyzylkum Desert in the

first three weeks of May (*BWP*). From this region, migrants may reach western Europe in as little as 10–15 days (Wallace 1999).

The pattern of occurrence in Britain & Ireland has undergone great change since the first known record in 1869; from being a rare vagrant, mostly in autumn on Fair Isle, records have become much more widespread and, especially in spring, much more numerous (Wallace 1999, Fraser *et al* 2000). Breeding was proven at six widespread localities in Britain during 1982–92, including Flamborough Head, where up to four pairs were present in 1992.

More than 60% of records are still in the Northern Isles (Fraser *et al* 2000) but, at both migration seasons, sightings have been made in most counties except those in central England, east Wales and central Ireland (Wallace 1999). Autumn records occur from early August to the beginning of November, with a peak in mid-September, and those in spring begin at the end of April and peak at the end of May (Dymond *et al* 1989). Breeding activity has been noted in Britain from 25 May to about 3 August (Wallace 1999), sometimes by brown-plumaged immature males which are generally much more common than red (older) males in Britain & Ireland. There are also a few winter sightings.

In 1993–96, spring occurrences outnumbered autumn ones for the first time (Wallace 1999).

Two same-autumn ring-recoveries of juvenile birds indicate headings at that season, but neither may be typical: one ringed in Rogaland, Norway on 29 August was caught at North Ronaldsay on 6 September, and another ringed on Fair Isle on 18 September was found on the Faeroes on 2 October. In spring, one on the Isle of May on 31 May was in Orkney eight days later, and one on North Ronaldsay on 6 June had been ringed on Helgoland as an adult female the previous 17 July.

The history of the Common Rosefinch illustrates, over the course of a few decades, many stages of the progression a species may show from occasional autumn vagrancy through regular spring and autumn occurrence to breeding colonization. If it eventually succeeds in establishing a breeding population in Britain & Ireland, greater knowledge of the species' dispersal patterns and migration routes, and of the pressures it experiences outside the breeding season, will benefit its conservation.

John H Marchant

Lapland Longspur (Lapland Bunting)
Calcarius lapponicus

The Lapland Bunting is one of the most abundant and widespread of arctic passerines. It nests, in five poorly differentiated races, from southern Norway across Siberia to the Bering Sea and from Alaska east across Canada to west and southeast Greenland (*BWP*). None are known to nest in northeast Greenland, Iceland or Svalbard. Eurasian birds belong to the nominate race, while the slightly larger and heavier-billed *subcalcaratus* occupies Greenland and most of the Canadian range. Wintering birds are found in northwest France, in Denmark and around the North Sea to southeast Scotland, across inland Eurasia from Hungary to China, and across North America from Pacific USA to Newfoundland (*BWP*).

Wintering is regular in Britain & Ireland. Between 200 and 500 birds are normally present, mostly in the coastal fringe of eastern Britain between Lothian and Kent, but many more in some years (*Winter Atlas*). Typical wintering habitat is saltmarsh or coastal fields with rough grassland or stubble but a few birds occur in similar country well inland. In Ireland, wintering groups have been noted in the south and southeast, mostly since the *Winter Atlas* of 1981–84 (*Birds in Ireland*). Passage migrants also occur in both spring and autumn. Breeding was recorded in the Scottish Highlands during 1977–80, with possibly 16 pairs in the first year and 11 pairs proved breeding in 1979 (Cumming 1979, Sharrock *et al* 1983), but no permanent colonization occurred.

Although *subcalcaratus* is not listed for Britain (BOU 1992), there is strong evidence that Lapland Buntings arrive in both Britain and Ireland from the west, presumably from Canada or Greenland, as well as from Scandinavia (Williamson & Davis 1956, *BWP*). The main wintering grounds of Nearctic birds are in North America, however, and most Scandinavian birds winter in southeast Europe. After moult in July–August, birds leave Greenland between mid-August and the end of September (*BWP*). A small passage is noted in Iceland, mainly from mid-

September to mid-October. Arrivals in Scotland and northwest Ireland, beginning in late August and peaking in the second half of September, may include many of these western birds. A regular passage on Scilly between mid-September and mid-November is probably of birds bound for wintering grounds in Brittany, where arrivals are earlier than those of presumably eastern origin in northeast France (*BWP*).

Arrivals on the east coast of Britain begin in the second week of September and, like those in Ireland, apparently include both passage migrants and wintering birds. There are no international ring-recoveries involving Britain & Ireland but recoveries, for example between Sweden and Belgium, link the wintering population of the southern North Sea with Scandinavia. An exceptional wintering flock of about 500 in Lincolnshire in 1986/87 contained at least two females ringed at the same site the previous winter, and another that was recaptured there in October 1988; wing lengths of these birds fitted the Norwegian population rather than *subcalcaratus* (A G Ball pers comm).

Numbers at the coast decrease during the winter and most winterers have departed by the end of March. During April and May, occasional individuals, perhaps including passage birds from continental wintering grounds, have been recorded at widely distributed, mainly coastal locations throughout Britain & Ireland. Arrivals on the breeding grounds begin with males, mostly in mid-May; females arrive a week or more later, depending on the state of thaw (Fox *et al* 1987).

Further ringing studies would help to clarify the distribution and patterns of occurrence in Britain & Ireland of birds of Nearctic and Eurasian origin, and to identify the winter destinations of coastal passage migrants.

John H Marchant

Cirl Bunting
Emberiza cirlus

The Cirl Bunting is not noted as a migrant in a British & Irish context but is not entirely a sedentary species. Ringing studies are proving valuable in addressing its conservation needs in southern England.

The species is endemic to the West Palearctic, with a range that covers most of Europe southwest of a line from southern England to Bulgaria, north and west Turkey, and North Africa between Morocco and Tunisia. In England & Wales, its range is restricted to warmer, drier and sunnier areas, and has contracted very markedly since the 1960s as a result largely of agricultural intensification (Wotton *et al* 2000). Breeding was formerly widespread in Wales, the south Midlands, and in south-coast counties from Cornwall to Kent, but is now almost entirely confined to a coastal strip of South Devon; the British population fell as low as 118 pairs in 1989, with 114 pairs in Devon, but has since recovered to 453 territories in Devon alone (Evans 1992, Wotton *et al* 2000). Breeding in the core areas is mostly on farmland with small fields and well supplied with trees and bushes. On the Continent, a wider range of bushy and scrubby habitats is used.

Throughout the range, the distribution changes little between the breeding season and winter (*BWP*). Most populations appear to be sedentary, but there is altitudinal movement in some areas as well as short-distance wandering and some longer, more directed movement. Ringing studies in continental Europe have provided a number of long-distance recoveries, mainly of birds moving south or west for the winter, of which the longest has been 725 km from Belgium to southwest France (*Der Zug*, *BWP*). Migrants are observed at Gibraltar and at the Col de Bretolet in Switzerland, and vagrants have occurred in the Canary Islands, Malta and Egypt (*BWP*).

The nesting season is long and may continue into September. After breeding, small flocks form and may visit habitats that are more exposed than those used for breeding. Observations outside the British breeding range or otherwise suggestive of long-distance movement are very rare. There are old records from as far north as Argyll, but very few in Scotland as a whole. Most remarkably, a bird trapped at the Isle of May on 11 June 1976, the sixth recorded on the island, had been ringed as a juvenile the previous July near Beachy Head in Sussex (*Birds in Scotland*). There are no Irish records (*Birds in Ireland*).

Weedy stubble fields are of particular value to wintering birds in Devon, with birds rarely venturing to forage more than 30 m from the hedgerow (Evans & Smith 1994). Colour-ringing studies in Devon have found that, in general, birds winter within a few kilometres of their breeding sites (Smith *et al* 1992b). Provision of extra foraging habitat close to the breeding areas, for example through the Countryside Stewardship Scheme, has been an effective conservation tool (Ovenden *et al* 1998, Wotton *et al* 2000, Peach *et al* 2001).

The ongoing threats to the UK population require that conservation-oriented research should continue. Further ringing studies may help to assess dispersal patterns and the possibilities for recolonization of areas from which the range has withdrawn in recent decades. They may also establish whether the English population has become isolated from that on the near Continent, where numbers have not declined (Tucker & Heath 1994).

John H Marchant

7 The future of migration studies for bird conservation science

Chris Wernham & Stephen Baillie

How can we conserve the populations of warblers that breed in Britain & Ireland if we do not know what threats await on their wintering grounds south of the Sahara or on their migration routes and fattening areas? How can we predict the effects of the loss and fragmentation of woodland within Britain & Ireland on their breeding populations if we do not know how far they usually disperse? Equally, how can we fulfil our international responsibilities to help conserve the large numbers of waterfowl, waders, thrushes and finches that spend the winter months, or passage periods, in Britain & Ireland, if we do not know which sites support the largest numbers and how and why they move about during their stay within our islands?

In the species accounts (Chapter 6), the expert authors have put forward their ideas about the conservation threats to each species and about the gaps in our current knowledge of their movements. Some have suggested ways in which the extra information required to conserve a species effectively might be obtained. In this, the final chapter, we attempt a synthesis of research needs concerning the movements of the birds of Britain & Ireland. We begin with a brief summary of why knowledge of movements is fundamental for bird conservation. We also provide a short account of the ways in which methods of studying bird movements are changing. The main part of the chapter consists of an overview of the current state of knowledge of different areas of research into movements across groups of species, finishing with our personal assessment of future research priorities.

Why does conservation require knowledge of bird movements?

Long-distance migrants, such as Swallows, Roseate Terns and many warblers that winter south of the Sahara, by definition have living requirements for parts of the year in areas that may be separated by thousands of kilometres. Threats to such species can occur at any stage of the annual cycle in differing locations: on the breeding grounds, while actually migrating, at stopover or 'fattening' sites or in the wintering areas. In order to conserve these species effectively, and to identify threats if a population appears to be declining, it is essential to know which geographical areas are used during the year, and when. On a more local scale within Britain & Ireland, some 'resident' or partially migrant species may make seasonal movements within our islands. For example, Twite and Meadow Pipits are known to make altitudinal movements away from their upland breeding areas to the lowlands (see the species accounts in Chapter 6) and there may be a wider tendency

for birds breeding in northern Britain and in upland areas to move south or west or to lower altitudes to find milder winter conditions (Chapter 5). Other species, such as Redwings and Fieldfares or seed-eating finches and buntings, may need to move about within the British & Irish landscape during the winter months in search of food. Such movements may be less clear-cut than those of the trans-Saharan migrants that vacate our countryside completely in winter but they can nevertheless have important implications for species conservation. We return to these issues in more detail later in the chapter.

When assessing the quality of the information on movements that is available for British & Irish birds, and what else needs to be collected, it is important to consider some of the mechanisms by which the existing knowledge is translated into practical conservation measures at the British, Irish, European and international scales. At the international scale, it has been recognized that migrating animals cross political boundaries; these arbitrary divisions have no meaning for them, but may have a profound impact on the health of their populations because of the large differences between countries in attitudes towards conservation. Therefore, the degree of protection afforded to sites and habitats that are equally essential for migratory birds throughout their annual cycles may vary greatly between countries.

International agreements

A small number of intergovernmental treaties are now in force that concern the conservation of migratory birds. The *Convention on Wetlands of International Importance especially as Waterfowl Habitat (1971)*, better known as the Ramsar Convention after the Iranian city where it was signed, now has more than 120 Contracting Parties (see www.ramsar.org). Signing obliges each country to designate at least one wetland site for inclusion on the Ramsar List, and also that the country makes 'wise use' of all the wetlands within its territory, establishes nature reserves in wetlands and provides staff training in wetland research, management and wardening. All Contracting Parties are obliged to consult with others when considering cross-border wetland areas, 'shared' water systems or 'shared' migratory species. The Convention has so far led to the designation of more than a thousand Wetlands of International Importance around the world.

A treaty with a wider remit for migratory species, the *Convention on the Conservation of Migratory Species of Wild Animals (1983)*, also known as the CMS or Bonn Convention, now has more than 70 signatories (see www.wcmc.org.uk/cms). The Parties agree to work together to conserve migratory species and their habitats by providing strict protection for

85 endangered species listed in Appendix 1 of the Convention (*eg* Red-breasted Goose, White-headed Duck and Spotted Eagle), making agreements for the conservation and management of other migratory species listed in Appendix 2 (*eg* all diver species, all migratory ducks, Corn Crake and Little Tern) and by undertaking cooperative research. The largest agreement developed under the Bonn Convention so far, and the most important one for migratory birds, is the *African-Eurasian Migratory Waterbird Agreement (1999)*, also known as AEWA (see www.unep-wcmc.org/AEWA). The AEWA covers 172 species of bird that are dependent on wetland habitats for at least part of their annual cycle, including pelicans, storks, flamingos, ducks, waders, terns, gulls and geese, and has been signed by 117 countries and the European Union. The Parties agree to engage in a wide range of conservation activities for wetland species (detailed in a comprehensive action plan), including practical species and habitat conservation and research, and the monitoring of populations. The action plan requires all countries to identify and conserve sites of national or international importance for waterbirds and demands specific research and monitoring actions, including the determination of migration routes and sites used through the year by participation in coordinated ringing programmes.

Legislation in Europe and site-based conservation in Britain & Ireland
As well as being signatories to the above international conventions and agreements, the UK and Ireland have obligations to protect bird populations under the 1979 European Union *Directive on the Conservation of Wild Birds (EC/79/409)*, often referred to as the 'Birds Directive' (see the useful site for information about nature conservation legislation at www.ecnc.nl/doc/europe/legislat/conventi.html). One of the main provisions of this legislation is the establishment of a European network of protected areas, known as Special Protection Areas (or SPAs) for birds. These, together with equivalent sites known as Special Areas for Conservation (SACs) created under the later 'Habitats Directive', form what is known as the *Natura 2000* network of protected sites across Europe (see www.europa.eu.int/comm/environment/nature/natura. htm). Various parts of the Birds Directive recognize that further research is needed for the protection, management and 'wise use' of bird populations and that migratory species have specific information needs (similar requirements to those defined earlier in the Ramsar and Bonn Conventions). The Directive also calls for particular information to be gathered on the movements (and survival rates) of quarry species

in order that their populations may be managed sustainably. Comprehensive recommendations for a UK network of protected areas for birds under the Birds Directive were made in 1990 (Stroud *et al* 1990, Pritchard *et al* 1992). A similar review has been carried out in Ireland (Way *et al* 1993). After further development work, detailed guidelines for selecting sites for SPAs in the UK were published (JNCC 1999) and a final set of terrestrial SPAs has recently been agreed (Stroud *et al* 2001, see www.jncc.gov.uk/UKSPA). This set of protected sites does not include those for bird species wholly reliant on the offshore environment whilst in UK waters, but these will be considered in a separate forthcoming JNCC review of information to designate marine SPAs (J B Reid pers comm).

The criteria used to select particular sites to be protected, whether as SPAs (*eg* JNCC 1999), Ramsar sites or some other designation, show instantly how important knowledge of the movements of individual species and populations is to allow such sites to be identified and, hence, protected through time. Often, sites are selected that are regularly used by 1% of a national population at some time during the year, or by 1% of a particular 'biogeographical population', or that regularly support 20,000 or more individuals of a given species. This means that, even at the most basic level, it is important to know the origins of populations using any given site, and how many individuals pass through a site during, for example, the autumn passage season: in most cases we still do not know this. The current designations are based largely on count data but the system would benefit from more detailed information on 'turnover' (see later). Most current selection criteria include some consideration of variation in the use of sites between years. They may allow inclusion of sites that support a significant proportion of a given population only once a decade, for example, during severe weather (see later). This, of course, requires that the seasonal movements of a population, and variations in these through time, are understood in some detail.

Wider-countryside conservation and agri-environment schemes
Of course, the conservation of birds cannot rely entirely on the designation of protected areas because many species are widely dispersed rather than concentrated at particular sites, even when they are migrating. The new SPA Review for the UK lists many species for which a network of protected sites will not be an effective conservation measure because they do not occur in sufficiently large concentrations. These include many common migratory passerines (such as Fieldfare, Swallow and Willow Warbler) and certain species whose numbers at particular sites are difficult to establish with any degree of confidence (such as Jack Snipe, Water Rail and Woodcock). It is now widely recognized that the creation of networks of protected sites must be carried out alongside conservation measures in the 'wider countryside'. For some species, particular measures are described in specific UK Biodiversity Action Plans (BAPs), which have been formulated in response to the signing of the *Convention of Biological Diversity* at the 'Earth Summit' in Rio de Janeiro in 1992 (see www.ukbap.org.uk/aboutBAP.htm). Several of these UK Plans, such as those for some of the declining farmland species (*eg* Turtle Dove, Tree Sparrow, Linnet, Reed Bunting and Corn Bunting), identify particular habitat management measures, the success of which would benefit greatly from a knowledge of the seasonal movements of the species concerned. For example, we need to know more about their winter ranging behaviour in order to take remedial action at a scale appropriate to conserving their populations.

A number of schemes currently operating in the UK are designed to benefit biodiversity in general, such as various agri-environmental schemes that offer payments to farmers for managing their land in a wildlife-friendly manner. These include the Environmentally Sensitive Areas (ESA) Scheme throughout the UK (see www.defra.gov.uk/erdp/ schemes/landbased/esas/esasindex.htm), Tir Gofal in Wales (www. cpat.org.uk/services/tirgofal/tirgofal.htm), Countryside Stewardship in England (www.defra.gov.uk/erdp/schemes/landbased/ccs/ccsindex.htm) and Rural Stewardship in Scotland (www.scotland.gov.uk/library3/

agri/rss-00.asp). They may benefit whole suites of birds if they are implemented effectively.

To obtain the maximum benefit from the types of actions that are encouraged by such schemes, a knowledge of bird movements on a local scale is extremely important. For example, one of the options under Rural Stewardship is to leave some areas of crops, such as legumes, brassicas or linseed, unharvested or partially harvested over the winter to provide cover and food for birds, potentially benefiting declining species such as the Skylark and several other farmland seed-eating species. The most appropriate scale to carry out such action depends on the normal ranging behaviour of such species during the winter months. It is also important to know the breeding origins of the birds that are in the area, and that will therefore benefit from the increased winter food availability.

We will return later to specific examples of the types of information on movements that are required for conserving birds effectively. More examples, particularly in relation to information from bird ringing, can be found in a number of review articles (eg Baillie 1995, 2001, Boobyer 1999, Davidson et al 1999, Spina 1999).

New developments in study methods

The immense value of bird ringing in studies of migration and other movements is demonstrated throughout this book. Chapter 1 explains that the traditional method of applying a single metal ring with a unique number and return address is only one means among many for studying bird movements. As the topic-based sections that follow in the current chapter will demonstrate, there is still a great deal that remains to be learnt about the movements of British and Irish bird populations even after almost a century of ringing, and this will require improvements to the collection of ring-recovery data as well as its integration with many other traditional and forward-looking study methods.

Bird ringing, and analytical methods for ring-recovery data

Recoveries of dead ringed birds can provide much information on movement patterns, particularly for larger species with relatively high recovery rates, but the interpretation of recovery patterns is not without difficulties, as already mentioned in Chapters 4 and 5. Variation in the chances of dead ringed birds being found and reported, and in mortality rates, with geographical area complicates the interpretation of recovery patterns and mean that care must be exercised in drawing conclusions from them. Similarly, investigations of changes in movement patterns over time (Chapter 5 and below) must take temporal changes in recovery rates into account. While these problems are not insurmountable when assessing movement patterns qualitatively, as long as any broad biases are taken into consideration (Chapter 4), they become increasingly important when investigating movements in a more quantitative manner (Chapter 5). For example, to determine rigorously the proportions of British & Irish Sandwich Terns that winter along the coast of the different countries in West Africa from recoveries of dead ringed birds it would be necessary to know how the chances of death and recovery vary across that geographical area.

Thus, there is a great need for further studies to allow us to partition variation in recovery rates from true geographical variation in the distributions of birds through the annual cycle. For species where many recoveries occur as a result of specific human-induced causes, such as hunting or accidental capture in fisheries, some quantitative measure of geographical variation in recovery rates might be obtainable from independent information, such as hunting bag or fisheries by-catch statistics. There is much research still required to validate the results from ring-recoveries against such independent data, for example comparing hunting pressures assessed by ringing (eg McCulloch et al 1992) against those from bag statistics, or ring-recovery patterns with the results of orientation studies to investigate departure directions (eg Busse

2000). There is also potential to estimate relative recovery probabilities in different geographical areas based on human spatial distribution (van Noordwijk 1995).

Despite the fact that quantitative information on rates of movement between different locations is important for understanding the population dynamics and evolutionary change of populations, much more attention was placed on developing quantitative approaches to estimating survival rates and other demographic parameters prior to the 1990s (Nichols & Kaiser 1999). Rigorous quantitative techniques now exist for analysing many aspects of animal movement: principal components analysis to estimate principal migration routes (eg Perdeck & Clason 1982), Fourier analysis to model the progression of migration with time (eg Perdeck 1977), clustering techniques to produce objective recovery core areas for population studies (eg Chu et al 1995, Pendleton & Sauer 1995), methods to address stopover durations and the turnover rates of migrants at particular sites (see Kaiser 1999 for a review) and numerous algorithms for estimating rates of movement based on recoveries of dead birds, recaptures or mixed data (see Nichols & Kaiser 1999 for a review). Great potential exists, therefore, to apply and further develop such quantitative methods for use with existing data both at the scale of Britain & Ireland and, more effectively, using data sets from across West Palearctic flyways. Within Britain & Ireland, quantitative approaches to the investigation of movement patterns based on ring-recoveries will benefit greatly from the routine computerization of records for all birds captured, as is now being actively encouraged in the British and Irish Ringing Scheme (Chapter 2).

The synthesis that follows in this chapter demonstrates that even the large numbers of birds of many species that have been ringed since 1909 have not produced sufficient records of dead birds for many important analyses. This is particularly true for smaller species with very low recovery rates. There is also evidence that the recovery rates of some species ringed in Britain & Ireland are falling (eg Baillie & Green 1987, Catchpole et al 1999, Wernham & Peach 1999). While some such decreases may be due to decreased hunting pressures on species that were previously legitimate quarry, 'observer fatigue' is also a possibility. Increased publicity for the value of reporting ringed birds, or freephone numbers to report them (eg US Fish & Wildlife Service 2001), might help to improve recovery rates for some species. More emphasis should also be placed on other means of increasing the chances of subsequently recording a bird once it is first handled. The routine computerization of all live recaptures of ringed birds, and the central collation of resightings of colour-marked individuals, both have the potential to increase markedly the volume and accessibility of the data collected for every bird that is marked. The information so collated could vastly improve our level of knowledge of several of the topics considered below, such as dispersal patterns and rates, and migration strategies, particularly if independent records of capture and resighting effort were kept for individual sites.

Remote-tracking devices

A range of devices now exists that can remotely sense the presence of birds at distances of a few centimetres or kilometres to a global scale. These include VHF radio-tags, passive implantable transponders (PITs), various data-logging devices, and satellite tags. Some introduction to the possibilities for studying bird movements using such techniques is provided in Chapter 1. There are a number of other useful reviews and publications to consult for further detailed information (eg Calvo & Furness 1992, Priede & Swift 1992, Gauthier-Clerc & Le Maho 2001, Kenward 2001, Redfern & Clark 2001). Here we briefly reiterate the main limitations and, thus, the potential of these techniques to increase knowledge of bird movements.

Radio-tracking generally allows the tracking of birds at distances of a maximum of several kilometres at ground level; the exact transmitter range depends on factors such as tag type, battery type, habitat, tracking location and the behaviour of the bird. Tags powered by 3.5V lithium thionyl-chloride batteries weigh 6–100 g, can last from four months to

six years and can have ranges of several kilometres, while those for smaller birds, weighing 0.35–6 g and powered by 1.5V silver oxide batteries, last up to around 12 months and have a range of several hundred metres only (Redfern & Clark 2001). The limited detection range in conventional radio-tracking means that it will continue to be used for intensive local work on bird movements, such as the measurement of home-range size in sedentary species), but is unlikely to find wider use for following long-distance migrations. However, it may have increasing value for certain specialist uses. For example, fixed automatic radio-tracking stations have been used to record the presence of tagged birds as they pass on migration (van Gils et al 2000, Green et al 2002), with a current range of around 1 km (Redfern & Clark 2001). This system could have greater potential if the detection range can be increased by some means, for example for detecting waders tagged on their British & Irish breeding grounds at locations along their flyways to the south.

Conventional radio-tags could also have a role in monitoring the stopover duration or turnover of migrants at given sites, particularly in habitats where other recapture methods present difficulties, if the cost (currently around £100 per tag) could be reduced so that they could be placed on large numbers of individual birds. PIT tags could have similar application. They are very small (0.06–0.8 g) and can be implanted under the skin or attached to feathers or a ring (Gauthier-Clerc & Le Maho 2001). They last a long time because they do not need internal battery power and are 'read' using radiowaves by a remote device. Each tag is relatively inexpensive but each 'reader' costs around £1,000. Their main limitation is the very low detection distance — only a few centimetres for the smaller tags to a maximum of one metre at present. This restricts their use to situations where birds pass very close to the reader antennae, such as at nest sites within a seabird colony (eg Becker & Wendeln 1997, Becker et al 2001).

The remote-sensing systems offering the most immediate advances for migration studies are satellite telemetry and various data logging devices. Whereas radio-tags generally have to be tracked manually and have very restricted range, satellite systems can track birds on migration automatically anywhere in the world. The main limitations are tag size and cost. There are currently two types of tag. Platform terminal transmitters (PTTs) transmit to satellites (eg ARGOS) that then transmit the location information back to a ground station. The smallest tags available currently weigh around 18 g and cost c £1,000–£3,000 each. There are additional charges (running into thousands of pounds per year) for receiving the data. Tags have a battery life of from several weeks to several months, depending on how often they transmit; they can be programmed to transmit at regular intervals and to vary this interval a few times during their battery life. The selection of appropriate transmission intervals is important, and necessitates some prior

knowledge of the progression of migration in order to obtain the maximum data quality. The larger the tag, the longer the battery life, or the greater the transmission power and hence the accuracy of the locations. Solar-powered tags are also available, allowing tags to transmit indefinitely, but they are larger. PTT tags give locations to a maximum accuracy of a few kilometres, and smaller ones (eg 30 g) may give an accuracy no better than several tens of kilometres (eg Britten et al 1999). Alternative global positioning system (GPS) tags are now available, which calculate their locations using satellite transmissions (eg from US NAVISTAR). They are larger (minimum 35 g) and more expensive (minimum c £2,000), but they can be accurate to within 5–10 m (Redfern & Clark 2001). The location information collected must be stored on the tag (so that the tag has to be retrieved to get it) or transmitted to the ground via satellite (which necessitates a heavier tag because of the extra circuitry required). These latter tags probably offer the greatest potential for migration studies to date, if they can be made smaller and less expensive.

Over recent decades, various types of data logger or data storage devices have been developed to measure the activity, physiology and environment of animals (Gauthier-Clerc & Le Maho 2001). Two such archival tags, with potential in migration studies, are based on the premise that it is not necessary to know the instantaneous position of a bird but, rather, that its movements can be derived by back-calculation (see Wilson 2001). The global location sensor (GLS) or geolocator measures and stores data on light intensity at very regular intervals and also contains a highly accurate quartz crystal clock; the current minimum weight is 16 g. A GLS recording every two minutes can function for 3.8 years. Various algorithms can then be used to calculate the latitude of the bird through time but, currently, the errors involved in positional fixes can be 20–150 km (Wilson 2001). Nevertheless, such a tag could be useful for larger species of long-distance migrant. An alternative archival tag, the dead reckoner, records information on speed, heading and height (or depth, for example for diving seabirds); speed can be recorded to an accuracy of 0.25 m/s, heading to within 5° and depth to within 30 cm. The absolute quality of the resulting location information relies on having known start and end points to each trip, however, and the smallest logger currently available weighs 80 g. Their accuracy has currently only been extensively evaluated with penguins making foraging trips in the order of tens of kilometres and returning to the breeding colony (Wilson 2001). The costs of such archival tags are currently high but, as they can measure environment conditions, such as light, salinity, water or air temperature, around birds that are on the move (Wilson et al 1994), the potential to develop their use in migration studies must be large. Any migration projects that use attached or implanted recording or transmitting devices on birds will, of course, also have to consider whether these methods affect the migratory behaviour of individuals (eg Calvo & Furness 1992) and ensure that the highest possible standards of bird welfare are met.

Chemical and biological marker techniques

Analyses of the body tissues of birds, or of signs of other organisms with which they have come into contact, can provide information on the locations that they have visited or the populations to which they belong (see Chapter 1 for an introduction). Studies of the variation shown by genetic markers, allozymes and DNA sequences allow dispersal rates among populations to be quantified (see Parker et al 1998 and Haig 1998 for reviews) and the future development of such techniques may allow the reliable differentiation of races or subpopulations using, for example, a given wintering area. Microsatellite DNA analysis has been used recently to differentiate the British & Irish race of Cormorant (carbo) from continental immigrants (sinensis) and, hence, to determine the proportions of immigrants in newly established inland breeding colonies in the south of England (Winney 1998, Goostrey et al 1998). It has also been used to compare individuals differentiated on the basis of field characteristics (gular pouch shape; Newson 2000). Analyses of certain

characteristics of the blood, which can indicate the rate of fuel use and fasting (*eg* Bairlein & Totzke 1992, Jenni-Eiermann & Jenni 1994), are likely to play an increasing role in research into the strategies used by long-distance migrants for their journeys. Methods for the detailed study of the ecophysiology of bird migration are outside the scope of the short review that we provide here; much further information is reviewed by Berthold (2001). At the other end of the spectrum of movement studies, genetic analyses might be used more widely to look at the degree of non-movement and, hence, to differentiate meta-populations of more sedentary species and the implications of these for their conservation; suitable target species of immediate conservation concern in Britain & Ireland might include some of the declining farmland passerines (*eg* Corn Bunting, House Sparrow and Yellowhammer; see also Lee *et al* 2001).

At a simpler level, analyses of the composition of pollen carried by birds may give clues to their origins or the stopover areas used on migration. For example, the presence of pollen from plants found only in the Mediterranean in the facial feathers of five species of *Sylvia* warbler caught in Denmark on return migration demonstrated that they used the Mediterranean Basin as an important stopover area in spring (Laursen *et al* 1997). Analysis of pollen in the lungs and air sacs of ducks has also been used to provide information on their migrations (Tamisier *et al* 1997).

Some non-invasive techniques based on the chemical composition of certain body tissues, such as feathers, perhaps offer some of the greatest potential in future wide-scale studies of bird migration. Analyses of stable isotopes can be used to provide information on the geographical areas where birds have been feeding, based on the fact that stable isotope 'signatures' within body tissues vary in line with those in local food webs, which in turn often vary because of several biogeographical processes (see Hobson 1999 for a recent review). Hence there is great potential to track the movements of birds between isotopically distinct food webs, if tissues that have an appropriate isotopic turnover rate can be found. For example, keratinous tissues, such as feathers and claws are metabolically inert once they are formed, so that their composition can reflect the locations where they were formed. Other metabolically active tissues, such as blood, may retain signatures for a few days to several weeks, and bone collagen for the lifetime of an individual (reflecting where it was hatched and reared). The ratios of the different stable isotopes in several abundant chemical elements have distributions in nature that vary, to some extent at least, in spatially predictable ways, including hydrogen, carbon, nitrogen, oxygen, sulphur, strontium and lead. For example, carbon isotope (^{13}C) content varies with the proportion of plants with different photosynthetic pathways (C3 *versus* C4 or CAM plants) at the base of the food chain, and hence broadly with latitude and biome (Peterson & Fry 1987, Tieszen & Boutton 1988). In North America, deuterium (^{2}H) content in growing-season rainfall shows a continent-wide pattern, from enriched values in the southeast to depleted values in the northwest (Fig 7.1), and the pattern is reflected in plant material and passed on to other organisms in the food web (Hobson 1999). Strontium (^{87}Sr) isotope content varies in terrestrial systems with rock type; for example, in North America ratios are highest in the Appalachian Mountains and lowest in the northern Midwest (Chamberlain *et al* 1997, see also review by Graustein 1988).

A number of pioneering studies have already demonstrated the great potential of stable isotope analyses in bird migration studies. For example, carbon and nitrogen isotope ratios have been investigated with a view to separating different subpopulations of wintering Lesser Snow Geese in North America based on differing winter diets (Alisauskas & Hobson 1993) and to confirm that two races of Willow Warbler, *trochilus* and *acredula*, winter in different areas of Africa (Chamberlain *et al* 2000). A combination of carbon, hydrogen and strontium ratios have been used to produce distinct 'signatures' for Black-throated Blue Warblers across their breeding range in eastern North America, and to show that individuals wintering in the Caribbean are mostly from the northernmost breeding areas (Chamberlain *et al* 1997). The latter project also demonstrated the added value of using multiple isotopes in such studies. Work on birds using marine habitats has, to date, focused largely on the use of isotopes for dietary studies (Hobson 1999), although there is some indication that studies of movements are also possible for certain species (*eg* for shearwaters, Minami *et al* 1995, Minami & Ogi 1997). Stable isotope analyses may also have an important role to play in work

Fig 7.1 Contour patterns of average deuterium (δD) levels in growing-season rainfall across North America, with the sampling stations shown as filled circles. (*Source*: Hobson 1999, Tracing origins and migration of wildlife using stable isotopes: a review, figure 1, *Oecologia*, volume 120, by permission of Springer-Verlag.)

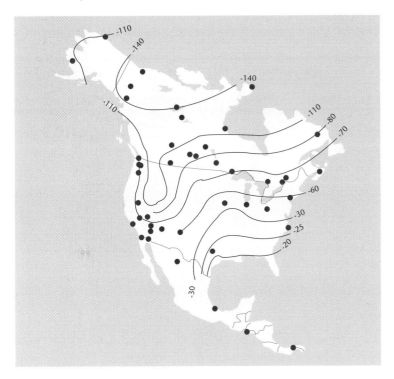

on migration strategies, for example by the use of blood sampling to investigate dietary changes and nutritional stresses during migratory journeys (*eg* Hobson & Clark 1993).

For stable isotope studies of bird migration to be successful, the chosen species must move between isotopically distinct areas or food webs, and a tissue into which isotopes are incorporated at an appropriate stage in the life cycle or annual cycle of the species must be selected for sampling. Much more research will be required to establish base-maps of spatial isotopic variation and to compare this with ratios in tissues grown by birds at known reference locations (*eg* Hobson & Wassenaar 1997, Hobson *et al* 1999). Much further work will also be required to quantify analytical processes and problems that introduce 'noise' into the results (see Hobson 1999 for a discussion of some such problems), including experimental approaches in the laboratory (Gannes *et al* 1997). More collaborative work between ecologists, biochemists and earth scientists will be required if the full potential of these techniques for studying migration is to be realized.

Integration of data at the individual and population levels

Much of the above discussion of future methods focuses on increasing knowledge of movements by studying individual birds, whether ringed, satellite tagged or sampled for their isotopic ratio composition. In contrast, Chapter 1 describes a number of approaches to studying bird movements at the level of populations, of which the breeding origins are often unknown, including the unsystematic observations collated in bird reports and a number of more systematic surveys (such as distribution atlases, Wetland Bird Survey (WeBS) counts, at-sea counts of seabirds and bird observatory census data).

The future improvement of our knowledge of many aspects of the movements of British and Irish birds is likely to require projects that integrate these two broad areas. For example, in order to improve knowledge of the populations of passerines that pass through Britain & Ireland during passage periods and how these have changed over time, projects integrating long-term census data collected at bird observatories

with ring-recovery data to assess breeding origins might be appropriate (*eg* Marchant 2002, see later). Similarly, an improved knowledge of the movements of passage and wintering wildfowl should involve projects that combine analyses of the seasonality of WeBS counts with ringing projects to establish breeding regions. Such an approach has been successfully adopted for goose populations (Madsen *et al* 1999) and has been used to some extent to produce atlases for wildfowl (Scott & Rose 1996) and waders (D A Stroud pers comm) at a flyway scale but much remains to be investigated (below). There is great potential to develop projects that integrate bird ringing and other intensive individual-based studies with wider-scale observational survey work. For example, an effective project to investigate the requirements for the conservation of immigrant thrushes when they are in Britain & Ireland for the winter might involve intensive ringing-recapture or resighting work and the collection of samples for isotopic analysis to assess individual movements and breeding origins, plus extensive survey work to monitor the spatial use of habitats by the overall wintering population and link the latter with the abundance and spatial distribution of food supplies. There are many other topics where such an integrated approach would be highly appropriate, and some are mentioned in the topic-based sections that follow.

Methods used to summarize how much is known about the movements of British & Irish birds

For this chapter, we have attempted to summarize the quality of information on movements that is currently available for our 188 main species, dividing this knowledge specifically into that concerning populations breeding in Britain & Ireland, populations that regularly spend the winter in Britain & Ireland and passage populations from abroad of species that do not regularly winter in Britain & Ireland. In order to do this, we have used information available from the standard analyses of the ring-recovery data that were carried out as part of this project, and information from other sources mentioned in the accounts by their individual authors. Throughout our synthesis, we attempted to classify the degree of knowledge available for separate species and seasonal populations, by topic, into good, moderate or poor categories. The full results of this exercise and the criteria used to classify populations are given in Appendix 6. The topics that we covered are listed in Table 7.1. We did not include those 73 species for which there are minor accounts in this book because, by definition, there is generally less information on the movements of specific populations of these species (due to the lack of ring-recoveries). However, in the topic-based sections that follow later in this chapter, many of the recommendations made for future research apply equally to the latter regularly occurring but rarely ringed species.

British & Irish breeding populations

For the species that breed regularly in Britain & Ireland, we looked first at to what extent our knowledge was sufficient to allocate a migratory status to each species. The degree to which the status could be tested directly with ring-recovery data varied between ecological groupings, being generally higher for seabirds/gulls, waders and wildfowl than for passerines and raptors/owls (Table 7.1). It was possible to allocate a status to all but three species (all passerines: Black Redstart, Firecrest and Skylark). For these three species, and some other breeding species with little ring-recovery information (*eg* Cetti's Warbler, Grasshopper Warbler, Tree Pipit and Wood Warbler), all aspects of their movements would benefit from future intensive studies involving ringing. For the purposes of the analyses that follow, we defined all species found or assumed to be long-distance or short-distance migrants (Appendix 6a) as 'migrant' and all species found or assumed to be sedentary as 'sedentary'.

We then made some assessment of whether the birds that have been ringed and recovered subsequently have been broadly representative of

Table 7.1 Summary of the quality of information available on the movements of bird populations present in Britain & Ireland during the year, based on knowledge from ring-recoveries and other information presented in the species accounts in Chapter 6. The proportions of species have been provided in any cell where a sample of more than two species was available. Entries in pink text show topics and grouping for which the proportion of species with poor knowledge is greater than one-third, and red text greater than two-thirds. Dashes in cells indicate topics not applicable to a given migrant type. See text and Appendix 6 for further explanation of the grading of the level of knowledge for each species and population.

British & Irish breeding populations	Passerines/near-passerines		Raptors/Owls		Seabirds/Gulls		Waders		Wildfowl	
	Migrant[1]	Sedentary	Migrant	Sedentary	Migrant	Sedentary	Migrant	Sedentary	Migrant	Sedentary
Percentage of species assumed (not tested)[2]	61	25	57	27	13	0	35	0	33	11
Ringing distribution (% graded 'poor')	20	23	0	9	0	1 species only	24	no species	67	22
Age of ringing (% with <10% ringed as nestlings)	39	48	0	0	9	1 species only	6	no species	53	56
Age of ringing (% with <10% ringed as fully grown)	5	13	100	73	48	1 species only	29	no species	0	11
Post-juvenile movements (% graded 'poor')	80	68	57	45	39	1 species only	71	no species	87	56
Natal dispersal (% graded 'poor')	34	20	29	27	9	1 species only	35	no species	67	22
Breeding dispersal (% graded 'poor')	43	20	57	45	43	1 species only	53	no species	67	56
Migration routes/timing (% graded 'poor')	10	—	29	—	9	—	41	—	40	—
Wintering areas (% graded 'poor')	51	—	43	—	13	—	41	—	33	—
Migration strategy (% graded 'poor')	66	—	75	—	85	—	75	—	100	—
Summering areas of immatures (% graded 'poor')	2 species only	—	80	—	17	—	71	—	17	—
Sex differences (% graded 'poor')	88	75	57	73	91	1 species only	100	no species	73	67
Age differences (% graded 'poor')	78	43	57	36	26	1 species only	59	no species	53	33
Regional differences (% graded 'poor')	88	68	86	64	43	1 species only	76	no species	93	67
Temporal change (% graded 'poor')	80	50	57	64	17	1 species only	65	no species	73	33

British & Irish wintering populations	Passerines/near-passerines		Raptors/Owls		Seabirds/Gulls		Waders		Wildfowl	
	Immigrant[3]	Resident	Immigrant	Resident	Immigrant	Resident	Immigrant	Resident	Immigrant	Resident
Percentage of species with 'poor knowledge'[4]	23		13		60		5		6	
Ringing distribution (% graded 'poor')	10	17	63	40	17	no species	10	no species	35	33
Migration routes/timing (% graded 'poor')	15	—	50	—	0	—	5	—	23	—
Breeding areas (% graded 'poor')	25	—	25	—	0	—	30	—	12	—
Migration strategy (% graded 'poor')	75	—	100	—	100	—	58	—	75	—
Sex differences (% graded 'poor')	60	—	75	—	83	—	95	—	65	—
Age differences (% graded 'poor')	45	—	75	—	17	—	70	—	65	—
Regional differences (% graded 'poor')	90	—	100	—	67	—	90	—	77	—
Winter movements (% graded 'poor')	15	41	50	80	33	no species	20	no species	31	0
Temporal change (% with no information)	70	100	88	100	83	no species	95	no species	88	100

Passage populations[5]	Passerines	Raptors/Owls	Seabirds/Gulls	Waders	Wildfowl
Existence and origins of passage populations (% graded 'poor')	43	67	84	24	53
Timing and geographical occurrence of passage (% graded 'poor')	51	92	89	29	53

Notes

1. 'Migrant' includes species categorized as either 'long-distance' or 'short-distance migrants';

2. 'Assumed' means that these species were categorized as migrant or sedentary from sources of knowledge other than rigorous tests of ring-recovery data;

3. 'Immigrant' includes species for which winter immigrant populations in Britain & Ireland are thought to exist; species occurring in winter for which immigration into Britain & Ireland is not thought to occur regularly are termed 'resident';

4. Species with poor knowledge are not included in the rest of the table entries for British & Irish wintering populations;

5. Excludes species that do not have regular passage populations from abroad passing through Britain & Ireland.

Fig 7.2 Summary of the degree of representativeness of existing ring-recovery data relating to British & Irish bird populations: (a) geographical distribution of ringing locations of British & Irish breeding birds that were later recovered, (b) age classes at ringing of British & Irish breeding birds that were later recovered, and (c) geographical distribution of ringing locations of birds ringed in Britain & Ireland outside the breeding season for birds later recovered. (See text and Appendix 6 for further explanation.)

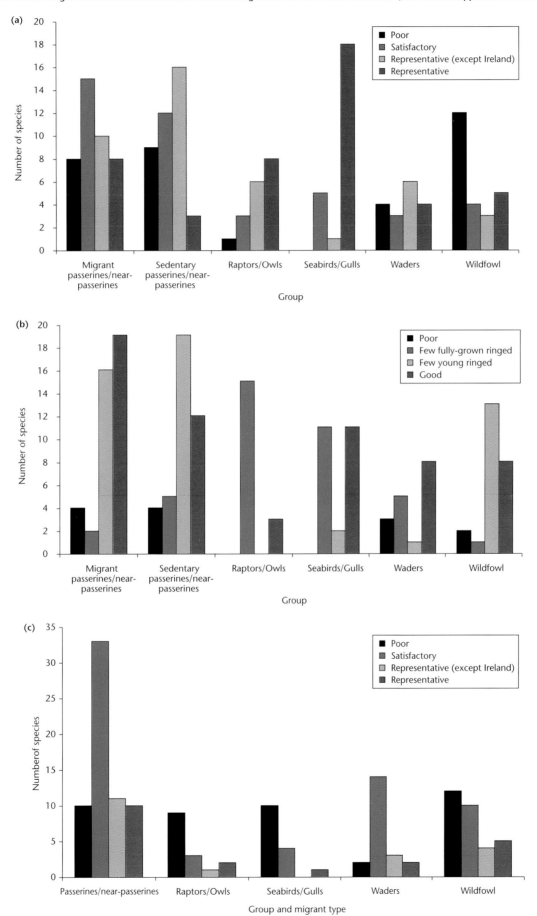

the breeding distribution of the species within Britain & Ireland, by comparison with the *1988–91 Atlas*. The results were most satisfactory for seabirds/gulls, with all species having been ringed at a satisfactory spread of locations, most even within Ireland (Fig 7.2a). Irish breeding birds were poorly represented in most other ecological groupings, and particularly within the passerines. It was rarely possible to test the movement patterns of Irish birds against those from geographical regions of Britain because of the low numbers of most species ringed there (see later). Wildfowl have received the least representative ringing effort during the breeding season, with many species showing poor geographical coverage (Fig 7.2a and Table 7.1).

We also assessed the age at which most birds later recovered had been ringed (Fig 7.2b). Many passerines and seabirds (particularly gulls) had satisfactory proportions of both chicks and fully grown birds ringed and later recovered. However, about half of all passerine species and wildfowl would benefit from greater numbers of chicks being ringed (Table 7.1). Conversely, most raptors/owls, around half of the seabird species and a quarter of the waders would benefit from more fully grown birds being ringed during the breeding season. The proportions of birds from the different age classes ringed affect the sample sizes that are available for some specific analyses, such as the assessment of juvenile, natal and breeding dispersal and differential migration of the age classes (see later). Some of the reasons for the distribution of ringing activity across Britain & Ireland and for the variation in the age classes ringed across the ecological groupings are discussed in more detail in Chapter 4.

The methods that we used when investigating the other topics shown in Table 7.1 for British & Irish breeding populations are given in Appendix 6.

Wintering populations

We first assessed to what extent our knowledge allowed us to determine whether a species that was present in Britain & Ireland during the winter comprised populations that were (i) entirely resident within Britain & Ireland (subsequently referred to as 'residents only'), (ii) entirely composed of immigrants from abroad ('immigrants only'), or (iii) a combination of these two types ('residents & immigrants'). It was more difficult to make direct tests of wintering status using the ring-recovery data than to make direct tests for breeding status because samples of birds ringed in winter could comprise variable proportions of resident and immigrant individuals, depending on the relative proportions of the two (or more) populations within the wintering area and on the pattern of ringing activity. Hence, for a species for which the wintering population within Britain & Ireland was categorized as sedentary by direct testing, additional information from other sources might exist (and be mentioned within the species account) to suggest or confirm the existence of winter immigrants from abroad. After considering both the direct tests of the ring-recovery data and any additional information provided by species-text authors, there were 29 species present in Britain & Ireland in winter that could not be allocated with certainty to one of the three categories of wintering species above (Appendix 6b); these

species, subsequently referred to as species with 'poor knowledge', constituted 60% of wintering seabirds, 23% of wintering passerines or near-passerines, 13% of raptors/owls, 6% of wildfowl and 5% of wintering wader species (Table 7.1). The proportion of seabird species in this category is particularly high because most can generally only be ringed when they are on land during the breeding season. At-sea surveys (Tasker *et al* 1984, Stone *et al* 1995) indicate that individuals of many species are found in British & Irish waters during the winter months but generally no information is available on their breeding origins, with a few exceptions (*eg* proportions of 'phases' of Arctic Skuas present through the year — see the species account).

In the analyses that follow, we refer to four categories of wintering species. *Immigrants only* are species that do not breed regularly in Britain & Ireland (they appear in section I of Appendix 6b but not as breeding species in Appendix 6a). *Residents only* are species for which there is thought to be no immigrant wintering population in Britain & Ireland from abroad (they appear in section III of Appendix 6b). *Residents & immigrants* are species for which the British & Irish wintering population comprises birds both from local and foreign breeding populations (they appear both in section I of Appendix 6b and as breeding species in Appendix 6a). Finally, species for which we have *poor knowledge* of the composition of wintering populations appear in section II of Appendix 6b.

We assessed whether the birds that have been ringed outside the breeding season and recovered subsequently have been broadly representative of the wintering distribution of the species within Britain & Ireland, by comparison with the *Winter Atlas*. The results across ecological groupings (Fig 7.2c and Table 7.1) differed substantially from those for ringing during the breeding season: most waders and passerines were sampled satisfactorily outside the breeding season, as were around 60% of wildfowl, but 60% of raptor/owl species and 67% of seabirds were poorly represented in the samples caught outside the breeding season, due to the difficulties of catching them as fully grown birds away from the nest.

The methods that we used when investigating the other topics shown in Table 7.1 for wintering and passage populations are given in Appendix 6, and are mentioned in more detail when necessary in the topic-based sections that follow.

Synthesis of knowledge and recommendations for future study

Dispersal movements of British & Irish breeding birds

Dispersal is an important biological process, which may contribute to the discovery and colonization of new breeding grounds, the reduction of overcrowding and avoidance of competition, population density regulation and genetic exchange to reduce inbreeding. Knowledge of the distances that individual birds disperse away from their natal and breeding areas is important in several areas of conservation biology, notably invasion and colonization processes, gene flow and the genetic structure of populations and source-sink population dynamics (and their effects on population density). An understanding of dispersal processes is also likely to be important in predicting the likely effects of climate change on bird populations (below), as dispersal processes may be important in range extension, which might result from climatic change (*eg* Thomas & Lennon 1999). It is often possible to assume that immigration and emigration are negligible when considering changes in populations at the scale of whole countries or regions of continents, but less for bird populations occupying much smaller areas, such as a particular seabird colony or piece of woodland. Knowledge of dispersal distances is important when considering the likely effects on bird populations of habitat degradation and fragmentation, which continue to have widespread effects on the countryside in both Britain and Ireland.

An example of the way in which information on dispersal rates feeds into the process of investigating population changes in a fragmented landscape, through population modelling (Baillie *et al* 2000), was discussed earlier in the book (see Chapter 2 and Fig 2.9). There is great potential to develop that kind of approach in conservation science, to look both at the likely effects of detrimental changes and those of positive conservation management. For example, the approach could be used to predict the effects on bird populations of projects designed to increase the area of native woodlands or the area of suitable marginal upland habitats for breeding waders once dispersal information is available for the relevant key species of interest. The measurement of dispersal distances is an important component of the BTO's Integrated Population Monitoring (IPM) programme (see Chapter 2 and Fig 2.3).

For our synthesis of natal and breeding dispersal information for British & Irish breeding birds, we combined information available from analyses carried out for this book with more rigorous analyses carried out previously for terrestrial species (Paradis *et al* 1998, see Appendix 2) and any information on more local studies provided by authors of the species accounts (see Appendix 6a). In general, the quality of information available on natal and breeding dispersal is higher for passerines/near-passerines than for non-passerines (Fig 7.3a & b and Table 7.1); within the former group, more migrant than sedentary species suffer from a lack of information. Those for which information is poor include a number of trans-Saharan migrants (*eg* Turtle Dove, Cuckoo, Tree Pipit, Nightingale, Whinchat, Grasshopper Warbler, Garden Warbler, Wood Warbler and Chiffchaff) and species that make nests from which it is often difficult or unsafe to extract nestlings for ringing (*eg* Rock Dove, Goldcrest, Bearded Tit, Marsh Tit and Treecreeper).

Generally for many raptor/owl and seabird species, satisfactory information is available on natal dispersal but not on breeding dispersal because most individuals are ringed as nestlings and few as breeding adults. So, for example, more information on breeding dispersal would be beneficial for all five species of tern, the two storm-petrels and even Gannet, Great Black-backed Gull and Great Skua. It is also required for several widespread raptors/owls (*eg* Goshawk, Buzzard, Merlin, Long-eared Owl and Short-eared Owl). Satisfactory information on natal and breeding dispersal is absent for many waders (*eg* Little Ringed Plover, Golden Plover, Dunlin and Snipe) and, particularly, for many common breeding waterfowl (*eg* Great Crested Grebe, Little Grebe, Gadwall, Teal, Shoveler and Tufted Duck). For many waterfowl species, information on breeding dispersal may be biased even if sample sizes appear satisfactory because of the difficulty of differentiating between British & Irish breeding adults and immigrants, when the breeding and autumn migration seasons overlap to a large extent (see Chapter 4). There is evidence for some species (*eg* Bullfinch; Newton 2000) that birds may disperse between breeding attempts within the same breeding season. These movements too have implications for population mixing and, particularly, for monitoring breeding populations and modelling population dynamics. They also have implications for the scale of provision of agri-environmental measures to improve habitats during the breeding season. They warrant further investigation for similar species.

The movements of juvenile birds in the first few months after they leave the nest are interesting biologically because they probably indicate an exploratory phase for the individuals concerned, when they build up knowledge of potential breeding areas. The relatively pronounced dispersal of migrant species (Paradis *et al* 1998) may be part of an 'imprinting' process that enables them to return safely to an appropriate breeding area on return migration (Baker 1993). For our synthesis, the only relevant information on juvenile movements that was available in a standard form involved the number of recoveries in each 30-day period after ringing for birds ringed as nestlings. We used this information in the first six months after ringing to provide an approximate guide to the level of knowledge currently available. This was most appropriate for those species that reach maturity the year after hatching, and least appropriate for many long-lived seabirds for which the age of first breeding may range from three years to as many as nine. Most ringed

seabirds do have relatively high recovery rates, however, which means that we have satisfactory information on the movements of the immature age classes for many species (see later). The same is true of a number of raptors/owls but, for the other ecological groupings, our knowledge of juvenile movements is relatively poor (Fig 7.3c).

Satellite-tracking (global surveillance) methods would be the ideal for measuring dispersal distances if the tags were small enough to fit on the smaller target species (most passerines) and cheap enough to monitor a large number of individuals (see Table 1.1). Neither of these criteria is likely to be met in the immediate future (see above and Chapter 1). Local studies based on retrapping or resighting marked birds within defined study areas can provide high-quality information on return rates but cannot provide true dispersal rates because dispersal and mortality are always confounded. Ring-recoveries still represent the most feasible method of studying dispersal on a wide geographical scale. Colour-marking could provide important data for some of the larger species but only if combined with systematic, wide-scale searches for marked birds and central collation of the resulting data (see above). The central collation and analysis of recapture data from across Britain & Ireland, with appropriate controls for spatial bias in ringing effort, perhaps has the most potential for providing high-quality dispersal information for the smaller passerines, which have low recovery rates as dead birds. There exists a general need to contrast the importance of the local *versus* long-distance components of bird dispersal, and to shift future emphasis away from the simple description of average dispersal patterns across species towards gaining better understanding of the processes involved.

Seasonal movements of migrants breeding in Britain & Ireland: migration routes and timing, wintering areas, and the summering areas of immatures

The effective conservation of any migrant species requires knowledge of the areas that individuals occupy at all stages of the annual cycle. To understand the possible threats that the species may experience, we also need to know what limits the way that movements are made, for example how much do individuals increase their fat reserves, what flight range does this give them and what alternative sites could they use to stop over if their preferred sites were threatened or destroyed? For species with delayed maturity, including many non-passerines, knowledge of the areas where immature birds spend summers before they begin breeding is also important, particularly given that these naive age classes may be more vulnerable to environmental and human-induced threats than experienced adults. All this information is essential for planning networks of protected areas for migrants and for fulfilling our responsibilities under national and international legislation (see above). As well as these direct conservation applications, a knowledge of migration patterns is important in addressing a range of other applied questions, such as the extent to which migrants are responsible for dispersing other organisms (diseases, parasites, plants) or the degree to which migrating species might conflict with human activities (flight lines of aircraft, wind turbines and so on).

For the current synthesis, we looked at the quality of information available on migration routes and timings (both of which can be addressed through ring-recovery data), and wintering areas, for species defined as long-distance migrants (wintering on average outside Britain & Ireland) or short-distance migrants (moving significantly but wintering on average within Britain & Ireland). For species that do not breed in the first year after hatching, we also considered the quality of information available on the summering areas used by immature birds. The criteria used to categorize species are given in Appendix 6a.

As expected, given the high reporting rates for ringed birds within Britain & Ireland (Chapter 4, Figs 4.8 & 4.9), the quality of information on migration and wintering areas is generally higher for short-distance than for long-distance migrants (Fig 7.4a). Also, more is generally known about migration routes than about the precise wintering areas of British & Irish breeding populations (compare Fig 7.4a & b), particularly for

Fig 7.3 Summary of the quality of existing information on (a) distance of natal dispersal, (b) distance of breeding dispersal, and (c) post-juvenile movements (in the first 6 months after ringing), for British & Irish breeding bird populations. (See text and Appendix 6 for further explanation.)

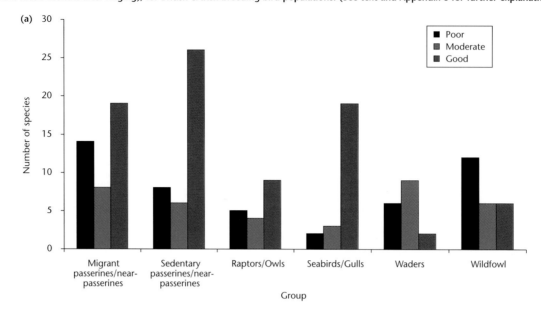

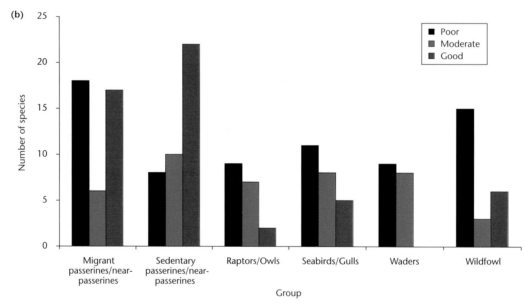

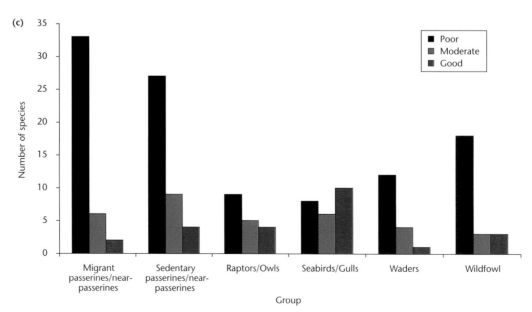

long-distance migrants (notably many passerines and wader species) that winter in Africa, where recovery rates are generally very low (see Fig 4.8). For those species where the information available on migration is coded as 'moderate', it is spring migration that is generally less well understood than autumn migration (17 species versus only one species where spring information is better, Appendix 6a). This at least partly results from the fact that autumn populations are swelled by juvenile birds (increasing the samples of recoveries obtained), many of which do not survive to make the return migration in spring. Also, spring migration may take place more rapidly and directly than autumn migration, or spring staging areas may differ from those used in autumn and have lower associated recovery rates. This may certainly be true for passerine species that winter south of the Sahara, which may fatten in France and Iberia on southward migration but in Africa on return migration in the spring. The quality of information available on the areas used by immature birds during summers before first breeding was generally high for seabirds, with their relatively high recovery rates and longer periods of immaturity, but poor for many species in the other groupings (Fig 7.4c).

For the larger species of non-passerine (seabirds, raptors, wildfowl and some of the larger waders), satellite tracking has great potential to fill some of the gaps in our knowledge of the movements of long-distance migrants. Some pioneering work is already under way or proposed in Britain & Ireland (eg on raptors, see www.ospreys.org.uk/AWOP/Satellite.htm and Fig 6 in the Osprey species account, and on seabirds, see www.gla.ac.uk/ibls/DEEB/rwf/ecql.html), and other studies are in progress throughout the world (see Chapter 1). For migratory species for which a satisfactory sample of ring-recovery information already exists, such as many seabirds, the global surveillance of even a small number of individuals will provide detailed observations on the timing, routes and sites used on migration against which the ring-recovery data can be calibrated and validated. For example, satellite tracking of a relatively large number of White Storks (75 individuals) has shown that many birds use the routes and sites suggested by ring-recoveries but has also identified an area in western Sudan and Chad where more satellite-tracked birds have been located than would be suggested by the distribution of ring-recoveries in that area (Berthold et al 2001). These authors conclude that the apparent difference could be due either to spatial variation in ring-reporting rates or to a recent change in the migratory behaviour of the storks, highlighting the added value of concurrent ringing and remote-tracking studies. For seabirds in particular, where rings are generally only recovered when the birds are close to land, satellite tracking has the potential to provide a huge amount of new information on their at-sea movements and spatial use of the sea areas that they visit outside (and within) the breeding season.

For smaller species, and those for which information on migration routes and wintering areas is currently negligible, satellite tracking is unlikely to provide the whole answer, at least not in the immediate future. For the smaller passerines and waders, standardized and coordinated programmes of ringing and recapture work across western Europe and throughout relevant parts of Africa (mostly North and West Africa for British & Irish breeding populations) would provide much more information on migration routes and timing than currently accrues from a reliance on the relatively small numbers of recoveries of dead birds, and could also provide important information on the strategies used by migrant birds (below). Sustained ringing at a network of sites across West Africa, south of the Sahara, would be much more likely to provide satisfactory information on the wintering ranges of the migrant passerines that breed in Britain & Ireland, through recoveries of dead birds and recaptures back on the breeding grounds (where recovery rates are relatively high), than a reliance on recoveries of ringed birds in Africa (where recovery rates are low). The establishment of ringing schemes in appropriate African countries, with expertise and support from European countries, would be the most appropriate mechanism by which to produce sufficient data in the longer term. Ringing effort would

need to be carefully recorded so that it could be taken into account in analyses. Two coordinated projects of this type, the Mettnau–Reit–Illmitz (MRI) Project (Berthold & Schlenker 1975, Berthold et al 1991, 1993) and the European Science Foundation (ESF) Network Project (eg Bairlein 1997b), have already demonstrated the potential of using standardized ringing during migration to study passerines, focusing on flyways further east than those used by most British & Irish breeding species. For a number of wader species, expedition work has been carried out along the flyways linking Britain & Ireland with West Africa, including colour-marking of some species, but many of the data remain to be analysed and made available to the conservation community (Davidson & Piersma 1986, Davidson et al 1998, 1999). For the larger wader species, and those with habits that make colour-ringing and resighting viable, this technique could be used to supplement or replace regular recaptures to provide additional information on migration and wintering areas.

For many long-distance migrant species, considerable potential exists to use chemical and biological markers, such as stable isotopes or DNA (above and Chapter 1), to elucidate their wintering areas and differentiate these from those of other breeding populations. Effective projects could be designed by combining the collection of samples from which to obtain signatures with conventional ringing and colour-marking work or satellite telemetry. Careful consideration would need to be given to the choice of tissue to be sampled in relation to the annual cycle of the target species. If samples of feathers are used (which are easy to collect via non-invasive techniques), then knowledge of the moulting strategy of the target species is required. Such projects are most likely to succeed when birds can be sampled both on the breeding grounds and across the potential wintering range, in order to establish base information on the geographical pattern of marker signatures, using a combination of different markers, and using a collaborative approach involving countries across Europe. A number of studies have already demonstrated the high potential of this approach with stable isotopes (eg Chamberlain et al 1997, 2000). Integrated studies combining chemical markers and conventional ringing might be particularly appropriate for further investigation of the wintering ranges of a number of widespread British & Irish trans-Saharan passerine migrants for which knowledge is currently poor (eg Garden Warbler, House Martin, Pied Flycatcher, Redstart, Tree Pipit, Wheatear, Whinchat, Willow Warbler and Wood Warbler), for some migrant raptors (eg Hobby and Marsh and Montagu's Harriers) and for some waders (eg Common Sandpiper, Dunlin, Little Ringed Plover and Ruff). Updated analyses of ring-recovery patterns at the European scale, as carried out previously for Der Zug and a number of other current EURING projects (eg Fiedler 1998), should be an important exploratory phase for any such collaborative project.

Migration strategies of long-distance migrants breeding in Britain & Ireland

The 'strategies' used on migration include components such as the duration of individual flights, the pattern of areas used for fattening and resting, the food requirements for fattening, and the amount of body reserves accumulated, which influence maximum flight durations and distances. Knowledge of the strategy used by each species is of great importance for effective conservation because it allows important staging areas and the effects of losses of such areas, or important habitats within them, to be predicted. Research on migration strategies is also of great importance in understanding the evolution of bird migration and testing modelling predictions, both for individual species (eg Weber & Houston 1997, Kokko 1999, Weber & Hedenström 2001) and whole communities (eg Howlett et al 2000).

For the current synthesis, we consulted the account for each of the main species to look for either specific direct information about the pattern of sites used on passage (which was rare to find) or indirect information, such as studies of fattening and predicted flight ranges or even assumptions made on the basis of the pattern of recoveries in autumn and spring. Only information specifically concerning the British

Fig 7.4 Summary of the quality of existing information on (a) migration routes and timings, (b) wintering areas, and (c) the summering areas of immature birds, for British & Irish breeding populations of long-distance migrants ('LDM') and short-distance migrants ('SDM'). (See text and Appendix 6 for further explanation.)

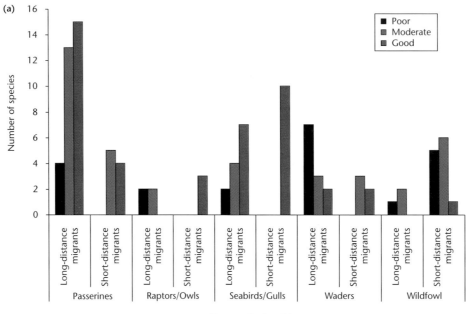

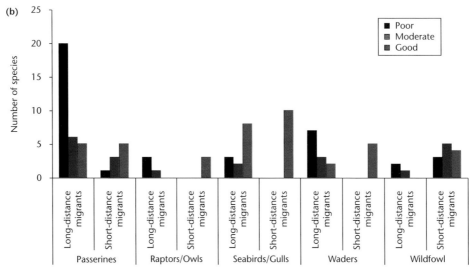

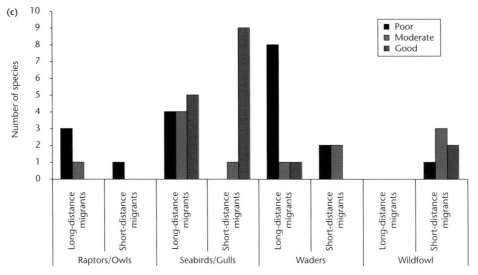

& Irish breeding population was considered when categorizing a species, and the process was only undertaken for species known or assumed to be long-distance migrants. The full results are provided in Appendix 6a. We did not find a single species for which there could be said to be comprehensive information on the migratory strategy of the British & Irish breeding population. For most species, there was either no information available (coded 'poor') or a small amount of knowledge, for example from a local study of changes in the body mass of a species during migration periods (*eg* Bibby & Green 1981, 1983, Baggott 1986, Norman 1987); we coded such species as having 'moderate' knowledge. Most of the species with some information available were passerines (*eg* Pied Wagtail, Sedge Warbler, Reed Warbler, Whitethroat, Blackcap, Willow Warbler and crossbills). For all ecological groupings, the number of species with poor information greatly outnumbered those for which there was some knowledge of migratory strategy (Table 7.1). Overall, we coded knowledge as 'poor' for 48 species and 'moderate' for only 17 species.

Studies of the migratory strategies of passerines breeding in mainland Europe are more advanced than those on British & Irish breeding populations, and some exemplary work has already been published. For example, a nationwide project in Sweden to study the autumn migration of Willow Warblers involved 18 bird observatories and many individual ringers during the period 1988–90, and collected data for 36,000 birds (Lindström *et al* 1996). The study resulted in important information on the birds' preparations for the early stages of migration. Ringing studies at roosts, undertaken as part of the international EURING Swallow Project (Spina 1998a), have also provided important new information on fattening strategies (Pilastro *et al* 1998a, Pilastro & Spina 1999). Work on the body condition and strategies used by long-distance migrant passerines further south on their migration routes has also been undertaken in the central Sahara Desert (*eg* Bairlein *et al* 1983, Bairlein 1985a, 1988, Biebach 1990).

On a larger geographical scale, the Italian-led 'Progetto Piccole Isole — Mediterranean Islands Project' was initiated in 1988 to study the strategies used by Palearctic-African passerine migrants during their passage across the Mediterranean in spring. The project has involved more than 500 ringers operating on 41 island and coastal sites around the Mediterranean, and more than 40,000 birds of over 200 species have been caught (Spina *et al* 1993, Spina & Pilastro 1999, Messineo *et al* 2001). It has produced important information on the strategies used by specific passerine migrants, in terms of the timing and sites used for fattening (*eg* Pilastro & Spina 1997, Grattarola *et al* 1999), the differential timings of movements (Spina *et al* 1994, see later) and the food requirements for fattening (Schwilch *et al* 2001). An ambitious ESF Network Project on songbird migration (Bairlein 1995, 1997b) was set up in the early 1990s with the aim of studying the movements of several mainly insectivorous passerine species between Europe and Africa, involving ringing at 40 stations in 18 countries. Leading on from this, a new ESF Scientific Programme on 'Optimality in Bird Migration' will run from 2000 to 2004 to carry out collaborative studies on the migration strategies of a number of European long-distance passerine migrants (F Bairlein pers comm, see www.esf.org). The project will carry out field studies on the body reserves of migrants, refuelling rates and the environmental factors that influence them, and the food supplies and habitats required during stopover; it will also be exemplary in including associated laboratory studies, and mathematical dynamic modelling approaches to bring field and lab data together to aid our understanding of migration routines and the decision-making processes used by migrant birds (Bairlein 2000).

With the relatively high density of ringers operating within Britain & Ireland, there is considerable scope to set up coordinated studies of particular target species to assess their migratory strategies both within our islands, and on the migration routes further south in collaboration with colleagues abroad. Many British & Irish ringers have carried out their own local studies on the body condition of migrants during passage periods (examples above and in the species accounts). This is expertise

that could be built upon to initiate nationwide and even flyway-wide studies of migratory strategy for an appropriate suite of target species using the westernmost flyways between Europe and Africa, following the ongoing work on the flyways further east. Existing information from local studies and ring-recovery patterns would be sufficient to select a set of contrasting species for study. Such a programme of research on migratory strategies would be highly complementary to the work required to elucidate further the migratory routes and wintering areas of many of the passerine species breeding in Britain & Ireland (above) and, together, these could form the basis of well-designed integrated research projects. Expedition work in West Africa has already demonstrated the potential for producing important information on the strategies used by Palearctic-African migrants there (*eg* Ash 1969, Loske 1990, Hjort *et al* 1996, Ottosson *et al* 2001).

For British & Irish breeding wader species, for which our knowledge of migration strategies is often poor (Stone-curlew, Little Ringed and Ringed Plovers, Golden Plover, Dunlin, Ruff, Black-tailed Godwit, Whimbrel and Greenshank), targeted studies originating on the breeding grounds are likely to represent the only means of separating the complex patterns of migratory movements involving both British & Irish breeding birds and those of passage populations from breeding areas abroad (see, for example, the accounts for Dunlin and Ringed Plover in Chapter 6). Much high-quality research has already been carried out on the migration strategies of waders on the likely flyways used by birds that breed in Britain & Ireland or pass through on passage (*eg* Piersma *et al* 1990, Zwarts *et al* 1990a, b, Piersma & Everaarts 1996, Piersma & Lindström 1997, Piersma & Gill 1998, Nebel *et al* 2000) but more is still required. The linking of this work to specific breeding populations and the definition of the strategies used by the different populations are major challenges that remain. For the smaller species, expedition work along migration routes and in wintering areas, to recapture birds that have been ringed or include resighting on the breeding grounds, or the use of biological or chemical markers (above), probably remain the only effective means of linking studies of migration strategies to specific breeding populations. The use of radio-telemetry, with tags attached on the breeding grounds, may be feasible for some species (*eg* Iverson *et al* 1996) but the costs and time required to relocate birds are likely to be high, meaning that only a small number of individuals can be studied (Davidson *et al* 1999).

For some larger species, such as several raptor/owl and seabird species, satellite telemetry, or the use of other types of remote logger (above), may prove feasible to provide high-resolution information on the migration routes of individuals and, therefore, on their migratory strategies. Indeed, for pelagic seabirds these are probably the only possibility for providing detailed information on the movements and activities of birds when they are at sea.

Differential movements of populations breeding in Britain & Ireland

Differential migration, whereby one or more sections of a population (such as age classes or sexes) undertake seasonal movements at different times or to different areas than other classes, and partial migration, where only a proportion of the population makes seasonal movements, both have important implications for the effective conservation of migratory species. Both result in the population being spread over differing geographical areas outside the breeding season, so that parts of the population may experience different competition for resources, predation pressures, weather factors and food availability (Cristol *et al* 1999 and references therein). For example, the adults of a given wildfowl or wader species might spend the winter further north than immature birds, in an area free from, say, hunting pressures, but the population as a whole may be threatened because immature birds are hunted in non-sustainable numbers in a more southerly wintering area. In order to conserve such migrant populations, threats in a number of different wintering areas may need to be considered in tandem, in order to predict their effects on the breeding population as a whole. Specific analyses to consider these phenomena for British & Irish breeding populations were carried out for this project, and the concepts and results of the analyses are discussed in detail in Chapter 5.

Here we consider the quality of information available on the differential movements of the age classes, sexes and regional subpopulations, based on the specific analyses described and discussed in Chapter 5 (which compared locations in winter). We divided the results into those for species categorized as significantly migratory and those thought to be sedentary. The criteria used to classify species, and the resultant categorizations, are given in Appendix 6a. As in Chapter 5, we did not exclude so-called 'sedentary' species from our appraisal; this was because one or more age or sex classes or regional subpopulations of a species could be migratory but this might not be apparent in the overall test for migratory status, if the larger data set were dominated by a sedentary portion of the population.

For all ecological groupings, the quality of information available on age differences in wintering areas was more satisfactory than that on sex differences (Fig 7.5 and Table 7.1). Of the 188 main species considered in the book, there was some information on sex differences for only 30 species, and of these the information was 'good' for only seven species (of which only two were classified as migrant). In total, some information was available for 15 passerine species, seven wildfowl species, six raptor/owl species, only two seabirds and no waders. Many species, across all ecological groups, would therefore benefit from greater samples of birds being sexed during ringing operations, and there is much scope for the further development of sexing methods, whether based on plumage characteristics, measurements of body size or molecular techniques based on samples of body tissues for validation use (eg Engelmoer 1984 for waders, Coulson et al 1983, Okill et al 1989, Hamer & Furness 1991, Granadeiro 1993 for seabirds). In general, the quality of information on age differences in wintering areas was satisfactory across a number of seabird/gull species, due to their relatively high recovery rates, but rather poor for most other ecological groupings; this was particularly so for migrant passerines, which often have very low recovery rates in their wintering areas (Fig 7.5a and Table 7.1). For the latter groupings, studies based in the wintering areas are likely to be required in order to investigate more effectively age and sex distributions there.

The types of approaches suggested above for increasing our knowledge of migration routes, wintering areas and migratory strategies, such as targeted expedition work along flyways, the establishment of long-term ringing schemes across Africa, and the use of biological and chemical markers, such as stable isotope signatures, could also provide important information on the differential movements of migrant species if based on carefully designed, integrated projects that also implement appropriate, and sometimes novel, ageing and sexing techniques. Such work could also further add to our knowledge of the differential timings of movements. The latter can be difficult to assess from recoveries alone because of potential biases caused by age- or sex-specific recovery rates from some common methods of recovery (such as hunting, see Chapters 4 and 5). The catching of birds along migration routes, the examination of the age and sex ratios of samples and their differential fattening rates can provide detailed information on differences in migratory strategy between individuals of different age and sex (eg Spina et al 1994 for migrants passing through the Mediterranean), and will have particularly high value when combined with approaches that identify the breeding origins of the populations under study (above).

In the case of differential movements of regional subpopulations, only for seabirds/gulls were there reasonable numbers of species for which our level of knowledge was at least 'moderate' (Fig 7.4c and Table 7.1), meaning that comparisons of wintering areas could be made between individuals breeding in at least three regions of Britain & Ireland. For all other ecological groupings, the majority of species were categorized as 'poor' knowledge, although, in general, slightly fewer resident than migrant species were coded as 'poor'. These deficiencies of course closely reflect the spatial biases in ringing effort across Britain &

Ireland (Chapter 4, Fig 4.5, and above), with seabirds/gulls being the only ecological grouping for which the spatial distribution of ringing effort has been good for a majority of species.

For species thought to be 'sedentary' on the basis of current analyses of ring-recovery data, the omission of information from some regions, and perhaps particularly from upland areas of northern and western Britain, might preclude the detection of important movements within Britain & Ireland, such as altitudinal movements, or movements of northern populations south and/or west in winter. Although less spectacular than the seasonal movements of long-distance migrants into southern Europe or Africa, such local movements may be important from a national conservation viewpoint. For example, the once-common House Sparrow is now a declining species in Britain & Ireland (Baillie et al 2001), and the limited ring-recoveries concerning upland breeding sites are suggestive of altitudinal movements as far as the coast in winter (Fig 4 in the species account). Knowledge of such movements may therefore be important for assessing the factors responsible for adverse changes in population size and for determining the geographical areas and habitats required to support the wintering population. Knowledge of the scale of seasonal movements is important if we are to recommend remedial conservation action, such as measures to be carried out as part of agri-environmental schemes.

For migrant species, an understanding of any differentiation of wintering areas or migration routes for British & Irish regional subpopulations may be important for identifying threats to breeding populations. For example, we know that drought conditions in the Sahel can affect the overwinter survival of trans-Saharan passerine migrants (eg Peach et al 1991, Szép 1995a, b) and that seasonal rainfall in West Africa may be very localized. There is much evidence from analyses at the European scale suggesting parallel migration routes (see Fig 3.1) and wintering areas (eg Der Zug) for individuals breeding at different longitudes, and some suggestion that such segregation may occur even at the scale of Britain & Ireland for some species (eg Sedge Warbler in Chapter 6; Chapter 5).

As expected, the under-ringed regions of Britain & Ireland (Fig 4.5) are generally those where human population density, and therefore the density of ringers, is low, or where the climate is less favourable for ringing (wetter and windier, for example). To address our lack of knowledge of the movements of regional subpopulations of many of the species that breed in Britain & Ireland, particularly many widespread passerines, there will be a general need to encourage more ringing and, particularly, recapturing in these areas; this could be achieved through financial incentives, such as regional subsidies on ring prices, using a similar approach to that adopted for target species (Clark et al 1998). As currently under-ringed areas are generally those with low human population density, a reliance on recoveries of dead ringed birds is unlikely to provide sufficient data on more local movements for most species however. For some of the larger non-passerines, such as waterfowl, raptors/owls and some waders, the establishment of specialist groups in appropriate target areas that currently lack data would be beneficial, and well-designed colour-marking programmes could make a large contribution to our knowledge of regional subpopulations by increasing the chances of re-recording marked individuals. There may be some potential for chemical markers to play a role in regional studies, if appropriate markers, with sufficient spatial resolution, could be identified. Pilot studies at the regional level within Britain & Ireland could form a useful component of any wider-scale studies that are initiated in future, in order to assess whether gradients of appropriate markers would be of a high-enough resolution at the scale of our islands.

Partial migration of birds breeding in Britain & Ireland
Obligate long-distance migration and completely sedentary life styles can be regarded as two extremes of a continuum of migratory behaviours displayed by birds. Partially migrant populations are, strictly speaking, those in which two or more discrete migration strategies exist, so that

Fig 7.5 Summary of the quality of existing information on the differential movements of (a) the immature and adult age classes, (b) the sexes, and (c) individuals from different geographical regions, for British & Irish breeding bird populations. (See text and Appendix 6 for further explanation.)

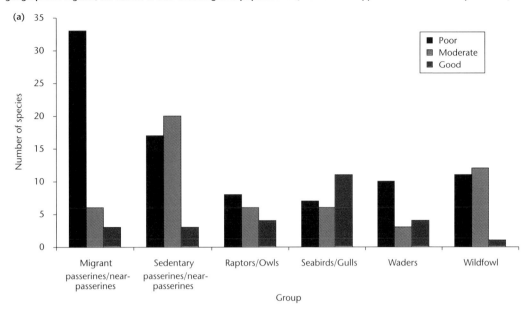

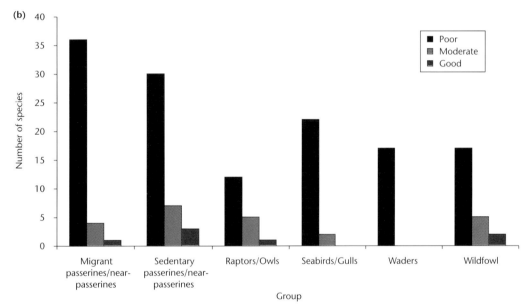

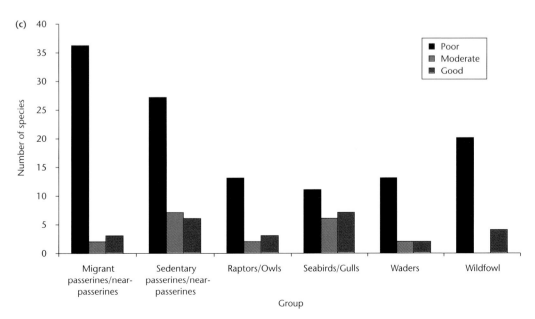

some individuals winter further away from their breeding areas than others. Partial migration has been defined to differ from differential migration in that the latter involves just one strategy that is expressed to varying extents in individuals of different age or sex (Lundberg 1988; see also the detailed discussion of this topic in Chapter 5). From a conservation perspective, the implications of partial migration strategies are similar to those of differential strategies, in that they result in sections of a population wintering in different areas and, hence, being susceptible to differing threats (above). Knowledge of partial migration strategies and how they co-exist and interact with differential strategies is important for understanding the evolution of migration (see Chapter 5 — *Differential migration, partial migration and the control of migratory strategy* section) and the ways in which migrants might respond to environmental changes (below).

The method used in this book for investigating the degree of migrancy of British & Irish breeding birds is described in detail in Chapter 5. Our level of knowledge of the movements of partially migrant species has already been discussed earlier in the section on the *Seasonal movements of migrants breeding in Britain & Ireland*. Major challenges for the future in this area of research concern ensuring that British & Irish breeding populations of potentially partially migrant species are sampled on a wide-enough geographical scale to identify this tendency, and quantifying and controlling for biases that may affect quantification of migratory tendency, such as spatial variation in reporting rates across wintering areas; these needs are discussed in detail in Chapter 5 (*Possible problems with the analyses and potential solutions* section). For species with sufficient ring-recovery data, there is also scope to investigate further the degree to which partial migration is facultative or obligate (*eg* Main 2000b), which has implications for understanding the ecological needs of such species as well as significant evolutionary importance. Analyses at the scale of continental Europe along the lines of those presented in Chapter 5, with further improvements as suggested there, could help us to understand the likely movements of those winter immigrants into Britain & Ireland that are partial migrants, and how partially (and differentially) migrant European birds might respond to environmental change.

Wintering populations: breeding origins, migration routes and timings, migratory strategies, and the importance of Britain & Ireland

Britain and Ireland are important wintering locations for individuals of a variety of species from populations breeding further north and east in Europe (*eg* Common Gull, Lapwing, Starling, Brambling) and further to the northwest in Iceland (*eg* Teal, Redwing) and even Greenland and arctic Canada (*eg* White-fronted Goose, Knot). We have an international responsibility to play our part in the global conservation of such migratory species and, to plan this effectively, knowledge of the breeding origins of the population(s) that winter within Britain & Ireland, and hence their international importance, is essential. As for the species that breed in Britain & Ireland, knowledge of the migration routes, timing of migration and strategies used by our winter immigrants is important for conservation efforts, for example in order to plan networks of protected sites along flyways, as well as being of intrinsic biological interest. Britain & Ireland is of international importance and thus has great international responsibility for high proportions of the total populations of a number of wader and wildfowl species (Stroud *et al* 2001).

We looked at the quality of information available on the breeding origins, migration routes and timings, and migratory strategies of species categorized as either 'immigrants only' or as 'residents & immigrants' (above). The criteria used to grade the quality of information available for each topic, and the results by species, are given in Appendix 6b.

In general, at least moderate information on the breeding origins of winter immigrants, and the routes taken to and from Britain & Ireland, is available for a majority of species in each of the ecological groupings (Fig 7.6a & b and Table 7.1). The highest-quality information is available for wildfowl and for waders. For the latter, the quality of information available on migration routes and timing is higher for more species than

that on breeding origins because many species breed in remote northern latitudes with very low recovery rates; for example, we have at least moderate information on the migration routes of the Bar-tailed Godwits, Grey Plovers, Green Sandpipers, Jack Snipe and Ruff that winter in Britain & Ireland but poor information on their breeding origins. The favourable information shown in Fig 7.6a & b for seabirds gives a rather biased picture in that it refers only to the gull species and Cormorant; the winter populations in British & Irish waters of a further nine seabird species, most of which are largely pelagic outside the breeding season (*eg* Fulmar, Gannet, Great Skua, Kittiwake, Guillemot, Razorbill and Puffin), may contain immigrants from abroad but there is currently little unbiased information on their origins available from ring-recoveries and therefore they have been coded as 'poor knowledge'. For all ecological groupings, the quality of information on migration routes and breeding origins was generally higher for species with 'immigrant only' populations than for those for which the wintering population also includes 'residents' because the available ring-recovery data are harder to interpret for 'mixed' populations; for example, all 14 species for which the knowledge of migration routes was coded as 'poor' had both resident and immigrant wintering populations (*eg* Red-throated Diver, Little Grebe, Goosander, Peregrine, Water Rail, Coot, Short-eared Owl, Song Thrush and Twite).

As for British & Irish breeding populations, the strategies used on migration by winter immigrants involve the duration of flights, patterns of areas used for fattening and resting, food requirements for fuelling, and the amount of body reserves accumulated, and their effects on maximum flight durations and distances. Knowledge of important staging areas and the effects on such migrants of losses of such areas, or important habitats within them, is extremely important when planning protected site networks on their flyways or predicting the effects on their populations of habitat change along the route. As for British & Irish breeding populations, we consulted the account for each of the main species to look for either specific direct information about the pattern of sites used on passage or indirect information, such as studies of fattening and predicted flight ranges or even assumptions made on the basis of the pattern of recoveries in autumn and spring. Only information specifically concerning immigrant populations present in Britain & Ireland in winter was considered when categorizing a species, and the process was undertaken only for species known or assumed to have winter immigrant populations within Britain & Ireland (*ie* those categorized as 'resident & immigrant' or 'immigrant only'). The full results are provided in Appendix 6b.

Some information on migratory strategy was given for only one-third of the species with immigrant winter populations (Fig 7.6c). 'Good' or 'moderate' information is available for a number of large, generally well-studied waterfowl (*eg* Bewick's and Whooper Swans and Greylag, Barnacle, Brent and Pink-footed Geese) and a number of wader species (*eg* Bar-tailed and Black-tailed Godwits, Knot, Grey Plover, Greenshank, Ruff, Dunlin and Turnstone), and also for a small number of passerines (Blackcap, Chaffinch, the redpolls, Robin, Siskin and Snow Bunting). However, for only three species (Bewick's Swan, Greylag Goose and Knot) did the species accounts suggest that comprehensive research has been undertaken on the migratory strategies of all the immigrant populations using Britain & Ireland in winter.

Given the large catchment breeding areas for the populations visiting Britain & Ireland in winter, from Greenland and arctic Canada in the west to Siberia in the east, any comprehensive research on the migrations of these species must be carried out cooperatively at an international scale. The first step for many species must be to collate existing ring-recovery data across the flyway, as this alone can provide much information on the seasonal patterns of movement between geographical areas or particular sites for some groupings (*eg* wildfowl and waders). For passerines, such preliminary research should build on the pioneering work carried out in Germany (*Der Zug*), and a similar approach will be appropriate for other ecological groupings. Once

Fig 7.6 Summary of the quality of existing information on (a) areas of breeding, (b) migration routes and timings, and (c) migration strategies, for bird populations wintering in Britain & Ireland. For (b), winter immigrant species are divided into those that also have resident breeding populations in Britain & Ireland ('resident & immigrant') and those that do not breed regularly in Britain & Ireland ('immigrant only'). (See text and Appendix 6 for further explanation.)

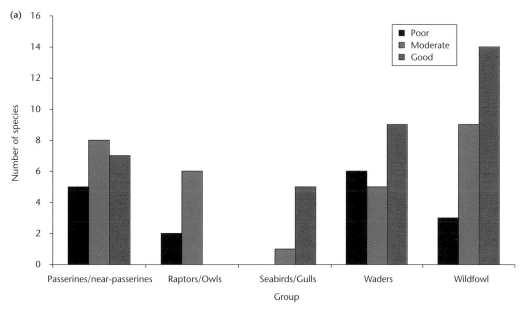

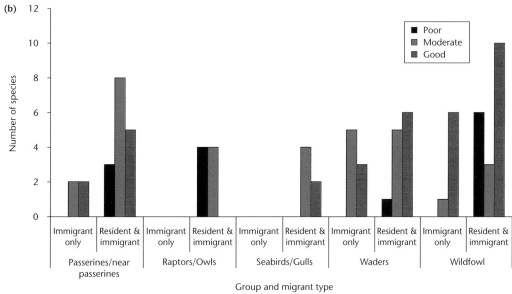

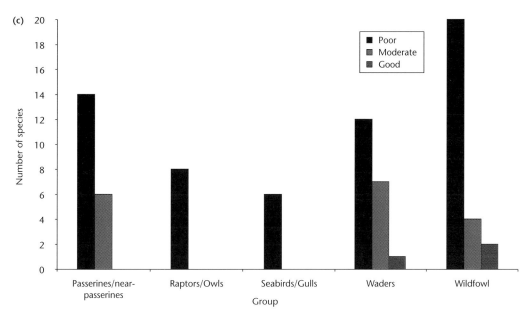

migration patterns have been described in these ways, it is possible to delineate populations, so that further research on strategies and the factors affecting individual birds at the different stages of their journeys can be appropriately targeted. Such work is now well developed for goose populations in the West Palearctic (Madsen *et al* 1999), and detailed studies have gone on to demonstrate the dynamic nature of population processes, such that future monitoring of movements will be essential (*eg* Mooij *et al* 1999 for White-fronted Goose). Recent developments along these lines have taken place for waders (D A Stroud pers comm) and are proposed to look at wildfowl movements at the European scale (Spina 1998c). Further research of this type for other ecological groupings will require the application of improved quantitative methods for delineating populations, by clustering ring-recoveries, and estimating rates of movement between them (Hestbeck *et al* 1991, Pendleton & Sauer 1995, above). For species for which it is unlikely that sufficient numbers of ring-recoveries will be obtained to link mixed populations of wintering birds with their breeding areas of origin, chemical and genetic marker techniques and other methods of differentiating individuals (such as biometric measurements, above) will be required. For example, a recent study using strontium isotopes has suggested that these can be used to differentiate Redshank from the Icelandic breeding population from Scottish-breeding individuals when populations are mixed in Scotland in winter (R Bullman & J Evans pers comm).

Once migratory populations have been satisfactorily delineated at the international scale, further research on migratory strategies could proceed based on similar principles and techniques to those discussed above for British & Irish breeding populations, for example involving ring-recapture and colour-marking approaches for passerines and smaller non-passerines and, perhaps, incorporating remote-tracking techniques for larger species (such as ducks, raptors and the larger waders). Ringers in Britain & Ireland could play a pivotal role in such cooperative projects involving populations whose wintering destinations are our islands, particularly on spring migration strategy, as well as in integrated projects that also address the winter ecology of immigrants or the separation and strategies used by wintering and passage populations; both of these last two topics are addressed further below.

Wintering populations: differential movements and use of Britain & Ireland

For British & Irish wintering populations, we considered the quality of information available on differential movements in a similar manner to those of British & Irish breeding populations (above), basing our appraisal on the specific analyses described and discussed in Chapter 5. These compared the locations during the breeding season and distances moved by birds present in Britain & Ireland during the winter that were recovered as adults. The regional analyses compared the locations abroad during the breeding season of birds ringed in different geographical areas of Britain & Ireland during the winter, and the proportions of birds ringed in each of these areas that were recovered abroad. Details of the methods employed are provided in Chapter 4. We

considered only species that were categorized as having immigrant wintering populations, and presented the results separately for those whose populations were 'immigrant only' from those that were a mixture of 'resident & immigrant'. The criteria used to classify species, and the resultant categorizations, are given in Appendix 6b.

Our knowledge of the differential movements of winter immigrants is generally rather poor (Table 7.1). Most information is available for age differences in the breeding origins of winter immigrants (Fig 7.7a), and is satisfactory for gulls and many passerines but poorer for some waders, wildfowl and, particularly, raptors/owls. For sex differences (Fig 7.7b), species with 'poor' knowledge form the majority in all ecological groupings, and 'good' information was available only for four species of wildfowl (Mallard, Pochard, Teal and Tufted Duck) and two passerines (Blackbird and Greenfinch). As for British & Irish breeding populations, many species ringed in Britain & Ireland during the winter months, across all ecological groupings, would benefit from improved ageing and sexing techniques to improve our knowledge of their differential movements (above). Again collaborative international analyses will be required in order to build up a complete picture of the differential movements of populations of winter immigrants to Britain & Ireland.

Information on regional differences in the breeding origins and proportion of immigrants in winter was poor for most species across all ecological groupings (Fig 7.7c). 'Good' or 'moderate' information was available only for 12 species, comprising six waterbirds (Brent, Barnacle and White-fronted Geese, Grey Heron, Mallard and Wigeon), two gulls (Black-headed and Herring), two waders (Golden Plover and Oystercatcher) and two passerines (Blackbird and Starling). Winter ringing, targeted in those geographical areas currently under-represented, would therefore be valuable for many species. The most successful approaches for generating increased information on these species will depend on their body size and the geographical areas and habitats that they utilize during the breeding season.

For larger species and those breeding in areas with relatively high ring-recovery rates, metal-ringing or colour-marking projects might generate sufficient data on a regional basis; potentially suitable widespread species requiring increased geographical coverage in winter include several wildfowl (Little Grebe, Gadwall, Teal, Shoveler, Pochard, Tufted Duck, Goldeneye, Goosander, Moorhen and Coot), three gull species (Common, Great Black-backed and Lesser Black-backed), some raptors/owls (Hen Harrier, Kestrel, Merlin, Short-eared Owl and Sparrowhawk) and a few waders (*eg* Curlew). For species of a suitable size, satellite telemetry projects integrated with widespread winter ringing could provide novel information on the origins of wintering individuals, as well as on their winter ecology when they are in Britain & Ireland (below).

For smaller species, and those breeding in remote areas where ring-recovery rates are likely to be very low, chemical and/or biological signature techniques (above) may prove the only means of differentiating the breeding origins of geographical subpopulations wintering in Britain & Ireland, assuming that appropriate markers can be found. Such techniques might provide suitable information for many passerine immigrants, including the four species with populations that are almost entirely immigrant (Brambling, Fieldfare, Redwing and Waxwing), and a number of others for which a knowledge of breeding origins would be of great interest on a regional basis (*eg* Rock Pipit, Goldcrest, Blackcap, Chiffchaff, Chaffinch, Siskin and the crossbills and redpolls). They would also be useful, and could provide fascinating regional information complementary to other sources, for a number of wintering wader species (*eg* Bar-tailed Godwit, Dunlin, Grey Plover, Jack Snipe, Knot, Redshank, Sanderling, Snipe, and Turnstone).

Of course chemical and biological signature techniques could also be wholly applicable to many of the larger species for which information on the movements of regional subpopulations is still required, for which their use could be complementary to conventional marking techniques and satellite tracking. In addition, they could be used valuably to investigate wintering populations of species for which we are still

Fig 7.7 Summary of the quality of existing information on the differential movements of (a) the immature and adult age classes, (b) the sexes, and (c) individuals wintering in different geographical regions, for bird populations wintering in Britain & Ireland. Winter immigrant species are divided into those that also have resident breeding populations in Britain & Ireland ('resident & immigrant') and those that do not breed regularly in Britain & Ireland ('immigrant only'). (See text and Appendix 6 for further explanation.)

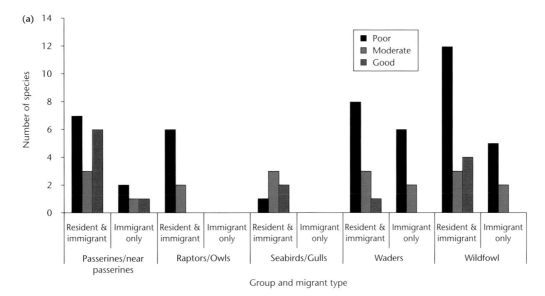

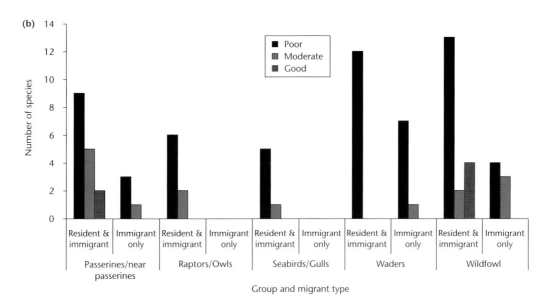

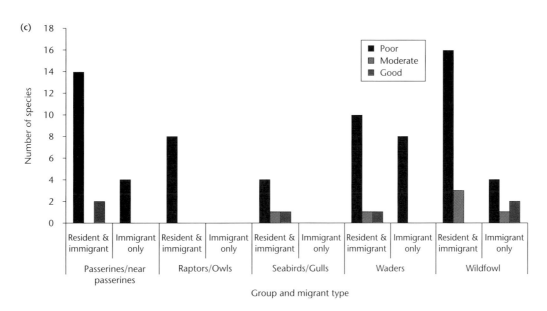

unclear whether immigration into Britain & Ireland occurs on a regular basis (*ie* those currently categorized as 'poor knowledge' in Appendix 6b). Some key species where such investigation would be valuable include a number of passerines and near-passerines (Kingfisher, Skylark, Meadow Pipit, Grey Wagtail, Stonechat, a number of corvid species and Goldfinch) and several other species (*eg* Great Crested Grebe, Buzzard and Marsh Harrier). The laboratory analyses required for the use of chemical and biological marker techniques are likely to remain relatively expensive; therefore, research to validate variation in the external characters of birds (such as plumage differences and biometrics, which are easy and cheap to measure) against measured differences in chemical and biological markers between populations from different breeding origins should be an integral part of projects involving such marker techniques. Variation in, for example, body size and plumage characteristics between individuals from different geographical origins is known to occur widely in birds (*eg* BWP) and is already used to separate the populations of some winter visitors to Britain & Ireland, particularly some waders (*eg* Ferns & Green 1979, Atkinson *et al* 1981, Furness & Baillie 1981a, Davidson *et al* 1986c, Nicoll *et al* 1988, 1991, Summers *et al* 1988b, 1989, 2001, see also Engelmoer & Roselaar 1998). The potential exists for such easily measured characteristics to be used to separate immigrants from residents in the British & Irish wintering population for a number of species (*eg* Robertson 1997).

Resource-related winter movements involving Britain & Ireland

In general, birds are more mobile in winter, when they are not constrained to a nest site, than during the breeding season. In addition, living conditions are naturally harsher in winter; food is generally less abundant for many species, there is less daylight in which to collect it, and the weather is less favourable than during the breeding season. From a practical conservation viewpoint, this means that, for any given species, it is generally more difficult to define a suitable network of protected areas, or put in place measures to improve conditions in winter (*eg* through agri-environmental schemes, above), when birds may be mobile, than during the breeding season. These issues are important in understanding the ecology, and therefore the conservation, of both migrant populations that visit Britain & Ireland for the winter and our resident species, as even these may show more localized but nonetheless important movements during the winter months. At the international scale, for example, ring-recoveries and counts have shown that many wildfowl move south and west in Europe in response to spells of severe weather (Ridgill & Fox 1990). This means that the numbers reaching Britain & Ireland from further afield for the winter, to escape severe conditions abroad, and the proportions remaining within our islands for the whole winter, are likely to vary depending on the severity of individual winters. Similarly, some waders may move out of Britain

& Ireland in response to cold winter weather, while others like Oystercatcher and Redshank generally remain on their usual wintering sites and can suffer greatly increased mortality in some years as a result (Baillie *et al* 1986, Clark *et al* 1993, Hulscher *et al* 1996). The effects of weather-related winter movements on populations may be exacerbated by higher direct hunting pressures, or disturbance on the areas where birds seek refuge from hunters (below), and such interactive effects must also be considered when planning networks of protected sites.

We considered the number of available ring-recoveries involving movements within a given winter, and between winters (see Chapter 4 for definitions), together with any additional information on winter movements provided by the authors of the species accounts. We considered the winter movements only of species with winter populations in Britain & Ireland, and excluded long-distance migrants for which the whole population departs in winter. Direct tests of relationships between winter movement distances and winter weather conditions could not be included in this project but authors used maps of winter movements to assess the fidelity of their species to wintering areas in general terms. The criteria that we used to grade species and the resultant classifications are shown in Appendix 6. We did not examine the temporal distribution of winter movement records for each species; so, for some species that we categorized as 'good', on the basis of having at least 30 within-winter and at least 30 between-winter movement records, the spread of data may still be insufficient to produce robust information on between-year variation in movement patterns in relation to weather conditions.

In general, the quality of information available on winter movements was satisfactory for many wader and wildfowl species (Fig 7.8 and Table 7.1). For these groupings, some detailed studies of resource-related winter movements have already been undertaken (*eg* Ridgill & Fox 1990) and much ringing-recapture and colour-mark resighting data exist, which could be analysed in more detail to provide further information for several species (*eg* Davidson *et al* 1999). There is much potential for existing and new ring-recapture and colour-marking data to be used to look at the local movements of waders and wildfowl, including use of particular areas within sites that are being considered for protection (*eg* Rehfisch *et al* 1996) as well as to further investigate larger-scale winter movements and the environmental conditions leading to these. Five species of wader were categorized as having only 'poor' information on winter movements (Common and Green Sandpipers, Golden Plover, Greenshank and Ruff). The wildfowl that would benefit most from further research into their winter movements are generally species that will be difficult to catch in winter because of their behaviour or the habitats they utilize (*eg* diving ducks like Goldeneye, Goosander and Scaup, Little and Great Crested Grebes and the diver species). These are species for which satellite telemetry or other remote data loggers might prove the most effective technique for gaining information on winter movements. In the case of seabirds, some information of a satisfactory quality is available for a small number of gull species but nothing is currently known of the movements of individuals from specific populations of most other species outside the breeding season because of their generally pelagic lifestyles and the difficulties of capturing individuals away from breeding sites (as discussed above). Once again, only remote tracking techniques are likely to shed light on the detailed pattern of the winter movements of such species. Very little information is available on the winter movements of raptors/owls and all species would benefit from increased research. The more migratory and diurnal species might be appropriate for satellite tracking and colour-marking projects to investigate their winter movements, whilst radio-telemetry could play an important role for the less mobile species.

The quality of information available on the winter movements of passerines/near-passerines is generally higher for species with immigrant populations than for 'resident only' species (Fig 7.8 and Table 7.1). Those for which our level of knowledge of winter movements is categorized as 'poor' include a number of insectivores (*eg* Green Woodpecker, Rock

Fig 7.8 Summary of the quality of existing information on movements within a winter for bird populations wintering in Britain & Ireland. The 'migrant' category consists of those species thought to have regular immigrant wintering populations. (See text and Appendix 6 for further explanation.)

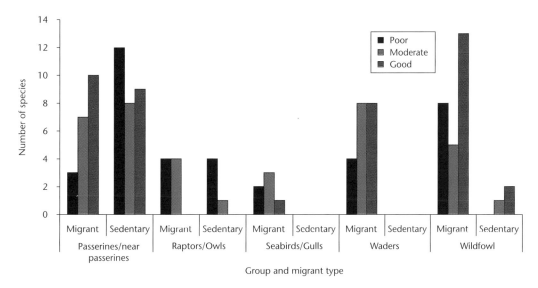

Pipit, Grey Wagtail, Stonechat, Nuthatch and Treecreeper), Kingfisher, Bearded Tit, two declining tit species (Marsh and Willow), some woodland finches (*eg* the crossbills and redpolls and Hawfinch), three corvids (Carrion Crow, Magpie and Raven) and the declining Corn Bunting. Information is only 'moderate' for a number of other farmland and seed-eating species, many of which are of immediate conservation concern (Gibbons *et al* 1996a), including Skylark, Chough, Tree Sparrow, Goldfinch, Linnet, Twite, Yellowhammer and Reed Bunting. For several of these species, intensive research has demonstrated that decreasing survival rates are driving the population declines, and has indicated that environmental factors outside the breeding season are important influences on population change (*eg* Siriwardena *et al* 1998b, Siriwardena 1999, Peach *et al* 1999). For most of these species, with their small body size and low recovery rates as dead birds, carefully planned ringing-recapture and/or colour-marking projects, perhaps combined with some intensive radio-telemetry work to provide additional detailed information on a smaller number of individuals, might be the most likely methods to succeed in increasing our knowledge of their winter movements. Such projects should be increasingly important for providing the information required to implement remedial conservation measures, such as specific agri-environmental incentives to farmers, at appropriate geographical scales. A pioneering BTO project is already under way to carry out one such intensive study, aimed at assessing the likely benefits to farmland seed-eating birds of increasing the area of overwinter cereal-crop stubbles available; it will involve the experimental provision of supplementary food at feeding stations with variable spacing and assessment of the range over which birds will travel to utilize such resources (Vickery 2002). As many such species roost communally during the winter months, research to identify the distances that individuals are able to travel to suitable roosting sites will also be important.

For species for which Britain & Ireland supports both resident and immigrant wintering populations, intensive work on winter movements will be of maximum value for conservation if projects incorporate techniques for differentiating resident and immigrant individuals (such as chemical and biological marker techniques or carefully validated approaches based on measuring body size, above). Within such projects, there is also much scope for investigating the environmental factors and characteristics of individual birds that influence winter site-fidelity or movement rates and also overwinter survival rates, and even for studying diets through the collection of faecal samples. Our knowledge of these topics outside the breeding season is currently very poor for

many passerine species with both resident and immigrant British & Irish wintering populations (Evans *et al* 1999). The same is true of our knowledge of 'immigrant only' passerine populations in Britain & Ireland. Although we have a reasonable number of winter movement records for the main four such species (Brambling, Fieldfare, Redwing and Waxwing), we still have a poor understanding of the factors that influence their movements once they reach Britain & Ireland, and hence their conservation needs, despite the fact that we have an important international responsibility to help conserve their populations. Such species would benefit from specific projects integrating intensive mark-recapture work with more extensive survey work to relate counts of birds to habitat use and food availability (such as that being undertaken during the BTO's Winter Farmland Bird Survey: Gillings & Wilson 1999, Gillings 2001a). Such integrated projects could also incorporate work on the breeding origins of immigrants (above) and provide information on the winter requirements of related species with both immigrant and resident populations (*eg* Blackbird, Song Thrush, Chaffinch and so on).

The importance of Britain & Ireland for passage populations
Just as Britain and Ireland are important for immigrant wintering populations, our islands also temporarily support large numbers of birds on spring and autumn passage. A few of the species with main species accounts in this book, such as Curlew Sandpiper, and Wryneck, and several of the species with minor accounts, such as Sooty Shearwater, Long-tailed Skua, Barred and Aquatic Warblers, are only present in Britain & Ireland in any numbers during passage periods. As with the wintering species, we have an international responsibility to contribute to the global conservation of such migratory species and, therefore, we need to know their breeding origins, the geographical areas and habitats within Britain & Ireland that are important to them and the timing of their needs whilst in our islands. Aquatic Warbler, indeed, is of global conservation concern (Tucker & Heath 1994).

Within the *Migration Atlas* project, we could not carry out the detailed analyses of the ring-recovery data that would be required specifically to look at the movements of passage populations for many species, particularly those (the majority) for which there are also British & Irish breeding or wintering populations that complicate greatly the interpretation of recovery patterns. Therefore, we base our synthesis on an appraisal of the existing volume of appropriate ring-recovery data and information on passage populations presented by each species-text author, such as counts of visible migrants and bird observatory data. We

Fig 7.9 Summary of the quality of existing information on the existence and origins of passage movements through Britain & Ireland of birds from foreign breeding populations. (See text and Appendix 6 for further explanation.)

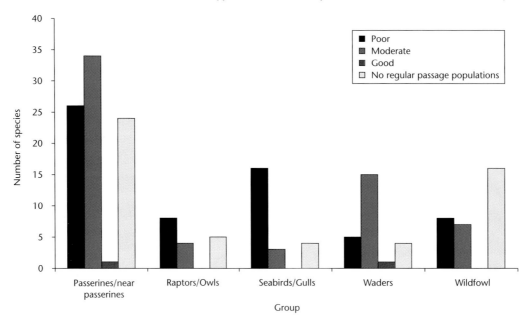

first assessed the quality of knowledge regarding the existence (or absence) of passage populations and their breeding origins, and then the level of knowledge regarding their timings and geographical occurrence within Britain & Ireland (Appendix 6).

The results were very similar for the two topics on passage populations that we addressed (Table 7.1). Hence although we have focused on the results of assessing the existence of passage populations and their breeding origins here (Fig 7.9), the results of assessing the timings of passage movements and the regional use of Britain & Ireland followed the same general pattern. Species could only be categorized as having 'good' knowledge using our criteria if information was sufficient to determine satisfactorily from which breeding areas the passage migrants through Britain & Ireland originated. Hence for many species, and particularly many passerines and near-passerines, detailed information on the timing of passage through Britain & Ireland may exist (eg from bird observatory data, R & F) but such species could only be classified as having 'moderate' knowledge because ring-recoveries linking such migrants to specific breeding areas were not available. The only two species classed as having 'good' information were Dunlin and Blackbird (see species accounts). The proportion of species for which there was 'poor' information was lowest among waders and highest among seabirds/gulls and raptors/owls (Fig 7.9 and Table 7.1).

The wader grouping contains the largest number of species with satisfactory information available on passage populations because of the large amount of work on their migrations, often by multi-national teams, which has been carried out along West Palearctic flyways (eg Pienkowski & Pienkowski 1983, Davidson & Piersma 1986, Rae et al 1986, Dick et al 1987, Summers et al 1989). For waders, there has been much research on the differentiation of individuals from varying source populations, through, for example, plumage characteristics, biometrics, moult patterns and genetic analyses (eg Hale 1971, Branson & Minton 1976, Greenwood 1986, Summers et al 1988b, 1989, Tomkovich 1992, Tomkovich & Soloviev 1996, Wennerberg et al 1999). We currently have rather poor knowledge of the passage populations of non-coastal wader species that require specialized catching methods (eg Dotterel, Golden Plover, Little Ringed Plover and Snipe). We have satisfactory knowledge of the passage of a number of waterfowl species because many are large (and often quarry) species with high recovery rates across their breeding range in Europe. The goose and swan species have generally been

investigated in sufficient detail through intensive studies to conclude that Britain & Ireland does not receive passage migrants on an annual basis. The waterfowl for which we currently have poor knowledge of passage populations tend to be diving species that are difficult to catch, and for which knowledge of movements in general is therefore poor (eg Red-throated Diver, Great Crested and Little Grebes, Goldeneye and Pochard) or relatively rare species (eg Garganey).

For many passage wildfowl and wader populations in Britain & Ireland, an improved knowledge of the numbers of individuals passing through the country, and particularly through specific sites ('turnover'), is the most pressing research need. This is a high conservation priority, given that the number of birds using a particular site is one of the major criteria used to designate sites for protection under national and international law. Recent appraisal of the analytical frameworks used to measure turnover to date has shown that most of the methods used regularly (eg the colour-marking of birds with cohort-specific rather than individual marks) may be flawed (Davidson et al 1999); they may give misleading results unless the use of a site by a population is highly synchronous. Further work in this area of research is likely to require well-planned projects to mark birds individually and record their presence at sites, either by visual observations of colour marks, recapturing, or remote sensing (Kaiser 1999, above and Chapter 1).

For small passerines, with their relatively low ring-recovery rates, the further investigation of the existence and specific breeding origins of passage populations in Britain & Ireland is unlikely to be achieved through ringing alone. Given that many passage migrants through Britain & Ireland will originate from populations that breed in remote areas further north and east on mainland Europe, colour-marking is also unlikely to be useful in tracing their breeding origins. Rather, more data need to be derived from the opportunity afforded by the trapping of birds for ringing, using techniques such as chemical and genetic signatures, plumage characteristics and biometrics (discussed under immigrant wintering populations above).

Projects to determine the existence and breeding origins of passage passerine populations need to be integrated with research on the timing and volume of passage movements. The Bird Observatories Network in Britain & Ireland (Durman 1976a) has a great deal to contribute to studies of bird migration, and particularly to research on passage migrants. Counts of the numbers of birds present in defined areas have

been made almost daily during passage times at many observatories, providing much information on the timing of major movements (*eg* *R & F*, Riddiford 1991, Marchant 2002). Most observatories also carry out regular trapping of birds for ringing during passage periods and, therefore, are in a unique position to collect data on breeding origins (using the methods suggested above) that can be linked with count data indicating the timing of movements at the same sites. Such data from coastal sites make a significant contribution to monitoring temporal change in the timings of bird migration (below). However, in order to build up a more comprehensive picture of how passage migrants from both British & Irish and foreign breeding populations utilize Britain & Ireland during migration, research projects need to include networks of inland sites, as well as the largely coastal observatories. Such research needs to integrate two major types of work: observations to record arrivals of migrants on a wide geographical scale (as is being carried out in the BTO's *Migration Watch* project, Balmer 2002) and regular trapping at a network of sites to collect data that can be used to assess the breeding origins of the different 'waves' of arrivals. The latter could form part of projects that also collect information on migration strategies (*eg* fattening rates, above).

Counts of grounded migrants at coastal sites may give a biased picture of the true numbers of birds that are regularly passing through Britain & Ireland, for a number of reasons. First, the number of birds that come ashore and land may be greatly influenced by prevailing weather conditions (see Chapter 3); hence coastal sites may record more continental immigrants at certain times than regularly pass through Britain & Ireland, particularly those on the east coast of Britain. In conditions suitable for migration, few birds may be counted but turnover may be high, with many birds overflying coastal count sites, while in poor weather conditions larger numbers may be grounded (see Chapter 1). There is a need to computerize and analyse further the wealth of information on passage movements that has been collected over many years by the Bird Observatories Network, and particularly to establish the effects of short-term weather factors on the numbers of migrants recorded; there may be a role for radar or similar technologies in showing the volume of migration taking place overhead in different weather conditions in such studies (Zehnder & Karlsson 2001, Chapter 1). Regular observations at inland sites, in addition to those made on the coast, are likely to be the only means of obtaining a fuller picture of the use of Britain & Ireland by passage migrants from foreign breeding populations, however. As for wildfowl and waders, counts of grounded passerine migrants are likely to produce biased information on the true volume of migration through an area and, in addition, they are much more difficult to make in most habitats used by passerines. The regular ringing and recapturing of individuals at migration sites during passage periods are most likely to produce high-quality information on turnover

rates and stopover durations at sites, and on the true numbers of birds passing through any given site in a season; rigorous analytical methods have been, and continue to be, developed for these kinds of data (see Kaiser 1999, Nichols & Kaiser 1999 and references therein). Standardized ringing at a network of sites in suitable habitats, including the collection of information to assess the breeding origins of the captured birds, could provide important information on the true spatial use of Britain & Ireland by both native breeding populations and those from abroad. Assessments of the true numbers of birds using particular sites, such as reedbeds, will provide important knowledge on which to base the designation of such sites for protection.

Raptors/owls and seabirds/gulls are ecological groupings for which research on the existence, breeding origins and size of passage populations utilizing Britain & Ireland is likely to remain particularly challenging. It is unlikely that large numbers of individuals of many of such species (except perhaps gulls) will be caught in Britain & Ireland outside the breeding season to provide ring-recoveries back on the breeding grounds. If methods can be developed to catch reasonable numbers, then colour-marking approaches could be successful for some species (*eg* some of the larger raptors and diurnal owls) but the collection of samples of biological or chemical markers from which to assess breeding origins is likely to be extremely valuable. Satellite telemetry and data logging techniques perhaps offer the most potential if fitted as part of intensive research projects on suitable target species.

The impacts of hunting on migratory bird populations

Most of the bird species that are hunted within Europe are to some extent migratory, implying that a coordinated approach to conserving such species, and to the regulation of hunting practices, is required at an international scale (Spina 1999). Existing European legislation (above) limits the number of legal quarry species, requires EU Member States to conserve their populations of wild birds and, specifically, to protect migratory populations during their movements to and from breeding areas. Despite these international legislative requirements, knowledge of the true impact of hunting on bird populations is poor both at national and international scales (Aebischer *et al* 1999).

Knowledge of the seasonal movements of individual populations is fundamental to determining the effects of hunting. In order to predict the likely impacts it is necessary to determine to which breeding populations the targeted individuals belong, the routes that are taken and the timing of migration. Our knowledge of these topics was discussed earlier in this chapter. Knowledge of any differential seasonal movements of individuals within a population (discussed above) may also be critical. For example, ring-recoveries were used recently to predict the likely impact of allowing the hunting season in Italy to be extended into February and March, months when more migratory birds would be moving northwards back to their breeding areas (Dall'Antonia *et al* 1996). By looking at the differential movements of the age classes of a number of species, the authors were able to show that increased hunting activity in those months would have a selective impact on adult birds. For example, the study showed that hunting after the end of January would disproportionately target adult male Ruff and therefore could affect the establishment of spring leks. There is also a strong link between the information that is required to predict the effects of hunting on bird populations and research into resource-related winter movements (discussed above). Periods of unusually cold weather can be stressful for birds, whether they use a strategy of seeking refuge in milder conditions elsewhere or remain site-faithful. Several European countries have a policy of imposing a statutory, temporary cold-weather ban on hunting if such weather conditions occur (Stroud 1992). Further research is needed on the combined effects of weather, hunting pressure and hunting disturbance, so that the effectiveness of cold-weather bans can be assessed and improved if necessary (Aebischer *et al* 1999).

As well as providing information on seasonal movements, ringing is an important tool for studying the impacts of hunting on bird populations because it can be used to measure harvest rates, temporal and geographical variation in hunting pressure, and survival rates (Nichols 1991a, McCulloch *et al* 1992, Aebischer *et al* 1999, Baillie 2001). The prediction of the impacts of hunting requires knowledge not just of mortality rates but also of the extent to which hunting mortality is 'additive' (additional to other causes of death) or 'compensatory' (where hunting keeps the population size below the threshold level at which other causes of mortality start to operate). A detailed consideration of these important topics is outside the scope of this synthesis (see Aebischer *et al* 1999 and Baillie 2001 for recent reviews). As well as being of biological importance for predicting the impacts of hunting on populations, knowledge of the way in which hunting pressure varies over time and across geographical areas (*eg* McCulloch *et al* 1992) is important for allowing unambiguous interpretation of movement patterns from ring-recoveries (see Chapter 4). Much work still needs to be carried out to compare measures of hunting pressure from ring-recovery data with independent information from population counts, hunting bag surveys or data on the numbers of hunters or cartridges sold (Aebischer *et al* 1999). Spatial and temporal variation in overall ring-reporting rates needs to be established more quantitatively at the international scale (see study methods section above). Assessment of the extent to which illegal hunting takes place is also very important in this context, as this may have complex influences on ring-reporting rates and patterns.

In North America, well-established annual survey programmes, many relying on intensive ringing efforts, have allowed four main flyways to be differentiated as the basis for setting annual hunting regulations (Crissey 1957, Nichols 1991b). The need for a similar coordinated hunting policy across Europe is clearly stated in the AEWA and the Bonn Convention (above) but much further cooperative research will be required before this can be established on a firm scientific basis. Flyway-scale studies of movements, such as those proposed in the EURING Waterfowl Atlas Project (Spina 1998c), will be fundamental in providing the knowledge on which to base such a policy.

Temporal change in movement patterns

Previous sections of this chapter demonstrate why we need to carry on collecting information on the movements of British & Irish birds, despite many decades of data collection so far. However, even if our knowledge of their current movements was complete, it would be important to carry on collecting new and comparable data because the world of nature is not static. There are a large number of natural and human-induced factors that could cause changes to bird movement patterns. It is important for us to know if patterns are changing because such changes might affect our ability to conserve species and populations effectively, for example if sites currently designated for protection become less suitable. As birds are widespread and a relatively easy taxon to monitor, such changes to movement patterns could alert us to changes that are occurring in the environment even when they are not detected by other monitoring methods. This could be particularly important for geographical areas and habitats that are remote or difficult to monitor directly: marine environments and the Arctic tundra, for example.

That changes to bird migration patterns can occur is no longer disputed: a recent review that considered changes in historical times (Sutherland 1998a) identified 43 cases globally for which alterations to routes could be identified. The reasons behind such changes, and the ability of species to alter their migration patterns in response to environmental perturbation are difficult to predict, however. It is now widely accepted that global temperatures are rising, and that the release of greenhouse gases from human activity is at least part of the cause (McCarthy *et al* 2001; see Hulme & Jenkins 1998 for Britain & Ireland). Undoubtedly, changes to the world's climate could have large and complex effects on bird migration patterns, although there is still considerable debate as to how exactly these might change (*eg* Lindström & Agrell 1999, Bairlein & Winkel 2001, Berthold 2001).

For small passerines, there is some expectation that resident populations breeding at higher latitudes will experience increasingly favourable conditions, such that their population densities might increase considerably. In addition, obligate partially migratory species may become largely sedentary (*eg* Blackbird, Chaffinch, Starling and Robin in continental Europe; Berthold 2001), as they are largely already in Britain & Ireland. Facultative partial migrant and eruptive species might experience more continuously favourable conditions for breeding, so that their populations increase, eruptions occur more often but the chances of returning to their original breeding population fall because of high competition. This could result in spreading populations and, eventually, fewer eruptions, a phenomenon that has already been noted in some species (*eg* Winkel 1993 for tits). These effects could lead to fewer winter immigrants into Britain & Ireland of some species, including wintering thrushes and Starling, Chaffinch and Brambling, and might be equally applicable to some non-passerines (*eg* Lapwing and Snipe, many duck species and gulls). If climatic warming occurs, short-distance migrant and partial migrant breeding species could become more resident over time within Britain & Ireland (*eg* Pied Wagtail, Goldfinch and Linnet), and some 'sedentary' species that we suspect may currently make local altitudinal movements, or movements south or west for the winter, within Britain & Ireland may cease to do so. Other climate change scenarios for Britain & Ireland predict cooling effects, however, due to a reduced influence of the Gulf Stream (Hansen *et al* 2001).

For long-distance migrants, the predictions are more complex (Berthold 2001). The increased populations of sedentary species might leave less habitat available for long-distance migrants on the breeding grounds, so that they are gradually 'squeezed out' of the breeding avifauna. Extensive studies by the BTO (O'Connor 1981, 1990) have suggested that the breeding densities of migrant passerines depend directly on the population size of resident species, so that late-returning species can only breed in habitats that have not been occupied by residents or earlier-returning migrants. Alternatively, or additionally, the reduced migratory behaviour of short-distance and partial migrant species might free up habitat at mid-latitudes, such as in Mediterranean areas, where long-distance migrants might remain to winter, rather than moving further south. There is some evidence that this may already be occurring, with small but increasing numbers of, for example, White Storks, Yellow Wagtails and House Martins wintering in Iberia (Berthold 2001). The migration routes of previous long-distance migrants might then be shorter, perhaps allowing them to return earlier or compete more successfully with residents for resources on the breeding grounds.

Of course the changes that occur in practice will depend both on how flexible and rapidly adaptable is the migratory behaviour of birds (Sutherland 1998a), and on how the habitats themselves change over time with latitude. There could undoubtedly be some effects that are specific to certain ecological groupings. For example, there is already some evidence that the populations of some wader species are switching from wintering on the west coast of Britain to the east coast, where food supplies may be more abundant, because winter weather in the east is becoming milder (Austin *et al* 2000). The elucidation of the effects of global climate change on seabird movements could be a complex process because any changes are likely to affect the physical, biological and biogeochemical characteristics of the oceans at different temporal and spatial scales, some of which could, in turn, produce further climatic change (see Chapter 6 in McCarthy *et al* 2001). There are likely to be complex effects on marine fisheries, which may impact the distribution and abundance of seabird prey. As well as overall widespread changes in world temperatures, global climate change may be responsible for increasingly unpredictable and severe weather effects (such as severe gales), which could, for example, affect the breeding success of seabirds (*eg* Heubeck 2000). Increased knowledge of the breeding dispersal ability of such species in the event of more frequent breeding disasters caused by severe summer weather would be useful in this respect. All-in-all, we have little idea of how climate change will affect the abundance of birds or their movement patterns and, therefore, it is important for us to monitor these variables in the long-term.

As well as global climate change, there are many other, more local factors that might influence bird movement patterns and, hence, make ongoing monitoring of changes in such patterns important. Many of these may be human-related, involving large-scale destruction of, say, important wintering areas so that populations are forced to move elsewhere, or more subtle human interventions in the natural environment, such as by the introduction of competing species. It is important for us to understand the links between migrants in breeding areas and those on the wintering grounds, and how they each respond to environmental change, if we are to predict the overall effects of such change on populations as a whole (*eg* Sutherland 1998b). At the scale of Britain & Ireland, one potentially important influence on the movements of birds has scarcely been considered — that of the widespread provision of increasing quantities and quality of supplementary food through the feeding of birds in gardens. Possible changes identified in the movements of some of our resident passerines (*eg* a reduction in the numbers of British Blackbirds that winter in Ireland, see the species account) might warrant further investigation with regard to this possible cause, and a project to investigate changes in movement patterns for similar species with regard to temporal and spatial variation in garden bird feeding might reveal some fascinating results.

The *Migration Atlas* project included a brief exploration only of the potential of existing ring-recovery data for investigating temporal changes in movement patterns, considering only the movements of populations breeding in Britain & Ireland and only movements between breeding and wintering areas (Chapter 5). We base our appraisal of the overall quality of information available for British & Irish breeding populations on these analyses, together with any additional information provided by the species-text authors in their accounts; for species wintering in Britain & Ireland, we used only the latter source of information (Appendix 6). The authors for the individual species accounts were asked explicitly to review any existing information on temporal change in the movement patterns of their species.

As for some of the other topics above, the quality of information available for testing for temporal change in the movement patterns of British & Irish breeding birds was generally satisfactory for many seabird/gull species (reflecting their relatively high ring-recovery rates) but generally poor for raptors/owls, wildfowl, most waders and, particularly, for migrant passerines (reflecting their low recovery rates in southern wintering areas (Table 7.1)). The level of knowledge for British & Irish wintering populations was poorer, across all species (Table 7.1), with some information on temporal change in movement patterns presented for only 12 of the 115 species thought to winter regularly. This suggests that we still have a great deal to do to improve our level of knowledge in this area, and supports the findings of a recent review (Sutherland 1998a) that revealed little specific information for British & Irish bird populations. Even for species where sufficient ring-recovery data exist to allow detailed investigations of temporal change in the future, much work still needs to be done to quantify potential biases within the data, such as those arising from changes in finding circumstances through time (Chapter 4). Hence, as well as addressing many of our gaps in knowledge of the other topics dealt with above, these results show the need to find ways of monitoring movements in the longer term.

Many of the recommendations made above for the individual subject areas and ecological groups above will also be relevant to achieving this aim, particularly those that seek to generate more information per bird handled. Thus, the development of long-term colour marking programmes and the systematic sampling of, say, isotope ratios in target populations through time (once suitable markers are established for target species) will be important, to complement the continuation of traditional ringing. Long-term observational surveys will also provide important population-level information on changes in movement

patterns to complement individual-based work, particularly where they record information on populations of known breeding origin (such as regular counts of wintering and staging geese; Madsen *et al* 1999).

We were not able to address temporal changes in the timing of bird movements within the current project (for reasons explained in Chapter 5). There are already indications that long-term changes in the timing of the seasonal migrations of birds are occurring however, which could be related to variation in global climate (*eg* Mason 1995, Huin & Sparks 1998, Sparks 1999, Jenkins & Watson 2000, Sokolov *et al* 2000, Bairlein & Winkel 2001, Zalakevicius & Zalakeviciute 2001; Fig 7.10). Long-term and widespread observational approaches, recording the arrival and departure dates of migrants, and their seasonal distribution of numbers, are likely to be effective first steps to assessing whether major changes in the timing of bird movements are occurring, particularly as they are often appropriate for volunteer observers to undertake. Such programmes already include, for example, the regular collection of census data at coastal bird observatories (*R & F*, above) and WeBS counts of waterfowl and waders (Pollitt *et al* 2000). The BTO has just initiated a new project, 'Migration Watch', asking volunteer observers to make regular observations of migrants seen at their usual birdwatching sites through the spring, with a view to gathering information on arrival times and recording the progress of spring arrivals, largely of passerines, through Britain and Ireland (Balmer 2002, see www.bto.org/migwatch). Projects to monitor the arrival times of migrants in the long term are run in other parts of Europe too (*eg* Slovak Republic — Sparks & Braslavská 2001; Norway — R Barrett pers comm) and there are plans to establish a European recording network (F Bairlein pers comm). Pioneering work has also been carried out in North America to record the timing of migration movements using NEXRAD (Next Generation Doppler Radar designed for weather forecasting) to record bird movements daily during spring and autumn, with volunteer birdwatchers ground-truthing the results by sending in observations from regular birdwatching sites (the *BirdCast* project; see www.birdsource.cornell.edu/BirdCast/home.html). Projects of this type, using volunteers and, particularly, using web-based recording and automated basic analysis, have great potential for long-term monitoring of the timing of bird movements in a cost-effective manner. Similar approaches might provide information on changes in the movements of other ecological groupings of species, for example based on sea-watching observations (Hope Jones & Tasker 1982).

Such observational projects to monitor the timing of movements will often only provide the first clues that changes are occurring, however. For example, autumn long-term census data on Willow Warblers from Dungeness Bird Observatory have recently been analysed, suggesting that the peak passage in autumn is now later than in the 1960s (Marchant 2002). However, this information alone did not allow the several possible hypotheses that could explain the change in timing to be evaluated. The long-term ring-recovery records were also required in order to differentiate the separate 'waves' of birds from different breeding areas, allowing the study to conclude that some wide-scale weather-related factor was more likely to be responsible for the change in timing than the decline in the population of birds breeding in southern Britain, as was previously suggested (Marchant 2002). In most cases, wide-scale population-level observational surveys will not act as a substitute for more intensive, individual-based work to assess the breeding origins of the populations that are affected, and hence the causal factors behind any observed changes. Rather, the wide-scale, observational, population-based monitoring work and the intensive, individual-based research will both generally be required, and projects that integrate the two will produce the highest-quality information and the most effective results for conservation purposes.

Seabird movements and the effects of the environment

The seabirds are an exceptional case because, gulls excepted, they present some unique difficulties for migration researchers. Most only come to

Fig 7.10 Contour maps showing the arrival dates of Swallows in Britain in years when they arrive (a) earlier than normal (1893, 1937 and 1944), (b) normally (1912, 1929 and 1933), and (c) later than normal (1908, 1916 and 1936), and (d) spring cumulative heat (day degrees above 0°C). White areas indicate the absence of data in at least one of the years shown on the map. (*Source*: Huin & Sparks 1998, by permission of *Bird Study*.)

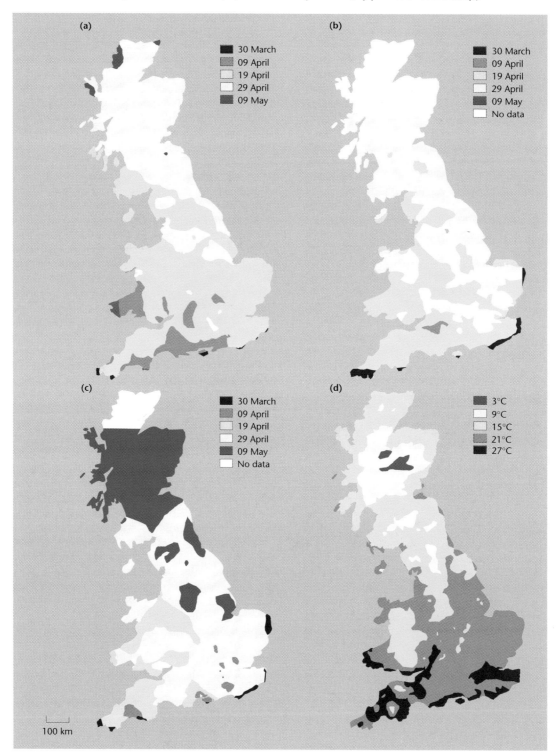

land for any length of time during the breeding season and, even then, many are difficult to catch in large numbers as fully grown birds because of disturbance risks at the colonies. This means our knowledge is poor for all those topics that involve capturing birds outside the breeding season, such as movements within the winter period, movements of passage populations and the existence and origins of immigrant wintering populations within our waters. At-sea surveys of seabirds carried out from ships have recently produced much important information on their

distributions in British and Irish waters and how these change seasonally (*eg* Stone *et al* 1995) but they are expensive to undertake on a regular basis (such as for long-term monitoring purposes) and do not provide information that can be linked to specific breeding populations. The use of remote-tracking devices and biological or chemical markers are currently the only possible techniques for investigating the movements of individual pelagic seabirds when they are away from breeding colonies. Even to use these effectively, methods of catching birds safely

Table 7.2 Priorities for future research on movements involving the birds of Britain & Ireland, with emphasis on topics of high conservation value.

Topic	Possible research methods
• Given the high profile of global climate change, analyses to assess whether movement patterns have shown temporal variation in relation to climate, and to predict future changes, are high priority, particularly for long-distance and partial migrants.	• To understand changes retrospectively: analyses of long-term data sets for selected key species at the scale of Britain & Ireland, Europe or flyway; • To monitor future changes and make predictions: multi-species analyses (as in Chapter 5) at the European scale; maintain existing ringing programmes that give sufficient recoveries; increase ringing in key wintering areas (Africa); evaluate the use of chemical and genetic marker techniques for monitoring movements.
• Because environmental change is particularly difficult to measure in marine systems, research on temporal change in the movements of seabirds in relation to environmental perturbation is a high priority.	• To understand changes retrospectively: analyses of long-term data sets for selected key species at the scale of Britain & Ireland or, preferably, an international scale appropriate to population range. • To monitor future changes and make predictions: maintain existing ringing programmes and validate them against other distributional and tracking data (below).
• For site-based conservation, research on movements between and within sites (including robust measures of turnover and resource-related movements) is of high priority, particularly for wildfowl and waders but also for other groupings for which a site-based approach to conservation is adopted.	• Improve collation and analysis of colour-mark resighting data. • Initiate focused studies using telemetry, resighting and recapture to evaluate turnover (demonstration studies). • Establish improved networks of ringing and observation stations. • Continue satellite telemetry studies of larger species.
• For conservation of birds in the wider countryside, research on movements within Britain & Ireland, and continental Europe, in relation to landscape-scale changes is high priority (for example, the movements of declining farmland birds in relation to food resources, the movements of winter visitors like thrushes and waders that are dependent on farmland, and increased knowledge of the dispersal patterns of key species of conservation concern).	• Analyses of existing data on a European scale (addressing both seasonal movements and dispersal movements). • Planned field studies involving volunteers and professionals (demonstration studies). • Develop spatially explicit population models incorporating data on movements. • Tests of best field methods (mark-recapture and resighting techniques, telemetry for local movements, chemical/genetic marker techniques).
• The filling of gaps in information on movements for species for which our overall knowledge is poor is a high priority. Research could be prioritized through the Birds of Conservation Concern listings (Gibbons et al 1996a), with 'Red-listed' and then 'Amber-listed' species with poor knowledge being the top priorities, although multi-species approaches should be adopted whenever possible to increase the general return of information.	• Existing ringing is unlikely to generate sufficient information in most cases. • Species-specific field methods likely to be most appropriate. • Tests of best field methods (mark-recapture and resighting techniques, telemetry for local movements, chemical/genetic marker techniques and biometric methods). • Use multi-species approaches to maximize data returns whenever possible. • Multi-species analyses at the European scale (as in Chapter 5) to aid prediction of likely movement patterns for species with few data.

at sea will need to be developed further in some cases. Some useful studies to investigate the breeding origins of seabirds could be based on corpses, for example from individuals caught accidentally in fishing nets or killed in oil spills (eg Boulinier 2001), with the usual caveat of the possible biases caused by movements of the corpses post-death (Chapter 4). An ambitious and exemplary integrated project, involving satellite tracking and isotope analyses, has recently been initiated to study the potential impacts of changes in fishery discard rates on a number of seabird species in the North Sea and Mediterranean, by following individual birds to establish where they are feeding during the winter months (see the Glasgow University website at www.gla.ac.uk/ibls/DEEB/rwf/ecql.html). Of course, all such work of this type will be expensive and labour-intensive, and can target only small numbers of individuals in most cases.

To balance these problems to some extent, many seabird species have relatively high ring-recovery rates, which mean that there are often at least moderate amounts of data available for our British & Irish breeding populations. However, the ring-recovery patterns must be interpreted with particular caution for this grouping; the majority of dead birds will only be reported when they are washed ashore (which may be some distance from the location where they died) or when they

are found as a result of particular recovery circumstances (such as hunting or accidental capture in fishing nets), which tend to be highly spatially aggregated (see Chapter 4). There are continuing threats to seabird populations, from pollution, accidental mortality in fishing nets, depletion of fish stocks or the construction of large offshore wind-farms for example, and the populations that breed in Britain & Ireland are internationally important (Stroud et al 2001). Some applied research on their movements has already been undertaken using ring-recovery data (eg Baillie & Mead 1982, Baillie et al 1994, Rehfisch et al 1999). However, much more research of high applied value could be carried out using the available data sets. The seabird analyses carried out for this book have only scratched the surface of what is possible: the data for many species would allow a much more detailed appraisal of the movements of British & Irish breeding populations, which should be combined with a quantitative approach to identifying and controlling for biases within the data.

Some of the possible biases within the ring-recovery data might be quantified further by validation against appropriate at-sea distributional data collected in the same periods of the annual cycle. Validation against data from individual birds followed using remote tracking will also be possible for some species, we hope, in the near future. Analyses of ring-recovery data to investigate in more detail whether there have been temporal changes in seabird movement patterns would be particularly valuable, given the complexities of monitoring long-term changes in the marine environment as a result of global climate change or depletion of fish stocks, for example. Further atlasing projects, using ring-recoveries to delineate parts of the breeding populations under threat, for example from oil spills in particular sea areas (*eg* Baillie *et al* 1994, see Figure 8 in the species account for Guillemot), would also be useful. These will be of much greater value if carried out at an international scale, such as a current project for Guillemots (Bakken 2000), allowing a much greater understanding of how populations mix outside the breeding season and which will be affected by adverse environmental changes.

Priorities for future research

In this chapter, we have highlighted a large number of gaps in our understanding of the movements of British & Irish bird populations and, indeed, European ones. The identification of such areas where knowledge is lacking has been one of the major achievements of the BTO's *Migration Atlas* project. It will provide a clear framework for the development of future research on the movements of our bird populations. The gaps that we have identified would all be worthy of filling, from both a pure and applied (conservation) viewpoint, if unlimited resources were available. In this final section, we present our personal view of areas of research that are of greatest priority in this field, with emphasis on those of high conservation value. We also identify some high-priority data-capture and analytical developments that are needed, if research in these areas is to be effective and provide robust results for conservation. Finally, we describe briefly the continuing role that we see for ringing in this future research on bird movements.

Research priorities

We have identified five main research areas that we feel are of highest priority for improving our understanding movements of bird populations that rely on Britain & Ireland during the year (Table 7.2). Our priorities are very much focused on those topics that warrant further research from an applied viewpoint, and on issues that are currently high on the conservation agenda both within Britain & Ireland and globally.

Some key analyses, such as multi-species investigations of movement patterns (similar to those that were carried out for Chapter 5 of this book) at a European scale, could provide an important basis on which to build more targeted research on several of the high-priority topics (Table 7.2). There is also a pressing need to assess the best field methods, for example to investigate the movements of certain species of high current conservation concern for which our knowledge of all movements is currently poor, and to develop methods through demonstration studies (see below).

We have not attempted to prioritize research topics by ecological grouping, although Table 7.2 gives some suggestions for groupings that fall within the topics that we have identified (such as seabirds, waders and waterfowl, farmland passerines, and the long-distant migrants likely to be most affected by global climate change). The topic-based sections earlier in this chapter provide further information on priorities by ecological grouping.

Data capture, analytical development and approaches

A number of approaches to data capture and analytical approaches have been identified in this chapter as being important for future research on bird movements. We concentrate on British & Irish birds, but many of the following recommendations apply equally to any international research on bird movements:

- European- or flyway-scale collaborative approaches are essential for many of the priority areas of research.

- Central collation of all capture data for individual birds (including the act of original ringing, subsequent recaptures and field sightings of colour-marked birds, as well as records of birds reported dead) is of high priority and would greatly increase the data available for both individual populations and multi-species analyses.

- Spatial and temporal variation in ring-reporting rates need to be further investigated, so that biases in the interpretation of recovery patterns may be reduced — this should involve both the application of analytical techniques that take account of geographical variation in reporting rates and validation against other sources of information on the spatial distribution of birds of known origin (*eg* telemetry studies, chemical and genetic marker studies, comparison with hunting bag statistics). Spatio-temporal variation in reporting rates should be incorporated into such studies where possible.

- Projects using standardized methods will be required to reduce some of the biases inherent in the ring-recovery data collected to date.

- Quantitative analytical methods for estimating rates of movement and the turnover of birds at particular sites require wider application and further development, and demonstration studies will be valuable.

- Stable isotope marker techniques have great future potential in wide-scale studies of bird migration but there is a need to investigate the resolution of such markers across Europe and the West Palearctic flyways, and produce appropriate base maps (following pioneering studies in North America).

- Satellite telemetry also has great potential in migration studies, particularly if tags can be substantially reduced in size (and cost), while maintaining or improving geographical accuracy.

- Integrated studies that combine traditional marking techniques with novel technologies and that combine individual- and population-based data, will have an important part to play in the future study of bird migration.

The role of ringing in the future study of bird movements

It is clear from this review that the traditional marking of birds with metal rings will continue to be valuable in studies of bird migration but, also, that in isolation it is unlikely to answer many further questions about the movements of British & Irish birds on an acceptable timescale. Our thoughts for the developments that should be of high priority are based on the British & Irish Ringing Scheme but in principle they would apply equally to any other scheme with similar aims:

- Existing ringing programmes that give sufficient recoveries must be maintained so that temporal change in movement patterns can be monitored.

- Information that has been under-used to date in studies of movements must be collated, made available (computerized) and analysed (*eg* original ringing data for all individuals captured, recapture data, resightings of colour-marked birds, and body size measurements that provide information on the origins and condition of ringed birds).

- The geographical spread of ringing effort must be improved wherever possible for appropriate species (in particular, there is a need to improve coverage of north and west Britain, and Ireland). On a larger scale, there is a need for more ringing in Africa and some poorly covered parts of Europe.

- The Ringing Scheme provides the basic infrastructure and skills through which novel techniques for studying bird migration (*eg* stable isotope and genetic markers, telemetry studies) will be applied in future.

This book is a tribute to the efforts of many thousands of mainly volunteer ringers who have contributed their time and expertise to provide much of our current knowledge of the movements of British &

Irish birds. To conserve our bird populations effectively, there is an urgent need to improve our knowledge of these movement patterns even further. This can only be achieved in practice through the continuing efforts of these volunteer ringers. They have the expertise and enthusiasm to maintain key existing ringing programmes and to work with professional bird ecologists in developing and applying the new approaches to the study of individual movements, and with volunteer birdwatchers in collecting important observational data, that will be needed in research on bird migration during the coming decade and beyond.

References

compiled by John H Marchant

Frequently cited references

The following key references are referred to throughout by their abbreviated titles, written in italics, and do not appear in the main list of references, ordered by author, that follows:

Short form	Full citation
1968–72 Atlas	Sharrock, J.T.R. (ed) 1976. *The Atlas of Breeding Birds in Britain and Ireland*. T. & A.D. Poyser, Berkhamsted.
1988–91 Atlas	Gibbons, D.W., J.B. Reid & R.A. Chapman (eds). 1993. *The New Atlas of Breeding Birds in Britain and Ireland: 1988–1991*. T. & A.D. Poyser, London.
Birds in Ireland	Hutchinson, C.D. 1989. *Birds in Ireland*. T. & A.D. Poyser, Calton.
Birds in Scotland	Thom, V.M. 1986. *Birds in Scotland*. T. & A.D. Poyser, Calton.
Birds in Wales	Lovegrove, R., G. Williams & I. Williams. 1994. *Birds in Wales*. T. & A.D. Poyser, London.
BWP	Cramp, S. & K.E.L. Simmons (eds). 1977. *Handbook of the Birds of Europe, the Middle East and North Africa: the birds of the Western Palearctic. Volume I. Ostrich to Ducks*. Oxford University Press, Oxford. Cramp, S. & K.E.L. Simmons (eds). 1980. *Handbook of the Birds of Europe, the Middle East and North Africa: the birds of the Western Palearctic. Volume II. Hawks to Bustards*. Oxford University Press, Oxford. Cramp, S. & K.E.L. Simmons (eds). 1983. *Handbook of the Birds of Europe, the Middle East and North Africa: the birds of the Western Palearctic. Volume III. Waders to Gulls*. Oxford University Press, Oxford. Cramp, S. (ed). 1985. *Handbook of the Birds of Europe, the Middle East and North Africa: the birds of the Western Palearctic. Volume IV. Terns to Woodpeckers*. Oxford University Press, Oxford. Cramp, S. (ed). 1988. *Handbook of the Birds of Europe, the Middle East and North Africa: the birds of the Western Palearctic. Volume V. Tyrant Flycatchers to Thrushes*. Oxford University Press, Oxford. Cramp, S. (ed). 1992. *Handbook of the Birds of Europe, the Middle East and North Africa: the birds of the Western Palearctic. Volume VI. Warblers*. Oxford University Press, Oxford.
	Cramp, S. & C.M. Perrins (eds). 1993. *Handbook of the Birds of Europe, the Middle East and North Africa: the birds of the Western Palearctic. Volume VII. Flycatchers to Shrikes*. Oxford University Press, Oxford. Cramp, S. & C.M. Perrins (eds). 1994. *Handbook of the Birds of Europe, the Middle East and North Africa: the birds of the Western Palearctic. Volume VIII. Crows to Finches*. Oxford University Press, Oxford. Cramp, S. & C.M. Perrins (eds). 1994. *Handbook of the Birds of Europe, the Middle East and North Africa: the birds of the Western Palearctic. Volume IX. Buntings and New World Warblers*. Oxford University Press, Oxford.
CBWP	Snow, D.W. & C.M. Perrins (eds). 1998. *The Birds of the Western Palearctic. Concise edition*. Oxford University Press, Oxford.
Der Zug	Zink, G. 1987. *Der Zug europäischer Singvögel*. Volume 1. AULA-Verlag, Wiesbaden. Zink, G. 1987. *Der Zug europäischer Singvögel*. Volume 2. AULA-Verlag, Wiesbaden. Zink, G. & F. Bairlein. 1995. *Der Zug europäischer Singvögel*. Volume 3. AULA-Verlag, Wiesbaden.
European Atlas	Hagemeijer, W.J.M. & M.J. Blair (eds). 1997. *The EBCC Atlas of European Breeding Birds: their distribution and abundance*. T. & A.D. Poyser, London.
Handbook	Witherby, H.F., F.C.R. Jourdain, N.F. Ticehurst & B.W. Tucker. 1938. *The Handbook of British Birds. Volume I (Crows to Flycatchers)*. H.F. & G. Witherby, London. Witherby, H.F., F.C.R. Jourdain, N.F. Ticehurst & B.W. Tucker. 1938. *The Handbook of British Birds. Volume II (Warblers to Owls)*. H.F. & G. Witherby, London. Witherby, H.F., F.C.R. Jourdain, N.F. Ticehurst & B.W. Tucker. 1939. *The Handbook of British Birds. Volume III (Hawks to Ducks)*. H.F. & G. Witherby, London. Witherby, H.F., F.C.R. Jourdain, N.F. Ticehurst & B.W. Tucker. 1940. *The Handbook of British Birds. Volume IV (Cormorants to Crane)*. H.F. & G. Witherby, London. Witherby, H.F., F.C.R. Jourdain, N.F. Ticehurst & B.W. Tucker. 1941. *The Handbook of British Birds. Volume V (Terns to Game-birds)*. H.F. & G. Witherby, London.

HBW	del Hoyo, J., A. Elliott & J. Sargatal (eds). 1992. *Handbook of the Birds of the World. Volume 1. Ostrich to Ducks.* Lynx Edicions, Barcelona. del Hoyo, J., A. Elliott & J. Sargatal (eds). 1994. *Handbook of the Birds of the World. Volume 2. New World Vultures to Guineafowl.* Lynx Edicions, Barcelona. del Hoyo, J., A. Elliott & J. Sargatal (eds). 1996. *Handbook of the Birds of the World. Volume 3. Hoatzin to Auks.* Lynx Edicions, Barcelona. del Hoyo, J., A. Elliott & J. Sargatal (eds). 1997. *Handbook of the Birds of the World. Volume 4. Sandgrouse to Cuckoos.* Lynx Edicions, Barcelona. del Hoyo, J., A. Elliott & J. Sargatal (eds). 1999. *Handbook of the Birds of the World. Volume 5. Barn-owls to Hummingbirds.* Lynx Edicions, Barcelona. del Hoyo, J., A. Elliott & J. Sargatal (eds). 2001. *Handbook of the Birds of the World. Volume 6. Mousebirds to Hornbills.* Lynx Edicions, Barcelona.
HVM	Bauer, K.M. & U.N. Glutz von Blotzheim. 1966. *Handbuch der Vögel Mitteleuropas. Volume 1. Gaviiformes – Phoenicopteriformes.* Akademische Verlagsgesellschaft, Frankfurt am Main. Bauer, K.M. & U.N. Glutz von Blotzheim. 1968. *Handbuch der Vögel Mitteleuropas. Volume 2. Anseriformes (1).* Akademische Verlagsgesellschaft, Frankfurt am Main. Bauer, K.M. & U.N. Glutz von Blotzheim. 1969. *Handbuch der Vögel Mitteleuropas. Volume 3. Anseriformes (2).* Akademische Verlagsgesellschaft, Frankfurt am Main. Glutz von Blotzheim, U.N., K.M. Bauer & E. Bezzel. 1971. *Handbuch der Vögel Mitteleuropas. Volume 4. Falconiformes.* Akademische Verlagsgesellschaft, Frankfurt am Main. Glutz von Blotzheim, U.N., K.M. Bauer & E. Bezzel. 1973. *Handbuch der Vögel Mitteleuropas. Volume 5. Galliformes und Gruiformes.* Akademische Verlagsgesellschaft, Frankfurt am Main. Glutz von Blotzheim, U.N., K.M. Bauer & E. Bezzel. 1975. *Handbuch der Vögel Mitteleuropas. Volume 6. Charadriiformes (1).* Akademische Verlagsgesellschaft, Wiesbaden. Glutz von Blotzheim, U.N., K.M. Bauer & E. Bezzel. 1977. *Handbuch der Vögel Mitteleuropas. Volume 7. Charadriiformes (2).* Akademische Verlagsgesellschaft, Wiesbaden. Glutz von Blotzheim, U.N. & K.M. Bauer. 1982. *Handbuch der Vögel Mitteleuropas. Volume 8. Charadriiformes (3).* Akademische Verlagsgesellschaft, Wiesbaden. Glutz von Blotzheim, U.N. & K.M. Bauer. 1980. *Handbuch der Vögel Mitteleuropas. Volume 9. Columbiformes – Piciformes.* Akademische Verlagsgesellschaft, Wiesbaden. Glutz von Blotzheim, U.N. & K.M. Bauer. 1985. *Handbuch der Vögel Mitteleuropas. Volume 10. Passeriformes (1).* Akademische Verlagsgesellschaft, Wiesbaden. Glutz von Blotzheim, U.N. & K.M. Bauer. 1988. *Handbuch der Vögel Mitteleuropas. Volume 11. Passeriformes (2).* Akademische Verlagsgesellschaft, Wiesbaden.

	Glutz von Blotzheim, U.N. & K.M. Bauer. 1991. *Handbuch der Vögel Mitteleuropas. Volume 12. Passeriformes (3).* Akademische Verlagsgesellschaft, Wiesbaden. Glutz von Blotzheim, U.N. & K.M. Bauer. 1993. *Handbuch der Vögel Mitteleuropas. Volume 13. Passeriformes (4).* Akademische Verlagsgesellschaft, Wiesbaden. Glutz von Blotzheim, U.N. & K.M. Bauer. 1997. *Handbuch der Vögel Mitteleuropas. Volume 14. Passeriformes (5).* Akademische Verlagsgesellschaft, Wiesbaden.
R & F	Riddiford, N. & P. Findley. 1981. *Seasonal movements of summer migrants.* BTO Guide 18. British Trust for Ornithology, Tring.
Winter Atlas	Lack, P. (ed). 1986. *The Atlas of Wintering Birds in Britain and Ireland.* T. & A.D. Poyser, Calton.

Author-date references, listed alphabetically

The reference list in this book is so long (2,878 entries) that the reader may benefit from some information on how it is constructed. This may aid the process of locating details for the brief 'author-date' references that are found in the text.

In keeping with usual convention, we have given the initials of the first author priority over date of publication, so that the publications of each individual come together in the list. In following this policy, we have deliberately introduced some apparent inconsistencies, aimed at keeping to this desired order even when an author has used more than one set of initials. Within the basic unit of the individual author, we have listed single-author references, then any with a second author, and thirdly any with two or more additional authors, before moving to the next individual in the alphabetized list.

Single-author references are alphabetized, first, by surname, second, by the author's full initials and, third, by date of publication. Where there are two authors, alphabetization follows the order 'first author, second author, date'. Where there are three or more authors, references in the text are in the form 'Author *et al* 2002'. So that such references can be more readily located, therefore, they are listed by first author and date, with the names of second and subsequent authors, which the reader would not know until consulting this list, given lower priority in the alphabetization process.

The process of collating references from so many different authors highlighted, first, that compiling a long list of references cannot be an exact science. There may be differences in the title of an article, or the authors' names, for example, between a journal article and its listing on the contents page in the same journal issue. A common-sense rather than a literal approach is sometimes needed. Second, it highlighted a very high incidence of discrepancies, many stemming from incontrovertible errors, between versions of the same reference arriving from different sources. We have attempted to resolve these by reference to the original publication wherever possible; any errors that remain are our own.

Abreu, M.V. 1989. The migration of raptors through Portugal. In *Raptors in the Modern World* (eds B.-U. Meyburg & R.D. Chancellor), pp 115–122. World Working Group on Birds of Prey and Owls, Berlin.

Adair, P. 1892. The short-eared owl (*Asio accipitrinus*, Pallas) and the kestrel (*Falco tinnunculus*, Linnæus) in the vole plague districts. *Annals of Scottish Natural History 1892*: 219–231.

Adams, M.C. 1966. Firecrests breeding in Hampshire. *British Birds* 59: 240–246.

Adams, S. 1995. Curlew Sandpipers on the Wash. *Wash Wader Ringing Group Report 1993–94*: 30–34.

Adriaens, P. 1999. The American Black Tern in Co. Dublin. *Birding World* 12: 378–379.

Adriaensen, F. 1988. An analysis of recoveries of Robins (*Erithacus rubecula*) ringed or recovered in Belgium: winter distributions. *Gerfaut* 78: 25–43.

Adriaensen, F., A.A. Dhondt & E. Matthysen. 1990. Bird migration. *Nature* 347: 23.

Adriaensen, F., P. Ulenaers & A.A. Dhondt. 1993. Ringing recoveries and the increase in numbers of European Great Crested Grebes. *Ardea* 81: 59–70.

Adriaensen, F., N. Verwimp & A.A. Dhondt. 1997. Are Belgian Kestrels *Falco tinnunculus* migratory: an analysis of ringing recoveries. *Ringing & Migration* 18: 91–101.

Adriaensen, F., N. Verwimp & A.A. Dhondt. 1998. Between cohort variation in dispersal distance in the European Kestrel *Falco tinnunculus* as shown by ringing recoveries. *Ardea* 86: 147–152.

Aebischer, N.J. 1995a. Philopatry and colony fidelity of Shags *Phalacrocorax aristotelis* on the east coast of Britain. *Ibis* 137: 11–18.

Aebischer, N.J. 1995b. Investigating the effects of hunting on the survival of British pigeons and doves by analysis of ringing recoveries. *Journal of Applied Statistics* 22: 923–934.

Aebischer, N.J. & J.C. Coulson. 1990. Survival of the Kittiwake in relation to sex, year, breeding experience and position in the colony. *Journal of Animal Ecology* 59: 1063–1071.

Aebischer, N.J. & G.R. Potts. 1994. Quail *Coturnix coturnix*. In *Birds in Europe: their conservation status* (eds G.M. Tucker & M.F. Heath), pp 222–223. Conservation series no. 3. BirdLife International, Cambridge.

Aebischer, N.J., G.R. Potts & M. Rehfisch. 1999. Using ringing data to study the effect of hunting on bird populations. *Ringing & Migration* 19 (suppl.): S67–81.

Aebischer, N.J., A.D. Evans, P.V. Grice & J.A. Vickery (eds). 2000. *Ecology and conservation of lowland farmland birds. Proceedings of the BOU Spring Conference 1999*. British Ornithologists' Union, Tring.

Aebischer, N.J., S.J. Browne & J.R. Calladine. 2001. An update on population trends, breeding ecology and migration of British Turtle Doves. In *Status, Management and Conservation of the Species Alectoris, Black Francolin, Thrush, Quail and Turtle Dove in the Mediterranean Region* (eds N. Kassinis & P. Panayides), pp 20–32. Game Fund Service, Ministry of Interior, Nicosia.

Aguilar, J.S. 1991. *Atlas de las Aves Marinas de Baleares*. Convenio de Vida Sivestre. CAIB-Icona.

Aidley, D.J. & R. Wilkinson. 1987. The annual cycle of six *Acrocephalus* warblers in a Nigerian reed-bed. *Bird Study* 34: 226–234.

Akriotis, T. 1991. Weight changes in the Wood Sandpiper *Tringa glareola* in south-eastern Greece during the spring migration. *Ringing & Migration* 12: 61–66.

Alerstam, T. 1990a. *Bird Migration*. Cambridge University Press, Cambridge.

Alerstam, T. 1990b. Ecological causes and consequences of bird orientation. *Experientia* 46: 405–415.

Alerstam, T. & A. Hedenström (eds). 1998. Optimal migration. *Journal of Avian Biology* 29: 337–636.

Alerstam, T. & G. Högstedt. 1980. Spring predictability and leap-frog migration. *Ornis Scandinavica* 11: 196–200.

Alerstam, T. & G. Högstedt. 1981. The evolution of hole-nesting in birds. *Ornis Scandinavica* 12: 188–193.

Alerstam, T. & G. Högstedt. 1985. Leap-frog arguments: reply to Pienkowski, Evans and Townshend. *Ornis Scandinavica* 16: 71–74.

Alerstam, T., C.-A. Bauer & G. Roos. 1974. Spring migration of Eiders *Somateria mollissima* in southern Scandinavia. *Ibis* 116: 194–210.

Alerstam, T., C. Hjort, G. Högstedt, P.-E. Jönsson, J. Karlsson & B. Larsson.

1986. Spring migration of birds across the Greenland Inlandice. *Meddelelser om Grønland, Bioscience* 21: 1–38.

Alerstam, T., G.A. Gudmundsson & K. Johannesson. 1992. Resources for long distance migration: intertidal exploitation of *Littorina* and *Mytilus* by Knots *Calidris canutus* in Iceland. *Oikos* 65: 179–189.

Alexander, I.H. & B. Cresswell. 1990. Foraging by Nightjars *Caprimulgus europaeus* away from their nesting areas. *Ibis* 132: 568–574.

Alexander, W.B. & D. Lack. 1944. Changes in status among British breeding birds. *British Birds* 38: 82–88.

Aley, J. & R. Aley. 1995. Red-breasted Nuthatch in Norfolk: new to Britain and Ireland. *British Birds* 88: 150–153.

Ali, S. & S.D. Ripley. 1980. *Handbook of birds of India and Pakistan. Volume 2*. Oxford University Press, Delhi.

Alisauskas, R.T. & K.A. Hobson. 1993. Determination of Lesser Snow Goose diets and winter distribution using stable isotope analysis. *Journal of Wildlife Management* 57: 49–54.

Allen, R.H. & G.E. Rutter. 1956. Moult migration of Shelduck from Cheshire in 1955. *British Birds* 49: 221–226.

Allen, R.H. & G.E. Rutter. 1957. Moult migration of Shelduck from Cheshire in 1956. *British Birds* 50: 344–346.

Allen, R.H. & G.E. Rutter. 1958. Moult migration of Shelduck from Cheshire in 1957. *British Birds* 51: 272–274.

Alonso, J.C., J.P. Veiga & J.A. Alonso. 1984. Familienauflösung und Abzug aus dem Winterquartier beim Kranich *Grus grus*. *Journal für Ornithologie* 125: 69–74.

Alonso, J.C., J.A. Alonso, F.J. Cantos & L. Bautista. 1990. Spring Crane *Grus grus* migration through Gallocanta, Spain. *Ardea* 78: 365–378.

Alonso, J.C., J.A. Alonso & L.M. Bautista. 1994. Carrying capacity of staging areas and facultative migration extension in common cranes. *Journal of Applied Ecology* 31: 212–222.

Alström, P. 1984. Sabine's Gulls in winter in Sweden. *British Birds* 77: 122.

Amat, J.A. & R.C. Soriguer. 1984. Kleptoparasitism of Coots by Gadwalls. *Ornis Scandinavica* 15: 188–194.

Anderson, A. 1982. The establishment and growth of a new Fulmar colony on sand dunes. *Bird Study* 29: 189–194.

Anderson, K.R. & C.D.T. Minton. 1978. Origins and movements of Oystercatchers on the Wash. *British Birds* 71: 439–447.

Andersson, M. 1971. Breeding behaviour of the Long-tailed Skua *Stercorarius longicaudus* (Vieillot). *Ornis Scandinavica* 2: 35–54.

Andersson, M. 1976. Population ecology of the Long-tailed Skua (*Stercorarius longicaudus* Vieill.) *Journal of Animal Ecology* 45: 537–559.

Andersson, T. 1954. Simflyttning hos skäggdopping (*Podiceps cristatus*) och gråhakedopping (*P. grisegena*). *Vår Fågelvärld* 13: 133–142.

Andrews, D.J., R.G. Mathers & E. Rainey. 1996. Brent Geese feeding on agricultural land around Strangford Lough, Co. Down. *Irish Birds* 5: 407–412.

Andrews, R., R. Higgins & J. Martin. 1999. The American Black Tern in Avon. *Birding World* 12: 416–418.

Anon. 1989. Red-necked Grebe breeding in Scotland. *Scottish Birds* 15: 133.

Anon. 1997. European news. *British Birds* 90: 238–250.

Anon. 2000. Request for records of nominate *cachinnans*, 'Caspian Gull'. *British Birds* 93: 303.

Antoniazza, M. 1998. *Resultats du recensement des oiseaux d'eau sur les lacs de Neuchâtel et de Morat*. Groupement d'Étude et de Gestion de la Grande Cariçaie, Champ-Pittet, Switzerland.

Aplin, O.V. 1890. On the distribution and sojourn in the British Islands of the Spotted Crake. *The Zoologist* 1890: 401–407.

Aplin, O.V. 1891. On the distribution and sojourn in the British Islands of the Spotted Crake. *The Zoologist* 1891: 88–96.

Appleton, G.F. & C.D.T. Minton. 1978. The primary moult of the Lapwing. *Bird Study* 25: 253–256.

Appleton, G.F., S.Y. Adams, J.A. Clark, J.R. Simons & W.J. Peach. 1997. Bird ringing in Britain and Ireland in 1995. *Ringing & Migration* 18: 113–158.

Appleyard, E.I. 1994. *Ring Ouzels of the Yorkshire Dales*. W.S. Maney & Son, Leeds.

Aquatic Warbler Conservation Team. 1999. World population, trends and conservation status of the Aquatic Warbler *Acrocephalus paludicola*. *Die Vogelwelt* 120: 65–85.

Arca, G. & C.F. Mason. 1985. Pesticide residues in eggs of Montagu's Harrier *Circus pygargus* from central Italy. *Avocetta* 9: 135–137.

Arcos, J.M. 1997. *Kleptoparasitic behaviour of Arctic Skuas* Stercorarius parasiticus *migrating through the northwestern Mediterranean*. Thesis, University of Barcelona. 31pp.

Arévalo, J.E. & A.G. Gosler. 1994. The behaviour of Treecreepers *Certhia familiaris* in mixed-species flocks in winter. *Bird Study* 41: 1–6.

Armstrong, E.A. 1955. *The Wren*. Collins, London.

Armstrong, E.A. 1958. *The Folklore of Birds*. Collins, London.

Arroyo, B.E., J.R. King & L.E. Palomares. 1995. Observations on the ecology of Montagu's and Marsh Harriers wintering in north-west Senegal. *Ostrich* 66: 37–40.

Arthur, D.S.C., P.R. Ellis, R.G. Lawie & M. Nicoll. 2000. Observations of wintering Ring Ouzels and their habitat in the High Atlas Mountains, Morocco. *Scottish Birds* 21: 109–115.

Asensio, B. 1986. La migración en España del jilguero (*Carduelis carduelis*, L.) según los resultados de anillamiento. *Ardeola* 33: 176–183.

Asensio, B. 1992. Migración e invernada de la Avefria (*Vanellus vanellus*) en la peninsula Iberica. *Doñana Acta Vertebrata* 19: 71–84.

Asensio, B. & C. Antón. 1990. Situación del Picogordo (*Coccothraustes coccothraustes*) en España. *Ardeola* 37: 29–35.

Ash, J.S. 1964. Observations in Hampshire and Dorset during the 1963 cold spell. *British Birds* 57: 221–241.

Ash, J.S. 1969. Spring weights of trans-Saharan migrants in Morocco. *Ibis* 111: 1–10.

Ash, J. 1977. Turtle Dove migration in southern Europe, the Middle East and North Africa. *British Birds* 70: 504–506.

Ash, J.S. 1980. Migrational status of Palaearctic birds in Ethiopia. In *Proceedings of the Fourth Pan-African Ornithological Conference* (ed D.W. Johnson), pp 199–208. SAOS, South Africa.

Ash, J.S. 1981. Bird-ringing results and ringed bird recoveries in Ethiopia. *Scopus* 5: 85–101.

Ashmole, M.J. 1962. The migration of European thrushes: a comparative study based on ringing recoveries. *Ibis* 104: 522–529.

Askins, J., R. Clarke & S. Piotrowski. 1996. *Orfordness Gull Report 1996*. Landguard Bird Observatory, Felixstowe.

Askokova, N.I., V.M. Konstantinov & A.N. Khokhlov. 1997. Synanthropization and synurbanization of the Magpie *Pica pica* in Russia. *Acta Ornithologica* 32: 128.

Aspinall, S.J. & R.H. Dennis. 1988. Goosanders and Red-breasted Mergansers in the Moray Firth. *Scottish Birds* 15: 65–70.

Atkinson, N.K., R.W. Summers, M. Nicoll & J.J.D. Greenwood. 1981. Population, movements and biometrics of the Purple Sandpiper *Calidris maritima* in eastern Scotland. *Ornis Scandinavica* 12: 18–27.

Atkinson, P.W. 1996. The origins, moult, movements and changes in number of Bar-tailed Godwits *Limosa lapponica* on the Wash, England. *Bird Study* 43: 60–72.

Atkinson, P.W. 1998. *The wintering ecology of the Twite* Carduelis flavirostris *and the consequences of habitat loss*. PhD thesis. University of East Anglia, Norwich.

Atkinson, P. 2001. Woodlarks' winter harbour. *BTO News* 234: 5.

Atkinson, P.W., N.A. Clark, J.A. Clark, M.C. Bell, P.J. Dare & P.L. Ireland. 2000. *The effects of changes in shellfish stocks and winter weather on shorebird populations: results of a 30-year study on the Wash, England*. Research Report 238. British Trust for Ornithology, Thetford.

Austin, G.E., J.S. Kirby & N.A. Clark. 1996. Movements and recovery circumstances of Canada Geese in Great Britain. In *Population dynamics of Canada Geese in Great Britain and implications for future management: a preliminary report to the Department of the Environment* (eds J.S. Kirby, G.E. Austin, J.M. Rowcliffe, C.V. Wernham, R.A. Pettifor & N.A. Clark), pp 126–159. Department of the Environment, Transport and the Regions, London.

Austin, G.E., I. Peachel & M.M. Rehfisch. 2000. Regional trends in coastal wintering waders in Britain. *Bird Study* 47: 352–361.

Avery, M.I. 1991. Little Tern. In *The status of seabirds in Britain and Ireland* (eds C. Lloyd, M.L. Tasker & K. Partridge), pp 234–242. T. & A.D. Poyser, London.

Avery, M.I., N.D. Coulthard, A.J. del Nevo, A. Leroux, F. Medeiros, O. Merne, L. Monteiro, A. Moralee, Y. Ntiamoa-Baidu, M. O'Briain & E. Wallace. 1995. A recovery plan for Roseate Terns in the East Atlantic: an international recovery programme. *Bird Conservation International* 5: 441–453.

Axell, H.E. 1966. Eruptions of Bearded Tits during 1959–65. *British Birds* 59: 513–543.

Axelsson, P., H. Källander & S. Nilsson. 1977. Stenknäcken och avenboken. *Anser* 16: 241–246.

Baccetti, N. & G. Cherubini (eds). 1997. Fourth European Conference on Cormorants, Bologna 1–3 November 1995. *Ricerche di Biologia della Selvaggina* 26 (suppl. 1): 1–594. Istituto per la Fauna Selvatica, Bologna.

Baccetti, N., A. Magnani & L. Serra. 1991. Migration pattern and fattening of Curlew Sandpiper at an Italian stopover site. *Wader Study Group Bulletin* 64: 17. (Abstract.)

Baccetti, N., A. De Faveri & L. Serra. 1992. Spring migration and body condition of Common Sandpipers *Actitis hypoleucos* on a small Mediterranean island. *Ringing & Migration* 13: 90–94.

Baccetti, N., R. Gambogi, A. Magnani, D. Piacentini & L. Serra. 1998. Stop-over strategy of Ruff *Philomachus pugnax* during the spring migration. *International Wader Studies* 10: 365–369.

Baggott, G.K. 1969. The moults, migrations and breeding seasons of the White Wagtail *Motacilla alba* – a review. *Bristol Ornithology* 2: 59–70.

Baggott, G.K. 1970. The timing of the moults of the Pied Wagtail. *Bird Study* 17: 45–46.

Baggott, G.K. 1986. The fat contents and flight ranges of four warbler species on migration in North Wales. *Ringing & Migration* 7: 25–36.

Bagworth, T. 1999. *Calf of Man Bird Observatory Report 1998*. Manx Natural Heritage, Douglas.

Baha el Din, S.M., W. Salama, A. Grieve & R.E. Green. 1996. Trapping and shooting of Corncrakes *Crex crex* on the Mediterranean coast of Egypt. *Bird Conservation International* 6: 213–217.

Bailey, M.A. & M.G. Rowan. 1987. Pied Wagtail roost at Claverton Down, Bath, 1980–1987. *Chew Valley Ringing Station Report 1984–1986*: 19–31.

Baillie, J. & B. Groombridge. 1996. *The 1996 IUCN Red List of Threatened Animals*. IUCN, Gland, Switzerland.

Baillie, S.R. 1984. *The movements of migratory birds in periods of severe cold weather*. Research Report 11. British Trust for Ornithology, Tring.

Baillie, S.R. 1990a. Integrated population monitoring of breeding birds in Britain and Ireland. *Ibis* 132: 151–166.

Baillie, S.R. 1990b. Mortality patterns of North Sea seabirds. In *Birds and the North Sea* (ed S.M.D. Alexander), pp 37–63. Tenth Anniversary Publication of the North Sea Bird Club, Aberdeen.

Baillie, S.R. 1991. Monitoring terrestrial breeding bird populations. In *Monitoring for Conservation and Ecology* (ed F.B. Goldsmith), pp 112–132. Chapman & Hall, London.

Baillie, S.R. 1995. Uses of ringing data for the conservation and management of bird populations: a ringing scheme perspective. *Journal of Applied Statistics* 22: 967–987.

Baillie, S.R. 2001. The contribution of ringing to the conservation and management of bird populations: a review. *Ardea* 89 (special issue): 167–184.

Baillie, S.R. & R.E. Green. 1987. The importance of variation in recovery rates when estimating survival rates from ringing recoveries. *Acta Ornithologica* 23: 41–60.

Baillie, S.R. & C.J. Mead. 1982. The effect of severe oil pollution during the winter of 1980–81 on British and Irish auks. *Ringing & Migration* 4: 33–44.

Baillie, S.R. & H. Milne. 1982. The influence of age on breeding in the Eider *Somateria mollissima*. *Bird Study* 29: 55–66.

Baillie, S.R. & H. Milne. 1989. Movements of Eiders *Somateria mollissima* on the east coast of Britain. *Ibis* 131: 321–335.

Baillie, S.R. & H. Milne. 1997. Eider population biology – the Forvie contribution. In *The Ythan, a festschrift for George Dunnet* (ed M.L. Gorman), pp 92–105. University of Aberdeen, Aberdeen.

Baillie, S.R. & W.J. Peach. 1992. Population limitation in Palaearctic-African migrant passerines. *Ibis* 134 (suppl. 1): 120–132.

Baillie, S.R., N.A. Clark & M.A. Ogilvie. 1986. *Cold weather movements of waterfowl and waders: an analysis of ringing recoveries*. Research Report 19. British Trust for Ornithology, Tring.

Baillie, S.R., C. Dudley & M.P. Harris. 1994. *Atlas of recoveries of Guillemots, Uria aalge, ringed in Scotland*. Report from BTO and ITE to Scottish Natural Heritage. British Trust for Ornithology, Thetford.

Baillie, S.R., C.V. Wernham & J.A. Clark. 1999a. Proceedings of the JNCC/BTO Workshop on the Conservation Uses of Ringing Data. *Ringing & Migration* 19 (suppl.).

Baillie, S.R., C.V. Wernham & J.A. Clark. 1999b. Development of the British and Irish Ringing Scheme and its role in conservation biology. *Ringing & Migration* 19 (suppl.): S5–19.

Baillie, S.R., R.W. Furness, J.A. Clark, R.E. Green, A.G. Gosler, S.J. Ormerod, W.J. Peach, D.A. Stroud, W.J. Sutherland & J.D. Wilson. 1999c. The Scientific Strategy of the BTO Ringing Scheme. *Ringing & Migration* 19 (suppl.): S129–143.

Baillie, S.R., P.M. North & A.G. Gosler (eds). 1999d. Large-scale studies of marked birds. Proceedings of the EURING97 Conference. *Bird Study* 46 (suppl.).

Baillie, S.R., W.J. Sutherland, S.N. Freeman, R.D. Gregory & E. Paradis. 2000. Consequences of large-scale processes for the conservation of bird populations. *Journal of Applied Ecology* 37 (suppl. 1): 88–102.

Baillie, S.R., H.Q.P. Crick, D.E. Balmer, R.I. Bashford, L.P. Beaven, S.N. Freeman, J.H. Marchant, D.G. Noble, M.J. Raven, G.M. Siriwardena, R. Thewlis & C.V. Wernham. 2001. *Breeding birds in the wider countryside: their conservation status 2000*. Research Report 252. British Trust for Ornithology, Thetford. www.bto.org/birdtrends

Baillon, F. & P. Dubois. 1991. Seawatching from Cape Verde, Senegal. *Birding World* 4: 440–442.

Bainbridge, I.P. & C.D.T. Minton. 1978. The migration and mortality of the Curlew in Britain and Ireland. *Bird Study* 25: 39–50.

Baines, D. 1994. Seasonal differences in habitat selection by Black Grouse *Tetrao tetrix* in the northern Pennines, England. *Ibis* 136: 39–43.

Baines, D. 1996. Seasonal variation in lek attendance and lekking behaviour by male Black Grouse *Tetrao tetrix*. *Ibis* 138: 177–180.

Baines, D. & P.J. Hudson. 1995. The decline of Black Grouse in Scotland and northern England. *Bird Study* 42: 122–131.

Baines, D. & R.W. Summers. 1997. Assessment of bird collisions with deer fences in Scottish forests. *Journal of Applied Ecology* 34: 941–948.

Baines, D., I.A. Wilson & G. Beeley. 1996. Timing of breeding in Black Grouse *Tetrao tetrix* and Capercaillie *Tetrao urogallus* and distribution of insect food for chicks. *Ibis* 138: 181–187.

Bairlein, F. 1985a. Body weights and fat deposition of Palaearctic passerine migrants in the central Sahara. *Oecologia* 68: 141–146.

Bairlein, F. 1985b. Offene Fragen der Erforschung des Zuges paläarktischer Vogelarten in Afrika. *Die Vogelwarte* 33: 144–155.

Bairlein, F. von. 1985c. Dismigration und Sterblichkeit in Süddeutschland beringter Schleiereulen (*Tyto alba*). *Die Vogelwarte* 33: 81–108.

Bairlein, F. 1987. The migratory strategy of the Garden Warbler: a survey of field and laboratory data. *Ringing & Migration* 8: 59–72.

Bairlein, F. 1988. How do migratory songbirds cross the Sahara? *Trends in Ecology & Evolution* 3: 191–194.

Bairlein, F. 1991. Body mass of Garden Warblers (*Sylvia borin*) on migration: a review of field data. *Die Vogelwarte* 36: 48–61.

Bairlein, F. 1995. *Manual of Field Methods*. European-African Songbird Migration Network, Wilhelmshaven.

Bairlein, F. 1997a. *Spatio-temporal course, ecology and energetics of Western Palaearctic-African songbird migrants: 1994–1996 summary report*. Institut für Vogelforschung, Wilhelmshaven.

Bairlein, F. 1997b. *The European-African Songbird Migration Network: summary report*. European-African Songbird Migration Network, Wilhelmshaven.

Bairlein, F. 2000. *Optimality in Bird Migration – towards an Understanding of Avian Migration Strategies*. Proposal to the European Science Foundation. Institut für Vogelforschung, Wilhelmshaven. (See www.esf.org)

Bairlein, F. 2001. Results of bird ringing in the study of migration routes. *Ardea* 89 (special issue): 7–19.

Bairlein, F. & U. Totzke. 1992. New aspects on migratory physiology of trans-Saharan passerine migrants. *Ornis Scandinavica* 23: 244–250.

Bairlein, F. & W. Winkel. 2001. Birds and climate change. In *Climate of the 21st Century: Changes and Risks* (eds J.L. Lozan, H. Graßl & H. Hupfer), pp 278–282. Wissenschaftliche Auswertungen, Hamburg.

Bairlein, F., P. Beck, W. Feiler & U. Querner. 1983. Autumn weights of some Palaearctic passerine migrants in the Sahara. *Ibis* 125: 404–407.

Bak, B. & H. Ettrup. 1982. Studies on the migration and mortality of the Lapwing (*Vanellus vanellus*) in Denmark. *Danish Review of Game Biology* 12: 1–20.

Baker, H. 1985. The status of the Canada Goose in the London Area. *London Bird Report* 49: 111–126.

Baker, J. 1998. The Yellow-legged Gull *Larus cachinnans* in Oxfordshire. *Birds of Oxfordshire 1997*: 72–76.

Baker, J.K. & G.P. Catley. 1987. Yellow-browed Warblers in Britain and Ireland, 1968–85. *British Birds* 80: 93–109.

Baker, R.R. 1978. *The Evolutionary Ecology of Animal Migration*. Hodder & Stoughton, London.

Baker, R.R. 1980. The significance of the Lesser Black-backed Gull for models of bird migration. *Bird Study* 27: 41–50.

Baker, R.R. 1984. *Bird Navigation: the Solution of a Mystery?* Hodder & Stoughton, London.

Baker, R.R. 1993. The function of post-fledging exploration: a pilot study of three species of passerines ringed in Britain. *Ornis Scandinavica* 24: 71–79.

Bakken, V. 2000. A recovery database of Common and Brünnich's Guillemots ringed in the Atlantic. *Seabird Group Newsletter* 86: 9–10.

Balfour, E. 1956. Crane in Orkney. *British Birds* 49: 38.

Balfour, E. & C.J. Cadbury. 1979. Polygyny, spacing, and sex ratio among Hen Harriers *Circus cyaneus* in Orkney, Scotland. *Ornis Scandinavica* 10: 133–141.

Balfour, E., A. Anderson & G. Dunnet. 1967. Orkney Cormorants – their breeding distribution and dispersal. *Scottish Birds* 4: 481–493.

Ballance, D.K. 2000. *Birds in Counties: an ornithological bibliography for the counties of England, Wales, Scotland and the Isle of Man*. Imperial College Press, London.

Balmer, D.E. 2001. RAS – four years on. *BTO News* 236: 14.

Balmer, D. 2002. Migration Watch: the new spring migration project. *BTO News* 238: 8–9.

Balmer, D. & J. Marchant. 1993. The sparrows fall. *British Birds* 86: 631–633.

Balmer, D.E. & W.J. Peach. 1996. *Review of natural avian mortality rates.* Research Report 175. British Trust for Ornithology, Thetford.

Balmer, D.E. & C.V. Wernham. 2001. *RAS Newsletter* 3. British Trust for Ornithology, Thetford.

Balmer, D.E., S.J. Browne & M.M. Rehfisch. 1996. A year in the life of Golden Pheasants *Chrysolophus pictus*. In *The Introduction and Naturalisation of Birds* (eds J.S. Holmes & J.R. Simons), pp 87–93. The Stationery Office, London.

Banks, K.W., H. Clark, I.R.K. Mackay, S.G. Mackay & R.M. Sellers. 1991. Origins, population structure, and movements of Snow Buntings *Plectrophenax nivalis* wintering in Highland Region, Scotland. *Bird Study* 38: 10–19.

Bannerman, D.A. 1961. *The Birds of the British Isles.* Volume 10. Oliver & Boyd, Edinburgh and London.

Bapat, N.N. & M.K. Himmatsinhji. 1992. Occurrence of *Larus minutus* Pallas in Kutch. *Journal of the Bombay Natural History Society* 89: 119–120.

Barnard, C. & D.B.A. Thompson. 1985. *Gulls and Plovers.* Croom Helm, London.

Barnes, J.A.G. 1952. The status of the Lesser Black-backed Gull. *British Birds* 45: 3–17.

Barre, N., P. Feldmann, G. Tayalay, P. Roc, M. Anselme & W. Smith. 1997. Introduction et extension de la tourterelle turque *Streptopelia decaocto* dans les Petites Antilles. *Alauda* 65: 245–250.

Barrett, J. & C.F. Barrett. 1985. Divers in the Moray Firth, Scotland. *Scottish Birds* 13: 149–154.

Barrett, R.T. 1988. The dispersal and migration of the Gannet *Sula bassana* from Norwegian breeding colonies. *Ringing & Migration* 9: 139–145.

Bartolomé, J., M. Fernández-Cruz & F. Campos. 1996. Band recoveries of Spanish Little Egrets, *Egretta garzetta*. *Colonial Waterbirds* 19: 220–225.

Barton, D. 1982. Notes on skuas and jaegers in the western Tasmanian Sea. *Emu* 82: 56–59.

Barton, N.W.H. & D.C. Houston. 1993. A comparison of digestive efficiency in birds of prey. *Ibis* 135: 363–371.

Bastian, H.-V. 1992. Breeding and natal dispersal of Whinchats *Saxicola rubetra*. *Ringing & Migration* 13: 13–19.

Batschelet, E. 1981. *Circular Statistics in Biology.* Academic Press, New York.

Batten, L.A. 1973. The colonisation of England by the Firecrest. *British Birds* 66: 159–166.

Batten, L.A. 1977. *Studies on the population dynamics and energetics of Blackbirds* Turdus merula *Linnaeus*. PhD thesis, University of London.

Batten, L.A., C.J. Bibby, P. Clement, G.D. Elliott & R.F. Porter. 1990. *Red Data Birds in Britain*. T. & A.D. Poyser, London.

Baudvin, H. 1986. La reproduction de la Chouette Effraie (*Tyto alba*). *Le Jean-le-Blanc* 25: 1–125.

Bavoux, C., G. Burneleau, P. Nicolau-Guillaumet & M. Picard. 1992. Le busard des roseaux *Circus a. aeruginosus* en Charente-Maritime (France). V. Déplacements et activité journalière des juvéniles en hiver. *Alauda* 60: 149–158.

Bavoux, C., G. Burneleau, P. Nicolau-Guillaumet & M. Picard. 1994. Le busard des roseaux *Circus a. aeruginosus* en Charente-Maritime (France). VII. Déplacements et activité journalière des adultes en hiver. *Alauda* 62: 281–288.

Bavoux, C., G. Burneleau, P. Nicolau-Guillaumet, M. Picard & C. Sahuc. 1998. Dependence and emancipation in juvenile Marsh Harriers *Circus a. aeruginosus*. In *Holarctic Birds of Prey* (eds R.D. Chancellor, B.-U. Meyburg & J.J. Ferrero), pp 91–100. ADENEX/World Working Group on Birds of Prey and Owls, Calamonte, Spain.

Baxter, E.V. & L.J. Rintoul. 1953. *The Birds of Scotland.* Oliver & Boyd, Edinburgh and London.

Beaman, M. & C. Galea. 1974. The visible migration of raptors over the Maltese islands. *Ibis* 116: 419–431.

Becker, P. 1995. Identification of Water Rail and *Porzana* crakes in Europe. *Dutch Birding* 17: 181–211.

Becker, P.H. & M. Erdelen. 1987. Die Bestandsentwicklung von Brutvögeln der deutschen Nordseeküste 1950–1979. *Journal für Ornithologie* 128: 1–32.

Becker, P.H. & H. Wendeln. 1996. Ring removal in terns caught in Africa – a major problem for population studies. *Ringing & Migration* 17: 31–32.

Becker, P.H. & H. Wendeln. 1997. A new application for transponders in population ecology of the Common Tern. *Condor* 99: 534–538.

Becker, P.H., H. Wendeln & J. Gonzáles-Solís. 2001. Population dynamics, recruitment, individual quality and reproductive strategies in Common Terns *Sterna hirundo* marked with transponders. *Ardea* 89 (special issue): 241–252.

Bedingfield, R.E. 1961. Canada Geese released by the Dorset Wildfowlers' Club, 1957 to 1960. *WAGBI Annual Report 1960–1961*: 28–29.

Beekman, J.H. 1997. International censuses of the northwest European Bewick's Swan population, January 1990 and 1995. *Swan Specialist Group Newsletter* 6: 7–9.

Beekman, J.H. & B. Laubek. 1997. Satellite tracking of Bewick's Swans on spring migrations. *Swan Specialist Group Newsletter* 6: 16–18.

Beekman, J., E. Rees & P. Bacon. 1994. Bewick's Swan *Cygnus columbianus*. In *Birds in Europe: their conservation status* (eds G.M. Tucker & M.F. Heath), pp 108–109. Conservation Series no. 3. BirdLife International, Cambridge.

Beekman, J., P. Berthold, E. Nowak & U. Querner. 1996. Implementation of satellite tracking in studying migration of Anatidae: an overview and a case study. In *Proceedings of the Anatidae 2000 Conference, Strasbourg, France, 5–9 December 1994* (eds M. Birkan, J. van Vessem, P. Havet, J. Madsen, B. Trolliet & M. Moser). *Gibier Faune Sauvage* 13: 157–176.

Begg, G.S. & J.B. Reid. 1997. Spatial variation in seabird density at a shallow sea tidal mixing front in the Irish Sea. *ICES Journal of Marine Science* 54: 552–565.

Belisle, M. & J.F. Giroux. 1995. Predation and kleptoparasitism by migrating parasitic jaegers. *Condor* 97: 771–781.

Bell, B.D. & R.J. Hornby. 1968. Territory, pair-bonds, mortality and movements in the Reed Bunting population. *Attenborough Ringing Report 1967*: 9–15.

Bell, C.P. 1996. Seasonality and time allocation as causes of leap-frog migration in the Yellow Wagtail *Motacilla flava*. *Journal of Avian Biology* 27: 334–342.

Bell, M.C. & C. Mitchell. 1996. *Survival in Surface Feeding Ducks.* Report to JNCC. Wildfowl & Wetlands Trust, Slimbridge.

Bell, M.C., A.D. Fox, M. Owen, J.M. Black & A.J. Walsh. 1993. Approaches to estimation of survival in two Arctic-nesting goose species. In *Marked Individuals in the Study of Bird Populations* (eds J.-D. Lebreton & P.M. North), pp 141–155. Birkhäuser Verlag, Basel.

Bell, M.V. 1988. Feeding behaviour of wintering Pink-footed and Greylag Geese in northeast Scotland. *Wildfowl* 39: 43–53.

Bell, N.A., P.A. Crowther & L.J. Degnan (eds). 1997. *Spurn Wildlife Number 7.* Yorkshire Naturalists' Union and Spurn Bird Observatory Committee.

Bellamy, P.E., N.J. Brown, B. Enoksson, L.G. Firbank, R.J. Fuller, S.A. Hinsley, A.G.M. Schotman & R.D. Swetnam. 1998. The influences of habitat, landscape structure and climate on distribution patterns of the Nuthatch (*Sitta europaea* L.). *Oecologia* 115: 127–136.

Bellrose, F.C. 1980. *Ducks, Geese & Swans of North America.* Stackpole Books, Harrisburg, Pennsylvania.

Belman, P.J. 1981. Ringing and recoveries of Greenland White-fronted Geese. In *Report of the 1979 Greenland White-fronted Goose Study Expedition to Eqalungmiut Nunât, West Greenland* (eds A.D. Fox & D.A. Stroud), pp 123–138. Greenland White-fronted Goose Study, Aberystwyth.

Belopol'skij, L.O. 1972. Ecological peculiarities in *Accipiter nisus* (L.) migrations. *Soviet Journal of Ecology* 3: 138–142.

Bengtson, S.-A. 1968. Breeding behaviour of the Grey Phalarope in West Spitsbergen. *Vår Fågelvärld* 27: 1–13.

Benkman, C.W. 1993a. Adaptation to single resources and the evolution of crossbill (*Loxia*) diversity. *Ecological Monographs* 63: 305–325.

Benkman, C.W. 1993b. Logging, conifers, and the conservation of crossbills. *Conservation Biology* 7: 473–479.

Benn, S. 1995. Successful breeding of Bluethroat in Scotland. *Scottish Birds* 18: 114.

Bensch, S. & B. Nielsen. 1999. Autumn migration speed of juvenile Reed and Sedge Warblers in relation to date and fat loads. *Condor* 101: 153–156.

Bent, A.C. 1946. *Life histories of North American Jays, Crows, and Titmice.* United States National Museum Bulletin 191. Smithsonian Institution, Washington DC.

Bentley, P. 1995. Understanding map projections, bird distribution, migration and vagrancy. *Birding World* 8: 231–239.

Beretzk, P., A. Keve, B. Nagy & J. Szijj. 1959. Economic importance of the Curlews and taxonomical position of the Hungarian populations. *Aquila* 65: 89–126.

Bergman, G. 1946. Der Steinwalzer, *Arenaria i. interpres* L., im seiner Beziehung zur Umwelt. *Acta Zoologica Fennica* 47: 1–144.

Bergström, R., H. Huldt & U. Nilsson (eds). 1992. *Swedish Game – Biology and Management.* Swedish Hunters' Association, Spånga.

Berrow, S.D., T.C. Kelly & A.A. Myers. 1991. Crows on estuaries: distribution and feeding behaviour of the Corvidae on four estuaries in southwest Ireland. *Irish Birds* 4: 393–412.

Berry, J. 1939. *The Status and Distribution of Wild Geese and Duck in Scotland.* International Wildfowl Inquiry. Volume 2. Cambridge University Press, Cambridge.

Berry, R.J. & J.L. Johnston. 1980. *The Natural History of Shetland.* Collins, London.

Berthold, P. 1973. Relationships between migratory restlessness and migration distance in six *Sylvia* species. *Ibis* 115: 594–599.

Berthold, P. 1984. The control of partial migration in birds: a review. *The Ring* 10: 253–265.

Berthold, P. 1985. A comparative study of juvenile development, migratory restlessness and migratory behaviour in the Redstart and Black Redstart. *Journal für Ornithologie* 126: 383–392.

Berthold, P. 1988. The biology of the genus *Sylvia* – a model and a challenge for Afro-European co-operation. *Tauraco* 1: 3–28.

Berthold, P. 1990. Genetics of migration. In *Bird Migration: physiology and ecophysiology* (ed E. Gwinner), pp 269–280. Springer Verlag, Berlin.

Berthold, P. (ed). 1991. *Orientation in birds.* Birkhäuser Verlag, Basel.

Berthold, P. 1993. *Bird Migration: a general survey.* Oxford University Press, Oxford.

Berthold, P. 1995. Microevolution of migratory behaviour illustrated by the Blackcap *Sylvia atricapilla* – 1993 Witherby lecture. *Bird Study* 42: 89–100.

Berthold, P. 1996. *Control of Bird Migration.* Chapman & Hall, London.

Berthold, P. 1999. A comprehensive theory for the evolution, control and adaptability of avian migration. *Ostrich* 70: 1–11.

Berthold, P. 2001. *Bird Migration: a general survey.* Second edition. Oxford University Press, Oxford.

Berthold, P. & U. Querner. 1995. Microevolutionary aspects of bird migration based on experimental results. *Israel Journal of Zoology* 41: 377–385.

Berthold, P. & R. Schlenker. 1975. Das Mettnau-Reit-Illmitz-Programm –

ein langfristiges Vogelfangprogramm der Vogelwarte Radolfzell. *Die Vogelwarte* 28: 97–123.

Berthold, P. & W. Winkel (eds). 2000. [Papers from *Bird Ringing 100 Years* conference, Helgoland 1999.] *Die Vogelwarte* 40: 249–324.

Berthold, P., E. Gwinner & H. Klein. 1970. Vergleichende Untersuchung der Jugundentwicklung eines ausgeprägten Zugvogels, *Sylvia borin*, und eines weniger ausgeprägten Zugvogels, *Sylvia atricapilla*. *Die Vogelwarte* 25: 297–331.

Berthold, P., G. Fliege, G. Heine, U. Querner & R. Schlenker. 1991. Autumn migration, resting behaviour, biometry and moult of small birds in central Europe. *Die Vogelwarte* 36: 1–221.

Berthold, P., A.J. Helbig, G. Mohr & U. Querner. 1992. Rapid microevoloution of migratory behaviour in a wild bird species. *Nature* 360: 668–669.

Berthold, P., A. Kaiser, U. Querner & R. Schlenker. 1993. Analyse von Fangzahlen im Hinblick auf die Bestandsentwicklung von Kleinvögeln nach 20 jährigem Betrieb der Station Mettnau, Süddeutschland. *Journal für Ornithologie* 134: 283–299.

Berthold, P., E. Nowak & U. Querner. 1995. Satellite-tracking of a migratory bird from central Europe to South African winter quarters – a case-report of the White Stork. *Journal für Ornithologie* 136: 73–76.

Berthold, P., W. van den Bossche, Y. Leshem, C. Kaatz, M. Kaatz, E. Nowak & U. Querner. 1997a. Satellite-tracking of the annual migration of a White Stork *Ciconia ciconia* and discussion of the orientation mechanisms of homeward migration. *Journal für Ornithologie* 138: 229–233.

Berthold, P., W. van den Bossche, Y. Leshem, C. Kaatz, M. Kaatz, E. Nowak & U. Querner. 1997b. Satellite-tracking of White Storks *Ciconia ciconia*: migration of an eastern individual to South Yemen. *Journal für Ornithologie* 138: 546–549.

Berthold, P., W. van den Bossche, W. Fiedler, C. Kaatz, M. Kaatz, Y. Leshem, E. Nowak & U. Querner. 2001. Detection of a new important staging area of the White Stork *Ciconia ciconia* by satellite tracking. *Ibis* 143: 450–455.

Bianki, V.V. 1979. Status of *Branta bernicla bernicla* in White Sea passage areas, USSR. In *Proceedings of the First Technical Meeting on Western Palaearctic Migratory Bird Management* (ed M. Smart), pp 21–24. International Waterfowl Research Bureau, Slimbridge.

Bianki, V.V. & T.D. Gerasimova. 1960. [Results of bird ringing between 1936 and 1958.] *Trudy Kandalakshskogo Gosudarstbennogo Zapovednika* 3: 199–262. (In Russian.)

Bibby, C.J. 1973. The Red-backed Shrike: a vanishing British species. *Bird Study* 20: 103–110.

Bibby, C.J. 1979. Mortality and movements of Dartford Warblers in England. *British Birds* 72: 10–22.

Bibby, C.J. 1981a. Wintering Bitterns in Britain. *British Birds* 74: 1–10.

Bibby, C.J. 1981b. An experiment on the recovery of dead birds from the North Sea. *Ornis Scandinavica* 12: 261–265.

Bibby, C.J. 1982. Polygyny and breeding ecology of the Cetti's Warbler *Cettia cetti*. *Ibis* 124: 288–301.

Bibby, C.J. 1983. Studies of west Palearctic birds 186. Bearded Tit. *British Birds* 76: 549–563.

Bibby, C.J. & R.E. Green. 1980. Foraging behaviour of migrant Pied Flycatchers *Ficedula hypoleuca* on temporary territories. *Journal of Animal Ecology* 49: 507–521.

Bibby, C.J. & R.E. Green. 1981. Autumn migration strategies of Reed and Sedge Warblers. *Ornis Scandinavica* 12: 1–12.

Bibby, C.J. & R.E. Green. 1983. Food and fattening of migrating warblers in some French marshlands. *Ringing & Migration* 4: 175–184.

Bibby, C.J. & M. Nattrass. 1986. Breeding status of the Merlin in Britain. *British Birds* 79: 170–185.

Biber, J.-P. & T. Salathé. 1991. Threats to migratory birds. In *Conserving Migratory Birds* (ed T. Salathé), pp 17–35. Technical Publication 12. International Council for Bird Preservation, Cambridge.

Biebach, H. 1983. Genetic determination of partial migration in the European Robin (*Erithacus rubecula*). *Auk* 100: 601–606.

Biebach, H. 1990. Strategies of trans-Saharan migrants. In *Bird Migration: the physiology and ecophysiology* (ed E. Gwinner), pp 352–367. Springer Verlag, Berlin.

Biebach, H. 1992. Flight-range estimates for small trans-Sahara migrants. *Ibis* 134 (suppl. 1): 47–54.

Bignal, E.M. & D.J. Curtis. 1989. *Choughs and Land-use in Europe*. Proceedings of an International Workshop on the Conservation of the Chough in the EC. Scottish Chough Study Group, Paisley.

Bijleveld, M. 1974. *Birds of Prey in Europe*. Macmillan, London.

Bijlsma, R.G. 1987. Explosieve toename van de Appelvink. *Limosa* 60: 155.

Bijlsma, R.G. 1993. *Ecologische Atlas van de Nederlandse Roofvogels*. Schuyt & Co, Haarlem.

Binet, D. 1997. Climate and pelagic fisheries in the Canary and Guinea currents 1964–1993: the role of trade winds and the southern oscillation. *Oceanologica Acta* 20: 177–190.

Bircham, P.M.M. 1989. *The birds of Cambridgeshire*. Cambridge University Press, Cambridge.

Bircham, P.M.M. & C.J. Bibby. 1978. Movements of birds to and from Cambridgeshire as indicated by ringing recoveries: 1. Thrushes. *Cambridge Bird Report* 52: 46–52.

BirdLife International. 2000. *Threatened Birds of the World*. Lynx Edicions, Barcelona, and BirdLife International, Cambridge.

Birkan, M. & J.M. Angibault. 1990. Utilisation de l'espace et rythme d'activité chez la perdrix grise (*Perdix perdix*). In *Proceedings from Sixteenth Congress of the International Union of Game Biologists* (ed P. Hell), pp 822–831. Forest Research Institute, Zvolen, Czechoslovakia.

Birkan, M., D. Serre, S. Skibniewski & E. Pelard. 1992. Spring–summer home range, habitat use and survival of Grey Partridge (*Perdix perdix*) in a semi-open habitat. In *Perdix VI, First International Symposium on Partridges, Quails & Francolins* (eds M. Birkan, G.R. Potts, N.J. Aebischer & S.D. Dowell). *Gibier Faune Sauvage* 9: 431–442.

Birkhead, M. & C. Perrins. 1986. *The Mute Swan*. Croom Helm, London.

Birkhead, T.R. 1974. Movements and mortality rates of British Guillemots. *Bird Study* 21: 241–254.

Birkhead, T.R. 1991. *The Magpies*. T. & A.D. Poyser, London.

Birkhead, T.R., S.F. Eden, K. Clarkson, S.F. Goodburn & J. Pellatt. 1986. Social organisation of a population of Magpies *Pica pica*. *Ardea* 74: 59–68.

Black, J.M. 1998. *Conservation and management plan for the Svalbard population of Barnacle Geese*. DN-Rapport 1998/1, pp 1–111. Directorate for Nature Management and Scottish Natural Heritage, Trondheim.

Black, J.M. & E.C. Rees. 1984. The structure and behaviour of the Whooper Swan population wintering at Caerlaverock, Dumfries and Galloway, Scotland: an introductory study. *Wildfowl* 35: 21–36.

Black, J.M., C. Deerenberg & M. Owen. 1991. Foraging behaviour and site selection of Barnacle Geese in a traditional and newly colonized spring staging area. *Ardea* 79: 349–358.

Blackwell, J.A. & W.H. Dowdeswell. 1951. Local movement in the Blue Tit. *British Birds* 44: 397–403.

Blair, M.J., H. McKay, A.J. Musgrove & M.M. Rehfisch. 2000. *Review of the status of introduced non-native waterbird species in the agreement area of African–Eurasian Waterbird Agreement*. Research Report 229. British Trust for Ornithology, Thetford.

Blake, B.F., M.L. Tasker, P. Hope Jones, T.J. Dixon, R. Mitchell & D.R. Langslow. 1984. *Seabird distribution in the North Sea*. Nature Conservancy Council, Huntingdon.

Blank, T.H. 1980. A day in the life of the Partridge. *The Field* 256: 807.

Blank, T.H. & J.S. Ash. 1956. The concept of territory in the Partridge *Perdix perdix*. *Ibis* 98: 379–389.

Blomert, A.-M., M. Engelmoer & Y. Ntiamoa-Baidu. 1990. The Banc d'Arguin, Mauritania, as a meeting point for Avocets during spring migration. *Ardea* 78: 185–192.

Blondel, J. 1967. Étude d'un cline chez le Rouge-queue à Front Blanc *Phoenicurus phoenicurus phoenicurus* (L.): la variation de la longueur d'aile, son utilisation dans l'étude des migrations. *Alauda* 35: 83–105, 163–193.

Bloomfield, A. & J. McCallum. 1999. The Stock Dove and its status in Norfolk. *Norfolk Bird Club Bulletin* 33: 5–6.

Blums, P., A. Mednis & J. Baumanis. 1989. [Long-distance dispersal in some European ducks.] *La Sauvagine* 309: 44–51. (In French.)

Blums, P., A. Mednis, I. Bauga, J.D. Nichols & J.E. Hines. 1996. Age-specific survival and philopatry in three species of European ducks: a long-term study. *Condor* 98: 61–74.

Blurton-Jones, N.G. 1956. Census of breeding Canada Geese. *Bird Study* 3: 153–170.

Boddy, M. 1983. Factors influencing timing of autumn dispersal or migration in first-year Dunnocks and Whitethroats. *Bird Study* 30: 39–46.

Boddy, M. 1984. Body weights of adult and juvenile Lesser Redpolls in central and southern England. *Ringing & Migration* 5: 91–100.

Boddy, M. 1992. Timing of Whitethroat *Sylvia communis* arrival, breeding and moult at a coastal site in Lincolnshire. *Ringing & Migration* 13: 65–72.

Boddy, M. 1993. Whitethroat *Sylvia communis* population studies during 1981–91 at a breeding site on the Lincolnshire coast. *Ringing & Migration* 14: 73–83.

Boddy, M. 1994. Survival/return rates and juvenile dispersal in an increasing population of Lesser Whitethroats *Sylvia curruca*. *Ringing & Migration* 15: 65–78.

Boddy, M. & A.C. Blackburn. 1978. Ringing studies at a Nottinghamshire Corn Bunting roost. *Ringing & Migration* 2: 27–33.

Boddy, M. & R.M. Sellers. 1983. Orientated movements of Greenfinches in southern Britain. *Ringing & Migration* 4: 129–138.

Boere, G.C. 1976. The significance of the Dutch Waddenzee in the annual life cycle of arctic, subarctic and boreal waders. Part I. The function as a moulting area. *Ardea* 64: 210–291.

Boere, G., K. Roselaar & M. Engelmoer. 1984. The breeding origins of Purple Sandpipers *Calidris maritima* present in the Netherlands. *Ardea* 72: 101–109.

Boisseau, S. & D.W. Yalden. 1998. The former status of the Crane *Grus grus* in Britain. *Ibis* 140: 482–500.

Boldreghini, P., P.L. Meininger & R. Santolini. 1992. Preliminary results of ringing Mediterranean Gulls *Larus melanocephalus* breeding in the Netherlands, Belgium and Italy. *Avocetta* 16: 73–74.

Boobyer, G. 1999. The requirements of the UK Statutory Conservation Agencies. *Ringing & Migration* 19 (suppl.): S20–27.

Booth, C.J. 1986. Raven breeding for first time at 6 years old. *Scottish Birds* 14: 51.

Booth, C., M. Cuthbert & P. Reynolds. 1984. *The Birds of Orkney*. The Orkney Press, Stromness.

Borzhonov, B.B. 1975. [Migration of Taimyr geese derived from ringing results.] *Materials for the All Union conference on bird migration, Moscow, 2–5 June 1975*. Moscow. (In Russian.)

Bossenmaier, E.F. & W.H. Marshall. 1958. *Field-feeding by waterfowl in South-eastern Manitoba*. Wildlife Monograph 1. The Wildlife Society, Bethesda, Maryland.

Bottoni, L., R. Massa & L. Fornasari. 1991. The migration of the Robin *Erithacus rubecula* in the central pre-Alps of Italy. *Ringing & Migration* 12: 48–53.

BOU. 1971. *The status of birds in Britain and Ireland*. Blackwell, Oxford.

BOU. 1991. British Ornithologists' Union Records Committee: fifteenth report (April 1991). *Ibis* 133: 438–441.

BOU. 1992. *Checklist of birds of Britain and Ireland.* Sixth edition. British Ornithologists' Union, Tring.

BOU. 1994. British Ornithologists' Union Records Committee: twentieth report (December 1993). *Ibis* 136: 253–255.

BOU. 1997. British Ornithologists' Union Records Committee: twenty-third report (July 1996). *Ibis* 139: 197–201.

BOU. 1999. British Ornithologists' Union Records Committee: 25th report (October 1998). *Ibis* 141: 175–180.

BOU. 2001. British Ornithologists' Union Records Committee: 27th report (October 2000). *Ibis* 143: 171–175.

Boulinier, T. 2001. Genetic study of Guillemots to trace the origin of seabirds killed in the Erika oil spill. *Seabird Group Newsletter* 87: 2–3.

Bourgonje, A. 1994. Overwinterende Oeverpiepers *Anthus spinoletta littoralis* in het Verdronken Land van Saeftinghe. *Limosa* 67: 117–118.

Bourne, W.R.P. 1971. Sooty Shearwaters in the Straits of Dover. *British Birds* 64: 468–469.

Bourne, W.R.P. 1990. The movements of Bulwer's Petrel and the larger shearwaters in the Atlantic Ocean. *Sea Swallow* 44: 49–52.

Bourne, W.R.P. 1992. Leach's Storm-petrels visiting ships at sea. *British Birds* 85: 556–557.

Bourne, W.R.P. & M. Beaman. 1980. Turtle Dove migration. *British Birds* 73: 232–233.

Bourne, W.R.P. & M.B. Casement. 1996. The migrations of the Arctic Tern. *Bulletin of the British Ornithologists' Club* 116: 117–123.

Bourne, W.R.P. & I.J. Patterson. 1962. The spring departure of Common Gulls (*Larus canus*) from Scotland. *Scottish Birds* 2: 3–17.

Bourne, W.R.P., E.J. Mackrill, A.M. Paterson & P. Yésou. 1988. The Yelkouan Shearwater *Puffinus (puffinus?) yelkouan*. *British Birds* 81: 306–319.

Boutin, J.-M. 2001. Elements for a Turtle Dove (*Streptopelia turtur*) management plan. *Game and Wildlife Science* 18: 87–112.

Bowden, C.G.R. & R.E. Green. 1991. *The ecology of Nightjars on pine plantations in Thetford Forest.* Report to Forestry Commission. Royal Society for the Protection of Birds, Sandy.

Bowes, A., P.C. Lack & M.R. Fletcher. 1984. Wintering gulls in Britain, January 1983. *Bird Study* 31: 161–170.

Bowey, K. 1992. The Mandarin in NE England – patterns and origins. *Birds in Durham 1991*: 16–20.

Bowley, J.J. 1996. The White Wagtail in autumn. *West Midland Bird Club Annual Report* 62: 11–13.

Boyd, A.W. 1957. Return of Great Grey Shrike to winter territories. *British Birds* 50: 271–272.

Boyd, H. 1954. The 'wreck' of Leach's Petrels in the autumn of 1952. *British Birds* 47: 137–163.

Boyd, H. 1955. The role of tradition in determining the winter distribution of Pinkfeet in Britain. *Wildfowl Trust Annual Report* 7: 107–122.

Boyd, H. 1956. Statistics of the British population of the Pink-footed Goose. *Journal of Animal Ecology* 25: 253–273.

Boyd, H. 1959a. Greylag Geese in Britain in winter. *Wildfowl Trust Annual Report* 10: 43–58.

Boyd, H. 1959b. Movements of marked sea and diving ducks in Europe. *Wildfowl Trust Annual Report* 10: 59–70.

Boyd, H. 1961. The number of Barnacle Geese in Europe in 1959/60. *Wildfowl Trust Annual Report* 12: 116–124.

Boyd, H. 1962. Population dynamics and the exploitation of ducks and geese. In *The Exploitation of Natural Animal Populations* (eds E.D. Le Cren & M.W. Holdgate), pp 85–95. Blackwell, Oxford.

Boyd, H. 1966. The assessment of weather on the breeding success of geese nesting in the arctic. *Statistician* 16: 171–180.

Boyd, H. & S.K. Eltringham. 1962. The Whooper Swan in Great Britain. *Bird Study* 9: 217–241.

Boyd, H. & J. Harrison. 1962. First-autumn dispersal of hand-reared Mallard. *Wildfowl Trust Annual Report* 13: 70–74.

Boyd, H. & M.A. Ogilvie. 1961. The distribution of Mallard ringed in southern England. *Wildfowl Trust Annual Report* 12: 125–136.

Boyd, H. & M.A. Ogilvie. 1964. Losses of Mute Swans in England in the winter of 1962–63. *Wildfowl Trust Annual Report* 15: 37–40.

Boyd, H. & T. Piersma. 2001a. Why do few Afro-Siberian Knots *Calidris canutus canutus* now visit Britain? *Bird Study* 48: 147–158.

Boyd, H. & T. Piersma. 2001b. Changing balance between survival and recruitment explains population trends in Red Knots *Calidris canutus islandica* wintering in Britain, 1969–1995. *Ardea* 89: 301–317.

Boyd, H. & P. Scott. 1955. The British population of the Pink-footed Goose, its numbers and losses. *Wildfowl Trust Annual Report* 7: 99–106.

Bozhko, S.I. 1980. *Der Karmingimpel.* Die Neue Brehm-Bücherei 529. A. Ziemsen Verlag, Wittenberg Lutherstadt.

Braaksma, S. & O. de Bruijn. 1976. De Kerkuilstand in Nederland. *Limosa* 49: 135–187.

Bradshaw, C. 1999. Rarities Committee announcements. *British Birds* 92: 113–114.

Brady, F. 1949. The fluctuations of some common shorebirds on the north Northumberland coast. *British Birds* 42: 297–307.

Bräger, I.S., J. Meißner & M. Thiel. 1995. Temporal and spatial abundance of wintering Common Eider *Somateria mollissima*, Long-tailed Duck *Clangula hyemalis*, and Common Scoter *Melanitta nigra* in shallow water areas of south-western Baltic Sea. *Ornis Fennica* 72: 14–18.

Braggs, J. (ed). 2000. *Kent Bird Report 1998.* Kent Ornithological Society.

Branson, N.J.B.A. (ed). 1985. *Wash Wader Ringing Group Report 1983–1984.* WWRG.

Branson, N.J.B.A. (ed). 1993. *Wash Wader Ringing Group Report 1991–1992.* WWRG.

Branson, N.J.B.A. & C.D.T. Minton. 1976. Moult, measurements and migrations of the Grey Plover. *Bird Study* 23: 257–266.

Branson, N.J.B.A., E.D. Ponting & C.D.T. Minton. 1978. Turnstone migrations in Britain and Europe. *Bird Study* 25: 181–187.

Branson, N.J.B.A., E.D. Ponting & C.D.T. Minton. 1979. Turnstone populations of the Wash. *Bird Study* 26: 47–54.

Brazil, M.A. 1983. Preliminary results from a study of Whooper Swan movements using neck collars. *Journal of the College of Dairying* 10: 79–90. Ebetsu, Hokkaido, Japan.

Brazil, M. 1991. *The Birds of Japan.* Christopher Helm, London.

Bregnballe, T., M. Frederiksen & J. Gregersen. 1997. Seasonal distribution and timing of migration of Cormorants *Phalacrocorax carbo sinensis* breeding in Denmark. *Bird Study* 44: 257–276.

Breiehagen, T. 1989. Nesting biology and mating system in an alpine population of Temminck's Stint *Calidris temminckii*. *Ibis* 131: 389–402.

Breife, B. 1989. Speglar massuppträdanden av bredstjärtad labb *Stercorarius pomarinus* i södra Skandinavien under hösten en god lämmeltillgång på den ryska tundran? [Heavy passages of Pomarine Skuas in southern Scandinavia – are they related to lemming cycles in the high arctic part of Russia?] *Calidris* 18: 3–10.

Brenchley, A. 1984. *Distribution of the Rook in relation to agriculture.* PhD thesis, University of Aberdeen.

Brenot, J.-F., M. Catusse & E. Menoni. 1996. Effets de la station de ski de fond du Plateau de Beille (Ariège) sur une importante population de Grand Tétras *Tetrao urogallus*. *Alauda* 64: 249–260.

Briggs, K. 1983. The distribution and reproduction of Ringed Plovers breeding coastally and inland in north-west England. *Bird Study* 30: 222–228.

Briggs, M., M. Kember, S. Tookey, D. Batchelor, P. Forrest, P. Findley, M. Griffiths, D. Howe, G. Cross & M. Sykes. 1998. Systematic list 1997. *Sandwich Bay Bird Observatory Report 1997*: 11–36.

Brindley, E., K. Norris, A. Cook, S. Babbs, C. Forster Brown, P. Massey, R. Thompson & R. Yaxley. 1998. The abundance and conservation status of Redshank *Tringa totanus* nesting on saltmarshes in Great Britain. *Biological Conservation* 86: 289–297.

Britten, M.W., P.L. Kennedy & S. Ambrose. 1999. Performance and accuracy evaluation of small satellite transmitters. *Journal of Wildlife Management* 63: 1349–1358.

Brooke, M. de L. 1978. The dispersal of female Manx Shearwaters *Puffinus puffinus*. *Ibis* 120: 545–551.

Brooke, M. 1990. *The Manx Shearwater.* T. & A.D. Poyser, London.

Brooke, M. de L. & N.B. Davies. 1987. Recent changes in host usage by Cuckoos *Cuculus canorus* in Britain. *Journal of Animal Ecology* 56: 873–883.

Brooke, M. de L. & N.B. Davies. 1988. Egg mimicry by Cuckoos *Cuculus canorus* in relation to discrimination by hosts. *Nature* 335: 630–632.

Brooke, R.K. 1974. The Spotted Crake *Porzana porzana* (Aves: Rallidae) in south central and southern Africa. *Durban Museum Novitates* 10: 43–52.

Broom, D.M., W.J.A. Dick, C.E. Johnson, D.I. Sales & A. Zahavi. 1976. Pied Wagtail roosting and feeding behaviour. *Bird Study* 23: 267–279.

Brown, A.F. & P.W. Atkinson. 1996. Habitat associations of coastal wintering passerines. *Bird Study* 43: 188–200.

Brown, A.F., H.Q.P. Crick & R.A. Stillman. 1995. The distribution, numbers and breeding ecology of Twite *Acanthis flavirostris* in the south Pennines of England. *Bird Study* 42: 107–121.

Brown, L. 1976. *British Birds of Prey.* Collins, London.

Brown, L. & D. Amadon. 1989. *Eagles, Hawks and Falcons of the World.* Wellfleet Press, Secaucus, New Jersey.

Brown, L.H., E.K. Urban & K. Newman. 1982. *The Birds of Africa.* Volume 1. Academic Press, London and New York.

Brown, M.J., E. Linton & E.C. Rees. 1992. Causes of mortality among wild swans in Britain. *Wildfowl* 43: 70–79.

Brown, R.G.B. 1955. The migration of the Coot in relation to Britain. *Bird Study* 2: 135–142.

Brown, R.G.B. 1979. Seabirds of the Senegal upwelling and adjacent waters. *Ibis* 121: 283–292.

Brown, R.G.B. 1985. The Atlantic Alcidae at sea. In *The Atlantic Alcidae: the evolution, distribution and biology of the auks inhabiting the Atlantic Ocean and adjacent water areas* (eds D.N. Nettleship & T.R. Birkhead), pp 383–426. Academic Press, London.

Brown, R.G.B. & D.E. Gaskin. 1988. The pelagic ecology of the Grey and Red-necked Phalaropes *Phalaropus fulicarius* and *P. lobatus* in the Bay of Fundy, eastern Canada. *Ibis* 130: 234–250.

Brown, S.C. 1974. Common Sandpiper biometrics. *Wader Study Group Bulletin* 11: 18–23.

Browne, S.J., G.E. Austin & M.M. Rehfisch. 1996. Evidence of decline in the United Kingdom's non-estuarine coastal waders. *Wader Study Group Bulletin* 80: 25–27.

Broyer, J. 1991. Situation des Wachtelkönigs in Frankreich. *Die Vogelwelt* 112: 71–77.

Bruderer, B. 1994. Nocturnal bird migration in the Negev (Israel) – a tracking radar study. *Ostrich* 65: 204–212.

Bruderer, B. & H. Bruderer. 1993. Distribution and habitat preference of Red-backed Shrikes *Lanius collurio* in southern Africa. *Ostrich* 64: 141–147.

Bruderer, B. & F. Liechti. 1995. Variation in density and height distribution of nocturnal migration in the south of Israel. *Israel Journal of Zoology* 41: 477–487.

Bruderer, B. & F. Liechti. 1998. Flight behaviour of nocturnally migrating birds in coastal areas – crossing or coasting. *Journal of Avian Biology* 29: 499–507.

Bruderer, B., S. Blitzblau & D. Peter. 1994. Migration and flight behaviour of Honey Buzzards *Pernis apivorus* in southern Israel observed by radar. *Ardea* 82: 111–122.

Bruderer, B., T. Steuri & M. Baumgartner. 1995a. Short-range high-precision surveillance of nocturnal migration and tracking of single targets. *Israel Journal of Zoology* 41: 207–220.

Bruderer, B., L.G. Underhill & F. Liechti. 1995b. Altitude choice by night migrants in a desert area predicted by meteorological factors. *Ibis* 137: 44–55.

Bruun, B. 1968. Migration of Little Gull (*Larus minutus*) in the North Atlantic region. *Dansk Ornithologisk Forenings Tidsskrift* 62: 126–136.

Bryant, D.M. 1978. Moulting Shelducks on the Forth Estuary. *Bird Study* 25: 103–108.

Bryant, D.M. 1981. Moulting Shelducks on the Wash. *Bird Study* 28: 157–158.

Bryant, D.M. & D.R. Waugh. 1976. Flightless Shelducks on the Forth. *Scottish Birds* 9: 124–125.

Buckland, S.T. & D.A. Elston. 1993. Empirical models for the spatial distribution of wildlife. *Journal of Applied Ecology* 30: 478–495.

Buckland, S.T., M.V. Bell & N. Picozzi. 1990. *The Birds of North-East Scotland.* North-East Scotland Bird Club, Aberdeen.

Buckton, S.T. & S.J. Ormerod. 1997. Use of a new standardised habitat survey for assessing the habitat preferences and distribution of upland river birds. *Bird Study* 44: 327–337.

Buckton, S.T., P.A. Brewin, A. Lewis, P.A. Stevens & S.J. Ormerod. 1998. The distribution of Dippers *Cinclus cinclus* in the acid sensitive region of upland Wales, 1984–1995. *Freshwater Biology* 39: 387–396.

Buczek, T. & M. Keller. 1994. Breeding ecology of the Marsh Harrier *Circus aeruginosus* in eastern Poland. Part 1. Population numbers and phenology of the onset of laying. *Acta Ornithologica* 29: 67–80.

Buffon, G.L.L. 1781. *Histoire Naturelle des Oiseaux.* Volume 2. L'Imprimerie Royale, Paris.

Bunn, D.S., A.B. Warburton & R.D.S. Wilson. 1982. *The Barn Owl.* T. & A.D. Poyser, Calton.

Burgess, J.P.C. 1982. Sexual differences and dispersal in the Blue Tit *Parus caeruleus*. *Ringing & Migration* 4: 25–32.

Burkitt, J.P. 1926. A study of the Robin by means of marked birds. *British Birds* 20: 91–101.

Burneleau, G. 1986. Sur les apparitions en France du Goéland à ailes blanches *Larus glaucoides* en 1984. *Alauda* 54: 15–24.

Burton, H., T. Lloyd Evans & D.N. Weir. 1970. Wrynecks breeding in Scotland. *Scottish Birds* 6: 154–156.

Burton, N.H.K. & P.R. Evans. 1997. Survival and winter site-fidelity of Turnstones *Arenaria interpres* and Purple Sandpipers *Calidris maritima* in northeast England. *Bird Study* 44: 35–44.

Burton, P.J.K. & J.M. Burton. 1963. Shearwater movements in the Outer Hebrides. *Scottish Birds* 2: 417–418.

Busche, G. 1994. The decline of wet meadow birds in Schleswig-Holstein, Germany from 1950 to 1992. *Journal für Ornithologie* 135: 137–177.

Busse, P. 1969. Results of ringing of European Corvidae. *Acta Ornithologica* 11: 263–328.

Busse, P. 1995. New technique of a field study of directional preferences of night passerine migrants. *The Ring* 17: 97–111.

Busse, P. 2000. Augmentation of ringing recovery data by means of field experiments: a new look at migration of nocturnal migrants. *Die Vogelwarte* 40: 265–270.

Bustnes, J.O. & K.E. Erikstad. 1993. Site fidelity in breeding Common Eider *Somateria mollissima* females. *Ornis Fennica* 70: 11–16.

Butler, D.J. 1982. Distribution, movements and feeding of birds of prey over the North Sea – based on observations submitted to the North Sea Bird Club, 1979–81. *North Sea Bird Club Annual Report 2, 1981*: 30–40.

Butler, P.J. & A.J. Woakes. 1998. Behaviour and energetics of Svalbard Barnacle Geese during their autumn migration. *Norsk Polarinstitutt Skrifter* 200: 165–174.

Butterfield, A. & K. Williamson. 1955. The passage of Black Terns through Britain in autumn 1954. *British Birds* 48: 300–307.

Buurma, L.S. 1995. Long-range surveillance radars as indicators of bird numbers aloft. *Israel Journal of Zoology* 41: 221–236.

Byers, C., U. Olsson & J. Curson. 1995. *Buntings and Sparrows*. Pica Press, Robertsbridge, East Sussex.

Byrkjedal, I. & D.B.A. Thompson. 1998. *Tundra plovers: the Eurasian, Pacific and American Golden Plovers and Grey Plover*. T. & A.D. Poyser, London.

Cabot, D. 1995. Performance of the Roseate Tern population breeding in north-west Europe – Ireland, Britain and France, 1960–94. *Proceedings of the Royal Irish Academy* 96B: 55–68.

Cabot, D. & B. West. 1983. Studies on the population of Barnacle Geese wintering on the Inishkea Islands, Co. Mayo. *Irish Birds* 2: 318–336.

Cabot, D., R. Nairn, S. Newton & M. Viney. 1984. *Biological Expedition to Jameson Land, Greenland 1984*. Barnacle Books, Dublin.

Cadbury, C.J. 1980. The status and habitats of the Corncrake in Britain, 1978–79. *Bird Study* 27: 203–218.

Cadbury, C.J. & P.J.S. Olney. 1978. Avocet population dynamics in England. *British Birds* 71: 102–121.

Cadbury, C.J., R.E. Green & G. Allport. 1987. Redshanks and other breeding waders of British saltmarshes. *RSPB Conservation Review* 1: 37–40.

Cade, M. 1983. The possibility of east Mediterranean Manx Shearwaters occurring in British waters. *British Birds* 76: 413.

Calladine, J. & M.P. Harris. 1997. Intermittent breeding in the Herring Gull *Larus argentatus* and the Lesser Black-backed Gull *Larus fuscus*. *Ibis* 139: 259–263.

Calladine, J.R., F. Buner & N.J. Aebischer. 1997. *The summer ecology and habitat use of the Turtle Dove: a pilot study*. Research Report 219. English Nature, Peterborough.

Callaghan, D.A. & A.J. Green. 1993. Wildfowl at risk. *Wildfowl* 44: 149–169.

Calvo, B. & R.W. Furness. 1992. A review of the use and the effects of marks and devices on birds. *Ringing & Migration* 13: 129–151.

Campbell, B. & J. Ferguson-Lees. 1972. *A Field Guide to Birds' Nests*. Constable, London.

Campbell, J.W. 1956. Crane in Outer Hebrides. *British Birds* 49: 281–282.

Campbell, L.H. 1978. Patterns of distribution and behaviour of flocks of seaducks wintering at Leith and Musselburgh, Scotland. *Biological Conservation* 14: 111–124.

Campbell, L.H. 1984. The impact of changes in sewage treatment on seaducks wintering in the Firth of Forth. *Biological Conservation* 28: 173–180.

Campbell, L.H. & H. Milne. 1983. Moulting Eiders in eastern Scotland. *Wildfowl* 34: 105–107.

Campbell, L.H. & G.P. Mudge. 1989. Conservation of Black-throated Divers in Scotland. *RSPB Conservation Review* 3: 72–74.

Campbell, L., J. Cayford & D. Pearson. 1996. Bearded Tits in Britain and Ireland. *British Birds* 89: 335–346.

Camphuysen, C.J. & M.F. Leopold. 1996. Invasies van de Kleine Alk *Alle alle*: voorkomen en achtergronden. *Sula* 10: 169–182.

Camphuysen, C.J. & J. van Dijk. 1983. Zee- en kustvogels langs de Nederlandse kust, 1974–79. *Limosa* 56: 81–230.

Camphuysen, C.J. & E.J. van IJzendoorn. 1988a. Invasie van Middelste Jager in Nederland in november 1985. *Dutch Birding* 10: 54–66.

Camphuysen, C.J. & E.J. van IJzendoorn. 1988b. Influx of Pomarine Skua in northwestern Europe in autumn 1985. *Dutch Birding* 10: 66–70.

Cannon, A. 1998. Garden reporting rates for Siskin and Redwing. *The Bird Table* 14: 1.

Cannon, A. 2000. *Garden BirdWatch Handbook*. Second edition. British Trust for Ornithology, Thetford.

Cantos, F.J. 1993. Evolucion de la invernada y fenologia de la Gaviota Sombria *Larus fuscus* en Madrid. *GIAM (Grupo Ibérico de Aves Marinas) Boletin* 16: 4.

Cantos, F.J. & J.L. Tellería. 1994. Stopover site fidelity of four migrant warblers in the Iberian Peninsula. *Journal of Avian Biology* 25: 131–134.

Carbone, C. & M. Owen. 1995. Differential migration of the sexes of Pochard *Aythya ferina*: results from a European survey. *Wildfowl* 46: 99–108.

Carboneras, C. 1988. The auks in the western Mediterranean. *Ringing & Migration* 9: 18–26.

Carey, C. & W.R. Dawson. 1999. A search for environmental cues used by birds for survival of cold winters. *Current Ornithology* 15: 1–31.

Carroll, J.P., R.D. Crawford & J.W. Schulz. 1995. Grey Partridge winter home range and use of habitat in North Dakota. *Journal of Wildlife Management* 59: 98–103.

Carson, C.A., G.A. Cornford & G.J. Thomas. 1977. Little Gulls nesting on the Ouse Washes. *British Birds* 70: 331–332.

Carss, D.N. 1994. Killing of piscivorous birds at Scottish finfish farms, 1984–87. *Biological Conservation* 68: 181–188.

Carter, I. 1998. The changing fortunes of the Red Kite in Suffolk. *Suffolk Birds* 46: 6–10.

Carter, S. & P. Evans. 1988. The Goosander in relation to salmon fisheries. *Ibis* 130: 589.

Casey, C. 1998. Distribution and conservation of the Corncrake in Ireland, 1993–1998. *Irish Birds* 6: 159–176.

Casey, S., N. Moore, L. Ryan, O.J. Merne, J.A. Coveney & A.J. del Nevo. 1995. The Roseate Tern conservation project on Rockabill, Co. Dublin: a six year review 1989–94. *Irish Birds* 5: 251–264.

Castle, P.E. & R. Clarke. 1995. Observations on the conservation of Hen Harriers *Circus cyaneus* wintering on Salisbury Plain: roosts and food. *Hobby* 21: 88–96.

Castro, G. & J.P. Myers. 1989. Flight range estimates for shorebirds. *Auk* 106: 474–476.

Catchpole, C.K. 1970. *Some aspects of behavioural ecology in two* Acrocephalus *species*. PhD thesis, University of Nottingham.

Catchpole, C.K. 1972. A comparative study of territory in the Reed Warbler *Acrocephalus scirpaceus* and Sedge Warbler *Acrocephalus schoenobaenus*. *Journal of Zoology, London* 166: 213–231.

Catchpole, E.A., S.N. Freeman, B.J.T. Morgan & M.P. Harris. 1998. Integrated recovery/recapture data analysis. *Biometrics* 54: 33–46.

Catchpole, E.A., B.J.T. Morgan, S.N. Freeman & W.J. Peach. 1999. Modelling the survival of British Lapwings *Vanellus vanellus* using ring-recovery data and weather covariates. *Bird Study* 46 (suppl.): S5–13.

Catry, P., R.A. Phillips, K.C. Hamer, N. Ratcliffe & R.W. Furness. 1998a. The incidence of nonbreeding by adult Great Skuas and Parasitic Jaegers from Foula, Shetland. *Condor* 100: 448–455.

Catry, P., N. Ratcliffe & R.W. Furness. 1998b. The influence of hatching date on different life-history stages of Great Skuas *Catharacta skua*. *Journal of Avian Biology* 29: 299–304.

Catt, D.C., D. Baines, N. Picozzi, R. Moss & R.W. Summers. 1998. Abundance and distribution of Capercaillie *Tetrao urogallus* in Scotland 1992–94. *Biological Conservation* 85: 257–267.

Cawthorne, R.A. & J.H. Marchant. 1980. The effects of the 1978/79 winter on British bird populations. *Bird Study* 27: 163–172.

Cayford, J. 1992. Barn Owl ecology on East Anglian farmland. *RSPB Conservation Review* 6: 45–50.

Cayford, J.T. & R.J. Waters. 1996. Population estimates for waders Charadrii wintering in Great Britain, 1987/88 – 1991/92. *Biological Conservation* 77: 7–17.

Cederroth, C., C. Johansson & L. Svensson. 1999. Taiga Flycatcher *Ficedula albicilla* in Sweden: the first record in western Europe. *Birding World* 12: 460–468.

Cederwall, G. 1978. Turturduvan *Streptopelia turtur* på Öland. *Calidris* 7: 12–22.

Chabrzyk, K.G. & J.C. Coulson. 1976. Survival and recruitment in the Herring Gull *Larus argentatus*. *Journal of Animal Ecology* 51: 187–203.

Chamberlain, C.P., J.D. Blum, R.T. Holmes, X. Feng, T.W. Sherry & G.R. Graves. 1997. The use of isotope tracers for identifying populations of migratory birds. *Oecologia* 109: 132–141.

Chamberlain, C.P., S. Bensch, X. Feng, S. Åkesson & T. Andersson. 2000. Stable isotopes examined across a migratory divide in Scandinavian Willow Warblers (*Phylloscopus trochilus trochilus* and *Phylloscopus trochilus acredula*) reflect their African winter quarters. *Proceedings of the Royal Society of London series B – Biological Sciences* 267: 43–48.

Chandler, R.J. 1981. Influxes into Britain and Ireland of Red-necked Grebes and other waterbirds during winter 1978/79. *British Birds* 74: 55–81.

Chandler, R.J. 1984. Proportions of adult male Smews and Red-breasted Mergansers in England and Wales in 1978/79. *British Birds* 77: 479–481.

Chapman, A H. 1999. *The Hobby*. Arlequin Press, Chelmsford.

Chapman, F.M. 1888. Observations on the nocturnal migration of birds. *Auk* 23: 210–217.

Charles, K.K. 1972. *Territorial behaviour and the limitation of population size in the Crow,* Corvus corone *and* Corvus cornix. PhD thesis, University of Aberdeen.

Chernichko, I.I., A.B. Grinchenko & V.D. Siokhin. 1991. Waders of the Sivash Gulf, Azov–Black Sea, USSR. *Wader Study Group Bulletin* 63: 37–38.

Chesney, M.C. 1987. The changes in bodymass and movements of Siskin on Tayside during late winter and early spring, 1986. *Tay Ringing Group Report 1984–86*: 26–32.

Chisholm, H. & C.J. Spray. 2002. Habitat usage and field choice by Mute Swans *Cygnus olor* and Whooper Swans *C. cygnus* in the Tweed Valley, Scotland. In *Proceedings of the Fourth International Swan Symposium, 2001* (eds E.C. Rees, S.L. Earnst & J. Coulson). *Waterbirds* 25, special edition 1: 177–182.

Choudhury, S. & J.M. Black. 1991. Testing the behavioural dominance and dispersal hypothesis in Pochard. *Ornis Scandinavica* 22: 155–159.

Christmas, S.E. 1978. The Sedge Warbler population of Holywell Meadow, Oxford. *Report of the Oxford Ornithological Society on the Birds of Oxfordshire for 1977*: 34–36.

Christmas, S.E., T.J. Christmas, A.P. Gosling & A.J. Parr. 1986. Feeding behaviour and geographical origins of Black-headed Gulls *Larus ridibundus* wintering in Central London. *Ringing & Migration* 7: 7–14.

Christophers, S.M. (ed). 1984. *Birds in Cornwall 1983*. Cornwall Birdwatching and Preservation Society.

Chu, D.S., J.D. Nichols, J.B. Hestbeck & J.E. Hines. 1995. Banding reference areas and survival rates of Green-winged Teal, 1950–89. *Journal of Wildlife Management* 59: 487–498.

Church, K.E., H.J. Harris & R.B. Stiehl. 1980. Habitat utilisation by Grey Partridge (*Perdix perdix* L.) pre-nesting pairs in east-central Wisconsin. In *Proceedings of Perdix II Grey Partridge Workshop* (eds R. Peterson & L. Nelson), pp 9–20. University of Moscow, Idaho.

Churcher, P.B. & J.H. Lawton. 1987. Predation by domestic cats in an English village. *Journal of the Zoological Society of London* 212: 439–455.

Clafton, F.R. 1971. Large weight gain by migrant Nightingale. *British Birds* 64: 320.

Clapham, C. 1979. The Turnstone populations of Morecambe Bay. *Ringing & Migration* 2: 144–150.

Clark, F. & D.A.C. McNeil. 1980. Cliff-nesting colonies of House Martins *Delichon urbica* in Great Britain. *Ibis* 122: 27–42.

Clark, H. & R. Sellers. 1997. Distribution and abundance of Twites wintering in Caithness. *Scottish Birds* 19: 1–9.

Clark, J.A., S.R. Baillie, N.A. Clark & R.H.W. Langston. 1993. *Estuary wader capacity following severe weather mortality*. Research Report 103. British Trust for Ornithology, Thetford.

Clark, J.A., S.Y. Adams, W.J. Peach & J.R. Simons. 1996. Report on bird ringing in Britain and Ireland for 1994. *Ringing & Migration* 17: 36–79.

Clark, J., S. Baillie, A. Gosler & A. Martin. 1998. Ring pricing for conservation and science. *Ringers' Bulletin* 9: 65–67.

Clark, J.A., C.V. Wernham, D.E. Balmer, S.Y. Adams, J.R. Blackburn, B.M. Griffin & J. King. 2000. Bird ringing in Britain and Ireland in 1998. *Ringing & Migration* 20: 39–93.

Clark, J.A., C.V. Wernham, D.E. Balmer, S.Y. Adams, B.M. Griffin, J.R. Blackburn, D. Anning & L.J. Milne. 2001. Bird ringing in Britain and Ireland in 1999. *Ringing & Migration* 20: 239–288.

Clark, J.M. 1984. *Birds of the Hants/Surrey Border*. Hobby Books, Fleet.

Clark, J.M. (ed). 1996. Birds in Hampshire, 1995. *Hampshire Bird Report 1995*: 5–121.

Clark, J.M. (ed). 1998. Birds in Hampshire, 1996. *Hampshire Bird Report 1996*: 8–137.

Clark, J.M. & J.A. Eyre (eds). 1993. *Birds of Hampshire*. Hampshire Ornithological Society.

Clark, N.A. 1978. Weights, moult and morphometrics of Spotted Redshanks in Britain. *Wader Study Group Bulletin* 22: 22–26.

Clark, N.A. 1983. *The ecology of Dunlin* (Calidris alpina *L.) wintering on the Severn Estuary*. PhD thesis, University of Edinburgh.

Clark, N.A. 1989. *Wader migration and distribution in south west estuaries*. Research Report 40. British Trust for Ornithology, Tring.

Clark, N.A., B.S. Turner & J.F. Young. 1982. Spring passage of Sanderlings *Calidris alba* on the Solway Firth. *Wader Study Group Bulletin* 36: 10–11.

Clark, R.J. 1975. *A field study of the Short-eared Owl* Asio flammeus (Pontoppidan) *in North America*. Wildlife Monograph 47. The Wildlife Society, Bethesda, Maryland.

Clarke, M.F., P. Griffioen & R.H. Loyn. 1999. Where do all the bush birds go? *Wingspan* 9 (suppl.): I–XVI.

Clarke, R. 1996. *Montagu's Harrier*. Arlequin Press, Chelmsford.

Clarke, R. & D. Watson. 1990. The Hen Harrier *Circus cyaneus* Winter Roost Survey in Britain and Ireland. *Bird Study* 37: 84–100.

Clarke, R. & D. Watson. 1997. The Hen Harrier Winter Roost Survey. *The Raptor* 24: 41–45.

Clausen, P. 1997. Dark-bellied Brent Geese *Branta b. bernicla* use of the White Sea, a progress report. In *Dark-bellied Brent Goose* Branta bernicla bernicla *Flyway Management Plan* (ed J. van Nugteren), pp 174–183. Dutch Society for the Preservation of the Wadden Sea / Ministry of Agriculture, Nature Management and Fisheries, Wageningen, the Netherlands.

Clausen, P. & J.O. Bustnes. 1998. Flyways of North-Atlantic Light-bellied Brent Geese *Branta bernicla hrota* reassessed by satellite telemetry. In *Research on Arctic Geese. Proceedings of the Svalbard Goose Symposium, Oslo, Norway, 23–26 September 1997* (eds F. Mehlum, J.M. Black & J. Madsen). *Norsk Polarinstitutt Skrifter* 200: 235–249.

Clausen, P. & S.M. Percival. 1992. Colour ringing of Light-bellied Brent Geese. *IWRB Goose Research Group Bulletin* 3: 33–38.

Clausen, P., J. Madsen, S.M. Percival, D. O'Connor & G.Q.A. Anderson. 1998. Population development and changes in winter site use by the Svalbard Light-bellied Brent Goose, *Branta bernicla hrota* 1980–1994. *Biological Conservation* 84: 157–165.

Clausen, P., J. Madsen, S.M. Percival, G.Q.A. Anderson, K. Koffijberg, F. Mehlum & D. Vangeluwe. 1999. Light-bellied Brent Goose *Branta bernicla hrota*: Svalbard. In *Goose populations of the Western Palaearctic; a review of status and distribution* (eds J. Madsen, G. Cracknell & A.D. Fox), pp 312–327. Wetlands International Publication 48. Wetlands International, Wageningen, the Netherlands, and National Environmental Research Institute, Rönde, Denmark.

Cleere, N. 1998. *Nightjars: a guide to Nightjars and related nightbirds*. Pica Press, Robertsbridge, East Sussex.

Clement, P. 1995. Southern and eastern races of Great Grey Shrikes in northwest Europe. *Birding World* 8: 300–309.

Clement, P. & R.E. Scott. 1999. Hume's Warbler in Sussex: new to Britain and Ireland. *British Birds* 92: 96–100.

Clement, P., A. Harris & J. Davis. 1993. *Finches and Sparrows: an identification guide*. Christopher Helm, London.

Clement, P., A.J. Helbig & B. Small. 1998. Taxonomy and identification of Chiffchaffs in the Western Palearctic. *British Birds* 91: 361–376.

Coleman, A.E. & C.D.T. Minton. 1979. Pairing and breeding of Mute Swans in relation to natal area. *Wildfowl* 30: 27–30.

Coleman, A.E., C.D.T. Minton & J.T. Coleman. 1991. Factors affecting the number of pairs and breeding success of Mute Swans (*Cygnus olor*) in an area of south Staffordshire, England between 1961 and 1985. In *Proceedings of the Third IWRB International Swan Symposium, Oxford 1989*, (eds J. Sears & P.J. Bacon), pp 103–110. *Wildfowl* suppl. 1.

Coleman, A.E., J.T. Coleman, P.A. Coleman & C.D.T. Minton. 2001. A 39 year study of a Mute Swan *Cygnus olor* population in the English Midlands. *Ardea* 89: 123–133.

Coles, C.F. & S.J. Petty. 1997. Dispersal behaviour and survival of juvenile Tawny Owls (*Strix aluco*) during the low point in a vole cycle. In *Biology and Conservation of Owls of the Northern Hemisphere* (eds J.R. Duncan, D.H. Johnson & T.H. Nicholls), pp 111–118. General Technical Report NC-190. USDA Forest Service, St Paul, Minnesota.

Colhoun, K. 1998. *I-WeBS Report 1996–97: results of the third winter of the Irish Wetland Bird Survey*. BirdWatch Ireland, Dublin.

Colhoun, K. 2000. *Irish Wetland Bird Survey*. Birdwatch Ireland, Dublin.

Collar, N.J., M.J. Crosby & A.J. Stattersfield. 1994. *Birds to Watch 2: the world list of threatened birds*. BirdLife International, Cambridge.

Collette, P. 1972. Contribution à l'étude de la migration prénuptiale du Bruant des Roseaux. *Aves* 9: 226–240.

Collins, R. & J. Whelan. 1993. Mute Swan herds in Dublin and Wicklow. *Irish Birds* 5: 11–22.

Collins, R. & J. Whelan. 1994. Movements in an Irish Mute Swan *Cygnus olor* population. *Ringing & Migration* 15: 40–49.

Combridge, P. & C. Parr. 1992. Influx of Little Egrets in Britain and Ireland in 1989. *British Birds* 85: 16–21.

Conder, P. 1989. *The Wheatear*. Christopher Helm, London.

Cook, A. 1975. Changes in the Carrion/Hooded Crow hybrid zone and the possible importance of climate. *Bird Study* 22: 165–169.

Cook, M. 1992. *The Birds of Moray and Nairn*. The Mercat Press, Edinburgh.

Cooke, F. & E.L. Mills. 1972. Summer distribution of pelagic birds off the coast of Argentina. *Ibis* 114: 245–251.

Coombes, R.A.H. 1947. On the races of the Bean Goose in the Netherlands. *Limosa* 20: 229–230.

Coombes, R.A.H. 1949. Sheld-duck: migration in summer. *Nature* 164: 1122–1123.

Coombes, R.A.H. 1950. The moult migration of the Shelduck. *Ibis* 92: 405–418.

Coombs, F. 1978. *The Crows – a study of the Corvids of Europe*. Batsford, London.

Coombs, C.F.B., A.J. Isaacson, R.K. Murton, R.J.P. Thearle & N.J. Westwood. 1981. Collared Doves (*Streptopelia decaocto*) in urban habitats. *Journal of Applied Ecology* 18: 41–62.

Cooper, J., L.G. Underhill & G. Avery. 1991. Primary moult and transequatorial migration of the Sooty Shearwater. *Condor* 93: 724–730.

Cooper, J.E.S. 1985. Spring migration of Siskins in north Sussex during 1984. *Ringing & Migration* 6: 61–65.

Cooper, R.H.W. 1987. *Migration strategies of shorebirds during the non-breeding season with particular reference to the Sanderling* (Calidris alba). PhD thesis, University of Durham.

Cormier, J.P. & F. Baillon. 1991. Concentration de busards cendrés *Circus pygargus* (L.) dans la region de M'bour (Sénégal) durant l'hiver 1988–1989: utilisation du milieu et régime alimentaire. *Alauda* 59: 163–168.

Cornwallis, R.K. 1961. Four invasions of Waxwings during 1956–60. *British Birds* 54: 1–30.

Cornwallis, R.K. & A.D. Townsend. 1968. Waxwings in Britain & Europe, 1965–66. *British Birds* 61: 97–118.

Corse, C.J. & R.W. Summers. 1999. The seasonal pattern of numbers, population structure and migration of Purple Sandpipers *Calidris maritima* in Orkney. *Ringing & Migration* 19: 275–282.

Cortone, P., A. Minganti, M. Pellegrini, F. Riga, A. Sigismondi & A. Zocchi. 1994. Population trends of the Red Kite *Milvus milvus* in Italy. In *Raptor Conservation Today* (eds B.-U. Meyburg & R.D. Chancellor), pp 29–32. World Working Group on Birds of Prey and Owls/Pica Press, Berlin.

Coulson, J.C. 1959. The plumage and leg-colour of the Kittiwake and comments on the non-breeding population. *British Birds* 52: 189–196.

Coulson, J.C. 1961. Movements and seasonal variation in mortality of Shags and Cormorants ringed on the Farne Islands, Northumberland. *British Birds* 54: 225–235.

Coulson, J.C. 1963. The status of the Kittiwake in the British Isles. *Bird Study* 10: 147–179.

Coulson, J.C. 1966. The movements of the Kittiwake. *Bird Study* 13: 107–115.

Coulson, J.C. 1983. The changing status of the Kittiwake *Rissa tridactyla* in the British Isles. *Bird Study* 30: 9–16.

Coulson, J.C. 1984. The population dynamics of the Eider Duck *Somateria mollissima* and evidence of extensive non-breeding by adult ducks. *Ibis* 126: 525–543.

Coulson, J.C. 1991. The population dynamics of culling Herring Gulls and Lesser Black-backed Gulls. In *Bird Population Studies: relevance to conservation and management* (eds C.M. Perrins, J.-D. Lebreton & G.J.M. Hirons), pp 479–497. Oxford University Press, Oxford.

Coulson, J.C. & M.G. Brazendale. 1968. Movements of Cormorants ringed in the British Isles and evidence of colony-specific dispersal. *British Birds* 61: 1–21.

Coulson, J.C. & J. Butterfield. 1985. Movements of British Herring Gulls. *Bird Study* 32: 91–103.

Coulson, J.C. & J. Butterfield. 1986. Studies on a colony of colour-ringed Herring Gulls *Larus argentatus*. II: Colony occupation and feeding outside the breeding season. *Bird Study* 33: 55–59.

Coulson, J.C. & G. Nève de Mévergnies. 1992. Where do young Kittiwakes *Rissa tridactyla* breed, philopatry or dispersal? *Ardea* 80: 187–197.

Coulson, J.C. & E. White. 1955. Abrasion and loss of rings among sea-birds. *Bird Study* 2: 41–44.

Coulson, J.C. & E. White. 1960. The effect of age and density of breeding birds on the time of breeding of the Kittiwake *Rissa tridactyla*. *Ibis* 102: 71–86.

Coulson, J.C., G.R. Potts, I.R. Deans & S.M. Fraser. 1968. Exceptional mortality of Shags and other seabirds, caused by paralytic shellfish poison. *British Birds* 61: 381–404.

Coulson, J.C., N. Duncan & C. Thomas. 1982a. Changes in the breeding biology of the Herring Gull (*Larus argentatus*) induced by reduction in the size and density of the colony. *Journal of Animal Ecology* 51: 739–756.

Coulson, J.C., P. Monaghan, J. Butterfield, N. Duncan, C.S. Thomas & H. Wright. 1982b. Variation in the wing-tip pattern of the Herring Gull in Britain. *Bird Study* 29: 111–120.

Coulson, J.C., C.S. Thomas, J.E.L. Butterfield, N. Duncan, P. Monaghan & C. Shedden. 1983. The use of head and bill length to sex live gulls *Laridae*. *Ibis* 125: 549–557.

Coulson, J.C., J. Butterfield, N. Duncan, S. Kearsey, P. Monaghan & C. Thomas. 1984a. Origin and behaviour of Great Black-backed Gulls wintering in northeast England. *British Birds* 77: 1–11.

Coulson, J.C., P. Monaghan, J.E.L. Butterfield, N. Duncan, K. Ensor, C. Shedden & C. Thomas. 1984b. Scandinavian Herring Gulls wintering in Britain. *Ornis Scandinavica* 15: 79–88.

Cowley, E. 1979. Sand Martin population trends in Britain, 1965–1978. *Bird Study* 26: 113–116.

Cox, S. 1984. *A New Guide to the Birds of Essex*. Essex Birdwatching and Preservation Society.

Craggs, J.D. 1982. *Hilbre, the Cheshire island: its history and natural history*. Liverpool University Press, Liverpool.

Cramp, S. 1955. The breeding of the Willow Warbler. *Bird Study* 2: 121–135.

Cramp, S. 1963. Movements of tits in Europe in 1959 and after. *British Birds* 56: 237–263.

Cramp, S., A. Pettet & J.T.R. Sharrock. 1960. The irruption of tits in autumn 1957. *British Birds* 53: 49–77, 99–117, 176–192.

Cramp, S., W.R.P. Bourne & D. Saunders. 1974. *The Seabirds of Britain and Ireland*. Collins, London.

Cranswick, P.A., R.J. Waters, J. Evans & M.S. Pollitt. 1995. *The Wetland Bird Survey 1993–94: wildfowl and wader counts*. BTO/WWT/RSPB/JNCC, Slimbridge.

Cranswick, P.A., J.M. Bowler, S.N. Delany, Ó. Einarsson, A. Garðarsson, J.G. McElwaine, O.J. Merne, E.C. Rees & J.H. Wells. 1996. Numbers of Whooper Swans *Cygnus cygnus* in Iceland, Ireland and Britain in January 1995: results of the international Whooper Swan census. *Wildfowl* 47: 17–30.

Cranswick, P.A., R.J. Waters, A.J. Musgrove & M.S. Pollitt. 1997. *The Wetland Bird Survey 1995–96: wildfowl and wader counts*. BTO/WWT/RSPB/JNCC, Slimbridge.

Cranswick, P.A., M.S. Pollitt, A.J. Musgrove & R.C. Hughes. 1999. *The Wetland Bird Survey 1997–98: wildfowl and wader counts*. BTO/WWT/RSPB/JNCC, Slimbridge.

Crawley, D. 1996. Stock Dove *Columba oenas*. In *Birds of Sussex* (ed P. James), pp 351–352. Sussex Ornithological Society.

Cresswell, B. & I. Alexander. 1992. Activity patterns of foraging Nightjars. In *Wildlife Telemetry: remote monitoring and tracking of animals* (eds I.G. Priede & S.M. Swift), pp 642–647. Ellis Horwood, Chichester.

Creutz, G. 1941. Vom Zug des Grauen Fliegenschnäppers, *Muscicapa striata striata* (Pallas). *Der Vogelzug* 12: 1–14.

Crick, H.Q.P. (ed). 1992. The ecology and conservation of Palaearctic-African migrants. *Ibis* 134 (suppl. 1).

Crick, H.Q.P. & S.R. Baillie. 1996. *A review of the BTO's Nest Record Scheme: its value to the Joint Nature Conservation Committee and country agencies, and its methodology*. Research Report 159. British Trust for Ornithology, Thetford.

Crick, H.Q.P. & D.A. Ratcliffe. 1995. The Peregrine *Falco peregrinus* breeding population of the United Kingdom in 1991. *Bird Study* 42: 1–19.

Crick, H.Q.P., D.W. Gibbons & R.D. Magrath. 1994. Seasonal changes in clutch size in British birds. *Journal of Animal Ecology* 62: 263–273.

Crick, H.Q.P., S.R. Baillie, D.E. Balmer, R.I. Bashford, L.P. Beaven, C. Dudley, D.E. Glue, R.D. Gregory, J.H. Marchant, W.J. Peach & A.M. Wilson. 1998. *Breeding birds in the wider countryside: their conservation status (1972–1996)*. Research Report 198. British Trust for Ornithology, Thetford.

Crissey, W.F. 1957. Forecasting waterfowl harvest by flyways. *Transatlantic North American Wildlife Conference* 22: 256–268.

Cristol, D.A., M.B. Baker & C. Carbone. 1999. Differential migration revisited: latitudinal segregation by age and sex class. *Current Ornithology* 15: 33–88.

Cross, A.V. & P.E. Davis. 1986. *Monitoring of Ravens and land use in Central Wales*. Report to the Nature Conservancy Council.

Cross, A.V. & P.E. Davis. 1998. *The Red Kites of Wales*. The Welsh Kite Trust, Llandrindod Wells.

Cuadrado, M. 1992. Year to year recurrence and site-fidelity of Blackcaps *Sylvia atricapilla* and Robins *Erithacus rubecula* in a Mediterranean wintering area. *Ringing & Migration* 13: 36–42.

Cuadrado, M., J.C. Senar & J.L. Copete. 1995. Do all Blackcaps *Sylvia atricapilla* show winter site fidelity? *Ibis* 137: 70–75.

Cubitt, M.G. 1995. Swinhoe's Storm-petrels at Tynemouth: new to Britain and Ireland. *British Birds* 88: 342–348.

Cullen, J.P. & P.P. Jennings. 1986. *Birds of the Isle of Man*. Bridgeen Publications, Douglas.

Cumming, I.G. 1979. Lapland Buntings breeding in Scotland. *British Birds* 72: 53–59.

Currie, D. & E. Matthysen. 1998. Nuthatches *Sitta europaea* do not delay postfledging dispersal in isolated forest fragments. *Belgian Journal of Zoology* 128: 49–54.

Curry, P.J. & J.A. Sayer. 1979. The inundation zone of the Niger as an environment for Palaearctic migrants. *Ibis* 121: 20–40.

Curry-Lindahl, K. 1981. *Bird Migration in Africa*. Volumes 1 & 2. Academic Press, London.

Curtis, W.F., P.A. Lassey & D.I.M. Wallace. 1985. Identifying the smaller shearwaters. *British Birds* 78: 123–138.

Cury, P. & A. Fontana. 1988. Competition et strategies demographiques comparées de deux espèces de sardinelles (*Sardinella aurita* et *Sardinella maderensis*) des côtes ouest-Africanes. *Aquatic Living Resources* 1: 165–180.

da Prato, S.R.D. & E.S. da Prato. 1983. Movements of Whitethroats *Sylvia communis* ringed in the British Isles. *Ringing & Migration* 4: 193–210.

da Prato, S.R.D., E.S. da Prato & D.J. Chittenden. 1980. Redwing migration through the British Isles. *Ringing & Migration* 3: 9–20.

Dagley, J.R. 1994. Golden Orioles in East Anglia and their conservation. *British Birds* 87: 205–219.

Dall'Antonia, P., F. Spina & R. Mantovani. 1996. Fenologia della migrazione di alcune specie di uccelli acquatici attraverso l'Italia. *Ricerche di Biologia della Selvaggina* 98: 1–72.

Danchin, E. & J.Y. Monnat. 1992. Population dynamics modelling of two neighbouring Kittiwakes *Rissa tridactyla* colonies. *Ardea* 80: 171–180.

Dare, P.J. & A.J. Mercer. 1974. The timing of wing-moult of the Oystercatcher *Haematopus ostralegus* in Wales. *Ibis* 116: 211–214.

Davenport, D.L. 1975. The spring passage of the Pomarine Skua on British and Irish coasts. *British Birds* 68: 456–462.

Davenport, D.L. 1981. The spring passage of Pomarine and Long-tailed Skuas off the south and west coasts of Britain and Ireland. *Irish Birds* 2: 73–79.

Davenport, D.L. 1982. Influxes into Britain of Hen Harriers, Long-eared Owls and Short-eared Owls in winter 1978/79. *British Birds* 75: 309–316.

Davenport, D.L. 1989. Seabird movements in Kent: autumn 1987. *Kent Bird Report* 36: 93–97.

Davenport, D.L. 1991. The spring passage of Long-tailed Skuas off North Uist in 1991. *Scottish Birds* 16: 85–89.

Davenport, D. 1992. The spring passage of Long-tailed and Pomarine Skuas in Britain and Ireland. *Birding World* 5: 92–95.

Davidson, N. 1998. Compiling estimates of East Atlantic Flyway wader populations wintering in coastal Europe in the early 1990s: a summary of the 1996 WSG wader populations workshop. *Wader Study Group Bulletin* 86: 18–25.

Davidson, N.C. & P.R. Evans. 1982. Mortality of Redshanks and Oystercatchers from starvation during severe weather. *Bird Study* 29: 183–188.

Davidson, N.C. & T. Piersma. 1986. International wader migration studies along the East Atlantic Flyway: preliminary results from spring 1986. *Wader Study Group Bulletin* 47: 2–3.

Davidson, N.C., P.R. Evans & M.W. Pienkowski. 1986a. The origins and destinations of waders using the coasts of Suffolk and Essex. *Ringing & Migration* 7: 37–49.

Davidson, N.C., K.-B. Strann, N.J. Crockford, P.R. Evans, J. Richardson, L.J. Standen, D.J. Townshend, J.D. Uttley, J.R. Wilson & A.G. Wood. 1986b. The origins of Knots *Calidris canutus* in arctic Norway in spring. *Ornis Scandinavica* 17: 175–179.

Davidson, N.C., J.D. Uttley & P.R. Evans. 1986c. Geographic variation in the lean mass of Dunlins wintering in Britain. *Ardea* 74: 191–198.

Davidson, N.C., D.A. Stroud, P.I. Rothwell & M.W. Pienkowski. 1998. Towards a flyway conservation strategy for waders. *International Wader Studies* 10: 24–38.

Davidson, N., D. Bryant & G. Boere. 1999. Conservation uses of ringing data: flyway networks for waterbirds. *Ringing & Migration* 19 (suppl.): S83–94.

Davies, A.K. & G.K. Baggott. 1989. Clutch size and nesting sites of the Mandarin Duck *Aix galericulata*. *Bird Study* 36: 32–36.

Davies, C. 2001. The European Bird Report. *British Birds* 94: 125–142.

Davies, M. 1988. The importance of Britain's Twites. *RSPB Conservation Review* 2: 91–94.

Davies, N.B. 1976. Food, flocking and territorial behaviour of the Pied Wagtail in winter. *Journal of Animal Ecology* 45: 235–253.

Davies, N.B. 1992. *Dunnock Behaviour and Social Evolution*. Oxford University Press, Oxford.

Davis, P. 1962. Robin recaptures on Fair Isle. *British Birds* 55: 225–229.

Davis, P. 1963. Aspects of spring migration at the bird observatories, 1963. *Bird Migration* 2: 279–318.

Davis, P. 1965. Recoveries of Swallows ringed in Britain and Ireland. *Bird Study* 12: 151–169.

Davis, P. 1966a. The movements of Pied Wagtails as shown by ringing. *Bird Study* 13: 147–162.

Davis, P. 1966b. The great immigration of early September 1965. *British Birds* 59: 353–376.

Davis, P. 1967. Migration seasons of the *Sylvia* warblers at British bird observatories. *Bird Study* 14: 65–95.

Davis, P.E. 1993. The Red Kite in Wales: setting the record straight. *British Birds* 86: 295–298.

Davis, P., C. Erard, N.O. Preuss, M. Tekke & J. Tricot. 1966. Invasion de Cailles (*Coturnix coturnix*) en Europe durant l'année 1964. *Aves* 3: 65–97.

Davis, P., T. Cross & J. Davis. 2001. Movement, settlement, breeding and survival of Red Kites *Milvus milvus* marked in Wales. *Welsh Birds* 3: 19–43.

Davis, P.G. 1981. *Trapping Methods for Bird Ringers*. British Trust for Ornithology, Tring.

Davis, R.A., R.N. Jones, C.D. MacInnes & A.J. Pakulak. 1985. Molt migration of large Canada Geese on the west coast of Hudson Bay. *Wilson Bulletin* 97: 296–305.

Daw, P.C. 1998. Systematic list for 1997. *Argyll Bird Report* 14: 6–93.

de Bruijn, O. 1994. Population ecology and conservation of the Barn Owl in farmland habitats in Liemers and Achterhoek (the Netherlands). *Ardea* 82: 5–109.

de By, R.A. 1990. Migration of Aquatic Warbler in western Europe. *Dutch Birding* 12: 165–181.

de Crousaz, G. 1966. À propos des mouvements saisonniers de la population alpine du Pipit spioncelle. *Nos Oiseaux* 28: 161–168.

de Juana, E. & A.M. Paterson. 1986. The status of the seabirds of the extreme western Mediterranean. In *Mediterranean Marine Avifauna: Population Studies and Conservation* (eds MEDMARAVIS & X. Monbailliu), pp 19–106. Springer-Verlag, Berlin.

de Kroon, G.H.J. 1979. Methods and provisional results of trapping results in the Netherlands. *Ringing & Migration* 2: 132–136.

de Kroon, G.H.J. 1980. *De Waterral*. Kosmos, Amsterdam and Antwerp.

De la Court, C. & E. Aguilera. 1997. Dispersal and migration in Eurasian Spoonbills *Platalea leucorodia*. *Ardea* 85: 193–202.

De Smet, W.M.A. 1970. Studie over de trek van de Koekoek *Cuculus canorus* L. Tweede deel: de Lentetrek van de Koekoek doorheen Europa. Ontleding van eigen gegevens. *Gerfaut* 60: 148–187.

Dean, A.R. 1984. Origins and distribution of British Glaucous Gulls. *British Birds* 77: 165–166.

Dean, A.R. & B.R. Dean. 1976. Glaucous and Iceland Gulls in the West Midlands. *British Birds* 69: 179–180.

Deán, J.I. 1998. Migratología del Jilguero (*Carduelis carduelis*) en Navarra. *Anuario Ornitologico de Navarra* 5: 43–50.

Dean, W.R.J. 1977. Moult of Little Stints in South Africa. *Ardea* 65: 73–79.

Deelder, C.L. 1949. On the autumn migration of the Scandinavian Chaffinch (*Fringilla c. coelebs* L.). *Ardea* 37: 1–88.

Dejaifve, P.-A. 1994. Écologie et comportement d'un migrateur paléarctique, le traquet tarier *Saxicola rubetra* (L.) au Zaïre et sa répartition hivernale en Afrique. *Revue d'Ecologie, La Terre et la Vie* 49: 35–52.

Dejonghe, J.F. 1989. Importance, structure, origins, biometrics and population dynamics of Kestrels *Falco tinnunculus* on spring migration at Cap Bon, Tunisia. *Alauda* 57: 17–45.

del Marmol, P. 1994. Interpretation des données belges de baguage de la poule d'eau, *Gallinula chloropus*, et de quelques autres rallides. *Gerfaut* 82–83: 3–23.

Delacour, J. 1959. *The Waterfowl of the World*. Country Life, London.

Delany, S. 1993. Introduced and escaped geese in Britain in summer 1991. *British Birds* 86: 591–599.

Delany, S., J.J.D. Greenwood & J. Kirby. 1992. *National Mute Swan Survey 1990*. Unpublished report to the Joint Nature Conservation Committee. 26 pp.

Delany, S., C. Reyes, E. Hubert, S. Pihl, E. Rees, L. Haanstra & A. van Strien. 1999. *Results from the International Waterbird Census in the Western Palearctic and Southwest Asia 1995 and 1996*. Publication 54. Wetlands International, Wageningen, the Netherlands.

Delestrade, A., R.H. McCleery & C.M. Perrins. 1996. Natal dispersal in a heterogeneous environment: the case of the Great Tit in Wytham. *Acta Oecologia* 17: 519–529.

Delingat, J. & V. Dierschke. 2000. Habitat utilization by Northern Wheatears (*Oenanthe oenanthe*) stopping over on an offshore island during migration. *Die Vogelwarte* 40: 271–278.

Delmée, E., P. Dachy & P. Simon. 1978. Quinze années d'observations sur la reproduction d'une population forestière de Chouettes hulottes (*Strix aluco*). *Gerfaut* 68: 590–650.

Dement'ev, G.P. & N.A. Gladkov (eds). 1966. *Birds of the Soviet Union*. Volume 1. Israel Program for Scientific Translations, Jerusalem.

Dement'ev, G.P. & N.A. Gladkov (eds). 1967. *Birds of the Soviet Union*. Volume 4. Israel Program for Scientific Translations, Jerusalem.

Dement'ev, G.P. & N.A. Gladkov (eds). 1969. *Birds of the Soviet Union*. Volume 3. Israel Program for Scientific Translations, Jerusalem.

Dementiev, V.F. 1956. [Migration of *Rissa tridactyla*.] *Proceedings of the Bird Ringing Bureau* 8: 22–32. (In Russian.)

Denby Wilkinson, A. 1950. The annual immigration of the Wood-pigeon and Stock-dove on the coast of East Sussex. *British Birds* 43: 233–238.

Dennis, M.K. 1992. Wintering Blackcaps and Chiffchaffs in the London area. *London Bird Report* 57: 145–152.

Dennis, M.K. 1996. *Breeding Birds of Essex*. Essex Birdwatching Society, Colchester.

Dennis, R. 1983. Population studies and conservation of Ospreys in Scotland. In *Biology and Management of Bald Eagle and Osprey* (ed D.M. Bird), pp 207–214. Harpell Press, Ste Anne de Bellevue, Québec.

Dennis, R. 1995a. Ospreys *Pandion haliaetus* in Scotland – a study of recolonization. *Die Vogelwelt* 116: 193–195.

Dennis, R. 1995b. *The experimental reintroduction of Ospreys to England*. Report to Scottish Natural Heritage.

Dennis, R. & H. Dixon. 1999. *Report on Translocation of young Ospreys from Scotland to Rutland Water Nature Reserve*. Anglian Water.

Dennis, R.H., P.M. Ellis, R.A. Broad & D.R. Langslow. 1984. The status of the Golden Eagle in Britain. *British Birds* 77: 592–607.

des Forges, G. & D.D. Harber. 1963. *A Guide to the Birds of Sussex*. Oliver & Boyd, Edinburgh.

DeSante, D.F., K.M. Burton, J.F. Saracco & B.L. Walker. 1995. Productivity indices and survival rate estimates from MAPS, a continent-wide programme of constant-effort mist-netting in North America. *Journal of Applied Statistics* 22: 935–947.

DeSante, D.F., D.R. O'Grady & P. Pyle. 1999. Measures of productivity and survival derived from standardised mist-netting are consistent with observed population changes. *Bird Study* 46 (suppl.): S178–188.

Desmots, D. & P. Yésou. 1996. Un nouvel afflux de Mouettes de Sabine *Larus sabini* aux Sables d'Olonne (Vendée). *Ornithos* 3: 11–13.

Devort, M., B. Trolliet & J. Veiga. 1988. Sur la migration postnuptiale de la Tourterelle des bois (*Streptopelia turtur turtur*) en Gironde. *Gibier Faune Sauvage* 5: 61–70.

Dhondt, A.A. 1979. Summer dispersal and survival of juvenile Great Tits in southern Sweden. *Oecologia* 42: 139–157.

Dhondt, A.A. 1989. Blue Tit. In *Lifetime Reproduction in Birds* (ed I. Newton), pp 15–33. Academic Press, London.

Dhondt, A.A. & J. Hublé. 1968. Fledging date and sex in relation to dispersal in young Great Tits. *Bird Study* 15: 127–134.

Dhondt, A.A. & G. Olaerts. 1981. Variations in survival and dispersal with ringing date as shown by recoveries of Belgian Great Tits *Parus major*. *Ibis* 123: 96–98.

Dias, S. & A.P. Fontoura. 1996. A dieta estival da rôla-brava (*Streptopelia turtur*) no Sul de Portugal. *Revista Florestal* 9: 227–241.

Dias, S., A.J. Pereira & A.P. Fontoura. 1996. The art of capturing doves: the past and the future of a traditional Portuguese technique. In *The Game and the Man: Proceedings of the XXII Congress of the International Union of Game Biologists, Sofia, 1995* (ed N. Botev), pp 367–372. IUGB, Sofia.

Dick, W.J.A. 1975. *Oxford and Cambridge Mauritanian Expedition 1973*. Privately published.

Dick, W.J.A., T. Piersma & P. Prokosch. 1987. Spring migration of the Siberian Knots *Calidris canutus canutus*: results of a co-operative Wader Study Group project. *Ornis Scandinavica* 18: 5–16.

Dierschke, V. 1994a. Phänologie und Fluktuation des Rastvorkommens der Strandläufer *Calidris*-Arten auf Helgoland. *Die Vogelwelt* 115: 59–68.

Dierschke, V. 1994b. The influence of oil-polluted plumage on survival and body mass of Purple Sandpipers *Calidris maritima* at Helgoland. *Die Vogelwelt* 115: 253–255.

Dierschke, V. 1998. Site fidelity and survival of Purple Sandpipers *Calidris maritima* at Helgoland (SE North Sea). *Ringing & Migration* 19: 41–48.

Dijkstra, C., S. Daan & J.B. Buker. 1990. Adaptive seasonal variation in the sex ratio of Kestrel broods. *Functional Ecology* 4: 143–148.

Dingle, H. 1996. *Migration: the biology of life on the move*. Oxford University Press, Oxford.

Dirksen, S., J. Beekman & T. Slagboom. 1991. Bewick's Swans *Cygnus columbianus bewickii* in the Netherlands: numbers, distribution and food choice during the winter season. In *Proceedings of the Third IWRB International Swan Symposium, Oxford 1989* (eds J. Sears & P.J. Bacon), pp 228–237. *Wildfowl*, suppl. 1.

Dirksen, S., R. Noordhuis, M. Poot, I. Tulp & J. van der Winden. 1998. Bewick's Swans exploiting stoneworts: recovering aquatic food sources increasingly important in autumn. *Swan Specialist Group Newsletter* 7: 12–13.

Dixon, C. 1895. *The Migration of British Birds*. Chapman & Hall, London.

Dobinson, H.M. & A.J. Richards. 1964. The effects of the severe winter of 1962/63 on birds in Britain. *British Birds* 57: 373–434.

Dobson, A.P. 1990. Survival rates and their relationship to life-history traits in some common British birds. *Current Ornithology* 7: 115–146.

Dolton, C.S. & M. de L. Brooke. 1999. Changes in the biomass of birds breeding in Great Britain, 1968–88. *Bird Study* 46: 274–278.

Donald, P.F. 1997. The Corn Bunting *Miliaria calandra* in Britain: a review of current status, patterns of decline and possible causes. In *The ecology and conservation of Corn Buntings* Miliaria calandra (eds P.F. Donald & N.J. Aebischer), pp 11–26. UK Nature Conservation no. 13. Joint Nature Conservation Committee, Peterborough.

Donald, P.F. & A.D. Evans. 1994. Habitat selection by Corn Buntings *Miliaria calandra* in winter. *Bird Study* 41: 199–210.

Donald, P.F. & A.D. Evans. 1995. Habitat selection and population size of Corn Buntings *Miliaria calandra* breeding in Britain in 1993. *Bird Study* 42: 190–204.

Donald, P.F. & R.J. Fuller. 1998. Ornithological atlas data: a review of uses and limitations. *Bird Study* 45: 129–145.

Donald, P.F., J.D. Wilson & M. Shepherd. 1994. The decline of the Corn Bunting. *British Birds* 87: 106–132.

Donker, J.K. 1959. Migration and distribution of Wigeon *Anas penelope* L. in Europe, based on ringing results. *Ardea* 47: 1–27.

Döring, V. & R. Helfrich. 1986. *Zur Ökologie einer Rebhuhnpopulations (Perdix perdix L. 1758) im Unteren Naheland (Rheinland-Pfalz; BRD)*. Schriften des Arbeitskreises Wildbiologie und Jagdwissenschaften an der Justus-Liebig-Universität Giessen, 15. Ferdinand Enke Verlag, Stuttgart.

dos Santos Júnior, J.R. 1979. A rola: notas de biologia e reprodução. *Cyanopica* 2: 5–27.

Dott, H.E.M. 1997. Declines in Turnstones and Purple Sandpipers wintering in south east Scotland. *Scottish Birds* 19: 101–104.

Doude van Troostwijk, W.J. 1974. Ringing data on White-fronted Geese *Anser a. albifrons* in the Netherlands, 1953–1968. *Ardea* 62: 98–110.

Dougall, T.W. 1991. Winter distribution and associated movements of northern Pied Wagtails *Motacilla alba yarrellii* as shown by ringing. *Ringing & Migration* 12: 1–15.

Dougall, T.W. 1992. Post-fledging dispersal of British Pied Wagtails *Motacilla alba yarrellii*. *Ringing & Migration* 13: 21–26.

Dougall, T.W. 1993. Post-juvenile moult and dispersal in the Meadow Pipit *Anthus pratensis*. *Ringing & Migration* 14: 137–142.

Dougall, T.W. 1996a. Movement and mortality of British-ringed Skylarks *Alauda arvensis*. *Bird Study* 17: 81–92.

Dougall, T.W. 1996b. Timing of autumn migration of Pied Wagtails *Motacilla alba yarrellii* in northern Britain. *Ringing & Migration* 17: 139–141.

Dougall, T.W. 1997. Biometrics and sex ratios of Skylarks *Alauda arvensis* in winter in south-east Scotland. *Ringing & Migration* 18: 37–49.

Dougall, T.W. & G.F. Appleton. 1989. Winter weights and age structure of a population of Pied Wagtails at a southern Scotland roost. *Ringing & Migration* 10: 83–88.

Dougall, T.W. & R.S. Craig. 1993. Ageing Meadow Pipits in autumn: a cautionary note. *Ringers' Bulletin* 8: 52.

Dougall, T.W. & R.S. Craig. 1997. Duration of post-juvenile moult in the Meadow Pipit *Anthus pratensis*. *Ringing & Migration* 18: 35–36.

Douse, A.F.G. 1981. *The use of agricultural land by Common Gulls (Larus canus L.) wintering in North-East Scotland*. PhD thesis, University of Aberdeen.

Dowsett-Lemaire, F. & R.J. Dowsett. 1987. European Reed and Marsh Warblers in Africa: migration patterns, moult and habitat. *Ostrich* 58: 65–85.

Doyle, F.I. & J.M.N. Smith. 1994. Population responses of Northern Goshawks to the 10-year cycle in numbers of Snowshoe Hares. *Studies in Avian Biology* 16: 122–129.

Draulans, D. & J. van Vessem. 1985. Age-related differences in the use of time and space by radio-tagged Grey Herons in winter. *Journal of Animal Ecology* 54: 771–780.

Drennan, D.J. 1997. Nesting of Eurasian Collared Doves (*Streptopelia decaocto*) in Barbour County, Alabama. *Alabama Birdlife* 43: 1–6.

Drent, P.J. 1984. Mortality and dispersal in summer and its consequences for the density of Great Tits *Parus major* at the onset of autumn. *Ardea* 72: 127–162.

Drent, R. & T. Piersma. 1990. An exploration of the energetics of leap-frog migration in arctic breeding waders. In *Bird Migration: the physiology and ecophysiology* (ed E. Gwinner), pp 399–412. Springer Verlag, Berlin.

Drent, R.H., B. Ebbinge & B. Weijand. 1981. Balancing the energy budgets of arctic breeding geese throughout the annual cycle: a progress report. *Verhandlungen der Ornithologischen Gesellschaft in Bayern* 23: 239–264.

du Feu, C.R. & J.M. McMeeking. 1991. Does constant effort netting measure juvenile abundance? *Ringing & Migration* 12: 118–123.

Dugan, P.J. 1981. *Seasonal movements of shorebirds in relation to spring behaviour and prey availability.* PhD thesis, University of Durham.

Dugan, P.J. 1982. Seasonal changes in patch use by a territorial Grey Plover: weather-dependent adjustments in foraging behaviour. *Journal of Animal Ecology* 51: 849–857.

Duncan, K. & M. Marquiss. 1993. The sex/age ratio, diving behaviour and habitat use of Goldeneye *Bucephala clangula* wintering in north east Scotland. *Wildfowl* 44: 111–120.

Duncan, K., D. Pullan & R. Smith. 1993. Visite au Maroc, à la recherche des Pluviers Guignards (*Charadrius morinellus*) – Octobre/Novembre 1991. *Porphyrio* 5: 6–45.

Duncan, R. 1987. Breeding Skylarks in Aberdeen. *Grampian Ringing Group Report* 5: 49–56.

Duncan, R. 1989a. Movements of Greenfinches in Grampian 1972–89. *Grampian Ringing Group Report* 6: 58–64.

Duncan, R. 1989b. A Waxwing invasion at last. *Grampian Ringing Group Report* 6: 77–87.

Duncan, R. 1992a. Female natal philopatry in a Scottish Wigeon population. *Scottish Birds* 16: 222.

Duncan, R. 1992b. The autumn dispersal of Grampian Teal ducklings. *Grampian Ringing Group Report* 7: 46–48.

Duncan, R. 1996. Movements of Greenfinches in Grampian. Part Two: The Norwegian story. *Grampian Ringing Group Report* 8: 39–47.

Duncker, H. 1912. Der Verbreitung der Gattung *Emberiza*. *Journal für Ornithologie* 60: 69–95.

Dunn, E.K. & C.J. Mead. 1982. Relationship between sardine fisheries and recovery rates of ringed terns in West Africa. *Seabird* 6: 98–104.

Dunn, J. 1983. Sabine's Gulls in Britain in winter. *British Birds* 76: 91.

Dunn, P.J. & E. Hirschfeld. 1991. Long-tailed Skuas in Britain and Ireland in autumn 1988. *British Birds* 84: 121–136.

Dunn, P.J. & P.A. Lassey. 1985. Little Gulls in Yorkshire. *Naturalist* 110: 91–98.

Dunnet, G.M. & I.J. Patterson. 1968. The rook problem in north-east Scotland. In *The Problems of Birds as Pests* (eds R.K. Murton & E.N. Wright), pp 119–139. Academic Press, London.

Dunnet, G.M., A. Anderson & R.M. Cormack. 1963. A study of survival of adult Fulmars with observations on the pre-laying exodus. *British Birds* 56: 2–18.

Dunnet, G.M., J.C. Ollason & A. Anderson. 1979. A 28–year study of breeding Fulmars (*Fulmarus glacialis*) in Orkney. *Ibis* 121: 293–300.

Durell, S.E.A. le V. dit, J.D. Goss-Custard, R.W.G. Caldow, H.M. Malcolm & D. Osborn. 2001. Sex, diet and feeding-method related differences in body condition in the Oystercatcher *Haematopus ostralegus*. *Ibis* 143: 107–119.

Durinck, J., H. Skov & P. Andell. 1993a. Seabird distribution and numbers in selected offshore parts of the Baltic Sea, winter 1992. *Ornis Svecica* 3: 11–26.

Durinck, J., K.D. Christensen, H. Skov & F. Danielsen. 1993b. Diet of the Common Scoter *Melanitta nigra* and Velvet Scoter *Melanitta fusca* wintering in the North Sea. *Ornis Fennica* 70: 215–218.

Durinck, J., H. Skov, F.P. Jensen & S. Pihl. 1994. *Important Marine Areas for Wintering Birds in the Baltic Sea.* EU DG XI research contract 2242/90–09–01. Ornis Consult, Copenhagen.

Durman, R.F. 1967. Weights and wing-lengths of Willow Warblers caught on Bardsey, 1961–65. *Bird Study* 14: 120–122.

Durman, R. 1976a. *Bird Observatories in Britain and Ireland.* T. & A.D. Poyser for the Bird Observatories Council, Berkhamsted.

Durman, R.F. 1976b. Ring Ousel migration. *Bird Study* 23: 197–205.

Durman, R.F. 1977. Ring Ousels in the Pentlands. *Edinburgh Ringing Report* 5: 24–27.

Dymond, J.N. 1980. *The Birds of Lundy.* Devon Birdwatching and Preservation Society, Plymouth.

Dymond, J.N. 1991. *The Birds of Fair Isle.* Privately published.

Dymond, J.N., P.A. Fraser & S.J.M. Gantlett. 1989. *Rare birds in Britain and Ireland.* T. & A.D. Poyser, Calton.

Dyrcz, A. & W. Zdunek. 1993. Breeding ecology of the Aquatic Warbler *Acrocephalus paludicola* on the Biebrza Marshes, northeast Poland. *Ibis* 135: 181–189.

Eastwood, E. 1967. *Radar Ornithology.* Methuen, London.

Ebbinge, B.S. 1991. The impact of hunting on mortality rates and spatial distribution of geese wintering in the western Palearctic. *Ardea* 79: 197–210.

Ebbinge, B.S. & A.K.M. St Joseph. 1992. The Brent Goose colour-ringing scheme: unravelling annual migratory movements from high arctic Siberia to the coasts of Western Europe. In *Population Limitation in Arctic Breeding Geese.* PhD thesis (B.S. Ebbinge), Groningen University, the Netherlands.

Ebbinge, B., H.T. van der Meulen & J.J. Smit. 1984. Changes in winter distribution and population size of Pink-footed Geese breeding in Svalbard. *Norsk Polarinstitutts Skrifter* 181: 11–17.

Ebbinge, B.S., J.B. van Biezen & H. van der Voet. 1991. Estimation of annual adult survival rates of Barnacle Geese *Branta leucopsis* using multiple sightings of marked individuals. *Ardea* 79: 73–112.

Ebbinge, B.S., C. Berrevoets, P. Clausen, B. Ganter, K. Günther, K. Koffijberg, R. Mahéo, J.M. Rowcliffe, A.K.M. St Joseph, P. Südbeck & E.E. Syroechkovski Jr. 1999. Dark-bellied Brent Goose *Branta bernicla bernicla*. In *Goose populations of the Western Palaearctic: a review of status and distribution* (eds J. Madsen, G. Cracknell & A.D. Fox), pp 312–327. Wetlands International Publication 48. Wetlands International, Wageningen, the Netherlands, and National Environmental Research Institute, Rönde, Denmark.

Eden, S.F. 1987. Natal philopatry of the Magpie *Pica pica*. *Ibis* 129: 477–490.

Edgar, R.D.M. 1996. Blackcap. In *Birds of Sussex* (ed P. James), pp 460–462. Sussex Ornithological Society.

Ehrenroth, B. 1973. Studies on migratory movements of the Willow Tit *Parus montanus borealis* Selys-Longchamps. *Ornis Scandinavica* 4: 87–96.

Ehrenroth, B. 1976. Autumn movements of the Long-tailed Tit *Aegithalos caudatus caudatus* L. at an inland locality in Central Sweden. *Ornis Fennica* 53: 73–86.

Einarsson, Ó. 1996. *Breeding biology of the Whooper Swan and factors affecting its breeding success, with notes on its social dynamics and life cycle in the wintering range.* PhD thesis, University of Bristol.

Einarsson, Ó. 2000. Iceland. In *Important Bird Areas in Europe: priority sites for conservation* (eds M.F. Heath & M.I. Evans), pp 341–363. BirdLife International, Cambridge.

Ekins, G. 1996. The Abberton Reservoir (51°45'N 0°45'E) tree-nesting Cormorant colony: a summary of recent research. *Essex Bird Report 1994*: 153–167.

Elgood, J.H. 1982. *The Birds of Nigeria.* British Ornithologists' Union, London.

Elkins, N. 1979. Nearctic landbirds in Britain and Ireland: a meteorological analysis. *British Birds* 72: 417–433.

Elkins, N. 1988a. *Weather and Bird Behaviour*. Second edition. T. & A.D. Poyser, Calton.

Elkins, N. 1988b. Recent transatlantic vagrancy of landbirds and waders. *British Birds* 81: 484–491.

Elkins, N. 1999. Recent records of Nearctic landbirds in Britain and Ireland. *British Birds* 92: 83–95.

Elkins, N. & M.R. Williams. 1969. Seabird movements in N.E. Scotland, 1968 and 1969. *Seabird Report* 1: 31–39.

Ellegren, H. 1990. Timing of autumn migration in Bluethroats *Luscinia svecica svecica* depends on timing of breeding. *Ornis Fennica* 67: 13–17.

Ellegren, H. 1991. Stopover ecology of autumn migrating Bluethroats *Luscinia svecica svecica* in relation to age and sex. *Ornis Scandinavica* 22: 340–348.

Ellegren, H. & T. Fransson. 1992. Fat loads and estimated flight-ranges in four *Sylvia* species analysed during autumn migration at Gotland, South-East Sweden. *Ringing & Migration* 13: 1–12.

Elliott, C.C.H., M. Waltner, L.G. Underhill, J.S. Pringle & W.J.A. Dick. 1976. The migration system of the Curlew Sandpiper *Calidris ferruginea* in Africa. *Ostrich* 47: 191–213.

Elliott, G.D. & M.I. Avery. 1991. A review of reports of Buzzard persecution 1975–1989. *Bird Study* 38: 52–56.

Ellis, P. 1983. The phenomenal migrant fall of October 1982. *Scottish Birds* 12: 246–251.

Ellis, P.M. 1990. Shore Larks nesting in Scotland in 1977. *Scottish Birds* 16: 43–44.

Ellis, P.M. & J.D. Okill. 1990. Breeding ecology of the Merlin *Falco columbarius* in Shetland. *Bird Study* 37: 101–110.

Elphick, D. 1979. An inland flock of Curlews *Numenius arquata* in mid Cheshire, England. *Wader Study Group Bulletin* 26: 31–35.

Eltringham, S.K. 1961. The moulting Shelduck of Bridgwater Bay. *Somerset Bird Report* 47: 59–61.

Eltringham, S.K. & H. Boyd. 1960. The Shelduck population in the Bridgwater Bay moulting area. *Wildfowl Trust Annual Report* 11: 107–117.

Eltringham, S.K. & H. Boyd. 1963. Moult migration of the Shelduck to Bridgwater Bay, Somerset. *British Birds* 56: 433–444.

Engel, K.A. & L.S. Young. 1989. Evaluation of techniques for capturing Common Ravens in Southwestern Idaho. *North American Bird Bander* 14: 5–8.

Engel, K.A. & L.S. Young. 1992. Movements and habitat use by Common Ravens from roost sites in southwestern Idaho. *Journal of Wildlife Management* 56: 596–602.

Engelmoer, M. 1984. *Analyse van Biometrische Gegevens 12 Soorten Holarctische Steltlopers*. Staatsbosbeheer, Utrecht.

Engelmoer, M. & A.-M. Blomert. 1985. *Broedbiologie van de Kluut langs de Friese Waddenkust seizoen 1983*. RIJP-rapport 39, Abw, Lelystad.

Engelmoer, M. & C.S. Roselaar. 1998. *Geographical Variation in Waders*. Kluwer Academic Publishers, Dordrecht.

Engler, H. 2000. *Die Teichralle*. Third edition. Die Neue Brehm-Bücherei 536. Westarp Wissenschaften, Hohenwarsleben.

Enoksson, B. 1987. Local movements in the Nuthatch (*Sitta europaea*). *Acta Regiae Societatis Scientiarum et Litterarum Gothoburgensis Zoologica* 14: 36–47.

Enoksson, B. 1990. Autumn territories and population regulation in the Nuthatch *Sitta europaea*: an experimental study. *Journal of Animal Ecology* 59: 1047–1062.

Enoksson, B., P. Angelstam & K. Larsson. 1995. Deciduous forest and resident birds: the problem of fragmentation within a coniferous forest landscape. *Landscape Ecology* 10: 267–275.

Ens, B.J., K.B. Briggs, U.N. Safriel & C.J. Smit. 1996. Life history decisions during the breeding season. In *The Oystercatcher: from individuals to populations* (ed J.D. Goss-Custard), pp 186–218. Oxford University Press, Oxford.

Erard, C. 1960. Sur l'aire de reproduction, les zones d'hivernage et les migrations de la Mouette Pygmée *Larus minutus* Pallas. *Alauda* 28: 196–228.

Eriksson, K. 1970. Ecology of migration and wintering of Fennoscandian Redpolls (*Carduelis flammea*). *Annales Zoologici Fennici* 7: 273–282.

Eriksson, K. 1971. Irruption and wintering ecology of the Great Spotted Woodpecker *Dendrocopos major*. *Ornis Fennica* 48: 69–76.

Eriksson, M.O.G. 2000. *Abstracts from 'Loons/Divers – Research and Management Workshop', 20–22 August 1999 at Viskadalen, Sweden*. The Swedish Union for Conservation of Nature, Stockholm.

Ernst, S. 1983. Die Birkenzeisiginvasion in Winter 1972/73 in Bezirk Karl-Marx-Stadt. *Die Falke* 30: 150–156.

Erritzoe, J. & R. Fuller. 1999. Sex differences in winter distribution of Long-eared Owls (*Asio otus*) in Denmark and neighbouring countries. *Die Vogelwarte* 40: 80–87.

Escalante, R. 1972. First Pomarine Skua specimen from Brazil. *Auk* 89: 663–665.

Etheridge, B., R.W. Summers & R.E. Green. 1997. The effects of illegal killing and destruction of nests by humans on the population dynamics of the Hen Harrier *Circus cyaneus* in Scotland. *Journal of Applied Ecology* 34: 1081–1105.

Etheridge, B., C. Crooke & T. Burns. 1998. *The Red Kite Newsletter for North Scotland 1997*. RSPB/SNH, Inverness.

Etheridge, B., C. Crooke & T. Burns. 1999. *The Red Kite Newsletter for North Scotland 1998*. RSPB/SNH, Inverness.

Etheridge, P. 2001. Dartford Warblers re-colonising Suffolk. *BTO News* 234: 23–24.

EURING. 1979. *Code manual: new EURING*. British Trust for Ornithology, Tring.

Evans, A.D. 1992. The numbers and distribution of Cirl Buntings *Emberiza cirlus* breeding in Britain in 1989. *Bird Study* 39: 17–22.

Evans, A.D. & K.W. Smith. 1994. Habitat selection of Cirl Buntings *Emberiza cirlus* wintering in Britain. *Bird Study* 41: 81–87.

Evans, A.D., M. Painter, R. Wynde & N. Michael. 1994. An inventory of lowland heathland: a foundation for an effective conservation strategy. *RSPB Conservation Review* 8: 24–30.

Evans, A.D., A.G. Gosler & J.D. Wilson. 1999. Increasing the conservation value of ringing studies of passerines, with emphasis on the non-breeding season. *Ringing & Migration* 19 (suppl.): S107–117.

Evans, I.M. & M.W. Pienkowski. 1991. World status of the Red Kite: a background to the experimental reintroduction to England and Scotland. *British Birds* 84: 171–187.

Evans, I.M., R.H. Dennis, D.C. Orr-Ewing, N. Kjellén, P.-O. Andersson, M. Sylvén, A. Senosiain & F. Compaired Carbo. 1997. The re-establishment of Red Kite breeding populations in Scotland and England. *British Birds* 90: 123–138.

Evans, I.M., R.W. Summers, L. O'Toole, D.C. Orr-Ewing, R. Evans, N. Snell & J. Smith. 1999. Evaluating the success of translocating Red Kites *Milvus milvus* to the UK. *Bird Study* 46: 129–144.

Evans, M. 1979a. Population composition, and return according to breeding status, of Bewick's Swans wintering at Slimbridge, 1963 to 1976. *Wildfowl* 30: 118–128.

Evans, M.E. 1979b. The effects of weather on the wintering Bewick's Swans *Cygnus columbianus bewickii* at Slimbridge, England. *Ornis Scandinavica* 10: 124–132.

Evans, M. 1979c. Aspects of the life-cycle of the Bewick's Swan based on recognition of individuals at a wintering site. *Bird Study* 26: 149–162.

Evans, M.E. 1982. Movements of Bewick's Swans *Cygnus columbianus bewickii* marked at Slimbridge, England from 1960 to 1979. *Ardea* 70: 59–75.

Evans, M. & J. Burn. 1996. An experimental analysis of mate choice in the wren: a monomorphic, polygynous passerine. *Behavioral Ecology* 7: 101–108.

Evans, M. & W.J.L. Sladen. 1980. A comparative analysis of the bill markings of whistling and Bewick's swans and out-of-range occurrences of the two taxa. *Auk* 97: 697–703.

Evans, P.R. 1966a. Wader migration in north-east England. *Transactions of the Natural History Society of Northumberland, Durham and Newcastle-upon-Tyne* 16: 126–151.

Evans, P.R. 1966b. Autumn movements, moult and measurements of the Lesser Redpoll *Carduelis flammea cabaret*. *Ibis* 108: 183–216.

Evans, P.R. 1966c. Some results from the ringing of Rock Pipits on Skokholm 1952–1965. *Report of Skokholm Bird Observatory 1966*: 22–27.

Evans, P.R. 1969. Ecological aspects of migration and pre-migratory fat deposition in the Lesser Redpoll, *Carduelis flammea cabaret*. *Condor* 71: 316–330.

Evans, P.R., D.M. Brearey & L.R. Goodyer. 1980. Studies on Sanderling at Teesmouth, NE England. *Wader Study Group Bulletin* 30: 18–21.

Evans, W. 1911. Notes of the recent immigration of Mealy Redpoll (*Acanthis linaria*), including the form known as Holboll's Redpoll. *Proceedings of the Royal Philosophical Society of Edinburgh* 18: 192–203.

Everett, M.J. 1967. Waxwings in Scotland, 1965/66 & 1966/67. *Scottish Birds* 4: 534–548.

Everett, M.J. 1971. Breeding status of Red-necked Phalaropes in Britain and Ireland. *British Birds* 64: 293–302.

Everitt, B.S. 1978. *Graphical Techniques for Multivariate Data*. Heinemann, London.

Ewins, P.J. 1988a. The timing of moult in Black Guillemots *Cepphus grylle* in Shetland. *Ringing & Migration* 9: 5–10.

Ewins, P.J. 1988b. An analysis of ringing recoveries of Black Guillemots *Cepphus grylle* in Britain and Ireland. *Ringing & Migration* 9: 95–102.

Ewins, P.J. & D.A. Kirk. 1988. The distribution of Black Guillemots *Cepphus grylle* outside the breeding season. *Seabird* 11: 50–61.

Exo, K.-M. & R. Hennes. 1978. Ringfunde des Steinkauzes (*Athene noctua*). *Auspicium* 6: 363–374.

Exo, K.-M. & R. Hennes. 1980. Beitrag zur Populationsökologie des Steinkauzes (*Athene noctua*) – eine Analyse deutscher und niederländischer Ringfunde. *Die Vogelwarte* 30: 162–179.

Eybert, M.C. & P. Constant. 1992. Validité de l'analyse des sacs fécaux pour l'étude du régime alimentaire des jeunes au nid de la linotte mélodieuse (*Carduelis cannabina*). *Canadian Journal of Zoology* 70: 2171–2177.

Eybert, M.C. & P. Constant. 1998. Diet of nestling Linnets (*Acanthis cannabina* L.). *Journal für Ornithologie* 139: 277–286.

Fajardo, I. 1990. Mortalidad de la Lechuza Común (*Tyto alba*) en España Central. *Ardeola* 37: 101–106.

Falk, K. & S. Moller. 1995. Satellite tracking of high-arctic Northern Fulmars. *Polar Biology* 15: 495–502.

Farmer, A.H. & A.H. Parent. 1997. Effects of the landscape on shorebird movements at spring migration stopovers. *Condor* 99: 698–707.

Farnsworth, S.J. 1994. Corn bunting *E. calandra* in Mauritania and West Africa. *Malimbus* 16: 124–125.

Feare, C.J. 1980. Local movements of Starlings in winter. In *Acta XVII Congressus Internationalis Ornithologici*, volume 2 (ed R. Nöhring), pp 1331–1336. Deutsche Ornithologen-Gesellschaft, Berlin.

Feare, C. 1984. *The Starling*. Oxford University Press, Oxford.

Feare, C.J. 1990. Pigeon control: towards a humane alternative. *Environmental Health* 98: 155–156.

Feare, C.J. 1994. Changes in numbers of Starlings and farming practice in Lincolnshire. *British Birds* 87: 200–204.

Feare, C.J. 1996. Rose-ringed Parakeet *Psittacula krameri*: a love-hate relationship in the making? In *The introduction and naturalisation of birds* (eds J.S. Holmes & J.R. Simons), pp 107–112. The Stationery Office, London.

Feare, C. & A. Craig. 1998. *Starlings and Mynas*. Christopher Helm, London.

Feare, C.J. & N. McGinnity. 1986. The relative importance of invertebrates and barley in the diet of Starlings *Sturnus vulgaris*. *Bird Study* 33: 164–167.

Feare, C.J., G.M. Dunnet & I.J. Patterson. 1974. Ecological studies of the Rook (*Corvus frugilegus* L.) in north-east Scotland. Food and feeding behaviour. *Journal of Applied Ecology* 11: 867–896.

Fedynich, A.M. & C.J. Godfrey. 1989. Gadwall pair recaptured in successive winters on the southern high plains of Texas. *Journal of Field Ornithology* 60: 168–170.

Feige, K.-D. 1986. *Der Pirol*. Die Neue Brehm-Bücherei 578. A. Ziemsen Verlag, Wittenberg Lutherstadt.

Fennell, J.F.M. & D.A. Stone. 1976. A winter roosting population of Reed Buntings in central England. *Ringing & Migration* 1: 108–114.

Ferguson, A. 1992. *Naturalised Rose-ringed Parakeets* Psittacula krameri *in the British Isles – a review of their biology and status and an ecological study on a group in the Isle of Thanet, Kent*. Thesis for the Diploma in Ecology and Conservation, Birkbeck College, University of London.

Ferguson-Lees, I.J. & K. Williamson. 1960. Recent reports and news – Phalaropes in abundance. *British Birds* 55: 529–531.

Fernandez, O. & P. Bayle. 1994. Tentative insolite de nidification du Fou de Bassan *Sula bassana* à Port-Frioul (Marseille, Bouches-du-Rhône). *Alauda* 62: 140–143.

Ferns, P.N. 1975. Feeding behaviour of autumn passage migrants in north east Portugal. *Ringing & Migration* 1: 3–11.

Ferns, P.N. 1980. The spring migration of Sanderlings *Calidris alba* through Britain in 1979. *Wader Study Group Bulletin* 30: 22–25.

Ferns, P.N. 1981. The spring passage of Turnstones through Britain in 1979. *Wader Study Group Bulletin* 31: 36–40.

Ferns, P.N. & G.H. Green. 1979. Observation on the breeding plumage and prenuptial moult of Dunlins, *Calidris alpina*, captured in Britain. *Gerfaut* 69: 287–303.

Ferns, P.N., G.H. Green & P.D. Round. 1979. Significance of the Somerset and Gwent Levels in Britain as feeding areas for migrant Whimbrels, *Numenius phaeopus*. *Biological Conservation* 16: 7–22.

Fiala, V. 1991. Der Durchzug der Watvögel (Limicolae) im Teichgebiet von Náměšt N. Osl. und seine Veränderungen 1957–1990. *Folia Zoologica* 40: 351–366.

Fiedler, W. 1998. Joint Vogelwarte Radolfzell-EURING migration project: a large-scale ringing recovery analysis of the migration of European bird species. *EURING Newsletter* 2: 31–35.

Figuerola, J. & A. Bertolero. 1995. The primary moult of Curlew Sandpiper in the Ebro Delta, North-east Spain. *Ringing & Migration* 16: 168–171.

Filchager, A.V. & V.V. Leonovich. 1992. Breeding range expansion of Barnacle and Brent Geese in the Russian-European north. *Polar Research* 11: 41–46.

Finlayson, J.C. 1980. The recurrence in winter quarters at Gibraltar of some scrub passerines. *Ringing & Migration* 3: 32–34.

Finlayson, C. 1992. *Birds of the Strait of Gibraltar*. T. & A.D. Poyser, London.

Fischer, A.G. 1960. Latitudinal variation in organic diversity. *Evolution* 14: 64–81.

Fisher, J. 1952. *The Fulmar*. Collins, London.

Fisher, P. 1998. The birds of the Wash, 1971–1996. *Norfolk Bird & Mammal Report 1997*: 565–588.

Fiuczynski, D. 1978. The population of the Hobby Falcon (*Falco subbuteo*). *Zoologisch Jahrbuch (Abteilung Systematik)* 105: 193–257.

Fjeldså, J. 1973. Distribution and geographical variation of the Horned Grebe *Podiceps auritus* (Linnaeus, 1758). *Ornis Scandinavica* 4: 55–86.

Fjeldså, J. & J.-K. Jensen. 1985. 'Invasion' af Hvidvingede og Kumlien's Måger *Larus glaucoides* og *kumlieni* på Nolsø på Færøerne. *Dansk Ornithologisk Forenings Tidsskrift* 79: 103–106.

Flamant, R. 1994. Aperçu des programmes de marquage d'oiseaux à l'aide de bagues de couleur, colliers et marques alaires en Europe. *Aves* 31: 65–186.

Flegg, J.J.M. 1973. A study of Treecreepers. *Bird Study* 20: 287–302.

Flegg, J.J.M. & C.J. Cox. 1975. Mortality in the Black-headed Gull. *British Birds* 68: 437–449.

Flegg, J.J.M. & C.J. Cox. 1976. Movement of Black-headed Gulls from colonies in England and Wales. *Bird Study* 19: 228–240.

Flegg, J.J.M. & D.E. Glue. 1973. A Water Rail study. *Bird Study* 20: 69–79.

Flegg, J.J.M. & R.A. Morgan. 1976. Mortality in British gulls. *Ringing & Migration* 1: 65–74.

Fleming, T.H. 1981. Winter roosting and feeding behaviour of Pied Wagtails *Motacilla alba* near Oxford, England. *Ibis* 123: 463–476.

Fliege, G. 1984. Das Zugverhalten des Stars (*Sturnus vulgaris*) in Europa: eine Analyse der Ringfunde. *Journal für Ornithologie* 125: 393–446.

Flint, P.R. & P.F. Stewart. 1983. *The Birds of Cyprus*. British Ornithologists' Union, London.

Fog, M. 1982. Number of Bean Goose (*Anser fabalis* sp.) in the wintering areas. *Aquila* 89: 123–125.

Fokkema, J., A.G. Bakker, D. Hollenga, J. Jukema & U. Rijpma. 1978. Sneeuwgorzen als wintergast. *Vanellus* 31: 130–135.

Forchammer, M. & L. Maagaard. 1991. Breeding biology of Sabine's Gull *Larus sabini* in Northeast Greenland. *Dansk Ornitologisk Forenings Tidsskrift* 85: 53–62.

Formozov, A.N. 1946. Snow cover as an integral factor of the environment and its importance in the ecology of mammals and birds. In *Materials for Fauna and Flora of the USSR*, New Series, Zoology, 5: 1–152. Moscow Society of Naturalists. (Translation published in 1964 by Boreal Institute for Northern Studies, University of Alberta, Canada.)

Forshaw, W.D. 1983. Numbers, distribution and behaviour of Pink-footed Geese in Lancashire. *Wildfowl* 34: 67–76.

Forslund, P. & K. Larsson. 1991. Breeding range expansion of the Barnacle Goose *Branta leucopsis* in the Baltic area. *Ardea* 79: 343–346.

Forsman, D. 1993. *Suomen Haukat ja Kotkat*. Kirjayhtymä, Helsinki.

Forsyth, I. 1993. Irish Ringing Report for 1992. *Irish Birds* 5: 103–117.

Forsyth, I. 1998. Irish Ringing Report for 1997. *Irish Birds* 6: 313–322.

Fouarge, J.G. 1968. Le Pouillot Siffleur *Phylloscopus sibilatrix* Bechstein. *Gerfaut* 58: 179–368.

Fouarge, J. 1981. La Fauvette à tête noire (*Sylvia atricapilla*), explanation des données Belges de baguage. *Gerfaut* 71: 677–716.

Fournier, O. & F. Spitz. 1969. Étude biometrique des Limicoles. II. Differenciation biometrique et cycle de presence des populations de *Tringa totanus* stationnant dans le Sud de la Vendée. *L'Oiseau et Revue Française d'Ornithologie* 39: 242–251.

Fowler, J.A. 1985. Monitoring Storm Petrel activity in Shetland. In *Population and Monitoring of Seabirds* (ed M.L. Tasker), pp 3–5. Proceedings of Second International Conference of the Seabird Group. The Seabird Group, Aberdeen.

Fowler, J. & L. Cohen. 1995. *Statistics for Ornithologists*. Second edition. BTO Guide 22. British Trust for Ornithology, Thetford.

Fowler, J.A. & M.V. Hounsome. 1998. Migration and arrival of immature Storm Petrels *Hydrobates pelagicus* in Shetland. *Ringing & Migration* 19: 91–94.

Fowler, J.A. & R. Swinfen. 1984. Scottish Storm Petrels in Iceland. *Scottish Birds* 13: 520.

Fowler, J.A., C.J. Miller & S. Cohen. 1984. Ectoparasite populations from breeding and wandering Storm Petrels. *Bird Study* 31: 126–130.

Fowler, J.A., M.E. Hulbert & G. Smith. 1986. Sex ratio in a sample of tape-lured Storm Petrels *Hydrobates pelagicus* from Shetland, Scotland. *Seabird* 9: 15–19.

Fowler, J.A., J.D. Okill & R. Riddington. 1996. Shetland Storm Petrels in Norway, Faeroe and Iceland. *Shetland Bird Report 1995*: 94–96.

Fox, A.D. 1988. Breeding status of Gadwall in Britain and Ireland. *British Birds* 81: 51–66.

Fox, A.D. & S.J. Aspinall. 1987. Pomarine Skuas in Britain and Ireland in autumn 1985. *British Birds* 80: 404–421.

Fox, A.D. & I.S. Francis. 2002. *Report of the 2001/2002 national census of Greenland White-fronted Geese in Britain*. Report to the Wildfowl & Wetlands Trust. Greenland White-fronted Goose Study, Rönde, Denmark.

Fox, A.D. & C. Mitchell. 1988. Migration and seasonal distribution of Gadwall from Britain and Ireland: a preliminary assessment. *Wildfowl* 39: 145–152.

Fox, A.D. & S.C. Ridgill. 1985. Spring activity patterns of migrating Greenland White-fronted Geese. *Wildfowl* 36: 21–28.

Fox, A.D. & D.G. Salmon. 1988. Changes in non-breeding distribution and habitat of Pochard in Britain. *Biological Conservation* 46: 303–316.

Fox, A.D. & D.G. Salmon. 1989. The winter status and distribution of Gadwall in Britain and Ireland. *Bird Study* 36: 37–44.

Fox, A.D. & D.A. Stroud. 1988. The breeding biology of the Greenland White-fronted Goose *Anser albifrons flavirostris*. *Meddelelser om Grønland, Bioscience* 27: 1–16.

Fox, A.D., J. Madsen & D.A. Stroud. 1983. A review of the summer ecology of the Greenland White-fronted Goose. *Dansk Ornitologisk Forenings Tidsskrift* 77: 43–55.

Fox, A.D., I.S. Francis, J. Madsen & J.M. Stroud. 1987. The breeding biology of the Lapland Bunting *Calcarius lapponicus* in West Greenland during two contrasting years. *Ibis* 129: 541–552.

Fox, A.D., H. Boyd & S. Warren. 1992. The phenology of spring pre-nesting feeding in Iceland-nesting geese. *Ecography* 15: 289–295.

Fox, A.D., C. Mitchell, A. Stewart, J.D. Fletcher, J.V.N. Turner, H. Boyd, P. Shimmings, D.G. Salmon, W.G. Haines & C. Tomlinson. 1994a. Winter movements and site-fidelity of Pink-footed Geese *Anser brachyrhynchus* ringed in Britain, with particular emphasis on those marked in Lancashire. *Bird Study* 41: 221–234.

Fox, A.D., D.W. Norriss, D.A. Stroud & H.J. Wilson. 1994b. *Greenland White-fronted Geese in Ireland and Britain 1982/83–1993/94 – the first twelve years of international conservation monitoring*. GWGS Research Report 8. Greenland White-fronted Goose Study, Aberystwyth, & National Parks and Wildlife Service, Dublin.

Fox, A.D., C. Glahder, C.R. Mitchell, D.A. Stroud, H. Boyd & J. Frikke. 1996. North American Canada Geese (*Branta canadensis*) in West Greenland. *Auk* 113: 231–233.

Fox, A.D., D.W. Norriss, D.A. Stroud, H.J. Wilson & O.J. Merne. 1998. The Greenland White-fronted Goose *Anser albifrons flavirostris* in Ireland and Britain 1982/83–1994/95: population change under conservation legislation. *Wildlife Biology* 4: 1–12.

Fox, A.D., J.Ó. Hilmarsson, Ó. Einarsson, H. Boyd, J.N. Kristiansen, D.A. Stroud, A.J. Walsh, C. Mitchell, I.S. Francis & T. Nygaard. 1999a. Phenology and distribution of ringing recoveries and resightings of individually marked Greenland White-fronted Geese *Anser albifrons flavirostris* staging in Iceland. *Wildfowl* 50: 31–45.

Fox, A.D., D.W. Norriss, H.J. Wilson, O.J. Merne, D.A. Stroud, A. Sigfusson & C. Glahder. 1999b. Greenland White-fronted Goose *Anser albifrons flavirostris*. In *Goose populations of the Western Palearctic: a review of status and distribution* (eds J. Madsen, G. Cracknell & A.D. Fox), pp 130–142. Wetlands International Publication 48. Wetlands International, Wageningen, the Netherlands, and National Environmental Research Institute, Rönde, Denmark.

Francis, C.M. & F. Cooke. 1986. Differential timing of spring migration in wood-warblers. *Auk* 103: 548–556.

Francis, I. & A. Thorpe. 1999. The breeding status of the Spotted Crake in north east Scotland. *Scottish Birds* 20: 14–17.

Francis, I.S. & A.D. Fox. 1987. Spring migration of Greenland White-fronted Geese through Iceland. *Wildfowl* 38: 7–12.

Fraser, P.A. & J.F. Ryan. 1995. Status of the Great Grey Shrike in Britain and Ireland. *British Birds* 88: 478–484.

Fraser, P.A., P.G. Lansdown & M.J. Rogers. 1997. Report on scarce migrant birds in Britain in 1995. *British Birds* 90: 413–439.

Fraser, P.A., P.G. Lansdown & M.J. Rogers. 1999a. Report on scarce migrant birds in Britain in 1996. *British Birds* 92: 120–154.

Fraser, P.A., P.G. Lansdown & M.J. Rogers. 1999b. Report on scarce migrant birds in Britain in 1997. *British Birds* 92: 618–658.

Fraser, P.A., P.G. Lansdown & M.J. Rogers. 2000. Report on scarce migrant birds in Britain in 1998. *British Birds* 93: 588–641.

Fremming, O.R. 1980. Kongeorn i Norge. *Viltrapport* 12: 1–63.

Frey, M. 1989a. Brutbiologie des Hänflings *Carduelis cannabina* unter den Einflüssen des Gebirgsklimas. *Der Ornithologische Beobachter* 86: 265–289.

Frey, M. 1989b. Nahrungsökologie und Raumnutzung einer subalpinen Population des Hänflings *Carduelis cannabina*. *Der Ornithologische Beobachter* 86: 291–305.

Frumkin, R. 1994. Intraspecific brood parasitism and dispersal in fledgling Sparrowhawks *Accipiter nisus*. *Ibis* 136: 426–433.

Fry, C.H. 1992. The Moreau ecological overview. *Ibis* 134 (suppl. 1) 1: 3–6.

Fry, C.H., J.S. Ash & I.J. Ferguson-Lees. 1970. Spring weights of some Palaearctic migrants at Lake Chad. *Ibis* 112: 58–82.

Fry, C.H., I.J. Ferguson-Lees & R.J. Dowsett. 1972. Flight muscle hypertrophy and ecophysiological variation of Yellow Wagtail *Motacilla flava* races at Lake Chad. *Journal of Zoology (London)* 167: 293–306.

Fry, C.H., S. Keith & E.K. Urban. 1988. *The Birds of Africa.* Volume 3. Academic Press, London.

Fry, C.H., K. Fry & A. Harris. 1992. *Kingfishers, Bee-eaters & Rollers.* Christopher Helm, London.

Frylestam, B. 1972. Über Wanderungen und Sterblichkeit beringter skandinavischer Schleiereulen *Tyto alba. Ornis Scandinavica* 3: 45–54.

Fuller, M.R., W.S. Seegar & P.W. Howey. 1995. The use of satellite systems for the study of bird migration. *Israel Journal of Zoology* 41: 243–252.

Fuller, R.J. 1982. *Bird Habitats in Britain.* T. & A.D. Poyser, Calton.

Fuller, R.J. & D.E. Glue. 1977. The breeding biology of the Stonechat and Whinchat. *Bird Study* 24: 215–228.

Fuller, R.J. & D. Lloyd. 1981. The distribution and habitats of wintering Golden Plovers in Britain, 1977–1978. *Bird Study* 28: 169–185.

Fuller, R.J. & R.E. Youngman. 1979. The utilisation of farmland by Golden Plovers wintering in southern England. *Bird Study* 26: 37–46.

Fuller, R.J., R.D. Gregory, D.W. Gibbons, J.H. Marchant, J.D. Wilson, S.R. Baillie & N. Carter. 1995. Population declines and range contractions among lowland farmland birds in Britain. *Conservation Biology* 9: 1425–1441.

Fuller, R.J., A.C.B. Henderson & A.M. Wilson. 1999. The Nightingale in England – problems and prospects. *British Wildlife* 10: 221–230.

Fuller, R.J., E. Ward, D. Hird & A.F. Brown. 2002. Declines of ground-nesting birds in two areas of upland farmland in the south Pennines of England. *Bird Study* 49: 146–152.

Furness, B.L. & R.W. Furness. 1982. Biometrics of Sabine's Gulls *Larus sabini* in the south Atlantic during the northern winter. *Cormorant* 10: 31–34.

Furness, R.W. 1978. Movements and mortality rates of Great Skuas ringed in Scotland. *Bird Study* 25: 229–238.

Furness, R.W. 1987. *The Skuas.* T. & A.D. Poyser, Calton.

Furness, R.W. & S.R. Baillie. 1981a. Age ratios, wing length and moult as indicators of the population structure of Redshank wintering on British estuaries. *Ringing & Migration* 3: 123–132.

Furness, R.W. & S.R. Baillie. 1981b. Factors affecting capture rate and biometrics of Storm Petrels on St Kilda. *Ringing & Migration* 3: 137–148.

Furness, R.W. & C.M. Todd. 1984. Diets and feeding of fulmars *Fulmarus glacialis* during the breeding season: a comparison between St. Kilda and Shetland colonies. *Ibis* 126: 379–387.

Furness, R.W., K. Ensor & A.V. Hudson. 1992. The use of fishery waste by gull populations around the British Isles. *Ardea* 80: 105–113.

Gabrey, S.W. 1996. Migration and dispersal in Great Lakes Ring-billed and Herring Gulls. *Journal of Field Ornithology* 67: 327–339.

Galbraith, H. 1977. The post-nuptial moult of a migratory population of Pied Wagtails. *Ringing & Migration* 1: 184–186.

Galbraith, H. 1988. Effects of agriculture on the breeding ecology of Lapwings *Vanellus vanellus. Journal of Applied Ecology* 25: 487–503.

Galbraith, H. 1989. Arrival and habitat use by Lapwings *Vanellus vanellus. Ibis* 139: 129–137.

Galbraith, H. & S.J. Tyler. 1982. The movements and mortality of the Dipper as shown by ringing recoveries. *Ringing & Migration* 4: 9–14.

Galbraith, H., S. Russell & R.W. Furness. 1981. Movements and mortality of Isle of May Shags as shown by ringing recoveries. *Ringing & Migration* 3: 181–189.

Galbraith, H., S.R. Baillie, R.W. Furness & S. Russell. 1986. Regional variations in the dispersal patterns of Shags *Phalacrocorax aristotelis* in northern Europe. *Ornis Scandinavica* 17: 68–74.

Galbraith, H., S. Murray, S. Rae, D.P. Whitfield & D.B.A. Thompson. 1993a. Numbers and distribution of Dotterel *Charadrius morinellus* breeding in Great Britain. *Bird Study* 40: 161–169.

Galbraith, H., S. Murray, K. Duncan, R. Smith, D.P. Whitfield & D.B.A. Thompson. 1993b. Diet and habitat use of the Dotterel *Charadrius morinellus* in Scotland. *Ibis* 135: 148–155.

Galea, G. & B. Massa. 1985. Notes on the raptor migration across the central Mediterranean. In *Conservation Studies on Raptors* (eds I. Newton & R.D. Chancellor), pp 257–261. Technical Publication 5. International Council for Bird Preservation, Cambridge.

Galushin, V.M. 1974. Synchronous fluctuations in populations of some raptors and their prey. *Ibis* 116: 127–134.

Galushin, V.M. 1994. Long-term changes in birds of prey populations within European Russia and neighbouring countries. In *Bird Numbers 1992: distribution, monitoring and ecological aspects* (eds E.J.M. Hagemeijer & T.J. Verstrael), pp 139–141. Proceedings of the Twelfth International Conference of IBCC and EOAC, Noordwijkerhout, the Netherlands. Statistics Netherlands, Voorburg/Heerlen and SOVON, Beek-Ubbergen.

Gamauf, A. 1987. Three-year study on a winter population of birds of prey in southern Burgenland, Austria. *Egretta* 30: 24–37.

Gannes, L.Z., D.M. O'Brien & C. Martínez del Rio. 1997. Stable isotopes in animal ecology: assumptions, caveats, and a call for more laboratory experiments. *Ecology* 78: 1271–1276.

Ganter, B., K. Larsson, E.V. Syroechkovsky, K.E. Litvin, A. Leito & J. Madsen. 1999. Barnacle Goose *Branta leucopsis*: Russia/Baltic. In *Goose populations of the Western Palearctic: a review of status and distribution* (eds J. Madsen, G. Cracknell & A.D. Fox), pp 270–283. Wetlands International Publication 48. Wetlands International, Wageningen, the Netherlands, and National Environmental Research Institute, Rönde, Denmark.

Gantlett, S.J.M. 1991. *The Birds of the Isles of Scilly.* Second edition. Privately published.

Garcia, J. & J. Guzman. 1990. El censo de laridos y cormoranes invernantes en Extremadura. Enero de 1990. *Alytes* 5: 143–150.

Garcia, J.T. & B.E. Arroyo. 1998. Migratory movements of western Montagu's Harrier *Circus pygargus*: a review. *Bird Study* 45: 188–194.

Garðarsson, A. 1991. Movements of Whooper Swans *Cygnus cygnus* neckbanded in Iceland. In *Proceedings of the Third IWRB International Swan Symposium, Oxford 1989* (eds J. Sears & P.J. Bacon), pp 189–194. *Wildfowl* suppl. 1.

Gardarsson, A. & G.A. Gudmundsson. 1996. Numbers of Light-bellied Brent Geese *Branta bernicla hrota* staging in Iceland in spring. *Wildfowl* 47: 62–66.

Garðarsson, A. & K.H. Skarphéðinsson. 1984. A census of the Icelandic Whooper Swan population. *Wildfowl* 35: 37–47.

Garðarsson, A. & K.H. Skarphéðinsson. 1985. Veturseta álfta á Íslandi. [Wintering Whooper Swans in Iceland.] *Bliki* 4: 45–56.

Garner, M.S. 1999. An interesting Shore Lark in Ireland. *Birding World* 12: 152–154.

Garnett, M.G.H. 1980. Moorland breeding and moulting of Canada Geese in Yorkshire. *Bird Study* 27: 219–226.

Garson, P.J. 1980. The breeding ecology of the Wren in Britain. *Bird Study* 27: 63–72.

Garthe, S. 1993. Durchzug und Wintervorkommen der Zwergmöwe (*Larus minutus*) bei Helgoland in den Jahren 1977 bis 1991. *Die Vogelwarte* 37: 118–129.

Garthe, S. 1997. Influence of hydrography, fishing activity and colony location on summer seabird distribution in the south-eastern North Sea. *ICES Journal of Marine Science* 54: 566–577.

Gaston, A.J. 1973. The ecology and behaviour of the Long-tailed Tit. *Ibis* 115: 330–351.

Gaston, A.J. & I.L. Jones. 1998. *The Auks: Alcidae*. Oxford University Press, Oxford.

Gates, J.M. & J.B. Hale. 1974. Seasonal movement, winter habitat use and population distribution of an east central Wisconsin Pheasant population. *Technical Bulletin of Department of Nature Resources, Wisconsin* 76: 1–55.

Gatter, W. 1972. Systematic observations of autumnal migration of birds of prey across the Randecker Maar, Suabian Alb. *Anzeiger Ornithologischen Gesellschaft in Bayern* 11: 194–209.

Gatter, W. 1993. Exploratory behaviour, migration and the evolution of migratory habits of the Crossbill, *Loxia curvirostra*. *Die Vogelwelt* 114: 38–55.

Gatter, W., R. Gardner & K. Penski. 1990. Abnahme ziehender Ringeltauben *Columbus palumba* in Süddeutschland. [Decline of migrating Wood Pigeons in southwest Germany.] *Die Vogelwelt* 111: 111–116.

Gauthier, J., J. Bédard & A. Reed. 1976. Overland migration by Common Eiders of the St. Lawrence estuary. *Wilson Bulletin* 88: 333–344.

Gauthier-Clerc, M. & Y. Le Maho. 2001. Beyond bird marking with rings. *Ardea* 89 (special issue): 221–230.

Gauthreaux, S.A. Jr. 1978. The ecological significance of behavioral dominance. *Perspectives in Ethology* 3: 17–54.

Gauthreaux, S.A. Jr. 1982. The ecology and evolution of avian migration systems. In *Avian Biology volume VI* (eds D.S. Farner, J.R. King & K.C. Parkes), pp 93–167. Academic Press, New York and London.

Gavrilov, E.I. & M.N. Korelov. 1968. [The Indian Sparrow as a distinct good species.] *Byulleten' Moskovskogo Obshchestva Ispytatelei Prirody (Otdel biologicheskii)* 73: 115–122. (In Russian.)

Geen, G.R. 1988. The autumn migration of Chiffchaffs at an inland site in south-east England. *Ringing & Migration* 9: 65–67.

Gelting, P. 1937. Studies on the food of the east Greenland Ptarmigan. *Meddelelser om Grønland* 116: 1–196.

Génard, M. & D. Lanusse. 1992. Use of marshlands by Common Cranes in winter in south-western France. *Ornis Fennica* 69: 19–28.

George, K. 1997. Red Kite wintering in north Harzvorland/Sachsen/Anhalt. *Newsletter of the World Working Group on Birds of Prey and Owls* 25/26: 24.

Géroudet, P. 1965. *Les Rapaces Diurnes et Nocturnes d'Europe*. Delachaux & Niestlé, Neuchâtel.

Gibb, J.A. & B.W. Tucker. 1947. The exceptional passage of Curlew Sandpipers and Little Stints in the autumn of 1946. *British Birds* 40: 354–359.

Gibbons, D.W. 1986. Brood parasitism and co-operative breeding in the Moorhen, *Gallinula chloropus*. *Behavioural Ecology and Sociobiology* 19: 221–232.

Gibbons, D.W. 1987. Juvenile helping in the Moorhen, *Gallinula chloropus*. *Animal Behaviour* 35: 170–181.

Gibbons, D.W. & S. Wotton. 1996. The Dartford Warbler in the United Kingdom in 1994. *British Birds* 89: 203–212.

Gibbons, D.W., M.I. Avery, S.R. Baillie, R.D. Gregory, J.S. Kirby, R.F. Porter, G.M. Tucker & G. Williams. 1996a. Bird species of conservation concern in the United Kingdom, Channel Islands and Isle of Man: revising the Red Data List. *RSPB Conservation Review* 10: 7–18.

Gibbons, D.W., M.I. Avery & A.F. Brown. 1996b. Population trends of breeding birds in the United Kingdom since 1800. *British Birds* 89: 291–305.

Gibbons, D.W., I.P. Bainbridge, G.P. Mudge, A.P. Tharme & P.M. Ellis. 1997. The status and distribution of the Red-throated Diver *Gavia stellata* in Britain in 1994. *Bird Study* 44: 194–205.

Gibbs, A., P.J. Grant, P.J. Oliver & C.A. Walker. 1965. Unusual numbers of Sooty Shearwaters in the eastern English Channel. *British Birds* 58: 56–58.

Gilbert, G. 2002. The status and habitat of Spotted Crakes *Porzana porzana* in Britain in 1999. *Bird Study* 49: 79–86.

Gilbert, G., G.A. Tyler & K.W. Smith. 2002. Local annual survival of booming male Great Bittern *Botaurus stellaris* in Britain, in the period 1990–1999. *Ibis* 144: 51–61.

Gill, J.A., J.A. Clark, N.A. Clark & W.J. Sutherland. 1995. Sex differences in the migration, moult and wintering areas of British-ringed Ruff. *Ringing & Migration* 16: 159–167.

Gill, M.F. 1977. Reared Pheasants: a review of research and management. *Game Conservancy Annual Review 1976*: 76–82.

Gillings, S. 1999. Lapwing. In *The Birds of Norfolk* (eds M. Taylor, M. Seago, P. Allard & D. Dorling), pp 252–253. Pica Press, Robertsbridge, East Sussex.

Gillings, S. 2001a. Winter plover hunts. *BTO News* 232: 14–15.

Gillings, S. 2001b. Factors affecting the distribution of Skylarks *Alauda arvensis* wintering in Britain and Ireland during the early 1980s. In *Proceedings of the BTO/RSPB/Tesco Conference on the Ecology and Conservation of Skylarks* Alauda arvensis (eds P.F. Donald & J.A. Vickery), pp 115–128. Royal Society for the Protection of Birds, Sandy.

Gillings, S. & R.J. Fuller. 2001. Habitat selection by Skylarks *Alauda arvensis* wintering in Britain in 1997/98. *Bird Study* 48: 293–307.

Gillings, S. & A. Wilson. 1999. Winter is almost upon us . . .. *BTO News* 224: 13.

Ginati, A., G. Lehmann & U. Schulz. 1995. New trends and capabilities of satellites for bird tracking and monitoring. *Israel Journal of Zoology* 41: 253–259.

Ginn, H.B. & D.S. Melville. 1983. *Moult in Birds*. BTO Guide 19. British Trust for Ornithology, Tring.

Giroux, J.-F. 1991. Roost fidelity of Pink-footed Geese *Anser brachyrhynchus* in north-east Scotland. *Bird Study* 38: 112–117.

Giroux, J.-F. & I.J. Patterson. 1995. Daily movements and habitat use by radio-tagged Pink-footed Geese *Anser brachyrhynchus* wintering in north-east Scotland. *Wildfowl* 46: 31–44.

Gladwin, T.W. & B.L. Sage. 1996. *The Birds of Hertfordshire*. Castlemead Publications, Ware, Hertfordshire.

Glahder, C.M. 1999a. *Sensitive areas and periods of the Greenland White-fronted Goose in West Greenland. Spring staging and moult as important bottleneck periods in the annual cycle of the goose subspecies*. PhD thesis, National Environmental Research Institute, Rönde, Denmark.

Glahder, C.M. 1999b. Spring staging areas of the Greenland White-fronted Goose (*Anser albifrons flavirostris*) in West Greenland. *Arctic* 52: 244–256.

Glahder, C.M., A.D. Fox & A.J. Walsh. 1996. *Effects of fitting dummy satellite transmitters to geese. A pilot project using radio telemetry on wintering Greenland White-fronted Geese*. Technical Report

169. National Environmental Research Institute, Rönde, Denmark.

Glahder, C.M., A.D. Fox & A.J. Walsh. 1997. Effects of fitting dummy satellite transmitters to Greenland White-fronted Geese *Anser albifrons flavirostris*. *Wildfowl* 48: 88–97.

Glahder, C.M., A.D. Fox & A.J. Walsh. 1999. Satellite tracking of Greenland White-fronted Geese. *Dansk Ornitologisk Forenings Tidsskrift* 93: 271–276.

Glaves, D.J. & M. Darlaston (eds). 1999. *Devon Bird Report 1997*. Devon Bird Watching and Preservation Society.

Glen, N.W. & C.M. Perrins. 1988. Cooperative breeding by Long-tailed Tits. *British Birds* 81: 630–641.

Glück, E. 1982. Jahresperiodik und Zug südwestdeustscher Stieglitze – Freilandbeobachtungen, Ringfundauswertungen und Zugaktivitätsuntersuchungen. *Die Vogelwarte* 31: 395–422.

Glue, D.E. 1971. Ringing recovery circumstances of small birds of prey. *Bird Study* 18: 137–146.

Glue, D.E. 1973. Seasonal mortality in four small birds of prey. *Ornis Scandinavica* 4: 97–102.

Glue, D. 1976. Long-eared Owl invasion. *BTO News* 78: 5.

Glue, D.E. 1977. Feeding ecology of the Short-eared Owl in Britain and Ireland. *Bird Study* 24: 70–78.

Glue, D. 1982. *The Garden Bird Book*. Macmillan, London.

Glue, D.E. & D. Scott. 1980. Breeding biology of the Little Owl. *British Birds* 69: 144–154.

Glue, D. & P. Whittington. 1987. Long-eared owls invade East Coast. *BTO News* 148: 1.

Gochfeld, M. 1983. The Roseate Tern: world distribution and status of a theatened species. *Biological Conservation* 25: 103–125.

Godfrey, J.D. & D.M. Bryant. 2000. State-dependent behaviour and energy expenditure: an experimental study of European Robins on winter territories. *Journal of Animal Ecology* 69: 301–313.

Goethe, F. 1961. The moult gatherings and moult migrations of Shelduck in north-west Germany. *British Birds* 54: 145–161.

Gomersall, C.H., J.S. Morton & R.M. Wynde. 1984. Status of breeding Red-throated Divers in Shetland, 1983. *Bird Study* 31: 223–229.

Goodacre, M.J. 1959. The origin of winter visitors to the British Isles. 4. Starling (*Sturnus vulgaris*). *Bird Study* 6: 180–192.

Goodacre, M.J. 1960. The origin of winter visitors to the British Isles. 6. Song Thrush (*Turdus philomelos*). *Bird Study* 7: 108–110.

Goodall, A. 1984. The 1983 spring Sanderling passage project on the Humber. *Lincolnshire Bird Report 1983*: 9–12.

Goodbody, I.M. 1951. Inland passage of Black Terns in the spring of 1950. *British Birds* 44: 170–173.

Goodwin, D. 1973. The buff variety of the Collared Dove. *British Birds* 66: 373–376.

Goodwin, D. 1986. *Crows of the World*. British Museum, London.

Goostrey, A., D.N. Carss, L.R. Noble & S.B. Piertney. 1998. Population introgression and differentiation in the Great Cormorant *Phalacrocorax carbo* in Europe. *Molecular Ecology* 7: 329–338.

Gopfert, M. 1986a. Reaktion einer Gebirgsstelzen-Winterpopulation (*Motacilla cinerea*) auf den extremen Kaltlufteinbruch in January 1985. *Journal für Ornithologie* 127: 96–97.

Gopfert, M. 1986b. Untersuchungen an einem gemeinsamen Schlafplatz uberwinternder Gebirgsstelzen (*Motacilla cinerea*) in Schwabisch Hall (Baden Wurttemburg). *Ökologie der Vögel* 8: 199–214.

Gosler, A.G. 1987. Pattern and process in the bill morphology of the Great Tit *Parus major*. *Ibis* 129: 451–476.

Gosler, A.G. 1991. On the use of greater covert moult and pectoral muscle as measures of condition in passerines with data on the Great Tit *Parus major*. *Bird Study* 38: 1–9.

Gosler, A.G. 1993. *The Great Tit*. Paul Hamlyn, London.

Gosler, A.G. & J.R. King. 1989. A sexually dimorphic plumage character in the Coal Tit *Parus ater* with notes on the Marsh Tit *P. palustris*. *Ringing & Migration* 10: 53–57.

Gosler, A.G., J.J.D. Greenwood & C. Perrins. 1995a. Predation risk and the cost of being fat. *Nature* 377: 621–622.

Gosler, A.G., J.J.D. Greenwood, J.K. Baker & J.R. King. 1995b. A comparison of wing length and primary length as size measures for small passerines. A report to the British Ringing Committee. *Ringing & Migration* 16: 65–78.

Gosling, A.P. 1986. A study of the movements and site fidelity of foreign ringed Black-headed Gulls in St James's Park, 1983–86. *London Bird Report* 50: 156–169.

Goss-Custard, J.D., S.E.A. le V. dit Durell, H.P. Sitters & R. Swinfen. 1982. Age-structure and survival of a wintering population of Oystercatchers. *Bird Study* 29: 83–98.

Goss-Custard, J.D., S.E.A. le V. dit Durell, C.P. Goater, J.B. Hulscher, R.H.D. Lambeck, P.L. Meininger & J. Urfi. 1996. How Oystercatchers survive the winter. In *The Oystercatcher: from individuals to populations* (ed J.D. Goss-Custard), pp 133–154. Oxford University Press, Oxford.

Graham, I.M., S.M. Redpath & S.J. Thirgood. 1995. The diet and breeding density of common buzzards *Buteo buteo* in relation to indexes of prey abundance. *Bird Study* 42: 165–173.

Granadeiro, J.P. 1991. On a Cory's Shearwater ringed at Selvagem Grande, Madeira (30°9'N, 15°52'W) and recovered on Berlenga Island, Portugal (39°24'N, 9°30'W). *Bocagiana* 145: 1–4.

Granadeiro, J.P. 1993. Variation in measurements of Cory's Shearwater between populations and sexing by discriminant analysis. *Ringing & Migration* 14: 103–112.

Grant, D.R. 1974. Local gull movements as a hazard to aircraft. *Bird Study* 21: 169–179.

Grant, J.R. & M.J. McGrady. 1999. Dispersal of Golden Eagles *Aquila chrysaetos* in Scotland. *Bird Study* 29: 169–174.

Grant, M.C. 1989. *The breeding ecology of Whimbrel* (Numenius phaeopus) *in Shetland, with particular reference to the effects of agricultural improvement of heathland nesting habitats*. PhD thesis, University of Durham.

Grant, M.C. 1991. Nesting densities, productivity and survival of breeding Whimbrel *Numenius phaeopus* in Shetland. *Bird Study* 38: 160–169.

Grant, P.J. 1987. Sabine's Gulls in winter. *British Birds* 80: 75–77.

Grattarola, A., A. Pilastro & F. Spina. 1999. Strategy of barrier crossing adopted by the Garden Warbler (*Sylvia borin*) during its spring migration across the Mediterranean area. *Journal für Ornithologie* 140: 419–430.

Graustein, W.C. 1988. ^{87}Sr/^{86}Sr ratios measure the sources and flow of strontium in terrestrial ecosystems. In *Stable Isotopes in Ecological Research* (eds P.W. Rundel, J.R. Ehleringer & K.A. Nagy), pp 491–512. Springer, Berlin.

Gray, D.B. 1974. Breeding behaviour of Whinchats. *Bird Study* 21: 280–282.

Green, M., T. Piersma, J. Jukema, P. de Goeij, B. Spaans & J. van Gils. 2002. Radio-telemetry observations of the first 650 km of the migration of Bar-tailed Godwits *Limosa lapponica* from the Wadden Sea to the Russian Arctic. *Ardea* 90: 71–80.

Green, P.T. 1981. Some results from trapping Rooks. *Ringing & Migration* 3: 203–212.

Green, R. 1983. Spring dispersal and agonistic behaviour of the Red-legged Partridge (*Alectoris rufa*). *Journal of Zoology* 201: 541–555.

Green, R.E. 1995a. Demography of Roseate Terns *Sterna dougallii* in Britain and Ireland. In *Proceedings of the Sixth Roseate Tern Workshop* (ed N. Ratcliffe), pp 8–12. Royal Society for the Protection of Birds, Sandy.

Green, R.E. 1995b. The decline of the Corncrake *Crex crex* in Britain continues. *Bird Study* 42: 66–75.

Green, R.E. 1996a. The status of the Golden Eagle in Britain in 1992. *Bird Study* 43: 20–27.

Green, R.E. 1996b. Factors affecting the population density of the Corncrake *Crex crex* in Britain and Ireland. *Journal of Applied Ecology* 33: 237–248.

Green, R.E. & G.H. Griffiths. 1994. Use of preferred nesting habitat by Stone Curlews *Burhinus oedicnemus* in relation to vegetation structure. *Journal of Zoology (London)* 233: 457–471.

Green, R.E. & M. Robins. 1993. The decline of the ornithological importance of the Somerset Levels and Moors, England and changes in the management of water levels. *Biological Conservation* 66: 95–106.

Green, R.E. & T.J. Stowe. 1993. The decline of the Corncrake *Crex crex* in Britain and Ireland in relation to habitat change. *Journal of Applied Ecology* 30: 689–695.

Green, R.E., D.P. Hodson & P.R. Holness. 1997. Survival and movements of Stone Curlews *Burhinus oedicnemus* ringed in England. *Ringing & Migration* 18: 102–112.

Green, R.E., G.A. Tyler & C.G.R. Bowden. 2000. Habitat selection, ranging behaviour and diet of the Stone Curlew (*Burhinus oedicnemus*) in southern England. *Journal of Zoology (London)* 250: 161–183.

Greenberg, R. 1980. Demographic aspects of long-distance migration. In *Migrant Birds in the Neotropics: ecology, behavior, distribution and conservation* (eds A. Keast & E.S. Morton), pp 493–504. Smithsonian Institution, Washington DC.

Greenwood, J.G. 1983. Post-nuptial primary moult of Dunlin *Calidris alpina*. *Ibis* 125: 223–228.

Greenwood, J.G. 1986. Geographical variation and taxonomy of the Dunlin *Calidris alpina* (L.). *Bulletin of the British Ornithologists' Club* 106: 43–56.

Greenwood, J.G. 1991. Duration of winter visits by Black Guillemots *Cepphus grylle* to an Irish breeding site. *Seabird* 13: 67–69.

Greenwood, J.J.D. 1968. Bluethroat nesting in Scotland. *British Birds* 61: 524–525.

Greenwood, J.J.D., R.J. Donally, C.J. Feare, N.J. Gordon & G. Waterston. 1971. A massive wreck of oiled birds: northeast Britain, winter 1970. *Scottish Birds* 6: 235–250.

Greenwood, P.J. 1980. Mating systems, philopatry and dispersal in birds and mammals. *Animal Behaviour* 28: 1140–1162.

Greenwood, P.J. & P.H. Harvey. 1982. The natal and breeding dispersal of birds. *Annual Review of Ecology and Systematics* 13: 1–21.

Greenwood, P.J., P.H. Harvey & C.M. Perrins. 1979. The role of dispersal in the Great Tit (*P. major*), the causes, consequences and heritability of natal dispersal. *Journal of Animal Ecology* 48: 123–142.

Gregory, R.D. 1999. Broad-scale habitat use of sparrows, finches and buntings in Britain. *Die Vogelwelt* 120, suppl.: 163–173.

Gregory, R.D. & J.H. Marchant. 1996. Population trends in Jays, Magpies, Jackdaws and Carrion Crows in the United Kingdom. *Bird Study* 43: 28–37.

Gregory, R.D., D.G. Noble, L.H. Campbell & D.W. Gibbons. 2000. *The State of the UK's Birds 1999*. RSPB/BTO, Sandy.

Greig-Smith, P.W. & G.M. Wilson. 1984. Patterns of activity and habitat use by a population of Bullfinches (*Pyrrhula pyrrhula*) in relation to bud-feeding in orchards. *Journal of Applied Ecology* 21: 401–422.

Grenmyr, U. 1997. Sex differences in recovery pattern and migratory direction of Goldcrests *Regulus regulus* ringed in northern Europe during autumn migration. *Ornis Svecica* 7: 81–90.

Grenmyr, U. 2000. Återfynd av kungsfåglar *Regulus regulus* funna i Sverige: tidsmässigt uppträdande samt köns- och åldersfördelning. *Ornis Svecica* 10: 129–139.

Gribble, F.C. 1983. Nightjars in Britain and Ireland in 1981. *Bird Study* 30: 165–176.

Griggs, T. 1998. Early birds. *Bird Watching* April 1998: 72.

Grimes, L. 1969. The Spotted Redshank *Tringa erythropus* in Ghana. *Ibis* 111: 246–251.

Grimes, L.G. 1977. A radar study of tern movements along the coast of Ghana. *Ibis* 119: 28–36.

Grobler, G.P.J. 2000. Thousands of House Martins perish in Northern Province. *Bird Numbers* 9: 34–35.

Gromadska, J. 1989. Breeding and wintering areas of Dunlin migrating through southern Baltic. *Ornis Scandinavica* 20: 132–144.

Groth, J.G. 1993. *Evolutionary differentiation in morphology, vocalisations, and allozymes among nomadic sibling species in the North American Red Crossbill (*Loxia curvirostra*) complex*. University of California Publications in Zoology 127, Berkeley, California.

Grüll, A. 1981. Untersuchungen über das Revier der Nachtigall (*Luscinia megarhynchos*). *Journal für Ornithologie* 122: 259–285.

Gudmundsson, G.A. 1993. The spring migration pattern of arctic birds in southwest Iceland, as recorded by radar. *Ibis* 135: 166–176.

Gudmundsson, G.A. 1997. [Winter distribution of Icelandic Golden Plovers *Pluvialis apricaria*.] *Bliki* 18: 55–58.

Gudmundsson, G.A. & T. Alerstam. 1998a. Why is there no transpolar bird migration? *Journal of Avian Biology* 29: 93–96.

Gudmundsson, G.A. & T. Alerstam. 1998b. Optimal map projections for analysing long-distance migration routes. *Journal of Avian Biology* 29: 597–605.

Gudmundsson, G.A. & A. Gardarsson. 1993. Numbers, geographic distribution and habitat utilization of waders (Charadrii) in spring on the shores of Iceland. *Ecography* 16: 82–93.

Gudmundsson, G.A. & C. Lindström. 1992. Spring migration of Sanderlings *Calidris alba* through SW Iceland: wherefrom and whereto? *Ardea* 80: 315–325.

Gudmundsson, G.A., T. Alerstam & B. Larsson. 1992. Radar observations of northbound migration of the Arctic Tern, *Sterna paradisaea*, at the Antarctic Peninsula. *Antarctic Science* 4: 163–170.

Gudmundsson, G.A., S. Benvenuti, T. Alerstam, F. Papi, K. Lilliendahl & S. Åkesson. 1995. Examining the limits of flight and orientation performance – satellite tracking of Brent Geese migrating across the Greenland ice-cap. *Proceedings of the Royal Society of London Series B – Biological Sciences* 261: 73–79.

Gullested, N., M. Owen & M.J. Nugent. 1984. Numbers and distribution of Barnacle Geese on Norwegian staging islands and the inportance of the staging areas to the Svalbard population. *Norsk Polarinstittut Skrifter* 181: 57–65.

Gustin, M. & T. Pizzari. 1998. Migratory pattern in the genus *Circus*: sex and age differential migration in Italy. *Ornis Svecica* 8: 23–26.

Guyomarc'h, J.-C. 1992. Structure, fonctionnement et microévolution des populations de caille des blés (*Coturnix c. coturnix*) dans le paléarctique occidentale. *Gibier Faune Sauvage* 9: 387–401.

Guyomarc'h, J.C. 1998. Bilan d'une recherche préliminaire sur les comportements de la Tourterelle des bois (*Streptopelia turtur*). In *Contributions à la Connaissance de la Biologie de l'Outarde et de la Tourterelle des Bois. Convention de Recherche Ponctuelle Annuelle ONC – Univ. Rennes-1 no. 97/27*, pp 1–10. Université de Rennes 1, Rennes.

Guyomarc'h, J.C., O. Combreau, M. Puigcerver, P. Fontoura, N. Aebischer & D.I.M. Wallace. 1998. *Coturnix coturnix* Quail. *BWP Update* 2: 27–46.

Gwinner, E. 1986. *Circannual Rhythms*. Springer Verlag, Berlin.

Gwinner, E. (ed). 1990. *Bird Migration: the physiology and ecophysiology*. Springer Verlag, Berlin.

Gwinner, E. 1996. Circannual clocks in avian reproduction and migration. *Ibis* 138: 47–63.

Haag-Wackernagel, D. 1995. Regulation of the street pigeon in Basel. *Wildlife Society Bulletin* 23: 256–260.

Hable, E. 1980. Beringungsergebnisse an der alpinen Population des Mornellregenpfeifers, *Eudromias morinellus* (L.). *Mitteilungen Abteilung für Zoologie und Botanik Landesmuseum 'Joanneum'* 9: 81–85.

Hafner, H., Y. Kayser, V. Boy, M. Fasola, A.-C. Juilliard, R. Pradel & F. Cézilly. 1998. Local survival, natal dispersal and recruitment in Little Egrets *Egretta garzetta*. *Journal of Avian Biology* 29: 216–227.

Haftorn, S. 1971. *Norges Fugler*. Universitetsforlaget, Oslo.

Hagen, Y. 1952. *Birds of Tristan da Cunha*. Results of the Norwegian Scientific Expedition to Tristan da Cunha 1937–1938, no. 20. I Kommisjon Hos Jacob Dybwad, Oslo.

Haig, S.M. 1987. *The population biology and life history patterns of the Piping Plover*. PhD thesis, University of North Dakota.

Haig, S.M. 1998. Molecular contributions to conservation. *Ecology* 79: 413–425.

Haig, S.M., C.L. Gratto-Trevor, T.D. Mullins & M.A. Colwell. 1997. Population identification of western hemisphere shorebirds throughout the annual cycle. *Molecular Ecology* 6: 413–427.

Haila, Y., A.O. Nicholls, I.K. Hanski & S. Raivio. 1996. Stochasticity in bird habitat selection: year-to-year changes in territory location in a boreal forest bird assemblage. *Oikos* 76: 536–552.

Hake, M., D. Blomqvist, E.P. Pierce, T. Järäs & O.C. Johansson. 1997. Population size, migration routes and breeding origin of Purple Sandpipers *Calidris maritima* wintering in Sweden. *Ornis Svecica* 7: 121–132.

Haldane, J.B.S. 1955. The calculation of mortality rates from ringing data. In *Proceedings of the Eleventh International Ornithological Congress, Basel 1954* (eds A. Portmann & E. Sutter), pp 454–458. Birkhäuser Verlag, Basel and Stuttgart.

Hale, W.G. 1971. A revision of the taxonomy of the Redshank *Tringa totanus*. *Zoological Journal of the Linnean Society, London* 50: 199–268.

Hale, W.G. 1973. The distribution of the Redshank *Tringa totanus* in the winter range. *Zoological Journal of the Linnean Society* 53: 177–236.

Hale, W.G. 1980. *Waders*. Collins, London.

Haller, H. 1982. Raumorganisation und Dynamik einer Population des Steinadlers *Aquila chrysaetos* in den Zentralalpen. *Der Ornithologische Beobachter* 79: 163–211.

Halley, D.J. 1996. Movements and mortality of Norwegian Goshawks *Accipiter gentilis*: an analysis of ringing data. *Fauna Norvegica serie C, Cinclus* 19: 55–67.

Halley, D.J. & M.P. Harris. 1993. Intercolony movement and behaviour of immature Guillemots *Uria aalge*. *Ibis* 135: 264–270.

Hamer, K.C. & R.W. Furness. 1991. Sexing Great Skuas *Catharacta skua* by discriminant analysis using external measurements. *Ringing & Migration* 12: 16–22.

Hamer, K.C., D.R. Thompson & C.M. Grey. 1997. Spatial variation in the feeding ecology, foraging ranges, and breeding energetics of Northern Fulmars in the north-east Atlantic Ocean. *ICES Journal of Marine Science* 54: 645–653.

Hancock, J. & J. Kushlan. 1984. *The Herons Handbook*. Croom Helm, London and Sydney.

Hancock, M.H., D.W. Gibbons & P.S. Thompson. 1997. The status of breeding Greenshank (*Tringa nebularia*) in the United Kingdom in 1995. *Bird Study* 44: 290–302.

Hancock, M., D. Baines, D. Gibbons, B. Etheridge & M. Shepherd. 1999. Status of male Black Grouse *Tetrao tetrix* in Britain in 1995–96. *Bird Study* 46: 1–16.

Haney, J.C. 1985. Wintering phalaropes off the southeastern United States: application of remote sensing imagery to seabird habitat analysis at oceanic fronts. *Journal of Field Ornithology* 56: 321–333.

Haney, J.C. & P.A. McGillivary. 1985. Aggregations of Cory's Shearwaters (*Calonectris diomedea*) at gulf stream fronts. *Wilson Bulletin* 97: 191–200.

Hanmer, D.B. 1986. Migrant Palaearctic passerines at Nchalo, Malaŵi. *Safring News* 15: 19–28.

Hansen, B., W.R. Turrell & S. Østerhus. 2001. Decreasing overflow from the Nordic seas into the Atlantic Ocean through the Faroe Bank channel since 1950. *Nature* 411: 927–930.

Hansen, J.M. 1984. The population of Long-tailed Skuas *Stercorarius longicaudus* at Kærelv, Scoresby Sund, East Greenland, 1979. *Dansk Ornithologisk Forenings Tidsskrift* 78: 99–104.

Hansen, K. 1978. Traek og spredning hos danske Musvitter *Parus major*. *Dansk Ornithologisk Forenings Tidsskrift* 72: 97–104.

Hanski, I., L. Hansson & H. Henttonen. 1991. Specialist predators, generalist predators and the microtine rodent cycle. *Journal of Animal Ecology* 60: 353–367.

Hanssen, O.J. 1981. Migratory movements of Scandinavian Goldcrests *Regulus regulus* (L.). *Fauna Norvegica serie C, Cinclus* 4: 1–8.

Harber, D.D. 1952. Mid-season movements of Swifts in Sussex. *British Birds* 45: 216–218.

Harber, D.D. 1964. The influx of Cranes in October 1963. *British Birds* 57: 502–508.

Hardman, J.A. 1974. Biology of the Skylark. *Annals of Applied Biology* 76: 337–341.

Hardy, A.R. 1992. Habitat use by farmland Tawny Owls *Strix aluco*. In *The Ecology and Conservation of European Owls* (eds C.A. Galbraith, I.R. Taylor & S.M. Percival), pp 55–63. Joint Nature Conservation Committee, Peterborough.

Hardy, A.R. & C.D.T. Minton. 1980. Dunlin migration in Britain and Ireland. *Bird Study* 27: 81–92.

Harper, D.G.C. 1985. Pairing strategies and mate choice in female Robins (*Erithacus rubecula*). *Animal Behaviour* 33: 862–875.

Harper, D.G.C. 1986. Individual territories in the European Robin. In *Acta XIX Congressus Internationalis Ornithologici* (ed H. Ouellet), pp 2355–2363. University of Ottawa Press, Ottawa.

Harper, D. 1995. Studies of West Palearctic birds 194: Corn Bunting *Miliaria calandra*. *British Birds* 88: 401–422.

Harper, W.G. 1959. Roosting movements of birds and migration departures from roosts as seen by radar. *Ibis* 101: 201–208.

Harradine, J. 1985. Duck shooting in the United Kingdom. *Wildfowl* 36: 81–94.

Harradine, J. 1988. The woodcock production survey in the United Kingdom and Ireland. In *Proceedings of the Third European Woodcock and Snipe Workshop* (ed P. Havet & G. Hirons), pp 87–91. International Waterfowl Research Bureau, Slimbridge.

Harrap, S. & D. Quinn. 1996. *Tits, Nuthatches and Treecreepers*. Christopher Helm, London.

Harris, M.P. 1962. Recoveries of ringed Great Black-backed Gulls. *Bird Study* 9: 192–197.

Harris, M.P. 1964a. Ring loss and wear of rings on marked Manx Shearwaters. *Bird Study* 11: 39–46.

Harris, M.P. 1964b. Recoveries of ringed Herring Gulls. *Bird Study* 11: 183–191.

Harris, M.P. 1966. Age of return to colony, age of breeding and adult survival of Manx Shearwaters. *Bird Study* 13: 84–95.

Harris, M.P. 1972. Inter-island movements of Manx Shearwaters. *Bird Study* 19: 167–171.

Harris, M.P. 1984a. *The Puffin*. T. & A.D. Poyser, Calton.

Harris, M.P. 1984b. Movements and mortality patterns of North Atlantic Puffins as shown by ringing. *Bird Study* 31: 131–140.

Harris, M.P. & M.L. Tasker. 1999. Conservation value of ringing seabirds in Britain and Ireland. *Ringing & Migration* 19 (suppl.): S95–106.

Harris, M.P. & S. Wanless. 1991. Population studies and conservation of Puffins *Fratercula arctica*. In *Bird Population Studies: relevance to conservation and management* (eds C.M. Perrins, J.-D. Lebreton & G.J.M. Hirons), pp 230–248. Oxford University Press, Oxford.

Harris, M.P. & S. Wanless. 1996. Differential responses of Guillemot *Uria aalge* and Shag *Phalacrocorax aristotelis* to a late winter wreck. *Bird Study* 43: 220–230.

Harris, M.P. & S. Wanless. 1997. Successful rehabilitation of oiled Guillemots *Uria aalge*. *Sula* 11: 183–185.

Harris, M. & S. Wanless. 1999. Transatlantic Gannets. *BTO News* 225: 5.

Harris, M.P. & R.F. Yule. 1977. The moult of the Puffin *Fratercula arctica*. *Ibis* 119: 535–541.

Harris, M.P., M. Heubeck & D. Suddaby. 1991. Results of an examination of Puffins *Fratercula arctica* washed ashore in Shetland in winter 1990–91. *Bird Study* 43: 63–66.

Harris, M.P., S.T. Buckland, S.M. Russell & S. Wanless. 1994. Year- and age-related variation in the survival of adult European Shags over a 24–year period. *Condor* 96: 600–605.

Harris, M.P., D.J. Halley & S. Wanless. 1996. Philopatry in the Common Guillemot *Uria aalge*. *Bird Study* 43: 134–137.

Harris, M.P., S.R. Baillie & C. Dudley. 1997. Ringing recoveries and colony attendance of Isle of May Guillemots. *Seabird* 19: 31–39.

Harris, P., J.A. Fowler & J.D. Okill. 1993. Initial results of Storm Petrel *Hydrobates pelagicus* ringing in Portugal. *Ringing & Migration* 14: 133–134.

Harrison, J.G. 1979. A new overland migration route of *Branta bernicla bernicla* in southeast England in autumn. In *Proceedings of the First Technical Meeting on Western Palaearctic Migratory Bird Management* (ed M. Smart), pp 60–63. International Waterfowl Research Bureau, Slimbridge.

Harrison, J.G. & M.A. Ogilvie. 1967. Immigrant Mute Swans in S.E. England. *Wildfowl Trust Annual Report* 18: 85–87.

Harrison, J.M. & J.G. Harrison. 1971. The occurrence of *Calidris alpina sakhalina* (Vieillot) in Britain. *Bulletin of the British Ornithologists' Club* 91: 39–40.

Harrison, J.M. & J.G. Harrison. 1972. Further notes on American and Schioler's Dunlin from Britain. *Bulletin of the British Ornithologists' Club* 92: 38–40.

Harrop, H.R., M. Mellor & D. Suddaby. 1993. Spring passage of Pomarine Skuas off Shetland in May 1992. *Scottish Birds* 17: 50–55.

Harvey, P.H. & M.D. Pagel. 1991. *The Comparative Method in Evolutionary Biology*. Oxford University Press, Oxford.

Harvey, P.V. & N. Riddiford. 1990. An uneven sex ratio of migrant Long-eared Owls. *Ringing & Migration* 11: 131–135.

Hashmi, D. 1991. Bestand und Verbreitung des Wachtelkönigs in der Bundesrepublik Deutschland vor 1990. *Die Vogelwelt* 112: 66–71.

Hashmi, D. & G.F. Fliege. 1994. Herbstzug der Sturmschwalbe (*Hydrobates pelagicus*) in der Meerenge von Gibraltar. *Journal für Ornithologie* 135: 203–207.

Hatch, S.A., B.D. Roberts & B.S. Fadley. 1993. Adult survival of Black-legged Kittiwakes *Rissa tridactyla* in a Pacific colony. *Ibis* 135: 247–254.

Hatchwell, B.J. 1999. Investment strategies of breeders in avian cooperative breeding systems. *American Naturalist* 154: 205–219.

Haukioja, E. 1971. Short-distance dispersal in the Reed Bunting *Emberiza schoeniclus*. *Ornis Fennica* 48: 45–67.

Haverschmidt, F. 1946. Observations on the breeding habits of the Little Owl. *Ardea* 34: 214–246.

Havlin, J. 1979. The dispersal of Feral Pigeons to the environs of a town. *Folia Zoologica* 28: 125–146.

Hawthorn, I. 1974. Moult and dispersal of juvenile Wrens. *Bird Study* 21: 88–91.

Hawthorn, I. 1975. Wrens wintering in a reed-bed. *Bird Study* 22: 19–23.

Hawthorn, I. & C.J. Mead. 1975. Wren movements and survival. *British Birds* 68: 349–358.

Hawthorn, I., R. Crockford, R.G. Smith & I. Weston. 1971. Wrens wintering in a reed-bed at Thatcham, Berkshire. *Bird Study* 18: 27–30.

Hawthorn, I., R. Crockford, R.G. Smith & I. Weston. 1976. The Wren on the Uists, Outer Hebrides. *Bird Study* 76: 301–303.

Hayman, P., J. Marchant & A.J. Prater. 1986. *Shorebirds: an identification guide to the waders of the world*. Croom Helm, London and Sydney.

Hays, H., J. DiCostanzo, G. Cormons, P. de T.Z. Antas, J.L.X. do Nascimento, I. de L.S. do Nascimento & R.E. Bremer. 1997. Recoveries of Roseate and Common Terns in South America. *Journal of Field Ornithology* 68: 79–90.

Hazevoet, C.J. 1995. *Birds of the Cape Verde Islands*. British Ornithologists' Union, Tring.

Hearn, R. & C. Mitchell. 1995. *Goose distribution and feeding around Loch Leven NNR*. Report to Scottish Natural Heritage. Wildfowl & Wetlands Trust, Slimbridge.

Heavisides, A. 1987. British and Irish Merlin recoveries, 1911–1984. *Ringing & Migration* 8: 29–41.

Hedenström, A. & J. Pettersson. 1987. Migration routes and wintering areas of Willow Warblers *Phylloscopus trochilus (L)* ringed in Fennoscandia. *Ornis Fennica* 64: 137–143.

Hedenström, A., Å. Lindström & J. Pettersson. 1995. Interrupted moult of adult Willow Warblers *Phylloscopus trochilus* during autumn migration through Sweden. *Ornis Svecica* 5: 69–74.

Heij, C.J. 1985. *Comparative ecology of the House Sparrow* Passer domesticus *in rural, suburban and urban situations*. Thesis, Vrije Universiteit te Amsterdam, the Netherlands.

Heinrich, B., D. Kaye, E. Knight & K. Schaumburg. 1994. Dispersal and association among Common Ravens. *Condor* 96: 545–551.

Helbig, A.J. & I. Seibold. 1999. Molecular phylogeny of Palearctic-African *Acrocephalus* and *Hippolais* warblers (Aves: Sylviidae). *Molecular Phylogenetics and Evolution* 11: 246–260.

Helbig, A.J., G. Orth, V. Laske & W. Wiltschko. 1987. Migratory orientation and activity of the Meadow Pipit (*Anthus pratensis*): a comparative observational and experimental field study. *Behaviour* 103: 276–293.

Helbig, A.J., P. Berthold, G. Mohr & U. Querner. 1994. Inheritance of a novel migratory direction in central European Blackcaps. *Naturwissenschaften* 81: 148–186.

Helle, T. & H. Mikkola. 1969. Hömötiaisen (*Parus montanus*) vaelluksista Keski-Suomessa 1965–68. *Ornis Fennica* 46: 136–139.

Hellmann, R. 1985. Zur 'Wanderunruhe' bei Blaumeisen (*Parus caeruleus*). *Journal für Ornithologie* 126: 207–210.

Hémery, G. & C. Jouanin. 1988. Statut et origine géographique des populations de Pétrels Culblanc (*Oceanodroma leucorhoa leucorhoa*) présentes dans le Golfe de Gascogne. *Alauda* 56: 238–245.

Hémon, Y.A., M. Saint-Jalme & J.C. Guyomarc'h. 1988. Structure et fonctionnement des populations reproductrices 'françaises' de cailles des blés. *Bulletin Mensuel de l'Office National de la Chasse* 127: 29–32.

Henderson, A.C.B. 1974. Seabird movements in Scotland, autumn 1973. *Seabird Report* 4: 65–78.

Henderson, I.G., W.J. Peach & S.R. Baillie. 1993. *The hunting of Snipe and Woodcock in Europe: a ringing recovery analysis*. Research Report 115. British Trust for Ornithology, Thetford.

Henderson, I.G., A. Wilson & D. Steele. 2000. *Population estimates and habitat associations of breeding waders in Northern Ireland in 1999: the results of an extensive survey*. Research Report 234. British Trust for Ornithology, Thetford.

Hengeveld, R. & F. van den Bosch. 1991. The expansion velocity of the Collared Dove *Streptopelia decaocto* population in Europe. *Ardea* 79: 67–72.

Henny, G.J. & N.E. Holgersen. 1974. Range expansion and population increase of the Gadwall in Eastern North America. *Wildfowl* 25: 95–101.

Herbert, I.J. 1991. The status and habitat of the Garden Warbler at Crom Estate, Co. Fermanagh, and a review of its status in Ireland. *Irish Birds* 14: 369–376.

Heredia, B., J.A. Alonso & F. Hiraldo. 1991. Space and habitat use by Red Kites *Milvus milvus* during winter in the Guadalquivir marshes: a comparison between resident and wintering populations. *Ibis* 133: 374–381.

Heredia, B., L. Rose & M. Painter. 1996. *Globally threatened birds in Europe. Action Plans*. Council of Europe Publishing, Germany.

Hereward, A.C. 1979. The autumn moult of the Yellow Wagtail. *Ringing & Migration* 2: 113–117.

Hernandez, M. 1988. Road mortality of the Little Owl (*Athene noctua*) in Spain. *Journal of Raptor Research* 22: 81–84.

Herremans, M. 1988a. Postjuvenile moult, phenology and biometry of Grey Wagtails *Motacilla cinerea* migrating over central Belgium. *Ringing & Migration* 9: 103–116.

Herremans, M. 1988b. Measurements and moult of irruptive common crossbills (*Loxia curvirostra curvirostra*) in central Belgium. *Gerfaut* 78: 243–260.

Herremans, M. 1990a. Body-moult and migration overlap in Reed Warblers (*Acrocephalus scirpaceus*) trapped during nocturnal migration. *Gerfaut* 80: 149–158.

Herremans, M. 1990b. Habitat and sampling related bias in sex ratio of trapped Blackcaps *Sylvia atricapilla*. *Ringing & Migration* 10: 31–34.

Herremans, M. 1997. Habitat segregation of male and female Red-backed Shrikes *Lanius collurio* and Lesser Grey Shrikes *Lanius minor* in the Kalahari basin, Botswana. *Journal of Avian Biology* 28: 240–248.

Herremans, M., D. Herremans-Tonnoeyr & W.D. Borello. 1995. Non-breeding site-fidelity of Red-backed Shrikes *Lanius collurio* in Botswana. *Ostrich* 66: 145–147.

Herrera, C.M. 1974. El paso otoñal de *Sylvia borin* y *Sylvia communis* en la Reserva Doñana. *Doñana Acta Vertebrata* 1: 83–119.

Herrera, C.M. 1978. On the breeding distribution pattern of European migrant birds: MacArthur's theme re-examined. *Auk* 95: 496–509.

Herrera, C.M. & M. Rodriguez. 1979. Year to year site constancy among three passerine species wintering at a southern Spanish locality. *Ringing & Migration* 2: 160.

Herroelen, P. 1998. Trek, overwintering en gedrag van Gierzwaluwen *Apus apus* in Congo en zuidelijk Afrika. [Migration, wintering and behaviour of Common Swifts in Congo and southern Africa]. *Oriolus* 64: 37–56.

Hestbeck, J.B., J.D. Nichols & R.A. Malecki. 1991. Estimates of movement and site fidelity using mark-resight data of wintering Canada Geese. *Ecology* 72: 523–533.

Heubeck, M. 2000. The not-so-perfect storm. *Seabird Group Newsletter* 86: 6–7.

Heubeck, M. & M.G. Richardson. 1980. Bird mortality following the *Esso Bernicia* oil spill, Shetland, December 1978. *Scottish Birds* 11: 97–108.

Heubeck, M., P.V. Harvey & J.D. Okill. 1991. Changes in the Shetland Guillemot *Uria aalge* population and the pattern of recoveries of ringed birds, 1959–1990. *Seabird* 13: 3–21.

Hewson, R. 1972. Changes in the number of stoats, rats and Little Owls in Yorkshire as shown by tunnel trapping. *Journal of Zoology* 168: 427–429.

Hibbert-Ware, A. 1937–38. Report of the Little Owl food inquiry, 1936–37. *British Birds* 31: 162–187, 205–229, 249–264.

Hickey, J.J. & D.W. Anderson. 1969. The Peregrine Falcon: life history and population literature. In *Peregrine Falcon populations: their biology and decline* (ed J.J. Hickey), pp 3–42. University of Wisconsin Press, Madison and London.

Higgins, P.J. & S.J.J.F. Davies (eds). 1996. *Handbook of Australian, New Zealand and Antarctic Birds. Volume 3. Snipe to Pigeons*. Oxford University Press, Melbourne.

Hildén, O. 1969. Activities of Finnish bird stations in 1968. *Ornis Fennica* 46: 179–187.

Hildén, O. 1971. Activities of Finnish bird stations in 1969. *Ornis Fennica* 48: 125–129.

Hildén, O. 1974. Finnish bird stations, their activities and aims. *Ornis Fennica* 51: 10–35.

Hildén, O. 1975. Breeding system of Temminck's Stint *Calidris temminckii*. *Ornis Fennica* 52: 117–146.

Hildén, O. 1979. The timing of arrival and departure of the Spotted Redshank *Tringa erythropus* in Finland. *Ornis Fennica* 56: 18–23.

Hildén, O. 1982. Winter ecology and partial migration of the Goldcrest *Regulus regulus* in Finland. *Ornis Fennica* 59: 99–122.

Hildén, O. 1990. Long-term study of a northern population of the Blue Tit *Parus caeruleus*. In *Population biology of passerine birds, an integrated approach* (eds J. Blondel, A. Gosler, J.-D. Lebreton & R.H. McCleery), pp 65–75. NATO ASI Series. Springer Verlag, Berlin.

Hildén, O. & M. Hildén. 1996. Wide fluctuations in the Finnish population of the Great Grey Shrike *Lanius excubitor* during recent decades. *Ornis Fennica* 73: 35–38.

Hildén, O. & S. Vuolanto. 1972. Breeding biology of the Red-necked Phalarope *Phalaropus lobatus* in Finland. *Ornis Fennica* 49: 57–85.

Hill, D. 1988. Population dynamics of the Avocet (*Recurvirostra avosetta*) breeding in Britain. *Journal of Animal Ecology* 57: 669–683.

Hill, D.A. & M.W. Ridley. 1987. Sexual segregation in winter, spring dispersal and habitat use in the Pheasant (*Phasianus colchicus*). *Journal of Zoology, London* 212: 657–668.

Hill, D.A. & P. Robertson. 1988. *The Pheasant: ecology, management and conservation*. BSP Professional Books, Oxford.

Hill, L.A. 1992. Observations at a colony of House Martins *Delichon urbica* in SW Spain with particular reference to moult. *Ringing & Migration* 13: 113–116.

Hill, L.A. 1997. Trans-Sahara recoveries of House Martins *Delichon urbica*, with discussion on ringing, roosting and sightings in Africa. *Safring News* 26: 7–12.

Hill, L.A. 2000. Post-breeding and post-juvenile moult of House Martins *Delichon urbica* at colonies in Spain. *Ringing & Migration* 20: 143–146.

Hill, L.A. 2002. A seven-year study of House Martins in Lincolnshire. *Lincolnshire Bird Report 1997* (in press).

Hinde, R.A. 1949. Exceptional inland passage of Black Tern 1948. *British Birds* 42: 113–117.

Hinsley, S.A., P.E. Bellamy & I. Newton. 1995. Bird species turnover and stochastic extinction in woodland fragments. *Ecography* 18: 41–50.

Hirons, G.J.M. 1976. *A population study of the Tawny Owl* (Strix aluco) *and its main prey species in woodland*. PhD thesis, University of Oxford.

Hirons, G. 1988. Some factors affecting age ratios among Woodcock wings collected from hunters in Britain. In *Proceedings of the Third European Woodcock and Snipe Workshop* (eds P. Havet & G. Hirons), pp 92–95. International Waterfowl Research Bureau, Slimbridge.

Hirons, G. & M. Linsley. 1989. Counting Woodcock. *Game Conservancy Annual Review* 20: 47–48.

Hirschfeld, E. & M. Ullman. 1985. Förekomsten av vittrut *Larus hyperboreus* i Skåne. *Anser* 24: 103–114.

Hjálmarsson, A.W. 1982. Vadfuglar. *Rit Landverndar* 8: 117–148.

Hjort, C., J. Pettersson, Å. Lindström & M.B. King. 1996. Fuel deposition and potential flight ranges of Blackcaps *Sylvia atricapilla* and Whitethroats *Sylvia communis* on spring migration in The Gambia. *Ornis Svecica* 6: 137–144.

Hobson, K.A. 1999. Tracing origins and migration of wildlife using stable isotopes: a review. *Oecologia* 120: 314–326.

Hobson, K.A. & R.W. Clark. 1993. Turnover of ^{13}C in cellular and plasma fractions of blood: implications for nondestructive sampling in avian dietary studies. *Auk* 110: 638–641.

Hobson, K.A. & L.I. Wassenaar. 1997. Linking breeding and wintering grounds of neotropical migrant songbirds using stable hydrogen isotope analysis of feathers. *Oecologia* 109: 142–148.

Hobson, K.A., L.I. Wassenaar & O.R. Taylor. 1999. Stable isotopes (δ^2H and $\delta^{13}C$) are geographic indicators of Monarch butterfly natal origins in eastern North America. *Oecologia* 120: 397–404.

Hodge, T.N. (ed). 1995. *Kent Bird Report 1993*. Kent Ornithological Society.

Hodge, T.N. (ed). 1998. *Kent Bird Report 1996*. Kent Ornithological Society.

Höglund, N.H. 1964. Der Habicht *Accipiter gentilis* Linné in Fennoscandia. *Viltrevy* 2: 195–270.

Hogstad, O. 1984. Variation in numbers, territoriality and flock size of a Goldcrest *Regulus regulus* population in winter. *Ibis* 126: 296–306.

Hogstedt, G. & C. Persson. 1982. Do Willow Warblers *Phylloscopus trochilus* of northern origin start their autumn migration at an earlier age than their southern conspecifics? *Holarctic Ecology* 5: 76–80.

Holland, J. & P.K. McGregor. 1997. Disappearing song dialects? The case of Cornish Corn Buntings *Miliaria calandra*. In *The ecology and conservation of Corn Buntings* Miliaria calandra (eds P.F. Donald & N.J. Aebischer), pp 181–185. UK Nature Conservation no. 13. Joint Nature Conservation Committee, Peterborough.

Holland, P.K. & D.W. Yalden. 1991. Population dynamics of Common Sandpipers *Actitis hypoleucos* breeding along an upland river system. *Bird Study* 38: 151–159.

Holland, P.K. & D.W. Yalden. 1994. An estimate of lifetime reproductive success for the Common Sandpiper *Actitis hypoleucos. Bird Study* 41: 110–119.

Holland, P.K., J.E. Robson & D.W. Yalden. 1982. The breeding biology of the Common Sandpiper *Actitis hypoleucos* in the Peak District. *Bird Study* 29: 99–110.

Holland, R., F. Bonadonna, L. Dall'Antonia, S. Benvenuti, T. Burt de Perera & T. Guilford. 2000. Short distance phase shifts revisited: tracking clock-shifted homing pigeons (Rock Dove *Columba livia*) close to the loft. *Ibis* 142: 111–118.

Holloway, S. 1996. *The Historical Atlas of Breeding Birds in Britain and Ireland: 1875–1900*. T. & A.D. Poyser, London.

Holmes, P.R., S.E. Christmas & A.J. Parr. 1987. A study of the return rate and dispersal of Sand Martins *Riparia riparia* at a single colony. *Bird Study* 34: 12–19.

Holmgren, N., H. Ellegren & J. Pettersson. 1993. The adaptation of the moult pattern in migratory Dunlins *Calidris alpina. Ornis Scandinavica* 24: 21–27.

Holyoak, D. 1971. Movements and mortality of Corvidae. *Bird Study* 18: 97–106.

Hölzinger, J., M. Mickley & K. Schilhansl. 1973. Untersuchungen zur Brut- und Ernährungs-biologie der Sumpfohreule (*Asio flammeus*) in einem süddeutschen Brutgebiet mit Bemerkungen zum Auftreten der Art in Mitteleuropa. *Anzeiger der Ornithologischen Gesellschaft in Bayern* 12: 176–197.

Honer, M.R. 1963. Observations on the Barn Owl (*Tyto alba guttata*) in the Netherlands in relation to its ecology and population fluctuations. *Ardea* 51: 158–195.

Honza, M. & I. Literak. 1997. Spatial distribution of four *Acrocephalus* warblers in reedbeds during the post-breeding migration. *Ringing & Migration* 18: 79–83.

Hoodless, A.N. 1994a. *Aspects of the ecology of the European Woodcock* Scolopax rusticola. PhD thesis, University of Durham.

Hoodless, A. 1994b. The density and distribution of Woodcock wintering in Cornwall, England. In *Proceedings of the Fourth European Woodcock and Snipe Workshop* (ed H. Kalchreuter), pp 27–34. International Waterfowl & Wetlands Research Bureau, Slimbridge.

Hoodless, A.N. & J.C. Coulson. 1994. Survival rates and movements of British and Continental Woodcock *Scolopax rusticola* in the British Isles. *Bird Study* 41: 48–60.

Hoodless, A.N. & J.C. Coulson. 1998. Breeding biology of the Woodcock *Scolopax rusticola* in Britain. *Bird Study* 45: 195–204.

Hope Jones, P. 1975. The migration of Redstarts through and from Britain. *Ringing & Migration* 1: 12–17.

Hope Jones, P. 1979. Roosting behaviour of Long-tailed Ducks in relation to possible oil pollution. *Wildfowl* 30: 155–158.

Hope Jones, P. & M.L. Tasker. 1982. *Seabird Movement at Coastal Sites around Great Britain and Ireland 1978–1980*. Nature Conservancy Council & The Seabird Group, Aberdeen.

Hope Jones, P., G. Howells, E.I.S. Rees & J. Wilson. 1970. Effect of 'Hamilton Trader' oil on birds in the Irish Sea in May 1969. *British Birds* 63: 97–110.

Hope Jones, P., C.J. Mead & R.F. Durman. 1977. The migration of the Pied Flycatcher from and through Britain. *Bird Study* 24: 2–14.

Hori, J. 1969. Social and population studies in the Shelduck. *Wildfowl* 20: 5–22.

Horton, N., T. Brough & J.B.A. Rochard. 1983. The importance of refuse tips to gulls wintering in an inland area of south-east England. *Journal of Applied Ecology* 20: 751–765.

Horton, N., T. Brough, M.R. Fletcher, J.B.A. Rochard & P.I. Stanley. 1984. The winter distribution of foreign Black-headed Gulls in the British Isles. *Bird Study* 31: 171–186.

Hötker, H. 1982. Studies of Meadow Pipit *Anthus pratensis* dispersal. *Ringing & Migration* 4: 45–50.

Hötker, H., A.B. Holger & S. Dietrich. 1990. Northward migration of waders wintering in Senegal in January. *Wader Study Group Bulletin* 59: 20–24.

Howard, R. & A. Moore. 1998. *A Complete Checklist of the Birds of the World*. Second edition. Academic Press, London.

Howells, R. 1986. Hen Harriers on Larkhill & Westdown Ranges. *Hobby* 12: 47–53.

Howey, D. & M. Bell. 1985. Pallas's Warblers and other migrants in Britain and Ireland in October 1982. *British Birds* 78: 381–392.

Howlett, P., I. Jüttner & S.J. Ormerod. 2000. Migration strategies of sylviid warblers: chance patterns or community dynamics? *Journal of Avian Biology* 31: 20–30.

Hoy, S.P. & R.G. Loxton. 1987. A pitfall trap study of habitat use by invertebrates on Ynys Enlli: IV Formicidae. *Bardsey Observatory Report* 31: 69–84.

Hudson, A.V., T.J. Stowe & S.J. Aspinall. 1990. Status and distribution of Corncrakes in Britain. *British Birds* 83: 173–186.

Hudson, P.J. 1992. *Grouse in Space and Time: the population biology of a managed gamebird*. Report of the Game Conservancy's Scottish Grouse Research Project & North of England Grouse Research Project. Game Conservancy, Fordingbridge.

Hudson, R. 1964. Recoveries in Great Britain and Ireland of birds ringed abroad. *British Birds* 57: 583–596.

Hudson, R. 1969. Recoveries in Great Britain and Ireland of birds ringed abroad. *British Birds* 62: 13–22.

Hudson, R. 1973. *Early and late dates for summer migrants*. BTO Guide 15. British Trust for Ornithology, Tring.

Hudson, R. & C.J. Mead. 1984. Origins and ages of auks wrecked in eastern Britain in February–March 1983. *Bird Study* 31: 89–94.

Hughes, B. 1996. *The feasibility of control measures for North American Ruddy Ducks* Oxyura jamaicensis *in the United Kingdom*. Report to the Department of the Environment. Wildfowl & Wetlands Trust, Slimbridge.

Hughes, B. & M. Grussu. 1995. The Ruddy Duck in Europe and the threat to the White-headed Duck. In *Britain's Birds in 1991–92: the conservation and monitoring review* (ed S.P. Carter), pp 17–19. British Trust for Ornithology/Joint Nature Conservation Committee, Thetford.

Hughes, B., K.A. Goverd & N.S. Jarrett. 1990. Dazzling waterbirds from a boat on Chew Valley Lake, Avon: the technique and results from the first two years' catching effort. *Chew Valley Ringing Station Report* 10: 60–74.

Hughes, B., R.M. Bevan, J.M. Bowler, L. Still, D.N. Carss, M. Marquiss, R.D. Hearn & J.H. Bruce. 1999. *Feeding Behaviour of Fish-eating Birds in Great Britain*. Department of the Environment, Transport and the Regions, London.

Hughes, B., J. Bruce, G. Ekins & S. Newson. 2000. *Movements and distribution of inland breeding Cormorants in England*. Research Report 360. English Nature, Peterborough.

Huin, N. & T.H. Sparks. 1998. Arrival and progression of the Swallow *Hirundo rustica* through Britain. *Bird Study* 45: 361–370.

Huin, N. & T.H. Sparks. 2000. Spring arrival patterns of the Cuckoo *Cuculus canorus,* Nightingale *Luscinia megarhynchos* and Spotted Flycatcher *Muscicapa striata* in Britain. *Bird Study* 47: 22–31.

Hulme, M. & G.J. Jenkins. 1998. *Climate Change Scenarios for the UK: scientific report.* UKCIP Technical Report 1. Climatic Research Unit, Norwich.

Hulscher, J.B., K.-M. Exo & N.A. Clark. 1996. Why do Oystercatchers migrate? In *The Oystercatcher: from individuals to populations* (ed J.D. Goss-Custard), pp 155–185. Oxford University Press, Oxford.

Hume, R.A. 1975. Identification and ageing of Glaucous and Iceland Gulls. *British Birds* 68: 24–37.

Hume, R.A. 1976. The pattern of Mediterranean Gull records at Blackpill, West Glamorgan. *British Birds* 69: 503–505.

Hume, R.A. 1984. Winter Sabine's Gulls. *British Birds* 77: 322.

Hume, R.A. 1993. *The Common Tern.* Hamlyn, London.

Hund, K. & R. Prinzinger. 1979. Untersuchungen zur Ortstreue, Paartreue und Überlebensrate nestjunger Vögel bei der Mehlschwalbe *Delichon urbica* in Oberschwaben. [Studies on site-tenacity, pair bond and nestling survival rate of House Martins in southwest Germany]. *Die Vogelwarte* 30: 107–117.

Hunter, E.N. 1970. Great Northern Diver breeding in Scotland. *Scottish Birds* 6: 195.

Hunter, E.N. & R.H. Dennis. 1972. Hybrid Great Northern Diver × Black-throated Diver in Wester Ross. *Scottish Birds* 7: 89–91.

Hurford, C. & P.G. Lansdown. 1995. *Birds of Glamorgan.* Privately published.

Hurrell, H.G. 1951. Movements of Swifts in summer. *British Birds* 44: 145–152.

Hustings, F. 1997. The decline of the Corn Bunting *Miliaria calandra* in the Netherlands. In *The ecology and conservation of Corn Buntings Miliaria calandra* (eds P.F. Donald & N.J. Aebischer), pp 42–51. UK Nature Conservation no. 13. Joint Nature Conservation Committee, Peterborough.

Hutchinson, C.D. 1980. Scarce passerine migrants in Ireland. *Irish Birds* 1: 502–514.

Hutchinson, C.D. & B. Neath. 1978. Little Gulls in Britain & Ireland. *British Birds* 71: 563–582.

Hutson, A.M., J.A. Burton & S.D.G. Stephens. 1970. Some preliminary results of Swift ringing at Beddington Sewage Farm, Surrey. *London Bird Report* 35: 81–87.

Huyskens, G. & P. Maes. 1971. La migración de aves marinas in el NW de España. *Ardeola* (special issue): 155–180.

Iborra, O., F. Dhermain & P. Vidal. 1991. L'hivernage du Grèbe à cou noir *Podiceps nigricollis* sur l'Étang de Berre (Bouches-du-Rhône). *Alauda* 59: 195–205.

Illner, H. 1992. Road deaths of Westphalian owls: methodological problems, influence of road type and possible effects on population levels. In *The Ecology and Conservation of European Owls* (eds C.A. Galbraith, I.R. Taylor & S.M. Percival), pp 94–100. Joint Nature Conservation Committee, Peterborough.

Image, R. 1987. Montagu's and Marsh Harriers in Norfolk 1982–1986. *Norfolk Bird and Mammal Report 1986*: 405–408.

Image, R.A. 1992. Montagu's and Marsh Harriers in West Norfolk 1987–1991. *Norfolk Bird and Mammal Report 1991*: 270–272.

Imboden, C. 1974. Migration, dispersal and breeding period of the Lapwing *Vanellus vanellus. Der Ornithologische Beobachter* 71: 5–134.

Inglis, I.R., A.J. Isaacson, R.J.P. Thearle & N.J. Westwood. 1990. The effects of changing agricultural practice upon Woodpigeon *Columba palumbus* numbers. *Ibis* 132: 262–272.

Inglis, I.R., A.J. Isaacson, G.C. Smith, P.J. Haynes & R.J.P. Thearle. 1997. The effect on the Woodpigeon (*Columba palumbus*) of the introduction of oilseed rape into Britain. *Agriculture, Ecosystems & Environment* 61: 113–121.

Ingolfsson, A. 1970. The moult of remiges and rectrices in Great Black-backed Gulls *Larus marinus* and Glaucous Gulls *Larus hyperboreus* in Iceland. *Ibis* 112: 83–92.

Insley, G.V. 1997. Skånsk grågås *Anser anser* utvandrad till Skottland. *Anser* 36: 272–274.

Insley, H. & R.C. Boswell. 1978. The timing of arrivals of Reed and Sedge Warblers at south coast ringing sites during autumn passage. *Ringing & Migration* 2: 1–9.

Insley, H. & L. Young. 1979. Ageing Collared Doves. *Ringers' Bulletin* 5: 72–74.

Insley, H., W.J. Peach, R.L. Swann & B. Etheridge. 1997. Survival rates of Redshank *Tringa totanus* wintering on the Moray Firth. *Bird Study* 44: 277–289.

Irwin, S. & J. O'Halloran. 1997. The wintering behaviour of Coot *Fulica atra* at Cork Lough, south-west Ireland. *Biology and Environment: Proceedings of the Royal Irish Academy* 97B: 157–162.

Isaksen, K. & V. Bakken. 1996. Migration routes and wintering areas of Little Auks *Alle alle* ringed on Svalbard. *Sula* 10: 229–238.

Isenmann, P. & M.-A. Bouchet. 1993. L'aire de distribution française et le statut taxonomique de la Pie-grièche grise meridionale *Lanius elegans meridionalis* (Temminck 1820). *Alauda* 61: 223–227.

Iverson, G.C., S.E. Warnock, R.W. Butler, M.A. Bishop & N. Warnock. 1996. Spring migration of Western Sandpipers (*Calidris mauri*) along the Pacific Coast of North America: a telemetry study. *Condor* 98: 10–22.

Izhaki, I. & A. Maitav. 1998. Blackcaps *Sylvia atricapilla* stopping over at the desert edge; inter- and intra-sexual differences in spring and autumn migration. *Ibis* 140: 234–243.

Jackson, D.B. 1994. Breeding dispersal and site-fidelity in three monogamous wader species in the Western Isles, U.K. *Ibis* 136: 463–473.

Jackson, D. 1999. The winter range of Redshank breeding in the Outer Hebrides. *Outer Hebrides (Western Isles) Bird Report 1998*: 104–106.

Jackson, R. & J. Jackson. 1976. Analysis of ringing and subsequent recoveries from a Yorkshire Blackbird roost. *Ringing & Migration* 1: 117–119.

Jackson, R.D. 1958. A study of a population of Robins, *Erithacus rubecula. Irish Naturalists Journal* 12: 229–236.

James, P. (ed). 1996. *The Birds of Sussex.* Sussex Ornithological Society.

Jardine, D., P. Cosgrove, M. Holmes & S. Bankier. 1994. Recoveries and controls of Siskins caught in Northumbria. *Birds in Northumbria 1993*: 95–100.

Jarry, G. 1994. Turtle Dove *Streptopelia turtur*. In *Birds in Europe: their conservation status* (eds G.M. Tucker & M.F. Heath), pp 320–321. Conservation Series no. 3. BirdLife International, Cambridge.

Jarry, G. 1995. Tourterelle des bois *Streptopelia turtur*. In *Nouvel Atlas des Oiseaux Nicheurs de France 1985–1989* (eds D. Yeatman-Berthelot & G. Jarry), pp 380–383. Société Ornithologique de France, Paris.

Jarry, G. & F. Baillon. 1991. *Hivernage de la Tourterelle des Bois* (Streptopelia turtur*) au Sénégal; étude d'une population dans la région de Nianing.* Rapport CRBPO/ORSTOM, Paris.

Jehl, J.R. Jr. 1990. Aspects of molt migration. In *Bird Migration: the physiology and ecophysiology* (ed E. Gwinner), pp 102–113. Springer Verlag, Berlin.

Jehl, J.R. Jr. 1996. Mass mortality events of Eared Grebes in North America. *Journal of Field Ornithology* 67: 471–476.

Jenkins, D. 1961. Population control in protected Partridges (*Perdix perdix*). *Journal of Animal Ecology* 30: 235–258.

Jenkins, D. & A. Watson. 2000. Dates of first arrival and song of birds during 1974–99 in mid-Deeside, Scotland. *Bird Study* 47: 249–251.

Jenkins, D., A. Watson & G.R. Miller. 1967. Population fluctuations in the Red Grouse *Lagopus lagopus scoticus. Journal of Animal Ecology* 36: 97–122.

Jenkins, R.K.B., S.T. Buckton & S.J. Ormerod. 1995. Local movements and population density of Water Rail *Rallus aquaticus* in a small inland reed bed. *Bird Study* 42: 82–87.

Jenni, L. 1982. Schweizerische Ringfunde von Bergfinken *Fringilla montifringilla*: ein Beitrag zum Problem der Masseneinflüge. *Der Ornithologische Beobachter* 79: 265–272.

Jenni, L. 1985. Der Herbstzug des Bergfinken *Fringilla montifringilla* in der Schweiz und Beziehungen zu Masseneinflügen in Mitteleuropa. *Die Vogelwarte* 33: 53–63.

Jenni, L. 1987. Mass concentrations of Bramblings *Fringilla montifringilla* in Europe 1900–1983 – their dependence upon beech mast and the effect of snow-cover. *Ornis Scandinavica* 18: 84–94.

Jenni, L. & C.J. Camphuysen. 2001. Bird Ringing 100 Years. Proceedings of the International Conference on Helgoland. *Ardea* 89 (special issue).

Jenni, L. & U. Schaffner. 1984. Herbstbewegungen von Haus- und Feldsperling *Passer domesticus* und *P. montanus* in der Schweiz. *Der Ornithologischer Beobachter* 81: 61–67.

Jenni, L. & R. Winkler. 1994. *Moult and ageing of European passerines.* Academic Press, London.

Jenni-Eiermann, S. & L. Jenni. 1994. Plasma metabolite levels predict individual body-mass changes in a small long-distance migrant, the Garden Warbler. *Auk* 111: 888–899.

Jennings, A.R. 1961. An analysis of 1,000 deaths in wild birds. *Bird Study* 8: 25–31.

Jespersen, P. & Å.V. Tåning (eds). 1950. *Studies in Bird Migration being the Collected Papers of H. Chr. C. Mortensen.* Munksgaard, Copenhagen.

JNCC. 1999. *The Birds Directive. Selection Guidelines for Special Protection Areas.* Joint Nature Conservation Committee, Peterborough.

John, A.W.G. & J. Roskell. 1985. Jay movements in autumn 1983. *British Birds* 78: 611–637.

Johnsgard, P.A. 1993. *Cormorants, Darters and Pelicans of the World.* Smithsonian Institution Press, Washington.

Johnson, C. 1985. Patterns of seasonal weight variation in waders on the Wash. *Ringing & Migration* 6: 19–32.

Johnson, E.D.H. 1961. The pair relationship and polygyny in the Stonechat. *British Birds* 54: 213–225.

Johnson, E.D.H. 1971. Observations on a resident population of Stonechats in Jersey. *British Birds* 64: 201–213, 267–279.

Johnson, I.G. 1970. The Water Pipit as a winter visitor to the British Isles. *Bird Study* 17: 297–319.

Johnson, R.F. & M. Janiga. 1995. *Feral Pigeons.* Oxford University Press, Oxford.

Johnstone, G.W. 1967. Blackgame and Capercaillie in relation to forestry in Britain. In *Wildlife in the Forest* (*Forestry* suppl., ed R.W.V. Palmer), pp 68–77. Oxford University Press, Oxford.

Johnstone, I.G. 1998. Territory structure of Robin *Erithacus rubecula* outside the breeding season. *Ibis* 140: 244–251.

Jones, E. 1979. Breeding of the Short-eared Owl in South West Ireland. *Irish Birds* 1: 377–380.

Jones, G. 1987a. Colonization patterns in Sand Martins *Riparia riparia*. *Bird Study* 34: 20–25.

Jones, G. 1987b. Selection against large size in the Sand Martin *Riparia riparia* during a dramatic population crash. *Ibis* 129: 274–280.

Jones, P. 1985. The migration strategies of Palearctic passerines in West Africa. In *Migratory Birds: problems and prospects* (eds A. McDonald & P. Goriup), pp 9–21. International Council for Bird Preservation, Cambridge.

Jones, P., J. Vickery, S. Holt & W. Cresswell. 1996. A preliminary assessment of some factors influencing the density and distribution of Palearctic passerine migrants wintering in the Sahel zone of West Africa. *Bird Study* 43: 73–84.

Jones, W.E. 1971. Sooty Shearwaters in the English Channel. *British Birds* 64: 322–324.

Jönsson, P.E. 1986. The migration and wintering of Baltic Dunlins *Calidris alpina schinzii*. *Vår Fågelvärld* (suppl.) 11: 71–78.

Jorgensen, O.H. 1976. Migration and aspects of population dynamics in the Grey Wagtail *Motacilla cinerea*. *Ornis Scandinavica* 7: 13–20.

Jukema, J. & J. Fokkema. 1992. Herkomst van in Nederland overwinterende Sneeuwgorzen *Plectrophenax nivalis*. *Limosa* 65: 67–72.

Júnior, T.V. 1991. Seabird mortality on longline fishing for tuna in southern Brazil. *Ciência e Cultura* 43: 388–390.

Kahlert, J., M. Coupe & F. Cooke. 1998. Winter segregation and timing of pair formation in Red-breasted Merganser *Mergus serrator*. *Wildfowl* 49: 161–172.

Kaiser, A. 1992. Fat deposition and theoretical flight range of small autumn migrants in southern Germany. *Bird Study* 39: 96–110.

Kaiser, A. 1999. Stopover strategies in birds: a review of methods for estimating stopover length. *Bird Study* 46 (suppl.): S299–308.

Kaiser, E. 1992. Populationsdynamik einer Mauersegler – *Apus apus* Kolonie unter besonderer Berücksichtigung der Nichtbrüter. *Die Vogelwelt* 113: 71–81.

Kålås, J.A. & I. Byrkjedal. 1984. Breeding chronology and mating system of the Eurasian Dotterel *Charadrius morinellus*. *Auk* 101: 838–847.

Källander, H. 1983. Återfynd av talgoxar och blåmesar ringmärkta i Sverige. *Vår Fågelvärld* 42: 413–424.

Kampp, K. 1982. Notes on the Long-tailed Skua *Stercorarius longicaudus* in West Greenland. *Dansk Ornithologisk Forenings Tidsskrift* 76: 129–135.

Kampp, K., A.D. Fox & D.A. Stroud. 1988. Mortality and movements of the Greenland White-fronted Goose (*Anser albifrons flavirostris*). *Dansk Ornithologisk Forenings Tidsskrift* 82: 25–36.

Kane, K.W.S. 1993. The altitude at which Quail *Coturnix coturnix* migrate. *Ibis* 135: 469–470.

Kapanen, M. 1977. Migration of the Arctic Skua in eastern Finland. *Ornis Fennica* 54: 123–126.

Karlin, A. & S. Raivio. 1987. Crane research in Finland in 1983. *Aquila* 93–94: 39–48.

Kasparek, M. 1996. Dismigration und Brutarealexpansion der Türkentaube *Streptopelia decaocto*. *Journal für Ornithologie* 137: 1–33.

Kear, J. 1963. The history of potato-eating by wildfowl in Britain. *Wildfowl Trust Annual Report* 14: 54–65.

Keijl, G.O. & E.V. Koopman. 1991. Veel Aalscholvers *Phalacrocorax carbo* en Dwergsterns *Sterna albifrons* op Rottumeroog, in juli en augustus 1990. *Sula* 5: 146–149.

Keith, J.O. & R.L. Bruggers. 1998. Review of hazards to raptors from pest control in Sahelian Africa. *Journal of Raptor Research* 32: 151–158.

Keith, L.B. 1961. *A study of waterfowl ecology on small impoundments in southeastern Alberta.* Wildlife Monograph 6. The Wildlife Society, Bethesda, Maryland.

Keith, S., E.K. Urban & C.H. Fry. 1992. *The Birds of Africa. Volume IV.* Academic Press, London.

Keller, M., B. Jędrzejewska & W. Jędrzejewski. 1989. Wintering tactics of the Kingfisher *Alcedo atthis*. *Ornis Fennica* 66: 157–160.

Kelsey, M.G. 1989. A comparison of the song and territorial behaviour of a long-distance migrant, the Marsh Warbler *Acrocephalus palustris*, in summer and winter. *Ibis* 131: 403–414.

Kelsey, M.G., G.H. Green, M.C. Garnett & P.V. Hayman. 1989. Marsh Warblers in Britain. *British Birds* 82: 239–256.

Kennedy, R.J. 1978. Mortality and site faithfulness of warblers. *Bird-Ringing in South West Lancashire, 1977*: 43–44.

Kenrick, H. 1940. A study of Blue Tits by colour-ringing. *British Birds* 33: 307–310.

Kenward, R.E. 2001. *A Manual for Wildlife Radio Tagging.* Academic Press, London.

Kenward, R.E., M. Marquiss & I. Newton. 1981. What happens to Goshawks trained for falconry? *Journal of Wildlife Management* 45: 802–806.

Kenward, R.E., V. Marcstrom & M. Karlbom. 1993. Post-nestling behaviour in Goshawks (*Accipiter gentilis*). I. The causes of dispersal. *Animal Behaviour* 46: 365–370.

Kenward, R.E., S.S. Walls & K.H. Hodder. 2001. Life path analysis: scaling indicates priming effects of social and habitat factors on dispersal distances. *Journal of Animal Ecology* 70: 1–13.

Kerr, I. 1989. The Merlin in winter in Northumberland. *Birds in Northumbria 1988*: 91–94.

Kershaw, M. 1998. *Long-term population trends in wintering Pintail (Anas acuta) in Great Britain 1966–1995*. Report to JNCC. Wildfowl & Wetlands Trust, Slimbridge.

Kershaw, M., R.A. Pettifor & M.C. Bell. 1998. *Trends in the number of wintering Pochard (Aythya ferina L.) in Britain, 1966–83, at a regional, habitat and site level*. Report to the WeBS partners. Wildfowl & Wetlands Trust, Slimbridge.

Ketterson, E.D. & V. Nolan Jr. 1976. Geographic variation and its climatic correlates in the sex ratio of eastern-wintering Dark-eyed Juncos (*Junco hyemalis hyemalis*). *Ecology* 57: 679–693.

Ketterson, E.D. & V. Nolan Jr. 1983. The evolution of differential bird migration. *Current Ornithology* 1: 357–402.

Kew, A., S. Wakeham & J. Clark. 1999. Curlew. *Wash Wader Ringing Group 1997–98 Report*: 74–75.

Kilpi, M. & P. Saurola. 1984. Migration and wintering strategies of juvenile and adult *Larus marinus, L. argentatus* and *L. fuscus*. *Ornis Fennica* 61: 1–8.

Kilpi, M. & P. Saurola. 1985. Movements and survival of Finnish Common Gulls (*Larus canus*). *Annales Zoologici Fennici* 22: 157–168.

King, B. 1976. Association between male North American Ruddy Ducks and stray ducklings. *British Birds* 69: 34.

King, D.T., K.J. Andrews, J.O. King, R.D. Flynt & J.F. Glahn. 1994. A night-lighting technique for capturing Cormorants. *Journal of Field Ornithology* 65: 254–257.

King, J.R. & J.L. Muddeman. 1995. Ageing and sexing Marsh Tits *Parus palustris*. *Ringing & Migration* 16: 172–177.

King, W.B. 1967. *Seabirds of the Tropical Pacific Ocean*. Smithsonian Institution, Washington DC.

Kirby, J.S. 1995. Winter population estimates for selected waterfowl species in Britain. *Biological Conservation* 73: 189–198.

Kirby, J.S. & P.C. Lack. 1993. Spatial dynamics of wintering Lapwings and Golden Plovers in Britain and Ireland, 1981/82 to 1983/84. *Bird Study* 40: 38–50.

Kirby, J.S. & C. Mitchell. 1993. Distribution and status of wintering Shovelers *Anas clypeata* in Great Britain. *Bird Study* 40: 170–180.

Kirby, J.S. & R.M. Sellers. 1997. Recent trends in the numbers and distribution of Cormorants *Phalacrocorax carbo* in Britain. *Ekologia Polska* 45: 71–76.

Kirby, J.S., K.K. Kirby & S.J. Woolfall. 1989. Curlew Sandpipers in Britain and Ireland in autumn 1988. *British Birds* 82: 399–409.

Kirby, J.S., E.C. Rees, O.J. Merne & A. Garðarsson. 1992. International census of Whooper Swans *Cygnus cygnus* in Britain, Ireland and Iceland: January 1991. *Wildfowl* 43: 20–26.

Kirby, J.S., R.J. Evans & A.D. Fox. 1993. Wintering seaducks in Britain and Ireland: populations, threats, conservation and research priorities. *Aquatic Conservation: Marine and Freshwater Ecosystems* 3: 105–137.

Kirby, J., S. Delany & J. Quinn. 1994. Mute Swans in Great Britain: a review, current status and long-term trends. *Hydrobiologia* 280: 467–482.

Kirby, J.S., W.G. Haines & G.E. Austin. 1999. Translocation of Canada Geese *Branta canadensis* in Great Britain. *Ringing & Migration* 19: 261–271.

Kistchinski, A.A. 1975. Breeding biology and behaviour of the Grey Phalarope *Phalaropus fulicarius* in East Siberia. *Ibis* 117: 285–301.

Kittle, T. 1975. Weights and moult of Green Sandpipers in Britain. *Ringing & Migration* 1: 52–55.

Kjellén, N. 1992. Differential timing of autumn migration between sex and age groups in raptors at Falsterbo, Sweden. *Ornis Scandinavica* 23: 420–434.

Kjellén, N. 1993. Age and sex ratio among raptors migrating past the Falsterbo peninsula in the autumn of 1992. *Anser* 32: 105–125.

Kjellén, N. 1994. Gladan: en Rovfågel på Frammarsch i Sverige. *Vår Fågelvärld* 53(6): 6–19.

Kjellén, N. 1996. Projekt Glada – Årsrapport 1995. *Anser* 35: 17–25.

Kjellén, N. 1998. Annual variation in numbers, age and sex ratios among migrating raptors at Falsterbo, Sweden from 1986–1995. *Journal für Ornithologie* 139: 157–171.

Kjellén, N., M. Hake & T. Alerstam. 1997. Strategies of two Ospreys *Pandion haliaetus* migrating between Sweden and tropical Africa as revealed by satellite tracking. *Journal of Avian Biology* 28: 15–23.

Klomp, N.I. & R.W. Furness. 1990. Variations in numbers of non-breeding Great Skuas attending a colony. *Ornis Scandinavica* 21: 270–276.

Klomp, N.I. & R.W. Furness. 1992a. The dispersal and philopatry of Great Skuas from Foula, Shetland. *Ringing & Migration* 13: 73–82.

Klomp, N.I. & R.W. Furness. 1992b. Non-breeders as a buffer against environmental stress: declines in numbers of Great Skuas on Foula, Shetland, and prediction of future recruitment. *Journal of Applied Ecology* 29: 341–348.

Kluyver, H.N. 1971. Regulation of numbers in populations of Great Tits (*Parus m. major*). In *Dynamics of populations* (eds P.J. den Boer & G.R. Gradwell), pp 507–523. Pudoc, Wageningen, the Netherlands.

Knox, A. 1988. Taxonomy of the Rock/Water Pipit superspecies *Anthus petrosus, spinoletta* and *rubescens*. *British Birds* 81: 206–211.

Knox, A.G. 1992. Species and pseudospecies: the structure of crossbill populations. *Biological Journal of the Linnean Society* 47: 325–335.

Koffijberg, K., B. Voslamber & E. van Winden. 1997. *Ganzen en zwanen in Nederland: overzicht van pleisterplaatsen in de periode 1985–94*. SOVON, Beek-Ubbergen, the Netherlands.

Köhler, P., U. Köhler, J. Pykal, E. van Krosigk & U. Firsching. 1995. Sustained pair bonds during moult migration? Pair formation during the break-up of family groups in Gadwall *Anas strepera*. *Journal für Ornithologie* 136: 167–175.

Kok, O.B., C.A. van Ee & D.G. Nel. 1991. Daylength determines departure date of the Spotted Flycatcher *Muscicapa striata* from its winter quarters. *Ardea* 79: 63–66.

Kokko, H. 1999. Competition for early arrival in migratory birds. *Journal of Animal Ecology* 68: 940–950.

Kolunen, H. & A. Peiponen. 1991. Delayed autumn migration of the Swift *Apus apus* from Finland in 1986. *Ornis Fennica* 68: 81–92.

Koopman, K. 1986. Primary molt and weight changes of ruffs in the Netherlands in relation to migration. *Ardea* 74: 69–77.

Korpimäki, E. 1992. Population dynamics of Fennoscandian owls in relation to wintering conditions and between-year fluctuations of food. In *The ecology and conservation of European owls* (eds C.A. Galbraith, I.R. Taylor & S. Percival), pp 1–10. UK Nature Conservation no. 5. Joint Nature Conservation Committee, Peterborough.

Korpimäki, E. 1994. Rapid or delayed tracking of multi-annual vole cycles by avian predators? *Journal of Animal Ecology* 63: 619–628.

Korpimäki, E. & K. Norrdahl. 1991. Numerical and functional responses of Kestrels, Short-eared Owls and Long-eared Owls to vole densities. *Ecology* 72: 814–826.

Koskimies, J. 1950. The life of the Swift, *Micropus apus* (L.) in relation to the weather. *Annales Academiae Scientiarum Fennicae Series A, IV Biologica* 15: 1–151.

Koskimies, P. 1989. *Distribution and numbers of Finnish breeding birds: appendix to Suomen Lintuatlas*. SLY:n Lintutieto Oy, Helsinki.

Kozulin, A. & M. Flade. 1999. Breeding habitat, abundance and conservation status of the Aquatic Warbler *Acrocephalus paludicola* in Belarus. *Die Vogelwelt* 120: 97–111.

Kramer, D. 1995. Inland spring passage of Arctic Terns in southern Britain. *British Birds* 88: 211–217.

Krebs, J.R. 1971. Territory and breeding density in the Great Tit. *Ecology* 52: 2–22.

Krüger, S. 1979. *Der Kernbeisser*. Die Neue Brehm-Bücherei 525. A. Ziemsen Verlag, Wittenberg Lutherstadt.

Krupa, R. 1997. Phenology and dynamics of autumn migration of Grey Plover (*Pluvialis squatarola*) through the Gulf of Gdansk in years 1984–1995. *The Ring* 19: 93–104.

Kruskal, J.B. & M. Wish. 1978. *Multidimensional Scaling*. Sage University Paper Series on Quantitative Applications in the Social Sciences, 07–011. Sage Publications, Beverly Hills, USA.

Kuresoo, A. 1991. Present status of Mute Swans *Cygnus olor*, Whooper Swans *C. cygnus* and Bewick's Swans, *C. bewickii* wintering in the Eastern Baltic region. In *Proceedings of the Third IWRB International Swan Symposium, Oxford 1989*, (eds J. Sears & P.J. Bacon), pp 201–208. *Wildfowl* suppl. 1.

Kuyken, E. & G. Burggraeve. 1971. Een Krombekstrandloper (*Calidris ferruginea*) na twee weken teruggemeld op de Kleine Antillen (Am.). *Gerfaut* 61: 162–163.

Kwei, E.A. 1964. Migration of *Sardinella aurita* (Val. et Cuv.). *Ghana Journal of Science* 4: 34–43.

Kyrkos, A. 1997. *Behavioural and demographic responses of Yellowhammers to variation in agricultural practices*. PhD thesis, University of Oxford.

Kyrkos, A., J.D. Wilson & R.J. Fuller. 1998. Farmland habitat change and abundance of Yellowhammers *Emberiza citrinella*: an analysis of Common Birds Census data. *Bird Study* 45: 232–246.

Lack, D. 1943. *The Life of the Robin*. H.F. & G. Witherby, London.

Lack, D. 1944. The problem of partial migration. *British Birds* 37: 122–130, 143–150.

Lack, D. 1951. Population ecology in birds: a review. In *Proceedings of the Tenth International Ornithological Congress, Uppsala 1950* (ed S. Hörstadius), pp 409–448. Almqvist & Wiksells, Uppsala, Sweden.

Lack, D. 1954a. Visible migration in SE England. *British Birds* 47: 1–15.

Lack, D. 1954b. *The Natural Regulation of Animal Numbers*. Clarendon Press, Oxford.

Lack, D. 1956. *Swifts in a Tower*. Methuen, London.

Lack, D. 1958a. Weather movements of Swifts 1955–1957. *Bird Study* 5: 128–142.

Lack, D. 1958b. Swifts over the sea at night. *Bird Study* 5: 126–127.

Lack, D. 1958c. Return and departure of Swifts at Oxford. *Ibis* 100: 477–502.

Lack, D. 1959a. Watching migration by radar. *British Birds* 52: 258–267.

Lack, D. 1959b. Migration across the North Sea studied by radar. Part 1. Survey through the year. *Ibis* 101: 209–234.

Lack, D. 1960. Migration across the North Sea studied by radar. Part 2. The spring departure 1956–59. *Ibis* 102: 26–57.

Lack, D. 1962. Migration across the southern North Sea studied by radar. Part 3. Movements in June and July. *Ibis* 104: 75–85.

Lack, D. 1963. Migration across the North Sea studied by radar. Part 4. Autumn. *Ibis* 105: 1–54.

Lack, D. 1966. *Population Studies of Birds*. Clarendon Press, Oxford.

Lack, D. & J.L.F. Parslow. 1962. Falls of migrants on the English coast in autumn 1960 and 1961. *Bird Migration* 2: 187–201.

Lack, D. & M.G. Ridpath. 1955. Do English Woodpigeons migrate? *British Birds* 48: 289–292.

Lack, P.C. 1988. The Winter Atlas in Britain and Ireland; a review of the methods, and the movements of the finches, buntings and sparrows. *Sitta* 2: 3–20.

Lack, P.C. 1989. Overall and regional trends in warbler populations of British farmland over 25 years. *Annales Zoologici Fennici* 26: 219–225.

Lack, P. 1990. Palaearctic-African systems. In *Biogeography and Ecology of Forest Bird Communities* (ed A. Keast), pp 345–356. SPB Academic Publishing, The Hague.

Lack, P. & D. Ferguson. 1993. *The Birds of Buckinghamshire*. Buckinghamshire Bird Club.

Lamarche, B. 1981. Liste commenté des oiseaux du Mali. *Malimbus* 3: 73–102.

Lambeck, R.H.D. 1990. Differences in migratory pattern and habitat choice between social classes of the Brent Goose *Branta b. bernicla*. *Ardea* 78: 426–440.

Lambeck, R.H.D., J.D. Goss-Custard & P. Triplet. 1996. Oystercatchers and man in the coastal zone. In *The Oystercatcher: from individuals to populations* (ed J.D. Goss-Custard), pp 289–326. Oxford University Press, Oxford.

Lampio, T. 1984. On the spring migration of the Bean Goose, *Anser fabalis*, in Finland. *Swedish Wildlife Research* 13: 59–72.

Lane, A.B. 1984. An enquiry into the responses of growers to attacks by pests on oilseed rape (*Brassica napus*), a relatively new crop in the United Kingdom. *Protection Ecology* 7: 73–78.

Langham, N.P.E. 1971. Seasonal movements of British terns in the Atlantic Ocean. *Bird Study* 18: 155–175.

Langslow, D.R. 1976. Weights of Blackcaps on migration. *Ringing & Migration* 1: 78–91.

Langslow, D.R. 1977a. Movements of Black Redstarts between Britain and Europe as related to occurrences at observatories. *Bird Study* 24: 169–178.

Langslow, D.R. 1977b. Weight increases and behaviour of Wrynecks on the Isle of May. *Scottish Birds* 9: 262–267.

Langslow, D.R. 1978. Recent increases in Blackcaps at bird observatories. *British Birds* 71: 345–354.

Langslow, D.R. 1979. Movements of Blackcaps ringed in Britain and Ireland. *Bird Study* 26: 239–252.

Langslow, D.R. 1981. Editorial. *Ringing & Migration* 3: 109–112.

Lapshin, N.V. 1988. [Post-nuptial moult in the Willow Warbler in the northwest USSR.] *Ornithologiya* 23: 100–110. (In Russian).

Laubek, B. 1995. Habitat use by Whooper Swans *Cygnus cygnus* and Bewick's Swans *Cygnus columbianus bewickii* wintering in Denmark: increasing agricultural conflicts. *Wildfowl* 46: 8 – 15.

Laubek, B., H.L. Knudsen & A. Ohtonen. 1998. Migration and winter range of Whooper Swans *Cygnus cygnus* breeding in different regions of Finland. In *The Northwest European Whooper Swan (Cygnus cygnus) population: ecological and management aspects of an expanding waterfowl population* (ed B. Laubek), pp 1–33. PhD thesis, University of Aarhus, Denmark.

Laubek, B., L. Nilsson, M. Wieloch, K. Koffijberg, C. Sudfelt & A. Follestad. 1999. Distribution, numbers and habitat choice of the NW European Whooper Swan *Cygnus cygnus* population: results of an international census in January 1995. *Die Vogelwelt* 120: 141–154.

Laursen, J.T. 1997. Invasion af Slørugle *Tyto alba* i Danmark i 1990–91. *Dansk Ornitologisk Forenings Tidsskrift* 91: 59–62.

Laursen, K. 1989. Estimates of sea duck wintering populations of the western Palearctic. *Danish Review of Game Biology* 13: 1–22.

Laursen, K., S. Pihl & J. Komdeur. 1992. New figures of seaduck winter populations in the Western Palearctic. *IWRB Seaduck Bulletin* 1: 6–8.

Laursen, K., E. Holm & I. Sørensen. 1997. Pollen as a marker in migratory warblers, Sylviidae. *Ardea* 85: 223–231.

Lawn, M.R. 1982. Pairing systems and site tenacity of the Willow Warbler *Phylloscopus trochilus* in southern England. *Ornis Scandinavica* 13: 193–199.

Lawn, M.R. 1984. Premigratory dispersal of juvenile Willow Warblers *Phylloscopus trochilus* in southern England. *Ringing & Migration* 5: 125–131.

Lawton, J.H. 1990. *Red Grouse populations and moorland management*. British Ecological Society Ecological Issues Series no. 2. Field Studies Council, Shrewsbury.

Lawton, N. 1999. Shorelarks in Norfolk – past and present. *Norfolk Bird Club Bulletin* 32: 4–8.

Le Grand, H.E. Jr. & E.S. Brinkley. 1996. Eurasian Collared Dove on the outer banks of North Carolina. *Chat* 60: 62–63.

Leach, I.H. 1981. Wintering Blackcaps in Britain and Ireland. *Bird Study* 28: 5–14.

Leader, P.J. 1999. Little Gull: the first record for Hong Kong. *Hong Kong Bird Report 1997*: 118–119.

Lebreton, J.-D. & P.M. North (eds). 1993. *Marked Individuals in the Study of Bird Populations.* Birkhäuser Verlag, Basel.

Lebreton, P. 1969. Sur le statut migratoire en France du Pigeon Ramier *Columba palumbus. L'Oiseau et la Revue Française d'Ornithologie* 39: 83–111.

Ledlie, R.C.B. & E.G. Pedlar. 1938. Nesting of the Little Ringed Plover in Hertfordshire. *British Birds* 32: 90–102.

Lee, D.S. 1995. The pelagic ecology of Manx Shearwaters *Puffinus puffinus* off the southeastern United States of America. *Marine Ornithology* 23: 107–119.

Lee, D.S. & S.W. Cardiff. 1993. Status of the Arctic Tern in the coastal and offshore waters of the southeastern United States. *Journal of Field Ornithology* 64: 158–163.

Lee, P.L.M., R.B. Bradbury, J.D. Wilson, N.S. Flanagan, L. Richardson, A.J. Perkins & J.R. Krebs. 2001. Microsatellite variation in the Yellowhammer *Emberiza citrinella*: population structure of a declining farmland bird. *Molecular Ecology* 10: 1633–1644.

Lehikoinen, E. & J. Hakala. 1988. Variation in weight of migratory Dippers *Cinclus cinclus* in their Finnish winter quarters. *Bird Study* 35: 101–108.

Lehman, P. 1988. A Eurasian Collared Dove at Cape May: first sighting in New Jersey. *New Jersey Audubon Society Records of New Jersey Birds* 24: 5–6.

Leibl, F. & P. Zach. 1992. Phänologie, Bestand und Brutbiologie des Schwarzhalstauchers in der Oberpfalz. *Die Vogelwelt* 113: 35–47.

Leinaas, H.P. & W.G. Ambrose. 1992. Utilization of different foraging habitats by the Purple Sandpiper *Calidris maritima* on a Spitsbergen beach. *Fauna Norvegica serie C, Cinclus* 15: 85–91.

Leisler, B., G. Heine & K.H. Siebenrock. 1983. Patterns of interspecific interactions among wintering Wheatears (*Oenanthe isabellina, Oenanthe oenanthe, Oenanthe pleschanka*) and resident chats in Kenya. *Journal für Ornithologie* 124: 393–413.

Lens, L. & A.A. Dhondt. 1992. The effect of a severe storm on a population of Crested Tits *Parus cristatus* in Belgium. *Bird Study* 39: 31–33.

Lens, L. & L.A. Wauters. 1996. Effects of population growth on Crested Tit *Parus cristatus* post-fledging settlement. *Ibis* 138: 545–551.

Lensink, R. 1997. Range expansion of raptors in Britain and the Nertherlands since the 1960s: testing an individual-based diffusion model. *Journal of Animal Ecology* 66: 811–826.

Lensink, R. 1999. Aspects of the biology of Egyptian Goose *Alopochen aegyptiacus* colonizing the Netherlands. *Bird Study* 46: 195–204.

Leonard, M.L., A.G. Horn & S.F. Eden. 1989. Does juvenile helping enhance breeder reproductive success? A removal experiment on moorhens. *Behavioural Ecology and Sociobiology* 25: 357–361.

Leopold, M.F., H.J.B. Baptist, P.A. Wolk & H.R. Offringa. 1995. De Zwarte Zeeëend *Melanitta nigra* in Nederland. *Limosa* 68: 49–64.

LeSchack, C.R. & G.R. Hepp. 1995. Kleptoparasitism of American Coots by Gadwalls and its relationship to social dominance and food abundance. *Auk* 112: 429–435.

LeSchack, C.R., S.K. McKnight & G.R. Hepp. 1997. Gadwall (*Anas strepera*). In *The Birds of North America* (eds A. Poole & F. Gill), no. 283. Academy of Natural Sciences, Philadelphia, and American Ornithologists' Union, Washington DC.

Leshem, Y. & Y. Yom-Tov. 1996. The use of thermals by soaring migrants. *Ibis* 138: 667–674.

Leshem, Y. & Y. Yom-Tov. 1998. Routes of migrating soaring birds. *Ibis* 140: 41–52.

Leslie, R. & C.M. Lessells. 1978. The migration of Dunlin *Calidris alpina* through northern Scandinavia. *Ornis Scandinavica* 9: 84–86.

Lessells, C.M. 1985. Natal and breeding dispersal of Canada Geese *Branta canadensis. Ibis* 127: 31–41.

Lever, C. 1977. *The naturalized animals of the British Isles.* Hutchinson, London.

Lever, C. 1987. *Naturalized Birds of the World.* Longman, London.

Lever, C. 1990. *The Mandarin Duck.* Shire, Princes Risborough.

Leverton, R. 1990. Passage Ring Ouzels in Sussex, 1962–1988. *Sussex Bird Report* 42: 87–92.

Leverton, R. 1993. Migrant Ring Ouzels at a stopover site on the South Downs. *British Birds* 86: 253–266.

Lewis, I. 1996. The Aquatic Warbler in Dorset. *Dorset Birds 1995*: 145–149.

Liechti, F., B. Bruderer & H. Paproth. 1995. Quantification of nocturnal bird migration by moonwatching – comparison with radar and infrared observations. *Journal of Field Ornithology* 66: 457–468.

Liley, D. 1999. *Predicting the population consequences of human disturbance and predation on Ringed Plovers.* PhD thesis, University of East Anglia.

Limbert, M. 1984. Vagrant races of Willow Tit in Britain. *British Birds* 77: 123.

Lind, H. 1957. A study of the movements of the Sheld-duck (L.). *Dansk Ornithologisk Forenings Tidsskrift* 51: 85–114.

Lindholm, A.K. 1999. Brood parasitism by the cuckoo on patchy reed warbler populations in Britain. *Journal of Animal Ecology* 68: 293–309.

Lindmeier, J.P. & R.L. Jessen. 1961. Results of capturing waterfowl in Minnesota by spotlighting. *Journal of Wildlife Management* 25: 430–431.

Lindström, Å. & J. Agrell. 1999. Global change and possible effects on the migration and reproduction of Arctic-breeding waders. *Ecological Bulletin* 47: 145–159.

Lindström, Å., S. Bensch & D. Hasselquist. 1985. Höstflyttningsstrategi hos unga blåhakar *Luscinia svecica.* [Autumn migration strategy of young Bluethroats.] *Vår Fågelvärld* 44: 197–206.

Lindström, Å., D.J. Pearson, D. Hasselquist, A. Hedenström, S. Bensch & S. Åkesson. 1993. The moult of Barred Warblers *Sylvia nisoria* in Kenya – evidence for a split wing-moult pattern initiated during the birds' first winter. *Ibis* 135: 403–409.

Lindström, Å., A. Hedenström & J. Pettersson. 1996. The autumn migration of Willow Warblers *Phylloscopus trochilus* in Sweden: results from a nation-wide co-operative project. *Ornis Svecica* 6: 145–172.

Little, B. & M. Davison. 1992. Merlins *Falco columbarius* using crow nests in Kielder Forest, Northumberland. *Bird Study* 39: 13–16.

Little, B. & R.W. Furness. 1985. Long-distance moult migration by British Goosanders *Mergus merganser. Ringing & Migration* 6: 77–82.

Litun, V.I. 1982. [Partridge (*Perdix daurica*).] In [*Migrations of Birds of Eastern Europe and Northern Asia: Falconiformes-Gruiformes*], (ed V.D. Ilyichev), pp 180–196. Nauka, Moscow. (In Russian.)

Lloyd, C. 1974. Movement and survival of British Razorbills. *Bird Study* 21: 102–116.

Lloyd, C. 1976. *The breeding biology and survival of the Razorbill* Alca torda *L.* DPhil thesis, University of Oxford.

Lloyd, C., M.L. Tasker & K. Partridge. 1991. *The Status of Seabirds in Britain and Ireland.* T. & A.D. Poyser, London.

Lock, L. & K. Cook. 1998. The Little Egret in Britain: a successful colonist. *British Birds* 91: 273–280.

Lockie, J.D. 1955. The breeding habits of Short-eared Owls after a vole plague. *Bird Study* 2: 53–69.

Lockley, R.M. 1942. *Shearwaters.* Dent, London.

Lockley, R.M. 1953. On the movements of the Manx Shearwater at sea during the breeding season. *British Birds* 46 (suppl.): 1–48.

Logie, J.W., D.M. Bryant, D.L. Howell & J.A. Vickery. 1996. Biological significance of UK critical loads estimates for flowing waters: assessments of dipper *Cinclus cinclus* populations in Scotland. *Journal of Applied Ecology* 33: 1065–1076.

Loman, J. 1985. Social organisation in a population of the Hooded Crow. *Ardea* 73: 61–75.

Long, R. & M. Long. 1982. Recurrence of warblers in winter. *Ringing & Migration* 4: 24.

Loske, K.-H. 1990. Spring weights and fat deposition of Palaearctic passerine migrants in Senegal. *Ringing & Migration* 11: 23–30.

Love, J.A. 1978. Leach's and Storm Petrels on North Rona: 1971–1974. *Ringing & Migration* 4: 249–253.

Lövei, G.L. 1998. Passerine migration between the Palaearctic and Africa. *Current Ornithology* 6: 143–174.

Lowery, G.H. Jr. 1951. A quantitative study of the nocturnal migration of birds. *University of Kansas Publications, Museum of Natural History* 3: 361–472.

Loxton, R.G. & P. Hope Jones. 1994. The breeding birds of Bardsey, Skomer, Skokholm and the Calf of Man. *Bardsey Observatory Report* 38: 84–159.

Loxton, R.G., T. Kittle & P. Hope Jones. 1999. *Atlas of recoveries of birds ringed by Bardsey Observatory*. Bardsey Bird and Field Observatory, Bethesda, Gwynedd.

Lozano, G.A., S. Perreault & R.E. Lemon. 1996. Age, arrival date and reproductive success of male American Redstarts *Setophaga ruticilla. Journal of Avian Biology* 27: 164–170.

Luigujoe, L., A. Kuresoo, J. Kespaik, A. Ader & A. Leito. 1996. Migration and staging of Bewick's Swan (*Cygnus columbianus bewickii*) in Estonia. In *Proceedings of the Anatidae 2000 Conference, Strasbourg, France, 5–9 December 1994* (eds M. Birkan, J. van Vessem, P. Havet, J. Madsen, B. Trolliet & M. Moser). *Gibier Faune Sauvage* 13: 451–461.

Lundberg, A. & R.V. Alatalo. 1992. *The Pied Flycatcher*. T. & A.D. Poyser, London.

Lundberg, P. 1988. The evolution of partial migration in birds. *Trends in Ecology & Evolution* 3: 172–175.

Lyster, I.H.J. 1971. Waxwings in Scotland, 1970/71. *Scottish Birds* 6: 420–438.

Lyver, P.O'B., H. Moller & C. Thompson. 1999. Changes in Sooty Shearwater *Puffinus griseus* chick production and harvest precede ENSO events. *Marine Ecology Progress Series* 188: 237–248.

Macdonald, M.A. 1977. An analysis of the recoveries of British-ringed Fulmars. *Bird Study* 24: 208–214.

Macdonald, R.A. & J. Whelan. 1986. Seasonal variations in feeding range and flock structure of the Rook *Corvus frugilegus* in eastern Ireland. *Ibis* 128: 540–557.

Mackay, I.R.K. & R.M. Sellers. 1989. Male-biassed sex ratio in Pied Wagtails wintering in Highland Region. *Scottish Birds* 15: 136–137.

Mackenzie, J.M.D. 1956. Tree-creepers using nest-boxes and other artificial nest-sites. *Scottish Naturalist* 68: 84–91.

MacKinnon, G.E. & J.C. Coulson. 1987. The temporal and geographical distribution of Continental Black-headed Gulls *Larus ridibundus* in the British Isles. *Bird Study* 34: 1–9.

Mackrill, E.J. 1988. First record of 'Balearic Shearwater' for the southern hemisphere. *British Birds* 81: 322.

Madge, S. & H. Burn. 1988. *Wildfowl: an identification guide to the Ducks, Geese and Swans of the world*. Christopher Helm, London.

Madge, S. & H. Burn. 1994. *Crows and Jays*. Christopher Helm, London.

Madsen, J. 1991. Status and trends of goose populations in the western palearctic in the 1980s. *Ardea* 79: 113–122.

Madsen, J. 1998. Experimental refuges for migratory waterfowl in Danish Wetlands. II. Tests of hunting disturbance effects. *Journal of Applied Ecology* 35: 398–417.

Madsen, J., G. Cracknell & A.D. Fox (eds). 1999. *Goose populations of the Western Palearctic: a review of status and distribution*. Wetlands International Publication 48. Wetlands International, Wageningen, the Netherlands, and National Environmental Research Institute, Rönde, Denmark.

Maguire, E. 1985. Tape-luring Meadow Pipits. *Ringers' Bulletin* 6: 84.

Main, I.G. 1996. Seasonal movements of British Greenfinches *Carduelis chloris. Bird Study* 43: 240–252.

Main, I.G. 1999. Overseas movements to and from Britain by Greenfinches *Carduelis chloris. Ringing & Migration* 19: 191–199.

Main, I.G. 2000a. The partial migration of Fennoscandian Greenfinches *Carduelis chloris. Ringing & Migration* 20: 167–180.

Main, I.G. 2000b. Obligate and facultative partial migration in the Blackbird (*Turdus merula*) and the Greenfinch (*Carduelis chloris*): uses and limitations of ringing data. *Die Vogelwarte* 40: 286–291.

Mainwood, A.R. 1976. The movements of Storm Petrels as shown by ringing. *Ringing & Migration* 1: 98–104.

Malecki, R.A., A.D. Fox & B.D.J. Batt. 2000. An aerial survey of nesting Greater White-fronted and Canada Geese in west Greenland. *Wildfowl* 51: 49–58.

Maltby-Prevett, L., H. Boyd & J.D. Heyland. 1975. Observations in Iceland and Northwest Europe of Brant from the Queen Elizabeth Islands, N.W.T., Canada. *Bird Banding* 46: 155–161.

Manly, B.F.J. 1986. *Multivariate statistical methods: a primer*. Chapman & Hall, London.

Marchant, J.H. 1982. Waders. In *Wildfowl and Wader counts 1981–82* (ed D.G. Salmon), pp 31–48. Wildfowl Trust, Slimbridge.

Marchant, J. 2002. Global warming and autumn migration – the observatory connection. *BTO News* 238: 14–15.

Marchant, J.H. & R.D. Gregory. 1999. Numbers of nesting Rooks *Corvus frugilegus* in the United Kingdom in 1996. *Bird Study* 46: 258–273.

Marchant, J.H., R. Hudson, S.P. Carter & P.A. Whittington. 1990. *Population trends in British breeding birds*. British Trust for Ornithology and Nature Conservancy Council, Tring.

Marchant, J., J. Clark & K. Wright. 2000. Redpolls and other splits. *Ringers' Bulletin* 10: 52.

Marchant, S. 1969. Turtle Dove migration in Iberia and the Middle East. *British Birds* 62: 84.

Marchant, S. & P.J. Higgins. 1991. *The Handbook of Australian, New Zealand and Antarctic Birds*. Volume 1. Oxford University Press, Melbourne.

Marcström, V. & R.E. Kenward. 1981. Movements of wintering Goshawks in Sweden. *Viltrevy* 12: 1–35.

Marion, L. 1989. Territorial feeding and colonial breeding are not mutually exclusive: the case of the Grey Heron (*Ardea cinerea*). *Journal of Animal Ecology* 58: 693–710.

Marks, J.S. 1985. Yearling male long-eared owls breed near natal nest. *Journal of Field Ornithology* 56: 181–182.

Marks, J.S., D.L. Evans & D.W. Holt. 1994. Long-eared Owl (*Asio otus*). In *The Birds of North America* (eds A. Poole & F. Gill), no. 133. Academy of Natural Sciences, Philadelphia, and American Ornithologists' Union, Washington DC.

Marler, P. 1956. Behaviour of the Chaffinch *Fringilla coelebs. Behaviour*, suppl. 5: 1–184.

Marquiss, M. 1980. Habitat and diet of male and female Hen Harriers in Scotland in winter. *British Birds* 73: 555–560.

Marquiss, M. 1981. The Goshawk in Britain – its provenance and current status. In *Understanding the Goshawk* (eds R.E. Kenward & I.M. Lindsay), pp 43–57. International Association for Falconry and Conservation of Birds of Prey, Oxford.

Marquiss, M. 1989. Grey Herons *Ardea cinerea* breeding in Scotland: numbers, distribution and census techniques. *Bird Study* 36: 181–191.

Marquiss, M. 1993. *Herons*. Colin Baxter Photography, Grantown-on-Spey.

Marquiss, M. & K. Duncan. 1993. Variation in the abundance of Red-breasted Mergansers *Mergus serrator* on a Scottish river in relation to season, year, river hydrography, salmon density and spring culling. *Ibis* 135: 33–41.

Marquiss, M. & K. Duncan. 1994a. Seasonal switching between habitats and changes in abundance of Goosanders *Mergus merganser* within a Scottish river system. *Wildfowl* 45: 198–208.

Marquiss, M. & K. Duncan. 1994b. Diurnal activity patterns of Goosanders *Mergus merganser* on a Scottish river system. *Wildfowl* 45: 209–221.

Marquiss, M. & I. Newton. 1982a. A radio-tracking study of the ranging behaviour and dispersion of European Sparrowhawks *Accipiter nisus*. *Journal of Animal Ecology* 51: 111–133.

Marquiss, M. & I. Newton. 1982b. The Goshawk in Britain. *British Birds* 75: 243–260.

Marquiss, M. & R. Rae. 1994. Seasonal trends in abundance, diet and breeding of Common Crossbills (*Loxia curvirostra*) in an area of mixed species conifer plantation following the 1990 crossbill 'irruption'. *Forestry* 67: 31–47.

Marquiss, M. & R. Rae. 1996. Movements of colour-ringed crossbills *Loxia* spp. *Grampian Ringing Group Report* 8: 35–38.

Marquiss, M. & R. Rae. 2002. Ecological differentiation in relation to bill size amongst sympatric, genetically undifferentiated crossbills *Loxia* spp. *Ibis* 144: 494–508.

Marquiss, M., I. Newton & D.A. Ratcliffe. 1978. The decline of the Raven, *Corvus corax* in relation to afforestation in southern Scotland and northern England. *Journal of Applied Ecology* 15: 129–144.

Marquiss, M., M. Nicoll & K. Brockie. 1983. Scottish Herons and the 1981/2 cold winter. *BTO News* 125: 4–5.

Marsden, S.J. & M.S. Sullivan. 2000. Intersexual differences in feeding ecology in a male-dominated wintering Pochard *Aythya ferina* population. *Ardea* 88: 1–7.

Marti, C. & H.R. Pauli. 1985. Wintergewicht, Masse und Alterbestimmung in einer alpinen Population des Birkhuhns, *Tetrao tetrix*. *Der Ornithologische Beobachter* 82: 153–168.

Marti, C.D. 1999. Natal and breeding dispersal in Barn Owls. *Journal of Raptor Research* 33: 181–189.

Martin, A.J. 1997. Site fidelity in wintering Siskins. *Stour Ringing Group Annual Report* 1996: 32–35.

Martin, G.R. & G. Katzir. 1994. Visual fields in the Stone-curlew *Burhinus oedicnemus*. *Ibis* 136: 448–453.

Martín, J.A. & A. Pérez. 1990. Movimientos del Martín Pescador (*Alcedo atthis*, L.) en España. *Ardeola* 37: 13–18.

Martínez, J.A. & G. López. 1995. Dispersal and causes of mortality of the Barn Owl (*Tyto alba*) in Spain. *Ardeola* 42: 29–37.

Mason, C.F. 1976. Breeding biology of the *Sylvia* warblers. *Bird Study* 23: 213–232.

Mason, C.F. 1995. Long-term trends in the arrival dates of spring migrants. *Bird Study* 42: 182–189.

Mason, C.F. 1997. Association between Willow Warbler *Phylloscopus trochilus* territories and birch in woodlands in southeastern England. *Ibis* 139: 411–412.

Mason, C.F. & F. Lyczynski. 1980. Breeding biology of the Pied and Yellow Wagtails. *Bird Study* 27: 1–10.

Mason, C.F. & S.M. Macdonald. 1988. Pollutant burden of a Great Northern Diver *Gavia immer*. *Bird Study* 35: 11–12.

Mather, J.R. 1969. The influx of northern Great Spotted Woodpeckers *Dendrocopos major major* at Spurn, Yorkshire, autumn 1968. *Spurn Bird Observatory Report 1968*: 52–56.

Mather, J.R. 1986. *The Birds of Yorkshire*. Croom Helm, London.

Mathiasson, S. 1991. Eurasian Whooper Swan *Cygnus cygnus* migration, with particular reference to birds wintering in southern Sweden. In *Proceedings of the Third IWRB International Swan Symposium, Oxford 1989* (eds J. Sears & P.J. Bacon), pp 201–208. *Wildfowl* suppl. 1.

Matthews, G.V.T. 1963. 'Nonsense' orientation as a population variant. *Ibis* 105: 185–197.

Matthysen, E. 1998. *The Nuthatches*. T. & A.D. Poyser, London.

Matthysen, E. 1999. Nuthatches (*Sitta europaea*: Aves) in forest fragments: demography of a patchy population. *Oecologia* 119: 501–509.

Matthysen, E. & F. Adriaensen. 1989. Directional dispersal by juveniles in a resident population of Nuthatches *Sitta europaea*. *Ringing & Migration* 10: 119–123.

Matthysen, E. & F. Adriaensen. 1998. Forest size and isolation have no effect on reproductive success of Eurasian Nuthatches (*Sitta europaea*). *Auk* 115: 955–963.

Matthysen, E. & D. Currie. 1996. Habitat fragmentation reduces disperser success in juvenile Nuthatches *Sitta europaea*: evidence from patterns of territory establishment. *Ecography* 19: 67–72.

Matthysen, E. & K.-H. Schmidt. 1987. Natal dispersal in the Nuthatch. *Ornis Scandinavica* 18: 313–316.

Matthysen, E., F. Adriaensen & A.A. Dhondt. 1995. Dispersal distances of Nuthatches, *Sitta europaea*, in a highly fragmented forest habitat. *Oikos* 72: 375–381.

May, C.A., J.H. Wetton, P.E. Davis, J.F.Y. Brookfield & D.T. Parkin. 1993. Single locus profiling reveals loss of variation in inbred populations of the Red Kite (*Milvus milvus*). *Proceedings of the Royal Society of London, Series B* 251: 165–170.

May, R. & J. Fisher. 1953. A Collared Turtle Dove in England. *British Birds* 46: 51–55.

Mayaud, N. 1954. Sur les migrations et l'hivernage de *Larus melanocephalus* Temminck. *Alauda* 22: 225–245.

Mayes, E. 1991. The winter ecology of Greenland White-fronted Geese *Anser albifrons flavirostris* on semi-natural grassland and intensive farmland. *Ardea* 79: 295–304.

Mayol, J. 1986. Human impact on seabirds in the Balearic Islands. In *Mediterranean Marine Avifauna: Population Studies and Conservation* (eds MEDMARAVIS & X. Monbailliu), pp 379–396. Springer-Verlag, Berlin.

McCallum, J. 1998. Observations of four North Norfolk birds. *Norfolk Bird Club Bulletin* 29: 10–13.

McCarthy, J.J., O.F. Canziani, N.A. Leary, D.J. Dokken & K.S. White (eds). 2001. *Climate Change 2001: impacts, adaption, and vulnerability*. Intergovernmental Panel on Climate Change/Cambridge University Press, Cambridge.

McCartney, P. 1986. Mediterranean races of Manx Shearwater in British waters. *British Birds* 79: 351–352.

McCleery, R.H. & J. Clobert. 1990. Differences in recruitment of young by resident and immigrant Great Tits in Wytham Wood. In *Population Biology of Passerine Birds, an integrated approach* (eds J. Blondel, A. Gosler, J.-D. Lebreton & R.H. McCleery), pp 423–440. NATO ASI Series. Springer Verlag, Berlin.

McCleery, R.H. & C.M. Perrins. 1991. The effects of predation on the numbers of Great Tits *Parus major*. In *Bird population studies: relevance to conservation and management* (eds C.M. Perrins, J.-D. Lebreton & G.J.M. Hirons), pp 129–147. Oxford University Press, Oxford.

McCulloch, M.N., G.M. Tucker & S.R. Baillie. 1992. The hunting of migratory birds in Europe: a ringing recovery analysis. *Ibis* 134 (suppl. 1): 55–65.

McElwaine, J.G., J.H. Wells & J.M. Bowler. 1995. Winter movements of Whooper Swans visiting Ireland: preliminary results. *Irish Birds* 5: 265–278.

McGrady, M.J., D.C. Orr-Ewing & T.J. Stowe. 1994. The re-introduction of the Red Kite *Milvus milvus* into Scotland. In *Raptor Conservation Today* (eds B.-U. Meyburg & R.D. Chancellor), pp 471–477. World Working Group on Birds of Prey and Owls/Pica Press, Berlin.

McGregor, P.K., J. Holland & M. Shepherd. 1997. The ecology of corn bunting *Miliaria calandra* song dialects and their potential use in conservation. In *The ecology and conservation of Corn Buntings Miliaria calandra* (eds P.F. Donald & N.J. Aebischer), pp 76–87. UK Nature Conservation no. 13. Joint Nature Conservation Committee, Peterborough.

McKelvie, C.L. 1990. *The Book of the Woodcock*. Swan Hill Press, Shrewsbury.

McKilligan, N.G. 1980. The winter exodus of the Rook from a Scottish Highland valley. *Bird Study* 27: 93–100.

McMinn, S. 1983. Cranes in Kent in October 1982. *British Birds* 76: 451–452.

McMinn, S. 1987. Cranes in 1963, 1982 and 1985. *British Birds* 80: 383.

McRae, S.B. 1997. Brood parasitism in the Moorhen: brief encounters between parasites and hosts and the significance of an evening laying hour. *Journal of Avian Biology* 27: 311–320.

Mead, C.J. 1970. The winter quarters of British Swallows. *Bird Study* 17: 229–240.

Mead, C.J. 1972. A change in the winter quarters of British Swallows (*Hirundo rustica*). In *Proceedings of the Fifteenth International Ornithological Congress* (ed K.H. Voous), pp 667–668. E.J. Brill, Leiden, the Netherlands.

Mead, C.J. 1973. Movements of British raptors. *Bird Study* 20: 259–286.

Mead, C.J. 1974a. The results of ringing auks in Britain and Ireland. *Bird Study* 21: 45–86.

Mead, C.J. 1974b. *Bird Ringing*. BTO Guide 16. British Trust for Ornithology, Tring.

Mead, C.J. 1978. Tern mortality in West Africa as shown by British and Dutch ringing results. *Ibis* 120: 110.

Mead, C.J. 1979a. Mortality and causes of death in British Sand Martins. *Bird Study* 26: 107–112.

Mead, C.J. 1979b. Colony fidelity and interchange in the Sand Martin. *Bird Study* 26: 99–106.

Mead, C.J. 1983. *Bird Migration*. Country Life Books, Feltham.

Mead, C.J. 1984. *Robins*. Whittet Books, London.

Mead, C.J. 1989. Seabird news around the world. Auk netfax. *BTO News* 163: 8.

Mead, C.J. 1993. Peregrine ringing returns affecting Britain and Ireland. In *The Peregrine Falcon* (D.A. Ratcliffe), second edition, pp 259–266. T. & A.D. Poyser, London.

Mead, C. 2000. *The State of the Nations' Birds*. Whittet Books, Suffolk.

Mead, C.J. & J.A. Clark. 1987. Report on bird-ringing in Britain and Ireland for 1986. *Ringing & Migration* 8: 135–200.

Mead, C.J. & J.A. Clark. 1988. Report on bird ringing in Britain and Ireland for 1987. *Ringing & Migration* 9: 169–204.

Mead, C.J. & J.A. Clark. 1989. Report on bird ringing in Britain and Ireland for 1988. *Ringing & Migration* 10: 158–196.

Mead, C.J. & J.A. Clark. 1991. Report on bird ringing in Britain and Ireland for 1990. *Ringing & Migration* 12: 139–175.

Mead, C.J. & J.A. Clark. 1993. Report on bird ringing in Britain and Ireland for 1992. *Ringing & Migration* 14: 152–200.

Mead, C.J. & J.D. Harrison. 1979a. Sand Martin movements within Britain and Ireland. *Bird Study* 26: 73–86.

Mead, C.J. & J.D. Harrison. 1979b. Overseas movements of British and Irish Sand Martins. *Bird Study* 26: 87–98.

Mead, C.J. & R. Hudson. 1984. Report on bird-ringing for 1983. *Ringing & Migration* 5: 153–192.

Mead, C.J. & B.R. Watmough. 1976. Suspended moult of trans-Saharan migrants in Iberia. *Bird Study* 23: 187–196.

Mead, C.J., J.J.M. Flegg & C.J. Cox. 1968. A factor inhibiting subspecific differentiation in the Lapwing. *Bird Study* 15: 105–106.

Mead, C.J., J.A. Clark & W.J. Peach. 1993. Report on bird ringing in Britain and Ireland for 1992. *Ringing & Migration* 14: 152–200.

Mead, C.J., J.A. Clark & W.J. Peach. 1995. Report on bird ringing in Britain and Ireland for 1993. *Ringing & Migration* 16: 16–64.

Mearns, R. 1982. Winter occupation of breeding territories and winter diet of Peregrines in south Scotland. *Ornis Scandinavica* 13: 79–83.

Mearns, R. & I. Newton. 1984. Turnover and dispersal in a Peregrine *Falco peregrinus* population. *Ibis* 126: 347–355.

Mebs, T. 1964. Über Wanderungen und bestandsgestaltende Faktoren beim Mäusebussard (*Buteo buteo*) nach deutschen Ringfunden. *Die Vogelwarte* 22: 180–194.

Meek, E.R. & B. Little. 1977a. The spread of the Goosander in Britain and Ireland. *British Birds* 70: 229–237.

Meek, E.R. & B. Little. 1977b. Ringing studies of Goosanders in Northumberland. *British Birds* 70: 273–283.

Meek, E.R., R.G. Adam & J. Hadasch. 1998a. Marsh Warblers breeding in Orkney in 1993: a first for Scotland. *Scottish Birds* 19: 170–171.

Meek, E.R., G.W. Rebecca, B. Ribbands & K. Fairclough. 1998b. Orkney Hen Harriers: a major population decline in the absence of persecution. *Scottish Birds* 19: 290–298.

Mehlum, F. 1983. Weight changes in migrating Robins *Erithacus rubecula* during stop-over at the island of Store Færder, Outer Oslofjord, Norway. *Fauna Norvegica serie C, Cinclus* 6: 57–61.

Mehlum, F. 1998. Areas in Svalbard important for geese during the pre-breeding, breeding and post-breeding periods. *Norsk Polarinstitutt Skrifter* 200: 41–55.

Meininger, P.L. & J.F. Bekhuis. 1990. De Zwartkopmeeuw *Larus melanocephalus* als broedvogel in Nederland en Europa. *Limosa* 63: 121–134.

Meininger, P.L. & U.G. Sørensen. 1986. The occurrence of skuas (Stercoraridae) in the Middle East, with special reference to Egypt and the northern Red Sea. *Die Vogelwarte* 33: 281–294.

Meininger, P.L. & U.G. Sørensen. 1993. Egypt as a major wintering area of Little Gulls. *British Birds* 86: 407–410.

Meissner, W. 1996. Timing and phenology of autumn migration of Common Sandpiper (*Actitis hypoleucos*) at the Gulf of Gdansk. *The Ring* 18: 59–72.

Meissner, W. 1997. Autumn migration and biometrics of the Common Sandpiper *Actitis hypoleucos* caught in the Gulf of Gdansk. *Ornis Fennica* 74: 131–139.

Meltofte, H. 1985. Populations and breeding schedules of waders, Charadrii, in high arctic Greenland. *Meddelelser om Grønland, Bioscience* 16: 1–43.

Meltofte, H. 1996a. Are African wintering waders really forced south by competition from northerly wintering conspecifics? Benefits and constraints of northern versus southern wintering and breeding in waders. *Ardea* 84: 31–44.

Meltofte, H. 1996b. Koncentrationer uden for yngletiden af Toppet Lappedykker *Podiceps cristatus* i Danmark. *Dansk Ornitologisk Forenings Tidsskrift* 90: 99–108.

Meltofte, H., J. Blew, J. Frikke, H.-U. Rösner & C.J. Smit. 1994. *Numbers and distribution of waterbirds in the Wadden Sea. Results and evaluation of 36 simultaneous counts in the Dutch-German-Danish Wadden Sea 1980–1991*. IWRB Publication 34/Wader Study Group Bulletin 74, special issue.

Melville, D.S. 1985. Long-tailed Skuas *Stercorarius longicaudus* in New Zealand. *Notornis* 32: 51–73.

Mendall, H.L. 1958. *The Ring-necked Duck in the North-east*. University of Maine Bulletin 60 (16). 317 pp.

Mendelssohn, H., U. Marder & Y. Yom-Tov. 1969. On the decline of migrant Quail (*Coturnix c. coturnix*) populations in Israel and Sinai. *Israel Journal of Zoology* 18: 317–323.

Mendelssohn, R. & P. Cury. 1987. Fluctuations of a fortnightly abundance index of the Ivorian coastal pelagic species and associated environmental conditions. *Canadian Journal of Fisheries and Aquatic Sciences* 44: 408–421.

Merne, O.J., D. Boertmann, H. Boyd, C. Mitchell, M. Ó Briain, A. Reed & A. Sigfusson. 1999. Light-bellied Brent Goose *Branta bernicla hrota*: Canada. In *Goose populations of the Western Palaearctic: a review of status and distribution* (eds J. Madsen, G. Cracknell & A.D. Fox), pp 312–327. Wetlands International Publication 48. Wetlands International, Wageningen, the Netherlands, and National Environmental Research Institute, Rönde, Denmark.

Messenger, D. 1993. Spring passage of Little Gulls across Northern England. *British Birds* 86: 397–406.

Messineo, A., A. Grattarola & F. Spina. 2001. Dieci anni di Progetto Piccole Isole. [Ten years of Mediterranean Islands Project.] *Biologia e Conservazione della Fauna* 106: 1–240.

Metcalfe, N.B. 1986. Variations in winter flocking associations and dispersion patterns in the Turnstone *Arenaria interpres. Journal of Zoology (London)* 209: 385–403.

Metcalfe, N.B. & R.W. Furness. 1984. Changing priorities: the effect of pre-migratory fattening on the trade-off between foraging and vigilance. *Behavioral Ecology & Sociobiology* 15: 203–206.

Metcalfe, N.B. & R.W. Furness. 1985. Survival, winter population stability and site fidelity in the Turnstone *Arenaria interpres. Bird Study* 32: 207–214.

Metcalfe, W.G. 1966. Observations of migrating Greater Shearwaters *Puffinus gravis* off the Brazilian coast. *Ibis* 108: 138–140.

Meyburg, B.-U., W. Scheller & C. Meyburg. 1995. Migration and wintering of the Lesser Spotted Eagle (*Aquila pomarina*) – a study by means of satellite telemetry. *Journal für Ornithologie* 136: 401–422.

Meyer, R.M. 1990. Observations on two Red-billed Choughs *Pyrrhocorax pyrrhocorax* in Cornwall: habitat use and food intake. *Bird Study* 37: 199–209.

Meyer, R. 2000. The return of the Red-billed Chough to England. *British Birds* 93: 249–252.

Mikkola, H. 1983. *Owls of Europe.* T. & A.D. Poyser, Calton.

Mikkola, K., E. Haapanen & F. Hosseinie. 1990. A continental rendezvous of the Red-necked Phalarope *Phalaropus lobatus* in Iran. *Ornis Fennica* 67: 141–142.

Millington, R. 1993. Identification and status of Kumlien's Gull. *Birding World* 6: 101–106.

Millsap, B.A. & S.L. Vana. 1984. Distribution of wintering Golden Eagles in the eastern United States. *Wilson Bulletin* 96: 692–701.

Milne, H. & F.W. Robertson. 1965. Polymorphisms in egg albumen protein and behaviour in the Eider duck. *Nature, London* 205: 367–369.

Milne, P. & O. O'Sullivan. 1997. Forty-fourth Irish Bird Report, 1996. *Irish Birds* 6: 61–90.

Milton, F. 1996. Storm Petrel ringing on the North Durham coast. *Birds in Durham 1994*: 94–99.

Milwright, R.D.P. 1984. Timing and duration of migratory waves of Redwings and Fieldfares in fenland orchards. *Wicken Fen Group Report* 12: 15–18.

Milwright, R.D.P. 1994. Fieldfare *Turdus pilaris* ringing recoveries during autumn, winter and spring, analysed in relation to river basins and watersheds in Europe and the Near East. *Ringing & Migration* 15: 129–189.

Milwright, R.D.P. 1998. Breeding biology of the Golden Oriole *Oriolus oriolus* in the fenland basin of eastern Britain. *Bird Study* 45: 320–330.

Milwright, R.D.P. 2002. Redwing *Turdus iliacus* migration and wintering areas as shown by recoveries of birds ringed in the breeding season in Fennoscandia, Poland, the Baltic Republics, Russia, Siberia and Iceland. *Ringing & Migration* 21: 5–15.

Minami, H. & H. Ogi. 1997. Determination of migratory dynamics of the Sooty Shearwater in the Pacific using stable carbon and nitrogen isotope analysis. *Marine Ecology Progress Series* 158: 249–256.

Minami, H., M. Minagawa & H. Ogi. 1995. Changes in stable carbon and nitrogen isotope ratios in Sooty and Short-tailed Shearwaters during their northward migration. *Condor* 97: 565–574.

Mineyev, Yu.N. 1991. Distribution and numbers of Bewick's Swans *Cygnus bewickii* in the European northeast of the USSR. In *Proceedings of the Third IWRB International Swan Symposium, Oxford 1989* (eds J. Sears & P.J. Bacon), pp 62–67. *Wildfowl* suppl. 1.

Ming, M. 1994. Decline of the Golden Pheasant in China. *World Pheasant Association News* 43: 41.

Minton, C.D.T. 1971. Mute Swan flocks. *Wildfowl* 22: 71–88.

Mitchell, C. 1997. Annual productivity in Eurasian Wigeon. *Duck Specialist Group Bulletin* 1: 7–9.

Mitchell, C. 1999. Greylag Goose *Anser anser*: Scotland. In *Goose populations of the Western Palearctic: a review of status and distribution* (eds J. Madsen, G. Cracknell & A.D. Fox), pp 172–177. Wetlands International Publication 48. Wetlands International, Wageningen, the Netherlands, and National Environmental Research Institute, Rönde, Denmark.

Mitchell, C.R. & M.A. Ogilvie. 1996. Fifty years of wildfowl ringing by the Wildfowl & Wetlands Trust. *Wildfowl* 47: 240–247.

Mitchell, C. & A. Sigfusson. 1999. Greylag Goose *Anser anser*: Iceland. In *Goose populations of the Western Palearctic: a review of status and distribution* (eds J. Madsen, G. Cracknell & A.D. Fox), pp 162–171. Wetlands International Publication 48. Wetlands International, Wageningen, the Netherlands, and National Environmental Research Institute, Rönde, Denmark.

Mitchell, C., R.L. Cromie & M. Brown. 1990. *Mallard as vectors of disease.* Report 162. Nature Conservancy Council, Peterborough.

Mitchell, C., M. Owen & B. Etheridge. 1995. *Within winter movements, winter site fidelity and age ratios of Wigeon in Britain and Ireland.* Report to JNCC. Wildfowl & Wetlands Trust, Slimbridge.

Mitchell, C., A.D. Fox, H. Boyd, A. Sigfusson & D. Boertmann. 1999. Pink-footed Goose *Anser brachyrhynchus*: Iceland/Greenland. In *Goose populations of the Western Palearctic: a review of status and distribution* (eds J. Madsen, G. Cracknell & A.D. Fox), pp 68–81. Wetlands International Publication 48. Wetlands International, Wageningen, the Netherlands, and National Environmental Research Institute, Rönde, Denmark.

Mitchell, J. 1970. Lesser Spotted Woodpeckers in Scotland. *Scottish Birds* 6: 210–212.

Miyabayashi, Y.Y. & T. Mundkur. 1999. *Atlas of key sites for Anatidae in the East Asian Flyway.* Wetlands International (Japan), Tokyo and Wetlands International (Asia Pacific), Kuala Lumpur.

Mjelstad, H. & M. Sætersdal. 1986. Density, population size and breeding distribution of Spotted Redshank *Tringa erythropus*, Bar-tailed Godwit *Limosa lapponica* and Jack Snipe *Lymnocryptes minimus* in Norway. *Fauna Norvegica serie C, Cinclus* 9: 13–16.

Möckel, R. 1992. Auswirkungen des 'Waldsterbens' auf die Populationsdynamik von Tannen- und Haubenmeise (*Parus ater, P. cristatus*) im Westerzgebirge. *Ökologie der Vögel* 14: 1–100.

Moen, S.M. 1991. Morphologic and genetic variation among breeding colonies of the Atlantic Puffin (*Fratercula arctica*). *Auk* 108: 755–763.

Mohr, R. 1967. Zum Vorkommen von *Acanthis flammea cabaret* im Rhein-Main-Nahe-Gebiet. *Journal für Ornithologie* 108: 484–490.

Møller, A.P. 1976. Turtelduens *Streptopelia turtur* forekomst i Danmark. *Dansk Ornithologisk Forenings Tidsskrift* 70: 99–102.

Møller, A.P. 1981a. Migration of European Sandwich Tern, *Sterna s. sandvicensis.* I. *Die Vogelwarte* 31: 74–94.

Møller, A.P. 1981b. Migration of European Sandwich Tern, *Sterna s. sandvicensis.* II. *Die Vogelwarte* 31: 149–168.

Møller, A.P. 1985. Communal roosting in the Magpie (*Pica pica*). *Journal für Ornithologie* 126: 405–419.

Møller, A.P. 1994. Phenotype-dependent arrival time and its consequences in a migratory bird. *Behavioral Ecology and Sociobiology* 35: 115–122.

Monaghan, P. & J.C. Coulson. 1977. The status of large gulls nesting on buildings. *Bird Study* 24: 89–104.

Monteiro, L.R., J.A. Ramos, R.W. Furness & A.J. del Nevo. 1996. Movements, morphology, breeding, molt, diet and feeding of seabirds in the Azores. *Colonial Waterbirds* 19: 82–97.

Monteiro, L.R., J.A. Ramos, J.C. Pereira, P.R. Monteiro, R.S. Feio, D.R. Thompson, S. Bearhop, R.W. Furness, M. Laranjo, G. Hilton, V.C. Neves, M.P. Groz & K.R. Thompson. 1999. Status and distribution of Fea's Petrel, Bulwer's Petrel, Manx Shearwater, Little Shearwater and Band-rumped Storm-petrel in the Azores Archipelago. *Waterbirds* 22: 358–366.

Montevecchi, W.A. & L.M. Tuck. 1987. *Newfoundland Birds: exploitation, study, conservation.* Publication 21 of the Nuttall Ornithological Club. Cambridge, Massachussetts.

Monval, J.-Y. & J.-Y. Pirot. 1989. *Results of the IWRB International Waterfowl Census, 1967–86.* Special Publication 8. International Waterfowl & Wetlands Research Bureau, Slimbridge.

Mooij, J.H. 1993. Development and management of wintering geese in the Lower Rhine area of North Rhine-Westphalia/Germany. *Die Vogelwarte* 37: 55–77.

Mooij, J.H. & I.O. Kostin. 1997. Bestände der Saat- und Bläßgans in Deutschland und der westlichen Paläarktis. *Beiträge zur Jagd- und Wildforschung* 22: 23–41.

Mooij, J.H., B.S. Ebbinge, I.O. Kostin, J. Burgers & B. Spaans. 1996. Panmixia in White-fronted Geese (*Anser a. albifrons*) of the western Palearctic. In *Ecology of geese wintering at the Lower Rhine area (Germany)* (ed J.H. Mooij), pp 107–130. Biologische Station im Kreis Wesel, Wesel, Germany.

Mooij, J.H., S. Faragó & J.S. Kirby. 1999. White-fronted Goose *Anser albifrons albifrons.* In *Goose populations of the Western Palearctic: a review of status and distribution* (eds J. Madsen, G. Cracknell & A.D. Fox), pp 94–128. Wetlands International Publication 48. Wetlands International, Wageningen, the Netherlands, and National Environmental Research Institute, Rönde, Denmark.

Moon, S.J. 1983. The eventual identification of a Royal Tern in Mid Glamorgan. *British Birds* 76: 335–339.

Moorcroft, D. & J.D. Wilson. 2000. The ecology of Linnets *Carduelis cannabina* on lowland farmland. In *Ecology and conservation of lowland farmland birds* (eds N.J. Aebischer, A.D. Evans, P.V. Grice & J.A. Vickery), pp 173–181. British Ornithologists' Union, Tring.

Moorcroft, D., R.B. Bradbury & J.D. Wilson. 1997. The diet of nestling Linnets *Carduelis cannabina* before and after agricultural intensification. In *The 1997 Brighton Crop Protection Conference – Weeds,* pp 923–928. British Crop Protection Council, Farnham.

Moore, C.C. & L.J. Lenehan. 1976. Carrion Crows in the Meath/Louth area. *Louth Bird Report* 1975: 3–6.

Moore, R. 1969. *The Birds of Devon.* David & Charles, Newton Abbot.

Morant, P.D., R.K. Brooke & R.W. Abrams. 1983. Recoveries in Southern Africa of seabirds breeding elsewhere. *Ringing & Migration* 4: 257–268.

Moreau, R.E. 1951. The British status of the Quail and some problems of its biology. *British Birds* 44: 257–276.

Moreau, R.E. 1956. Quail in the British Isles, 1950–53. *British Birds* 49: 161–166.

Moreau, R.E. 1961. Problems of Mediterranean-Saharan migration. *Ibis* 103a: 373–427, 580–623.

Moreau, R.E. 1967. Water birds over the Sahara. *Ibis* 109: 232–259.

Moreau, R.E. 1972. *The Palaearctic-African Bird Migration Systems.* Academic Press, London.

Morel, G.J. & J. Betlem. 1992. The use of *Acacia nilotica* riverine forests of Senegal by birds, particularly Palearctic migrants. In *Proceedings of the Seventh Pan-African Ornithological Congress* (ed L. Bennun), pp 495–502. PAOC Committee, Nairobi, Kenya.

Morel, G.J. & M.Y. Morel. 1988. Nouvelles données sur l'hivernage de la Tourterelle des bois, *Streptopelia turtur,* en Afrique de l'Ouest: nord de la Guinée. *Alauda* 56: 85–91.

Morel, M.Y. 1985. La Tourterelle des bois, *Streptopelia turtur,* en Sénégambie: évolution de la population au cours de l'année et identification des races. *Alauda* 53: 100–110.

Morel, M.Y. 1987. La Tourterelle des bois, *Streptopelia turtur,* dans l'ouest africain: mouvements migratoires et régime alimentaire. *Malimbus* 9: 23–42.

Morgan, D.H.W. 1993. Feral Rose-ringed Parakeets in Britain. *British Birds* 86: 561–564.

Morgan, R. 1982. The breeding biology of the Nightingale *Luscinia megarhynchos* in Britain. *Bird Study* 29: 667–672.

Morgan, R. & D. Glue. 1977. Breeding, mortality and movements of Kingfishers. *Bird Study* 24: 15–24.

Morgan, R.A. & R.J. O'Connor. 1980. Farmland habitat and Yellowhammer distribution in Britain. *Bird Study* 27: 155–162.

Morley, J.V. 1966. Moult migration of Shelducks from Bridgwater Bay. *British Birds* 59: 141–147.

Morris, A., D. Burges, R.J. Fuller, A.D. Evans & K.W. Smith. 1994. The status and distribution of Nightjars *Caprimulgus europaeus* in Britain in 1992. *Bird Study* 41: 181–191.

Morrison, R.I.G. 1984. Migration systems of some New World shorebirds. In *Shorebirds: Migration and Foraging Behavior* (eds J. Burger & B.L. Olla), pp 125–202. Plenum Press, New York.

Morrison, R.I.G. & N.C. Davidson. 1990. Migration, body condition and behavior of shorebirds during spring migration at Alert, Ellesmere Island, N.W.T. In *Canada's Missing Dimension: Science and History in the Canadian Arctic Islands* (ed C.R. Harington), pp 544–567. Canadian Museum of Nature, Ottawa.

Morton, R. 1986. Rapid territory establishment by a Wood Warbler. *Ringing & Migration* 7: 56.

Moser, M.E. 1985. Curlew Sandpiper influx. *BTO News* 141: 1.

Moser, M.E. 1988. Limits to the numbers of Grey Plovers *Pluvialis squatarola* wintering on British estuaries: an analysis of long-term population trends. *Journal of Applied Ecology* 25: 473–485.

Moser, M. & M. Carrier. 1983. Patterns of population turnover in Ringed Plovers and Turnstones during their spring passage through the Solway Firth in 1983. *Wader Study Group Bulletin* 39: 37–41.

Moser, M.E. & R.W. Summers. 1987. Wader populations on the non-estuarine coasts of Britain and Northern Ireland: results of the 1984–85 Winter Shorebird Count. *Bird Study* 34: 71–81.

Moss, D. 1990. Migration patterns of the Wader populations of north-west Wales. *Scan Ringing Group Report 1989–90*: 47–52.

Moss, D. 1992. Dispersal of Cormorants and Shags ringed on Puffin Island. *Scan Ringing Group Report 1991–92*: 34–40.

Moss, D. & G.M. Moss. 1993. Breeding biology of the Little Grebe *Tachybaptus ruficollis* in Britain and Ireland. *Bird Study* 40: 107–114.

Moss, R. 1987. Demography of Capercaillie *Tetrao urogallus* in north-east Scotland. II. Age and sex distribution. *Ornis Scandinavica* 18: 135–140.

Moss, R. & J. Oswald. 1985. Population dynamics of Capercaillie in a North-east Scottish glen. *Ornis Scandinavica* 16: 229–238.

Moss, R. & D.N. Weir. 1987. Demography of Capercaillie *Tetrao urogallus* in north-east Scotland. III. Production and recruitment of young. *Ornis Scandinavica* 18: 141–145.

Moss, R., N. Picozzi, R.W. Summers & D. Baines. 2000. Capercaillie *Tetrao urogallus* in Scotland – demography of a declining population. *Ibis* 142: 259–267.

Moss, S. 1995. *Birds and weather: a birdwatcher's guide.* Hamlyn, London.

Mougin, J.L., C. Jouanin, B. Despin & F. Roux. 1986. The age of first breeding of Cory's Shearwater on Selvagem Grande and problems of ring loss. *Ringing & Migration* 7: 130–134.

Mougin, J.L., C. Jouanin & F. Roux. 1988. Les migrations du Puffin cendré *Calonectris diomedea. L'Oiseau et la Revue Française d'Ornithologie* 58: 303–319.

Mountfort, G. 1957. *The Hawfinch.* Collins, London.

Mountfort, G. 1981. Diurnal migration of Turtle Doves. *British Birds* 74: 265–266.

Mudge, G.P. & P.N. Ferns. 1982. The feeding ecology of five species of gulls (Aves: Larini) in the inner Bristol Channel. *Journal of Zoology, London* 197: 497–510.

Mudge, G.P. & T.R. Talbot. 1993. The breeding biology and causes of nest failure of Scottish Black-throated Divers *Gavia arctica*. *Ibis* 135: 113–120.

Mueller, H.C., D.D. Berger & G. Allez. 1977. The periodic invasions of Goshawks. *Auk* 94: 652–663.

Müller, W. 1997. Breeding and wintering population of the Red Kite in Switzerland. *Newsletter of the World Working Group on Birds of Prey and Owls* 25/26: 23–24.

Munk, H. 1951. Danske Stormmagers (*Larus canus* L.) traek. *Dansk Ornithologisk Forenings Tidsskrift* 45: 192–196.

Murray, R.D. 1987. Bluethroats in Scotland during 1985. *Scottish Birds* 14: 168–174.

Murray, R.D. 1991. Quail in Scotland, 1989. *Scottish Bird Report 1989* 22: 45–50.

Murray, R. (ed). 1993. *Scottish Bird Report 1991*. Scottish Ornithologists' Club, Edinburgh.

Murray, R. (ed). 1998. *Scottish Bird Report 1996*. Scottish Ornithologists' Club, Edinburgh.

Murray, R. (ed). 1999. *Scottish Bird Report 1997*. Scottish Ornithologists' Club, Edinburgh.

Murray, S. & S. Wanless. 1997. The status of the Gannet in Scotland in 1994–95. *Scottish Birds* 19: 10–27.

Murton, R.K. 1965. *The Woodpigeon*. Collins, London.

Murton, R.K. 1966. Natural selection and the breeding seasons of the Stock Dove and Wood Pigeon. *Bird Study* 13: 311–327.

Murton, R.K. 1968. Breeding, migration and survival of Turtle Doves. *British Birds* 61: 193–212.

Murton, R.K. & M.G. Ridpath. 1962. The autumn movements of the Woodpigeon. *Bird Study* 9: 7–41.

Murton, R.K. & N. Westwood. 1966. The foods of the Rock Dove and Feral Pigeon. *Bird Study* 13: 130–140.

Murton, R.K., A.J. Isaacson & N.J. Westwood. 1963. The feeding ecology of the woodpigeon. *British Birds* 56: 345–375.

Murton, R.K., N.J. Westwood & A.J. Isaacson. 1964a. The feeding habits of the Woodpigeon *Columba palumbus*, Stock Dove *C. oenas* and the Turtle Dove *Streptopelia turtur*. *Ibis* 106: 174–188.

Murton, R.K., N.J. Westwood & A.J. Isaacson. 1964b. A preliminary investigation of the factors regulating population size in the Woodpigeon. *Ibis* 106: 482–507.

Murton, R.K., R.J.P. Thearle & J. Thompson. 1972. Ecological studies of the Feral Pigeon *Columba livia* var. 1. Population, breeding biology and methods of control. *Journal of Applied Ecology* 9: 835–874.

Murton, R.K., R.J.P. Thearle & C.F.B. Coombs. 1974. Ecological studies of the Feral Pigeon *Columba livia* var. 3. Reproduction and plumage polymorphism. *Journal of Applied Ecology* 11: 841–854.

Myers, J.P. 1981. A test of three hypotheses for latitudinal segregation of the sexes in wintering birds. *Canadian Journal of Zoology* 59: 1527–1534.

Myers, J.P., G. Castro, B. Harrington, M. Howe, J. Maron, E. Ortiz, M. Sallaberry, C.T. Schick & E. Tabilo. 1984. The pan-American shorebird program: a progress report. *Wader Study Group Bulletin* 42: 26–31.

Myers, J.P., C.T. Schick & G. Castro. 1988. Structure in Sanderling (*Calidris alba*) populations: the magnitude of intra- and interyear dispersal during the non-breeding season. *Proceedings of the International Ornithological Congress* 19: 604–615.

Myers, J.P., M. Sallaberry, A.E. Ortiz, G. Castro, L.M. Gordon, J.L. Maron, C.T. Schick, E. Tabilo, P. Antas & T. Below. 1990. Migration routes of New World Sanderlings (*Calidris alba*). *Auk* 107: 172–180.

Myrberget, S. 1972. Fluctuations in a north Norwegian population of Willow Grouse. In *Proceedings of the XVth International Ornithological Congress* (ed K.H. Voous), pp 107–120. E.J. Brill, Leiden.

Myrberget, S. 1973. Ringing of Black Guillemots on the west coast of Scandinavia. *Sterna* 12: 33–40.

Naef-Daenzer, B. 1994. Radiotracking of Great and Blue Tits: new tools to assess territoriality, home-range use and resource distribution. *Ardea* 82: 335–347.

Nankinov, D. 1994. Migrations of the Turtle Dove (*Streptopelia turtur*) in Bulgaria: a review. *Gibier Faune Sauvage* 11: 249–261.

Nankinov, D.N. 1996. Dotterel in Bulgaria and routes of its migration in Eurasia. *Berkut* 5: 141–146.

Natorp, O. 1951. Massenansammlungen von Baumfalken. *Die Vogelwelt* 72: 55–56.

Naumann, J.A. 1833. *Naturgeschichte der Vögel Deutschlands*. Volume 6. Gera-Untermhaus, Leipzig.

Naylor, K.A. 1996. *A reference manual of rare birds in Great Britain and Ireland. Volume 1*. Privately published.

Naylor, K.A. 1998. *A reference manual of rare birds in Great Britain and Ireland. Volume 2*. Privately published.

Nebel, S., T. Piersma, J. van Gils, A. Dekinga & B. Spaans. 2000. Length of stopover, fuel storage and a sex-bias in the occurrence of Red Knots *Calidris c. canutus* and *C. c. islandica* in the Wadden Sea during southward migration. *Ardea* 88: 165–176.

Nelson, B. 1978. *The Gannet*. T. & A.D. Poyser, Berkhamsted.

Nelson, B. 1997. *Morus bassanus* Northern Gannet. *BWP Update* 1: 131–143.

Nelson, T.H. 1907. *The Birds of Yorkshire*. A. Brown & Sons, London.

Nethersole-Thompson, D. 1973. *The Dotterel*. Collins, London.

Nethersole-Thompson, D. 1975. *Pine Crossbills*. T. & A.D. Poyser, Berkhamsted.

Nethersole-Thompson, D. & M. Nethersole-Thompson. 1979. *Greenshanks*. T. & A.D. Poyser, Berkhamsted.

Nethersole-Thompson, D. & M. Nethersole-Thompson. 1986. *Waders, their breeding, haunts and watchers*. T. & A.D. Poyser, Calton.

Nettleship, D.N. & A.R. Lock. 1973. Tenth census of seabirds in the sanctuaries of the north shore of the St Lawrence. *Canadian Field Naturalist* 87: 395–402.

Neves, T. & F. Olmos. 1998. Albatross mortality in fisheries off the coast of Brazil. In *Albatross biology and conservation* (eds G. Robertson & R. Gale), pp 214–219. Surrey Beatty & Sons, Chipping Norton, Australia.

Newby, J.E. 1980. The birds of the Ouadi Rime – Ouadi Achim Faunal Reserve: a contribution to the study of the Chadian avifauna. *Malimbus* 2: 29–50.

Newby, J., J. Grettenberger & J. Watkins. 1987. The birds of the Northern Air, Niger. *Malimbus* 9: 4–16.

Newell, R.G. 1968. Influx of Great Shearwaters in autumn 1965. *British Birds* 61: 145–159.

Newnham, J.A. 1984. Some aspects of the sea-bird movements observed from the Sussex coast during the spring 1983. *Sussex Bird Report* 36: 60–63.

Newson, S.E. 2000. *Colonisation and range expansion of inland breeding Great Cormorants Phalacrocorax carbo in England*. PhD thesis, University of Bristol.

Newton, I. 1966. The moult of the Bullfinch *Pyrrhula pyrrhula*. *Ibis* 108: 41–67.

Newton, I. 1967a. The adaptive radiation and feeding ecology of some British finches. *Ibis* 109: 33–98.

Newton, I. 1967b. Attacks on fruit buds by Redpolls *Carduelis flammea*. *Ibis* 109: 440–441.

Newton, I. 1967c. The feeding ecology of the Bullfinch (*Pyrrhula pyrrhula*) in southern England. *Journal of Applied Ecology* 36: 721–744.

Newton, I. 1972. *Finches*. Collins, London.

Newton, I. 1979. *Population Ecology of Raptors*. T. & A.D. Poyser, Berkhamsted.

Newton, I. 1986. *The Sparrowhawk*. T. & A.D. Poyser, Calton.

Newton, I. 1991. Habitat variation and population regulation in Sparrowhawks. *Ibis* 133 (suppl. 1): 76–88.

Newton, I. 2000. Movements of Bullfinches *Pyrrhula pyrrhula* within the breeding season. *Bird Study* 47: 372–376.

Newton, I. & C.R.G. Campbell. 1973. Feeding geese on farmland in East-central Scotland. *Journal of Applied Ecology* 10: 781–801.

Newton, I. & L. Dale. 1996a. Relationships between migration and latitude among west European birds. *Journal of Animal Ecology* 65: 137–146.

Newton, I. & L. Dale. 1996b. Bird migration at different latitudes in eastern North America. *Auk* 113: 626–635.

Newton, I. & I. Wyllie. 1992. Fidelity to nesting territory among European Sparrowhawks in three areas. *Journal of Raptor Research* 26: 108–114.

Newton, I., E. Meek & B. Little. 1978. Breeding ecology of the Merlin in Northumberland. *British Birds* 71: 376–398.

Newton, I., P.E. Davis & J.E. Davis. 1982. Ravens and Buzzards in relation to sheep-farming and forestry in Wales. *Journal of Applied Ecology* 19: 681–706.

Newton, I., E. Meek & B. Little. 1986. Population and breeding of Northumbrian Merlins. *British Birds* 79: 155–170.

Newton, I., P.E. Davis & J.E. Davis. 1989. Age of first breeding, dispersal and survival of Red Kites *Milvus milvus* in Wales. *Ibis* 131: 16–21.

Newton, I., I. Wyllie & L. Dale. 1999. Trends in the numbers and mortality patterns of Sparrowhawks and Kestrels in Britain, as revealed by carcass analyses. *Journal of Zoology* 248: 139–147.

Nichols, J.D. 1991a. Responses of North American Duck populations to exploitation. In *Bird Population Studies: relevance to conservation and management* (eds C.M. Perrins, J.-D. Lebreton & G.J.M. Hirons), pp 168–189. Oxford University Press, Oxford.

Nichols, J.D. 1991b. Extensive monitoring programmes viewed as long-term population studies: the case of North American waterfowl. *Ibis* 133 (suppl.): 89–98.

Nichols, J.D. 1996. Sources of variation in migratory movements of animal populations: statistical inference and a selective review of empirical results for birds. In *Population Dynamics in Ecological Space and Time* (eds O.E. Rhodes Jr., R.K. Chesser & M.H. Smith), pp 147–197. University of Chicago Press, Chicago.

Nichols, J.D. & A. Kaiser. 1999. Quantitative studies of bird movement: a methodological review. *Bird Study* 46 (suppl.): S289–298.

Nicoll, M., R.W. Summers, L.G. Underhill, K. Brockie & R. Rae. 1988. Regional, seasonal and annual variation in the structure of Purple Sandpiper *Calidris maritima* populations in Britain. *Ibis* 130: 221–233.

Nicoll, M., R. Rae, R.W. Summers, K.-B. Strann & K. Brockie. 1991. The biometrics of Norwegian and Svalbard Purple Sandpipers *Calidris maritima*. *Ringing & Migration* 12: 67–71.

Nieboer, E. 1973. *Geographical and ecological differentiation in the genus Circus.* Dissertation, University of Amsterdam, the Netherlands.

Nightingale, B. & K. Allsopp. 1995. The ornithological year 1994. *British Birds* 88: 457–472.

Nightingale, B. & K. Allsopp. 1998. The ornithological year 1997. *British Birds* 91: 526–539.

Nikiforov, M.E. 1992. Size and mobility of Grey Partridge (*Perdix perdix*) winter coveys in Belorussia. In *Perdix VI, First International Symposium on Partridges, Quails and Francolins* (eds M. Birkan, G.R. Potts, N.J. Aebischer & S.D. Dowell). *Gibier Faune Sauvage* 9: 447–453.

Nikolaus, G. 1987. *Distribution atlas of Sudan's birds with notes on habitat and status.* Bonner Zoologische Monographia 25. Zoologisches Forschungsinstitut and Museum Alexander Koering, Bonn.

Nikolaus, G. & I. Chernichko. 1995. The loop migration of Curlew Sandpiper with special reference to the Sivash, Black Sea. *Wader Study Group Bulletin* 76: 16. (Abstract.)

Nilsson, J.-Å. 1989. Causes and consequences of natal dispersal in the Marsh Tit, *Parus palustris*. *Journal of Animal Ecology* 58: 619–636.

Nilsson, L. 1969. The migration of the Goldeneye in north-west Europe. *Wildfowl* 20: 112–118.

Nilsson, L. 1970. Local and seasonal variation in sex-ratios of diving ducks in south Sweden during the non-breeding season. *Ornis Scandinavica* 1: 115–128.

Nilsson, L. 1984a. The impact of hard winters on waterfowl populations of south Sweden. *Wildfowl* 35: 71–80.

Nilsson, L. 1984b. Migrations of Fennoscandian Bean Geese, *Anser fabalis*. *Swedish Wildlife Research* 13: 83–106.

Nilsson, L. & M.K. Pirkola. 1991. Migration pattern of Finnish Bean Geese *Anser fabalis*. *Ornis Svecica* 1: 69–80.

Nisbet, I.C.T. 1956. Records of Wood Sandpipers in Britain in the autumn of 1952. *British Birds* 49: 49–62.

Nisbet, I.C.T. 1959. Wader migration in North America and its relation to transatlantic crossings. *British Birds* 52: 205–215.

Nisbet, I.C.T. 1962. South-eastern rarities at Fair Isle. *British Birds* 55: 74–86.

Nisbet, I.C.T. 1984. Migration and winter quarters of North American Roseate Terns as shown by banding recoveries. *Journal of Field Ornithology* 55: 1–17.

Nisbet, I.C.T. 1997. Status, biology and management of the Black Tern: symposium summary and overview. *Colonial Waterbirds* 20: 622–625.

Nisbet, I.C.T. & D. Cabot. 1995. Transatlantic recovery of a ringed Roseate Tern *Sterna dougallii*. *Ringing & Migration* 16: 14–15.

Nisbet, I.C.T. & C. Safina. 1996. Transatlantic recoveries of ringed Common Terns *Sterna hirundo*. *Ringing & Migration* 17: 28–30.

Nisbet, I.C.T. & A.E. Vine. 1956. Migration of Little Stints, Curlew Sandpipers and Ruffs through Great Britain in the autumn of 1953. *British Birds* 49: 121–134.

Noble, D.G., R.I. Bashford, J.H. Marchant, S.R. Baillie & R.D. Gregory. 1999. *The Breeding Bird Survey 1998.* Research Report 225. British Trust for Ornithology, Thetford.

Noer, H. 1991. Distributions and movements of Eider *Somateria mollissima* populations wintering in Danish waters, analysed from ringing recoveries. *Danish Review of Game Biology* 14: 1–32.

Nolet, B.A., V.A. Andreev, P. Clausen, M.J.M. Poot & E.G.J. Wessel. 2001. Significance of the White Sea as a stopover for Bewick's Swans *Cygnus columbianus bewickii* in spring. *Ibis* 143: 63–71.

Noordhuis, R. & A.L. Spaans. 1992. Interspecific competition for food between Herring *Larus argentatus* and Lesser Black-backed Gulls *L. fuscus* in the Dutch Wadden Sea area. *Ardea* 80: 115–132.

Norberg, U.M. 1990. *Vertebrate Flight: mechanics, physiology, morphology, ecology and evolution.* Springer Verlag, Heidelberg.

Nore, T., J.-P. Malafosse, G. Nore & E. Buffard. 1992. La dispersion des jeunes de première année dans une population sédentaire de busard variable (*Buteo buteo*). *Revue d'Ecologie-La Terre et La Vie* 47: 259–286.

Norman, D. 1994a. *The Fieldfare.* Hamlyn, London.

Norman, D. 1994b. The return rate of adult male Wood Warblers *Phylloscopus sibilatrix* to a peripheral breeding area. *Ringing & Migration* 15: 79–83.

Norman, D.M. 1970. Grey Wagtails at Prawle. *Devon Birds* 23: 10–15.

Norman, S.C. 1987. Body weights of Willow Warblers during autumn migration within Britain. *Ringing & Migration* 8: 73–82.

Norman, S.C. 1991. Post-juvenile moult in relation to dispersal and migration in the Chiffchaff. *Ringing & Migration* 12: 80–85.

Norman, S.C. 1992. Dispersal and site fidelity in Lesser Whitethroat *Sylvia curruca*. *Ringing & Migration* 13: 167–174.

Norman, S.C. 1994. Dispersal and return rates of Willow Warblers *Phylloscopus trochilus* in relation to age, sex and season. *Ringing & Migration* 15: 8–16.

Norman, S.C. 1997. Juvenile wing-shape, wing moult and weight in the family *Sylviidae*. *Ibis* 139: 617–630.

Norman, S.C. 1999. Biometrics and post-juvenile moult in the Goldcrest *Regulus regulus*. *Ringing & Migration* 19: 175–180.

Norman, S.C. & W. Norman. 1985. Autumn movements of Willow Warblers ringed in the British Isles. *Ringing & Migration* 6: 7–18.

Norman, W. 1986. Winter movements of Blue and Great Tits in the North York Moors. *South Cleveland Ringing Group Report* 8: 30–40.

Norris, C.A. 1945. Summary of a report on the distribution and status of the Corncrake (*Crex crex*). *British Birds* 38: 142–148, 162–168.

Norris, C.A. 1947. Report on the distribution and status of the Corncrake. *British Birds* 40: 226–244.

Norris, K., E. Brindley, A. Cook, S. Babbs, C. Forster Brown & R. Yaxley. 1998. Is the density of Redshank *Tringa totanus* nesting on saltmarshes in Great Britain declining due to changes in grazing management? *Journal of Applied Ecology* 35: 621–634.

Norriss, D.W. 1995. The 1991 survey and weather impacts on the Peregrine *Falco peregrinus* breeding population in the Republic of Ireland. *Bird Study* 42: 20–30.

North, P.M. 1979. Relating Grey Heron survival rates to winter weather conditions. *Bird Study* 26: 23–28.

North, P.M. 1980. An analysis of Razorbill movements away from the breeding colony. *Bird Study* 27: 11–20.

Nowak, E. 1989. Ausbreitung der Türkentaube (*Streptopelia decaocto*) in der USSR: Umfrage 1988. *Journal für Ornithologie* 130: 513–527.

Nowak, E. & P. Berthold. 1987. Die Satelliten-Telemetrie in der Erforschung von Tierwanderungen: eine Übersicht. *Journal für Ornithologie* 128: 405–422.

Ntiamoa-Baidu, Y. 1991. Species protection as a strategy for conservation action in Africa: the case of the roseate tern in Ghana. In *Conserving Migratory Birds* (ed T. Salathé), pp 169–176. Technical Publication 12. International Council for Bird Preservation, Cambridge.

Ntiamoa-Baidu, Y. 1992. Terns in coastal Ghana. In *Proceedings of the Seventh Pan-African Ornithological Congress* (ed L. Bennun), pp 37–43. PAOC Committee, Nairobi, Kenya.

Ntiamoa-Baidu, Y., S.K. Nyame & A.A. Nuoh. 1992. Preliminary report on tern trapping in coastal Ghana. In *Proceedings of the Roseate Tern Workshop* (ed G. Rolland), pp 47–52. SEPNB, Brest, Brittany.

Nuttall, R. 2001. Barn Swallow *Hirundo rustica* ringing in southern Africa (1998/99 – 2000/01). *EURING Newsletter* 3: 37–38.

Nyrup, H. 1992. Forekomsten af kjover i Nordjylland, 1975–1989. *Dansk Ornitologisk Forenings Tidsskrift* 86: 257–261.

Ó Briain, M. & B. Healy. 1991. Winter distribution of Light-bellied Brent Geese *Branta bernicla hrota* in Ireland. *Ardea* 79: 317–326.

Ó Briain, M., T.D. Carruthers & V. Sheridan. 1986. Transitory staging of Brent Geese in Ireland. *Irish Birds* 3: 286.

O'Brien, M. 1996. The number of breeding waders in lowland Scotland. *Scottish Birds* 18: 231–241.

O'Brien, M. & S. Murray. 1998. Estimating the breeding wader populations on farmland in northern England in 1993. *Wader Study Group Bulletin* 85: 60–65.

O'Brien, M. & K.W. Smith. 1992. Changes in the status of waders breeding on wet lowland grasslands in England and Wales between 1982 and 1989. *Bird Study* 39: 165–176.

O'Connor, R.J. 1980. Pattern and process in Great Tit (*Parus major*) populations in Britain. *Ardea* 68: 165–183.

O'Connor, R.J. 1981. Comparisons between migrant and non-migrant birds in Britain. In *Animal Migration* (ed D.J. Aidley), pp 167–195. Cambridge University Press, Cambridge.

O'Connor, R.J. 1984. Science and the Ringing Scheme: a prospective. *Ringing & Migration* 5: 6–14.

O'Connor, R.J. 1990. Some ecological aspects of migrants and residents. In *Bird Migration: the physiology and ecophysiology* (ed E. Gwinner), pp 175–182. Springer-Verlag, Berlin.

O'Connor, R.J. & C.J. Mead. 1984. The Stock Dove in Britain, 1930–80. *British Birds* 77: 181–201.

O'Connor, R.J. & M. Shrubb. 1986. *Farming and Birds*. Cambridge University Press, Cambridge.

O'Donoghue, P.D., T.F. Cross & J. O'Halloran. 1996. Carrion Crows in Ireland, 1969–1993. *Irish Birds* 5: 399–406.

O'Halloran, J., A.A. Myers & P.F. Duggan. 1991. Lead poisoning in Mute Swans, *Cygnus olor*, in Ireland: a review. In *Proceedings of the Third IWRB International Swan Symposium, Oxford 1989* (eds J. Sears & P.J. Bacon), pp 389–395. *Wildfowl* suppl. 1.

O'Halloran, J., P. Smiddy & B. O'Mahony. 2000. Movements of Dippers *Cinclus cinclus* in southwest Ireland. *Ringing & Migration* 20: 147–151.

O'Sullivan, J.M. 1976. Bearded Tits in Britain and Ireland, 1966–74. *British Birds* 69: 473–489.

O'Sullivan, O. & P. Smiddy. 1992. Thirty-ninth Irish bird report 1991. *Irish Birds* 4: 571–610.

OAG Münster. 1984. Inland wader counts – third progress report. *Wader Study Group Bulletin* 30: 15–17.

OAG Münster. 1989. Observations on the spring migrations of Ruffs *Philomachus pugnax*. *Journal für Ornithologie* 130: 175–182.

OAG Münster. 1996. Gibt es tatsächlich einen Weibchenüberschuß bei überwinternder Kampfläufern *Philomachus pugnax* in Afrika? [Do females really outnumber males in Ruff *Philomachus pugnax* wintering in Africa?] *Journal für Ornithologie* 137: 91–100.

Oatley, T.B. 1999. Uneven recovery pattern of ringed European Swifts *Apus apus* in southern Africa. *Ostrich* 70: 236.

Oatley, T.B. 2000. Migrant European Swallows *Hirundo rustica* in southern Africa: a southern perspective. *Ostrich* 71: 205–209.

Odin, N. 1997. Snow Buntings at Felixstowe Ferry – early 1997. *The Harrier* 111: 7–9.

Oelke, H. 1969. Die Brandgans (*Tadorna tadorna*) im Mausergebiet Grosser Knechtsand. *Journal für Ornithologie* 110: 170–175.

Ogilvie, M.A. 1969. The status of the Canada Goose in Britain 1967–1969. *Wildfowl* 28: 79–85.

Ogilvie, M.A. 1972a. Large numbered leg bands for individual identification of swans. *Journal of Wildlife Management* 36: 1261–1265.

Ogilvie, M.A. 1972b. Distribution, numbers and migration. In *The Swans* (eds P. Scott & the Wildfowl Trust), pp 29–56. Michael Joseph, London.

Ogilvie, M.A. 1983. *A migration study of the Teal* (Anas crecca) *in Europe using ringing recoveries*. PhD thesis, University of Bristol.

Ogilvie, M.A. 1987. Movements of Tufted Ducks ringed in Britain: a preliminary assessment. *Wildfowl* 38: 28–36.

Ogilvie, M.A. & W.A. Cook. 1971. Differential migration of the sexes and other aspects of the recovery overseas of Mallard ringed at Borough Fen Decoy, Northamptonshire. *Wildfowl* 22: 89–97.

Ogilvie, M.A. & W.A. Cook. 1972. British recoveries of Mallard ringed at Borough Fen Decoy, Northamptonshire. *Wildfowl* 23: 103–110.

Ogilvie, M.A. & M. Owen. 1984. Some results from the ringing of Barnacle Geese *Branta leucopsis* in Svalbard and Britain. *Norsk Polarinstitutt Skrifter* 181: 49–55.

Ogilvie, M. & the Rare Breeding Birds Panel. 1995. Rare breeding birds in the United Kingdom in 1992. *British Birds* 88: 67–93.

Ogilvie, M. & the Rare Breeding Birds Panel. 1999a. Rare breeding birds in the United Kingdom in 1996. *British Birds* 92: 120–154.

Ogilvie, M. & the Rare Breeding Birds Panel. 1999b. Rare breeding birds in the United Kingdom in 1997. *British Birds* 92: 389–428.

Ogilvie, M.A., D. Boertmann, D. Cabot, O. Merne, S.M. Percival & A. Sigfusson. 1999c. Barnacle Goose *Branta leucopsis*: Greenland. In *Goose populations of the Western Palearctic: a review of status and distribution* (eds J. Madsen, G. Cracknell & A.D. Fox), pp 246–256. Wetlands International Publication 48. Wetlands International, Wageningen, the Netherlands, and National Environmental Research Institute, Rönde, Denmark.

Ogilvie, M. & the Rare Breeding Birds Panel. 2000. Rare breeding birds in the United Kingdom in 1998. *British Birds* 93: 358–393.

Okill, J.D. 1981. Catching and ringing Red-throated Divers. *Ringers' Bulletin* 5: 120–122.

Okill, J.D. 1992. Natal dispersal and breeding site fidelity of Red-throated Divers *Gavia stellata* in Shetland. *Ringing & Migration* 13: 57–58.

Okill, J.D. 1993. *The recoveries of ringed birds during the Braer oil spill, Shetland 1993*. Report to the Environmental Steering Group on the Oil Spill in Shetland.

Okill, J.D. 1994. Ringing recoveries of Red-throated Divers *Gavia stellata* in Britain and Ireland. *Ringing & Migration* 15: 107–118.

Okill, J.D., J.A. Ginnever & A. Jones. 1980. Shetland's Merlins. *Shetland Bird Report 1979*: 51–54.

Okill, J.D., D.D. French & S. Wanless. 1989. Sexing Red-throated Divers in Shetland. *Ringing & Migration* 10: 26–30.

Oliver, P.J. 1971. Sooty Shearwaters in the English Channel. *British Birds* 64: 56–60.

Olney, P.J.S. 1963. The food and feeding habits of Tufted Duck *Aythya fuligula*. *Ibis* 105: 55–62.

Olney, P.J.S. 1968. The food and feeding habits of Pochard. *Biological Conservation* 1: 71–78.

Olsen, K.M. & H. Larsson. 1997. *Skuas and Jaegers: a guide to the skuas and jaegers of the world*. Pica Press, Robertsbridge, East Sussex.

Olson, B.O. 1980. *Project Stenfalk Rapport 1975–1978*. Svenska Naturskyddsforeningen, Stockholm.

Olsson, K.-A. 1975. Mindre strandpiparens *Charadrius dubius* flyttning baserad på resultat från ringmärkning. *Anser* 14: 217–224.

Olsson, V. 1981. Vårfagelns *Lanius excubitor* flyttning och övervintringsområde. *Vår Fågelvärld* 40: 447–454.

Onno, S.K. 1965. [Attachment to the nest (Ortstreue) in the Common Gull, Common Tern and Arctic Tern.] *Soobshch. pribalt. Kom. Izuch. Migr. Ptits* 3: 140–162. Estonian Academy of Science, Tartu. (In Russian.)

Orchel, J. 1992. *Forest Merlins in Scotland*. The Hawk and Owl Trust, London.

Orell, M. & Ojanen, M. 1979. Mortality rates of the Great Tit *Parus major* in a northern population. *Ardea* 67: 130–137.

Orford, N. 1973. Breeding distribution of the Twite in central Britain. *Bird Study* 20: 51–62, 121–126.

Oring, L.W. & D.B. Lank. 1984. Breeding area fidelity, natal philopatry, and the social systems of sandpipers. In *Behaviour of Marine Animals*, volume 5 (eds J. Burger & B.L. Olla), pp 125–147. Plenum Press, New York.

Ormerod, S.J. 1989. The influence of weather on the body mass of migrating Swallows *Hirundo rustica* in South Wales. *Ringing & Migration* 10: 65–74.

Ormerod, S.J. 1990. Time of passage, habitat use and mass change of *Acrocephalus* warblers in a South Wales reedswamp. *Ringing & Migration* 11: 1–11.

Ormerod, S.J. 1991. Pre-migratory and migratory movements of Swallows *Hirundo rustica* in Britain and Ireland. *Bird Study* 38: 170–178.

Ormerod, S.J. & S.J. Tyler. 1991. The influence of stream acidification and riparian land-use on the feeding ecology of Grey Wagtails *Motacilla cinerea*. *Ibis* 133: 53–61.

Ormerod, S.J. & S.J. Tyler. 1992. Patterns of contamination by organochlorines and mercury in the eggs of two river passerines in Britain and Ireland with reference to individual PCB congeners. *Environmental Pollution* 76: 233–244.

Ormerod, S.J. & S.J. Tyler. 1993. The adaptive significance of brood size and time of breeding in the Dipper *Cinclus cinclus* as seen from post-fledging survival. *Journal of Zoology* 231: 371–381.

Ormerod, S.J., S.J. Tyler, S.J. Pester & A.V. Cross. 1988. Censussing distribution and population of birds along upland rivers using measured ringing effort: a preliminary study. *Ringing & Migration* 9: 71–82.

Ormerod, S.J., S.J. Tyler & I. Jüttner. 2000. Effects of point-source contamination on breeding performance and post-fledging survival in the Dipper *Cinclus cinclus*. *Environmental Pollution* 110: 505–513.

Ortiz, N.E. & G.R. Smith. 1994. Landfill sites, botulism and gulls. *Epidemiology and Infection* 112: 385–391.

Ortlieb, R. 1982. *Der Rotmilan*. Die Neue Brehm-Bücherei 532. A. Ziemsen Verlag, Wittenberg Lutherstadt.

Osborn, K. 1985. A possible eastern Common Gull on Fair Isle. *British Birds* 78: 454.

Osborn, K. & Shetland Bird Club. 1999. Birds. In *A naturalist's Shetland* (ed J.L. Johnston), pp 438–489. T. & A.D. Poyser, London.

Ostapenko, V.A. 1997. [Mandarin Duck – *Aix galericulata* (L.).] In [*Migrations of Birds of Eastern Europe and Northern Asia: Anseriformes*] (eds V.V. Bianki & I.N. Dobrynina), p 305. Nauka, Moscow. (In Russian.)

Österlöf, S. 1977. Migration, wintering areas, and site tenacity of the European Osprey *Pandion haliaetus* (L.). *Ornis Scandinavica* 8: 61–78.

Ottosson, U., S. Rumsey & C. Hjort. 2001. Migration of four Sylvia warblers through northern Senegal. *Ringing & Migration* 20: 344–351.

Ouden, J.E. & L. Stougie. 1990. Voorjaarstek van Dwergmeeuwen *Larus minutus* langs de Nordzeekust. *Sula* 4: 90–98.

Ovenden, G.N., A.R.H. Swash & D. Smallshire. 1998. Agri-environment schemes and their contribution to the conservation of biodiversity in England. *Journal of Applied Ecology* 35: 955–960.

Overskaug, K. & E. Kristiansen. 1994. Sex ratio of accidentally killed Long-eared Owls in Norway. *Ringing & Migration* 15: 104–106.

Owen, M. 1976. Factors affecting the distribution of geese in the British Isles. *Wildfowl* 27: 143–147.

Owen, M. 1980. *Wild Geese of the World*. Batsford, London.

Owen, M. 1983. The aliens. *Wildfowl World* 89: 16–19.

Owen, M. & J.M. Black. 1989. Factors affecting the survival of Barnacle Geese on migration from the breeding grounds. *Journal of Animal Ecology* 58: 603–618.

Owen, M. & J.M. Black. 1991. The importance of migration mortality in non-passerine birds. In *Bird Population Studies: relevance to conservation and management* (eds C.M. Perrins, J.-D. Lebreton & G.J.M. Hirons), pp 360–372. Oxford University Press, Oxford.

Owen, M. & M. Dix. 1986. Sex ratios in some common British wintering ducks. *Wildfowl* 37: 104–112.

Owen, M. & N. Gullestad. 1984. Migration routes of Svalbard Barnacle Geese *Branta leucopsis* with a preliminary report on the importance of the Bjørnøya staging area. *Norsk Polarinstitutt Skrifter* 181: 67–77.

Owen, M. & C. Mitchell. 1988. Movements and migrations of Wigeon *Anas penelope* wintering in Britain and Ireland. *Bird Study* 35: 47–59.

Owen, M. & D.G. Salmon. 1988. Feral Greylag Geese *Anser anser* in Britain and Ireland, 1960–1988. *Bird Study* 35: 37–45.

Owen, M., G.L. Atkinson-Willes & D.G. Salmon. 1986. *Wildfowl in Great Britain*. Second edition. Cambridge University Press, Cambridge.

Owen, M., J.M. Black, M.C. Agger & C.R.G. Campbell. 1987. The use of the Solway Firth by an increasing population of Barnacle Geese in relation to changes in refuge management. *Biological Conservation* 39: 63–81.

Owen, M., J.M. Black & H. Liber. 1988. Pair bond duration and the timing of its formation in Barnacle Geese. In *Wildfowl in Winter* (ed M. Weller), pp 23–38. University of Minnesota Press, Minneapolis.

Owen, M., J.S. Kirby & D.G. Salmon. 1994. Canada Geese in Great Britain: history, problems and prospects. In *Biology and management of Canada geese* (eds D.H. Rusch, M.D. Samuel, D.D. Humburg & B.D. Sullivan). Northern Prairie Wildlife Research Center, Jamestown ND.

Owens, I.P.F., T. Burke & D.B.A. Thompson. 1994. Extraordinary sex roles in the Eurasian Dotterel: female mating arenas, female-female competition and female mate choice. *American Naturalist* 144: 76–100.

Page, G.W., L.E. Stenzel & J.E. Kjelmyr. 1999. Using atlas data to model the distribution of woodpecker species in the Jura, France. *Condor* 101: 461–471.

Pain, D.J., C. Bavoux & G. Burneleau. 1997. Seasonal blood lead concentrations in Marsh Harriers *Circus aeruginosus* from Charente-Maritime, France: relationship with the hunting season. *Biological Conservation* 81: 1–7.

Pain, J. 1990. Water Pipits *Anthus spinoletta* on Hampshire watercress beds. *Hampshire Bird Report 1989*: 84–86.

Pajuelo, L., F. de Lope & E. da Silva. 1992. Biología de la reproducción del Avión Común (*Delichon urbica*) en Badajoz, España. *Ardeola* 39: 15–23.

Palmer, R.S. 1976a. *Handbook of North American Birds*. Volume 2. Yale University Press, New Haven and London.

Palmer, R.S. 1976b. *Handbook of North American Birds*. Volume 3. Yale University Press, New Haven and London.

Palokangas, P., R.V. Alatalo & E. Korpimäki. 1992. Female choice in the Kestrel under different availability of mating options. *Animal Behaviour* 43: 659–665.

Paludan, K. 1963. Partridge markings in Denmark. *Danish Review of Game Biology* 4: 25–58.

Paradis, E., S.R. Baillie, W.J. Sutherland & R.D. Gregory. 1998. Patterns of natal and breeding dispersal in birds. *Journal of Animal Ecology* 67: 518–536.

Parasharya, B.M., A. Mukherjee & T.V. Patel. 1999. Sight records of the Little Gull *Larus minutus* from Gujarat. *Journal of the Bombay Natural History Society* 96: 142.

Parker, P.G., A.A. Snow, M.D. Schug, G.C. Booton & P.A. Fuerst. 1998. What molecules can tell us about populations: choosing and using a molecular marker. *Ecology* 79: 361–382.

Parkes, K.C. 1952. Geographical variation in the Horned Grebe. *Condor* 54: 314–315.

Parkin, D.T. & J.M. McMeeking. 1985. The increase of Canada Geese in Nottinghamshire from 1980. *Bird Study* 32: 132–140.

Parmelee, D.F. 1970. Breeding behaviour of the Sanderling in the Canadian high Arctic. *Living Bird* 9: 97–145.

Parr, R. 1980. Population study of Golden Plover *Pluvialis apricaria*, using marked birds. *Ornis Scandinavica* 11: 179–189.

Parr, R. 1992. The decline to extinction of a population of Golden Plover in northeast Scotland. *Ornis Scandinavica* 23: 152–158.

Parr, R. & A. Watson. 1988. Habitat preferences of Black Grouse on moorland-dominated ground in north-east Scotland. *Ardea* 76: 175–180.

Parr, S.J. 1991. Occupation of new conifer plantations by Merlins in Wales. *Bird Study* 38: 103–111.

Parr, S.J., R.J. Haycock & M.E. Smith. 1997. The impact of the Sea Empress oil spill on birds of the Pembrokeshire coast and islands. In *Proceedings of the 1997 International Oil Spill Conference*, pp 217–225. Publication 4651. American Petroleum Institute, Washington DC.

Parrinder, E.D. 1989. Little Ringed Plovers *Charadrius dubius* in Britain in 1984. *Bird Study* 36: 147–153.

Parrinder, E.R. & E.D. Parrinder. 1975. Little Ringed Plovers in Britain 1968–73. *British Birds* 68: 359–368.

Parslow, J.L.F. 1962. Immigration of night-migrants into southern England in spring 1962. *Bird Migration* 2: 106–175.

Parslow, J.L.F. 1967. Changes in status among breeding birds in Britain & Ireland. *British Birds* 60: 2–47.

Parslow, J.L.F. 1973. *Breeding birds of Britain and Ireland*. T. & A.D. Poyser, Berkhamsted.

Parslow-Otsu, M. 1991. Bean Geese in the Yare Valley, Norfolk. *British Birds* 84: 161–170.

Parslow-Otsu, M. & G.D. Elliott. 1991. Red-necked Grebe breeding in England. *British Birds* 84: 188–191.

Parsons, J. & N. Duncan. 1978. Recoveries and dispersal of Herring Gulls from the Isle of May. *Journal of Animal Ecology* 47: 993–1005.

Paterson, A.M. 1986. Kleptoparasitic feeding by migrating skuas in Malaga Bay, Spain. *Ringing & Migration* 7: 51–55.

Patrimonio, O. 1990. *Le Milan Royal (*Milvus milvus*) en Corse: répartition et reproduction*. Travaux Scientifiques du Parc Naturel Régional et des Réserves Naturelles de Corse.

Pattenden, B. 1989. The Aquatic Warbler (*Acrocephalus paludicola*) in Cornwall and the Isles of Scilly. *Cornwall Bird Report 1988*: 132–134.

Patterson, I.J. 1965. Timing and spacing of broods in the Black-headed Gull *Larus ridibundus*. *Ibis* 107: 433–459.

Patterson, I.J. 1982. *The Shelduck: a study in behavioural ecology*. Cambridge University Press, Cambridge.

Patterson, I.J., G.M. Dunnet & R.A. Fordham. 1971. Ecological studies of the Rook, *Corvus frugilegus* L., in north-east Scotland. Dispersion. *Journal of Applied Ecology* 8: 815–833.

Patterson, I.J., S. Abdul-Jalil & M.L. East. 1989. Damage to winter cereals by Greylag and Pink-footed Geese in north-east Scotland. *Journal of Applied Ecology* 26: 879–895.

Pauli, H.-R. 1974. Zur Winterökologie des Birkhuhns *Tetrao tetrix* in den Schweizer Alpen. *Der Ornithologische Beobachter* 71: 247–278.

Paulson, D.R. 1993. *Shorebirds of the Pacific Northwest*. University of Washington Press, Seattle and London.

Paulus, S.L. 1983. Dominance relations, resource use, and pairing chronology of Gadwalls in winter. *Auk* 100: 947–952.

Payevsky, V.A. 1994. Age and sex structure, mortality and spatial winter distribution of Siskins migrating through eastern Baltic area. *Die Vogelwarte* 37: 190–198.

Payn, W.H. 1978. *The Birds of Suffolk*. Ancient House Publishing, Ipswich.

Peach, W.J. 1993. Combining mark-recapture data sets for small passerines. In *Marked Individuals in the Study of Bird Populations* (eds J.-D. Lebreton & P.M. North), pp 107–122. Birkhäuser Verlag, Basel.

Peach, W.J. & J.A. Fowler. 1989. Movements of wing-tagged Starlings *Sturnus vulgaris* from an urban communal roost in winter. *Bird Study* 36: 16–22.

Peach, W.J., S.T. Buckland & S.R. Baillie. 1990. Estimating survival rates using mark-recapture data from multiple ringing sites. *The Ring* 13: 87–102.

Peach, W., S. Baillie & L. Underhill. 1991. Survival of British Sedge Warblers *Acrocephalus schoenobaenus* in relation to west African rainfall. *Ibis* 133: 300–305.

Peach, W.J., P.S. Thompson & J.C. Coulson. 1994. Annual and long-term variation in the survival rates of British Lapwings *Vanellus vanellus*. *Journal of Animal Ecology* 63: 60–70.

Peach, W.J., H.Q.P. Crick & J.H. Marchant. 1995a. The demography of the decline in the British Willow Warbler population. *Journal of Applied Statistics* 22: 905–922.

Peach, W., C.R. du Feu & J.M. McMeeking. 1995b. Site-tenacity and survival of Wrens *Troglodytes troglodytes* and Treecreepers *Certhia familiaris* in a Nottinghamshire wood. *Ibis* 137: 497–507.

Peach, W.J., S.T. Buckland & S.R. Baillie. 1996. The use of constant-effort mist-netting to measure between-year changes in the abundance and productivity of common passerines. *Bird Study* 43: 142–156.

Peach, W., J. Clark, A. Gosler & A. Evans. 1997. Grants from the Bob Spencer Memorial Fund. *Ringers' Bulletin* 9: 63.

Peach, W.J., S.R. Baillie & D.E. Balmer. 1998. Long-term changes in the abundance of passerines in Britain and Ireland as measured by constant effort mist-netting. *Bird Study* 45: 257–275.

Peach, W.J., G.M. Siriwardena & R.D. Gregory. 1999. Long-term changes in over-winter survival rates explain the decline of Reed Buntings

Emberiza schoeniclus in Britain. *Journal of Applied Ecology* 36: 798–811.

Peach, W.J., L.J. Lovett, S.R. Wotton & C. Jeffs. 2001. Countryside Stewardship delivers Cirl Buntings (*Emberiza cirlus*) in Devon, UK. *Biological Conservation* 101: 361–373.

Peal, R.E.F. 1972. European ringing of the Wryneck (*Jynx torquilla*). In *Proceedings of the XVth International Ornithological Congress* (ed K.H. Voous), pp 675–676. E.J. Brill, Leiden.

Pearson, D.J. 1972. The wintering and migration of Palaearctic passerines at Kampala, southern Uganda. *Ibis* 114: 43–60.

Pearson, D.J. 1973. Moult of some Palearctic warblers wintering in Uganda. *Bird Study* 20: 24–36.

Pearson, D.J. 1975. Moult and its relation to eruptive activity in the Bearded Reedling. *Bird Study* 22: 205–227.

Pearson, D.J. 1981. The wintering and moult of Ruffs *Philomachus pugnax* in the Kenyan rift valley. *Ibis* 123: 158–182.

Pearson, D.J. 1982. The migration and wintering of Palaearctic *Acrocephalus* warblers in Kenya and Uganda. *Scopus* 6: 49–59.

Pearson, D.J. 1984. The moult of the Little Stint *Calidris minuta* in the Kenyan rift valley. *Ibis* 126: 1–15.

Pearson, D.J. 1987. The status, migrations and seasonality of the Little Stint in Kenya. *Ringing & Migration* 8: 91–108.

Pearson, D.J. & G.C. Backhurst. 1976. The southward migration of Palaearctic birds over Ngulia, Kenya. *Ibis* 118: 78–105.

Pearson, D.J., G. Nikolaus & J.S. Ash. 1988. The southward migration of Palaearctic passerines through northeast and east tropical Africa: a review. In *Proceedings of the Sixth Pan-African Ornithological Congress* (ed G.C. Backhurst), pp 243–261. Sixth PAOC Organizing Committee, Nairobi, Kenya.

Pedersen, M.B. 1989. Aspekter af Enkeltbekkasinens *Lymnocryptes minimus* overvintringsstrategi i Danmark. *Dansk Ornitologisk Forenings Tidsskrift* 83: 69–73.

Pedersen, M.B. 1994. Jack Snipe *Lymnocryptes minimus*. In *Birds in Europe: their conservation status* (eds G.M. Tucker & M.F. Heath), pp 266–267. Conservation Series no. 3. BirdLife International, Cambridge.

Peiponen, V.A. 1967. Südliche Fortpflanzung und Zug von *Carduelis flammea* im Jahre 1965. *Annales Zoologici Fennici* 4: 547–559.

Peirò, V. & M. Candela. 1995. Analyse des prélèvement dans la province d'Alicante. *Bulletin de l'Office National de la Chasse* 205: 22–31.

Pendleton, G.W. & J.R. Sauer. 1995. Delineating bird populations using ring recoveries. *Journal of Applied Statistics* 22: 1049–1055.

Penhallurick, R.D. 1978a. *The Birds of Cornwall and the Isles of Scilly*. Headland Publications, Penzance.

Penhallurick, R.D. 1978b. Chiffchaffs wintering at sewage-works in west Cornwall. *British Birds* 71: 183–186.

Pennycuick, C.J. 1989. *Bird Flight Performance: a practical calculation manual*. Oxford University Press, Oxford.

Pennycuick, C.J., Ó. Einarsson, T.A.M. Bradbury & M. Owen. 1996. Migrating Whooper Swans *Cygnus cygnus*: satellite tracks and flight performance calculations. *Journal of Avian Biology* 27: 118–134.

Pennycuick, C.J., T.A.M. Bradbury, Ó. Einarsson & M. Owen. 1999. Response to weather and light conditions of migratory Whooper Swans *Cygnus cygnus* and flying height profiles, observed with the Argos satellite system. *Ibis* 141: 434–443.

Percival, S.M. 1990. *Population trends in British Barn Owls* Tyto alba *and Tawny Owls* Strix aluco *in relation to environmental change*. Research Report 57. British Trust for Ornithology, Tring.

Percival, S.M. 1991. The population structure of Greenland Barnacle Geese *Branta leucopsis* on the wintering grounds on Islay. *Ibis* 133: 357–364.

Percival, S.M. 1993. The effects of reseeding, fertiliser application and disturbance on the use of grasslands by Barnacle Geese, and the implications for refuge management. *Journal of Applied Ecology* 30: 437–443.

Percival, S.M. & T. Percival. 1997. Feeding ecology of Barnacle Geese on their spring staging grounds in northern Iceland. *Ecogeography* 20: 461–465.

Perdeck, A.C. 1958. Two types of orientation in migrating Starlings, *Sturnus vulgaris* L., and Chaffinches, *Fringilla coelebs* L., as revealed by displacement experiments. *Ardea* 46: 1–37.

Perdeck, A.C. 1967. The Starling as a passage migrant in Holland. *Bird Study* 14: 129–152.

Perdeck, A.C. 1970. The standard direction of the Scandinavian Chaffinch during autumn migration throughout its area of passage. *Ardea* 58: 142–170.

Perdeck, A.C. 1977. The analysis of ringing data: pitfalls and prospects. *Die Vogelwarte* 29: 33–44.

Perdeck, A.C. & C. Clason. 1982. Flyways of Anatidae ringed in the Netherlands – an analysis based on ringing recoveries. *Proceedings of the Technical Meeting on Western Palearctic Migratory Bird Management* 2: 65–88.

Perdeck, A.C. & C. Clason. 1983. Sexual differences in migration and winter quarters of ducks ringed in the Netherlands. *Wildfowl* 34: 137–143.

Perrett, D.H. 1951. Observations on Shelduck. *Report of the Mid-Somerset Naturalists' Society* 1: 21–22.

Perring, F.H. & S.M. Walters. 1976. *Atlas of the British Flora*. Second edition. Botanical Society of the British Isles, London.

Perrins, C.M. 1965. Population fluctuations and clutch size in the Great Tit, *Parus major* L. *Journal of Animal Ecology* 34: 601–647.

Perrins, C.M. 1966. The effect of beech crops on Great Tit populations and movements. *British Birds* 59: 419–432.

Perrins, C.M. 1971. Age of first breeding and adult survival rates in the Swift. *Bird Study* 18: 61–70.

Perrins, C.M. 1979. *British Tits*. Collins, London.

Perrins, C.M. 1991. Survival rates of young Mute Swans *Cygnus olor*. In *Proceedings of the Third IWRB International Swan Symposium, Oxford 1989*, (eds J. Sears & P.J. Bacon), pp 95–103. *Wildfowl* suppl. 1.

Perrins, C.M. & M. de L. Brooke. 1976. Manx Shearwaters in the Bay of Biscay. *Bird Study* 23: 295–299.

Perrins, C. & P. Martin. 1999. *The impact of lost and discarded fishing line and tackle on Mute Swans – Phase 1*. R&D Technical Report W200. Environment Agency, Bristol.

Perrins, C.M. & J. Sears. 1991. Collisions with overhead wires as a cause of mortality in Mute Swans, *Cygnus olor*. *Wildfowl* 42: 5–11.

Perry, K.W. 2000. *The Ecology and Conservation of Great Crested Grebes* Podiceps cristatus *at Lough Neagh, Northern Ireland*. DPhil thesis, the University of Ulster at Coleraine, Co. Londonderry.

Perry, K.W., M. Antoniazza & K.R. Day. 1999. Abundance and habitat use by breeding Great Crested Grebes at Lough Neagh (N. Ireland) and at Lake Neuchâtel (Switzerland). *Irish Birds* 6: 269–276.

Persson, C. 1987. Sand Martin *Riparia riparia* populations in south-west Scania, Sweden, 1964 to 1968. *Journal of Zoology, London (B)* 1: 619–637.

Peterjohn, B.G. & J.R. Sauer. 1997. Population trends of Black Terns from the North American Breeding Bird Survey, 1966–1996. *Colonial Waterbirds* 20: 566–573.

Petersen, A. 1998. *Íslenskir Fuglar*. Vaka-Helgafell, Reykjavik.

Peterson, B.J. & B. Fry. 1987. Stable isotopes in ecosystem studies. *Annual Review of Ecology and Systematics* 18: 293–320.

Peterz, M. & B. Olden. 1987. Origin and mortality of Guillemots *Uria aalge* on the Swedish west coast. *Seabird* 16: 22–27.

Pettersson, J. & D. Hasselquist. 1985. Fat deposition and migration capacity of Robins *Erithacus rubecula* and Goldcrests *Regulus regulus* at Ottenby, Sweden. *Ringing & Migration* 6: 66–76.

Petty, S.J. 1992. Ecology of the Tawny Owl *Strix aluco* in the spruce forests of Northumberland and Argyll. PhD thesis, Open University, Milton Keynes.

Petty, S.J. 1996a. History of the Northern Goshawk *Accipiter gentilis* in Britain. In *The Introduction and Naturalisation of Birds* (eds J.S. Holmes & J.R. Simons), pp 95–102. The Stationery Office, London.

Petty, S.J. 1996b. *Reducing disturbance to Goshawks during the breeding season*. Research Information Note 267. Forestry Commission, Edinburgh.

Petty, S.J. & D.I.K. Anderson. 1996. *Population growth and breeding performance of Goshawks in the English/Scottish Borders during 1987–1996*. Forestry Commission Northern Research Station, Edinburgh.

Petty, S.J. & S.J. Thirgood. 1989. A radio tracking study of post-fledging mortality and movements of Tawny Owls in Argyll. *Ringing & Migration* 10: 75–82.

Petty, S.J., I.J. Patterson, D.I.K. Anderson, B. Little & M. Davison. 1995. Numbers, breeding performance and diet of the Sparrowhawk *Accipiter nisus* and Merlin *Falco columbarius* in relation to cone crops and seed-eating finches. *Forest Ecology and Management* 79: 133–146.

Petursson, G. & G. Thrainsson. 1999. Sjaldgaefir fuglar a Islandi fyrir 1981. *Fjölrit Náttúrufræðistofnunar* 37: 111.

Pfander, P.F. 1992. On the reasons for the late breeding of Hobbies in the south of the range. In *Modern Ornithology 1991* (ed E.N. Kurochkin), pp 77–85. Nauka, Moscow.

Philippona, J. 1992. Een huiszwaluwkolonie in Spanje. *Het Vogeljaar* 3: 126–127.

Phillipps, H. 1997. Common Tern recovery: more details. *Birding-Aus Mailing List Archive 1997* at http://www.cse.unsw.edu.au/archives/birding-aus/hypermail/1997/0217.html.

Phillips, J. 2000. Autumn vagrancy: 'reverse migration' and migratory orientation. *Ringing & Migration* 20: 35–38.

Phillips, J.H. 1963a. The distribution of the Sooty Shearwater around the British Isles. *British Birds* 56: 197–203.

Phillips, J.H. 1963b. The pelagic distribution of the Sooty Shearwater *Procellaria grisea*. *Ibis* 105: 340–353.

Phillips, J.H. & S.L.B. Lee. 1966. Movements of Manx Shearwaters off Erris Head, Western Ireland, in the autumn. *Bird Study* 13: 284–296.

Phillips, N.J. 1994. Autumn migration and weights of Blackcaps *Sylvia atricapilla* and Garden Warblers *S. borin* at an inland site in southern England. *Ringing & Migration* 15: 17–26.

Phillips, V.E. 1991. Pochard *Aythya ferina* use of chironomid-rich feeding habitat in winter. *Bird Study* 38: 118–122.

Pianka, E.R. 1966. Latitudinal gradients in species diversity: a review of concepts. *American Naturalist* 100: 33–46.

Picozzi, N. 1983. Growth and sex of nestling Merlins in Orkney. *Ibis* 125: 377–382.

Picozzi, N. 1984. Breeding biology of polygynous Hen Harriers *Circus c. cyaneus* in Orkney. *Ornis Scandinavica* 15: 1–10.

Picozzi, N. & R. Hewson. 1970. Kestrels, Short-eared Owls and Field Voles in Eskdalemuir in 1970. *Scottish Birds* 6: 185–190.

Pienkowski, M.W. 1975. *Studies on coastal birds and wetlands in Morocco in 1972*. University of East Anglia, Norwich.

Pienkowski, M.W. 1976. Recurrence of waders on autumn migration sites in Morocco. *Die Vogelwarte* 28: 293–297.

Pienkowski, M.W. 1984. Breeding biology and population dynamics of Ringed Plovers *Charadrius hiaticula* in Britain and Greenland: nest predation as a possible factor limiting distribution and time of breeding. *Journal of Zoology, London* 202: 83–114.

Pienkowski, M.W. & P.R. Evans. 1978. Shelducks on the Firth of Forth. *Edinburgh Ringing Group Report* 6: 10–18.

Pienkowski, M.W. & P.R. Evans. 1979. The origins of Shelducks moulting on the Forth. *Bird Study* 26: 195–196.

Pienkowski, M.W. & A. Pienkowski. 1983. WSG project on the movement of wader populations in western Europe, eighth progress report. *Wader Study Group Bulletin* 38: 13–22.

Pienkowski, M.W., P.J. Knight, D.J. Stanyard & F.B. Argyle. 1976. The primary moult of waders on the Atlantic coast of Morocco. *Ibis* 118: 347–365.

Pienkowski, M.W., P.R. Evans & D.J. Townshend. 1985. Leap-frog and other migration patterns of waders: a critique of the Alerstam and Högstedt hypothesis, and some alternatives. *Ornis Scandinavica* 16: 61–70.

Piersma, T. 1986. Breeding waders in Europe: a review of population size estimates and a bibliography of information sources. *Wader Study Group Bulletin* 48 (suppl.): 1–116.

Piersma, T. 1988a. Body size, nutrient reserves and diet of Red-necked and Slavonian Grebes *Podiceps grisegena* and *P. auritus* on Lake IJsselmeer, the Netherlands. *Bird Study* 35: 13–24.

Piersma, T. 1988b. The annual moult cycle of Great Crested Grebes. *Ardea* 76: 82–95.

Piersma, T. & A.J. Baker. 2000. Life history characteristics and the conservation of migratory shorebirds. In *Behaviour and conservation* (eds L.M. Gosling & W.J. Sutherland), pp 105–124. Cambridge University Press, Cambridge.

Piersma, T. & N.C. Davidson (eds). 1992. The Migration of Knots. *Wader Study Group Bulletin* 64 (suppl.). 209 pp.

Piersma, T. & J.M. Everaarts. 1996. Build-up of red blood cells in refuelling Bar-tailed Godwits in relation to individual migratory quality. *Condor* 98: 363–370.

Piersma, T. & R.E. Gill Jr. 1998. Guts don't fly: small digestive organs in obese Bar-tailed Godwits. *Auk* 115: 196–203.

Piersma, T. & A. Koolhaas. 1997. *Shorebirds, shellfish(eries) and sediments around Griend, western Wadden Sea, 1988–1996*. NIOZ report 1997-7. NIOZ, Texel, the Netherlands.

Piersma, T. & Å. Lindström. 1997. Rapid reversible changes in organ size as a component of adaptive behaviour. *Trends in Ecology & Evolution* 12: 134–138.

Piersma, T. & Y. Ntiamoa-Baidu. 1995. *Waterbird ecology and the management of coastal wetlands in Ghana*. NIOZ report 1995–6. NIOZ/Ghana Wildlife Society.

Piersma, T., J.J. Vlug & J.H.P. Westhof. 1986. Twintig jaar ruiende futen bij de Mokkebank, 1966–85. *Vanellus* 39: 27–37.

Piersma, T., M. Klaassen, J.H. Bruggemann, A.-M. Blomert, A. Gueye, Y. Ntiamoa-Baidu & N.E. van Brederode. 1990. Seasonal timing of the spring departure of waders from the Banc d'Arguin, Mauritania. *Ardea* 78: 123–134.

Piersma, T., R. Joekstra, A. Dekinga, A. Koolhaas, P. Wolf, P. Battley & P. Wiersma. 1993. Scale and intensity of intertidal habitat use by Knots *Calidris canutus* in the western Wadden Sea in relation to food, friends and foes. *Netherlands Journal of Sea Research* 31: 331–357.

Piersma, T., J. van Gils & P. Wiersma. 1996. Family Scolopacidae (Sandpipers, Snipes and Phalaropes). In *Handbook of the Birds of the World, Volume 3* (eds J. del Hoyo, A. Elliott & J. Sargatal), pp 444–533. Lynx Edicions, Barcelona.

Piersma, T., R. van Aelst, K. Kurk, H. Berkhoudt & L.R.M. Maas. 1998. A new pressure sensory mechanism for prey detection in birds: the use of principles of seabed dynamics? *Proceedings of the Royal Society of London* 265: 1377–1383.

Pilastro, A. & F. Spina. 1997. Ecological and morphological correlates of residual fat reserves in passerine migrants at their spring arrival in southern Europe. *Journal of Avian Biology* 28: 309–318.

Pilastro, A. & F. Spina. 1999. Fat accumulation in pre-migratory roosting Barn Swallows in Europe. In *Proceedings of the Twenty-second International Ornithological Congress, Durban* (eds N.J. Adams & R.H. Slotow). BirdLife South Africa, Johannesburg. (CD-ROM).

Pilastro, A., F. Spina & P. Micheloni. 1998a. Geographical variation in pre-migratory condition of Swallows *Hirundo rustica* in Italy. *Ringing & Migration* 19: 67–74.

Pilastro, A., S. Macchio, A. Massi, A. Montemaggiori & F. Spina. 1998b. Spring migratory routes of eight trans-Saharan passerines through the central and western Mediterranean; results from a network of insular and coastal ringing sites. *Ibis* 140: 591–598.

Pinowski, J. 1965. Dispersal of young Tree Sparrows (*Passer m. montanus* L.). *Bulletin de l'Académie Polonaise des Sciences classe II, Série des Sciences Biologique* 13: 509–514.

Pirot, J.-Y. & D. Pont. 1987. Le Canard Souchet (*Anas clypeata* L.) hivernant en Camargue: alimentation, comportement et dispersion nocturne. *Revue d'Ecologie (Terre et Vie)* 42: 59–79.

Pithon, J.A. & C. Dytham. 1999. Census of the British Ring-necked Parakeet *Psittacula krameri* population by simultaneous counts of roosts. *Bird Study* 46: 112–115.

Pithon, J.A. & C. Dytham. 2001. Determination of the origin of British feral Rose-ringed Parakeets. *British Birds* 94: 74–79.

Pitts, M. & M. Roberts. 1998. *Fairweather Eden: life in Britain half a million years ago as revealed by the excavations at Boxgrove*. Century, London.

Pollitt, M.S., P.A. Cranswick, A.J. Musgrove, C. Hall, R.D. Hearn, J.A. Robinson & S.J. Holloway. 2000. *The Wetland Bird Survey 1998–99: Wildfowl and Wader Counts*. BTO/WWT/RSPB/JNCC, Slimbridge.

Pollock, C.M., R. Mavor, C.R. Weir, A. Reid, R.W. White, M.L. Tasker, A. Webb & J.B. Reid. 2000. *The distribution of seabirds and marine mammals in the Atlantic Frontier, north and west of Scotland*. Joint Nature Conservation Committee, Aberdeen.

Poole, A.F. 1989. *Ospreys: a Natural and Unnatural History*. Cambridge University Press, Cambridge.

Poorter, E.P.R. 1990. Pleisterplaasten van Nederlandse Lepelaars (*Platalea leucorodia*). *Technisch Rapport* 4. Vogelbescherming Nederland, Zeist.

Porter, J.M. & J.C. Coulson. 1987. Long-term changes in recruitment to the breeding group and the quality of recruits in a Kittiwake *Rissa tridactyla* colony. *Journal of Animal Ecology* 56: 675–689.

Porter, R.F. 1993. Autumn migration of passerines and near passerines at the Bosphorus, Turkey. *Sandgrouse* 5: 45–74.

Post, P.W. 1967. Manx, Audubon's and Little Shearwaters in the northwestern North Atlantic. *Bird-Banding* 38: 278–305.

Post, P.W. & R.H. Lewis. 1995. Lesser Black-backed Gull in the Americas. Occurrence and sub-specific identity. Part II. Field identification. *Birding* 27: 370–381.

Potts, G.R. 1969. The influence of eruptive movements, age, population size and other factors on the survival of the Shag *Phalacrocorax aristotelis (L.)*. *Journal of Animal Ecology* 38: 53–102.

Potts, G.R. 1986. *The Partridge: pesticides, predation and conservation*. Collins, London.

Pounder, B. 1976. Waterfowl at effluent discharges in Scottish coastal waters. *Scottish Birds* 9: 5–36.

Power, D.M. & D.M. Ainley. 1986. Seabird geographic variation: similarity among populations of Leach's Storm-Petrel. *Auk* 103: 575–585.

Powers, K.D. & J. Cherry. 1983. Loon migrations off the coast of the north-eastern United States. *Wilson Bulletin* 95: 125–132.

Prakash, V. 1989. Population and distribution of raptors in Keoladea National Park, Bharatpur, India. In *Raptors in the Modern World* (eds B.-U. Meyburg & R.D. Chancellor), pp 129–137. World Working Group on Birds of Prey and Owls, Berlin.

Prater, A.J. 1973. The wintering population of Ruffs in Britain and Ireland. *Bird Study* 20: 245–250.

Prater, A.J. 1975. The wintering population of the Black-tailed Godwit. *Bird Study* 22: 169–176.

Prater, A.J. 1981. *Estuary Birds of Britain and Ireland*. T. & A.D. Poyser, Calton.

Prater, A.J. 1989. Ringed Plover *Charadrius hiaticula* breeding population of the United Kingdom. *Bird Study* 36: 154–160.

Prater, A.J. & M. Davies. 1978. Wintering Sanderlings in Britain. *Bird Study* 25: 33–38.

Pravosudov, V.V. 1993. Social organisation of the Nuthatch *Sitta europaea asiatica*. *Ornis Scandinavica* 24: 290–296.

Prestt, I. 1965. An enquiry into the recent breeding status of some of the smaller birds of prey and crows in Britain. *Bird Study* 12: 196–221.

Preuss, N.O. 1981. Preliminary results of neck-collared *Cygnus cygnus cygnus*. In *Proceedings of the Second International Swan Symposium, Sapporo, Japan 1980* (eds G.V.T. Matthews & M. Smart), pp 141–144. International Waterfowl Research Bureau, Slimbridge.

Preuss, N.O. 2001. Hans Christian Cornelius Mortensen: aspects of his life and of the history of bird ringing. *Ardea* 89 (special issue): 1–6.

Prevost, Y.A. 1982. *The wintering ecology of Ospreys in Senegambia*. PhD thesis, University of Edinburgh.

Priede, I.G. & S.M. Swift (eds). 1992. *Wildlife Telemetry: remote monitoring and tracking of animals*. Ellis Horwood, Chichester.

Prins, H.H.T. 1986. Spring migration of Cuckoo through the Rift Valley in northern Tanzania. *Ardea* 74: 215–217.

Pritchard, D.E., S.D. Housden, G.P. Mudge, C.A. Galbraith & M.W. Pienkowski. 1992. *Important Bird Areas in the United Kingdom including the Channel Islands and the Isle of Man*. RSPB/JNCC, Sandy.

Prokosch, P. 1988. Das Schleswig-Holsteinische Wattenmeer als Frühjahrs-Aufenthaltsgebiet arktischer Watvogel-Populationen am Beispiel von Kiebitzregenpfeifer (*Pluvialis squatarola*, L. 1758), Knutt (*Calidris canutus*, L. 1758) und Pfuhlschnepfe (*Limosa lapponica*, L. 1758). *Corax* 12: 274–442.

Prop, J., M.R. van Eerden & R.H. Drent. 1984. Reproductive success of the Barnacle Goose *Branta leucopsis* in relation to food exploitation on the breeding grounds, western Svalbard. *Norsk Polarinstitutt Skrifter* 181: 87–117.

Prŷs-Jones, R.P. 1977. *Aspects of Reed Bunting ecology, with comparisons with the Yellowhammer*. DPhil thesis, University of Oxford.

Prŷs-Jones, R.P. 1984. Migration patterns of the Reed Bunting, *Emberiza schoeniclus schoeniclus*, and the dependence of wintering distribution on environmental conditions. *Gerfaut* 74: 15–37.

Ptushenko, E.S. & A.A. Inozemtsev. 1968. *Biologiya i khozyaystvennoe znachenie ptits Moskovskoy oblasti i sopredel'nykh territoriy*. MGU, Moscow.

Pulich, W. Jr. 1982. Documentation and status of Cory's Shearwater in the western Gulf of Mexico. *Wilson Bulletin* 94: 381–385.

Pulliainen, E. & L. Saari. 1991. Breeding biology of the Wood Sandpiper *Tringa glareola* in eastern Finnish Lapland. *Ornis Fennica* 68: 127–128.

Quinn, A. & P. Clement. 1971. *The Beachy Head Bird Report 1960 to 1970*. Beachy Head Ringing Group.

Quinn, J.L. & Y. Kokorev. 1999. A westward extension to the known breeding range of Sabine's Gull *Larus sabini* in Siberia. *Bulletin of the British Ornithologists' Club* 119: 206.

Quinn, J.L., L. Still, J.S. Kirby, M.C. Carrier & P. Lambdon. 1997. Scaup *Aythya marila* numbers and the cockle *Cardium edule* fishery on the Solway Firth: are they related? *Wildfowl* 47: 187–193.

Rabbitts, B. (ed). 1999. *Outer Hebrides (Western Isles) Bird Report 1998*.

Rabøl, J. 1969. Reversed migration as the cause of westward vagrancy by four *Phylloscopus* warblers. *British Birds* 62: 89–92.

Rabøl, J. 1973. Orientation experiments with Whitethroats *Sylvia communis* and Lesser Whitethroat *Sylvia curruca*. *Dansk Ornithologisk Forenings Tidsskrift* 67: 85–94.

Rabøl, J. 1985. The orientation of vagrant passerines on the Faeroe Islands, September 1984. *Dansk Ornithologisk Forenings Tidsskrift* 79: 133–140.

Rabouam, C., V. Bretagnolle, Y. Bigot & G. Periquet. 2000. Genetic relationships of Cory's Shearwater: parentage, mating assortment, and geographic differentiation revealed by DNA fingerprinting. *Auk* 113: 651–662.

Radford, M.C. 1960. Common Gull movements shown by ringing returns. *Bird Study* 7: 81–93.

Radford, M.C. 1962. British ringing recoveries of the Black-headed Gull. *Bird Study* 9: 42–55.

Radford, M.C. 1968. The autumn migration records of the Red-breasted Flycatcher. *Bird Study* 15: 154–160.

Rae, R. 1986. Clap-netting Snow Buntings. *Ringers' Bulletin* 6: 116.

Rae, R., M. Nicoll & R.W. Summers. 1986. The distribution of Hardangervidda Purple Sandpipers outwith the breeding season. *Scottish Birds* 14: 68–73.

Rafe, R.W. (ed). 1996. The 1994 Suffolk Bird Report. *Suffolk Birds* 44: 28–146.

Rands, M.R.W. 1986. The survival of gamebird (Galliformes) chicks in relation to pesticide use on cereals. *Ibis* 128: 57–64.

Rands, M.R.W. 1987. Recruitment of Grey and Red-legged Partridges (*Perdix perdix* and *Alectoris rufa*) in relation to population density and habitat. *Journal of Zoology, London* 212: 407–418.

Rankin, M.N. & E.A.G. Duffey. 1948. A study of the bird life of the North Atlantic. *British Birds* 41 (suppl.): 1–42.

Ratcliffe, D.A. 1976. Observations on the breeding of the Golden Plover in Great Britain. *Bird Study* 23: 63–116.

Ratcliffe, D.A. 1993. *The Peregrine Falcon*. Second edition. T. & A.D. Poyser, London.

Ratcliffe, D.A. 1997. *The Raven*. T. & A.D. Poyser, London.

Ratcliffe, N. 1997. Estimates of Roseate Tern survival and natal fidelity in Britain and Ireland from ring resightings. *Proceedings of the Seventh Roseate Tern Workshop* (ed L.R. Monteiro), pp 28–30. University of Azores, Horta, Portugal.

Raven, S. & J.C. Coulson. 1997. The distribution and abundance of *Larus* gulls nesting on buildings in Britain and Ireland. *Bird Study* 44: 13–34.

Rebecca, G.W. 1987. Merlin ringing: some results from Grampian. *Grampian Ringing Group Report* 5: 31–43.

Rebecca, G.W. 1989. Merlins at offshore locations in the North Sea. *North Sea Bird Club Annual Report 8, 1987–88*: 69–77.

Rebecca, G.W. & I.P. Bainbridge. 1998. The breeding status of the Merlin *Falco columbarius* in Britain in 1993–94. *Bird Study* 45: 172–187.

Redfern, C.P.F. 1979. Survival in relation to sex in Reed Warbler populations. *Wicken Fen Group Report* 10: 34–38.

Redfern, C.P.F. & P.J. Alker. 1996. Plumage development and post-juvenile moult in the Sedge Warbler *Acrocephalus schoenobaenus*. *Journal of Avian Biology* 27: 157–163.

Redfern, C.P.F. & J.A. Clark. 2001. *Ringers' Manual*. British Trust for Ornithology, Thetford.

Redman, P.S. & W.D. Hooke. 1954. Firecrests in Britain 1952–1953. *British Birds* 47: 324–335.

Redpath, S.M. 1995. Habitat fragmentation and the individual: Tawny Owl *Strix aluco* in woodland patches. *Journal of Animal Ecology* 64: 652–661.

Ree, V. 1977. Underartene av svartstrupe, *Saxicola torquata* (L.), i Norge. *Fauna* 30: 41–47.

Reed, A. 1975. Migration, homing and mortality of Eiders *Somateria mollissima dresseri* of the St Lawrence Estuary, Quebec. *Ornis Scandinavica* 6: 41–47.

Reed, A. 1993. Duration of family bonds of Brent Geese *Branta bernicla* on the Pacific coast of North America. *Wildfowl* 44: 33–38.

Reed, A. & A.J. Erskine. 1986. Populations of the Common Eider in eastern North America: their size and status. In *Eider Ducks in Canada* (ed A. Reed), pp 156–175. CWS Report 47. Canadian Wildlife Service, Ottawa.

Reed, S. 1995. Factors limiting the distribution and population size of Twite (*Carduelis flavirostris*) in the Pennines. *Naturalist* 120: 93–102.

Reed, T. 1985. Estimates of British breeding wader populations. *Wader Study Group Bulletin* 45: 11–12.

Rees, E.C. 1982. The effect of photoperiod on the timing of spring migration in the Bewick's Swan. *Wildfowl* 33: 119–132.

Rees, E.C. 1987. Conflict of choice within pairs of Bewick's Swans regarding their migratory movement to and from the wintering grounds. *Animal Behaviour* 35: 1685–1693.

Rees, E.C. 1988. *Aspects of the migration and movements of individual Bewick's Swans*. PhD thesis, University of Bristol.

Rees, E.C. 1991. Distribution within the USSR of Bewick's Swans *Cygnus columbianus bewickii* marked in Britain. In *Proceedings of the Third IWRB International Swan Symposium, Oxford 1989* (eds J. Sears & P.J. Bacon), pp 209–213. *Wildfowl* suppl. 1.

Rees, E.C. & P.J. Bacon. 1996. Migratory tradition in Bewick's Swan (*Cygnus columbianus bewickii*). In *Proceedings of the Anatidae 2000 Conference, Strasbourg, France, 5–9 December 1994* (eds M. Birkan, J. van Vessem, P. Havet, J. Madsen, B. Trolliet & M. Moser). *Gibier Faune Sauvage* 13: 407–420.

Rees, E.C. & J.M. Bowler. 1991. Feeding activities of Bewick's Swans *Cygnus columbianus bewickii* at a migratory site in Estonia. In *Proceedings of the Third IWRB International Swan Symposium, Oxford 1989* (eds J. Sears & P.J. Bacon), pp 249–255. *Wildfowl* suppl. 1.

Rees, E. & J. Bowler. 1997. Fifty years of swan research and conservation by The Wildfowl & Wetlands Trust. *Wildfowl* 47: 249–263.

Rees, E.C., J.M. Bowler & L. Butler. 1990. Bewick's and Whooper Swans: the 1989–90 season. *Wildfowl* 41: 176–181.

Rees, E.C., P. Lievesley, R.A. Pettifor & C. Perrins. 1996. Mate fidelity in swans: an interspecific comparison. In *Partnerships in Birds: the Study of Monogamy* (ed J.M. Black), pp 118–137. Oxford University Press, Oxford.

Rees, E.C., J.M. Bowler & J.H. Beekman. 1997a. *Cygnus columbianus* Bewick's Swan and Whistling Swan. *BWP Update* 1: 63–74.

Rees, E., Ó. Einarsson & B. Laubek. 1997b. *Cygnus cygnus* Whooper Swan. *BWP Update* 1: 27–35.

Rees, E.C., J.S. Kirby & A. Gilburn. 1997c. Site selection by swans wintering in Britain and Ireland; the importance of habitat and geographic location. *Ibis* 139: 337–352.

Rees, G.H. 1986. Mediterranean races of Manx Shearwater in British waters. *British Birds* 79: 351.

Rehfisch, M.M., N.A. Clark, R.H.W. Langston & J.J.D. Greenwood. 1996. A guide to the provision of refuges for waders: an analysis of 30 years of ringing data from the Wash, England. *Journal of Applied Ecology* 33: 673–687.

Rehfisch, M.M., C.V. Wernham & J.H. Marchant (eds). 1999. *Population, distribution, movements and survival of fish-eating birds in Great Britain*. Department of the Environment, Transport and the Regions, London.

Reinikainen, A. 1937. The irregular migrations of the Crossbill, *Loxia c. curvirostra*, and their relation to the cone-crop of conifers. *Ornis Fennica* 14: 55–64.

Renssen, T.A. & R.L. Vogel. 1993. Recente ontwikkelingen van de Raaf *Corvus corax* in Nederland. *Limosa* 66: 107–166.

Reymond, A. & O. Zuchuat. 1995. Axial migration routes in Cormorants *Phalacrocorax carbo* passing through or wintering in Switzerland. *Ardea* 83: 275–280.

Reynolds, A. 1978. Chiffchaffs at Rye Meads. *Ringing & Migration* 2: 38–41.

Richardson, M.G. 1990. The distribution and status of Whimbrel *Numenius p. phaeopus* in Shetland and Britain. *Bird Study* 37: 61–68.

Richardson, R.A., M.J. Seago & A. Church. 1957. Collared Doves in Norfolk: a bird new to the British List. *British Birds* 50: 239–246.

Richardson, W.J. 1978. Timing and amount of bird migration in relation to weather – a review. *Oikos* 30: 224–272.

Richardson, W.J. 1991. Wind and orientation of migrating birds: a review. In *Orientation in Birds* (ed P. Berthold), pp 226–249. Birkhäuser Verlag, Basel.

Richdale, L.E. 1963. Biology of the Sooty Shearwater *Puffinus griseus*. *Proceedings of the Zoological Society of London* 141: 1–117.

Richner, H. 1986. Winter feeding strategies of individually marked herons. *Animal Behaviour* 34: 881–886.

Richner, H. 1988. Temporal and spatial patterns in the abundance of wintering Red-breasted Mergansers *Mergus serrator* in an estuary. *Ibis* 130: 73–78.

Riddiford, N. 1985. Grounded migrants versus radar: a case study. *Bird Study* 32: 116–121.

Riddiford, N.J. 1991. *Migration strategies and population fluctuations: an explanation of the occurrence of birds at Dungeness Bird Observatory during the 25 year period 1953–77*. MPhil thesis, Leicester Polytechnic.

Riddington, R. 1992. *Some aspects of the dispersal and post-fledging ecology of a population of Great Tits (*Parus major*)*. DPhil thesis, University of Oxford.

Riddington, R. & N. Ward. 1998. The invasion of Northern Bullfinches to Britain in autumn 1994, with particular reference to the Northern Isles. *Ringing & Migration* 9: 48–52.

Riddle, G. 1986. Kestrels attending oil installations in the North Sea. *North Sea Bird Club Annual Report 6, 1985*: 63–70.

Ridgill, S.C. & A.D. Fox. 1990. *Cold weather movements of waterfowl in Western Europe*. Special Publication 13. International Waterfowl & Wetlands Research Bureau, Slimbridge.

Ridley, M.W. 1980. The breeding behaviour and feeding ecology of Grey Phalaropes *Phalaropus fulicarius* in Svalbard. *Ibis* 122: 210–226.

Rimmer, C.C. & C.H. Darmstadt. 1996. Non-breeding site fidelity in Northern Shrikes. *Journal of Field Ornithology* 67: 360–366.

Ristow, D., F. Feldmann, N. Scharlau & M. Wink. 1990. Population structure, philopatry and mortality of Cory's Shearwater *Calonectris diomedea*. *Die Vogelwelt* 111: 172–181.

Ristow, D., P. Berthold, D. Hashmi & U. Querner. 2000. Satellite tracking of Cory's Shearwater migration. *Condor* 10: 696–699.

Roalkvam, R. 1994. Gråhegre *Ardea cinerea*. In *Norsk Fugleatlas* (eds J.O. Gjershaug, P.G. Thingstad, S. Eldøy & S. Byrkjeland), pp 52–53. Norsk Ornitologisk Forening, Klæbu.

Robbins, C.S. 1980. Prediction of future Nearctic landbird vagrants to Europe. *British Birds* 73: 448–457.

Robel, R.J. 1969. Movements and flock stratification within a population of Blackcocks in Scotland. *Journal of Animal Ecology* 38: 755–763.

Roberts, G. 1991. Winter movements of Sanderlings (*Calidris alba*) between feeding sites. *Acta Oecologica* 12: 281–294.

Roberts, J.L. & N. Bowman. 1986. Diet and ecology of Short-eared Owls *Asio flammeus* breeding on heather moor. *Bird Study* 33: 12–17.

Roberts, J.L. & M.S. Jones. 1999. Increase of a population of Ravens (*Corvus corax*) in N.E. Wales – its dynamics and possible causation. *Welsh Birds* 2: 121–130.

Roberts, P.J. 1985. The Choughs of Bardsey. *British Birds* 78: 217–232.

Roberts, P. 1986. *The Birds of Bardsey*. Bardsey Bird and Field Observatory.

Roberts, P.J. 1989. The numbers, distribution and movements of Chough in Wales. In *Choughs and Land-use in Europe* (eds E.M. Bignal & D.J. Curtis), pp 9–11. Scottish Chough Study Group, Paisley.

Roberts, S.J., J.M.S. Lewis & I.T. Williams. 1999. Breeding European Honey-Buzzards in Britain. *British Birds* 92: 326–345.

Robertson, D.G. 1997. The structure of a Goldfinch (*Carduelis carduelis*) flock in winter. *Tay Ringing Group Report 1996–97*: 4–7.

Robertson, I.S. 1982. The origin of migrant Merlins on Fair Isle. *British Birds* 75: 108–111.

Robertson, P.A. 1996. Naturalised introduced gamebirds in Britain. In *The Introduction and Naturalisation of Birds* (eds J.S. Holmes & J.R. Simons), pp 63–69. The Stationery Office, London.

Robinson, J.A. 1999. Migration and morphometrics of the Red-breasted Merganser *Mergus serrator* in northern Eurasia and the implications for conservation of this species in Britain & Ireland. *Wildfowl* 50: 139–148.

Rock, P. 1993. *Roof-nesting gulls in Bristol*. Unpublished report.

Rock, P. 1994. *Roof-nesting gulls in Bristol*. Unpublished report.

Rock, P. 1999. The efficacy of the colour-ringing system used for Herring *Larus argentatus* and Lesser Black-backed Gulls *Larus fuscus* in Bristol, 1980–1997. *Ringing & Migration* 19: 306–310.

Rodebrand, S. 1996. Ängshöken *Circus pygargus* på Öland. *Calidris* 25: 99–116.

Rödl, T. 1994. The wintering of territorial Stonechat pairs *Saxicola torquata* in Israel. *Journal für Ornithologie* 136: 423–433.

Rodrigues, M. & H.Q.P. Crick. 1997. The breeding biology of the Chiffchaff *Phylloscopus collybita* in Britain: a comparison of an intensive study with records of the BTO nest record scheme. *Bird Study* 44: 374–383.

Rodwell, S.P., A. Sauvage, S.J.R. Rumsey & A. Braunlich. 1996. An annotated check-list of birds occurring at the Parc National des Oiseaux du Djoudj in Senegal, 1984–1994. *Malimbus* 18: 74–111.

Rogacheva, H. 1992. *The Birds of Central Siberia*. Husum Druck- und Verlagsgesellschaft, Husum, Germany.

Rogers, M.J. (ed). 1984. *The Isles of Scilly Bird Report 1983*. Cornwall Bird Watching and Preservation Society.

Rogers, M.J. & the Rarities Committee. 1986. Report on rare birds in Great Britain in 1985. *British Birds* 79: 526–588.

Rogers, M.J. & the Rarities Committee. 1998. Report on rare birds in Great Britain in 1997. *British Birds* 91: 455–517.

Roggeman, W. 1977. Selectieve lijst van terugvangsten van in Belgie geringde vogels. *Gerfaut* 67: 277–320.

Rönkä, A. 1996. Distribution, status and population trends in the Temminck's Stint *Calidris temminckii* in the Finnish Bothnian Bay. *Ornis Fennica* 73: 1–11.

Roper, P. 1995. The status of Water Pipits at Rye Meads Sewage Works, Hertfordshire. *Rye Meads Ringing Group 13th Report 1992–1994*: 53–58.

Rose, P.M. 1995. *Western Palearctic and South-West Asia Waterfowl Census 1994*. Publication 35. International Waterfowl & Wetlands Research Bureau, Slimbridge.

Rose, P.M. & D.A. Scott. 1994. *Waterfowl population estimates*. Special Publication 29. International Waterfowl & Wetlands Research Bureau, Slimbridge.

Rose, P.M. & D.A. Scott. 1997. *Waterfowl population estimates*. Second edition. Special Publication 44. Wetlands International, Wageningen, the Netherlands.

Roselaar, C.S. 1979. Fluctuaties in aantallen Krombekstrandlopers *Calidris ferruginea*. *Watervogels* 4: 202–210.

Round, P.D. & R.L. Swann. 1977. Aspects of the breeding of Cory's Shearwaters *Calonectris diomedea* in Crete. *Ibis* 119: 350–353.

Rüger, A., C. Prentice & M. Owen. 1986. *Results of the IWRB International Waterfowl Census 1967–1983*. Special Publication 6. International Waterfowl Research Bureau, Slimbridge.

Rumsey, S.J.R. 1975. Mist-netting Grasshopper Warblers. *Ringers' Bulletin* 4: 104.

Russell, A.F. 1999. *Ecological constraints and the cooperative breeding system of the Long-tailed Tit* Aegithalos caudatus. PhD thesis, University of Sheffield.

Ruttledge, R.F. 1970. Winter distribution and numbers of Scaup, Long-tailed Duck and Common Scoter in Ireland. *Bird Study* 17: 241–246.

Ruttledge, R.F. 1990. Exceptional influx of Little Gulls on the North Wicklow coast. *Irish Birding News* 1: 73–74.

Ruttledge, R.F. & M.A. Ogilvie. 1979. The past and current status of the Greenland White-fronted Goose in Ireland and Britain. *Irish Birds* 1: 293–363.

Ruxton, J. 1962. Goose Conservation: Canada Goose. *WAGBI Annual Report 1961–1962*: 36–40.

Ryan, P.G. 1989. The distribution and abundance of Long-tailed Skuas off southern Africa. *Ostrich* 60: 89–90.

Rydzewski, W. 1951. A historical review of bird marking. *Dansk Ornithologisk Forenings Tidsskrift* 45: 61–95.

Rydzewski, W. 1956. The nomadic movements and migrations of the European Common Heron *Ardea cinerea* L. *Ardea* 44: 171–188.

Rymkevich, T.A. & J.G. Bojarinova. 1996. Variation in the extent of post-juvenile moult in the Great Tit near Lake Ladoga (Russia). *Bird Study* 43: 47–59.

Sæther, B.-E. 1979. Trekket hos den norske populasjon av Gråtrost *Turdus pilaris* basert på ringmerking. *Fauna Norvegica serie C, Cinclus* 2: 7–14.

Sæther, B.-E., J. Tufto, S. Engen, K. Jerstad, O.W. Rostad & J.E. Skåtan. 2000. Population dynamical consequences of climate change for a small temperate songbird. *Science* 287: 854–856.

Sagot, F. 1991. Milan royal *Milvus milvus*. In *Atlas des oiseaux de France en hiver* (eds D. Yeatman-Berthelot & G. Jarry), pp 146–147. Société Ornithologique de France, Paris.

Saino, N. & S. Villa. 1992. Pair composition and reproductive success across a hybrid zone of Carrion Crows and Hooded Crows. *Auk* 109: 543–555.

Salewski, V., F. Bairlein & B. Leisler. 2000. Site fidelity of Palearctic passerine migrants in the Northern Guinea savanna zone, West Africa. *Die Vogelwarte* 40: 298–301.

Salmon, D.G. 1981. *Wildfowl & Wader Counts 1980–81. The results of the National Wildfowl Counts and Birds of Estuaries Enquiry.* Wildfowl Trust, Slimbridge.

Salmon, D.G. 1982. *Wildfowl & Wader Counts 1981–82. The results of the National Wildfowl Counts and Birds of Estuaries Enquiry.* Wildfowl Trust, Slimbridge.

Salmon, D.G. (ed). 1987. Wildfowl. In *Wildfowl & Wader Counts 1986–1987* (eds D.G. Salmon, R.P. Prŷs-Jones & J.S. Kirby), pp 7–38. Wildfowl Trust, Slimbridge.

Salmon, D.G. (ed). 1988. The numbers and distribution of Scaup *Aythya marila* in Britain and Ireland. *Biological Conservation* 43: 267–278.

Salmon, D.G. & J.M. Black. 1986. The January 1986 Whooper Swan census in Britain, Ireland and Iceland. *Wildfowl* 37: 172–174.

Salomonsen, F. 1947. The geographical variation in the European Whimbrels. *Dansk Ornithologisk Forenings Tidsskrift* 41: 143–145.

Salomonsen, F. 1950. *Grønlands Fugle.* [The Birds of Greenland.] Munkgaard, Copenhagen.

Salomonsen, F. 1956. The Greenland bird ringing system. *The Ring* 7: 130–133.

Salomonsen, F. 1967a. *Fuglene på Grønland.* Rhodos, Copenhagen.

Salomonsen, F. 1967b. Migratory movements of the Arctic Tern (*Sterna paradisaea*) in the southern ocean. *Kongelige Danske Videnskabernes Selskabs Biol. Meddelelser* 24: 1–42.

Salomonsen, F. 1968. The moult migration. *Wildfowl* 19: 5–24.

Salomonsen, F. 1971. Tolvte foreløbige liste over genfundne grønlandske ringfugle. *Dansk Ornithologisk Forenings Tidsskrift* 65: 11–19.

Salomonsen, F. 1979. Ornithological and ecological studies in S.W. Greenland (59° 46' – 62° 27' N. Lat.). *Meddelelser om Grønland* 204: 1–214.

Salvi, A. 1987. Crane, *Grus grus*, migration in France from autumn 1981 to spring 1984. *Aquila* 93–94: 107–113.

Samuel, M.D., J.Y. Takekawa, V.V. Baranyuk & D.L. Orthmeyer. 1999. Effects of avian cholera on survival of Lesser Snow Geese *Anser caerulescens*: an experimental approach. *Bird Study* 46 (suppl.): S239–247.

Sandberg, R., J. Pettersson & K. Persson. 1991. Migratory orientation of free-flying Robins *Erithacus rubecula* and Pied Flycatchers *Ficedula hypoleuca* – release experiments. *Ornis Scandinavica* 22: 1–11.

Sandell, M. & H.G. Smith. 1991. Dominance, prior occupancy, and winter residency in the Great Tit *Parus major*. *Behavioral Ecology and Sociobiology* 29: 147–152.

Saniga, M. 1998. Diet of Capercaillie (*Tetrao urogallus*) in a Central-European spruce-beech-fir and mountain spruce forest. *Folia Zoologica* 47: 115–124.

Santos, T., B. Asensio, J. Bueno, F.J. Cantos & J. Munoz-Colo. 1988. Spatial and temporal trends of the catching of presaharian passerines in Spain. In *Invernada de aves en la peninsula Iberica* (ed J.-L. Tellería), pp 167–184. Monograph 1. Sociedad Española de Ornitología (SEO), Madrid.

Sarker, S.U. & N.J. Sarker. 1985. Migratory raptorial birds of Bangladesh. In *Conservation Studies on Raptors* (eds I. Newton & R.D. Chancellor), pp 205–209. Technical Publication 5. International Council for Bird Preservation, Cambridge.

SAS Institute. 1990. *SAS/STAT User's Guide. Version 6, fourth edition. Volume 2, GLM-VARCOMP.* SAS Institute, Cary, North Carolina.

SAS Institute. 1996. *SAS/STAT Software: changes and enhancements through release 6.11.* SAS Institute, Cary, North Carolina.

Sauer, J.R., J.E. Hines, G. Gough, I. Thomas & B.G. Peterjohn. 1997. *The North American Breeding Bird Survey Results and Analysis. Version 96.2.* Patuxent Wildlife Research Center, Laurel, Maryland.

Saurola, P. 1979. Virikkeitä viklolöydöistä. *Lintumies* 14: 59–64.

Saurola, P. 1994. African non-breeding areas of Fennoscandian Ospreys *Pandion haliaetus*: a ring recovery analysis. *Ostrich* 65: 127–136.

Sauvage, A., S. Rumsey & S. Rodwell. 1998. Recurrence of Palaearctic birds in the lower Senegal river valley. *Malimbus* 20: 33–53.

Savage, C.D.W. 1952. *The Mandarin Duck.* A. & C. Black, London.

Scebba, S. & G.L. Lövei. 1985. Winter recurrence, weights and wing lengths of Wrynecks *Jynx torquilla* on a southern Italian island. *Ringing & Migration* 6: 83–86.

Scebba, S. & G. Moschetti. 1996. Migration pattern and weight changes of Wood Sandpiper in a stopover site in southern Italy. *Ringing & Migration* 17: 101–104.

Schäffer, N. 1995. Rufverhalten und Funktion des Rufens beim Wachtelkönig *Crex crex*. *Die Vogelwelt* 116: 141–151.

Schamel, D. & D.M. Tracey. 1991. Breeding site fidelity and natal philopatry in the sex role-reversed Red and Red-necked Phalaropes. *Journal of Field Ornithology* 62: 390–398.

Schaub, M., R. Schwilch & L. Jenni. 1999. Does tape-luring of migrating Eurasian Reed Warblers increase number of recruits or capture probability? *Auk* 116: 1047–1053.

Schaub, M., R. Pradel, L. Jenni & J.-D. Lebreton. 2001. Migrating birds stop over longer than usually thought: an improved capture-recapture analysis. *Ecology* 82: 852–859.

Schekkerman, H. 1999. Sex bias and seasonal patterns in tape-lured samples of migrating Skylarks *Alauda arvensis*. *Ringing & Migration* 19: 299–305.

Schekkerman, H., G. Nehls, H. Hötker, P.S. Tomkovich, W. Kania, P. Chylarecki, M. Soloviev & M. van Roomen. 1998. Growth of Little Stint *Calidris minuta* chicks on the Taimyr Peninsula. *Bird Study* 45: 77–84.

Schiavini, A., E. Frere, P. Gandini, N. García & E. Crespo. 1998. Albatross-fisheries interactions in Patagonian shelf waters. In *Albatross biology and conservation* (eds G. Robertson & R. Gale), pp 208–213. Surrey Beatty & Sons, Chipping Norton, Australia.

Schifferli, A. 1963. Vom Zug der Buchfinken (♂♂ und ♀♀) *Fringilla coelebs* in der Schweiz. In *Proceedings of the Thirteenth International Ornithological Congress* (ed C.G. Sibley), pp 468–474. American Ornithologists' Union, Baton Rouge, Louisiana.

Schildmacher, H. 1963. Beobachtungen zu den Invasionen des Jahres 1962 von *Dendrocopos major* und *Loxia curvirostra*. *Ornis Fennica* 40: 66–68.

Schipper, W.J.A. 1978. Comparison of breeding ecology in three European harriers (*Circus*). *Ardea* 66: 77–102.

Schloss, W. 1982. Ringfunde der Gebirgstelze (*Motacilla cinerea*). *Auspicium* 7: 169–183.

Schmidt, G.A.J. 1983. The moult migration of the Common Eider *Somateria mollissima* across Schleswig-Holstein towards the North Sea. *Ornis Fennica* (suppl.) 3: 48–50.

Schmidt, K. & E. Hantge. 1954. Studien an einer farbig beringten Population des Braunkehlchens (*Saxicola rubetra*). *Journal für Ornithologie* 95: 130–173.

Schmidt, K.-H., M. März & E. Matthysen. 1992. Breeding success and laying date of Nuthatches *Sitta europaea* in relation to habitat, weather and breeding density. *Bird Study* 39: 23–30.

Schmidt, R.C. & G. Vauk. 1981. Zug, Rast, Ringfunde auf Helgoland durchziehender Wald und Sumpfohreulen (*Asio otus* und *Asio flammeus*). *Die Vogelwelt* 102: 180–189.

Schneider, W. 1937. Beringungs-Ergebnisse an der mitteleuropäischen Schleiereule (*Tyto alba guttata* Brehm). *Der Vogelzug* 8: 159–170.

Schönfeld, M. 1974. Ringfundauswertung der 1964–1972 in der DDR beringten Schleiereulen *Tyto alba guttata* Brehm. *Vogelwarte Hiddensee* 4: 90–122.

Schroth, K.E. 1991. Survival, movements, and habitat selection of released Capercaillie in the north-east Black Forest in 1984–1989. *Ornis Scandinavica* 22: 249–254.

Schulze-Hagen, K., B. Leisler, H.M. Schäfer & V. Schmidt. 1999. The breeding system of the Aquatic Warbler *Acrocephalus paludicola* – a review of new results. *Die Vogelwelt* 120: 87–96.

Schütz, E. 1974. Über den Zug von *Gavia arctica* in der Paläarktis. *Ornis Fennica* 51: 183–194.

Schwabl, H. 1983. Expression and significance of the winter strategies in a partially migratory population of European Blackbirds (*Turdus merula*). *Journal für Ornithologie* 124: 101–116.

Schwabl, H. & B. Silverin. 1990. Control of partial migration and autumnal behaviour. In *Bird Migration: physiology and ecophysiology* (ed E. Gwinner), pp 144–155. Springer Verlag, Berlin.

Schwan, M.W. & D.D. Williams. 1978. Temperature regulation in the Common Raven of interior Alaska. *Comparative Biochemistry and Physiology A* 60: 31–36.

Schwarz, J. & M. Flade. 2000. Results of the German Common Birds Census. Part 1: Population changes of urban breeding birds since 1989. *Die Vogelwelt* 121: 97–106.

Schwilch, R., R. Mantovani, F. Spina & L. Jenni. 2001. Nectar consumption of warblers after long-distance flights during spring migration. *Ibis* 143: 24–32.

Scott, D.A. 1970. *The breeding biology of the Storm Petrel*. DPhil thesis, University of Oxford.

Scott, D. 1999. *Report on the Conservation Status of Migratory Waterbirds in the Agreement Area*. AEWA Report. Wetlands International, Wageningen, the Netherlands.

Scott, D.A. & P.M. Rose. 1996. *Atlas of Anatidae Populations in Africa and Western Eurasia*. Special Publication 41. Wetlands International, Wageningen, the Netherlands.

Scott, D.K. 1984. Winter territoriality of Mute Swans *Cygnus olor*. *Ibis* 126: 168–176.

Scott, D.K. 1988. Reproductive success in Bewick's Swans. In *Reproductive Success* (ed T.H. Clutton-Brock), pp 220–236. University of Chicago Press, Chicago and London.

Scott, G.A. 1963. First nesting of the Little Gull *Larus minutus* in Ontario and in the New World. *Auk* 80: 548–549.

Scott, G.W., D.C. Jardine, G. Hills & B. Sweeney. 1998. Changes in Nightjar *Caprimulgus europaeus* populations in upland forests in Yorkshire. *Bird Study* 45: 219–225.

Scott, P. 1953. Marking of Geese. *Wildfowl Trust Annual Report* 5: 19–21.

Scott, P. & J. Fisher. 1953. *A Thousand Geese*. Collins, London.

Scott, P., J. Fisher & F. Gudmundsson. 1955. The Wildfowl Trust's second expedition to central Iceland, 1953. *Wildfowl Trust Annual Report* 7: 63–98.

Scott, R.E. 1968. Rough-legged Buzzards in Britain in the winter of 1966/67. *British Birds* 61: 449–465.

Scott, R.E. 1978. Rough-legged Buzzards in Britain in 1973/74 and 1974/75. *British Birds* 71: 325–338.

Scott, W.E.D. 1881. Some observations on the migration of birds. *Bulletin of the Nuttall Ornithological Club* 6: 97–100.

Seago, M.J. (ed). 1997. *Norfolk Bird & Mammal Report 1996*. Norfolk & Norwich Naturalists' Society, Norwich, Norfolk.

Sears, J. 1988. Regional and seasonal variations in lead poisoning in the Mute Swan *Cygnus olor* in relation to the distribution of lead and lead weights in the Thames area, England. *Biological Conservation* 46: 115–134.

Sears, J. & M.I. Avery. 1993. Population and productivity trends of little terns *Sterna albifrons* in Britain 1969–89. *Seabird* 15: 3–16.

Sears, J. & A. Hunt. 1991. Lead poisoning in Mute Swans *Cygnus olor* in England. In *Proceedings of the Third IWRB International Swan Symposium, Oxford 1989* (eds J. Sears & P.J. Bacon), pp 383–388. *Wildfowl* suppl. 1.

Seel, D.C. 1977. Migration of the northwestern European population of the Cuckoo *Cuculus canorus*, as shown by ringing. *Ibis* 119: 309–322.

Seigne, J.W. 1930. *A bird watcher's note book: studies of woodcock, snipe and other birds*. P. Allan & Co, London.

Sellers, R.M. 1984. Movements of Coal, Marsh and Willow Tits in Britain. *Ringing & Migration* 5: 79–89.

Sellers, R.M. 1986. Biometrics of the Siskin. *Ringing & Migration* 7: 99–111.

Sellers, R.M., G.R. Ekins, B. Hughes & J.S. Kirby. 1997. Population development of inland breeding Cormorants in Great Britain. *Ricerche di Biologia della Selvaggina* 26 (suppl. 1): 11–21.

Sells, J.D. 1998. Coal Tits, Marsh Tits and the Batsford nestbox scheme. *The Gloucestershire Naturalist* 11: 74–79.

Senar, J.C., P.J.K. Burton & N.B. Metcalfe. 1992. Variation in the nomadic tendency of a wintering finch *Carduelis spinus* and its relationship with body condition. *Ornis Scandinavica* 23: 63–72.

Senar, J.C., J. Lleonart & N.B. Metcalfe. 1994. Wing-shape variation between resident and transient wintering Siskins *Carduelis spinus*. *Journal of Avian Biology* 25: 50–54.

Serebryakov, V.V., V.N. Grishenko & A.M. Poluda. 1991. The migration of swans, *Cygnus* spp, in the Ukraine, USSR. In *Proceedings of the Third IWRB International Swan Symposium, Oxford 1989* (eds J. Sears & P.J. Bacon), pp 218–223. *Wildfowl* suppl. 1.

Serle, W., G.J. Morel & W. Hartwig. 1977. *A Field Guide to the Birds of West Africa*. Collins, Glasgow.

Serra, L., A. Magnani & N. Baccetti. 1990. Weights and duration of stays in Ruffs *Philomachus pugnax* during spring migration: some data from Italy. *Wader Study Group Bulletin* 58: 19–22.

Sharrock, J.T.R. 1969. Grey Wagtail passage and population fluctuations in 1956–67. *Bird Study* 16: 17–34.

Sharrock, J.T.R. 1971. Scarce migrants in Britain and Ireland during 1958–67. *British Birds* 64: 93–113.

Sharrock, J.T.R. 1973. *The Natural History of Cape Clear Island*. T. & A.D. Poyser, Berkhamsted.

Sharrock, J.T.R. 1974. *Scarce Migrant Birds in Britain and Ireland*. T. & A.D. Poyser, Berkhamsted.

Sharrock, J.T.R. & the Rare Breeding Birds Panel. 1983. Rare breeding birds in the United Kingdom in 1981. *British Birds* 76: 1–25.

Shaw, G. 1990. Timing and fidelity of breeding for Siskins in Scottish conifer plantations. *Bird Study* 37: 30–35.

Shaw, G. 1995. Habitat selection by Short-eared Owls *Asio flammeus* in young coniferous forests. *Bird Study* 42: 158–164.

Shawyer, C.R. 1998. *The Barn Owl*. Arlequin Press, Chelmsford.

Shchadilov, Yu.M., A.V. Belousova, E.C. Rees & J.M. Bowler. 1998. Long-term study of the nesting success of Bewick's Swans in the coastal tundra in the Nenetskiy Autonomous Okrug. *Casarca* 4: 217–228.

Shealer, D.A. & S.W. Kress. 1994. Post-breeding movements and prey selection of Roseate Terns at Stratton Island, Maine. *Journal of Field Ornithology* 65: 349–362.

Shepherd, M., I.R. Hartley & P.K. McGregor. 1997. Natal philopatry and breeding site fidelity of Corn Buntings *Miliaria calandra* on the Uists. In *The ecology and conservation of Corn Buntings* Miliaria calandra (eds P.F. Donald & N.J. Aebischer), pp 103–114. UK Nature Conservation no. 13. Joint Nature Conservation Committee, Peterborough.

Sheppard, J.R. 1982. Whooper and Bewick's Swans in north west Ireland. *Irish Birds* 2: 48–59.

Sheppard, R. 1993. *Ireland's Wetland Wealth.* Irish Wildbird Conservancy, Dublin.

Sheppard, R. & R.E. Green. 1995. Status of the Corncrake in Ireland in 1993. *Irish Birds* 5: 125–138.

Sherrington, P. 1993. Golden Eagle migration in the Front Ranges of the Alberta Rocky Mountains. *Birders Journal* 2: 195–204.

Shevareva, T. 1970. Geographical distribution of the main dabbling duck populations in the USSR and the main directions of their migrations. In *Proceedings of the International Regional Meeting on Conservation of Wildfowl Resources, Leningrad, USSR, 25–30 September 1968* (ed Y.A. Isakov), pp 46–55. Moscow.

Shewell, E.L. 1959. The waterfowl of Barberspan. *Ostrich* suppl. 3: 160–179.

Shields, G.F. 1990. Analysis of mitochondrial DNA of Pacific Black Brant *Branta bernicla nigricans. Auk* 107: 620–623.

Shirihai, H. 1996. *The Birds of Israel.* Academic Press, London and San Diego.

Short, L.L. 1982. *Woodpeckers of the World.* Delaware Museum of Natural History, Delaware.

Shubin, A.O. 1998. The importance of the western Caspian coast for migrating and wintering waders. *International Wader Studies* 10: 403–412.

Shurtleff, L.L. & C. Savage. 1996. *The Wood Duck and the Mandarin.* University of California Press, Berkeley and Los Angeles.

Sibley, C.G., J.E. Ahlquist & B.L. Monroe Jr. 1988. A classification of the living birds of the world based on DNA-DNA hybridization studies. *Auk* 105: 409–423.

Siefke, A. 1994. Movements of Carrion Crow *Corvus corone* ringed or recovered in eastern Germany. *Die Vogelwelt* 115: 83–89.

Sillett, T.S. & R.T. Holmes. 2002. Variation in survivorship of a migratory songbird throughout its annual cycle. *Journal of Animal Ecology* 71: 296–308.

Simms, E. 1979. *The Public Life of the Street Pigeon.* Hutchinson, London.

Simms, E. 1992. *British Larks, Pipits and Wagtails.* HarperCollins, London.

Sinclair, J.C. & B. Rose 1982. Southern African records of the Manx Shearwater *Puffinus puffinus. Cormorant* 10: 81–86.

Siriwardena, G.M. 1999. Survival or breeding performance – are these causing farmland bird declines? *BTO News* 220: 8–9.

Siriwardena, G.M., S.R. Baillie, S.T. Buckland, R.M. Fewster, J.H. Marchant & J.D. Wilson. 1998a. Trends in the abundance of farmland birds: a quantitative comparison of smoothed Common Birds Census indices. *Journal of Applied Ecology* 35: 24–43.

Siriwardena, G.M., S.R. Baillie & J.D. Wilson. 1998b. Variation in the survival rates of some British passerines with respect to their population trends on farmland. *Bird Study* 45: 276–292.

Siriwardena, G.M., S.R. Baillie & J.D. Wilson. 1999. Temporal variation in the annual survival rates of six granivorous birds with contrasting population trends. *Ibis* 141: 621–636.

Siriwardena, G.M., S.R. Baillie, H.Q.P. Crick, J.D. Wilson & S. Gates. 2000. The demography of lowland farmland birds. In *Ecology and conservation of lowland farmland birds* (eds N.J. Aebischer, A.D. Evans, P.V. Grice & J.A. Vickery), pp 117–133. British Ornithologists' Union, Tring.

Sitters, H.P. 1986. Woodlarks in Britain, 1968–83. *British Birds* 79: 105–116.

Sitters, H.P., R.J. Fuller, R.A. Hoblyn, M.T. Wright, N. Cowie & C.G.R. Bowden. 1996. The Woodlark *Lullula arborea* in Britain: population trends, distribution and habitat occupancy. *Bird Study* 43: 172–187.

Skeel, M.A. 1983. Nesting success, density, philopatry, and nest-site selection of the Whimbrel (*Numenius phaeopus*) in different habitats. *Canadian Journal of Zoology* 61: 218–225.

Skov, H., J. Durinck, M.F. Leopold & M.L. Tasker. 1995. *Important Bird Areas for seabirds in the North Sea.* BirdLife International, Cambridge.

Slack, R.S., C.B. Slack, R.N. Roberts & D.E. Emond. 1987. Spring migration of Long-eared Owls and Northern Saw-whet Owls at Nine Mile Point, New York. *Wilson Bulletin* 99: 480–485.

Slagsvold, T. 1979. Age and sex distribution of Hooded Crows *Corvus corone cornix* in Norway. *Fauna Norvegica serie C, Cinclus* 2: 60–64.

Slagsvold, T. 1980. Morphology of the Hooded Crow *Corvus corone cornix* in relation to locality, season, and year. *Fauna Norvegica serie C, Cinclus* 3: 16–35.

Slagsvold, T. & T. Grasaas. 1979. Autumn population size of the Capercaillie *Tetrao urogallus* in relation to weather. *Ornis Scandinavica* 10: 37–41.

Smaldon, R. 1993. Goosanders roosting on Dartmoor reservoirs in winter 1992/93. *Devon Birds* 46: 40–44.

Small, B. 2002. The Horned Lark on the Isles of Scilly. *Birding World* 15: 111–120.

Smit, C. & T. Piersma. 1989. Numbers, midwinter distribution and migration of wader populations using the East Atlantic Flyway. In *Flyways and reserve networks for waterbirds* (eds H. Boyd & J.-Y. Pirot), pp 24–63. Special Publication 9. International Waterfowl & Wetlands Research Bureau, Slimbridge.

Smith, A.J.M. 1975. Studies of breeding Sandwich Terns. *British Birds* 68: 142–156.

Smith, D.G. 1981. Winter roost site fidelity by Long-eared Owls in central Pennsylvania. *American Birds* 35: 339.

Smith, H.G. & J.-Å. Nilsson. 1987. Intraspecific variation in migratory pattern of a partial migrant, the blue tit (*Parus caeruleus*) – an evaluation of different hypotheses. *Auk* 104: 109–115.

Smith, K.D. 1965. On the birds of Morocco. *Ibis* 107: 493–526.

Smith, K.D. 1968. Spring migration through southeast Morocco. *Ibis* 110: 452–472.

Smith, K.W., J.M. Reed & B.E. Trevis. 1992a. Habitat use and site fidelity of Green Sandpipers *Tringa ochropus* wintering in southern England. *Bird Study* 39: 155–164.

Smith, K., J. Waldon & G. Williams. 1992b. Action for Cirl Buntings. *RSPB Conservation Review* 6: 40–44.

Smith, K.W., J.M. Reed & B.E. Trevis. 1999. Nocturnal and diurnal activity patterns and roosting sites of Green Sandpipers *Tringa ochropus* wintering in southern England. *Ringing & Migration* 19: 315–322.

Smith, L. 2001. The Long Mynd Breeding Bird Project: Ring Ouzel. *Shropshire Bird Report 1999*: 3–22.

Smith, P.H. 1987. The changing status of Little Gulls *Larus minutus* in north Merseyside, England. *Seabird* 10: 12–21.

Smith, P.W. 1987. The Eurasian Collared Dove arrives in the Americas. *American Birds* 41: 1371–1379.

Smith, R.D. 1992. Age determination, wing-feather colour and wing-length change in Snow Buntings. *Ringing & Migration* 13: 43–51.

Smith, R.D. 1994a. *Snow Buntings* Plectrophenax nivalis: *the behavioural ecology and site use of an itinerant flock species in the non-breeding season.* PhD thesis, University of Glasgow.

Smith, R.D. 1994b. *Snow Buntings breeding in the Cairngorms: population dynamics and the influence of recreation.* Research publication 1. Scottish Natural Heritage, Edinburgh.

Smith, R.D. 1996. Racial composition of breeding and wintering Snow Buntings *Plectrophenax nivalis* in the north-east Scottish uplands. *Ringing & Migration* 17: 123–136.

Smith, R.D. & M. Marquiss. 1994. Breeding seasons and nesting success of Snow Buntings in north-east Scotland. *Scottish Birds* 17: 223–234.

Smith, R.D., M. Marquiss, R. Rae & N.B. Metcalfe. 1993. Age and sex variation in choice of wintering site by Snow Buntings: the effect of altitude. *Ardea* 81: 47–52.

Smith, S. 1950. *The Yellow Wagtail*. Collins, London.

Smith, S., J. Harradine & J. Bateley. 1995. *Farmers, Woodpigeons and Woodpigeon Shooting*. British Association for Shooting and Conservation, Wrexham.

Smith, S., G. Thompson & C.M. Perrins. 2001. A census of the Manx Shearwater *Puffinus puffinus* on Skomer, Skokholm and Middleholm, west Wales. *Bird Study* 48: 330–340.

Smith, S.J. 1996. A study of moorland breeding chats. *Gwent Bird Report* 30 (1994): 8–11.

Smith, V.W. 1963. Arrival dates of the Garden Warbler *Sylvia borin* in central Nigeria. *Ibis* 105: 561–563.

Smith, V.W. 1966. Autumn and spring weights of some Palaearctic migrants in central Nigeria. *Ibis* 108: 492–512.

Smith, V.W. & D. Ebbutt. 1965. Notes on Yellow Wagtails *Motacilla flava* wintering in central Nigeria. *Ibis* 107: 390–393.

Snell, R.R. 1991. Variably plumaged Icelandic Herring Gulls: relict founders not hybrids. *Auk* 108: 329–341.

Snow, B.K. & D.W. Snow. 1984. Long-term defence of fruit by Mistle Thrushes *Turdus viscivorus*. *Ibis* 126: 39–49.

Snow, D.W. 1953. The migration of the Greenland Wheatear. *Ibis* 95: 376–378.

Snow, D.W. 1958. *A Study of Blackbirds*. British Museum, London.

Snow, D.W. 1966. The migration and dispersal of British Blackbirds. *Bird Study* 13: 237–253.

Snow, D.W. 1968. Movements and mortality in British Kestrels. *Bird Study* 15: 65–83.

Snow, D.W. 1969. Some vital statistics of British Mistle Thrushes. *Bird Study* 16: 34–44.

Snow, D.W. 1978. Long-distance movements of British Blackbirds. *Ringing & Migration* 2: 52–54.

Snow, W.D., H.L. Mendall & W.B. Krohn. 1989. Capturing Common Eiders by night-lighting in coastal Maine. *Journal of Field Ornithology* 61: 67–72.

Sokal, R.R. & F.J. Rohlf. 1995. *Biometry: the principles and practice of statistics in biological research*. Third edition. Freeman, New York.

Sokolov, L.V., V.D. Yefremov, M.Y. Markovets, A.P. Shapoval & M.E. Shumakov. 2000. Monitoring of numbers in passage populations of passerines over 42 years (1958–1999) on the Courish Spit of the Baltic Sea. *Avian Ecology and Behaviour* 4: 31–53.

Sorenson, L.H. 1977. Analysis of Common Gull (*Larus canus*) recoveries recorded from 1931 to 1972 by the Zoological Museum in Copenhagen. *Gerfaut* 67: 133–160.

Southern, H.N. 1939. Spring migration of Redstarts over Europe. *British Birds* 33: 34–36.

Southern, H.N. 1970. The natural control of a population of Tawny Owls. *Journal of Zoology* 162: 197–285.

Southern, H.N., R. Vaughan & R.C. Muir. 1954. The behaviour of young Tawny Owls after fledging. *Bird Study* 1: 101–110.

Southern, W.E., S.R. Patton, L.K. Southern & L.A. Hanner. 1985. Effects of nine years of fox predation on two species of breeding gulls. *Auk* 102: 827–833.

SOVON. 1987. *Atlas van de Nederlandse Vogels*. SOVON, Arnhem, the Netherlands.

Sowls, L.K. 1955. *Prairie Ducks*. Stackpole Co, Harrisburg, Pennsylvania.

Spaans, A.L. 1977. Are Starlings faithful to their winter quarters? *Ardea* 65: 83–87.

Spaans, A.L., M. Bukacinska, D. Bukacinski & N.D. van Swelm. 1994. *The relationship between food supply, reproductive parameters and population dynamics in Dutch Lesser Black-backed Gulls*, Larus

fuscus: *a pilot study.* IBN Research Report 9. Institute for Forestry and Natural Research, Wageningen, the Netherlands.

Spaar, R. 1995. Flight behaviour of Steppe Buzzards (*Buteo buteo vulpinus*) during spring migration in southern Israel – a tracking-radar study. *Israel Journal of Zoology* 41: 489–500.

Spaar, R. 1997. Flight strategies of migrating raptors; a comparative study of interspecific variation in flight characteristics. *Ibis* 139: 523–535.

Spaar, R. & B. Bruderer. 1997. Optimal flight behaviour of soaring migrants: a case study of migrating Steppe Buzzards, *Buteo buteo vulpinus*. *Behavioral Ecology* 8: 288–297.

Spaepen, J.F. 1988. Estimation of the survival rates of Meadow Pipits – a comparison of two different methods. *Ringing & Migration* 9: 117–128.

Spaepen, J.F. 1989. Spring migration of the Meadow Pipit (*Anthus pratensis*) through Belgium. *Gerfaut* 79: 91–100.

Spaepen, J.F. 1995. A study of the migration of the Skylark, *Alauda arvensis*, based on European ringing data. *Gerfaut* 85: 63–89.

Spaepen, J. & F. van Cauteren. 1968. Migration of the Skylark, *Alauda arvensis* L. (new results). *Gerfaut* 58: 24–77.

Sparks, T. 1999. Phenology and the changing pattern of bird migration in Britain. *International Journal of Biometeorology* 42: 134–138.

Sparks, T.H. & O. Braslavská. 2001. The effects of temperature, altitude and latitude on the arrival and departure dates of the Swallow *Hirundo rustica* in the Slovak Republic. *International Journal of Biometeorology* 45: 212–216.

Spear, L.B. & D.G. Ainley. 1999. Migration routes of Sooty Shearwaters in the Pacific Ocean. *Condor* 101: 205–218.

Speek, B.J. & G. Speek. 1984. *Thieme's Vogeltrekatlas*. B.V.W.J. Thieme & Cie, Zutphen, the Netherlands.

Spencer, R. 1957. Report on bird ringing for 1956. *British Birds* 50: 449–485.

Spencer, R. 1975. Changes in the distribution of recoveries of ringed Blackbirds. *Bird Study* 22: 177–190.

Spencer, R. 1976. Introduction. In *Bird Observatories in Britain and Ireland* (ed R. Durman), pp 11–28. T. & A.D. Poyser, Berkhamsted, for the Bird Observatories Council.

Spencer, R. 1984. *The Ringer's Manual*. Third edition. BTO, Tring.

Spencer, R. & G.H. Gush. 1973. Siskins feeding in gardens. *British Birds* 66: 91–99.

Spencer, R. & R. Hudson. 1978. Report on bird ringing for 1976. *Ringing & Migration* 1: 189–252.

Spencer, R. & R. Hudson. 1979. Report on bird-ringing for 1978. *Ringing & Migration* 2: 161–208.

Spencer, R. & R. Hudson. 1980. Report on bird-ringing for 1979. *Ringing & Migration* 3: 65–108.

Spina, F. 1998a. The EURING Swallow Project: results from the first pilot year. *EURING Newsletter* 2: 22–27.

Spina, F. 1998b. The EURING Swallow Project: a large-scale approach to the study and conservation of a long-distance migrant. In *Migrating birds know no boundaries* (eds Y. Leshem, E. Lachman & P. Berthold). *Torgos* 28: 151–162.

Spina, F. 1998c. The waterbird migration atlas. *EURING Newsletter* 2: 36.

Spina, F. 1999. Value of ringing information for bird conservation in Europe. *Ringing & Migration* 19 (suppl.): S29–40.

Spina, F. 2001. EURING Swallow Project. Third newsletter years 1999–2000. *EURING Newsletter* 3: 29–34.

Spina, F. & A. Pilastro. 1999. Strategy of sea and desert crossing in spring passerine migrants as suggested by the analysis of intra- and interspecific variation of residual fat levels. In *Proceedings of the Twenty-second International Ornithological Congress, Durban* (eds N.J. Adams & R.H. Slotow), pp 1958–1976. BirdLife South Africa, Johannesburg. (CD-ROM).

Spina, F., A. Massi, A. Montemaggiori & N. Baccetti. 1993. Spring migration across the Central Mediterranean: general results from the 'Progetto Piccole Isole'. *Die Vogelwarte* 37 (suppl.): 1–94.

Spina, F., A. Massi & A. Montemaggiori. 1994. Back from Africa: who's running ahead? Aspects of differential migration of sex and age classes in Palearctic-African spring migrants. *Ostrich* 65: 137–150.

Spitznagel, A. 1995. Die Farbvariabilität der Wasseramsel (*Cinclus cinclus*) und der Einfluß ökologischer und ethologischer Faktoren. *Acta Ornithoecologica* 3: 167–180.

Sporne, S. 1980. Just for a Lark. *Ringers' Bulletin* 5: 111.

Spray, C.J. 1981. An isolated population of *Cygnus olor* in Scotland. In *Proceedings of the Second International Swan Symposium, Sapporo 1980*, (eds G.V.T. Matthews & M. Smart), pp 191–208.

Spray, C.J. 1991. Population dynamics of Mute Swans, *Cygnus olor* in the Outer Hebrides, Scotland. In *Proceedings of the Third IWRB International Swan Symposium, Oxford 1989* (eds J. Sears & P.J. Bacon), p 143. *Wildfowl* suppl. 1.

Spray, C.J. 1992. *Mute Swan survey of the Outer Hebrides 1992.* Unpublished report to the Joint Nature Conservation Committee.

Spray, C.J. & N.K. Atkinson. 1991. Moult and dispersal of Mute Swans *Cygnus olor* in East Scotland: a preliminary analysis. In *Proceedings of the Third IWRB International Swan Symposium, Oxford 1989* (eds J. Sears & P.J. Bacon), p 325. *Wildfowl* suppl. 1.

Spray, C.J. & K. Bayes. 1992. The effect of neck collars on the behaviour, weight and breeding success of Mute Swans *Cygnus olor*. *Wildfowl* 43: 49–57.

Spray, C.J. & H. Milne. 1988. The incidence of lead poisoning among Whooper and Mute Swans *Cygnus cygnus* and *C. olor* in Scotland. *Biological Conservation* 44: 265–281.

Spray, C.J., M. Fraser & J. Coleman. 1996. *The swans of Berwick-upon-Tweed*. Northumbrian Water, Durham. 15 pp.

Sproll, A. & W. Fiedler. 2001. Digging in old data: migration and causes of death in White Storks (*Ciconia ciconia*) according to ringing recovery data of the Vogelwarte Rossitten (Eastern Prussia) before the Second World War. *EURING Newsletter* 3: 54–59.

Squires, J.R. & L.F. Ruggiero. 1995. Winter movements of adult Northern Goshawks that nested in southcentral Wyoming. *Journal of Raptor Research* 29: 5–9.

St Joseph, A.K.M. 1979. The seasonal distribution and movements of *Branta bernicla* in western Europe. In *Proceedings of the First Technical Meeting on Western Palaearctic Migratory Bird Management* (ed M. Smart), pp 45–57. International Waterfowl Research Bureau, Slimbridge.

Staav, R. 1975. Flyttning hos nordiska blåhakar *Luscinia s. svecica*. *Vår Fågelvärld* 34: 212–220.

Stanford, W.P. 1953. Winter distribution of the Grey Phalarope *Phalaropus fulicarius*. *Ibis* 95: 483–491.

Stanley, P.I. & C.D.T. Minton. 1972. The unprecedented westward migration of Curlew Sandpipers in autumn 1969. *British Birds* 65: 365–380.

Stanley, P.I., T. Brough, M.R. Fletcher, N. Horton & J.B.A. Rochard. 1981. The origins of Herring Gulls wintering inland in southeast England. *Bird Study* 28: 123–132.

Steedman, A. (ed). 1988. *Locust Handbook*. Overseas Development Natural Resources Institute, London.

Stenhouse, I.J. & W.A. Montevecchi. 1996. Winter distribution and wrecks of Little Auks (Dovekies) *Alle a. alle* in the Northwest Atlantic. *Sula* 10: 219–228.

Sterling, T. & A. Dzubin. 1967. Canada Goose molt migrations to the Northwest Territories. *Transactions of the North American Wildlife and Natural Resources Conference* 32: 355–373.

Stevenson, H. 1870. *The Birds of Norfolk.* Volume 2. Stevenson & Co, Norwich.

Stewart, P.A. 1952. Dispersal, breeding behavior and longevity of banded Barn Owls in North America. *Auk* 69: 227–245.

Steyn, P. & R.K. Brooke. 1971. Cold induced mortality of birds in Rhodesia during November 1968. In *Proceedings of the Third Pan-African Ornithological Congress* (ed G.L. Maclean). *Ostrich* (suppl. 8): 272–282.

Stiefel, A. 1991. Situation des Wachtelkönigs in Ostdeutschland (vormalige DDR). *Die Vogelwelt* 112: 57–66.

Stiefel, A., S.G. Priklonski & A.V. Postelnych. 1985. [Common Sandpiper –*Actitis hypoleucos* (L)]. In [*Migrations of Birds of Eastern Europe and Northern Asia: Gruiformes-Charadriiformes*] (eds J.A. Viksne & H.A. Michelson), pp 126–140. Nauka, Moscow. (In Russian.)

Stientien, E.W.M., A. Jonard & A. Brenninkmeijer. 1998. Tern trapping along the Senegalese coast. *Sula* 12: 19–26.

Stoate, C. 1995. The impact of Desert Locust *Schistocerca gregaria* swarms on pre-migratory fattening of Whitethroats *Sylvia communis* in the western Sahel. *Ibis* 37: 420–422.

Stoate, C. 1997. Abundance of Whitethroats *Sylvia communis* and potential invertebrate prey in two Sahelian sylvi-agricultural habitats. *Malimbus* 19: 7–11.

Stoate, C. & S.J. Moreby. 1995. Premigratory diet of trans-Saharan migrant passerines in the western Sahel. *Bird Study* 42: 101–106.

Stokes, D.L. & P.D. Boersma. 1998. Satellite tracking of Magellanic Penguin migration. *Condor* 100: 376–381.

Stone, B.H., J. Sears, P.A. Cranswick, R.D. Gregory, D.W. Gibbons, M.M. Rehfisch, N.J. Aebischer & J.B. Reid. 1997. Population estimates of birds in Britain and in the United Kingdom. *British Birds* 90: 1–22.

Stone, C.J., A. Webb & M.L. Tasker. 1994. The distribution of Manx Shearwaters *Puffinus puffinus* in north-west European waters. *Bird Study* 41: 170–180.

Stone, C.J., A. Webb, C. Barton, N. Ratcliffe, T.C. Reed, M.L. Tasker, C.J. Camphuysen & M.W. Pienkowski. 1995. *An atlas of seabird distribution in north-west European waters.* Joint Nature Conservation Committee and Nederlands Instituut voor Onderzoek der Zee, Peterborough.

Storch, I. 1997. Male territoriality, female range use and spatial organization of Capercaillie *Tetrao urogallus* leks. *Wildlife Biology* 3: 149–161.

Storer, R.W. & J.R. Jehl. 1985. Moult patterns and moult migration in the Black-necked Grebe *Podiceps nigricollis*. *Ornis Scandinavica* 16: 253–260.

Storey, A.E. & J. Lien. 1985. Development of the first North American colony of Manx Shearwaters. *Auk* 102: 395–401.

Stott, M. 1998. Hen Harrier breeding success on English grouse moors. *British Birds* 91: 107–108.

Stowe, T.J. & A.V. Hudson. 1988. Corncrake studies in the Western Isles. *RSPB Conservation Review* 2: 38–42.

Stowe, T.J. & A.V. Hudson. 1991. Corncrakes outside the breeding grounds, and ideas for a conservation strategy. *Die Vogelwelt* 112: 103–107.

Stowe, T.J., A.V. Newton, R.E. Green & E. Mayes. 1993. The decline of the Corncrake *Crex crex* in Britain and Ireland in relation to habitat. *Journal of Applied Ecology* 30: 53–62.

Strang, C.A. 1977. Variation and distribution of Glaucous Gulls in western Alaska. *Condor* 79: 170–175.

Strann, K.-B. & W. Vader. 1992. The nominate Lesser Black-backed Gull *Larus fuscus fuscus*, a gull with tern-like feeding biology, and its recent decrease in northern Norway. *Ardea* 80: 133–142.

Stroud, D.A. 1992. *Greenland White-fronted Goose* Anser albifrons flavirostris *international conservation plan*. National Parks and Wildlife Service/International Waterfowl & Wetlands Research Bureau. (Draft.)

Stroud, D.A. & A.D. Fox. 1981. The status of the Greenland White-front in East Greenland. In *Report of the 1979 Greenland White-fronted Goose Study Expedition to Eqalungmiut Nunât, West Greenland* (eds A.D. Fox & D.A. Stroud), pp 146–147. Greenland White-fronted Goose Study, Aberystwyth.

Stroud, D.A., G.P. Mudge & M.W. Pienkowski. 1990. *Protecting Internationally Important Bird Sites: a Review of the EEC Special*

Protection Area Network in Great Britain. Nature Conservancy Council, Peterborough.

Stroud, D.A., D. Chambers, S. Cook, N. Buxton, B. Fraser, P. Clement, P. Lewis, I. McLean, H. Baker & S. Whitehead. 2001. *The UK SPA Review: its scope and content.* Volumes 1–3. Joint Nature Conservation Committee, Peterborough.

Stroud, J.M. 1992. *Statutory suspension of wildfowling in severe weather: review of past winter weather and actions.* Report 75. Joint Nature Conservation Committee, Peterborough.

Strowger, J. 1998. The status and breeding biology of the Dotterel *Charadrius morinellus* in northern England during 1972–95. *Bird Study* 45: 85–91.

Stuart, D. 1948. Vital statistics of the Mochrum Cormorant colony. *British Birds* 41: 194–199.

Stubbs, F.J. 1910. Ceremonial gatherings of the Magpie. *British Birds* 3: 334–336.

Studer-Thiersch, A. 1969. Das Zugverhalten schweizerischer Stare *Sturnus vulgaris* nach Ringfunden. *Ornithologische Beobachter* 66: 105–144.

Sulkava, S., K. Huhtala & R. Tornberg. 1994. Regulation of Goshawk *Accipiter gentilis* breeding in western Finland over the last 30 years. In *Raptor Conservation Today. Proceedings of the Fourth World Conference on Birds of Prey and Owls* (eds B.-U. Meyburg & R.D. Chancellor), pp 67–76. World Working Group on Birds of Prey and Owls/Pica Press, Bodmin.

Summers, D.D.B. 1979. Bullfinch dispersal and migration in relation to fruit bud damage. *British Birds* 72: 249–263.

Summers, R.W. 1986. Breeding production of Dark-bellied Brent Geese *Branta bernicla bernicla* in relation to lemming cycles. *Bird Study* 34: 161–171.

Summers, R.W. 1994. The migration patterns of the Purple Sandpiper *Calidris maritima. Ostrich* 65: 167–173.

Summers, R.W. 1995. Diurnal and tidal activity patterns of Purple Sandpipers on the Isle of May, Fife. *Scottish Birds* 18: 51–54.

Summers, R.W. 1998. Territory sizes of Crested Tits at Abernethy Forest, Strathspey. *Scottish Birds* 19: 177–179.

Summers, R.W. 2000. The habitat requirements of the Crested Tit *Parus cristatus* in Scotland. *Scottish Forestry* 54: 197–201.

Summers, R.W. & M. Canham. 2001. The distribution of Crested Tits in Scotland during the 1990s. *Scottish Birds* 22: 20–27.

Summers, R.W. & S.J. Cross. 1987. Winter movements and habitat use by Starlings in Norfolk. *Ringing & Migration* 8: 11–18.

Summers, R.W. & C.J. Feare. 1995. Roost departure by Starlings *Sturnus vulgaris*: effects of competition and choice of feeding site. *Journal of Avian Biology* 26: 289–295.

Summers, R.W. & S. Laing. 1990. Movements of Cormorants from the Lamb, Firth of Forth. *Scottish Birds* 16: 29–32.

Summers, R.W. & R. Proctor. 1999. Tree and cone selection by crossbills *Loxia* sp. and red squirrels *Sciurus vulgaris* at Abernethy Forest, Strathspey. *Forest Ecology and Management* 118: 173–182.

Summers, R.W. & M. Waltner. 1978. Seasonal variations in the mass of waders in southern Africa, with special reference to migration. *Ostrich* 50: 21–37.

Summers, R.W., L.G. Underhill, M. Waltner & D.A. Whitelaw. 1987. Population, biometrics and movements of the sanderling *Calidris alba* in southern Africa. *Ostrich* 58: 24–39.

Summers, R.W., C.J. Corse, M. Nicoll, R. Smith & D.P. Whitfield. 1988a. The biometrics and wintering area of Icelandic Purple Sandpipers. *Ringing & Migration* 9: 133–138.

Summers, R.W., M. Nicoll, L.G. Underhill & A. Petersen. 1988b. Methods for estimating the proportions of Icelandic and British Redshanks *Tringa totanus* in mixed populations wintering on British coasts. *Bird Study* 35: 169–180.

Summers, R.W., L.G. Underhill, C.F. Clinning & M. Nicoll. 1989. Populations, migrations, biometrics and moult of the Turnstone

Arenaria i. interpres on the East Atlantic coastline, with special reference to the Siberian population. *Ardea* 77: 145–168.

Summers, R.W., S. Smith, M. Nicoll & N.K. Atkinson. 1990. Tidal and sexual differences in the diet of Purple Sandpipers *Calidris maritima* in Scotland. *Bird Study* 37: 187–194.

Summers, R.W., L.G. Underhill, R.J. Howells, J.A. Vickery & R. Prŷs-Jones. 1996. Phenology of migration and use of wintering sites by the increasing population of Dark-bellied Brent Geese *Branta bernicla bernicla. Journal of Zoology* 239: 197–208.

Summers, R.W., T. Piersma, K.-B. Strann & P. Wiersma. 1998. How do Purple Sandpipers *Calidris maritima* survive the winter north of the Arctic Circle? *Ardea* 86: 51–58.

Summers, R.W., R.A. Mavor, S.T. Buckland & A.M. MacLennan. 1999. Winter population size and habitat selection of Crested Tits *Parus cristatus* in Scotland. *Bird Study* 46: 230–242.

Summers, R.W., M. Nicoll & W.J. Peach. 2001. Numbers, migration phenology and survival of Purple Sandpipers *Calidris maritima* at Gourdon, eastern Scotland. *Bird Study* 48: 139–146.

Summers, R., D.C. Jardine, M. Marquiss & R. Rae. 2002. The distribution and habitats of crossbills *Loxia* spp. in Britain, with special reference to the Scottish Crossbill *Loxia scotica. Ibis* 144: 393–410.

Summers-Smith, D. 1956. Movements of House Sparrows. *British Birds* 49: 465–488.

Summers-Smith, D. 1963. *The House Sparrow.* Collins, London.

Summers-Smith, J.D. 1988. *The Sparrows.* T. & A.D. Poyser, Calton.

Summers-Smith, J.D. 1995. *The Tree Sparrow.* Privately published.

Summers-Smith, J.D. 1999. Current status of the House Sparrow in Britain. *British Wildlife* 10: 381–386.

Sutcliffe, S.J. 1986. Changes in the gull populations of SW Wales. *Bird Study* 33: 91–97.

Sutherland, W.J. 1988. The heritability of migration. *Nature* 334: 471–472.

Sutherland, W.J. 1998a. Evidence for flexibility and constraint in migration systems. *Journal of Avian Biology* 29: 441–446.

Sutherland, W.J. 1998b. The effect of local change in habitat quality on populations of migratory species. *Journal of Applied Ecology* 35: 418–421.

Sutherland, W.J. & G. Allport. 1991. The distribution and ecology of naturalized Egyptian Geese *Alopochen aegyptiacus* in Britain. *Bird Study* 38: 128–134.

Svärdson, G. 1951. Swift (*Apus apus* L.) movements in summer. In *Proceedings of the Tenth International Ornithological Congress* (ed S. Hörstadius), pp 335–338. Almqvist & Wiksells, Uppsala, Sweden.

Svazas, S. & V. Pareigis. 1992. The significance of Lithuanian Baltic coastal waters for wintering populations of the Velvet Scoter. *IWRB Seaduck Bulletin* 1: 41–42. (Abstract.)

Svensson, L. 1992. *Identification Guide to European Passerines.* Fourth edition. Lars Svensson, Stockholm.

Swanberg, P.O. 1987. Migration routes of Swedish Cranes (*Grus grus*) present knowledge. *Aquila* 93–94: 63–73.

Swann, R.L. 1975. Seasonal variations in suburban Blackbird roosts in Aberdeen. *Ringing & Migration* 1: 37–42.

Swann, R.L. 1980. Fieldfare and Blackbird weights during the winter of 1978–79 at Drumnadrochit, Inverness-shire. *Ringing & Migration* 3: 37–40.

Swann, R. 1981. Bar-tailed Godwits on the Moray Firth. *Highland Ringing Group Report* 4: 3–5.

Swann, R.L. 1988. Are all large Chaffinch flocks composed of continentals? *Ringing & Migration* 9: 1–4.

Swann, B. 1998. Greylag Geese in Highland – 1996/97. *Wildfowl Ringers Newsletter (WWT)* 3: 16–21.

Swann, R.L. & B. Etheridge. 1995. A comparison of breeding success and prey of the Common Buzzard *Buteo buteo* in two areas of northern Scotland. *Bird Study* 42: 37–43.

Swann, R.L. & A.D.K. Ramsay. 1979. An analysis of Shag recoveries from northwest Scotland. *Ringing & Migration* 2: 137–143.

Swann, R.L. & A.D.K. Ramsay. 1983. Movements from and age of return to an expanding Scottish Guillemot colony. *Bird Study* 30: 207–214.

Swann, R.L., D.G. Aiton, J. Carruthers, R.J. Graham & A.D.K. Ramsay. 1994. An analysis of Shag *Phalacrocorax aristotelis* ring recovery and breeding success data during a period of population change on the Isle of Canna. *Seabird* 16: 50–56.

Swaysland, W. 1903. *Familiar Wild Birds.* Cassell & Co, London.

Swennen, C. 1990. Dispersal and migratory movements of Eiders *Somateria mollissima* breeding in the Netherlands. *Ornis Scandinavica* 21: 17–27.

Swingland, I.R. 1983. Intraspecific differences in movement. In *The Ecology of Animal Movement* (eds I.R. Swingland & P.J. Greenwood), pp 102–115. Clarendon Press, Oxford.

Symonds, F.L. & D.R. Langslow. 1984. Geographical origins and movements of shorebirds using the Firth of Forth. *Ringing & Migration* 5: 145–152.

Symonds, F.L., D.R. Langslow & M.W. Pienkowski. 1984. Movements of wintering shorebirds within the Firth of Forth: species differences in usage of an intertidal complex. *Biological Conservation* 28: 187–215.

Syroechkovski, E.E. Jr. & E.G. Lappo. 1994. Migration phenology of waders (Charadrii) on the Taimyr Peninsula, northern Russia. *Ostrich* 65: 181–190.

Syroechkovskiy, Y.V., K.Y. Litvin & B.S. Ebbinge. 1992. Breeding success of geese and swans on Vaygach Island (USSR) during 1986–1988; interplay of weather and Arctic Fox predation. In *Population limitation in Arctic-breeding geese,* pp 181–190. PhD thesis of B.S. Ebbinge, University of Groningen, the Netherlands.

Szép, T. 1995a. Relationship between west African rainfall and the survival of central European Sand Martins *Riparia riparia. Ibis* 137: 162–168.

Szép, T. 1995b. Survival rates of Hungarian Sand Martins and their relationship with Sahel rainfall. *Journal of Applied Statistics* 22: 891–904.

Szulc-Olech, B. 1965. The resting period of migrant Robins on autumn passage. *Bird Study* 12: 1–7.

Tamisier, A., P. Cour, P. Richard, O. Dehorter & F. Pelsy-Mozimann. 1997. Pollen in lungs and air sacs. A spatio-temporal marker for long-distance migrants. In *Limnology and Waterfowl: monitoring, modelling and management* (eds S. Faragó & J. Kerekes), pp 187–188. Wetlands International, Wageningen.

Tapper, S. 1992. *Game heritage: an ecological review from shooting and gamekeeping records.* Game Conservancy, Fordingbridge.

Tapper, S.C. & G.J.M. Hirons. 1983. Recent trends in woodcock bags in Britain. In *Proceedings of the Second European Woodcock and Snipe Workshop* (ed H. Kalchreuter), pp 132–137. International Waterfowl Research Bureau, Slimbridge.

Tasker, M.L. 1982. Moulting Shelducks on the Humber. *Bird Study* 29: 164–166.

Tasker, M.L., P. Hope Jones, T. Dixon & B.F. Blake. 1984. Counting seabirds at sea from ships: a review of methods employed and a suggestion for a standardized approach. *Auk* 101: 567–577.

Tasker, M.L., P. Hope Jones, B.F. Blake & T.J. Dixon. 1985. Distribution and feeding habits of the great skua *Catharacta skua* in the North Sea. *Seabird* 8: 34–43.

Tasker, M.L., P. Hope Jones, B.F. Blake, T.J. Dixon & A.W. Wallis. 1986. Seabirds associated with oil production platforms in the North Sea. *Ringing & Migration* 7: 7–14.

Tasker, M.L., A. Webb, A.J. Hall, M.W. Pienkowski & D.R. Langslow. 1987. *Seabirds in the North Sea.* Nature Conservancy Council, Peterborough.

Tasker, M.L., P.R. Moore & R.A. Schofield. 1988. The seabirds of St. Kilda, 1987. *Scottish Birds* 15: 21–29.

Tast, J. 1968. Changes in the distribution, habitat requirements and nest sites of the linnet *Carduelis cannabina* (L.) in Finland. *Annales Zoologici Fennici* 5: 159–178.

Tatner, P. 1982. Factors influencing the distribution of Magpies *Pica pica* in an urban environment. *Bird Study* 29: 227–234.

Tatner, P. 1986. Survival rates of urban Magpies. *Ringing & Migration* 7: 112–118.

Taverner, J.H. 1970. Mediterranean Gulls nesting in Hampshire. *British Birds* 63: 67–79.

Taylor, B. & B. van Perlo. 1998. *Rails: a guide to the rails, crakes, gallinules and coots of the world.* Pica Press, Robertsbridge, East Sussex.

Taylor, D.W., D.L. Davenport & J.J.M. Flegg. 1981. *The Birds of Kent.* Kent Ornithological Society, Meopham, Kent.

Taylor, I. 1994. *Barn Owls: predator-prey relationships and conservation.* Cambridge University Press, Cambridge.

Taylor, I.R. 1979. The kleptoparasitic behaviour of the Arctic Skua *Stercorarius parasiticus* with three species of tern. *Ibis* 121: 274–282.

Taylor, M. 1984. The patterns of migration and partial migration at a north Norfolk bird-ringing site. *Ringing & Migration* 5: 65–78.

Taylor, M. 1997. The origins of Rock Pipits in Norfolk. *Norfolk Bird Report 1995*: 606–607.

Taylor, M., M. Seago, P. Allard & D. Dorling. 1999. *The Birds of Norfolk.* Pica Press, Robertsbridge, East Sussex.

Taylor, P.B. 1987. A field study of the Spotted Crake *Porzana porzana* at Ndola, Zambia. *Ostrich* 58: 107–117.

Taylor, R.C. 1980. Migration of the Ringed Plover *Charadrius hiaticula. Ornis Scandinavica* 11: 30–42.

Tellería, J.L. 1980. Autumn migration of Cory's Shearwater through the Straits of Gibraltar. *Bird Study* 27: 21–26.

Tellería, J.L. 1981. *La Migración de las Aves en el Estrecho de Gibraltar.* Universidad Complutense, Madrid.

Tellería, J.L. & T. Santos. 1985. Avifauna invernante en los medios agricolas del norte de España. I. Caracterizacion biogeografica. [Wintering avifauna in the agricultural landscapes of Northern Spain. I. Biogeographical patterns.] *Ardeola* 32: 203–225.

Temminck, C.-J. 1820. *Manuel d'Ornithologie, ou tableau systématique des oiseaux qui se trouvent en Europe.* Volume 4. H. Cousin, Paris.

Terborgh, J. 1989. *Where have all the birds gone?* Princeton University Press, Princeton, New Jersey.

Terrill, S.B. 1990. Ecophysiological aspects of movements by migrants in the wintering quarters. In *Bird Migration: physiology and ecophysiology* (ed E. Gwinner), pp 130–143. Springer Verlag, Berlin.

Terrill, S.B. 1991. Evolutionary aspects of orientation and migration in birds. In *Orientation in Birds* (ed P. Berthold), pp 180–201. Birkhäuser Verlag, Basel.

Terrill, S.B. & K.P. Able. 1988. Bird migration terminology. *Auk* 105: 205–206.

Tessen, D.D. 1975. The nesting season: June 1 – July 31, 1975. Western Great Lakes Region. *American Birds* 29: 974–979.

Thevenot, M. & A. Salvi. 1987. Wintering of Common Cranes (*Grus grus*) in Morocco from 1980 to 1985. *Aquila* 93–94: 233–235.

Thibault, J.-C. 1993. Natal philopatry in the Cory's Shearwater (*Calonectris diomedea*) on Lavezzi Island, Corsica. *Colonial Waterbirds* 16: 77–82.

Thibault, J.-C., V. Bretagnolle & C. Rabouam. 1997. *Calonectris diomedea* Cory's Shearwater. *BWP Update* 1: 75–98.

Thiede, W. 1986. Das Herbstvorkommen der Zwergmöwe (*Larus minutus*) in den türkischen Meerengen. *Die Vogelwelt* 107: 71–72.

Thiollay, J.-M. 1985a. The birds of Ivory Coast: status and distribution. *Malimbus* 7: 1–59.

Thiollay, J.-M. 1985b. The situation of raptors wintering in West Africa. *World Working Group on Birds of Prey Newsletter* 2: 3–4.

Thiollay, J.-M. 1989. Distribution and ecology of Palearctic birds of prey wintering in west and central Africa. In *Raptors in the Modern*

World (eds B.-U. Meyburg & R.D. Chancellor), pp 95–107. World Working Group on Birds of Prey and Owls, Berlin.

Thomas, C.D. & J.K. Lennon. 1999. Birds extend their ranges northwards. *Nature* 399: 213.

Thomas, G.J. 1972. A review of gull damage and management methods at nature reserves. *Biological Conservation* 4: 115–127.

Thompson, D.B.A., P.S. Thompson & D. Nethersole-Thompson. 1988. Fidelity and philopatry in breeding Redshanks (*Tringa totanus*) and Greenshanks (*Tringa nebularia*). *Proceedings of the International Ornithological Congress* 19: 563–574.

Thompson, K.R. 1987. *The ecology of the Manx Shearwater* Puffinus puffinus *on Rhum, West Scotland*. PhD thesis, University of Glasgow.

Thompson, P.S. 1988. *Long-term trends in the use of gardens by birds*. Research Report 32. British Trust for Ornithology, Tring.

Thompson, P.S. & W.G. Hale. 1989. Breeding site fidelity and natal philopatry in the Redshank *Tringa totanus*. *Ibis* 131: 214–224.

Thompson, P.S. & D.B.A. Thompson. 1991. Greenshanks *Tringa nebularia* and long-term studies of breeding waders. *Ibis* 133 (suppl.): 99–112.

Thompson, P.S., D. Baines, J.C. Coulson & G. Longrigg. 1994. Age at first breeding, philopatry and breeding site-fidelity in the Lapwing *Vanellus vanellus*. *Ibis* 136: 474–484.

Thomsen, P. & P. Jacobsen. 1979. *The Birds of Tunisia*. Nature-Travels, Copenhagen.

Thomson, A.L. 1965. The transequatorial migration of the Manx Shearwater (Puffin des Anglais). *L'Oiseau et la Revue Française d'Ornithologie* 35: 130–140.

Thomson, A.L. 1966. An analysis of recoveries of Great Skuas ringed in Shetland. *British Birds* 59: 1–15.

Thomson, A.L. 1974. The migration of the Gannet: a reassessment of British and Irish ringing data. *British Birds* 67: 89–103.

Thomson, D.L. & P.A. Cotton. 2000. Understanding the decline of the British population of Song Thrushes *Turdus philomelos*. In *Ecology and conservation of lowland farmland birds* (eds N.J. Aebischer, A.D. Evans, P.V. Grice & J.A. Vickery), pp 151–155. British Ornithologists' Union, Tring.

Thomson, D.L., S.R. Baillie & W.J. Peach. 1997. The demography and age-specific annual survival of Song Thrushes during periods of population stability and decline. *Journal of Animal Ecology* 66: 414–424.

Thorpe, J.P. & A.M. Sapsford. 1992. Population structure of Goldcrests *Regulus regulus* caught on migration at the Calf of Man Bird Observatory in 1989. *Ringing & Migration* 13: 103–112.

Thorpe, J.P. & R. Spencer. 1992. A large fall of Greenland Wheatears following exceptional weather conditions. *Ringing & Migration* 13: 125–126.

Thorup, K. 1998. Vagrancy of Yellow-browed Warbler *Phylloscopus inornatus* and Pallas's Warbler *Ph. proregulus* in north-west Europe: misorientation on great circles? *Ringing & Migration* 19: 7–12.

Tiainen, J. 1980. Adaptedness of the Willow Tit *Parus montanus* to the migratory habit. *Ornis Fennica* 57: 77–81.

Tiainen, J., I.K. Hanski, T. Pakkala, J. Piiroinen & R. Yrölä. 1989. Clutch size, nestling growth and nestling mortality of the Starling *Sturnus vulgaris* in south Finnish agroenvironments. *Ornis Fennica* 66: 41–48.

Ticehurst, N.F. 1957. *The Mute Swan in England: its history, and the ancient custom of swan keeping*. Cleaver-Hume, London.

Tieszen, L.L. & T.W. Boutton. 1988. Stable isotopes in terrestrial ecosystem research. In *Stable Isotopes in Ecological Research* (eds P.W. Rundel, J.R. Ehleringer & K.A. Nagy), pp 167–195. Springer Verlag, Berlin.

Timmerman, A., M.F. Morzer Bruyns & J. Philippona. 1979. Survey of the winter distribution of Palearctic geese in Europe, western Asia and North Africa. *Limosa* 49: 230–292.

Tobias, J. 1997. Food availability as a determinant of pairing behaviour in the European Robin. *Journal of Animal Ecology* 66: 629–639.

Tomes, R.F. 1901. Birds. In *The Victoria County History of Worcestershire*, volume 1, pp 139–170. Constable, London.

Tomiałojć, L. 1999. A long-term study of changing predation impact on breeding Woodpigeons. In *Advances in Vertebrate Pest Management* (eds D.P. Cowan & C.J. Feare), pp 205–218. Filander Verlag, Fürth.

Tomkovich, P.S. 1992. An analysis of the geographic variability in Knots *Calidris canutus* based on museum skins. *Wader Study Group Bulletin* 64 (suppl.): 17–23.

Tomkovich, P.S. & M.Yu. Soloviev. 1994. Site fidelity in high arctic breeding waders. *Ostrich* 65: 174–180.

Tomkovich, P.S. & M.Y. Soloviev. 1996. Distribution, migrations and biometrics of Knots *Calidris canutus canutus* on Taimyr, Siberia. *Ardea* 84: 85–98.

Toms, M.P. & J.A. Clark. 1998. Bird ringing in Britain and Ireland in 1996. *Ringing & Migration* 19: 95–168.

Toms, M.P., J.A. Clark & D.E. Balmer. 1999. Bird ringing in Britain and Ireland in 1997. *Ringing & Migration* 19: 215–255.

Toms, M.P., H.Q.P. Crick & C.R. Shawyer. 2000. *Project Barn Owl Final Report*. Research Report 197. British Trust for Ornithology, Thetford.

Toms, M.P., H.Q.P. Crick & C.R. Shawyer. 2001. The status of breeding Barn Owls *Tyto alba* in the United Kingdom 1995–97. *Bird Study* 48: 23–37.

Townshend, D.J. 1981. The importance of field feeding to the survival of wintering male and female Curlews *Numenius arquata* on the Tees Estuary. In *Feeding and survival strategies in estuarine organisms* (eds N.V. Jones & W.J. Wolff), pp 261–273. Plenum Press, New York.

Townshend, D.J. 1982. The Lazarus syndrome in Grey Plovers. *Wader Study Group Bulletin* 34: 11–12.

Townshend, D.J. 1985. Decisions for a lifetime: establishment of spatial defence and movement patterns by juvenile Grey Plovers *Pluvialis squatarola*. *Journal of Animal Ecology* 54: 267–274.

Townshend, D.J., P.J. Dugan & M.W. Pienkowski. 1984. The unsociable plover – use of intertidal areas by Grey Plovers. In *Coastal waders and wildfowl in winter* (eds P.R. Evans, J.D. Goss-Custard & W.G. Hale), pp 140–159. Cambridge University Press, Cambridge.

Toyne, E.P. 1995. Autumnal nest building by Goshawks. *Welsh Birds* 1: 11–13.

Triplet, P. & P. Yésou. 1998. Mid-winter counts of waders in the Senegal delta, West Africa, 1993–1997. *Wader Study Group Bulletin* 85: 66–73.

Trodd, P. & D. Kramer. 1991. *The Birds of Bedfordshire*. Castlemead Publications, Welwyn Garden City.

Troy, D.M. 1983. Recaptures of Redpolls – movements of an irruptive species. *Journal of Field Ornithology* 54: 146–151.

Trump, D.P.C., D.A. Stone, C.F.B. Coombs & C.J. Feare. 1994. Mute Swans in the Wylye Valley – population dynamics and habitat use. *International Journal of Pest Management* 40: 88–93.

Tubbs, C.R. 1974. *The Buzzard*. David & Charles, Newton Abbot.

Tubbs, C.R. 1977. Wildfowl and waders in Langstone Harbour. *British Birds* 70: 177–199.

Tuck, G. & H. Heinzel. 1980. *A field guide to seabirds of Australia and the world*. Collins, Sydney.

Tucker, G.M. & M.F. Heath. 1994. *Birds in Europe: their conservation status*. Conservation Series no. 3. BirdLife International, Cambridge.

Tucker, G.M., M.N. McCulloch & S.R. Baillie. 1990. *The conservation of migratory birds in the Western Palearctic-African flyway: review on the importance of losses incurred to migratory birds during migration*. Research Report 58. British Trust for Ornithology, Tring.

Turnbull, S.C. 1984. Feeding flocks of Wheatears and Meadow Pipits after heavy spring snowfalls. *British Birds* 77: 159.

Turner, A. & C. Rose. 1989. *Swallows and Martins of the World*. Christopher Helm, London.

Turner, J.R.G., J.J. Lennon & J.A. Lawrenson. 1988. British bird distributions and the energy theory. *Nature* 335: 539–541.

Turpie, J.K. 1995. Nonbreeding territoriality: causes and consequences of seasonal and individual variation in Grey Plover *Pluvialis squatarola* behaviour. *Journal of Animal Ecology* 64: 429–438.

Tveit, G. 1984. Autumn migration, wintering areas and survival of Bean Geese *Anser fabalis* marked on the moulting grounds in Finnmark, North Norway. *Swedish Wildlife Research* 13: 73–82.

Tyack, A.J., S.S. Walls & R.E. Kenward. 1998. Behaviour in the post-nestling dependence period of radio-tagged Common Buzzards *Buteo buteo*. *Ibis* 140: 58–63.

Tye, A. 1982. *Social organization and feeding in the Wheatear and Fieldfare.* PhD thesis, University of Cambridge.

Tyler, G.A. & R.E. Green. 1996. The incidence of nocturnal song by male Corncrakes *Crex crex* is reduced during pairing. *Bird Study* 43: 214–219.

Tyler, S.J. 1979. Mortality and movements of Grey Wagtails. *Ringing & Migration* 2: 122–131.

Tyler, S.J. & M. Green. 1994. The status and breeding ecology of Ring Ouzels *Turdus torquatus* in Wales with reference to soil acidity. *Welsh Bird Report* 7: 78–89.

Tyler, S.J. & S.J. Ormerod. 1994. *The Dippers.* T. & A.D. Poyser, London.

Tyler, S.J., S.J. Ormerod & J.M.S. Lewis. 1990. Breeding and natal dispersal amongst Welsh Dippers *Cinclus cinclus*. *Bird Study* 37: 18–23.

Tyrväinen, H. 1970. The mass occurrence of the Fieldfare (*Turdus pilaris* L.) in the winter of 1964/65 in Finland. *Annales Zoologici Fennici* 7: 349–357.

Tyrväinen, H. 1975. The winter irruption of Fieldfare *Turdus pilaris* and the supply of rowan-berries. *Ornis Fennica* 52: 23–31.

UK Biodiversity Group. 1999. *Tranche 2 Action Plans: Terrestrial and freshwater species and habitats.* Volume VI. English Nature, Peterborough.

Ulfstrand, S., G. Roos, T. Alerstam & L. Österdahl. 1974. Visible bird migration at Falsterbo, Sweden. *Vår Fågelvärld* suppl. 8.

Ullman, M. 1989. Varför är nordliga taigasångare *Phylloscopus inornatus* och kungsfågelsångare *Ph. proregulus* tidigare än sydliga? *Vår Fågelvärld* 48: 467–475.

Ulmschneider, H. 1990. *Post-nesting ecology of the Long-eared Owl (*Asio otus*) in southwestern Idaho.* Masters thesis, Boise State University, Idaho.

Ulmschneider, H.M. 1993. Wintering and nesting site use by Long-eared Owls in the Snake River Birds of Prey Area. In *Snake River Birds of Prey Area 1993 Research and Monitoring Annual Report* (ed K. Steenhof), pp 318–323. Bureau of Land Management, Boise, Idaho.

Underhill, L.G. 1995. The relationship between breeding and non-breeding localities of waders: the Curlew Sandpiper *Calidris ferruginea* as an extreme example. *Ostrich* 66: 41–45.

Underhill, L.G., R.P. Prŷs-Jones, R.J. Dowsett, P. Herroelen, D.N. Johnston, M.R. Lawn, S.C. Norman, D.J. Pearson & A.J. Tree. 1992. The biannual primary moult of Willow Warblers *Phylloscopus trochilus* in Europe and Africa. *Ibis* 134: 286–297.

Underhill, L.G., R.P. Prŷs-Jones, E.E. Syroechkovski, N.M. Groen, V. Karpov, H.G. Lappo, M.W.J. van Roomen, A. Rybkin, H. Schekkerman, H. Spiekman & R.W. Summers. 1993. Breeding of waders (Charadrii) and Brent Geese *Branta bernicla* at Pronchosheva Lake, north-eastern Taimyr, Russia, in a peak and a decreasing lemming year. *Ibis* 135: 277–292.

Underhill, M.C., T. Gittings, D.A. Callaghan, B. Hughes, J.S. Kirby & S. Delany. 1998. Status and distribution of breeding Common Scoters *Melanitta nigra nigra* in Britain and Ireland in 1995. *Bird Study* 45: 146–156.

Underhill-Day, J.C. 1981. Status of Bitterns in Europe since 1976. *British Birds* 74: 10–16.

Underhill-Day, J.C. 1984. Population and breeding biology of Marsh Harriers in Britain since 1900. *Journal of Applied Ecology* 21: 773–787.

Underhill-Day, J.C. 1990. *The status and breeding biology of Marsh Harrier* Circus aeruginosus *and Montagu's Harrier* Circus pygargus *in Britain since 1900.* PhD thesis, CNAA.

Underhill-Day, J.C. 1998. Breeding Marsh Harriers in the United Kingdom, 1983–1995. *British Birds* 91: 210–218.

Underhill-Day, J.C. & J. Wilson. 1978. Breeding Bitterns in Britain. *British Birds* 71: 285–300.

Underwood, L.A. & T.J. Stowe. 1984. Massive wreck of seabirds in eastern Britain, 1983. *Bird Study* 31: 79–88.

Upton, A.J., G. Pickerell & M. Heubeck. 2000. *Seabird numbers and breeding success in Britain and Ireland, 1999.* UK Nature Conservation no. 24. Joint Nature Conservation Committee, Peterborough.

Urban, E.K., C.H. Fry & S. Keith. 1986. *The Birds of Africa.* Volume 2. Academic Press, London and Orlando.

Urban, E.K., C.H. Fry & S. Keith. 1997. *The Birds of Africa.* Volume 5. Academic Press, London and San Diego.

Urcun, J.-P. & J. Bried. 1998a. The autumn migration of Red Kite *Milvus milvus* through the Pyrenees. In *Holarctic Birds of Prey* (eds R.D. Chancellor, B.-U. Meyburg & J.J. Ferrero), pp 641–654. ADENEX/World Working Group on Birds of Prey and Owls, Calamonte, Spain.

Urcun, J.-P. & J. Bried. 1998b. The autumn migration of raptors through the Pyrenees. In *Holarctic Birds of Prey* (eds R.D. Chancellor, B.-U. Meyburg & J.J. Ferrero), pp 655–690. ADENEX/World Working Group on Birds of Prey and Owls, Calamonte, Spain.

US Fish & Wildlife Service. 2001. *Adaptive Harvest Management: 2001 hunting season.* United States Department of the Interior, Washington DC.

van Balen, J.H. 1980. Population fluctuations in the Great Tit and feeding conditions in winter. *Ardea* 68: 143–164.

van Balen, J.H. & F. Hage. 1989. The effect of environmental factors on tit movements. *Ornis Scandinavica* 20: 99–104.

van den Bergh, L.M.J. 1984. Movements of Bean Geese *Anser fabalis* between West and Central European wintering areas. *Limosa* 57: 116–118.

van den Brink, B. & K.-H. Loske. 1990. Botswana and Namibia as regular wintering quarters for European Reed Warblers? *Ostrich* 61: 146–147.

van den Brink, B., R.G. Bijlsma & T.M. van der Have. 2000. European Swallows *Hirundo rustica* in Botswana during three non-breeding seasons: the effect of rainfall on moult. *Ostrich* 71: 198–204.

van der Hut, R.M.G., J. de Jong & E.R. Osieck. 1992. *Biologie en bescherming van de Kerkuil* Tyto alba: *aanzet tot het beschermingsplan.* Technisch rapport 7. Vogelbescherming Nederland, Zeist.

van der Poel, A.M. 1984. Overwinteringsgebieden, plaatstrouw en levensverwachting van Nederlandse Futen *Podiceps cristatus*. *Limosa* 57: 43–46.

van der Poel, A.M. 1985. Is de stadsfuut (*Podiceps cristatus*) echt anders? *Het Vogeljaar* 33: 97–106.

van Eerden, M.R. & J. Gregersen. 1995. Long-term changes in the northwest European population of Cormorants *Phalacrocorax carbo sinensis*. *Ardea* 83: 61–79.

van Eerden, M.R. & M.J. Munsterman. 1995. Sex and age dependent distribution in wintering Cormorants *Phalacrocorax carbo sinensis* in western Europe. *Ardea* 83: 285–297.

van Gils, J. & T. Piersma. 1999. Day- and night-time movements of radio-marked Red Knots staging in the western Wadden Sea in July-August 1995. *Wader Study Group Bulletin* 89: 36–44.

van Gils, J., T. Piersma, A. Dekinga & B. Spaans. 2000. Voortdurend in de lucht: zenderonderzoek aan Kanoeten *Calidris canutus* in de westelijke Waddenzee. [Distributional ecology of individually radio-marked Knots *Calidris canutus* in the western Dutch Wadden Sea in August–October 1999.] *Limosa* 73: 29–34.

van Impe, J. 1966. Notes sur la migration d'automne de *Larus minutus* sur la côte Belge. *Alauda* 34: 63–65.

van Impe, J. 1978. La rupture de la cohesion familiale chez l'Oie Rieuse, *Anser albifrons albifrons*, dans les quartiers d'hivernage. *Gerfaut* 68: 651–679.

van Impe, J. 1987. La migration d'automne, les quartiers d'hivernage et de reproduction de *Anser fabalis fabalis* et de *Anser fabalis rossicus* en relation avec la loi de Bergmann. *Gerfaut* 77: 63–88.

van Impe, J. 1991. Overleving, sterfte en trek van in België geringde jonge Kluten (*Recurvirosta avosetta*). *Gerfaut* 81: 217–243.

van Impe, J. & S. Derasse. 1994. [The recent increase of Yellow-browed Warbler and of Pallas's Warbler in Europe: are vagrants really wandering birds?] *Oriolus* 60: 3–17.

van Noordwijk, A.J. 1984. Problems in the analysis of dispersal and a critique on its heritability in the Great Tit. *Journal of Animal Ecology* 53: 533–544.

van Noordwijk, A.J. 1995. On bias due to observer distribution in the analysis of data on natal dispersal in birds. *Journal of Applied Statistics* 22: 683–694.

van Rhijn, J.G. 1991. *The Ruff*. T. & A.D. Poyser, London.

van Vessem, J. & D. Draulans. 1987. Spatial distribution and time budget of radio-tagged Grey Herons, *Ardea cinerea*, during the breeding season. *Journal of the Zoological Society of London* 213: 507–534.

Veiga, J.P. 1986. Settlement and fat accumulation by migrant Pied Flycatchers in Spain. *Ringing & Migration* 7: 85–98.

Veit, R.R. 1985. Long-tailed Jaegers wintering along the Falkland Current. *American Birds* 39: 873–878.

Veit, R.R., P. Pyle & J.A. McGowan. 1996. Ocean warming and long-term change in pelagic bird abundance within the California current system. *Marine Ecology Progress Series* 139: 11–18.

Verboom, J., A. Schotman, P. Opdam & J.A.J. Metz. 1991. European nuthatch metapopulations in a fragmented agricultural landscape. *Oikos* 61: 149–156.

Vercauteren, P. 1991. Overwinteren van Goudhaantjes, *Regulus regulus*, in Vlaanderen. *De Giervalk* 81: 35–55.

Verheyen, R. 1954. Les pinsons du Nord en Belgique. *Gerfaut* 44: 324–342.

Verhulst, S., C.M. Perrins & R. Riddington. 1997. Natal dispersal of Great Tits in a patchy environment. *Ecology* 78: 864–872.

Vernon, J.D.R. 1969. Spring migration of the Common Gull in Britain and Ireland. *Bird Study* 16: 101–107.

Vernon, J.D.R. 1972. Feeding habitats and food of the Black-headed and Common Gulls. *Bird Study* 19: 173–192.

Veron, P.K. 1988. Movements of Gannets ringed on Les Étacs and Ortac, Alderney, Channel Islands. *Ringing & Migration* 9: 37–43.

Vickery, J. 2002. Exciting new farmland bird projects. Winter feeding project. *BTO News* 238: 16–17.

Vickery, J.A. & J.A. Gill. 1999. Managing grassland for wild geese in Britain: a review. *Biological Conservation* 89: 93–106.

Vickery, J.A., W.J. Sutherland, A.R. Watkinson, S.J. Lane & J.M. Rowcliffe. 1995. Habitat switching by Dark-bellied Brent Geese *Branta b. bernicla* (L.) in relation to food depletion. *Oecologia* 103: 499–508.

Viitala, J., E. Korpimäki, P. Palokangas & M. Koivula. 1995. Attraction of Kestrels to vole scent marks visible in ultraviolet light. *Nature (London)* 373: 425–427.

Viker, M. 1994. Skogdue *Columba oenas*. In *Norsk Fugleatlas* (eds J.O. Gjershaug, P.G. Thingstad, S. Eldøy & S. Byrkjeland), pp 262–263. Norsk Ornitologisk Forening, Klæbu.

Village, A. 1985a. Turnover, age and sex ratios of Kestrels (*Falco tinnunculus*) in south Scotland. *Journal of Zoology, London, series A* 206: 175–189.

Village, A. 1985b. Spring arrival times and assortative mating of Kestrels in south Scotland. *Journal of Animal Ecology* 54: 857–868.

Village, A. 1987. Numbers, territory-size and turnover of Short-eared Owls *Asio flammeus* in relation to vole abundance. *Ornis Scandinavica* 18: 198–204.

Village, A. 1990. *The Kestrel*. T. & A.D. Poyser, London.

Vinicombe, K. 1971. Sabine's Gulls hawking flying insects inland. *British Birds* 64: 503–504.

Vinicombe, K. 1982. Breeding and population fluctuations of the Little Grebe. *British Birds* 75: 204–218.

Vinicombe, K., J. Marchant & A. Knox. 1993. Review of status and categorisation of feral birds on the British List. *British Birds* 86: 605–614.

Viñuela, J. 1996. Situación del Milano Real en el Mediterráneo. In *Biologia y conservación de las Rapaces Mediterraneas* (eds J. Muntaner & J. Mayol), pp 361–370. Mongrafias de la SEO 4. SEO/BirdLife International, Madrid.

Viñuela, J. 1997. Road transects as a large-scale census method for raptors: the case of the Red Kite *Milvus milvus* in Spain. *Bird Study* 44: 155–165.

Vlug, J.J. 1976. Zomerconcentraties van de Fuut *Podiceps cristatus*. *Natura* 73: 121–132.

Vodoladzskaya, T. 1997. Magpie ecology in urban landscape of Kazan, Russia. *Acta Ornithologica* 32: 132.

Voelker, G. 2001. Morphological correlates of migratory distance and flight display in the avian genus *Anthus*. *Biological Journal of the Linnean Society* 73: 425–435.

Voipio, P. 1990. Group of Black-throated Divers *Gavia arctica* preparing for the autumn migration. *Ornis Fennica* 67: 142–143.

Voisin, C. 1985. Migration et stabilité des populations chez l'Aigrette garzette *Egretta garzetta*. *Oiseau* 55: 39–43.

Voisin, C. 1991. *The Herons of Europe*. T. & A.D. Poyser, London.

von Haartman, L. 1968. The evolution of resident versus migratory habit in birds: some considerations. *Ornis Fennica* 45: 1–7.

von Keller, H., H.-R. Pauli & U.N. Glutz von Blotzheim. 1979. Zur Winternahrung des Birkhuhns *Tetrao tetrix* im subalpinen Fichtenwald der Nordalpenzone. *Der Ornithologische Beobachter* 76: 9–32.

von Lambert, K. 1967. Beobachtungen zum Zug und Winterquartier der Schwaldbenmöwe (*Xema sabini*) im östlichen Atlantik. *Die Vogelwarte* 24: 99–106.

von Lübcke, W. 1980. Mortalität, Maße und Gewichte von Wacholderdrosseln (*Turdus pilaris*) an der deutschen Nordseeküst im Februar 1978. *Beiträge zur Naturkunde Niedersachsens* 33: 147–152.

von Sauter, U. 1956. Beiträge zur Ökologie der Schleiereule (*Tyto alba*) nach den Ringfunden. *Die Vogelwarte* 18: 109–151.

Vooren, C.M. & A. Chiaradia. 1989. *Stercorarius longicaudus* and *S. parasiticus* in southern Brazil. *Ardea* 77: 233–235.

Voous, K.H. & J. Wattel. 1963. Distribution and migration of the Greater Shearwater. *Ardea* 51: 143–157.

Wainwright, C.B. 1957. How to make and use a duck trap. *Wildfowl Trust Annual Report* 8: 44–47.

Walker, A.F.G. 1970. The moult migration of Yorkshire Canada Geese. *Wildfowl* 21: 99–104.

Walker, F.J. 1996. Observations of North Atlantic Gannets *Morus bassanus* from Cape St Vincent, Portugal. *Seabird* 18: 40–48.

Wallace, D.I.M. 1972. Seabirds at Lagos and in the Gulf of Guinea. *Ibis* 115: 559–571.

Wallace, D.I.M. 1999. History of the Common Rosefinch in Britain and Ireland, 1869–1996. *British Birds* 92: 445–471.

Wallace, D.I.M. & W.R.P. Bourne. 1981. Seabird movements along the east coast of England. *British Birds* 74: 417–426.

Wallin, K., M.L. Wallin, T. Jaras & P. Strandvik. 1987. Leap-frog migration in the Swedish Kestrel *Falco tinnunculus* population.

Proceedings of the Fifth Nordic Ornithological Congress 1985: 213–222.

Walls, S.S. & R.E. Kenward. 1995. Movements of radio-tagged Buzzards *Buteo buteo* in their first year. *Ibis* 137: 177–182.

Walls, S.S. & R.E. Kenward. 1998. Movements of radio-tagged Buzzards *Buteo buteo* in early life. *Ibis* 140: 561–568.

Walls, S.S., S. Mañosa, R.M. Fuller, K.H. Hodder & R.E. Kenward. 1999. Is dispersal enterprise or exile? Evidence from radio-tagged Buzzards. *Journal of Avian Biology* 30: 407–415.

Walters, J. 1987. Primary moult in Black Terns and Common Terns. *Ringing & Migration* 8: 83–90.

Walters-Davies, P. & P.E. Davis. 1973. The ecology and conservation of the Red Kite in Wales. *British Birds* 66: 183–224, 241–270.

Wanless, S. & M.P. Harris. 1992. At-sea activity budgets of a pursuit-diving seabird monitored by radio-telemetry. In *Wildlife Telemetry: remote monitoring and tracking of animals* (eds I.G. Priede & S.M. Swift), pp 591–598. Ellis Horwood, Chichester.

Wanless, S. & M.P. Harris. 1997. *Phalacrocorax aristotelis* Shag. *BWP Update* 1: 3–13.

Wanless, S. & J.D. Okill. 1994. Body measurements and flight performance of adult and juvenile Gannets *Morus bassanus*. *Ringing & Migration* 15: 101–103.

Wanless, S., M.P. Harris, J. Calladine & P. Rothery. 1996. Modelling responses of Herring Gull and Lesser Black-backed Gull populations to restriction of reproductive output: implications for control measures. *Journal of Applied Ecology* 33: 1420–1432.

Ward, R.M. 2000. Migration patterns and moult of Common Terns *Sterna hirundo* and Sandwich Terns *Sterna sandvicensis* using Teesmouth in late summer. *Ringing & Migration* 20: 19–28.

Warham, J. 1990. *The Petrels: their ecology and breeding systems*. Academic Press, London.

Warham, J. 1996. *The Behaviour, Population Biology and Physiology of the Petrels*. Academic Press, London.

Warham, J., G.J. Wilson & B.R. Keeley. 1982. Annual cycle of the Sooty Shearwater at Snares Island, New Zealand. *Notornis* 29: 269–292.

Warren, S.M. 1990. *An analysis of the Irish Wildlife Service Greenland White-fronted Goose project 1983/84–1989/90*. Report to National Parks & Wildlife Service, Dublin. Wildfowl & Wetlands Trust, Slimbridge.

Warren, S.M., A.D. Fox, A.J. Walsh, O.J. Merne & H.J. Wilson. 1992a. Wintering site interchange among Greenland White-fronted Geese *Anser albifrons flavirostris* captured at Wexford Slobs, Ireland. *Bird Study* 39: 186–194.

Warren, S.M., A.D. Fox, A. Walsh & P. O'Sullivan. 1992b. Age of first pairing and breeding among Greenland White-fronted Geese. *Condor* 94: 791–793.

Warren, S.M., A.D. Fox, A. Walsh & P. O'Sullivan. 1993. Extended parent-offspring relationships in Greenland White-fronted Geese (*Anser albifrons flavirostris*). *Auk* 110: 145–148.

Waters, R. 1994. Wintering gulls 1953–1993. *BTO News* 190: 9–10.

Waters, R.J., P.A. Cranswick, A.J. Musgrove & M.S. Pollitt. 1998. *The Wetland Bird Survey 1996–97: Wildfowl and Wader Counts*. BTO/WWT/RSPB/JNCC, Slimbridge.

Waterston, G. 1966. *Ospreys in Speyside*. Royal Society for the Protection of Birds, Sandy.

Watkins, D. 1993. *A national plan for shorebird conservation in Australia*. Report 90. Royal Australasian Ornithologists' Union, Melbourne.

Watson, A. 1965. A population study of Ptarmigan (*Lagopus mutus*) in Scotland. *Journal of Animal Ecology* 34: 135–172.

Watson, A. 1972. The behaviour of the Ptarmigan. *British Birds* 65: 6–26, 93–117.

Watson, A. 1982. Effects of human impact on Ptarmigan and Red Grouse near ski lifts in Scotland. *Institute of Terrestrial Ecology Annual Report for 1981*: 51.

Watson, D. 1977. *The Hen Harrier*. T. & A.D. Poyser, Berkhamsted.

Watson, J. 1997. *The Golden Eagle*. T. & A.D. Poyser, London.

Watson, J., S.R. Rae & R. Stillman. 1992. Nesting density and breeding success of Golden Eagles in relation to food supply in Scotland. *Journal of Animal Ecology* 61: 543–550.

Way, L.S., P. Grice, A. MacKay, C.A. Galbraith, D.A. Stroud & M.W. Pienkowski. 1993. *Ireland's Internationally Important Bird Sites: a review of sites for the EC Special Protection Area Network*. Report to the National Parks and Wildlife Service of the Office of Public Works, Dublin and the Department of the Environment (Northern Ireland), Belfast. Joint Nature Conservation Committee, Peterborough.

Webb, A., N.M. Harrison, G.M. Leaper, R.D. Steele, M.L. Tasker & M.W. Pienkowski. 1990. *Seabird Distribution west of Britain*. Final report of Phase 3 of the NCC Seabirds at Sea Project, November 1986–March 1990. Nature Conservancy Council, Aberdeen.

Weber, T.P. & A. Hedenström. 2001. Long-distance migrants as a model system of structural and physiological plasticity. *Evolutionary Ecology Research* 3: 255–271.

Weber, T.P. & A.I. Houston. 1997. A general model for time-minimising avian migration. *Journal of Theoretical Biology* 185: 447–458.

Weeden, R.B. 1964. Spatial separation of sexes in Rock and Willow Ptarmigan in winter. *Auk* 81: 534–541.

Wege, M.L. 1980. *Migration behaviour of Giant Canada Geese*. PhD thesis, University of California, Davis.

Wegge, P. & B.B. Larsen. 1987. Spacing of adult and subadult male common capercaillies during the breeding season. *Auk* 104: 481–490.

Wendeln, H. & P.H. Becker. 1999. Significance of ring removal in Africa for a Common Tern *Sterna hirundo* colony. *Ringing & Migration* 19: 210–212.

Wenink, P.W., A.J. Baker, H.U. Rosner & M.G.J. Tilanus. 1996. Global mitochondrial DNA phylogeography of holarctic breeding dunlins (*Calidris alpina*). *Evolution* 50: 318–330.

Wennerberg, L., N.M.A. Holmgren, P.-E. Jönsson & T. von Schantz. 1999. Genetic and morphological variation in Dunlin *Calidris alpina* breeding in the Palearctic tundra. *Ibis* 141: 391–398.

Wernham, C.V. & D.E. Balmer. 2001. Constant effort ringing in Europe – outline of project aims for participant ringing schemes. *EURING Newsletter* 3: 27–28.

Wernham, C.V. & W.J. Peach. 1999. Use of ring recoveries to monitor long-term changes in the survival rates of British and Irish Cormorants *Phalacrocorax carbo*. *Bird Study* 46 (suppl.): S189–197.

Wernham, C.V. & A.J. Williams. 1999. Rehabilitation of oiled seabirds. In *Proceedings of the Twenty-second International Ornithological Congress, Durban* (eds N.J. Adams & R.H. Slotow), pp 3168–3170. BirdLife South Africa, Johannesburg. (CD-ROM).

Wernham, C.V., W.J. Peach & S.J. Browne. 1997. *Survival rates of rehabilitated Guillemots*. Research Report 186. British Trust for Ornithology, Thetford.

Wernham, C.V., S.R. Baillie, J.A. Clark, H.Q.P. Crick & G.M. Siriwardena. 1998. The BTO Integrated Population Monitoring programme: the contribution of ringing. *Acta Zoologica Lituanica, Ornithologia* 8: 93–104.

Wernham, C.V., S.R. Baillie & J.A. Clark. 1999. Improving the role of ringing data in conservation – how your data are contributing. *Ringers' Bulletin* 10: 21–23.

Wessels, H. 1987. Crane (*Grus grus*) migration over the Netherlands. *Aquila* 93–94: 91–105.

West, R.H. 1896. Flight of birds across the moon's disc. *Nature (London)* 53: 131.

Westerhoff, D. & C.R. Tubbs. 1991. Dartford Warblers *Sylvia undata*, their habitat and conservation in the New Forest, Hampshire, England in 1988. *Biological Conservation* 56: 89–100.

Whilde, A. 1989. The Chough in Ireland: numbers and distribution. In *Choughs and Land-use in Europe* (eds E.M. Bignal & D.J. Curtis), pp 12–13. Scottish Chough Study Group, Paisley.

White, G. 1789. *The Natural History and Antiquities of Selborne*. B. White & Son, London.

White, R.W., J.B. Reid, A.D. Black & K.W. Gillon. 1999. *Seabird and marine mammal dispersion in the waters around the Falkland Islands 1998–1999.* Joint Nature Conservation Committee, Peterborough.

White-Robinson, R. 1984. *The ecology of Canada Geese (*Branta canadensis*) in Nottinghamshire, and their importance in relation to agriculture.* PhD thesis, University of Nottingham.

Whitfield, D.P. 1985. *Social organisation and feeding behaviour of wintering Turnstone* Arenaria interpres. PhD thesis, University of Edinburgh.

Whitfield, D.P. 1990. Individual feeding specialisations in wintering Turnstone *Arenaria interpres. Journal of Animal Ecology* 59: 193–211.

Whitfield, D.P. 1995. Behaviour and ecology of a polyandrous population of Grey Phalaropes *Phalaropus fulicarius* in Iceland. *Journal of Avian Biology* 26: 349–352.

Whitfield, D.P. 2002. The status of breeding Dotterel *Charadrius morinellus* in Britain in 1999. *Bird Study* 49 (in press).

Whitfield, D.P. & J. Magnusson. 1987. The migration of high arctic waders through Melrakkasletta, north-east Iceland. In *The conservation of international flyway populations of waders* (eds N.C. Davidson & M.W. Pienkowski), pp 85–89. *Wader Study Group Bulletin* 49 (suppl.). IWRB Special Publication 7.

Whitfield, D.P., K. Duncan, D. Pullan & R.D. Smith. 1996. Recoveries of Scottish-ringed Dotterel *Charadrius morinellus* in the non-breeding season: evidence for seasonal shifts in wintering distribution. *Ringing & Migration* 17: 105–110.

Whittingham, M.J., S.M. Percival & A.F. Brown. 1999. The use of radio telemetry to measure habitat choice by young Golden Plover *Pluvialis apricaria* chicks. *Bird Study* 46: 363–368.

Whittington, P.A., B.M. Dyer, R.J.M. Crawford & A.J. Williams. 1999. First recorded breeding of Leach's Storm-Petrel *Oceanodroma leucorhoa* in the southern hemisphere, at Dyer Island, South Africa. *Ibis* 141: 327–330.

Widén, P. 1985. Breeding and movements of Goshawks in boreal forests in Sweden. *Holarctic Ecology* 8: 273–279.

Widgery, J.P. 1970. Ringing controls and territorial feeding behaviour of Black-headed Gulls in Hyde Park and Kensington Gardens. *London Bird Report* 34: 88–89.

Widmer, M. 1996. Phänologie, Siedlungsdichte und Populationsökologie der Gartengrasmücke *Sylvia borin* in einem subalpinen Habitat der Zentralalpen. *Journal für Ornithologie* 137: 479–501.

Wieloch, M. 1991. Population trends of the Mute Swan *Cygnus olor* in the Palearctic. In *Proceedings of the Third IWRB International Swan Symposium, Oxford 1989* (eds J. Sears & P.J. Bacon), pp 22–32. *Wildfowl* suppl. 1.

Wijnandts, H. 1984. Ecological energetics of the Long-eared Owl (*Asio otus*). *Ardea* 72: 1–92.

Wiktander, U. 1998. *Reproduction and survival in the Lesser Spotted Woodpecker. Effects of life history, mating system and age.* PhD thesis, University of Lund, Sweden.

Wiktander, U., O. Olsson & S.G. Nilsson. 2000. Parental care and social mating system in the Lesser Spotted Woodpecker *Dendrocopos minor. Journal of Avian Biology* 31: 447–456.

Wilbur, H.M. 1969. The breeding biology of Leach's Petrel *Oceanodroma leucorhoa. Auk* 86: 433–442.

Williams, A.J. & L.G. Underhill. 1997. Common Tern *Sterna hirundo.* In *The atlas of southern African birds: volume 1 – non-passerines* (eds J.A. Harrison, D.G. Allan, L.G. Underhill, M. Herremans, A.J. Tree, V. Parker & C.J. Brown), pp 476–477. BirdLife South Africa, Johannesburg.

Williams, R.S.R. 1996. *Ecology and population dynamics of the Long-eared Owl* Asio otus. PhD thesis, University of East Anglia.

Williams, R.S.R. 1998. Uneven sex ratio of the Long-eared Owl *Asio otus* in northern India. *Journal of the Bombay Natural History Society* 95: 343–344.

Williams, T.C. & J.M. Williams. 1978. An oceanic mass migration of land birds. *Scientific American* 239: 138–145.

Williamson, K. 1954a. Northern Chiffchaffs and their area of origin. *British Birds* 47: 49–58.

Williamson, K. 1954b. The migration of the Iceland Merlin. *British Birds* 47: 434–441.

Williamson, K. 1958–62. Reports from bird observatories, autumn migration. *Bird Migration* 1: 2–27, 97–147, 249–272; 2: 121–131.

Williamson, K. 1959. Meadow Pipit migration. *Bird Migration* 1: 88–91.

Williamson, K. 1960. *The genera* Cettia, Locustella, Acrocephalus *and* Hippolais. BTO Guide 7. British Trust for Ornithology, Oxford.

Williamson, K. 1961. The concept of 'Cyclonic Approach'. *Bird Migration* 1: 235–240.

Williamson, K. 1962a. *The genus* Phylloscopus. BTO Guide 8. British Trust for Ornithology, Oxford.

Williamson, K. 1962b. An eruptive dispersal of Dunnocks (*Prunella modularis*). *Bird Migration* 2: 111–113.

Williamson, K. 1963a. Movements as an indicator of population changes. *Bird Migration* 2: 207–223.

Williamson, K. 1963b. Aspects of autumn movements at the Bird Observatories. *Bird Migration* 2: 224–251.

Williamson, K. 1964. *The genus* Sylvia. BTO Guide 9. British Trust for Ornithology, Tring.

Williamson, K. 1965. *Fair Isle and its birds*. Oliver & Boyd, Edinburgh.

Williamson, K. & P. Davis. 1956. The autumn 1953 invasion of Lapland Buntings and its source. *British Birds* 49: 6–25.

Wilson, A. & R. Slack. 1996. *Rare and Scarce Birds in Yorkshire*. Privately published.

Wilson, A.M., J.A. Vickery & S.J. Browne. 2001. Numbers and distribution of Northern Lapwings *Vanellus vanellus* breeding in England and Wales in 1998. *Bird Study* 48: 2–17.

Wilson, A.M., A.C.B. Henderson & R.J. Fuller. 2002. Status of the Common Nightingale *Luscinia megarhynchos* in England at the end of the 20th century with particular reference to climate change. *Bird Study* 49 (in press).

Wilson, H.J., D.W. Norriss, A. Walsh, A.D. Fox & D.A. Stroud. 1991. Winter site fidelity in Greenland White-fronted Geese: implications for conservation and management. *Ardea* 79: 287–294.

Wilson, J. 1983. Wintering site fidelity of woodcock in Ireland. In *Proceedings of the Second European Woodcock and Snipe Workshop* (ed H. Kalchreuter), pp 18–27. International Waterfowl Research Bureau, Slimbridge.

Wilson, J. 1993. Colonisation by Bearded Tits of Leighton Moss, Lancashire. *British Birds* 86: 352–358.

Wilson, J.D., R. Taylor & L.B. Muirhead. 1996. Field use by farmland birds in winter: an analysis of field type preferences using resampling methods. *Bird Study* 43: 320–332.

Wilson, J.D., A.J. Morris, B.E. Arroyo, S.C. Clark & R.B. Bradbury. 1999. A review of the abundance and diversity of invertebrate and plant foods of granivorous birds in northern Europe in relation to agricultural change. *Agriculture, Ecosystems & Environment* 75: 13–30.

Wilson, J.R. 1981. The migration of High Arctic shorebirds through Iceland. *Bird Study* 28: 21–32.

Wilson, J.R. 1986. The migration of shorebirds through north-east and east Iceland. *Wader Study Group Bulletin* 46: 18–20.

Wilson, J.R. 1997. Sanderlings in Iceland. *Wader Study Group Bulletin* 82: 44–45.

Wilson, J.R., M.A. Czajkowski & M.W. Pienkowski. 1980. The migration through Europe and wintering in West Africa of Curlew Sandpipers. *Wildfowl* 31: 107–122.

Wilson, R.P. 2001. Beyond rings on birds for determination of movements: wither the archival tag? *Ardea* 89 (special issue): 231–240.

Wilson, R.P., B.M. Culik, R. Bannasch & J. Lage. 1994. Monitoring Antarctic environmental variables using penguins. *Marine Ecology Progress Series* 106: 199–202.

Wiltschko, W., P. Weindler & R. Wiltschko. 1998. Interaction of magnetic and celestial cues in the migratory orientation of passerines. *Journal of Avian Biology* 29: 606–617.

Winkel, W. 1993. Zum Migrationsverhalten von Kohl- und Blaumeise. *Jahresbericht Institut für Vogelforschung 'Vogelwarte Helgoland'* 1: 9.

Winkler, D.W. & S.D. Cooper. 1986. Ecology of migrant Black-necked Grebes *Podiceps nigricollis* at Mono Lake, California. *Ibis* 128: 483–491.

Winkler, H., D.A. Christie & D. Nurney. 1995. *Woodpeckers: a guide to the woodpeckers, piculets and wrynecks of the world*. Pica Press, Robertsbridge, East Sussex.

Winney, B.J. 1998. *Cormorant population genetics and Turaco phylogenetics*. PhD thesis, University of Nottingham.

Winstanley, D., R. Spencer & K. Williamson. 1974. Where have all the Whitethroats gone? *Bird Study* 21: 1–14.

Witherby, H.F. 1921. On the British taken examples of the 'Levantine' Shearwater. *British Birds* 15: 151–153.

Witt, K. 1982. Der Bergpieper (*Anthus sp. spinoletta*) als Gast im nördlichen Mitteleuropa. *Die Vogelwelt* 103: 90–111.

Wood, J.B. 1976. *The biology of Yellow Wagtails* Motacilla flava *L. overwintering in Nigeria*. PhD thesis, University of Aberdeen.

Wood, B. 1979. Changes in numbers of over-wintering Yellow Wagtails *Motacilla flava* and their food supplies in a West African savanna. *Ibis* 121: 228–231.

Wood, B. 1982a. Weights and migration strategy of Blackcaps *Sylvia atricapilla* wintering in Tunisia. *Ibis* 124: 66–72.

Wood, B. 1982b. The trans-Saharan spring migration of Yellow Wagtails (*Motacilla flava*). *Journal of Zoology (London)* 197: 267–283.

Wood, B. 1989. Comments on Bairlein's hypothesis of trans-Saharan migration by short stages with stopovers. *Ringing & Migration* 10: 48–52.

Wood, B. 1992. Yellow Wagtail *Motacilla flava* migration from West Africa to Europe: pointers towards a conservation strategy for migrants on passage. *Ibis* 134 (suppl. 1): 66–76.

Wood, K.A. 1989. Seasonal abundance, marine habitats and behaviour of skuas off central New South Wales. *Corella* 13: 97–104.

Woodcock, A. 1992. The Burham, Eccles and New Hythe Nightingales. *Kent Bird Report* 40 (1991): 137–140.

Woods, R.W. 1988. *Guide to Birds of the Falkland Islands*. Anthony Nelson, Oswestry.

Woods, R.W. & A. Woods. 1997. *Atlas of breeding birds of the Falkland Islands*. Anthony Nelson, Oswestry.

Wooller, R.D. & J.C. Coulson. 1977. Factors affecting the age of first breeding of the Kittiwake *Rissa tridactyla*. *Ibis* 119: 339–349.

Wormell, P. 1976. The Manx Shearwaters of Rhum. *Scottish Birds* 9: 103–118.

Wotton, S.R. & S. Gillings. 2000. The status of breeding Woodlarks *Lullula arborea* in Britain in 1997. *Bird Study* 47: 212–224.

Wotton, S., D.W. Gibbons, M. Dilger & P.V. Grice. 1998. Cetti's Warblers in the United Kingdom and the Channel Islands in 1996. *British Birds* 91: 77–89.

Wotton, S.R., R.H.W. Langston, D.W. Gibbons & A.J. Pierce. 2000. The status of the Cirl Bunting *Emberiza cirlus* in the UK and the Channel Islands in 1998. *Bird Study* 47: 138–146.

Woutersen, K. 1980. Migrating Little Gulls in the Netherlands. *British Birds* 73: 192–193.

Wright, M., A. Brenchley, S. Evans, T. Howe & D. Underwood. 2000. Roosting behaviour of Swifts. *British Birds* 93: 145.

Wuorinen, J.D. 1992. Do Arctic Skuas *Stercorarius parasiticus* exploit and follow terns during the fall migration. *Ornis Fennica* 69: 198–200.

Wyllie, I. 1981. *The Cuckoo*. Batsford, London.

Wyllie, I. 1985. Post-fledging period and dispersal of young Sparrowhawks *Accipiter nisus*. *Bird Study* 32: 196–198.

Wyllie, I., L. Dale & I. Newton. 1996. Unequal sex-ratio, mortality and pollutant residues in Long-eared Owls in Britain. *British Birds* 89: 429–436.

Wymenga, E., M. Engelmoer, C.J. Smit & T.M. van Spanje. 1990. Geographical breeding origin and migration of waders wintering in West Africa. *Ardea* 78: 83–112.

Wynne-Edwards, V.C. 1935. On the habits and distribution of birds on the North Atlantic. *Proceedings of the Boston Society of Natural History* 40: 233–346.

Wynne-Edwards, V.C. 1952. Geographical variation in the bill of the Fulmar (*Fulmarus glacialis*). *Scottish Naturalist* 64: 84–101.

Wynne-Edwards, V.C. 1962. *Animal Dispersion in Relation to Social Behaviour*. Oliver & Boyd, Edinburgh.

Yalden, D.W. & J.W. Pearce-Higgins. 1997. Density-dependence and winter weather as factors affecting the size of a population of Golden Plovers *Pluvialis apricaria*. *Bird Study* 44: 227–234.

Yeatman, L., G. Olioso & D. Berthelot. 1991. *Atlas des Oiseaux de France en hiver*. Société ornithologique de France, Paris.

Yésou, P. 1985a. The breeding chronology of the Avocet. *Wader Study Group Bulletin* 45: 10.

Yésou, P. 1985b. Nouvelles données sur la mue de *Puffinus p. mauretanicus*. *L'Oiseau* 55: 177–182.

Yésou, P. 1986. Mediterranean races of Manx Shearwater in British waters. *British Birds* 79: 354.

Yésou, P. 1995. Individual migration strategies in Cormorants *Phalacrocorax carbo* passing through or wintering in western France. *Ardea* 83: 267–274.

Yésou, P., A.M. Paterson, E.J. Mackrill & W.R.P. Bourne. 1990. Plumage variation and identification of the 'Yelkouan Shearwater'. *British Birds* 83: 299–319.

Yoerg, S.I. 1994. Development of foraging behaviour in the Eurasian Dipper *Cinclus cinclus* from fledging until dispersal. *Animal Behaviour* 47: 577–588.

Yosef, R. 1995a. Foraging behaviour of arctic, pomarine and long-tailed skua on migration in the Red Sea. *Bulletin of the Ornithological Society of the Middle East* 34: 12–13.

Yosef, R. 1995b. Spring 1994 raptor migration at Eilat, Israel. *Journal of Raptor Research* 29: 127–134.

Young, C.M. 1964. *An ecological study of the Common Shelduck* (Tadorna tadorna, L.) *with special reference to regulation of the Ythan population*. PhD thesis, University of Aberdeen.

Young, J.G. 1972. Distribution, status and movements of feral Greylag Geese in southwest Scotland. *Scottish Birds* 7: 170–182.

Young-Powell, M. 1994. Migration of Jays in Norfolk. *Norfolk Bird Club Bulletin* 8: 14.

Zalakevicius, M. & R. Zalakeviciute. 2001. Global climate change impact on birds: a review of research in Lithuania. *Folia Zoologica* 50: 1–17.

Zamora, R. 1990. The fruit diet of Ring Ouzels *Turdus torquatus* wintering in the Sierra Nevada (southeast Spain). *Alauda* 58: 67–70.

Zar, J.H. 1984. *Biostatistical Analysis*. Second edition. Prentice-Hall, New Jersey.

Zehnder, S. & L. Karlsson. 2001. Do ringing numbers reflect true migratory activity of nocturnal migrants? *Journal für Ornithologie* 142: 173–183.

Zeiske, O. 1995. Traditional or flexible response – Curlew Sandpiper *Calidris ferruginea* on post-breeding migration via the East Atlantic Flyway show different migration strategies with clear sexual tendencies. *Wader Study Group Bulletin* 76: 19.

Zheng, G. & Z. Zhang. 1993. The distribution and status of Pheasants in China. In *Pheasants in Asia 1992* (ed D. Jenkins), pp 15–19. World Pheasant Association, Reading.

REFERENCES

Zicus, M.C. 1981. Molt migration of Canada Geese from Crex Meadows, Wisconsin. *Journal of Wildlife Management* 45: 54–63.

Zijlstra, M. 1987. Bruine Kiekendief *Circus aeruginosus* in Flevoland in de winter. *Ardea* 60: 57–62.

Zink, G. 1958. Vom Zug der Großen Rohrdommel (*Botaurus stellaris*) nach den Ringfunden. *Die Vogelwarte* 19: 243–247.

Zino, P.A., F. Zino, T. Maul & J.M. Biscoito. 1987. The laying, incubation and fledging periods of Cory's Shearwater *Calonectris diomedea borealis* on Selvagem Grande in 1984. *Ibis* 129: 393–398.

Zöckler, C. & I. Lysenko. 2000. *Water Birds on the Edge. First circumpolar assessment of climate change impact on arctic breeding water birds.* World Conservation Monitoring Centre, Cambridge.

Zoutendyk, P. 1968. The occurrence of Sabine's Gull *Xema sabini* off the Cape Peninsula. *Ostrich* 39: 9–11.

Zuckerbrot, Y.D., U.N. Safriel & U. Paz. 1980. Autumn migration of Quail *Coturnix coturnix* at the north coast of the Sinai Peninsula. *Ibis* 122: 1–14.

Zwarts, L. 1990. Increased prey availability drives premigration hyperphagia in Whimbrels and allows them to leave the Banc d'Arguin, Mauritania, in time. *Ardea* 78: 297–300.

Zwarts, L., A.-M. Blomert & R. Hupkes. 1990a. Increase of feeding time in waders preparing for spring migration from the Banc d'Arguin, Mauritania. *Ardea* 78: 237–256.

Zwarts, L., B. Ens, M. Kersten & T. Piersma. 1990b. Moult, mass and flight range of waders ready to take off for long-distance migrations. *Ardea* 78: 339–364.

Zwickel, F.C. 1966. Winter food habits of Capercaillie in north-east Scotland. *British Birds* 59: 325–336.

Appendix 1a
Recovery types and finding circumstance classes used in the book

Recovery types

Type	Description	EURING codes*
'Dead'	Found by members of the public; such birds are generally dead but occasionally alive (*eg* trapped in greenhouse).	All except those defined as 'Recaught' or 'Resighted' below.
'Recaught'	Caught by ringers alive and released again.	IFCI=8; IFCN=8 and IFCI=20 or 27
'Resighted'	Field reports of individually marked birds.	IFCI=28 or 29

Finding circumstance classes

Class	Description	EURING codes*
'Deliberately taken by Man'	Birds shot, trapped and poisoned for any reason (*eg* hunting, pest control, protection of public health).	IFCI=10–19; IFCI=20 (unless IFCN=8); IFCI=21–26
'Human-related'	Most common are road, rail and air traffic collisions, collisions with man-made structures, attracted to lights, entered buildings.	IFCI=40–49
'Accidental capture'	Most commonly via by-catching in fisheries, entanglement in fish pond nets and crop protection nets.	IFCI=33 or 34
'Natural (environmental)'	Most common are poor condition due to cold or hot weather, other weather-related causes (*eg* storms), drowning in natural water-bodies, capture in natural holes, tangling in natural materials and collision with natural objects.	IFCI=70–78
'Natural (illness)'	Breaks, contusions, trauma, malformations and disease.	IFCI=50–59
'Pollution'	Oiling, entanglement in discarded human materials, accidental poisoning, radioactivity and electrocution.	IFCI=30–32 or 35–38
'Domestic predator'	Taken by cats or other domestic animals.	IFCI=61 or 62
'Natural predator'	Taken by any predator other than domestic animals.	IFCI=60 or 63–69
'Additional rare classes'	Found on ships (but not attracted to lights or caught in nets), joined domestic animals and caught due to ring.	IFCI=6, 7 or 9

* Refers to the definitions used for coding in the ring-recovery database (source: EURING 1979). Abbreviations IFCN and IFCI refer to the terms 'finding condition' and 'finding circumstances' respectively, as defined by EURING (1979).

Appendix 1b
Tests for biases in recovery locations due to finding circumstances

For each species, the mean latitudes and longitudes of recoveries due to deliberate taking by Man, human-related causes, pollution, accidental capture and domestic predators were compared in turn to those due to other, more natural causes ('**other**'). Negative values indicate locations south of the Equator for latitude and west of the Greenwich Meridian for longitude. All coordinates are given in decimal degrees. A minimum sample of 10 recoveries in each group was required for a test to be carried out and only those species with at least 10 recoveries in the 'other' group could be tested. Tests were made both for birds ringed in Britain & Ireland during the breeding season and recovered in winter (Table I) and for those ringed in Britain & Ireland in winter and recovered during the breeding season (Table II). Full methods are provided in **Chapter 4**. The number of records available for each cause of recovery is indicated. Only species for which at least one of the comparisons could be carried out are included. For each latitude or longitude test, the significance of the result is indicated. For significant results, the difference between the two means tested in each case is also shown. Significance codes are as follows:-

S significant at P<0.05;
S* significant but sample <30 in one or both groups;
NS non-significant (P>0.05);
NS* non-significant but sample <30 in one or both groups;
NT not tested (insufficient sample for the given finding circumstance class).

For each species with at least one significant result, the proportion is given of the total number of recoveries with known cause that is attributable to significant causes ('**% of total**'). The '**overall result**' indicates whether finding circumstances are likely to have introduced significant bias into the recovery pattern presented for that species. This is the result presented under 'finding circumstances' in the standard *statistical analyses* table in each main species account, coded as follows:-

S at least one result significant and >50% of the recoveries of known cause are due to this cause (or multiple causes);
S* as above but the only significant tests are based on a sample of <30 in at least one class;
NS all the tests had samples of at least 30 and none was significant;
NS* all tests were non-significant but tests had a sample of <30 for at least one class;
(NS) at least one significant result was demonstrated but the proportion of the total recoveries due to the significant cause(s) was <50%;
NT not tested because the sample size was <10 in all other groups.

In addition, a small number of species had insufficient recoveries in the 'other' class to allow testing but, nonetheless, had more than 10 recoveries in one of the potential biasing classes. These are coded as [**Not tested***] in the *statistical analyses* table in each account and were as follows:-

Breeding-winter analyses: Deliberately taken by Man, n=10–29: Wigeon, Gadwall, Pintail, Dotterel, Golden Plover, Little Owl, Swift and Blackcap; Deliberately taken by Man, n=30+: Greylag Goose (n=106), Teal (n=38), Shoveler (n=32), Pochard (n=58), Snipe (n=61) and Woodcock (n=268); Human-related, n=10–29: Little Owl and Grey Wagtail.

Winter-breeding analyses: Deliberately taken by Man, n=10–29: Pink-footed Goose, Shoveler and Woodcock; Deliberately taken by Man, n=30+: Wigeon (n=105), Pintail (n=42) and Pochard (n=78); Human-related, n=10–29: Long-tailed Tit.

Table I Ringed in the breeding season and recovered in winter

Species*	Other			Deliberately taken by Man					Human-related					Pollution				
	Mean latitude	Mean longitude	Number of records	Mean latitude	Mean longitude	Number of records	Test result and differences (latitude)	Test result and differences (longitude)	Mean latitude	Mean longitude	Number of records	Test result and differences (latitude)	Test result and differences (longitude)	Mean latitude	Mean longitude	Number of records	Test result and differences (latitude)	Test result and differences (longitude)
retdi	56.59	−2.86	13	48.30	−4.50	1	NT	NT	—	—	0	NT	NT	—	—	2	NT	NT
fulma	54.70	−0.02	53	61.49	−7.13	34	S −6.79	S 7.10	—	—	4	NS*	NS*	53.17	−0.09	11	NS*	NS*
mansh	−11.52	−42.62	54	—	—	5	NT	NT	—	—	0	NT	NT	—	—	1	NT	NT
stope	−11.26	18.93	10	—	—	0	NT	NT	—	—	1	NT	NT	—	—	0	NT	NT
ganne	47.37	−2.54	181	39.41	−4.97	57	S 7.96	S 2.43	52.04	−2.91	30	NS	NS	49.62	−0.40	57	NS	S −2.14
cormo	52.60	−3.21	883	52.01	−4.24	871	S 0.59	S 1.03	54.15	−1.52	32	NS	NS	52.40	−2.09	61	NS	S −1.12
shag	54.55	−3.51	1261	54.58	−4.61	187	NS	S 1.09	53.60	−1.76	51	NS	NS	55.79	−2.69	121	S −1.23	S −0.82
grehe	53.17	−1.50	328	52.53	−2.18	62	S 0.64	S 0.68	52.59	−1.88	531	S −0.36	S −0.15	—	—	9	NT	NT
mutsw	52.22	−2.04	1241	52.68	−1.18	75	S −0.46	S −0.85	53.03	−1.35	109	NS	NS	52.69	−1.72	132	S −0.47	NS* −0.32
cango	52.84	−1.31	288	52.75	−1.47	1492	S	S 0.16	—	—	0	NT	NT	52.23	−1.55	11	NS*	NS*
sheld	53.02	0.99	45	52.11	−3.70	22	S*	S 4.69	52.20	−0.05	15	NS*	NS*	—	—	1	NT	NT
malla	52.32	−0.41	92	52.56	−0.82	2380	NS	NS*	—	—	5	NS*	NS*	—	—	2	NT	NT
tufdu	52.25	0.13	24	52.54	−2.49	218	NS*	S*	—	—	4	NT	NT	—	—	1	NT	NT
eider	56.65	−2.23	346	56.98	−1.72	40	NS*	NS*	—	—	10	NS*	NS*	56.39	−2.61	128	S 0.26	S 0.37
goosa	54.98	−3.12	12	55.09	−2.72	14	S −0.32	S −0.50	55.80	−2.43	222	NS	NS*	—	—	0	NT	NT
henha	56.66	−1.91	32	—	—	7	NT	NT	53.25	−1.88	34	S −1.08	S	—	—	0	NT	NT
sparr	53.27	−1.87	229	53.51	−2.38	57	NS	NS 0.51	55.57	−3.80	260	NS	NS	—	—	4	NS*	NT
buzza	54.68	−3.66	60	54.72	−3.23	10	NS	NS	52.93	−1.56	52	NS	NS	—	—	3	NS*	NT
kestr	52.80	−1.44	520	51.63	−1.76	67	NS	NS*	54.34	−1.72	21	NS*	S −0.59	—	—	7	NS*	NT
merli	53.67	−2.32	57	—	—	7	NT	NT	55.27	−3.33	10	NS*	NS*	—	—	3	NS*	NT
pereg	54.55	−4.11	61	54.04	−4.18	12	NS*	NS*	52.37	−0.62	3	NS*	NT	—	—	2	NS*	NT
moorh	53.10	−1.23	32	52.40	0.02	16	S* −1.26	NS	—	—	18	NS*	NS*	—	—	1	NS*	NT
coot	52.55	−1.67	20	51.50	0.55	24	S* −2.22	NS	54.93	−3.22	0	NT	NT	—	—	0	NT	NT
oyste	53.86	−2.78	259	49.22	−4.25	101	NS* 4.64	S* 1.46	—	—	25	S −1.64	S	—	—	2	NS*	NT
rinpl	50.77	−2.39	36	49.53	−3.58	17	NS*	NS*	53.93	−3.61	5	NS*	NS*	—	—	0	NT	NT
lapwi	52.29	−4.39	154	47.75	−4.96	516	S 4.54	S 0.57	—	—	5	NS*	NS*	—	—	2	NS*	NT
dunli	50.84	−1.83	17	—	—	9	NT	NT	—	—	0	NT	NT	—	—	2	NS*	NT
curle	53.78	−4.36	57	52.92	−5.85	115	S* 0.85	S 1.48	—	—	5	NT	NT	—	—	0	NT	NT
redsh	52.51	−1.11	60	50.80	−2.61	59	S 1.71	S 1.49	53.18	−2.75	136	NS*	NS	—	—	2	NS*	NT
gresk	45.94	−1.25	153	42.01	−3.62	47	S 3.92	NS	56.05	−3.28	13	NS	NS	—	—	0	NT	NT
blhgu	52.80	−3.00	790	49.83	−4.26	166	S 2.96	S 1.25	43.69	−5.59	24	S	S	47.05	−1.08	18	NS*	NS*
comgu	56.03	−4.42	70	53.44	−7.22	11	S* 2.59	S 2.80	54.22	−3.43	15	NS	NS	52.82	−2.76	18	NS*	NS*
lbbgu	42.70	−5.65	327	38.38	−7.18	266	S* 4.32	S 1.53	55.25	−3.00	64	NS	NS	43.64	−4.75	10	NS*	NS*
hergu	54.14	−3.30	744	54.17	−2.94	744	NS	NS	—	—	753	NS	NS	53.42	−3.25	31	NS*	NS*
gpbgu	54.30	−3.43	148	54.50	−3.75	100	NS	NS	—	—	151	NS	NS	52.55	−3.22	13	NS*	NS*
kitti	50.77	0.02	129	52.65	−9.55	59	S	NS	—	—	13	NS*	NS*	53.47	1.41	31	S* 1.74	NS*
sante	7.28	−2.38	322	8.83	−5.72	627	S	S	—	—	25	S	S	8.47	−3.39	18	S −2.70	NS*
roste	6.84	−0.91	38	5.66	−1.34	131	NS	NS	—	—	5	NS	NS	—	—	5	NS*	NT
comte	10.44	−5.98	49	2.96	2.24	103	S* 1.18	NS	—	—	8	NS	NS	—	—	5	NS*	NT
arcte	−18.03	20.24	25	10.76	−8.16	11	S* −21.00	S* 17.99	—	—	9	S	S	—	—	0	NT	NT
guill	53.46	−0.11	628	58.45	−1.50	214	S −4.98	S 1.39	53.00	−2.02	1	NT	NT	52.33	0.77	477	S 1.13	S −0.88
razor	47.35	−2.66	256	46.92	−0.89	139	NS	S −1.76	53.76	−2.09	2	S −1.03	NS	50.80	−0.57	163	S −3.44	S −2.08
blagu	58.52	−2.54	18	—	—	0	NT	NT	53.36	−1.42	0	NT	NT	—	—	4	NS*	NT
puffi	51.97	−2.17	104	57.68	−5.44	18	S* −5.70	S*	52.19	−1.15	1	NS*	S*	52.46	−1.30	19	NS*	NT
stodo	52.41	−0.92	17	52.74	−1.62	72	NS*	NS*	—	—	3	NS	NS	—	—	0	NT	NT
woodp	52.70	−1.08	49	52.96	−1.36	507	NS	NS	—	—	2	NS	NS	—	—	1	NT	NT
coldo	52.46	−2.08	13	—	—	7	NT	NT	—	—	2	NS	NS	—	—	0	NT	NT
barow	52.89	−2.01	422	53.55	−1.67	25	S* −0.65	S*	53.00	−1.66	753	NS	NS	—	—	6	NS*	NT
tawow	53.84	−1.94	88	—	—	6	NT	NT	53.76	−1.45	151	NS*	NS*	—	—	4	NS*	NT
loeow	54.91	−0.23	11	—	—	2	NT	NT	53.36	−1.32	13	NS*	NS*	—	—	1	NT	NT
kingf	52.16	−0.77	46	—	—	1	NT	NT	52.19	−1.56	25	NS*	NS*	—	—	0	NT	NT
grswo	52.37	−1.34	10	—	—	1	NT	NT	—	—	5	NT	NT	—	—	0	NT	NT
swall	−28.01	25.17	40	—	—	0	NT	NT	—	—	8	NT	NT	—	—	0	NT	NT
meapi	42.98	−4.77	18	38.85	−5.88	33	S* 4.13	S* 5.40	52.12	−1.46	46	S −1.03	S	—	—	1	NT	NT
piewa	51.09	−1.43	188	40.86	−6.83	41	NS 10.22	NS	—	—	6	S	S	—	—	0	NT	NT
dippe	54.68	−2.76	15	—	—	1	NT	NT	—	—	3	NS*	NS	—	—	1	NT	NT
wren	52.62	−1.19	47	—	—	7	NT	NT	53.06	−1.27	18	NS*	NS	—	—	0	NT	NT
dunno	52.32	−0.96	151	52.52	−2.66	10	S 0.61	S	52.74	−1.35	69	NS*	NS	—	—	0	NT	NT
robin	52.36	−1.32	247	51.65	−1.82	22	NS	NS	52.57	−1.37	126	NS	NS	—	—	0	NT	NT
blabi	52.73	−1.39	844	52.91	−2.59	51	NS	NS	52.61	−1.19	337	NS	NS	—	—	6	NS*	NT
sonth	52.30	−1.99	506	53.68	−2.87	93	S*	S*	52.64	−1.66	188	S −0.33	NS*	52.63	−1.31	13	NS*	NT
misth	52.64	−1.69	51	53.41	−4.92	64	S 4.08	NS	52.66	−1.45	15	NS	NS	—	—	0	NT	NT
bluti	52.42	−1.28	267	52.65	−1.33	24	S* 3.94	NS	52.32	−1.32	148	NS*	NS	—	—	5	NS*	NT
greti	52.64	−1.52	137	52.31	−0.13	175	S*	S*	52.51	−1.56	77	S −0.56	NS*	—	—	5	NS*	NT
nutha	51.87	−1.79	16	—	—	22	NS*	NS	—	—	3	NT	NT	—	—	0	NT	NT
jay	52.69	−1.23	30	—	—	16	NT	NT	—	—	5	NT	NT	—	—	1	NT	NT
magpi	52.92	−2.57	35	—	—	12	NT	NT	—	—	1	NT	NT	—	—	0	NT	NT
choug	54.62	−5.40	15	—	—	0	NT	NT	—	—	0	NT	NT	—	—	0	NT	NT
jackd	53.19	−2.03	56	52.08	−0.62	93	S* −0.60	S	52.68	−3.64	14	NS*	S* 1.61	—	—	0	NT	NT
rook	53.74	−2.10	52	52.45	−1.54	45	NS	NS	—	—	4	NS	NS	—	—	0	NT	NT
crow	54.16	−2.25	57	52.67	−1.37	2	NT	NT	—	—	1	NT	NT	—	—	1	NT	NT
raven	54.25	−3.93	49	53.30	−2.59	37	S*	S*	—	—	5	NS	NS	—	—	0	NT	NT
starl	52.83	−1.07	790	52.91	−2.66	51	S	S	52.90	−1.12	212	NS	NS	—	—	5	NS*	NT
housp	52.34	−0.99	210	53.41	−4.92	93	S*	NS	52.91	−1.29	48	NS	NS	—	—	2	NS*	NT
tresp	52.65	−0.59	21	52.65	−1.33	24	S −0.85	S*	—	—	41	S −0.56	NS	—	—	0	NT	NT
chaff	52.84	−1.47	79	52.60	−1.36	175	NT	NT	53.49	−1.77	56	NS	NS	—	—	5	NS*	NT
grefi	52.19	−1.02	200	42.90	−2.76	22	S	S	52.75	−1.55	10	S	S	—	—	2	NS*	NT
goldf	47.98	−0.38	35	43.01	−2.04	9	S 5.07	S 2.37	48.92	−1.07	12	NS*	NS*	—	—	0	NT	NT
linne	48.30	−1.20	73	51.66	0.08	32	S 5.28	S 0.83	49.30	−1.22	68	S −0.56	NS	—	—	5	NS*	NT
bullf	52.22	−0.84	130			65	S 0.56	S −0.92	52.71	−1.26	8	S −0.48	NS*	—	—	0	NT	NT
yelha	52.58	−0.19	20			105	NT	NS				NT	NS	—	—	0	NT	NT
reebu	52.69	−1.34	41			89	NT	NT	52.54	−1.82	15	NS*	NS*	—	—	2	NT	NT

continued

Table I *Continued*

	Accidental capture					Domestic predator						
Species*	Mean latitude	Mean longitude	Number of records	Test result and differences (latitude)	Test result and differences (longitude)	Mean latitude	Mean longitude	Number of records	Test result and differences (latitude)	Test result and differences (longitude)	% of total	Overall result
retdi	—	—	8	NT	NT	—	—	0	NT	NT	—	NT
fulma	—	—	8	NT	NT	—	—	0	NT	NT	30.1	(NS)
mansh	—	—	0	NT	NT	—	—	0	NT	NT	—	NT
stope	—	—	0	NT	NT	—	—	0	NT	NT	—	NT
ganne	37.61	−7.33	84	S 9.76	S 4.79	—	—	0	NT	NT	52.1	S
cormo	50.40	−3.94	153	S 2.20	S 0.73	—	—	0	NT	NT	54.3	S
shag	53.59	−5.65	140	S 0.96	S 2.13	—	—	0	NT	NT	25.6	(NS)
grehe	54.72	−3.36	11	S* −1.54	S* 1.86	—	—	0	NT	NT	15.8	(NS)
mutsw	—	—	5	NT	NT	—	—	6	NT	NT	37.1	(NS)
cango	—	—	0	NT	NT	—	—	1	NT	NT	78.5	S
sheld	—	—	0	NT	NT	—	—	0	NT	NT	32.4	(NS)
malla	—	—	0	NT	NT	—	—	2	NT	NT	—	NS
tufdu	53.31	—	13	NS*	S* −4.20	—	—	0	NT	NT	88.5	S
eider	—	4.34	6	NT	NT	—	—	0	NT	NT	32.1	(NS)
goosa	—	—	0	NT	NT	—	—	0	NT	NT	—	NS*
henha	—	—	2	NT	NT	—	—	0	NT	NT	—	NS*
sparr	—	—	6	NT	NT	—	—	4	NT	NT	10.9	(NS)
buzza	—	—	3	NT	NT	—	—	0	NT	NT	30.9	(NS)
kestr	—	—	5	NT	NT	—	—	4	NT	NT	7.8	(NS)
merli	—	—	0	NT	NT	—	—	3	NT	NT	42.6	NS*
pereg	—	—	1	NT	NT	—	—	9	NT	NT	—	(NS)
mooh	—	—	0	NT	NT	—	—	9	NT	NT	23.5	(NS)
coot	—	—	3	NT	NT	—	—	1	NT	NT	50.0	S
oyste	—	—	0	NT	NT	—	—	0	NT	NT	26.4	(NS)
rinpl	—	—	0	NT	NT	—	—	1	NT	NT	—	NS*
lapwi	—	—	0	NT	NT	—	—	4	NT	NT	77.2	S
dunli	—	—	2	NT	NT	—	—	0	NT	NT	—	NT
curle	—	—	3	NT	NT	—	—	1	NT	NT	63.9	S
redsh	—	—	0	NT	NT	—	—	0	NT	NT	47.2	(NS)
gresk	41.71	−4.17	16	NS*	NS*	52.71	−3.09	16	NS*	NS*	19.7	(NS)
blhgu	—	—	6	NT	NT	—	—	1	NT	NT	14.7	(NS)
comgu	—	—	2	NT	NT	—	—	0	NT	NT	11.2	(NS)
lbbgu	36.45	−7.48	13	S*	NS* 6.25	—	—	0	NT	NT	43.6	NS
hergu	54.58	−3.88	17	NS*	NS*	—	—	0	NT	NT	—	(NS)
gbbgu	—	—	9	NT	NT	—	—	0	NT	NT	6.0	(NS)
kitti	12.15	−11.51	8	NS*	S 9.12	—	—	0	NT	NT	38.3	(NS)
sante	—	—	47	NS*	NT	—	—	1	NT	NT	65.8	S
roste	—	—	1	NT	NT	—	—	0	NT	NT	74.4	S
comte	—	—	5	NT	NT	—	—	0	NT	NT	—	NS
arcte	—	—	5	NT	NT	—	—	0	NT	NT	26.8	(NS)
guill	57.73	7.13	506	S −4.26	S −7.24	—	—	1	NT	NT	65.5	S
razor	42.91	−4.59	149	S 4.44	S 1.93	—	—	2	NT	NT	63.6	S
blagu	—	—	0	NT	NT	—	—	0	NT	NT	—	NT
puffi	—	—	1	NT	NT	—	—	0	NT	NT	12.6	(NS)
stodo	—	—	0	NT	NT	—	—	0	NT	NT	—	NS*
woodp	—	—	0	NT	NT	—	—	0	NT	NT	—	NT
coldo	—	—	0	NT	NT	—	—	3	NT	NT	—	NT
barow	—	—	1	NT	NT	—	—	0	NT	NT	2.1	(NS)
tawow	—	—	3	NT	NT	—	—	0	NT	NT	—	NS
loeow	—	—	0	NT	NT	—	—	8	NT	NT	—	NS*
kingf	—	—	0	NT	NT	—	—	2	NT	NT	—	NS*
grswo	—	—	0	NT	NT	—	—	1	NT	NT	—	NT
swall	—	—	0	NT	NT	—	—	1	NT	NT	—	NT
meapi	—	—	0	NT	NT	51.57	−1.00	32	NS	NT	60.0	S
piewa	—	—	0	NT	NT	—	—	7	NT	NT	28.2	(NS)
dippe	—	—	0	NT	NT	—	—	2	NT	NT	—	NT
wren	—	—	0	NT	NT	52.17	−0.92	43	NS	NS	—	NS
dunno	—	—	4	NT	NT	52.46	−0.93	87	NS	NS	3.1	(NS)
robin	52.68	−1.50	16	NS*	NS*	52.48	−1.29	172	NS	NS	—	NS
blabi	53.08	−3.51	14	NS*	S* 2.12	52.49	−1.23	251	S	S	21.6	(NS)
sonth	51.72	−3.96	12	NS*	S* 1.96	52.06	−1.11	139	S 0.24	S −0.88	47.5	(NS)
misth	—	—	0	NT	NT	—	—	9	NT	NT	15.7	(NS)
bluti	—	—	5	NT	NT	52.41	−1.53	178	NS	NS	—	NS
greti	—	—	5	NT	NT	52.33	−1.47	74	NS	NS	—	NS
nutha	—	—	1	NT	NT	—	—	0	NT	NT	—	NT
jay	—	—	2	NT	NT	—	—	2	NT	NT	72.1	S
magpi	—	—	2	NT	NT	—	—	2	NT	NT	50.0	S
choug	—	—	1	NT	NT	—	—	0	NT	NT	—	NT
jackd	—	—	0	NT	NT	—	—	4	NT	NT	12.4	(NS)
rook	—	—	0	NT	NT	—	—	0	NT	NT	—	NS
crow	—	—	0	NT	NT	—	—	0	NT	NT	—	NS
raven	—	—	2	NT	NT	—	—	0	NT	NT	30.8	(NS)
starl	—	—	1	NT	NT	52.35	−0.89	248	S 0.48	S	17.3	(NS)
housp	—	—	5	NT	NT	52.17	−0.78	71	NS	NS	19.6	(NS)
tresp	—	—	0	NT	NT	—	—	2	NT	NT	—	NT
chaff	—	—	2	NT	NT	52.21	−0.78	23	NS*	NS*	14.9	NS
grefi	—	—	2	NT	NT	51.97	−0.83	80	NS	NT	55.1	(NS)
goldf	—	—	0	NT	NT	—	—	8	NT	NT	53.6	(NS)
linne	—	—	0	NT	NT	—	—	6	NT	NT	61.5	S
bullf	—	—	0	NT	NT	51.90	−0.90	51	S 0.32	S	—	NT
yelha	52.27	1.58	1	NT	NT	—	—	9	NT	NT	—	NS
reebu	51.10	−1.30	1	NT	NT	52.40	−1.75	19	NS*	NS*	—	NS*

* A key to the five-letter codes used to refer to each species is provided in Appendix 2.

Table II Ringed in winter and recovered in the breeding season

Species*	Other — Mean latitude	Other — Mean longitude	Other — Number of records	Deliberately taken by Man — Mean latitude	Deliberately taken by Man — Mean longitude	Deliberately taken by Man — Number of records	Deliberately — Test result and differences (latitude)	Deliberately — Test result and differences (longitude)	Human-related — Mean latitude	Human-related — Mean longitude	Human-related — Number of records	Human-related — Test result and differences (latitude)	Human-related — Test result and differences (longitude)	Pollution — Mean latitude	Pollution — Mean longitude	Pollution — Number of records	Pollution — Test result and differences (latitude)	Pollution — Test result and differences (longitude)
mutsw	52.58	−1.64	409	52.37	−1.38	36	NS	NS	52.37	−1.56	180	NS	NS	52.29	−1.38	91	NS	NS
whosw	64.44	−17.79	19	—	—	3	NT	NT	—	—	4	NT	NT	—	—	0	NT	NT
cango	51.64	−1.84	15	—	—	6	NT	NT	—	—	2	NT	NT	—	—	0	NT	NT
sheld	56.23	1.22	14	—	—	0	NT	NT	—	—	0	NT	NT	—	—	1	NT	NT
teal	61.16	19.63	47	62.54	38.92	91	NS	S −19.29	—	—	8	NT	NT	—	—	1	NT	NT
malla	54.33	4.77	133	56.58	13.89	654	S −2.24	S −9.12	53.75	3.03	33	NS	NS	—	—	0	NT	NT
tufdu	55.72	8.22	41	60.15	31.83	154	S −4.43	S −23.60	—	—	5	NT	NT	—	—	2	NT	NT
eider	57.28	−2.07	81	57.31	−2.01	12	NS*	NS*	—	—	1	NT	NT	—	—	4	NT	NT
sparr	52.77	−2.20	19	—	—	2	NT	NT	52.69	−2.19	19	NS*	NS*	—	—	0	NT	NT
moorh	53.21	−0.55	39	—	—	4	NT	NT	52.20	0.09	21	S* 1.01	S*	—	—	0	NT	NT
coot	51.78	−0.51	27	—	—	9	NT	NT	—	—	4	NT	NT	—	—	0	NT	NT
oyste	58.66	−1.52	448	59.34	−0.70	20	NS*	NS*	58.55	−0.92	135	NS	NS	60.78	0.74	13	S* −2.12	S*
knot	69.56	−46.44	10	71.65	−57.44	39	NS*	NS*	—	—	0	NT	NT	—	—	0	NT	NT
dunli	56.64	12.38	18	—	—	4	NT	NT	—	—	0	NT	NT	—	—	0	NT	NT
curle	60.52	14.29	24	—	—	2	NT	NT	—	—	0	NT	NT	—	—	1	NT	NT
redsh	59.27	−10.07	30	—	—	5	NT	NT	62.14	−14.25	8	NS*	NS*	—	—	0	NT	NT
blhgu	56.46	12.28	999	59.95	18.83	403	S −3.48	S −6.55	56.52	11.43	19	NS	NS	57.44	14.61	34	NS*	NS*
comgu	59.62	12.80	43	58.45	12.66	30	NS	NS	—	—	150	NS	NS	—	—	0	NT	NT
lbbgu	54.74	−2.96	46	55.58	−4.24	86	NS	NS	—	—	4	NT	NT	—	—	2	NT	NT
hergu	56.56	−0.83	337	57.79	1.50	57	NS	S −2.33	58.72	0.68	7	NT	NT	—	—	9	NT	NT
gbbgu	61.93	7.78	26	—	—	5	NT	NT	—	—	24	S* −2.15	S*	—	—	2	NT	NT
woodp	51.75	−0.46	16	52.22	−0.59	84	NS*	NS*	—	—	7	NT	NT	—	—	0	NT	NT
coldo	52.52	−1.23	36	52.15	−1.12	11	NS*	NS*	51.86	−1.17	4	NS*	NS*	—	—	0	NT	NT
barow	52.64	−1.91	11	—	—	0	NT	NT	52.80	−1.31	13	NS*	NS*	—	—	2	NT	NT
tawow	53.27	−1.98	14	—	—	3	NT	NT	52.40	−1.28	13	NS*	NS*	—	—	0	NT	NT
grswo	52.19	−1.42	32	—	—	2	NT	NT	52.10	−0.98	13	NS	NS*	—	—	0	NT	NT
piewa	52.65	−1.55	157	—	—	4	NT	NT	52.23	−1.15	20	NS	S −0.40	—	—	3	NT	NT
dunno	52.60	−1.20	214	—	—	6	NT	NT	52.59	−1.20	85	NS	NS	—	—	2	NT	NT
robin	52.39	−1.13	178	—	—	5	NT	NT	52.51	−1.57	121	NS	S 0.44	—	—	5	NT	NT
blabi	53.14	−0.00	1696	54.63	3.55	105	S −1.48	S −3.55	53.16	−0.28	77	NS	NS	53.34	−0.24	28	NS*	NS*
field	61.36	15.17	69	62.09	20.25	37	NS	S −5.07	62.79	17.29	942	NS*	NS*	—	—	3	NT	NT
sonth	52.43	−0.95	391	52.67	−1.29	19	NS*	NS*	52.56	−1.06	18	NS	NS	—	—	0	NT	NT
redwi	58.04	18.80	31	—	—	8	NT	NT	63.70	23.55	270	S* −5.65	NS*	—	—	2	NT	NT
misth	52.32	−1.06	101	—	—	4	NT	NT	52.19	−1.25	12	NS*	NS*	—	—	0	NT	NT
coati	52.55	−1.64	38	—	—	0	NT	NT	52.54	−0.91	39	NS*	NS*	—	—	0	NT	NT
bluti	52.26	−1.15	588	52.37	−1.13	19	NS*	NS*	52.40	−1.19	12	NS	NS	—	—	5	NT	NT
greti	52.51	−1.39	218	—	—	8	NT	NT	52.48	−1.23	358	NS	NS	—	—	3	NT	NT
nutha	52.05	−1.97	14	—	—	0	NT	NT	—	—	109	NT	NT	—	—	0	NT	NT
jay	51.63	−0.65	28	51.94	−1.11	21	NS*	NS*	51.50	−0.48	5	NS*	NS*	—	—	1	NT	NT
magpi	52.56	−2.46	14	52.92	−1.60	17	NS*	NS*	—	—	13	NT	NT	—	—	0	NT	NT
jackd	52.24	−3.02	38	52.66	−2.87	37	NS	NS	—	—	3	NT	NT	—	—	0	NT	NT
rook	53.66	−2.73	34	53.28	−2.70	26	NS*	NS*	—	—	5	NT	NT	—	—	0	NT	NT
starl	53.87	3.59	3600	53.50	4.48	663	S 0.36	S −0.89	53.58	1.50	702	S 0.28	S 2.08	52.83	2.30	24	NS*	NS*
housp	52.56	−0.75	348	52.34	−0.62	29	NS*	NS*	52.46	−0.87	147	NS	NS	—	—	5	NT	NT
tresp	52.74	−0.88	36	—	—	3	NT	NT	52.71	−0.65	13	NS*	NS*	—	—	0	NT	NT
chaff	54.06	1.61	283	54.56	−0.74	20	NS*	NS*	54.08	−0.04	274	NS	S 1.65	—	—	3	NT	NT
grefi	52.47	−0.97	1432	52.68	−1.52	66	NS	S 0.54	52.57	−1.02	1188	NS	NS	52.31	−0.90	15	NS	NS
goldf	51.98	−1.00	12	—	—	0	NT	NT	52.98	−1.69	12	NS*	NS*	—	—	0	NT	NT
siski	57.38	−2.79	41	—	—	1	NT	NT	57.44	2.47	26	S*	S* −5.27	—	—	1	NT	NT
linne	52.78	−0.86	30	—	—	0	NT	NT	52.99	0.00	23	NS*	NS*	—	—	0	NT	NT
redpo	53.65	−1.50	10	—	—	0	NT	NT	—	—	6	NT	NT	—	—	0	NT	NT
bulfi	52.18	−0.70	93	52.21	−0.63	13	NS*	NS*	52.30	−0.99	85	NS	NS	—	—	1	NT	NT
yelha	52.66	−1.48	33	—	—	2	NT	NT	53.12	−1.13	60	NS	NS	—	—	0	NT	NT
reebu	53.03	−1.17	19	—	—	0	NT	NT	53.50	0.24	16	NS*	NS*	—	—	0	NT	NT

continued

Table II *Continued*

	Accidental capture					Domestic predator						
Species*	Mean latitude	Mean longitude	Number of records	Test result and differences (latitude)	Test result and differences (longitude)	Mean latitude	Mean longitude	Number of records	Test result and differences (latitude)	Test result and differences (longitude)	% of total	Overall result
mutsw	—	—	4	NT	NT	—	—	1	NT	NT	—	NS
whosw	—	—	0	NT	NT	—	—	0	NT	NT	—	NT
cango	—	—	0	NT	NT	—	—	0	NT	NT	—	NT
sheld	—	—	0	NT	NT	—	—	0	NT	NT	—	NT
teal	63.19	24.60	63	S −2.03	S −4.97	—	—	1	NT	NT	73.0	S
malla	61.57	23.00	21	S* −7.23	S* −18.23	—	—	3	NT	NT	80.0	S
tufdu	59.90	17.28	43	S −4.18	S −9.05	—	—	1	NT	NT	80.0	S
eider	—	—	5	NT	NT	—	—	0	NT	NT	—	NS*
sparr	—	—	0	NT	NT	—	—	1	NT	NT	—	NS*
moorh	—	—	1	NT	NT	52.69	1.46	10	NS*	NS*	28.0	(NS)
coot	—	—	0	NT	NT	—	—	0	NT	NT	—	NT
oyste	—	—	3	NT	NT	58.97	1.69	11	NS*	NS*	2.1	(NS)
knot	—	—	0	NT	NT	—	—	1	NT	NT	—	NS*
dunli	—	—	1	NT	NT	—	—	1	NT	NT	—	NT
curle	—	—	1	NT	NT	—	—	2	NT	NT	—	NT
redsh	—	—	0	NT	NT	—	—	4	NT	NT	—	NS*
blhgu	61.40	21.77	39	S −4.93	S −9.49	52.11	−1.34	8	NT	NT	66.6	S
comgu	—	—	7	NT	NT	—	—	1	NT	NT	—	NT
lbbgu	—	—	0	NT	NT	—	—	0	NT	NT	—	NS
hergu	—	—	5	NT	NT	—	—	0	NT	NT	18.8	(NS)
gbbgu	—	—	1	NT	NT	—	—	0	NT	NT	—	NT
woodp	—	—	0	NT	NT	—	—	1	NT	NT	—	NS*
coldo	—	—	0	NT	NT	52.11	−1.34	12	NS*	NS*	—	NS*
barow	—	—	0	NT	NT	—	—	0	NT	NT	—	NS*
tawow	—	—	0	NT	NT	—	—	0	NT	NT	—	NS*
grswo	—	—	1	NT	NT	—	—	5	NT	NT	—	NS*
piewa	—	—	0	NT	NT	52.28	−1.35	29	NS*	NS*	30.6	(NS)
dunno	—	—	4	NT	NT	52.24	−1.05	198	S 0.36	NS	36.3	(NS)
robin	—	—	9	NT	NT	52.23	−1.10	173	S 0.32	NS	17.2	(NS)
blabi	53.46	0.39	145	NS	NS	52.81	−0.83	607	S	S 0.83	20.2	(NS)
field	—	—	9	NT	NT	—	—	9	NT	NT	26.0	(NS)
sonth	53.12	−1.18	32	S −0.69	NS	52.32	−0.83	159	S	NS	3.7	(NS)
redwi	—	—	4	NT	NT	51.99	−0.75	7	NT	NT	19.4	(NS)
misth	—	—	0	NT	NT	52.45	−1.19	12	NT	NS*	—	NS
coati	—	—	0	NT	NT	52.14	−1.07	29	NS*	NS*	—	NS*
bluti	52.79	−2.16	11	NS*	S* 1.00	52.29	−1.21	356	NS	NS	0.8	(NS)
greti	52.50	−1.86	11	NS*	NS*	52.14	−1.69	179	NS*	NS*	—	NS
nutha	—	—	0	NT	NT	—	—	10	NS*	NS*	—	NS*
jay	—	—	2	NT	NT	—	—	4	NT	NT	—	NS*
magpi	—	—	0	NT	NT	—	—	6	NT	NT	—	NS*
jackd	—	—	1	NT	NT	—	—	0	NT	NT	—	NS
rook	—	—	0	NT	NT	—	—	0	NT	NT	—	NS*
starl	53.44	1.89	40	NS	NS	53.51	2.20	1168	S 0.35	S 1.39	40.9	NS*
housp	—	—	5	NT	NT	52.26	−0.95	139	S 0.29	NS	20.7	(NS)
tresp	—	—	1	NT	NT	52.28	−0.90	19	NS*	NS*	—	NS*
chaff	—	—	1	NT	NT	53.28	−0.12	83	S 0.77	S 1.73	53.8	S
grefi	52.33	−0.64	46	NS	NS	52.27	−0.92	925	S 0.20	NS	27.0	(NS)
goldf	—	—	0	NT	NT	—	—	4	NT	NT	—	NS*
siski	—	—	0	NT	NT	—	—	6	NT	NT	34.7	(NS)
linne	—	—	0	NT	NT	—	—	7	NT	NT	—	NS*
redpo	—	—	1	NT	NT	—	—	8	NT	NT	—	NT
bullf	—	—	9	NT	NT	51.96	−0.80	69	NS*	NS*	—	NS*
yelha	—	—	0	NT	NT	52.94	−1.92	16	NS*	NS*	—	NS
reebu	—	—	0	NT	NT	—	—	9	NT	NT	—	NS*

* A key to the five-letter codes used to refer to each species is provided in Appendix 2.

Species	5-letter species code	Definition of seasons[1]				Geographical region group[2]	Ecological grouping for analyses[3]	Age of first breeding[4]	Breeding dispersal[5]			Natal dispersal[5]		
		Breeding start	Autumn start	Winter start	Spring start				Number of records	Mean (km)	Standard deviation (km)	Number of records	Mean (km)	Standard deviation (km)
Red-throated Diver	retdi	mMAY	mSEP	sDEC	sAPR	Terrestrial	WF	2	—	—	—	—	—	—
Little Grebe	litgr	sMAY	sSEP	sNOV	sMAR	Terrestrial	WF	1	—	—	—	—	—	—
Great Crested Grebe	grcgr	mAPR	mSEP	mNOV	mFEB	Terrestrial	WF	2	—	—	—	—	—	—
Fulmar	fulma	sMAY	mAUG	mNOV	sMAR	Seabird	SG	9	—	—	—	—	—	—
Manx Shearwater	mansh	sMAY	sAUG	sNOV	mJAN	Seabird	SG	5	—	—	—	—	—	—
Storm Petrel	stope	mMAY	sOCT	sDEC	sMAR	Seabird	SG	4	—	—	—	—	—	—
Leach's Petrel	leape	mMAY	sOCT	sDEC	sMAR	Seabird	SG	5	—	—	—	—	—	—
Northern Gannet	ganne	sMAY	sSEP	sDEC	sMAR	Seabird	SG	5	—	—	—	—	—	—
Cormorant	cormo	sAPR	sAUG	sNOV	sFEB	Seabird	SG	3	—	—	—	—	—	—
Shag	shag	mMAR	sAUG	sNOV	sFEB	Seabird	SG	4	—	—	—	—	—	—
Grey Heron	grehe	sAPR	sAUG	mNOV	sFEB	Terrestrial	WF	2	4	7.8	2.4	440	68.4	84.7
Mute Swan	mutsw	mMAR	sOCT	mDEC	mFEB	Terrestrial	WF	3	497	18	48	49	34.3	35.9
Bewick's Swan	bewsw	sJUN	mSEP	sDEC	mMAR	Terrestrial	WF	4	—	—	—	—	—	—
Whooper Swan	whosw	mMAY	sOCT	sDEC	mMAR	Terrestrial	WF	4	—	—	—	—	—	—
Pink-footed Goose	pifgo	sMAY	sOCT	sNOV	sAPR	Terrestrial	WF	3	—	—	—	—	—	—
White-fronted Goose	whfgo	sJUN	mSEP	mDEC	mMAR	Terrestrial	WF	3	—	—	—	—	—	—
Greylag Goose	grego	mAPR	sAUG	sDEC	mFEB	Terrestrial	WF	3	—	—	—	—	—	—
Canada Goose	cango	sAPR	mJUL	sNOV	mFEB	Terrestrial	WF	3	365	8.9	10.8	173	7	10.6
Barnacle Goose	bargo	sJUN	mSEP	sDEC	mAPR	Terrestrial	WF	3	—	—	—	—	—	—
Brent Goose	brego	mJUN	sSEP	sDEC	mMAR	Terrestrial	WF	2	—	—	—	—	—	—
Shelduck	sheld	sMAY	sSEP	sDEC	sMAR	Coastal wader	WF	2	—	—	—	—	—	—
Mandarin	manda	sMAY	sAUG	sNOV	sFEB	Terrestrial	WF	1	—	—	—	—	—	—
Wigeon	wigeo	mMAY	mAUG	sDEC	mMAR	Terrestrial	WF	1	—	—	—	—	—	—
Gadwall	gadwa	sMAY	mAUG	sDEC	sMAR	Terrestrial	WF	1	—	—	—	—	—	—
Eurasian & Green-winged Teals	teal	sMAY	mJUL	mNOV	sMAR	Terrestrial	WF	1	—	—	—	—	—	—
Mallard	malla	sMAY	sSEP	sNOV	sMAR	Terrestrial	WF	1	328	18.6	21.6	666	19.9	21.6
Pintail	pinta	mMAY	sSEP	sDEC	mMAR	Terrestrial	WF	1	—	—	—	—	—	—
Garganey	garga	sMAY	sAUG	sNOV	sMAR	Terrestrial	WF	1	—	—	—	—	—	—
Shoveler	shove	mAPR	sAUG	sDEC	sMAR	Terrestrial	WF	1	—	—	—	—	—	—
Pochard	pocha	sMAY	sSEP	sDEC	sMAR	Terrestrial	WF	1	—	—	—	—	—	—
Tufted Duck	tufdu	mMAY	mSEP	sDEC	mMAR	Terrestrial	WF	1	—	—	—	—	—	—
Scaup	scaup	sMAY	mSEP	mNOV	mMAR	Terrestrial	WF	2	—	—	—	—	—	—
Eider	eider	sMAY	sSEP	mNOV	mMAR	Coastal wader	WF	3	—	—	—	—	—	—
Goldeneye	golde	sMAY	sOCT	mDEC	sMAR	Terrestrial	WF	2	—	—	—	—	—	—
Goosander	goosa	mMAY	sAUG	mDEC	mMAR	Terrestrial	WF	2	—	—	—	—	—	—
Red Kite	redki	sMAY	mJUL	sNOV	mFEB	Terrestrial	RO	2	—	—	—	—	—	—
Marsh Harrier	marha	sMAY	sAUG	mNOV	sMAR	Terrestrial	RO	3	—	—	—	—	—	—
Hen Harrier	henha	sMAY	mAUG	mNOV	sMAR	Terrestrial	RO	2	—	—	—	18	22	19.4
Montagu's Harrier	monha	mMAY	mAUG	mOCT	mMAR	Terrestrial	RO	3	—	—	—	—	—	—
Northern Goshawk	gosha	sMAY	sAUG	mNOV	sMAR	Terrestrial	RO	2	—	—	—	9	41.4	45.1
Sparrowhawk	sparr	sMAY	sAUG	mNOV	sMAR	Terrestrial	RO	1	17	17.3	36.2	231	15.6	22
Common Buzzard	buzza	mAPR	sSEP	sNOV	sMAR	Terrestrial	RO	3	—	—	—	41	24.2	24.1
Golden Eagle	golea	sAPR	sAUG	sDEC	sMAR	Terrestrial	RO	4	—	—	—	—	—	—
Osprey	ospre	mMAY	sAUG	sNOV	mMAR	Terrestrial	RO	3	—	—	—	—	—	—
Kestrel	kestr	sMAY	sAUG	mNOV	sMAR	Terrestrial	RO	1	27	14.8	47.4	395	42.8	58
Merlin	merli	sMAY	sAUG	sNOV	sMAR	Terrestrial	RO	1	—	—	—	39	35.1	23
Hobby	hobby	sJUN	mSEP	mNOV	sAPR	Terrestrial	RO	2	—	—	—	—	—	—
Peregrine	pereg	sAPR	sAUG	mNOV	sMAR	Terrestrial	RO	2	—	—	—	21	21.7	10.7
Grey Partridge	grepa	sMAY	sAUG	sNOV	mFEB	Terrestrial	PN	1	—	—	—	—	—	—
Water Rail	watra	mAPR	sSEP	mNOV	sMAR	Terrestrial	WF	1	—	—	—	—	—	—
Moorhen	moorh	sMAY	mSEP	mNOV	sMAR	Terrestrial	WF	1	31	4.9	8	38	4.5	10.3
Coot	coot	sMAY	sSEP	mNOV	sMAR	Terrestrial	WF	2	32	20.5	25.8	25	23.2	28.1
Eurasian Oystercatcher	oyste	sAPR	mJUL	sOCT	sMAR	Coastal wader	WD	4	—	—	—	—	—	—
Stone-curlew	stocu	mAPR	mAUG	mNOV	sMAR	Terrestrial	WD	1	—	—	—	—	—	—
Little Ringed Plover	lirpl	sMAY	mJUL	sNOV	sMAR	Terrestrial	WD	2	—	—	—	—	—	—
Ringed Plover	rinpl	sMAY	mAUG	sNOV	sMAR	Coastal wader	WD	1	—	—	—	—	—	—
Dotterel	dotte	mMAY	sAUG	mOCT	mAPR	Terrestrial	WD	2	—	—	—	—	—	—

Continued

Species	5-letter species code	Breeding start	Autumn start	Winter start	Spring start	Geographical region group[2]	Ecological grouping for analyses[3]	Age of first breeding[4]	Breeding dispersal[5] Number of records	Breeding dispersal[5] Mean (km)	Breeding dispersal[5] Standard deviation (km)	Natal dispersal[5] Number of records	Natal dispersal[5] Mean (km)	Natal dispersal[5] Standard deviation (km)
Golden Plover	golpl	mMAY	sAUG	sDEC	mMAR	Terrestrial	WD	1	—	—	—	—	—	—
Grey Plover	grepl	sJUN	sAUG	mNOV	mMAR	Coastal wader	WD	2	—	—	—	—	—	—
Lapwing	lapwi	sAPR	sAUG	mNOV	sFEB	Terrestrial	WD	2	—	—	—	—	—	—
Knot	knot	sJUN	sAUG	sDEC	sAPR	Coastal wader	WD	1	—	—	—	—	—	—
Sanderling	sande	mJUN	sAUG	sDEC	sMAY	Coastal wader	WD	2	—	—	—	—	—	—
Curlew Sandpiper	cursa	mJUN	mJUL	sOCT	sMAY	Coastal wader	WD	2	—	—	—	—	—	—
Purple Sandpiper	pursa	mJUN	mAUG	sDEC	mAPR	Coastal wader	WD	2	—	—	—	—	—	—
Dunlin	dunli	sJUN	sAUG	mOCT	sAPR	Coastal wader	WD	2	—	—	—	—	—	—
Ruff	ruff	sMAY	mJUL	mOCT	sMAR	Coastal wader	WD	2	—	—	—	—	—	—
Jack Snipe	jacsn	sMAY	sSEP	mNOV	sMAR	Terrestrial	WD	2	—	—	—	—	—	—
Common Snipe	snipe	mAPR	sAUG	mNOV	sMAR	Terrestrial	WD	2	—	—	—	—	—	—
Woodcock	woodc	mAPR	sAUG	mNOV	sMAR	Terrestrial	WD	2	—	—	—	—	—	—
Black-tailed Godwit	bltgo	mAPR	mJUL	mOCT	mFEB	Coastal wader	WD	2	—	—	—	—	—	—
Bar-tailed Godwit	batgo	sJUN	mJUL	sNOV	sAPR	Coastal wader	WD	2	—	—	—	—	—	—
Whimbrel	whimb	mMAY	sAUG	mNOV	mMAR	Coastal wader	WD	2	—	—	—	—	—	—
Curlew	curle	sMAY	sAUG	mOCT	mMAR	Terrestrial	WD	2	—	—	—	—	—	—
Redshank	redsh	sMAY	sJUL	mOCT	sMAR	Coastal wader	WD	1	—	—	—	—	—	—
Greenshank	gresh	sMAY	mJUL	sOCT	sAPR	Terrestrial	WD	2	—	—	—	—	—	—
Green Sandpiper	gresa	sMAY	sJUL	sOCT	mMAR	Terrestrial	WD	2	—	—	—	—	—	—
Common Sandpiper	comsa	mMAY	mJUL	sOCT	mMAR	Terrestrial	WD	2	—	—	—	—	—	—
Turnstone	turns	mMAY	sAUG	mOCT	sAPR	Coastal wader	WD	2	—	—	—	—	—	—
Arctic Skua	arcsk	mMAY	mAUG	mNOV	sAPR	Seabird	SG	4	—	—	—	—	—	—
Great Skua	gresk	mMAY	sSEP	mNOV	mMAR	Seabird	SG	7	—	—	—	—	—	—
Black-headed Gull	blhgu	sMAY	sAUG	sNOV	sMAR	Terrestrial	SG	2	110	44.5	72.5	1478	47	69.2
Common Gull	comgu	mMAY	sAUG	mNOV	sMAR	Terrestrial	SG	3	19	16.6	34.4	159	21.1	30
Lesser Black-backed Gull	lbbgu	sMAY	sAUG	mNOV	sMAR	Terrestrial	SG	4	190	38.2	37.4	1882	28.2	40.7
Herring Gull	hergu	sMAY	mAUG	mNOV	sMAR	Terrestrial	SG	4	—	—	—	—	—	—
Great Black-backed Gull	gbbgu	sMAY	mAUG	mNOV	sMAR	Seabird	SG	4	—	—	—	—	—	—
Kittiwake	kitti	sMAY	mAUG	mNOV	sMAR	Seabird	SG	4	—	—	—	—	—	—
Sandwich Tern	sante	sMAY	mAUG	mOCT	mMAR	Seabird	SG	3	—	—	—	—	—	—
Roseate Tern	roste	sJUN	mAUG	mOCT	mAPR	Seabird	SG	2	—	—	—	—	—	—
Common Tern	comte	mMAY	mAUG	mOCT	sMAR	Seabird	SG	3	—	—	—	—	—	—
Arctic Tern	arcte	mMAY	mAUG	sNOV	mMAR	Seabird	SG	4	—	—	—	—	—	—
Little Tern	litte	mMAY	mAUG	mOCT	sAPR	Seabird	SG	3	—	—	—	—	—	—
Guillemot	guill	sMAY	sAUG	sNOV	sFEB	Seabird	SG	5	—	—	—	—	—	—
Razorbill	razor	sAPR	sAUG	sNOV	sFEB	Seabird	SG	4	—	—	—	—	—	—
Black Guillemot	blagu	sMAY	sSEP	sDEC	sMAR	Seabird	SG	4	—	—	—	—	—	—
Puffin	puffi	sAPR	mAUG	sNOV	sFEB	Seabird	SG	5	—	—	—	—	—	—
Rock Dove & Feral Pigeon	rocdo	mFEB	mSEP	sNOV	sJAN	Terrestrial	PN	1	—	—	—	—	—	—
Stock Dove	stodo	mAPR	mSEP	mNOV	sMAR	Terrestrial	PN	1	19	5.6	6.5	96	10.4	15.6
Woodpigeon	woodp	mAPR	mSEP	mNOV	sMAR	Terrestrial	PN	1	233	10.9	24.1	718	10.7	19.3
Collared Dove	coldo	mAPR	mSEP	mNOV	sMAR	Terrestrial	PN	1	102	4.1	9.3	37	9.3	11.5
Turtle Dove	turdo	sMAY	sSEP	mNOV	sMAR	Terrestrial	PN	1	12	3.8	6.1	4	8.8	10.8
Cuckoo	cucko	mMAY	sAUG	sOCT	mMAR	Terrestrial	PN	2	—	—	—	—	—	—
Barn Owl	barow	sAPR	sNOV	sJAN	sMAR	Terrestrial	RO	1	24	16.9	36.3	445	23.9	36.6
Little Owl	litow	sAPR	sAUG	sNOV	sFEB	Terrestrial	RO	1	19	11.1	41.6	82	14.5	26.4
Tawny Owl	tawow	mFEB	sJUL	sOCT	sJAN	Terrestrial	RO	1	24	3.1	7.4	282	8.3	13.5
Long-eared Owl	loeow	sMAY	sJUL	mNOV	mMAR	Terrestrial	RO	1	6	4.8	4	38	47.8	56.9
Short-eared Owl	sheow	sMAY	mJUL	mNOV	sMAR	Terrestrial	RO	1	—	—	—	—	—	—
Nightjar	nijar	mMAY	mAUG	mNOV	mMAR	Terrestrial	PN	1	—	—	—	—	—	—
Common Swift	swift	mMAY	sAUG	mOCT	mMAR	Terrestrial	PN	4	644	10.8	34	30	36.8	37.1
Common Kingfisher	kingf	sMAY	sSEP	mNOV	mMAR	Terrestrial	PN	1	12	9.5	10.8	67	21.5	39.6
Wryneck	wryne	mMAY	mAUG	mOCT	mMAR	Terrestrial	PN	1	—	—	—	—	—	—
Green Woodpecker	grewo	sMAY	mJUL	mOCT	sMAR	Terrestrial	PN	1	19	1.7	2.5	14	7.6	10.1
Great Spotted Woodpecker	grswo	sMAY	mJUL	mOCT	sMAR	Terrestrial	PN	1	30	3.7	10.4	15	16.5	19.8
Skylark	skyla	mAPR	mAUG	mNOV	mFEB	Terrestrial	PN	1	15	0.7	1.9	32	5.5	23.1
Sand Martin	sanma	mMAY	sAUG	sNOV	mMAR	Terrestrial	PN	1	144	7.7	13.4	70	20.9	22.8
Swallow	swall	mMAY	mAUG	sDEC	mFEB	Terrestrial	PN	1	76	4.8	9.4	395	14.1	28.4
House Martin	houma	mMAY	mAUG	sDEC	sMAR	Terrestrial	PN	1	191	4.2	8.3	72	10.4	12.2
Tree Pipit	trepi	sMAY	sAUG	mNOV	sMAR	Terrestrial	PN	1	—	—	—	—	—	—
Meadow Pipit	meapi	sAPR	sAUG	sDEC	sMAR	Terrestrial	PN	1	—	—	—	—	—	—
Rock Pipit	rocpi	mAPR	sAUG	mNOV	mMAR	Terrestrial	PN	1	—	—	—	—	—	—
Yellow Wagtail	yelwa	mMAY	sAUG	mOCT	sMAR	Terrestrial	PN	1	14	3	3.8	28	12.5	11.5
Grey Wagtail	grewa	sAPR	sAUG	sNOV	sMAR	Terrestrial	PN	1	—	—	—	20	26.6	29.5
Pied Wagtail	piewa	sAPR	mAUG	sNOV	sMAR	Terrestrial	PN	1	47	8	30.5	157	16.1	23.6
Waxwing	waxwi	sJUN	sAUG	sOCT	sMAR	Terrestrial	PN	1	—	—	—	—	—	—
Dipper	dippe	sAPR	mJUL	sOCT	sJAN	Terrestrial	PN	1	12	1.2	3.2	56	8	10.9
Wren	wren	sMAY	mAUG	sDEC	sMAR	Terrestrial	PN	1	33	6.5	14.5	40	8.9	14.7
Dunnock	dunno	sAPR	mAUG	sNOV	sMAR	Terrestrial	PN	1	190	1.4	8.3	237	2.1	7.2
European Robin	robin	sMAY	sAUG	sNOV	sMAR	Terrestrial	PN	1	147	8	35.9	409	6	20.2
Nightingale	nigal	mMAY	mJUL	mSEP	sAPR	Terrestrial	PN	1	—	—	—	—	—	—
Black Redstart	blare	mAPR	mJUL	sNOV	sMAR	Terrestrial	PN	1	—	—	—	—	—	—
Redstart	redst	mMAY	mAUG	sNOV	mMAR	Terrestrial	PN	1	—	—	—	18	12.2	11.9
Whinchat	whinc	mMAY	sAUG	mNOV	mMAR	Terrestrial	PN	1	—	—	—	—	—	—
Stonechat	stoch	mAPR	mAUG	sNOV	sMAR	Terrestrial	PN	1	—	—	—	—	—	—
Wheatear	wheat	mMAY	sAUG	mNOV	mFEB	Terrestrial	PN	1	6	17.2	39.2	21	18.9	28.9
Ring Ouzel	rinou	sJUN	mJUL	sNOV	sAPR	Terrestrial	PN	1	—	—	—	—	—	—
Blackbird	blabi	sMAY	sAUG	sDEC	sMAR	Terrestrial	PN	1	1806	3.2	20.6	2189	3.3	20.3
Fieldfare	field	sMAY	sOCT	sDEC	sMAR	Terrestrial	PN	1	—	—	—	—	—	—

Continued

Species	5-letter species code	Definition of seasons[1]				Geographical region group[2]	Ecological grouping for analyses[3]	Age of first breeding[4]	Breeding dispersal[5]			Natal dispersal[5]		
		Breeding start	Autumn start	Winter start	Spring start				Number of records	Mean (km)	Standard deviation (km)	Number of records	Mean (km)	Standard deviation (km)
Song Thrush	sonth	sMAY	mAUG	sNOV	mMAR	Terrestrial	PN	1	397	4	21.8	779	7	21.6
Redwing	redwi	sMAY	sOCT	mNOV	sMAR	Terrestrial	PN	1	—	—	—	—	—	—
Mistle Thrush	misth	sAPR	mJUL	sNOV	sMAR	Terrestrial	PN	1	89	2.3	5.8	92	8.3	17.4
Cetti's Warbler	cetwa	mMAY	sAUG	sNOV	mFEB	Terrestrial	PN	1	—	—	—	—	—	—
Grasshopper Warbler	grawa	mMAY	sAUG	sNOV	sMAR	Terrestrial	PN	1	—	—	—	—	—	—
Sedge Warbler	sedwa	sJUN	sAUG	sNOV	sMAR	Terrestrial	PN	1	29	30.6	58.3	70	40.4	57.8
Reed Warbler	reewa	sJUN	sAUG	sNOV	mMAR	Terrestrial	PN	1	53	32.4	61.6	77	47	68.6
Lesser Whitethroat	leswh	sJUN	sAUG	mOCT	sMAR	Terrestrial	PN	1	19	16.4	21.2	26	32.3	24.3
Whitethroat	white	sJUN	sAUG	sNOV	sAPR	Terrestrial	PN	1	51	11.1	19	89	14.4	19
Garden Warbler	garwa	sJUN	sAUG	mNOV	mMAR	Terrestrial	PN	1	—	—	—	—	—	—
Blackcap	blaca	sJUN	mAUG	sNOV	mFEB	Terrestrial	PN	1	64	27.5	32	74	41.2	37.9
Wood Warbler	woowa	mMAY	sAUG	mNOV	sAPR	Terrestrial	PN	1	—	—	—	—	—	—
Chiffchaff	chiff	mMAY	sAUG	mNOV	sMAR	Terrestrial	PN	1	—	—	—	—	—	—
Willow Warbler	wilwa	mMAY	sAUG	mNOV	mMAR	Terrestrial	PN	1	58	16.9	39.6	79	20.8	46.3
Goldcrest	goldc	sMAY	mAUG	sNOV	sAPR	Terrestrial	PN	1	—	—	—	—	—	—
Firecrest	firec	mMAY	mAUG	sDEC	sMAR	Terrestrial	PN	1	—	—	—	—	—	—
Spotted Flycatcher	spofl	sJUN	sAUG	mNOV	sAPR	Terrestrial	PN	1	38	5.9	12.1	47	12.8	17.6
Pied Flycatcher	piefl	sMAY	mJUL	sNOV	mMAR	Terrestrial	PN	1	238	20.6	17.7	1551	20.6	16.5
Bearded Tit	beati	mAPR	mAUG	sNOV	sMAR	Terrestrial	PN	1	—	—	—	—	—	—
Long-tailed Tit	lotti	sAPR	sJUL	sDEC	mFEB	Terrestrial	PN	1	32	3.7	6.1	21	8.3	8.3
Marsh Tit	marti	mAPR	sJUL	mNOV	mFEB	Terrestrial	PN	1	—	—	—	—	—	—
Willow Tit	wilti	mAPR	sJUL	mNOV	mFEB	Terrestrial	PN	1	14	1.7	3.1	14	4.6	5.3
Coal Tit	coati	mAPR	sJUL	mNOV	mFEB	Terrestrial	PN	1	22	1.2	3.1	35	9.4	10.8
Blue Tit	bluti	mAPR	mJUL	mNOV	mFEB	Terrestrial	PN	1	201	2.3	10.2	703	5.3	15.2
Great Tit	greti	mAPR	mJUL	mNOV	mFEB	Terrestrial	PN	1	173	2.5	12.3	560	5.3	17.9
Nuthatch	nutha	sAPR	mJUL	mNOV	mFEB	Terrestrial	PN	1	22	0.8	1.6	30	6.5	8.8
Treecreeper	treec	mAPR	mJUL	mNOV	mFEB	Terrestrial	PN	1	—	—	—	—	—	—
Jay	jay	mMAY	mJUL	mOCT	mAPR	Terrestrial	PN	2	76	2.8	8.1	42	3.5	6.3
Magpie	magpi	mMAR	mJUL	mOCT	mJAN	Terrestrial	PN	2	33	2.1	7.5	205	7.9	18.2
Chough	choug	sAPR	sJUL	sOCT	sJAN	Terrestrial	PN	3	—	—	—	—	—	—
Jackdaw	jackd	sAPR	mJUL	sNOV	sMAR	Terrestrial	PN	2	51	6	12.8	51	8.6	11.6
Rook	rook	sAPR	sJUL	mNOV	sMAR	Terrestrial	PN	2	96	3.1	4.7	84	8.5	13
Carrion Crow	crow	mAPR	mJUL	sNOV	mMAR	Terrestrial	PN	2	20	3.7	4.3	206	9.9	12.8
Raven	raven	mFEB	mJUN	mSEP	sJAN	Terrestrial	PN	3	—	—	—	212	39.6	37.6
Common Starling	starl	mAPR	mJUL	sNOV	sMAR	Terrestrial	PN	2	1672	3.4	19.1	401	9.5	28.1
House Sparrow	housp	sAPR	sAUG	sNOV	sMAR	Terrestrial	PN	1	526	1.9	22.4	531	1.7	6.9
Tree Sparrow	tresp	mAPR	mAUG	mNOV	mMAR	Terrestrial	PN	1	38	5	23.3	54	8	17.5
Chaffinch	chaff	sMAY	sAUG	sNOV	mMAR	Terrestrial	PN	1	120	2.8	9.9	64	3.6	5.6
Brambling	bramb	mMAY	mJUL	sNOV	sMAR	Terrestrial	PN	1	—	—	—	—	—	—
Greenfinch	grefi	sMAY	mAUG	mNOV	mMAR	Terrestrial	PN	1	283	7.5	22.1	99	4.2	6.4
Goldfinch	goldf	sMAY	mAUG	sNOV	sAPR	Terrestrial	PN	1	63	10.6	20.8	85	11.1	18.2
Siskin	siski	sMAY	mJUL	sNOV	sMAR	Terrestrial	PN	1	—	—	—	—	—	—
Linnet	linne	sMAY	sSEP	sNOV	sAPR	Terrestrial	PN	1	110	3.5	8.3	147	4.4	8.8
Twite	twite	mMAY	sAUG	mNOV	sMAR	Terrestrial	PN	1	—	—	—	—	—	—
Lesser & Common Redpolls	redpo	sMAY	mAUG	mNOV	sMAR	Terrestrial	PN	1	45	21.9	25.1	31	22.7	31
Common, Scottish & Parrot Crossbills	cross	sFEB	sJUL	sOCT	sJAN	Terrestrial	PN	1	—	—	—	—	—	—
Bullfinch	bullf	sMAY	sSEP	sNOV	mMAR	Terrestrial	PN	1	194	2.5	5.2	195	4.6	9.8
Hawfinch	hawfi	sMAY	mJUL	sNOV	sMAR	Terrestrial	PN	1	—	—	—	—	—	—
Snow Bunting	snobu	sJUN	mAUG	sDEC	mMAR	Terrestrial	PN	1	—	—	—	—	—	—
Yellowhammer	yelha	sMAY	sSEP	sNOV	sAPR	Terrestrial	PN	1	56	0.8	2.8	27	8.4	13.8
Reed Bunting	reebu	mAPR	sSEP	mNOV	mFEB	Terrestrial	PN	1	79	3.8	9.3	58	5.4	13.1

Notes

1. In the analyses, quantitative results, maps and tables presented in this book, four mutually exclusive **seasons** were defined to the nearest half-month for each species (see 'Definition of seasons' section of **Chapter 4**), together covering the entire year. The starting half-month for each season is given here, where 's' indicates the start of a month and 'm' indicates the middle of a month. For example, an entry of 'sAPR' for 'breeding start' and 'mJUL' for 'autumn start' indicates that the breeding season started on 1 April and ended on 15 July and that autumn started on 16 July.

2. In the analyses, quantitative results, maps and tables presented in this book, Britain & Ireland was divided into five geographical 'regions', which differed for three groups of species to reflect their use of habitats within the islands (see 'Definition of geographical regions' section of **Chapter 4**). The group into which each species was placed for such analyses is given here.

3. In the analyses and quantitative results presented in this book (see Chapters 5 and 7), each species was placed into one of five ecological groupings The group into which each species was placed for such analyses is given here: passerines and near-passerines ('**PN**'), raptors and owls ('**RO**'), seabirds and gulls ('**SG**'), wildfowl ('**WF**') and waders ('**WD**').

4. An assumed **age of first breeding** was taken from the literature and used to define individuals as either immature or adult at recovery (see 'Definition of age classes' section of **Chapter 4**). All individuals were assumed to start breeding at this age for the purposes of the book. The age of first breeding applied for each species in the book is given here, where '1' indicates the year after the hatching year (as for most passerines), '2' the year after that and so on.

5. Basic analyses of natal and breeding dispersal were carried out for as many species as possible for this book (see 'Dispersal and fidelity' section of **Chapter 4**). Results from more rigorous previous BTO analyses (Paradis et al 1998) are presented here: sample sizes ('**total number of records**'), arithmetic mean dispersal distances ('**mean**') and standard deviations.

Appendix 3a

Tests to assess the migratory status (Table I) and temporal change in degree of migrancy (Table II) of British & Irish breeding birds, and the species-specific ecological parameter values used in tests of relationships between degree of migrancy and ecological correlates (Table III)

Table I gives the results of tests designed to reveal whether species are migratory or not, and the degree to which they are migratory, by comparing the ringing locations of birds ringed during the breeding season in Britain & Ireland with their finding locations during the winter. Negative coordinates indicate locations south of the Equator for latitude and west of the Greenwich Meridian for longitude. All coordinates are given in decimal degrees. The methods are explained more fully in Chapter 4—see the sections on *'Migratory tendency and seasonal locations'* and *'Partial migration: quantifying migratory strategy'*. Only species with at least 10 appropriate recoveries were tested and only those with at least 20 such recoveries were allocated migratory scores. The results of the individual tests of latitude and longitude, and the overall result are given, coded as:-

S significant (P<0.05);
S* significant but based on a sample of <30 recoveries;
NS not significant (P>0.05);
NS* not significant but based on a sample of <30 recoveries.

The tests were also carried out using adult birds only—see the section titled *'Where natal dispersal and migratory movements are confounded'* in Chapter 4. The overall result for the analyses with only adults included are given, coded as above or as '**NT**' if tests could not be carried out because the sample of recoveries available was <10. Species for which the result using adults alone differed from the result for all age classes are flagged with '~' in the '**overall result**' column.

Table II gives the results of exploratory tests to assess whether the degree of migrancy has changed over time. The tests considered birds ringed in Britain & Ireland during the breeding season and recovered in winter; the frequency distributions of distances moved of the samples before and after the median year of recovery were compared (full details of the tests are given in Chapter 5).

Table III gives the parameter values used in tests of relationships between the degree of migrancy and various ecological correlates. The derivation and use of these values in the analyses, and their sources, are explained in Chapter 5.

Table I Migratory status and migrancy scores

		Tests of migratory status								Migrancy score		
Species[1]	Number of records	Mean ringing latitude	Mean finding latitude	Latitude test result	Mean ringing longitude	Mean finding longitude	Longitude test result	Overall result	Result for adults only	Standardized score	Allocated migrancy score	Species 2-letter code[2]
retdi	24	59.958	54.544	S*	−2.025	−3.24	NS*	S*	NT	−1.042	3	RH
fulma	111	58.735	56.962	S	−2.836	−3.053	NS	S~	NS*	−0.006	2	F
mansh	61	52.388	−8.042	S	−5.365	−41.593	S	S	NT	−2.357	4	MX
stope	17	56.309	−12.268	S*	−6.08	15.732	S*	S*	NT	—	—	—
ganne	387	55.167	43.933	S	−3.79	−3.873	NS	S	NT	−0.375	2	GX
cormo	2006	54.31	52.168	S	−4.425	−3.679	S	S	NT	0.126	2	CA
shag	1745	55.021	54.563	S	−4.097	−3.709	S	S~	NS*	0.273	2	SA
grehe	462	53.414	53.182	NS	−1.507	−1.677	NS	NS	NT	0.817	0	H
mutsw	1997	52.372	52.368	NS	−1.942	−1.942	NS	NS	NS	0.778	0	MS
grego	114	54.476	54.364	NS	−3.302	−3.289	NS	NS	NT	0.679	0	GJ
cango	1902	53.035	52.783	S	−1.575	−1.444	S	S	NT	0.667	1	CG
sheld	68	53.825	52.739	S	−1.3	−0.588	NS	S	NT	−0.559	3	SU
wigeo	12	55.688	54.656	NS*	−2.559	−2.4	NS*	NS*	NT	—	—	—
gadwa	26	52.608	49.143	S*	0.311	0.165	NS*	S*	S*	−0.323	2	GA
teal	38	54.166	51.378	S	−1.807	−2.329	NS	S~	NS*	−0.150	2	T
malla	2492	52.574	52.554	NS	−0.873	−0.81	NS	NS	NS	0.810	0	MA
pinta	11	52.412	51.093	NS*	−0.198	0.55	NS*	NS*	NT	—	—	—
shove	33	52.247	46.315	S	0.271	−0.99	NS	S	S*	−0.832	3	SV
pocha	65	51.824	50.259	S	0.816	−0.064	NS	S	S	0.066	2	PO
tufdu	261	53.482	52.534	S	−0.855	−1.843	S	S	S	0.099	2	TU
eider	524	56.921	56.608	S	−1.96	−2.283	S	S	S	0.633	1	E
goosa	26	54.876	55.044	NS*	−2.386	−2.912	S*	S*	NT	−0.420	2	GD
henha	53	58.013	56.059	S	−3.481	−2.478	NS	S	NT	0.007	2	HH
sparr	522	53.338	53.287	NS	−1.931	−1.924	NS	NS	NS*	0.807	0	SH
buzza	110	55.068	55.002	NS	−3.791	−3.645	NS	NS	NT	0.260	0	BZ
kestr	863	53.552	52.754	S	−1.887	−1.488	S	S~	NS	0.566	1	K
merli	122	55.606	53.827	S	−2.641	−2.072	S	S	NT	0.440	1	ML
pereg	97	54.776	54.69	NS	−3.806	−3.949	NS	NS	NT	0.408	0	PE
moorh	68	52.759	52.801	NS	−0.812	−0.842	NS	NS	NS*	0.611	0	MH
coot	48	52.19	51.957	NS	−0.209	−0.423	NS	NS	NT	0.316	0	CO
oyste	383	55.299	52.67	S	−2.837	−3.187	NS	S~	NS*	0.217	2	OC
stocu	16	51.983	38.274	S*	−0.184	−4.083	S*	S*	NT	—	—	—
rinpl	56	53.076	49.943	S	−0.827	−3.05	S	S	S*	0.459	1	RP
dotte	15	56.946	32.851	S*	−3.831	−7.287	S*	S*	NT	—	—	—
golpl	21	55.618	49.797	S*	−2.38	−3.683	S*	S*	NT	−0.614	3	GP
lapwi	701	54.508	49.016	S	−2.525	−4.769	S	S	NT	−0.485	2	L
dunli	28	52.922	48.967	S*	0.005	−2.797	S*	S*	NT	−0.153	2	DN
snipe	65	53.897	52.165	S	−2.597	−5.322	S	S	NT	−0.278	2	SN
woodc	277	55.107	54.044	S	−3.133	−4.082	S	S	NT	0.547	1	WK
curle	181	54.849	53.284	S	−2.618	−5.326	S	S	NT	−0.199	2	CU
redsh	125	54.361	51.765	S	−2.279	−1.986	NS	S	S	−0.065	2	RK
gresk	240	60.182	44.85	S	−1.909	−1.993	NS	S	NT	−0.088	2	NX
blhgu	1134	53.599	52.41	S	−2.149	−3.163	S	S~	NS	0.595	1	BH
comgu	98	57.299	55.707	S	−4.293	−4.578	NS	S	NT	0.437	1	CM
lbbgu	654	53.956	40.665	S	−3.439	−6.39	S	S	NT	−0.509	2	LB
hergu	977	54.874	54.161	S	−3.923	−3.286	S	S	NT	0.550	1	HG
gbbgu	220	55.436	54.292	S	−4.348	−3.518	S	S	NT	0.181	2	GB
kitti	240	55.541	51.598	S	−2.31	−2.376	NS	S~	NS*	0.082	2	KI
sante	1043	55.183	8.409	S	−2.536	−4.871	S	S	NT	−1.652	3	TE
roste	179	53.557	6.137	S	−5.046	−1.323	S	S	NT	−3.968	4	RS
comte	172	53.889	10.896	S	−2.365	−8.127	S	S	NT	−0.475	2	CN
arcte	47	56.921	−10.334	S	−2.604	12.732	S	S	NT	−1.283	3	AE
guill	1830	56.93	54.921	S	−3.979	1.951	S	S	S*	−0.479	2	GU
razor	710	54.154	47.143	S	−5.524	−2.238	S	S	S*	−0.498	2	RA
blagu	22	59.039	58.487	NS*	−2.435	−2.599	NS*	NS*	NT	0.375	0	TY
puffi	143	56.172	52.729	S	−3.398	−2.407	NS	S	S*	−0.224	2	PU
stodo	92	52.755	52.643	NS	−1.533	−1.476	NS	NS	NT	0.759	0	SD
woodp	559	53.107	52.953	NS	−1.297	−1.337	NS	NS	NS	0.762	0	WP
coldo	25	52.695	52.59	NS*	−1.518	−1.549	NS*	NS*	NS*	0.609	0	CD
barow	1200	52.989	52.981	NS	−2.089	−2.024	NS	NS	NS	0.742	0	BO
litow	32	52.239	52.171	NS	−1.038	−1.099	NS	NS	NT	0.126	0	LO

Table I Continued

		Tests of migratory status								Migrancy score		
Species[1]	Number of records	Mean ringing latitude	Mean finding latitude	Latitude test result	Mean ringing longitude	Mean finding longitude	Longitude test result	Overall result	Result for adults only	Standardized score	Allocated migrancy score	Species 2-letter code[2]
tawow	253	53.755	53.747	NS	−2.074	−2.048	NS	NS	NS*	0.737	0	TO
loeow	25	54.022	54.136	NS*	−1.712	−0.916	NS*	NS*	NT	0.609	0	LE
sheow	16	54.145	52.192	NS*	−2.522	−3.679	NS*	NS*	NT	—	—	—
swift	20	52.63	−9.976	S*	−1.423	28.25	S*	S*	NT	−3.283	4	SI
kingf	82	52.159	52.168	NS	−0.972	−0.958	NS	NS	NS*	0.234	0	KF
grswo	18	52.227	52.23	NS*	−1.207	−1.215	NS*	NS*	NS*	—	—	—
swall	56	53.171	−27.137	S	−2.015	25.538	S	S	NT	−3.765	4	SL
meapi	55	54.059	41.053	S	−2.232	−5.244	S	S	NT	−2.007	4	MP
grewa	32	53.689	52.36	S	−2.382	−2.125	NS	S	NT	−0.588	3	GL
piewa	308	53.123	49.949	S	−1.451	−2.11	S	S	S	0.207	2	PW
dippe	29	54.332	54.273	NS*	−2.795	−2.789	NS*	NS*	NT	0.337	0	DI
wren	109	52.642	52.547	NS	−1.2	−1.13	NS	NS	NS*	0.618	0	WR
dunno	321	52.504	52.456	NS	−1.145	−1.1	NS	NS	NS	0.857	0	D
robin	590	52.59	52.431	NS	−1.366	−1.355	NS	NS	NS	0.839	0	R
stoch	18	53.422	48.297	S*	−3.107	−2.799	NS*	S*	NT	—	—	—
rinou	11	54.316	40.709	S*	−2.588	−1.712	NS*	S*	NT	—	—	—
blabi	1525	52.736	52.68	NS	−1.221	−1.405	S	S~	NS	0.801	1	B
sonth	963	52.714	51.832	S	−1.136	−1.991	S	S	S	0.570	1	ST
misth	89	52.863	51.925	S	−1.325	−1.207	NS	S~	NS*	0.513	1	M
blaca	35	52.049	36.898	S	−1.459	−3.019	S	S	S*	−2.931	4	BC
goldc	14	52.115	51.807	NS*	−2.172	−1.605	NS*	NS*	NT	—	—	—
piefl	13	53.216	31.494	S*	−3.395	−4.884	NS*	S*	NT	—	—	—
lotti	17	52.128	52.086	NS*	−0.947	−0.95	NS*	NS*	NT	—	—	—
coati	14	52.034	52.06	NS*	−1.092	−1.124	NS*	NS*	NT	—	—	—
bluti	621	52.4	52.396	NS	−1.367	−1.375	NS	NS	NS	0.825	0	BT
greti	308	52.497	52.484	NS	−1.458	−1.488	NS	NS	NS	0.769	0	GT
nutha	27	51.945	51.942	NS*	−1.808	−1.777	NS*	NS*	NT	0.361	0	NH
jay	129	52.152	52.202	NS	−0.72	−0.751	NS	NS	NS*	0.731	0	J
magpi	91	52.623	52.631	NS	−2.021	−2.024	NS	NS	NT	0.535	0	MG
choug	18	54.639	54.408	NS*	−5.305	−5.046	NS*	NS*	NT	—	—	—
jackd	113	52.9	52.894	NS	−2.029	−2.048	NS	NS	NS*	0.704	0	JD
rook	108	53.53	53.497	NS	−2.264	−2.35	NS	NS	NS*	0.497	0	RO
crow	156	53.848	53.846	NS	−2.443	−2.44	NS	NS	NT	0.550	0	C
raven	78	53.968	53.924	NS	−4.468	−4.292	NS	NS	NT	0.024	0	RN
starl	1433	52.766	52.737	NS	−1.038	−1.086	NS	NS	NS	0.837	0	SG
housp	358	52.393	52.39	NS	−0.963	−0.961	NS	NS	NS	0.830	0	HS
tresp	28	52.801	52.694	NS*	−0.759	−0.741	NS*	NS*	NS*	0.729	0	TS
chaff	154	52.954	52.929	NS	−1.468	−1.418	NS	NS	NS	0.805	0	CH
grefi	382	52.371	52.257	NS	−0.855	−1.071	NS	NS~	S	0.502	0	GR
goldf	118	52.047	45.538	S	−0.375	−1.813	S	S	S	−1.079	3	GO
siski	12	56.995	52.02	S*	−3.867	−2.013	S*	S*	S*	—	—	—
linne	197	52.714	45.572	S	−0.735	−1.636	S	S	S	−1.178	3	LI
redpo	19	53.061	50.527	S*	−1.161	1.95	S*	S*	S*	—	—	—
bullf	338	52.144	52.129	NS	−0.688	−0.695	NS	NS	NS	0.706	0	BF
yelha	39	52.49	52.5	NS	−0.464	−0.475	NS	NS	NS*	0.720	0	Y
reebu	80	52.661	52.559	NS	−1.442	−1.554	NS	NS	NS	0.613	0	RB

Notes
1. See key in Appendix 2.
2. See Figure 5.5 for a graphical display of species by migrancy index values. These two-letter codes are used extensively in BTO fieldwork, and exist for nearly all British and Irish bird species.

Table II Temporal change tests

Species[1]	Number of records	Dividing year	Standardized index Test statistic (K-S D)[2]	Significance[3]	Absolute index Test statistic (K-S D)[2]	Significance[3]	Direction of effect[4]
fulma	111	1984	0.174	NS	0.184	NS	—
mansh	61	1969	0.323	*	0.317	*	Complex change[7]
ganne	387	1968	0.203	***	0.220	***	Fewer after median
cormo	2006	1973	0.019	NS	0.019	NS	—
shag	1745	1978	0.101	***	0.070	**	Fewer after median
grehe	462	1972	0.049	NS	0.035	NS	—
mutsw	1997	1983	0.065	**	0.002	NS	More after median [5]
grego	114	mid 1988	0.211	NS	0.018	NS	—
cango	1902	1982	0.049	NS	0.013	NS	—
sheld	68	mid 1974	0.177	NS	0.177	NS	—
malla	2492	1970	0.024	NS	0.021	NS	—
pocha	65	1982	0.176	NS	0.214	NS	—
tufdu	261	1978	0.283	***	0.261	***	Fewer after median
eider	524	1972	0.161	***	0.011	NS	Complex change[5, 8]
henha	53	1972	0.269	NS	0.273	NS	—
sparr	522	1985	0.033	NS	0.007	NS	—
buzza	110	1982	0.343	***	0.020	NS	Fewer after median [5]
kestr	863	1982	0.173	***	0.067	NS	Fewer after median [5]
merli	122	1988	0.149	NS	0.073	NS	—
pereg	97	1988	0.141	NS	0.060	NS	—
moorh	68	mid 1965	0.235	NS	0.029	NS	—
coot	48	mid 1973	0.042	NS	0.083	NS	—
oyste	383	1977	0.177	***	0.148	**	Fewer after median
rinpl	56	mid 1967	0.143	NS	0.179	NS	—
lapwi	701	1953	0.309	***	0.330	***	More after median
snipe	65	1953	0.149	NS	0.104	NS	—
woodc	277	1935	0.120	NS	0.120	NS	—
curle	181	1954	0.231	**	0.231	**	Fewer after median
redsh	125	1963	0.170	NS	0.177	NS	—
gresk	240	1977	0.183	**	0.193	**	More after median
blhgu	1134	1966	0.088	**	0.066	NS	Fewer after median [5]
comgu	98	1983	0.183	NS	0.112	NS	—
lbbgu	654	1969	0.077	NS	0.077	NS	—
hergu	977	1973	0.037	NS	0.041	NS	—
gbbgu	220	1979	0.109	NS	0.090	NS	—
kitti	240	1980	0.109	NS	0.109	NS	—
sante	1043	1972	0.085	**	0.113	***	Complex change[9]
roste	179	1969	0.167	NS	0.170	NS	—
comte	172	1978	0.105	NS	0.291	***	Fewer after median [6]
arcte	47	1980	0.196	NS	0.196	NS	—
guill	1830	1987	0.064	**	0.048	NS	More after median [5]
razor	710	1981	0.102	**	0.107	**	Complex change[10]
puffi	143	1984	0.254	**	0.258	**	Fewer after median
stodo	92	mid 1970	0.065	NS	0.000	NS	—
woodp	559	1967	0.071	NS	0.016	NS	—
barow	1207	1990	0.025	NS	0.005	NS	—
tawow	253	1985	0.109	NS	0.000	NS	—
kingf	82	1978	0.085	NS	0.000	NS	—
swall	56	mid 1968	0.107	NS	0.214	NS	—
meapi	55	1964	0.112	NS	0.139	NS	—
piewa	308	1968	0.179	**	0.187	***	Fewer after median
wren	109	1982	0.038	NS	0.010	NS	—
dunno	321	1975	0.019	NS	0.019	NS	—
robin	590	1975	0.021	NS	0.022	NS	—
blabi	1525	1971	0.081	**	0.056	NS	Fewer after median [5]
sonth	963	1964	0.197	***	0.158	***	Fewer after median
misth	89	1963	0.226	NS	0.156	NS	—
bluti	621	1981	0.018	NS	0.003	NS	—
greti	308	1983	0.053	NS	0.006	NS	—
jay	129	1978	0.062	NS	0.015	NS	—

Table II Continued

Species[1]	Number of records	Dividing year	Standardized index		Absolute index		Direction of effect[4]
			Test statistic (K-S D)[2]	Significance[3]	Test statistic (K-S D)[2]	Significance[3]	
magpi	91	1981	0.108	NS	0.000	NS	—
jackd	113	1972	0.092	NS	0.018	NS	—
rook	108	1971	0.105	NS	0.000	NS	—
crow	156	mid 1973	0.090	NS	0.000	NS	—
raven	78	1976	0.185	NS	0.023	NS	—
starl	1433	1965	0.006	NS	0.007	NS	—
housp	358	1966	0.046	NS	0.000	NS	—
chaff	154	1977	0.027	NS	0.026	NS	—
grefi	382	1975	0.067	NS	0.059	NS	—
goldf	118	1971	0.165	NS	0.206	NS	—
linne	197	1965	0.241	***	0.260	***	More after median
bullf	338	1973	0.023	NS	0.000	NS	—
reebu	80	1979	0.162	NS	0.048	NS	—

Notes
1. See key in Appendix 2.
2. Kolmogorov–Smirnov statistic (see Chapter 5).
3. Significance levels for tests: * $P<0.05$, ** $P<0.01$, *** $P<0.001$, NS $P>0.05$ (not significant).
4. Changes in the proportion of long-distance movements after the median year are indicated. See later footnotes for explanations of more complex changes.
5. Significant only with the standardized index because the difference was small in terms of absolute distance.
6. A slight shift towards shorter migratory distances, detected only by the distance resolution with the absolute index.
7. Bimodal distribution, with a tendency towards a greater number of long-distance movements and more variation in long-distance movements after the median year.
8. Possible bimodal distribution, with a tendency for a greater number of short-distance movements but also longer long-distance movements after the median year.
9. Major difference suggests fewer long-distance movements after the median year, but the pattern is rather complex.
10. Major difference suggests more long-distance movements after the median year, but the pattern is rather complex.

Table III Parameter values for ecological correlate testing in Chapter 5*

Species[1]	Species grouping	Family	Phylogenetic group[2]	Body length (cm)	Wing span (cm)	Male wing length (mm)	Female wing length (mm)	Male weight (g)	Female weight (g)	Social organization[3]	Diet[4]	UK population (individuals)	Annual survival rate	First egg date (week number)	Length of breeding season (weeks)	Rearing strategy[5]	Nesting strategy[6]	Clutch size	Egg length (mm)	Egg width (mm)	Egg volume (cubic cm)
retdi	Seabird	Gaviidae	Ciconiides	61	112	288	283	1635	1500	s	verts	2400	—	20	14	f	0	2	75	48	90.48
fulma	Seabird	Procellariidae	Ciconiides	47	107	340	323	880	730	c	fish	1086000	0.97	20	15	c	0	1	74	51	100.78
mansh	Seabird	Procellariidae	Ciconiides	34	82	237	234	428	411	c	verts	470000	0.972	19	18	c	0	1	61	42	56.34
ganne	Seabird	Sulidae	Ciconiides	94	173	490	490	3000	3000	c	fish	402000	0.94	16	20	c	0	3	79	50	103.42
cormo	Seabird	Phalacrocoracidae	Ciconiides	90	145	347	331	2500	2100	c	verts	15200	0.725	13	19	c	0	3.5	66	41	58.09
shag	Seabird	Phalacrocoracidae	Ciconiides	73	98	270	260	1960	1800	c	fish	75000	0.855	11	21	c	0	3.1	63	39	50.18
grehe	Waterbird	Ardeidae	Ciconiides	94	185	463	436	1550	1550	t	verts	22000	0.732	9	29	f	0	4	61	43	59.06
mutsw	Waterbird	Anatidae	Anserides	152	230	600	550	11500	9000	t	veg	29000	0.795	13	32	f	0	6	113	74	324.01
grego	Waterbird	Anatidae	Anserides	82	163	468	449	3550	2950	c	veg	105000	0.77	—	—	f	0	5	85	58	149.73
cango	Waterbird	Anatidae	Anserides	95	168	505	481	4800	4300	c	veg	47200	0.72	12	15	f	0	5.9	86	58	151.49
sheld	Waterbird	Anatidae	Anserides	63	122	329	300	1225	1000	t	inverts	21800	—	17	15	f	0	9	66	47	76.34
gadwa	Waterbird	Anatidae	Anserides	52	90	271	252	825	700	t	veg	1580	—	—	—	c	0	10	55	39	43.80
teal	Waterbird	Anatidae	Anserides	36	61	188	180	350	300	s	inverts/veg	4400	0.541	—	33	f	0	9	45	33	25.66
malla	Waterbird	Anatidae	Anserides	58	90	285	265	1100	975	t	inverts/veg	230000	0.625	9	13	f	0	11	57	41	50.17
shove	Waterbird	Anatidae	Anserides	48	77	244	230	650	610	s	inverts/veg	2500	—	16	16	f	0	10	52	37	37.28
pocha	Waterbird	Anatidae	Anserides	45	77	217	208	975	875	s	inverts/veg	657	0.54	16	16	f	0	9	62	44	62.85
tufdu	Waterbird	Anatidae	Anserides	44	70	207	198	800	725	c	inverts/veg	17000	0.94	19	16	f	0	9.5	59	41	51.93
eider	Waterbird	Anatidae	Anserides	60	94	302	299	2250	2250	c	inverts	65000	0.94	17	17	f	0	5	77	52	109.02
goosa	Waterbird	Anatidae	Anserides	62	90	285	263	1700	1300	s	verts	5200	0.6	13	15	f	0	9.5	68	47	78.65
henha	Raptor	Accipitridae	Falconides	48	110	337	375	350	500	s	verts	1340	0.81	18	12	c	0	5	46	36	31.22
sparr	Raptor	Accipitridae	Falconides	33	63	204	243	153	314	t	verts	68000	0.65	18	11	c	0	5	40	32	21.45
buzza	Raptor	Accipitridae	Falconides	54	120	376	397	775	1000	t	verts	29000	0.81	14	14	c	0	3	55	44	55.76
kestr	Raptor	Falconidae	Falconides	34	75	246	250	184	220	s	verts	104000	0.587	14	13	c	0	4.5	39	31	19.62
merli	Raptor	Falconidae	Falconides	28	56	198	215	170	235	s	verts	2660	—	17	12	c	0	4	40	31	20.13
pereg	Raptor	Falconidae	Falconides	42	103	306	358	664	1110	t	verts	2570	0.7	13	16	c	0	3	51	39	40.62
moorh	Waterbird	Rallidae	Miscellaneous	33	52	186	177	345	295	t	inverts/veg	520000	0.623	12	23	f	0	7	43	31	21.64
coot	Waterbird	Rallidae	Miscellaneous	37	79	220	205	850	750	t	veg	48000	0.697	12	21	c	0	6	53	36	35.97
oyste	Wader	Haematopodidae	Charadrioidea	43	83	257	259	550	550	t	inverts	78000	0.88	16	16	f	0	3	57	40	47.75
rinpl	Wader	Charadriidae	Charadrioidea	19	53	134	134	60	60	s	inverts	17200	0.772	15	15	f	0	3.5	36	26	12.74
golpl	Wader	Charadriidae	Charadrioidea	28	72	190	191	216	214	s	inverts	45200	0.593	14	14	f	0	4	52	35	33.35
lapwi	Wader	Charadriidae	Charadrioidea	29	84	230	222	220	220	c	inverts	550000	0.752	12	16	f	0	4	47	33	26.80
dunli	Wader	Charadriidae	Charadrioidea	18	40	114	116	48	48	s	inverts	19050	0.83	18	11	f	0	4	34	25	11.13
snipe	Wader	Charadriidae	Charadrioidea	26	45	135	135	110	110	s	inverts	122000	0.62	13	16	f	0	4	39	29	17.17
woodc	Wader	Charadriidae	Charadrioidea	34	58	200	200	305	305	t	inverts	32000	0.58	11	18	f	0	4	44	34	26.63
curle	Wader	Charadriidae	Charadrioidea	55	90	289	306	800	800	c	inverts	81000	0.736	15	14	f	0	4	68	48	82.04
redsh	Wader	Charadriidae	Charadrioidea	28	63	157	161	107	125	c	inverts	77000	0.74	15	11	f	0	4	45	32	24.13
gresk	Seabird	Stercorariidae	Laroidea	55	136	398	411	1310	1510	c	verts	17000	0.93	19	13	c	0	2	71	50	92.94
blhgu	Seabird	Laridae	Laroidea	35	105	303	298	325	250	c	inverts/various	380000	0.79	16	16	c	0	2.5	52	37	37.28
comgu	Seabird	Laridae	Laroidea	41	120	361	339	400	390	c	inverts/various	137000	0.896	17	13	c	0	3	58	41	51.05
lbbgu	Seabird	Laridae	Laroidea	60	145	438	403	810	700	c	inverts/various	170000	0.91	17	13	c	0	3	67	47	77.50
hergu	Seabird	Laridae	Laroidea	61	146	451	425	1170	950	c	inverts/various	360000	0.9	16	14	c	0	3	70	48	84.45
gbbgu	Seabird	Laridae	Laroidea	71	158	501	472	1700	1500	s	inverts/various	40000	—	16	15	c	0	10	77	54	117.57
kitti	Seabird	Laridae	Laroidea	39	105	308	297	425	390	c	fish	1000000	0.835	20	11	c	0	2	57	41	50.17
sante	Seabird	Sternidae	Laroidea	39	100	310	307	245	245	c	verts	34000	—	19	14	c	0	1.5	51	36	34.61
roste	Seabird	Sternidae	Laroidea	36	76	236	235	113	113	c	verts	144	—	22	9	c	0	1.5	43	30	20.26
comte	Seabird	Sternidae	Laroidea	33	88	272	275	130	130	c	verts	28000	0.81	19	13	c	0	2.5	41	31	20.63
arcte	Seabird	Sternidae	Laroidea	34	80	280	270	113	113	c	verts	88000	0.9	20	12	c	0	2	41	30	19.32
guill	Seabird	Alcidae	Laroidea	40	67	197	197	853	870	c	fish	1100000	0.93	18	10	c	0	1	82	50	107.34

Table III *Continued*

Species[1]	Species grouping	Family	Phylogenetic group[2]	Body length (cm)	Wing span (cm)	Male wing length (mm)	Female wing length (mm)	Male weight (g)	Female weight (g)	Social organization[3]	Diet[4]	UK population (individuals)	Annual survival rate	First egg date (week number)	Length of breeding season (weeks)	Rearing strategy[5]	Nesting strategy[6]	Clutch size	Egg length (mm)	Egg width (mm)	Egg volume (cubic cm)
razor	Seabird	Alcidae	Laroidea	38	68	208	208	700	700	c	fish	160000	0.89	19	9	c	o	1	75	48	90.48
blagu	Seabird	Alcidae	Laroidea	31	55	176	176	420	420	c	verts	37000	—	19	13	c	o	1.5	59	40	49.43
puffi	Seabird	Alcidae	Laroidea	28	55	157	157	400	400	c	fish	903000	0.975	18	15	c	o	1	63	44	63.87
stodo	Passerine	Columbidae	Miscellaneous	33	66	222	216	320	285	s	seeds/inverts	480000	—	14	23	c	h	2	38	29	16.73
woodp	Passerine	Columbidae	Miscellaneous	41	78	253	250	470	430	t	seeds/inverts	4900000	0.57	15	29	c	o	2	41	29	18.06
coldo	Passerine	Columbidae	Miscellaneous	32	51	183	176	205	200	s	seeds/inverts	420000	0.6	15	29	c	o	1	30.5	23.6	8.89
barow	Raptor	Tytonidae	Miscellaneous	34	89	290	290	295	295	t	verts	9000	0.6	13	27	c	h	5.5	41	32	21.98
litow	Raptor	Strigidae	Miscellaneous	22	56	161	165	165	185	t	verts	18000	0.648	14	13	c	h	3.6	36	30	16.97
tawow	Raptor	Strigidae	Miscellaneous	38	99	267	278	370	520	t	verts	40000	0.7	10	24	c	h	2.7	47	39	37.43
loeow	Raptor	Strigidae	Miscellaneous	36	95	296	298	275	305	t	verts	7000	0.69	10	14	c	h	4.2	40	32	21.45
swift	Passerine	Apodidae	Miscellaneous	17	45	172	172	44	44	c	inverts	170000	0.77	18	13	c	h	2.4	25	16	3.35
kingf	Passerine	Alcedinidae	Miscellaneous	17	25	79	79	40	40	t	fish	9600	—	14	18	c	h	6.7	23	19	4.35
swall	Passerine	Hirundinidae	Sylvioidea	18	33	125	122	19	19	t	inverts	1220000	0.374	19	16	c	h	4.5	20.3	14.2	2.14
meapi	Passerine	Motacillidae	Passeroidea	15	24	82	77	19	19	t	inverts/veg	4000000	0.543	15	14	c	o	4.5	19.5	14.4	2.12
grewa	Passerine	Motacillidae	Passeroidea	19	26	86	83	18	18	t	inverts	76000	—	13	15	c	o	5	19	14.3	2.03
piewa	Passerine	Motacillidae	Passeroidea	18	28	92	89	21	21	t	inverts	640000	0.485	15	14	c	o	5.5	20.5	15.3	2.51
dippe	Passerine	Cinclidae	Muscicapoidea	18	28	96	87	68	59	t	inverts	28000	0.54	10	15	c	h	4.5	26	18.7	4.76
wren	Passerine	Troglodytidae	Sylvioidea	10	15	50	48	10	9	t	inverts	15200000	0.319	16	14	c	o	5.7	21.6	16.4	3.04
dunno	Passerine	Prunellidae	Passeroidea	15	20	71	69	21	20	t	inverts/veg	4200000	0.473	13	18	c	o	5	19.2	14.5	2.11
robin	Passerine	Turdidae	Muscicapoidea	14	21	73	71	18	17	t	inverts/veg	9000000	0.419	13	13	c	o	5	19.6	15	2.31
blabi	Passerine	Turdidae	Muscicapoidea	25	36	133	126	103	103	t	inverts/veg	9400000	0.65	11	18	c	o	4	29.3	21.4	7.03
sonth	Passerine	Turdidae	Muscicapoidea	23	35	115	115	83	83	t	inverts/veg	2200000	0.563	11	19	c	o	4	27.1	20.4	5.91
misth	Passerine	Turdidae	Muscicapoidea	27	45	157	147	125	125	t	inverts/veg	500000	0.621	11	12	c	o	4	30.2	22.3	7.86
blaca	Passerine	Sylviidae	Sylvioidea	13	22	76	74	21	21	t	inverts	1180000	0.436	17	11	c	o	5	19.7	14.7	2.23
bluti	Passerine	Paridae	Sylvioidea	12	19	66	63	11	11	t	inverts/veg	7000000	0.532	15	12	c	h	11	16	13	1.42
greti	Passerine	Paridae	Sylvioidea	14	24	77	74	18	17	t	inverts/veg	3400000	0.542	15	12	c	h	9.9	17.5	13.5	1.67
nutha	Passerine	Sittidae	Sylvioidea	14	25	87	85	24	24	t	inverts/veg	260000	0.5	14	10	c	h	7	19.2	14.3	2.06
jay	Passerine	Corvidae	Corvoidea	35	55	170	162	186	179	t	inverts/various	320000	—	16	10	c	o	4.5	31.7	23	8.78
magpi	Passerine	Corvidae	Corvoidea	45	56	198	186	241	198	t	inverts/various	1300000	0.695	13	11	c	o	6	33.8	23.9	10.11
jackd	Passerine	Corvidae	Corvoidea	34	71	240	231	230	225	c	inverts/various	860000	0.694	15	10	c	h	4.5	35	25.2	11.64
rook	Passerine	Corvidae	Corvoidea	45	90	134	130	320	300	c	inverts/various	1890000	0.749	11	11	c	o	4	39.8	29.9	18.63
crow	Passerine	Corvidae	Corvoidea	46	99	329	315	540	470	t	inverts/various	2000000	0.608	13	12	c	o	4	42.9	29.9	20.08
raven	Passerine	Corvidae	Corvoidea	64	135	430	420	1270	1057	t	inverts/various	15000	—	9	20	c	o	4.5	48.8	33.8	29.19
starl	Passerine	Sturnidae	Muscicapoidea	22	40	134	130	80	75	c	inverts	2400000	0.687	15	11	c	h	4.5	29.7	21.2	6.99
housp	Passerine	Passeridae	Passeroidea	15	24	80	76	31	31	c	seeds/inverts	6700000	0.571	14	15	c	h	4	22.2	15.7	2.87
tresp	Passerine	Passeridae	Passeroidea	14	21	71	69	24	23	c	seeds/inverts	220000	0.336	16	12	c	h	5	19.3	14	1.98
chaff	Passerine	Fringillidae	Passeroidea	15	27	91	84	25	23	t	seeds/inverts	11600000	0.589	15	10	c	o	4.5	19.3	14.6	2.15
grefi	Passerine	Fringillidae	Passeroidea	15	26	88	86	28	28	s	seeds/inverts	1120000	0.443	16	14	c	o	5	20	14.6	2.23
goldf	Passerine	Fringillidae	Passeroidea	12	23	81	78	17	17	s	seeds/inverts	460000	0.371	17	13	c	o	4	17	12.8	1.46
linne	Passerine	Fringillidae	Passeroidea	14	23	82	79	20	18	s	seeds/inverts	1080000	0.371	16	18	c	o	5	18	13.3	1.67
bullf	Passerine	Fringillidae	Passeroidea	16	26	82	82	21	21	s	seeds/inverts	400000	0.419	17	16	c	o	4.5	20.8	14.9	2.42
yelha	Passerine	Emberizidae	Passeroidea	16	26	88	85	31	31	t	seeds/inverts	2400000	0.536	16	16	c	o	3.5	21.7	16.4	3.06
reebu	Passerine	Emberizidae	Passeroidea	16	25	74	71	21	20	t	seeds/inverts	480000	0.542	17	14	c	o	4.5	19.5	14.6	2.18

Notes

* The data presented in this table were used in simple, exploratory analyses of the correlates of migratory tendency, as described in Chapter 5. They were taken (or calculated) from published sources, as indicated in the text, but should not be regarded as definitive. We refer the reader to the source material for more detail.

1. See key in Appendix 2.
2. Phylogenetic group: groupings for statistical control purposes only, based on superfamilies as defined by Sibley *et al* (1988), but with broader categories including higher taxonomic levels and a 'miscellaneous' group.
3. Social organization codes: 'c'—colonial; 't'—territorial; 's'—semicolonial.
4. Diet category abbreviations: 'verts'—vertebrates; 'inverts'—invertebrates; 'veg'—vegetation.
5. Rearing strategy codes: 'f'—nidifugous; 'c'—nidicolous.
6. Nesting strategy codes: 'h'—hole-nesting; 'o'—open-nesting.

Appendix 3b
Tests of migratory status for British & Irish wintering birds

This appendix gives the results of tests designed to reveal whether species are migratory or not, and the degree to which they are migratory, by comparing the ringing locations of birds ringed during the winter in Britain & Ireland with their finding locations during the breeding season. The methods are explained more fully in Chapter 4—see the sections on *'Migratory tendency and seasonal locations'* and *'Partial migration: quantifying migratory strategy'*. The results are in the same format and coded as described under Appendix 3a. No migratory scores were allocated for wintering populations.

Species*	Number of records	Mean ringing latitude	Mean finding latitude	Latitude test result	Mean ringing longitude	Mean finding longitude	Longitude test result	Overall result	Result for adults only
mutsw	722	52.464	52.475	NS	−1.587	−1.573	NS	NS	NT
whosw	26	54.588	64.593	S*	−2.977	−17.631	S*	S*	NT
pifgo	26	55.219	64.644	S*	−2.904	−15.77	S*	S*	NT
cango	23	51.613	51.707	NS*	−1.369	−1.44	NS*	NS*	NT
bargo	12	54.746	66.966	S*	−5.69	−7.147	NS*	S*	NT
sheld	15	56.699	56.263	NS*	−2.37	1.694	S*	S*	NT
wigeo	115	53.135	63.936	S	−0.929	54.27	S	S	S
gadwa	15	52.068	52.03	NS*	−1.335	4.296	S*	S*	NT
teal	211	52.069	62.42	S	−0.45	29.067	S	S	S
malla	844	52.23	56.226	S	−0.608	12.203	S	S	S
pinta	47	51.888	64.26	S	−2.297	40.639	S	S	NT
shove	17	51.803	59.633	S*	−1.53	35.016	S*	S*	NT
pocha	105	51.976	55.393	S	−1.05	35.401	S	S	S
tufdu	248	52.158	59.1	S	−0.333	23.989	S	S	S
eider	103	57.37	57.287	NS	−2.026	−2.073	NS	NS	NT
sparr	41	52.676	52.762	NS	−2.306	−2.316	NS	NS	NT
kestr	15	52.716	52.837	NS*	−1.285	−1.288	NS*	NS*	NT
moorh	75	52.697	52.851	NS	−1.077	−0.155	S	S	NT
coot	40	51.801	52.449	S	−0.435	3.081	S	S	NT
oyste	635	53.958	58.714	S	−2.809	−1.219	S	S	NT
lapwi	11	53.331	56.575	NS*	−1.765	13.338	S*	S*	NT
knot	50	53.67	71.374	S	−1.44	−55.713	S	S	S
dunli	25	52.667	57.686	S*	−1.622	17.535	S*	S*	NT
snipe	10	52.972	59.508	S*	−1.649	24.005	S*	S*	NT
woodc	19	52.886	58.122	S*	−5.646	20.028	S*	S*	NT
curle	38	53.531	60.241	S	−3.201	14.254	S	S	NT
redsh	60	54.698	60.697	S	−2.58	−12.315	S	S	S*
turns	15	53.552	68.262	S*	−1.87	−35.233	S*	S*	NT
blhgu	1635	52.117	57.49	S	−0.529	14.124	S	S	S
comgu	86	52.951	59.613	S	−0.376	13.322	S	S	NT
lbbgu	141	52.112	55.269	S	−2.086	−3.707	S	S	S
hergu	438	54.601	56.992	S	−2.114	−0.234	S	S	S*
gbbgu	41	54.479	62.629	S	−1.233	8.952	S	S	NT
woodp	105	52.158	52.155	NS	−0.52	−0.581	NS	NS	NS*
coldo	72	52.208	52.28	NS	−0.819	−1.228	NS	NS	NT
barow	26	52.627	52.69	NS*	−1.731	−1.818	NS*	NS*	NT
tawow	30	52.891	52.888	NS	−1.728	−1.732	NS	NS	NT

Continued

Species[*]	Number of records	Mean ringing latitude	Mean finding latitude	Latitude test result	Mean ringing longitude	Mean finding longitude	Longitude test result	Overall result	Result for adults only
grewo	13	51.553	51.539	NS*	−0.655	−0.631	NS*	NS*	NT
grswo	61	52.163	52.133	NS	−1.242	−1.246	NS	NS	NT
piewa	278	51.916	52.485	S	−1.139	−1.394	S	S	S
wren	25	52.507	52.591	NS*	−0.395	−0.36	NS*	NS*	NT
dunno	545	52.484	52.485	NS	−1.152	−1.153	NS	NS	NS*
robin	448	52.357	52.375	NS	−1.204	−1.224	NS	NS	NS
blabi	3528	52.838	53.155	S	−1.253	−0.101	S	S	S
field	142	52.4	61.843	S	−0.812	16.672	S	S	NT
sonth	875	52.433	52.482	NS	−1.104	−0.982	NS	NS	NS
redwi	62	52.978	59.842	S	−1.676	21.665	S	S	NT
misth	160	52.245	52.268	NS	−1.07	−1.07	NS	NS	NS*
goldc	15	52.197	52.178	NS*	−1.089	−1.19	NS*	NS*	NT
lotti	22	52.205	52.2	NS*	−0.865	−0.868	NS*	NS*	NT
coati	79	52.507	52.515	NS	−1.387	−1.367	NS	NS	NT
bluti	1349	52.279	52.273	NS	−1.172	−1.152	NS	NS	NS
greti	529	52.424	52.429	NS	−1.321	−1.309	NS	NS	NS
nutha	29	52.076	52.094	NS*	−1.668	−1.668	NS*	NS*	NT
jay	69	51.771	51.736	NS	−0.745	−0.766	NS	NS	NT
magpi	40	52.677	52.671	NS	−1.964	−1.946	NS	NS	NT
jackd	81	52.404	52.5	NS	−3.313	−3.022	NS	NS	NT
rook	63	53.435	53.454	NS	−2.727	−2.645	NS	NS	NT
starl	6214	52.94	53.729	S	−1.231	3.175	S	S	NT
housp	673	52.453	52.459	NS	−0.807	−0.814	NS	NS	NS
tresp	72	52.435	52.555	NS	−0.92	−0.845	NS	NS	NT
chaff	664	52.871	54.002	S	−1.777	0.654	S	S	S
bramb	11	53.285	61.942	S*	−1.746	19.786	S*	S*	NT
grefi	3679	52.395	52.458	S	−1.153	−0.984	S	S	S
goldf	28	52.187	52.572	NS*	−1.221	−1.609	NS*	NS*	NT
siski	75	54.114	57.417	S	−2.2	−0.345	NS	S	S*
linne	60	52.472	52.801	NS	−0.802	−0.601	NS	NS	NT
redpo	26	52.024	54.886	S*	−1.089	−1.647	NS*	S*	NT
bullf	270	52.152	52.157	NS	−0.809	−0.799	NS	NS	NS
yelha	111	52.979	52.99	NS	−1.386	−1.373	NS	NS	NS*
reebu	44	52.619	53.008	NS	−1.132	−0.565	NS	NS	NT
corbu	13	52.947	52.872	NS*	−1.016	−0.718	NS*	NS*	NT

* See the key in Appendix 2.

Appendix 4a
Tests of differential migration for British & Irish birds: age differences in migration patterns

This appendix gives the results of tests for differential migration patterns between two age classes of bird. A sample of 10 records in each class was required for testing and only those species for which the sample was sufficient for at least one set of tests to be carried out are included here. Only recoveries for which the age class was known accurately were tested. For movements of the British & Irish breeding population (**Table I**), the tests compared the recovery locations in winter, autumn or spring of birds ringed in Britain & Ireland during the breeding season and recovered as immatures with those recovered as adults. For the wintering population (**Table II**), the tests considered the recovery locations during the breeding season, autumn or spring of birds ringed as either immatures or adults in Britain & Ireland during the winter and <u>recovered as adults</u>. Negative coordinates are locations south of the Equator for latitude or west of the Greenwich Meridian for longitude. Coordinates are given in decimal degrees. Full details of the methods are given in the *'Differential migration'* section of Chapter 4.

For each test, the number of records available for each class, and the mean latitudes and longitudes of recovery for each class are provided. For movements between the breeding season and winter (Table I) and between the winter and the breeding season (Table II), tests of distances moved were also carried out: the median distance moved by each class and the 5th ('**P5**') and 95th ('**P95**') percentiles for each class are also given. For each season, results are presented separately for each test (latitude, longitude or distance as appropriate) and a summary result ('**overall result**') is also given.

The entries under each result column are coded as follows:-

S Significant result (P<0.05) and each class had a sample of at least 30 birds;

NS both classes had samples >30 and the test was not significant;

NT not tested because the sample size was <10 for at least one class.

For each overall result, an asterisk (*) indicates a sample of <30 records in at least one class and a tilde (~) indicates that differences in ringing and recovery locations were confounded for at least one of the tests (see *'Biases caused by differences in ringing locations'* section of Chapter 4). The overall results for breeding-to-winter and winter-to-breeding movements are flagged in the '**statistical analyses**' table in each main species account (see Chapter 6).

Table I British & Irish breeding population (age differences)

Species[1]	Ecological grouping[2]	Migrant type[3]	Number of adult records	Number of immature records	Mean winter latitude of adults	Mean winter latitude of immatures	Winter latitude test result	Mean winter longitude of adults	Mean winter longitude of immatures	Winter longitude test result	Median distance moved by adults (km)	Adult P5	Adult P95	Median distance moved by immatures (km)	Immature P5	Immature P95	Distance test result	Overall result
							Winter tests											
retdi	WF	Migrant	11	13	55.145	54.034	NS	-3.837	-2.735	NS	435	186	1047	472	19	1547	NS	NS*
fulma	SG	Migrant	21	68	57.739	56.327	NS	-0.354	-4.73	NS	430	7	1249	676	71	3253	NS	NS*
mansh	SG	Migrant	5	49	—	-12.736	NT	—	-45.439	NT	—	—	—	9347	49	11224	NT	NT
ganne	SG	Migrant	137	235	49.695	40.299	S	-1.644	-5.186	S	639	23	2017	1380	182	4427	S	S
cormo	SG	Migrant	310	1695	52.271	52.152	NS	-3.689	-3.678	NS	179	13	1060	222	25	1069	S	S
shag	SG	Migrant	160	1565	55.657	54.445	S	-3.373	-3.735	NS-	58.5	0	308.5	96	11	471	S	S
grehe	WF	Sedentary	62	400	53.114	53.192	NS	-1.899	-1.643	NS-	22.5	0	223	47.5	1.5	299	S	S-
mutsw	WF	Sedentary	797	976	52.24	52.488	S-	-1.956	-1.964	NS	10	0	89	10	0	76	S	S-
grego	WF	Sedentary	48	21	54.478	53.925	NS-	-3.391	-2.743	NS-	13	0	179	13	0	25	NS	NS*~
cango	WF	Migrant	797	457	52.804	52.886	NS	-1.377	-1.407	NS	16	0	289	6	0	54	S	S
sheld	WF	Migrant	39	29	53.201	52.117	NS-	1.361	-3.203	S	316	2	716	227	0	811	NS	S*
wigeo	WF	Sedentary	7	5	—	—	NT	—	—	NT	—	—	—	—	—	—	NT	NT
gadwa	WF	Migrant	17	9	49.192	50.973	NS	-0.542	-2.789	NS-	301	6	1880	386.5	3	1523	NS	NS*~
teal	WF	Migrant	24	14	51.615	52.68	S-	-2.06	-1.152	S-	171	0	1459	15	0	200	S	S-
malla	WF	Sedentary	1522	889	52.469	45.836	NS	-0.559	0.13	NS	23	0	358	717	56	2142	S	NS*
shove	WF	Migrant	20	13	46.626	52.723	NS-	-1.715	-2.874	S	659	0	1749.5	264	6	981	S	S-
tufdu	WF	Migrant	205	55	52.484	57.12	S-	-1.545	-2.201	NS	226	6	715	6.5	0	126	S	S~
eider	WF	Migrant	330	160	56.377	55.006	NT	-2.293	-3.012	NT	74	0	162	86.5	22	265	NT	NT
goosa	WF	Migrant	4	22	—	55.308	S	—	-2.427	NS	—	—	—	262	3	1413	S	S*
henha	RO	Migrant	15	38	57.961	53.214	NS	-2.607	-1.992	NS	47	0	942	12	0	120	S	S
sparr	RO	Sedentary	214	307	53.38	55.012	NS	-1.82	-3.568	NS-	9	0	70	20	0	106	NS	NS*~
buzza	RO	Sedentary	16	94	54.948	52.701	NS	-4.1	-1.446	NS	15	0	67	64	0	700	NS	S
kestr	RO	Migrant	277	586	52.866	53.635	NS	-1.576	-2.124	NS	23	0	522	107	9	1121	S	NS*
merli	RO	Migrant	45	77	54.157	54.808	NS-	-1.982	-3.797	NS	79	11	389	49.5	8	357	NS	NS*~
pereg	RO	Sedentary	33	64	54.461	52.752	NS	-4.244	-1.223	NS-	54	20	297	0	0	31.5	NS	NS*
moorh	WF	Sedentary	43	20	52.637	51.585	NS	-0.562	0.093	NS-	3	0	76	106.5	0	739.5	S	S
coot	WF	Migrant	20	20	52.225	52.354	NS	-1.048	-3.61	S	62	0	283	250	0	1421	NS	NS-
oyste	WD	Migrant	141	229	53.17	—	NT	-2.528	—	NT	69	0	971	—	—	—	NT	NT
stocu	WD	[Migrant]	10	6	40.059	52.492	S	-3.863	-2.364	NS	1497	7	2262	95	5	1285	NS	S*
rinpl	WD	Migrant	33	23	48.153	48.599	S	-3.529	-4.708	NS	261	0	3866	533.5	13	1786	NS	S*
lapwi	WD	Migrant	308	392	49.555	52.928	S	-4.859	-5.429	NS	472	11	1637	180	0	628	S	S*
snipe	WD	Migrant	23	31	51.831	54.058	NS	-5.954	-4.198	NS	483	2	936	11	0	667	S	S*
woodc	WD	Migrant	76	189	54.252	53.417	NS	-3.727	-5.938	NS-	11	0	579	334	0	642	NS	NS-
curle	WD	Migrant	80	99	53.147	51.659	NS	-4.713	-2.571	S	181	0	674.5	289	12	1368	S	S
redsh	WD	Migrant	74	51	51.837	—	NS	-1.583	—	NT	87.5	0	973	—	—	—	S	S
arcsk	SG	[Migrant]	1	8	—	44.648	NT	—	-2.44	NT	—	—	—	—	—	—	NT	NT
gresk	SG	Migrant	33	206	45.711	51.989	NS	0.926	-3.433	NS	1661	877	2863	1725.5	749	3234	NS	NS
blhgu	SG	Migrant	547	587	52.861	56.055	S	-2.873	-4.913	NS	84	7	583	141	12	1391	NS	NS
comgu	SG	Migrant	28	70	54.839	39.911	NS	-3.74	-6.733	S	106	5	912	86	4	601	S	NS*
lbbgu	SG	Migrant	153	495	43.041	54.042	S	-5.293	-3.298	S	1201	25	2567	1701	38	2892	S	S
hergu	SG	Migrant	268	695	54.459	54.402	NS	-3.293	-3.854	NS	45.5	2	504	88	5	533	S	S
gbbgu	SG	Migrant	54	165	53.99	50.691	NS-	-2.436	-5.233	S	54.5	0	930	115	13	720	S	S
kitti	SG	Migrant	110	113	52.16	8.459	NS	0.587	-5.249	S	671	0	1894	717	91	3585	NS	NS*
sante	SG	Migrant	208	835	8.199	6.143	NS	-3.332	-1.273	S	5138.5	1458	10203	5407	2119	7758	S	S
roste	SG	Migrant	26	152	6.115	11.261	NS	-1.662	-8.737	NS	5313.5	4969	5580	5312	5172	5630	NS	NS*
comte	SG	Migrant	27	144	9.026	-12.793	NS	-4.963	14.355	NS	5087	31	10063	5051.5	2996	5627	NS	NS*
arcte	SG	Migrant	5	42	—	55.124	NT	—	2.244	NT	—	—	—	8321.5	5015	10795	NT	NT
guill	SG	Migrant	204	1547	53.798	45.951	S	0.39	-2.868	S	608	51	1118	683	119	1124	S	S
razor	SG	Migrant	158	488	49.949	52.095	S	-0.754	-5.733	S	683.5	91	1514	973.5	170	2305	S	S
puffi	SG	Migrant	71	44	54.945	52.907	S	-0.831	-1.573	NS-	472	73	2101	686.5	119	3157	S	S
stodo	PN	Sedentary	45	46	52.42	52.835	NS-	-1.354	-1.401	NS	10	0	41	10.5	0	76	NS	NS-
woodp	PN	[Migrant]	316	240	53.049	—	NS-	-1.296	—	NT	6	0	81	28	0	281	NT	NT
turdo	PN	[Migrant]	0	0	—	—	NT	—	—	NT	—	—	—	—	—	—	NT	NT
barow	RO	Sedentary	355	848	53.109	52.931	NS	-2.168	-1.955	NS-	10	0	61	13	0	119	S	S

Table 1 Continued

					Winter tests													
Species[1]	Ecological grouping[2]	Migrant type[3]	Number of adult records	Number of immature records	Mean winter latitude of adults	Mean winter latitude of immatures	Winter latitude test result	Mean winter longitude of adults	Mean winter longitude of immatures	Winter longitude test result	Median distance moved by adults (km)	Adult P5	Adult P95	Median distance moved by immatures (km)	Immature P5	Immature P95	Distance test result	Overall result
litow	RO	Sedentary	12	20	52.47	51.992	NS–	-0.967	-1.179	NS–	0	0	33	17	0	128.5	S	S*
tawow	RO	Sedentary	86	167	53.706	53.768	NS	-2.09	-2.027	NS	3	0	26	6	0	35	NS	NS
loeow	RO	Sedentary	14	11	55.04	52.986	S	-0.384	-1.592	NS	6	0	1447	70	3	345	NS	S*
sheow	RO	Sedentary	8	8	—	—	NT	—	—	NT	—	—	—	—	—	—	NT	NT
swift	PN	Migrant	10	0	-5.785	—	NT	25.583	—	NT	7985.5	8	8681	—	—	—	NT	NT
kingf	PN	Sedentary	31	46	52.001	52.364	NS–	-1.078	-0.992	NS	11	0	82	7.5	0	60	NS	NS–
sanma	PN	[Migrant]	7	1	—	—	NT	—	—	NT	—	—	—	—	—	—	NT	NT
swall	PN	Migrant	20	35	-27.135	-27.026	NS	24.403	26.046	NS	9635.5	5953	9888	9691	6756	10301	NS	NS*
houma	PN	Migrant	0	0	—	—	NT	—	—	NT	—	—	—	—	—	—	NT	NT
meapi	PN	Migrant	28	27	42.031	40.042	NS	-4.435	-6.082	NS	1493.5	19	2091	1667	74	2516	NS	NS*
yelwa	PN	[Migrant]	6	0	—	—	NT	—	—	NT	—	—	—	—	—	—	NT	NT
grewa	PN	Migrant	10	22	52.707	52.202	NS	-2.59	-1.914	NS	94	12	546	164.5	25	556	NS	NS*~
piewa	PN	Migrant	146	161	50.794	49.173	S	-1.578	-2.606	S	12	0	1266	92	0	1747	S	S
dippe	PN	Sedentary	14	15	54.122	54.413	NS–	-2.713	-2.86	NS–	4	0	95	6	0	46	NS	NS*~
wren	PN	Sedentary	48	57	52.444	52.641	NS	-0.918	-1.336	NS–	0	0	52	1	0	268	NS	NS–
dunno	PN	Sedentary	169	128	52.412	52.524	NS	-1.052	-1.181	NS	0	0	10	0	0	8	NS	NS
robin	PN	Sedentary	306	283	52.379	52.468	NS	-1.248	-1.462	NS–	0	0	123	0	0	56	NT	NS–
redst	PN	[Migrant]	1	0	—	—	NT	—	—	NT	—	—	—	—	—	—	NT	NT
wheat	PN	[Migrant]	1	1	—	—	NT	—	—	NT	—	—	—	—	—	—	S	NT
blabi	PN	Migrant	1040	481	52.599	52.859	S–	-1.314	-1.607	S–	0	0	45	0	0	189	S	S–
sonth	PN	Migrant	535	386	52.069	51.538	S	-2.033	-1.972	NS	3	0	540	12	0	939	S	S
misth	PN	Migrant	52	37	52.432	51.211	S	-1.286	-1.095	NS	2	0	734	9	0	883	S	S
sedwa	PN	[Migrant]	0	1	—	—	NT	—	—	NT	—	—	—	—	—	—	NT	NT
reewa	PN	[Migrant]	4	2	—	—	NT	—	—	NT	—	—	—	—	—	—	NT	NT
white	PN	[Migrant]	1	1	37.193	—	NT	-2.26	—	NT	1795.5	833	1979	—	—	—	NT	NT
blaca	PN	Migrant	26	9	—	—	NT	—	—	NT	—	—	—	—	—	—	NT	NT
wilwa	PN	[Migrant]	3	2	—	—	NT	—	—	NT	—	—	—	—	—	—	NT	NT
spofl	PN	[Migrant]	4	0	—	—	NT	—	—	NT	—	—	—	—	—	—	NT	NT
piefl	PN	Migrant	9	4	—	—	NT	—	—	NT	—	—	—	—	—	—	NT	NT
bluti	PN	Sedentary	238	382	52.372	52.412	NS	-1.328	-1.403	NS	2	0	29	3	0	40	S	S
greti	PN	Sedentary	108	200	52.29	52.589	NS–	-1.328	-1.575	NS–	1	0	41	2	0	37.5	NS	S
jay	PN	Sedentary	67	46	52.143	52.364	NS–	-0.735	-0.836	NS–	0	0	24	4	0	136	S	NS*
magpi	PN	Sedentary	25	63	52.696	52.858	NT	-1.88	-2.062	NS–	1	0	11	2	0	25	NS	S
jackd	PN	Sedentary	67	31	52.746	53.229	NS–	-2.219	-2.296	NS	4	0	37	10	0	185	S	S
rook	PN	Sedentary	53	53	53.537	53.428	NS	-2.138	-2.603	NS–	6	0	54	13	0	63	S	NS–
crow	PN	Sedentary	48	106	54.125	53.722	NS–	-2.477	-2.437	NS	5.5	0	30	5.5	0	25	NS	NS*
raven	PN	Sedentary	13	64	54.082	53.884	NS	-4.185	-4.348	NS	23	0	146	36	5	98	NS	S
starl	PN	Sedentary	635	622	52.674	52.862	NS	-1.001	-1.136	NS	0	0	49	7	0	189	S	NS–
housp	PN	Sedentary	256	70	52.393	52.388	NS	-0.864	-1.091	NS–	0	0	6	0	0	11	NS	NS*~
tresp	PN	Sedentary	16	11	52.575	52.858	NS–	-0.355	-1.217	NS–	0	0	318	0	0	45	NS	NS–
chaff	PN	Sedentary	116	34	52.977	52.726	NS–	-1.461	-1.292	NS	0	0	74	1	0	30	NS	NS–
grefi	PN	Sedentary	274	104	52.189	52.477	NS–	-1.094	-1.1	NS	5	0	228	7	0	186	NS	NS–
goldf	PN	Migrant	69	49	46.003	44.881	NS	-1.587	-2.132	NS–	878	1	1290	926	2	1550	NS	NS–
linne	PN	Migrant	106	78	46.026	44.982	NS	-1.484	-1.85	NS–	868	1	1622	904	4	1747	NS	NS–
redpo	PN	Migrant	18	1	50.526	—	NT	2.253	—	NT	444.5	4	862	—	—	—	NT	NT
bulff	PN	Sedentary	206	127	52.133	52.108	NS–	-0.622	-0.837	NS–	0	0	37	2	0	24	NS	NS–
yelha	PN	Sedentary	26	10	52.657	52.318	NS–	-0.29	-1.385	NS–	0	0	11	4	0	85	S	S*
reebu	PN	Sedentary	56	22	52.54	52.534	NS	-1.583	-1.506	NS	2	0	135	6	0	152	NS	NS*

continued

Table 1 *Continued*

Species[1]	Number of adult records	Number of immature records	Mean autumn latitude of adults	Mean autumn latitude of immatures	Autumn latitude test result	Mean autumn longitude of adults	Mean autumn longitude of immatures	Autumn longitude test result	Overall result
					Autumn tests				
retdi	3	5	—	—	NT	—	—	NT	NT
fulma	22	199	56.354	56.391	NS	3.821	-2.452	S	S*
mansh	121	526	44.486	47.57	NS	-11.128	-7.619	S	S
ganne	99	917	51.127	46.992	S	-2.269	-3.647	S	S
cormo	163	1852	52.486	52.394	NS	-3.951	-4.173	NS~	NS~
shag	160	1412	55.671	54.736	S	-3.523	-4.33	S~	S~
grehe	51	324	53.308	53.048	NS~	-2.023	-2.446	NS~	NS~
mutsw	775	1249	52.255	52.704	S~	-1.9	-1.86	NS	NS~
grego	72	60	54.47	54.843	NS~	-3.607	-3.661	NS	NS~
cango	826	507	52.989	53.051	NS	-1.411	-1.383	NS	NS
sheld	27	75	53.885	53.986	NS	7.008	-1.043	S	S*
wigeo	14	12	55.493	53.701	NS	5.478	-2.351	NS	NS*
gadwa	35	22	51.651	51.17	NS~	0.887	1.348	NS~	NS*~
teal	15	23	52.999	53.521	NS~	0.2	-3.369	S	S*
malla	1076	737	52.922	52.593	S	0.537	-0.749	S	S
shove	34	29	51.034	52.823	S	3.435	0.355	NS	S*
tufdu	145	101	53.442	53.366	NS	1.239	-1.229	S	S
eider	120	50	56.614	57.214	S~	-0.155	-2.209	S	S~
goosa	12	33	59.276	55.91	S	4.561	-1.902	S	S*
henha	9	42	—	56.387	NT	—	-3.371	NT	NT
sparr	128	731	53.353	53.288	NS	-2.184	-1.903	S~	S~
buzza	5	67	—	54.933	NT	—	-3.74	NT	NT
kestr	257	755	52.905	52.692	NS~	-1.286	-1.439	NS	NS~
merli	41	206	53.434	54.732	S	-1.883	-2.058	NS	S
pereg	38	90	54.906	54.935	NS	-4.096	-3.652	NS~	NS~
moorh	21	22	52.311	53.14	S~	-1.46	-2.725	NS~	S*~
coot	2	16	—	50.757	NT	—	-0.416	NT	NT
oyste	115	241	55.512	53.58	S	-1.431	-3.206	S	S
stocu	22	25	45.996	46.903	NS	-1.358	-0.681	NS	NS*
rinpl	37	20	50.113	52.247	NS	-1.138	-2.293	NS	NS*
lapwi	95	227	53.939	54.46	NS	-2.853	-3.074	NS	NS
snipe	23	48	54.774	53.837	NS	-3.703	-4.108	NS~	NS*~
woodc	35	85	55.452	55.602	NS	-2.962	-3.723	NS	NS
curle	31	90	53.469	54.26	S~	-3.338	-4.268	NS	S~
redsh	18	76	53.313	51.884	NS	-2.98	-1.9	NS	NS*
arcsk	19	35	56.531	49.086	NS	-1.72	-2.05	NS~	NS*~
gresk	54	336	55.971	52.518	S	0.553	2.047	NS	S
blhgu	423	1036	53.825	54.00	NS	-2.703	-2.795	NS	NS
comgu	52	222	56.889	56.996	NS	-4.334	-4.523	NS	NS
lbbgu	461	1291	51.475	49.642	S	-3.441	-4.289	S	S
hergu	485	1610	54.367	54.495	NS	-3.467	-3.846	S~	S~
gbbgu	65	346	54.435	55.553	S~	-3.831	-4.044	NS	S~
kitti	66	210	56.206	55.72	NS	-16.248	-16.707	NS~	NS~
sante	142	328	38.928	37.298	NS	-4.388	-4.838	NS	NS*
roste	13	37	35.554	36.429	NS	-4.707	-7.399	NS	NS*
comte	36	196	43.116	45.317	NS	-3.505	-3.093	NS	NS
arcte	18	109	37.804	24.607	NS~	2.693	-3.093	NS	NS*~
guill	71	637	56.544	55.958	NS~	-0.1	0.66	NS	NS~
razor	32	194	54.369	52.603	NS	-3.522	-1.059	S	S
puffi	32	29	56.705	52.192	S	-2.438	-2.595	NS	S*
stodo	9	17	—	52.083	NT	—	-2.112	NT	NT
woodp	98	67	52.395	52.939	S~	-1.176	-1.432	NS~	S~
turdo	57	28	41.336	41.978	NS	-4.35	-3.906	NS	NS*
barow	0	0	—	—	NT	—	—	NT	NT

Table 1 *Continued*

Species[1]	Number of adult records	Number of immature records	Mean autumn latitude of adults	Mean autumn latitude of immatures	Autumn latitude test result	Mean autumn longitude of adults	Mean autumn longitude of immatures	Autumn longitude test result	Overall result
					Autumn tests				
litow	30	52	52.604	52.069	S–	-1.294	-0.885	NS–	S–
tawow	142	207	53.561	53.623	NS	-1.997	-1.949	NS	NS
loeow	9	19	—	54.078	NT	—	-2.005	NT	NT
sheow	12	32	53.653	53.248	NS–	1.427	-2.307	NS	NS*–
swift	47	15	50.503	51.409	NS	-1.572	-0.186	S	S*
kingf	19	64	51.623	51.986	NS–	-0.829	-1.105	NS–	NS*–
sanma	66	34	47.776	49.877	NS	-1.601	-1.445	NS	NS
swall	112	311	48.883	48.739	NS	-0.735	-0.83	NS	NS
houma	74	25	51.655	52.414	NS–	-1.053	-1.045	NS	NS*–
meapi	19	53	46.923	45.798	NS	-4.392	-3.144	NS	NS*–
yelwa	13	15	41.785	44.781	NS	-6.934	-4.166	S	S*
grewa	3	7	—	—	NT	—	—	NT	NT
piewa	32	69	51.893	50.352	NS	-1.784	-2.123	NS	NS
dippe	6	21	—	54.751	NT	—	-2.837	NT	NT
wren	28	80	51.929	52.58	NS–	-1.071	-1.49	NS–	NS*–
dunno	72	140	52.635	52.664	NS	-0.9	-1.207	NS–	NS–
robin	136	352	52.177	52.509	NS–	-1.312	-1.423	NS	NS–
redst	13	35	40.837	45.44	S	-4.522	-3.08	NS	S*
wheat	15	37	44.133	44.587	NS–	-3.294	-3.748	NS	NS*–
blabi	848	1074	52.62	52.941	S–	-1.076	-1.58	S–	S–
sonth	148	296	52.531	52.793	S	-1.31	-1.676	S	S
misth	37	40	52.255	52.595	NS–	-1.26	-1.644	NS–	NS–
sedwa	9	47	—	49.956	NT	—	-1.131	NT	NT
reewa	56	95	41.173	48.721	S	-6.276	-2.501	S	S
white	29	53	45.968	48.641	NS	-3.434	-2.486	NS	NS*
blaca	23	33	42.861	47.764	S	-3.157	-1.784	NS	S*
wilwa	17	71	44.766	50.43	S	-4.389	-1.84	S	S*
spofl	17	39	43.877	44.738	NS	-2.895	-3.232	NS–	NS*–
piefl	30	160	42.942	47.672	S	-5.76	-3.583	S	S
bluti	169	525	52.316	52.574	S–	-1.374	-1.45	S	S–
greti	124	324	52.346	52.434	NS	-1.373	-1.388	NS	NS
jay	23	17	51.903	52.655	S–	-0.687	-1.366	NS–	S*–
magpi	15	96	53.707	52.88	S–	-2.309	-2.289	NS	S*–
jackd	65	87	53.11	53.416	NS–	-2.69	-2.63	NS	NS–
rook	58	156	53.979	53.979	NS	-2.063	-2.581	NS–	NS–
crow	20	110	54.282	53.946	NS–	-3.533	-3.056	NS–	NS*–
raven	8	61	—	54.222	NT	—	-4.477	NT	NT
starl	576	811	52.709	52.837	NS	-1.039	-1.058	NS	NS
housp	214	100	52.484	52.569	NS	-1.114	-1.143	NS	NS
tresp	9	12	—	52.521	NT	—	-0.679	NT	NT
chaff	41	36	52.955	53.197	NS–	-1.358	-2.033	NS–	NS–
grefi	110	57	52.246	52.537	NS–	-1.108	-1.343	NS–	NS–
goldf	26	23	48.016	47.084	NS	-1.051	-0.413	NS	NS*
linne	74	114	45.395	45.224	NS	-1.479	-1.337	NS	NS
redpo	34	14	51.429	52.025	NS	2.369	1.79	NS	NS*
bullf	22	39	51.877	52.339	NS–	-0.689	-0.66	NS	NS*–
yelha	10	9	53.078	—	NT	-0.805	—	NT	NT
reebu	7	10	—	52.578	NT	—	-1.059	NT	NT

continued

Table 1 *Continued*

Species[1]	Number of adult records	Number of immature records	Spring tests					Autumn longitude test result	Overall result
			Mean spring latitude of adults	Mean spring latitude of immatures	Spring latitude test result	Mean spring longitude of adults	Mean spring longitude of immatures		
retdi	5	7	—	—	NT	—	—	NT	NT
fulma	24	85	56.008	57.637	NS	1.422	-4.899	S	S*
mansh	156	55	46.85	45.724	NS	-6.541	-7.117	NS	NS
ganne	139	114	53.731	45.739	S	-2.136	-3.085	NS	S
cormo	255	736	52.918	53.435	NS~	-3.294	-3.582	NS	NS~
shag	356	1022	55.864	54.881	S	-2.491	-2.877	S~	S~
grehe	61	284	53.36	53.799	NS	-1.431	-2.109	S	S
mutsw	388	398	52.17	52.52	NS~	-2.08	-1.978	NS	NS~
grego	7	1	—	—	NT	—	—	NT	NT
cango	81	49	52.766	52.711	NS	-1.603	-1.105	S~	S~
sheld	15	3	55.311	—	NT	-0.415	—	NT	NT
wigeo	2	0	—	—	NT	—	—	NT	NT
gadwa	0	1	—	—	NT	—	—	NT	NT
teal	0	2	—	—	NT	—	—	NT	NT
malla	107	28	52.62	52.368	NS~	1.583	1.993	NS~	NS~
shove	3	3	—	—	NT	—	—	NT	NT
tufdu	34	3	58.21	—	NT	28.256	—	NT	NT
eider	196	75	56.291	57.145	NS~	-1.93	-2.132	S~	S~
goosa	2	4	—	—	NT	—	—	NT	NT
henha	9	16	52.922	56.614	NT	-1.666	-2.494	NT	NT
sparr	220	207	53.052	53.046	NS	-1.31	-1.811	NS	NS
buzza	8	52	54.882	55.151	NS	-2.468	-3.909	NS	NS
kestr	106	143	54.186	52.804	NS	-4.029	-1.495	NS	NS
merli	38	28	52.905	54.221	NS	-1.943	-2.331	NS	NS
pereg	12	19	56.15	54.094	NS~	-1.93	-3.855	NS	NS*
moorh	27	19	—	53.787	NT	—	-2.684	NS	NS*
coot	9	3	—	—	NT	—	—	S	NS~
oyste	42	44	48.343	54.389	S	-2.007	-3.563	S	S
stocu	2	5	—	—	NT	—	—	NT	NT
rinpl	23	7	—	—	NT	—	—	NT	NT
lapwi	176	223	50.131	49.168	NS	-3.746	-4.06	NS~	NS~
snipe	0	1	—	—	NT	—	—	NT	NT
woodc	1	9	—	—	NT	—	—	NT	NT
curle	13	10	54.271	52.858	NS	-1.666	-3.23	NS	NS*
redsh	20	11	53.259	52.243	NS	-2.396	-2.091	NS~	NS~
arcsk	0	3	—	—	NT	—	—	NT	NT
gresk	23	105	55.116	51.689	NS	-0.604	-1.559	NS	NS*
blhgu	283	192	53.446	53.337	NS	-1.895	-2.33	NS	NS
comgu	19	41	56.563	56.448	NS	-4.385	-4.897	NS	NS*
lbbgu	144	184	50.706	42.681	S	-4.058	-5.828	S	S
hergu	255	392	54.713	54.3	S	-3.644	-3.166	S	S
gbbgu	60	117	55.047	55.177	NS	-4.392	-3.933	NS~	NS~
kitti	68	54	54.054	53.308	NS	-1.397	0.343	NS	NS
sante	87	155	28.466	4.381	S	-3.17	-3.433	S	S
roste	7	15	—	7.565	NT	—	-5.577	NT	NT
comte	20	46	46.575	8.644	S	-2.628	-8.587	S	S*
arcte	23	11	55.731	29.145	S	-1.917	6.793	S	S*
guill	251	1201	54.344	53.912	NS	-1.377	0.835	S	S
razor	336	344	51.636	47.929	S	-1.142	-2.687	S	S
puffi	156	60	52.871	51.328	S	-0.978	-0.829	NS	S
stodo	25	23	52.551	53.002	NS~	-1.278	-1.189	NS	NS~
woodp	142	74	53.188	53.292	NS	-1.315	-1.275	NS	NS
turdo	5	3	—	—	NT	—	—	NT	NT
barow	0	0	—	—	NT	—	—	NT	NT

Table 1 *Continued*

Species[1]	Number of adult records	Number of immature records	Mean spring latitude of adults	Mean spring latitude of immatures	Spring latitude test result	Mean spring longitude of adults	Mean spring longitude of immatures	Autumn longitude test result	Overall result
litow	17	12	52.604	52.067	NS–	–1.234	–1.518	NS–	NS*–
tawow	43	64	53.927	53.428	NS–	–2.013	–2.099	NS	NS–
loeow	12	2	53.376	—	NT	–1.772	—	NT	NT
sheow	3	2	—	—	NT	—	—	NT	NT
swift	74	5	50.825	—	NT	–0.996	—	NT	NT
kingf	7	15	—	52.918	NT	—	–1.906	NT	NT
sanma	88	21	47.647	45.988	NS	–0.84	–0.786	NS	NS*
swall	133	115	50.18	45.541	S	–0.709	0.635	NS	S
houma	12	1	50.113	—	NT	0.096	—	NT	NT
meapi	5	4	—	—	NT	—	—	NT	NT
yelwa	13	4	40.576	—	NT	–4.195	—	NT	NT
grewa	2	3	—	—	NT	—	—	NT	NT
piewa	45	26	51.218	50.901	NS–	–1.519	–1.293	NS–	NS*–
dippe	10	13	53.993	54.908	NS–	–3.049	–2.796	NS–	NS*–
wren	38	33	52.27	52.238	NS	–1.163	–1.491	NS–	NS–
dunno	81	59	52.34	52.449	NS	–0.985	–1.027	NS	NS
robin	180	138	52.382	52.439	NS	–0.934	–1.331	NS	NS*
redst	12	15	43.425	45.81	NS	–3.403	–3.248	S	S
wheat	9	11	—	48.233	NT	—	–2.665	NT	NT
blabi	1283	527	52.613	52.757	NS	–1.215	–1.329	NS	NS
sonth	283	177	52.537	52.57	NS	–1.25	–1.489	NS–	NS–
misth	17	10	53.083	53.211	NS	–1.87	–1.529	NS*	NS*–
sedwa	15	16	51.294	49.92	NS	–1.661	–0.827	NS*	NS*–
reewa	35	8	44.763	—	NT	–2.991	—	NT	NT
white	36	18	51.351	51.104	NS	–0.846	–1.456	NS	NS*–
blaca	62	45	46.76	48.696	NS	–0.73	–0.411	NS	NS
wilwa	65	56	50.424	50.567	NS	–1.162	–1.515	NS–	NS–
spofl	12	5	50.272	—	NT	–1.731	—	NT	NT
piefl	52	55	42.633	40.551	NS	–3.4	–3.365	NS	NS
bluti	243	290	52.346	52.371	NS	–1.247	–1.382	NS	NS*–
greti	125	170	52.502	52.687	NS	–1.285	–1.599	NS–	NS*–
jay	11	4	51.742	—	NT	–1.561	—	NT	NT
magpi	13	41	52.193	52.778	NS–	–1.364	–2.101	NS–	NS*–
jackd	31	19	53.042	53.003	NS	–2.491	–2.625	NS	NS*
rook	43	25	53.919	53.175	NS–	–1.894	–1.38	NS–	NS*–
crow	11	43	53.178	53.71	NS–	–1.215	–2.156	NS–	NS*–
raven	7	23	—	54.583	NT	—	–4.078	NT	NT
starl	245	204	52.573	52.544	NS	–1.062	–1.102	NS	NS
housp	93	23	52.339	52.162	NS	–0.508	–0.813	NS	NS*–
tresp	18	4	53.227	—	NT	–1.862	—	NT	NT
chaff	147	36	52.564	52.679	NS	–1.812	–1.222	NS–	NS–
grefi	207	56	52.189	51.922	NS–	–0.935	–1.004	NS	NS–
goldf	21	9	47.311	—	NT	–1.158	—	NT	NT
linne	28	19	50.935	51.787	NS–	–0.885	–0.549	NS	NS*–
redpo	15	1	52.357	—	NT	–0.132	—	NT	NT
bullf	56	38	51.908	52.146	NS–	–0.395	–1.153	S–	S–
yelha	11	1	52.455	—	NT	–0.662	—	NT	NT
reebu	69	17	52.255	52.067	NS	–1.336	–1.338	NS	NS*

Notes

1. See key in Appendix 2.
2. Ecological groupings used in the synthesis of differential movements in Chapter 5: 'PN'—passerine/near-passerine; 'RO'—raptor/owl; 'SG'—seabird/gull; 'WF'—wildfowl; 'WD'—wader.
3. Migrant types: 'Migrant'—significantly migrant according to the tests carried out in Chapter 5 (Appendix 3a); 'Sedentary'—not significantly migrant; brackets indicate migrant types allocated based on previous knowledge rather than rigorous statistical testing of ring-recovery data.

Table II British & Irish wintering population (age differences)

					Breeding season tests													
Species[1]	Ecological grouping[2]	Are there winter immigrants from abroad?[3]	Number of adult records	Number of immature records	Mean breeding latitude of adults	Mean breeding latitude of immatures	Breeding latitude test result	Mean breeding longitude of adults	Mean breeding longitude of immatures	Breeding longitude test result	Median distance moved by adults (km)	Adult P5	Adult P95	Median distance moved by immatures (km)	Immature P5	Immature P95	Distance test result	Overall result
mutsu	WF	None or unknown	205	400	52.709	52.384	S~	-1.829	-1.468	S~	11	0	76	11	0	66.5	NS	S~
pifgo	WF	Yes	8	10	—	65.768	NT	—	-16.87	NT	—	—	—	1548	207	2534	NT	NT
whfgo	WF	Yes	1	3	—	—	NT	—	—	NT	—	—	—	—	—	—	NT	NT
cango	WF	None or unknown	9	4	—	—	NT	—	—	NT	—	—	—	—	—	—	NT	NT
wigeo	WF	Yes	75	40	64.742	62.439	S	55.602	51.791	NS	3752	1734	4828	3401	1414.5	4764	NS	S
gadwa	WF	Yes	5	10	—	51.886	NT	—	4.218	NT	—	—	—	303	0	1476	NT	S
teal	WF	Yes	163	42	62.416	62.532	NS	27.72	33.658	S	2022	510	3416	2123	989	3374	S	S
malla	WF	Yes	537	264	56.213	56.159	NS	12.306	11.747	NS	840	0	2236	788	0	2172	NS	NS
pinta	WF	Yes	36	11	64.115	64.738	NS	42.13	35.848	NS	3149.5	990	4153	2208	1472	3813	NS	NS*
pocha	WF	Yes	77	28	55.5	55.098	NS	35.732	34.498	NS	2134	329	4762	1943.5	355	4445	NS	NS*
tufdu	WF	Yes	140	107	59.315	58.889	NS	22.894	25.677	NS	1705.5	3.5	3923	1695	23	4152	NS	NS
eider	WF	None or unknown	60	33	57.313	57.235	NS	-2.084	-2.067	NS	1	0	79	1	0	80	NS	NS
sparr	RO	Yes	15	26	52.777	52.752	NS	-2.513	-2.202	NS~	3	0	29	4	0	49	NS	NS~
kestr	RO	Yes	11	4	52.795	—	NT	-1.141	—	NT	2	0	193	—	—	—	NT	NT
moorh	WF	Yes	49	25	52.974	52.652	NS~	-0.723	1.047	S	0	0	80	6	0	775	S	S*
oyste	WD	Yes	396	155	58.879	58.434	NS	-0.972	-1.227	NS	559	4	1610	579	0	1490	NS	NS
knot	WD	Yes	45	5	73.027	—	NT	-59.255	—	NT	3498	1630	4146	—	—	—	NT	NS*
dunli	WD	Yes	10	13	56.762	56.572	NS	12.741	14.126	NS	820.5	0	4076	729	171	3406	NS	NS*
snipe	WD	Yes	2	3	—	—	NT	—	—	NT	—	—	—	—	—	—	NT	NT
curle	WD	Yes	18	20	60.515	59.995	NS~	13.429	14.994	NS	1791	4	2238	1435	0	2370	NS	S*
redsh	WD	Yes	48	12	60.561	61.243	NS~	-12.254	-12.559	NS	1039.5	0	1851	1218.5	0	1720	NS	NS*~
blhgu	SG	Yes	812	819	57.474	57.474	NS	13.841	14.443	NS	1026.5	17	2144	1121	43	2101	NS	NS
comgu	SG	Yes	57	24	58.874	60.308	NS	12.283	14.23	NS	954	100	2087	1219.5	234	2169	NS	NS*
lbbgu	SG	Yes	119	19	55.332	54.368	S	-3.776	-2.865	NS	238	143	1772	232	86	1112	NS	NS*
hergu	SG	Yes	269	139	57.585	55.675	S	-0.019	-1.065	NS	111	3	2171	116	4	1503	NS	NS*
gbbgu	SG	Yes	24	10	64.208	61.874	NS	9.711	11.12	NS	1116.5	62	2381	1139	35	2078	NS	NS*~
woodp	PN	None or unknown	83	22	52.087	52.41	NS~	-0.556	-0.677	NS	6	0	47	12.5	0	47	NS	NS*~
coldo	PN	None or unknown	61	11	52.197	52.741	NS	-1.134	-1.75	NS	8	0	377	2	0	397	NS	NS*
grswo	PN	None or unknown	51	10	52.223	51.672	NS~	-1.31	-0.924	NS~	1	0	19	1	0	35	NS	NS*~
piewa	PN	None or unknown	105	172	52.664	52.382	NS~	-1.269	-1.475	NS~	4	0	466	7.5	0	507	S	S
wren	PN	None or unknown	21	4	52.355	—	NT	-0.434	—	NT	0	0	72	0	0	—	NT	NT
dunno	PN	None or unknown	441	104	52.473	52.535	NS	-1.12	-1.293	NS	0	0	4	0	0	3	NS	NS
robin	PN	Yes	369	79	52.314	52.659	NS	-1.196	-1.356	NS	0	0	8	0	0	46	NS	NS
blabi	PN	Yes	1947	1581	53.134	53.182	NS	-0.202	0.023	NS	0	0	825	0	0	837	S	S
field	PN	Yes	81	61	61.767	61.944	NS	15.983	17.588	NS~	1416	906	2078	1583	841	2181	NS	NS*~
sonth	PN	Yes	686	188	52.455	52.573	NS	-1.023	-0.829	NS	0	0	106	0	0	165	NS	NS
redwi	PN	Yes	188	27	59.684	60.046	NS	20.427	23.263	NS	1884	0	3661	1983	0	3986	NS	NS*
misth	PN	None or unknown	116	44	52.328	52.111	NS~	-1.02	-1.203	NT	0	0	24	0	0	13	NT	NS~
blaca	PN	Yes	2	0	—	—	NT	—	—	NT	—	—	—	—	—	—	NT	NT
coati	PN	None or unknown	54	25	52.407	52.749	NS~	-1.543	-0.985	NS~	0	0	10	0	0	6	NS	NS*~
bluti	PN	None or unknown	603	746	52.301	52.25	NS	-1.14	-1.162	NS	0	0	23	0	0	19	NS	NS
greti	PN	None or unknown	317	212	52.452	52.396	NS	-1.302	-1.319	NS	0	0	15	0	0	39	S	S
jay	PN	None or unknown	15	47	51.713	51.774	NS	-0.536	-0.876	NS~	1	0	28	0	0	56	NS	NS*~
jackd	PN	None or unknown	24	42	52.731	52.619	NS	-4.17	-2.946	NS	7	0	77	5.5	0	156	NS	NS*
rook	PN	Yes	22	38	54.041	53.103	S~	-2.378	-2.692	NS	6	0	13	4.5	0	146	NS	S*~
starl	PN	Yes	1505	3341	53.703	53.809	NS	2.666	3.536	S	6	0	1754	11	0	1789	S	S~
housp	PN	None or unknown	623	49	52.418	52.887	S~	-0.834	-0.486	NS~	0	0	15	0	0	57	S	S~
chaff	PN	Yes	395	269	53.706	54.437	S	0.425	0.991	NS	0	0	1356	3	0	1442	S	S
bramb	PN	Yes	4	7	—	—	NT	—	—	NT	—	—	—	—	—	—	NT	NT
grefi	PN	None or unknown	1877	1802	52.436	52.481	NS	-0.991	-0.976	NS	5	0	138	7	0	123	S	NS*~
goldf	PN	Yes	17	11	52.727	52.333	NS~	-1.035	-2.498	S	7	0	367	3	0	239	NS	S*
siski	PN	Yes	34	41	58.002	56.934	NS	2.669	-2.807	S	497.5	98	2246	98	4	1097	S	S*
linne	PN	None or unknown	47	12	52.787	52.788	NS	-0.528	-0.943	NS~	10	0	183	24.5	0	258	S	S*
bullf	PN	None or unknown	149	121	52.103	52.223	NS	-0.767	-0.839	NS	0	0	21	2	0	12	NS	NS
yelha	PN	None or unknown	75	36	52.986	52.999	NS	-1.424	-1.267	NS	0	0	38	2	0	52	NS	NS
reebu	PN	Yes	28	16	52.841	53.301	NS	-1.048	0.283	NS	2	0	94	4	0	1664	NS	NS*

continued

Table II *Continued*

Species[1]	Number of adult records	Number of immature records	Autumn tests						Overall result
			Mean autumn latitude of adults	Mean autumn latitude of immatures	Autumn latitude test result	Mean autumn longitude of adults	Mean autumn longitude of immatures	Autumn longitude test result	
mutsw	80	141	52.473	52.259	NS–	−1.689	−1.518	NS	NS–
pifgo	22	14	55.585	56.667	NS	−2.994	−3.411	NS	NS*
whfgo	23	28	55.89	57.884	NS	7.841	−3.48	S	S*
cango	18	12	51.98	52.983	NS–	−1.474	−2.482	S–	S*–
wigeo	260	215	55.993	56.5	NS	14.935	18.178	NS	NS
gadwa	49	43	50.594	51.259	NS	2.153	1.363	NS	NS
teal	1332	438	55.88	55.749	NS	11.319	11.526	NS–	NS–
malla	1158	514	54.46	54.465	NS	5.637	6.376	NS–	NS–
pinta	81	24	55.109	54.157	NS	10.27	11.049	NS	NS*
pocha	106	64	52.611	52.317	NS	12.93	13.696	NS	NS
tufdu	119	108	54.147	54.18	NS	6.545	7.312	NS	NS
eider	31	0	57.26	—	NT	−1.544	—	NT	NT
sparr	7	11	—	53.488	NT	—	−3.073	NT	NT
kestr	14	11	51.789	53.066	S	−0.519	−1.212	NS–	S*
moorh	9	4	—	—	NT	—	—	NT	NT
oyste	209	65	57.454	56.208	NS	−1.578	0.24	S	S
knot	70	10	53.85	53.405	NS	0.298	−0.747	NS–	NS*–
dunli	36	45	54.737	54.079	NS	9.556	11.587	NS	NS
snipe	22	27	54.825	55.306	NS	6.46	12.45	NS	NS*
curle	13	14	52.941	54.516	NS	−0.009	2.637	NS	NS*
redsh	61	11	56.171	55.966	NS	−5.545	−4.629	NS	NS*
blhgu	311	357	54.188	54.15	NS	6.316	6.111	NS	NS
comgu	30	16	59.173	56.254	S	10.163	4.929	S	S*
lbbgu	26	4	53.076	—	NT	−2.116	—	NT	NT
hergu	108	63	55.954	55.174	NS	−0.409	−0.017	NS	NS
gbbgu	19	6	59.123	—	NT	7.591	—	NT	NT
woodp	16	1	51.773	—	NT	−0.418	—	NT	NT
coldo	16	3	52.407	—	NT	−2.55	—	NT	NT
grswo	9	3	—	—	NT	—	—	NT	NT
piewa	14	11	53.299	52.112	NS	−1.616	−1.009	NS	NS*
wren	8	5	—	—	NT	—	—	NT	NT
dunno	45	20	52.351	52.587	NS–	−0.891	−0.878	NS	NS*–
robin	123	38	52.453	53.278	S–	−1.399	−1.704	NS–	S–
blabi	702	525	53.754	53.918	NS	1.174	1.458	NS	NS
field	29	19	49.732	49.663	NS	7.61	5.935	NS	NS*
sonth	85	34	51.985	51.958	NS	−0.854	−0.621	NS–	NS–
redwi	46	31	49.792	46.042	S	6.191	3.564	S	S
misth	23	6	52.072	—	NT	−0.75	—	NT	NT
blaca	0	0	—	—	NT	—	—	NT	NT
coati	21	5	52.71	—	NT	−1.33	—	NT	NT
bluti	200	203	52.157	52.362	NS–	−1.199	−1.381	NS	NS–
greti	107	57	52.531	52.128	NS–	−1.632	−1.552	NS	NS–
jay	9	20	—	51.946	NT	—	−1.236	NT	NT
jackd	6	5	—	—	NT	—	—	NT	NT
rook	4	17	—	53.37	NT	—	−2.872	NT	NT
starl	420	942	53.637	53.858	NS–	2.941	4.68	S	S
housp	135	14	52.507	53.569	S–	−0.796	−0.57	NS–	S*–
chaff	137	71	53.802	53.576	NS	4.28	1.389	S	S
bramb	15	12	51.976	51.451	NS	5.659	6.672	NS	NS*
grefi	197	224	52.512	52.408	NS	−1.161	−0.996	NS	NS
goldf	2	1	—	—	NT	—	—	NT	NT
siski	4	4	—	—	NT	—	—	NT	NT
linne	7	2	—	—	NT	—	—	NT	NT
bullf	8	6	—	—	NT	—	—	NT	NT
yelha	7	6	—	—	NT	—	—	NT	NT
reebu	6	1	—	—	NT	—	—	NT	NT

continued

Table II *Continued*

			Spring tests						
Species[1]	Number of adult records	Number of immature records	Mean spring latitude of adults	Mean spring latitude of immatures	Spring latitude test result	Mean spring longitude of adults	Mean spring longitude of immatures	Spring longitude test result	Overall result
mutsw	39	109	52.322	52.654	NS~	−0.571	−1.477	S	S
pifgo	1	4	—	—	NT	—	—	NT	NT
whfgo	13	12	59.582	61.714	NS	39.186	36.075	NS	NS
cango	4	2	—	—	NT	—	—	NT	NT
wigeo	58	43	60.196	59.925	NS~	47.975	42.477	NS	NS~
gadwa	2	0	—	—	NT	—	—	NT	NT
teal	97	24	54.024	51.242	S	11.542	8.042	NS	S
malla	123	63	53.669	53.317	NS~	3.266	3.666	NS~	NS~
pinta	17	4	61.809	—	NT	43.498	—	NT	NT
pocha	30	10	54.402	52.894	NS	22.582	25.433	NS	NS
tufdu	36	26	59.412	58.583	NS	26.597	27.186	NS	NS
eider	35	18	57.226	57.268	NS	−2.111	−2.049	NS	NS
sparr	18	40	53.162	52.485	NS~	−2.334	−1.871	NS~	NS~
kestr	10	10	51.962	53.108	NS~	−1.28	−0.367	NS~	NS~
moorh	17	25	52.792	52.673	NS	−0.434	−0.583	NS	NS
oyste	95	53	56.023	55.065	NS	−2.002	−2.903	NS	NS
knot	34	2	59.921	—	NT	−14.45	—	NT	NT
dunli	21	34	54.078	54.329	NS	3.284	5.239	NS	NS
snipe	1	2	—	—	NT	—	—	NT	NT
curle	10	7	57.351	—	NT	7.591	—	NT	NT
redsh	63	22	53.972	54.524	NS	−2.177	−1.514	NS	NS
blhgu	237	300	54.723	54.507	NS	8.317	7.034	NS	NS
comgu	23	17	58.194	56.751	S~	11.1	9.008	NS~	S~
lbbgu	9	3	—	—	NT	—	—	NT	NT
hergu	43	37	56.98	55.421	NS	−0.225	−1.632	NS	NS
gbbgu	9	4	—	—	NT	—	—	NT	NT
woodp	23	16	52.022	52.173	NS	−0.529	0.174	S~	S~
coldo	9	6	—	—	NT	—	—	NT	NT
grswo	8	3	—	—	NT	—	—	NT	NT
piewa	22	47	52.052	51.739	NS	−1.03	−1.051	NS	NS
wren	12	11	51.663	52.241	NS~	−0.967	−1.105	NS	NS~
dunno	48	35	52.87	52.755	NS	−1.46	−1.021	NS~	NS~
robin	173	84	52.469	53.033	S~	−1.213	−1.209	NS	S~
blabi	1350	1508	53.26	53.349	NS	0.115	0.211	NS	NS
field	12	15	52.842	53.682	NS	8.389	6.987	NS	NS
sonth	189	121	52.602	52.568	NS	−1.208	−0.709	S	S
redwi	47	45	50.894	51.509	NS	3.71	1.815	NS	NS
misth	16	6	—	—	NT	−1.482	—	NT	NT
blaca	10	13	51.999	50.96	NS	−2.323	−0.453	NS	NS
coati	27	40	53.08	53.105	NS	−1.831	−1.638	NS	NS
bluti	501	754	52.288	52.264	NS~	−1.158	−1.219	NS~	NS~
greti	150	147	52.448	52.377	NS	−1.372	−1.28	NS	NS
jay	2	17	—	52.188	NT	—	−0.753	NT	NT
jackd	5	6	—	—	NT	—	—	NT	NT
rook	2	6	—	—	NT	—	—	NT	NT
starl	195	682	53.357	53.38	NS	1.584	1.506	NS	NS
housp	70	13	52.178	52.374	NS	−0.477	−0.627	NS	NS
chaff	322	250	53.497	53.779	NS~	0.242	0.129	NS~	NS~
bramb	16	38	53.695	54.436	NS	4.463	4.834	NS	NS
grefi	866	1231	52.263	52.42	S~	−0.952	−1.016	NS	S~
goldf	6	6	—	—	NT	—	—	NT	NT
siski	90	131	54.037	54.531	NS~	−0.37	−1.954	S	S
linne	3	6	—	—	NT	—	—	NT	NT
bullf	26	43	52.4	52.15	NS~	−0.792	−1.072	NS~	NS~
yelha	18	13	53.214	53.193	NS	−1.621	−1.795	NS	NS
reebu	41	31	52.746	53.04	NS~	−0.314	−1.12	NS	NS~

Notes

1. See key in Appendix 2.
2. Ecological groupings: see Appendix 4a – Table I (above).
3. Winter immigrants: as defined in Chapter 5 and Appendix 6b.

This appendix gives the results of tests for differential migration patterns between the sexes. A sample of 10 records in each class was required for testing and only those species for which the sample was sufficient for at least one set of tests to be carried out are included here. Only recoveries for which the sex was known accurately were tested. For movements of the British & Irish breeding population (**Table I**), the tests compared the recovery locations in winter, autumn and spring of males and females ringed in Britain & Ireland during the breeding season. For the wintering population (**Table II**), the tests compared the recovery locations of males and females in the breeding season, autumn and spring for birds ringed in Britain & Ireland during the winter. Negative coordinates are locations south of the Equator for latitude or west of the Greenwich Meridian for longitude. Coordinates are given in decimal degrees. Full details of the methods are given in the *'Differential migration'* section of Chapter 4. Entries in the results columns follow those in Appendix 4a.

Table I British & Irish breeding population (sex differences)

Species[1]	Ecological grouping[2]	Migrant type[3]	Number of male records	Number of female records	Mean winter latitude of males	Mean winter latitude of females	Winter latitude test result	Mean winter longitude of males	Mean winter longitude of females	Winter longitude test result	Median distance moved by males (km)	Male P5	Male P95	Median distance moved by females (km)	Female P5	Female P95	Distance test result	Overall result
shag	SG	Migrant	11	12	56.27	55.71	NS	-2.579	-1.939	NS	43	5	169	95.5	19	685	NS	NS*
mutsw	WF	Sedentary	573	451	52.548	52.554	NS	-2.306	-2.225	NS	8	0	85	8	0	73	NS	NS
grego	WF	Sedentary	33	30	55.316	54.865	NS-	-4.514	-4.223	NS-	16	0	65	11	0	54	NS	NS-
cango	WF	Migrant	183	199	52.142	52.127	NS	-1.826	-1.93	NS	15	0	154	5	0	142	NS	NS
sheld	WF	Migrant	13	8	53.149	—	NT	0.435	—	NT	231	2	716	—	—	—	NT	NT
gadwa	WF	Migrant	7	12	—	49.752	NT	—	0.391	NT	—	—	—	312	6	1880	NT	NT
malla	WF	Sedentary	1376	712	52.339	52.573	S-	-0.665	-0.597	NS	26	0	318	17	0	320	S	S-
shove	WF	Migrant	20	9	45.983	—	NT	-2.327	—	NT	661.5	126.5	1953.5	—	—	—	NT	NT
pocha	WF	Migrant	51	12	50.438	50.9	NS	0.743	-2.903	S	297	7	1143	429	8	1301	NS	S*
tufdu	WF	Migrant	144	88	52.31	52.993	S-	-1.418	-2.588	NS-	246	11	628	253.5	0	981	NS	S-
eider	WF	Migrant	116	252	56.707	56.398	S-	-2.392	-2.27	NS	100	0	162	22.5	0	148	S	S-
henha	RO	Migrant	15	13	53.615	58.463	S	-3.452	-1.931	NS	406	0	1588	16	0	1312	S	S*
gosha	RO	[Sedentary]	3	4	—	—	NT	—	—	NT	—	—	—	—	—	—	NT	NT
sparr	RO	Sedentary	185	197	53.179	53.213	NS	-1.733	-1.829	NS	7	0	100	13	2	81	S	S
kestr	RO	Migrant	68	82	52.754	52.792	S-	-1.213	-1.311	NS	8	0	304	31	0	717	S	S-
merli	RO	Migrant	29	29	54.075	53.729	NS-	-2.149	-1.644	NS	122	5	856	126	21	461	NS	NS*-
pereg	RO	Sedentary	33	28	54.813	54.333	NS-	-3.64	-4.537	S	49	2	357	83	22	376	NS	S*
lbbgu	SG	Migrant	4	2	—	—	NT	—	—	NT	—	—	—	—	—	—	NT	NT
guil	SG	Migrant	13	10	54.734	54.808	NS	5.778	5.007	NS	777	121	953	833	565	1105	NS	NS*
barow	RO	Sedentary	49	72	53.26	53.265	NS	-2.491	-2.775	NS-	10	0	42	10	0	101	NS	NS-
swall	PN	Migrant	2	0	—	—	NT	—	—	NT	—	—	—	—	—	—	NT	NT
piewa	PN	Migrant	24	20	51.438	51.573	NS	-1.349	-0.501	NS	4	0	739	15.5	1	592	S	S*
dunno	PN	Sedentary	21	16	52.368	53.066	NS-	-1.307	-1.744	NS-	1	0	9	0.5	0	9	NS	NS*-
robin	PN	Sedentary	18	22	52.906	52.808	NS	-1.477	-1.333	NS	0	0	48	5.5	0	179	NS	NS*
blabi	PN	Migrant	552	321	52.535	52.578	NS	-1.08	-1.271	NS	0	0	11	1	0	27	NS	NS
sonth	PN	Migrant	25	17	51.859	51.564	NS-	-0.904	-0.5	NS-	2	0	529	1	0	1089	NS	NS*-
blaca	PN	Migrant	13	6	37.167	—	NT	-3.149	—	NT	1840	98	2022	—	—	—	NT	NT
bluti	PN	Sedentary	15	21	52.171	52.304	NS	-1.681	-1.34	NS-	2	0	23	2	0	27	NS	NS*-
greti	PN	Sedentary	24	26	52.495	52.906	NS-	-1.093	-1.928	NS-	2	0	13	1.5	0	43	NS	NS*-
starl	PN	Sedentary	316	242	52.527	52.676	NS	-1.01	-0.839	NS	0	0	47	0	0	109	NS	NS
housp	PN	Sedentary	131	80	52.315	52.253	NS	-0.913	-0.731	NS	0	0	4	0	0	6	NS	NS
chaff	PN	Sedentary	55	39	53.211	52.694	NS-	-1.697	-0.835	NS-	0	0	8	0	0	395	NS	NS-
grefi	PN	Sedentary	195	114	52.158	51.99	NS	-0.871	-1.062	NS	5	0	228	9.5	0	291	NS	NS
goldf	PN	Migrant	28	23	45.433	46.842	NS	-1.765	-2.107	NS	922.5	0	1382	876	1	1243	NS	NS*
linne	PN	Migrant	45	41	44.597	45.492	NS	-1.75	-1.277	NS	900	3	1747	889	5	1622	NS	NS
redpo	PN	Migrant	11	3	50.647	—	NT	2.205	—	NT	455	71	862	—	—	—	NT	NT
bullf	PN	Sedentary	158	81	52.161	52.00	NS	-0.746	-0.431	NS-	1	0	31	0	0	53	NS	NS-
reebu	PN	Sedentary	30	16	52.3	52.979	NS-	-1.626	-1.67	NS	2	0	75	2.5	0	247	NS	NS*-

continued

Table I *Continued*

Species[1]	Number of male records	Number of female records	Autumn tests						Overall result
			Mean autumn latitude of males	Mean autumn latitude of females	Autumn latitude test result	Mean autumn longitude of males	Mean autumn longitude of females	Autumn longitude test result	
shag	9	8	—	—	NT	—	—	NT	NT
mutsw	578	482	52.764	52.964	NS-	-2.084	-2.166	NS	NS-
grego	45	45	55.153	55.497	NS	-3.943	-4.981	NS	NS
cango	165	123	52.456	52.34	NS	-1.708	-1.714	NS	NS
sheld	11	10	53.759	53.407	NS	4.34	2.309	NS	NS
gadwa	16	28	49.854	52.432	S	1.672	0.172	NS	S
malla	942	589	52.773	52.591	NS	0.42	-0.019	NS	NS
shove	24	22	51.255	51.857	NS	2.625	1.129	NS	NS
pocha	31	19	51.251	50.517	NS	0.732	1.935	NS	NS
tufdu	106	112	53.356	53.713	S-	1.276	-0.547	NS	S-
eider	44	77	56.956	56.576	S-	1.354	-1.831	S	S-
henha	14	17	55.112	57.642	S	-1.66	-3.318	NS	S
gosha	13	18	53.071	52.7	NS-	-3.023	-2.564	NS-	NS-
sparr	281	402	53.157	53.454	S-	-1.888	-1.911	NS	S-
kestr	40	71	53.01	53.002	NS	-1.382	-0.883	NS	NS
merli	41	68	54.134	54.089	NS	-1.942	-1.914	NS	NS
pereg	34	41	54.45	55.042	NS	-3.748	-3.447	NS	NS
lbgu	11	12	50.411	52.828	NS	-5.212	-3.617	NS	NS
guill	3	4	—	—	NT	—	—	NT	NT
barow	0	0	—	—	NT	—	—	NT	NT
swall	12	20	44.421	52.588	NS	0.942	-1.711	NS	NS
piewa	9	2	—	—	NT	—	—	NT	NT
dunno	7	5	—	—	NT	—	—	NT	NT
robin	9	12	—	52.923	NT	—	—	NT	NT
blabi	445	317	52.454	52.579	NS	-0.992	-1.441	NS	NS
sonth	8	11	—	52.665	NT	—	-1.011	NT	NT
blaca	17	12	46.281	47.497	NS	-1.421	-1.297	NS-	NS
bluti	11	21	52.555	52.061	NS-	-0.921	-1.874	NS	NS-
greti	26	17	52.603	52.102	NS-	-1.1	-1.622	NS	NS-
starl	274	268	52.684	52.742	NS	-0.947	-1.092	NS	NS
housp	112	67	52.59	52.525	NS	-1.098	-0.956	NS	NS
chaff	32	20	52.892	53.881	NS	-1.532	-1.159	NS	NS
grefi	72	56	52.268	52.011	NS-	-1.307	-1.313	S-	S-
goldf	5	11	—	47.228	NT	—	-0.579	NT	NT
linne	29	38	46.417	45.391	NS	-1.625	-1.648	NS-	NS-
redpo	14	11	51.263	51.786	NS-	2.015	2.252	NS	NS-
bulf	16	18	51.88	52.309	NS-	-0.416	-0.571	NS	NS-
reebu	5	3	—	—	NT	—	—	NT	NT

continued

Table I *Continued*

Species[1]	Number of male records	Number of female records	Mean spring latitude of males	Mean spring latitude of females	Spring latitude test result	Mean spring longitude of males	Mean spring longitude of females	Spring longitude test result	Overall result
shag	34	35	56.942	56.873	NS	−2.526	−2.053	NS	NS
mutsw	238	205	52.58	52.608	NS	−2.263	−2.14	NS	NS
grego	6	1	—	—	NT	—	—	NT	NT
cango	26	10	52.082	52.271	NS	−1.246	−2.249	S	S*
sheld	3	4	—	—	NT	—	—	NT	NT
gadwa	0	0	—	—	NT	—	—	NT	NT
malla	52	61	53.194	52.293	S	4.262	−0.333	S	S
shove	2	3	—	—	NT	—	—	NT	NT
pocha	6	1	—	—	NT	—	—	NT	NT
tufdu	27	7	58.265	—	NT	29.187	—	NT	NT
eider	66	143	56.883	56.158	S−	−1.881	−1.956	NS	S−
henha	9	7	—	—	NT	—	—	NT	NT
gosha	5	5	—	—	NT	—	—	NT	NT
sparr	156	169	52.868	53.108	NS−	−1.662	−1.686	NS	NS−
kestr	36	21	52.653	51.712	NS	−1.248	−1.915	NS	NS*
merli	13	14	55.242	55.766	NS	−2.032	−2.262	NS	NS*
pereg	8	6	—	—	NT	—	—	NT	NT
lbbgu	1	4	—	—	NT	—	—	NT	NT
guill	8	9	—	—	NT	—	—	NT	NT
barow	0	0	—	—	NT	—	—	NT	NT
swall	16	22	50.088	50.236	NS	−1.943	0.564	S	S*
piewa	10	9	52.098	—	NT	−1.204	—	NT	NT
dunno	12	3	52.516	—	NT	−1.542	—	NT	NT
robin	10	8	52.657	—	NT	−0.502	—	NT	NT
blabi	637	423	52.53	52.531	NS	−1.162	−1.049	NS	NS
sonth	16	12	52.114	52.25	NS	−0.71	−1.619	NS−	NS*−
blaca	47	19	47.665	50.142	NS	−0.025	−1.749	NS	NS*
bluti	7	24	—	52.512	NT	—	−1.988	NT	NT
greti	30	13	52.526	53.127	NS−	−1.7	−1.575	NS	NS*−
starl	135	94	52.393	52.431	NS	−0.836	−1.04	NS−	NS−
housp	42	23	52.177	52.286	NS	−0.214	−0.439	NS−	NS*−
chaff	81	54	52.456	52.409	NS	−1.593	−2.052	NS−	NS−
grefi	142	72	52.115	52.108	NS	−0.866	−1.034	NS	NS
goldf	9	6	—	—	NT	—	—	NT	NT
linne	17	14	51.242	51.045	NS	−0.552	−0.624	NS	NS*
redpo	5	3	—	—	NT	—	—	NT	NT
bullf	44	23	51.869	51.949	NS	−0.462	−0.678	NS−	NS*−
reebu	33	21	51.938	52.127	NS	−1.388	−0.953	NS−	NS*−

Notes
1. See key in Appendix 2.
2. Ecological groupings used in the synthesis of differential movements in Chapter 5: 'PN'—passerine/near-passerine; 'RO'—raptor/owl; 'SG'—seabird/gull; 'WF'—wildfowl; 'WD'—wader.
3. Migrant types: 'Migrant'—significantly migrant according to the tests carried out in Chapter 5 (Appendix 3a); 'Sedentary'—not significantly migrant; brackets indicate migrant types allocated based on previous knowledge rather than rigorous statistical testing of ring-recovery data.

Table II British & Irish wintering population (sex differences)

Species[1]	Ecological grouping[2]	Are there winter immigrants from abroad?[3]	Number of male records	Number of female records	Mean breeding latitude of males	Mean breeding latitude of females	Breeding latitude test result	Mean breeding longitude of males	Mean breeding longitude of females	Breeding longitude test result	Median distance moved by males (km)	Male P5	Male P95	Median distance moved by females (km)	Female P5	Female P95	Distance test result	Overall result
mutsw	WF	None or unknown	159	128	52.723	52.578	NS	−2.06	−1.927	NS	9	0	61	13	0	77	NS	NS
whosw	WF	Yes	14	12	64.361	64.865	NS	−17.844	−17.383	NS−	1432	0	1748	1364	1222	1743	NS	NS*−
pifgo	WF	Yes	11	11	63.899	66.378	NS	−15.189	−18.837	NS	1397	0	1645	1541	1189	2534	NS	NS*
whfgo	WF	Yes	2	3	—	—	NT	—	—	NT	—	—	—	—	—	—	NT	NT
bargo	WF	Yes	7	2	—	—	NT	—	—	NT	—	—	—	—	—	—	NT	NT
sheld	WF	Yes	8	6	—	—	NT	—	—	NT	—	—	—	—	—	—	NT	NT
wigeo	WF	Yes	85	28	64.107	63.251	NS	57.434	47.476	S	3811	1734	4531	3043.5	1655	4878	S	S*
gadwa	WF	Yes	8	6	—	—	NT	—	—	NT	—	—	—	—	—	—	NT	NT
teal	WF	Yes	126	75	62.808	61.795	NS	28.933	29.98	NS	2050	510	3374	2085	510	3603	NS	NS
malla	WF	Yes	447	378	55.464	57.068	S	10.273	14.376	S	697	0	2131	1190.5	0	2195	S	S
pinta	WF	Yes	30	17	63.957	64.797	NS	44.359	33.985	NS	3366.5	990	4114	2225	1746	4264	NS	NS*
pocha	WF	Yes	69	36	56.252	53.749	S	39.429	27.884	S	2587	618	4728	1784	322	4165	S	S
tufdu	WF	Yes	149	91	59.339	58.484	NS	25.322	20.639	NS	1809	10	4085	1575	1	4026	NS	NS
eider	WF	None or unknown	64	38	57.275	57.306	NS	−2.076	−2.071	NS	1	0	73	0	0	114	NS	NS
sparr	RO	Yes	26	14	52.652	52.955	NS−	−2.415	−1.685	NS−	4	0	28	4.5	0	49	NS	NS*−
blhgu	SG	Yes	22	18	55.806	54.729	NS	11.332	10.377	NS	965	137	1718	902	43	1992	NS	NS*
grswo	PN	None or unknown	32	26	51.987	52.229	NS−	−1.077	−1.377	NS−	0	0	13	0	0	39	NS	NS*−
piewa	PN	None or unknown	92	79	52.369	52.363	NS−	−1.451	−1.352	NS	5.5	0	528	7	0	637	NS	NS
blabi	PN	Yes	2008	1405	53.173	53.145	NS	−0.136	−0.001	NS	0	0	869	0	0	817	S	S
field	PN	Yes	48	66	61.955	61.592	NS	15.771	17.119	NS	1473.5	797	2245	1566.5	783	2135	NT	NT
blaca	PN	Yes	1	1	—	—	NT	—	—	NT	—	—	—	—	—	—	NT	NT
bluti	PN	None or unknown	110	101	52.183	52.035	NS	−0.953	−0.801	NS	0	0	7	0	0	41	NS	NS
greti	PN	None or unknown	226	203	52.46	52.386	NS	−1.276	−1.281	NS	0	0	15	0	0	32	NS	NS
starl	PN	Yes	2437	1996	53.845	53.666	NS−	3.368	2.918	NS	7	0	1823	10	0	1704	NS	NS−
housp	PN	None or unknown	372	276	52.499	52.433	NS	−0.852	−0.758	NS−	0	0	15	0	0	21	NS	NS−
chaff	PN	Yes	394	257	54.021	54.055	NS	0.611	0.872	NS	2	0	1275	2	0	1696	NT	NT
bramb	PN	Yes	9	1	—	—	NT	—	—	NT	—	—	—	—	—	—	NT	NT
grefi	PN	Yes	2107	1430	52.494	52.417	NS	−0.994	−0.957	NS	6	0	128	6	0	140	NS	NS
siski	PN	Yes	50	23	57.533	57.152	NS−	0.678	−2.227	NS	260.5	0	2147	490	0	1363	NS	NS*−
linne	PN	None or unknown	39	18	52.898	52.537	NS−	−0.329	−0.972	NS	10	0	261	20	0	258	NS	NS*−
bullf	PN	None or unknown	178	89	52.141	52.207	NS	−0.741	−0.941	NS−	0	0	14	0	0	11	NS	NS−
yelha	PN	None or unknown	55	35	53.01	52.625	NS−	−1.136	−1.3	NS	2	0	52	2	0	47	NS	NS−
reebu	PN	Yes	30	12	52.646	53.978	S	−0.881	0.362	NS	2	0	163	29	0	1664	S	S*

continued

Table II *Continued*

Species[1]	Number of male records	Number of female records	Autumn tests						Overall result
			Mean autumn latitude of males	Mean autumn latitude of females	Autumn latitude test result	Mean autumn longitude of males	Mean autumn longitude of females	Autumn longitude test result	
mutsw	50	44	52.329	52.718	NS~	−1.794	−1.992	NS	NS~
whosw	7	4	—	—	NT	—	—	NT	NT
pifgo	18	15	55.852	56.854	NS	−2.699	−4.55	NS	NS*
whfgo	32	20	56.816	58.058	NS	1.149	2.681	NS	NS*
bargo	20	14	62.851	60.177	NS	−12.07	−12.314	NS	NT
sheld	9	4	—	—	NT	—	—	NT	NT
wigeo	283	185	55.481	57.386	S	12.674	22.41	S	S
gadwa	61	28	50.473	52.031	S	1.987	1.489	NS	S*
teal	1032	663	55.283	56.84	S	10.352	13.564	S	S
malla	969	728	54.093	54.938	S	4.818	7.409	S	S
pinta	49	54	54.372	54.983	NS	8.991	11.45	NS	NS
pocha	114	55	52.733	52.027	NS	15.033	9.703	NS	NS
tufdu	128	92	53.915	54.619	NS	5.553	8.741	NS	NS*
eider	22	11	57.226	57.341	NS	−1.357	−2.00	NS	NS*
sparr	9	7	—	—	NT	—	—	NT	NT
blhgu	6	6	—	—	NT	—	—	NT	NT
grswo	4	7	—	—	NT	—	—	NT	NT
piewa	15	1	52.763	—	NT	−1.466	—	NT	NT
blabi	690	500	53.914	53.692	NS~	1.257	1.325	NS	NS~
field	18	17	49.343	49.451	NS	5.709	7.544	NS	NS*
blaca	0	0	—	—	NT	—	—	NT	NT
bluti	14	28	52.649	52.275	NS~	−1.287	−1.356	NS	NS*~
greti	75	47	52.438	52.347	NS	−1.692	−1.88	NS	NS
starl	712	515	53.603	53.985	S~	3.546	3.575	NS	S~
housp	83	59	52.411	52.773	NS~	−0.688	−0.769	NS	NS~
chaff	138	61	53.75	53.814	NS	2.996	3.979	NS	NS
bramb	15	9	51.905	—	NT	6.861	—	NT	NT
grefi	214	187	52.486	52.427	NS	−1.211	−0.885	S~	S~
siski	2	6	—	—	NT	—	—	NT	NT
linne	1	6	—	—	NT	—	—	NT	NT
bullf	8	6	—	—	NT	—	—	NT	NT
yelha	7	4	—	—	NT	—	—	NT	NT
reebu	7	0	—	—	NT	—	—	NT	NT

continued

Table II *Continued*

Species[1]	Number of male records	Number of female records	Mean spring latitude of males	Mean spring latitude of females	Spring latitude test result	Mean spring longitude of males	Mean spring longitude of females	Spring longitude test result	Overall result
					Spring tests				
mutsw	34	35	52.707	53.04	NS-	-1.879	-1.763	NS	NS-
whosw	8	16	—	62.802	NT	—	-13.56	NT	NT
pifgo	1	2	—	—	NT	—	—	NT	NT
whfgo	10	17	58.717	58.281	NS	25.685	33.729	NS	NS*
bargo	9	5	—	—	NT	—	—	NT	NT
sheld	15	11	55.784	55.506	NS-	-0.734	-1.31	NS-	NS*~
wigeo	83	29	59.845	60.37	NS	46.988	41.367	NS	NS*
gadwa	1	1	—	—	NT	—	—	NT	NT
teal	83	63	54.597	52.944	NS	14.819	8.295	S	S
malla	139	104	53.65	53.361	NS	4.97	2.105	S	S
pinta	20	3	61.359	—	NT	46.354	—	NT	NT
pocha	37	4	54.086	—	NT	23.705	—	NT	NT
tufdu	46	24	59.21	58.577	NS	28.738	23.132	NS	NS*
eider	39	24	57.202	57.348	NS	-2.122	-1.997	NS	NS*
sparr	46	15	52.794	52.245	NS-	-2.121	-1.566	NS-	NS*~
blhgu	3	4	—	—	NT	—	—	NT	NT
grswo	11	9	52.858	—	NT	-1.556	—	NT	NT
piewa	27	20	51.76	51.595	NS	-1.292	-0.945	NS-	NS*~
blabi	1896	1198	53.332	53.255	NS	0.173	0.264	NS	NS
field	11	19	53.536	52.787	NS-	4.75	5.442	NS-	NS*~
blaca	15	14	51.529	51.111	NS-	-1.647	-0.137	NS-	NS*~
bluti	129	101	52.09	52.416	S-	-0.837	-1.009	NS	S~
greti	201	95	52.439	52.41	NS	-1.361	-1.389	NS	NS
starl	680	444	53.419	53.335	NS	1.192	1.127	NS	NS
housp	86	57	52.36	52.514	NS	-0.673	-0.514	NS	NS
chaff	390	261	53.66	53.351	NS	0.143	0.043	NS	NS
bramb	36	21	54.533	52.848	NS	5.602	2.44	NS	NS*
grefi	1457	881	52.347	52.297	NS	-0.962	-0.99	NS	NS
siski	143	90	54.417	53.783	NS	-1.019	-1.823	NS	NS
linne	9	3	—	—	NT	—	—	NT	NT
bullf	53	29	52.111	52.276	NS	-0.819	-1.056	NS-	NS*~
yelha	28	10	53.08	53.622	NS-	-1.719	-1.304	NS-	NS*~
reebu	73	27	52.865	52.619	NS-	-0.552	-1.127	NS	NS*~

Notes
1. See key in Appendix 2.
2. Ecological groupings: see Appendix 4a—Table I (above).
3. Winter immigrants: as defined in Chapter 5 and Appendix 6b.

Appendix 4c
Dual effects of age and sex on movement patterns

In the analyses presented in this book, the effects of age and sex on movement patterns were considered separately, to give the maximum possible sample sizes for each test. To assess whether the effects of age and sex were confounded in the results, statistical tests were carried out to compare the frequencies of the different sex and age (immature or adult at ringing) classes. For a test to be carried out, a minimum of five records in each age-by-sex class was required. If a test result was 'significant', then the effects of age and sex on movement patterns may be confounded and the results of the separate tests for age classes and sexes (Appendix 4a and b) should be interpreted with caution. The methods are explained in the *'Biases caused by the confounding of age and sex effects'* section of Chapter 4 and the results of the tests are flagged after the titles **'age differences'** and **'sex differences'** in the **statistical analyses** table in each main species account (see Chapter 6). For the age

difference tests, the percentage of each age class that was female is given and the outcome of the chi-squared test is given under **'age test result'**. For the sex difference tests, the percentage of each sex that was adult and the **'sex test result'** are given. The test results are coded as follows:-

S   Significant at P<0.05 and a sample of at least 30 in each of the four classes;

S*   Significant at P<0.05 but a sample of <30 in at least one class;

NS   Not significant and a sample of at least 30 in each class;

NS*   Not significant but a sample of <30 in at least one class;

NT   Not tested due to insufficient records (<5 in at least one class);

(NS)   Not tested (as above) but no significant confounding effect likely because the majority of records come from only one sex or age class for the age and sex tests respectively (see methods in Chapter 4).

Species*	Number of adult records	Number of immature records	% of adults that were female	% of immatures that were female	Age test result	Number of male records	Number of female records	% of females that were adult	% of males that were adult	Sex test result
cormo	14	24	42.9	41.7	NS*	22	16	37.5	36.4	NS*
shag	328	19	47.6	47.4	NS*	182	165	94.5	94.5	NS*
mutsw	2804	1899	45.5	47.1	NS	2534	2169	58.8	60.3	NS
grego	96	43	50.0	44.2	NS*	72	67	71.6	66.7	NS*
cango	390	148	45.9	49.3	NS	286	252	71.0	73.8	NS
sheld	74	22	44.6	72.7	S*	47	49	67.3	87.2	S*
gadwa	51	24	66.7	54.2	NS*	28	47	72.3	60.7	NS*
malla	3288	1534	35.0	41.7	S	3032	1790	64.2	70.5	S
pinta	23	13	43.5	46.2	NS*	20	16	62.5	65.0	NS*
shove	67	32	37.3	56.3	NS*	56	43	58.1	75.0	NS*
pocha	154	4	27.3	0.0	NT	116	42	100.0	96.6	(NS)
tufdu	518	153	42.5	45.1	NS	382	289	76.1	78.0	NS
eider	1673	231	80.6	55.8	S	427	1477	91.3	76.1	S
goosa	25	18	76.0	50.0	NS*	15	28	67.9	40.0	NS*
henha	61	133	60.7	48.9	NS*	92	102	36.3	26.1	NS*
gosha	23	65	56.5	50.8	NS*	42	46	28.3	23.8	NS*
sparr	839	1223	52.9	55.8	NS	936	1126	39.4	42.2	NS
buzza	6	29	50.0	41.4	NT	20	15	20.0	15.0	(NS)*
kestr	305	194	39.3	73.2	S	237	262	45.8	78.1	S
merli	110	181	65.5	61.3	NS	108	183	39.3	35.2	NS
pereg	144	163	54.2	48.5	NS	150	157	49.7	44.0	NS
rinpl	45	0	40.0	NONE	NT	27	18	100.0	100.0	(NS)*
blhgu	28	1	46.4	100.0	NT	15	14	92.9	100.0	(NS)*
lbbgu	137	7	45.3	57.1	NT	78	66	93.9	96.2	(NS)
hergu	154	10	54.5	50.0	NS*	75	89	94.4	93.3	NS*

Continued

Species*	Number of adult records	Number of immature records	% of adults that were female	% of immatures that were female	Age test result	Number of male records	Number of female records	% of females that were adult	% of males that were adult	Sex test result
guill	3	47	33.3	48.9	NT	26	24	4.2	7.7	(NS)*
woodp	25	0	56.0	NONE	NT	11	14	100.0	100.0	(NS)*
barow	165	133	60.0	56.4	NS	124	174	56.9	53.2	NS
tawow	73	3	71.2	66.7	NT	22	54	96.3	95.5	(NS)*
kingf	55	36	36.4	22.2	NS*	63	28	71.4	55.6	NS*
grswo	54	1	42.6	0.0	NT	32	23	100.0	96.9	(NS)*
sanma	62	0	51.6	NONE	NT	30	32	100.0	100.0	(NS)
swall	257	2	58.8	50.0	NT	107	152	99.3	99.1	(NS)
houma	65	0	53.8	NONE	NT	30	35	100.0	100.0	(NS)
yelwa	25	3	36.0	0.0	NT	19	9	100.0	84.2	NT
piewa	180	14	43.9	35.7	NS*	110	84	94.0	91.8	NS*
wren	48	4	62.5	0.0	NT	22	30	100.0	81.8	(NS)*
dunno	178	0	36.5	NONE	NT	113	65	100.0	100.0	(NS)
robin	128	3	53.1	0.0	NT	63	68	100.0	95.2	(NS)
blabi	4607	929	37.9	44.9	S	3373	2163	80.7	84.8	S
sonth	184	1	47.3	0.0	NT	98	87	100.0	99.0	(NS)
misth	45	1	57.8	0.0	NT	20	26	100.0	95.0	(NS)*
reewa	38	0	42.1	NONE	NT	22	16	100.0	100.0	(NS)*
white	49	2	59.2	0.0	NT	22	29	100.0	90.9	(NS)*
blaca	186	45	46.2	31.1	NS*	131	100	86.0	76.3	NS*
wilwa	53	9	39.6	22.2	NT	39	23	91.3	82.1	(NS)*
piefl	205	10	61.0	40.0	NT	86	129	96.9	93.0	(NS)
bluti	193	11	75.1	45.5	S*	54	150	96.7	88.9	S*
greti	290	38	45.9	36.8	NS*	181	147	90.5	86.7	NS*
jackd	44	0	59.1	NONE	NT	18	26	100.0	100.0	(NS)*
rook	42	1	61.9	100.0	NT	16	27	96.3	100.0	(NS)*
starl	3091	518	46.5	56.2	S	1881	1728	83.2	87.9	S
housp	1331	63	40.0	33.3	NS*	841	553	96.2	95.0	NS*
chaff	463	58	45.1	44.8	NS*	286	235	88.9	88.8	NS*
grefi	1360	182	37.8	40.7	NS	954	588	87.4	88.7	NS
goldf	168	15	45.8	46.7	NS*	99	84	91.7	91.9	NS*
siski	70	3	35.7	66.7	NT	46	27	92.6	97.8	(NS)*
linne	356	79	43.3	45.6	NS	245	190	81.1	82.4	NS
redpo	96	3	33.3	0.0	NT	67	32	100.0	95.5	(NS)
bullf	706	115	30.0	47.0	S	555	266	79.7	89.0	S
yelha	76	6	30.3	16.7	NT	58	24	95.8	91.4	(NS)*
reebu	156	19	41.0	31.6	NS*	105	70	91.4	87.6	NS*

* See key in Appendix 2.

Appendix 5a
Comparisons of the movement patterns of birds present in different regions of Britain & Ireland: British & Irish breeding populations

This appendix gives the results of tests for differences in the movements of birds present in the standard regions of Britain & Ireland[1] used throughout the book (see *'Definition of geographical regions'* section of Chapter 4) for birds ringed in Britain & Ireland during the breeding season and recovered in winter. Terrestrial species (**Table I**) and seabirds (**Table II**) are listed separately because the geographical region definitions differed between these groups of species. Details of the testing methods are given in the *'Differential movements of regional subpopulations'* section of Chapter 4. Only regions with at least 10 appropriate recoveries could be included in the tests for any given species. The median distances moved between breeding season ringing locations and winter recovery locations and the 5th (**'P5'**) and 95th (**'P95'**) percentiles, are given for each region. The mean latitudes and longitudes for winter recoveries from each breeding region are also shown. Negative values for coordinates indicate locations south of the Equator for latitude or west of the Greenwich Meridian for longitude. Coordinates are given in decimal degrees. The results of tests between regions for distances, latitude and longitude are coded as follows:-

S significant ($P<0.05$);

S* significant but based on a sample of <30 recoveries for at least one region;

NS not significant ($P>0.05$);

NS* not significant but based on a sample of <30 recoveries for at least one region.

The **'overall result'** column is coded as above, and indicates whether the movement patterns of the species differed significantly between one or more regions. For sedentary species, the overall result is only coded as significant if the distance test result was significant (because the tests of latitude and longitude were not appropriate for these species, see Chapters 4 and 5). For species that move between breeding and wintering areas (Short-distance and Long-distance Migrants), the overall result is significant if any one of the three test results (distance, latitude or longitude) was significant.

Table I Terrestrial species

| Species[2] | Migrant type | Number of regions tested | Number of records for each region[1] | | | | | Distance tests | | | | | | | | | | | | | | | Distance test result |
			NE	NW	SE	SW	I	NE median distance (km)	NE P5	NE P95	NW median distance (km)	NW P5	NW P95	SE median distance (km)	SE P5	SE P95	SW median distance (km)	SW P5	SW P95	I median distance (km)	I P5	I P95	
grehe	Sedentary	5	55	64	233	88	22	38	0	242	62.5	3	245	49	0	336	28	0	171	33	3	242	S*
mutsw	Sedentary	5	200	107	640	1027	23	33.5	0	127.5	11	0	93	11	0	54	9	0	60	25	0	127.5	S*
grego	Sedentary	2	<10	63	40	<10	<10	—	—	—	17	0	179	10.5	0	37.5	—	—	—	—	—	—	S*
cango	Short-distance migrant	4	45	368	653	836	<10	0	0	36	24	0	529	13	0	86	7	0	106	—	—	—	S
malla	Sedentary	5	143	88	1746	353	162	0	0	139	9.5	0	135	23	0	346	13	0	291	21.5	0	139	S
sparr	Sedentary	5	39	114	236	112	21	14	1	89	25.5	0	189	8	0	52	10	0	57	6	0	89	S*
kestr	Short-distance migrant	5	88	208	297	259	11	61.5	0	876	126.5	2	700	26	7	343	34	0	666	32	0	876	S*
lapwi	Long-distance migrant	4	80	348	108	163	<10	697.5	50	1976	435	12	1642	585	7	1671	580	0	1649	—	—	—	S
snipe	Short-distance migrant	3	<10	19	18	24	<10	—	—	—	300	0	817	259	0	1291	292	0	581	—	—	—	NS*
woodc	Short-distance migrant	5	92	109	33	30	13	13.5	0	1018	9	0	578	13	0	566	15	0	553	0	0	1018	NS*
curle	Short-distance migrant	4	34	103	15	27	<10	370	0	776	319	13	639	7	0	601	327	14	640	—	—	—	S*
blhgu	Short-distance migrant	5	112	373	359	217	73	162.5	11	1404	105	11	534	113	6	1323	108	11	1263	82	5	1404	NS
lbbgu	Long-distance migrant	4	123	309	17	197	<10	2098	182	3207	1701	24	2892	1803	103	2946	1376	230	2386	—	—	—	NS*
hergu	Short-distance migrant	5	354	271	12	273	67	75	3	617	85	4	409	53	0	484	83	7	378	34	0	617	S
woodp	Sedentary	4	81	54	321	97	<10	8	0	97	27	0	196	11	0	177	17	0	320	—	—	—	S
barow	Sedentary	4	39	280	444	439	<10	8	0	135	13	0	98.5	11	0	108	12	0	113	—	—	—	NS
tawow	Sedentary	4	27	55	61	110	<10	6	0	41	6	0	57	3	0	15	4	0	26	—	—	—	S*
swall	Long-distance migrant	2	<10	<10	18	19	<10	—	—	—	—	—	—	9577	5416	9835	9691	571	10092	—	—	—	NS*
meapi	Long-distance migrant	3	17	<10	15	15	<10	2045	0	2609	—	—	—	1459	0	1736	1605	274	2016	—	—	—	S*
piewa	Long-distance migrant	4	43	42	153	69	<10	545	8	1962	543	4	1734	9	0	1494	38	0	1772	—	—	—	S
wren	Sedentary	3	10	<10	67	27	<10	1	0	280	—	—	—	0	0	140	1	0	138	—	—	—	NS*
dunno	Sedentary	4	22	16	195	80	<10	0	0	9	0	0	44	0	0	9	0	0	9.5	—	—	—	NS*
robin	Sedentary	5	38	44	340	155	13	0	0	217	5.5	0	293	0	0	49	0	0	78	0	0	217	S*
blabi	Short-distance migrant	5	150	107	905	333	30	0	0	111	0	0	446	0	0	16	0	0	12	0	0	111	S
sonth	Short-distance migrant	4	80	97	573	206	<10	14.5	0	1043	196	0	584	4	0	826	5	0	540	—	—	—	S
bluti	Sedentary	4	30	44	364	181	<10	2	0	61	6	0	48	2	0	36	1	0	29	—	—	—	NS*
greti	Sedentary	4	18	26	180	80	<10	4	0	44	6	0	40	2	0	37.5	2	0	40	—	—	—	S*
jackd	Sedentary	5	14	10	52	24	13	4	0	45	12.5	0	168	3.5	0	185	5.5	0	105	7	0	45	NS*
rook	Sedentary	3	21	<10	43	17	<10	8	0	54	—	—	—	9	0	47	11	0	147	—	—	—	NS*
crow	Sedentary	5	23	26	47	43	17	5	0	46	5	0	30	6	0	22	5	0	28	7	0	46	NS*
starl	Sedentary	5	120	79	905	303	26	4	0	284.5	5	0	225	2	0	116	0	0	139	0	0	284.5	S*
housp	Sedentary	4	22	13	244	75	<10	0	0	4	0	0	35	0	0	7	0	0	6	—	—	—	NS*
chaff	Sedentary	4	10	29	88	24	<10	1.5	0	17	0	0	15	0	0	33	0	0	28	—	—	—	NS*
grefi	Sedentary	4	20	24	267	68	<10	4.5	0	55	4.5	0	186	9	0	245	2	0	158	—	—	—	S*
linne	Long-distance migrant	3	19	<10	130	42	<10	1234	0	1628	—	—	—	880.5	7	1733	879.5	5	1428	—	—	—	NS*

continued

Table 1 *Continued*

	Latitude tests						Longitude tests						
Species[2]	NE mean winter latitude	NW mean winter latitude	SE mean winter latitude	SW mean winter latitude	I mean winter latitude	Winter latitude test result	NE mean winter longitude	NW mean winter longitude	SE mean winter longitude	SW mean winter longitude	I mean winter longitude	Winter longitude test result	Overall result
grehe	55.85	55.483	51.888	52.979	54.363	S*	−3.345	−3.285	−0.179	−2.182	−6.679	S*	S*
mutsw	56.2	55.351	51.889	51.599	52.932	S*	−2.635	−4.241	−0.586	−2.296	−7.157	S*	S*
grego	—	56.0	51.837	—	—	S*	—	−5.319	−0.016	—	—	S*	S*
cango	54.09	54.119	52.322	52.484	—	S	−1.064	−1.901	−0.308	−2.151	—	S	S
malla	56.33	55.076	52.172	51.999	53.188	S	−3.036	−3.227	0.378	−2.328	−7.032	S	S
sparr	56.25	55.096	51.972	53.045	54.072	S*	−2.51	−3.145	−0.67	−2.315	−6.215	S*	S*
kestr	55.74	53.668	51.814	52.085	52.793	S*	−1.825	−2.079	−0.478	−1.815	−7.187	S*	S*
lapwi	49.32	50.476	46.232	47.542	—	S	−5.616	−5.488	−2.789	−4.075	—	S	S
snipe	—	53.75	49.739	52.406	—	S*	—	−7.022	−3.013	−5.414	—	S*	S*
woodc	54.64	54.492	52.205	52.504	54.314	S*	−4.155	−4.539	−1.55	−3.512	−7.471	S*	S*
curle	55.24	53.376	52.131	51.236	—	S	−5.934	−6.213	0.753	−4.31	—	S	S
blhgu	54.21	53.552	50.918	51.637	53.452	S	−4.232	−3.537	−1.515	−3.451	−6.855	S	S
lbbgu	38.95	41.896	38.462	40.047	—	S*	−6.558	−6.066	−5.391	−6.785	—	NS*	S*
hergu	55.55	54.536	51.222	52.216	53.797	S*	−2.264	−3.734	0.756	−3.634	−6.176	S*	S*
woodp	55.89	55.425	51.976	52.28	—	S	−2.313	−3.505	−0.289	−2.475	—	S	NS
barow	55.35	54.939	52.288	52.237	—	S	−1.766	−3.611	−0.288	−2.706	—	S	S*
tawow	56.09	55.654	52.336	53.003	—	S*	−2.455	−3.286	−0.381	−2.254	—	S*	NS*
swall	—	—	−28.788	−24.324	—	NS*	—	—	25.137	25.524	—	NS*	NS*
meapi	40.87	—	42.214	39.341	—	NS*	−5.581	—	−4.081	−6.434	—	NS*	S
piewa	51.28	49.761	50.516	47.912	—	S	−2.456	−3.224	−0.81	−4.02	—	S	S
wren	56.27	—	51.935	52.188	—	S*	−2.327	—	−0.209	−2.305	—	S*	NS*
dunno	54.95	55.012	52.065	52.063	53.688	S*	−1.829	−3.078	−0.102	−2.452	—	S*	NS*
robin	55.41	54.739	51.956	51.984	54.074	S	−2.259	−3.201	−0.255	−2.602	−6.381	S*	S
blabi	56.0	54.741	51.933	52.435	—	S	−2.342	−4.614	−0.298	−2.517	−6.339	S	S
sonth	54.4	53.41	51.146	51.936	—	S	−3.841	−5.519	−0.703	−3.04	—	S	S
bluti	55.36	55.053	51.947	52.142	—	S*	−2.07	−2.922	−0.511	−2.569	—	S*	S
greti	55.85	55.246	51.887	52.092	—	S*	−2.406	−3.245	−0.584	−2.513	—	S*	S*
jackd	55.85	55.204	51.681	52.341	53.824	S*	−2.441	−3.675	−0.196	−2.819	−6.359	S*	NS*
rook	57.12	—	51.848	51.649	—	S*	−2.188	—	−0.251	−2.888	—	S*	NS*
crow	58.68	54.989	51.989	52.42	54.339	S*	−1.994	−3.259	−0.558	−2.852	−5.952	S*	NS*
starl	56.41	55.174	51.929	52.92	54.452	S*	−2.108	−3.347	−0.229	−2.232	−5.980	S*	S*
housp	56.13	55.322	51.805	52.613	—	S*	−1.997	−3.06	−0.184	−2.54	—	S*	NS*
chaff	56.74	55.285	51.941	52.097	—	S*	−2.794	−3.269	−0.172	−2.403	—	S*	NS*
grefi	56.13	55.228	51.755	52.024	—	S*	−2.449	−3.118	−0.331	−2.529	—	S*	S*
linne	47.66	—	45.061	45.789	—	NS*	−2.404	—	−1.262	−2.252	—	S*	S*

Table II Seabirds

Species[2]	Migrant type	Number of regions tested	Number of records for each region[1]					Distance tests															Distance test result
			NE	NW	N	SW	SE	NE median distance (km)	NE P5	NE P95	NW median distance (km)	NW P5	NW P95	N median distance (km)	N P5	N P95	SW median distance (km)	SW P5	SW P95	SE median distance (km)	SE P5	SE P95	
fulma	Short-distance migrant	3	15	11	84	<10	<10	636	7	3253	478	0	3379	447	4	1816	—	—	—	—	—	—	NS*
ganne	Long-distance migrant	4	208	73	17	89	<10	822.5	33	4282	1480	260	4469	1689	89	4942	767	89	3745	—	—	—	S*
cormo	Short-distance migrant	5	346	804	225	616	15	83.5	19	623	247	25	1179	175	12	533	311	26	1068	153	60	1799	S*
shag	Short-distance migrant	4	559	480	215	491	<10	142	6	557	61.5	12	227	76	6	412	117	10	340	—	—	—	S
kitti	Short-distance migrant	5	164	17	24	20	15	675	25	3309	788	215	2199	847.5	224	3463	654	22	1296	548	0	1289	NS*
sante	Long-distance migrant	5	596	198	114	58	77	5467.5	1701	7949	5420	4387	10039	5588.5	2299	7874	5206.5	1785	9845	5225	1695	9160	S
comte	Long-distance migrant	3	27	69	<10	12	<10	5469	3739	5757	5125	2139	5793	—	—	—	4383	380	5292	—	—	—	S*
guill	Short-distance migrant	4	166	421	925	318	<10	639	58	935	761	98	1455	718	148	1078	346	83	1013	—	—	—	S
razor	Long-distance migrant	3	197	197	74	431	<10	656	240	2009	916	170	2352	859	336	2557	935	111	1725	—	—	—	S
puffi	Short-distance migrant	4	78	10	33	22	<10	468	58	872	2301.5	1100	3360	1443	94	2970	548.5	196	2179	—	—	—	S*

continued

Species[2]	Latitude tests						Longitude tests						
	NE mean winter latitude	NW mean winter latitude	N mean winter latitude	SW mean winter latitude	SE mean winter latitude	Winter latitude test result	NE mean winter longitude	NW mean winter longitude	N mean winter longitude	SW mean winter longitude	SE mean winter longitude	Winter longitude test result	Overall result
fulma	57.483	54.57	56.213	—	—	NS*	-2.467	-12.266	-0.023	0.8	—	NS*	NS*
ganne	42.073	40.822	45.457	43.278	—	S*	-6.281	-4.719	-2.943	-4.891	—	S*	S*
cormo	57.43	51.649	54.724	49.561	49.431	S*	-2.969	-3.96	-1.995	-4.623	0.624	S*	S*
shag	59.041	55.134	54.738	51.857	51.780	S	-2.213	-5.443	-1.237	-5.484	—	S	S
kitti	55.123	51.22	51.525	48.166	—	S*	-10.342	0.278	-1.929	-3.056	2.662	NS*	S*
sante	10.186	3.879	10.172	4.538	6.681	S	-6.606	-3.023	-5.529	-2.41	-3.758	S	S*
comte	9.173	10.497	—	14.744	—	NS*	-10.97	-8.242	—	-10.542	—	NS*	S*
guill	57.076	53.968	54.872	49.963	—	S	4.661	-0.349	3.179	-3.506	—	S	S
razor	—	48.897	50.727	45.579	—	S	—	-2.054	2.237	-3.005	—	S	S
puffi	48.802	41.345	57.489	46.834	—	S*	-5.362	-14.552	0.864	-4.483	—	S*	S*

Notes

1. The standard regional definitions for terrestrial species are coded: 'NW'—Northwest; 'NE'—Northeast; 'SW'—Southwest; 'SE'—Southeast and 'I'—Ireland. For seabirds they are coded: 'NE'—Northeast; 'NW'—Northwest; 'N'—North; 'SW'—Southwest and 'SE'—Southeast. See Figure 4.12 for a map showing the boundaries adopted.
2. See key in Appendix 2.

Appendix 5b
Comparisons of the movement patterns of birds present in different regions of Britain & Ireland: British & Irish breeding populations by median recovery location

This appendix gives the results of tests for differences in the seasonal movements of the regional subpopulations of terrestrial birds present in Britain & Ireland during the breeding season. For recoveries in autumn (**Table I**) and recoveries in winter (**Table II**) separately, we divided recoveries around the median recovery latitude or longitude for that species and season and compared the proportions of birds from the north and south of Britain & Ireland (latitude tests) and from the east and west (longitude tests) that were reported in the two recovery areas in each case. Details of the testing methods and the regional divisions used are given in footnote 4 of Chapter 5. Only species for which the

expected number of records was at least five in each cell of the two-by-two contingency table were included in each set of tests. The median latitudes and longitudes used in the tests are shown in decimal degrees, with negative values for locations south of the Equator for latitude or west of the Greenwich Meridian for longitude. The results of tests are coded as follows:-

S   significant (P<0.05);
NS not significant (P>0.05);
NS* not significant but based on a sample of <30 recoveries.

Table I Autumn results

Species*	Migrant type	Number of records	Median latitude of recovery in autumn	% from North, of birds in northern area in autumn	% from North, of birds in southern area in autumn	North–South test result	Median longitude of recovery in autumn	% from East, of birds in eastern area in autumn	% from East, of birds in western area in autumn	East–West test result
tufdu	Short-distance migrant	41	52.6	23.8	20.0	NS	5.8	100.0	95.0	NS
kestr	Short-distance migrant	64	48.6	46.8	40.6	NS	0.8	31.2	28.1	NS
stocu	Long-distance migrant	33	—	—	—	NT	−1.3	82.3	87.5	NS
lapwi	Long-distance migrant	22	46.5	36.3	54.5	NS*	−1.3	50.0	70.0	NS*
blhgu	Short-distance migrant	27	49.4	21.4	23.0	NS*	—	—	—	NT
lbbgu	Long-distance migrant	837	40.6	44.8	37.8	S	−8.7	17.9	17.9	NS
hergu	Short-distance migrant	37	51.4	78.9	44.4	S	2.4	89.4	44.4	S
turdo	Long-distance migrant	84	—	—	—	NT	−4.9	85.7	78.5	NS
cucko	Long-distance migrant	22	—	—	—	NT	6.2	72.7	54.5	NS*
swift	Long-distance migrant	28	—	—	—	NT	−1.9	71.4	78.5	NS*
sanma	Long-distance migrant	334	47.3	20.8	15.0	NS	−1.0	55.6	46.6	NS
swall	Long-distance migrant	114	39.5	14.0	17.5	NS	1.1	52.5	43.6	NS
meapi	Long-distance migrant	52	43.4	42.3	57.6	NS	−2.0	42.3	73.0	S
yelwa	Long-distance migrant	22	—	—	—	NT	−8.6	81.8	54.5	NS*
piewa	Long-distance migrant	22	43.5	35.7	12.5	NS*	—	—	—	NT
redst	Long-distance migrant	37	41.9	63.1	55.5	NS	−2.7	15.7	11.1	NS
wheat	Long-distance migrant	36	40.2	55.5	61.1	NS	−4.1	33.3	38.8	NS
sedwa	Long-distance migrant	225	47.9	28.4	23.8	NS	−2.2	54.8	37.5	S
reewa	Long-distance migrant	161	—	—	—	NT	−2.9	61.7	80.0	S
white	Long-distance migrant	37	42.2	15.7	16.6	NS	−6.8	57.8	61.1	NS
blaca	Long-distance migrant	42	—	—	—	NT	−2.4	66.6	71.4	NS
chiff	Long-distance migrant	18	—	—	—	NT	−5.7	55.5	66.6	NS*
wilwa	Long-distance migrant	51	43.4	46.1	24	NS	−2.4	46.1	48.0	NS
spofl	Long-distance migrant	35	40.2	27.7	17.6	NS	−4.1	47.3	75.0	NS
piefl	Long-distance migrant	101	42.5	25.0	30.6	NS	—	—	—	NT
goldf	Long-distance migrant	36	—	—	—	NT	−1.3	83.3	55.5	NS
linne	Long-distance migrant	172	43.8	9.3	6.9	NS	−1.2	68.6	74.4	NS
redpo	Short-distance migrant	64	50.7	31.2	28.1	NS	—	—	—	NT

Table II Winter results

Species*	Migrant type	Number of records	North–South tests				East–West tests			
			Median latitude of recovery	% from North, of birds in northern wintering area	% from North, of birds in southern wintering area	North–South test result	Median longitude of recovery	% from East, of birds in eastern wintering area	% from East, of birds in western wintering area	East–West test result
tufdu	Short-distance migrant	64	51.7	96.8	75.0	S	—	—	—	NT
kestr	Short-distance migrant	91	48.5	51.0	65.9	NS	−0.2	41.3	28.8	NS
lapwi	Long-distance migrant	380	43.5	56.8	55.0	NS	−2.7	38.9	36.8	NS
blhgu	Short-distance migrant	155	43.4	70.5	67.5	NS	−4.1	65.3	49.3	S
lbbgu	Long-distance migrant	1000	37.3	45.1	39.2	NS	−8.6	21.9	21.0	NS
hergu	Short-distance migrant	82	51.0	9.0	57.8	S	1.6	86.0	38.4	S
sanma	Long-distance migrant	143	16.4	73.5	72.7	NS	−16.3	48.8	70.0	NS
swall	Long-distance migrant	95	−29.8	56.0	77.7	S	26.4	45.8	44.6	NS
meapi	Long-distance migrant	63	38.7	59.3	54.8	NS	−6.8	56.2	41.9	NS
piewa	Long-distance migrant	114	41.5	46.5	76.7	S	−7.2	42.1	42.1	NS
sonth	Short-distance migrant	129	46.0	92.3	89.0	NS	−1.8	87.6	81.2	NS
blaca	Long-distance migrant	61	36.2	96.7	96.6	NS	−5.0	67.7	63.3	NS
piefl	Long-distance migrant	32	34.9	75.0	68.7	NS	—	—	—	NT
goldf	Long-distance migrant	130	—	—	—	NT	−2.1	83.0	84.6	NS
linne	Long-distance migrant	222	43.6	93.8	84.4	S	−1.4	84.8	67.2	S

* See key in Appendix 2.

Appendix 5c
Regional differences in the movement patterns of British & Irish wintering birds

This appendix presents the results of tests for differences between wintering regions of Britain & Ireland in the breeding origins of winter immigrants (latitude and longitude tests) and the proportion of winter immigrants (tests of proportions recovered abroad). A minimum of 10 appropriate recoveries from a given wintering region was required for the region to be included in the analyses. The mean latitudes and longitudes of breeding-season recoveries abroad for birds ringed in each wintering region, and the percentages recovered abroad for birds ringed in each region of Britain & Ireland in winter, are shown. For coordinates, negative values indicate locations south of the Equator for latitude or west of the Greenwich Meridian for longitude. Coordinates are given in decimal degrees. For the tests of proportions, an expected value of at least 5 was required in each cell of the contingency table. The full methods of testing are described in Chapter 4. The results of tests between regions for latitude, longitude and proportions of recoveries abroad are coded as follows:-

S   significant (P<0.05);

S*   significant but based on a sample of <30 recoveries for at least one region;

NS   not significant (P>0.05);

NS*   not significant but based on a sample of <30 recoveries for at least one region;

NT   not tested (insufficient data).

The 'overall result' indicates whether significant differences between regions were detected in one or more of the three tests.

Species[1]	Grouping for regional split[2]	Number of regions tested	Migrant type[3]	Number of records by region[2]					Breeding latitude tests						Breeding longitude tests					
				Region 1	Region 2	Region 3	Region 4	Region 5	Mean breeding latitude Region 1	Mean breeding latitude Region 2	Mean breeding latitude Region 3	Mean breeding latitude Region 4	Mean breeding latitude Region 5	Breeding latitude test result	Mean breeding longitude Region 1	Mean breeding longitude Region 2	Mean breeding longitude Region 3	Mean breeding longitude Region 4	Mean breeding longitude Region 5	Breeding longitude test result
pifgo	Terrestrial	2	Immigrant only	<10	10	<10	11	<10	—	64.793	—	66.117	—	NS*	—	−15.412	—	−19.122	—	NS*
wigeo	Terrestrial	3	Resident & immigrant	<10	21	89	24	<10	—	63.498	63.899	64.806	—	NS*	—	45.46	55.915	55.485	—	NS*
teal	Terrestrial	2	Resident & immigrant	<10	<10	206	52	<10	—	—	62.132	63.031	—	NS	—	—	29.797	31.742	—	NS
malla	Terrestrial	4	Resident & immigrant	13	<10	527	132	11	57.595	—	57.693	56.861	59.744	NS*	11.254	—	17.252	16.643	18.82	NS*
pocha	Terrestrial	2	Resident & immigrant	<10	<10	65	55	<10	—	—	56.174	55.274	—	NS	—	—	35.778	36.914	—	NS
tufdu	Terrestrial	2	Resident & immigrant	<10	<10	181	36	<10	—	—	60.00	62.725	—	S	—	—	30.315	31.403	—	NS
oyste	Wader	4	Resident & immigrant	16	102	41	138	<10	62.765	61.387	58.504	62.322	—	S*	−0.826	7.77	0.279	−1.47	—	S*
knot	Wader	2	Immigrant only	<10	26	<10	31	<10	—	73.682	55.91	71.468	—	NS*	—	−61.429	—	−55.221	—	NS*
dunli	Wader	2	Resident & immigrant	<10	<10	17	11	<10	—	—	58.99	57.167	—	NS*	—	—	14.948	13.491	—	NS*
blhgu	Terrestrial	4	Resident & immigrant	54	68	1266	293	<10	60.836	60.442	58.148	57.874	—	S	17.117	14.687	16.759	15.636	—	S
comgu	Terrestrial	2	Resident & immigrant	<10	15	89	<10	<10	—	63.881	58.99	—	—	S*	—	12.285	14.83	—	—	NS*
hergu	Terrestrial	3	Resident & immigrant	10	32	32	<10	<10	68.821	68.139	63.767	—	—	S*	18.965	19.577	16.315	—	—	NS*
blabi	Terrestrial	4	Resident & immigrant	15	54	188	87	<10	57.725	57.992	56.359	57.713	—	S*	12.653	12.957	13.186	13.279	—	NS*
field	Terrestrial	2	Immigrant only	<10	32	125	32	<10	—	—	61.101	61.956	—	NS	—	—	16.654	18.386	—	NS
redwi	Terrestrial	2	Immigrant only	<10	<10	29	29	<10	—	—	61.001	59.661	—	NS*	—	—	25.823	25.742	—	NS*
starl	Terrestrial	5	Resident & immigrant	87	255	1202	617	22	58.518	59.465	55.21	55.811	57.155	S*	14.003	13.024	15.587	15.188	14.642	S*
chaff	Terrestrial	2	Resident & immigrant	<10	<10	49	76	<10	—	—	59.063	59.733	—	NS	—	—	13.953	13.827	—	NS

continued

Tests of proportions recovered abroad

Species[1]	Recovered abroad from Region 1	Recovered abroad from Region 2	Recovered abroad from Region 3	Recovered abroad from Region 4	Recovered abroad from Region 5	Proportion recovered abroad—test result	Overall result
pifgo	—	—	—	—	—	NT	NS*
wigeo	—	—	—	—	—	NT	NS*
teal	—	—	—	—	—	NT	NS
malla	52%	—	81%	46%	—	S*	S*
pocha	—	—	—	—	—	NT	NS
tufdu	—	—	77%	86%	—	NS	S
oyste	10%	72%	37%	31%	22%	S	S
knot	—	—	—	—	—	NT	NS*
dunli	—	—	—	—	—	NT	NS*
blhgu	82%	74%	84%	83%	—	NS	S*
comgu	—	—	—	—	—	NT	S*
hergu	4%	13%	27%	18%	—	S	S
blabi	7%	12%	0%	6%	10%	S	S
field	—	—	—	—	—	NT	NS
redwi	20%	—	76%	78%	16%	NS	NS*
starl	20%	29%	26%	29%	16%	S	S
chaff	—	—	14%	25%	—	S	S

Notes

1. See key in Appendix 2.
2. For species categorized as 'Terrestrial', the region numbers are: 1—Northwest; 2—Northeast; 3—Southeast; 4—Southwest; 5—Ireland. For 'Waders', the region numbers are: 1—North; 2—East; 3—South; 4—West; 5—Ireland. The regional boundaries adopted for the analyses are shown in Figure 4.12.
3. Migrant type as defined in Appendix 6b.

Appendix 6
Summary of current knowledge of the movements of British & Irish birds, by species and population

In this appendix, we summarize the quality of information on movements that is currently available for the 188 main species included in this book, dividing this knowledge into (a) the British & Irish breeding population, (b) the British & Irish wintering population and (c) species for which there are passage populations from abroad that do not regularly winter in Britain & Ireland. The contents represent a synthesis of the information available from the ring-recovery data and analyses presented in this book, and information from other sources mentioned in the species accounts by their authors. We cannot assume that every author has found and included every piece of relevant information but we are confident that these appendices provide a satisfactory summary of the relative quality of knowledge across species (see Chapter 7 for a further description of the rationale for this summary, the methods employed and a synthesis of the results).

The codes '●●●' (good), '●●' (moderate) and '●' (poor) are used throughout to reflect the relative quality of information available on each topic. Other codes and the derivation of the values for each topic are detailed in the footnotes in Appendix 6c.

Species[1]	Ecological grouping[2]	Distribution of ringing effort[3]	Age of ringing[4]	Juvenile movements[5]	Natal dispersal[6]	Breeding dispersal[6]	Migrant type[7]	Routes and timing of migration[8]	Wintering area[9]	Sex differences[10]	Age differences[10]	Regional differences[11]	Migration strategy[12]	Summering areas of immatures[13]	Temporal change in wintering areas[14]
retdi	WF	•	•••	•	••	••	Short-distance migrant*	•	••	•	••	•	—	••	•
litgr	WF	•	FG (-Y)	•	•	•	[Short-distance migrant]	•	•	•	•	•	—	—	•
grcgr	WF	•	•	•	•	•	[Short-distance migrant]	•	•	•	•	•	—	•	•
fulma	SG	••	•••	•	•••	••	Short-distance migrant	•••	•••	•	••	••	—	•••	••
mansh	SG	•••	•••	•	•••	••	Long-distance migrant	•••	•••	•	•	•	•	••	••
stope	SG	•••	FG (-Y)	•	•	•	Long-distance migrant*	••	••	•	•	•	•	•	•
leape	SG	•••	FG (-Y)	•	•	•	[Long-distance migrant]	•	•	•	•	•	•	•	•
ganne	SG	•••	Y (-FG)	•••	•••	•	Long-distance migrant	•••	•••	•	•••	••	•	••	•••
cormo	SG	••	Y (-FG)	•••	•••	••	Short-distance migrant	•••	•••	•	•••	•••	—	•••	•••
shag	SG	•••	Y (-FG)	•••	•••	•••	Short-distance migrant	•••	•••	••	••	••	—	•••	•••
grehe	WF	•••	Y (-FG)	•••	•••	•	Sedentary	—	—	•	••	••	—	—	•••
mutsw	WF	•••	•••	•••	•••	•••	Sedentary	—	—	•••	•••	•••	—	—	••
grego	WF	•••	FG (-Y)	•	••	•	Sedentary	—	—	••	••	•	—	—	••
cango	WF	••• (-I)	•••	••	•••	•••	Short-distance migrant	•••	•••	•••	•••	•••	—	••	•••
sheld	WF	••	•••	•	••	••	Short-distance migrant	••	•••	•	••	•	—	•••	••
manda	WF	•	FG (-Y)	•	•	•	[Short-distance migrant]	•	••	•	•	•	—	—	•
wigeo	WF	•••	FG (-Y)	•	••	•	Sedentary*	—	—	•	•	•	—	—	••
gadwa	WF	••• (-I)	FG (-Y)	•	•	•	Long-distance migrant*	•• (-S)	••	•	•	•	•	—	•
teal	WF	•	FG (-Y)	•	•	•	Short-distance migrant	•• (-S)	••	•	••	•	—	—	•
malla	WF	•••	FG (-Y)	•••	•••	•••	Sedentary	—	—	••	••	•••	—	—	•••
pinta	WF	•	•	•	•	•	Sedentary*	—	—	•	•	•	—	—	••
garga	WF	•	FG (-Y)	•	•	•	[Long-distance migrant]	•	•	•	•	•	—	—	•
shove	WF	•	•••	•	•	•	Long-distance migrant*	•• (-S)	••	•	••	•	•	—	•
pocha	WF	•	FG (-Y)	•	•	•	Short-distance migrant*	••	••	••	••	•	—	—	•
tufdu	WF	••	FG (-Y)	•	•	••	Short-distance migrant*	•• (-S)	•••	••	••	•	—	—	•••
eider	WF	••	•••	••	•••	•••	Short-distance migrant*	••	•••	••	••	•	—	•••	•••
golde	WF	•	FG (-Y)	•	•	•	[Short-distance migrant]	•	•	•	•	•	—	—	•
goosa	WF	•	•••	•	••	••	Short-distance migrant*	••	••	•	•	•	—	••	••
redki	RO	•••	Y (-FG)	••	••	••	[Sedentary]	—	—	•	•	•	—	—	•
marha	RO	••	Y (-FG)	•	•	•	[Long-distance migrant]	•	•	•	•	•	•	—	••
henha	RO	••• (-I)	Y (-FG)	••	••	••	Short-distance migrant*	•••	••	••	••	•	—	•	••
monha	RO	•••	Y (-FG)	•	••	•	[Long-distance migrant]	•• (-S)	•	••	••	•	•	•	••
gosha	RO	•••	Y (-FG)	•	•	•	[Sedentary]	—	—	•	•	••	—	—	••
sparr	RO	••• (-I)	Y (-FG)	•••	•••	•••	Sedentary	—	—	•••	•••	•••	—	—	••
buzza	RO	••• (-I)	Y (-FG)	••	•••	•	Sedentary	—	—	•	••	•	—	—	••
golea	RO	•	Y (-FG)	•	•	•	[Sedentary]	—	—	•	•	•	—	—	••
ospre	RO	••	Y (-FG)	•	••	••	[Long-distance migrant]	••	••	•	••	••	—	•	•
kestr	RO	••• (-I)	Y (-FG)	•••	•••	••	Short-distance migrant	•••	•••	••	•••	•••	—	—	••
merli	RO	•••	Y (-FG)	••	•••	•	Short-distance migrant	•••	•••	••	•••	•	—	—	••
hobby	RO	•••	Y (-FG)	•	•	•	[Long-distance migrant]	•	•	••	••	•	—	•	•
pereg	RO	••	Y (-FG)	••	•••	••	Sedentary	—	—	••	••	•	—	—	••
grepa	PN	•	FG (-Y)	•	•	•	[Sedentary]	—	—	•	•	•	—	—	•
watra	WF	•	FG (-Y)	•	•	•	[Sedentary]	—	—	•	•	•	—	—	•
moorh	WF	••• (-I)	•••	••	•••	•••	Sedentary	—	—	•	••	••	—	—	••
coot	WF	••	FG (-Y)	•	••	•••	Sedentary	—	—	•	••	•	—	—	••
oyste	WD	••• (-I)	•••	••	•••	••	Short-distance migrant	•••	•••	•	•••	••	—	••	•••
stocu	WD	•••	Y (-FG)	•	•	•	Long-distance migrant*	•• (-S)	••	•	•	•	—	••	••
lirpl	WD	•••	•••	•	•	•	[Long-distance migrant]	•• (-S)	•	•	•	•	—	••	••
rinpl	WD	••• (-I)	•••	•	••	••	Long-distance migrant*	•••	•••	•	••	•	—	—	••
dotte	WD	•••	•	•	••	••	Long-distance migrant*	••	••	•	•	•	••	••	••
golpl	WD	•	Y (-FG)	•	•	•	Long-distance migrant*	••	••	•	•	•	•	•	•
lapwi	WD	••• (-I)	Y (-FG)	•••	•••	••	Long-distance migrant	•••	•••	•	•••	•••	••	•••	••
dunli	WD	•	FG (-Y)	••	•••	••	Long-distance migrant*	•	•••	•	••	••	•	••	•
ruff	WD	•	•	•	•	•	[Long-distance migrant]	•	•	•	•	••	•	•	•
snipe	WD	••	•••	•	•	•	Short-distance migrant	•• (-S)	•••	•	••	••	—	•	••
woodc	WD	••• (-I)	•••	•	••	••	Short-distance migrant	•• (-S)	•••	•	••	•••	—	•	••
bltgo	WD	••	Y (-FG)	•	••	•	[Long-distance migrant]	•	•	•	•	•	—	•	•

Continued

Species[1]	Ecological grouping[2]	Distribution of ringing effort[3]	Age of ringing[4]	Juvenile movements[5]	Natal dispersal[6]	Breeding dispersal[6]	Migrant type[7]	Routes and timing of migration[8]	Wintering area[9]	Sex differences[10]	Age differences[10]	Regional differences[11]	Migration strategy[12]	Summering areas of immatures[13]	Temporal change in wintering areas[14]
whimb	WD	●●●	●●●	●	●●	●●	[Long-distance migrant]	●	●	●	●	●	●	●	●
curle	WD	●●● (-I)	Y (-FG)	●●	●●	●	Short-distance migrant	●● (-S)	●●●	●	●●●	●	—	●●	●●
redsh	WD	●●● (-I)	●●●	●●	●●	●●	Short-distance migrant*	●●●	●●●	●	●●●	●	—	—	●●●
gresh	WD	●	●	●	●●	●●	[Long-distance migrant]	●	●	●	●	●	●	●	●
comsa	WD	●●	●●●	●	●●	●	[Long-distance migrant]	●	●	●	●	●	●●	●	●
arcsk	SG	●●●	●●●	●	●●●	●●	[Long-distance migrant]	●	●	●	●	●	●	●●	●●
gresk	SG	●●●	Y (-FG)	●●●	●●●	●	Long-distance migrant	●●●	●●●	●	●●●	●	●	●●●	●●●
blhgu	SG	●●●	Y (-FG)	●●●	●●●	●●●	Short-distance migrant	●●●	●●●	●	●●●	●●●	—	●●●	●●●
comgu	SG	●●●	Y (-FG)	●●	●●●	●●	Short-distance migrant	●●●	●●●	●	●●	●	—	●●●	●●●
lbbgu	SG	●●●	●●●	●●●	●●●	●●●	Long-distance migrant	●●●	●●●	●	●●●	●●	—	●●●	●●●
hergu	SG	●●●	●●●	●●●	●●●	●●●	Short-distance migrant	●●●	●●●	●	●●●	●●●	—	●●●	●●●
gbbgu	SG	●●●	Y (-FG)	●●	●●	●	Short-distance migrant	●●●	●●●	●	●●●	●	—	●●●	●●●
kitti	SG	●●	●●●	●●	●●●	●●	Short-distance migrant	●●●	●●●	●	●●●	●●●	—	●●●	●●●
sante	SG	●●●	Y (-FG)	●●●	●●●	●	Long-distance migrant	●●●	●●●	●	●●●	●●●	●	●●●	●●●
roste	SG	●●●	Y (-FG)	●●	●●●	●	Long-distance migrant	●●	●●●	●	●●	●	●●	●●	●●●
comte	SG	●●●	Y (-FG)	●●	●●●	●	Long-distance migrant	●●●	●●●	●	●●	●●	●●	●●●	●●●
arcte	SG	●●●	Y (-FG)	●●	●●●	●	Long-distance migrant	●● (-S)	●●	●	●	●	●	●	●●
litte	SG	●●	●●●	●	●●	●	[Long-distance migrant]	●● (-S)	●	●	●	●	●	●	●●
guill	SG	●●● (-I)	●●●	●●●	●●●	●●	Short-distance migrant*	●●●	●●●	●●	●●●	●●●	—	●●●	●●
razor	SG	●●●	●●●	●●●	●●●	●●	Long-distance migrant*	●●●	●●●	●	●●●	●●	—	●●●	●●
blagu	SG	●●	●●●	●	●●	●	Sedentary	—	—	●	●	●	—	—	●
puffi	SG	●●●	●●●	●	●●●	●●●	Short-distance migrant*	●●●	●●●	●	●●●	●●	—	●●	●●
rocdo	PN	●	●	●	●	●	[Sedentary]	—	—	●	●	●	—	—	●
stodo	PN	●●● (-I)	●●●	●●	●●●	●●	Sedentary	—	—	●	●●	●	—	—	●●
woodp	PN	●●● (-I)	●●●	●●●	●●●	●●●	Sedentary	—	—	●	●●	●●●	—	—	●●●
coldo	PN	●●	FG (-Y)	●	●●●	●●●	Sedentary*	—	—	●	●	●	—	—	●●
turdo	PN	●●●	●●●	●	●	●●	[Long-distance migrant]	●● (-S)	●	●	●	●	●●	—	●
cucko	PN	●●	●●●	●	●	●	[Long-distance migrant]	●● (-S)	●	●	●	●	●	●	●
barow	RO	●●● (-I)	Y (-FG)	●●●	●●●	●●	Sedentary	—	—	●●	●●	●●●	—	—	●●
litow	RO	●●●	●●●	●	●●●	●●	Sedentary	—	—	●	●●	●	—	—	●
tawow	RO	●●●	Y (-FG)	●●●	●●●	●●●	Sedentary	—	—	●	●●●	●●	—	—	●●
loeow	RO	●●● (-I)	●●●	●	●●●	●	Sedentary*	—	—	●	●●	●	—	—	●
sheow	RO	●●●	Y (-FG)	●	●	●	Sedentary*	—	—	●	●	●	—	—	●
nijar	PN	●●	●●●	●	●●	●	[Long-distance migrant]	●●	●	●	●	●	●	—	●
swift	PN	●●	FG (-Y)	●	●●●	●●●	Long-distance migrant*	●●●	●●	●	●	●	●	●	●
kingf	PN	●●● (-I)	FG (-Y)	●	●●●	●●	Sedentary	—	—	●	●●	●	—	—	●●
grewo	PN	●	FG (-Y)	●	●●	●●	[Sedentary]	—	—	●	●	●	—	—	●
grswo	PN	●●	FG (-Y)	●	●●	●●●	Sedentary*	—	—	●	●	●	—	—	●
skyla	PN	●	●●●	●	●●●	●●	?	?	?	●	●	●	?	?	?
sanma	PN	●●● (-I)	FG (-Y)	●	●●●	●●●	[Long-distance migrant]	●●●	●	●	●●	●	●●	—	●
swall	PN	●●● (-I)	●●●	●●	●●●	●●●	Long-distance migrant	●●●	●●●	●	●●	●	●	—	●●
houma	PN	●●● (-I)	FG (-Y)	●	●●●	●●●	[Long-distance migrant]	●● (-S)	●	●	●●	●	●●	—	●●
trepi	PN	●	●●●	●	●	●	[Long-distance migrant]	●●	●	●	●	●	●	—	●●
meapi	PN	●	●●●	●	●●	●	Long-distance migrant	●●●	●●●	●	●●	●●	●	—	●●
rocpi	PN	●	Y (-FG)	●	●	●	[Sedentary]	—	—	●	●	●	—	—	●
yelwa	PN	●●●	FG (-Y)	●	●●	●	[Long-distance migrant]	●●	●	●	●	●	●	—	●
grewa	PN	●●● (-I)	Y (-FG)	●	●●	●	Short-distance migrant	●●	●●	●	●●	●	—	—	●●
piewa	PN	●●● (-I)	●●●	●●	●●●	●●●	Long-distance migrant*	●●●	●●●	●●	●●●	●●●	●●	—	●●●
dippe	PN	●●	Y (-FG)	●●	●●●	●●●	Sedentary*	—	—	●	●●	●	—	—	●●
wren	PN	●●	FG (-Y)	●	●●●	●●●	Sedentary	—	—	●	●●	●●	—	—	●●
dunno	PN	●●● (-I)	●●●	●	●●●	●●●	Sedentary	—	—	●●	●●●	●●	—	—	●●●
robin	PN	●●● (-I)	●●●	●	●●●	●●●	Sedentary	—	—	●●	●●	●●●	—	—	●●●
nigal	PN	●●●	●●●	●	●	●●	[Long-distance migrant]	●	●	●	●	●	●	—	●
blare	PN	●●	●●●	●	●	●	?	?	?	●	●	●	?	—	?
redst	PN	●●	●●●	●	●●	●	[Long-distance migrant]	●●●	●	●	●	●	●	—	●
whinc	PN	●●	●●●	●	●	●	[Long-distance migrant]	●● (-S)	●	●	●	●	●	—	●
stoch	PN	●	Y (-FG)	●	●	●	Long-distance migrant*	●	●●	●	●	●	●	—	●
wheat	PN	●●	●●●	●	●●	●	[Long-distance migrant]	●●	●	●	●	●	●	—	●
rinou	PN	●●	●●●	●	●●	●	Long-distance migrant*	●● (-S)	●●	●	●	●	●	—	●
blabi	PN	●●●	●●●	●●●	●●●	●●●	Short-distance migrant	●●●	●●●	●●	●●	●●●	—	—	●●●
sonth	PN	●●● (-I)	●●●	●●●	●●●	●●●	Short-distance migrant*	●●●	●●●	●●	●●●	●●●	—	—	●●●
misth	PN	●●	●●●	●	●●●	●●●	Short-distance migrant	●●●	●●●	●	●●●	●	—	—	●●
cetwa	PN	●●●	FG (-Y)	●	●	●	[Sedentary]	—	—	●	●	●	—	—	●
grawa	PN	●	●	●	●	●	[Long-distance migrant]	●	●	●	●	●	●	—	●
sedwa	PN	●●● (-I)	FG (-Y)	●	●●●	●●	[Long-distance migrant]	●●●	●	●	●	●	●	—	●
reewa	PN	●●●	FG (-Y)	●●	●●●	●●●	[Long-distance migrant]	●●●	●	●	●	●	●	—	●
leswh	PN	●●●	FG (-Y)	●	●●	●●	[Long-distance migrant]	●●	●	●	●	●	●	—	●
white	PN	●●	FG (-Y)	●	●●	●●●	[Long-distance migrant]	●●	●	●	●	●	●	—	●
garwa	PN	●●	FG (-Y)	●	●	●	[Long-distance migrant]	●●	●	●	●	●	●	—	●
blaca	PN	●●● (-I)	FG (-Y)	●	●●●	●●●	Long-distance migrant*	●●●	●●	●	●	●	●●	—	●
woowa	PN	●	●	●	●	●	[Long-distance migrant]	●	●	●	●	●	●	—	●
chiff	PN	●●● (-I)	FG (-Y)	●	●	●	[Long-distance migrant]	●●	●●	●	●	●	●	—	●
wilwa	PN	●●● (-I)	FG (-Y)	●●	●●	●●●	[Long-distance migrant]	●●●	●●	●	●	●	●●	—	●
goldc	PN	●●	●	●	●	●	Sedentary*	—	—	●	●	●	—	—	●
firec	PN	●	●	●	●	●	?	?	?	●	●	●	?	—	?
spofl	PN	●●	●●●	●	●●●	●●●	[Long-distance migrant]	●●●	●	●	●	●	●	—	●
piefl	PN	●●●	●●●	●	●●●	●●●	Long-distance migrant*	●●●	●	●	●	●	●●	—	●
beati	PN	●●●	FG (-Y)	●	●	●	[Short-distance migrant]	●●	●	●	●	●	●	—	●
lotti	PN	●●	FG (-Y)	●	●●	●●●	Sedentary*	—	—	●	●	●	—	—	●
marti	PN	●●	FG (-Y)	●	●	●	[Sedentary]	—	—	●	●	●	—	—	●

Continued

Species[1]	Ecological grouping[2]	Distribution of ringing effort[3]	Age of ringing[4]	Juvenile movements[5]	Natal dispersal[6]	Breeding dispersal[6]	Migrant type[7]	Routes and timing of migration[8]	Wintering area[9]	Sex differences[10]	Age differences[10]	Regional differences[11]	Migration strategy[12]	Summering areas of immatures[13]	Temporal change in wintering areas[14]
wilti	PN	●●	FG (-Y)	●	●●	●●	[Sedentary]	—	—	●	●	●	—	—	●
coati	PN	●	FG (-Y)	●	●●●	●●	Sedentary*	—	—	●	●	●	—	—	●
bluti	PN	●●● (-I)	●●●	●●●	●●●	●●●	Sedentary	—	—	●●	●●●	●●●	—	—	●●
greti	PN	●●● (-I)	●●●	●●●	●●●	●●●	Sedentary	—	—	●●	●●	●●	—	—	●●
nutha	PN	●●●	●●●	●	●●●	●●	Sedentary*	—	—	●	●	●	—	—	●
treec	PN	●	FG (-Y)	●	●	●●	[Sedentary]	—	—	●	●	●	—	—	●
jay	PN	●●	●●●	●	●●●	●●●	Sedentary	—	—	●	●●	●	—	—	●●●
magpi	PN	●●● (-I)	●●●	●●	●●●	●●●	Sedentary	—	—	●	●●	●	—	—	●
choug	PN	●●● (-I)	Y (-FG)	●●	●●●	●●	Sedentary*	—	—	●	●	●	—	—	●
jackd	PN	●●● (-I)	●●●	●●	●●●	●●●	Sedentary	—	—	●	●●	●●●	—	—	●●●
rook	PN	●●● (-I)	●●●	●●	●●●	●●●	Sedentary	—	—	●	●●	●●	—	—	●●●
crow	PN	●●●	Y (-FG)	●●	●●●	●●	Sedentary	—	—	●●	●●	●●●	—	—	●●●
raven	PN	●●	Y (-FG)	●●	●●●	●●	Sedentary	—	—	●	●●	●	—	—	●●
starl	PN	●●● (-I)	FG (-Y)	●●●	●●●	●●●	Sedentary	—	—	●●●	●●●	●●●	—	—	●●●
housp	PN	●●● (-I)	FG (-Y)	●	●●●	●●●	Sedentary	—	—	●●●	●●	●●	—	—	●●●
tresp	PN	●●	●●●	●	●●●	●●●	Sedentary*	—	—	●	●●	●	—	—	●
chaff	PN	●●● (-I)	FG (-Y)	●	●●●	●●●	Sedentary	—	—	●●	●●	●●	—	—	●●●
grefi	PN	●●● (-I)	FG (-Y)	●	●●●	●●●	Sedentary*	—	—	●●●	●●	●●	—	—	●●●
goldf	PN	●●	FG (-Y)	●	●●●	●●●	Long-distance migrant*	●●●	●●●	●●	●●	●	●	—	●●●
siski	PN	●●	FG (-Y)	●	●	●●	Short-distance migrant*	●● (-A)	●●●	●	●	●	—	—	●
linne	PN	●●	●●●	●	●●●	●●●	Long-distance migrant*	●●●	●●●	●●●	●●	●●	●	—	●●●
twite	PN	●	●●●	●	●	●	[Short-distance migrant]	●●	●●	●	●	●	—	—	●
redpo	PN	●●	FG (-Y)	●	●●●	●●●	Short-distance migrant**	●●●	●●●	●	●	●	—	—	●
cross	PN	●	●	●	●	●	[Long-distance migrant]*	●●	—	●	●	●	●●	—	●
bullf	PN	●●● (-I)	FG (-Y)	●	●●●	●●●	Sedentary	—	—	●●	●●	●	—	—	●●●
hawfi	PN	●	●	●	●	●	[Sedentary]	—	—	●	●	●	—	—	●
snobu	PN	●	●	●●	●●●	●●	[Short-distance migrant]	●●	●●	●	●	●	—	—	●
yelha	PN	●●	FG (-Y)	●	●●	●●●	Sedentary	—	—	●	●●	●	—	—	●
reebu	PN	●●	FG (-Y)	●	●●●	●●●	Sedentary	—	—	●●	●●	●	—	—	●●
corbu	PN	●	●	●	●●	●	[Sedentary]	—	—	●	●	●	—	—	●

Appendix 6b
British & Irish wintering populations

Table I Known or assumed to have a regular immigrant wintering population

Species[1]	Ecological grouping[2]	Distribution of ringing effort[3]	Winter movements[15]	Migrant type[7]	Routes and timing of migration[8]	Breeding origins[16]	Sex differences[10]	Age differences[10]	Regional differences[11]	Migration strategy[12]	Temporal change in movements[17]	Existence and origins of passage populations[18]	Timing and spatial occurrence of passage[19]
retdi	WF	●	●	[Long-distance migrant]	●	●●	●	●	●	●	No information	●	●
litgr	WF	●	●	[Long-distance migrant]	●	●	●	●	●	●	No information	●	●
cormo	SG	●	●●	[Short-distance migrant]	●●●	●●●	●	●	●	●	Some information	No regular passage	No regular passage
grehe	WF	●	●	[Long-distance migrant]	●●●	●●●	●	●	●●	●	No information	No regular passage	No regular passage
*bewsw	WF	●●● (-I)	●●●	[Long-distance migrant]	●●●	●●	●●	●●	●	●●●	No information	No regular passage	No regular passage
*whosw	WF	●●	●●●	Long-distance migrant*	●●●	●●●	●●	●	●	●●	No information	No regular passage	No regular passage
*pifgo	WF	●●●	●●●	Long-distance migrant*	●●●	●●●	●●	●	●	●	No information	No regular passage	No regular passage
*whfgo	WF	●●	●● (-W)	[Long-distance migrant]	●●●	●●●	●	●	●●	●	No information	No regular passage	No regular passage
grego	WF	●●● (-I)	●●●	[Long-distance migrant]	●●●	●●●	●	●	●	●●●	No information	No regular passage	No regular passage
*bargo	WF	●●●	●●●	Long-distance migrant*	●●●	●●●	●	●	●●●	●●	Some information	No regular passage	No regular passage
*brego	WF	●●●	●●	[Long-distance migrant]	●●●	●●	●	●●	●●●	●●	No information	No regular passage	No regular passage
sheld	WF	●●	●●	Short-distance migrant*	●●	●●	●	●	●	●	No information	No regular passage	No regular passage
wigeo	WF	●●	●●●	Long-distance migrant*	●●●	●●●	●●	●●●	●●	●	No information	●●	●●
gadwa	WF	●●	●● (-W)	Long-distance migrant*	●● (-S)	●●●	●	●	●	●	No information	●●	●●
teal	WF	●●	●●●	Long-distance migrant*	●●●	●●●	●●●	●●●	●	●	No information	●●	●●
malla	WF	●●●	●●●	Long-distance migrant*	●●●	●●●	●●●	●●●	●●	●	Some information	●●	●●
pinta	WF	●●	●●●	Long-distance migrant	●●●	●●●	●●	●●	●	●	No information	●●	●●
garga	WF	●	●	[Long-distance migrant]	●	●	●	●	●	●	No information	●●	●●
shove	WF	●	●●	Long-distance migrant*	●●●	●●●	●	●	●	●	No information	●●	●
pocha	WF	●	●●●	Long-distance migrant*	●●●	●●●	●●●	●●	●	●	No information	●	●
tufdu	WF	●●	●●●	Long-distance migrant*	●●●	●●●	●●●	●●●	●	●	No information	●●	●●
*scaup	WF	●	●	[Long-distance migrant]	●●	●●	●	●	●	●	Some information	No regular passage	No regular passage
golde	WF	●	●	[Long-distance migrant]	●●	●●	●	●	●	●	No information	●	●
goosa	WF	●	●	[Long-distance migrant]	●	●●	●	●	●	●	No information	No regular passage	No regular passage
redki	RO	●	●●	[Long-distance migrant]	●	●●	●	●	●	●	No information	No regular passage	No regular passage
henha	RO	●	●●	[Long-distance migrant]	●	●●	●	●	●	●	No information	●	●
sparr	RO	●●● (-I)	●● (-W)	Sedentary	●●	●●	●●	●●	●	●	No information	●●	●●
kestr	RO	●●	●●	Sedentary*	●●	●	●	●	●	●	No information	●●	●
merli	RO	●	●	[Long-distance migrant]	●●	●●	●	●	●	●	No information	No regular passage	No regular passage
pereg	RO	●	●	[Long-distance migrant]	●	●●	●	●	●	●	No information	●	●
watra	WF	●●	●	[Long-distance migrant]	●	●	●	●	●	●	No information	●	●
moorh	WF	●●● (-I)	●●●	Short-distance migrant	●●●	●●	●	●●	●	●	No information	No regular passage	No regular passage
coot	WF	●●	●●●	Long-distance migrant	●	●●	●	●	●	●	No information	●	●
oyste	WD	●●	●●●	Short-distance migrant	●●●	●●●	●	●●●	●●●	●	No information	No regular passage	No regular passage
rinpl	WD	●●	●●	[Long-distance migrant]	●●	●●	●	●	●	●	No information	●●	●●
golpl	WD	●	●	[Long-distance migrant]	●●	●●	●	●	●●	●	No information	●●	●●
*grepl	WD	●●	●● (-W)	[Long-distance migrant]	●●●	●	●	●●	●	●●	No information	●●	●●
lapwi	WD	●●	●● (-W)	Long-distance migrant*	●●	●●●	●	●	●	●	No information	No regular passage	No regular passage
*knot	WD	●●● (-I)	●●●	Long-distance migrant*	●●●	●●●	●	●	●	●●●	No information	●●	●●
*sande	WD	●●	●●	[Long-distance migrant]	●●	●●	●	●	●	●	No information	●●	●●
*pursa	WD	●●	●●	[Long-distance migrant]	●●	●●	●	●	●	●	No information	●	●
dunli	WD	●●●	●●●	Long-distance migrant*	●●●	●●	●	●●	●	●●	Some information	●●●	●●●
ruff	WD	●●	●	[Long-distance migrant]	●●	●	●	●	●	●●	No information	●●	●●
*jacsn	WD	●●	●● (-W)	[Long-distance migrant]	●●	●	●	●	●	●	No information	●●	●●
snipe	WD	●●	●●●	Long-distance migrant*	●●●	●●●	●	●	●	●	No information	●	●
woodc	WD	●●	●●●	Long-distance migrant*	●●●	●●●	●	●	●	●	No information	No regular passage	No regular passage
bltgo	WD	●●	●●●	[Long-distance migrant]	●●●	●●●	●	●●	●	●●	No information	No regular passage	No regular passage
*batgo	WD	●●	●●	[Long-distance migrant]	●●	●	●●	●●	●	●●	No information	●●	●●
curle	WD	●●	●● (-W)	Long-distance migrant	●● (-S)	●●●	●	●●	●	●	No information	●●	●●
redsh	WD	●●● (-I)	●●●	Long-distance migrant*	●●●	●●●	●	●●	●	●●	No information	●●	●
gresh	WD	●●	●	[Long-distance migrant]	●	●	●	●	●	●	No information	●●	●●
*gresa	WD	●●●	●	[Long-distance migrant]	●●	●●	●	●	●	●	No information	●●	●●
*turns	WD	●●● (-I)	●●●	Long-distance migrant*	●●●	●●●	●	●	●	●●	No information	●●	●●
blhgu	SG	●●●	●●●	Long-distance migrant*	●●●	●●●	●	●●●	●●●	●	No information	●	●
comgu	SG	●●	●●	Long-distance migrant	●●	●●●	●	●●	●	●	No information	●	●
lbbgu	SG	●●	●	Short-distance migrant*	●●	●●●	●	●●	●	●	No information	●	●
hergu	SG	●●	●● (-W)	Short-distance migrant*	●●	●●●	●	●●●	●●	●	No information	No regular passage	No regular passage

Table I Continued

Species[1]	Ecological grouping[2]	Distribution of ringing effort[3]	Winter movements[15]	Migrant type[7]	Routes and timing of migration[8]	Breeding origins[16]	Sex differences[10]	Age differences[10]	Regional differences[11]	Migration strategy[12]	Temporal change in movements[17]	Existence and origins of passage populations[18]	Timing and spatial occurrence of passage[19]
gbbgu	SG	●●	●	Long-distance migrant	●●	●●	●	●●	●	●	No information	No regular passage	No regular passage
loeow	RO	●●	●	[Long-distance migrant]	●●	●●	●●	●●	●	●	Some information	●	●
sheow	RO	●	●	[Long-distance migrant]	●	●	●	●	●	●	No information	●	●
rocpi	PN	●	●	[Long-distance migrant]	●●	●	●	●	●	●	No information	●●	●
*waxwi	PN	●●●	●● (-B)	[Long-distance migrant]	●● (-S)	●	●	●	●	●	No information	No regular passage	No regular passage
robin	PN	●●● (-I)	●●●	Sedentary	●●●	●●	●	●●●	●	●●	No information	●●	●●
blabi	PN	●●●	●●●	Short-distance migrant*	●●●	●●●	●●●	●●	●●●	●	Some information	●●●	●●●
*field	PN	●●	●●●	Long-distance migrant	●●●	●●●	●●	●●●	●	●	Some information	●●	●●
sonth	PN	●●● (-I)	●●●	Sedentary	●	●●	●	●●●	●	●	No information	●●	●●
*redwi	PN	●●	●●●	Long-distance migrant	●●●	●●●	●●	●●	●	●	No information	●●	●●
blaca	PN	●●●	●●	[Long-distance migrant]	●●	●	●	●	●	●●	No information	●●	●●
chiff	PN	●●● (-I)	●	[Long-distance migrant]	●	●	●	●	●	●	No information	●●	●●
goldc	PN	●●	●● (-B)	Sedentary*	●● (-S)	●	●●	●	●	●	No information	●	●
rook	PN	●●	●●	Sedentary	●●	●●●	●	●●	●	●	Some information	No regular passage	No regular passage
starl	PN	●●● (-I)	●●●	Long-distance migrant	●●●	●●	●●	●●●	●●●	●	Some information	●●	●●
chaff	PN	●●● (-I)	●●●	Short-distance migrant*	●●	●●	●●	●●●	●	●●	Some information	●	●
*bramb	PN	●●	●●●	Long-distance migrant*	●●	●●	●	●	●	●	No information	●	●
grefi	PN	●●●	●●●	Short-distance migrant*	●●●	●●●	●●●	●●●	●	●	Some information	No regular passage	No regular passage
siski	PN	●●●	●●●	Short-distance migrant*	●●●	●●●	●●	●●●	●	●●	No information	●●	●●
twite	PN	●	●●	[Long-distance migrant]	●●	●	●	●	●	●	No information	No regular passage	No regular passage
redpo	PN	●●	●	Short-distance migrant*	●●	●●	●	●	●	●●	No information	●	●
cross	PN	●	●	[Long-distance migrant]*	?	?	●	●	●	?	?	●●	●●
snobu	PN	●●	●●	[Long-distance migrant]	●●	●●	●	●	●	●●	No information	●●	●●
reebu	PN	●●	●●	Sedentary	●●	●●	●	●●	●	●	No information	●●	●●

Table II May have a regular immigrant wintering population (poor knowledge)

Species[1]	Ecological grouping[2]	Distribution of ringing effort[3]	Winter movements[15]	Migrant type[7]	Routes and timing of migration[8]	Breeding origins[16]	Sex differences[10]	Age differences[10]	Regional differences[11]	Migration strategy[12]	Temporal change in movements[17]	Existence and origins of passage populations[18]	Timing and spatial occurrence of passage[19]
grcgr	WF	●	●	?	?	?	●	●	●	?	?	●	●
fulma	SG	●	●	?	?	?	●	●	●	?	?	●	●
ganne	SG	●	●	?	?	?	●	●	●	?	?	●	●
shag	SG	●	●	[Short-distance migrant]	?	?	●	●	●	?	?	No regular passage	No regular passage
manda	WF	●	●	[Short-distance migrant]	?	?	●	●	●	?	?	No regular passage	No regular passage
marha	RO	●	●	?	?	?	●	●	●	?	?	●	●
buzza	RO	●	●	?	?	?	●	●	●	?	?	●	●
comsa	WD	●●	●	?	?	?	●	●	●	?	?	●●	●●
gresk	SG	●	●	?	?	?	●	●	●	?	?	●●	●
kitti	SG	●	●	?	?	?	●	●	●	?	?	●	●
guill	SG	●	●	?	?	?	●	●	●	?	?	●	●
razor	SG	●	●	?	?	?	●	●	●	?	?	●	●
blagu	SG	●	●	?	?	?	●	●	●	?	?	●	●
puffi	SG	●	●	?	?	?	●	●	●	?	?	●	●
kingf	PN	●●	●	?	?	?	●	●	●	?	?	●	●
skyla	PN	●●	●● (-B)	?	?	?	●	●	●	?	?	●●	●
meapi	PN	●●	●●	[Short-distance migrant]	?	?	●	●	●	?	?	●●	●●
grewa	PN	●●	●	?	?	?	●	●	●	?	?	●●	●●
dippe	PN	●●	●●	?	?	?	●	●	●	?	?	●●	●
blare	PN	●●	●	?	?	?	●	●	●	?	?	●	●
stoch	PN	●	●	?	?	?	●	●	●	?	?	●	●
cetwa	PN	●●●	●	?	?	?	●	●	●	?	?	●	●
firec	PN	●●●	●	?	?	?	●	●	●	?	?	●	●
jay	PN	●●	●●●	Sedentary	?	?	●	●●	●	?	?	●●	●●
jackd	PN	●●	●●	Sedentary	?	?	●	●●	●	?	?	●●	●●
crow	PN	●●	●	?	?	?	●	●	●	?	Some information	●●	●●
goldf	PN	●●	●● (-B)	Sedentary*	?	?	●	●●	●	?	?	●	●
hawfi	PN	●	●	?	?	?	●	●	●	?	?	●	●

Table III Wintering population thought to be the same as the breeding population

Species[1]	Ecological grouping[2]	Distribution of ringing effort[3]	Winter movements[15]	Migrant type[7]	Routes and timing of migration[8]	Breeding origins[16]	Sex differences[10]	Age differences[10]	Regional differences[11]	Migration strategy[12]	Temporal change in movements[17]	Existence and origins of passage populations[18]	Timing and spatial occurrence of passage[19]
mutsw	WF	●●●	●●●	Sedentary	—	—	●●●	●●	●	—	No information	No regular passage	No regular passage
cango	WF	●●● (-I)	●●●	Sedentary*	—	—	●	●	●	—	No information	No regular passage	No regular passage
eider	WF	●	●● (-W)	Sedentary	—	—	●●●	●●●	●	—	No information	No regular passage	No regular passage
gosha	RO	●	●	[Sedentary]	—	—	●	●	●	—	No information	●	●
golea	RO	●	●	[Sedentary]	—	—	●	●	●	—	No information	No regular passage	No regular passage
grepa	PN	●	●	[Sedentary]	—	—	●	●	●	—	No information	No regular passage	No regular passage
rocdo	PN	●	●	[Sedentary]	—	—	●	●	●	—	No information	No regular passage	No regular passage
stodo	PN	●	●	[Sedentary]	—	—	●	●	●	—	No information	●	●
woodp	PN	●●	●●●	Sedentary	—	—	●	●●	●	—	No information	●	●
coldo	PN	●●	●●	Sedentary	—	—	●	●●	●	—	No information	No regular passage	No regular passage
barow	RO	●●	●●	Sedentary*	—	—	●	●	●	—	No information	●●	●
litow	RO	●●●	●	[Sedentary]	—	—	●	●	●	—	No information	No regular passage	No regular passage
tawow	RO	●●●	●	Sedentary	—	—	●	●	●	—	No information	No regular passage	No regular passage
grewo	PN	●●	●	Sedentary	—	—	●	●	●	—	No information	No regular passage	No regular passage
grswo	PN	●●	●●	Sedentary*	—	—	●●	●●	●	—	No information	●●	●
piewa	PN	●●● (-I)	●●●	Short-distance migrant*	As breeding population	As breeding population	●●●	●●	●	—	As breeding population	●●	●●
wren	PN	●●	●●	Sedentary*	—	—	●	●	●	—	No information	●	●
dunno	PN	●●● (-I)	●●●	Sedentary	—	—	●	●●●	●	—	No information	●●	●●
misth	PN	●●	●●●	Sedentary	—	—	●	●●	●	—	No information	No regular passage	No regular passage
beati	PN	●●●	●	[Short-distance migrant]	As breeding population	As breeding population	●	●	●	—	As breeding population	No regular passage	No regular passage
lotti	PN	●●	●●	Sedentary*	—	—	●	●	●	—	No information	No regular passage	No regular passage
marti	PN	●●	●	[Sedentary]	—	—	●	●	●	—	No information	No regular passage	No regular passage
wilti	PN	●●	●	[Sedentary]	—	—	●	●	●	—	No information	No regular passage	No regular passage
coati	PN	●●● (-I)	●●●	Sedentary	—	—	●	●●	●	—	No information	●●	●●
bluti	PN	●●●	●●●	Sedentary	—	—	●●●	●●●	●	—	No information	No regular passage	No regular passage
greti	PN	●●● (-I)	●●●	Sedentary	—	—	●●●	●●●	●	—	No information	No regular passage	No regular passage
nutha	PN	●●●	●	Sedentary*	—	—	●	●	●	—	No information	No regular passage	No regular passage
treec	PN	●	●	[Sedentary]	—	—	●	●	●	—	No information	No regular passage	No regular passage
magpi	PN	●●	●	Sedentary	—	—	●	●	●	—	No information	No regular passage	No regular passage
choug	PN	●●● (-I)	●●	[Sedentary]	—	—	●	●	●	—	No information	No regular passage	No regular passage
raven	PN	●	●	[Sedentary]	—	—	●	●	●	—	No information	No regular passage	No regular passage
housp	PN	●●● (-I)	●●●	Sedentary	—	—	●●●	●●	●	—	No information	No regular passage	No regular passage
tresp	PN	●●	●●	Sedentary	—	—	●	●	●	—	No information	No regular passage	No regular passage
linne	PN	●●	●●	Sedentary	—	—	●●	●●	●	—	No information	●●	●
bullf	PN	●●	●●●	Sedentary	—	—	●●	●●●	●	—	No information	No regular passage	No regular passage
yelha	PN	●●	●●	Sedentary	—	—	●●	●●●	●	—	No information	●	●
corbu	PN	●●	●	Sedentary*	—	—	●	●	●	—	—	No regular passage	No regular passage

Appendix 6c
Passage populations from abroad for species that do not regularly winter in Britain & Ireland

Species[1]	Ecological grouping[2]	Distribution of ringing effort[3]	Winter movements[15]	Migrant type[7]	Routes and timing of migration[8]	Breeding origins[16]	Sex differences[10]	Age differences[10]	Regional differences[11]	Migration strategy[12]	Temporal change in movements[17]	Existence and origins of passage populations[18]	Timing and spatial occurrence of passage[19]
stope	SG	—	—	NONE	—	—	—	—	—	—	—	●	●
leape	SG	—	—	NONE	—	—	—	—	—	—	—	●	●
ospre	RO	—	—	NONE	—	—	—	—	—	—	—	●●	●
hobby	RO	—	—	NONE	—	—	—	—	—	—	—	●	●
lirpl	WD	—	—	NONE	—	—	—	—	—	—	—	●	●
dotte	WD	—	—	NONE	—	—	—	—	—	—	—	●	●
cursa	WD	—	—	PASS	—	—	—	—	—	—	—	●●	●●
whimb	WD	—	—	NONE	—	—	—	—	—	—	—	●●	●●
arcsk	SG	—	—	NONE	—	—	—	—	—	—	—	●●	●●
sante	SG	—	—	NONE	—	—	—	—	—	—	—	●●	●●
roste	SG	—	—	NONE	—	—	—	—	—	—	—	●	●
comte	SG	—	—	NONE	—	—	—	—	—	—	—	●●	●●
arcte	SG	—	—	NONE	—	—	—	—	—	—	—	●	●
litte	SG	—	—	NONE	—	—	—	—	—	—	—	●	●
cucko	PN	—	—	NONE	—	—	—	—	—	—	—	●	●
nijar	PN	—	—	NONE	—	—	—	—	—	—	—	●	●
swift	PN	—	—	NONE	—	—	—	—	—	—	—	●	●
wryne	PN	—	—	PASS	—	—	—	—	—	—	—	●●	●●
swall	PN	—	—	NONE	—	—	—	—	—	—	—	●●	●●
houma	PN	—	—	NONE	—	—	—	—	—	—	—	●	●
trepi	PN	—	—	NONE	—	—	—	—	—	—	—	●	●●
yelwa	PN	—	—	NONE	—	—	—	—	—	—	—	●●	●●
nigal	PN	—	—	NONE	—	—	—	—	—	—	—	●●	●●
redst	PN	—	—	NONE	—	—	—	—	—	—	—	●●	●●
whinc	PN	—	—	NONE	—	—	—	—	—	—	—	●●	●●
wheat	PN	—	—	NONE	—	—	—	—	—	—	—	●●	●●
rinou	PN	—	—	NONE	—	—	—	—	—	—	—	●●	●●
grawa	PN	—	—	NONE	—	—	—	—	—	—	—	●	●
sedwa	PN	—	—	NONE	—	—	—	—	—	—	—	●●	●●
leswh	PN	—	—	NONE	—	—	—	—	—	—	—	●	●
garwa	PN	—	—	NONE	—	—	—	—	—	—	—	●●	●●
woowa	PN	—	—	NONE	—	—	—	—	—	—	—	●	●
wilwa	PN	—	—	NONE	—	—	—	—	—	—	—	●●	●●
spofl	PN	—	—	NONE	—	—	—	—	—	—	—	●	●
piefl	PN	—	—	NONE	—	—	—	—	—	—	—	●●	●●

Notes

1. See key in Appendix 2. Species marked with asterisks (*) in Appendices 6b and 6c do not have regular breeding populations in Britain & Ireland, or have small breeding populations with insufficient information on their movements to allow their treatment as breeding species in these analyses.

2. **Ecological grouping**: 'PN'—passerine/near-passerine; 'RO'—raptor/owl; 'SG'—seabird/gull; 'WF'—wildfowl; 'WD'—wader.

3. **Distribution of ringing effort** during the breeding season (Appendix 6a) or outside it (Appendix 6b) of birds later recovered: '●●●'—spatially representative of the distribution of the British & Irish population as given in the *1988–91 Atlas* (breeding population) or *Winter Atlas* (wintering population); '●●● (-I)'—as '●●●' but with Ireland poorly represented; '●●'—satisfactory but with some areas under-represented; '●'—poor, ringing very localized relative to the distribution of the species or no birds ringed at all in the given season. Based on the standard Figs 1a (breeding) and 1b (outside breeding season) in each main account in Chapter 6.

4. **Age at ringing of birds later recovered**: '●●●'—good, satisfactory proportions of both fully grown birds and chicks ringed during the breeding season; 'FG (-Y)'—birds ringed as chicks poorly represented in the sample of recoveries (generally <10% ringed as chicks); 'Y (-FG)' — birds ringed when fully grown poorly represented in the sample of recoveries (generally <10% ringed when fully grown); '●'—poor as the sample of birds that were ringed during the breeding season in the recovery sample is small or zero. Based on Figure 2 in each main species account.

5. **Dispersal of juveniles**: Based on the availability of recoveries of dead birds that were ringed as chicks in 30-day periods for the first six months after ringing, and any further information available from the accounts. '●●●'—good, sample >29 recoveries in each period or intensive study results available; '●●'—10–29 recoveries in each period or some other source of information available; '●'—insufficient data.

6. **Natal and breeding dispersal**: Information was available from the current project and from Paradis *et al* (1998), using slightly different methods (see Chapter 4 and Appendix 2), and from additional sources mentioned by individual authors. '●●●'—good, sample of >29 appropriate recoveries and no major biases identified; '●●'—10–29 appropriate recoveries (or more but with caveats attached) or information from an intensive local study available; '●'—insufficient data.

7. **Migrant type**: The classes are those used in the standard tables in the main species accounts (see Chapter 6). 'NONE' indicates that there is no regular breeding population (Appendix 6a) or wintering population (Appendix 6b & c) in Britain & Ireland—a species is coded as 'NONE' in Appendix 6b if immigrant wintering birds are unlikely to occur in most years (although they may occur in some years *eg* due to severe weather movements). 'PASS' indicates that there is no regular breeding or wintering population but the species passes through Britain & Ireland on migration. '?' indicates that there is insufficient information to allocate a status. Brackets indicate that the status is based on knowledge from sources other than the statistical tests carried out for this book, and asterisks (*) indicate small sample size or other caveat. **Note that this column affects entries in subsequent columns, some of which will be empty if the species is classified as sedentary. However, also note that for analyses for the British & Irish wintering population, the ringed sample may have included a majority of 'residents'. Hence, for some species classified as sedentary (*eg* Robin and Song Thrush), migratory information may be given if there is additional evidence for an immigrant wintering population.**

Notes *continued*

8. **Routes and timing of migration:** Based on the information available in autumn and spring from recoveries of dead individuals defined as *British & Irish breeders*, and any other sources indicated by the species authors. '●●●'—good, >29 recoveries for each of spring and autumn and account indicates that migration movements are well known; '●●' — <30 recoveries for either autumn or spring but both samples >9; '●● (-S)'—poor information (<10 recoveries or other caveats) for spring; '●● (-A)'—poor information (<10 recoveries or other caveats) for autumn; '●'—poor information for both seasons.

9. **Wintering area:** Based on the information available in winter from recoveries of dead individuals defined as *British & Irish breeders*, and any other sources indicated by the species authors. '●●●'—good, >29 recoveries; '●●'—10–29 recoveries (or more with other caveats); '●'—poor.

10. **Sex and age differences in movement patterns:** Based on the tests comparing recoveries in wintering areas (breeding populations) and breeding areas (wintering populations) described in Chapter 4 and Appendix 4 and supplemented by information reviewed by individual authors. '●●●'—good, tested directly with a sample of at least 30 appropriate recoveries; '●●'—tested directly (but with <30 recoveries or other caveat) or supplementary information available from other source; '●'—poor.

11. **Regional differences in movement patterns:** Based on the tests comparing recoveries in wintering areas (breeding populations) and breeding areas (wintering populations) described in Chapter 4 and Appendix 5 and supplemented by information reviewed by individual authors. '●●●'—good, tested directly for at least four regions with satisfactory samples; '●●'—moderate, tested for three regions, or four but with smaller samples, or other supplementary information mentioned in the accounts; '●'—tested for a maximum of two regions and no other information sources mentioned in accounts.

12. **Migration strategy:** Based on the species accounts (either on direct references to the patterns of sites used on migration or indirect information, such as studies of migratory fattening and predicted flight ranges). Only information on the specific populations under consideration was considered relevant for inclusion here (see Chapter 7). '●●●'—good information from intensive, well-planned study; '●●'—some information available in the species account but incomplete; '●'—little or no information available. Only applicable to long-distance migrants.

13. **Summering areas of immature birds:** Based on the information available during the breeding season from recoveries of dead individuals defined as *British & Irish breeders*, and any other sources indicated by the species authors. '●●●'—good, >29 recoveries available for each immature age class; '●●'—10–29 recoveries available for each age class (or more with other caveats) or information available from other source; '●'—poor. Only applicable to species with an age of first breeding of at least two years.

14. **Temporal change in wintering areas:** Based on the tests comparing recoveries in wintering areas (split by the median year of recovery, see Chapter 5 and Appendix 3a) and supplemented by information reviewed by species-text authors. '●●●'—good, tested directly with a sample of at least 100 appropriate recoveries and a median year of between 1960 and 1980 inclusive; '●●'—tested directly (but either the sample was <100 or the median lay outside the years 1960-80) or information available from another source; '●'—insufficient data (sample <100 and median outside the years 1960-80) or no information.

15. **Winter movements:** Based on the samples of winter–winter recoveries available (see Chapter 4) and any additional information reviewed by individual authors. '●●●'—at least 30 between-winter and 30 within-winter recoveries available; '●●'—<30 recoveries for either between- or within-winter samples but both >9; '●● (-W)'—poor information (<10 recoveries or other caveats) for within-winter movements; '●● (-B)'—poor information (<10 recoveries or other caveats) for between-winter movements; '●'—poor information for both types of winter movement. Not applicable to species that do not winter in Britain & Ireland.

16. **Breeding origins of winter immigrants:** Based on the information available on locations abroad during the breeding season from dead individuals that were present in Britain & Ireland during the winter, and any other sources indicated by the species authors. '●●●'—good, >29 recoveries; '●●'—10–29 recoveries (or more with other caveats); '●'—poor.

17. **Temporal change in the breeding origins of winter immigrants:** These were not tested directly for this book: the entries are based on whether the individual authors present any evidence for changes (in area of origin, route or number of immigrants) in the movements of winter immigrants to Britain & Ireland (coded as 'Some information') or whether no mention is made in the account ('No information').

18. **Existence and origins of regular passage population(s):** Based on information from ringed birds present in Britain & Ireland in autumn and spring and at appropriate locations abroad during passage and during the breeding season. '●●●'—good information, confirming regular passage of migrants from populations breeding outside Britain & Ireland, and with at least 30 records abroad during the breeding season to confirm their breeding origins; '●●'—regular passage populations known to exist but information on their breeding origins is less satisfactory or uncertain; '●'—little information on whether passage movements occur (but they cannot be ruled out based on existing knowledge); 'No regular passage'—no regular passage suspected (although sporadic irruptions or falls may occur).

19. **Timing and spatial occurrence of passage migrants:** These are complex issues that have not been addressed in detail, through specific analyses: the codes are based on an exploratory assessment of the amount of data that may be available for future analysis and on information presented by individual authors within the species accounts. '●●●'—good information, based on specific, intensive study and/or interpretation of existing data; '●●'—moderate knowledge (from *eg* ring-recoveries and/or bird observatory data) but requiring much further analysis and interpretation; '●'—little or no information currently available, although regular passage is suspected; 'No regular passage'—no regular passage suspected.

Appendix 7
Migrancy information for the minor species included in this book

This appendix presents the migrancy categories allocated to the minor species included in this book, based on information provided in the species accounts in Chapter 6. The use of this information in describing the composition of British & Irish bird communities is described in Chapter 5.

Species	Ecological grouping[1]	British & Irish breeding population		British & Irish wintering population		Winter immigrants from abroad?	Presence of passage population(s) from abroad?
		Presence	Migrant type[2]	Presence	Migrant type[3]		
Black-throated Diver	WF	Yes	?	Yes	Long-distance migrant	Yes	?
Great Northern Diver	WF	No	—	Yes	Long-distance migrant	Yes	?
Red-necked Grebe	WF	No	—	Yes	Long-distance migrant	Yes	?
Slavonian Grebe	WF	Yes	Long-distance migrant	Yes	Long-distance migrant	Yes	?
Black-necked Grebe	WF	Yes	?	Yes	Long-distance migrant	Yes	Yes
Cory's Shearwater	SG	No	—	No	—	—	Yes
Great Shearwater	SG	No	—	No	—	—	Yes
Sooty Shearwater	SG	No	—	No	—	—	Yes
Balearic Shearwater	SG	No	—	No	—	—	Yes
Bittern	WF	Yes	?	Yes	Long-distance migrant	Yes	No
Little Egret	WF	Yes	?	Yes	Long-distance migrant	Yes	Yes
Spoonbill	WF	No	—	No	—	—	Yes
Bean Goose	WF	No	—	Yes	Long-distance migrant	Yes	No
Egyptian Goose	WF	Yes	Sedentary	Yes	Sedentary	No	No
Long-tailed Duck	WF	No	—	Yes	Long-distance migrant	Yes	No
Common Scoter	WF	Yes	Short-distance migrant	Yes	Long-distance migrant	Yes	Yes
Velvet Scoter	WF	No	—	Yes	Long-distance migrant	Yes	Yes
Smew	WF	No	—	Yes	Long-distance migrant	Yes	?
Red-breasted Merganser	WF	Yes	Short-distance migrant	Yes	Long-distance migrant	Yes	?
Ruddy Duck	WF	Yes	?	Yes	?	?	?
Honey-buzzard	RO	Yes	Long-distance migrant	No	—	—	Yes
Rough-legged Buzzard	RO	No	—	Yes	Long-distance migrant	Yes	Yes
Red Grouse	PN	Yes	Sedentary	Yes	Sedentary	No	No
Ptarmigan	PN	Yes	Sedentary	Yes	Sedentary	No	No
Black Grouse	PN	Yes	Sedentary	Yes	Sedentary	No	No
Capercaillie	PN	Yes	Sedentary	Yes	Sedentary	No	No
Red-legged Partridge	PN	Yes	Sedentary	Yes	Sedentary	No	No
Quail	PN	Yes	Long-distance migrant	No	—	—	Yes
Pheasant	PN	Yes	Sedentary	Yes	Sedentary	No	No
Golden Pheasant	PN	Yes	Sedentary	Yes	Sedentary	No	No
Lady Amherst's Pheasant	PN	Yes	Sedentary	Yes	Sedentary	No	No
Spotted Crake	WF	Yes	Long-distance migrant	No	—	—	Yes
Corncrake	PN	Yes	Long-distance migrant	No	—	—	?
Common Crane	WF	Yes	Sedentary	Yes	Sedentary	No	No
Avocet	WD	Yes	Long-distance migrant	Yes	?	?	?
Little Stint	WD	No	—	No	—	—	Yes

Continued

Species	Ecological grouping[1]	British & Irish breeding population		British & Irish wintering population		Winter immigrants from abroad?	Presence of passage population(s) from abroad?
		Presence	Migrant type[2]	Presence	Migrant type[3]		
Temminck's Stint	WD	Yes	Long-distance migrant	No	—	—	Yes
Pectoral Sandpiper	WD	No	—	No	—	—	Yes
Spotted Redshank	WD	No	—	Yes	Long-distance migrant	Yes	Yes
Wood Sandpiper	WD	Yes	Long-distance migrant	No	—	—	Yes
Red-necked Phalarope	WD	Yes	Long-distance migrant	No	—	—	Yes
Grey Phalarope	WD	No	—	No	—	—	Yes
Pomarine Skua	SG	No	—	No	—	—	Yes
Long-tailed Skua	SG	No	—	No	—	—	Yes
Mediterranean Gull	SG	Yes	?	Yes	Long-distance migrant	Yes	?
Little Gull	SG	No	—	Yes	Long-distance migrant	Yes	Yes
Sabine's Gull	SG	No	—	No	—	—	Yes
Iceland Gull	SG	No	—	Yes	Long-distance migrant	Yes	Yes
Glaucous Gull	SG	No	—	Yes	Long-distance migrant	Yes	Yes
Black Tern	SG	No	—	No	—	—	Yes
Little Auk	SG	No	—	Yes	Long-distance migrant	Yes	Yes
Rose-ringed Parakeet	PN	Yes	?	Yes	As breeding population	No	No
Hoopoe	PN	No	—	No	—	—	Yes
Lesser Spotted Woodpecker	PN	Yes	Sedentary	Yes	Sedentary	No	No
Wood Lark	PN	Yes	?	Yes	?	?	Yes
Shore Lark	PN	No	—	Yes	Long-distance migrant	Yes	?
Richard's Pipit	PN	No	—	No	—	—	Yes
Water Pipit	PN	No	—	Yes	Long-distance migrant	Yes	Yes
Bluethroat	PN	No	—	No	—	—	Yes
Aquatic Warbler	PN	No	—	No	—	—	Yes
Marsh Warbler	PN	Yes	Long-distance migrant	No	—	—	Yes
Icterine Warbler	PN	No	—	No	—	—	Yes
Dartford Warbler	PN	Yes	Sedentary	Yes	Sedentary	No	No
Barred Warbler	PN	No	—	No	—	—	Yes
Yellow-browed Warbler	PN	No	—	No	—	—	Yes
Red-breasted Flycatcher	PN	No	—	No	—	—	Yes
Crested Tit	PN	Yes	Sedentary	Yes	Sedentary	No	No
Golden Oriole	PN	Yes	Long-distance migrant	No	—	—	Yes
Red-backed Shrike	PN	No	—	No	—	—	Yes
Great Grey Shrike	PN	No	—	Yes	Long-distance migrant	Yes	Yes
Common Rosefinch	PN	No	—	No	—	—	Yes
Lapland Bunting	PN	No	—	Yes	Long-distance migrant	Yes	Yes
Cirl Bunting	PN	Yes	Sedentary	Yes	Sedentary	No	No

Notes

1. Ecological grouping classes: 'PN'—passerine/near-passerine; 'RO'—raptor/owl; 'SG'—seabird/gull; 'WF'—wildfowl; 'WD'—wader.
2. Migrant type (British & Irish breeding population): 'Long-distance migrant'—at least part of population known to winter outside Britain & Ireland; 'Short-distance migrant'—seasonal movements known to occur but thought to be largely within Britain & Ireland; 'Sedentary'—regular seasonal movements not thought to occur.
3. Migrant type (British & Irish wintering population): 'Long-distance migrant'—includes immigrants from abroad; 'Sedentary'—resident population only; 'As breeding population'—movements unknown but no winter immigration thought to occur.

Appendix 8a
Scientific names of organisms mentioned in the text

Vernacular names are ordered alphabetically within each section of this list, followed by the scientific name.

Birds
The list omits bird species for which the scientific name can be found in a species-text heading in this book, or in Table 3.1.

African Black Swift	*Apus barbatus*
African Penguin	*Spheniscus demersus*
African Reed Warbler	*Acrocephalus baeticatus*
Alpine Chough	*Pyrrhocorax graculus*
American Robin	*Turdus migratorius*
Audouin's Gull	*Larus audouinii*
Bar-headed Goose	*Anser indicus*
Black Kite	*Milvus migrans*
Black-browed Albatross	*Diomedea melanophris*
Black-capped Chickadee	*Parus atricapillus*
Blackpoll Warbler	*Dendroica striata*
Black-throated Blue Warbler	*Dendroica caerulescens*
Booted Eagle	*Hieraaetus pennatus*
Brown Creeper	*Certhia americana*
Brown Skua	*Catharacta antarctica*
Buff-bellied Pipit	*Anthus rubescens*
Buff-breasted Sandpiper	*Tryngites subruficollis*
Chilean Skua	*Catharacta chilensis*
Dark-eyed Junco	*Junco hyemalis*
Desert Wheatear	*Oenanthe deserti*
Eagle Owl	*Bubo bubo*
Eleonora's Falcon	*Falco eleonorae*
European Bee-eater	*Merops apiaster*
Ferruginous Duck	*Aythya nyroca*
Grey Fantail	*Rhipidura fuliginosa*
Grey-cheeked Thrush	*Catharus minimus*
Gyr Falcon	*Falco rusticolus*
Hume's Leaf Warbler	*Phylloscopus humei*
Ivory Gull	*Pagophila eburnea*
Killdeer	*Charadrius vociferus*
Lesser Snow Goose	*Anser caerulescens caerulescens*
Lesser Spotted Eagle	*Aquila pomarina*
Magellanic Penguin	*Spheniscus magellanicus*
Melodious Warbler	*Hippolais polyglotta*
Nutcracker	*Nucifraga caryocatactes*
Ortolan Bunting	*Emberiza hortulana*
Pallas's Sandgrouse	*Syrrhaptes paradoxus*
Pallas's Warbler	*Phylloscopus proregulus*
Pigeon Guillemot	*Cepphus columba*
Red-billed Quelea	*Quelea quelea*
Red-breasted Goose	*Branta ruficollis*
Red-breasted Nuthatch	*Sitta canadensis*
Red-eyed Vireo	*Vireo olivaceus*
Red-rumped Swallow	*Hirundo daurica*
Rock Sandpiper	*Calidris ptilocnemis*
Ross's Gull	*Rhodostethia rosea*
Serin	*Serinus serinus*
Short-toed Treecreeper	*Certhia brachydactyla*
Song Sparrow	*Melospiza melodia*
South Polar Skua	*Catharacta maccormicki*
Spotless Starling	*Sturnus unicolor*
Spotted Eagle	*Aquila clanga*
Tawny Pipit	*Anthus campestris*
Thayer's Gull	*Larus thayeri*
Wallcreeper	*Tichodroma muraria*
White-headed Duck	*Oxyura leucocephala*
White-rumped Sandpiper	*Calidris fuscicollis*
White-winged Black Tern	*Chlidonias leucopterus*
Willow Ptarmigan	*Lagopus lagopus*
Wood Duck	*Aix sponsa*

Other animals
Vernacular names may in some cases be used loosely to include related species or genera.

Anchovy	Engraulidae
ant	Formicidae
Arctic Fox	*Alopex lagopus*
Atlantic Salmon	*Salmo salar*
beetle	Coleoptera
Blue Mussel, Edible Mussel	*Mytilus edulis*
caterpillar	Lepidoptera (larva)
Cockle, Edible Cockle	*Cerastoderma edule*
Common Skate	*Raja batis*
dragonfly	Odonata
earthworm	Oligochaeta
earwig	Dermaptera
Field Vole, Short-tailed Vole	*Microtus agrestis*
grasshopper	Orthoptera
Grey Squirrel	*Sciurus carolinensis*
Herring	*Clupea harengus*
kelp fly	Coelopidae
locust	*Locusta* and related genera
Microtine rodent	*Microtus* and related genera
millipede	Diplopoda
mink, American Mink	*Mustela vison*
moth	Lepidoptera
Mountain Cranefly	*Tipula montana*
Norway Lemming	*Lemmus lemmus*

otter	*Lutra lutra*	Dwarf Willow	*Salix herbacea*
Pike	*Esox lucius*	eel-grass	*Zostera* species
Plum-reed Aphid	*Hyalopterus pruni*	Elder, elderberry	*Sambucus nigra*
rabbit	*Oryctolagus cuniculus*	elephant grass	*Pennisetum* species
rat	*Rattus* species	Glasswort	*Salicornia* species
Red Fox	*Vulpes vulpes*	Gorse	*Ulex* species
Sand-eel	*Ammodytes* and related genera	Hare's-tail Cottongrass	*Eriophorum vaginatum*
Sardine	*Sardinella* and related genera	Hawthorn	*Crataegus monogyna*
shrimp	*Crangon* and related genera	Hazel	*Corylus avellana*
Snowshoe Hare	*Lepus americanus*	Heather	*Calluna* or *Erica* species
spider	Araneae	Holly	*Ilex aquifolium*
Sprat	*Sprattus* and related genera	Holm Oak	*Quercus ilex*
springtail	Collembola	hornbeam	*Carpinus betulus*
squirrel	*Sciurus* species	Juniper	*Juniperus communis*
termite	Isoptera	Larch	*Larix* species
Trout	*Salmo* species	mangrove	Rhizophoraceae
Winkle	*Littorina littorea*	Nettle	*Urtica* species
Wood lemming	*Myopus schisticolor*	Norway Spruce	*Picea abies*
Woodmouse	*Apodemus sylvaticus*	Oak	*Quercus* species
Zebra Mussel	*Dreissena polymorpha*	pea	Fabaceae
		Pine	*Pinus* species

Plants

Vernacular names may in some cases be used loosely to include related species or genera.

		poplar	*Populus* species
		Reedmace, Bulrush	*Typha* species
		Rowan	*Sorbus aucuparia*
		Scots Pine	*Pinus sylvestris*
Alder	*Alnus glutinosa*	Sea Aster	*Aster tripolium*
Annual Seablite	*Suaeda maritima*	Sea Lavender	*Limonium vulgare*
Aspen	*Populus tremula*	Sedge	*Carex* species
Beech	*Fagus sylvatica*	Sessile Oak	*Quercus petraea*
Bilberry	*Vaccinium myrtillus*	Spruce	*Picea* species
Birch	*Betula* species	Sunflower	*Helianthus annuus*
Black Poplar (hybrid)	*Populus x canadensis*	Sweet Chestnut	*Castanea sativa*
Blackthorn	*Prunus spinosa*	watercress	*Rorippa* species
blue gum	*Eucalyptus* species	Western Hemlock	*Tsuga heterophylla*
Bracken	*Pteridium aquilinum*	Wheat	*Triticum* species
cherry	*Prunus* species	Whitebeam	*Sorbus* species
Common Reed, reed	*Phragmites australis*	Willow	*Salix* species
Crowberry	*Empetrum nigrum*	Willowherb	*Chamerion* and related genera
Douglas Fir	*Pseudotsuga menziesii*	Yew	*Taxus baccata*
Dwarf Birch	*Betula nana*		

Appendix 8b
Abbreviations used in the text

The following abbreviations and acronyms have been used in the text:

asl	above sea-level
BBS	BTO/JNCC/RSPB Breeding Bird Survey
BOURC	British Ornithologists' Union Records Committee
BTO	British Trust for Ornithology
CBC	BTO/JNCC Common Birds Census
CEH	Centre for Ecology & Hydrology (formerly Institute of Terrestrial Ecology)
EU	European Union
EURING	European Union for Bird Ringing
ITE	Institute of Terrestrial Ecology (now Centre for Ecology & Hydrology)
JNCC	Joint Nature Conservation Committee
MAFF	Ministry of Agriculture, Fisheries & Food (now Department for Food and Rural Affairs)
RSPB	Royal Society for the Protection of Birds
SNH	Scottish Natural Heritage
WeBS	BTO/WWT/RSPB/JNCC Wetland Bird Survey
WWT	Wildfowl & Wetlands Trust

Index to species accounts

Index of artists

We record with gratitude, below, the names of artists who have contributed original illustrations for this book, and the page numbers on which their work appears.

Artist	List of page numbers
Ray Bishop	410, 412, 414, 417, 420, 423, 487, 490, 493, 496, 612, 614, 617, 619, 621, 623, 626
Keith Brockie	jacket, 222, 225, 227, 230, 232, 235, 238, 241, 243, 246, 250, 253, 256
Chris Butler	581, 584, 587, 590, 592, 594, 596, 599, 602, 606, 609
Lawrence Chappell	117, 120, 124, 128, 130, 133, 139, 143
Mark Cornish	633, 635, 670, 673, 675, 678
Simon Gillings	70, 336, 340, 342, 344, 347, 381, 385, 388, 392, 395, 468, 470, 474, 477, 480, 483, 715, 719, 728
Su Gough	31, 38, 540, 542, 544, 548, 733, 753
Maxine Grover	455, 458, 462, 465
Brendel Lang	79, 84, 88, 100, 738, 748
Liz Mackley	269, 273, 276, 278, 281, 284, 287, 290, 293, 297, 300, 303, 306, 311
Harriet Mead	14, 103, 109, 112, 114, 178, 181, 183, 186, 189, 193, 196, 199, 202, 680, 730, 734
Dan Powell	426, 429, 432, 434, 437, 637, 641, 644, 648, 651, 654, 657, 660, 663, 666, 668
Rosemary Powell	518, 521, 527, 530, 534, 538
John Reaney	204, 208, 212, 214, 217, 219, 351, 353, 356, 361, 365, 369, 373, 377, 690
Derek Robertson	261, 263, 266, 314, 316, 319, 323, 326, 329, 332, 397, 401, 405, 407, 759
Rob Robinson	83, 90, 750
Gerard Russell	552, 555, 559, 562, 565, 568, 571, 575, 579
Richard Thewlis	441, 443, 446, 449, 451, 453
Mike Toms	259, 629
Lyn Wells	1, 23, 146, 149, 154, 158, 161, 166, 169, 172, 175, 498, 502, 505, 507, 510, 512, 515
Andy Wilson	headings on preliminary pages, 731, 760
Peter Wilson	44, 711